Glencoe

Algebra 2

Integration
Applications
Connections

Solutions Manual

GLENCOE
McGraw-Hill
New York, New York Columbus, Ohio Woodland Hills, California Peoria, Illinois

Glencoe/McGraw-Hill
A Division of The McGraw-Hill Companies

Send all inquiries to:
Glencoe/McGraw-Hill
8787 Orion Place
Columbus, OH 43240-4027

Algebra 2
Solutions Manual

ISBN: 0-02-825152-0

5 6 7 8 9 10 024 03 02 01 00

Contents

Chapter 1 Analyzing Equations and Inequalities

1-1A A Graphing Technology: Expressions

Page 6 Exercises

1. 5 [×] [(] 4 [+] 7 [)] [÷] 6 [ENTER] 9.17
2. 231.5 [^] 6 [ENTER] 1.54×10^{14}
3. [(] 52 [×] 4 [)] [^] 3 [+] 76 [÷] 6 [ENTER] 8,998,924.67
4. 3 [(] [(] 4 [+] [(] 3 [(] 4 [+] 6 [)] [)] [÷] 5 [)] [÷] 4 [)] [+] 11 [ENTER] 18.5
5. 112 [−] 2 [(] 16 [+] 2 [(] 14 [−] 2 [(] 7 [+] 1 [)] [)] [)] [−] 4 [x^2] [ENTER] 72
6. [(] [(] [(−)] 4 [+] 11 [)] [x^2] [÷] 4 [)] [×] 3 [ENTER] 36.75
7. [(] 1.12 [×] 10 [^] 4 [)] [(] 3.65 [×] 10 [^] [(−)] 3 [)] [ENTER] 40.88
8. [(] 5.24 [×] 10 [^] [(−)] 6 [)] [(] 3.24 [×] 10 [^] 4 [ENTER] 0.17
9. Use [STO▸] and [ENTER]; 10, 0, −17.78, −20.56, 26.67
10. Use [STO▸] and [ENTER]; 56, 0.48

1-1 Expressions and Formulas

Page 10 Check for Understanding

1. The operation with the innermost group is evaluated first.
2. First, solve the parenthesis to get 66. Multiply 66 and 12 to get 792. Divide 792 by 2 to get 396. Then subtract 396 from $\frac{1}{3}$ to get $-395\,\frac{2}{3}$.
3. See students' work.
4. See students' work.
5. Both formulas will work to find the volume of ≈ 3690 cm^3.
6. $7 - 6 \div 3 = 7 - 2$
   $= 5$
7. $9(4 + 2) = 9(6)$
   $= 54$
8. $18 \cdot 6 + 12 = 108 + 12$
   $= 120$
9. $25 \cdot 2 - 3 = 50 - 3$
   $= 47$
10. $\frac{45(4 + 32)}{10} = \frac{45(36)}{10}$
    $= \frac{1620}{10}$
    $= 162$
11. $(4 - 3)^5 \cdot 9 = (1)^5 \cdot 9$
    $= 9$
12. $a + b - c = 3 + (-4) - 5$
    $= -6$
13. $a + c^2 = 3 + 5^2$
    $= 3 + 25$
    $= 28$
14. $a(b + c) = 3(-4 + 5)$
    $= 3(1)$
    $= 3$
15. $C = \frac{5(F - 32)}{9}$
    $= \frac{5(98.6 - 32)}{9}$
    $= \frac{5(66.6)}{9}$
    $= \frac{333}{9}$
    $= 37$
    98.6° F = 37° C
16. $C = \frac{5(F - 32)}{9}$
    $= \frac{5(32 - 32)}{9}$
    $= \frac{5(0)}{9}$
    $= \frac{0}{9}$
    $= 0$
    32° F = 0° C
17. $A = \ell w$
    $= (a + 6)(a - 6)$ in^2

Pages 10–12 Exercises

18. $4(3^2 + 3) = 4(9 + 3)$
    $= 4(12)$
    $= 48$
19. $2(9 + 2) - 3 = 2(11) - 3$
    $= 22 - 3$
    $= 19$
20. $(7 + 5)3 - 3 = (12)3 - 3$
    $= 36 - 3$
    $= 33$
21. $4 + 2^2 - 15 + 4 = 4 + 4 - 15 + 4$
    $= -3$
22. $10 + 16 \div 4 + 8 = 10 + 4 + 8$
    $= 22$
23. $5 + 9(3) \div 3 - 8 = 5 + 27 \div 3 - 8$
    $= 5 + 9 - 8$
    $= 6$
24. $7 - [4 + (6 \cdot 5)] = 7 - [4 + 30]$
    $= 7 - [34]$
    $= -27$
25. $[21 - (9 - 2)] \div 2 = [21 - 7] \div 2$
    $= [14] \div 2$
    $= 7$
26. $4 + [9 \div (9 - 2(4))] = 4 + [9 \div (9 - 8)]$
    $= 4 + [9 \div 1]$
    $= 4 + 9$
    $= 13$
27. $[(-7 + 4) \times 5 - 2] \div 6 = [(-3) \times 5 - 2] \div 6$
    $= [(-15) - 2] \div 6$
    $= [-17] \div 6$
    $= -\frac{17}{6}$ or $-2.8\overline{3}$
28. $\frac{1}{2}(5^2 + 3) = \frac{1}{2}(25 + 3)$
    $= \frac{1}{2}(28)$
    $= 14$
29. $\frac{14(8 - 15)}{2} = \frac{14(-7)}{2}$
    $= \frac{-98}{2}$
    $= -49$
30. $-3(2^2 + 3) = -3(4 + 3)$
    $= -3(7)$
    $= -21$
31. $4 + (49 \div 7) \times 8 \div 2 = 4 + 7 \times 8 \div 2$
    $= 4 + 56 \div 2$
    $= 4 + 28$
    $= 32$
32. $0.4(0.6 + 3.2) \div 2 = 0.4(3.8) \div 2$
    $= 1.52 \div 2$
    $= 0.76$
33. $0.5(2.3 + 25) \div 1.5 = 0.5(27.3) \div 1.5$
    $= 13.65 \div 1.5$
    $= 9.1$

34. $3 + [8 \div (9 + 2(-4))] = 3 + [8 \div (9 + (-8))]$
$= 3 + [8 \div 1]$
$= 3 + 8$
$= 11$

35. $\frac{1}{3} - \frac{12(77 \div 11)}{9} = \frac{1}{3} - \frac{12(7)}{9}$
$= \frac{1}{3} - \frac{84}{9}$
$= \frac{1}{3} - 9\frac{1}{3}$
$= -9$

36. $d(3 + c) = 4\left(3 + \frac{1}{2}\right)$
$= 4\left(3\frac{1}{2}\right)$
$= 14$

37. $a + b + d = -5 + 0.25 + 4$
$= -0.75$

38. $a + 2b - c = -5 + 2(0.25) - \frac{1}{2}$
$= -5 + 0.5 - \frac{1}{2}$
$= -5$

39. $a + 10 \div c = -5 + 10 \div \frac{1}{2}$
$= -5 + 20$
$= 15$

40. $2^d + a = 2^4 + (-5)$
$= 16 + (-5)$
$= 11$

41. $\frac{3ab}{cd} = \frac{3(-5)(0.25)}{\left(\frac{1}{2}\right)(4)}$
$= \frac{-3.75}{2}$
$= -1.875$

42. $\frac{3a + 4c}{2c} = \frac{3(-5) + 4\left(\frac{1}{2}\right)}{2\left(\frac{1}{2}\right)}$
$= \frac{-15 + 2}{1}$
$= -13$

43. $(a + c)^2 - bd = \left(-5 + \frac{1}{2}\right)^2 - (0.25)(4)$
$= \left(-4\frac{1}{2}\right)^2 - 1$
$= 20.25 - 1$
$= 19.25$

44. $A = \frac{1}{2}bh$
$= 0.5(x + 4)(x + 8) \text{ ft}^2$

45. $A = \frac{h}{2}(b_1 + b_2) = \frac{6}{2}(22 + 17)$
$= 3(39)$
$= 117$

46. $A = \frac{h}{2}(b_1 + b_2) = \frac{10}{2}(52 + 17)$
$= 5(69)$
$= 345$

47. $A = \frac{h}{2}(b_1 + b_2) = \frac{4}{2}(12.50 + 6.25)$
$= 2(18.75)$
$= 37.5$

48. $A = \frac{h}{2}(b_1 + b_2) = \frac{\frac{5}{8}}{2}\left(\frac{3}{4} + \frac{1}{2}\right)$
$= \frac{5}{16}\left(\frac{5}{4}\right)$
$= \frac{25}{64}$

49. $I = prt$
$= (1500)\ (0.065)\ (3)$
$= 292.50$; \$292.50

50. $I = prt$
$= (2500)\ (0.0725)\ (2)$
$= 362.50$; \$362.50

51. $I = prt$
$= (20{,}005)\ (0.079)\ (2.25)$
≈ 3555.89; \$3555.89

52. $I = prt$
$= (65{,}283.21)\ (0.0932)\ (6.5)$
$\approx 39{,}548.57$; \$39,548.57

53a. 528 **53b.** 52.5 **53c.** 28.8

```
PROGRAM:AREA
:Disp "HEIGHT = ?"
:Input H
:Disp "BASE = ?"
:Input B
:Disp "AREA ="
H · B/2
```

53d. 46.23 cm^2 **53e.** 5253.36 cm^2

54a. $(1 + 3) \cdot 2^2$ **54b.** $[1 + (3 \cdot 2)]^2$

54c. $1 + 3 \cdot 2^2$ **54d.** $1 + (3 \cdot 2)^2$

55a. $SA = 2\ell w + 2\ell h + 2wh$
$= 2(3a + 4)\ a + 2(3a + 4)\ 2a + 2a(2a)$
$= 6a^2 + 8a + 12a^2 + 16a + 4a^2$
$= 22a^2 + 24a$

55b. $SA = 22a^2 + 24a$
$= 22(4^2) + 24(4)$
$= 22(16) + 24(4)$
$= 352 + 96$
$= 448$; 448 square units

55c. $SA = 22a^2 + 24a$
$= 22(6.2^2) + 24(6.2)$
$= 22(38.44) + 24(6.2)$
$= 845.68 + 148.8$
$= 994.48$; 994.48 square units

56a. $5 \times 20 = 100$ mg

56b. 24 hours $\div$ 6 hours $= 4$ doses/day
30 days $\times$ 4 doses $= 120$ tablets

57a. 2, 3, 5, 7, 11, 13, 17, 19, 23, 29, 31, 37, 41, 43, 47, 53, 57, 59, 61, 67, 71, 73, 79, 83, 89

57b. Answers will vary; sample answers are 2, 3, 5, 7.

57c. 496, 8128

58a. $2.9t^2 + 5.8t + 50 = 2.9(0^2) + 5.8(0) + 50$
$= 0 + 0 + 50$
$= 50$
average salary = \$50,000

58b. $2.9t^2 + 5.8t + 50 = 2.9(19^2) + 5.8(19) + 50$
$= 1046.9 + 110.2 + 50$
$= 1207.1$
average salary = \$1,207,100

58c. To find the salary for 1970, use -5; for 1965, use -10.

1-2 Properties of Real Numbers

Pages 16–17 Check for Understanding

1. It is irrational because it is neither a repeating nor a terminating decimal.

2. Natural numbers belong in the set of whole numbers, which are in the set of integers, which are in the set of rational numbers.

3. Sample answers:
Rational numbers: 30, −8, $\frac{1}{2}$, $\sqrt{9}$, $4\frac{1}{3}$;
Irrational numbers: $\sqrt{2}$, π, $\sqrt{11}$, $\sqrt{15}$, $\sqrt{17}$.

4. Use the commutative property when you can switch the order of the numbers around the operation without affecting the answer. Use the associative property when you can move the parentheses or regroup the numbers in a given problem without affecting the answer.

5a. See students' work. **5b.** See students' work.
5c. See students' work. **6.** $7 - 6 = 1$; R, Q, Z, W, N
7. $6 - 7 = -1$; R, Q, Z
8. $6 \div 2^2 = 6 \div 4 = 1.5$; R, Q
9. $\sqrt{49 + 8} = \sqrt{57} \approx 7.550$; R, I
10. false; −1 **11.** true
12. commutative (×) **13.** additive inverse
14. commutative (+)
15. $-7; \frac{1}{7}$ **16.** $\frac{2}{3}; -\frac{3}{2}$
17. $2(4c + 5d) + 6(2c - d) = 2(4c) + 2(5d) + 6(2c) - 6(d)$
$= 8c + 10d + 12c - 6d$
$= 20c + 4d$
18. $3x + 5y + 7x - 3y = 10x + 2y$
19. $(5 + 7)3 = (12)3 = 36$; \$36.00

Pages 17–18 Exercises

20. $2.9 + 3.7 = 6.6$; R, Q **21.** $-56 \div 8 = -7$; R, Q, Z
22. $58 \div 100 = 0.58$; R, Q
23. $-4.2 \times 10 = -42$; R, Q, Z
24. $1 - 5 = -4$; R, Q, Z
25. $\sqrt{25} - 6 = 5 - 6 = -1$; R, Q, Z
26. $3^3 + 2^2 = 27 + 4 = 31$; R, Q, Z, W, N
27. $1\frac{1}{2} + \frac{3}{4} = 2\frac{1}{4}$; R, Q
28. $10 \times (-3.9) = -39$; R, Q, Z
29. $4 \div 2^3 = 4 \div 8 = \frac{1}{2}$; R, Q
30. $-81 \div (-9) = 9$; R, Q, Z, W, N
31. $\sqrt{64 + 3} = \sqrt{67} \approx 8.185$; RI
32. false; 1.5 **33.** true **34.** false; 1.5 **35.** true
36. true **37.** true **38.** distributive
39. commutative (+) **40.** additive identity
41. addititve inverse **42.** distributive
43. commutative (×) **44.** multiplicative identity
45. multiplicative inverse
46. $-8; \frac{1}{8}$ **47.** $-0.2; 5$ **48.** $1.25; -0.8$
49. $1; -1$ **50.** $-\frac{5}{6}, \frac{6}{5}$ **51.** $3\frac{5}{7}; \frac{7}{26}$
52. $6x - 2y - 3x + 2y = 3x$
53. $4(14c - 10d) - 6(d + 4c)$
$= 4(14c) - 4(10d) - 6(d) - 6(4c)$
$= 56c - 40d - 6d - 24c$
$= 32c - 46d$

54. $\frac{1}{2}(17 - 4x) - \frac{3}{4}(6 - 16x)$
$= \frac{1}{2}(17) - \frac{1}{2}(4x) - \frac{3}{4}(6) + \frac{3}{4}(16x)$
$= \frac{17}{2} - 2x - \frac{9}{2} + 12x$
$= 4 + 10x$

55. $\frac{3}{4}(2x - 5y) + \frac{1}{2}\left(\frac{2}{3}x + 4y\right)$
$= \frac{3}{4}(2x) - \frac{3}{4}(5y) + \frac{1}{2}\left(\frac{2}{3}x\right) + \frac{1}{2}(4y)$
$= \frac{3}{2}x - \frac{15}{4}y + \frac{1}{3}x + 2y$
$= \frac{11}{6}x - \frac{7}{4}y$

56. $\frac{1}{4}(12 + 20a) + \frac{3}{4}(12 + 20a)$
$= \frac{1}{4}(12) + \frac{1}{4}(20a) + \frac{3}{4}(12) + \frac{3}{4}(20a)$
$= 3 + 5a + 9 + 15a$
$= 12 + 20a$

57. $7(0.2m + 0.3n) + 5(0.6m - n)$
$= 7(0.2m) + 7(0.3n) + 5(0.6m) - 5(n)$
$= 1.4m + 2.1n + 3m - 5n$
$= 4.4m - 2.9n$

58a. 0 **58b.** $\frac{1}{a}$; multiplicative inverse of a
58c. 1
59a. $638 - 577 = 61$; $6 + 1 = 7$ (not divisible by 9); no
59b. $1050 - 1095 = -45$; $4 + 5 = 9$; yes
59c. This method works because the difference between a number and the number whose digits are reversed is 9.

60. Sample answers:
$A = 78 \times 36$
$= 2808$ ft^2

$A = 39 \times 36 + 39 \times 36$
$= 1404 + 1404$
$= 2808$ ft^2

61. $0.2(0.5 + 2.2) \div 6 = 0.2(2.7) \div 6$
$= 0.54 \div 6$
$= 0.09$

62. $8 - [21 - (3 \cdot 5)] = 8 - [21 - 15]$
$= 8 - 6$
$= 2$

63. $3(13 - 7) + (7 - 5)^2 = 3(6) + (2)^2$
$= 18 + 4$
$= 22$

64. $17 - [22 \div (21 - 2(5))] = 17 - [22 \div (21 - 10)]$
$= 17 - [22 \div 11]$
$= 17 - 2$
$= 15$

65. $\frac{3a + 4c}{b} = \frac{3(-3) + 4(0.5)}{2}$
$= \frac{-9 + 2}{2}$
$= \frac{-7}{2}$
$= -3.5$

66. $d - [c \div (a - b(a))] = 17 - [12 \div (-1 - 5(-1))]$
$= 17 - [12 \div (-1 + 5)]$
$= 17 - [12 \div 4]$
$= 17 - [3]$
$= 14$

67. 2 hours $\times \frac{60 \text{ min}}{\text{hour}} \times \frac{60 \text{ seconds}}{\text{min}} = 7200$ seconds
7200 seconds $\div 5 = 1440$ times

68. $A = \frac{h}{2}(b_1 + b_2)$
$= \frac{3}{2}(4 + 8)$
$= \frac{3}{2}(12)$
$= 18$

69. $I = prt$
$= (2500)(0.0737)(4)$
$= 737$; \$737

70. Sears Tower: $Y = \frac{F}{3}$
$= \frac{1454}{3}$
≈ 484.67; about 484.67 yards

Petronas Tower: $1454 + 22 = 1476$
$Y = \frac{F}{3}$
$= \frac{1476}{3}$
$= 492$; 492 yards

71. $12 + 18 \div 6 + 7 = 12 + 3 + 7 = 22$

1-3 Integration: Statistics Graphs and Measures of Central Tendency

Pages 22–23 Check for Understanding

1. The number of overall scored for the floor exercises of the Buckeye Gymnastics team members is closer to the higher marks of 8.5 to 10.
2. stem 9, leaf 8
3. It does not affect it.
4. mode
5. See students' work.
6. 2; 2; $\frac{0+2+2+3+4}{5} = 2.2$
7. 8; no mode; $\frac{4+5+8+10+12}{5} = 7.8$
8. 7; 7; $\frac{7+7+7+7+7}{5} = 7$

9a.

Stem	Leaf
2	2 3 4 4 7 8 8 9 9
3	1 1 3 4 4 4 9
4	1

2|2 = 22,000

9b. $(22{,}000 + 23{,}000 + 24{,}000 + 24{,}000 + 27{,}000 + 28{,}000 + 28{,}000 + 29{,}000 + 29{,}000 + 31{,}000 + 31{,}000 + 33{,}000 + 34{,}000 + 34{,}000 + 34{,}000 + 39{,}000 + 41{,}000) \div 17 \approx \$30{,}059$

9c. \$29,000

9d. \$34,000

9e. See students' work.

Pages 23–26 Exercises

10. 256, 276, 298, 388, 399
298; no mode;
$\frac{256 + 276 + 298 + 388 + 399}{5} = \frac{1617}{5} = 323.4$

11. 3, 7, 34, 58, 75
34; no mode; $\frac{3 + 7 + 34 + 58 + 75}{5} = \frac{177}{5} = 35.4$

12. 2.1, 2.1, 2.1, 4.8, 4.8, 5.7
$\frac{2.1 + 4.8}{2} = \frac{6.9}{2} = 3.45$; 2.1;
$\frac{2.1 + 2.1 + 2.1 + 4.8 + 4.8 + 5.7}{6} = \frac{21.6}{6} = 3.6$

13. 50, 50, 55, 65, 65, 70, 75, 80
$\frac{65 + 65}{2} = \frac{130}{2} = 65$; 50 and 65;
$\frac{50 + 50 + 55 + 65 + 65 + 70 + 75 + 80}{8} = \frac{510}{8} = 63.75$

14. 45, 61, 89, 89, 93, 102
$\frac{89 + 89}{2} = \frac{178}{2} = 89$; 89;
$\frac{45 + 61 + 89 + 89 + 93 + 102}{6} = \frac{479}{6} = 79.8\overline{3}$

15. 10.7, 12.5, 13.3, 15.4
$\frac{12.5 + 13.3}{2} = \frac{25.8}{2} = 12.9$; no mode;
$\frac{10.7 + 12.5 + 13.3 + 15.4}{4} = \frac{51.9}{4} = 12.975$

16. 101, 101, 121, 153, 192
121; 101; $\frac{101 + 101 + 121 + 153 + 192}{5} = \frac{668}{5} = 133.6$

17. 42, 43, 43, 43, 51, 54, 55
43; 43; $\frac{42 + 43 + 43 + 43 + 51 + 54 + 55}{7} = \frac{331}{7} \approx 47.29$

18. 1947, 1989, 1999, 2000, 2004, 2301, 2324, 2738, 2938
2004; no mode;
$\frac{1947 + 1989 + 1999 + 2000 + 2004 + 2301 + 2324 + 2738 + 2938}{9}$
$= \frac{20{,}240}{9} = 2248.\overline{8}$

19. 71; 71 and 88; $(55 + 55 + 60 + 64 + 65 + 66 + 67 + 68 + 70 + 71 + 71 + 71 + 72 + 72 + 75 + 76 + 76 + 80 + 85 + 86 + 88 + 88 + 88) \div 23 = 1669 \div 23 \approx 73$

20. $\frac{100 + 100 + 88 + 76 + 95 + 88 + 93}{7} = \frac{640}{7} \approx 91.4$

21a. Mean; it is higher.

21b. Mode; it is lower and is what most employees make. It reflects the most representative worker.

22a. [2nd] [LIST] [▶] 3 [2nd] [{] 3 [,] 5 [,] 7 [,] 5 [,] 3 [,] 8 [,] 2 [2nd] [}] [)] [ENTER] 4.714285714; [2nd] [LIST] [▶] 4 [2nd] [{] 3 [,] 5 [,] 7 [,] 5 [,] 3 [,] 8 [,] 2 [2nd] [}] [)] [ENTER] 5

22b. [2nd] [LIST] [▶] 3 [2nd] [{] 45.7 [,] 64.8 [,] 33.2 [,] 66.1 [,] 54.4 [,] 64.5 [2nd] [}] [)] [ENTER] $54.78\overline{3}$; [2nd] [LIST] [▶] 4 [2nd] [{] 45.7 [,] 64.8 [,] 33.2 [,] 66.1 [,] 54.4 [,] 64.5 [2nd] [}] [)] [ENTER] 59.45

23a. The graphs of the data look different because a different scale is used in each graph.

23b. Sample answer: Graph A might be used by an employer to show an employee she cannot get a big raise. It appears that sales are steady but not rising drastically enough to warrant a big raise.

23c. Sample answer: Graph B might be used by a company owner to show a prospective buyer. It looks like there is a dramatic rise in sales.

24a. See students' work.

24b. See students' work.

24c. See students' work.

25a.

Employed	Stem	Unemployed
	0	2 2 2 3 3 3 4 4 6 6
	1	2
	2	
0 4 8	3	
6	4	
3 4 7	5	
4	6	
	7	
0 8	8	
	9	
	10	
	11	
	12	
	13	
4	14	*|1|2 = 1,200,000*

25b. Answers will vary. Sample answer: The number of employed people in these states is much higher than the number of unemployed people.

25c. Divide the number of unemployed people by the total number of employed and unemployed people.

25d.

California $\frac{1,197,000}{14,411,000 + 1,197,000} = \frac{1,197,000}{15,608,000} \approx$ 0.0767 or 7.7%

Florida $\frac{445,000}{6,384,000 + 445,000} = \frac{445,000}{6,829,000} \approx 0.0652$ or 6.5%

Illinois $\frac{378,000}{5,672,000 + 378,000} = \frac{378,000}{6,050,000} \approx 0.0624$ or 6.2%

Massachusetts $\frac{205,000}{2,979,000 + 205,000} = \frac{205,000}{3,184,000} \approx$ 0.0643 or 6.4%

Michigan $\frac{247,000}{4,570,000 + 247,000} = \frac{247,000}{4,817,000} \approx 0.0512$ or 5.1%

New Jersey $\frac{277,000}{3,830,000 + 277,000} = \frac{277,000}{4,107,000} \approx 0.0674$ or 6.7%

New York $\frac{561,000}{8,048,000 + 561,000} = \frac{561,000}{8,609,000} \approx 0.0651$ or 6.5%

North Carolina $\frac{180,000}{3,443,000 + 180,000} = \frac{180,000}{3,623,000} \approx$ 0.0496 or 5.0%

Ohio $\frac{274,000}{5,282,000 + 274,000} = \frac{274,000}{5,556,000} \approx 0.0493$ or 4.9%

Pennsylvania $\frac{344,000}{5,428,000 + 344,000} = \frac{344,000}{5,772,000} \approx$ 0.0595 or 6.0%

Texas $\frac{555,000}{8,842,000 + 555,000} = \frac{555,000}{9,397,000} \approx 0.0590$ or 5.9%

26a. \$695, \$695, \$895, \$999, \$1100, \$1200, \$1300, \$1499

$\frac{999 + 1100}{2} = \frac{2099}{2} = \$1049.50$; \$695;

$\frac{695 + 695 + 895 + 999 + 1100 + 1200 + 1300 + 1499}{8}$

$= \frac{8383}{8} \approx \$1047.88$

26b. Mode; it is the least expensive price.

26c. Mean; it is the most representative of the prices of the cameras.

27. 425, 2500, 3250, 3550, 12,500, 12,600, 28,180, 38,900, 42,500, 73,000, 170,000, 175,000

$\frac{12,600 + 28,180}{2} = \frac{40,780}{2} = \$20,390$; no mode; (425 + 2500 + 3250 + 3550 + 12,500 + 12,600 + 28,180 + 38,900 + 42,500 + 73,000 + 170,000 + 175,000) ÷ 12 = 562,405 ÷ 12 ≈ \$46,867.08

The median is most representative of the data since there is such a wide range of costs.

28a. $\frac{2,200,000 + 2,100,000}{2} = \frac{4,300,000}{2} = 2,150,000$;
2,000,000;
(3,000,000 + 2,918,236 + 2,472,500 + 2,390,000 + 2,300,000 + 2,200,000 + 2,100,000 + 2,097,416, + 2,006,688 + 2,000,000 + 2,000,000 + 2,000,000) ÷ 12 = 27,484,840 ÷ 12 = $2,290,403.\overline{3}$ or about 2,290,403

28b. Mode; it is lower.

28c. Mean; it is higher.

29a.

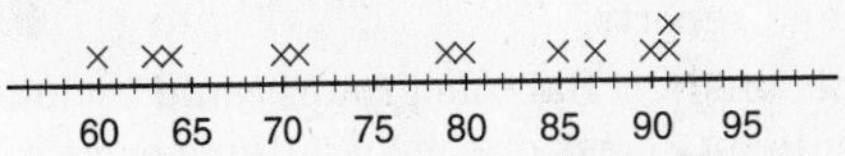

29b. 79.5; 91;

$\frac{60 + 63 + 64 + 70 + 71 + 79 + 80 + 85 + 87 + 90 + 91 + 91}{12}$

$= \frac{931}{12} \approx 77.58$

29c.

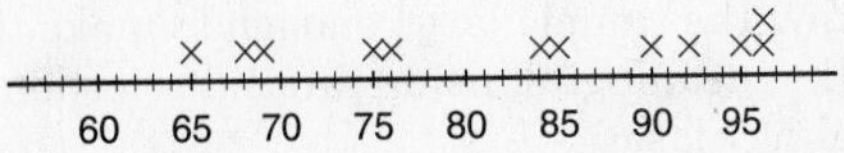

29d. They each increase by 5 since the temperature increased by 5 degrees; different.

29e. All points on the original line plot would be shifted 5 to the right to obtain the new line plot.

30. commutative (+)

31. $a(3 + 5) - 6(3a - 1) = a(8) - 6(3a) + 6$
$= 8a - 18a + 6$
$= -10a + 6$

32. $\frac{2}{3}(6a - 18) + 3(2a - 9)$
$= \frac{2}{3}(6a) - \frac{2}{3}(18) + 3(2a) - 3(9)$
$= 4a - 12 + 6a - 27$
$= 10a - 39$

33. $\frac{7(3 + 2)}{4 - 9} = \frac{7(5)}{-5}$
$= \frac{35}{-5}$
$= -7$

34. $(r + 7) \div s = (20 + 7) \div 3$
$= 27 \div 3$
$= 9$

35. $C = \frac{5(F - 32)}{9}$
$= \frac{5(787.1 - 32)}{9}$
$= \frac{5(755.1)}{9}$
$= \frac{3775.5}{9}$
$= 419.5$; 419.5° C

Page 26 Mathematics and Society

1. Sample answer: Examples include tracking population movements, measuring fertility trends and birthrates, determining the needs for social programs and legislation, deciding how federal funds should be spent, and determining seats in the House of Representatives. Businesses could use the data for marketing purposes and to help them decide where to locate offices, factories, and other facilities. Chambers of commerce could use the data to promote their cities and to guide the development of facilities and services. Public-service agencies could use the data to target their services to selected areas and population groups. School districts could predict enrollment trends and forecast needs for new schools.
2. Sample answer: Use of paperwork and forms would be greatly reduced. Fewer people would be needed to distribute forms, record and monitor responses, and follow up on non-respondents. There would also be savings in the costs of data entry and computer processing. With the volume of data greatly reduced, the number of processing errors should decline, thus improving accuracy of data and reports.
3. Sample answer: Sample groups could include students in a class or school, attendees at a concert or sporting event, people who listen to a particular radio station, people who shop at a certain store or shopping mall, people who buy certain products, and a wide variety of other possibilities. Planning considerations including making the sample large enough to make the results meaningful, using random selection, and avoiding biases.

1-4 Solving Equations

Pages 30–31 Check for Understanding

1. See students' work.
2. See students' work.
3. An equation has an equals sign in it; it conveys a complete mathematical sentence. An expression does not have an equals sign in it; it is only part of a mathematical sentence.

4. $5s = 250$ **5.** yes **6.** $3 - 2n$ **7.** $5x - 3$

8. subtraction (=) **9.** multiplication (=)

10. $10 + 5x = 110$; $5x = 100$; $x = 20$

11. $-2(a + 4) = 2$; $-2a - 8 = 2$; $-2a = 10$; $a = -5$

12. $3b + 4b + 5b = 30$; $12b = 30$; $b = 2.5$

13. $7 + 5n = -58$; $5n = -65$; $n = -13$

14. $-1.4t + 3 = -7.5$; $-1.4t = -10.5$; $t = 7.5$

15. $-\frac{2}{3}k = 14$; $\left(-\frac{3}{2}\right)\left(-\frac{2}{3}\right)k = 14\left(-\frac{3}{2}\right)$; $k = -21$

16. $2x - 3m = 6$; $2x = 6 + 3m$; $x = \frac{6 + 3m}{2}$

17. $V = \frac{1}{3}\pi r^2 h$; $3V = \pi r^2 h$; $\frac{3V}{\pi r^2} = h$

18. Let x = age of Marisa's parents.
$16 + 2x = 100$
$2x = 84$
$x = 42$, Check: $16 + 2(42) = 100$ ✓

Pages 31–34 Exercises

19. $14 - x^2$ **20.** $2(n + 11)$ **21.** $4(n + n^2)$ **22.** $5x^2$

23. $7 + 3n$ **24.** $(x + 13)^2$ **25.** reflexive (=)

26. symmetric (=) **27.** addition (=)

28. transitive (=) **29.** subtraction (=)

30. substitution (=)

31. $3y + 16 = 22$; $3y = 6$; $y = 2$

32. $14 - x = -7$; $-x = -21$; $x = 21$

33. $34 - 10w = 6w + 2$; $34 - 16w = 2$; $-16w = -32$; $w = 2$

34. $t + 2t + 3t + 4t + 5t = 45$; $15t = 45$; $t = 3$

35. $\frac{1}{8} - \frac{3}{4}x = \frac{1}{16}$; $-\frac{3}{4}x = -\frac{1}{16}$; $x = \frac{1}{12}$

36. $\frac{3}{4} - \frac{3}{5}x = \frac{2}{5}x + \frac{2}{4}$; $\frac{3}{4} - x = \frac{2}{4}$; $-x = -\frac{1}{4}$; $x = \frac{1}{4}$

37. $5 = -5(y + 3)$; $5 = -5y - 15$; $20 = -5y$; $-4 = y$

38. $2d + 5 = 8d + 2$; $-6d + 5 = 2$; $-6d = -3$; $d = \frac{1}{2}$

39. $280 - 26f = 1098$; $-26f = 818$; $f = -\frac{409}{13}$

40. $3(4 - 5k) = 2k - 4$; $12 - 15k = 2k - 4$; $12 - 17k = -4$; $-17k = -16$; $k = \frac{16}{17}$

41. $4m - 9 = 5m + 7$; $-m - 9 = 7$; $-m = 16$; $m = -16$

42. $32g + 245 = 3829$; $32g = 3584$; $g = 112$

43. $12x - 24 = -14x + 28$; $26x - 24 = 28$; $26x = 52$; $x = 2$

44. $18 = -6(p + 5)$; $18 = -6p - 30$; $48 = -6p$; $-8 = p$

45. $4.5(b + 1) - 2 = 4(b + 3)$
$4.5b + 4.5 - 2 = 4b + 12$
$4.5b + 2.5 = 4b + 12$
$0.5b + 2.5 = 12$
$0.5b = 9.5$
$b = 19$

46. $2.3n + 1 = 1.3n + 7$
$n + 1 = 7$
$n = 6$

47. $\frac{5}{7}x - 4 = \frac{3}{7}x + 1$
$\frac{2}{7}x - 4 = 1$
$\frac{2}{7}x = 5$
$x = \frac{35}{2}$

48. $\frac{3}{4}n - 2 = \frac{1}{2}n + 7$
$\frac{1}{4}n - 2 = 7$
$\frac{1}{4}n = 9$
$n = 36$

49. $x(y + 2) = z$
$y + 2 = \frac{z}{x}$
$y = \frac{z}{x} - 2$

50. $I = prt$
$\frac{I}{pr} = t$

51. $5a - 6b = 9$
$-6b = -5a + 9$
$b = \frac{5a - 9}{6}$

52. $de - 4f = 5g$
$de = 5g + 4f$
$e = \frac{5g + 4f}{d}$

53. $F = G\frac{Mm}{r^2}$
$\frac{F}{G} = \frac{Mm}{r^2}$
$\frac{Fr^2}{G} = Mm$
$\frac{Fr^2}{Gm} = M$

54. $qr + s = t$
$qr = t - s$
$q = \frac{t - s}{r}$

55. Let x = the number of adult tickets. Thus, $5x$ is the number of student tickets.
$30x + 15(5x) = 420$
$30x + 75x = 420$
$105x = 420$
$x = 4$
4 adult tickets
5(4) = 20 student tickets

56. Let x = percent.
$\frac{17{,}099}{18{,}999} = \frac{x}{100}$
$1{,}709{,}900 = 18{,}999x$
$89.999 \approx x$
Sheila's price is about 90% of the dealership's price.

57. Let x = plant price.
$2x + 18 = 32$
$2x = 14$
$x = 7$
Each plant costs $7.00

58. Let s = the length of the equal sides.
$116 = 36 + s + s$
$116 = 36 + 2s$
$80 = 2s$
$40 = s$
The length of one of the equal sides is 40 cm.

59. the product of twice a number and the sum of the number and four added to twice the sum of the number and six

60. $\pi(1^2)h = \pi(2^2)1$
$\pi h = 4\pi$
$h = \frac{4\pi}{\pi}$
$h = 4$; 4 units

61. $\frac{50 \text{ miles}}{\text{hour}} \times x \text{ hours} = 510 \text{ miles}$
$x \text{ hours} = 10.2$
54.75 hours + 10.2 hours = 64.95 hours
Yes, the last day's trip will take him only 10.2 hours, which will bring the driver's total time to 64.95 hours.

62. 93,000,000 + 69,000,000 = 162,000,000 miles

63. 13,200 − 5280 = 7920 miles

64a.

Stem	Leaf
2	7
3	1 2 3
4	1 5
5	6 6
6	0 7
7	0

2|7 = 270

64b. 450; 560; (270 + 310 + 320 + 330 + 410 + 450 + 560 + 560 + 600 + 670 + 700) ÷ 11 = 5180 ÷ 11 = $470.\overline{90}$

65. 179, 180, 216, 219, 399, 399
$\frac{216 + 219}{2} = \frac{435}{2} = 217.5$; 399;
$\frac{179 + 180 + 216 + 219 + 399 + 399}{6} = \frac{1592}{6} = 265.\overline{3}$

66a. 92 **66b.** 10

67.

January	Stem	July
1	1	
1 2 6	2	
0 5	3	
1 1 4	4	
1 3 7	5	6
	6	5
	7	0 3 3 5 8 9
	8	1 2 3 6

|3|5 = 35°

68. 10, 11, 12, 12, 13, 13, 15
12; 12 and 13;
$\frac{10 + 11 + 12 + 12 + 13 + 13 + 15}{7} = \frac{86}{7} \approx 12.3$

69. $2(9a - 2) - 3(5 + a) = 2(9a) - 2(2) - 3(5) - 3(a)$
$= 18a - 4 - 15 - 3a$
$= 15a - 19$

70. commutative (+)

71. additive identity

72. $\sqrt{9 \div 3} = \sqrt{3}$; I R

73. $I = prt$
$= (20{,}000)\ (0.145)\ (6)$
$= 17{,}400$; $17,400

74. $3^b - a + c = 3^2 - 13 + 9$
$= 9 - 13 + 9$
$= 5$

75. $4 - [32 \div (16 - 12)] = 4 - [32 \div 4]$
$= 4 - 8$
$= -4$

76. $[18 - (5 + 22)] \times 2 = [18 - 27] \times 2$
$= -9 \times 2$
$= -18$

Page 34 Self Test

1. $m + n - p = 2 + (-3) - 4$
$= -5$

2. $m(n + p) = 2(-3 + 4)$
$= 2(1)$
$= 2$

3. $7 - 8 = -1$; R, Q, Z

4. $3.9 + 2.6 = 6.5$; R, Q

5. $\sqrt{36 + 5} = \sqrt{41} \approx 6.403$; R, I

6a.

Stem	Leaf
3	0 0 0 2 3 5 6 7 7 7 7 7 8 9 9
4	0 0 2 5 8 8 8 8 9
5	0 0 3 8 9 9

4|8 = $48

6b. 40; 37 and 48; (30 + 30 + 30 + 32 + 33 + 35 + 36 + 37 + 37 + 37 + 37 + 38 + 39 + 39 + 40 + 40 + 42 + 45 + 48 + 48 + 48 + 48 + 49 + 50 + 50 + 53 + 58 + 59 + 59) ÷ 29 = 1227 ÷ 29 ≈ 42.3

7. $4.5 - 3.9m = 20.1$
$-3.9m = 15.6$
$m = -4$

8. $9 = 16d + 51$
$-42 = 16d$
$-2.625 = d$

9. $2y - 8 = 14 - 9y$
$11y - 8 = 14$
$11y = 22$
$y = 2$

10. $285 - 38x = 2033$
$-38x = 1748$
$x = -46$

1-5A Graphing Technology: Using Tables to Estimate Solutions

Page 36 Exercises

1. $4x + 6 = 9$
$4x - 3 = 0$; build table of values; 0.75

2. $3.5x + 7 = 11$
$3.5x - 4 = 0$; build table of values; 1.14

3. $-1.25 - 0.3x = 8$
$-9.25 - 0.3x = 0$; build table of values; -30.83

4. $5(x - 3) = -2$
$5x - 15 = -2$
$5x - 13 = 0$; build table of values; 2.6

5. $2x + 1 = 12 - x$
$3x + 1 = 12$
$3x - 11 = 0$; build table of values; 3.67

6. $|6x + 4| - 7 = 2$
$|6x + 4| - 9 = 0$; build table of values; 0.83, -2.17

7. $|3 - x| = 5$
$|3 - x| - 5 = 0$; build table of values; -2, 8

8. $|2.21 + 0.55x| = 1.75$
$|2.21 + 0.55x| - 1.75 = 0$; build table of values; -0.84, -7.2

9. $|\frac{1}{2}x - 5| = 17$
$|\frac{1}{2}x - 5| - 17 = 0$; build table of values; 44, -24

10. $40 = \frac{5}{9}(x - 32)$
$40 = \frac{5}{9}x - \frac{160}{9}$
$0 = \frac{5}{9}x - \frac{520}{9}$; build table of values; 104

1-5 Solving Absolute Value Equations

Pages 40–41 Check for Understanding

1. Absolute value represents the number of units x is away from zero.

2. $|x - 7| + 4 = 0$
$|x - 7| = -4$
This equation can have no solution because an absolute value cannot have a negative solution.

3. Explanations will vary; $-a$ could be a positive number if the original a is negative; $-(-a) = a$.

4. Sometimes true; true if x is positive, false if x is 0 or negative.

5. See students' work.

6. $|x + 6| = |2.5 + 6|$
$= |8.5|$
$= 8.5$

7. $|-2x| = |-2(2.5)|$
$= |-5|$
$= 5$

8. $-|x + 10| = -|2.5 + 10|$
$= -|12.5|$
$= -12.5$

9. $|x + 5| = 18$ means $x + 5 = 18$ or $-(x + 5) = 18$
$x + 5 = 18$ or $-(x + 5) = 18$
$x = 13$; $x + 5 = -18$
$x = -23$

10. $|x + 9| = 25$ means $x + 9 = 25$ or $-(x + 9) = 25$
$x + 9 = 25$ or $-(x + 9) = 25$
$x = 16$; $x + 9 = -25$
$x = -34$

11. $|x - 6| = 12$ means $x - 6 = 12$ or $-(x - 6) = 12$
$x - 6 = 12$ or $-(x - 6) = 12$
$x = 18$; $x - 6 = -12$
$x = -6$

12. $|x - 3| = 15$ means $x - 3 = 15$ or $-(x - 3) = 15$
$x - 3 = 15$ or $-(x - 3) = 15$
$x = 18$; $x - 3 = -15$
$x = -12$

13. $|3 + x| = 45$ means $3 + x = 45$ or $-(3 + x) = 45$
$3 + x = 45$ or $-(3 + x) = 45$
$x = 42$; $3 + x = -45$
$x = -48$

14. $6|5x + 2| = 312$
$|5x + 2| = 52$
$|5x + 2| = 52$ means $5x + 2 = 52$ or $-(5x + 2) = 52$
$5x + 2 = 52$ or $-(5x + 2) = 52$
$5x = 50$; $5x + 2 = -52$
$x = 10$; $5x = -54$
$x = -10.8$

15a. $|x - 16| = 0.2$

15b. $|x - 16| = 0.2$ means $x - 16 = 0.2$ or $-(x - 16) = 0.2$
$x - 16 = 0.2$ or $-(x - 16) = 0.2$
$x = 16.2$; $x - 16 = -0.2$
$x = 15.8$

Pages 41–42 Exercises

16. $|-4x| = |-4(-4)|$
$= |16|$
$= 16$

17. $|2y - 5| = |2(5) - 5|$
$= |10 - 5|$
$= |5|$
$= 5$

18. $|3z| = |3(1.2)|$
$= |3.6|$
$= 3.6$

19. $|x + 5| = |-4 + 5|$
$= |1|$
$= 1$

20. $|-2y| = |-2(5)|$
$= |-10|$
$= 10$

21. $-|2z - 4| = -|2(1.2) - 4|$
$= -|2.4 - 4|$
$= -|-1.6|$
$= -1.6$

22. $6 - |4y + 10| = 6 - |4(5) + 10|$
$= 6 - |20 + 10|$
$= 6 - |30|$
$= 6 - 30$
$= -24$

23. $7 - |3z + 10| = 7 - |3(1.2) + 10|$
$= 7 - |3.6 + 10|$
$= 7 - |13.6|$
$= 7 - 13.6$
$= -6.6$

24. $3|x + 4| + |3x| = 3|-4 + 4| + |3(-4)|$
$= 3|0| + |-12|$
$= 3(0) + 12$
$= 0 + 12$
$= 12$

25. $|x - 3| = 17$
$x - 3 = 17$ or $x - 3 = -17$
$x = 20$ $\quad x = -14$

26. $|x + 6| = 18$
$x + 6 = 18$ or $x + 6 = -18$
$x = 12$ $\quad x = -24$

27. $|x + 11| = 42$
$x + 11 = 42$ or $x + 11 = -42$
$x = 31$ $\quad x = -53$

28. $3|x + 6| = 36$
$|x + 6| = 12$
$x + 6 = 12$ or $x + 6 = -12$
$x = 6$ $\quad x = -18$

29. $11|x - 9| = 121$
$|x - 9| = 11$
$x - 9 = 11$ or $x - 9 = -11$
$x = 20$ $\quad x = -2$

30. $|2x + 9| = 30$
$2x + 9 = 30$ or $2x + 9 = -30$
$2x = 21$ $\quad 2x = -39$
$x = 10.5$ $\quad x = -19.5$

31. $8|x - 3| = 88$
$|x - 3| = 11$
$x - 3 = 11$ or $x - 3 = -11$
$x = 14$ $\quad x = -8$

32. $|2x + 7| = 0$
$2x + 7 = 0$
$2x = -7$
$x = -\frac{7}{2}$

33. $|4x - 3| = -27$
no solution

34. $8|4x - 3| = 64$
$|4x - 3| = 8$
$4x - 3 = 8$ or $4x - 3 = -8$
$4x = 11$ $\quad 4x = -5$
$x = \frac{11}{4}$ $\quad x = -\frac{5}{4}$

35. $3|3x + 2| = 51$
$|3x + 2| = 17$
$3x + 2 = 17$ or $3x + 2 = -17$
$3x = 15$ $\quad 3x = -19$
$x = 5$ $\quad x = -\frac{19}{3}$

36. $5|x + 4| = 45$
$|x + 4| = 9$
$x + 4 = 9$ or $x + 4 = -9$
$x = 5$ $\quad x = -13$

37. $4|6x - 1| = 29$
$|6x - 1| = \frac{29}{4}$
$6x - 1 = \frac{29}{4}$ or $6x - 1 = -\frac{29}{4}$
$6x = \frac{33}{4}$ $\quad 6x = -\frac{25}{4}$
$x = \frac{11}{8}$ $\quad x = -\frac{25}{24}$

38. $|3t - 5| = 2t$
$3t - 5 = 2t$ or $3t - 5 = -2t$
$t - 5 = 0$ $\quad 5t - 5 = 0$
$t = 5$ $\quad 5t = 5$
$t = 1$

39. $|2a + 7| = a - 4$
$2a + 7 = a - 4$ or $2a + 7 = -(a - 4)$
$a + 7 = -4$ $\quad 2a + 7 = -a + 4$
$a = -11$ $\quad 3a + 7 = 4$
$3a = -3$
$a = -1$

Check:
$|2a + 7| = a - 4$ $\quad |2a + 7| = a - 4$
$|2(-11) + 7| \stackrel{?}{=} -11 - 4$ $\quad |2(-1) + 7 \stackrel{?}{=} -1 - 4$
$|-22 + 7| \stackrel{?}{=} -15$ $\quad |-2 + 7| \stackrel{?}{=} -5$
$|-15| \neq -15$ $\quad |5| \neq -5$
No solution.

40. $|x - 3| + 7 = 2$
$|x - 3| = -5$
No solution

41. $3|x + 6| = 9x - 6$
$|x + 6| = \frac{9x - 6}{3}$
$|x + 6| = 3x - 2$
$x + 6 = 3x - 2$ or $x + 6 = -(3x - 2)$
$-2x + 6 = -2$ $\quad x + 6 = -3x + 2$
$-2x = -8$ $\quad 4x + 6 = 2$
$x = 4$ $\quad 4x = -4$
$x = -1$

Check:
$3|x + 6| = 9x - 6$ $\quad 3|x + 6| = 9x - 6$
$3|4 + 6| \stackrel{?}{=} 9(4) - 6$ $\quad 3|-1 + 6| \stackrel{?}{=} 9(-1) - 6$
$3|10| \stackrel{?}{=} 36 - 6$ $\quad 3|5| \stackrel{?}{=} -9 - 6$
$30 = 30$ ✓ $\quad 15 \neq -15$

42. $5|3x - 4| = x + 1$
$|3x - 4| = \frac{x + 1}{5}$
$3x - 4 = \frac{x + 1}{5}$ or $3x - 4 = -\left(\frac{x + 1}{5}\right)$
$5(3x - 4) = 5\left(\frac{x + 1}{5}\right)$ $\quad 5(3x - 4) = -5\left(\frac{x + 1}{5}\right)$
$15x - 20 = x + 1$ $\quad 15x - 20 = -x - 1$
$14x - 20 = 1$ $\quad 16x - 20 = -1$
$14x = 21$ $\quad 16x = 19$
$x = \frac{3}{2}$ $\quad x = \frac{19}{16}$

43a. [Y=] [X,T,θ,n] [x^2] [−] 2 [X,T,θ,n] [−] 4; run program; −1.2, 3.2

43b. [Y=] [X,T,θ,n] [^] 3 [−] 3 [X,T,θ,n] ; run program; −1.7, 0, 1.7

43c. [Y=] [2nd] [ABS] [(] 3 [X,T,θ,n] [−] 2 [)] [−] 4; run program; −0.7, 2

43d. [Y=] 5 [X,T,θ,n] [^] 3 [+] 3 [X,T,θ,n] [x^2] [−] 25 [X,T,θ,n] [−] 15; run program; −2.2, −0.6, 2.2

44. $|x + 2| = |2x - 4|$

$x + 2 = 2x - 4$ or $x + 2 = -(2x - 4)$

$2 = x - 4$ $\quad x + 2 = -2x + 4$

$6 = x$ $\quad 3x + 2 = 4$

$3x = 2$

$x = \frac{2}{3}$

See students' work for explanations.

45a. $|x - 697| = 5$

45b. $|x - 697| = 5$

$x - 697 = 5$ or $x - 697 = -5$

$x = 702$ $\quad x = 692$

46a. $|x + 257°| = 2°$

46b. $|x + 257°| = 2°$

$x + 257° = 2°$ or $x + 257° = -2°$

$x = -255°C$ $\quad x = -259°C$

47. TAW, TAX, TAY, TBW, TBX, TBY, TCW, TCX, TCY, UAW, UAX, UAY, UBW, UBX, UBY, UCW, UCX, UCY, VAW, VAX, VAY, VBW, VBX, VBY, VCW, VCX, VCY

48. $4 + 3x$ **49.** $3 - 2x = 18$ **50.** $P = 4s$

$-2x = 15$ $\quad 42 = 4s$

$x = -\frac{15}{2}$ $\quad 10.5 = s$

side = 10.5 inches

51. $p + 5$

52. −35, −32, −31, −29, −29, −28, −27

−29; −29;

$\frac{-35 + (-32) + (-31) + (-29) + (-29) + (-28) + (-27)}{7}$

$= \frac{-211}{7} \approx -30.1$

53. $\frac{141 + 145}{2} = 143$; 141; (130 + 132 + 133 + 133 + 135 + 137 + 141 + 141 + 141 + 145 + 147 + 148 + 149 + 149 + 155 + 156 + 157 + 157) ÷ 18 = 2586 ÷ 18 ≈ 143.7

54. multiplicative identity

55. $-2.4 \times 10 = -24$; Z, Q, R

56. $12a^2 + bc = 12(3)^2 + 7(-2)$

$= 12(9) + (-14)$

$= 108 - 14$

$= 94$

1-6 Solving Inequalities

Page 46–47 Check for Understanding

1. 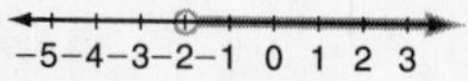

2. $\frac{1}{2}(5x) \le 10$

3a. $6 > 3$; $6 > -3$; $-6 < 3$; $-6 < -3$

3b. $\frac{6}{2} > \frac{3}{2}$ $\quad \frac{6}{2} > \frac{-3}{2}$ $\quad \frac{-6}{2} < \frac{3}{2}$ $\quad \frac{-6}{2} < \frac{-3}{2}$

$3 > \frac{3}{2}$ $\quad 3 > \frac{-3}{2}$ $\quad -3 < \frac{3}{2}$ $\quad -3 < \frac{-3}{2}$; yes

3c. $\frac{6}{-2} > \frac{3}{-2}$ $\quad \frac{6}{-2} > \frac{-3}{-2}$ $\quad \frac{-6}{-2} < \frac{3}{-2}$ $\quad \frac{-6}{-2} < \frac{-3}{-2}$

$-3 \not> \frac{-3}{2}$ $\quad -3 \not> \frac{3}{2}$ $\quad 3 \not< \frac{-3}{2}$ $\quad 3 \not< \frac{3}{2}$

No; when you multiply both sides of an inequality by a negative number, the inequality sign must be reversed to keep the inequality true.

4. $x > 4.5 \rightarrow \{x \mid x > 4.5\}$

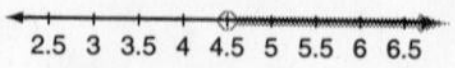

5. $7 \le 4a$

$1.75 \le a \rightarrow \{a \mid a \ge 1.75\}$

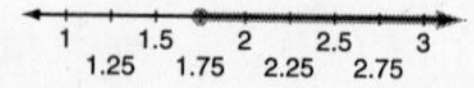

6. $7 - b \ge 5$

$-b \ge -2$

$b \le 2 \rightarrow \{b \mid b \le 2\}$

7. $3x + 4 \ge 19$

$3x \ge 15$

$x \ge 5 \rightarrow \{x \mid x \ge 5\}$

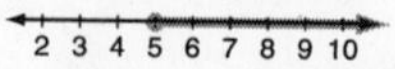

8. $2c + 15 \ge 3$

$2c \ge -12$

$c \ge -6 \rightarrow \{c \mid c \ge -6\}$

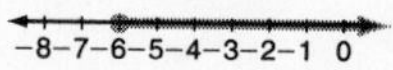

9. $\frac{d}{10} - 2 \le 0$

$\frac{d}{10} \le 2$

$d \le 20 \rightarrow \{d \mid d \le 20\}$

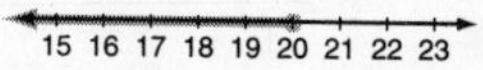

10. $-0.5y < 6$

$y > -12 \rightarrow \{y \mid y > -12\}$

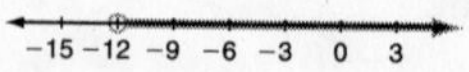

11. $\frac{7x + 1}{8} > \frac{7x}{8} + 1$

$8\left(\frac{7x+1}{8}\right) > 8\left(\frac{7x}{8}\right) + 8(1)$

$7x + 1 > 7x + 8$

$1 > 8$ false, so $\varnothing$

12. Let x = the number.

$4x < 32$

13. Let n = the number.

$n + 15 \ge 27$

Pages 47–48 Exercises

14. $6x < 30$

$x < 5 \rightarrow \{x \mid x < 5\}$

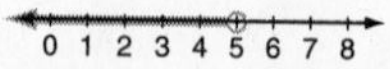

15. $-5r > 25$

$r < -5 \rightarrow \{r \mid r < -5\}$

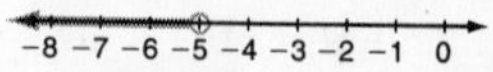

16. $11 - 5y < -77$

$-5y < -88$

$y > 17.6 \rightarrow \{y \mid y > 17.6\}$

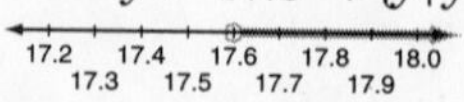

17. $0.06 + x < 2$

$x < 1.94 \rightarrow \{x \mid x < 1.94\}$

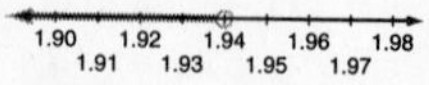

18. $15 - 5t \ge 55$

$-5t \ge 40$

$t \le -8 \rightarrow \{t \mid t \le -8\}$

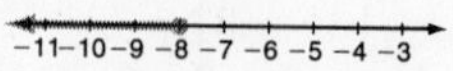

19. $6x + 4 \ge 34$

$6x \ge 30$

$x \ge 5 \rightarrow \{x \mid x \ge 5\}$

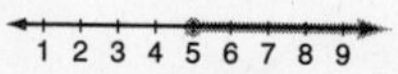

20. $3(4x + 7) < 21$
$12x + 21 < 21$
$12x < 0$
$x < 0 \rightarrow \{x \mid x < 0\}$

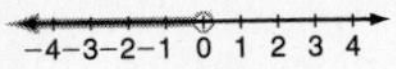

21. $8x + 5 \geq 10$
$8x \geq 5$
$x \geq \frac{5}{8} \rightarrow \left\{x \mid x \geq \frac{5}{8}\right\}$

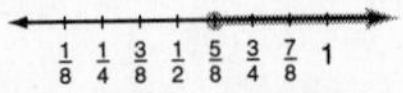

22. $40 \leq -6(5r - 7)$
$40 \leq -30r + 42$
$-2 \leq -30r$
$\frac{1}{15} \geq r \rightarrow \left\{r \mid r \leq \frac{1}{15}\right\}$

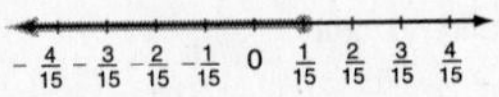

23. $7x - 5 > 3x + 4$
$4x - 5 > 4$
$4x > 9$
$x > 2.25 \rightarrow \{x \mid x > 2.25\}$

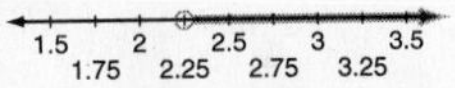

24. $9(2x + 3) > 10$
$18x + 27 > 10$
$18x > -17$
$x > -\frac{17}{18} \rightarrow \left\{x \mid x > -\frac{17}{18}\right\}$

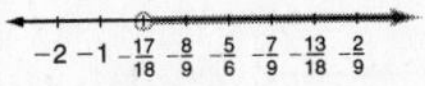

25. $5(3z - 3) \leq 60$
$15z - 15 \leq 60$
$15z \leq 75$
$z \leq 5 \rightarrow \{z \mid z \leq 5\}$

26. $7 - 2m \geq 0$
$-2m \geq -7$
$m \leq 3.5 \rightarrow \{m \mid m \leq 3.5\}$

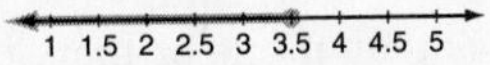

27. $2(m - 5) - 3(2m - 5) < 5m + 1$
$2m - 10 - 6m + 15 < 5m + 1$
$-4m + 5 < 5m + 1$
$-9m + 5 < 1$
$-9m < -4$
$m > \frac{4}{9} \rightarrow \left\{m \mid m > \frac{4}{9}\right\}$

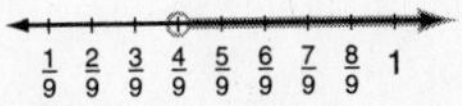

28. $0.01x - 4.23 \geq 0$
$0.01x \geq 4.23$
$x \geq 423 \rightarrow \{x \mid x \geq 423\}$

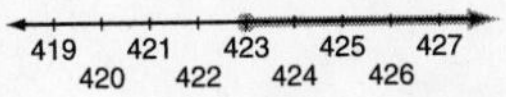

29. $3b - 2(b - 5) < 2(b + 4)$
$3b - 2b + 10 < 2b + 8$
$b + 10 < 2b + 8$
$-b + 10 < 8$
$-b < -2$
$b > 2 \rightarrow \{b \mid b > 2\}$

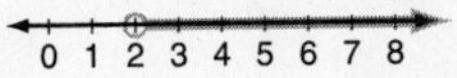

30. $0.75x - 0.5 < 0$
$0.75x < 0.5$
$x < \frac{0.5}{0.75}$
$x < \frac{2}{3} \rightarrow \left\{x \mid x < \frac{2}{3}\right\}$

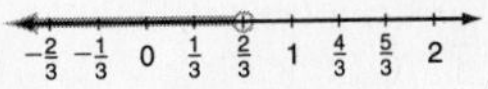

31. $2.55x - 4.24 \leq 0$
$2.55x \leq 4.24$
$x \leq 1.66 \rightarrow \{x \mid x \leq 1.66\}$

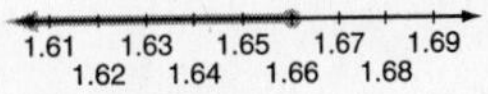

32. $\frac{2x + 3}{5} \leq 0.03$
$2x + 3 \leq 0.15$
$2x \leq -2.85$
$x \leq -1.425 \rightarrow \{x \mid x \leq -1.425\}$

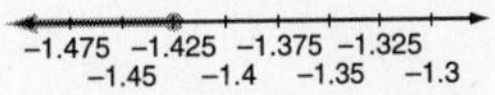

33. $\frac{3x - 3}{5} < \frac{6(x - 1)}{10}$
$10\left(\frac{3x - 3}{5}\right) < \left(\frac{6(x - 1)}{10}\right)10$
$2(3x - 3) < 6(x - 1)$
$6x - 3 < 6x - 6$
$-3 < -6$ false, so $\varnothing$

34. $\frac{4x + 2}{5} \geq -0.04$
$4x + 2 \geq -0.2$
$4x \geq -2.2$
$x \geq -0.55 \rightarrow \{x \mid x \geq -0.55\}$

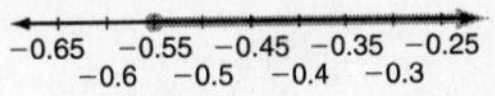

35. $-x \geq \frac{x + 4}{7}$
$-7x \geq x + 4$
$-8x \geq 4$
$x \leq -\frac{1}{2} \rightarrow \left\{x \mid x \leq \frac{1}{2}\right\}$

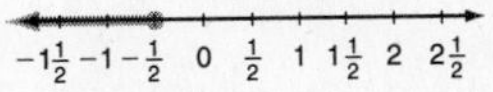

36. $\frac{x + 8}{4} - 1 > \frac{x}{3}$
$\left(\frac{x + 8}{4}\right)12 - (1)12 > \left(\frac{x}{3}\right)12$
$3(x + 8) - 12 > 4x$
$3x + 24 - 12 > 4x$
$3x + 12 > 4x$
$-x + 12 > 0$
$-x > -12$
$x < 12 \rightarrow \{x \mid x < 12\}$

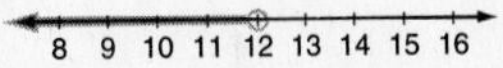

37. $20\left(\frac{1}{5} - \frac{w}{4}\right) \geq -2w$
$4 - 5w \geq -2w$
$4 - 3w \geq 0$
$-3w \geq -4$
$w \leq \frac{4}{3} \rightarrow \left\{w \mid w \leq \frac{4}{3}\right\}$

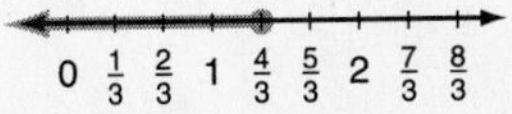

38. Let x = the number.
$11x < 53$
$x < 4.\overline{81} \rightarrow \{x \mid x < 4.\overline{81}\}$

39. Let x = the number.
$\frac{3}{4}x - 25 \geq 8$
$\frac{3}{4}x \geq 33$
$x \geq 44 \rightarrow \{x \mid x \geq 44\}$

40. Let x = the number.
$-5x < 321$
$x > -64.2 \rightarrow \{x \mid x > -64.2\}$

41. Let x = the number.
$57 > 0.5x$
$114 > x \rightarrow \{x \mid x < 114\}$

42. Let x = the number.
$90 - 5 \geq 10x$
$85 \geq 10x$
$8.5 \geq x \rightarrow \{x \mid x \leq 8.5\}$

43. Let x = the number.
$62 < -6x$
$-10.\overline{3} > x \rightarrow \{x \mid x < -10.\overline{3}\}$

44. [Y=] [(-)] 49 [2nd] [TEST] [3] 7 [(] 2 [X,T,θ,n] [+] 3 [)] [GRAPH] $\{x \mid x < -5\}$

45. [Y=] 8 [X,T,θ,n] [+] 3 [(] 2 [+] 7.5 [)] [2nd] [TEST] [5] 25 [GRAPH] $\{r \mid r < -0.4375\}$

46. [Y=] 2 [(] 3 [X,T,θ,n] [+] 4 [)] [−] 3 [2nd] [TEST] [6] 2 [(] [(-)] 1 [)] [GRAPH]
$\{k \mid k \leq -1.1\overline{6}\}$

47. [Y=] [(-)] 5 [X,T,θ,n] [+] 4 [(] 3 [−] 5 [)] [2nd] [TEST] [5] 7 [GRAPH] $\{s \mid s > -3\}$

48. $3x - 2 \geq 0$ $\quad$ $5x - 1 \leq 0$
$3x \geq 2$ $\quad$ $5x \leq 1$
$x \geq \frac{2}{3}$ $\quad$ $x \leq \frac{1}{5}$
There are no numbers that satisfy both inequalities; $\varnothing$.

49a. $2500 \times 0.30 = 750$; $3300 \times 0.30 = 990$;
$750 \leq x \leq 990$

49b. 990 Calories

50. $2(4.99) + x \leq 75$

51. $|x - 4| = 11$
$x - 4 = 11$ or $x - 4 = -11$
$x = 15$ $\quad$ $x = -7$

52. $|x - 8| = 3x - 4$
$x - 8 = 3x - 4$ or $x - 8 = -(3x - 4)$
$-2x - 8 = -4$ $\quad$ $x - 8 = -3x + 4$
$-2x = 4$ $\quad$ $4x - 8 = 4$
$x = -2$ $\quad$ $4x = 12$
$x = 3$

Check:
$|x - 8| = 3x - 4$ $\quad$ $|x - 8| = 3x - 4$
$|-2 - 8| \stackrel{?}{=} 3(-2) - 4$ $\quad$ $|3 - 8| \stackrel{?}{=} 3(3) - 4$
$|-10| \stackrel{?}{=} -6 - 4$ $\quad$ $|-5| \stackrel{?}{=} 9 - 4$
$10 \neq -10$ $\quad$ $5 = 5$ ✓

53. $|2x - 4| + 1.2 = |2(-3) - 4| + 1.2$
$= |-6 - 4| + 1.2$
$= |-10| + 1.2$
$= 10 + 1.2$
$= 11.2$

54. Square: perimeter = $4x$
Triangle: perimeter = $3x$
$4x + 3x < 50$
$7x < 50$
$x < 7.143$
The possible whole number lengths are 1 cm, 2 cm, 3 cm, 4 cm, 5 cm, 6 cm, 7 cm.

55. $68x + 373 = 802$
$68x = 429$
$x \approx 6.309$

56. 2, 8, 43, 44, 56
43; no mode; $\frac{2 + 8 + 43 + 44 + 56}{5} = \frac{153}{5} = 30.6$

57. distributive

58. $5(3m - 7n) + 3(4m + n) = 15m - 35n + 12m + 3n$
$= 27m - 32n$

59. $I = \frac{E}{R + r}$
$= \frac{1.5}{2.35 + 0.15}$
$= \frac{1.5}{2.5}$
$= 0.6$; 0.6 amperes

1-7 Solving Absolute Value Inequalities

Page 52 Check for Understanding

1. Sample answer: $|x + 9| < -2$

2. $|x| < 5$

3. Because the absolute value of $x + 2 \geq 0$ and $0 > -4$.

4. A compound inequality containing *and* is true only if both inequalities are true. A compound inequality containing *or* is true if one or more of the inequalities is true.

5. $|x| < 18$

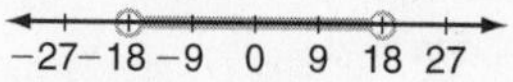

6. $|x| < 3$

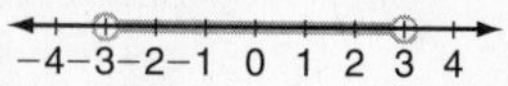

7. $|x| < 4$

8. $|x| \leq 2$

9. $3x + 1 < 7$ or $7 < 2x - 9$
$3x < 6$ $\quad$ $16 < 2x$
$x < 2$ $\quad$ $8 < x$
$\{x \mid x < 2 \text{ or } x > 8\}$

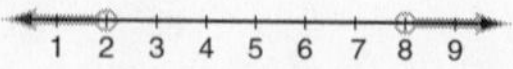

10. $|x| \geq 4$
$x \geq 4$ or $x \leq -4$
$\{x \mid x \geq 4 \text{ or } x \leq -4\}$

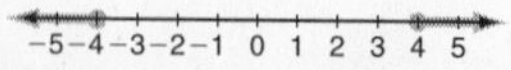

11. $|x + 2| > 3$
$x + 2 > 3$ or $x + 2 < -3$
$x > 1$ $\quad$ $x < -5$
$\{x \mid x > 1 \text{ or } x < -5\}$

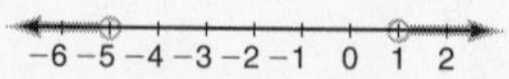

12. $1 \le x - 2 \times 2 \le 7$
$1 + 2 \le x - 2 + 2 \le 7 + 2$
$3 \le x \le 9$
$\{x \mid 3 \le x \le 9\}$

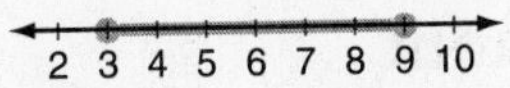

13. $|3x + 12| > 42$
$3x + 12 > 42$ or $3x + 12 < -42$
$3x > 30 \qquad 3x < -54$
$x > 10 \qquad x < -18$
$\{x \mid x > 10 \text{ or } x < -18\}$

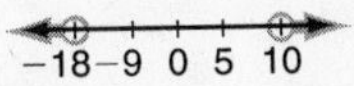

14. $|x| \ge x$
$x \ge x$ or $x \le -x$
$0 \ge 0 \qquad 2x \le 0$
true, so $\qquad x \le 0$
all reals

Pages 53–54 Exercises

15. $|x| < 7$
$-7 < x < 7$
$\{x \mid -7 < x < 7\}$

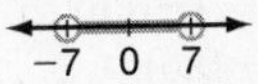

16. $|x| \le 15$
$-15 \le x \le 15$
$\{x \mid -15 \le x \le 15\}$

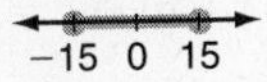

17. $|x| > 11$
$x > 11$ or $x < -11$
$\{x \mid x > 11 \text{ or } x < -11\}$

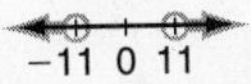

18. $|x| \le 5$
$-5 \le x \le 5$
$\{x \mid -5 \le x \le 5\}$

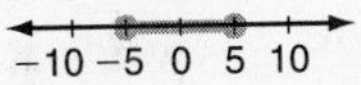

19. $|x| < 8$
$-8 < x < 8$
$\{x \mid -8 < x < 8\}$

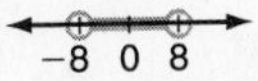

20. $|x| \le 10$
$-10 \le x \le 10$
$\{x \mid -10 \le x \le 10\}$

21. $|x| < 3$ **22.** $|x| \le 1$ **23.** $|x| \ge 4$
24. $|x| < 2.8$ **25.** $|x + 1| > 2$ **26.** $|x - 1| < 1$

27. $|8x| \le 10$
$-10 \le 8x \le 10$
$-\frac{5}{4} \le x \le \frac{5}{4}$
$\left\{x \mid \frac{5}{4} \le x \le \frac{5}{4}\right\}$

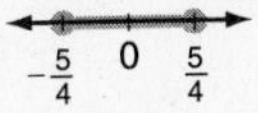

28. $|2x| < 6$
$-6 < 2x < 6$
$-3 < x < 3$
$\{x \mid -3 < x < 3\}$

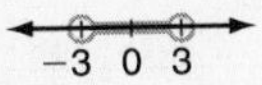

29. $|x| > 5$
$x > 5$ or $x < -5$
$\{x \mid x > 5 \text{ or } x < -5\}$

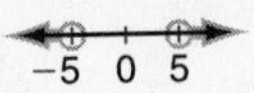

30. $|2x - 9| \le 27$
$-27 \le 2x - 9 \le 27$
$-18 \le 2x \le 36$
$-9 \le x \le 18$
$\{x \mid -9 \le x \le 18\}$

31. $|3x| \ge 7$
$3x \ge 7$ or $3x \le -7$
$x \ge \frac{7}{3} \qquad x \le -\frac{7}{3}$
$\left\{x \mid x \ge \frac{7}{3} \text{ or } x \le -\frac{7}{3}\right\}$

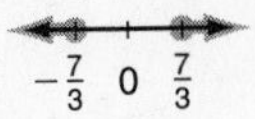

32. $|5x| < -25$
$\varnothing$

33. $|2x| > 1$
$2x > 1$or $2x < -1$
$x > \frac{1}{2} \qquad x < -\frac{1}{2}$
$\left\{x \mid x > \frac{1}{2} \text{ or } x < -\frac{1}{2}\right\}$

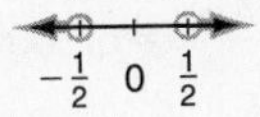

34. $x - 4 < 1$ or $x + 2 > 1$
$x < 5 \qquad x > -1$
all reals

35. $|x - 6| \le -12$
$\varnothing$

36. $-1 < 3x + 2 < 14$
$-3 < 3x < 12$
$-1 < x < 4$
$\{x \mid -1 < x < 4\}$

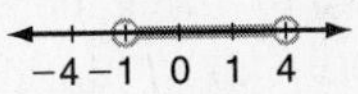

37. $|3x + 11| > 1$
$3x + 11 > 1$ or $3x + 11 < -1$
$3x > -10 \qquad 3x < -12$
$x > -\frac{10}{3} \qquad x < -4$
$\left\{x \mid x > -\frac{10}{3} \text{ or } x < -4\right\}$

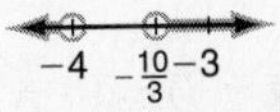

38. $|x| \le x$
$-x \le x \le x$
Statement is true for all positive reals. However, negative reals would make the inequality false. Therefore, only nonnegative reals are in the solution set.
$\{x \mid x \ge 0\}$

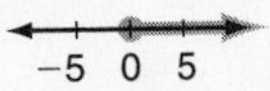

39. $x + 6 \ge -1$ or $x - 2 \le 4$
$x \ge -7 \qquad x \le 6$
all reals

40. $-4 \le 4x + 24 \le 4$
$-28 \le 4x \le -20$
$-7 \le x \le -5$
$\{x \mid -7 \le x \le -5\}$

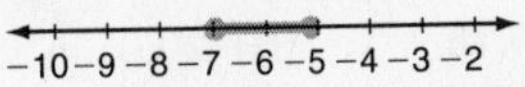

41. $|3x| + 3 \le 0$
$|3x| \le -3$
$\varnothing$

42. $|5x - 7| < 81$
$-81 < 5x - 7 < 81$
$-74 < 5x < 88$
$-14.8 < x < 17.6$
$\{x \mid -14.8 < x < 17.6\}$

43. $2x - 1 < -5$ or $3x + 2 \ge 5$
$2x < -4 \qquad 3x \ge 3$
$x < -2 \qquad x \ge 1$
$\{x \mid x < -2 \text{ or } x \ge 1\}$

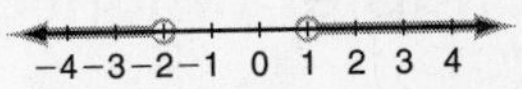

44. $|x + 2| - x \geq 0$
$|x + 2| \geq x$
$x + 2 \geq x$ or $x + 2 \leq -x$
$2 \geq 0$ $\quad 2x + 2 \leq 0$
true, so $\quad 2x \leq -2$
all reals $\quad x \leq -1$

45. $|x + 1| + |x - 1| \leq 2$
$-2 \leq x + 1 + x - 1 \leq 2$
$-2 \leq 2x \leq 2$
$-1 \leq x \leq 1$
$\{x \mid -1 \leq x \leq 1\}$

46a. $45 \leq s \leq 65$ **46b.** $45 \leq s \leq 55$

47a. range = 76,000 − 40,000 = 36,000
half of range = $\frac{36,000}{2}$ = 18,000
salary halfway between the highest and lowest salaries = $\frac{76,000 + 40,000}{2}$ = 58,000
$|x - 58,000| \leq 18,000$

47b. See students' work.

48. $1.20x = 10.50$ $\quad 1.40x = 10.50$
$x = 8.75$ $\quad x = 7.5$
7.5 to 8.75 gallons

49. $9(x + 2) < 72$
$x + 2 < 8$
$x < 6$
$\{x \mid x < 6\}$

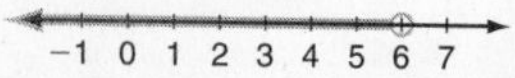

50. $3(3x + 2) > 7x - 2$
$9x + 6 > 7x - 2$
$2x + 6 > -2$
$2x > -8$
$x > -4$
$\{x \mid x > -4\}$

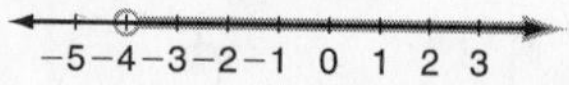

51. $8x + 5 < 7x - 3$
$x + 5 < -3$
$x < -8$
$\{x \mid x < -8\}$

52. $-4(3m - 7) - (3 - m) < 13$
$-12m + 28 - 3 + m < 13$
$-11m + 25 < 13$
$-11m < -12$
$m > \frac{12}{11}$
$\left\{m \mid m > \frac{12}{11}\right\}$

53. $|3x - 4| = 1$
$3x - 4 = 1$ or $3x - 4 = -1$
$3x = 5$ $\quad 3x = 3$
$x = \frac{5}{3}$ $\quad x = 1$

54. $|7(-3) + 10| = |-21 + 10|$
$= |-11|$
$= 11$

55a. $(0.50)6 + (0.35)x = 10$

55b. $(0.50)6 + (0.35)x = 10$
$3 + (0.35)x = 10$
$0.35x = 7$
$x = 20$

56. $y = 8(0.3) + 1.2$
$= 2.4 + 1.2$
$= 3.6$

57. 19.75, 19.80, 20.01, 20.19, 20.3, 20.5, 20.7, 20.7, 21.6, 21.6, 21.7, 21.8, 22, 22.2, 22.6
20.7; 20.7 and 21.6; (19.75 + 19.80 + 20.01 + 20.19 + 20.3 + 20.5 + 20.7 + 20.7 + 21.6 + 21.6 + 21.7 + 21.8 + 22 + 22.2 + 22.6) ÷ 15 = 315.45 ÷ 15 = 21.03

Chapter 1 Highlights

Page 55 Understanding and Using the Vocabulary

1. j **2.** h **3.** f **4.** k **5.** b **6.** e **7.** l **8.** g **9.** c **10.** a **11.** i **12.** d

Chapter 1 Study Guide and Assessment

Pages 56–58 Skills and Concepts

13. $6(5 - 8) \div 9 + 4 = 6(-3) \div 9 + 4$
$= -18 \div 9 + 4$
$= -2 + 4$
$= 2$

14. $(3 + 7)^2 - 16 \div 2 = (10)^2 - 16 \div 2$
$= 100 - 8$
$= 92$

15. $(6 + 5)4 - 3 = (11)4 - 3$
$= 44 - 3$
$= 41$

16. $-7 + [28 \div (18 - 7(2))] = -7 + [28 \div (18 - 14)]$
$= -7 + [28 \div 4]$
$= -7 + [7]$
$= 0$

17. $\frac{8c + ab}{a} = \frac{8(-0.5) + 4(5)}{4}$
$= \frac{-4 + 20}{4}$
$= \frac{16}{4}$
$= 4$

18. $(a - d + b) \div c = (4 - (-3) + 5) \div (-0.5)$
$= (4 + 3 + 5) \div (-0.5)$
$= 12 \div (-0.5)$
$= -24$

19. $4 - 12 = -8$; Z, Q, R

20. $42 \div 8 = 5.25$; Q, R

21. $\sqrt{2 + 3} = \sqrt{5}$; I, R

22. $2^3 + 10 = 8 + 10 = 18$; N, W, Z, Q, R

23. $2\pi(8.75) \approx 54.978$; I, R

24. $-20 \div 2^2 = -20 \div 4 = -5$; Z, Q, R

25. multiplicative inverse

26. associative (×)

27. $7a + 2b - 5a - 6b = 2a - 4b$

28. $3(a + 4b) - 2(4a + 2b) = 3a + 12b - 8a - 4b$
$= -5a + 8b$

29. 5, 18, 25, 64, 92
25; no mode; $\frac{5 + 18 + 25 + 64 + 92}{5} = \frac{204}{5} = 40.8$

30. 35, 41, 48, 48, 52, 59, 61, 66
$\frac{48 + 52}{2} = 50$; 48;
$\frac{35 + 41 + 48 + 48 + 52 + 59 + 61 + 66}{8} = \frac{410}{8} = 51.25$

31. 2.9, 3.6, 4.6, 6.1, 6.1, 8.9, 10
6.1; 6.1; $\frac{2.9 + 3.6 + 4.6 + 6.1 + 6.1 + 8.9 + 10}{7} = \frac{42.2}{7} \approx 6.0$

32. 3, 6, 7, 7, 7, 7, 9, 10, 10, 10, 10, 10, 13, 14, 14, 16, 17, 17, 19, 20, 21, 31
$\frac{10 + 10}{2} = \frac{20}{2} = 10$; 10; (3 + 6 + 7 + 7 + 7 + 7 + 9 + 10 + 10 + 10 + 10 + 10 + 13 + 14 + 14 + 16 + 17 + 17 + 19 + 20 + 21 + 31) ÷ 22 = 278 ÷ 22 ≈ 12.6

33. $$\begin{aligned} 12z + 36 &= 8z - 48 \\ 4z + 36 &= -48 \\ 4z &= -84 \\ z &= -21 \end{aligned}$$

34. $$\begin{aligned} 4.2x + 6.4 &= 40 \\ 4.2x &= 33.6 \\ x &= 8 \end{aligned}$$

35. $$\begin{aligned} 14y - 3 &= 25 \\ 14y &= 28 \\ y &= 2 \end{aligned}$$

36. $$\begin{aligned} 7w + 2 &= 3w + 94 \\ 4w + 2 &= 94 \\ 4w &= 92 \\ w &= 23 \end{aligned}$$

37. $$\begin{aligned} 4 - 2(1 - w) &= -38 \\ 4 - 2 + 2w &= -38 \\ 2 + 2w &= -38 \\ 2w &= -40 \\ w &= -20 \end{aligned}$$

38. $$\begin{aligned} 4y - \tfrac{1}{10} &= 3y + \tfrac{4}{5} \\ y - \tfrac{1}{10} &= \tfrac{4}{5} \\ y &= \tfrac{9}{10} \end{aligned}$$

39. $$\begin{aligned} 48 + 5y &= 96 - 3y \\ 48 + 8y &= 96 \\ 8y &= 48 \\ y &= 6 \end{aligned}$$

40. $$\begin{aligned} \tfrac{x}{3} + \tfrac{x}{2} &= \tfrac{3}{4} \\ 12\left(\tfrac{x}{3}\right) + 12\left(\tfrac{x}{2}\right) &= 12\left(\tfrac{3}{4}\right) \\ 4x + 6x &= 9 \\ 10x &= 9 \\ x &= \tfrac{9}{10} \end{aligned}$$

41. $$\begin{aligned} A &= p + prt \\ A - p &= prt \\ \tfrac{A-p}{pr} &= t \end{aligned}$$

42. $$\begin{aligned} df - 3g &= 4h \\ df &= 4h + 3g \\ f &= \tfrac{4h + 3g}{d} \end{aligned}$$

43. $$\begin{aligned} \tfrac{3a^2 - 1}{2b} &= c \\ 3a^2 - 1 &= 2bc \\ \tfrac{3a^2 - 1}{2c} &= b \end{aligned}$$

44. $$\begin{aligned} s &= \tfrac{1}{2}gt^2 \\ 2s &= gt^2 \\ \tfrac{2s}{t^2} &= g \end{aligned}$$

45. $$\begin{aligned} |y - 5| - 2 &= 10 \\ |y - 5| &= 12 \end{aligned}$$
$y - 5 = 12$ or $y - 5 = -12$
$y = 17$ $\quad$ $y = -7$

46. $|5y - 8| = 12$
$5y - 8 = 12$ or $5y - 8 = -12$
$5y = 20$ $\quad$ $5y = -4$
$y = 4$ $\quad$ $y = -\frac{4}{5}$

47. $|2x - 36| = 14$
$2x - 36 = 14$ or $2x - 36 = -14$
$2x = 50$ $\quad$ $2x = 22$
$x = 25$ $\quad$ $x = 11$

48. $$\begin{aligned} |x + 4| + 3 &= 17 \\ |x + 4| &= 14 \end{aligned}$$
$x + 4 = 14$ or $x + 4 = -14$
$x = 10$ $\quad$ $x = -18$

49. $$\begin{aligned} |q - 3| + 7 &= 2 \\ |q - 3| &= -5 \end{aligned}$$
no solution

50. $$\begin{aligned} 4|3x + 4| &= 4x + 8 \\ |3x + 4| &= x + 2 \end{aligned}$$
$3x + 4 = x + 2$ or $3x + 4 = -(x + 2)$
$2x + 4 = 2$ $\quad$ $3x + 4 = -x - 2$
$2x = -2$ $\quad$ $4x + 4 = -2$
$x = -1$ $\quad$ $4x = -6$
$x = -\frac{3}{2}$

51. $$\begin{aligned} 2|w + 6| &= 10 \\ |w + 6| &= 5 \end{aligned}$$
$w + 6 = 5$ or $w + 6 = -5$
$w = -1$ $\quad$ $w = -11$

52. $$\begin{aligned} 5|6 - 5x| &= 15x - 35 \\ |6 - 5x| &= 3x - 7 \end{aligned}$$
$6 - 5x = 3x - 7$ or $6 - 5x = -(3x - 7)$
$6 - 8x = -7$ $\quad$ $6 - 5x = -3x + 7$
$-8x = -13$ $\quad$ $6 - 2x = 7$
$x = \frac{13}{8}$ $\quad$ $-2x = 1$
$x = -\frac{1}{2}$

Check:

$$\begin{aligned} 5|6 - 5x| &= 15x - 35 \\ 5\left|6 - \tfrac{65}{8}\right| &\overset{?}{=} \tfrac{195}{8} - 35 \\ 5\left|-\tfrac{17}{8}\right| &\overset{?}{=} -\tfrac{85}{8} \\ 5\left(\tfrac{17}{8}\right) &\overset{?}{=} -\tfrac{85}{8} \\ \tfrac{85}{8} &\neq -\tfrac{85}{8} \end{aligned}$$

$$\begin{aligned} 5|6 - 5x| &= 15x - 35 \\ 5\left|6 + \tfrac{5}{2}\right| &\overset{?}{=} -\tfrac{15}{2} - 35 \\ 5\left|\tfrac{17}{2}\right| &\overset{?}{=} -\tfrac{85}{2} \\ 5\left(\tfrac{17}{2}\right) &\overset{?}{=} -\tfrac{85}{2} \\ \tfrac{85}{2} &\neq -\tfrac{85}{2} \end{aligned}$$

no solution

53. $$\begin{aligned} 5z - 6 &> 14 \\ 5z &> 20 \\ z &> 4 \rightarrow \{z \mid z > 4\} \end{aligned}$$

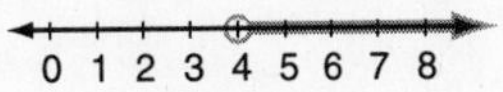

54. $$\begin{aligned} 5(x - 2) &< 75 \\ 5x - 10 &< 75 \\ 5x &< 85 \\ x &< 17 \rightarrow \{x \mid x < 17\} \end{aligned}$$

55. $$\begin{aligned} 57 - 4t &\geq 13 \\ -4t &\geq -44 \\ t &\leq 11 \rightarrow \{t \mid t \leq 11\} \end{aligned}$$

56. $$\begin{aligned} -3(2x + 5) &> 13x - 4 \\ -6x - 15 &> 13x - 4 \\ -19x - 15 &> -4 \\ -19x &> 11 \\ x &< -0.58 \rightarrow \{x \mid x < -0.58\} \end{aligned}$$

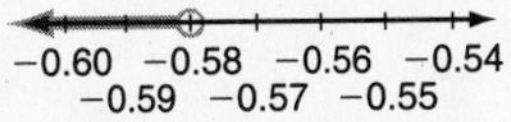

57. $$\begin{aligned} 18 - 2(y + 6) &< 76 \\ 18 - 2y - 12 &< 76 \\ -2y + 6 &< 76 \\ -2y &< 70 \\ y &> -35 \rightarrow \{y \mid y > -35\} \end{aligned}$$

58. $$\begin{aligned} 3(6 - 5x) &\leq 12x - 36 \\ 18 - 15x &\leq 12x - 36 \\ 18 - 27x &\leq -36 \\ -27x &\leq -54 \\ x &\geq 2 \rightarrow \{x \mid x \geq 2\} \end{aligned}$$

59. $2 - 3z \geq 7(8 - 2z) + 12$
$2 - 3z \geq 56 - 14z + 12$
$2 - 3z \geq 68 - 14z$
$2 + 11z \geq 68$
$11z \geq 66$
$z \geq 6 \rightarrow \{z \mid z \geq 6\}$

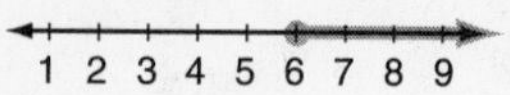

60. $8(2x - 1) > 11x - 17$
$16x - 8 > 11x - 17$
$5x - 8 > -17$
$5x > -9$
$x > -1.8 \rightarrow \{x \mid x > -1.8\}$

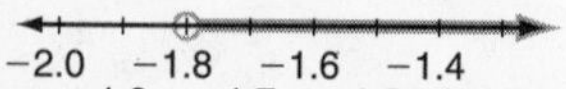

61. $11 < 3x + 2 < 20$
$9 < 3x < 18$
$3 < x < 6$
$\{x \mid 3 < x < 6\}$

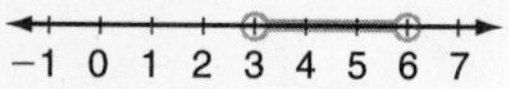

62. $4x - 10 < -10$ or $6x + 4 \geq 10$
$4x < 0$ $\quad$ $6x \geq 6$
$x < 0$ $\quad$ $x \geq 1$
$\{x \mid x < 0 \text{ or } x \geq 1\}$

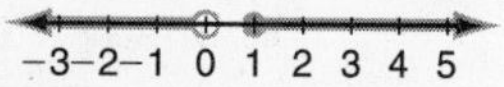

63. $-1 < 3(y - 2) \leq 9$
$-1 < 3y - 6 \leq 9$
$5 < 3y \leq 15$
$\frac{5}{3} < y \leq 5$
$\left\{y \mid \frac{5}{3} < y \leq 5\right\}$

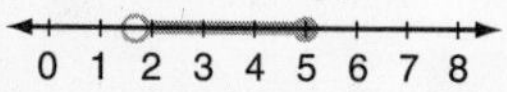

64. $5y - 4 > 16$ or $3y + 2 < 1$
$5y > 20$ $\quad$ $3y < -1$
$y > 4$ $\quad$ $y < -\frac{1}{3}$
$\left\{y \mid y > 4 \text{ or } y < -\frac{1}{3}\right\}$

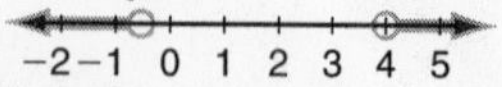

65. $|2x + 6| \leq 4$
$-4 \leq 2x + 6 \leq 4$
$-10 \leq 2x \leq -2$
$-5 \leq x \leq -1$
$\{x \mid -5 \leq x \leq -1\}$

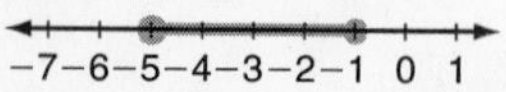

66. $7 + |9 - 5x| > 1$
$|9 - 5x| > -6$
all reals

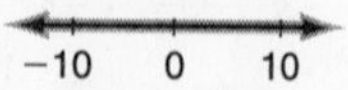

67. $|4x| + 3 \leq 0$
$|4x| \leq -3$
no solution; $\varnothing$

68. $|x| + 1 < 12$
$|x| < 11$
$-11 < x < 11$
$\{x \mid -11 < x < 11\}$

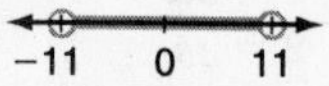

69. $|3x| < 27$
$-27 < 3x < 27$
$-9 < x < 9$
$\{x \mid -9 < x < 9\}$

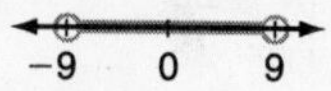

70. $|2x + 3| - 6 \geq 7$
$|2x + 3| \geq 13$
$2x + 3 \geq 13$ or $2x + 3 \leq -13$
$2x \geq 10$ $\quad$ $2x \leq -16$
$x \geq 5$ $\quad$ $x \leq -8$
$\{x \mid x \geq 5 \text{ or } x \leq -8\}$

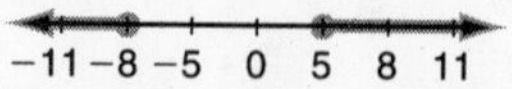

Page 58 Applications and Problem Solving

71. Let w = width
Length = $w + 15$

$P = 2\ell + 2w$
$150 = 2(w + 15) + 2(w)$
$150 = 2w + 30 + 2w$
$150 = 4w + 30$
$120 = 4w$
$30 = w$

Length = $w + 15 = 30 + 15 = 45$
Dimensions are 30 cm by 45 cm.

72. $2011 - 972 - 114 = 925$
$925 \div 7400 = 0.125$
Gasoline cost/mile = 12.5¢

73. Let q = score on last quiz.
$\frac{73 + 75 + 89 + 91 + q}{5} \geq 85$
$73 + 75 + 89 + 91 + q \geq 425$
$328 + q \geq 425$
$q \geq 97$
You must score at least 97.

74. $3x + 0.75 + 2x + 0.75 = 9$
$5x + 1.50 = 9$
$5x = 7.50$
$x = 1.50$; \$1.50

75. 22, 183, 421, 660, 2782, 3658, 3742, 3777, 3787, 4632, 4773, 5016, 5625, 6946, 7455, 9219, 10,918
3777; no mode; (22 + 183 + 421 + 660 + 2782 + 3658 + 3742 + 3777 + 3787 + 4632 + 4773 + 5016 + 5625 + 6946 + 7455 + 9219 + 10,918) ÷ 17 = 73,616 ÷ 17 ≈ 4330.4

Page 59 Alternative Assessment; Thinking Critically

- Sample answers:

$x + 3$	three more than a number the sum of a number and three
$n - 3$	three less than a number three substracted from a number
$2w$	twice the value of a number two times a number

- When both a and b are positive numbers, both are negative numbers, or a least one of the numbers is 0.

2-1 Relations and Functions

Page 68 Check for Understanding

1. Sample answer:

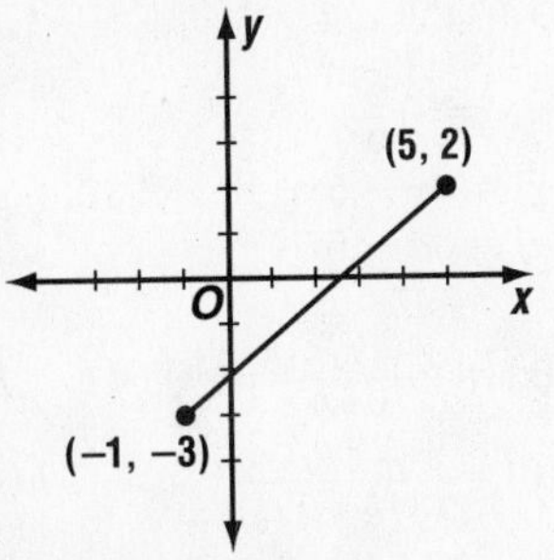

2. See students' work. The graph of a discrete function consists of points that are not connected. A continuous function can be graphed with a straight line or a smooth curve.
3. Any vertical line where $x = a$ is not a function.
4.

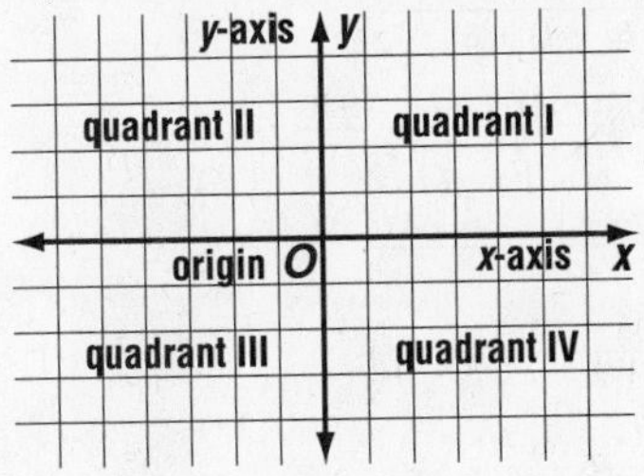

See students' work for graphs of points.

5. The four ways are a mapping, table, graph, and an equation or function. Sample answers:

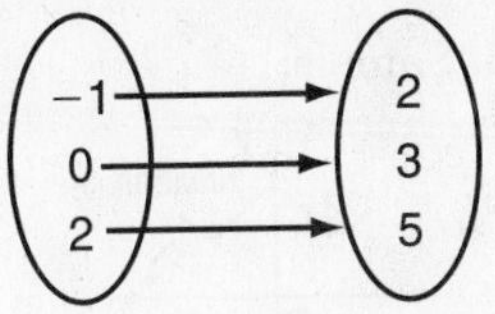

x	y
−1	2
0	3
2	5

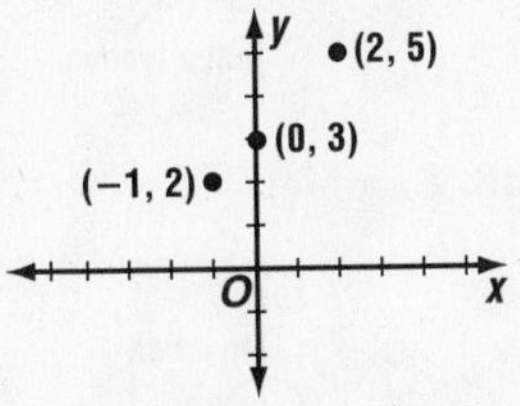

$y = x + 3$

6. See students' work. Sample answer: D = $\{0 < x < 20\}$, R = $\{0 < y < 105\}$
7. function 8. function 9. not a function
10. D = {7}, R = {−1, 2, 5, 8}; not a function

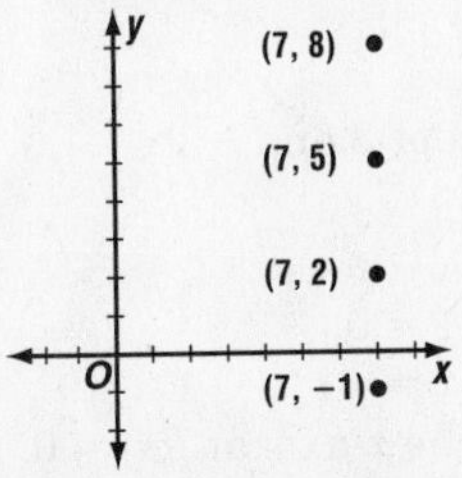

11. D = {3, 4, 6}, R = {2.5}; function; discrete

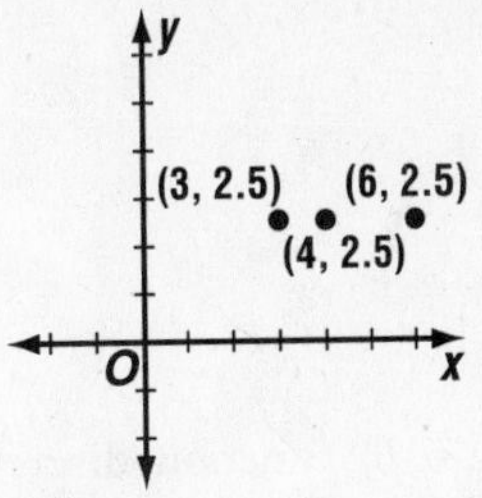

12. D = {all reals}, R = {all reals}; function; continuous

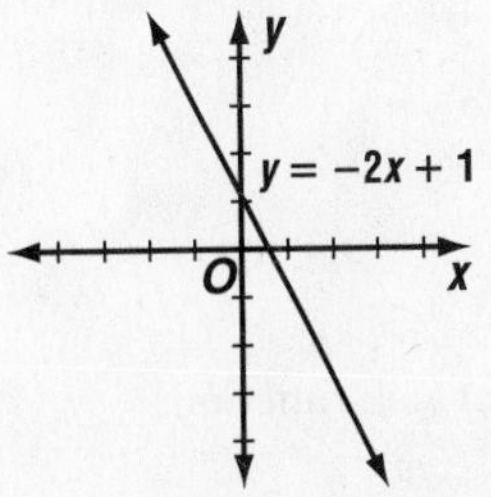

13. D = $\{x \mid x \geq 0\}$, R = {all reals}; not a function

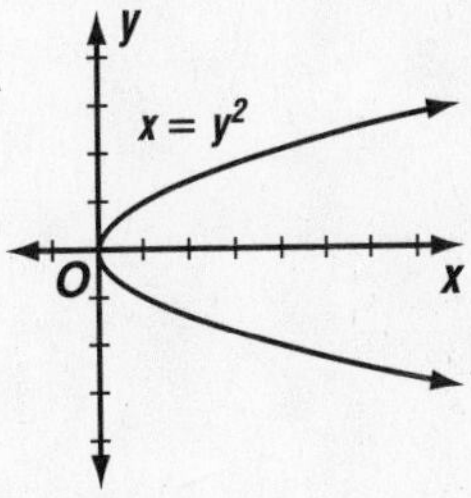

14. $f(x) = x^2 - 3x$
$f(5) = 5^2 - 3(5)$
$= 25 - 15$
$= 10$
15. $h(x) = x^3 + 1$
$h(-2) = (-2)^3 + 1$
$= -8 + 1$
$= -7$

Pages 69–71 Exercises

16. function
17. not a function
18. function
19. not a function
20. function
21. not a function
22. function
23. not a function
24. not a function
25. D = {3, 4, 6}, R = {5}; function; discrete

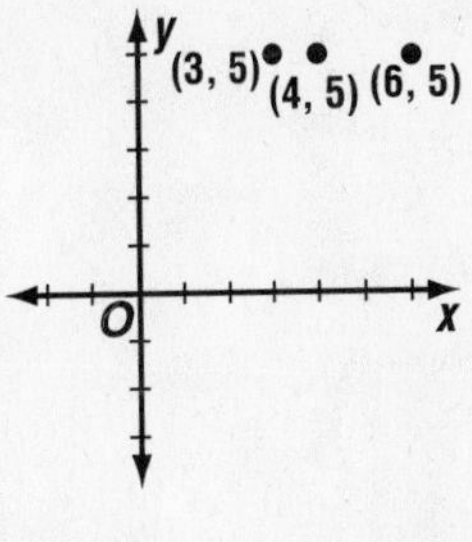

26. D = {−2, 3}, R = {5, 7, 8}; not a function

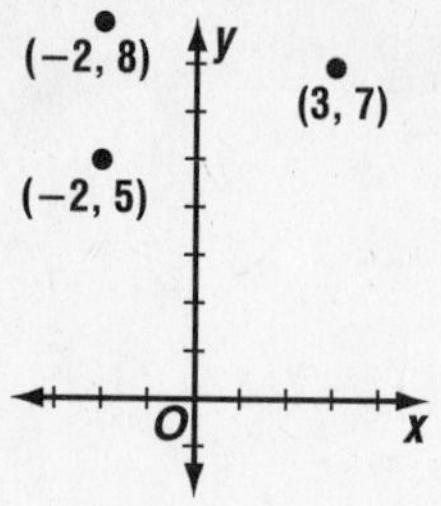

27. D = {3, 4, 5, 6}, R = {3, 4, 5, 6}; function, discrete

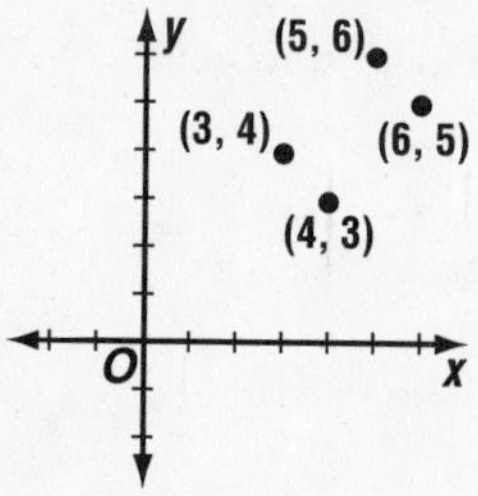

28. D = {all reals}, R = {all reals}; function; continuous

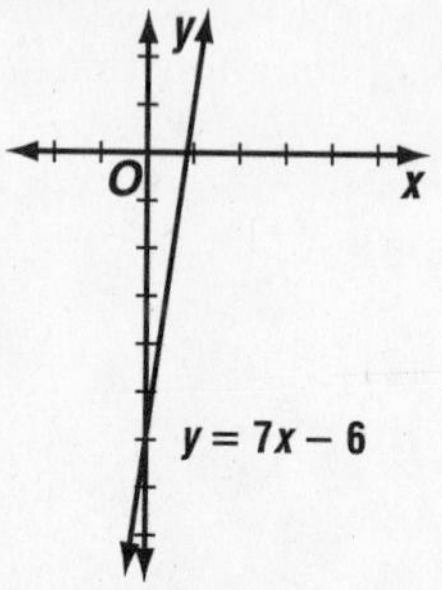

29. D = {all reals}, R = {all reals}; function; continuous

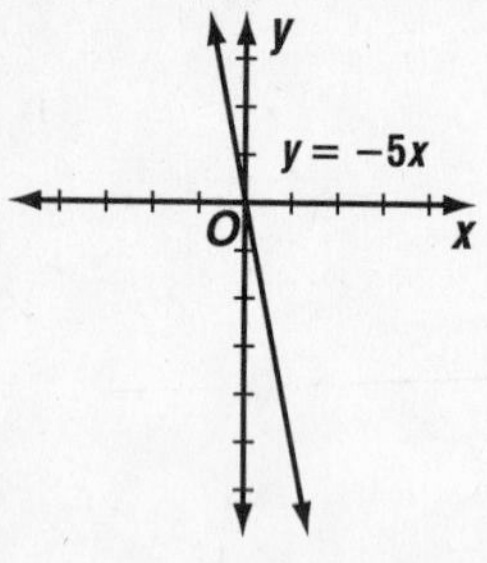

30. D = {all reals ≥ 1}; R = {all reals}; not a function

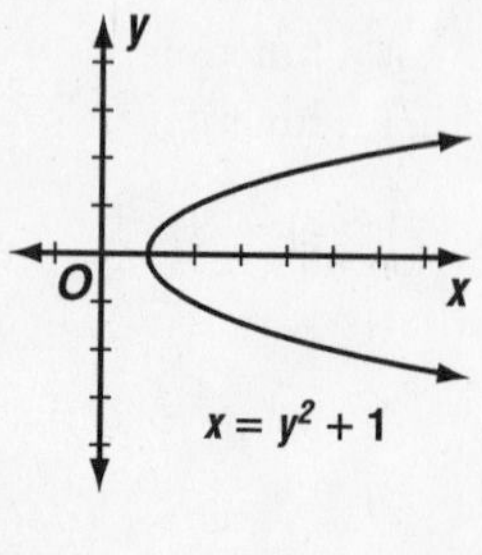

31. no 32. yes 33. yes

34. $f(x) = 3x - 5$
$f(-3) = 3(-3) - 5$
$= -9 - 5$
$= -14$

35. $g(x) = x^2 - x$
$g(3) = 3^2 - 3$
$= 9 - 3$
$= 6$

36. $g(x) = x^2 - x$
$g\left(\frac{1}{3}\right) = \left(\frac{1}{3}\right)^2 - \frac{1}{3}$
$= \frac{1}{9} - \frac{1}{3}$
$= -\frac{2}{9}$

37. $f(x) = 3x - 5$
$f\left(\frac{2}{3}\right) = 3\left(\frac{2}{3}\right) - 5$
$= 2 - 5$
$= -3$

38. $f(x) = 3x - 5$
$f(a) = 3a - 5$

39. $g(x) = x^2 - x$
$g(5n) = (5n)^2 - 5n$
$= 25n^2 - 5n$

40. $h(x) = \frac{x^2 + 5x - 6}{x + 3}$
$h(3) = \frac{3^2 + 5(3) - 6}{3 + 3}$
$= \frac{9 + 15 - 6}{6}$
$= \frac{18}{6}$
$= 3$

41. $h(x) = \frac{x^2 + 5x - 6}{x + 3}$
$h(-2) = \frac{(-2)^2 + 5(-2) - 6}{-2 + 3}$
$= \frac{4 - 10 - 6}{1}$
$= -12$

42. $h(x) = \frac{x^2 + 5x - 6}{x + 3}$
$h(a - 1) = \frac{(a - 1)^2 + 5(a - 1) - 6}{(a - 1) + 3}$
$= \frac{(a - 1)(a - 1) + 5a - 5 - 6}{a - 1 + 3}$
$= \frac{a^2 - 2a + 1 + 5a - 11}{a + 2}$
$= \frac{a^2 + 3a - 10}{a + 2}$

43. Sample answer: $f(x) = 2.5x$

44. $g: x \to x^2 + x$
$g: (-2) \to (-2)^2 + (-2)$
$\to 4 - 2$
$\to 2$

45. Sample:

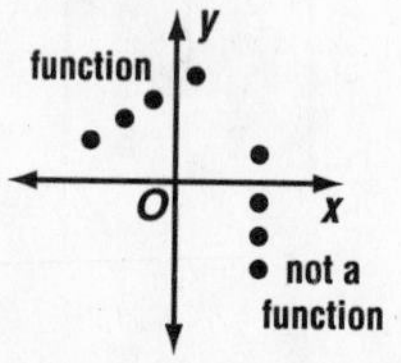

46. Sample:

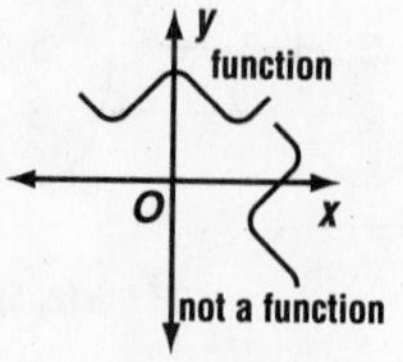

47. Sample:

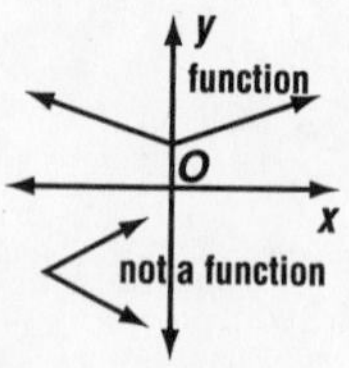

48. Sample:

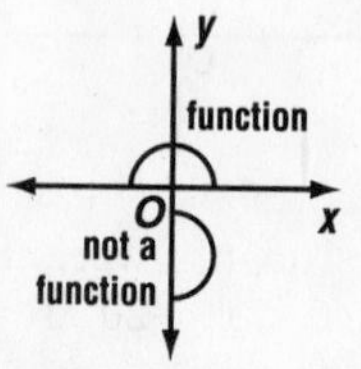

49. $x^2 - 9 = 0$
$x^2 = 9$
$x = \pm 3$
D = {all real numbers except 3 and −3}

50. $x^2 + 2x + 1 = 0$
$(x + 1)(x + 1) = 0$
$x + 1 = 0$ or $x + 1 = 0$
$x = -1$ $x = -1$
The graph of $f(x)$ crosses the x-axis at $f(x) = 0$.

51a. D = {years}, R = {stock price}

51b. {(83, 19), (84, 20), (85, 25), (86, 25), (87, 28), (88, 29), (89, 45), (90, 30), (91, 39), (92, 50), (93, 55)}

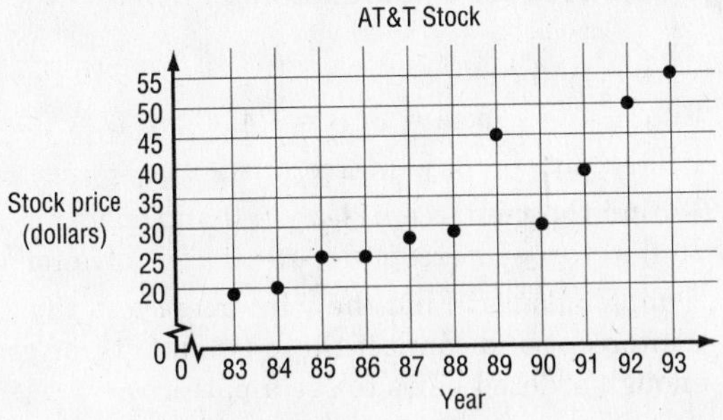

51c. yes

51d. Sample answer: Yes; even when it dropped in value, it rose even higher.

52.

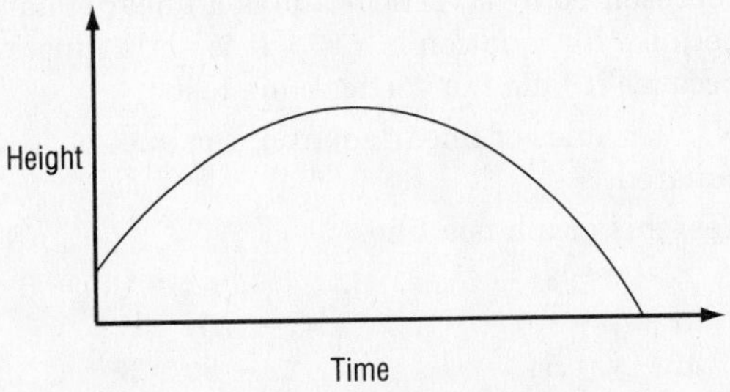

The graph is a function; it passes the vertical line test.

53. D = $\{-3 \le x \le 3\}$, R = $\{-3 \le y \le 3\}$; no

54a. D = {year}, R = {Latino members}

54b. {(1981, 6), (1983, 8), (1985, 10), (1987, 11), (1989, 10), (1991, 11), (1993, 17), (1995, 15)}

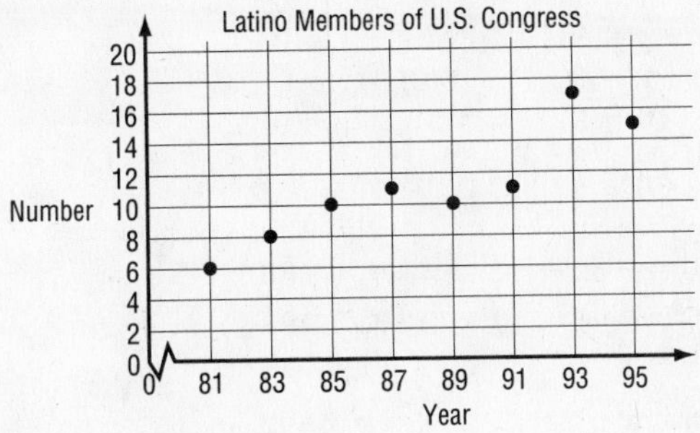

54c. yes; discrete

54d. No; 10 and 11 are paired with more than one year.

55. $|y + 1| < 7$
$-7 < y + 1 < 7$
$-8 < y < 6$
$\{y \mid -8 < y < 6\}$

56. $|5 - m| < 1$
$-1 < 5 - m < 1$
$-6 < -m < -4$
$6 > m > 4$
$\{m \mid 4 < m < 6\}$

57. $x - 5 < 0.1$
$x < 5.1$
$\{x \mid x < 5.1\}$

58. $3|2x - 5| = -\frac{1}{3}$
$|2x - 5| = -\frac{1}{9}$
no solution

59a. 27.89 − 25.04 = 2.85; $2.85

59b. 32.67 − 2.85 = 29.82; $29.82

60. substitution (=)

61. $x + 2x^2 - 7$

62a. Team A: 28, 69, 72, 110, 147, 212, 212, 281

$$\frac{28 + 69 + 72 + 110 + 147 + 212 + 212 + 281}{8} = \frac{1131}{8} \approx$$

141.38; $\frac{110 + 147}{2} = \frac{257}{2} = 128.5$; 212

Team B: 69, 88, 101, 111, 143, 154, 205, 236

$$\frac{69 + 88 + 101 + 111 + 143 + 154 + 205 + 236}{8} = \frac{1107}{8} \approx$$

138.38; $\frac{111 + 143}{2} = \frac{254}{2} = 127$; none

62b.

Team A	Stem	Team B
1 1 8	2	0 3
1 4	1	0 1 4 5
2 6 7	0	6 8
8|2| = 280 to 289		*|2|3 = 230 to 239*

62c. Team B; they had the lower mean.

63. $3(5a + 6b) + 8(2a - b) = 15a + 18b + 16a - 8b$
$= 31a + 10b$

64. $3^2(2^2 - 1^2) + 4^2 = 9(4 - 1) + 16$
$= 9(3) + 16$
$= 27 + 16$
$= 43$

2-2A Graphing Technology: Linear Functions

Page 72 Exercises

1. Y= 3 X,T,θ,n − 3 ZOOM 6

[−10, 10] by [−10, 10]

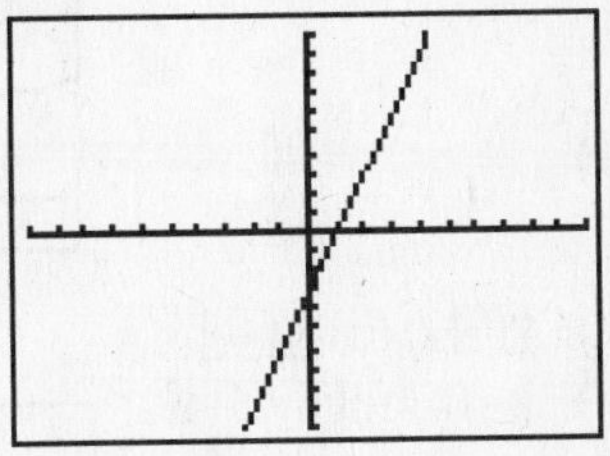

2. Y= (−) 2 X,T,θ,n + 5 ZOOM 6

[−10, 10] by [−10, 10]

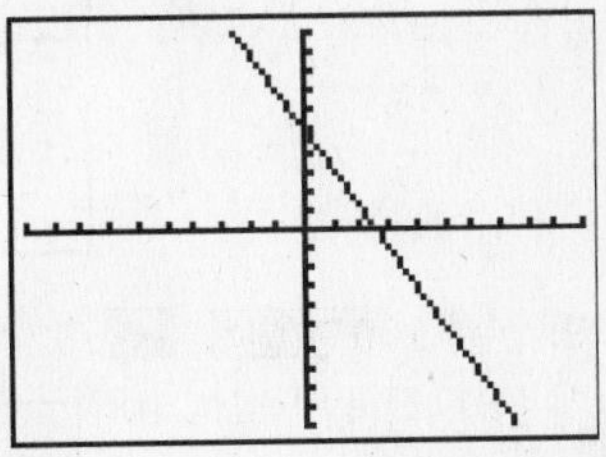

3. Y= 4 − X,T,θ,n ZOOM 6

[−10, 10] by [−10, 10]

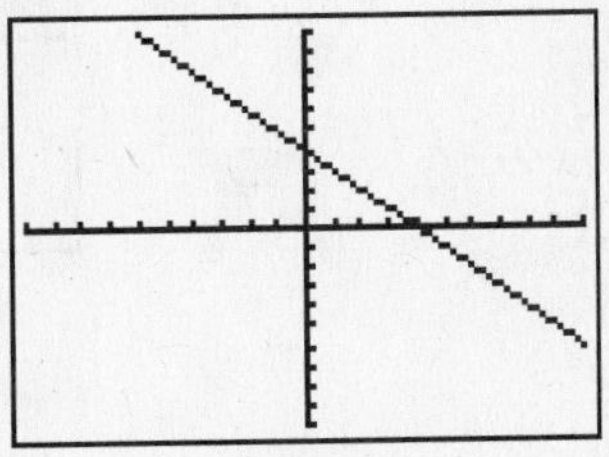

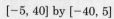

4. [Y=] 5 [X,T,θ,n] [−] 35
[−5, 40] by [−40, 5]

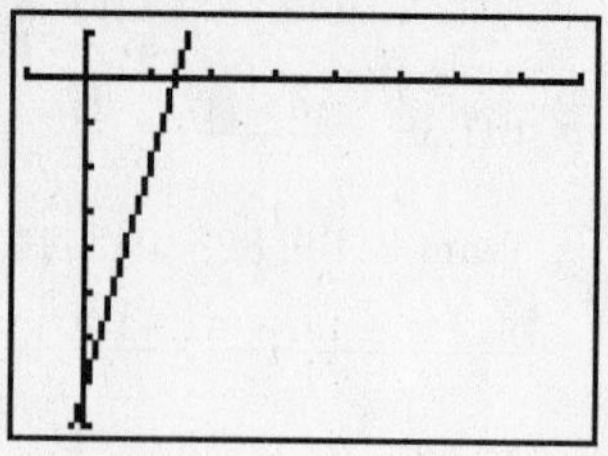

5. [Y=] [(−)] 12 [X,T,θ,n]
[−10, 10] by [−20, 5]

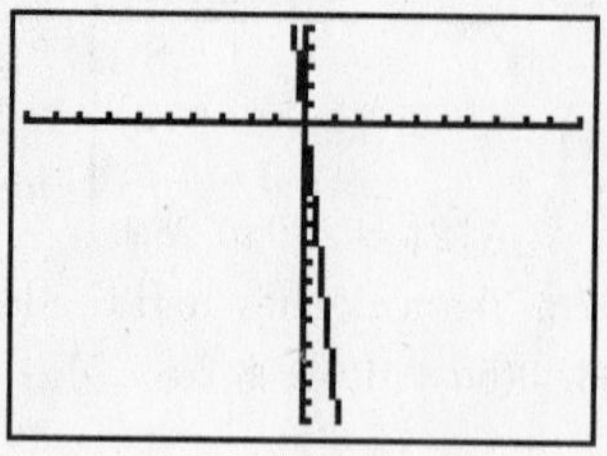

6. [Y=] 0.1 [X,T,θ,n] [−] 1
[−5, 15] by [−10, 10]

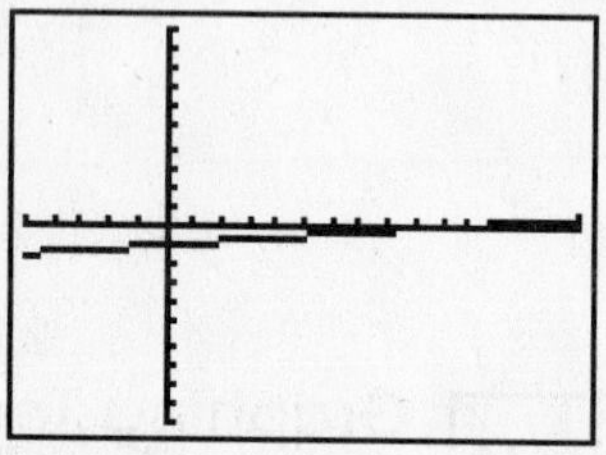

7. [Y=] [(−)] 0.3 [X,T,θ,n] [+] 15
[−5, 50] by [−5, 50]

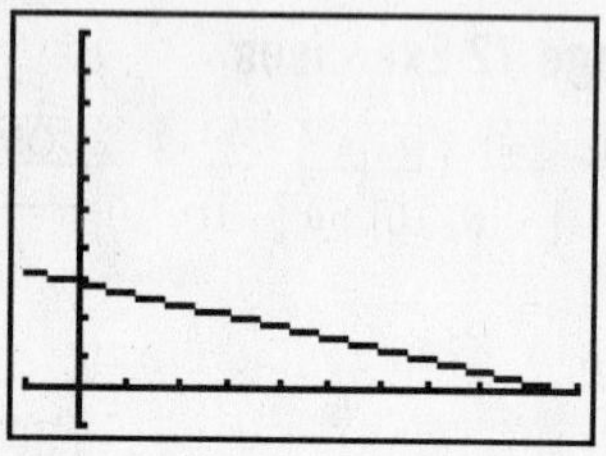

8. [Y=] 0.01 [X,T,θ,n]
[−10, 10] by [−1,1]

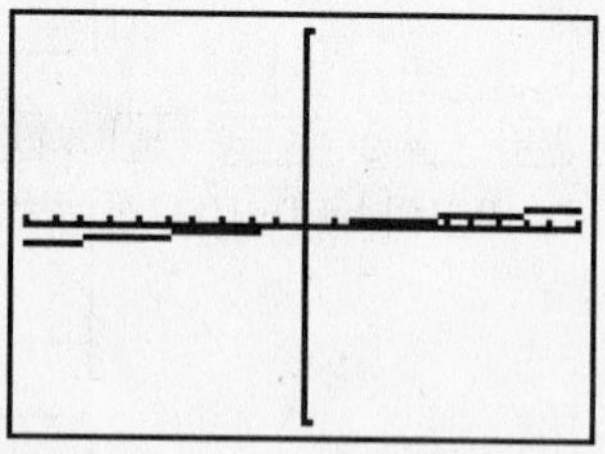

9. [Y=] 100 [X,T,θ,n] [+] 5
[−1, 1] by [−10, 10]

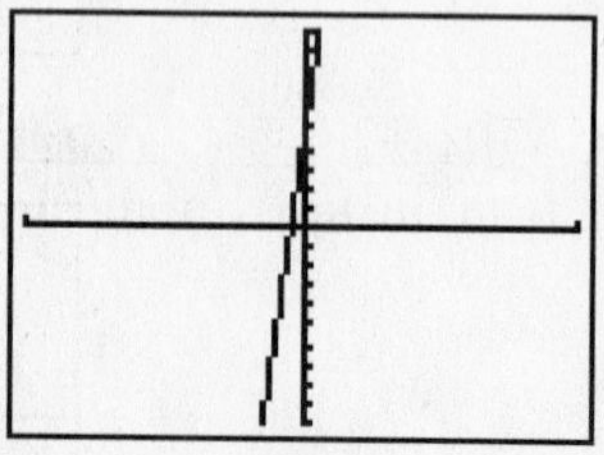

2-2 Linear Equations

Page 76 Check for Understanding

1. $4y = 3x + 5$
$-3x + 4y = 5$
$3x - 4y = -5$; $A = 3$, $B = -4$, $C = -5$

2. x-intercept $= -3$; y-intercept $= -2$

3. To find the x-intercept, let $y = 0$ and solve for x. To find the y-intercept, let $x = 0$ and solve for y.

4. Sample answer: Find the y-intercept and the x-intercept and connect these two points, or graph enough ordered pairs to see a pattern.

5. Sample answer: The equation represented by a horizontal line is a linear equation because its equation is $y = c$, and it is a function because it passes the vertical line test. The equation represented by a vertical line is a linear equation because its equation is $x = c$. It is not a function because it fails the vertical line test.

6. No; variables of linear equations cannot be squared.

7. Yes; this graph is a line.

8. $y = 3x - 5$
$-3x + y = -5$
$3x - y = 5$
$A = 3$, $B = -1$, $C = 5$

9. $4x = 10y + 6$
$4x - 10y = 6$
$2x - 5y = 3$
$A = 2$, $B = -5$, $C = 3$

10. $y = \frac{2}{3}x + 1$
$-\frac{2}{3}x + y = 1$
$-3\left(-\frac{2}{3}x\right) + (-3)y = -3(1)$
$2x - 3y = -3$
$A = 2$, $B = -3$, $C = -3$

11. $6x + y = 9$
$6x + 0 = 9$
$6x = 9$
$x = \frac{3}{2}$

$6x + y = 9$
$6(0) + y = 9$
$y = 9$

12. $y = -3x - 5$
$0 = -3x - 5$
$5 = -3x$
$-\frac{5}{3} = x$

$y = -3x - 5$
$y = -3(0) - 5$
$y = -5$

13. $f(x) = x - 2$
$0 = x - 2$
$2 = x$

$f(x) = x - 2$
$y = 0 - 2$
$y = -2$

14. $3x + 2y = 6$
$3x + 2(0) = 6$
$3x = 6$
$x = 2$
$(2, 0)$

$3x + 2y = 6$
$3(0) + 2y = 6$
$2y = 6$
$y = 3$
$(0, 3)$

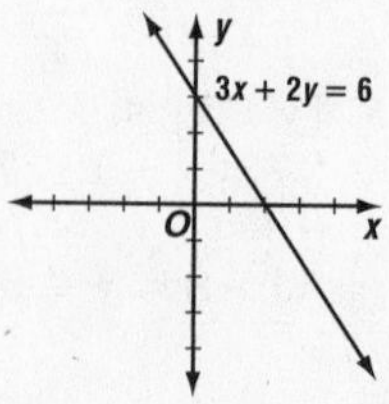

15.

x	y
0	0
1	−2
−1	2

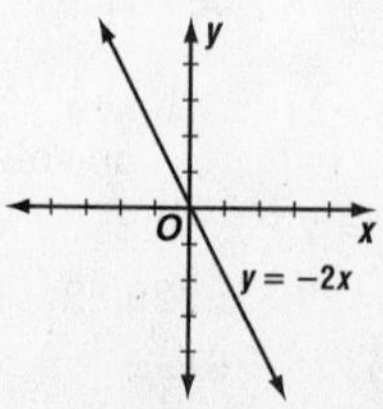

16. $4x + 8y = 12$ $\quad 4x + 8y = 12$
$4x + 8(0) = 12$ $\quad 4(0) + 8y = 12$
$4x = 12$ $\quad 8y = 12$
$x = 3$ $\quad y = \frac{3}{2}$
$(3, 0)$ $\quad \left(0, \frac{3}{2}\right)$

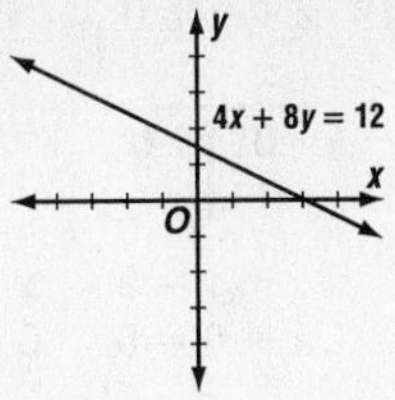

17. $f(x) = 0.718x$
$= 0.718(100)$
$= 71.8$; $71.80

Pages 77–78 Exercises

18. Yes, this graph is a line.
19. No; variables may not appear in the denominator.
20. No; variables may not be multiplied.
21. Yes, this graph is a line.

22. $y = -3x + 4$
$3x + y = 4$
$A = 3, B = 1, C = 4$

23. $y = 12x$
$-12x + y = 0$
$12x - y = 0$
$A = 12, B = -1, C = 0$

24. $x = 4y - 5$
$x - 4y = -5$
$A = 1, B = -4, C = -5$

25. $5y = 10x - 25$
$-10x + 5y = -25$
$2x - y = 5$
$A = 2, B = -1, C = 5$

26. $\frac{1}{2}x + \frac{1}{2}y = 6$
$x + y = 12$
$A = 1, B = 1, C = 12$

27. $0.25y = 10$
$y = 40$
$A = 0, B = 1, C = 40$

28. $y + 6 = 5x$ $\quad y + 6 = 5x$
$0 + 6 = 5x$ $\quad y + 6 = 5(0)$
$6 = 5x$ $\quad y + 6 = 0$
$\frac{6}{5} = x$ $\quad y = -6$

29. $3x = y$ $\quad 3x = y$
$3x = 0$ $\quad 3(0) = y$
$x = 0$ $\quad 0 = y$

30. $y = -2$
$0 \neq -2$; false, so no x-intercept
y-intercept is -2

31. $x = 8$
x-intercept is 8
$0 = 8$; false, so no y-intercept

32. $g(x) = 4x - 1$ $\quad g(x) = 4x - 1$
$0 = 4x - 1$ $\quad y = 4(0) - 1$
$1 = 4x$ $\quad y = 0 - 1$
$\frac{1}{4} = x$ $\quad y = -1$

33. $5x + 3y = 15$ $\quad 5x + 3y = 15$
$5x + 3(0) = 15$ $\quad 5(0) + 3y = 15$
$5x + 0 = 15$ $\quad 0 + 3y = 15$
$5x = 15$ $\quad 3y = 15$
$x = 3$ $\quad y = 5$

34.

x	y
0	0
1	1
2	2

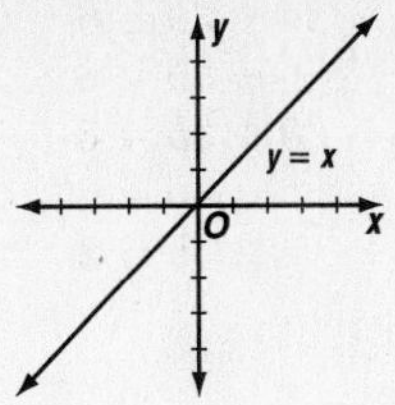

35. $y = 4x + 2$ $\quad y = 4x + 2$
$0 = 4x + 2$ $\quad y = 4(0) + 2$
$-2 = 4x$ $\quad y = 0 + 2$
$-\frac{1}{2} = x$ $\quad y = 2$

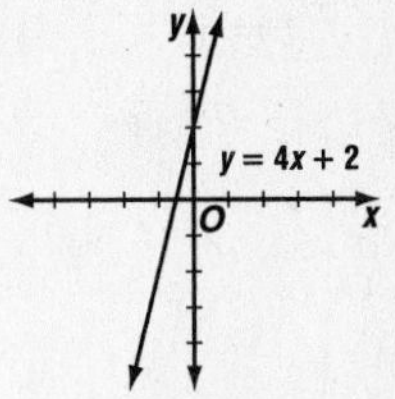

36. $x + y = 7$ $\quad x + y = 7$
$x + 0 = 7$ $\quad 0 + y = 7$
$x = 7$ $\quad y = 7$

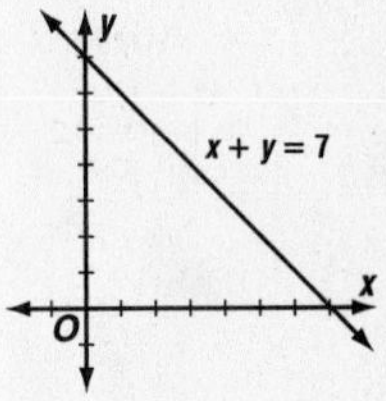

37. $2x - y = 5$ $\quad 2x - y = 5$
$2x - 0 = 5$ $\quad 2(0) - y = 5$
$2x = 5$ $\quad 0 - y = 5$
$x = \frac{5}{2}$ $\quad -y = 5$
$y = -5$

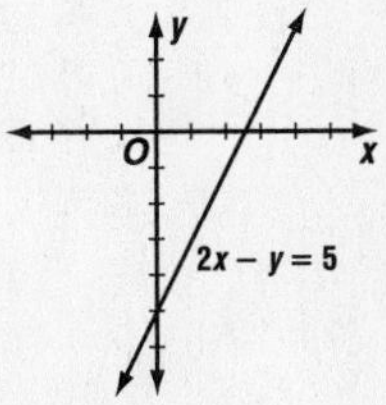

38. $2x + 5y = 10$ $\quad 2x + 5y = 10$
$2x + 5(0) = 10$ $\quad 2(0) + 5y = 10$
$2x + 0 = 10$ $\quad 0 + 5y = 10$
$2x = 10$ $\quad 5y = 10$
$x = 5$ $\quad y = 2$

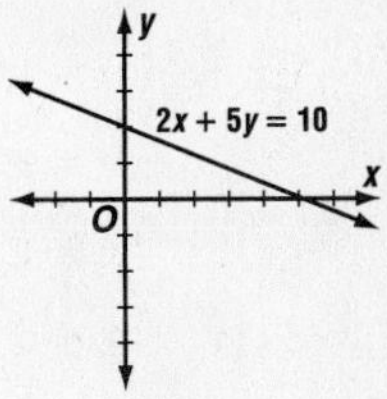

39. $y = 0.5x - 3$ $\quad y = 0.5x - 3$
$0 = 0.5x - 3$ $\quad y = 0.5(0) - 3$
$3 = 0.5x$ $\quad y = 0 - 3$
$6 = x$ $\quad y = -3$

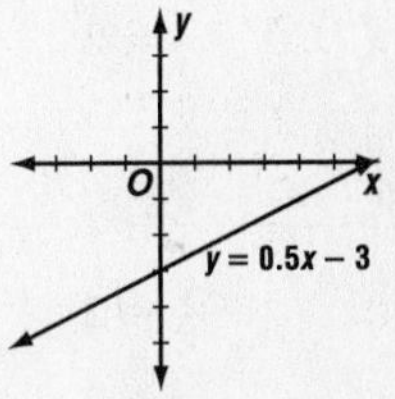

40. $b = 2a - 3$ $\quad b = 2a - 3$
$0 = 2a - 3$ $\quad b = 2(0) - 3$
$3 = 2a$ $\quad b = 0 - 3$
$\frac{3}{2} = a$ $\quad b = -3$

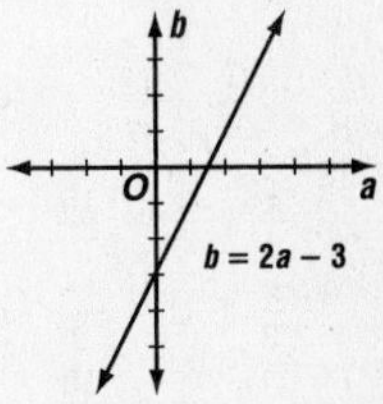

41. $x - y = 6$ $\quad x - y = 6$
$x - 0 = 6$ $\quad 0 - y = 6$
$x = 6$ $\quad -y = 6$
$y = -6$

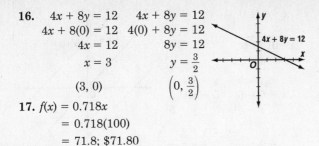

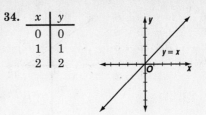

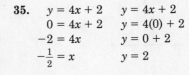

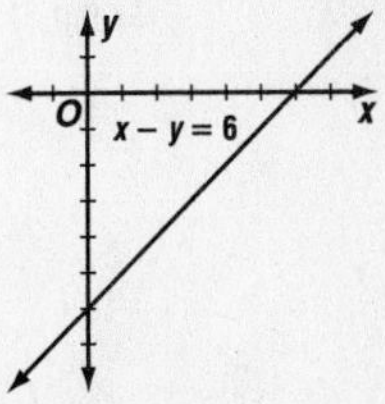

42. $2a + 3b = 6$ $\quad$ $2a + 3b = 6$
$2a + 3(0) = 6$ $\quad$ $2(0) + 3b = 6$
$2a + 0 = 6$ $\quad$ $0 + 3b = 6$
$2a = 6$ $\quad$ $3b = 6$
$a = 3$ $\quad$ $b = 2$

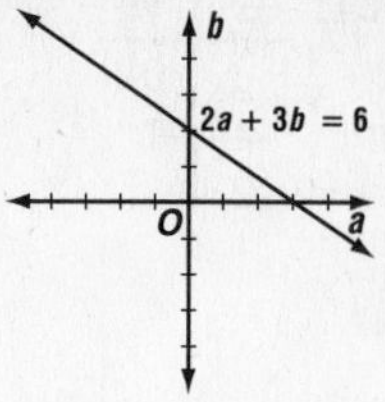

43. $3 = 3x$
$1 = x$

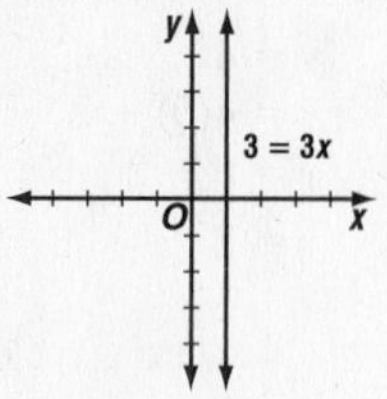

44. $x + 2y = 7$ $\quad$ $x + 2y = 7$
$x + 2(0) = 7$ $\quad$ $0 + 2y = 7$
$x + 0 = 7$ $\quad$ $2y = 7$
$x = 7$ $\quad$ $y = \frac{7}{2}$

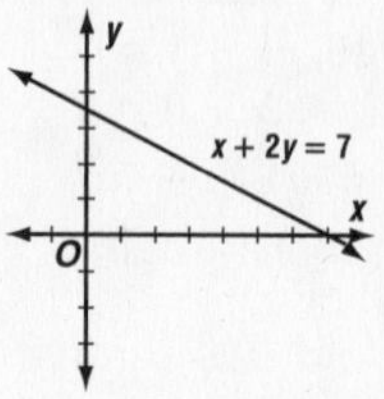

45. $4x + 3y = 12$ $\quad$ $4x + 3y = 12$
$4x + 3(0) = 12$ $\quad$ $4(0) + 3y = 12$
$4x + 0 = 12$ $\quad$ $0 + 3y = 12$
$4x = 12$ $\quad$ $3y = 12$
$x = 3$ $\quad$ $y = 4$

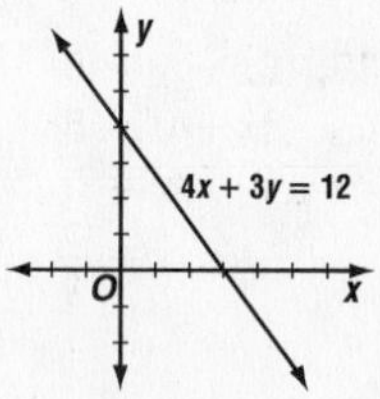

46. $\frac{1}{3}x + \frac{1}{2}y = 1$ $\quad$ $\frac{1}{3}x + \frac{1}{2}y = 1$
$\frac{1}{3}x + \frac{1}{2}(0) = 1$ $\quad$ $\frac{1}{3}(0) + \frac{1}{2}y = 1$
$\frac{1}{3}x + 0 = 1$ $\quad$ $0 + \frac{1}{2}y = 1$
$\frac{1}{3}x = 1$ $\quad$ $\frac{1}{2}y = 1$
$x = 3$ $\quad$ $y = 2$

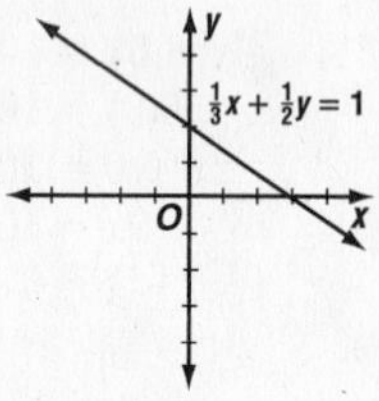

47. $\frac{x}{4} - \frac{y}{3} = 2$ $\quad$ $\frac{x}{4} - \frac{y}{3} = 2$
$\frac{x}{4} - \frac{0}{3} = 2$ $\quad$ $\frac{0}{4} - \frac{y}{3} = 2$
$\frac{x}{4} - 0 = 2$ $\quad$ $0 - \frac{y}{3} = 2$
$\frac{x}{4} = 2$ $\quad$ $-\frac{y}{3} = 2$
$x = 8$ $\quad$ $y = -6$

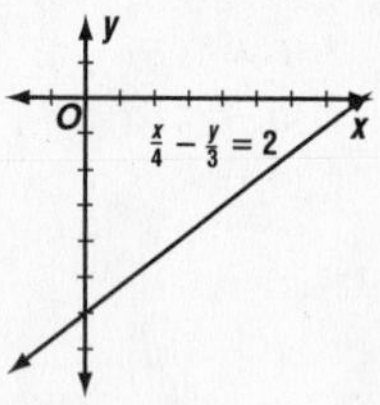

48. $\frac{x}{3} + \frac{y}{2} = \frac{15}{2}$ $\quad$ $\frac{x}{3} + \frac{y}{2} = \frac{15}{2}$
$\frac{x}{3} + \frac{0}{2} = \frac{15}{2}$ $\quad$ $\frac{0}{3} + \frac{y}{2} = \frac{15}{2}$
$\frac{x}{3} + 0 = \frac{15}{2}$ $\quad$ $0 + \frac{y}{2} = \frac{15}{2}$
$\frac{x}{3} = \frac{15}{2}$ $\quad$ $\frac{y}{2} = \frac{15}{2}$
$x = 22.5$ $\quad$ $y = 15$

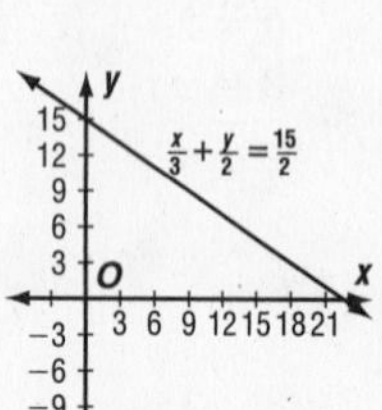

49. $x + y = 0$

x	y
0	0
1	−1

$x + y = 5$ $\quad$ $x + y = 5$
$x + 0 = 5$ $\quad$ $0 + y = 5$
$x = 5$ $\quad$ $y = 5$

$x + y = -5$ $\quad$ $x + y = -5$
$x + 0 = -5$ $\quad$ $0 + y = -5$
$x = -5$ $\quad$ $y = -5$

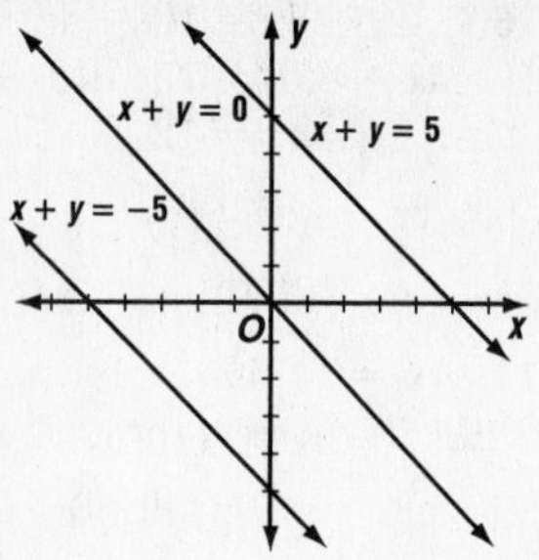

49a. same slope, different y-intercepts, look parallel

49b. Sample answer: $x + y = 2$

50a. $t(d) = 35d + 20$
$0 = 35d + 20$
$-20 = 35d$
$-\frac{4}{7} = \text{d}$

$t(d) = 35d + 20$
$t(d) = 35(0) + 20$
$t(d) = 0 + 20$
$t(d) = 20$

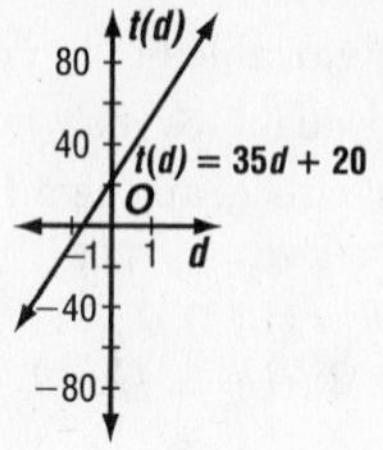

50b. $t(d) = 35d + 20$
$= 35(3) + 20$
$= 105 + 20$
$= 125$; 125°C

50c. Continuous; there is an infinite number of elements in the domain.

50d. $t(d) = 35d + 20$
$195 = 35d + 20$
$175 = 35d$
$5 = d$; 5 kilometers

51a. Let t = time from sound signal leaving boat to returning. So $4760t$ = distance from boat to fish and back.
$d(t) = \frac{1}{2}(4760t)$ or $2380t$

51b. $d(t) = 2380t$
$= 2380\ (0.05)$
$= 119$; 119 feet

52. $\frac{5280 \text{ ft}}{\text{mile}} = \frac{1850 \text{ feet}}{x}$ $\quad$ $f(x) = 1.15x$
$1850 = 5280x$ $\quad$ $\approx 1.15(0.35)$
$0.35 \approx x$ $\quad$ ≈ 0.403; 0.403 tons/in^2

53a. $1.50x + 1.25y = 375$

53b. $1.50x + 1.25y = 375$ $\quad$ $1.50x + 1.25y = 375$
$1.50x + 1.25(0) = 375$ $\quad$ $1.50(0) + 1.25y = 375$
$1.50x + 0 = 375$ $\quad$ $0 + 1.25y = 375$
$1.50x = 375$ $\quad$ $1.25y = 375$
$x = 250$ $\quad$ $y = 300$

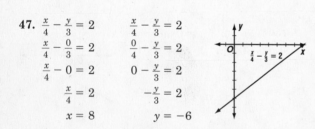

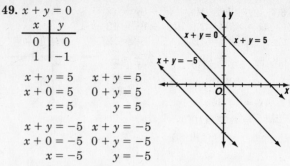

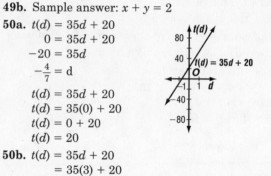

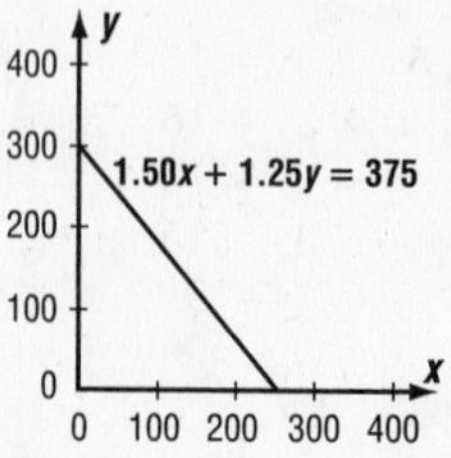

53c. Yes, it is a function. Discrete; it is possible to list the elements of the domain.

53d.
$$\begin{aligned} 1.50x + 1.25y &= 375 \\ 1.50(100) + 1.25(200) &\stackrel{?}{=} 375 \\ 150 + 250 &\stackrel{?}{=} 375 \\ 400 &\neq 375 \end{aligned}$$
They exceed their goal.

54. a and c

55. $|x + 7| > -2$
true for all x

56.
$$\begin{aligned} 5(2x - 7) &> 10 \\ 10x - 35 &> 10 \\ 10x &> 45 \\ x &> \frac{9}{2} \end{aligned}$$
$\{x \mid x > \frac{9}{2}\}$

57.
$$\begin{aligned} 7|3x + 5| &= 35 \\ |3x + 5| &= 5 \end{aligned}$$
$3x + 5 = 5$ or $3x + 5 = -5$
$3x = 0$ $\quad 3x = -10$
$x = 0$ $\quad x = -\frac{10}{3}$

58.
$$\begin{aligned} x + 28.3 &= 56.0 \\ x &= 27.7 \end{aligned}$$

59.
$$\begin{aligned} 87 + 92 + 81 + x &\geq 350 \\ 260 + x &\geq 350 \\ x &\geq 90 \end{aligned}$$
You must score 90 or higher.

60a. 25,895, 25,910, 25,925, 26,000, 26,041, 26,090, 26,291, 26,360, 26,400, 26,470, 26,504, 26,660, 26,750, 26,760, 26,810, 27,790, 27,890, 28,208, 29,064, 29,108
(25,895 + 25,910 + 25,925 + 26,000 + 26,041 + 26,090 + 26,291 + 26,360 + 26,400 + 26,470 + 26,504 + 26,660 + 26,750 + 26,760 + 26,810 + 27,790 + 27,890 + 28,208 + 29,064 + 29,108) ÷ 20 = 536,926 ÷ 20 = 26,846.3; $\frac{26{,}470 + 26{,}504}{2} = \frac{52{,}974}{2} = 26{,}487$; no mode

60b.

Stem	Leaf
29	0 1
28	2
27	7 8
26	0 0 0 2 3 4 4 5 6 7 7 8
25	8 9 9

28 | 2 = 28,200 feet to 28,299 feet

61.
$$\begin{aligned} (9s - 4) - 3(2s - 6) &= 9s - 4 - 6s + 18 \\ &= 3s + 14 \end{aligned}$$

62.
$$\begin{aligned} [19 - (8 - 1)] \div 3 &= [19 - 7] \div 3 \\ &= [12] \div 3 \\ &= 4 \end{aligned}$$

2-2B Graphing Technology: Using Graphs to Estimate Solutions

Page 79 Exercises

1. [Y=] 2 [X,T,θ,n] [−] 1 [ENTER] 2 [ZOOM] 6 [2nd] [CALC] 5 [ENTER] [ENTER] [ENTER] 1.5
$$\begin{aligned} 2x - 1 &= 2 \\ 2x &= 3 \\ x &= 1.5 \end{aligned}$$

2. [Y=] 3 [X,T,θ,n] [+] 9 [ENTER] 25 [ZOOM] 6 [2nd] [CALC] 5 [ENTER] [ENTER] [ENTER] $5.\overline{3}$
$$\begin{aligned} 3x + 9 &= 25 \\ 3x &= 16 \\ x &= 5.\overline{3} \end{aligned}$$

3. [Y=] 2 [X,T,θ,n] [+] 1 [ENTER] 16 [−] [X,T,θ,n] [ZOOM] 6 [2nd] [CALC] 5 [ENTER] [ENTER] [ENTER] 5
$$\begin{aligned} 2x + 1 &= 16 - x \\ 3x + 1 &= 16 \\ 3x &= 15 \\ x &= 5 \end{aligned}$$

4. [Y=] 4 [X,T,θ,n] [+] 3 [ENTER] 5 [X,T,θ,n] [+] 7 [ZOOM] 6 [2nd] [CALC] 5 [ENTER] [ENTER] [ENTER] −4
$$\begin{aligned} 4x + 3 &= 5x + 7 \\ 3 &= x + 7 \\ -4 &= x \end{aligned}$$

5. [Y=] 7 [X,T,θ,n] [+] 9 [ENTER] 3 [(] [X,T,θ,n] [+] 3 [)] [ZOOM] 6 [2nd] [CALC] 5 [ENTER] [ENTER] [ENTER] 0
$$\begin{aligned} 7x + 9 &= 3(x + 3) \\ 7x + 9 &= 3x + 9 \\ 4x + 9 &= 9 \\ 4x &= 0 \\ x &= 0 \end{aligned}$$

6. [Y=] 5 [(] 8 [−] 2 [X,T,θ,n] [)] [ENTER] 4 [X,T,θ,n] [−] 2 [ZOOM] 6 [2nd] [CALC] 5 [ENTER] [ENTER] [ENTER] 3
$$\begin{aligned} 5(8 - 2x) &= 4x - 2 \\ 40 - 10x &= 4x - 2 \\ 40 - 14x &= -2 \\ -14x &= -42 \\ x &= 3 \end{aligned}$$

7. [Y=] [(−)] 1.5 [X,T,θ,n] [ENTER] [(−)] 2 [X,T,θ,n] [+] 5.75 [Graph] [2nd] [CALC] 5 [ENTER] [ENTER] [ENTER] 11.5 (WINDOW: [−10, 15] by [−20, 10])
$$\begin{aligned} -1.5x &= -2x + 5.75 \\ 0.5x &= 5.75 \\ x &= 11.5 \end{aligned}$$

8. [Y=] 16 [X,T,θ,n] [−] 3.8 [ENTER] 12 [X,T,θ,n] [−] 3.8 [ZOOM] 6 [2nd] [CALC] 5 [ENTER] [ENTER] [ENTER] 0
$$\begin{aligned} 16x - 3.8 &= 12x - 3.8 \\ 4x - 3.8 &= -3.8 \\ 4x &= 0 \\ x &= 0 \end{aligned}$$

9. [Y=] 5.2 [X,T,θ,n] [+] 0.7 [ENTER] 2.8 [+] 2.2 [X,T,θ,n] [ZOOM] 6 [2nd] [CALC] 5 [ENTER] [ENTER] [ENTER] 0.7

$$\begin{aligned} 5.2x + 0.7 &= 2.8 + 2.2x \\ 3x + 0.7 &= 2.8 \\ 3x &= 2.1 \\ x &= 0.7 \end{aligned}$$

10. [Y=] [(-)] 2 [(] 3 [X,T,θ,n] [-] 5 [)] [+] 3 [X,T,θ,n] [ENTER] 2 [-] [X,T,θ,n] [ZOOM] 6 [2nd] [CALC] 5 [ENTER] [ENTER] [ENTER] 4

$$\begin{aligned} -2(3x - 5) + 3x &= 2 - x \\ -6x + 10 + 3x &= 2 - x \\ -3x + 10 &= 2 - x \\ -2x + 10 &= 2 \\ -2x &= -8 \\ x &= 4 \end{aligned}$$

2-3 Slope

Pages 84–85 Check for Understanding

1. Find the ratio of the difference of y values to the difference of x values. $\frac{4-3}{-2-(-1)} = \frac{1}{-1}$ or -1

2.

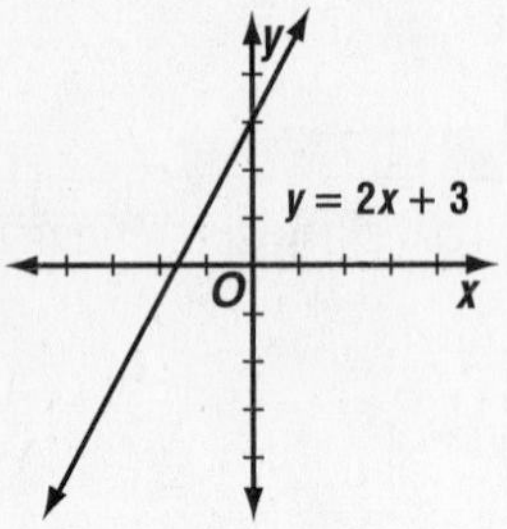

3. c

4. Their slopes are equal.

5. See students' work.

6. $m = \frac{y_2 - y_1}{x_2 - x_1}$
$= \frac{-2 - 0}{0 - (-3)}$
$= -\frac{2}{3}$

7. $m = \frac{y_2 - y_1}{x_2 - x_1}$
$= \frac{3 - 0}{1 - (-2)}$
$= \frac{3}{3}$
$= 1$

8. undefined

9. $m = \frac{1 - 1}{3 - 1}$
$= \frac{0}{2}$
$= 0$; horizontal

10. $m = \frac{-2 - 0}{3 - (-1)}$
$= \frac{-2}{4}$
$= -\frac{1}{2}$; falls

11. $m = \frac{2 - 4}{1 - 3}$
$= \frac{-2}{-2}$
$= 1$; rises

12. $2x - y = 4$, $2x - 0 = 4$, $2x = 4$, $x = 2$, $(2, 0)$
$2x - y = 4$, $2(0) - y = 4$, $0 - y = 4$, $y = -4$, $(0, -4)$
$m = \frac{-4 - 0}{0 - 2} = \frac{-4}{-2} = 2$

13. $x + y = 3$, $x + 0 = 3$, $x = 3$, $(3, 0)$
$x + y = 3$, $0 + y = 3$, $y = 3$, $(0, 3)$
$m = \frac{3 - 0}{0 - 3} = \frac{3}{-3} = -1$

14. $2x + 3y = 6$, $2x + 3(0) = 6$, $2x + 0 = 6$, $2x = 6$, $x = 3$, $(3, 0)$
$2x + 3y = 6$, $2(0) + 3y = 6$, $0 + 3y = 6$, $3y = 6$, $y = 2$, $(0, 2)$
$m = \frac{2 - 0}{0 - 3} = -\frac{2}{3}$

15. $m = \frac{2 - (-1)}{3 - (-1)}$
$= \frac{3}{4}; -\frac{4}{3}$

16. Graph (0, 0), then using the definition of slope, go up 3 units and 1 unit to the right. Plot the point. Connect the points.

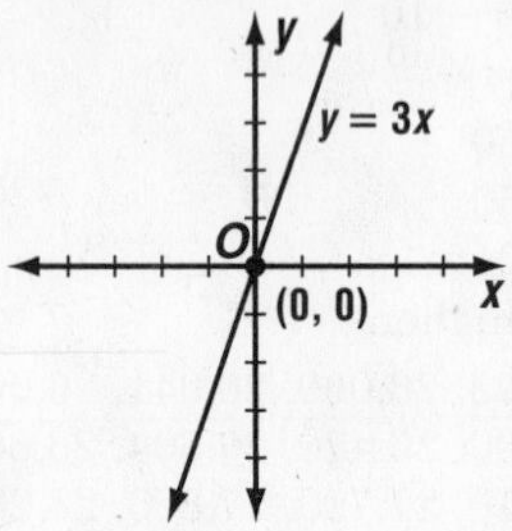

17. $6y - 10x = 30$, $6(0) - 10x = 30$, $-10x = 30$, $x = -3$, $(-3, 0)$
$6y - 10x = 30$, $6y - 10(0) = 30$, $6y - 0 = 30$, $6y = 30$, $y = 5$, $(0, 5)$
$m = \frac{5 - 0}{0 - (-3)} = \frac{5}{3}$

Graph (0, 3), then go up 5 units and 3 units to the right.

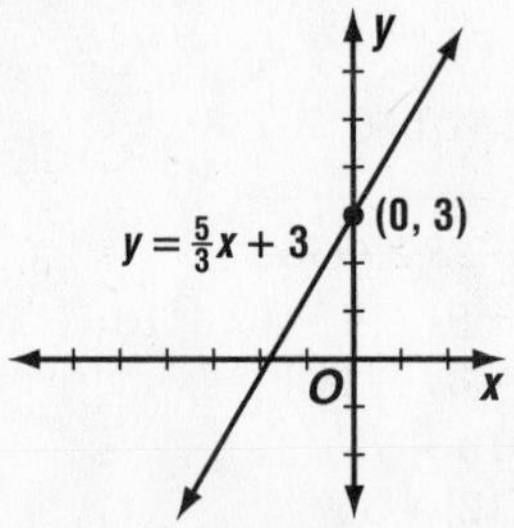

Pages 85–87 Exercises

18. $m = \frac{-4 - 1}{8 - 6}$
$= -\frac{5}{2}$; falls

19. $m = \frac{-5 - 8}{5 - 6}$
$= \frac{-13}{-1}$
$= 13$; rises

20. $m = \frac{1 - (-5)}{4 - (-6)}$
$= \frac{6}{10}$
$= \frac{3}{5}$; rises

21. $m = \frac{8 - 8}{1 - 7}$
$= \frac{0}{-6}$
$= 0$; horizontal

22. $m = \frac{-9 - 3}{1 - 2.5}$
$= \frac{-12}{-1.5}$
$= 8$; rises

23. $m = \frac{-2 - 2}{a - a}$
$= \frac{-4}{0}$
undefined; vertical

24.
$$x + y = 5 \qquad x + y = 5 \qquad m = \frac{5-0}{0-5}$$
$$x + 0 = 5 \qquad 0 + y = 5 \qquad = \frac{5}{-5}$$
$$x = 5 \qquad y = 5 \qquad = -1$$
$$(5, 0) \qquad (0, 5)$$

25.
$$3x + 9 = 0$$
$$3x = -9$$
$$x = -3$$

This is the equation of a vertical line; the slope is undefined.

26.
$$2x - y = 8 \qquad 2x - y = 8 \qquad m = \frac{-8-0}{0-4}$$
$$2x - 0 = 8 \qquad 2(0) - y = 8 \qquad = \frac{-8}{-4}$$
$$2x = 8 \qquad 0 - y = 8 \qquad = 2$$
$$x = 4 \qquad -y = 8$$
$$(4, 0) \qquad y = -8$$
$$(0, -8)$$

27.
$$2x + 3y + 32 = 0 \qquad 2x + 3y + 32 = 0$$
$$2x + 3(0) + 32 = 0 \qquad 2(0) + 3y + 32 = 0$$
$$2x + 0 = -32 \qquad 0 + 3y = -32$$
$$2x = -32 \qquad 3y = -32$$
$$x = -16 \qquad y = \frac{-32}{3}$$
$$(-16, 0) \qquad \left(0, -\frac{32}{3}\right)$$
$$\text{m} = \frac{-\frac{32}{3} - 0}{0 - (-16)} = \frac{-\frac{32}{3}}{16} = -\frac{2}{3}$$

28.
$$3x - 4y = 0 \qquad 3x - 4y = 0 \qquad m = \frac{\frac{3}{4} - 0}{1 - 0}$$
$$3x - 4(0) = 0 \qquad 3(1) - 4y = 0$$
$$3x - 0 = 0 \qquad 3 - 4y = 0 \qquad = \frac{\frac{3}{4}}{1}$$
$$3x = 0 \qquad -4y = -3$$
$$x = 0 \qquad y = \frac{3}{4} \qquad = \frac{3}{4}$$
$$(0, 0) \qquad \left(1, \frac{3}{4}\right)$$

29. $y = 5$

This is the equation of a horizontal line; the slope is 0.

30.
$$m = \frac{y_2 - y_1}{x_2 - x_1}$$
$$\frac{-8}{3} = \frac{-6-2}{4-r}$$
$$\frac{-8}{3} = \frac{-8}{4-r}$$
$$-8(4-r) = -8(3)$$
$$-32 + 8r = -24$$
$$8r = 8$$
$$r = 1$$

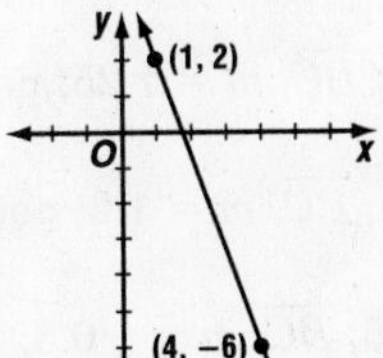

31.
$$m = \frac{y_2 - y_1}{x_2 - x_1}$$
$$2 = \frac{3-r}{2-5}$$
$$2 = \frac{3-r}{-3}$$
$$-6 = 3 - r$$
$$-9 = -r$$
$$9 = r$$

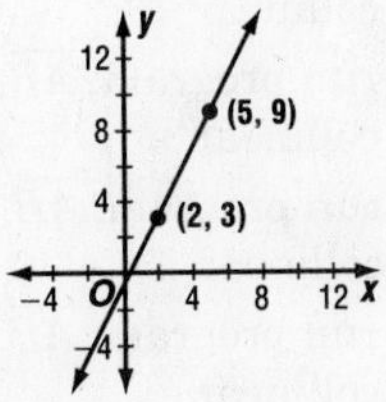

32.
$$m = \frac{y_2 - y_1}{x_2 - x_1}$$
$$\frac{1}{2} = \frac{4-6}{8-r}$$
$$\frac{1}{2} = \frac{-2}{8-r}$$
$$-4 = 8 - r$$
$$-12 = -r$$
$$12 = r$$

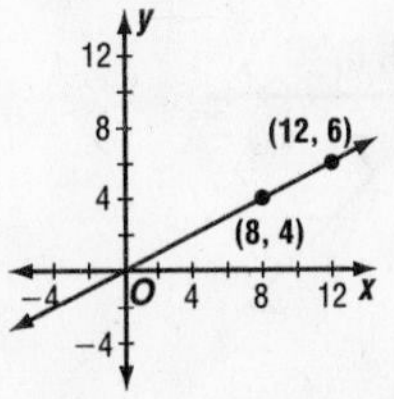

33.
$$m = \frac{y_2 - y_1}{x_2 - x_1}$$
$$\frac{1}{3} = \frac{2-r}{9-6}$$
$$\frac{1}{3} = \frac{2-r}{3}$$
$$3 = 6 - 3r$$
$$-3 = -3r$$
$$1 = r$$

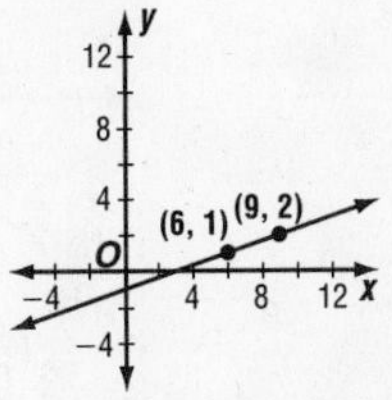

34. Graph (2, 6), then go up 2 units and 3 units to the right.

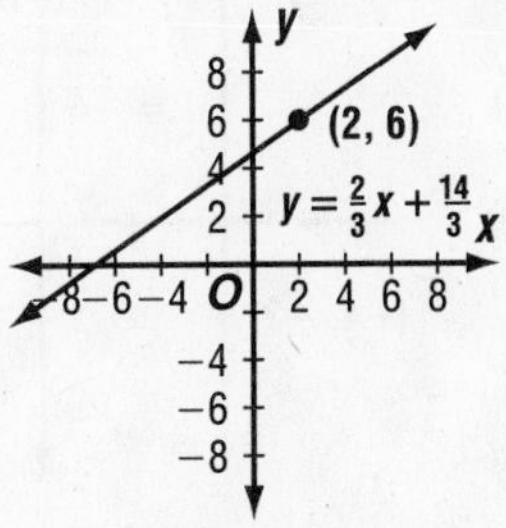

35. Graph (−2, 2), then go down 1 unit and 1 unit to the right.

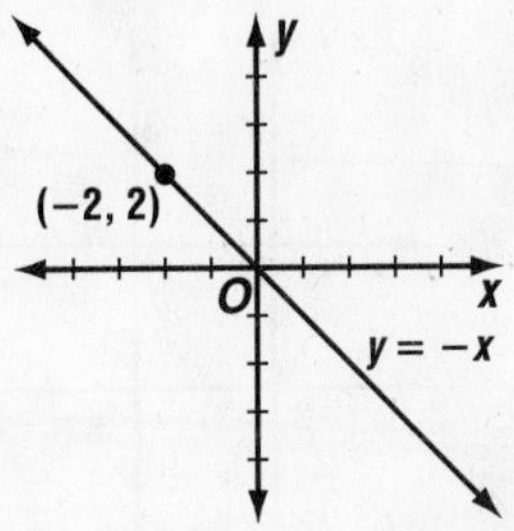

36. The perpendicular slope is $\frac{2}{3}$. Graph (−4, 1), then go up 2 units and 3 units to the right.

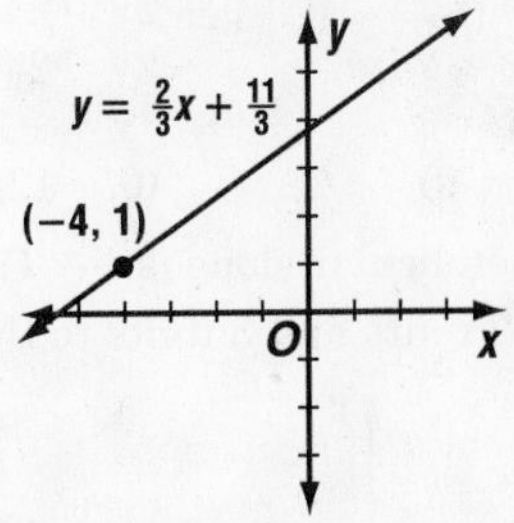

37. $y = 3$ is a horizontal line. A line perpendicular is a vertical line. Graph (3, 3,), then draw a vertical line.

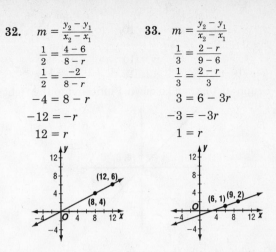

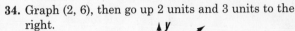

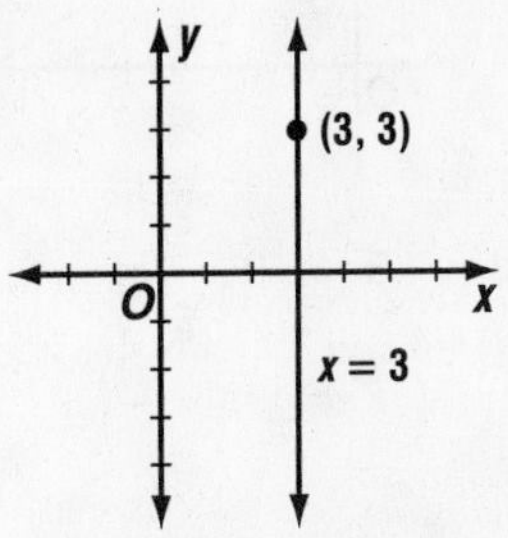

38. $x + y = 10$ $\quad$ $x + y = 10$ $\quad$ $m = \frac{10 - 0}{0 - 10}$

$x + 0 = 10$ $\quad$ $0 + y = 10$ $\quad$ $= \frac{10}{-10}$

$x = 10$ $\quad$ $y = 10$ $\quad$ $= -1$

$(10, 0)$ $\quad$ $(0, 10)$

Graph (0, 0), then go down 1 unit and to the right 1 unit.

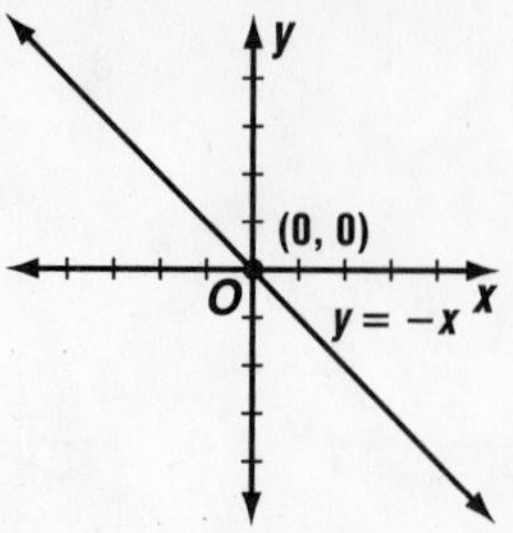

39. Graph (−4, −2), then draw a vertical line.

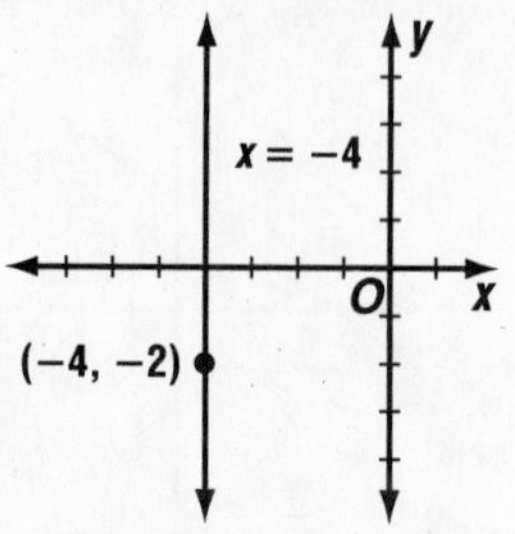

40. Graph (−3, −3), then draw one horizontal line and one vertical line through that point.

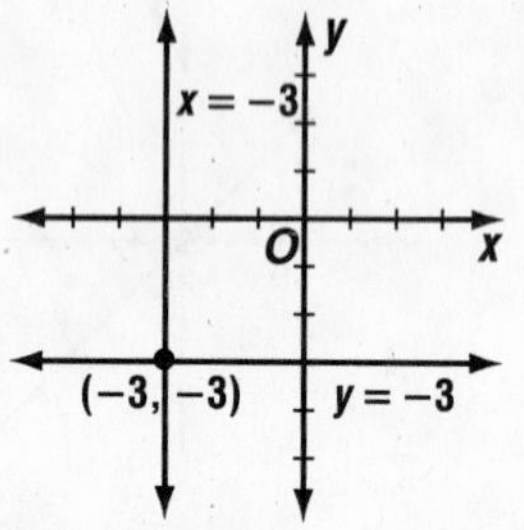

41. $3x - 2y = 24$ $\quad$ $3x - 2y = 24$ $\quad$ $m = \frac{-12 - 0}{0 - 8}$

$3x - 2(0) = 24$ $\quad$ $3(0) - 2y = 24$ $\quad$ $= \frac{-12}{-8}$

$3x - 0 = 24$ $\quad$ $0 - 2y = 24$ $\quad$ $= \frac{3}{2}$

$3x = 24$ $\quad$ $-2y = 24$

$x = 8$ $\quad$ $y = -12$

$(8, 0)$ $\quad$ $(0, -12)$

The perpendicular slope is $-\frac{2}{3}$. Graph (8, 0), then go down 2 units and 3 units to the right.

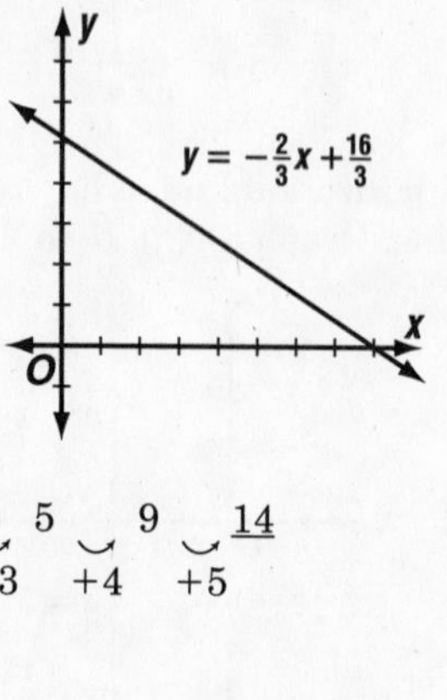

42. 0 $\quad$ 2 $\quad$ 5 $\quad$ 9 $\quad$ <u>14</u>

+2 $\quad$ +3 $\quad$ +4 $\quad$ +5

43. The slope of diagonal $\overline{BD}$ is $\frac{0 - (-4)}{9 - 6} = \frac{4}{3}$. The slope of diagonal $\overline{AC}$ is $\frac{0 - (-4)}{5 - 10} = -\frac{4}{5}$. Since $\left(\frac{4}{3}\right)\left(-\frac{4}{5}\right) \neq -1$, the diagonals are not perpendicular.

44. The slope of diagonal $\overline{AC}$ is $\frac{b}{a}$; the slope of diagonal $\overline{BD}$ is $-\frac{b}{a}$. Since $\left(\frac{b}{a}\right)\left(-\frac{b}{a}\right) \neq -1$, the diagonals are not perpendicular.

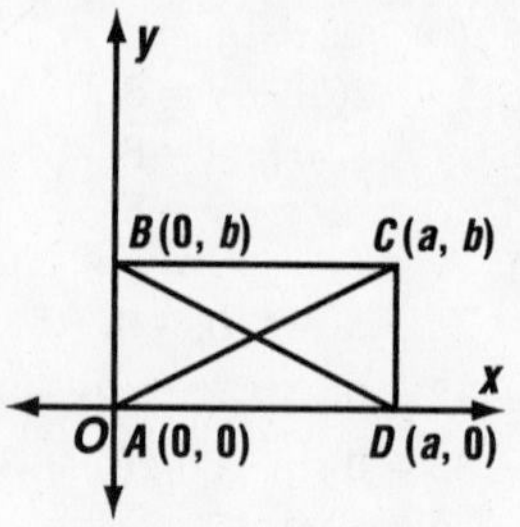

45a. Graphs have the same y-intercept; as slope increases, the lines get steeper.

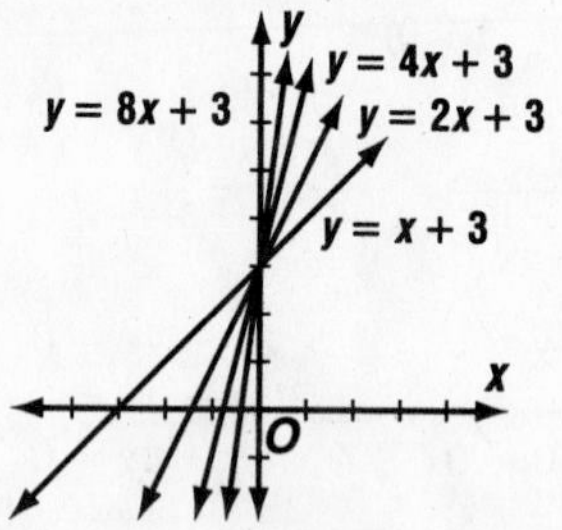

45b. Graphs have the same y-intercept; as the absolute value of the slope increases, the lines get steeper.

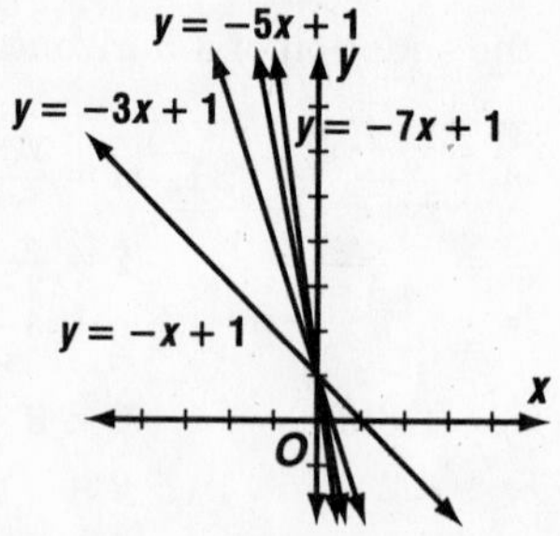

46a. run program; $\overline{AB}$, $m = 0.5$; $\overline{BC}$, $m = 0.5$; collinear

46b. run program; $\overline{AB}$, $m = 1.5$; $\overline{BC}$, $m = 1.25$; not collinear

46c. run program; $\overline{AB}$, $m = 1.34$; $\overline{BC}$, $m = 1.2$; not collinear

46d. run program; $\overline{AB}$, $m = -0.5$; $\overline{BC}$, $m = -0.5$; collinear

47.
$$\begin{aligned} ax + 2y &= 8 \\ ax + 2(0) &= 8 \\ ax + 0 &= 8 \\ ax &= 8 \\ x &= \frac{8}{a} \\ &\left(\frac{8}{a}, 0\right) \end{aligned} \qquad \begin{aligned} ax + 2y &= 8 \\ a(0) + 2y &= 8 \\ 0 + 2y &= 8 \\ 2y &= 8 \\ y &= 4 \\ &(0, 4) \end{aligned} \qquad \begin{aligned} m &= \frac{4 - 0}{0 - \frac{8}{a}} \\ &= \frac{4}{\frac{-8}{a}} \\ &= \frac{4a}{-8} \\ &= -\frac{a}{2} \end{aligned}$$

$$\begin{aligned} 2x + y &= -3 \\ 2x + 0 &= -3 \\ 2x &= -3 \\ x &= -\frac{3}{2} \\ &\left(-\frac{3}{2}, 0\right) \end{aligned} \qquad \begin{aligned} 2x + y &= -3 \\ 2(0) + y &= -3 \\ 0 + y &= -3 \\ y &= -3 \\ &(0, -3) \end{aligned} \qquad \begin{aligned} m &= \frac{-3 - 0}{0 - \left(-\frac{3}{2}\right)} \\ &= \frac{-3}{\frac{3}{2}} \\ &= -2 \end{aligned}$$

If $-\frac{a}{2}$ is perpendicular to -2, then $-\frac{a}{2} = \frac{1}{2}$.

$$\begin{aligned} -\frac{a}{2} &= \frac{1}{2} \\ -2a &= 2 \\ a &= -1 \end{aligned}$$

48a.

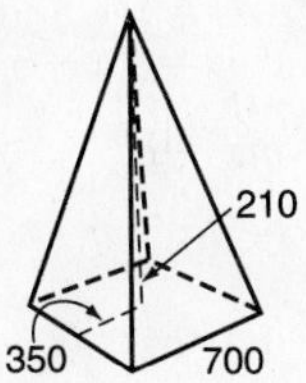

slope $\approx \frac{210}{350}$ or 0.6

48b.

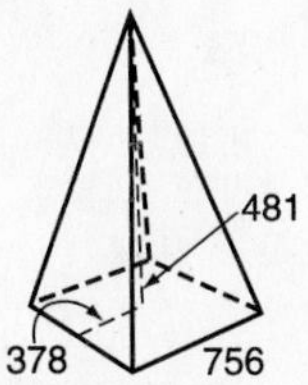

slope $\approx \frac{481}{378}$ or 1.3

49a. 6, 10, 15, 21, 28, <u>36</u>
(differences: +4, +5, +6, +7, +8)

49b. 1, 4, 9, 16, 25, <u>36</u>
(differences: +3, +5, +7, +9, +11)

50. Cassette tapes: $\frac{345 - 360}{1994 - 1991} = \frac{-15}{3} = -5$

CD's: $\frac{662 - 333}{1994 - 1991} = \frac{329}{3} \approx 110$

51.
$$\begin{aligned} y &= -2x + 4 \\ 2x + y &= 4 \end{aligned}$$

52a.

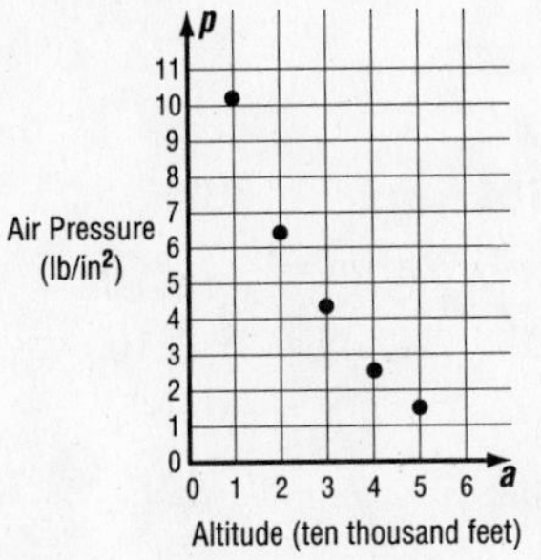

52b. about 0.5 lb/in^2

53.
$$\begin{aligned} 5 < 2x &+ 7 < 13 \\ -2 < 2x &< 6 \\ -1 < x &< 3 \end{aligned}$$
$\{x \mid -1 < x < 3\}$

54. Let x = the lesser number.
$$\begin{aligned} 2x + 2x &\geq 85 \\ 4x &\geq 85 \\ x &\geq 21.25 \end{aligned}$$

55. $|7 + 3a| = 11 - a$

$7 + 3a = 11 - a$ or $7 + 3a = -(11 - a)$
$$\begin{aligned} 7 + 4a &= 11 \\ 4a &= 4 \\ a &= 1 \end{aligned} \qquad \begin{aligned} 7 + 3a &= -11 + a \\ 7 + 2a &= -11 \\ 2a &= -18 \\ a &= -9 \end{aligned}$$

56.
$$\begin{aligned} 0.75(8a + 20) - 2(a - 1) &= 3 \\ 6a + 15 - 2a + 2 &= 3 \\ 4a + 17 &= 3 \\ 4a &= -14 \\ a &= -\frac{7}{2} \end{aligned}$$

57. 45, 97, 98, 100, 101, 105

$\frac{45 + 97 + 98 + 100 + 101 + 105}{6} = \frac{546}{6} = 91$;

$\frac{98 + 100}{2} = \frac{198}{2} = 99$; no mode

58.
$$\begin{aligned} \frac{1}{3}(15a + 9b) - \frac{1}{7}(28b - 84a) &= 5a + 3b - 4b + 12a \\ &= 17a - b \end{aligned}$$

59.
$$\begin{aligned} 3 + (21 \div 7) \times 8 \div 4 &= 3 + 3 \times 8 \div 4 \\ &= 3 + 24 \div 4 \\ &= 3 + 6 \\ &= 9 \end{aligned}$$

Page 87 Self Test

1a. D = {0, 5, 10, 15, 20, 25, 30, 35, 40},
R = {30, 27, 16, 9, 4, 1, −2, −4, −5}

1b.

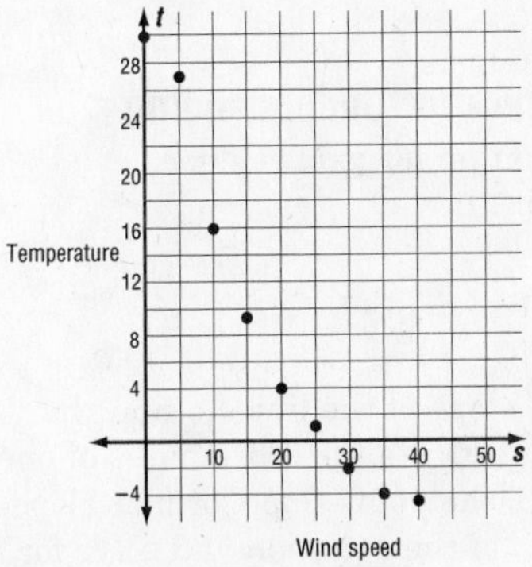

Yes, this is a function.

2.
$$\begin{aligned} f(x) &= 100x - 5x^2 \\ f(15) &= 100(15) - 5(15)^2 \\ &= 1500 - 5(225) \\ &= 1500 - 1125 \\ &= 375 \end{aligned}$$

3.
$$\begin{aligned} y &= -6x + 4 \\ 6x + y &= 4 \end{aligned}$$

4. $3x + 5y = 30$ | $3x + 5y = 30$
$3x + 5(0) = 30$ | $3(0) + 5y = 30$
$3x + 0 = 30$ | $0 + 5y = 30$
$3x = 30$ | $5y = 30$
$x = 10$ | $y = 6$
$(10, 0)$ | $(0, 6)$

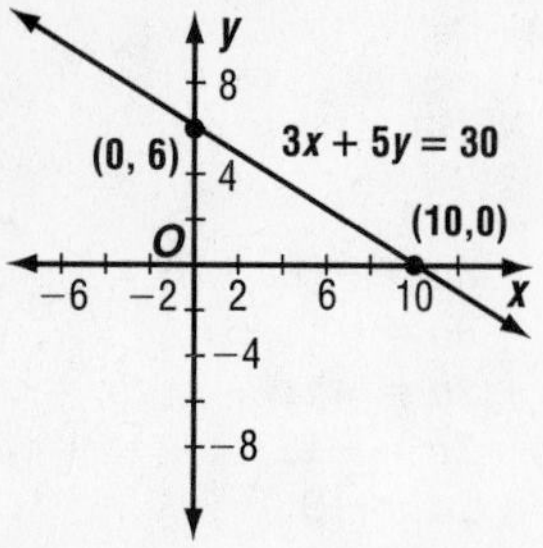

5. $2x + 3y = 6$ | $2x + 3y = 6$ | $m = \frac{2-0}{0-3}$
$2x + 3(0) = 6$ | $2(0) + 3y = 6$ | $= -\frac{2}{3}$
$2x + 0 = 6$ | $0 + 3y = 6$
$2x = 6$ | $3y = 6$
$x = 3$ | $y = 2$
$(3, 0)$ | $(0, 2)$

Graph $(4, -3)$, then go down 2 units and 3 units to the right.

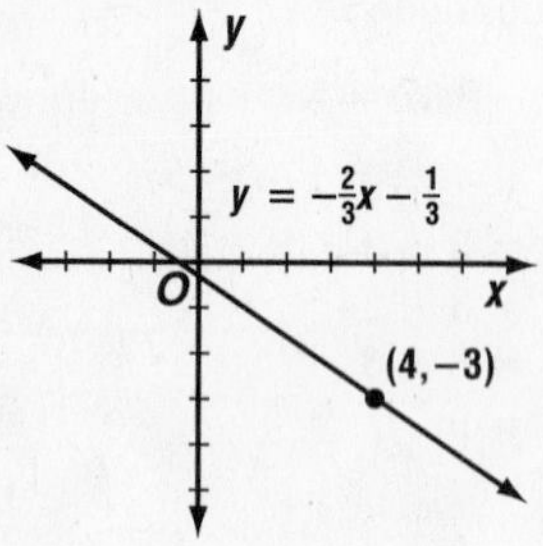

2-4 Writing Linear Equations

Pages 91–92 Check for Understanding

1. Solve the equation for y; m = slope, b = y-intercept.
2. $y = mx + b$
   $y = 5x + (-4)$
   $y = 5x - 4$
3. First find the slope of the line. To find the y-intercept, substitute the coordinates of one of the points into the point-slope form or slope-intercept form of the equation and solve for b. Write the equation in slope-intercept form.
4. b; it has a negative slope and a positive y-intercept.
5. Karen is correct because even though one line is written in slope-intercept form, they are the same line.

   $y = 4x + 2$
   $-4x + y = 2$
   $4x - y = -2$

6. $y = 10x + 250$; $m = 10$, representing the amount of money added to the account each month; y-intercept = 250, representing the amount already in savings

7. $y = mx + b$
   $y = 7x - 3$

8. $y = mx + b$
   $y = 1.5x + 0$
   $y = 1.5x$

9. $y = mx + b$
   $y = -\frac{1}{3}x + 4$

10. $m = 2$; $b = -5$

11. $2y = 4x + 6$
    $y = 2x + 3$
    $m = 2$; $b = 3$

12. $3x + 2y = 10$
    $2y = -3x + 10$
    $y = -\frac{3}{2}x + 5$
    $m = -\frac{3}{2}$; $b = 5$

13. $m = \frac{7-2}{0-(-4)}$
    $= \frac{5}{4}$
    $y - y_1 = m(x - x_1)$
    $y - 7 = \frac{5}{4}(x - 0)$
    $y - 7 = \frac{5}{4}x$
    $y = \frac{5}{4}x + 7$

14. $m = \frac{2-(-5)}{2-0}$
    $= \frac{7}{2}$
    $y - y_1 = m(x - x_1)$
    $y - (-5) = \frac{7}{2}(x - 0)$
    $y + 5 = \frac{7}{2}x$
    $y = \frac{7}{2}x - 5$

15. $m = \frac{-1-(-3)}{3-(-3)}$
    $= \frac{2}{6}$
    $= \frac{1}{3}$
    $y - y_1 = m(x - x_1)$
    $y - (-1) = \frac{1}{3}(x - 3)$
    $y + 1 = \frac{1}{3}x - 1$
    $y = \frac{1}{3}x - 2$

16. $y = mx + b$
    $4 = 0.5(6) + b$
    $4 = 3 + b$
    $1 = b$
    $y = 0.5x + 1$

17. $m = \frac{-4-1}{8-6}$
    $= -\frac{5}{2}$
    $y - y_1 = m(x - x_1)$
    $y - 1 = -\frac{5}{2}(x - 6)$
    $y - 1 = -\frac{5}{2}x + 15$
    $y = -\frac{5}{2}x + 16$

18. $m = 4$
    $y = mx + b$
    $5 = 4(0) + b$
    $5 = b$
    $y = 4x + 5$

19. $m = 1$; perpendicular $m = -1$
    $y = mx + b$
    $-2 = -1(0) + b$
    $-2 = b$
    $y = -x - 2$

20. $y = 75x + 6000$

Pages 92–94 Exercises

21. $m = -\frac{2}{3}$; $b = -4$

22. $m = \frac{3}{4}$; $b = 0$

23. $-y = 0.3x + 6$
    $y = -0.3x - 6$
    $m = -0.3$; $b = -6$

24. $4y = 2x - 10$
    $y = \frac{1}{2}x - \frac{5}{2}$
    $m = \frac{1}{2}$; $b = -\frac{5}{2}$

25. $-5y = 3x - 30$
    $y = -\frac{3}{5}x + 6$
    $m = -\frac{3}{5}$; $b = 6$

26. $y = cx + d$
    $m = c$; $b = d$

27. $m = \frac{2-0}{2.5-0}$
$= \frac{2}{2.5}$
$= \frac{4}{5}$
$y - y_1 = m(x - x_1)$
$y - 0 = \frac{4}{5}(x - 0)$
$y = \frac{4}{5}x$

28. The slope of any horizontal line is 0.
$y - y_1 = m(x - x_1)$
$y - (-4) = 0(x - 0)$
$y + 4 = 0$
$y = -4$

29. $m = \frac{-2-3}{7-4}$
$= -\frac{5}{3}$
$y - y_1 = m(x - x_1)$
$y - 3 = -\frac{5}{3}(x - 4)$
$y - 3 = -\frac{5}{3}x + \frac{20}{3}$
$y = -\frac{5}{3}x + \frac{29}{3}$

30. $y = mx + b$
$4 = 0.25(0) + b$
$4 = b$
$y = 0.25x + 4$

31. $y = mx + b$
$-3 = (-0.5)(2) + b$
$-3 = -1 + b$
$-2 = b$
$y = -0.5x - 2$

32. $y = mx + b$
$0 = 4(0) + b$
$0 = b$
$y = 4x$

33. $m = \frac{1-5}{3-(-2)}$
$= -\frac{4}{5}$
$y - y_1 = m(x - x_1)$
$y - 1 = -\frac{4}{5}(x - 3)$
$y - 1 = -\frac{4}{5}x + \frac{12}{5}$
$y = -\frac{4}{5}x + \frac{17}{5}$

34. $m = \frac{8-1}{7-7}$
$= \frac{7}{0}$
undefined; no slope-intercept form, $x = 7$

35. $m = \frac{0-(-3)}{0-(-2)}$
$= \frac{3}{2}$
$y - y_1 = m(x - x_1)$
$y - 0 = \frac{3}{2}(x - 0)$
$y = \frac{3}{2}x$

36. $(-4, 0), (0, 4)$
$m = \frac{4-0}{0-(-4)}$
$= \frac{4}{4}$
$= 1$
$y - y_1 = m(x - x_1)$
$y - 4 = 1(x - 0)$
$y - 4 = x$
$y = x + 4$

37. $\left(\frac{1}{3}, 0\right), \left(0, -\frac{1}{4}\right)$
$m = \dfrac{-\frac{1}{4} - 0}{0 - \frac{1}{3}}$
$= \dfrac{-\frac{1}{4}}{-\frac{1}{3}}$
$= \frac{3}{4}$
$y - y_1 = m(x - x_1)$
$y - 0 = \frac{3}{4}\left(x - \frac{1}{3}\right)$
$y = \frac{3}{4}x - \frac{1}{4}$

38. $(0, 0), (0, 4)$
$m = \frac{4-0}{0-0}$
$= \frac{4}{0}$
undefined; no slope-intercept form
$x = 0$

39. $m = \frac{2}{3}$
$y = mx + b$
$6 = \frac{2}{3}(4) + b$
$6 = \frac{8}{3} + b$
$\frac{10}{3} = b$
$y = \frac{2}{3}x + \frac{10}{3}$

40. $m = -3$
perpendicular $m = \frac{1}{3}$
$y = mx + b$
$0 = \frac{1}{3}(-2) + b$
$0 = -\frac{2}{3} + b$
$\frac{2}{3} = b$
$y = \frac{1}{3}x + \frac{2}{3}$

41. $m = \frac{6-3}{0-3}$
$= \frac{3}{-3}$
$= -1$
$y = mx + b$
$-1 = (-1)(-3) + b$
$-1 = 3 + b$
$-4 = b$
$y = -x - 4$

42. $3x - \frac{1}{5}y = 3$
$-\frac{1}{5}y = -3x + 3$
$y = 15x - 15$
$m = 15$
perpendicular $m = -\frac{1}{15}$
$y = mx + b$
$-5 = \left(-\frac{1}{15}\right)(6) + b$
$-5 = -\frac{2}{5} + b$
$-\frac{23}{5} = b$
$y = -\frac{1}{15}x - \frac{23}{5}$

43. $5x + ky = 8$
$5(3) + k(-1) = 8$
$15 - k = 8$
$-k = -7$
$k = 7$

44. $4x - ky = 7$
$4(4) - k(3) = 7$
$16 - 3k = 7$
$-3k = -9$
$k = 3$

45. $3x + 8y = k$
$3(0) + 8(0.5) = k$
$0 + 4 = k$
$4 = k$

46. $kx + 3y = 11$
$k(7) + 3(2) = 11$
$7k + 6 = 11$
$7k = 5$
$k = \frac{5}{7}$

47. $2y = 6x + 14$
$y = 3x + 7$

$3x - y = 6$
$-y = -3x + 6$
$y = 3x - 6$

The lines are parallel with different y-intercepts.

48. $2y - 4 = x$
$2y = x + 4$
$y = \frac{1}{2}x + 2$

$y = -2x + 2$

The lines are perpendicular and intersect at their y-intercepts.

49. $3x + 5y = 15$
$5y = -3x + 15$
$y = -\frac{3}{5}x + 3$

$y = -\frac{3}{5}x + 3$

The lines are the same.

50. $\overline{BC}$: $m = \frac{10-4}{-6-6}$
$= \frac{6}{-12}$
$= -\frac{1}{2}$
perpendicular $m = 2$
$y = mx + b$
$-8 = 2(-6) + b$
$-8 = -12 + b$
$4 = b$
$y = 2x + 4$

51. 1999 is 10 years after 1989.

$y = 0.4x + 4.6$
$= 0.4(10) + 4.6$
$= 4 + 4.6$
$= 8.6$; 8.6 billion hours

52a. $d = 180(c - 2)$
$d = 180c - 360$

52b. $m = 180$
$b = -360$

52c. $d = 180c - 360$
$= 180(5) - 360$
$= 900 - 360$
$= 540$; 540°

53. $y = 8.33x$

54. Benny's: $20 + 3x = y$ Carmelita's: $30 + 2x = y$
$30 + 2x < 20 + 3x$
$30 - x < 20$
$-x < -10$
$x > 10$; when the number of miles is greater than 10.

55a. $m = \frac{9 - 3.2}{4 - 0}$
$= \frac{5.8}{4}$
$= 1.45$
$y = mx + b$
$3.2 = 1.45(0) + b$
$3.2 = b$
$y = 1.45x + 3.2$

55b. 2000 is 9 years after 1991.
$y = 1.45x + 3.2$
$= 1.45(9) + 3.2$
$= 13.05 + 3.2$
$= 16.25$; 16.25 million

55c. The slope is the average increase in subscribers; the y-intercept is the number of subscribers in 1990.

56. From 1:30 to 3:00 is $1\frac{1}{2}$ hours.
$y = 40x + 32$
$= 40\left(1\frac{1}{2}\right) + 32$
$= 60 + 32$
$= 92$; 92 miles

57. $g(x) = x(2 - x)$
$= 2x - x^2$
No, variables must be of first degree.

58. $h(a + 1) = h(4 + 1)$
$= h(5)$
$h(x) = 3x - 1$
$h(5) = 3(5) - 1$
$= 15 - 1$
$= 14$

59. $|x - 2| \leq -99$
no solution

60. $2(r - 4) + 5 \geq 9$
$2r - 8 + 5 \geq 9$
$2r - 3 \geq 9$
$2r \geq 12$
$r \geq 6$
$\{r \mid r \geq 6\}$

61. $|x - 3| = 2x$

$x - 3 = 2x$ or $x - 3 = -2x$
$-x - 3 = 0$ $3x - 3 = 0$
$-x = 3$ $3x = 3$
$x = -3$ $x = 1$

Check:

$|x - 3| \stackrel{?}{=} 2x$ $|x - 3| \stackrel{?}{=} 2x$
$|-3 - 3| \stackrel{?}{=} 2(-3)$ $|1 - 3| \stackrel{?}{=} 2(1)$
$|-6| \neq -6$ $|-2| = 2$ ✓

62. $\frac{1}{5}(4 + n)$

63. \$4.50 (20), \$5.00 (100), \$5.90 (60), \$6.25 (10), \$7.75 (10)
$((4.50 \times 20) + (5.00 \times 100) + (5.90 \times 60) + (6.25 \times 10) + (7.75 \times 10)) \div 200 = 1084 \div 200 =$ 5.42 or \$5.42; \$5.00; \$5.00

64. commutative (+)

65. $(5a + 3d)^2 - e^2 = (5(3) + 3(0.5))^2 - (0.3)^2$
$= (15 + 1.5)^2 - 0.09$
$= (16.5)^2 - 0.09$
$= 272.25 - 0.09$
$= 272.16$

Page 94 Mathematics and Society

1. Sample answer: shrubs, trees, fences, and so on
2. Sample answer: People also count landmarks when traveling.
3. Sample answer: The landmarks on graphs are units used to provide numerical scales.

2-5 Integration: Statistics Modeling Real-World Data Using Scatter Plots

Page 98 Check for Understanding

1. Sample answer: Best-fit lines help to make predictions.
2. See students' work.
3. c; the points increase
4. Sample answer: Juanita is probably correct because typing speed will eventually level off.
5. See students' work.

6. $w = 5h - 187$
$= 5(66) - 187$
$= 330 - 187$
$= 143$; 143 pounds

7. $w = 5h - 187$
$= 5(72) - 187$
$= 360 - 187$
$= 173$; 173 pounds

8. $w = 5h - 187$
$= 5(78) - 187$
$= 390 - 187$
$= 203$; 203 pounds

9a.

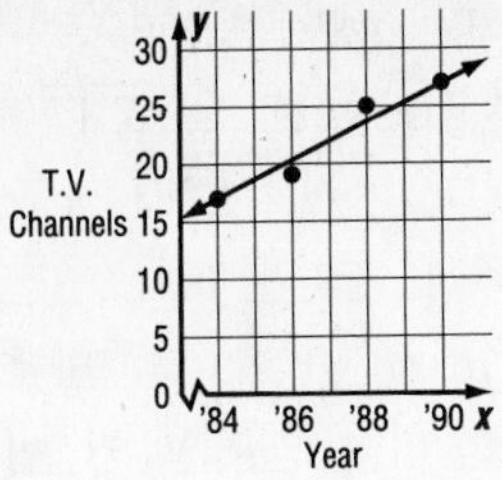

9b. Let x = years since 1984.

$$m = \frac{27 - 17}{6 - 0}$$
$$= \frac{10}{6}$$
$$= \frac{5}{3}$$
$$y = mx + b$$
$$17 = \frac{3}{5}(0) + b$$
$$17 = 0 + b$$
$$17 = b$$

9c. $x = 1999 - 1984$ or 15

$$y = \frac{5}{3}x + 17$$
$$= \frac{5}{3}(15) + 17$$
$$= 25 + 17$$
$$= 42\text{; about } 42$$

Pages 98–100 Exercises

10. Let x = years since 1982.

$$m = \frac{42 - 57}{12 - 0}$$
$$= \frac{-15}{12}$$
$$= -\frac{5}{4}$$
$$y = mx + b$$
$$57 = -\frac{5}{4}(0) + b$$
$$57 = 0 + b$$
$$57 = b$$
$$x = 2000 - 1982 \text{ or } 18$$
$$y = -\frac{5}{4}x + 57$$
$$= -\frac{5}{4}(18) + 57$$
$$= -22.5 + 57$$
$$= 34.5\text{; about } 35\%$$

11a.

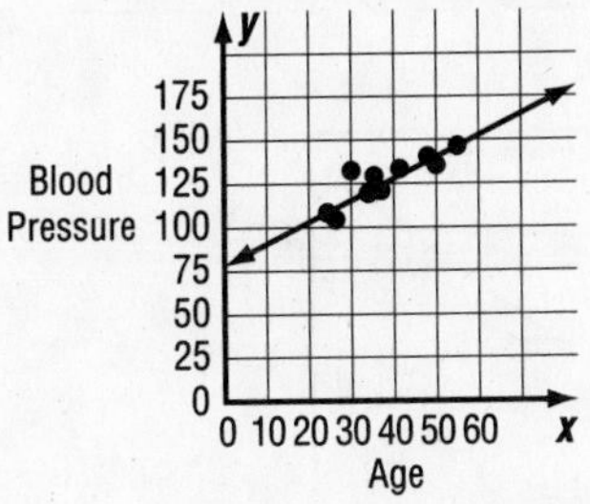

11b. Sample answer: $m = \frac{140 - 108}{48 - 24}$

$$= \frac{32}{24}$$
$$= \frac{4}{3}$$
$$y = mx + b$$
$$140 = \frac{4}{3}(48) + b$$
$$140 = 64 + b$$
$$76 = b$$
$$y = \frac{4}{3}x + 76$$

11c. Sample answer: based on equation for 10b

$$y = \frac{4}{3}x + 76$$
$$= \frac{4}{3}(54) + 76$$
$$= 72 + 76$$
$$= 148$$

12a.

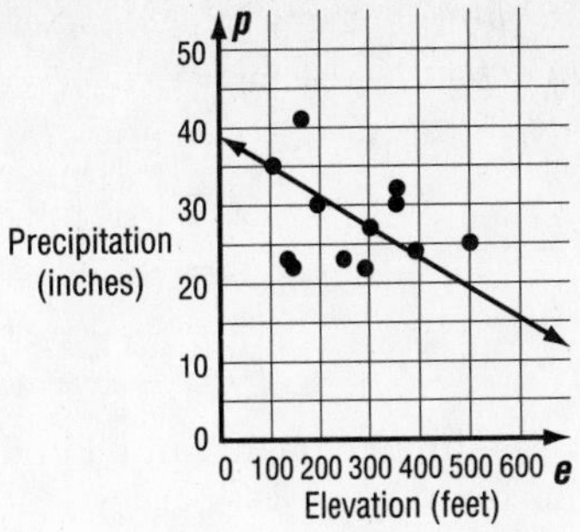

12b. Sample answer: $m = \frac{35 - 27}{111 - 308}$

$$= \frac{8}{-197}$$
$$\approx -0.04$$
$$y = mx + b$$
$$35 = -0.04(111) + b$$
$$35 = -4.44 + b$$
$$39.44 = b$$
$$p = -0.04e + 39.44$$

12c. See students' work.

13a.

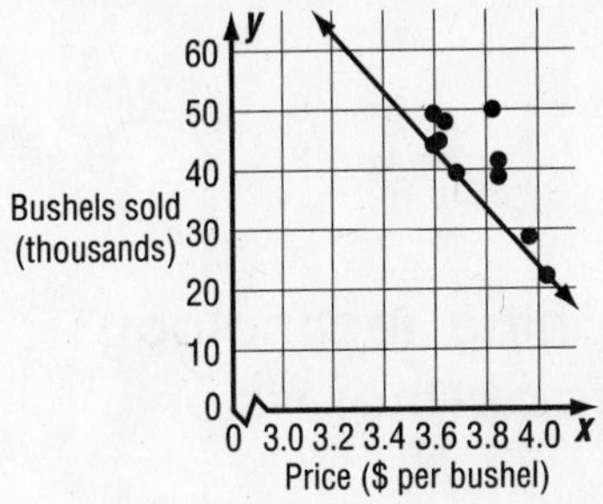

Sample answer: $m = \frac{23 - 46}{4.05 - 3.60}$

$$= \frac{-23}{0.45}$$
$$\approx -50$$
$$y = mx + b$$
$$46 = (-50)(3.60) + b$$
$$46 = -180 + b$$
$$226 = b$$
$$y = -50x + 226$$

13b. Sample answer: based on answer for 13a

$$y = -50x + 226$$
$$= -50(3.90) + 226$$
$$= -195 + 226$$
$$= 31$$

about 31,000 bushels

13c. Sample answer: based on answer for 13a

$$y = -50x + 226$$
$$25.5 = -50x + 226$$
$$-200.5 = -50x$$
$$4.01 = x$$

about \$4.01

14. One best-fit line may not be accurate enough because the graph "flattens out" at the top and doesn't follow the same pattern as the first part of the graph.

15. line b: $y = mx + b$

$3 = 3(3) + b$

$3 = 9 + b$

$-6 = b$

$y = 3x - 6$

line a: perpendicular

slope $= -\frac{1}{3}$

$y = mx + b$

$3 = \left(-\frac{1}{3}\right)(3) + b$

$3 = -1 + b$

$4 = b$

$y = -\frac{1}{3}x + 4$

line c: only passes through quandrants I and II, so it must be horizontal: $y = 3$

16. $g(x) = -\frac{4x}{2} + 7$

$g(3) = -\frac{4(3)}{2} + 7$

$= -\frac{12}{2} + 7$

$= -6 + 7$

$= 1$

17. $|x + 4| > 3$

$x + 4 > 3$ or $x + 4 < -3$

$x > -1$ $\quad x < -7$

$\{x \mid x < -7 \text{ or } x > -1\}$

18. Let x = the number.

$x + x^2$

19. $3(2x + 2) - 2(x - 1) = 6x + 6 - 2x + 2$

$= 4x + 8$

2-5B Graphing Technology: Lines of Regression

Page 102 Exercises

1. [−5, 25] by [−20, 5] with Xscl = 5 and Yscl = 5

[STAT] 1 [▲] [CLEAR] [ENTER] [▶] [▲] [CLEAR] [ENTER] [◀] −2 [ENTER] 1 [ENTER] 4 [ENTER] 10 [ENTER] 23 [ENTER] 25 [ENTER] [▶] 1 [ENTER] [(−)] 0.5 [ENTER] 2 [ENTER] [(−)] 4.5 [ENTER] [(−)] 10 [ENTER] [(−)] 11.5 [ENTER] [2nd] [STAT PLOT] 1 [ENTER] [▼] [ENTER] [▼] [ENTER] [▼] [▶] [ENTER] [▼] [ENTER] [GRAPH] [STAT] [▶] 5 [2nd] [L1] [,] [2nd] [L2] [ENTER] [Y=] [VARS] 5 [▶] [▶] 7 [GRAPH]

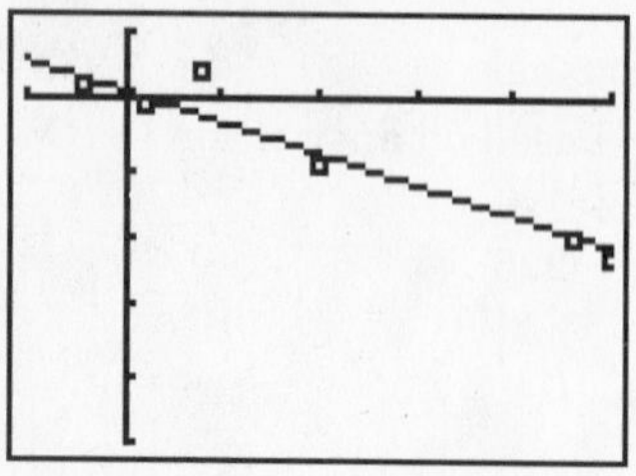

2. [−2, 8] by [−10, 10] with Xscl = 1 and Yscl = 1.

[STAT] 1 [▲] [CLEAR] [ENTER] [▶] [▲] [CLEAR] [ENTER] [◀] 0.2 [ENTER] 1 [ENTER] 3 [ENTER] 4 [ENTER] 5 [ENTER] 8 [ENTER] [▶] 0.11 [ENTER] 0.31 [ENTER] 0.9 [ENTER] 1.25 [ENTER] 1.75 [ENTER] 2.3 [ENTER] [2nd] [STAT PLOT] 1 [ENTER] [▼] [ENTER] [▼] [ENTER] [▼] [▶] [ENTER] [▼] [ENTER] [GRAPH] [STAT] [▶] 5 [2nd] [L1] [,] [2nd] [L2] [ENTER] [Y=] [VARS] 5 [▶] [▶] 7 [GRAPH]

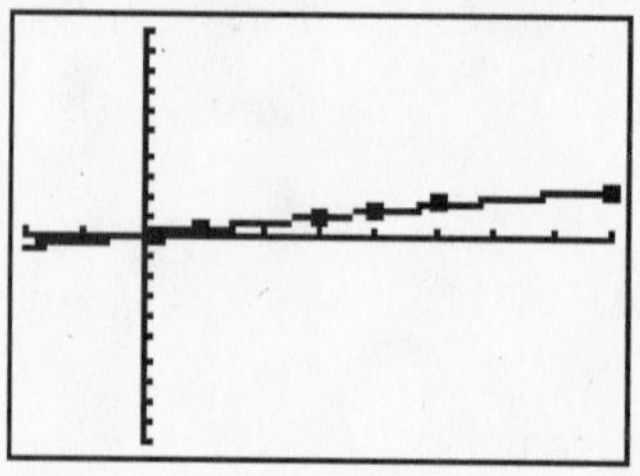

3a. [0, 45] by [3000, 20000] with Xscl = 2 and Yscl = 500

[STAT] 1 [▲] [CLEAR] [ENTER] [▶] [▲] [CLEAR] [ENTER] [◀] 10 [ENTER] 20 [ENTER] 30 [ENTER] 35 [ENTER] 40 [ENTER] [▶] 3257 [ENTER] 5323 [ENTER] 11197 [ENTER] 15624 [ENTER] 19822 [ENTER] [2nd] [STAT PLOT] 1 [ENTER] [▼] [ENTER] [▼] [ENTER] [▼] [▶] [ENTER] [▼] [ENTER] [GRAPH] [STAT] [▶] 5 [2nd] [L1] [,] [2nd] [L2] [ENTER] [Y=] [VARS] 5 [▶] [▶] 7 [GRAPH]

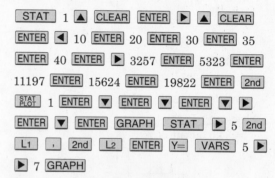

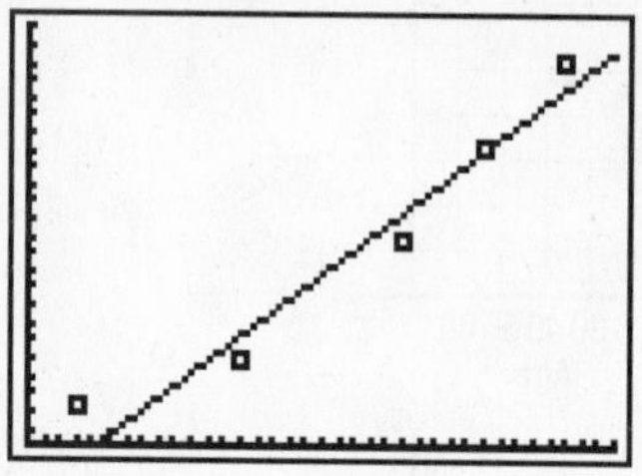

[TRACE] and use arrow keys to predict salary at 2000; about $23,879

3b. [0, 45] by [2000, 30000] with Xscl = 2 and Yscl = 5000

(Keep data in L_1 from 3a.). [STAT] 1 [▶] [▲] [CLEAR] [ENTER] 5368 [ENTER] 8966 [ENTER] 18612 [ENTER] 24195 [ENTER] 27678 [ENTER] [2nd] [STAT PLOT] 1 [ENTER] [▼] [ENTER] [▼] [ENTER] [▼] [▶] [ENTER] [▼] [ENTER] [GRAPH] [STAT] [▶] 5 [2nd] [L1] [,] [2nd] [L2] [ENTER] [Y=] [VARS] 5 [▶] [▶] 7 [GRAPH]

(continued on next page)

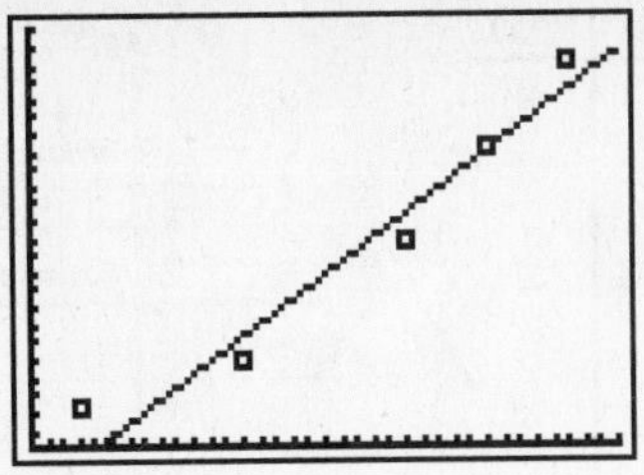

TRACE and use arrow keys to predict salary at 2000; about $35,015

3c. The women's average income since 1950 has increased at a greater rate than the men's; however, the men's average income was greater than the women's in 1950 and remained greater in 1990.

2-6 Special Functions

Page 106 Check for Understanding

1. 3.32 is close to π due to measurement error and rounding.
2. d
3. $[-4.1] = -5$ instead of -4 because $-4 > -4.1$.
4. One part of the graph is a reflection of the other.
5. The graphs have the same shape, but different y-intercepts. The graph of $f(x) = |x|$ has its vertex at the origin; the graph of $f(x) = |x| - 2$ has its vertex at $(0, -2)$

6. A;

x	$\|3x - 2\|$	$f(x)$
-1	$\|3(-1) - 2\|$	5
0	$\|3(0) - 2\|$	2
1	$\|3(1) - 2\|$	1
2	$\|3(2) - 2\|$	4
3	$\|3(3) - 2\|$	7

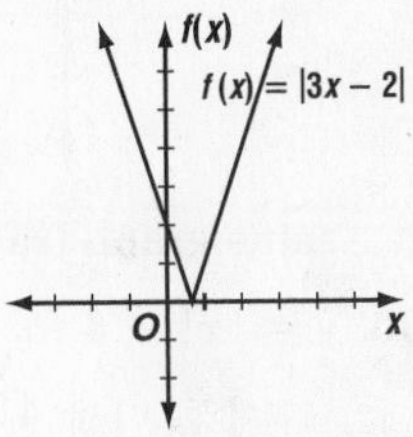

7. G;

x	$-[x]$	$g(x)$
0	$-[0]$	0
$\frac{1}{2}$	$-\left[\frac{1}{2}\right]$	0
1	$-[1]$	-1
$1\frac{1}{2}$	$-\left[1\frac{1}{2}\right]$	-1
2	$-[2]$	-2
$-\frac{1}{2}$	$-\left[-\frac{1}{2}\right]$	1
-1	$-[-1]$	1

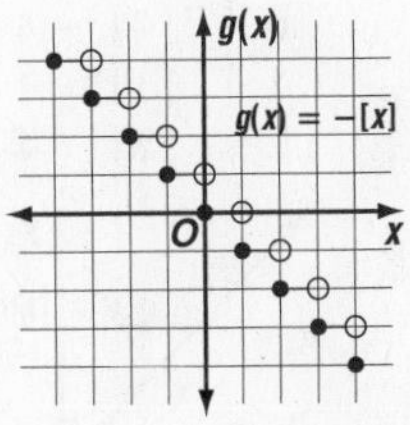

8. D;

x	$2x$	$f(x)$
-2	$2(-2)$	-4
-1	$2(-1)$	-2
0	$2(0)$	0
1	$2(1)$	2
2	$2(2)$	4

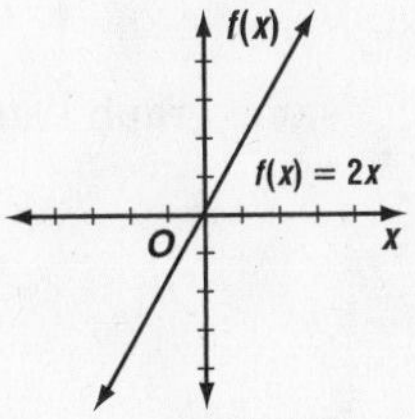

9. C;

x	$h(x)$
-2	0.5
-1	0.5
0	0.5
1	0.5
2	0.5

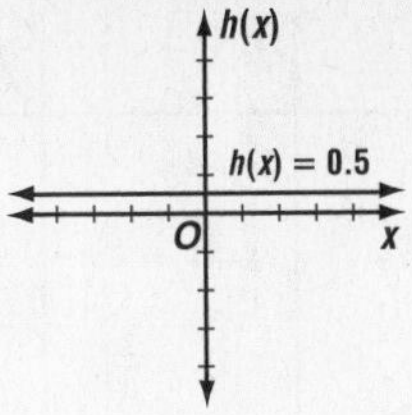

10.
$g(x) = |x - 5|$
$g(4) = |4 - 5|$
$= |-1|$
$= 1$

11.
$f(x) = 2[x - 1]$
$f(6.9) = 2[6.9 - 1]$
$= 2[5.9]$
$= 2(5)$
$= 10$

12. step function

Pages 106–108 Exercises

13.
$h(x) = [2x + 3]$
$h(2) = [2(2) + 3]$
$= [4 + 3]$
$= [7]$
$= 7$

14.
$h(x) = [2x + 3]$
$h(-2) = [2(-2) + 3]$
$= [-4 + 3]$
$= [-1]$
$= -1$

15.
$h(x) = [2x + 3]$
$h(-2.3) = [2(-2.3) + 3]$
$= [-4.6 + 3]$
$= [-1.6]$
$= -2$

16.
$h(x) = [2x + 3]$
$h\left(\frac{1}{4}\right) = \left[2\left(\frac{1}{4}\right) + 3\right]$
$= \left[\frac{1}{2} + 3\right]$
$= \left[3\frac{1}{2}\right]$
$= 3$

17. D;

x	$h(x)$
-1	-1
0	0
1	1

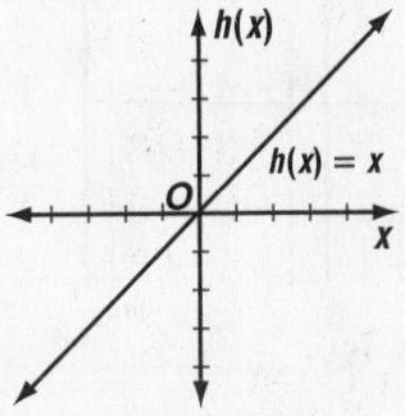

18. A;

x	$\|2x\|$	$f(x)$
-2	$\|2(-2)\|$	4
-1	$\|2(-1)\|$	2
0	$\|2(0)\|$	0
1	$\|2(1)\|$	2
2	$\|2(2)\|$	4

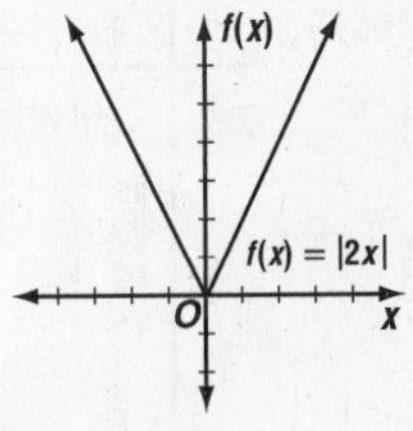

19. C;

x	$g(x)$
0	-3
1	-3

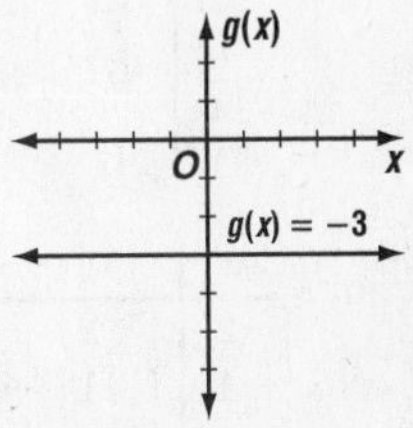

20. G;

x	$[2x + 1]$	$f(x)$
0	$[2(0) + 1]$	1
$\frac{1}{4}$	$\left[2\left(\frac{1}{4}\right) + 1\right]$	1
$\frac{1}{2}$	$\left[2\left(\frac{1}{2}\right) + 1\right]$	2
$\frac{3}{4}$	$\left[2\left(\frac{3}{4}\right) + 1\right]$	2

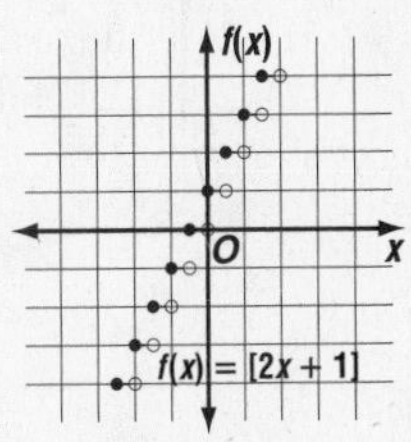

21. A;

x	$\left\lvert x - \frac{1}{4} \right\rvert$	$f(x)$
-2	$\left\lvert -2 - \frac{1}{4} \right\rvert$	$2\frac{1}{4}$
-1	$\left\lvert -1 - \frac{1}{4} \right\rvert$	$1\frac{1}{4}$
0	$\left\lvert 0 - \frac{1}{4} \right\rvert$	$\frac{1}{4}$
$\frac{1}{4}$	$\left\lvert \frac{1}{4} - \frac{1}{4} \right\rvert$	0
1	$\left\lvert 1 - \frac{1}{4} \right\rvert$	$\frac{3}{4}$
2	$\left\lvert 2 - \frac{1}{4} \right\rvert$	$1\frac{3}{4}$

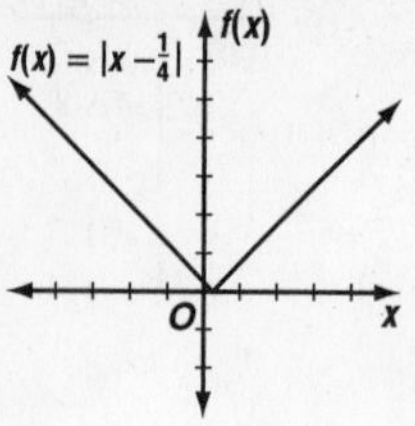

22. D;

x	$-\frac{2}{3}x$	$f(x)$
-1	$-\frac{2}{3}(-1)$	$\frac{2}{3}$
0	$-\frac{2}{3}(0)$	0
1	$-\frac{2}{3}(1)$	$-\frac{2}{3}$
2	$-\frac{2}{3}(2)$	$-\frac{4}{3}$

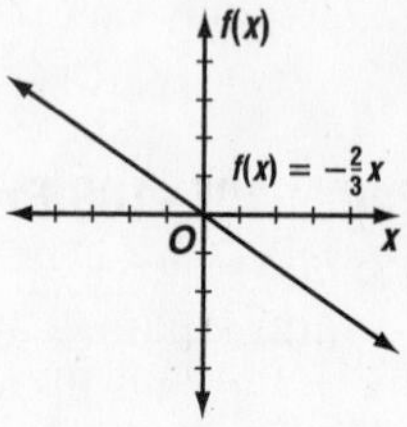

23. D;

x	$x + 3$	$f(x)$
-2	$-2 + 3$	1
-1	$-1 + 3$	2
0	$0 + 3$	3
1	$1 + 3$	4

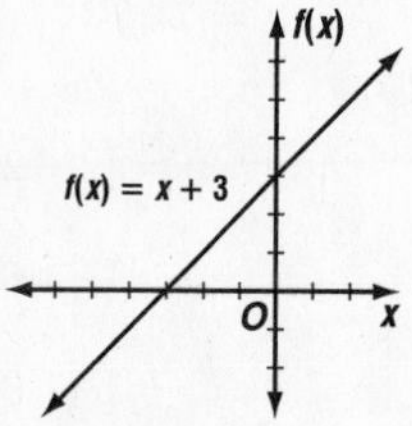

24. A;

x	$\lvert x + 3 \rvert$	$f(x)$
-5	$\lvert -5 + 3 \rvert$	2
-4	$\lvert -4 + 3 \rvert$	1
-3	$\lvert -3 + 3 \rvert$	0
-2	$\lvert -2 + 3 \rvert$	1
-1	$\lvert -1 + 3 \rvert$	2

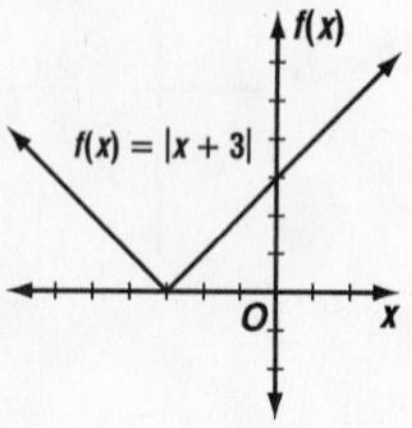

25. G;

x	$[x + 3]$	$f(x)$
-1	$[-1 + 3]$	2
$-\frac{1}{2}$	$\left[-\frac{1}{2} + 3\right]$	2
$-\frac{1}{4}$	$\left[-\frac{1}{4} + 3\right]$	2
0	$[0 + 3]$	3
$\frac{1}{2}$	$\left[\frac{1}{2} + 3\right]$	3
$\frac{3}{4}$	$\left[\frac{3}{4} + 3\right]$	3
1	$[1 + 3]$	4

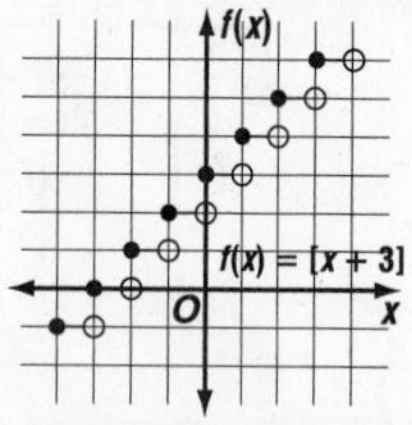

26. A;

x	$\lvert x \rvert + 3$	$g(x)$
-2	$\lvert -2 \rvert + 3$	5
-1	$\lvert -1 \rvert + 3$	4
0	$\lvert 0 \rvert + 3$	3
1	$\lvert 1 \rvert + 3$	4
2	$\lvert 2 \rvert + 3$	5

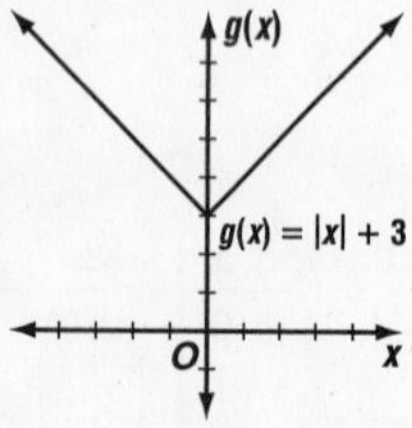

27. G;

x	$[x] + 3$	$g(x)$
-1	$[-1] + 3$	2
$-\frac{1}{2}$	$\left[-\frac{1}{2}\right] + 3$	2
$-\frac{1}{4}$	$\left[-\frac{1}{4}\right] + 3$	2
0	$[0] + 3$	3
$\frac{1}{2}$	$\left[\frac{1}{2}\right] + 3$	3
$\frac{3}{4}$	$\left[\frac{3}{4}\right] + 3$	3
1	$[1] + 3$	4

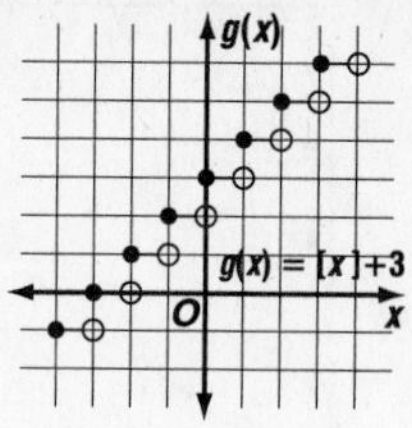

28. A;

x	$3\lvert x \rvert$	$g(x)$
-2	$3\lvert -2 \rvert$	6
-1	$3\lvert -1 \rvert$	3
0	$3\lvert 0 \rvert$	0
1	$3\lvert 1 \rvert$	3
2	$3\lvert 2 \rvert$	6

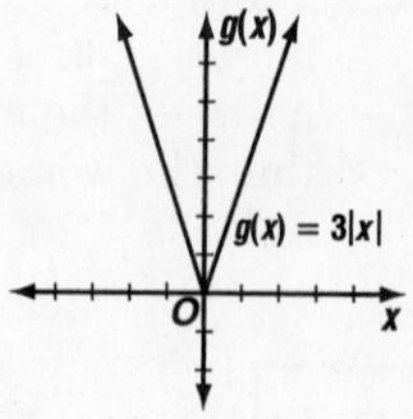

29. $y = \lvert x + 2 \rvert$

x	$\lvert x + 2 \rvert$	y
-3	$\lvert -3 + 2 \rvert$	1
-2	$\lvert -2 + 2 \rvert$	0
-1	$\lvert -1 + 2 \rvert$	1
0	$\lvert 0 + 2 \rvert$	2

$y = \lvert x - 2 \rvert$

x	$\lvert x - 2 \rvert$	y
0	$\lvert 0 - 2 \rvert$	2
1	$\lvert 1 - 2 \rvert$	1
2	$\lvert 2 - 2 \rvert$	0
3	$\lvert 3 - 2 \rvert$	1

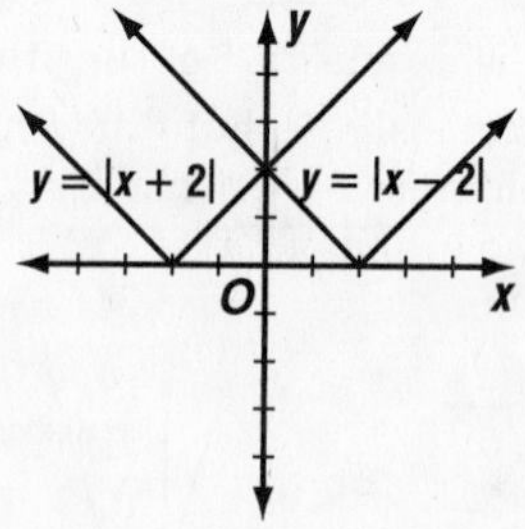

same graph translated four units right

30. $y = \lvert x \rvert + 4$

x	$\lvert x \rvert + 4$	y
-1	$\lvert -1 \rvert + 4$	5
0	$\lvert 0 \rvert + 4$	4
1	$\lvert 1 \rvert + 4$	5
2	$\lvert 2 \rvert + 4$	6

$y = \lvert x \rvert - 4$

x	$\lvert x \rvert - 4$	y
-1	$\lvert -1 \rvert - 4$	-3
0	$\lvert 0 \rvert - 4$	-4
1	$\lvert 1 \rvert - 4$	-3
2	$\lvert 2 \rvert - 4$	-2

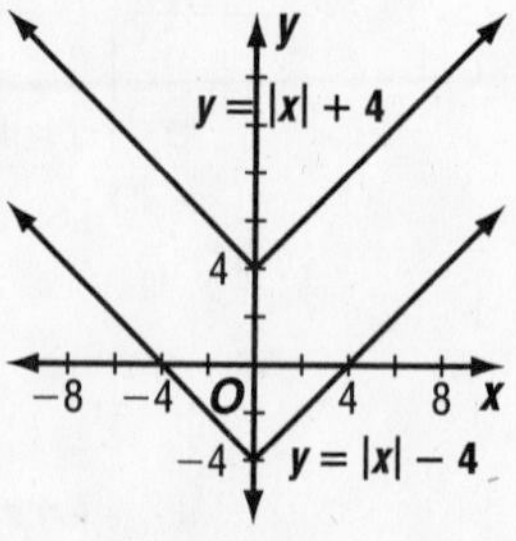

same graph translated eight units down

31. $y = |x + 2|$

x	$\lvert x + 2\rvert$	y
-4	$\lvert -4 + 2\rvert$	2
-3	$\lvert -3 + 2\rvert$	1
-2	$\lvert -2 + 2\rvert$	0
-1	$\lvert -1 + 2\rvert$	1

$y = |x + 2| - 1$

x	$\lvert x + 2\rvert - 1$	y
-4	$\lvert -4 + 2\rvert - 1$	1
-3	$\lvert -3 + 2\rvert - 1$	0
-2	$\lvert -2 + 2\rvert - 1$	-1
-1	$\lvert -1 + 2\rvert - 1$	0

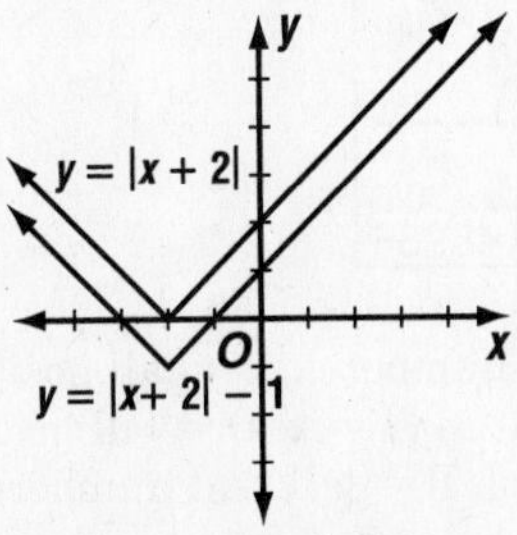

same graph translated one unit down

32. $y = 2[x]$

x	$2[x]$	y
0	$2[0]$	0
$\frac{1}{2}$	$2\left[\frac{1}{2}\right]$	0
$\frac{3}{4}$	$2\left[\frac{3}{4}\right]$	0
1	$2[1]$	2

$y = [2x]$

x	$[2x]$	y
0	$[2(0)]$	0
$\frac{1}{2}$	$\left[2\left(\frac{1}{2}\right)\right]$	1
$\frac{3}{4}$	$\left[2\left(\frac{3}{4}\right)\right]$	1
1	$[2(1)]$	2

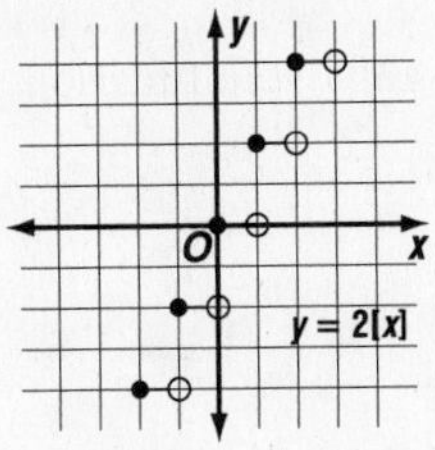

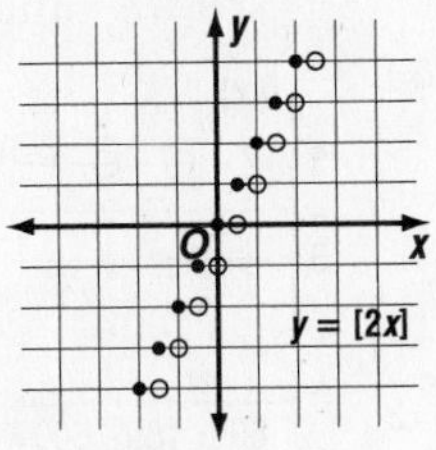

$2[x]$ steps 2 units vertically at 1-unit intervals;
$[2x]$ steps 1 unit vertically at 0.5-unit intervals.

33. $y = [x + 5]$

x	$[x + 5]$	y
0	$[0 + 5]$	5
$\frac{1}{2}$	$\left[\frac{1}{2} + 5\right]$	5
$\frac{3}{4}$	$\left[\frac{3}{4} + 5\right]$	5
1	$[1 + 5]$	6

$y = [x] + 5$

x	$[x] + 5$	y
0	$[0] + 5$	5
$\frac{1}{2}$	$\left[\frac{1}{2}\right] + 5$	5
$\frac{3}{4}$	$\left[\frac{3}{4}\right] + 5$	5
1	$[1] + 5$	6

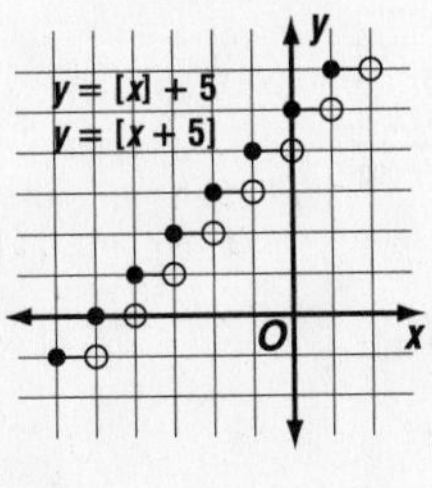

Graphs are the same.

34. $y = 2|2x|$

x	$\lvert 2x\rvert$	y
-1	$\lvert 2(-1)\rvert$	2
0	$\lvert 2(0)\rvert$	0
1	$\lvert 2(1)\rvert$	2
2	$\lvert 2(2)\rvert$	4

$y = 2|x|$

x	$2\lvert x\rvert$	y
-1	$2\lvert -1\rvert$	2
0	$2\lvert 0\rvert$	0
1	$2\lvert 1\rvert$	2
2	$2\lvert 2\rvert$	4

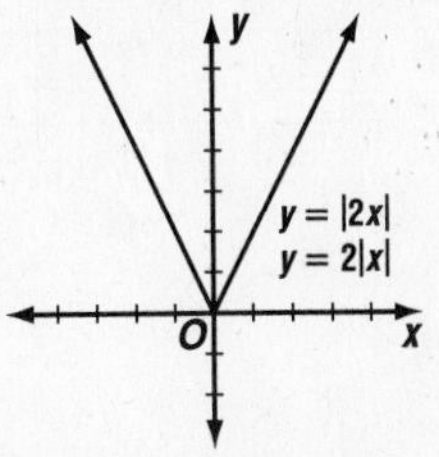

Graphs are the same.

35. $y = -2|4x|$

x	$-2\lvert 4x\rvert$	y
-1	$-2\lvert 4(-1)\rvert$	-8
0	$-2\lvert 4(0)\rvert$	0
1	$-2\lvert 4(1)\rvert$	-8

$y = 4|-2x|$

x	$4\lvert -2x\rvert$	y
-1	$4\lvert -2(-1)\rvert$	8
0	$4\lvert -2(0)\rvert$	0
1	$4\lvert -2(1)\rvert$	8

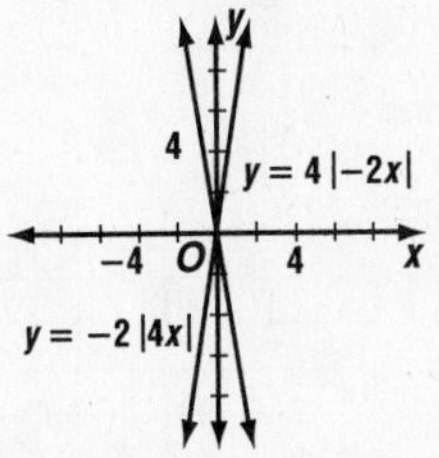

same graph reflected over x-axis

36. $y = -3[x]$

x	$-3[x]$	y
0	$-3[0]$	0
$\frac{1}{2}$	$-3\left[\frac{1}{2}\right]$	0
$\frac{3}{4}$	$-3\left[\frac{3}{4}\right]$	0
1	$-3[1]$	-3
$1\frac{1}{2}$	$-3\left[1\frac{1}{2}\right]$	-3
$1\frac{3}{4}$	$-3\left[1\frac{3}{4}\right]$	-3

$y = [-3x]$

x	$[-3x]$	y
0	$[-3(0)]$	0
$\frac{1}{6}$	$\left[-3\left(\frac{1}{6}\right)\right]$	-1
$\frac{1}{3}$	$\left[-3\left(\frac{1}{3}\right)\right]$	-1
$\frac{1}{2}$	$\left[-3\left(\frac{1}{2}\right)\right]$	-2
$\frac{2}{3}$	$\left[-3\left(\frac{2}{3}\right)\right]$	-2
1	$[-3(1)]$	-3

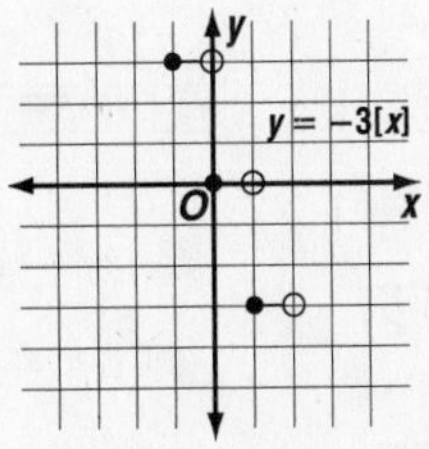

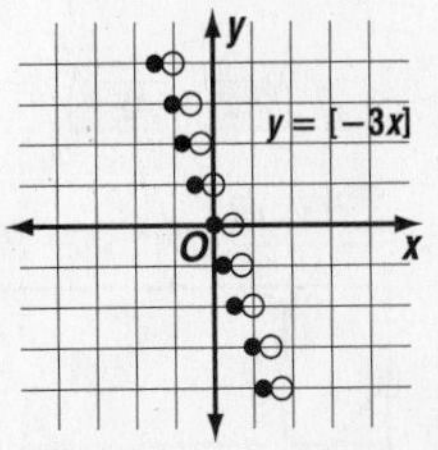

$-3[x]$ steps 3 units vertically at 1-unit intervals;
$[-3x]$ steps 1 unit vertically at $\frac{1}{3}$-unit intervals.

37. $y = [|x|]$

x	$[\lvert x \rvert]$	y
-2	$[\lvert -2 \rvert]$	2
$-1\frac{1}{2}$	$\left[\left\lvert -1\frac{1}{2} \right\rvert\right]$	1
-1	$[\lvert -1 \rvert]$	1
$-\frac{1}{2}$	$\left[\left\lvert -\frac{1}{2} \right\rvert\right]$	0
0	$[\lvert 0 \rvert]$	0
$\frac{1}{2}$	$\left[\left\lvert \frac{1}{2} \right\rvert\right]$	0
1	$[\lvert 1 \rvert]$	1

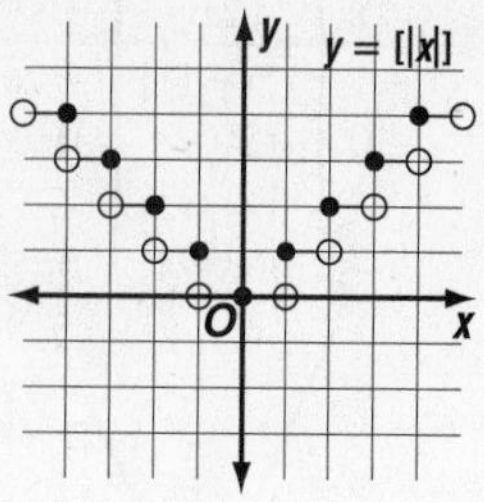

38. $y = |[x]|$

x	$\lvert [x] \rvert$	y
-2	$\lvert [-2] \rvert$	2
$-1\frac{1}{2}$	$\left\lvert\left[-1\frac{1}{2} \right]\right\rvert$	2
-1	$\lvert [-1] \rvert$	1
$-\frac{1}{2}$	$\left\lvert\left[-\frac{1}{2} \right]\right\rvert$	1
0	$\lvert [0] \rvert$	0
$\frac{1}{2}$	$\left\lvert\left[\frac{1}{2} \right]\right\rvert$	0
1	$\lvert [1] \rvert$	1

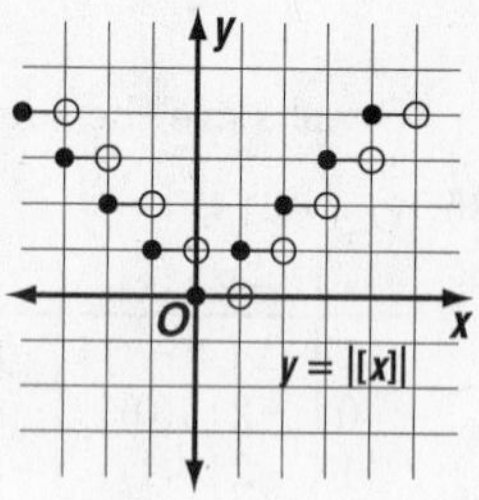

39. $y = x - [x]$

x	$x - [x]$	y
0	$0 - [0]$	0
$\frac{1}{2}$	$\frac{1}{2} - \left[\frac{1}{2}\right]$	$\frac{1}{2}$
$\frac{3}{4}$	$\frac{3}{4} - \left[\frac{3}{4}\right]$	$\frac{3}{4}$
1	$1 - [1]$	0
$1\frac{1}{2}$	$1\frac{1}{2} - \left[1\frac{1}{2}\right]$	$\frac{1}{2}$

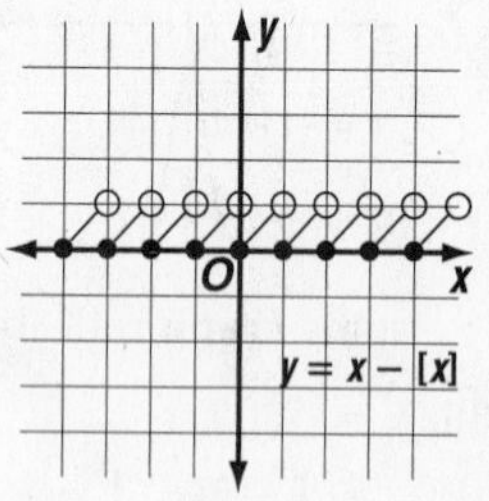

40. $y = x + |x|$

x	$x + \lvert x \rvert$	y
-2	$-2 + \lvert -2 \rvert$	0
-1	$-1 + \lvert -1 \rvert$	0
0	$0 + \lvert 0 \rvert$	0
1	$1 + \lvert 1 \rvert$	2
2	$2 + \lvert 2 \rvert$	4
3	$3 + \lvert 3 \rvert$	6

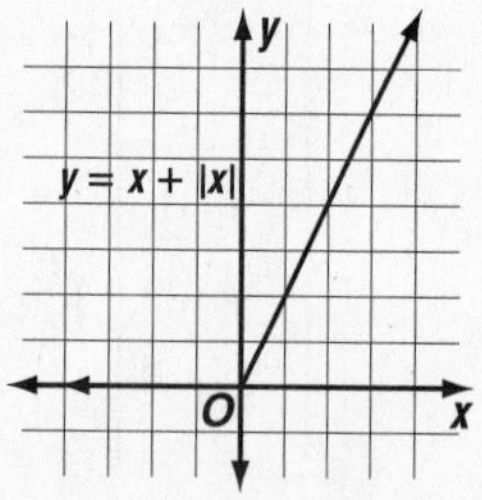

41. Y= 2nd ABS (2 X,T,θ,n − 4) ENTER 6 GRAPH ; $x = -1$ or 5

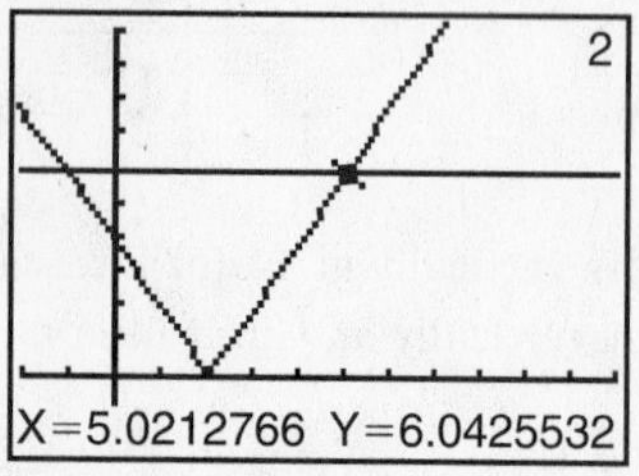

42. Y= 2nd ABS (X,T,θ,n + 2) ENTER 4 GRAPH ; $x = 2$ or -6

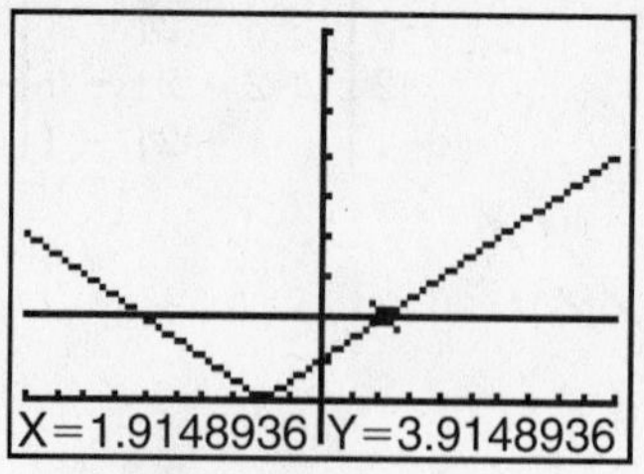

43. $y = |x|$: D = {all real numbers}, R = {all positive real numbers and zero}; $|y| = x$: D = {all positive real numbers and zero}, R = {all real numbers}

44a. Sample answer:

$$m = \frac{39 - 0}{4 - 0}$$
$$= \frac{39}{4}$$
$$= 9.75$$
$$y = 9.75x$$

44b. direct variation

44c. Sample answer: based on equation for 44a

$$x = 1999 - 1991 \text{ or } 8$$
$$y = 9.75x$$
$$= 9.75(8)$$
$$= 78;\ 78 \text{ million}$$

45a.

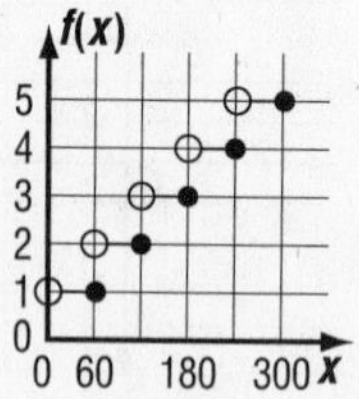

45b. step function

46a. $5.25 \times 0.25 \approx 1.31$
$\$5.25 - 1.31 = \$3.94$
$y = 3.94x$

46b.
$$y = 3.94x$$
$$100 = 3.94x$$
$$25.38 \approx x$$
about 25 hours

46c. direct variation

47a.

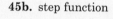

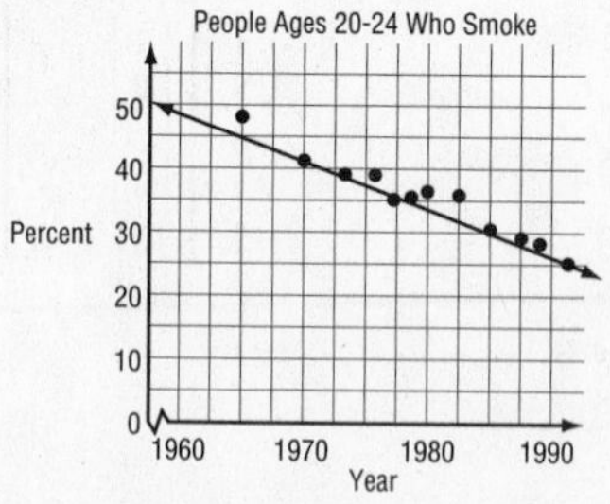

$$m = \frac{41.5 - 25.0}{1970 - 1993}$$
$$= \frac{16.5}{-23}$$
$$\approx -0.72$$

$$y = mx + b$$
$$25.0 = (-0.72)(1993) + b$$
$$25.0 = -1434.96 + b$$
$$1460 \approx b$$
$$y = -0.72x + 1460$$

47b.
$$y = -0.72x + 1460$$
$$= -0.72(2000) + 1460$$
$$= -1440 + 1460$$
$$= 20;\ 20\%$$

48. $y = mx + b$

$-5 = \left(\frac{2}{3}\right)(6) + b$

$-5 = 4 + b$

$-9 = b$

$y = \frac{2}{3}x - 9$

49. $y - 2x = 4$

$y = 2x + 4$

slope = 2, perpendicular slope = $-\frac{1}{2}$; graph (0, 3), then go down 1 unit and 2 units to the right

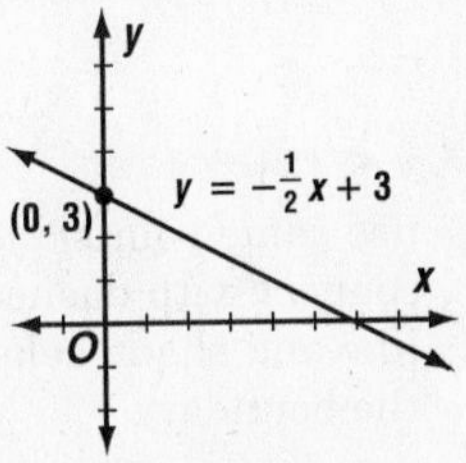

50. $b = 3a - 2$ | $b = 3a - 2$

$0 = 3a - 2$ | $b = 3(0) - 2$

$2 = 3a$ | $= 0 - 2$

$\frac{2}{3} = a$ | $= -2$

$\left(\frac{2}{3}, 0\right)$ | $(0, -2)$

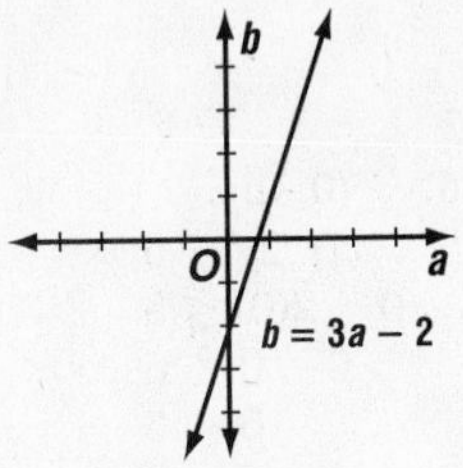

51. $h(x) = \frac{x^2 + 2x - 5}{x^2 - 2}$

$h(-1) = \frac{(-1)^2 + 2(-1) - 5}{(-1)^2 - 2}$

$= \frac{1 - 2 - 5}{1 - 2}$

$= \frac{-6}{-1}$

$= 6$

52. $28 - 6y < 23$

$-6y < -5$

$y > \frac{5}{6}$

$\{y \mid y > \frac{5}{6}\}$

53a. 51

53b. 1

53c. 16

53d. 5 or 11

54. $3 + \{8 \div [9 - 2(4)]\} = 3 + \{8 \div [9 - 8]\}$

$= 3 + \{8 \div 1\}$

$= 3 + 8$

$= 11$

2-7A Graphing Technology: Linear Inequalities

Page 109 Exercises

1. ZOOM 6 2nd DRAW 7 3 , 10) ENTER

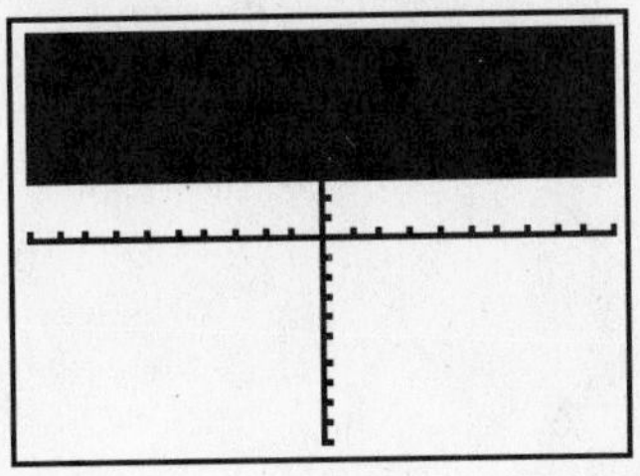

2. ZOOM 6 2nd DRAW 7 X,T,θ,n + 2 , 10) ENTER

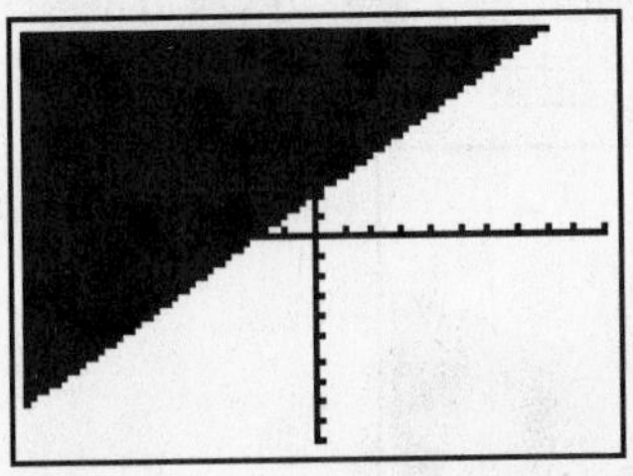

3. ZOOM 6 2nd DRAW 7 (−) 10 , (−) 2 X,T,θ,n − 4) ENTER

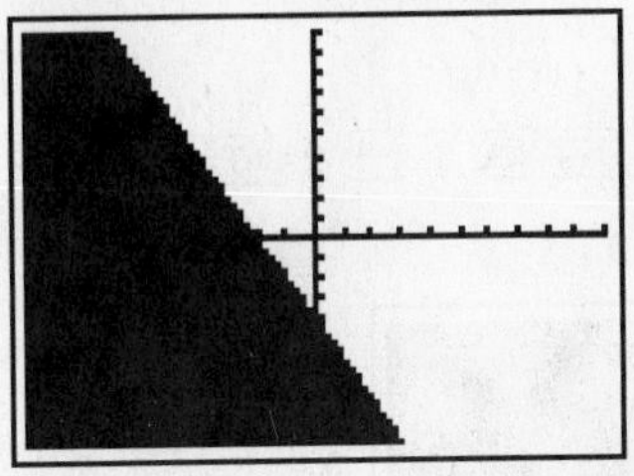

4. ZOOM 6 2nd DRAW 7 (1 ÷ 3) X,T,θ,n + 7 , 10) ENTER

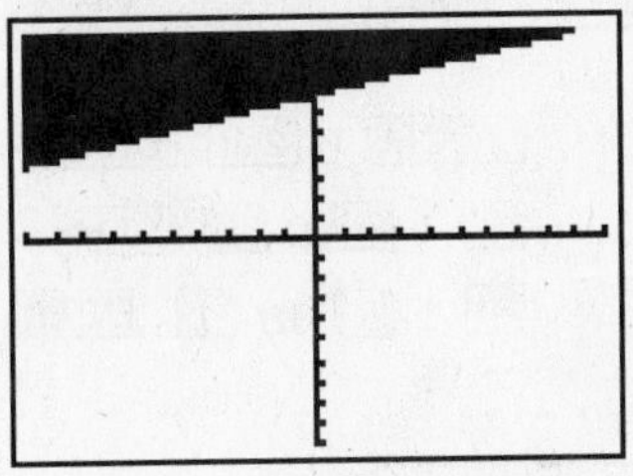

5. ZOOM 6 2nd DRAW 7 (1 ÷ 2) X,T,θ,n − 3 , 10) ENTER

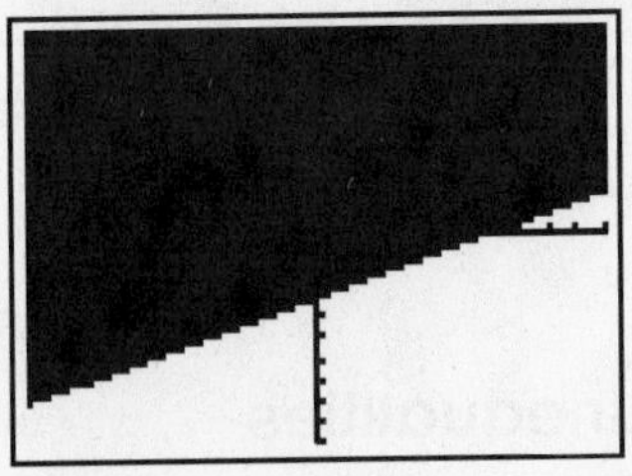

6. $y \geq x - 7$; ZOOM 6 2nd DRAW 7 X,T,θ,n − 7 , 10) ENTER

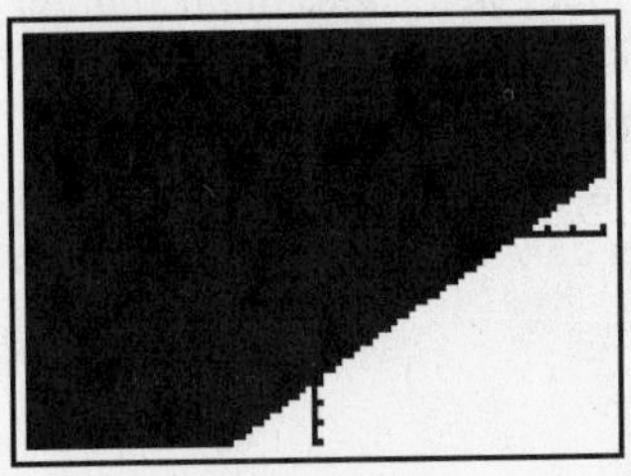

7. $y + 1 \le 0.5x$
$y \le 0.5x - 1;$

[ZOOM] 6 [2nd] [DRAW] 7 [(−)] 10 [,] 0.5 [X,T,θ,n] [−] 1 [)] [ENTER]

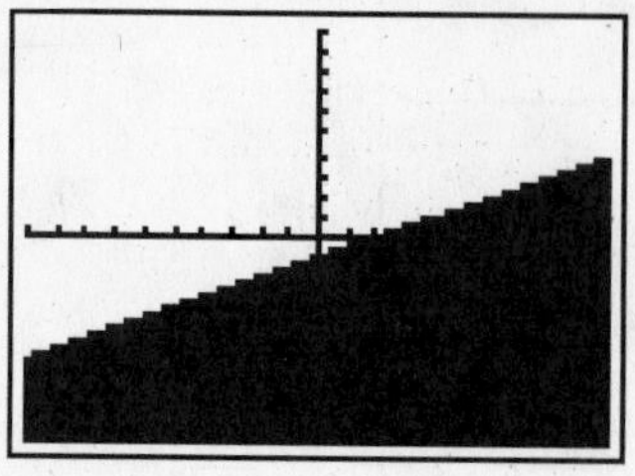

8. $y - 3 > -2x$
$y > -2x + 3$

[ZOOM] 6 [2nd] [DRAW] 7 [(−)] 2 [X,T,θ,n] [+] 3 [,] 10 [)] [ENTER]

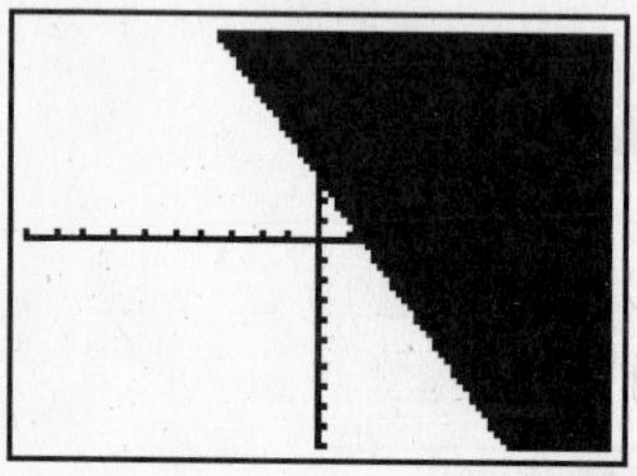

9. $2 \ge x - 2y$
$2y + 2 \ge x$
$2y \ge x - 2$
$y \ge \frac{1}{2}x - 1$

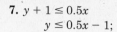

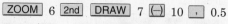

[ZOOM] 6 [2nd] [DRAW] 7 [(] 1 [÷] 2 [)] [X,T,θ,n] [−] 1 [,] 10 [)] [ENTER]

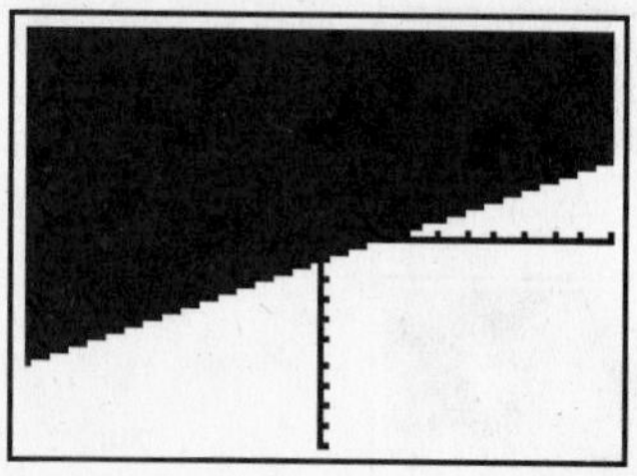

2-7 Linear Inequalities

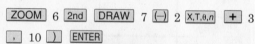

Pages 112–113 Check for Understanding

1. The boundary is a dashed line if the inequality is $<$ or $>$. The boundary is a solid line if the inequality is $\ge$ or $\le$.
2. When you substitute the value (0, 2) into $y \ge -8x + 2$, you get a true statement $2 \ge 2$.
3. c; the boundary is dashed, shading is below the line.
4. $y = |x| + 1$

x	$\lvert x\rvert + 1$	y
−1	$\lvert -1\rvert + 1$	2
0	$\lvert 0\rvert + 1$	1
1	$\lvert 1\rvert + 1$	2
2	$\lvert 2\rvert + 1$	3

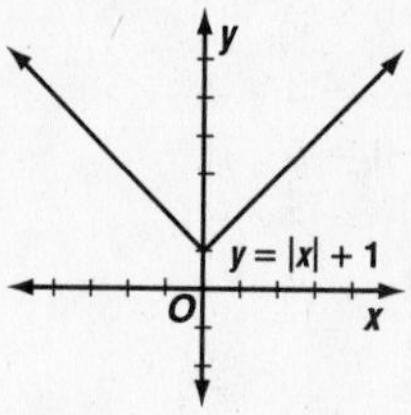

$y < |x| + 1$
use same points, but connect with dashed line and shade below the boundary

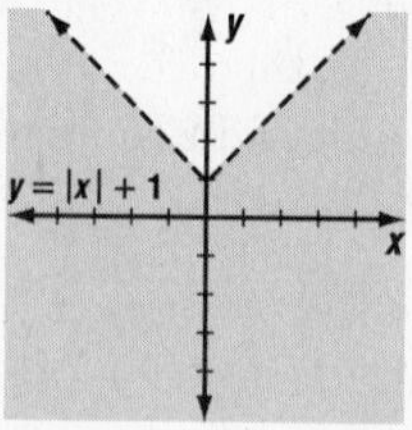

5. (0, 0)
$x + 2y \overset{?}{<} 5$
$0 + 2(0) \overset{?}{<} 5$
$0 + 0 \overset{?}{<} 5$
$0 < 5$
true

(3, −4)
$x + 2y \overset{?}{<} 5$
$3 + 2(-4) \overset{?}{<} 5$
$3 - 8 \overset{?}{<} 5$
$-5 < 5$
true

(−1, 3)
$x + 2y \overset{?}{<} 5$
$-1 + 2(3) \overset{?}{<} 5$
$-1 + 6 \overset{?}{<} 5$
$5 \not< 5$
false

6. (0, 0)
$4x + 3y \overset{?}{\le} 0$
$4(0) + 3(0) \overset{?}{\le} 0$
$0 + 0 \overset{?}{\le} 0$
$0 \le 0$
true

(3, −4)
$4x + 3y \overset{?}{\le} 0$
$4(3) + 3(-4) \overset{?}{\le} 0$
$12 - 12 \overset{?}{\le} 0$
$0 \le 0$
true

(−1, 3)
$4x + 3y \overset{?}{\le} 0$
$4(-1) + 3(3) \overset{?}{\le} 0$
$-4 + 9 \overset{?}{\le} 0$
$5 \not\le 0$
false

7. (0, 0)
$5x - y \overset{?}{\ge} 6$
$5(0) - 0 \overset{?}{\ge} 6$
$0 - 0 \overset{?}{\ge} 6$
$0 \not\ge 6$
false

(3, −4)
$5x - y \overset{?}{\ge} 6$
$5(3) - (-4) \overset{?}{\ge} 6$
$15 + 4 \overset{?}{\ge} 6$
$19 \ge 6$
true

(−1, 3)
$5x - y \overset{?}{\ge} 6$
$5(-1) - 3 \overset{?}{\ge} 6$
$-5 - 3 \overset{?}{\ge} 6$
$-8 \not\ge 6$
false

8. $y = 2$ is a horizontal line. All points above the line would be $y > 2$.

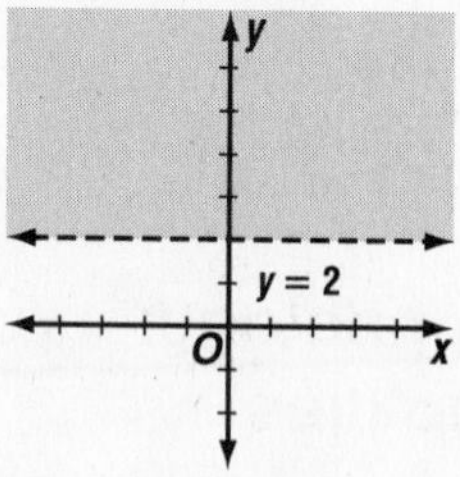

9. $x - y \ge 0$
$-y \ge -x$
$y \le x$
y-intercept = 0
slope = 1

Test (2, 0).
$x - y \overset{?}{\ge} 0$
$2 - 0 \overset{?}{\ge} 0$
$2 \ge 0$; true

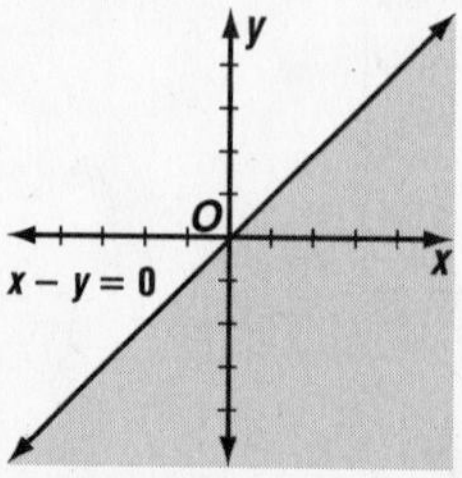

10. $y > 2x$
y-intercept = 0
slope = 2

Test (0, 2).
$y \overset{?}{>} 2x$
$2 \overset{?}{>} 2(0)$
$2 > 0$; true

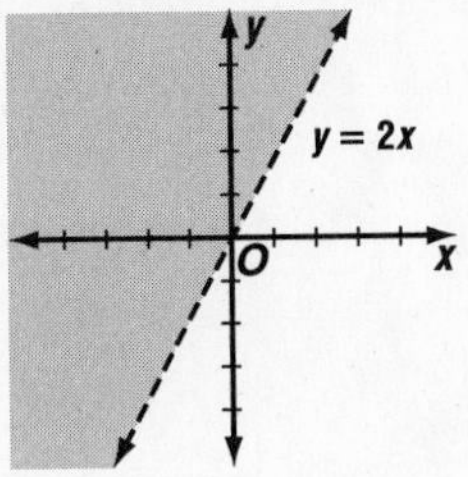

11. $y > |2x|$

x	$\lvert 2x \rvert$	y
-1	$\lvert -2(-1) \rvert$	2
0	$\lvert -2(0) \rvert$	0
1	$\lvert -2(1) \rvert$	2

Test (0, 1).
$y \overset{?}{>} |2x|$
$1 \overset{?}{>} |2(0)|$
$1 > 0$; true

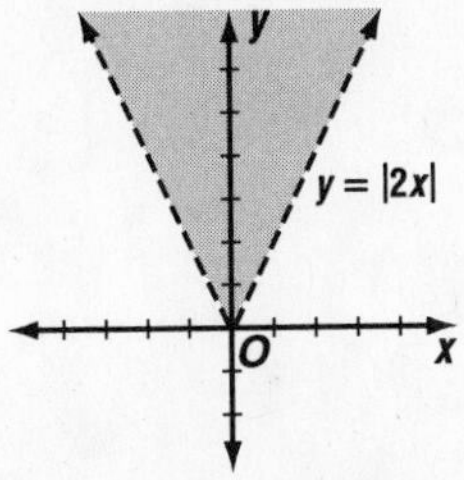

12. $x = 4$ is a vertical line. All points to the right of the line would be $x > 4$.

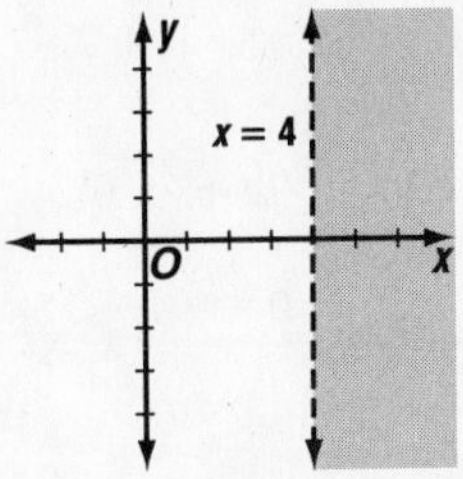

Pages 113–114 Exercises

13. $x + y > -5$

$x + y = -5$
$x + 0 = -5$
$x = -5$
$(-5, 0)$

$x + y = -5$
$0 + y = -5$
$y = -5$
$(0, -5)$

Test (0, 0).
$x + y \overset{?}{>} -5$
$0 + 0 \overset{?}{>} -5$
$0 > -5$; true

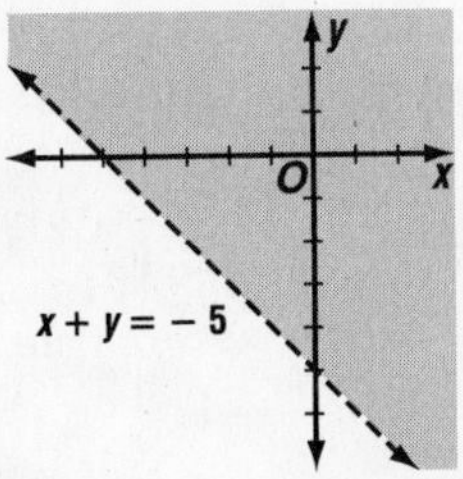

14. $y + 1 < 4$
$y < 3$
slope = 0; horizontal line

Test (0, 0).
$y + 1 \overset{?}{<} 4$
$0 + 1 \overset{?}{<} 4$
$1 < 4$; true

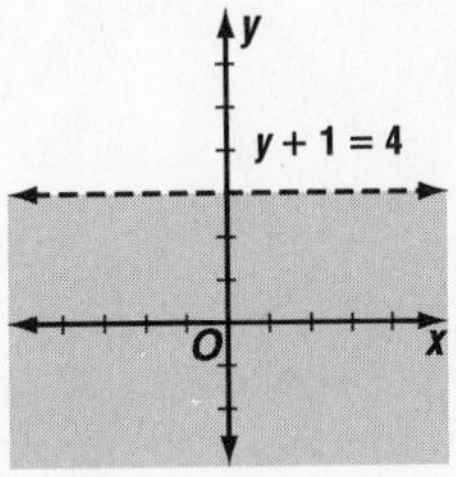

15. $y > 6x - 2$

$y = 6x - 2$
$0 = 6x - 2$
$2 = 6x$
$\frac{1}{3} = x$
$\left(\frac{1}{3}, 0\right)$

$y = 6x - 2$
$y = 6(0) - 2$
$y = 0 - 2$
$y = -2$
$(0, -2)$

Test (0, 0).
$y \overset{?}{>} 6x - 2$
$0 \overset{?}{>} 6(0) - 2$
$0 \overset{?}{>} 0 - 2$
$0 > -2$; true

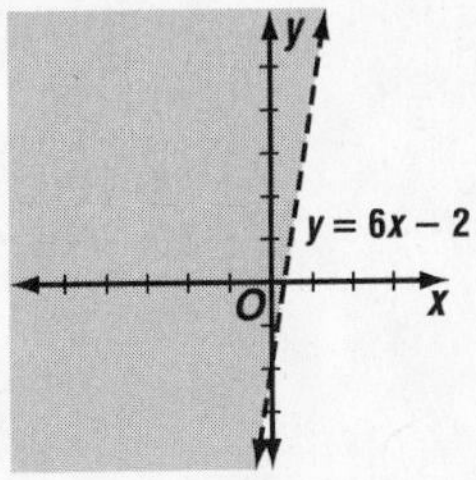

16. $x - 5 \leq y$

$x - 5 = y$
$x - 5 = 0$
$x = 5$
$(5, 0)$

$x - 5 = y$
$0 - 5 = y$
$-5 = y$
$(0, -5)$

Test (0, 0).
$x - 5 \overset{?}{\leq} y$
$0 - 5 \leq 0$
$-5 \leq 0$; true

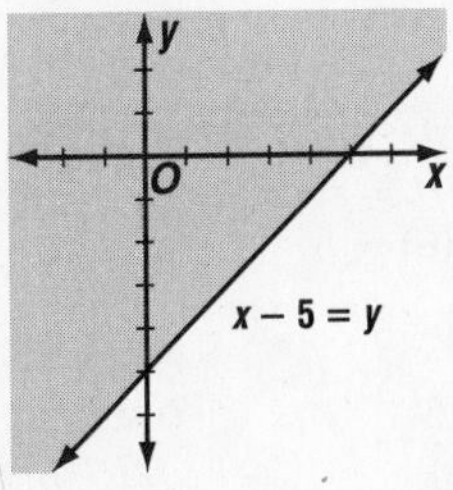

17. $y \geq -4x + 3$

$y = -4x + 3$
$0 = -4x + 3$
$-3 = -4x$
$\frac{3}{4} = x$
$\left(\frac{3}{4}, 0\right)$

$y = -4x + 3$
$y = -4(0) + 3$
$y = 0 + 3$
$y = 3$
$(0, 3)$

Test (2, 0).
$y \overset{?}{\geq} -4x + 3$
$0 \overset{?}{\geq} -4(2) + 3$
$0 \overset{?}{\geq} -8 + 3$
$0 \geq -5$; true

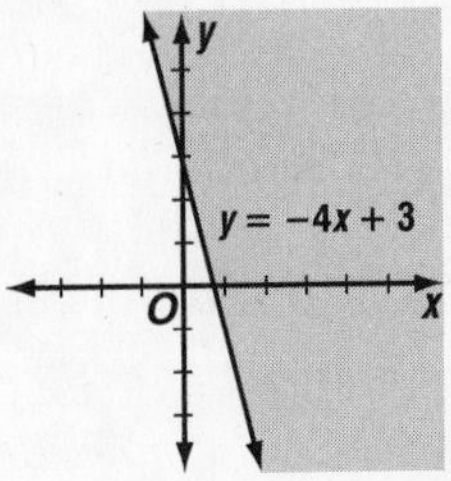

18. $y - 2 < 3x$

$y - 2 = 3x$	$y - 2 = 3x$	Test (0, 0).
$0 - 2 = 3x$	$y - 2 = 3(0)$	$y - 2 < 3x$
$-2 = 3x$	$y - 2 = 0$	$0 - 2 \overset{?}{<} 3(0)$
$-\frac{2}{3} = x$	$y = 2$	$-2 < 0$; true
$\left(-\frac{2}{3}, 0\right)$	$(0, 2)$	

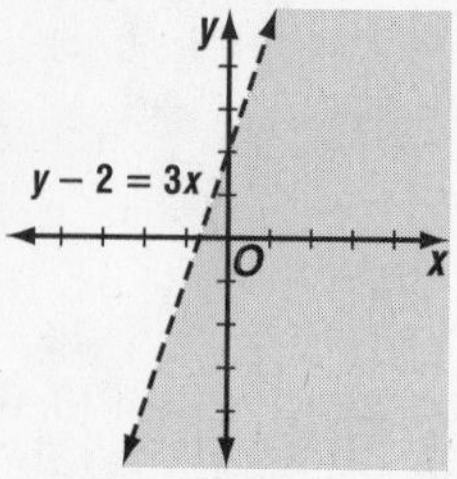

19. $y > \frac{1}{3}x + 5$

$y = \frac{1}{3}x + 5$	$y = \frac{1}{3}x + 5$	Test (0, 10).
$0 = \frac{1}{3}x + 5$	$y = \frac{1}{3}(0) + 5$	$y > \frac{1}{3}x + 5$
$-5 = \frac{1}{3}x$	$y = 0 + 5$	$10 \overset{?}{>} \frac{1}{3}(0) + 5$
$-15 = x$	$y = 5$	$10 \overset{?}{>} 0 + 5$
$(-15, 0)$	$(0, 5)$	$10 > 5$; true

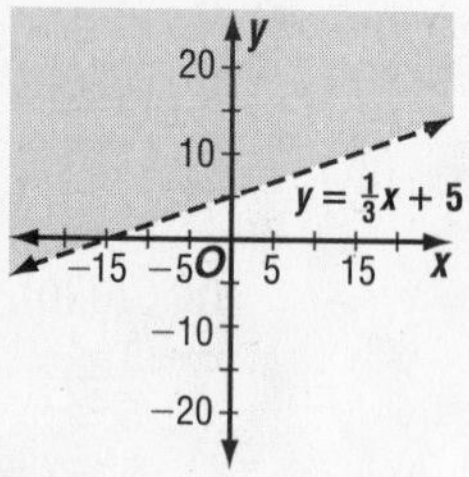

20. $y \geq \frac{1}{2}x - 5$

$y = \frac{1}{2}x - 5$	$y = \frac{1}{2}x - 5$	Test (0, 0).
$0 = \frac{1}{2}x - 5$	$y = \frac{1}{2}(0) - 5$	$y \geq \frac{1}{2}x - 5$
$5 = \frac{1}{2}x$	$y = 0 - 5$	$0 \overset{?}{\geq} \frac{1}{2}(0) - 5$
$10 = x$	$y = -5$	$0 \overset{?}{\geq} 0 - 5$
$(10, 0)$	$(0, -5)$	$0 \geq -5$; true

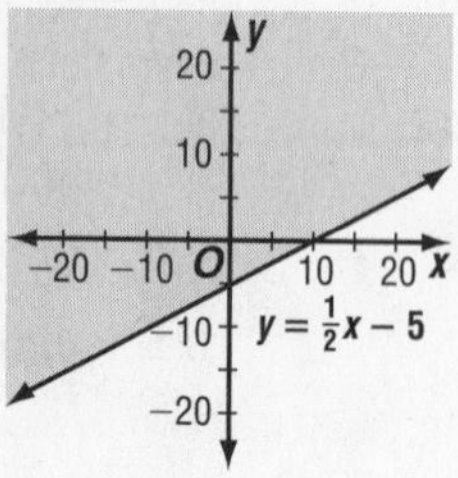

21. $3 \geq x - 3y$

$3 = x - 3y$	$3 = x - 3y$	Test (0, 0).
$3 = x - 3(0)$	$3 = 0 - 3y$	$3 \geq x - 3y$
$3 = x - 0$	$3 = -3y$	$3 \overset{?}{\geq} 0 - 3(0)$
$3 = x$	$-1 = y$	$3 \overset{?}{\geq} 0 - 0$
$(3, 0)$	$(0, -1)$	$3 \geq 0$; true

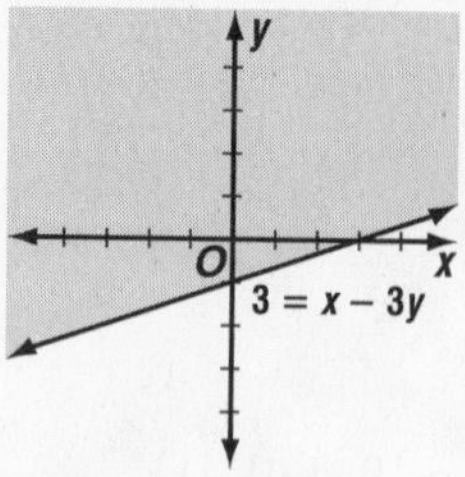

22. $y \leq |x|$

when $x < 0$	when $x \geq 0$	Test (0, −1).
$y \leq -x$	$y \leq x$	$y \leq \lvert x \rvert$
		$-1 \overset{?}{\leq} \lvert 0 \rvert$
		$-1 \leq 0$; true

x	y
−1	1
−2	2

x	y
0	0
1	1

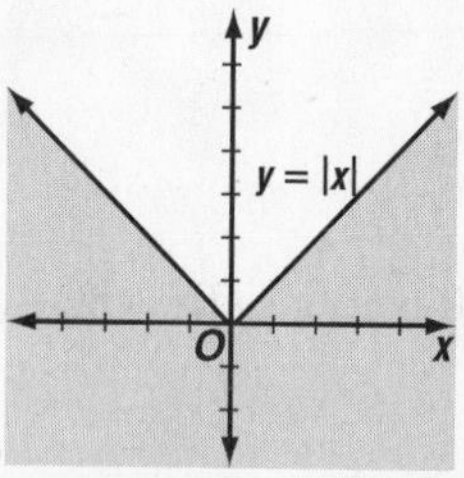

23. $y + |x| < 3$

when $x < 0$	when $x \geq 0$	Test (0, 0).
$y - x < 3$	$y + x < 3$	$y + \lvert x \rvert < 3$
		$0 + \lvert 0 \rvert \overset{?}{<} 3$
		$0 < 3$; true

x	y
−1	2
−2	1

x	y
0	3
1	2

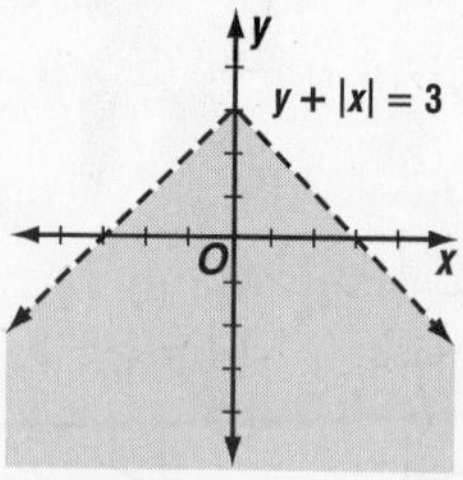

24. $y > |4x|$

when $x < 0$	when $x \geq 0$	Test (0, 2).
$y > -4x$	$y > 4x$	$y > \lvert 4x \rvert$
		$2 \overset{?}{>} \lvert 4(0) \rvert$
		$2 \overset{?}{>} \lvert 0 \rvert$
		$2 > 0$; true

x	y
−1	4
−2	8

x	y
0	0
1	4

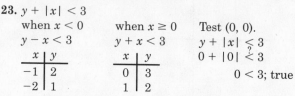

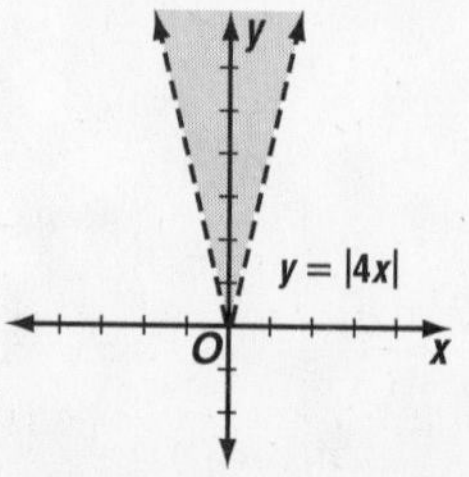

25. $x = -2$ is a vertical line. All points to the left would be $x < -2$.

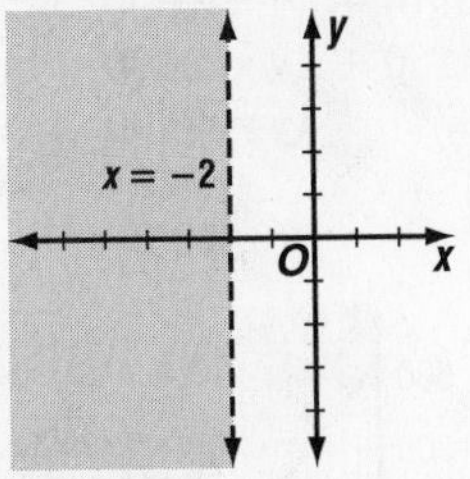

26.

$x + 2y = 5$
$x + 2(0) = 5$
$x + 0 = 5$
$x = 5$
$(5, 0)$

$x + 2y = 5$
$0 + 2y = 5$
$2y = 5$
$y = \frac{5}{2}$
$\left(0, \frac{5}{2}\right)$

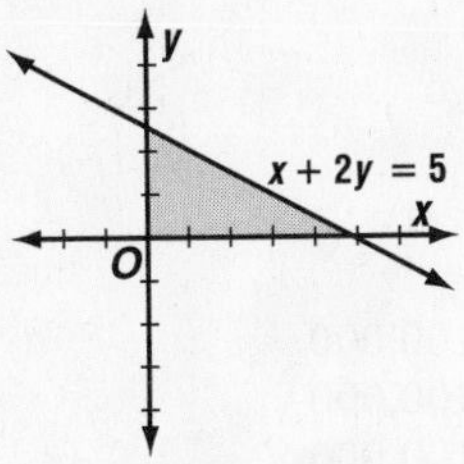

27. $x = -3$ and $x = -6$ are vertical lines. $y = 4$ is a horizontal line.

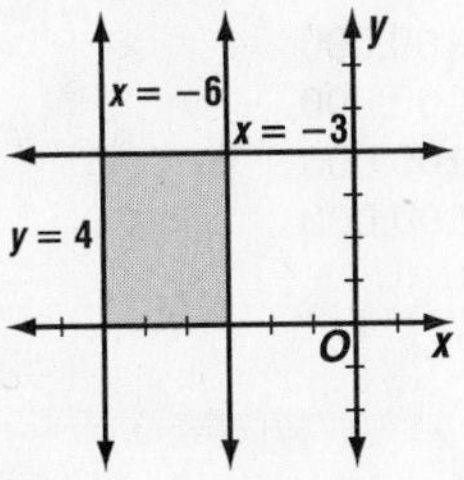

28.

$3x - y = 4$
$3x - 0 = 4$
$3x = 4$
$x = \frac{4}{3}$
$\left(\frac{4}{3}, 0\right)$

$3x - y = 4$
$3(0) - y = 4$
$0 - y = 4$
$-y = 4$
$y = -4$
$(0, -4)$

$x - y = 5$
$x - 0 = 5$
$x = 5$
$(5, 0)$

$x - y = 5$
$0 - y = 5$
$-y = 5$
$y = -5$
$(0, -5)$

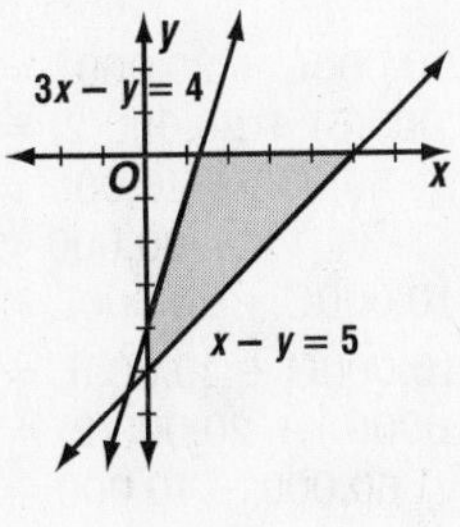

29. $|x| \le |y|$

Boundary is $|x| = |y|$.

x	$\|x\|$	y
-2	$\|-2\|$	2, 2
-1	$\|-1\|$	1, −1
0	$\|0\|$	0
1	$\|1\|$	1, −1
2	$\|2\|$	2, −2

Test (0, 1).
$|x| \overset{?}{\le} |y|$
$|0| \overset{?}{\le} |1|$
$0 \le 1$; true

Test (0, −1).
$|x| \overset{?}{\le} |y|$
$|0| \overset{?}{\le} |-1|$
$0 \le 1$; true

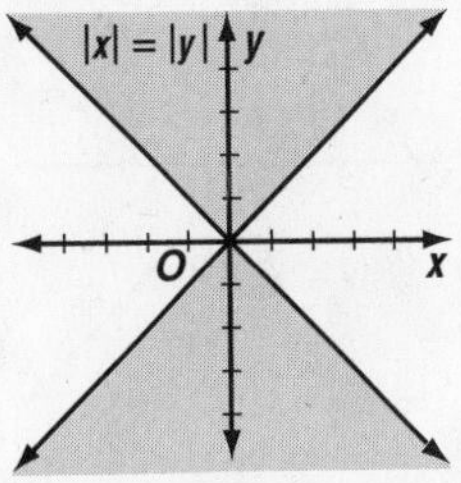

30. $|x| - |y| = 1$
$-|y| = -|x| + 1$
$|y| = |x| - 1$

x	$\|x\| - 1$	y
0	$\|0\| - 1$	$\varnothing$
1	$\|1\| - 1$	0
2	$\|2\| - 1$	1, −1
3	$\|3\| - 1$	2, −2
-1	$\|-1\| - 1$	0
-2	$\|-2\| - 1$	1, −1

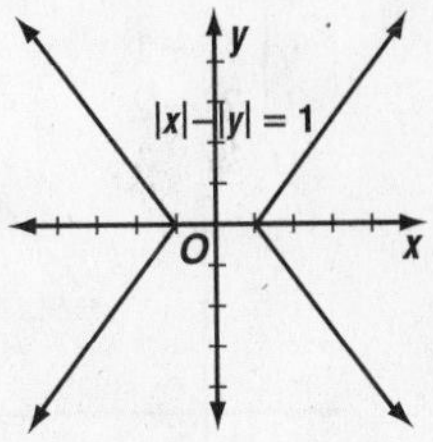

31. $|x| + |y| \ge 1$
$|y| \ge -|x| + 1$
Boundary is $|y| = -|x| + 1$

x	$-\|x\| + 1$	y
0	$-\|0\| + 1$	1, −1
1	$-\|1\| + 1$	0
-1	$-\|-1\| + 1$	0
2	$-\|2\| + 1$	$\varnothing$
-2	$-\|-2\| + 1$	$\varnothing$

Test (0, 2).
$|x| + |y| \overset{?}{\ge} 1$
$|0| + |2| \overset{?}{\ge} 1$
$0 + 2 \overset{?}{\ge} 1$
$2 \ge 1$; true

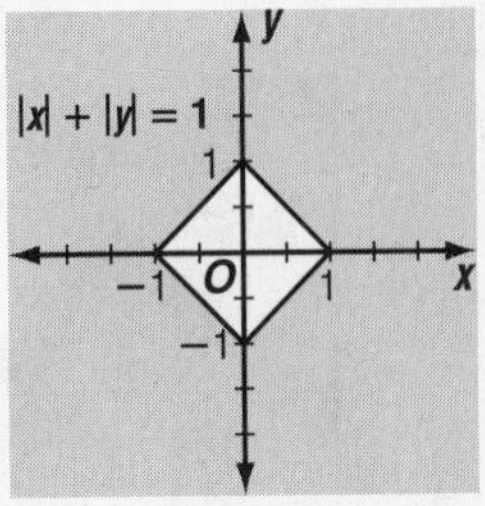

32. $|x + y| > 1$

$x + y > 1$ or $x + y < -1$

$y > -x + 1$ $\quad$ $y < -x - 1$

Boundary is $y = -x + 1$. Boundary is $y = -x - 1$.

x	y
-1	2
0	1
1	0

x	y
-1	0
0	-1
1	-2

Test (0, 2).

$|x + y| \overset{?}{>} 1$

$|0 + 2| \overset{?}{>} 1$

$2 > 1$; true

Test (0, −2).

$|x + y| \overset{?}{>} 1$

$|0 + -2| \overset{?}{>} 1$

$|-2| \overset{?}{>} 1$

$2 > 1$; true

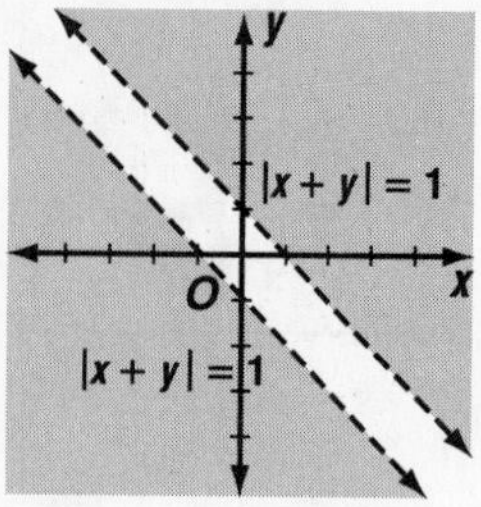

33. $|y| < x$

Boundary $|y| = x$

x	y
-1	$\varnothing$
0	0
1	1, −1
2	2, −2

Test (1, 0).

$|y| \overset{?}{<} x$

$|0| \overset{?}{<} 1$

$0 < 1$; true

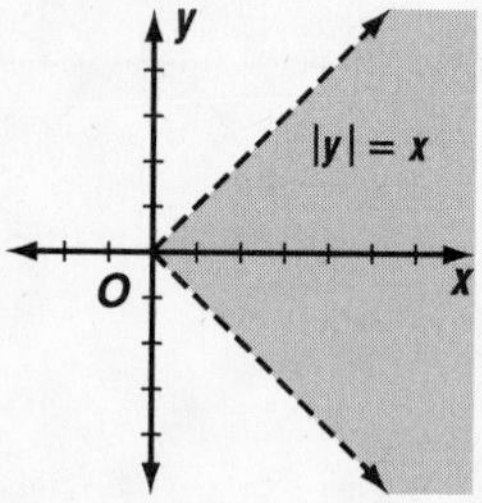

The boundary is dashed; it is shaped like a "v" on its side. The interior of the "v" is shaded.

34. $s > 50e + 25$

$s = 50e + 25$	$s = 50e + 25$	Test (0, 50).
$0 = 50e + 25$	$s = 50(0) + 25$	$s \overset{?}{>} 50e + 25$
$-25 = 50e$	$s = 0 + 25$	$50 \overset{?}{>} 50(0) + 25$
$-\frac{1}{2} = e$	$s = 25$	$50 \overset{?}{>} 0 + 25$
$\left(-\frac{1}{2}, 0\right)$	(0, 25)	$50 > 25$; true

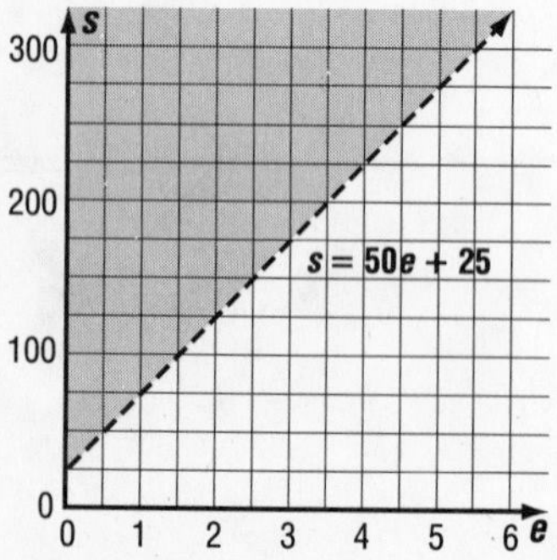

35a. $5x + 4y \geq 2500$

35b. $5x + 4y \geq 2500$

$5x + 4y = 2500$	$5x + 4y = 2500$
$5x + 4(0) = 2500$	$5(0) + 4y = 2500$
$5x + 0 = 2500$	$0 + 4y = 2500$
$5x = 2500$	$4y = 2500$
$x = 500$	$y = 625$
(500, 0)	(0, 625)

Test (0, 700).

$5x + 4y \overset{?}{\geq} 2500$

$5(0) + 4(700) \overset{?}{\geq} 2500$

$0 + 2800 \overset{?}{\geq} 2500$

$2800 \geq 2500$

true

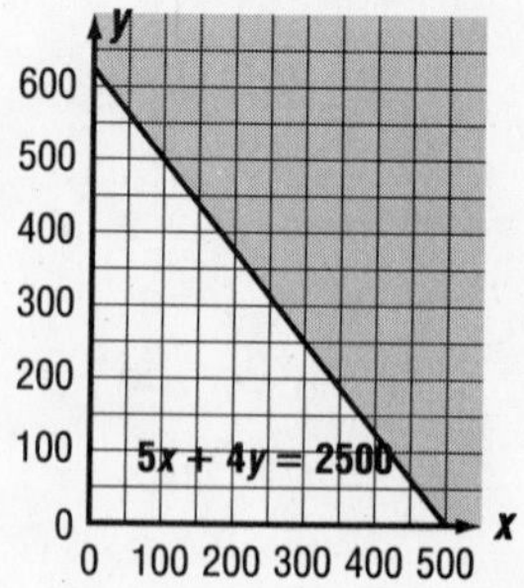

35c.

$5x + 4y \overset{?}{\geq} 2500$

$5(175) + 4(435) \overset{?}{\geq} 2500$

$875 + 1740 \overset{?}{\geq} 2500$

$2615 \geq 2500$; true

yes

36a. $10{,}000C + 20{,}000L = 100{,}000$

$10{,}000C + 20{,}000(0) = 100{,}000$

$10{,}000C + 0 = 100{,}000$

$10{,}000C = 100{,}000$

$C = 10$

(10, 0)

$10{,}000C + 20{,}000L = 100{,}000$

$10{,}000(0) + 20{,}000L = 100{,}000$

$0 + 20{,}000L = 100{,}000$

$20{,}000L = 100{,}000$

$L = 5$

(0, 5)

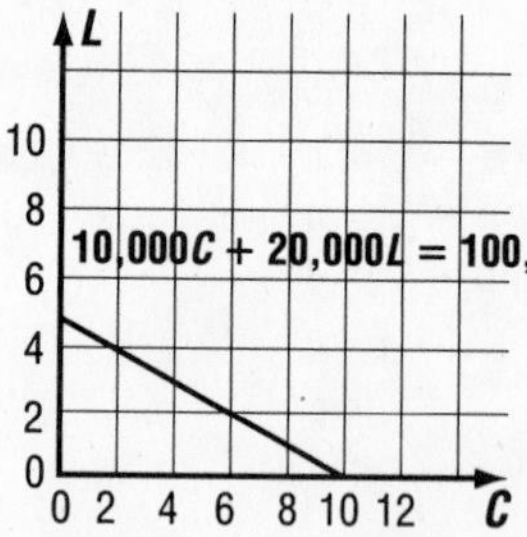

36b. $10{,}000C + 20{,}000L = 100{,}000$

$10{,}000(5) + 20{,}000(2) \overset{?}{=} 100{,}000$

$50{,}000 + 40{,}000 \overset{?}{=} 100{,}000$

$90{,}000 < 100{,}000$; below

$10{,}000C + 20{,}000L < 100{,}000$

36c. $10{,}000C + 20{,}000L = 100{,}000$

$10{,}000(6) + 20{,}000(2) \overset{?}{=} 100{,}000$

$60{,}000 + 40{,}000 \overset{?}{=} 100{,}000$

$100{,}000 = 100{,}000$

$10{,}000C + 20{,}000L = 100{,}000$

36d. $10{,}000C + 20{,}000L = 100{,}000$

$10{,}000(9) + 20{,}000(2) \overset{?}{=} 100{,}000$

$90{,}000 + 40{,}000 \overset{?}{=} 100{,}000$

$130{,}000 > 100{,}000$

$10{,}000C + 20{,}000L > 100{,}000$

37a. $m + v \geq 1200$

37b. $m + v \geq 1200$

$m + v = 1200$	$m + v = 1200$	Test (0, 1400).
$0 + v = 1200$	$m + 0 = 1200$	$m + v \overset{?}{\geq} 1200$
$v = 1200$	$m = 1200$	$1400 + 0 \overset{?}{\geq} 1200$
(1200, 0)	(0, 1200)	$1400 \geq 1200$
		true

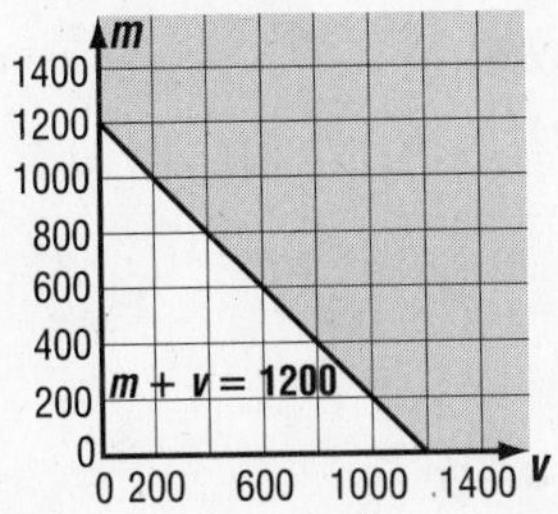

37c. $D = \{200 \leq m \leq 800\}$, $R = \{200 \leq v \leq 800\}$

38. $y = [x] - 4$

x	$[x] - 4$	y
0	$[0] - 4$	-4
$\frac{1}{2}$	$\left[\frac{1}{2}\right] - 4$	-4
1	$[1] - 4$	-3
$1\frac{1}{2}$	$\left[1\frac{1}{2}\right] - 4$	-3
2	$[2] - 4$	-2

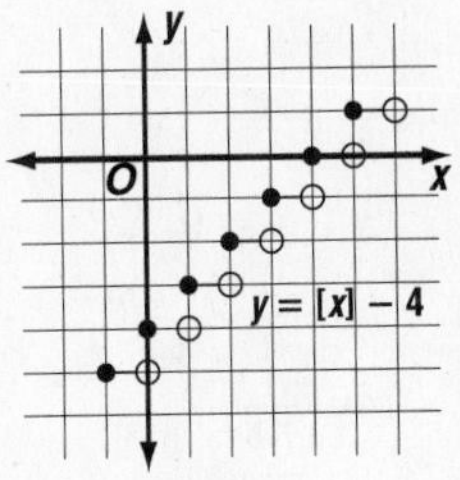

39a.

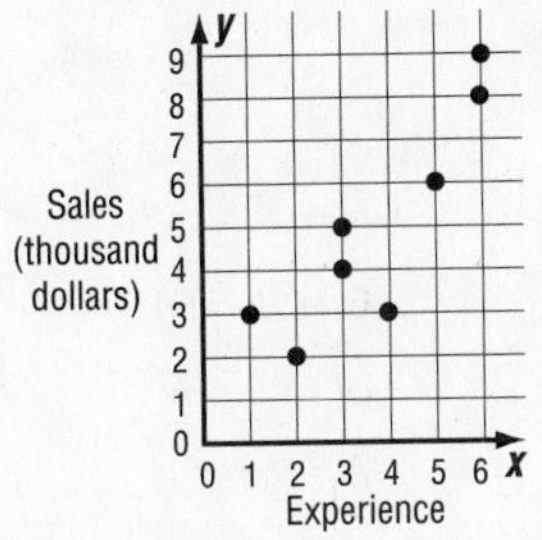

39b. $m = \frac{8000 - 0}{6 - 0}$

$= \frac{8000}{6}$

≈ 1333

$y = mx + b$

$8000 = 1333(6) + b$

$8000 = 8000 + b$

$0 = b$

$y = 1333x$

39c. $y = 1333x$

$= 1333(8)$

$= 10{,}664$; \$10,664

40. $y = mx + b$

$-5 = \left(\frac{2}{3}\right)6 + b$

$-5 = 4 + b$

$-9 = b$

$y = \frac{2}{3}x - 9$

41. $x - 2y = 3$

$-2y = -x + 3$

$y = \frac{1}{2}x - \frac{3}{2}$

slope $= \frac{1}{2}$, perpendicular

slope $= -2$

Graph (−2, 7), then go down 2 units and over 1 unit to the right.

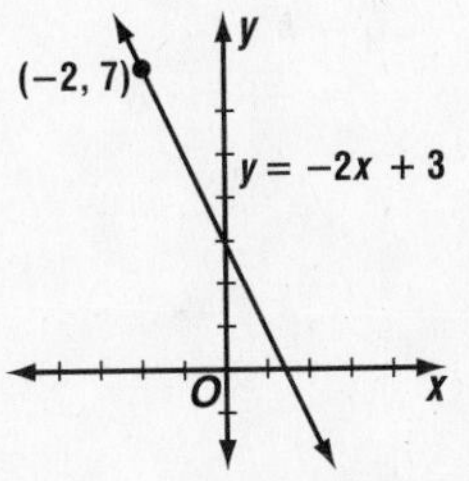

42.

$4x + 5y = 10$	$4x + 5y = 10$
$4x + 5(0) = 10$	$4(0) + 5y = 10$
$4x + 0 = 10$	$0 + 5y = 10$
$4x = 10$	$5y = 10$
$x = \frac{5}{2}$	$y = 2$

43. (7, 2)

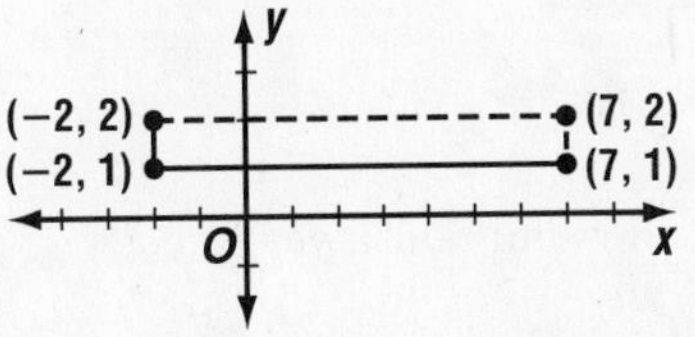

Chapter 2 Highlights

Page 115 Understanding and Using the Vocabulary

1. prediction equation
2. identity function
3. constant function
4. direct variation
5. absolute value function
6. standard form
7. parallel lines
8. domain
9. perpendicular lines
10. range
11. slope

Chapter 2 Study Guide and Assessment

Pages 116–118 Skills and Concepts

12. $D = \{-4, 4\}$, $R = \{-7, 7\}$, no

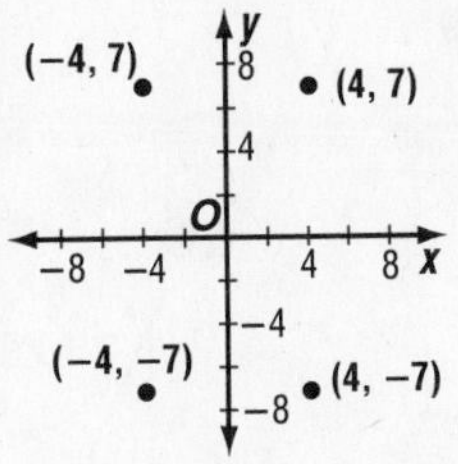

13. $D = \{1, 3, 5, 7, 9\}$, $R = \{1, 2, 3, 4, 5\}$; yes

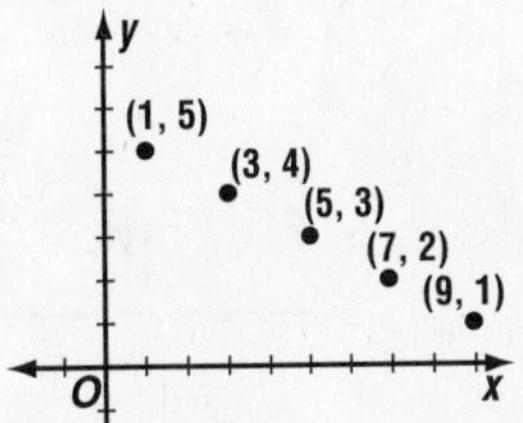

14. D = {all reals}, R = {all reals}; yes

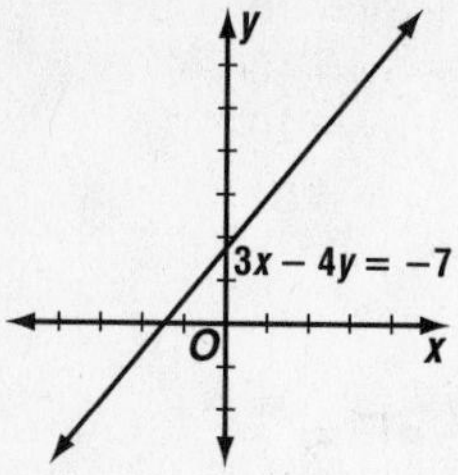

15. D = {all reals}, R = {all reals}; yes

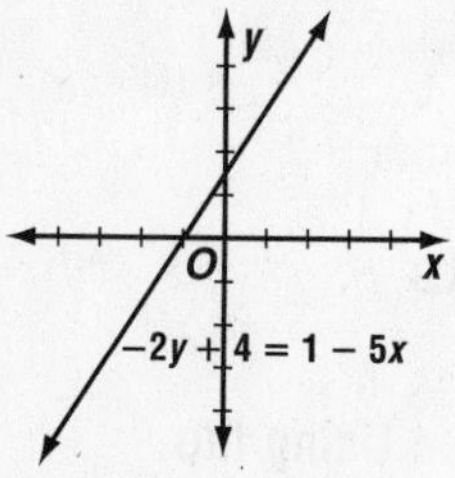

16. $f(x) = 4x^2 + 5x - 9$
$f(6) = 4(6)^2 + 5(6) - 9$
$= 4(36) + 30 - 9$
$= 144 + 30 - 9$
$= 165$

17. $f(x) = 4x^2 + 5x - 9$
$f(-2) = 4(-2)^2 + 5(-2) - 9$
$= 4(4) - 10 - 9$
$= 16 - 10 - 9$
$= -3$

18. $f(x) = 4x^2 + 5x - 9$
$f(3y) = 4(3y)^2 + 5(3y) - 9$
$= 4(9y^2) + 15y - 9$
$= 36y^2 + 15y - 9$

19. $f(x) = 4x^2 + 5x - 9$
$f(-2v) = 4(-2v)^2 + 5(-2v) - 9$
$= 4(4v^2) - 10v - 9$
$= 16v^2 - 10v - 9$

20. No, x is squared.

21. yes

$2x + y = 11$	$2x + y = 11$
$2x + 0 = 11$	$2(0) + y = 11$
$2x = 11$	$0 + y = 11$
$x = \frac{11}{2}$	$y = 11$
$\left(\frac{11}{2}, 0\right)$	$(0, 11)$

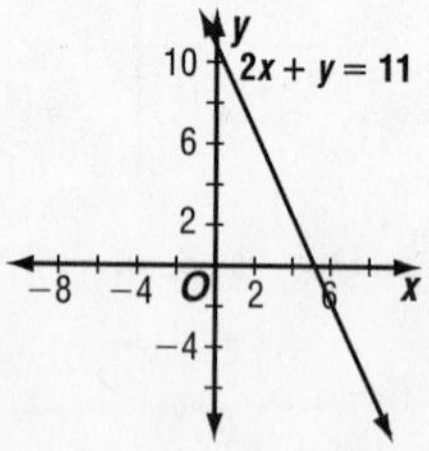

22. Yes, $y = 7$ is horizontal.

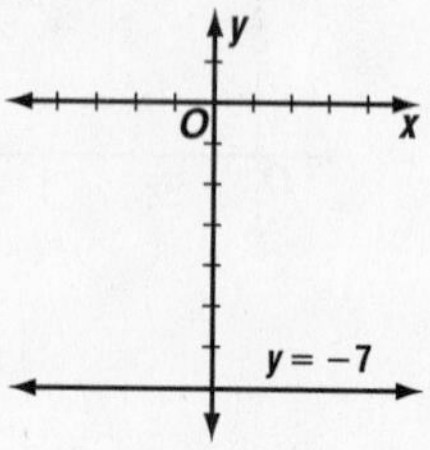

23. No, x and y are squared.

24. $y = 7x + 15$
$-7x + y = 15$
$7x - y = -15$

25. $0.5x = -0.2y - 0.4$
$0.5x + 0.2y = -0.4$
$5x + 2y = -4$

26. $\frac{2}{3}x - \frac{3}{4}y = 6$
$12\left(\frac{2}{3}\right)x - 12\left(\frac{3}{4}\right)y = 12(6)$
$8x - 9y = 72$

27. $-\frac{1}{5}y = x + 4$
$-x - \frac{1}{5}y = 4$
$-5(-x) - (-5)\left(\frac{1}{5}\right)y = -5(4)$
$5x + y = -20$

28. $6x = -12y + 48$
$6x + 12y = 48$
$x + 2y = 8$

29. $y - x = -9$
$-x + y = -9$
$x - y = 9$

30. $m = \frac{7 - (-3)}{6 - (-6)}$
$= \frac{10}{12}$
$= \frac{5}{6}$

31. $m = \frac{-7 - (-5.5)}{11 - 5.5}$
$= \frac{-1.5}{5.5}$
$= \frac{-15}{55}$
$= -\frac{3}{11}$

32. $m = \frac{-41 - 24}{10 - (-3)}$
$= \frac{-65}{13}$
$= -5$

33. $y = mx + b$
$9 = \frac{3}{4}(-6) + b$
$9 = -\frac{9}{2} + b$
$\frac{27}{2} = b$
$y = \frac{3}{4}x + \frac{27}{2}$

34. $\left(\frac{3}{2}, 0\right)$
$y = mx + b$
$0 = 2\left(\frac{3}{2}\right) + b$
$0 = 3 + b$
$-3 = b$
$y = 2x - 3$

35. $m = \frac{2 - (-8)}{-3 - 3}$
$= \frac{10}{-6}$
$= -\frac{5}{3}$
$y = mx + b$
$2 = -\frac{5}{3}(-3) + b$
$2 = 5 + b$
$-3 = b$
$y = -\frac{5}{3}x - 3$

36. $m = \frac{0.35 - 0.7}{0.7 - 0.35}$
$= \frac{-0.35}{0.35}$
$= -1$
$y = mx + b$
$0.35 = -1(0.7) + b$
$0.35 = -0.7 + b$
$1.05 = b$
$y = -x + 1.05$

37. parallel slope $= -3$
$y = mx + b$
$2 = -3(1) + b$
$2 = -3 + b$
$5 = b$
$y = -3x + 5$

38. $x - 3y = 14$
$-3y = -x + 14$
$y = \frac{1}{3}x - \frac{14}{3}$
parallel slope $= \frac{1}{3}$
$y = mx + b$
$2 = \frac{1}{3}(-1) + b$
$2 = -\frac{1}{3} + b$
$\frac{7}{3} = b$
$y = \frac{1}{3}x + \frac{7}{3}$

39. $4x - 3y = 12$

$-3y = -4x + 12$

$y = \frac{4}{3}x - 4$

perpendicular slope $= -\frac{3}{4}$

$y = mx + b$

$2 = \left(-\frac{3}{4}\right)(3) + b$

$2 = -\frac{9}{4} + b$

$\frac{17}{4} = b$

$y = -\frac{3}{4}x + \frac{17}{4}$

40. perpendicular slope $= \frac{3}{2}$

$y = mx + b$

$3 = \frac{3}{2}(1) + b$

$3 = \frac{3}{2} + b$

$\frac{3}{2} = b$

$y = \frac{3}{2}x + \frac{3}{2}$

41a.

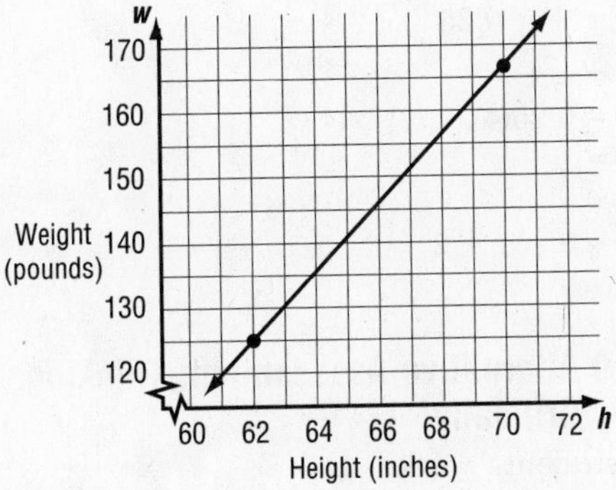

41b. $m = \frac{167 - 125}{70 - 62}$

$= \frac{42}{8}$

$= 5.25$

$w = 5.25h - 200.5$

$y = mx + b$

$167 = 5.25(70) + b$

$167 = 367.5 + b$

$-200.5 = b$

41c. $w = 5.25h - 200.5$

$= 5.25(77) - 200.5$

$= 404.25 - 200.5$

$= 203.75$; 203.75 pounds

41d. $w = 5.25h - 200.5$

$155 = 5.25h - 200.5$

$355.5 = 5.25h$

$67.7 \approx h$; 67.71 inches

42. A;

x	$\|x\| + 4$	$f(x)$
-1	$\|-1\| + 4$	5
0	$\|0\| + 4$	4
1	$\|1\| + 4$	5
2	$\|2\| + 4$	6

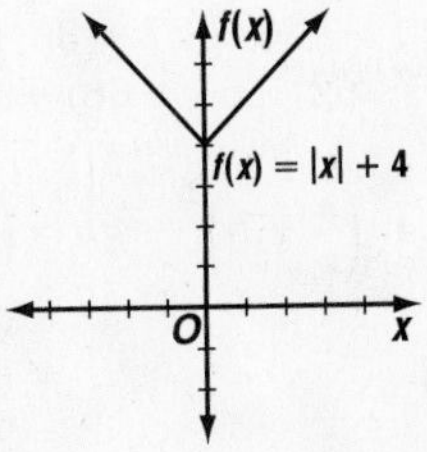

43. G;

x	$[x] - 2$	$f(x)$
0	$[0] - 2$	-2
$\frac{1}{2}$	$\left[\frac{1}{2}\right] - 2$	-2
1	$[1] - 2$	-1
$1\frac{1}{2}$	$\left[1\frac{1}{2}\right] - 2$	-1
2	$[2] - 2$	0

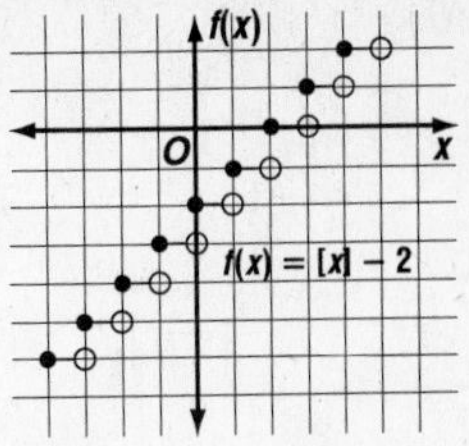

44. C;

x	$g(x)$
-2	$\frac{2}{3}$
0	$\frac{2}{3}$
3	$\frac{2}{3}$

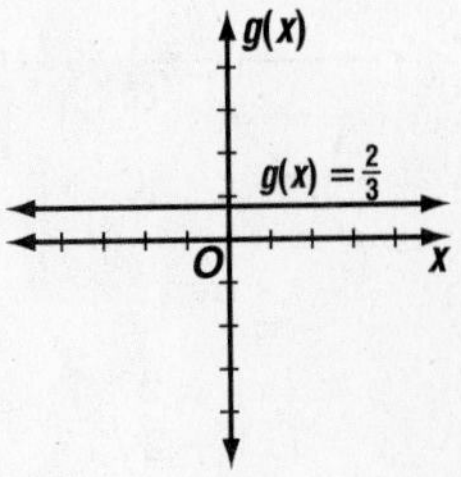

45. D;

x	$3x$	$h(x)$
-1	$3(-1)$	-3
0	$3(0)$	0
1	$3(1)$	3

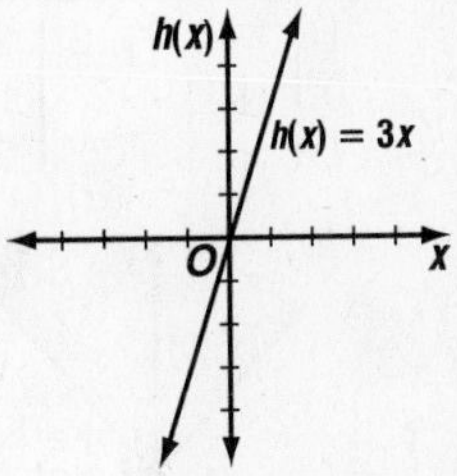

46. G;

x	$[2x + 1]$	$h(x)$
0	$[2(0) + 1]$	1
$\frac{1}{4}$	$\left[2\left(\frac{1}{4}\right) + 1\right]$	1
$\frac{1}{2}$	$\left[2\left(\frac{1}{2}\right) + 1\right]$	2
$\frac{3}{4}$	$\left[2\left(\frac{3}{4}\right) + 1\right]$	2
1	$[2(1) + 1]$	3

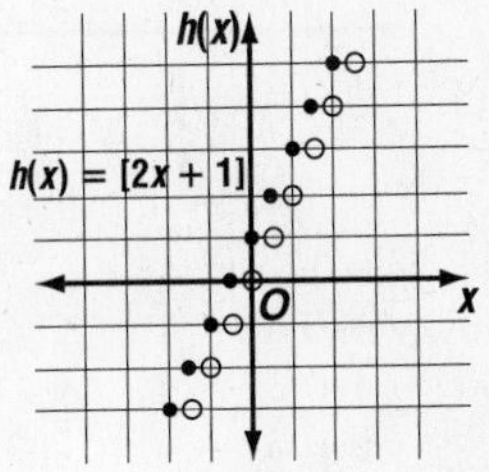

47. A;

x	$\|x - 1\| + 7$	$g(x)$
-1	$\|-1 - 1\| + 7$	9
0	$\|0 - 1\| + 7$	8
1	$\|1 - 1\| + 7$	7
2	$\|2 - 1\| + 7$	8

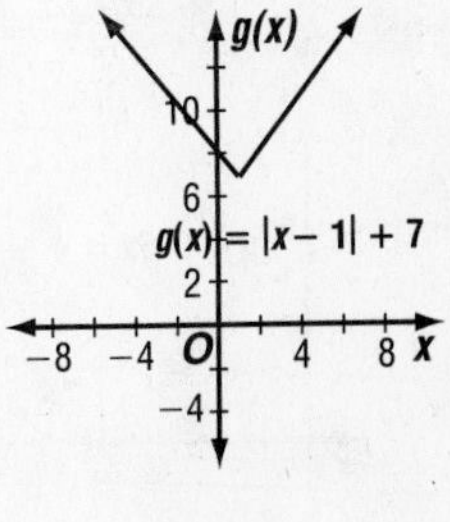

48. $y \leq 3x - 5$

$y = 3x - 5$

$0 = 3x - 5$

$5 = 3x$

$\frac{5}{3} = x$

$\left(\frac{5}{3}, 0\right)$

$y = 3x - 5$

$y = 3(0) - 5$

$y = 0 - 5$

$y = -5$

$(0, -5)$

Test $(0, -6)$.

$y \overset{?}{\leq} 3x - 5$

$-6 \overset{?}{\leq} 3(0) - 5$

$-6 \overset{?}{\leq} 0 - 5$

$-6 \leq -5$; true

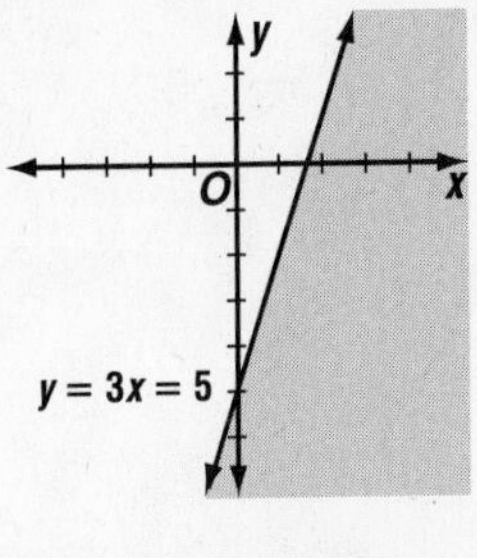

49. $x > y - 1$

$x = y - 1$	$x = y - 1$	Test (0, 0).
$x = 0 - 1$	$0 = y - 1$	$x \overset{?}{>} y - 1$
$x = -1$	$1 = y$	$0 \overset{?}{>} 0 - 1$
$(-1, 0)$	$(0, 1)$	$0 > -1$; true

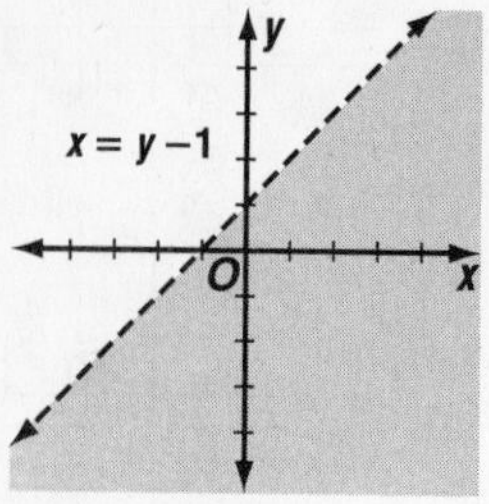

50. $y \geq |x| + 2$

$y = |x| + 2$

x	$\lvert x\rvert + 2$	y
-1	$\lvert -1\rvert + 2$	3
0	$\lvert 0\rvert + 2$	2
1	$\lvert 1\rvert + 2$	3

Test (0, 4).

$y \overset{?}{\geq} |x| + 2$

$4 \overset{?}{\geq} |0| + 2$

$4 \geq 2$; true

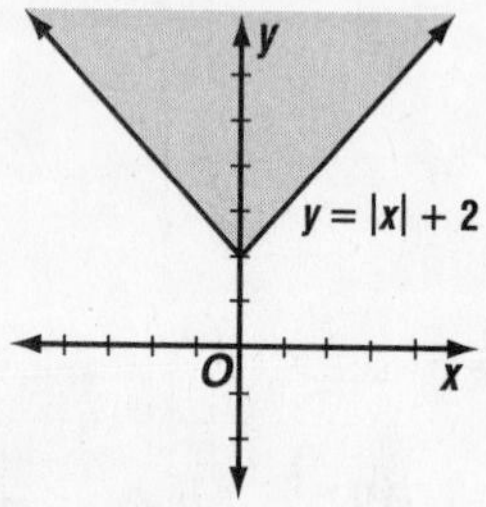

51. $y + 0.5x < 4$

$y + 0.5x = 4$	$y + 0.5x = 4$	Test (0, 0).
$0 + 0.5x = 4$	$y + 0.5(0) = 4$	$y + 0.5x \overset{?}{<} 4$
$0.5x = 4$	$y + 0 = 4$	$0 + 0.5(0) \overset{?}{<} 4$
$x = 8$	$y = 4$	$0 + 0 \overset{?}{<} 4$
$(8, 0)$	$(0, 4)$	$0 < 4$; true

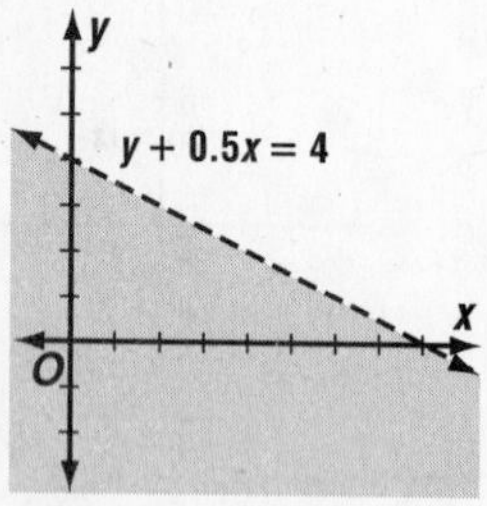

Page 118 Applications and Problem Solving

52. $40 \times \$7.00 = 280$

$p = 280 + 0.50(x - 25)$ if $x > 25$; $p = 280$ if $x < 25$

53. $b = 110 + 5 + 0.02(110)$

$= 110 + 5 + 2.2$

$= 117.2$; \$117.20

54. a: (0, 4), (4, −4)

$m = \frac{-4 - 4}{4 - 0}$

$= \frac{-8}{4}$

$= -2$

$y = mx + b$

$4 = -2(0) + b$

$4 = b$

$y = -2x + 4$

b: (−4, −4), (0, 4)

$m = \frac{4 - (-4)}{0 - (-4)}$

$= \frac{8}{4}$

$= 2$

$y = mx + b$

$4 = 2(0) + b$

$4 = b$

$y = 2x + 4$

c: (−4, −4), (4, 3)

$m = \frac{3 - (-4)}{4 - (-4)}$

$= \frac{7}{8}$ or 0.875

$y = mx + b$

$3 = 0.875(4) + b$

$3 = 3.5 + b$

$-0.5 = b$

$y = 0.875x - 0.5$

d: (−4, 1), (4, −4)

$m = \frac{-4 - 1}{4 - (-4)}$

$m = -\frac{5}{8}$ or -0.625

$y = mx + b$

$1 = -0.625(-4) + b$

$1 = 2.5 + b$

$-1.5 = b$

$y = -0.625x - 1.5$

e: (−4, 1), (4, 3)

$m = \frac{3 - 1}{4 - (-4)}$

$= \frac{2}{8}$ or 0.25

$y = mx + b$

$3 = 0.25(4) + b$

$3 = 1 + b$

$2 = b$

$y = 0.25x + 2$

Page 119 Alternative Assessment; Thinking Critically

- See students' work.

Chapter Entrance Exam Practice, Chapters 1–2

Pages 120–121

1. C

2. $3(a + 2b) - c = 0$

$3a + 6b - c = 0$

$3a + 6b = c$

$6b = c - 3a$

$b = \frac{c - 3a}{6}$; B

3. $(3 + 7 + 12 + 12 + 15 + 18 + 18 + 23 + 25 + 25 + 26 + 27 + 36 + 40 + 43 + 43 + 43 + 50 + 53 + 62 + 66 + 68) \div 22 = 715 \div 22 = 32.5$; 32.5 years; A

4. $\left(\frac{a}{x} + b\right)^2 - gh = \left(\frac{9}{3} + 2\right)^2 - 4(6)$

$= (3 + 2)^2 - 4(6)$

$= (5)^2 - 4(6)$

$= 25 - 24$

$= 1$; D

5. $2x - 4y = 8$

$-4y = -2x + 8$

$y = \frac{1}{2}x - 2$

slope $= \frac{1}{2}$

$2x - 4y = 8$

$2(6) - 4(1) \stackrel{?}{=} 8$

$12 - 4 \stackrel{?}{=} 8$

$8 = 8$

$2x - y = 8$

$-y = -2x + 8$

$y = 2x + 8$

not parallel

$4x - 8y = 16$

$-8y = -4x + 16$

$y = \frac{1}{2}x - 2$

not perpendicular

C

6. B

7. The dashed line passes through (0, 2) and (5, 0).

$m = \frac{0 - 2}{5 - 0}$

$= -\frac{2}{5}$

$b = 2$

$y = mx + b$

$y = -\frac{2}{5}x + 2$

$5y = -2x + 10$

$2x + 5y = 10$

Test (0, 0).

$2x + 5y < 10$

$2(0) + 5(0) \stackrel{?}{<} 10$

$0 + 0 \stackrel{?}{<} 10$

$0 < 10$

$y > 2 - \frac{2}{5}x$

$0 \stackrel{?}{>} 2 - \frac{2}{5}(0)$

$0 \stackrel{?}{>} 2 - 0$

$0 \not> 2$

A

8. D

9. $8|2b - 3| = 64$

$|2b - 3| = 8$

$2b - 3 = 8$ or $2b - 3 = -8$

$2b = 11$ $2b = -5$

$b = 5.5$ $b = -2.5$

10. Let x = length of the rug.
Then the width equals $\frac{x}{3} + 4$.

$x + \left(\frac{x}{3} + 4\right) + x + \left(\frac{x}{3} + 4\right) = 64$

$\frac{8x}{3} + 8 = 64$

$\frac{8x}{3} = 56$

$x = 21$; 21 feet

$\frac{x}{3} + 4 = \frac{21}{3} + 4$

$= 7 + 4$

$= 11$; 11 feet

11. Intercity Car Rental $= 20 + 0.2x$

$= 20 + 0.2(875)$

$= 20 + 175$

$= 195$

Big Wheels Car Rental $= 10 + 0.23x$

$= 10 + 0.23(875)$

$= 10 + 201.25$

$= 211.25$

$211.25 - 195 = 16.25$

Intercity Car Rental would be \$16.25 cheaper.

12. $\frac{x + 8}{4} - 1 > \frac{x}{3}$ and $7 < 2x - 11$

$3x + 24 - 12 > 4x$ $18 < 2x$

$3x + 12 > 4x$ $9 < x$

$12 > x$

$\{x \mid 9 < x < 12\}$

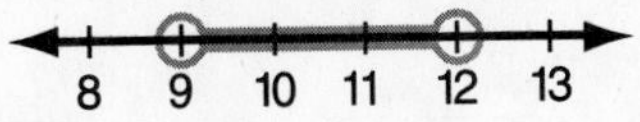

13. $m = \frac{-1 - (-7)}{-3 - 4}$

$= -\frac{6}{7}$

slope of perpendicular line $= \frac{7}{6}$

14. $125 + 86 + 98 + 72 + 63 + 135 = 579$

$1025 - 579 = 446$; \$446

15. See students' work.

16. $m = \frac{2 - (-1)}{-3 - 5}$

$= -\frac{3}{8}$

$-\frac{3}{8} < \frac{8}{3}$; B

17. $g^2 + (k - p) \div g = 3^2 + (-2 - 4) \div 3$

$= 9 + (-6) \div 3$

$= 9 - 2$

$= 7$

$\left(\frac{p}{k} + m\right)^2 \div g + k = \left(\frac{4}{-2} + 5\right)^2 \div 3 + (-2)$

$= (-2 + 5)^2 \div 3 + (-2)$

$= (3)^2 \div 3 + (-2)$

$= 9 \div 3 + (-2)$

$= 3 + (-2)$

$= 1$

$7 > 1$; A

18. $y - 3 \geq 4x$ $3x + 5 < 10$

$\frac{y - 3}{4} \geq x$ $3x < 5$

$x < \frac{5}{3}$

There is not enough information since we do not know the value of y. D

19. 12, 19, 27, 33, 38, 41

$\frac{27 + 33}{2} = \frac{60}{2} = 30$

$\frac{14 + 23 + 35 + 18 + 32 + 27 + 39}{7} = \frac{188}{7} \approx 26.86$

$30 > 26.86$; A

20. $-d + a + c = -d + a + b$

$= (b + a) - d$; C

Chapter 3 Solving Systems of Linear Equations and Inequalities

3-1A Graphing Technology: Systems of Equations

Page 125 Exercises

1. [Y=] 3 [X,T,θ,n] [–] 2 [ENTER] [(–)] 0.5 [X,T,θ,n] [+] 5 [ZOOM] 6

   Use [TRACE] and [ZOOM] or the INTERCEPT feature to find accurate solution; (2, 4).

2. [Y=] [(] 1 [÷] 4 [)] [X,T,θ,n] [+] 3 [ENTER] [(–)] 2 [X,T,θ,n] [+] 21 [ENTER] 6

   Use [TRACE] and [ZOOM] or the INTERCEPT feature to find accurate solution; (8, 5).

3. $2x + 3y = 8$ $\qquad$ $3x - 8y = -13$

   $3y = -2x + 8$ $\qquad$ $-8y = -3x - 13$

   $y = -\frac{2}{3}x + \frac{8}{3}$ $\qquad$ $y = \frac{3}{8}x + \frac{13}{8}$

   [Y=] [(–)] [(] 2 [÷] 3 [)] [X,T,θ,n] [+] [(] 8 [÷] 3 [)] [ENTER] [(] 3 [÷] 8 [)] [X,T,θ,n] [+] [(] 13 [÷] 8 [)] [ZOOM] 6

   Use [TRACE] and [ZOOM] or the INTERCEPT feature to find accurate solution; (1, 2).

4. $8 = 2x - y$

   $8 + y = 2x$

   $y = 2x - 8$

   [Y=] [(–)] [X,T,θ,n] [+] 7 [ENTER] 2 [X,T,θ,n] [–] 8 [ZOOM] 6

   Use [TRACE] and [ZOOM] or the INTERCEPT feature to find accurate solution; (5, 2).

5. [Y=] 0.125 [X,T,θ,n] [–] 3.005 [ENTER] [(–)] 2.58 [ZOOM] 6

   Use [TRACE] and [ZOOM] or the INTERCEPT feature to find accurate solution; (3.40, −2.58).

6. $\frac{1}{2}x + \frac{1}{3}y = 1$ $\qquad$ $3x + 2y = 6$

   $\frac{1}{3}y = -\frac{1}{2}x + 1$ $\qquad$ $2y = -3x + 6$

   $y = -\frac{3}{2}x + 3$ $\qquad$ $y = -\frac{3}{2}x + 3$

   [Y=] [(–)] [(] 3 [÷] 2 [)] [X,T,θ,n] [+] 3 [ENTER] [(–)] [(] 3 [÷] 2 [)] [X,T,θ,n] [+] 3 [ZOOM] 6

   The lines are the same; infinitely many.

7. $3.14x + 2.03y = 1.99$

   $2.03y = -3.14x + 1.99$

   $y \approx -1.55x + 0.98$

   $9.32x - 3.77y = -4.21$

   $-3.77y = -9.32x - 4.21$

   $y \approx 2.47 + 1.12$

   [Y=] [(–)] 1.55 [X,T,θ,n] [+] 0.98 [ENTER] 2.47 [X,T,θ,n] [+] 1.12 [ZOOM] 6

   Use [TRACE] and [ZOOM] or the INTERCEPT feature to find accurate solution; (−0.03, 1.03).

8. $12y = 4x - 16$ $\qquad$ $9y - 3x = 3$

   $y = \frac{1}{3}x - \frac{4}{3}$ $\qquad$ $9y = 3x + 3$

   $y = \frac{1}{3}x + \frac{1}{3}$

   [Y=] [(] 1 [÷] 3 [)] [X,T,θ,n] [–] [(] 4 [÷] 3 [)] [ENTER] [(] 1 [÷] 3 [)] [X,T,θ,n] [+] [(] 1 [÷] 3 [)] [ZOOM] 6

   Lines are parallel; no solution.

3-1 Graphing Systems of Equations

Pages 129–130 Check for Understanding

1a. inconsistent, because lines are parallel

1b. same slopes, different intercepts

2.

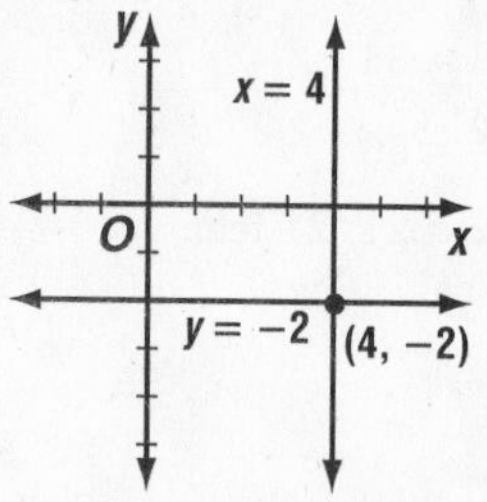

a horizontal line and a vertical line intersecting at (4, −2)

3. Two straight lines cannot intersect in exactly two points.

4. Sample answer: $x + y = 5$ and $x - y = 5$

5a. The break-even point was (75, 2250). Selling 100 shirts is above this point so she would make a profit. The profit would be about $300.

5b. Profit = income − cost

   $600 = 30x - (900 + 18x)$

   $600 = 30x - 900 - 18x$

   $600 = 12x - 900$

   $1500 = 12x$

   $125 = x$; 125 sweatshirts

6. Write the equations in slope-intercept form. If the equations have different slopes, the graphs of the equations are intersecting lines. If the equations have the same slope but different y-intercepts, the graphs of the equations are two parallel lines. If the equations have the same slope and the same y-intercept, the graphs of the equations are two coincident lines.

7. 0; inconsistent

8. 1; consistent, independent; (1, 2.5)

9. $5x - y = 3$ $\quad y = 5x - 3$
$-y = -5x + 3$
$y = 5x - 3$

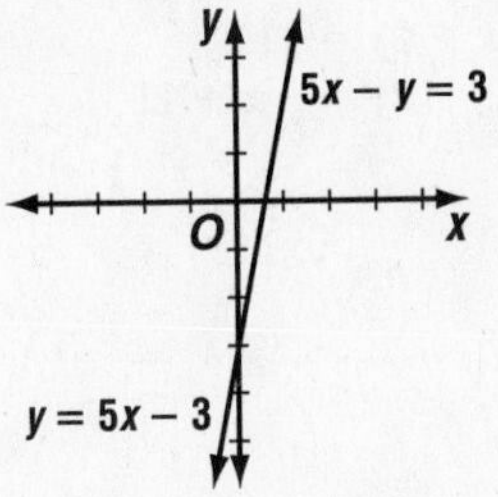

$y = 5x - 3$; consistent, dependent

10. $2x - 3y = 7$ $\quad 2x + 3y = 7$
$-3y = -2x + 7$ $\quad 3y = -2x + 7$
$y = \frac{2}{3}x - \frac{7}{3}$ $\quad y = -\frac{2}{3}x + \frac{7}{3}$

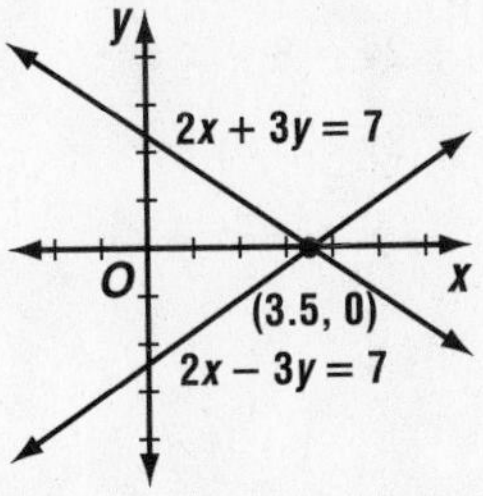

(3.5, 0); consistent, independent

11. $x + y = 6$ $\quad 3x + 3y = 3$
$y = -x + 6$ $\quad 3y = -3x + 3$
$y = -x + 1$

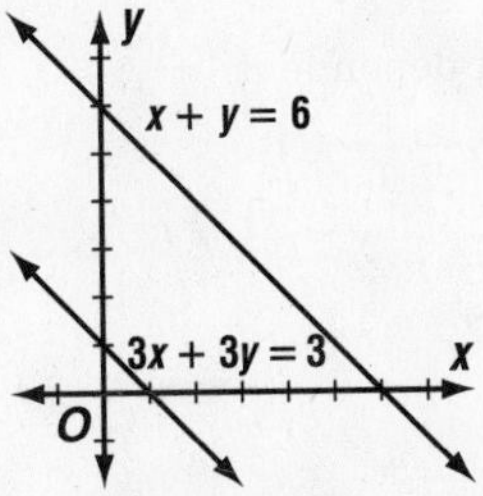

no solution; inconsistent

12. $\frac{1}{2}x - y = 0$ $\quad \frac{1}{4}x + \frac{1}{2}y = -2$
$-y = -\frac{1}{2}x$ $\quad \frac{1}{2}y = -\frac{1}{4}x - 2$
$y = \frac{1}{2}x$ $\quad y = -\frac{1}{2}x - 4$

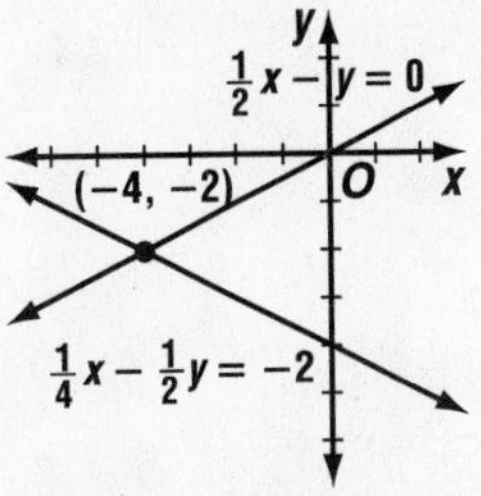

(−4, −2); consistent, independent

13. $x + y = 4$ $\quad y = x - 2$; a
$y = -x + 4$

Pages 130–132 Exercises

14. 1; consistent, independent; (−1, 4)

15. 1; consistent, independent; (−3, 0)

16. 0; inconsistent

17. 1; consistent, independent; (−1, 3)

18. $2x + 3y = 12$ $\quad 2x - y = 4$
$3y = -2x + 12$ $\quad -y = -2x + 4$
$y = -\frac{2}{3}x + 4$ $\quad y = 2x - 4$

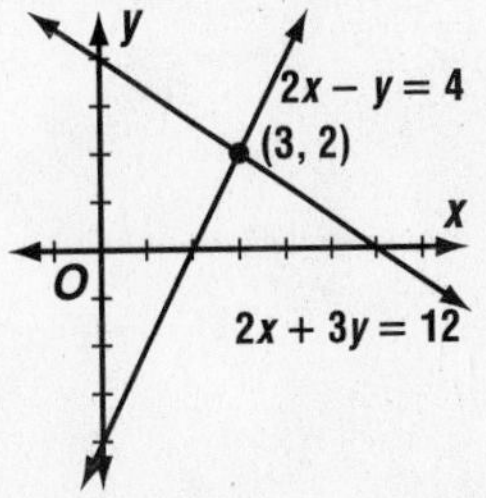

(3, 2); consistent, independent

19. $3x - y = 8$ $\quad x - y = 8$
$-y = -3x + 8$ $\quad -y = -x + 8$
$y = 3x - 8$ $\quad y = x - 8$

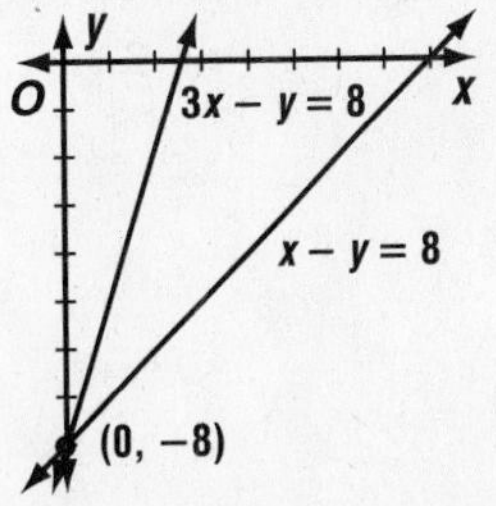

(0, −8); consistent, independent

20. $4x - 6y = 5$ $\quad$ $2x - 3y = 5$

$-6y = -4x + 5$ $\quad$ $-3y = -2x + 5$

$y = \frac{2}{3}x - \frac{5}{6}$ $\quad$ $y = \frac{2}{3}x - \frac{5}{3}$

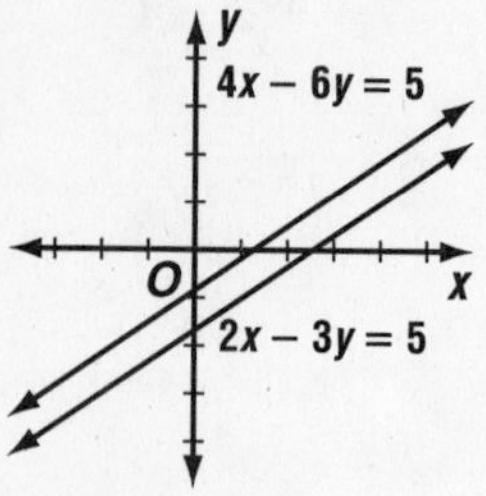

no solution; inconsistent

21. $x + 2y = 6$ $\quad$ $2x + y = 9$

$2y = -x + 6$ $\quad$ $y = -2x + 9$

$y = -\frac{1}{2}x + 3$

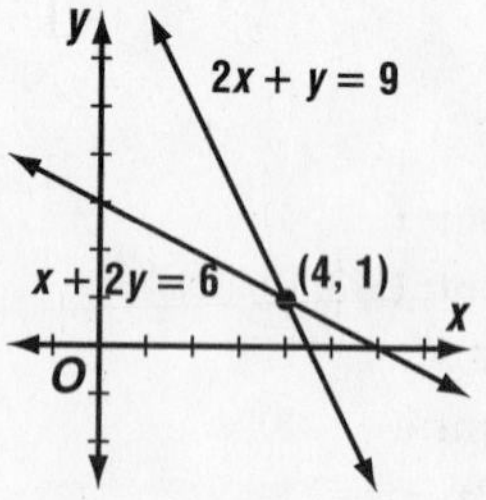

(4, 1); consistent, independent

22. $x + 1 = y$ $\quad$ $2x - 2y = 8$

$y = x + 1$ $\quad$ $-2y = -2x + 8$

$y = x - 4$

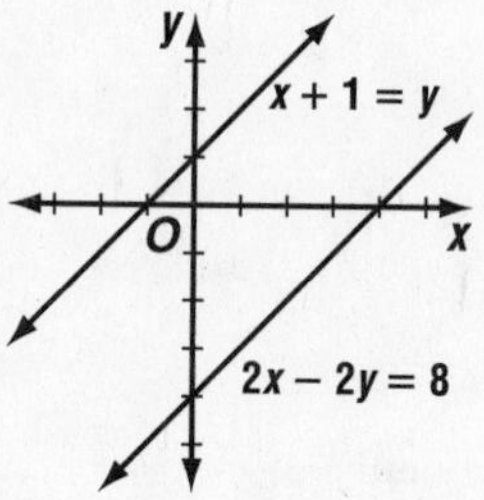

no solution; inconsistent

23. $2x + 4y = 8$ $\quad$ $x + 2y = 4$

$4y = -2x + 8$ $\quad$ $2y = -x + 4$

$y = -\frac{1}{2}x + 2$ $\quad$ $y = -\frac{1}{2}x + 2$

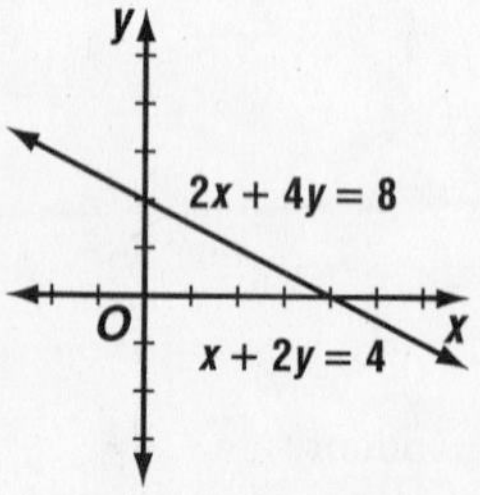

$x + 2y = 4$; consistent, dependent

24. $3x - 8y = 4$ $\quad$ $6x - 42 = 16y$

$-8y = -3x - 4$ $\quad$ $16y = 6x - 42$

$y = \frac{3}{8}x + \frac{1}{2}$ $\quad$ $y = \frac{3}{8}x - \frac{21}{8}$

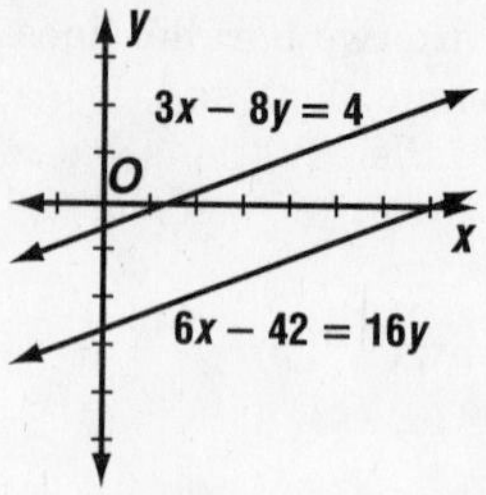

no solution; inconsistent

25. $3x + 6 = 7y$ $\quad$ $x + 2y = 11$

$7y = 3x + 6$ $\quad$ $2y = -x + 11$

$y = \frac{3}{7}x + \frac{6}{7}$ $\quad$ $y = -\frac{1}{2}x + \frac{11}{2}$

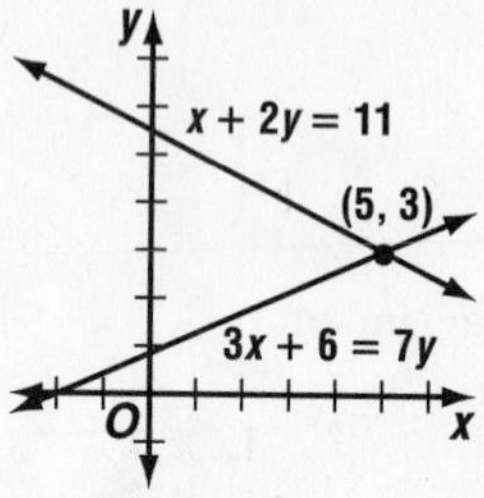

(5, 3); consistent, independent

26. $\frac{3}{4}x + \frac{1}{6}y = \frac{2}{3}$ $\quad$ $9x + 2y = 8$

$\frac{1}{6}y = -\frac{3}{4}x + \frac{2}{3}$ $\quad$ $2y = -9x + 8$

$y = -\frac{9}{2}x + 4$ $\quad$ $y = -\frac{9}{2}x + 4$

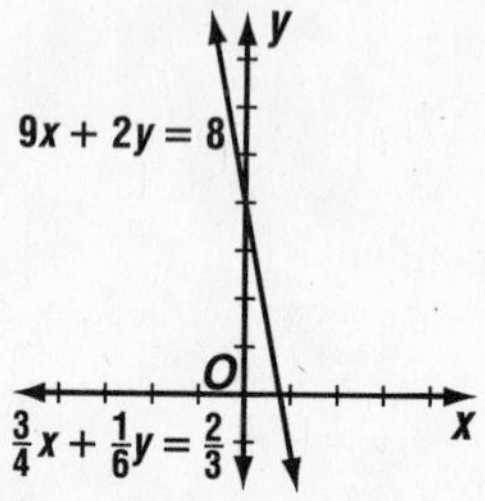

$9x + 2y = 8$; consistent, dependent

27. $\frac{2}{3}x + y = -3$ $\quad$ $y - \frac{1}{3}x = 6$

$y = -\frac{2}{3}x - 3$ $\quad$ $y = \frac{1}{3}x + 6$

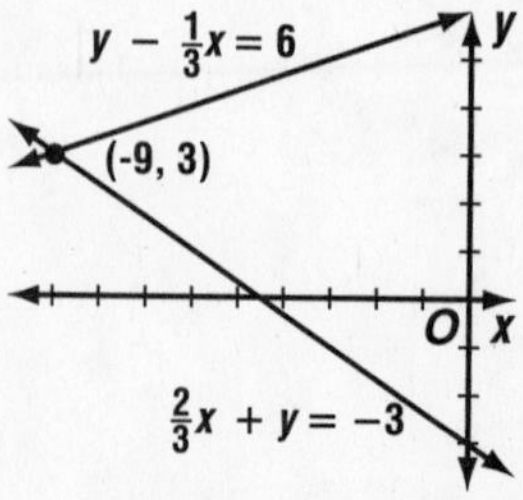

(−9, 3); consistent, independent

28. $\frac{4}{3}x + \frac{1}{5}y = 3$ $\qquad$ $\frac{2}{3}x - \frac{3}{5}y = 5$

$\frac{1}{5}y = -\frac{4}{3}x + 3$ $\qquad$ $-\frac{3}{5}y = -\frac{2}{3}x + 5$

$y = -\frac{20}{3}x + 15$ $\qquad$ $y = \frac{10}{9}x - \frac{25}{3}$

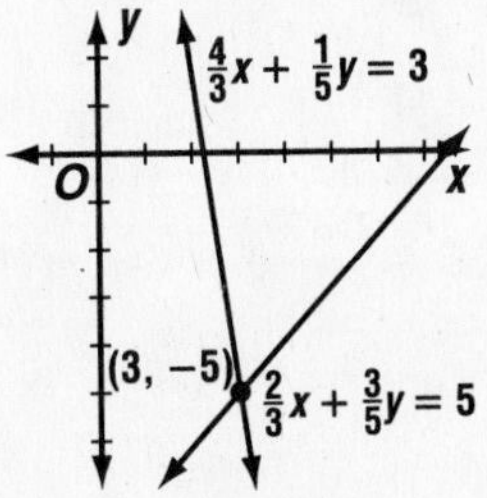

(3, −5); consistent, independent

29. $9x + 8y = 8$ $\qquad$ $\frac{3}{4}x + \frac{2}{3}y = 8$

$8y = -9x + 8$ $\qquad$ $\frac{2}{3}y = -\frac{3}{4}x + 8$

$y = -\frac{9}{8}x + 1$ $\qquad$ $y = -\frac{9}{8}x + 12$

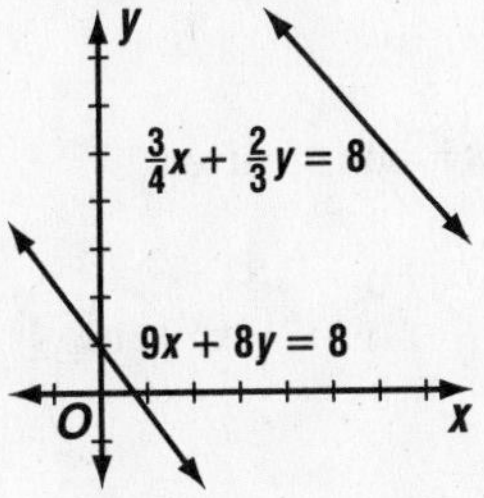

no solution; inconsistent

30. $3x + 4y = 7$ $\qquad$ $1.5x + 2y = 3.5$

$4y = -3x + 7$ $\qquad$ $2y = -1.5x + 3.5$

$y = -\frac{3}{4}x + \frac{7}{4}$ $\qquad$ $y = -0.75x + 1.75$

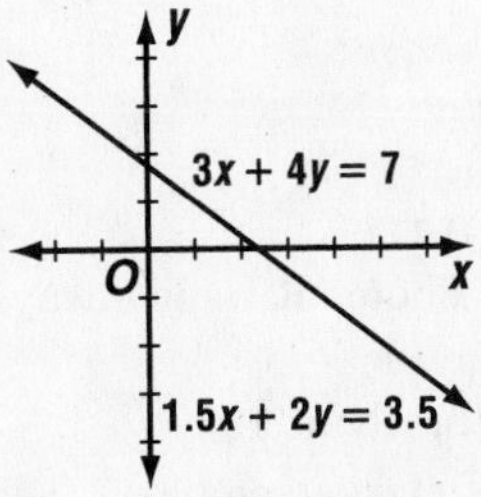

$3x + 4y = 7$; consistent, dependent

31. $1.2x + 2.5y = 4$ $\qquad$ $0.8x - 1.5y = -10$

$2.5y = -1.2x + 4$ $\qquad$ $-1.5y = -0.8x - 10$

$y = -0.48x + 1.6$ $\qquad$ $y = 0.5\overline{3}x + 6.\overline{6}$

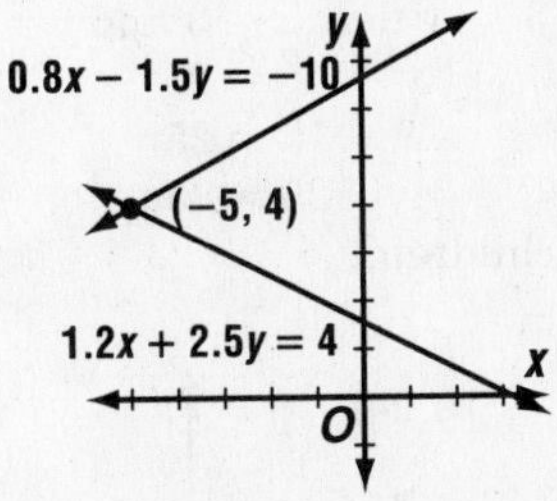

(−5, 4); consistent, independent

32. $5x - 7y = 70$ $\qquad$ $-10x + 14y = 120$

$-7y = -5x + 70$ $\qquad$ $14y = 10x + 120$

$x = \frac{5}{7}x - 10$ $\qquad$ $y = \frac{5}{7}x + \frac{60}{7}$

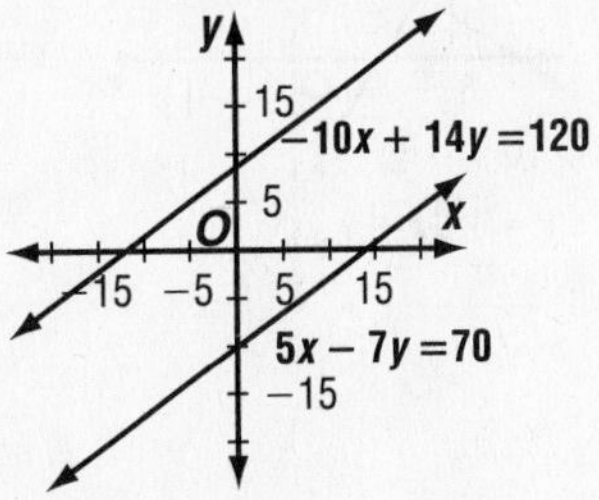

no solution; inconsistent

33. $5x - 3y = 8$

$mx + ny = 4$

Since the system is consistent and dependent, the lines are the same and one equation is a multiple of the other. Compare constants: $4 = \frac{1}{2} \cdot 8$, so the second equation is half of the first.

$m = \frac{1}{2} \cdot 5$ $\qquad$ $n = \frac{1}{2} \cdot (-3)$

$= \frac{5}{2}$ $\qquad$ $= -\frac{3}{2}$

34. $4x - 5y = 10$

$mx - y = n$

Since the system is consistent and independent, the lines are intersecting and the slopes must be different.

$4x - 5y = 10$ $\qquad$ $mx - y = n$

$-5y = -4x + 10$ $\qquad$ $-y = -mx - n$

$y = \frac{4}{5}x - 2$ $\qquad$ $y = mx + n$

$m \neq \frac{4}{5}$

$n =$ any real number

35. $3x + 4y = 8$

$mx + 2y = n$

Since the system is inconsistent, the lines are parallel so the slopes must be the same and y-intercepts must be different.

$3x + 4y = 8$ $\qquad$ $mx + 2y = n$

$4y = -3x + 8$ $\qquad$ $2y = -mx + n$

$y = -\frac{3}{4}x + 2$ $\qquad$ $y = -\frac{m}{2}x + \frac{n}{2}$

$-\frac{3}{4} = -\frac{m}{2}$ $\qquad$ $2 \neq \frac{n}{2}$

$-4m = -6$ $\qquad$ $4 \neq n$

$m = \frac{3}{2}$

$m = \frac{3}{2}, n \neq 4$

36. $2x + 7y = 5$

$x + my = n$

Since the system is consistent and dependent, the lines are the same and one equation is a multiple of the other. For x, the second equation coefficient is half of the first equation coefficient.

$m = \frac{1}{2} \cdot 7$ $\qquad$ $n = \frac{1}{2} \cdot 5$

$= \frac{7}{2}$ $\qquad$ $= \frac{5}{2}$

37. $y = -\frac{3}{2} - 6$
$y = \frac{2}{3}x + 7$
$(-6, 3)$

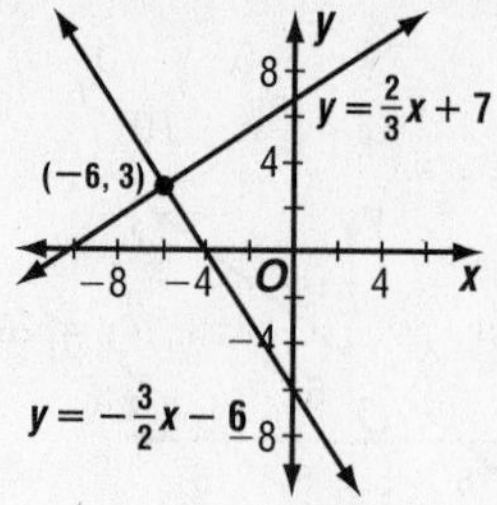

38. base = $s - 2$
side = s
Perimeter = side + side + base

$16 = s + s + s - 2$
$16 = 3s - 2$
$18 = 3s$
$6 = s$

base $= s - 2$
$= 6 - 2$
$= 4$

6 centimeters, 6 centimeters, 4 centimeters

39. $3.6x + 4.8y = -7.2$
$4.8y = -3.6x - 7.2$
$y = -0.75x - 1.5$
$5.8x - 7.1y = 32.9$
$-7.1y = -5.8x + 32.9$
$y = \frac{5.8}{7.1}x - \frac{32.9}{7.1}$

[Y=] [(−)] 0.75 [X,T,θ,n] [−] 1.5 [ENTER] [(] 5.8 [÷] 7.1 [)] [X,T,θ,n] [−] [(] 32.9 [÷] 7.1 [)] [ZOOM] 6 [2nd] [CALC] 5 [ENTER] [ENTER] [ENTER]; $(2, -3)$

40. $-14x + 18y = 75$
$18y = 14x + 75$
$y = \frac{7}{9}x + \frac{25}{6}$

$9.1x - 11.7y = 36$
$-11.7y = -9.1x + 36$
$y = \frac{9.1}{11.7}x - \frac{36}{11.7}$

[Y=] [(] 7 [÷] 9 [)] [X,T,θ,n] [+] [(] 25 [÷] 6 [)] [ENTER] [(] 9.1 [÷] 11.7 [)] [X,T,θ,n] [−] [(] 36 [÷] 11.7 [)] [ZOOM] 6; parallel lines, no solution

41. $3.6x - 2y = 4$
$-2y = -3.6 + 4$
$y = 1.8x - 2$

$-2.7x + y = 3$
$y = 2.7x + 3$

[Y=] 1.8 [X,T,θ,n] [−] 2 [ENTER] 2.7 [X,T,θ,n] [+] 3 [ZOOM] 6 [2nd] [CALC] 5 [ENTER] [ENTER] [ENTER]; $(-5.56, -12.00)$

42. $7x + 13.5y = 31$
$13.5y = -7x + 31$
$y = -\frac{7}{13.5}x + -\frac{31}{13.5}$

$9.8x + 18.9y = 43.4$
$18.9y = -9.8x + 43.4$
$y = -\frac{9.8}{18.9}x + -\frac{43.4}{18.9}$

[Y=] [(−)] [(] 7 [÷] 13.5 [)] [X,T,θ,n] [+] [(] 31 [÷] 13.5 [)] [ENTER] [(−)] [(] 9.8 [÷] 18.9 [)] [X,T,θ,n] [+] [(] 43.4 [÷] 18.9 [)] [ZOOM] 6; same line; $7x + 13.5y = 31$

43a. equations must be multiples; $\frac{a}{d} = \frac{b}{e} = \frac{c}{f}$

43b. slopes must be different; $\frac{a}{d} \neq \frac{b}{e}$

43c. slopes must be equal, intercepts different; $\frac{a}{d} = \frac{b}{e} = \frac{c}{f}$

44a. Let c = regular price, and let d = discount price. Graph $d = \frac{2}{3}c$ and $d = c - 1$.

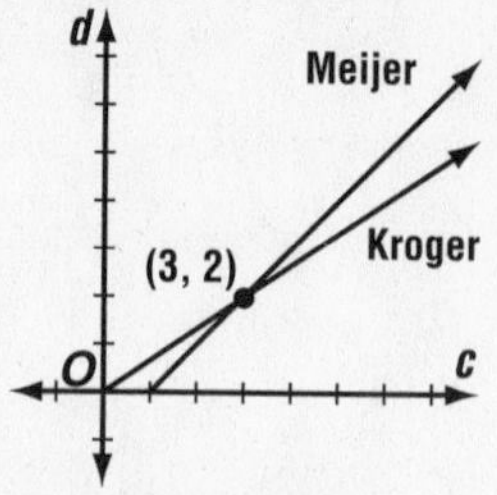

44b. the regular price where the discount prices would be the same

44c. For cereals that cost more than \$3, Kroger had the better deal.

44d. For cereals that cost less than \$3, Meijer had the better deal.

45. $9 - 2 = 7$
Let x = field goals and y = points after touchdown.

$x + y = 7$
$y = -x + 7$

$3x + y = 13$
$y = -3x + 13$

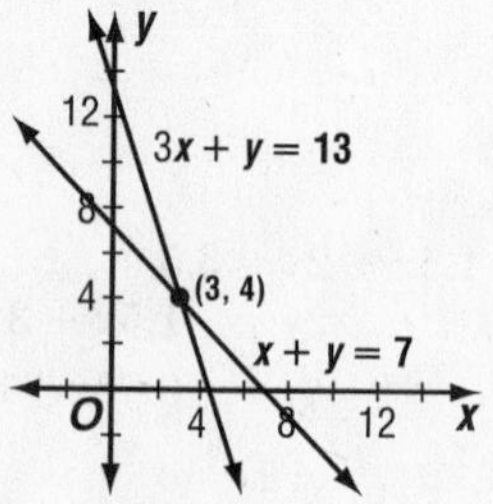

3 field goals, 4 points after

46. Photo Shop: $y = 1.60 + 0.11x$
Photos R Us: $y = 1.20 + 0.11x$
These lines are parallel. Photos R Us is always cheaper.

47a. butter

47b. about 1957

47c. Yes, the consumption of margarine has decreased in recent years.

47d. See students' work.

48. Let x = number of boys, y = number of girls.
$x^2 + y^2 = 25$

Guess $x = 4$ and $y = 5$.
$4^2 + 5^2 \stackrel{?}{=} 25$
$16 + 25 \stackrel{?}{=} 25$
$31 \neq 25$

Guess $x = 3$ and $y = 4$.
$3^2 + 4^2 \stackrel{?}{=} 25$
$9 + 16 \stackrel{?}{=} 25$
$25 = 25$

There are 3 + 4 or 7 children.

49. $y = |x| + 1$

x	$\|x\| + 1$	y
−1	$\|-1\| + 1$	2
0	$\|0\| + 1$	1
1	$\|1\| + 1$	2
2	$\|2\| + 1$	3

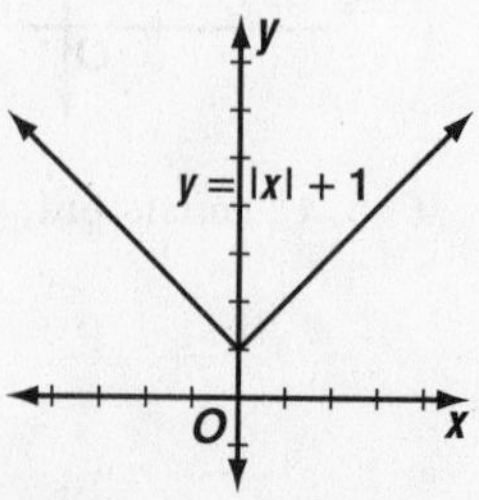

50. $d = 12.79t$; direct variation

51a. Sample answer:

$$m = \frac{44 - 38}{870 - 3240} = \frac{6}{-2370} = -0.003$$

$$y = mx + b$$
$$44 = -0.003(870) + b$$
$$44 = -2.61 + b$$
$$47 \approx b$$

$$y = -0.003x + 47$$

51b. $y = -0.003x + 47$
$= -0.003(3000) + 47$
$= -9 + 47$
$= 38$; about 38%

52. slope of $y = 8x - 4$ is 8, perpendicular slope is $-\frac{1}{8}$

$y = mx + b$
$7 = -\frac{1}{8}(-16) + b$
$7 = 2 + b$
$5 = b$
$y = -\frac{1}{8}x + 5$

53. perpendicular slope $= \frac{1}{3}$

Graph (4, −2), then go up 1 unit and 3 units to the right.

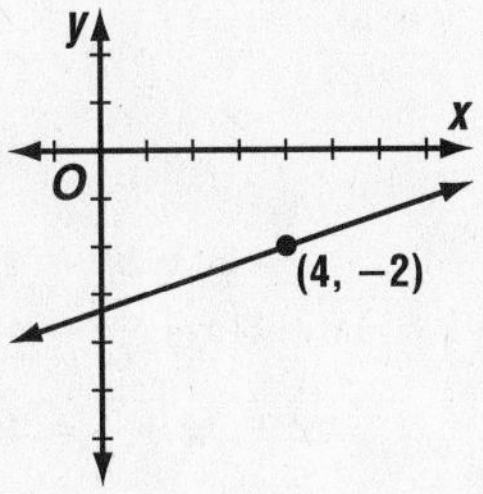

54. $m = \frac{y_2 - y_1}{x_2 - x_1} = \frac{2 - 4}{2 - 5} = \frac{-2}{-3} = \frac{2}{3}$

55. $x = \frac{1}{3}y + 3$
$x - \frac{1}{3}y = 3$
$3x - y = 9$

56. $[25 - (5 - 2)^2 + 5] \div 7 = [25 - 3^2 + 5] \div 7$
$= [25 - 9 + 5] \div 7$
$= 21 \div 7$
$= 3$

3-2 Solving Systems of Equations Algebraically

Page 137 Check for Understanding

1. By subtracting the equations, the variable c would disappear.

2. One of the equations is already solved for a variable, one of the variables has a coefficient of 1, or equations are in slope-intercept form.

3a. $y = 4x + 3 \rightarrow 4x + 3 = y$; $y = 2x - 5$
$4x + 3 = 2x - 5$

3b. Solve $4x + 3 = 2x - 5$ for x, and then use one equation to solve for y.

3c. $4x + 3 = 2x - 5$
$2x = -8$
$x = -4$

$y = 4x + 3$
$y = 4(-4) + 3$
$= -16 + 3$
$= -13$

(−4, −13)

4. Juanita; $-20 = 28$ is an incorrect statement; therefore there are no solutions, and the graph is parallel lines.

5. Let one cup represent x. $y = x + 2$ is represented by one cup and 2 positive counters. $x + 2y = -5$ is represented by one cup representing the x and 2 representations of $y = x + 2$. On the other side of the mat, place five negative counters.

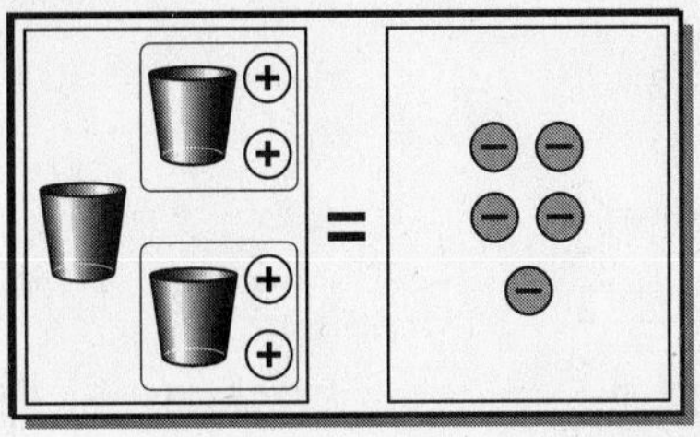

The value of x that solves the system is −3.
$y = x + 2$
$= -3 + 2$
$= -1$; The solution is (−3, −1).

6. $x + y = 4$
$x = 4 - y$

$x - 2y = 1$
$(4 - y) - 2y = 1$
$4 - 3y = 1$
$-3y = -3$
$y = 1$

$x + y = 4$
$x + 1 = 4$
$x = 3$

(3, 1)

7. $p - 3q = -17$
$p = 3q - 17$

$2p + 3q = 2$
$2(3q - 17) + 3q = 2$
$6q - 34 + 3q = 2$
$9q - 34 = 2$
$9q = 36$
$q = 4$

$p - 3q = -17$
$p - 3(4) = -17$
$p - 12 = -17$
$p = -5$
(−5, 4)

8. $m + n = 6$
$(+)\ m - n = 5$
$2m = 11$
$m = 5.5$

$m + n = 6$
$5.5 + n = 6$
$n = 0.5$
(5.5, 0.5)

9. $5x + 3y = 0 \rightarrow$ Multiply by $-4 \rightarrow -20x - 12y = 0$
$4x + 5y = 13 \rightarrow$ Multiply by $5 \rightarrow 20x + 25y = 65$

$-20x - 12y = 0$
$(+)\ 20x + 25y = 65$
$13y = 65$
$y = 5$

$5x + 3y = 0$
$5x + 3(5) = 0$
$5x + 15 = 0$
$5x = -15$
$x = -3$

(−3, 5)

10. $4a - b = 26$
$(-)\ 8a - b = 54$
$-4a = -28$
$a = 7$

$4a - b = 26$
$4(7) - b = 26$
$28 - b = 26$
$-b = -2$
$b = 2$

(7, 2)

11. $6x + 9y = -45 \rightarrow \quad \rightarrow 6x + 9y = -45$

$2x + 3y = -15 \rightarrow$ Multiply by $-3 \rightarrow -6x - 9y = 45$

$$\begin{aligned} 6x + 9y &= -45 \\ (+)\ -6x - 9y &= 45 \\ \hline 0 &= 0 \end{aligned}$$

true, so solution is infinite; $2x + 3y = -15$

12. $4s + t = 6$

$t = -4s + 6$

$$\begin{aligned} 3s - 2t &= 10 \\ 3s - 2(-4s + 6) &= 10 \\ 3s + 8s - 12 &= 10 \\ 11s - 12 &= 10 \\ 11s &= 22 \\ s &= 2 \end{aligned}$$

$$\begin{aligned} 4s + t &= 6 \\ 4(2) + t &= 6 \\ 8 + t &= 6 \\ t &= -2 \end{aligned}$$

$(2, -2)$

13.

$$\begin{aligned} \tfrac{1}{4}x + y &= \tfrac{7}{2} \\ (+)2x - y &= 4 \\ \hline \tfrac{9}{4}x \quad &= \tfrac{15}{2} \\ x &= \tfrac{10}{3} \end{aligned}$$

$$\begin{aligned} 2x - y &= 4 \\ 2\left(\tfrac{10}{3}\right) - y &= 4 \\ \tfrac{20}{3} - y &= 4 \\ -y &= -\tfrac{8}{3} \\ y &= \tfrac{8}{3} \end{aligned}$$

$\left(\frac{10}{3}, \frac{8}{3}\right)$

14. Let x = one angle and y = the other angle.

$x + y = 180$

$x = \frac{2}{3}y - 5$

$$\begin{aligned} x + y &= 180 \\ \left(\tfrac{2}{3}y - 5\right) + y &= 180 \\ \tfrac{5}{3}y - 5 &= 180 \\ \tfrac{5}{3}y &= 185 \\ y &= 111;\ 111° \end{aligned}$$

$$\begin{aligned} x &= \tfrac{2}{3}y - 5 \\ &= \tfrac{2}{3}(111) - 5 \\ &= 74 - 5 \\ &= 69;\ 69° \end{aligned}$$

Pages 137–140 Exercises

15. $3x + y = 7$

$y = -3x + 7$

$$\begin{aligned} 4x - 3y &= 18 \\ 4x - 3(-3x + 7) &= 18 \\ 4x + 9x - 21 &= 18 \\ 13x - 21 &= 18 \\ 13x &= 39 \\ x &= 3 \end{aligned}$$

$$\begin{aligned} 3x + y &= 7 \\ 3(3) + y &= 7 \\ 9 + y &= 7 \\ y &= -2 \end{aligned}$$

$(3, -2)$

16. $x + 3y = 13$

$x = -3y + 13$

$$\begin{aligned} -3x + 2y &= 27 \\ -3(-3y + 13) + 2y &= 27 \\ 9y - 39 + 2y &= 27 \\ 11y - 39 &= 27 \\ 11y &= 66 \\ y &= 6 \end{aligned}$$

$$\begin{aligned} x + 3y &= 13 \\ x + 3(6) &= 13 \\ x + 18 &= 13 \\ x &= -5 \end{aligned}$$

$(-5, 6)$

17. $r = 8s - 10$

$$\begin{aligned} 3r + 9s &= 36 \\ 3(8s - 10) + 9s &= 36 \\ 24s - 30 + 9s &= 36 \\ 33s - 30 &= 36 \\ 33s &= 66 \\ s &= 2 \end{aligned}$$

$$\begin{aligned} r &= 8s - 10 \\ &= 8(2) - 10 \\ &= 16 - 10 \\ &= 6 \end{aligned}$$

$(6, 2)$

18. $n = 3m + 7$

$$\begin{aligned} 4m + 9n &= 1 \\ 4m + 9(3m + 7) &= 1 \\ 4m + 27m + 63 &= 1 \\ 31m + 63 &= 1 \\ 31m &= -62 \\ m &= -2 \end{aligned}$$

$$\begin{aligned} n &= 3m + 7 \\ &= 3(-2) + 7 \\ &= -6 + 7 \\ &= 1 \end{aligned}$$

$(-2, 1)$

19. $2x - 10y = -11$

$-10y = -2x - 11$

$y = \frac{1}{5}x + \frac{11}{10}$

$$\begin{aligned} 4x + 6y &= -9 \\ 4x + 6\left(\tfrac{1}{5}x + \tfrac{11}{10}\right) &= -9 \\ 4x + \tfrac{6}{5}x + \tfrac{33}{5} &= -9 \\ \tfrac{26}{5}x + \tfrac{33}{5} &= -9 \\ \tfrac{26}{5}x &= -\tfrac{78}{5} \\ x &= -3 \end{aligned}$$

$$\begin{aligned} 4x + 6y &= -9 \\ 4(-3) + 6y &= -9 \\ -12 + 6y &= -9 \\ 6y &= 3 \\ y &= \tfrac{1}{2} \end{aligned}$$

$\left(-3, \frac{1}{2}\right)$

20. $6x - 6y = -1$

$-6y = -6x - 1$

$y = x + \frac{1}{6}$

$$\begin{aligned} 4x + 3y &= 4 \\ 4x + 3\left(x + \tfrac{1}{6}\right) &= 4 \\ 4x + 3x + \tfrac{1}{2} &= 4 \\ 7x + \tfrac{1}{2} &= 4 \\ 7x &= \tfrac{7}{2} \\ x &= \tfrac{1}{2} \end{aligned}$$

$$\begin{aligned} 4x + 3y &= 4 \\ 4\left(\tfrac{1}{2}\right) + 3y &= 4 \\ 2 + 3y &= 4 \\ 3y &= 2 \\ y &= \tfrac{2}{3} \end{aligned}$$

$\left(\frac{1}{2}, \frac{2}{3}\right)$

21. $x - 3y = -12 \rightarrow$ Multiply by $-2 \rightarrow -2x + 6y = 24$

$2x + 11y = -7 \rightarrow \quad \rightarrow 2x + 11y = -7$

$$\begin{aligned} -2x + 6y &= 24 \\ (+)\ 2x + 11y &= -7 \\ \hline 17y &= 17 \\ y &= 1 \end{aligned}$$

$$\begin{aligned} x - 3y &= -12 \\ x - 3(1) &= -12 \\ x - 3 &= -12 \\ x &= -9 \end{aligned}$$

$(-9, 1)$

22. $3x - 4y = 1 \rightarrow \quad \rightarrow 3x - 4y = 1$

$5x + 2y = 45 \rightarrow$ Multiply by $2 \rightarrow 10x + 4y = 90$

$$\begin{aligned} 3x - 4y &= 1 \\ (+)\ 10x + 4y &= 90 \\ \hline 13x \quad &= 91 \\ x &= 7 \end{aligned}$$

$$\begin{aligned} 3x - 4y &= 1 \\ 3(7) - 4y &= 1 \\ 21 - 4y &= 1 \\ -4y &= -20 \\ y &= 5 \end{aligned}$$

$(7, 5)$

23. $4p + 5q = 7 \rightarrow$ Multiply by 2 $\rightarrow 8p + 10q = 14$
$3p - 2q = 34 \rightarrow$ Multiply by 5 $\rightarrow 15p - 10q = 170$

$$\begin{array}{rl} 8p + 10q &= 14 \\ (+)\ 15p - 10q &= 170 \\ \hline 23p &= 184 \\ p &= 8 \end{array} \qquad \begin{array}{rl} 3p - 2q &= 34 \\ 3(8) - 2q &= 34 \\ 24 - 2q &= 34 \\ -2q &= 10 \\ q &= -5 \end{array}$$

$(8, -5)$

24. $5c - 6d = -27 \rightarrow \qquad \rightarrow 5c - 6d = -27$
$7c + 3d = -15 \rightarrow$ Multiply by 2 $\rightarrow 14c + 6d = -30$

$$\begin{array}{rl} 5c - 6d &= -27 \\ (+)\ 14c + 6d &= -30 \\ \hline 19c &= -57 \\ c &= -3 \end{array} \qquad \begin{array}{rl} 7c + 3d &= -15 \\ 7(-3) + 3d &= -15 \\ -21 + 3d &= -15 \\ 3d &= 6 \\ d &= 2 \end{array}$$

$(-3, 2)$

25. $\frac{1}{3}x + \frac{1}{2}y = 7 \rightarrow$ Multiply by 2 $\rightarrow \frac{2}{3}x + y = 14$
$\frac{2}{3}x - y = -2 \rightarrow \qquad \rightarrow \frac{2}{3}x - y = -2$

$$\begin{array}{rl} \frac{2}{3}x + y &= 14 \\ (+)\ \frac{2}{3}x - y &= -2 \\ \hline \frac{4}{3}x &= 12 \\ x &= 9 \end{array} \qquad \begin{array}{rl} \frac{2}{3}x - y &= -2 \\ \frac{2}{3}(9) - y &= -2 \\ 6 - y &= -2 \\ -y &= -8 \\ y &= 8 \end{array}$$

$(9, 8)$

26. $\frac{2}{5}x - \frac{1}{2}y = 6 \rightarrow$ Multiply by 3 $\rightarrow \frac{6}{5}x - \frac{3}{2}y = 18$
$\frac{4}{5}x + \frac{3}{2}y = -8 \rightarrow \qquad \rightarrow \frac{4}{5}x + \frac{3}{2}y = -8$

$$\begin{array}{rl} \frac{6}{5}x - \frac{3}{2}y &= 18 \\ (+)\ \frac{4}{5}x + \frac{3}{2}y &= -8 \\ \hline 2x &= 10 \\ x &= 5 \end{array} \qquad \begin{array}{rl} \frac{2}{5}x - \frac{1}{2}y &= 6 \\ \frac{2}{5}(5) - \frac{1}{2}y &= 6 \\ 2 - \frac{1}{2}y &= 6 \\ -\frac{1}{2}y &= 4 \\ y &= -8; \end{array}$$

$(5, -8)$

27. $x + 3y = -1$

$$\begin{array}{rl} x &= -3y - 1 \end{array} \qquad \begin{array}{rl} 3x - 7y &= 5 \\ 3(-3y - 1) - 7y &= 5 \\ -9y - 3 - 7y &= 5 \\ -16y - 3 &= 5 \\ -16y &= 8 \\ y &= -\frac{1}{2} \end{array}$$

$$\begin{array}{rl} x + 3y &= -1 \\ x + 3(-\frac{1}{2}) &= -1 \\ x - \frac{3}{2} &= -1 \\ x &= \frac{1}{2} \end{array}$$

$\left(\frac{1}{2}, -\frac{1}{2}\right)$

28. $2p - 5q = -53 \rightarrow$ Multiply by $-3 \rightarrow -6p + 15q = 159$
$6p + 7q = 39 \rightarrow \qquad \rightarrow 6p + 7q = 39$

$$\begin{array}{rl} -6p + 15q &= 159 \\ (+)\ 6p + 7q &= 39 \\ \hline 22q &= 198 \\ q &= 9 \end{array} \qquad \begin{array}{rl} 2p - 5q &= -53 \\ 2p - 5(9) &= -53 \\ 2p - 45 &= -53 \\ 2p &= -8 \\ p &= -4 \end{array}$$

$(-4, 9)$

29. $2a - b = 8 \rightarrow$ Multiply by $-3 \rightarrow -6a + 3b = -24$
$6a - 3b = -9 \rightarrow \qquad \rightarrow 6a - 3b = -9$

$$\begin{array}{rl} -6a + 3b &= -24 \\ (+)\ 6a - 3b &= -9 \\ \hline 0 &= -33 \end{array}$$

false, no solution

30. $3u + 5v = -12 \rightarrow$ Multiply by 3 $\rightarrow 9u + 15v = -36$
$2u - 3v = -8 \rightarrow$ Multiply by 5 $\rightarrow 10u - 15v = -40$

$$\begin{array}{rl} 9u + 15v &= -36 \\ (+)\ 10u - 15v &= -40 \\ \hline 19u &= -76 \\ u &= -4 \end{array} \qquad \begin{array}{rl} 2u - 3v &= -8 \\ 2(-4) - 3v &= -8 \\ -8 - 3v &= -8 \\ -3v &= 0 \\ v &= 0 \end{array}$$

$(-4, 0)$

31. $y = 5x + 37$

$$\begin{array}{rl} 2x - 3y &= -20 \\ 2x - 3(5x + 37) &= -20 \\ 2x - 15x - 111 &= -20 \\ -13x - 111 &= -20 \\ -13x &= 91 \\ x &= -7 \end{array} \qquad \begin{array}{rl} y &= 5x + 37 \\ &= 5(-7) + 37 \\ &= -35 + 37 \\ &= 2 \end{array}$$

$(-7, 2)$

32. $t = 4s + 3$

$$\begin{array}{rl} 5s - t &= 2 \\ 5s - (4s + 3) &= 2 \\ 5s - 4s - 3 &= 2 \\ s - 3 &= 2 \\ s &= 5 \end{array} \qquad \begin{array}{rl} t &= 4s + 3 \\ &= 4(5) + 3 \\ &= 20 + 3 \\ &= 23 \end{array}$$

$(5, 23)$

33. $y = 3x - 27$
$y = \frac{1}{2}x - 7$

$$\begin{array}{rl} 3x - 27 &= \frac{1}{2}x - 7 \\ \frac{5}{2}x - 27 &= -7 \\ \frac{5}{2}x &= 20 \\ x &= 8 \end{array} \qquad \begin{array}{rl} y &= \frac{1}{2}x - 7 \\ &= \frac{1}{2}(8) - 7 \\ &= 4 - 7 \\ &= -3 \end{array}$$

$(8, -3)$

34. $2.5m - 1.3n = -0.9 \rightarrow$ Multiply by $-4 \rightarrow$
$-10m + 5.2n = -3.6$
$10m - 5.2n = 3.6 \rightarrow \qquad \rightarrow 10m - 5.2n = 3.6$

$$\begin{array}{rl} -10m + 5.2n &= -3.6 \\ (+)\ 10m - 5.2n &= 3.6 \\ \hline 0 &= 0 \end{array}$$

true, infinite solutions; $2.5m - 1.3n = 0.9$

35. $\frac{1}{4}x + \frac{3}{5}y = -3 \rightarrow$ Multiply by $-3 \rightarrow -\frac{3}{4}x - \frac{9}{5}y = 9$
$\frac{3}{4}x - \frac{2}{5}y = 13 \rightarrow \qquad \rightarrow \frac{3}{4}x - \frac{2}{5}y = 13$

$$\begin{array}{rl} -\frac{3}{4}x - \frac{9}{5}y &= 9 \\ (+)\ \frac{3}{4}x - \frac{2}{5}y &= 13 \\ \hline -\frac{11}{5}y &= 22 \\ y &= -10 \end{array} \qquad \begin{array}{rl} \frac{1}{4}x + \frac{3}{5}y &= -3 \\ \frac{1}{4}x + \frac{3}{5}(-10) &= -3 \\ \frac{1}{4}x - 6 &= -3 \\ \frac{1}{4}x &= 3 \\ x &= 12 \end{array}$$

$(12, -10)$

36. $\frac{3}{5}s - \frac{1}{6}t = 1 \rightarrow$ Multiply by 5 $\rightarrow \frac{15}{5}s - \frac{5}{6}t = 5$
$\frac{1}{5}s + \frac{5}{6}t = 11 \rightarrow \qquad \rightarrow \frac{1}{5}s + \frac{5}{6}t = 11$

$$\begin{array}{rl} \frac{15}{5}s - \frac{5}{6}t &= 5 \\ (+)\ \frac{1}{5}s + \frac{5}{6}t &= 11 \\ \hline \frac{16}{5}s &= 16 \\ s &= 5 \end{array} \qquad \begin{array}{rl} \frac{3}{5}s - \frac{1}{6}t &= 1 \\ \frac{3}{5}(5) - \frac{1}{6}t &= 1 \\ 3 - \frac{1}{6}t &= 1 \\ -\frac{1}{6}t &= 2 \\ t &= 12 \end{array}$$

$(5, 12)$

37. $1.5a - 0.2b = -8.3 \rightarrow$ Multiply by 2 $\rightarrow$ $3a - 0.4b = -16.6$

$0.4a + 0.4b = -0.4 \rightarrow\ \rightarrow 0.4a + 0.4b = -0.4$

$3a - 0.4b = -16.6$
$(+)\ 0.4a + 0.4b = -0.4$
$3.4a = -17$
$a = -5$

$3a - 0.4b = -16.6$
$3(-5) - 0.4b = -16.6$
$-15 - 0.4b = -16.6$
$-0.4b = -1.6$
$b = 4$

$(-5, 4)$

38. $4m + 9n = 3 \rightarrow\ \rightarrow 4m + 9n = 3$

$8m - 3n = -8 \rightarrow$ Multiply by 3 $\rightarrow 24m - 9n = -24$

$4m + 9n = 3$
$(+) 24m - 9n = -24$
$28m = -21$
$m = -\frac{3}{4}$

$4m + 9n = 3$
$4\left(-\frac{3}{4}\right) + 9n = 3$
$-3 + 9n = 3$
$9n = 6$
$n = \frac{2}{3}$

$\left(-\frac{3}{4}, \frac{2}{3}\right)$

39. $x + 2y = 9$
$x = -2y + 9$

$5x - 3y = -7$
$5(-2y + 9) - 3y = -7$
$-10y + 45 - 3y = -7$
$-13y + 45 = -7$
$-13y = -52$
$y = 4$

$x + 2y = 9$
$x + 2(4) = 9$
$x + 8 = 9$
$x = 1$ $(1, 4)$

$5x - 3y = -7 \rightarrow$ Multiply by $-7 \rightarrow -35x + 21y = 49$
$3x - 7y = 1 \rightarrow$ Multiply by 3 $\rightarrow 9x - 21y = 3$

$-35x + 21y = 49$
$(+)\ 9x - 21y = 3$
$-26x = 52$
$x = -2$

$3x - 7y = 1$
$3(-2) - 7y = 1$
$-6 - 7y = 1$
$-7y = 7$
$y = -1$

$(-2, -1)$

$x + 2y = 9$
$x = -2y + 9$

$3x - 7y = 1$
$3(-2y + 9) - 7y = 1$
$-6y + 27 - 7y = 1$
$-13y + 27 = 1$
$-13y = -26$
$y = 2$

$x + 2y = 9$
$x + 2(2) = 9$
$x + 4 = 9$
$x = 5$ $(5, 2)$

40. $2x + y = -12$
$2x - y - 4 = 0 \rightarrow$

$2x + y = -12$
$(+) 2x - y = 4$
$4x = -8$
$x = -2$

$2x + y = -12$
$2(-2) + y = -12$
$-4 + y = -12$
$y = -8$

$(-2, -8)$

$2x + y = -12$
$(+)\ 2x - y = -8$
$4x = -20$
$x = -5$

$2x + y = -12$
$2(-5) + y = -12$
$-10 + y = -12$
$y = -2$

$(-5, -2)$

(Continued next column)

$2x - y = -8 \rightarrow$ Multiply by 2 $\rightarrow 4x - 2y = -16$
$4x + 2y = 24 \rightarrow\ \rightarrow 4x + 2y = 24$

$4x - 2y = -16$
$(+)\ 4x + 2y = 24$
$8x = 8$
$x = 1$

$2x - y = -8$
$2(1) - y = -8$
$2 - y = -8$
$-y = -10$
$y = 10$ $(1, 10)$

$2x - y - 4 = 0$
$-y - 4 = -2x$
$-y = -2x + 4$
$y = 2x + 4$

$4x + 2y = 24$
$4x + 2(2x - 4) = 24$
$4x + 4x - 8 = 24$
$8x - 8 = 24$
$8x = 32$
$x = 4$

$4x + 2y = 24$
$4(4) + 2y = 24$
$16 + 2y = 24$
$2y = 8$
$y = 4$ $(4, 4)$

41a. run program, $A = 1$, $B = -3$, $C = 6$, $D = 2$, $E = 6$, $F = 24$; $(9, 1)$

41b. run program, $A = 1$, $B = 4$, $C = 2$, $D = -1$, $E = 1$, $F = -7$; $(6, -1)$

41c. run program, $A = 2$, $B = -1$, $C = 36$, $D = 3$, $E = -.5$, $F = 26$; $(4, -28)$

41d. run program, $A = 2$, $B = 1$, $C = 45$, $D = 3$, $E = -1$, $F = 5$; $(10, 25)$

42. Let $n = \frac{1}{x}$ and $m = \frac{1}{y}$.

$\frac{1}{x} + \frac{3}{y} = \frac{3}{4} \rightarrow n + 3m = \frac{3}{4} \rightarrow -3n - 9m = -\frac{9}{4}$
$\frac{3}{x} - \frac{2}{y} = \frac{5}{12} \rightarrow 3n - 2m = \frac{5}{12} \rightarrow 3n - 2m = \frac{5}{12}$

$-3n - 9m = -\frac{9}{4}$
$(+)\ 3n - 2m = \frac{5}{12}$
$-11m = -\frac{11}{6}$
$m = \frac{1}{6}$

$n + 3m = \frac{3}{4}$
$n + 3\left(\frac{1}{6}\right) = \frac{3}{4}$
$n + \frac{1}{2} = \frac{3}{4}$
$n = \frac{1}{4}$

$n = \frac{1}{x}$
$\frac{1}{4} = \frac{1}{x}$
$x = 4$

$m = \frac{1}{y}$
$\frac{1}{6} = \frac{1}{y}$
$y = 6$ $(4, 6)$

43. Let x = cups of hot chocolate and y = cups of coffee.

$x + y = 295 \rightarrow x = 295 - y$
$0.75x + 0.50y = 200$
$0.75(295 - y) + 0.50y = 200$
$221.25 - 0.75y + 0.50y = 200$
$221.25 - 0.25y = 200$
$-0.25y = -21.25$
$y = 85$ cups of coffee

$x + y = 295$
$x + 85 = 295$
$x = 210$ cups hot chocolate

44. Let x = weight of Tweedledum and y = weight of Tweedledee.

$x + 2y = 362$
$x = -2y + 362$

$y + 2x = 361$
$y + 2(-2y + 362) = 361$
$y - 4y + 724 = 361$
$-3y + 724 = 361$
$-3y = -363$
$y = 121$ pounds

$x + 2y = 362$
$x + 2(121) = 362$
$x + 242 = 362$
$x = 120$ pounds

45a. $p = 17.99 + 0.43d$

45b. $3.67 - 2.72 = 0.95$; $p = 3.67 + 0.95d$

45c. $p = 17.99 + 0.43d$

$p = 3.67 + 0.95d$

$17.99 + 0.43d = 3.67 + 0.95d$

$17.99 = 3.67 + 0.52d$

$14.32 = 0.52d$

$27.5 \approx d$

$27.5 \times 10 = 275$; $1990 + 275 = 2265$; during the year 2265

46. $y = x$ $\quad y = -2.5x + 2.5$ $\quad y = x$

$y = -2.5y + 2.5$ $\quad \frac{5}{7} = x$

$3.5y = 2.5$

$y = \frac{2.5}{3.5}$

$y = \frac{5}{7}$ $\quad \left(\frac{5}{7}, \frac{5}{7}\right)$

47. Sample answer: 20¢ a mile or \$15 plus 10¢ a mile

48. $y = 2x - 5$ $\quad x + y = -3$

$y = -x - 3$

both y-intercepts negative; b

49. step function

50. $g(x) = |4x + 17|$

$g(-2) = |4(-2) + 17|$

$= |-8 + 17|$

$= |9|$

$= 9$

51a. Sample answer:

$m = \frac{32 - 25}{25 - 17}$ $\quad$ When $x = 0$, $y = 8$.

$= \frac{7}{8}$ $\quad y = \frac{7}{8}x + 8$

51b. $2010 - 1971 = 39$; $y = \frac{7}{8}x + 8$

$= \frac{7}{8}(39) + 8$

$= 34.125 + 8$

$= 42.125$; about 42¢

52. $-5x = 6 - 2y$

$-5x + 2y = 6$

$2y = 5x + 6$ $\quad$ slope $= \frac{5}{2}$

$y = \frac{5}{2}x + 3$ $\quad$ y-intercept $= 3$

53. $kx - 3y = 12$

$k(2) - 3(2) = 12$

$2k - 6 = 12$

$2k = 18$

$k = 9$

54. $x = 9$ is a vertical line.

x-intercept $= 9$

y-intercept $=$ none

55. 2, 3, 5, 7, 11, 13, 17, 19, 23, 29, 31

$\frac{2 + 3 + 5 + 7 + 11 + 13 + 17 + 19 + 23 + 29 + 31}{11} = \frac{160}{11} \approx$

14.55; 13; no mode

3-3 Cramer's Rule

Page 144 Check for Understanding

1. $\begin{vmatrix} 0 & a \\ 0 & b \end{vmatrix} = 0 \cdot b - 0 \cdot c = 0 - 0 = 0$

$\begin{vmatrix} 0 & 0 \\ a & b \end{vmatrix} = 0 \cdot b - a \cdot 0 = 0 - 0 = 0$

2. $\begin{vmatrix} a & b \\ c & d \end{vmatrix} = ad - bc$; $ad = bc$

3. The lines are parallel or coincident.

4. $e = 18$, $f = -4$, $a = 2$, $c = 3$, $b = -5$, $d = 8$, $2x - 5y = 18$, $3x + 8y = -4$

5. $\begin{vmatrix} 5 & 2 \\ 4 & 1 \end{vmatrix} = 5(1) - 4(2)$

$= -3$

6. $\begin{vmatrix} 6 & -2 \\ 7 & 3 \end{vmatrix} = 6(3) - 7(-2)$

$= 32$

7. $\begin{vmatrix} \frac{2}{5} & 6 \\ \frac{1}{3} & 2 \end{vmatrix} = \frac{2}{5}(2) - \frac{1}{3}(6)$

$= \frac{4}{5} - 2$

$= -\frac{6}{5}$

8. $x = \frac{\begin{vmatrix} 1 & -1 \\ 19 & 2 \end{vmatrix}}{\begin{vmatrix} 2 & -1 \\ 3 & 2 \end{vmatrix}}$ $\quad y = \frac{\begin{vmatrix} 2 & 1 \\ 3 & 19 \end{vmatrix}}{\begin{vmatrix} 2 & -1 \\ 3 & 2 \end{vmatrix}}$

$= \frac{1(2) - 19(-1)}{2(2) - 3(-1)}$ $\quad = \frac{2(19) - 3(1)}{2(2) - 3(-1)}$

$= \frac{21}{7}$ $\quad = \frac{35}{7}$

$= 3$ $\quad = 5$ $\quad (3, 5)$

9. $x = \frac{\begin{vmatrix} 8 & 2 \\ 7 & -3 \end{vmatrix}}{\begin{vmatrix} 5 & 2 \\ 2 & -3 \end{vmatrix}}$ $\quad y = \frac{\begin{vmatrix} 5 & 8 \\ 2 & 7 \end{vmatrix}}{\begin{vmatrix} 5 & 2 \\ 2 & -3 \end{vmatrix}}$

$= \frac{8(-3) - 7(2)}{5(-3) - 2(2)}$ $\quad = \frac{5(7) - 2(8)}{5(-3) - 2(2)}$

$= \frac{-38}{-19}$ $\quad = \frac{19}{-19}$

$= 2$ $\quad = -1$ $\quad (2, -1)$

10. $x = \frac{\begin{vmatrix} 0 & -\frac{1}{9} \\ 15 & 1 \end{vmatrix}}{\begin{vmatrix} \frac{1}{6} & -\frac{1}{9} \\ 1 & 1 \end{vmatrix}}$ $\quad y = \frac{\begin{vmatrix} \frac{1}{6} & 0 \\ 1 & 15 \end{vmatrix}}{\begin{vmatrix} \frac{1}{6} & -\frac{1}{9} \\ 1 & 1 \end{vmatrix}}$

$= \frac{0(1) - 15\left(-\frac{1}{9}\right)}{\frac{1}{6}(1) - 1\left(-\frac{1}{9}\right)}$ $\quad = \frac{\frac{1}{6}(15) - 1(0)}{\frac{1}{6}(1) - 1\left(-\frac{1}{9}\right)}$

$= \frac{\frac{5}{3}}{\frac{5}{18}}$ $\quad = \frac{\frac{5}{2}}{\frac{5}{18}}$

$= 6$ $\quad = 9$ $\quad (6, 9)$

11. $m = \frac{\begin{vmatrix} 2 & -5 \\ -5 & 4 \end{vmatrix}}{\begin{vmatrix} 2 & -5 \\ 3 & 4 \end{vmatrix}}$ $\quad n = \frac{\begin{vmatrix} 2 & 2 \\ 3 & -5 \end{vmatrix}}{\begin{vmatrix} 2 & -5 \\ 3 & 4 \end{vmatrix}}$

$= \frac{2(4) - (-5)(-5)}{2(4) - 3(-5)}$ $\quad = \frac{2(-5) - 3(2)}{2(4) - 3(-5)}$

$= \frac{-17}{23}$ $\quad = \frac{-16}{23}$ $\quad \left(-\frac{17}{23}, -\frac{16}{23}\right)$

12. $x = \dfrac{\begin{vmatrix} -4 & 1 \\ -9 & -3 \end{vmatrix}}{\begin{vmatrix} 4 & 1 \\ 2 & -3 \end{vmatrix}}$ $\quad y = \dfrac{\begin{vmatrix} 4 & -4 \\ 2 & -9 \end{vmatrix}}{\begin{vmatrix} 4 & 1 \\ 2 & -3 \end{vmatrix}}$

$= \dfrac{-4(-3) - (-9)(1)}{4(-3) - 2(1)}$ $\quad = \dfrac{4(-9) - 2(-4)}{4(-3) - 2(1)}$

$= \dfrac{21}{-14}$ $\quad = \dfrac{-28}{-14}$

$= -\dfrac{3}{2}$ $\quad = 2$ $\quad \left(-\dfrac{3}{2}, 2\right)$

Pages 144–146 Exercises

13. $\begin{vmatrix} 8 & 5 \\ 6 & -2 \end{vmatrix} = 8(-2) - 6(5)$
$= -46$

14. $\begin{vmatrix} -2 & 4 \\ 8 & -7 \end{vmatrix} = -2(-7) - 8(4)$
$= -18$

15. $\begin{vmatrix} -8 & 3 \\ -9 & 7 \end{vmatrix} = -8(7) - (-9)(3)$
$= -29$

16. $\begin{vmatrix} -6 & -2 \\ 8 & 5 \end{vmatrix} = -6(5) - 8(-2)$
$= -14$

17. $\begin{vmatrix} 2 & -7 \\ -5 & 3 \end{vmatrix} = 2(3) - (-5)(-7)$
$= -29$

18. $\begin{vmatrix} 21 & 43 \\ 17 & -29 \end{vmatrix} = 21(-29) - 17(43)$
$= -1340$

19. $\begin{vmatrix} -54 & 39 \\ 18 & -13 \end{vmatrix} = -54(-13) - 18(39)$
$= 0$

20. $\begin{vmatrix} -3.2 & -5.8 \\ 4.1 & 3.9 \end{vmatrix} = -3.2(3.9) - 4.1(-5.8)$
$= 11.3$

21. $\begin{vmatrix} 7 & -5.2 \\ 1.3 & 2.29 \end{vmatrix} = 7(2.29) - 1.3(-5.2)$
$= 22.79$

22. $x = \dfrac{\begin{vmatrix} 13 & 7 \\ 13 & -5 \end{vmatrix}}{\begin{vmatrix} 5 & 7 \\ 2 & -5 \end{vmatrix}}$ $\quad y = \dfrac{\begin{vmatrix} 5 & 13 \\ 2 & 13 \end{vmatrix}}{\begin{vmatrix} 5 & 7 \\ 2 & -5 \end{vmatrix}}$

$= \dfrac{13(-5) - 13(7)}{5(-5) - 2(7)}$ $\quad = \dfrac{5(13) - 2(13)}{5(-5) - 2(7)}$

$= \dfrac{-156}{-39}$ $\quad = \dfrac{39}{-39}$

$= 4$ $\quad = -1$ $\quad (4, -1)$

23. $a = \dfrac{\begin{vmatrix} 33 & 5 \\ 51 & 7 \end{vmatrix}}{\begin{vmatrix} 3 & 5 \\ 5 & 7 \end{vmatrix}}$ $\quad b = \dfrac{\begin{vmatrix} 3 & 33 \\ 5 & 51 \end{vmatrix}}{\begin{vmatrix} 3 & 5 \\ 5 & 7 \end{vmatrix}}$

$= \dfrac{33(7) - 51(5)}{3(7) - 5(5)}$ $\quad = \dfrac{3(51) - 5(33)}{3(7) - 5(5)}$

$= \dfrac{-24}{-4}$ $\quad = \dfrac{-12}{-4}$

$= 6$ $\quad = 3$ $\quad (6, 3)$

24. $m = \dfrac{\begin{vmatrix} 4 & 7 \\ -20 & -2 \end{vmatrix}}{\begin{vmatrix} 2 & 7 \\ 1 & -2 \end{vmatrix}}$ $\quad n = \dfrac{\begin{vmatrix} 2 & 4 \\ 1 & -20 \end{vmatrix}}{\begin{vmatrix} 2 & 7 \\ 1 & -2 \end{vmatrix}}$

$= \dfrac{4(-2) - (-20)(7)}{2(-2) - 1(7)}$ $\quad = \dfrac{2(-20) - 1(4)}{2(-2) - 1(7)}$

$= \dfrac{132}{-11}$ $\quad = \dfrac{-44}{-11}$

$= -12$ $\quad = 4$ $\quad (-12, 4)$

25. $x = \dfrac{\begin{vmatrix} 4 & -2 \\ 1 & -\frac{2}{3} \end{vmatrix}}{\begin{vmatrix} 3 & -2 \\ \frac{1}{2} & -\frac{2}{3} \end{vmatrix}}$ $\quad y = \dfrac{\begin{vmatrix} 3 & 4 \\ \frac{1}{2} & 1 \end{vmatrix}}{\begin{vmatrix} 3 & -2 \\ \frac{1}{2} & -\frac{2}{3} \end{vmatrix}}$

$= \dfrac{4\left(-\frac{2}{3}\right) - 1(-2)}{3\left(-\frac{2}{3}\right) - \frac{1}{2}(-2)}$ $\quad = \dfrac{3(1) - \frac{1}{2}(4)}{3\left(-\frac{2}{3}\right) - \frac{1}{2}(-2)}$

$= \dfrac{-\frac{8}{3} + 2}{-2 + 1}$ $\quad = \dfrac{1}{-1}$

$= \dfrac{-\frac{2}{3}}{-1}$ $\quad = -1$

$= \dfrac{2}{3}$ $\quad \left(\dfrac{2}{3}, -1\right)$

26. $x = \dfrac{\begin{vmatrix} 0.5 & 0.7 \\ -7.4 & -0.6 \end{vmatrix}}{\begin{vmatrix} 1.5 & 0.7 \\ 2.2 & -0.6 \end{vmatrix}}$ $\quad y = \dfrac{\begin{vmatrix} 1.5 & 0.5 \\ 2.2 & -7.4 \end{vmatrix}}{\begin{vmatrix} 1.5 & 0.7 \\ 2.2 & -0.6 \end{vmatrix}}$

$= \dfrac{0.5(-0.6) - (-7.4)(0.7)}{1.5(-0.6) - 2.2(0.7)}$ $\quad = \dfrac{1.5(-7.4) - 2.2(0.5)}{1.5(-0.6) - 2.2(0.7)}$

$= \dfrac{4.88}{-2.44}$ $\quad = \dfrac{-12.2}{-2.44}$

$= -2$ $\quad = 5$ $\quad (-2, 5)$

27. $u = \dfrac{\begin{vmatrix} 6 & 3 \\ -9 & -1 \end{vmatrix}}{\begin{vmatrix} 4 & 3 \\ 8 & -1 \end{vmatrix}}$ $\quad v = \dfrac{\begin{vmatrix} 4 & 6 \\ 8 & -9 \end{vmatrix}}{\begin{vmatrix} 4 & 3 \\ 8 & -1 \end{vmatrix}}$

$= \dfrac{6(-1) - (-9)(3)}{4(-1) - 8(3)}$ $\quad = \dfrac{4(-9) - 8(6)}{4(-1) - 8(3)}$

$= \dfrac{21}{-28}$ $\quad = \dfrac{-84}{-28}$

$= -\dfrac{3}{4}$ $\quad = 3$ $\quad \left(-\dfrac{3}{4}, 3\right)$

28. $r = \dfrac{\begin{vmatrix} -4 & \frac{3}{4} \\ 10 & -\frac{7}{8} \end{vmatrix}}{\begin{vmatrix} \frac{1}{2} & \frac{3}{4} \\ \frac{3}{4} & -\frac{7}{8} \end{vmatrix}}$ $\quad s = \dfrac{\begin{vmatrix} \frac{1}{2} & -4 \\ \frac{3}{4} & 10 \end{vmatrix}}{\begin{vmatrix} \frac{1}{2} & \frac{3}{4} \\ \frac{3}{4} & -\frac{7}{8} \end{vmatrix}}$

$= \dfrac{-4\left(-\frac{7}{8}\right) - 10\left(\frac{3}{4}\right)}{\frac{1}{2}\left(-\frac{7}{8}\right) - \frac{3}{4}\left(\frac{3}{4}\right)}$ $\quad = \dfrac{\frac{1}{2}(10) - \frac{3}{4}(-4)}{\frac{1}{2}\left(-\frac{7}{8}\right) - \frac{3}{4}\left(\frac{3}{4}\right)}$

$= \dfrac{\frac{7}{2} - \frac{15}{2}}{-\frac{7}{16} - \frac{9}{16}}$ $\quad = \dfrac{8}{-1}$

$= \dfrac{-4}{-1}$ $\quad = -8$

$= 4$ $\quad (4, -8)$

29. $x = \dfrac{\begin{vmatrix} 5 & \frac{2}{5} \\ -3 & -\frac{1}{2} \end{vmatrix}}{\begin{vmatrix} \frac{1}{3} & \frac{2}{5} \\ \frac{2}{3} & -\frac{1}{2} \end{vmatrix}}$ $\quad y = \dfrac{\begin{vmatrix} \frac{1}{3} & 5 \\ \frac{2}{3} & -3 \end{vmatrix}}{\begin{vmatrix} \frac{1}{3} & \frac{2}{5} \\ \frac{2}{3} & -\frac{1}{2} \end{vmatrix}}$

$= \dfrac{5\left(-\frac{1}{2}\right) - (-3)\left(\frac{2}{5}\right)}{\frac{1}{3}\left(-\frac{1}{2}\right) - \frac{2}{3}\left(\frac{2}{5}\right)}$ $\quad = \dfrac{\frac{1}{3}(-3) - \frac{2}{3}(5)}{\frac{1}{3}\left(-\frac{1}{2}\right) - \frac{2}{3}\left(\frac{2}{5}\right)}$

$= \dfrac{-\frac{5}{2} + \frac{6}{5}}{-\frac{1}{6} - \frac{4}{15}}$ $\quad = \dfrac{-1 - \frac{10}{3}}{\frac{-13}{30}}$

$= \dfrac{-\frac{13}{10}}{-\frac{13}{30}}$ $\quad = \dfrac{\frac{-13}{3}}{\frac{-13}{30}}$

$= 3$ $\quad = 10$ $\quad (3, 10)$

30. $x = \dfrac{\begin{vmatrix} -1 & -1 \\ -\frac{1}{4} & \frac{1}{2} \end{vmatrix}}{\begin{vmatrix} \frac{1}{2} & -1 \\ \frac{3}{4} & \frac{1}{2} \end{vmatrix}}$ $\quad y = \dfrac{\begin{vmatrix} \frac{1}{2} & -1 \\ \frac{3}{4} & -\frac{1}{4} \end{vmatrix}}{\begin{vmatrix} \frac{1}{2} & -1 \\ \frac{3}{4} & \frac{1}{2} \end{vmatrix}}$

$= \dfrac{-1\left(\frac{1}{2}\right) - \left(-\frac{1}{4}\right)(-1)}{\frac{1}{2}\left(\frac{1}{2}\right) - \frac{3}{4}(-1)}$ $\quad = \dfrac{\frac{1}{2}\left(-\frac{1}{4}\right) - \frac{3}{4}(-1)}{\frac{1}{2}\left(\frac{1}{2}\right) - \frac{3}{4}(-1)}$

$= \dfrac{-\frac{3}{4}}{1}$ $\quad = \dfrac{\frac{5}{8}}{1}$

$= -\frac{3}{4}$ $\quad = \frac{5}{8}$ $\quad \left(-\frac{3}{4}, \frac{5}{8}\right)$

31. $a = \dfrac{\begin{vmatrix} \frac{11}{12} & \frac{1}{2} \\ \frac{1}{8} & -\frac{1}{4} \end{vmatrix}}{\begin{vmatrix} \frac{3}{4} & \frac{1}{2} \\ \frac{1}{2} & -\frac{1}{4} \end{vmatrix}}$ $\quad b = \dfrac{\begin{vmatrix} \frac{3}{4} & \frac{11}{12} \\ \frac{1}{2} & \frac{1}{8} \end{vmatrix}}{\begin{vmatrix} \frac{3}{4} & \frac{1}{2} \\ \frac{1}{2} & -\frac{1}{4} \end{vmatrix}}$

$= \dfrac{\frac{11}{12}\left(-\frac{1}{4}\right) - \frac{1}{8}\left(\frac{1}{2}\right)}{\frac{3}{4}\left(-\frac{1}{4}\right) - \frac{1}{2}\left(\frac{1}{2}\right)}$ $\quad = \dfrac{\frac{3}{4}\left(\frac{1}{8}\right) - \frac{1}{2}\left(\frac{11}{12}\right)}{\frac{3}{4}\left(-\frac{1}{4}\right) - \frac{1}{2}\left(\frac{1}{2}\right)}$

$= \dfrac{-\frac{14}{48}}{-\frac{7}{16}}$ $\quad = \dfrac{-\frac{35}{96}}{-\frac{7}{16}}$

$= \frac{2}{3}$ $\quad = \frac{5}{6}$ $\quad \left(\frac{2}{3}, \frac{5}{6}\right)$

32. $0.2a = 0.3b$

$0.2a - 0.3b = 0$

$a = \dfrac{\begin{vmatrix} 0 & -0.3 \\ 0.2 & -0.2 \end{vmatrix}}{\begin{vmatrix} 0.2 & -0.3 \\ 0.4 & -0.2 \end{vmatrix}}$ $\quad b = \dfrac{\begin{vmatrix} 0.2 & 0 \\ 0.4 & 0.2 \end{vmatrix}}{\begin{vmatrix} 0.2 & -0.3 \\ 0.4 & -0.2 \end{vmatrix}}$

$= \dfrac{0(-0.2) - 0.2(-0.3)}{0.2(-0.2) - 0.4(-0.3)}$ $\quad = \dfrac{0.2(0.2) - 0.4(0)}{0.2(-0.2) - 0.4(-0.3)}$

$= \dfrac{0.06}{0.08}$ $\quad = \dfrac{0.04}{0.08}$

$= 0.75$ $\quad = 0.5$ $\quad (0.75, 0.5)$

33. $2(x - y) = 10$

$2x - 2y = 10$

$x = \dfrac{\begin{vmatrix} -5 & 4 \\ 10 & -2 \end{vmatrix}}{\begin{vmatrix} 3.5 & 4 \\ 2 & -2 \end{vmatrix}}$ $\quad y = \dfrac{\begin{vmatrix} 3.5 & -5 \\ 2 & 10 \end{vmatrix}}{\begin{vmatrix} 3.5 & 4 \\ 2 & -2 \end{vmatrix}}$

$= \dfrac{-5(-2) - 10(4)}{3.5(-2) - 2(4)}$ $\quad = \dfrac{3.5(10) - 2(-5)}{3.5(-2) - 2(4)}$

$= \dfrac{-30}{-15}$ $\quad = \dfrac{45}{-15}$

$= 2$ $\quad = -3$ $\quad (2, -3)$

34. $x - 4y = -6$
$5x + y = 33$

$$x = \frac{\begin{vmatrix} -6 & -4 \\ 33 & 1 \end{vmatrix}}{\begin{vmatrix} 1 & -4 \\ 5 & 1 \end{vmatrix}} = \frac{(-6)(1) - 33(-4)}{1(1) - 5(-4)} = \frac{126}{21} = 6$$

$$y = \frac{\begin{vmatrix} 1 & -6 \\ 5 & 33 \end{vmatrix}}{\begin{vmatrix} 1 & -4 \\ 5 & 1 \end{vmatrix}} = \frac{1(33) - 5(-6)}{1(1) - 5(-4)} = \frac{63}{21} = 3$$

(6, 3)

$x - 4y = -6$
$2x - y = 2$

$$x = \frac{\begin{vmatrix} -6 & -4 \\ 2 & -1 \end{vmatrix}}{\begin{vmatrix} 1 & -4 \\ 2 & -1 \end{vmatrix}} = \frac{-6(-1) - 2(-4)}{1(-1) - 2(-4)} = \frac{14}{7} = 2$$

$$y = \frac{\begin{vmatrix} 1 & -6 \\ 2 & 2 \end{vmatrix}}{\begin{vmatrix} 1 & -4 \\ 2 & -1 \end{vmatrix}} = \frac{1(2) - 2(-6)}{1(-1) - 2(-4)} = \frac{14}{7} = 2$$

(2, 2)

$5x + y = 33$
$2x - y = 2$

$$x = \frac{\begin{vmatrix} 33 & 1 \\ 2 & -1 \end{vmatrix}}{\begin{vmatrix} 5 & 1 \\ 2 & -1 \end{vmatrix}} = \frac{33(-1) - 2(1)}{5(-1) - 2(1)} = \frac{-35}{-7} = 5$$

$$y = \frac{\begin{vmatrix} 5 & 33 \\ 2 & 2 \end{vmatrix}}{\begin{vmatrix} 5 & 1 \\ 2 & -1 \end{vmatrix}} = \frac{5(2) - 2(33)}{5(-1) - 2(1)} = \frac{-56}{-7} = 8$$

(5, 8)

35. In both cases, the denominator is 0. If the numerator is also 0, there is an infinite number of solutions. If the numerator is not 0, there are no solutions.

36. Men's: $y = 72.43 - 2.42x$
$2.42x + y = 72.43$
Women's: $y = 78.74 - 3.16x$
$3.16x + y = 78.74$

$$x = \frac{\begin{vmatrix} 72.43 & 1 \\ 78.74 & 1 \end{vmatrix}}{\begin{vmatrix} 2.42 & 1 \\ 3.16 & 1 \end{vmatrix}} = \frac{-6.31}{-0.74} \approx 9$$

Winter Olympics are held every four years. The women's times will be faster than the men's: 1994 + 9(4) = 2030; the 2030 Winter Olympics.

37. $\frac{30 \text{ miles}}{\text{hour}} \cdot \frac{1 \text{ hour}}{60 \text{ min}} = \frac{1}{2}$ mile/min

$\frac{5 \text{ miles}}{\text{hour}} \cdot \frac{1 \text{ hour}}{60 \text{ min}} = \frac{1}{12}$ mile/min

Let x = time riding and y = time walking.

$x + y = 75$
$\frac{1}{2}x + \frac{1}{12}y = 18$

$$x = \frac{\begin{vmatrix} 75 & 1 \\ 18 & \frac{1}{12} \end{vmatrix}}{\begin{vmatrix} 1 & 1 \\ \frac{1}{2} & \frac{1}{12} \end{vmatrix}} = \frac{75\left(\frac{1}{12}\right) - 18(1)}{1\left(\frac{1}{12}\right) - \frac{1}{2}(1)} = \frac{-11.75}{-\frac{5}{12}} = 28.2;\ 28.2 \text{ minutes}$$

38. Let x = New York voters and y = Texas voters.
Clinton: $0.50x + 0.37y = 5{,}700{,}000$
Bush: $0.34x + 0.41y = 4{,}800{,}000$

$$x = \frac{\begin{vmatrix} 5{,}700{,}000 & 0.37 \\ 4{,}800{,}000 & 0.41 \end{vmatrix}}{\begin{vmatrix} 0.50 & 0.37 \\ 0.34 & 0.41 \end{vmatrix}} = \frac{5{,}700{,}000(0.41) - 4{,}800{,}000(0.37)}{0.50(0.41) - 0.34(0.37)} = \frac{561{,}000}{0.0792} \approx 7{,}083{,}333.333$$

about 7,100,000 people

$$y = \frac{\begin{vmatrix} 0.50 & 5{,}700{,}000 \\ 0.34 & 4{,}800{,}000 \end{vmatrix}}{\begin{vmatrix} 0.50 & 0.37 \\ 0.34 & 0.41 \end{vmatrix}} = \frac{0.50(4{,}800{,}000) - 0.34(5{,}700{,}000)}{0.50(0.41) - 0.34(0.37)} = \frac{462{,}000}{0.0792} \approx 5{,}833{,}333.333$$

about 5,800,000 people

39. $2x + y = 0$
$y = -2x$

$5x + 3y = 1$
$5x + 3(-2x) = 1$
$5x - 6x = 1$
$-1x = 1$
$x = -1$

$2x + y = 0$
$2(-1) + y = 0$
$-2 + y = 0$
$y = 2$
(−1, 2)

40. Let x = cost of film and y = cost of batteries.

$8x + 2y = 23$
$6x + 2y = 18$

$8x + 2y = 23$
$(-)\ 6x + 2y = 18$
$2x = 5$
$x = 2.50$

$8x + 2y = 23$
$8(2.50) + 2y = 23$
$20 + 2y = 23$
$2y = 3$
$y = 1.50$

film: \$2.50, batteries: \$1.50

41. $y = -3x$
$y - x = 4$
$y = x + 4$
$(-1, 3)$; consistent and independent

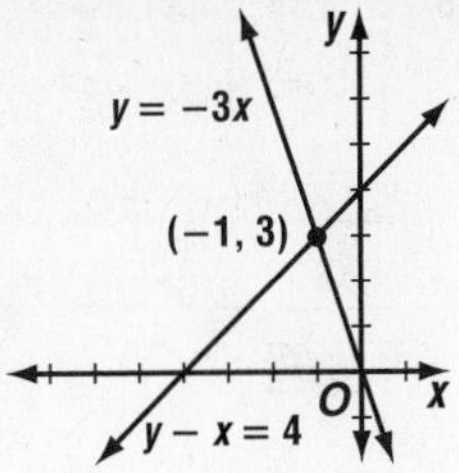

42. $f(x) = [5x - 3]$
$f\left(-\frac{1}{2}\right) = \left[5\left(-\frac{1}{2}\right) - 3\right]$
$= [-2.5 - 3]$
$= [-5.5]$
$= -6$

43. $m = \frac{3 - (-5)}{0 - 8}$
$= \frac{8}{-8}$
$= -1$

When $x = 0$, $y = 3$.
$y = -x + 3$

44. $\frac{w - 6}{3} \leq 6 - w$
$w - 6 \leq 18 - 3w$
$4w - 6 \leq 18$
$4w \leq 24$
$w \leq 6$
$\{w \mid w \leq 6\}$

45. $A = \frac{1}{2}h(b_1 + b_2)$
$= \frac{1}{2}(10)(15 + 9)$
$= \frac{1}{2}(10)(24)$
$= 120$; 120 square units

Page 146 Mathematics and Society

1. ability to perform more work in less time, ability to solve complex and newer problems that previously could not be solved, and less need to buy and maintain as many computers
2. Answers will vary. Sample answer: people passing through many gates instead of just one to enter a stadium
3. If it works, we will have a powerful new tool to use and new applications to be developed. We will find solutions to problems that were previously too large to solve. If it doesn't work, we will learn that our knowledge of quantum mechanics is incomplete and/or incorrect. We may need to try a new way to build quantum computers, or perhaps we'll learn that they cannot be built at all.

3-4A Graphing Technology: Systems of Linear Inequalities

Page 147 Exercises

1. [ZOOM] 6 [2nd] [DRAW] 7 [X,T,θ,n] [,] 5 [)] [ENTER]

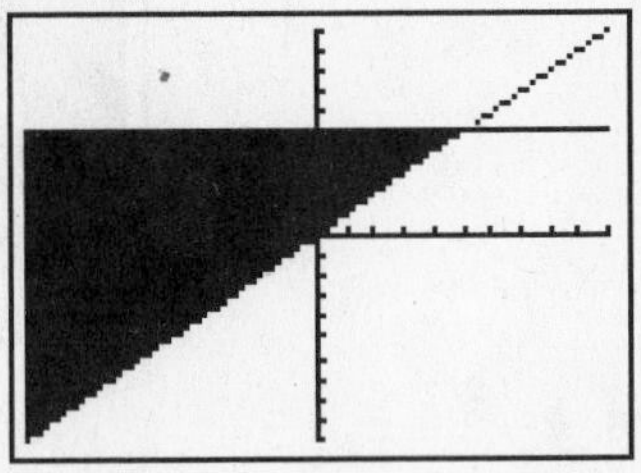

2. [ZOOM] 6 [2nd] [DRAW] 7 [(−)] 2 [X,T,θ,n] [+] 4 [,] [X,T,θ,n] [−] 1 [)] [ENTER]

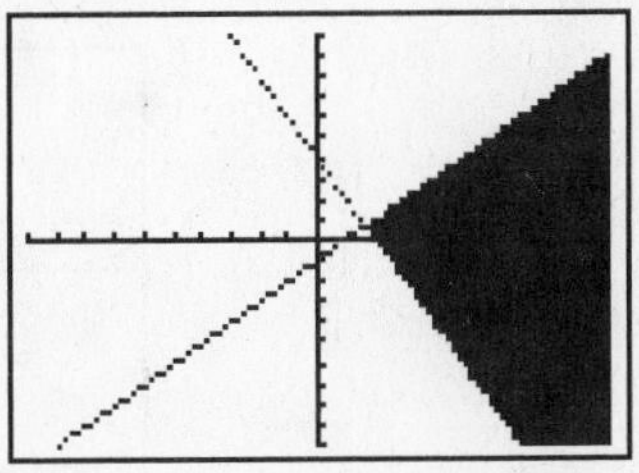

3. [ZOOM] 6 [2nd] [DRAW] 7...0.5 [X,T,θ,n] [,] 6 [X,T,θ,n] [−] 3 [)] [ENTER]

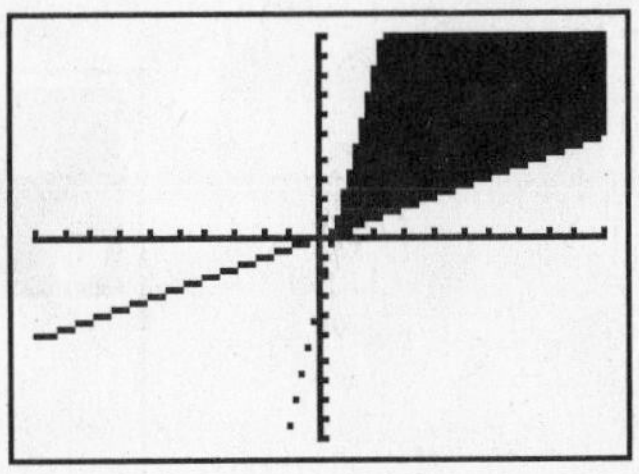

4. [ZOOM] 6 [2nd] [DRAW] 7 [(−)] 0.5 [X,T,θ,n] [−] 3 [,] 0.1 [X,T,θ,n] [+] 1 [)] [ENTER]

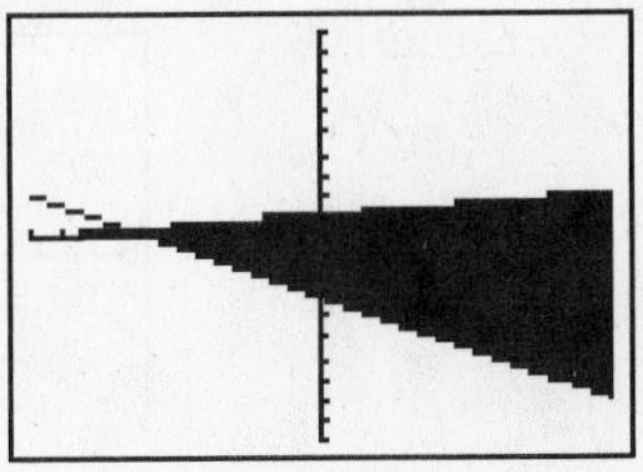

5. $3x - 4y \le 12$ $\quad\quad 2x + y \le 10$

$-4y \le -3x + 12 \quad\quad y \le -2x + 10$

$y \ge \frac{3}{4}x - 3$

ZOOM 6 2nd DRAW 7 (3 ÷ 4)
X,T,θ,n − 3 , (−) 2 X,T,θ,n + 10)
ENTER

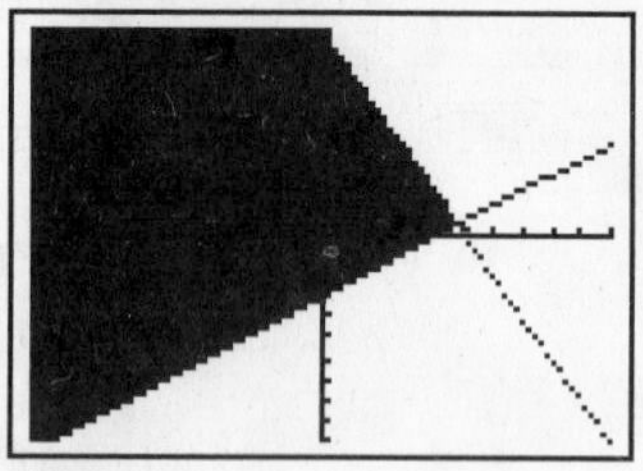

6. $y - 2 \le x$ $\quad\quad y \ge -3x + 5$

$y \le x + 2$

ZOOM 6 2nd DRAW 7 (−) 3 X,T,θ,n + 5
, X,T,θ,n + 2) ENTER

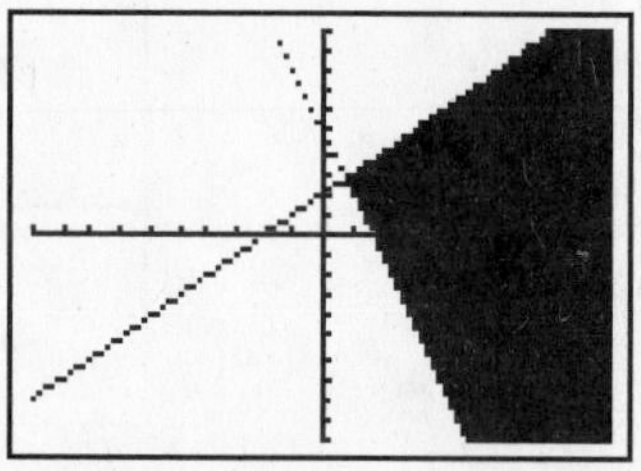

7. ZOOM 6 2nd DRAW 7...0 , (−) 2 X,T,θ,n
+ 12) ENTER

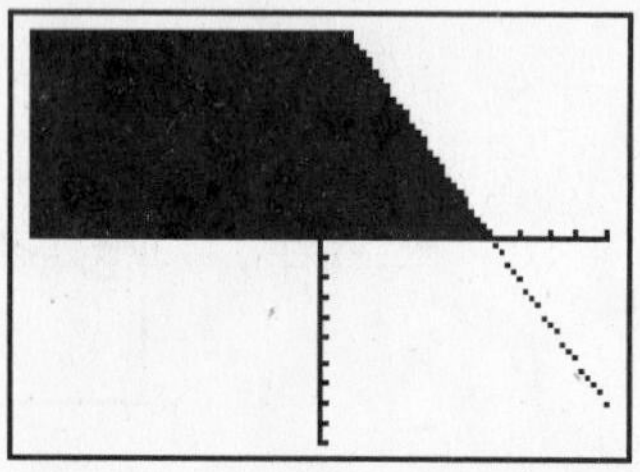

8. ZOOM 6 2nd DRAW 7 (−) (1 ÷ 5)
X,T,θ,n + 3 , (2 ÷ 3) X,T,θ,n −
1) ENTER

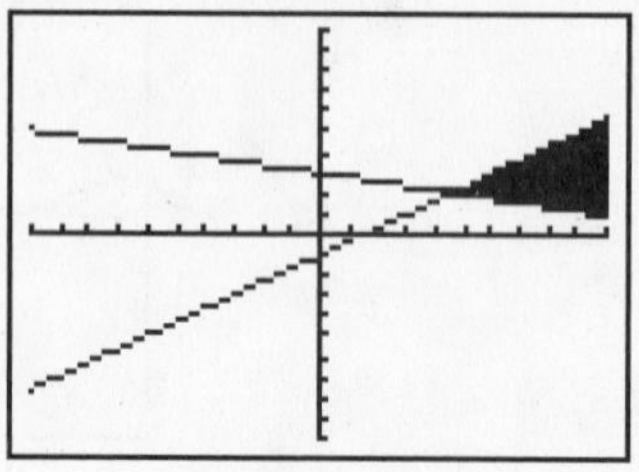

9. $-5y \le -2x$ $\quad\quad 2y \le 3x - 8$

$y \ge \frac{2}{5}x \quad\quad y \le \frac{3}{2}x - 4$

ZOOM 6 2nd DRAW 7 (2 ÷ 5)
X,T,θ,n , (3 ÷ 2) X,T,θ,n − 4)
ENTER

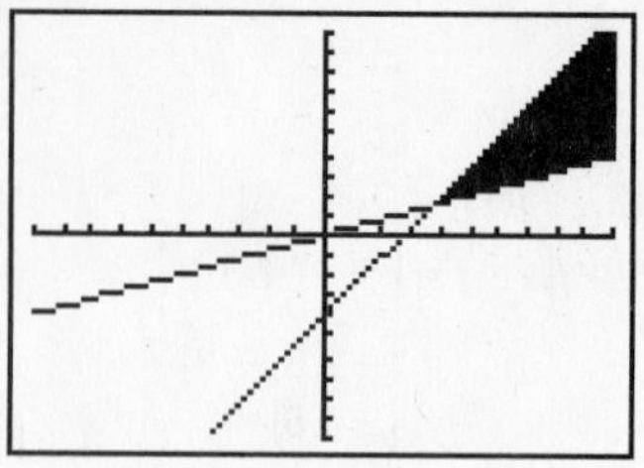

3-4 Graphing Systems of Inequalities

Page 150 Check for Understanding

1. When the coordinates of the point are substituted into each inequality, the resulting statements are true.

2a. two separate regions

2b. no overlapping regions, no solution

3. $|x| \ge 2$ is equivalent to $x > 2$ or $x \le -2$ which is two separate regions. $|x| \le 2$ is equivalent to $x \ge -2$ and $x \le 2$, which is a single overlapping region.

4.

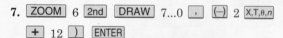

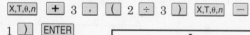

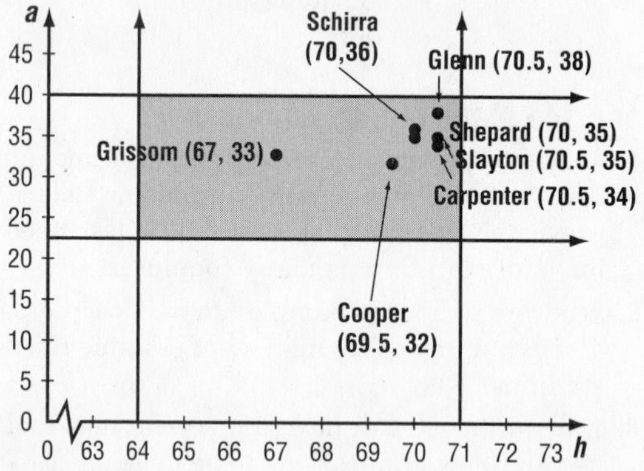

Sample answer: The astronauts ages were between 22 and 40 and their heights between 64 and 71 inches.

5. Sample answer: $x < 5$ and $x > 7$

6. See students' work.

7. Test (0, 5).

$x + y \ge 1 \quad\quad x - y \le 0$

$0 + 5 \overset{?}{\ge} 1 \quad\quad 0 - 5 \overset{?}{\le} 0$

$5 \ge 1$; true $\quad\quad -5 \le 0$; true

The shaded area shown in c satisfies both inequalities.

8. $x \leq 1$, vertical line
$y > 3$, horizontal line

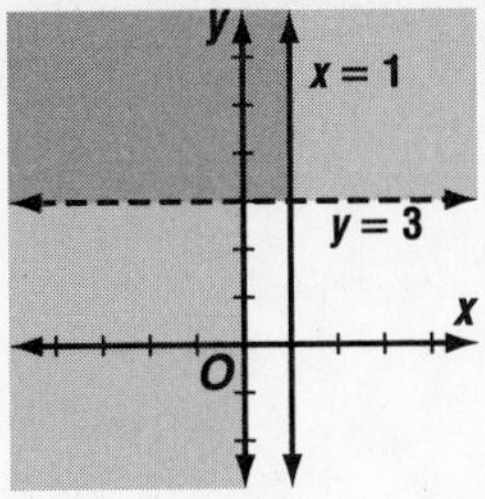

9. $y \geq 2x - 2$
$y \leq -x + 2$

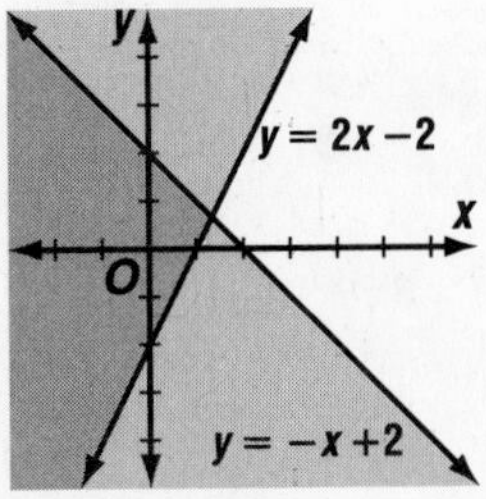

10. $x - 3y \leq -3$
$-3y \leq -x - 3$
$y \geq \frac{1}{3}x + 1$

$2x + 3y < 12$
$3y < -2x + 12$
$y < -\frac{2}{3}x + 4$

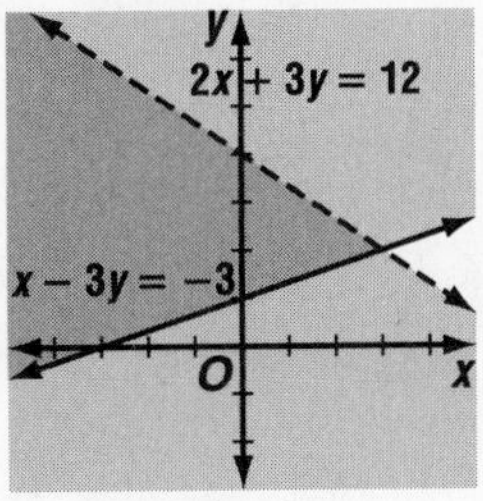

11. $x - 3y \geq -9$
$-3y \geq -x - 9$
$y \leq \frac{1}{3}x + 3$

$4x - y \leq 4$
$-y \leq -4x + 4$
$y \geq 4x - 4$

$x + 2y \geq -2$
$2y \geq -x - 2$
$y \geq -\frac{1}{2}x - 1$

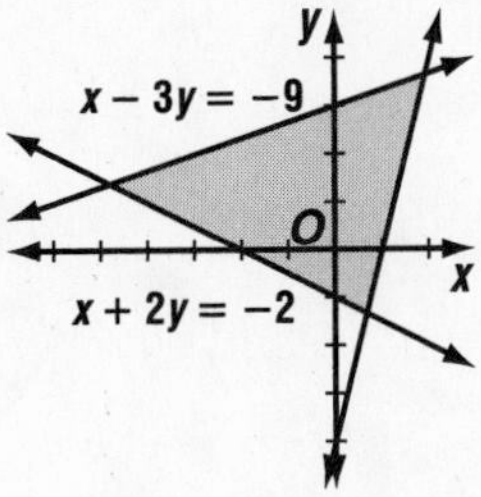

12. $x \geq 0$
$y \geq 0$

$x + y \leq 6$
$y \leq -x + 6$

$A = \frac{1}{2}bh$
$= \frac{1}{2}(6)(6)$
$= 18$; 18 square units

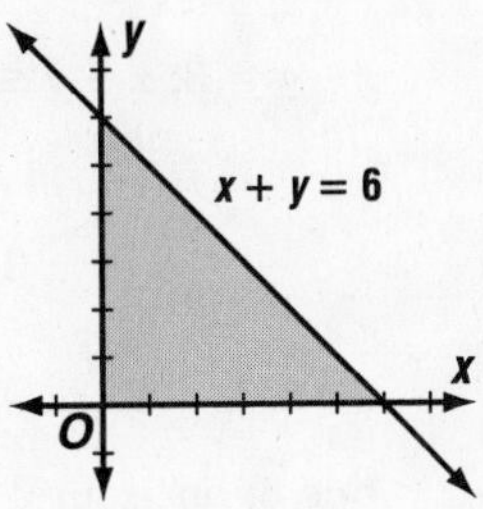

Pages 151–152 Exercises

13. $x < 2$; vertical line
$y \geq 1$; horizontal line

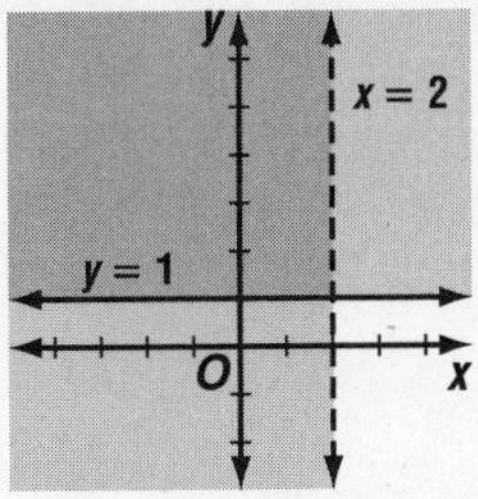

14. $x - y \leq 3$
$-y \leq -x + 3$
$y \geq x - 3$

$x + y \geq 2$
$y \geq -x + 2$

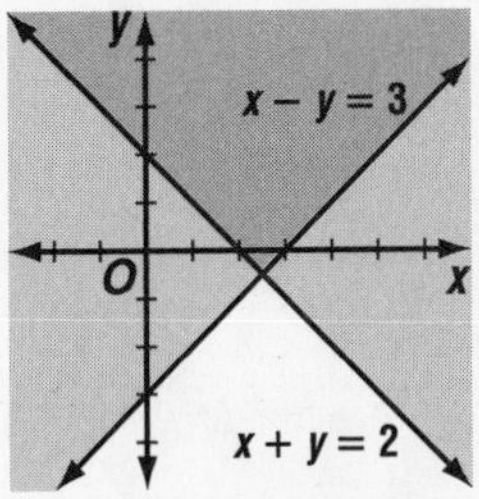

15. $x + y > 2$
$y > -x + 2$

$y > 3$

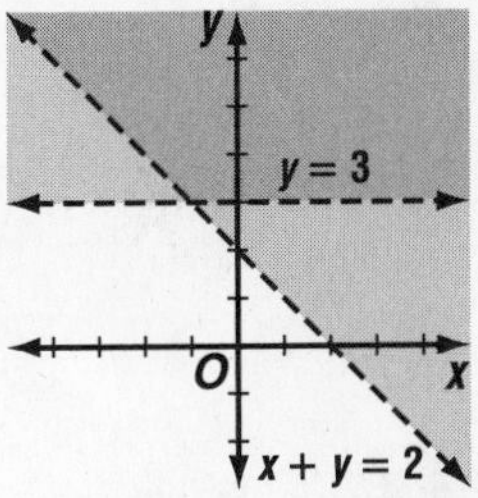

16. $y - x \leq 3$
$y \leq x + 3$

$y \geq x + 2$

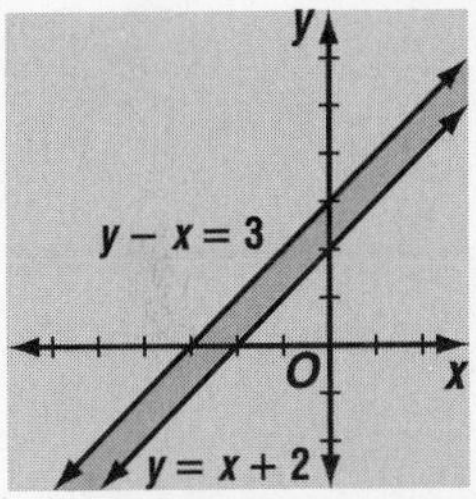

17. $y \geq x - 3$
$y \geq -x + 1$

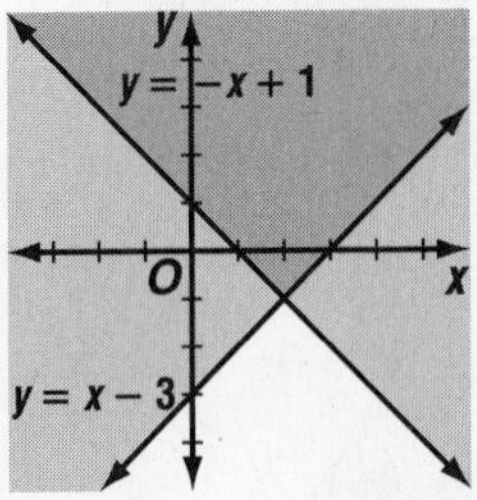

18. $y < -x - 3$

$x > y - 2$
$x + 2 > y$
$y < x + 2$

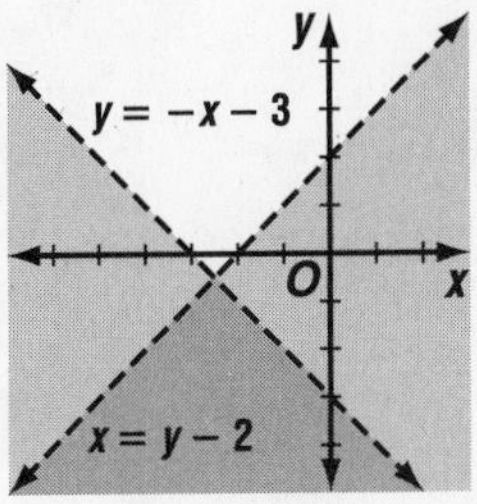

19. $y \le 2x - 3$

$y \le \frac{1}{2}x + 1$

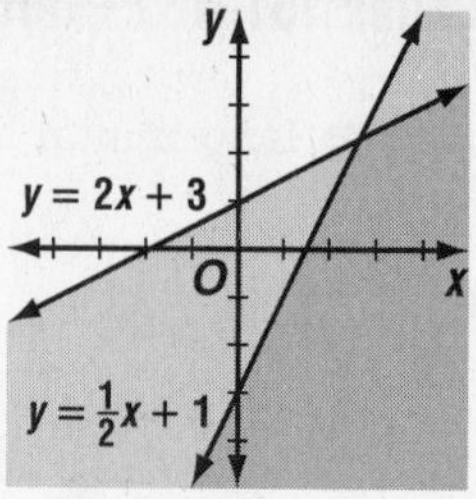

20. $y > \frac{2}{3}x - 1$

$y \le -\frac{3}{4}x + 2$

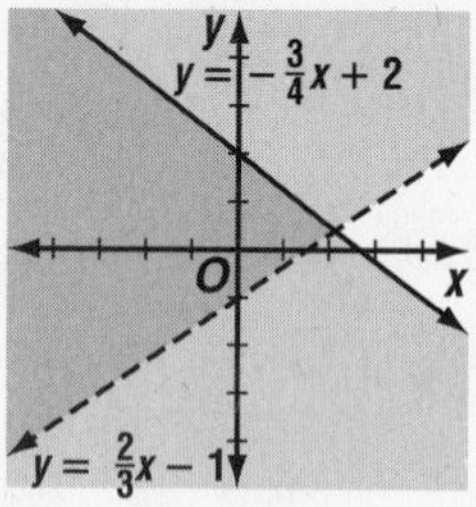

21. $|x| < 3$ $\quad$ $|y| > 2$

$-3 < x < 3$ $\quad$ $y > 2$ or $y < -2$

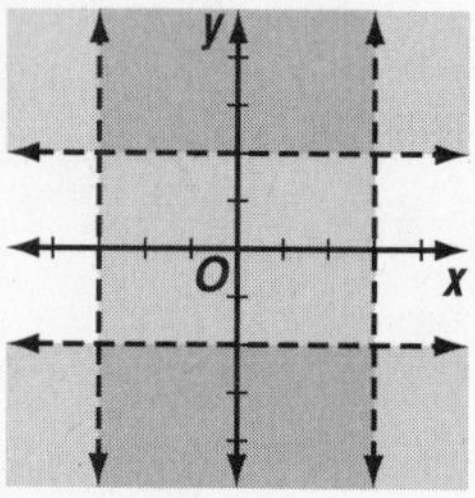

22. $|x + 1| \le 2$ $\quad$ $x - 2y \ge 1$

$-2 \le x + 1 \le 2$ $\quad$ $-2y \ge -x + 1$

$-3 \le \quad x \quad \le 1$ $\quad$ $y \le \frac{1}{2}x - \frac{1}{2}$

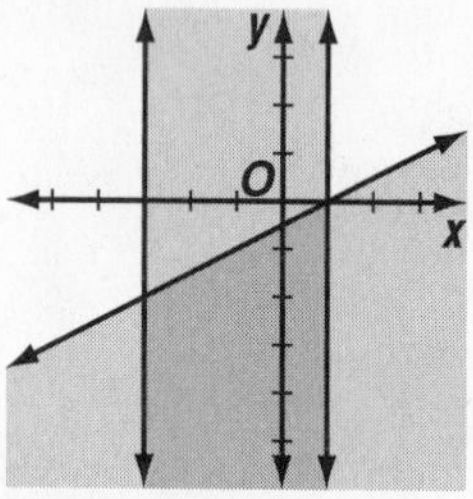

23. $3x + 2y \le 6$ $\quad$ $4x - y < 2$

$2y \le -3x + 6$ $\quad$ $-y < -4x + 2$

$y \le -\frac{3}{2}x + 3$ $\quad$ $y > 4x - 2$

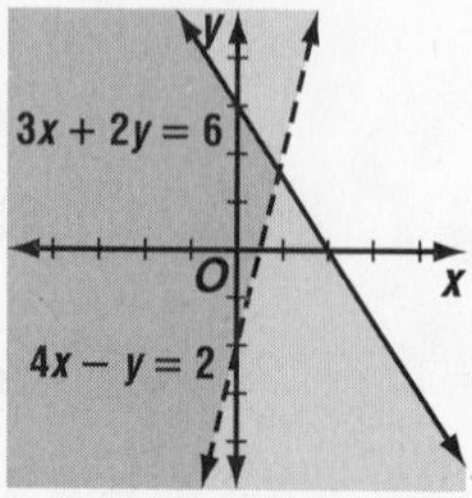

24. $4x - 3y \ge 7$ $\quad$ $y < 2$

$-3y \ge -4x + 7$

$y \le \frac{4}{3}x - \frac{7}{3}$

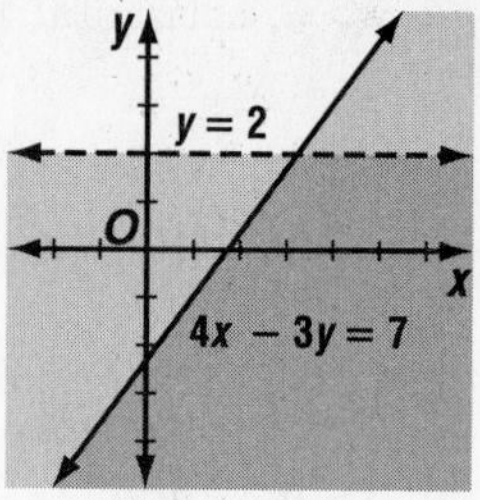

25. $x - 3y > 2$ $\quad$ $2x - y < 4$

$-3y > -x + 2$ $\quad$ $-y < -2x + 4$

$y < \frac{1}{3}x - \frac{2}{3}$ $\quad$ $y > 2x - 4$

$3x + 4y > 0$

$4y > -3x$

$y > -\frac{3}{4}x$

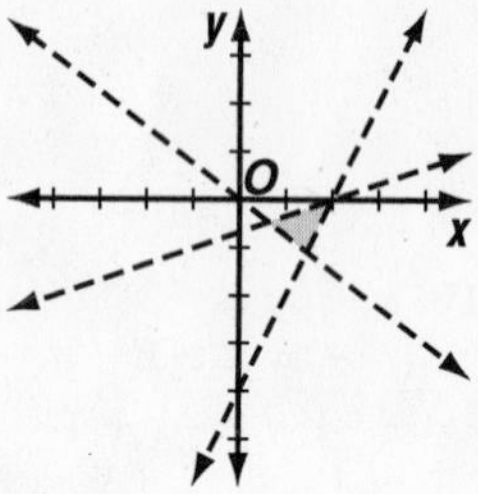

26. $5x - y < 0$ $\quad$ $4x + 3y > 6$

$-y < -5x$ $\quad$ $3y > -4x + 6$

$y > 5x$ $\quad$ $y > -\frac{4}{3}x + 2$

$x - 3y > 3$

$-3y > -x + 3$

$y < \frac{1}{3}x - 1$

$\varnothing$

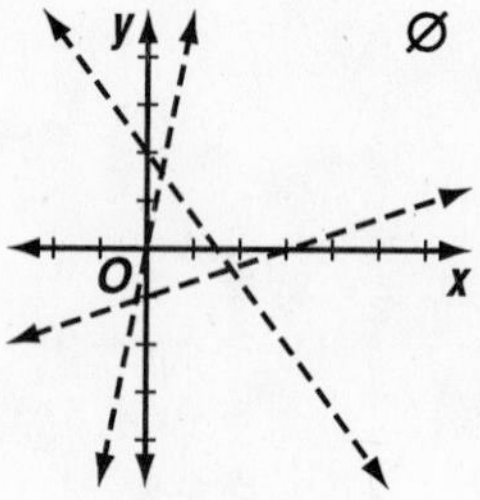

27. $y < 2x + 1$ $\quad$ $3x + y > 8$

$y > 2x - 2$ $\quad$ $y > -3x + 8$

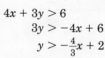

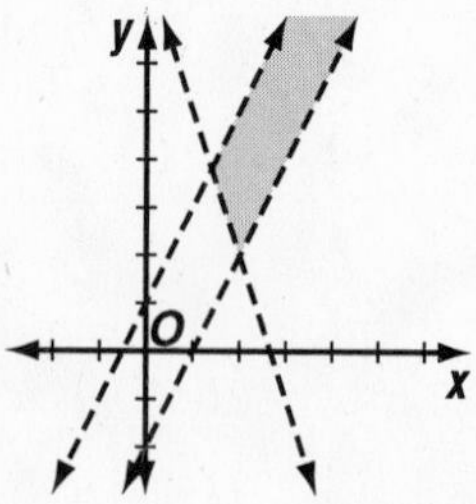

28a. line 1: y-intercept = 3, slope = -1

$y = mx + b$

$y = -1x + 3$

$x + y = 3$; $x + y \le 3$

line 2: y-intercept = 3, slope = $\frac{4}{3}$

$y = mx + b$

$y = \frac{4}{3}x + 3$

$-\frac{4}{3}x + y = 3$

$4x - 3y = -9$; $4x - 3y \ge -9$

line 3: horizontal line; $y = -1$; $y \ge -1$

28b. current triangle: $A = \frac{1}{2}bh$

$= \frac{1}{2}(7)(4)$

$= 14$

$14 \times 4 = 56$

Experiment by moving the horizontal line.

$y \geq -5$, $b = 14$ and $h = 8$.

$A = \frac{1}{2}bh$

$= \frac{1}{2}(14)(8)$

$= 56$; true

29. Sample answer: $x + y \leq 4$, $x - y \leq 4$, $x \geq -1$

30a. parallelogram

30b. $m = \frac{-2-(-3)}{-4-(-1)}$

$= \frac{1}{-3} = -\frac{1}{3}$

$y = mx + b$

$-2 = \left(-\frac{1}{3}\right)(-4) + b$

$-2 = \frac{4}{3} + b$

$-\frac{10}{3} = b$

$y = -\frac{1}{3}x - \frac{10}{3}$

$\frac{1}{3}x + y = -\frac{10}{3}$

$x + 3y = -10$

$x + 3y \geq -10$

$m = \frac{-3-3}{-1-5}$

$= \frac{-6}{-6} = 1$

$y = mx + b$

$3 = 1(5) + b$

$3 = 5 + b$

$-2 = b$

$y = x - 2$

$-x + y = -2$

$x - y = 2$

$x - y \leq 2$

$m = \frac{4-3}{2-5}$

$= \frac{1}{-3} = -\frac{1}{3}$

$y = mx + b$

$4 = -\frac{1}{3}(2) + b$

$4 = -\frac{2}{3} + b$

$\frac{14}{3} = b$

$y = -\frac{1}{3}x + \frac{14}{3}$

$\frac{1}{3}x + y = \frac{14}{3}$

$x + 3y = 14$

$x + 3y \leq 14$

$m = \frac{4-(-2)}{2-(-4)}$

$= \frac{6}{6} = 1$

$y = mx + b$

$4 = 1(2) + b$

$4 = 2 + b$

$2 = b$

$y = x + 2$

$-x + y = 2$

$x - y = -2$

$x - y \geq -2$ or $y - x \leq 2$

30c. Counting the number of squares, there are 24 square units.

31. $|x| + |y| \leq 5$

$|y| \leq 5 - |x|$

If $x \geq 0$, $|y| \leq 5 - x$.

$-(5 - x) \leq y \leq 5 - x$

$-5 + x \leq y \leq 5 - x$

$y \geq -5 + x$ and

$y \leq 5 - x$

If $x < 0$, $|y| \leq 5 + x$.

$-(5 + x) \leq y \leq 5 + x$

$-5 - x \leq y \leq 5 + x$

$y \geq -5 - x$ and

$y \geq 5 + x$

$|x| + |y| \geq 2$

$|y| \geq 2 - |x|$

If $x \geq 0$, $|y| \leq 2 - x$.

$-(2 - x) \leq y \leq 2 - x$

$-2 + x \leq y \leq 2 - x$

$y \geq -2 + x$ and

$y \leq 2 - x$

If $x < 0$, $|y| \leq 2 + x$.

$-(2 + x) \leq y \leq 2 + x$

$-2 - x \leq y \leq 2 + x$

$y \geq -2 - x$ and

$y \leq 2 + x$

(Continued next column)

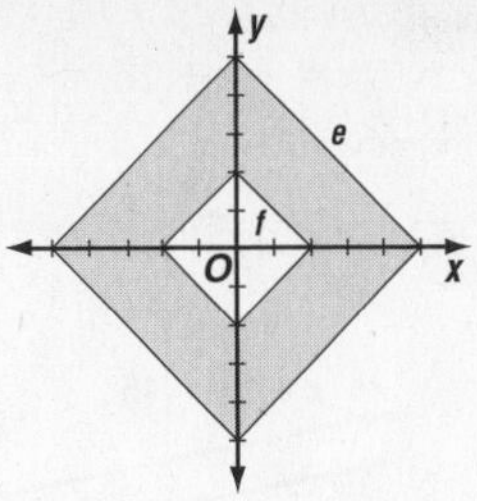

$c^2 = a^2 + b^2$

$e^2 = 5^2 + 5^2$

$= 50$

$c^2 = a^2 + b^2$

$f^2 = 2^2 + 2^2$

$= 8$

area = area of larger square − area of smaller square

$A = 50 - 8$

$= 42$; 42 square units

32. $540 \leq v \leq 650$ and $620 \leq m \leq 720$

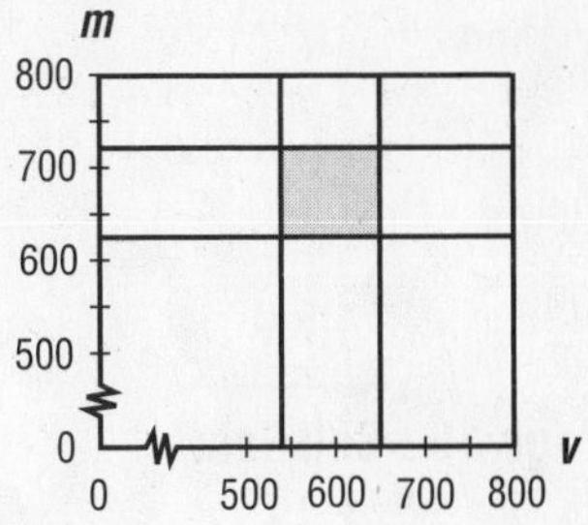

33. $s \geq 7$ and $s + a \leq 16$

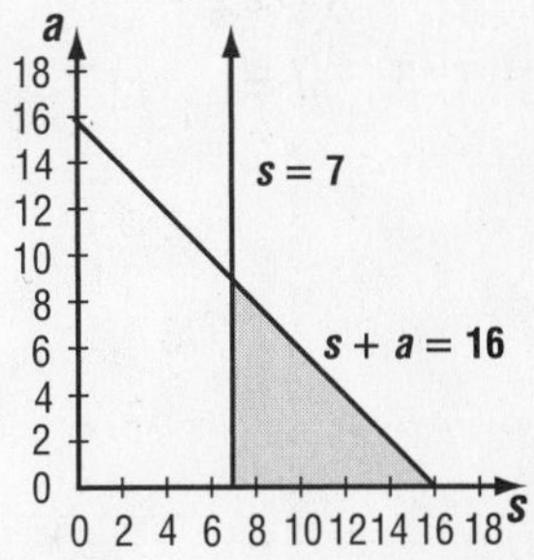

34. $x = \frac{\begin{vmatrix} 1 & -4 \\ 13 & 3 \end{vmatrix}}{\begin{vmatrix} 1 & -4 \\ 2 & 3 \end{vmatrix}}$

$= \frac{1(3) - 13(-4)}{1(3) - 2(-4)}$

$= 5$

$y = \frac{\begin{vmatrix} 1 & 1 \\ 2 & 13 \end{vmatrix}}{\begin{vmatrix} 1 & -4 \\ 2 & 3 \end{vmatrix}}$

$= \frac{1(13) - 2(1)}{1(3) - 2(-4)}$

$= 1$ (5, 1)

35. $4a - 3b = -4 \rightarrow$ Multiply by 2 $\rightarrow 8a - 6b = -8$

$3a - 2b = -4 \rightarrow$ Multiply by $-3 \rightarrow -9a + 6b = 12$

$8a - 6b = -8$

$(+)\ -9a + 6b = 12$

$-a = 4$

$a = -4$

$4a - 3b = -4$

$4(-4) - 3b = -4$

$-16 - 3b = -4$

$-3b = 12$

$b = -4$

$(-4, -4)$

36. $r - s = 8$

$r = 8 + s$

$2r + s = 1$

$2(8 + s) + s = 1$

$16 + 2s + s = 1$

$16 + 3s = 1$

$3s = -15$

$s = -5$

$r - s = 8$

$r - (-5) = 8$

$r = 3$

$(3, -5)$

37. $x + 5y = 10$ $x + 5y = 15$

$5y = -x + 10$ $5y = -x + 15$

$y = -\frac{1}{5}x + 2$ $y = -\frac{1}{5}x + 3$

no solution

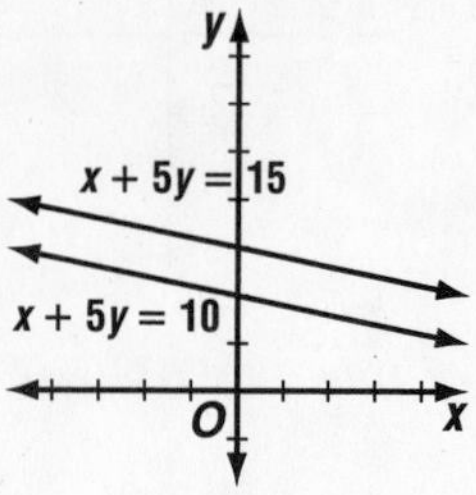

38. check by substitution; d

39. Let x = Tyler's money. Then $x + 8$ = Salina's money.

$x + 8 + 1 + x - 3 = 12$

$2x + 6 = 12$

$2x = 6$

$x = 3$; \$3.00

Page 152 Self Test

1. $2x - 5y = 14$ $x - y = 1$

$-5y = -2x + 14$ $-y = -x + 1$

$y = \frac{2}{5}x - \frac{14}{5}$ $y = x - 1$

$(-3, -4)$

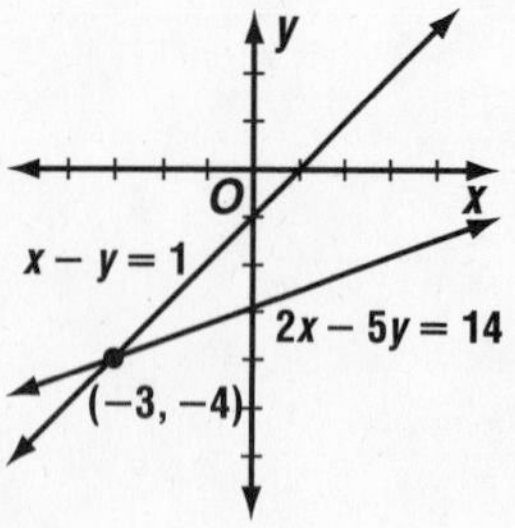

2. $4x - 3y = -9$ $x + 2y = -5$

$-3y = -4x - 9$ $2y = -x - 5$

$y = \frac{4}{3}x + 3$ $y = -\frac{1}{2}x - \frac{5}{2}$

$(-3, -1)$

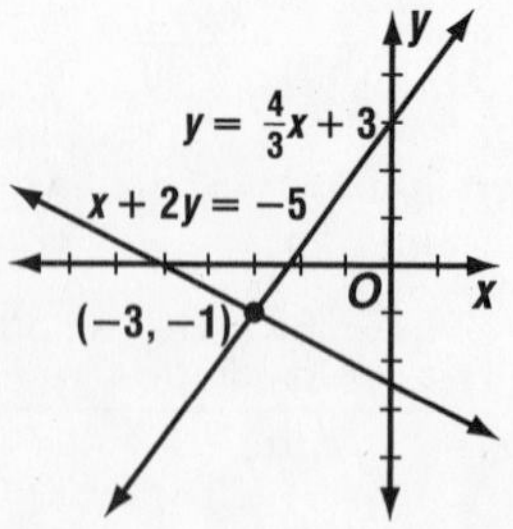

3. $y = 3x$ $x + 21 = -2y$ $y = 3x$

$x + 21 = -2(3x)$ $y = 3(-3)$

$x + 21 = -6x$ $y = -9$

$21 = -7x$

$-3 = x$

$(-3, -9)$

4. $4a + 3b = -2 \rightarrow$ Multiply by 5 $\rightarrow 20a + 15b = -10$

$5a + 7b = 17 \rightarrow$ Multiply by $-4 \rightarrow$

$-20a - 28b = -68$

$20a + 15b = -10$

$\underline{(+) -20a - 28b = -68}$

$-13b = -78$

$b = 6$

$4a + 3b = -2$

$4a + 3(6) = -2$

$4a + 18 = -2$

$4a = -20$

$a = -5$ $(-5, 6)$

5. $\begin{vmatrix} -5 & -2 \\ -3 & 11 \end{vmatrix} = -5(11) - (-3)(-2)$

$= -61$

6. $x = \dfrac{\begin{vmatrix} 2 & -7 \\ 4 & -13 \end{vmatrix}}{\begin{vmatrix} 3 & -7 \\ 6 & -13 \end{vmatrix}}$ $y = \dfrac{\begin{vmatrix} 3 & 2 \\ 6 & 4 \end{vmatrix}}{\begin{vmatrix} 3 & -7 \\ 6 & -13 \end{vmatrix}}$

$= \frac{2(-13) - 4(-7)}{3(-13) - 6(-7)}$ $= \frac{3(4) - 6(2)}{3(-13) - 6(-7)}$

$= \frac{2}{3}$ $= \frac{0}{3}$

$= 0$ $\left(\frac{2}{3}, 0\right)$

7. $x = \dfrac{\begin{vmatrix} -7 & 5 \\ 7 & -3 \end{vmatrix}}{\begin{vmatrix} 6 & 5 \\ 2 & -3 \end{vmatrix}}$ $y = \dfrac{\begin{vmatrix} 6 & -7 \\ 2 & 7 \end{vmatrix}}{\begin{vmatrix} 6 & 5 \\ 2 & -3 \end{vmatrix}}$

$= \frac{-7(-3) - 7(5)}{6(-3) - 2(5)}$ $= \frac{6(7) - 2(-7)}{6(-3) - 2(5)}$

$= \frac{-14}{-28}$ $= \frac{56}{-28}$

$= \frac{1}{2}$ $= -2$ $\left(\frac{1}{2}, -2\right)$

8. Let x = hotel cost and y = lift ticket cost.

$3x + 2y = 245 \rightarrow$ Multiply by $-3 \rightarrow$

$-9x - 6y = -735$

$5x + 3y = 400 \rightarrow$ Multiply by $2 \rightarrow 10x + 6y = 800$

$-9x - 6y = -735$

$\underline{(+)\ 10x + 6y = 800}$

$x = 65$

$3x + 2y = 245$

$3(65) + 2y = 245$

$195 + 2y = 245$

$2y = 50$

$y = 25$;

hotel, \$65; lift ticket, \$25

9. $x + y > 2$ $x - 2y \leq -1$

$y > -x + 2$ $-2y \leq -x - 1$

$y \geq \frac{1}{2}x + \frac{1}{2}$

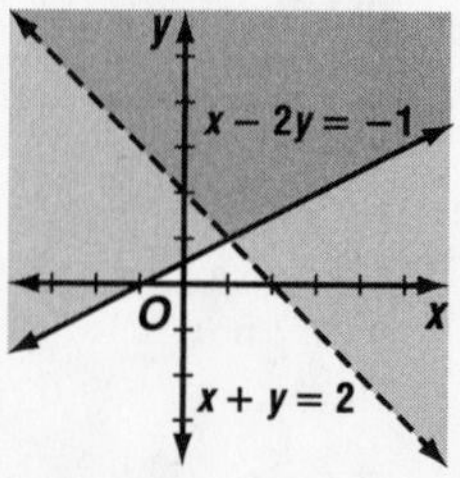

10. $y < 2$

$y \geq 2x$

$y \geq x + 1$

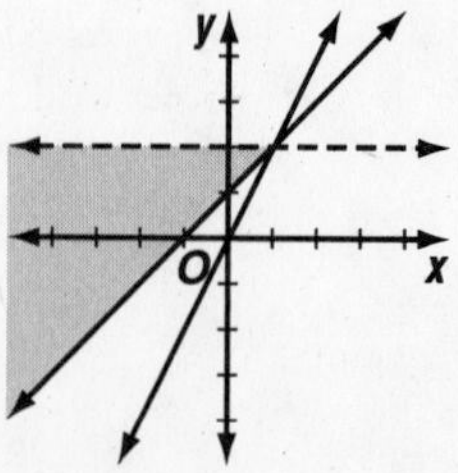

3-5 Linear Programming

Pages 156–157 Check for Understanding

1a. $(-1, 3), (3, 5), (5, -1), (-2, -2)$

1b.

(x, y)	$2x + 3y$	$f(x, y)$
$(-1, 3)$	$2(-1) + 3(3)$	7
$(3, 5)$	$2(3) + 3(5)$	21
$(5, -1)$	$2(5) + 3(-1)$	7
$(-2, -2)$	$2(-2) + 3(-2)$	-10

maximum: $f(3, 5) = 21$
minimum: $f(-2, -2) = -10$

2. Sample answer: the process of finding a maximum or a minimum value of a function by using the coordinates of the vertices of the polygon formed by the graphs of the constraints

3. Sample answer: a difficult problem with a solution that is not obvious

4.

(x, y)	$x + 2y$	$f(x, y)$
$(-3, 2)$	$-3 + 2(2)$	1
$(4, 1)$	$4 + 2(1)$	6
$(2, 6)$	$2 + 2(6)$	14
$(1, -2)$	$1 + 2(-2)$	-3

maximum: $f(2, 6) = 14$
minimum: $f(1, -2) = -3$

5.

(x, y)	$4x - y$	$f(x, y)$
$(-3, 2)$	$4(-3) - 2$	-14
$(4, 1)$	$4(4) - 1$	15
$(2, 6)$	$4(2) - 6$	2
$(1, -2)$	$4(1) - (-2)$	6

maximum: $f(4, 1) = 15$
minimum: $f(-3, 2) = -14$

6. $y \geq 1$ $x \leq 6$ $y \leq 2x + 1$

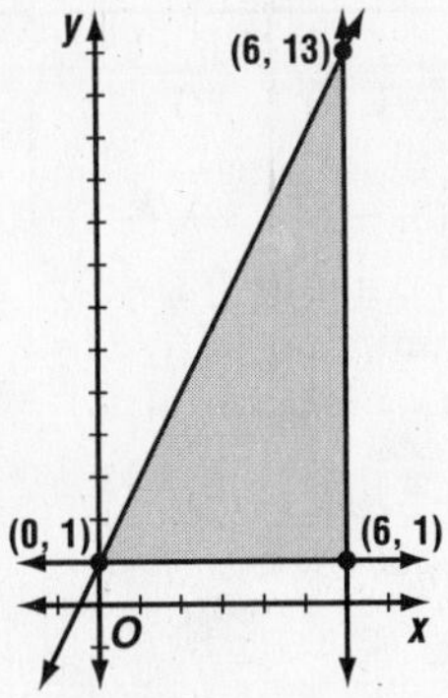

vertices: $(0, 1), (6, 13), (6, 1)$

(x, y)	$x + y$	$f(x, y)$
$(0, 1)$	$0 + 1$	1
$(6, 13)$	$6 + 13$	19
$(6, 1)$	$6 + 1$	7

maximum: $f(6, 13) = 19$
minimum: $f(0, 1) = 1$

7. $4y \leq x + 8$ $x + y \geq 2$ $y \geq 2x - 5$
$y \leq \frac{1}{4}x + 2$ $y \geq -x + 2$

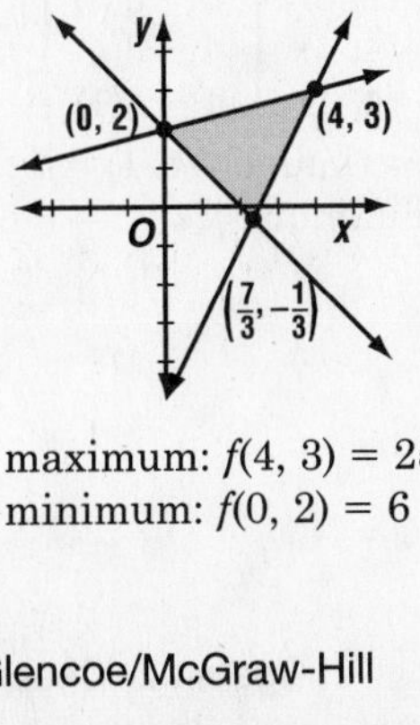

vertices: $(0, 2), (4, 3), \left(\frac{7}{3}, -\frac{1}{3}\right)$

(x, y)	$4x + 3y$	$f(x, y)$
$(0, 2)$	$4(0) + 3(2)$	6
$(4, 3)$	$4(4) + 3(3)$	25
$\left(\frac{7}{3}, -\frac{1}{3}\right)$	$4\left(\frac{7}{3}\right) + 3\left(-\frac{1}{3}\right)$	$\frac{25}{3}$

maximum: $f(4, 3) = 25$
minimum: $f(0, 2) = 6$

8. $y \geq 2$ $1 \leq x \leq 5$ $y \leq x + 3$

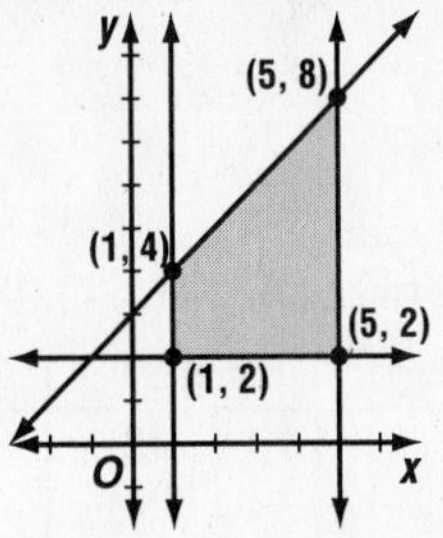

vertices: $(1, 4), (5, 8), (5, 2), (1, 2)$

(x, y)	$3x - 2y$	$f(x, y)$
$(1, 4)$	$3(1) - 2(4)$	-5
$(5, 8)$	$3(5) - 2(8)$	-1
$(5, 2)$	$3(5) - 2(2)$	11
$(1, 2)$	$3(1) - 2(2)$	-1

maximum: $f(5, 2) = 11$
minimum: $f(1, 4) = -5$

9a. Gauss used the strategy of solving a simpler problem as in Example 3.

9b.

$$\begin{aligned} s &= 1 + 2 + 3 + \ldots + 2000 \\ (+)\ s &= 2000 + 1999 + 1998 + \ldots + 1 \\ \hline 2s &= 2001 + 2001 + 2001 + \ldots + 2001 \\ 2s &= 2000 \cdot 2001 \\ 2s &= 4{,}002{,}000 \\ s &= 2{,}001{,}000 \end{aligned}$$

Pages 157–159 Exercises

10.

(x, y)	$x - y$	$f(x, y)$
$(-1, 3)$	$-1 - 3$	-4
$(3, 5)$	$3 - 5$	-2
$(4, -1)$	$4 - (-1)$	5
$(-1, -2)$	$-1 - (-2)$	1

maximum: $f(4, -1) = 5$
minimum: $f(-1, 3) = -4$

11.

(x, y)	$3x + 2y$	$f(x, y)$
$(-1, 3)$	$3(-1) + 2(3)$	3
$(3, 5)$	$3(3) + 2(5)$	19
$(4, -1)$	$3(4) + 2(-1)$	10
$(-1, -2)$	$3(-1) + 2(-2)$	-7

maximum: $f(3, 5) = 19$
minimum: $f(-1, -2) = -7$

12.

(x, y)	$3y - x$	$f(x, y)$
$(-1, 3)$	$3(3) - (-1)$	10
$(3, 5)$	$3(5) - 3$	12
$(4, -1)$	$3(-1) - 4$	-7
$(-1, -2)$	$3(-2) - (-1)$	-5

maximum: $f(3, 5) = 12$
minimum: $f(4, -1) = -7$

13.

(x, y)	$-2x - y$	$f(x, y)$
$(-1, 3)$	$-2(-1) - 3$	-1
$(3, 5)$	$-2(3) - 5$	-11
$(4, -1)$	$-2(4) - (-1)$	-7
$(-1, -2)$	$-2(-1) - (-2)$	4

maximum: $f(-1, -2) = 4$
minimum: $f(3, 5) = -11$

14. $2x + 3y \ge 6$ $3x - 2y \ge -4$

$3y \ge -2x + 6$ $-2y \ge -3x - 4$

$y \ge -\frac{2}{3}x + 2$ $y \le \frac{3}{2}x + 2$

$5x + y \le 15$

$y \le -5x + 15$

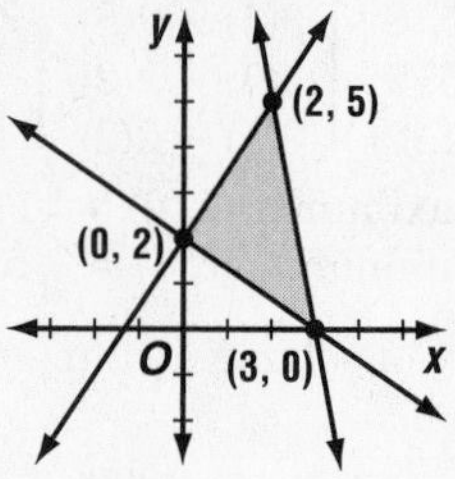

vertices: (0, 2), (2, 5), (3, 0)

(x, y)	$x + 3y$	$f(x, y)$
(0, 2)	0 + 3(2)	6
(2, 5)	2 + 3(5)	17
(3, 0)	3 + 3(0)	3

maximum: $f(2, 5) = 17$

minimum: $f(3,0) = 3$

15. $x \ge 1$ $2x + y \le 6$

$y \ge 0$ $y \le -2x + 6$

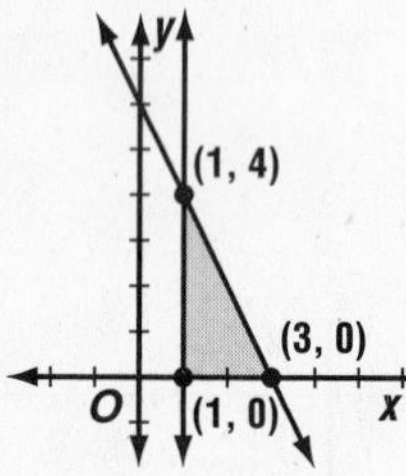

vertices: (1, 0), (1, 4), (3, 0)

(x, y)	$3x + y$	$f(x, y)$
(1, 0)	3(1) + 0	3
(1, 4)	3(1) + 4	7
(3, 0)	3(3) + 0	9

maximum: $f(3, 0) = 9$

minimum: $f(1, 0) = 3$

16. $x + y \ge 4$ $3x - 2y \le 12$ $x - 4 \ge -16$

$y \ge -x + 4$ $-2y \le -3x + 12$ $-4y \ge -x - 16$

$y \ge \frac{3}{2}x - 6$ $y \le \frac{1}{4}x + 4$

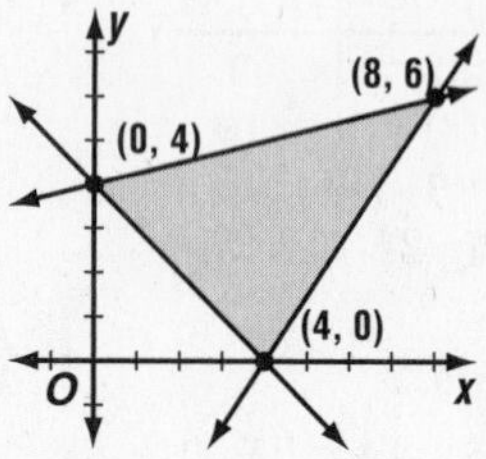

vertices: (0, 4), (8, 6), (4, 0)

(x, y)	$x - 2y$	$f(x, y)$
(0, 4)	0 − 2(4)	−8
(8, 6)	8 − 2(6)	−4
(4, 0)	4 − 2(0)	4

maximum: $f(4, 0) = 4$

minimum: $f(0, 4) = -8$

17. $y \le 2x + 1$ $1 \le y \le 3$ $y \le -0.5x + 6$

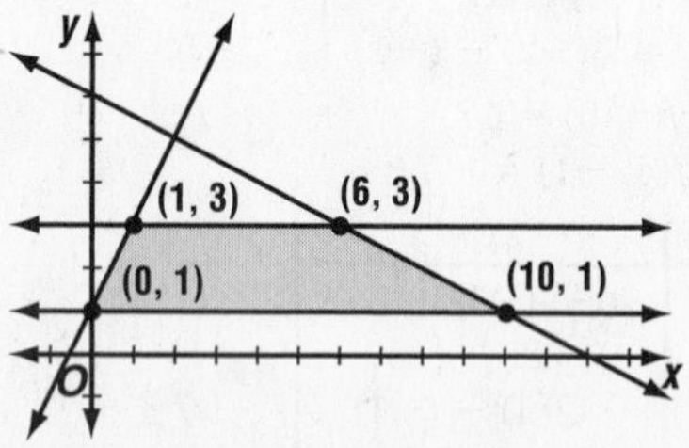

vertices: (0, 1), (1, 3), (6, 3), (10, 1)

(x, y)	$3x + y$	$f(x, y)$
(0, 1)	3(0) + 1	1
(1, 3)	3(1) + 3	6
(6, 3)	3(6) + 3	21
(10, 1)	3(10) + 1	31

maximum: $f(10, 1) = 31$

minimum: $f(0, 1) = 1$

18. $y \le x + 6$ $y + 2x \ge 6$ $2 \le x \le 6$

$y \ge -2x + 6$

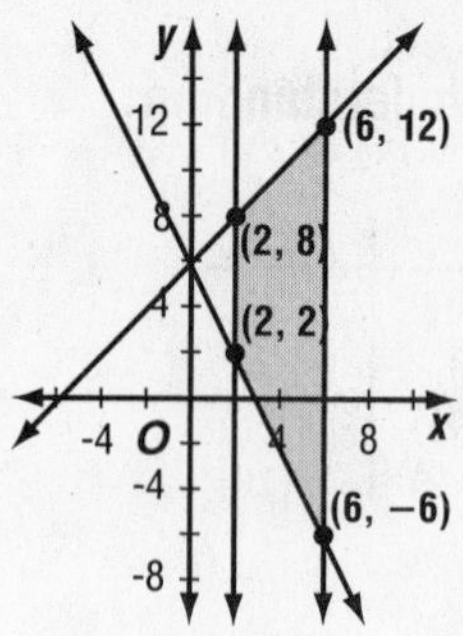

vertices: (2, 2), (2, 8), (6, 12), (6, −6)

(x, y)	$-x + 3y$	$f(x, y)$
(2, 2)	−2 + 3(2)	4
(2, 8)	−2 + 3(8)	22
(6, 12)	−6 + 3(12)	30
(6, −6)	−6 + 3(−6)	−24

maximum: $f(6, 12) = 30$

minimum: $f(6, -6) = -24$

19. $x + y \ge 2$ $2y \ge 3x - 6$ $4y \le x + 8$

$y \ge -x + 2$ $y \ge \frac{3}{2}x - 3$ $y \le \frac{1}{4}x + 2$

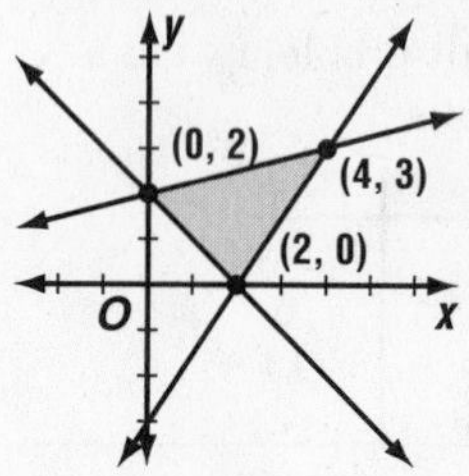

vertices: (0, 2), (4, 3), (2, 0)

(x, y)	$3y + x$	$f(x, y)$
(0, 2)	3(2) + 0	6
(4, 3)	3(3) + 4	13
(2, 0)	3(0) + 2	2

maximum: $f(4, 3) = 13$

minimum: $f(2, 0) = 2$

20. $x - 3y \ge -7$ $5x + y \le 13$

$-3y \ge -x - 7$ $y \le -5x + 13$

$y \le \frac{1}{3}x + \frac{7}{3}$

$x + 6y \ge -9$ $3x - 2y \ge -7$

$6y \ge -x - 9$ $-2y \ge -3x - 7$

$y \ge -\frac{1}{6}x - \frac{3}{2}$ $y \le \frac{3}{2}x + \frac{7}{2}$

vertices: (−3, −1), (−1, 2), (2, 3), (3, −2)

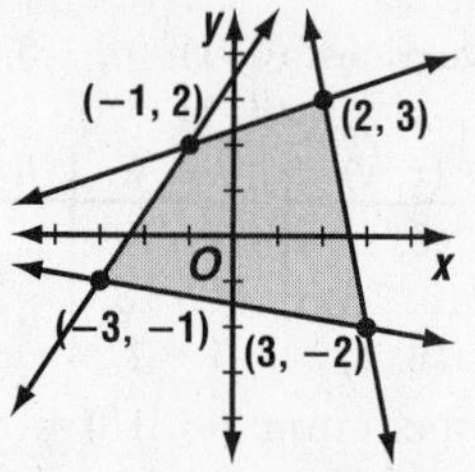

(x, y)	$x - y$	$f(x, y)$
(−3, −1)	−3 −(−1)	−2
(−1, 2)	−1 − 2	−3
(2, 3)	2 − 3	−1
(3, −2)	3 − (−2)	5

maximum: $f(3, -2) = 5$

minimum $f(-1, 2) = -3$

21. $x \ge 2$ $x - 2y \ge -4$

$x \le 4$ $-2y \ge -x - 4$

$y \ge 1$ $y \le \frac{1}{2}x + 2$

vertices: (2, 1), (2, 3), (4, 4), (4, 1)

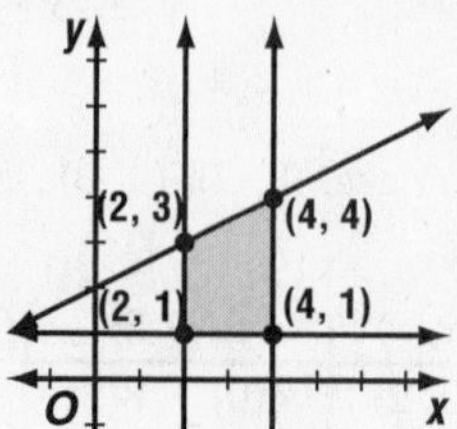

(x, y)	$x - 3y$	$f(x, y)$
(2, 1)	2 − 3(1)	−1
(2, 3)	2 − 3(3)	−7
(4, 4)	4 − 3(4)	−8
(4, 1)	4 − 3(1)	1

maximum: $f(4, 1) = 1$

minimum: $f(4, 4) = -8$

22. $x \geq 0$ $\quad x + 2y \leq 6$ $\quad 2y - x \leq 2$

$y \geq 0$ $\quad 2y \leq -x + 6$ $\quad 2y \leq x + 2$

$y \leq -\frac{1}{2}x + 3$ $\quad y \leq \frac{1}{2}x + 1$

$x + y \leq 5$

$y \leq -x + 5$

vertices: (0, 0), (0, 1), (2, 2), (4, 1), (5, 0)

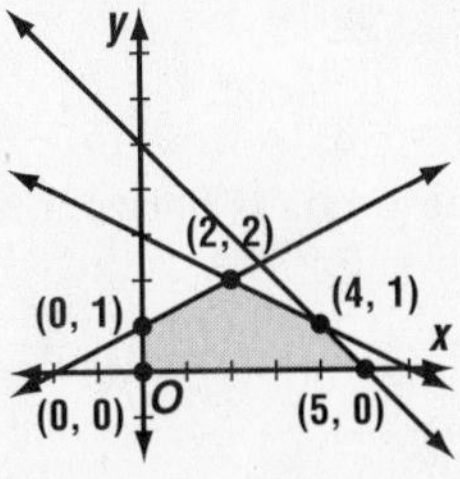

(x, y)	3x − 5y	f(x, y)
(0, 0)	3(0) − 5(0)	0
(0, 1)	3(0) − 5(1)	−5
(2, 2)	3(2) − 5(2)	−4
(4, 1)	3(4) − 5(1)	7
(5, 0)	3(5) − 5(0)	15

maximum: $f(5, 0) = 15$
minimum: $f(0, 1) = -5$

23. $-x + y \leq 2$ $\quad x + y \leq 6$

$y \leq x + 2$ $\quad y \leq -x + 6$

[ZOOM] 6 [Y=] 0 [ENTER] [X,T,θ,n] [+] 2 [ENTER]
[(−)] [X,T,θ,n] [+] 6 [GRAPH] [2nd] [DRAW] 4
[ENTER] [▶] (until the line reaches 5) [ENTER]

vertices: (5, 0), (0, 0), (0, 2), (2, 4), (5, 1)

(x, y)	5x − 3y	f(x, y)
(5, 0)	5(5) − 3(0)	25
(0, 0)	5(0) − 3(0)	0
(0, 2)	5(0) − 3(2)	−6
(2, 4)	5(2) − 3(4)	−2
(5, 1)	5(5) − 3(1)	22

maximum: $f(5, 0) = 25$
minimum: $f(0, 2) = -6$

24. $x + y \geq 1$

$y \geq -x + 1$

[Y=] 5 [ENTER] [(−)] [X,T,θ,n] [+] 1 [ENTER] 0
[GRAPH] [2nd] [DRAW] 4 [ENTER] [▶] (until the line reaches 3) [ENTER]

vertices: (0, 1), (0, 5), (3, 5), (3, 0), (1, 0)

(x, y)	2x + 8y + 10	f(x, y)
(0, 1)	2(0) + 8(1) + 10	18
(0, 5)	2(0) + 8(5) + 10	50
(3, 5)	2(3) + 8(5) + 10	56
(3, 0)	2(3) + 8(0) + 10	16
(1, 0)	2(1) + 8(0) + 10	12

maximum: $f(3, 5) = 56$
minimum: $f(1, 0) = 12$

25. $5x \leq -2$ $\quad 1.2x - y \geq -2.9$

$x \leq -\frac{2}{5}$ $\quad -y \geq -1.2x - 2.9$

$y \leq 1.2x + 2.9$

[Y=] 1 [ENTER] [(−)] 2 [ENTER] 1.2 [X,T,θ,n] [+] 2.9
[GRAPH] [2nd] [DRAW] 4 [◀] (until the line reaches −0.4) [ENTER]

(Continued next column)

vertices: (−4.08, −2), (−1.58, 1), (−0.4, 1), (−0.4, −2)

(x, y)	4x + 2y	f(x, y)
(−4.08, −2)	4(−4.08) + 2(−2)	−20.32
(−1.58, 1)	4(−1.58) + 2(1)	−4.32
(−0.4, 1)	4(−0.4) + 2(1)	0.4
(−0.4, −2)	4(−0.4) + 2(−2)	−5.6

maximum: $f(-0.4, 1) = 0.4$
minimum: $f(-4.08, -2) = -20.32$

26a. Sample answer: $f(x, y) = -2x - y$

26b. Sample answer: $f(x, y) = 3y - 2x$

26c. Sample answer: $f(x, y) = x + y$

26d. Sample answer: $f(x, y) = -x - 3y$

26e. Sample answer: $f(x, y) = x + 2y$

27. Let x = hours tutoring and y = hours at Pizza King.

$x + y \leq 20$ $\quad 3 \leq x \leq 8$ $\quad y \geq 0$

$y \leq -x + 20$

vertices: (3, 0), (3, 17), (8, 12), (8, 0)

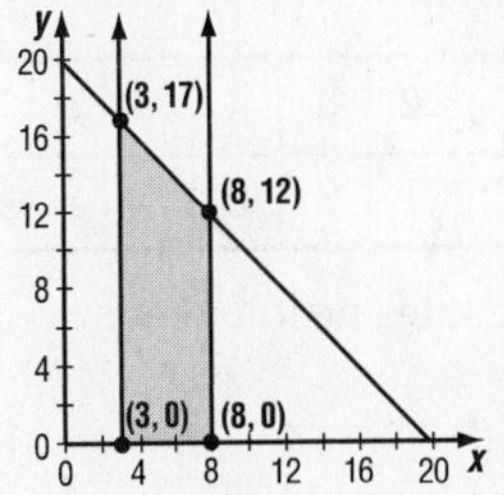

$f(x, y) = 10x + 7y$

(x, y)	10x + 7y	f(x, y)
(3, 0)	10(3) + 7(0)	30
(3, 17)	10(3) + 7(17)	149
(8, 12)	10(8) + 7(12)	164
(8, 0)	10(8) + 7(0)	80

maximum earnings: $164

28. Let x = notebook paper and y = newsprint.

$x + y \leq 200$ $\quad x \geq 10$ $\quad y \geq 80$

$y \leq -x + 200$

vertices: (10, 80), (10, 190), (120, 80)

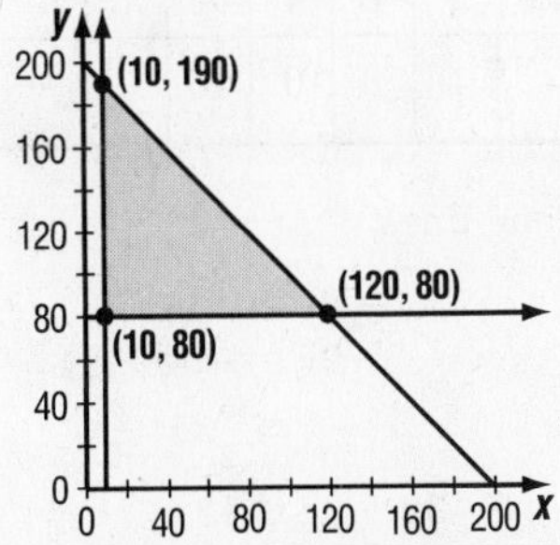

$f(x, y) = 500x + 350y$

(x, y)	500x + 350y	f(x, y)
(10, 80)	500(10) + 350(80)	33,000
(10, 190)	500(10) + 350(190)	71,500
(120, 80)	500(120) + 350(80)	88,000

maximum profit: $88,000
Produce 120 units of notebook paper and 80 units of newsprint.

29. $0 \le c \le 1200$ $\quad 0 \le s \le 1400$ $\quad c + s \le 1350$
$7c + 6s \le 8400$
vertices: (0, 1350), (300, 1050), (1200, 0), (0, 0)

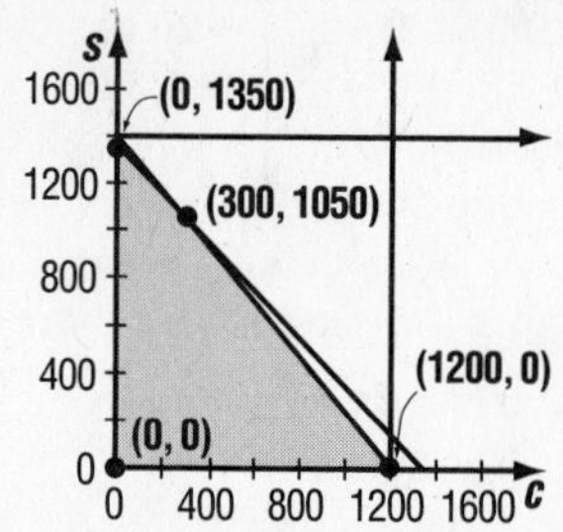

(c, s)	30c + 26s	f(c, s)
(0, 1350)	30(0) + 26(1350)	35,100
(300, 1050)	30(300) + 26(1050)	36,300
(1200, 0)	30(1200) + 26(0)	36,000
(0, 0)	30(0) + 26(0)	0

maximum profit: $36,300
Sample answer: No, he could only increase his income by $100.

30.

Number of Teams	2	3	4	...	n
Number of Games	1	2	3	...	$n - 1$

Thus, for 30 teams, 29 games need to be played.

31.

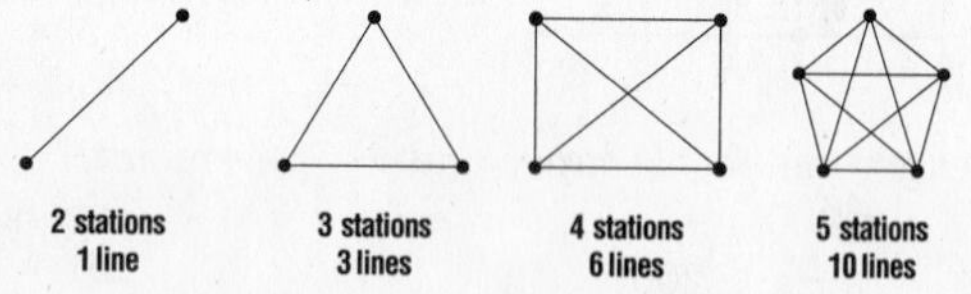

Number of stations	2	3	4	5	...	n
Number of lines	1	3	6	10	...	$\frac{n(n-1)}{2}$

$\frac{16(15)}{2} = 120$ telephone lines

32a. $x - 2y \le -1$
$-2y \le -x - 1$
$y \ge \frac{1}{2}x + \frac{1}{2}$

$5x - 2y \ge -21$
$-2y \ge -5x - 21$
$y \le \frac{5}{2}x + \frac{21}{2}$

$x - 2y \ge -9$
$-2y \ge -x - 9$
$y \le \frac{1}{2}x + \frac{9}{2}$

$3x + 2y \le 13$
$2y \le -3x + 13$
$y \le -\frac{3}{2}x + \frac{13}{2}$

32b.

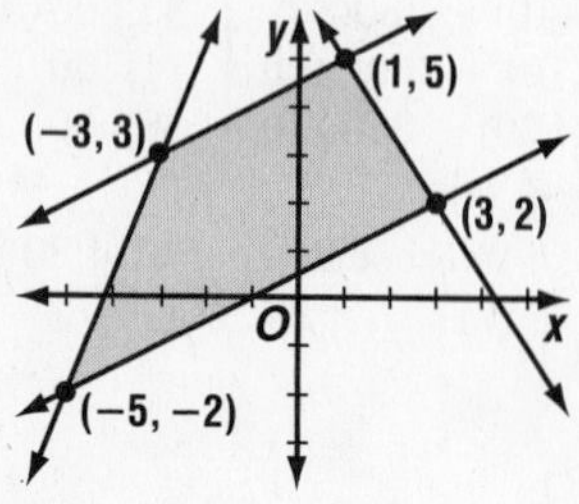

trapezoid
(−5, −2), (−3, 3), (1, 5), (3, 2)

33. $x = \dfrac{\begin{vmatrix} 9 & 2 \\ 19 & -3 \end{vmatrix}}{\begin{vmatrix} 3 & 2 \\ 2 & -3 \end{vmatrix}}$ $\qquad y = \dfrac{\begin{vmatrix} 3 & 9 \\ 2 & 19 \end{vmatrix}}{\begin{vmatrix} 3 & 2 \\ 2 & -3 \end{vmatrix}}$

$= \frac{9(-3) - 19(2)}{3(-3) - 2(2)}$ $\qquad = \frac{3(19) - 2(9)}{3(-3) - 2(2)}$

$= \frac{-65}{-13}$ $\qquad = \frac{39}{-13}$

$= 5$ $\qquad = -3$ $\qquad (5, -3)$

34. A line perpendicular to the y-axis is horizontal. It will cross the y-axis at 9. $y = 9$

35. no, by the vertical line test

36. $c = 12.95 + 0.15m$
$90 = 12.95 + 0.15m$
$77.05 = 0.15m$
$513.\overline{6} = m$; $513\frac{2}{3}$ miles

37. $4(12 - 5b) - 3(4b - 2) = 48 - 20b - 12b + 6$
$= 54 - 32b$

3-6 Applications of Linear Programming

Page 162 Check for Understanding

1. Lula; if the region is not bounded, there may be no minimum.

2. The vertices represent the extreme possibilities and therefore must produce the maximum and minimum.

3. Write the restrictions as inequalities, graph the inequalities, identify the vertices of the polygon formed, and substitute the coordinates of the vertices in the expression to be maximized or minimized.

4a. If p = plain pages, then $0 \le p \le 40$.

4b. If c = pages with charts or graphs, then $0 \ge c \le 16$.

4c. $c + p \le 50$

4d. $c + p \le 50$
$p \le -c + 50$

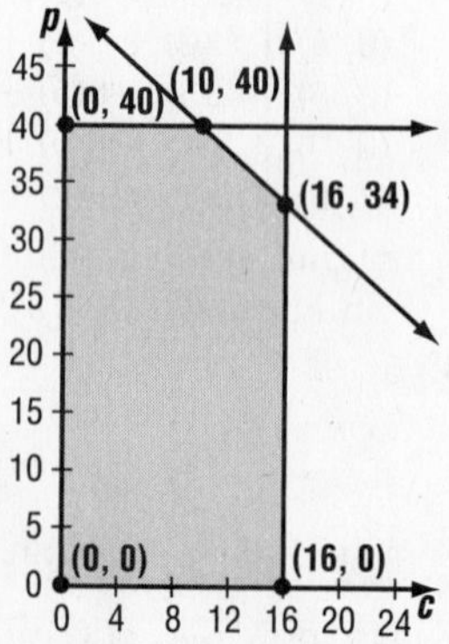

4e. (0, 0), (0, 40), (10, 40), (16, 34), (16, 0)

4f. $f(c, p) = 8.00c + 3.50p$

4g.

(c, p)	$8.00c + 3.50p$	$f(c, p)$
(0, 0)	8.00(0) + 3.50(0)	0
(0, 40)	8.00(0) + 3.50(40)	140
(10, 40)	8.00(10) + 3.50(40)	220
(16, 34)	8.00(16) + 3.50(34)	247
(16, 0)	8.00(16) + 3.50(0)	128

(16, 34)

4h. \$247

Pages 162–164 Exercises

5a. $w \geq 0,\ d \geq 0,\ 8w + 5d \leq 80,\ 2w + 5d \leq 50$

5b. $8w + 5d \leq 80$ $\quad$ $2w + 5d \leq 50$

$5d \leq -8w + 80$ $\quad$ $5d \leq -2w + 50$

$d \leq -\frac{8}{5}w + 16$ $\quad$ $d \leq -\frac{2}{5}w + 10$

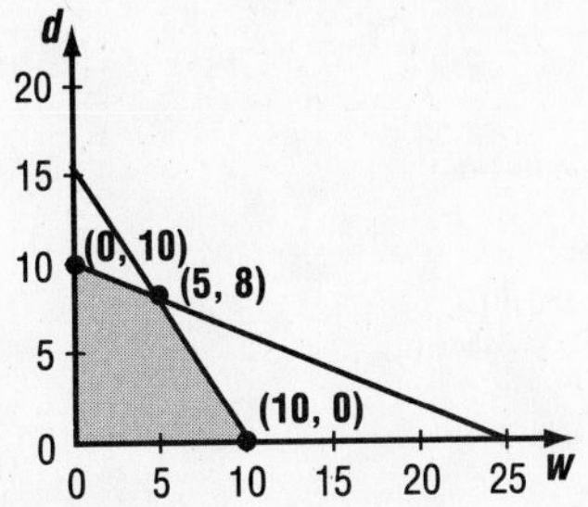

5c. $f(w, d) = 17w + 29d$

5d.

(w, d)	$17w + 29d$	$f(w, d)$
(0, 0)	17(0) + 29(0)	0
(0, 10)	17(0) + 29(10)	290
(5, 8)	17(5) + 29(8)	317
(10, 0)	17(10) + 29(0)	170

5 Wallbangers and 8 Dingbats should be produced for a \$317 profit.

6a. $c \geq 0,\ b \geq 0,\ 6c + 30b \leq 600,\ c + b \leq 60$

6b. $6c + 30b \leq 600$ $\quad$ $c + b \leq 60$

$30b \leq -6c + 600$ $\quad$ $b \leq -c + 60$

$b \leq -\frac{1}{5}c + 20$

vertices: (0, 0), (0, 20), (50, 10), (60, 0)

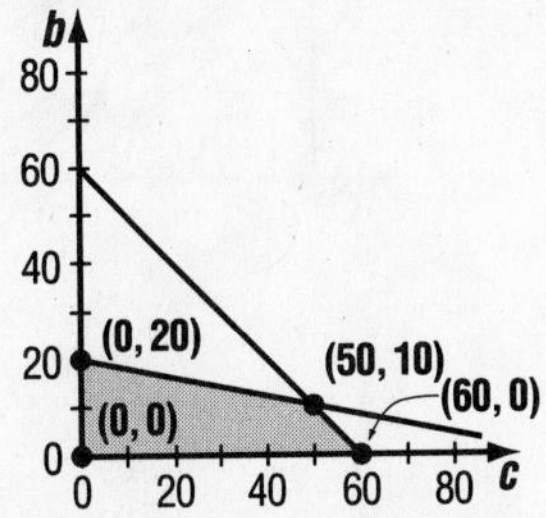

$f(c, b) = 2.50c + 7.50b$

(c, b)	$2.50c + 7.50b$	$f(c, b)$
(0, 0)	2.50(0) + 7.50(0)	0
(0, 20)	2.50(0) + 7.50(20)	150
(50, 10)	2.50(50)+ 7.50(10)	200
(60, 0)	2.50(60) + 7.50(0)	150

50 cars and 10 buses should be accepted for a \$200 income.

6c. $f(c, b) = 4.00c + 8.00b$

(c, b)	$4.00c + 8.00b$	$f(c, b)$
(0, 0)	4.00(0) + 8.00(0)	0
(0, 20)	4.00(0) + 8.00(20)	160
(50, 10)	4.00(50) + 8.00(10)	280
(60, 0)	4.00(60) + 8.00(0)	240

50 cars and 10 buses should be accepted for a \$280 income.

7a. $x + y \geq 40$ $\quad$ $x + \frac{1}{3}y \geq 20$

$y \geq -x + 40$ $\quad$ $\frac{1}{3}y \geq -x + 20$

$y \geq -3x + 60$

$\frac{1}{2}x + y \geq 30$ $\quad$ $x + y \leq 100$

$y \geq -\frac{1}{2}x + 30$ $\quad$ $y \leq -x + 100$

vertices: (0, 60), (0, 100), (100, 0), (60, 0), (20, 20), (10, 30)

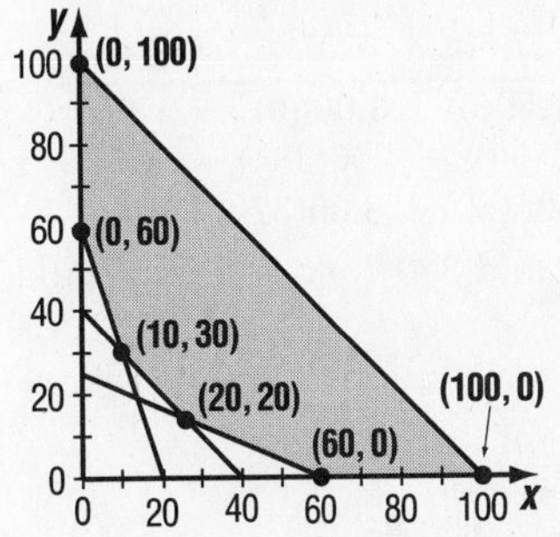

$f(x, y) = 0.80x + 0.40y$

(x, y)	$0.80x + 0.40y$	$f(x, y)$
(0, 60)	0.80(0) + 0.40(60)	24
(0, 100)	0.80(0) + 0.40(100)	40
(100, 0)	0.80(100) + 0.40(0)	80
(60, 0)	0.80(60) + 0.40(0)	48
(20, 20)	0.80(20) + 0.40(20)	24
(10, 30)	0.80 (10) + 0.40(30)	20

least cost: \$20

7b. $f(x, y) = 1.00x + 0.40y$

(x, y)	$1.00x + 0.40y$	$f(x, y)$
(0, 60)	1.00(0) + 0.40(60)	24
(0, 100)	1.00(0) + 0.40(100)	40
(100, 0)	1.00(100) + 0.40(0)	100
(60, 0)	1.00(60) + 0.40(0)	60
(20, 20)	1.00(20) + 0.40(20)	28
(10, 30)	1.00(10) + 0.40(30)	22

No; the vertex at (10, 30) still produces the least cost (\$22).

8a. Let s = Silent Sally and t = Talking Tommy

$t \geq 2s$ $\quad \frac{t}{8} + \frac{s}{20} \leq 48$ $\quad t \geq 0$

$5t + 2s \leq 1920$ $\quad s \geq 0$

$5t \leq -2s + 1920$

$t \leq -\frac{2}{5}s + 384$

vertices: (0, 0), (0, 384), (160, 320)

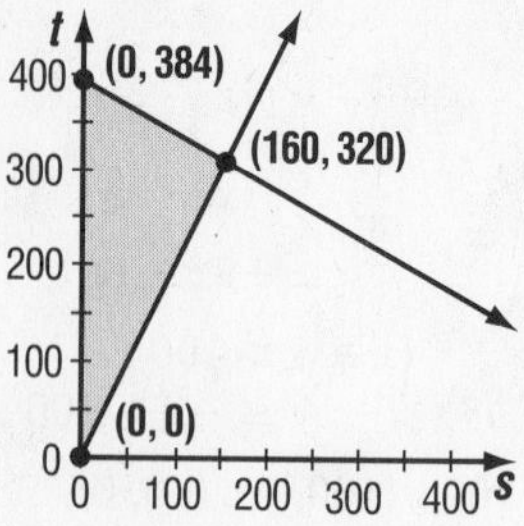

$P(s, t) = 7.50s + 3.00\,t$

(s, t)	$7.50s + 3.00t$	$P(s, t)$
(0, 0)	7.50(0) + 3.00 (0)	0
(0, 384)	7.50(0) + 3.00(384)	1152
(160, 320)	7.50(160) + 3.00(320)	2160

160 Sally dolls and 320 Tommy dolls should be produced.

8b. \$2160

9a. A = 4 blue + 1 red

B = 1 blue + 6 red

$a \geq 0$, $b \geq 0$, $4a + b \leq 32$, $a + 6b \leq 54$

9b. $4a + b \leq 32$ $\quad a + 6b \leq 54$

$b \leq -4a + 32$ $\quad 6b \leq -a + 54$

$b \leq -\frac{1}{6}a + 9$

vertices (0, 0), (0, 9), (6, 8), (8, 0)

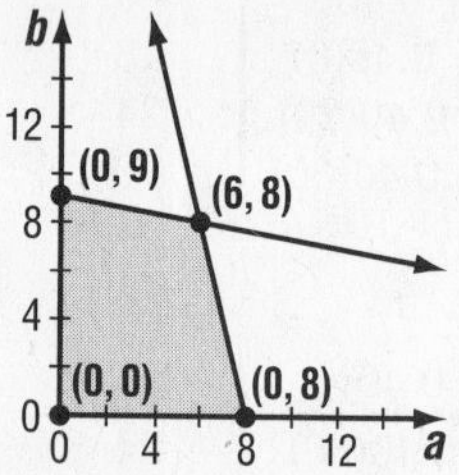

$f(a, b) = a + b$

(a, b)	$a + b$	$f(a, b)$
(0, 0)	0 + 0	0
(0, 9)	0 + 9	9
(6, 8)	6 + 8	14
(8, 0)	8 + 0	8

14 gallons

10. Let c = console televisions and w = wide-screen televisions.

$c \leq 450$ $\quad c \geq 0$ $\quad 600c + 900w \leq 360{,}000$

$w \leq 200$ $\quad w \geq 0$ $\quad 900w \leq -600c + 360{,}000$

$w \leq -\frac{2}{3}c + 400$

vertices: (0, 0), (0, 200), (300, 200), (450, 100), (450, 0)

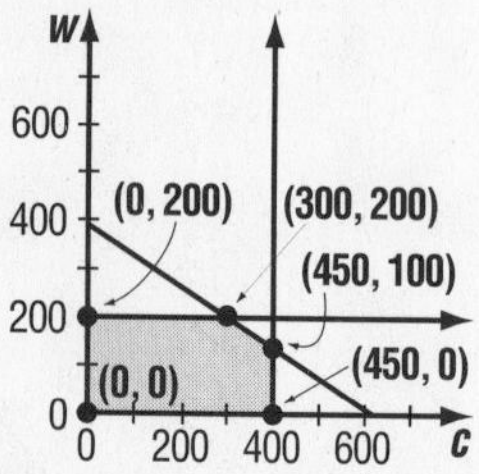

(Continued next column)

$P(c, w) = 125c + 200w$

(c, w)	$125c + 200\,w$	$P(c, w)$
(0, 0)	125(0) + 200(0)	0
(0, 200)	125(0) + 200(200)	40,000
(300, 200)	125(300) + 200(200)	77,500
(450, 100)	125(450) + 200(100)	76,250
(450, 0)	125(450) + 200(0)	56,250

They should produce 300 console and 200 wide-screens for a profit of \$77,500.

11a. Let m = multiple choice and s = short answer.

$0 \leq m \leq 20$ $\quad 1.5m + 2s \leq 50$

$0 \leq s \leq 20$ $\quad 2s \leq -1.5m + 50$

$s \leq -\frac{3}{4}m + 25$

vertices: (0, 0), (0, 20), (6, 20), (20, 10), (20, 0)

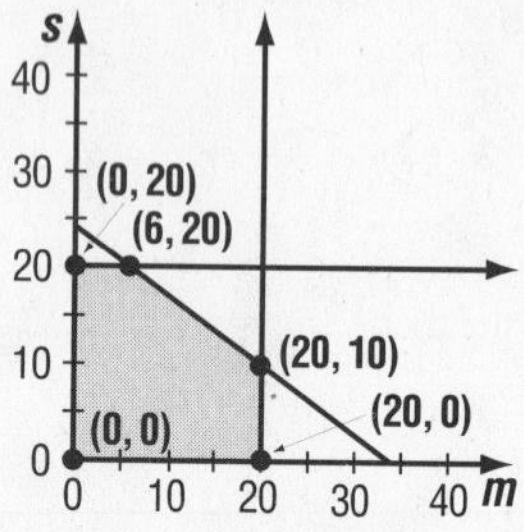

$f(m, s) = 2m + 3s$

(m, s)	$2m + 3s$	$f(m, s)$
(0, 0)	2(0) + 3(0)	0
(0, 20)	2(0) + 3(20)	60
(6, 20)	2(6) + 3(20)	72
(20, 10)	2(20) + 3(10)	70
(20, 0)	2(20) + 3(0)	40

Maximum score: 72

11b. Sample answer: Take a speed reading course so that she can read and answer the multiple-choice questions in less time.

12a. $0 \leq x \leq 5$

$0 \leq y \leq 6$

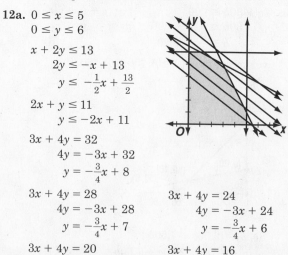

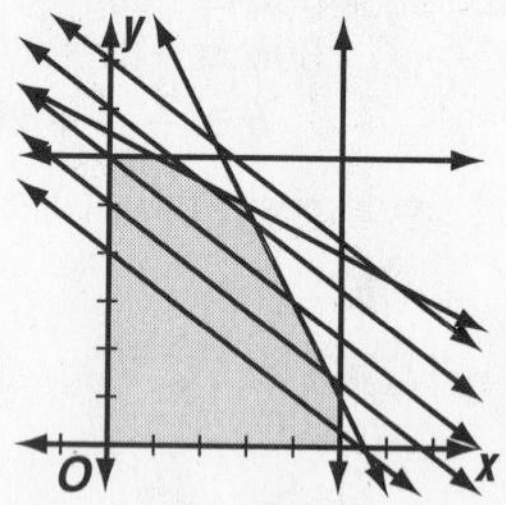

$x + 2y \leq 13$

$2y \leq -x + 13$

$y \leq -\frac{1}{2}x + \frac{13}{2}$

$2x + y \leq 11$

$y \leq -2x + 11$

$3x + 4y = 32$

$4y = -3x + 32$

$y = -\frac{3}{4}x + 8$

$3x + 4y = 28$

$4y = -3x + 28$

$y = -\frac{3}{4}x + 7$

$3x + 4y = 24$

$4y = -3x + 24$

$y = -\frac{3}{4}x + 6$

$3x + 4y = 20$

$4y = -3x + 20$

$y = -\frac{3}{4}x + 5$

$3x + 4y = 16$

$4y = -3x + 16$

$y = -\frac{3}{4}x + 4$

The maximum is located at (3, 5) and is between 32 and 28.

12b. $3x + 6y = 42$
$6y = -3x + 42$
$y = -\frac{1}{2}x + 7$

$3x + 6y = 36$
$6y = -3x + 36$
$y = -\frac{1}{2}x + 6$

$3x + 6y = 30$
$6y = -3x + 30$
$y = -\frac{1}{2}x + 5$

$3x + 6y = 24$
$6y = -3x + 24$
$y = -\frac{1}{2}x + 4$

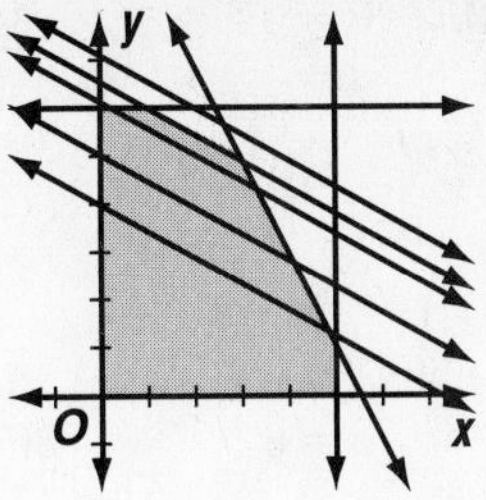

The maximum is reached at any point on the equation $x + 2y = 13$ where $1 \le x \le 3$.

13. $x \ge 0$ $y \ge 3$ $y \ge 2x + 1$ $y \le -0.5x + 6$

vertices: (0, 3), (0, 6), (2, 5), (1, 3)

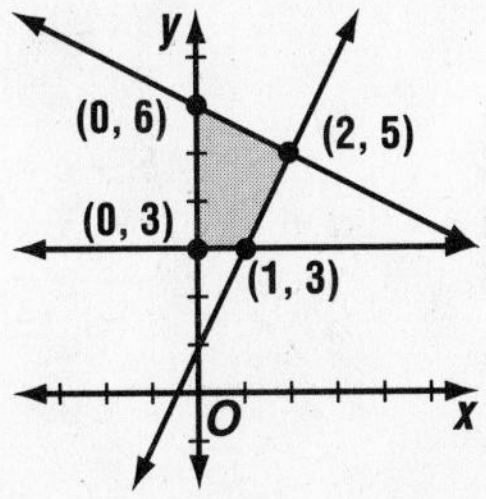

(x, y)	$3x - 2y$	$f(x\ y)$
(0, 3)	3(0) − 2(3)	−6
(0, 6)	3(0) − 2(6)	−12
(2, 5)	3(2) − 2(5)	−4
(1, 3)	3(1) − 2(3)	−3

maximum: $f(1, 3) = -3$
minimum: $f(0, 6) = -12$

14. Sample answer: $x \ge 0, y \ge 0, x + y \le 6$

15. 10:00 − 2:00 = 4 hours

(0, 195), (4, 415) $m = \frac{195 - 415}{0 - 4}$
$= \frac{-220}{-4}$
$= 55$; 55 mph

16. $5y - 25x = -10$
$5y = 25x - 10$
$y = 5x - 2$

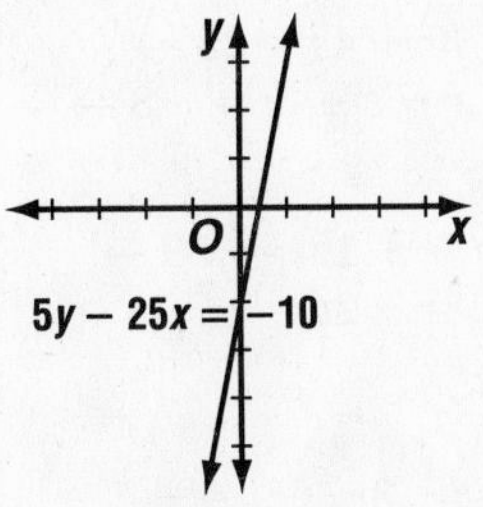

17. $|x| < 4$

3-7 Solving Systems of Equations in Three Variables

Page 169 Check for Understanding

1. The third question tells us that $c = 2r$.

2a. Sample answer: The system may produce an obvious error, such as $0 = 5$.

2b. Sample answer: The system may produce two equations in three unknowns.

3.
$3x - 7y + 2z = 43$
$3(4) - 7(-3) + 2(5) \stackrel{?}{=} 43$
$12 + 21 + 10 \stackrel{?}{=} 43$
$43 = 43$; true

$5x + 2y - 3z = -1$
$5(4) + 2(-3) - 3(5) \stackrel{?}{=} -1$
$20 - 6 - 15 \stackrel{?}{=} -1$
$-1 = -1$; true

$2x + 5y - z = -12$
$2(4) + 5(-3) - 5 = -12$
$8 - 15 - 5 = -12$
$-12 = -12$; true; yes

4.
$5a - 3b + c = -3$
$5(-2) - 3(0) + 7 \stackrel{?}{=} -3$
$-10 - 0 + 7 \stackrel{?}{=} -3$
$-3 = -3$; true

$7a + 2b - 3c = -35$
$7(-2) + 2(0) - 3(7) \stackrel{?}{=} -35$
$-14 + 0 - 21 \stackrel{?}{=} -35$
$-35 = -35$; true

$a - 6b + 7c = 51$
$-2 - 6(0) + 7(7) \stackrel{?}{=} 51$
$-2 - 0 + 49 \stackrel{?}{=} 51$
$47 \ne 51$; false; no

5.
$4x - 3y + 5z = 43 \rightarrow$ $-4x + 3y - 5z = -43$
$2x + y = 9 \rightarrow$ $(+)\ 4x + 2y = 18$
$5y - 5z = -25$

$5y - 5z = -25 \rightarrow$ $-10y + 10z = 50$
$3y - 2z = -9 \rightarrow$ $(+)\ 15y - 10z = -45$
$5y = 5$
$y = 1$

$2x + y = 9$
$2x + 1 = 9$
$2x = 8$
$x = 4$

$3y - 2z = -9$
$3(1) - 2z = -9$
$3 - 2z = -9$
$-2z = -12$
$z = 6$ (4, 1, 6)

6.
$6a - 2b = 18 \rightarrow$ $-6a + 2b = -18$
$a + 6c = -28 \rightarrow$ $(+)\ 6a + 36c = -168$
$2b + 36c = -186$

$2b + 36c = -186 \rightarrow$ $-6b - 108c = 558$
$3b + 5c = -34 \rightarrow$ $(+)\ 6b + 10c = -68$
$-98c = 490$
$c = -5$

$a + 6c = -28$
$a + 6(-5) = -28$
$a - 30 = -28$
$a = 2$

$6a - 2b = 18$
$6(2) - 2b = 18$
$12 - 2b = 18$
$-2b = 6$
$b = -3$ (2, −3, −5)

7. $4x + 3y + 2z = 34 \rightarrow$ $\quad -4x - 3y - 2z = -34$
$2x + 4y + 3z = 45 \rightarrow$ $\quad (+)\ 4x + 8y + 6z = 90$
$5y + 4z = 56$

$2x + 4y + 3z = 45 \rightarrow$ $\quad 6x + 12y + 9z = 135$
$3x + 2y + 4z = 47 \rightarrow$ $\quad (+)\ -6x - 4y - 8z = -94$
$8y + z = 41$

$5y + 4z = 56 \rightarrow$ $\quad -5y - 4z = -56$
$8y + z = 41 \rightarrow$ $\quad (+)\ 32y + 4z = 164$
$27y = 108$
$y = 4$

$8y + z = 41$, $8(4) + z = 41$, $32 + z = 41$, $z = 9$

$2x + 4y + 3z = 45$, $2x + 4(4) + 3(9) = 45$, $2x + 16 + 27 = 45$, $2x = 2$, $x = 1$ $\quad (1, 4, 9)$

8. $x + y + z = -1 \rightarrow$ $\quad 2x + 2y + 2z = -2$
$3x - 2y - 4z = 16 \rightarrow$ $\quad (+)\ 3x - 2y - 4z = 16$
$5x - 2z = 14$

$x + y + z = -1$
$(+)\ 2x - y + z = 19$
$3x + 2z = 18$

$5x - 2z = 14$
$(+)\ 3x + 2z = 18$
$8x = 32$
$x = 4$

$3x + 2z = 18$, $3(4) + 2z = 18$, $12 + 2z = 18$, $2z = 6$, $z = 3$

$x + y + z = -1$, $4 + y + 3 = -1$, $y + 7 = -1$, $y = -8$ $\quad (4, -8, 3)$

9. Sample answer: $x + y + z = -9$, $x + y - z = 1$, $x - y + z = -13$

10. Sample answer: $x + y + z = 1$, $x + y - z = -11$, $x - y + z = 7$

Pages 169–171 Exercises

11. $3a + 7b - 4c = -17$
$3(2) + 7(-1) - 4(4) \stackrel{?}{=} -17$
$6 - 7 - 16 \stackrel{?}{=} -17$
$-17 = -17$; true

$2a - 8b - c = 8$
$2(2) - 8(-1) - 4 \stackrel{?}{=} 8$
$4 + 8 - 4 \stackrel{?}{=} 8$
$8 = 8$; true

$6a - b + 3c \stackrel{?}{=} 23$
$6(2) - (-1) + 3(4) \stackrel{?}{=} 23$
$12 + 1 + 12 = 23$
$25 \neq 23$; false; no

12. $x + 3z = -5$
$-2 + 3(-1) \stackrel{?}{=} -5$
$-2 - 3 \stackrel{?}{=} -5$
$-5 = -5$; true

$5x - 2y = -22$
$5(-2) - 2(6) \stackrel{?}{=} -22$
$-10 - 12 \stackrel{?}{=} -22$
$-22 = -22$; true

$5y - 6z = 36$
$5(6) - 6(-1) \stackrel{?}{=} 36$
$30 + 6 \stackrel{?}{=} 36$
$36 = 36$; true; yes

13. $-3t = 12$, $t = -4$

$6s + 5t = 10$, $6s + 5(-4) = 10$, $6s - 20 = 10$, $6s = 30$, $s = 5$

$5r + 2s = 0$, $5r + 2(5) = 0$, $5r + 10 = 0$, $5r = -10$, $r = -2$

$(-2, 5, -4)$

14. $2a = 12$, $a = 6$

$3a + b = 13$, $3(6) + b = 13$, $18 + b = 13$, $b = -5$

$2b - c = -13$, $2(-5) - c = -13$, $-10 - c = -13$, $-c = -3$, $c = 3$

$(6, -5, 3)$

15. $x + y - z = -1$
$(+)\ x + y + z = 3$
$2x + 2y = 2$
$x + y = 1$

$x + y + z = 3$
$(+)\ 3x - 2y - z = -4$
$4x - y = -1$

$4x - y = -1$
$(+)\ x + y = 1$
$5x = 0$
$x = 0$

$x + y = 1$, $0 + y = 1$, $y = 1$

$x + y + z = 3$, $0 + 1 + z = 3$, $1 + z = 3$, $z = 2$

$(0, 1, 2)$

16. $3b = -3$, $b = -1$

$b + c = 4$, $-1 + c = 4$, $c = 5$

$2a + 4b - c = -3$, $2a + 4(-1) - 5 = -3$, $2a - 9 = -3$, $2a = 6$, $a = 3$

$(3, -1, 5)$

17. $-2y + 3z = 9 \rightarrow$ $\quad -2y + 3z = 9$
$7x - z = 27 \rightarrow$ $\quad (+)\ 21x - 3z = 81$
$21x - 2y = 90$

$21x - 2y = 90 \rightarrow$ $\quad 147x - 14y = 630$
$5x + 7y = -1 \rightarrow$ $\quad (+)\ 10x + 14y = -2$
$157x = 628$
$x = 4$

$5x + 7y = -1$, $5(4) + 7y = -1$, $20 + 7y = -1$, $7y = -21$, $y = -3$

$7x - z = 27$, $7(4) - z = 27$, $28 - z = 27$, $-z = -1$, $z = 1$ $\quad (4, -3, 1)$

18. $2s - t = 15 \rightarrow$ $\quad 4s - 2t = 30$
$3r + 2t = -7 \rightarrow$ $\quad (+)\ 3r + 2t = -7$
$3r + 4s = 23$

$3r + 4s = 23 \rightarrow$ $\quad 3r + 4s = 23$
$r - s + 3t = -8 \rightarrow$ $\quad (+)\ 4r - 4s + 12t = -32$
$7r + 12t = -9$

$7r + 12t = -9 \rightarrow$ $\quad 7r + 12t = -9$
$3r + 2t = -7 \rightarrow$ $\quad (+)\ -18r - 12t = 42$
$-11r = 33$
$r = -3$

$3r + 2t = -7$, $3(-3) + 2t = -7$, $-9 + 2t = -7$, $2t = 2$, $t = 1$

$2s - t = 15$, $2s - 1 = 15$, $2s = 16$, $s = 8$

$(-3, 8, 1)$

19.
$$\begin{array}{ll} 5a - b + 3c = 5 \rightarrow & 35a - 7b + 21c = 35 \\ 2a + 7b - 2c = 5 \rightarrow & (+)\ 2a + 7b - 2c = 5 \\ \hline & 37a + 19c = 40 \end{array}$$

$$\begin{array}{ll} 5a - b + 3c = 5 \rightarrow & -25a + 5b - 15c = -25 \\ 4a - 5b - 7c = -65 \rightarrow & (+)\ 4a - 5b - 7c = -65 \\ \hline & -21a - 22c = -90 \end{array}$$

$$\begin{array}{ll} 37a + 19c = 40 \rightarrow & 777a + 399c = 840 \\ -21a - 22c = -90 \rightarrow & (+)\ -777a - 814c = -3330 \\ \hline & -415c = -2490 \\ & c = 6 \end{array}$$

$$\begin{array}{rr} 37a + 19c = 40 & 5a - b + 3c = 5 \\ 37a + 19(6) = 40 & 5(-2) - b + 3(6) = 5 \\ 37a + 114 = 40 & -10 - b + 18 = 5 \\ 37a = -74 & -b = -3 \\ a = -2 & b = 3 \end{array}$$

$(-2, 3, 6)$

20.
$$\begin{array}{ll} 6x + 2y - 3z = -17 \rightarrow & 6x + 2y - 3z = -17 \\ 7x - 5y + z = 72 \rightarrow & (+)\ 21x - 15y + 3z = 216 \\ \hline & 27x - 13y = 199 \end{array}$$

$$\begin{array}{ll} 7x - 5y + z = 72 \rightarrow & -21x + 15y - 3z = -216 \\ 2x + 8y + 3z = -21 \rightarrow & (+)\ 2x + 8y + 3z = -21 \\ \hline & -19x + 23y = -237 \end{array}$$

$$\begin{array}{ll} 27x - 13y = 199 \rightarrow & 621x - 299y = 4577 \\ -19x + 23y = -237 \rightarrow & (+)\ -247x + 299y = -3081 \\ \hline & 374x = 1496 \\ & x = 4 \end{array}$$

$$\begin{array}{rr} 27x - 13y = 199 & 7x - 5y + z = 72 \\ 27(4) - 13y = 199 & 7(4) - 5(-7) + z = 72 \\ 108 - 13y = 199 & 28 + 35 + z = 72 \\ -13y = 91 & z = 9 \\ y = -7 & (4, -7, 9) \end{array}$$

21.
$$\begin{array}{ll} 3x + 4y - 3z = 5 \rightarrow & 3x + 4y - 3z = 5 \\ x + 6y + 2z = 3 \rightarrow & (+)\ -3x - 18y - 6z = -9 \\ \hline & -14y - 9z = -4 \end{array}$$

$$\begin{array}{ll} x + 6y + 2z = 3 \rightarrow & -6x - 36y - 12z = -18 \\ 6x + 2y + 3z = 4 \rightarrow & (+)\ 6x + 2y + 3z = 4 \\ \hline & -34y - 9z = -14 \end{array}$$

$$\begin{array}{rr} -14y - 9z = -4 & -14y - 9z = -4 \\ (-)\ -34y - 9z = -14 & -14\left(\frac{1}{2}\right) - 9z = -4 \\ \hline 20y = 10 & -7 - 9z = -4 \\ y = \frac{1}{2} & -9z = 3 \\ & z = -\frac{1}{3} \end{array}$$

$$\begin{array}{r} x + 6y + 2z = 3 \\ x + 6\left(\frac{1}{2}\right) + 2\left(-\frac{1}{3}\right) = 3 \\ x + 3 - \frac{2}{3} = 3 \\ x + \frac{7}{3} = 3 \\ x = \frac{2}{3} \end{array}$$

$\left(\frac{2}{3}, \frac{1}{2}, -\frac{1}{3}\right)$

22.
$$\begin{array}{ll} 4x + 7y - z = -10 \rightarrow & 24x + 42y - 6z = -60 \\ 6x - 3y + 6z = 3 \rightarrow & (+)\ 6x - 3y + 6z = 3 \\ \hline & 30x + 39y = -57 \end{array}$$

$$\begin{array}{ll} 4x + 7y - z = -10 \rightarrow & 32x + 56y - 8z = -80 \\ 2x + y + 8z = 9 \rightarrow & (+)\ 2x + y + 8z = 9 \\ \hline & 34x + 57y = -71 \end{array}$$

$$\begin{array}{ll} 30x + 39y = -57 \rightarrow & 1020x + 1326y = -1938 \\ 34x + 57y = -71 \rightarrow & (+)\ -1020x - 1710y = 2130 \\ \hline & -384y = 192 \\ & y = -\frac{1}{2} \end{array}$$

$$\begin{array}{rr} 30x + 39y = -57 & 4x + 7y - z = -10 \\ 30x + 39\left(-\frac{1}{2}\right) = -57 & 4\left(-\frac{5}{4}\right) + 7\left(-\frac{1}{2}\right) - z = -10 \\ 30x - \frac{39}{2} = -57 & -5 - \frac{7}{2} - z = -10 \\ 30x = -\frac{75}{2} & -\frac{17}{2} - z = -10 \\ x = -\frac{5}{4} & -z = -\frac{3}{2} \\ & z = \frac{3}{2} \end{array}$$

$\left(-\frac{5}{4}, -\frac{1}{2}, \frac{3}{2}\right)$

23.
$$\begin{array}{ll} 2r + 3s + 4t = 3 \rightarrow & 6r + 9s + 12t = 9 \\ 5r - 9s + 6t = 1 \rightarrow & (+)\ 5r - 9s + 6t = 1 \\ \hline & 11r + 18t = 10 \end{array}$$

$$\begin{array}{ll} 2r + 3s + 4t = 3 \rightarrow & 4r + 6s + 8t = 6 \\ \frac{1}{3}r - \frac{1}{2}s + \frac{1}{3}t = \frac{1}{12} \rightarrow & (+)\ 4r - 6s + 4t = 1 \\ \hline & 8r + 12t = 7 \end{array}$$

$$\begin{array}{ll} 11r + 18t = 10 \rightarrow & 44r + 72t = 40 \\ 8r + 12t = 7 \rightarrow & (+)\ -48r - 72t = -42 \\ \hline & -4r = -2 \\ & r = \frac{1}{2} \end{array}$$

$$\begin{array}{rr} 8r + 12t = 7 & 2r + 3s + 4t = 3 \\ 8\left(\frac{1}{2}\right) + 12t = 7 & 2\left(\frac{1}{2}\right) + 3s + 4\left(\frac{1}{4}\right) = 3 \\ 4 + 12t = 7 & 1 + 3s + 1 = 3 \\ 12t = 3 & 3s = 1 \\ t = \frac{1}{4} & s = \frac{1}{3} \end{array}$$

$\left(\frac{1}{2}, \frac{1}{3}, \frac{1}{4}\right)$

24.
$$\begin{array}{ll} 2x + y + z = 7 \rightarrow & 2x + y + z = 7 \\ \frac{2x}{3} - y + \frac{z}{3} = -\frac{1}{3} \rightarrow & (+)\ -2x + 3y - z = 1 \\ \hline & 4y = 8 \\ & y = 2 \end{array}$$

$$\begin{array}{rr} 2x + y + z = 7 & 12x - 2y - 2z = 2 \\ 2x + 2 + z = 7 & 12x - 2(2) - 2z = 2 \\ 2x + z = 5 & 12x - 4 - 2z = 2 \\ & 12x - 2z = 6 \end{array}$$

$$\begin{array}{ll} 2x + z = 5 \rightarrow & 4x + 2z = 10 \\ 12x - 2z = 6 \rightarrow & (+)\ 12x - 2z = 6 \\ \hline & 16x = 16 \\ & x = 1 \end{array}$$

$$\begin{array}{r} 2x + z = 5 \\ 2(1) + z = 5 \\ z = 3 \end{array}$$

$(1, 2, 3)$

25. Let x = 1st number, y = 2nd number, and z = 3rd number.

$x + y + z = 12$
$x = 5y$
$x + z = 9$

$x + z = 9$
$5y + z = 9$

$x + y + z = 12$
$5y + y + z = 12$
$6y + z = 12$

$$\begin{array}{r} 5y + z = 9 \\ (-)\ 6y + z = 12 \\ \hline -1y \quad = -3 \\ y = 3 \end{array}$$

$x = 5y$
$x = 5(3)$
$x = 15$

$x + y = 9$
$15 + z = 9$
$z = -6$
15, 3, −6

26. Let x = 1st number, y = 2nd number, and z = 3rd number.

$x + y + z = 20$
$x = y + z$
$z = 3x$

$x = y + z$
$x = y + 3x$
$-2x = y$

$x + y + z = 20$
$x + (-2x) + 3x = 20$
$2x = 20$
$x = 10$

$-2x = y$
$-2(10) = y$
$-20 = y$

$z = 3x$
$z = 3(10)$
$z = 30$
10, −20, 30

27. Let x = 1st number, y = 2nd number, and z = 3rd number.

$x + y + z = 18$
$x = 8(y + z) \rightarrow x = 8y + 8z \rightarrow x - 8y - 8z = 0$
$x + z = 11$

$$\begin{array}{r} x + y + z = 18 \\ (-)\ x - 8y - 8z = 0 \\ \hline 9y + 9z = 18 \end{array} \qquad \begin{array}{r} x + y + z = 18 \\ (-)\ x \quad + z = 11 \\ \hline y \quad = 7 \end{array}$$

$9y + 9z = 18$
$9(7) + 9z = 18$
$63 + 9z = 18$
$9z = -45$
$z = -5$

$x + z = 11$
$x + (-5) = 11$
$x = 16$
16, 7, −5

28.

$$\begin{array}{r} w + x + y + z = 2 \\ (+)\ 2w - x - y + 2z = 7 \\ \hline 3w \quad + 3z = 9 \end{array} \qquad \begin{array}{r} w + x + y + z = 2 \\ (+)\ 3w - 2x - y - 3z = -2 \\ \hline 4w - x \quad - 2z = 0 \end{array}$$

$$\begin{array}{rr} 2w - x - y + 2z = 7 \rightarrow & 4w - 2x - 2y + 4z = 14 \\ 2w + 3x + 2y - z = -2 \rightarrow & (+)\ 2w + 3x + 2y - z = -2 \\ \hline & 6w + x \quad + 3z = 12 \end{array}$$

$$\begin{array}{r} 4w - x - 2z = 0 \\ (+)\ 6w + x + 3z = 12 \\ \hline 10w \quad + z = 12 \end{array}$$

$$\begin{array}{rr} 10w + z = 12 \rightarrow & -30w - 3z = -36 \\ 3w + 3z = 9 \rightarrow & (+)\ 3w + 3z = 9 \\ \hline & -27w \quad = -27 \\ & w = 1 \end{array}$$

$3w + 3z = 9$
$3(1) + 3z = 9$
$3z = 6$
$z = 2$

$4w - x - 2z = 0$
$4(1) - x - 2(2) = 0$
$4 - x - 4 = 0$
$-x = 0$
$x = 0$

$w + x + y + z = 2$
$1 + 0 + y + 2 = 2$
$y + 3 = 2$
$y = -1$
1, 0, −1, 2

29. Let x = 1-year, y = 2-year, and z = 3-year.

$0.034x + 0.05y + 0.06z = 800$
$y = x + 1000 \rightarrow -x + y = 1000$
$z = 15000 - (x + y)$

$-x + y = 1000 \rightarrow$
$0.034x + 0.05y + 0.06z = 800 \rightarrow$

$$\begin{array}{r} -0.034x + 0.034y \qquad = 34 \\ (+)\ 0.034x + 0.05y + 0.06z = 800 \\ \hline 0.084y + 0.06z = 834 \end{array}$$

$z = 15000 - x - y$
$z = 15000 - (y - 1000) - y$
$z = 15000 - y + 1000 - y$
$z = 16000 - 2y$
$2y + z = 1600$

$$\begin{array}{rr} 0.084y + 0.06z = 834 \rightarrow & 0.084y + 0.06z = 834 \\ 2y + z = 16000 \rightarrow & -0.12y - 0.06z = -960 \\ \hline & -0.036y \qquad = -126 \\ & y = 3500 \end{array}$$

$y = x + 1000$
$3500 = x + 1000$
$2500 = x$

$z = 15000 - (x + y)$
$= 15000 - (2500 + 3500)$
$= 9000$

1-year, \$2500; 2-year, \$3500; 3-year, \$9000

30. Let x = hamburger cost, y = cheeseburger cost, and z = jumbo cost.

$3x + 5y + 6z = 25.24$
$2x + 7y + 5z = 25.68$
$4x + 4y + 7z = 26.59$

$$\begin{array}{rr} 3x + 5y + 6z = 25.24 \rightarrow & 6x + 10y + 12z = 50.48 \\ 2x + 7y + 5z = 25.68 \rightarrow & (+)\ -6x - 21y - 15z = -77.04 \\ \hline & -11y - 3z = -26.56 \end{array}$$

$$\begin{array}{rr} 2x + 7y + 5z = 25.68 \rightarrow & -4x - 14y - 10z = -51.36 \\ 4x + 4y + 7z = 26.59 \rightarrow & (+)\ 4x + 4y + 7z = 26.59 \\ \hline & -10y - 3z = -24.77 \end{array}$$

$$\begin{array}{r} -11y - 3z = -26.56 \\ (-)\ -10y - 3z = -24.77 \\ \hline -1y \quad = -1.79 \\ y = 1.79 \end{array}$$

$-10y - 3z = -24.77$
$-10(1.79) - 3z = -24.77$
$-17.9 - 3z = -24.77$
$-3z = -6.87$
$z = 2.29$

$2x + 7y + 5z = 25.68$
$2x + 7(1.79) + 5(2.29) = 25.68$
$2x + 12.53 + 11.45 = 25.68$
$2x = 1.70$
$x = 0.85$

Hamburger, \$0.85; Double Cheeseburger, \$1.79; Jumbo Jack, \$2.29

31. Let x = 3-point goal, y = 2-point goal, and z = 1-point free throw.

$y = x + z \rightarrow -x + y - z = 0$
$2y - 1 = 3x + z \rightarrow -3x + 2y - z = 1$
$3x + 2y + z = 35$

$$\begin{array}{r} -x + y - z = 0 \\ (-)\ -3x + 2y - z = 1 \\ \hline 2x - y \quad = -1 \end{array} \qquad \begin{array}{r} -x + y - z = 0 \\ (+)\ 3x + 2y + z = 35 \\ \hline 2x + 3y \quad = 35 \end{array}$$

$$\begin{array}{r} 2x - y = -1 \\ (-)\ 2x + 3y = 35 \\ \hline -4y = -36 \\ y = 9 \end{array}$$

$2x + 3y = 35$
$2x + 3(9) = 35$
$2x + 27 = 35$
$2x = 8$
$x = 4$

$y = x + z$
$9 = 4 + z$
$5 = z$

3-pointers, 4; 2-pointers, 9; free throws, 5

32a. Let x = jean jackets and y = leather jackets.
$0 \le x \le 30 \quad 0 \le y \le 20 \quad 10x + 20y \le 500$

$$20y \le -10x + 500$$
$$y \le -\frac{1}{2}x + 25$$

vertices: (0,0), (0, 20), (10, 20), (30, 10), (30, 0)

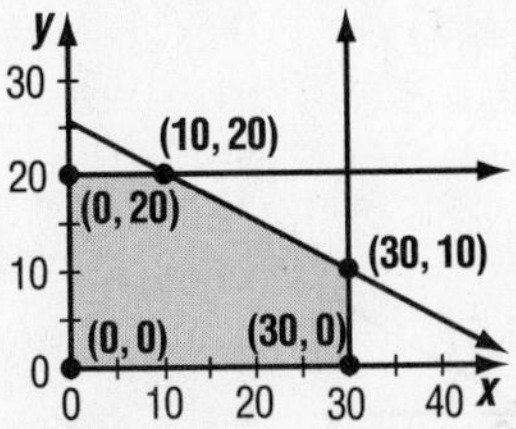

$P(x, y) = x + y$

(x, y)	$x + y$	$P(x, y)$
(0,0)	0 + 0	0
(0, 20)	0 + 20	20
(10, 20)	10 + 20	30
(30, 10)	30 + 10	40
(30, 0)	30 + 0	30

30 jean jackets and 10 leather jackets should be produced.

32b. $P(x, y) = x + 3y$

(x, y)	$x + 3y$	$P(x, y)$
(0, 0)	0 + 3(0)	0
(0, 20)	0 + 3(20)	60
(10, 20)	10 + 3(20)	70
(30, 10)	30 + 3(10)	60
(30, 0)	30 + 3(0)	30

10 jean jackets and 20 leather jackets should be produced.

33. $x + y \ge 4 \qquad x \le 2y$
$y \ge -x + 4 \qquad 2y \ge x$
$y \ge \frac{1}{2}x$ a

34a. $c = 0.95(t-1) + 0.50$
$= 0.95(2-1) + 0.50$
$= 1.45$; \$1.45

$c = 0.95(t - 1) + 0.50$
$= 0.95(3-1) + 0.50$
$= 0.95(2) + 0.50$
$= 2.4$; \$2.40

$c = 0.95(t- 1) + 0.50$
$= 0.95(3- 1) + 0.50$
$= 0.95(2) + 0.50$
$= 2.4$; \$2.40

$c = 0.95(t - 1) + 0.50$
$= 0.95(3-1) + 0.50$
$= 0.95(2) + 0.50$
$= 2.4$; \$2.40

$c = 0.95(t - 1) + 0.50$
$= 0.95(4 - 1) + 0.50$
$= 0.95(3) + 0.50$
$= 3.35$; \$3.35

$c = 0.95(t - 1) + 0.50$
$= 0.95(4 - 1) + 0.50$
$= 0.95(3) + 0.50$
$= 3.35$; \$3.35

34b. (2, 1.45), (2.25, 2.40), (2.5, 2.40), (3, 2.40), (3.75, 3.35), (4, 3.35)

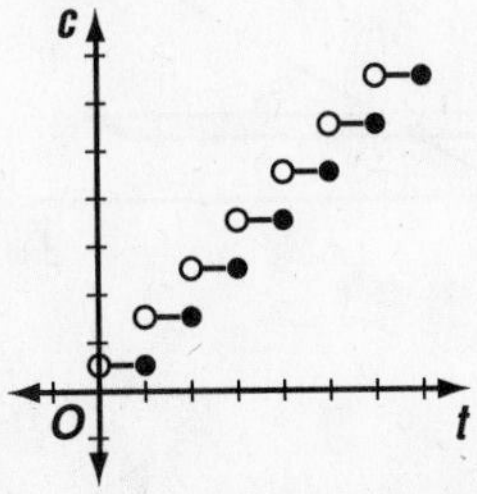

34c. \$7.15

34d. It is a series of steps with open circles on the left and closed circles on the right; a step function.

35a. $y = 0.25x + 20$; $y = 0.25x + 35$

35b. parallel (same slopes)

35c. \$15, the luxury car is alway \$15 more for equal miles.

36. $f(x) = x^2 + 3x$
$f(5) = 5^2 + 3(5)$
$= 25 + 15$
$= 40$

37. $2|-x - 6| = -3x$
$|-x - 6| = -\frac{3}{2}x$

$-x - 6 = -\frac{3}{2}x$ or $-x - 6 = \frac{3}{2}x$
$\frac{1}{2}x - 6 = 0 \qquad -\frac{5}{2}x - 6 = 0$
$\frac{1}{2}x = 6 \qquad -\frac{5}{2}x = 6$
$x = 12 \qquad x = -\frac{12}{5}$

Check:
$2|-x - 6| = -3x \qquad 2|-x - 6| = -3x$
$2|-12 - 6| \stackrel{?}{=} -3(12) \qquad 2\left|-\left(-\frac{12}{5}\right) - 6\right| \stackrel{?}{=} -3\left(-\frac{12}{5}\right)$
$2|-18| \stackrel{?}{=} -36 \qquad 2\left|\frac{12}{5} - 6\right| \stackrel{?}{=} \frac{36}{5}$
$2(18) \stackrel{?}{=} -36 \qquad 2\left|-\frac{18}{5}\right| \stackrel{?}{=} \frac{36}{5}$
$36 \ne -36$; false $\qquad 2\left(\frac{18}{5}\right) \stackrel{?}{=} \frac{36}{5}$
$\frac{36}{5} = \frac{36}{5}$; true

3-7B Modeling Mathematics: Graphing Equations in Three Variables

Page 173 Exercises

1. 1

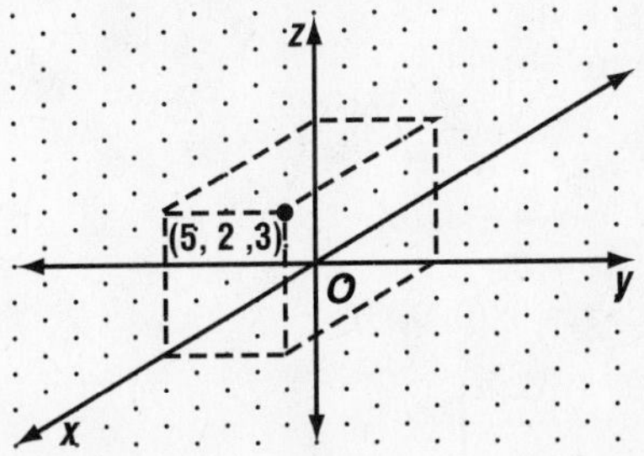

2. 4

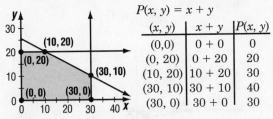

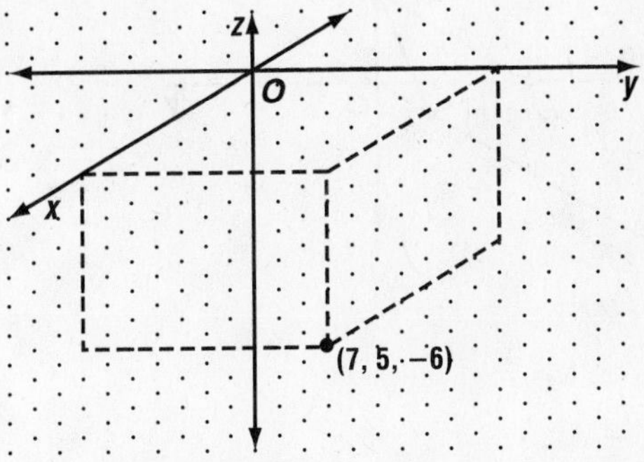

3. none

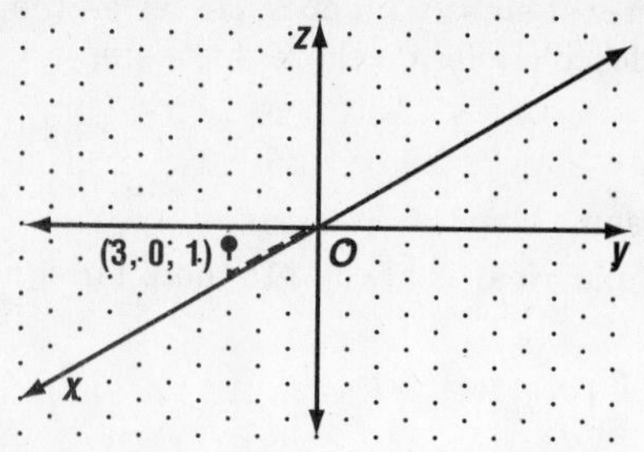

4. 2

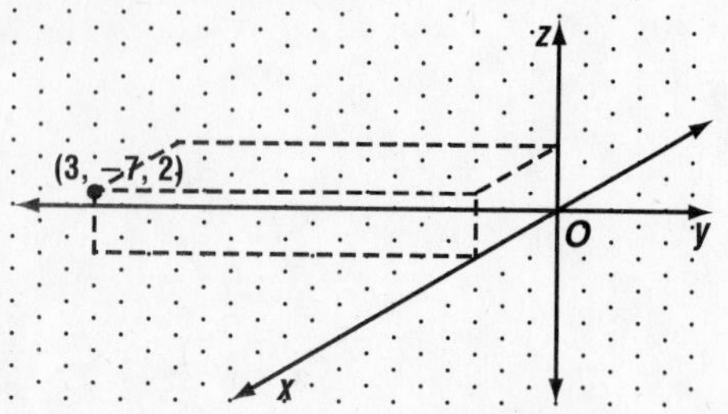

5. $4x + y + 2z = 4$
x-intercept: $4x = 4$
$x = 1$; (1, 0, 0)
y-intercept: $y = 4$; (0, 4, 0)
z-intercept: $2z = 4$
$z = 2$; (0, 0, 2)

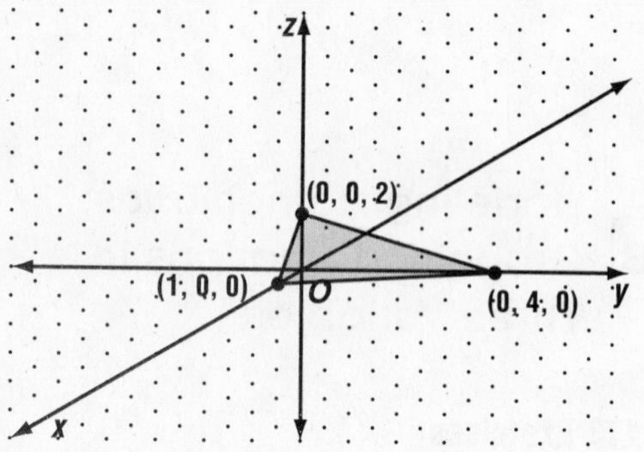

6. $3x - 2y + 2z = 6$
x-intercept: $3x = 6$
$x = 2$; (2, 0, 0)
y-intercept: $-2y = 6$
$y = -3$; (0, −3, 0)
z-intercept: $2z = 6$
$z = 3$; (0, 0, 3)

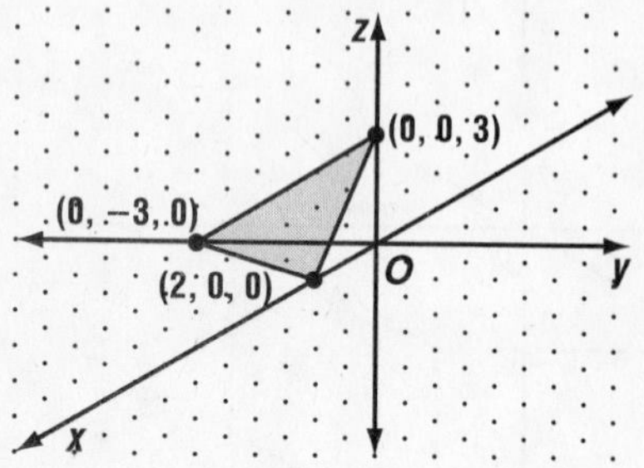

7. $3x - y + 6z = 3$
x-intercept: $3x = 3$
$x = 1$; (1, 0, 0)
y-intercept: $-y = 3$
$y = -3$; (0, −3, 0)
z-intercept: $6z = 3$
$z = \frac{1}{2}$; $\left(0, 0, \frac{1}{2}\right)$

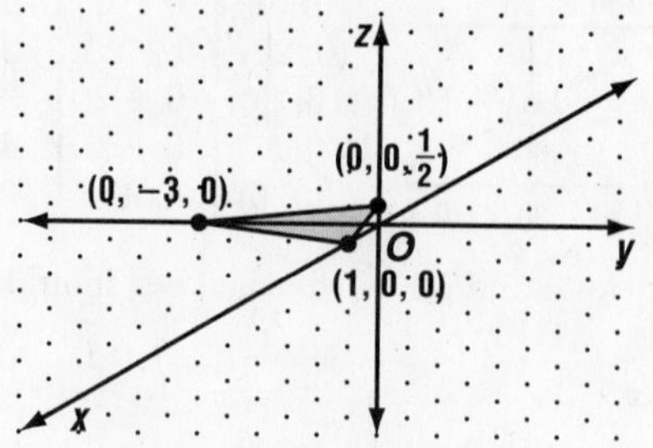

8. $4x + 5y - 10z = 20$
x-intercept: $4x = 20$
$x = 5$; (5, 0, 0)
y-intercept: $5y = 20$
$y = 4$; (0, 4, 0)
z-intercept: $-10z = 20$
$z = -2$; (0, 0, −2)

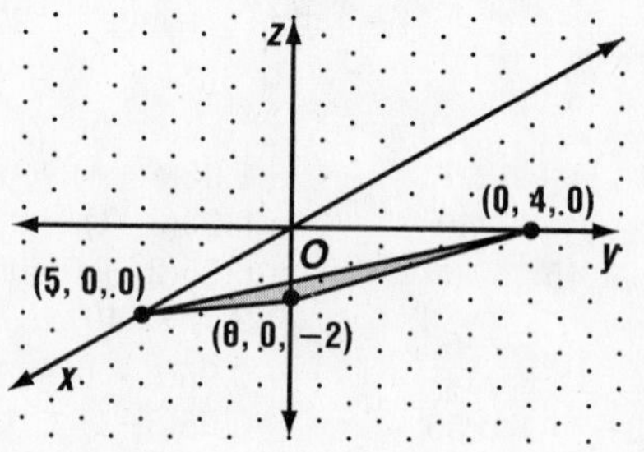

9. $3z - 2x = 6$
x-intercept: $-2x = 6$
$x = -3$; (−3, 0, 0)
y-intercept: none
z-intercept: $3z = 6$
$z = 2$; (0, 0, 2)

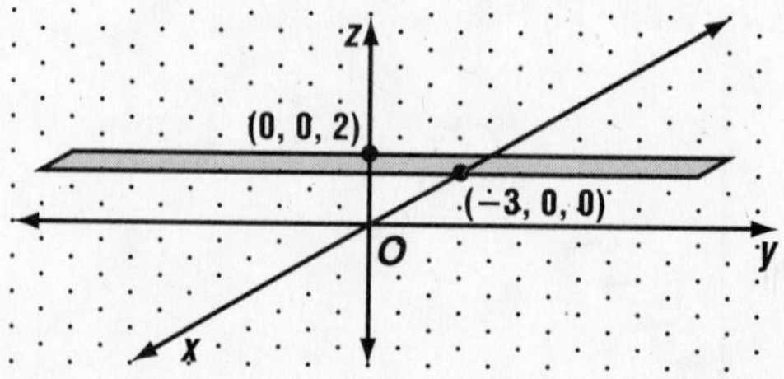

10. $3x - 4y = -12$
x-intercept: $3x = -12$
$x = -4$
(−4, 0, 0)
y-intercept: $-4y = -12$
$y = 3$
(0, 3, 0)
z-intercept: none

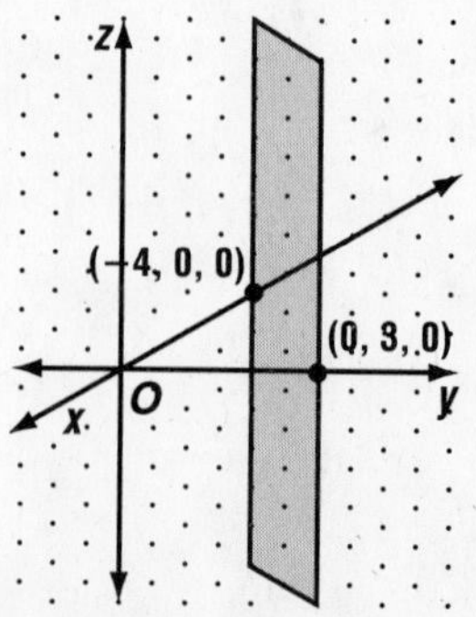

11. Sample answer: $5x - 5y + 2z = 10$

12. Sample answer: $12x + 2y - 3z = 6$

13. Two-dimensional graphs are divided into quandrants and three-dimensional graphs are divided into octants.

14a. a point at 2

14b. a line perpendicular to the x-axis at $x = 2$

14c. a plane perpendicular to the x-axis at $x = 2$

14d. One is a point (one-dimensional), one is a line (two-dimensional), and one is plane (three dimensional).

Chapter 3 Highlights

Page 175 Understanding and Using the Vocabulary

1. c	2. b	3. f	4. j
5. a	6. e	7. i	8. h
9. d	10. g	11. k	

Chapter 3 Study Guide and Assessment

Pages 176–178 Skills and Concepts

12. $3x + 2y = 12$ $\quad$ $x - 2y = 4$

$2y = -3x + 12$ $\quad$ $-2y = -x + 4$

$y = -\frac{3}{2}x + 6$ $\quad$ $y = \frac{1}{2}x - 2$

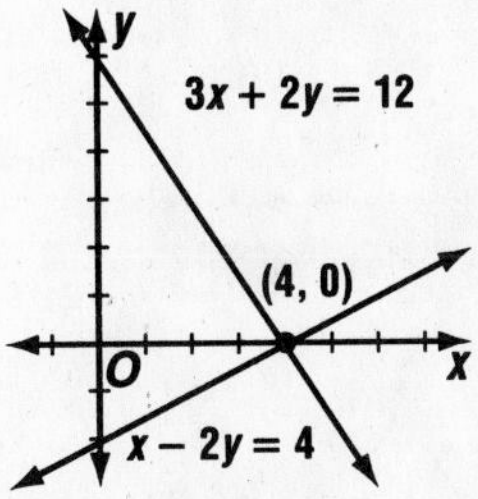

(4, 0); consistent, independent

13. $8x - 10y = 7$ $\quad$ $4x - 5y = 7$

$-10y = -8x + 7$ $\quad$ $-5y = -4x + 7$

$y = \frac{4}{5}x - \frac{7}{10}$ $\quad$ $y = \frac{4}{5}x - \frac{7}{5}$

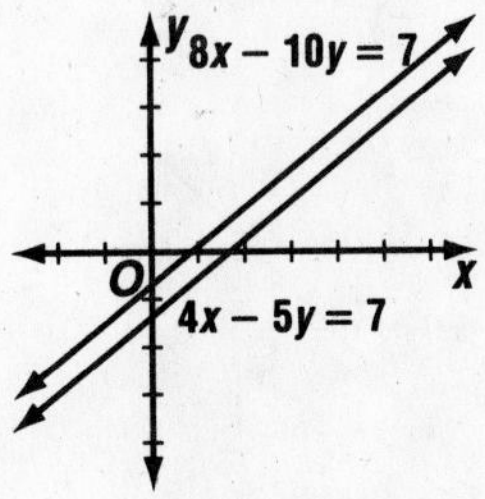

no solution; inconsistent

14. $y - 2x = 8$ $\quad$ $y = \frac{1}{2}x - 4$

$y = 2x + 8$

$(-8, -8)$; consistent, independent

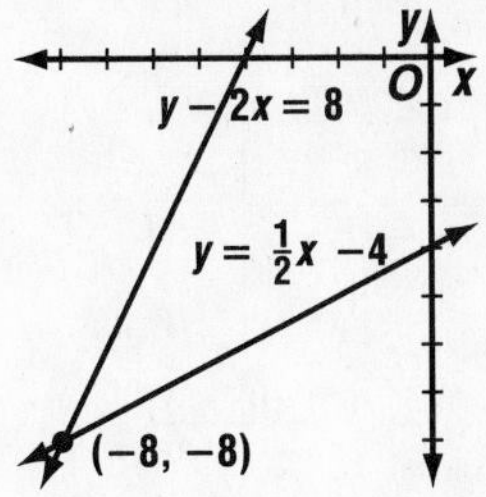

15. $20y + 13x = 10$ $\quad$ $0.65x + y = 0.5$

$20y = -13x + 10$ $\quad$ $y = -0.65x + 0.5$

$y = -0.65 + 0.5$

$20y - 13x = 10$; consistent, dependent

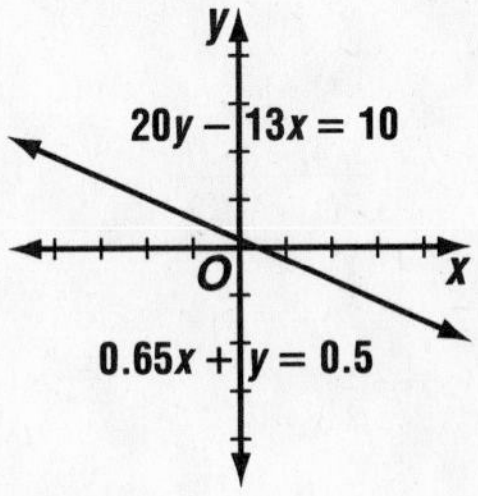

16.
$$\begin{aligned} x + y &= 4 \\ (+)\ x - y &= 8.5 \\ \hline 2x &= 12.5 \\ x &= 6.25 \end{aligned} \qquad \begin{aligned} x + y &= 4 \\ 6.25 + y &= 4 \\ y &= -2.25 \end{aligned}$$

$(6.25, -2.25)$

17. $2x + 3y = -6 \rightarrow$ Multiply by $-2 \rightarrow$ $-4x - 6y = 12$

$3x + 2y = 25 \rightarrow$ Multiply by $3 \rightarrow$ $(+)\ 9x + 6y = 75$

$5x = 87$

$x = 17.4$

$$\begin{aligned} 2x + 3y &= -6 \\ 2(17.4) + 3y &= -6 \\ 34.8 + 3y &= -6 \\ 3y &= -40.8 \\ y &= -13.6 \end{aligned}$$

$(17.4, -13.6)$

18.
$$\begin{aligned} 7y - 2x &= 10 \\ -3y + x &= -3 \\ x &= 3y - 3 \end{aligned} \qquad \begin{aligned} 7y - 2x &= 10 \\ 7y - 2(3y - 3) &= 10 \\ 7y - 6y + 6 &= 10 \\ y + 6 &= 10 \\ y &= 4 \end{aligned} \qquad \begin{aligned} -3y + x &= -3 \\ -3(4) + x &= -3 \\ -12 + x &= -3 \\ x &= 9 \end{aligned}$$

$(9, 4)$

19. $-6y - 2x = 0 \rightarrow$ Multiply by $3 \rightarrow$ $-18y - 6x = 0$

$11y + 3x = 4 \rightarrow$ Multiply by $2 \rightarrow$ $(+)\ 22y + 6x = 8$

$4y = 8$

$y = 2$

$$\begin{aligned} 11y + 3x &= 4 \\ 11(2) + 3x &= 4 \\ 22 + 3x &= 4 \\ 3x &= -18 \\ x &= -6 \end{aligned}$$

$(-6, 2)$

20. $3x - 5y = -13 \rightarrow$ Multiply by $2 \rightarrow$ $6x - 10y = -26$

$4x + 2y = 0 \rightarrow$ Multiply by $5 \rightarrow$ $(+)\ 20x + 10y = 0$

$26x = -26$

$x = -1$

$$\begin{aligned} 4x + 2y &= 0 \\ 4(-1) + 2y &= 0 \\ -4 + 2y &= 0 \\ 2y &= 4 \\ y &= 2 \end{aligned}$$

$(-1, 2)$

21. $\begin{array}{r} c + d = 5 \\ (+)\ 2c - d = 4 \\ \hline 3c \quad = 9 \\ c = 3 \end{array}$ $\quad$ $\begin{array}{r} c + d = 5 \\ 3 + d = 5 \\ d = 2 \end{array}$ $\quad (3, 2)$

22. $x = \dfrac{\begin{vmatrix} 4 & -3 \\ 2 & 5 \end{vmatrix}}{\begin{vmatrix} 2 & -3 \\ 1 & 5 \end{vmatrix}} = \dfrac{4(5) - 2(-3)}{2(5) - 1(-3)} = \dfrac{26}{13} = 2$ $\quad$ $y = \dfrac{\begin{vmatrix} 2 & 4 \\ 1 & 2 \end{vmatrix}}{\begin{vmatrix} 2 & -3 \\ 1 & 5 \end{vmatrix}} = \dfrac{2(2) - 1(4)}{2(5) - 1(-3)} = \dfrac{0}{13} = 0$ $\quad (2, 0)$

23. $x = \dfrac{\begin{vmatrix} 5 & 3 \\ 3 & 4 \end{vmatrix}}{\begin{vmatrix} 7 & 3 \\ 2 & 4 \end{vmatrix}} = \dfrac{5(4) - 3(3)}{7(4) - 2(3)} = \dfrac{11}{22} = \dfrac{1}{2}$ $\quad$ $y = \dfrac{\begin{vmatrix} 7 & 5 \\ 2 & 3 \end{vmatrix}}{\begin{vmatrix} 7 & 3 \\ 2 & 4 \end{vmatrix}} = \dfrac{7(3) - 2(5)}{7(4) - 2(3)} = \dfrac{11}{22} = \dfrac{1}{2}$ $\quad \left(\dfrac{1}{2}, \dfrac{1}{2}\right)$

24. $x = \dfrac{\begin{vmatrix} 7 & -1 \\ 7 & 3 \end{vmatrix}}{\begin{vmatrix} 2 & -1 \\ 1 & 3 \end{vmatrix}} = \dfrac{7(3) - 7(-1)}{2(3) - 1(-1)} = \dfrac{28}{7} = 4$ $\quad$ $y = \dfrac{\begin{vmatrix} 2 & 7 \\ 1 & 7 \end{vmatrix}}{\begin{vmatrix} 2 & -1 \\ 1 & 3 \end{vmatrix}} = \dfrac{2(7) - 1(7)}{2(3) - 1(-1)} = \dfrac{7}{7} = 1$ $\quad (4, 1)$

25. $\begin{array}{r} u + 11 = 8v \\ u - 8v + 11 = 0 \\ u - 8v = -11 \end{array}$ $\quad$ $\begin{array}{r} 8(u - v) = 3 \\ 8u - 8v = 3 \end{array}$

$u = \dfrac{\begin{vmatrix} -11 & -8 \\ 3 & -8 \end{vmatrix}}{\begin{vmatrix} 1 & -8 \\ 8 & -8 \end{vmatrix}} = \dfrac{-11(-8) - 3(-8)}{1(-8) - 8(-8)} = \dfrac{112}{56} = 2$ $\quad$ $v = \dfrac{\begin{vmatrix} 1 & -11 \\ 8 & 3 \end{vmatrix}}{\begin{vmatrix} 1 & -8 \\ 8 & -8 \end{vmatrix}} = \dfrac{1(3) - 8(-11)}{1(-8) - 8(-8)} = \dfrac{91}{56} = \dfrac{13}{8}$ $\quad \left(2, \dfrac{13}{8}\right)$

26. $f = \dfrac{\begin{vmatrix} -1 & -2 \\ -16 & 3 \end{vmatrix}}{\begin{vmatrix} 1 & -2 \\ 2 & 3 \end{vmatrix}} = \dfrac{-1(3) - (-16)(-2)}{1(3) - 2(-2)} = \dfrac{-35}{7} = -5$ $\quad$ $g = \dfrac{\begin{vmatrix} 1 & -1 \\ 2 & -16 \end{vmatrix}}{\begin{vmatrix} 1 & -2 \\ 2 & 3 \end{vmatrix}} = \dfrac{1(-16) - 2(-1)}{1(3) - 2(-2)} = \dfrac{-14}{7} = -2$ $\quad (-5, -2)$

27. $m = \dfrac{\begin{vmatrix} 0 & -1 \\ -6 & 10 \end{vmatrix}}{\begin{vmatrix} 1 & -1 \\ 4 & 10 \end{vmatrix}} = \dfrac{0(10) - (-6)(-1)}{1(10) - 4(-1)} = -\dfrac{6}{14} = -\dfrac{3}{7}$ $\quad$ $n = \dfrac{\begin{vmatrix} 1 & 0 \\ 4 & -6 \end{vmatrix}}{\begin{vmatrix} 1 & -1 \\ 4 & 10 \end{vmatrix}} = \dfrac{1(-6) - 4(0)}{1(10) - 4(-1)} = -\dfrac{6}{14} = -\dfrac{3}{7}$ $\quad \left(-\dfrac{3}{7}, -\dfrac{3}{7}\right)$

28. $y \le 4$
$y > -3$

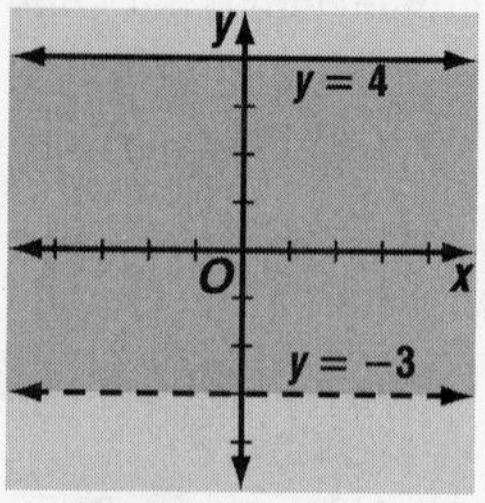

29. $y > 3$
$x \le 1$

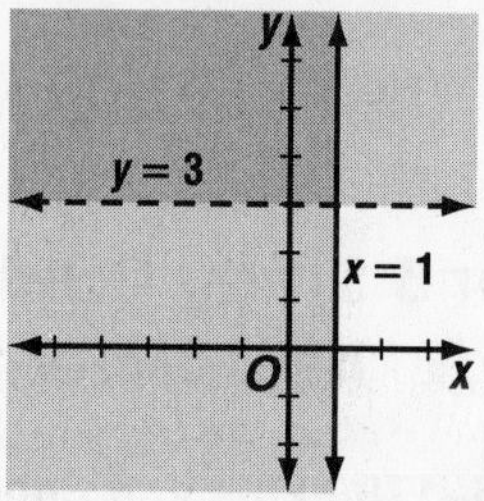

30. $y < x + 1$
$x > 5$

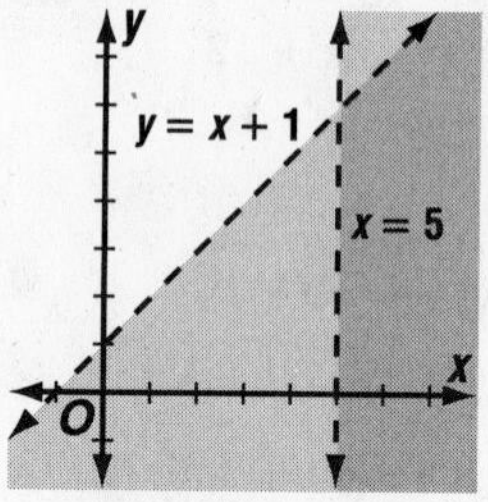

31. $x + y \ge 3$
$y \ge -x + 3$
$x \le 0$

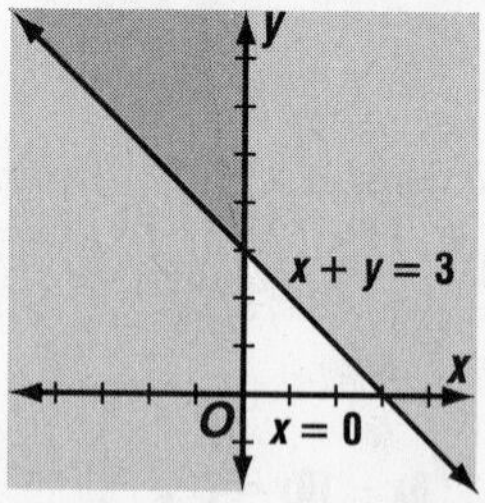

32. $y \le x + 4$
$2y \ge x - 3$
$y \ge \frac{1}{2}x - \frac{3}{2}$

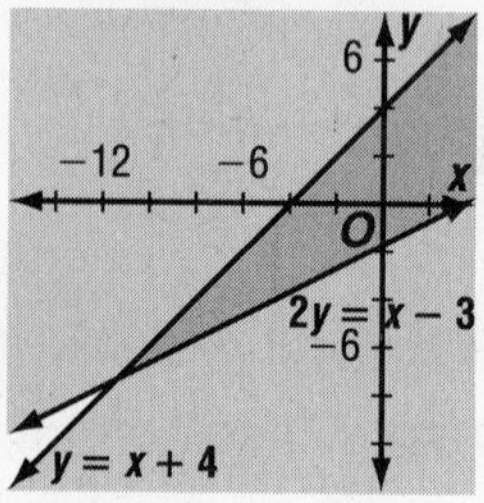

33. $y < 2$
$y \geq -7$
$y \geq 2x$
$y \leq x + 1$

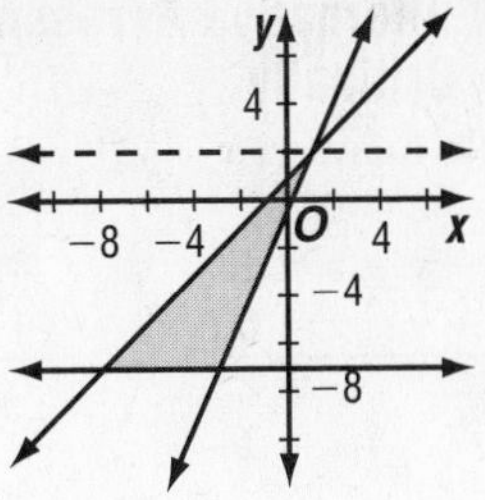

34. $x \geq -5$ $\quad x \leq 4$ $\quad y \geq -1$ $\quad y \leq 3$
vertices: (4, 3), (4, −1), (−5, −1), (−5, 3)

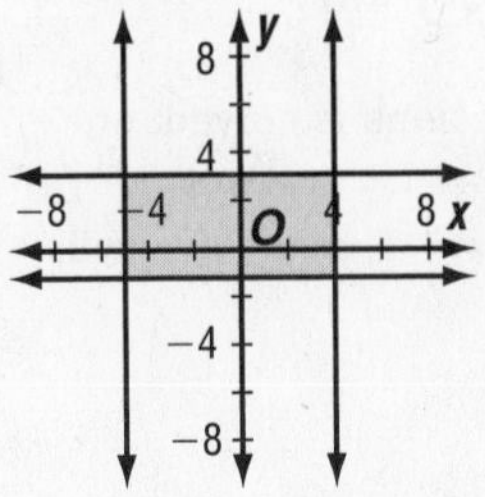

(x, y)	−2x + y	f(x, y)
(4, 3)	−2(4) + 3	−5
(4, −1)	−2(4) + (−1)	−9
(−5, −1)	−2(−5) + (−1)	9
(−5, 3)	−2(−5) + 3	13

maximum: $f(-5, 3) = 13$
minimum: $f(4, -1) = -9$

35. $x \geq 0$ $\quad x + 3y \leq 15$ $\quad 4x + y \leq 16$
$y \geq 0$ $\quad 3y \leq -x + 15$ $\quad y \leq -4x + 16$
$y \leq -\frac{1}{3}x + 5$
vertices: (0, 0), (0, 5), (3, 4), (4, 0)

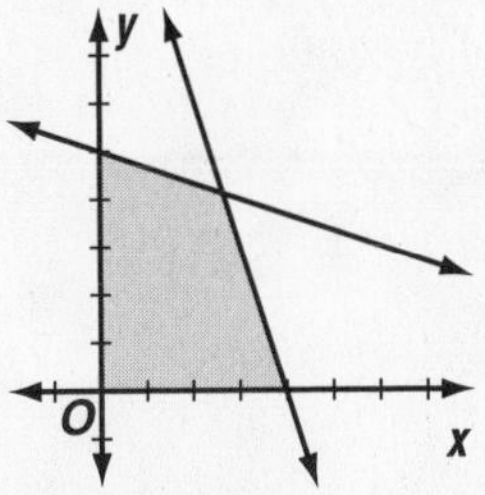

(x, y)	3x + 2y	f(x, y)
(0, 0)	3(0) + 2(0)	0
(0, 5)	3(0) + 2(5)	10
(3, 4)	3(3) + 2(4)	17
(4, 0)	3(4) + 2(0)	12

maximum: $f(3, 4) = 17$
minimum: $f(0, 0) = 0$

36. Let x = adult tickets and y = student tickets.
$x + y \leq 150$ $\quad y \geq \frac{1}{2}x$ $\quad x \geq 0$ $\quad y \geq 0$
$y \leq -x + 150$
vertices: (0, 0), (0, 150), (100, 50)

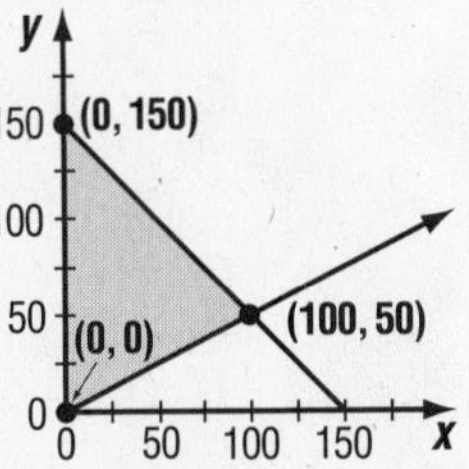

$f(x, y) = 2x + y$

(x, y)	2x + y	f(x, y)
(0, 0)	2(0) + 0	0
(0, 150)	2(0) + 150	150
(100, 50)	2(100) + 50	250

100 adults and 50 students should attend.

37. $x + 4y - z = 6 \rightarrow$ $\quad 3x + 12y - 3z = 18$
$3x + 2y + 3z = 16 \rightarrow$ $\quad (+)\ 3x + 2y + 3z = 16$
$\quad 6x + 14y = 34$

$x + 4y - z = 6$
$(+)\ 2x - y + z = 3$
$3x + 3y = 9$

$6x + 14y = 34 \rightarrow$ $\quad 6x + 14y = 34$
$3x + 3y = 9 \rightarrow$ $\quad (+)\ -6x - 6y = -18$
$\quad 8y = 16$
$\quad y = 2$

$3x + 3y = 9$
$3x + 3(2) = 9$
$3x + 6 = 9$
$3x = 3$
$x = 1$

$2x - y + z = 3$
$2(1) - 2 + z = 3$
$2 - 2 + z = 3$
$z = 3$
(1, 2, 3)

38. $2a + b - c = 5$
$(+)\ a - b + 3c = 9$
$3a + 2c = 14$

$3a + 2c = 14$
$(-)\ 3a - 6c = 6$
$8c = 8$
$c = 1$

$3a + 2c = 14$
$3a + 2(1) = 14$
$3a + 2 = 14$
$3a = 12$
$a = 4$

$2a + b - c = 5$
$2(4) + b - 1 = 5$
$8 + b - 1 = 5$
$b = -2$
(4, −2, 1)

39. $3e = -3$
$e = -1$

$e + f = 4$
$-1 + f = 4$
$f = 5$

$2d + 4e - f = -3$
$2d + 4(-1) - 5 = -3$
$2d - 4 - 5 = -3$
$2d = 6$
$d = 3$

(3, −1, 5)

Page 178 Applications and Problem Solving

40. Let x = student tickets and y = nonstudent tickets.
$x + y \geq 1000$ $\quad 4x + 6y \geq 4800$
$y \geq 1000 - x$ $\quad 6y \geq -4x + 4800$
$x \geq 0$ $\quad y \geq -\frac{2}{3}x + 800$
$y \geq 0$
vertices: (0, 1000), (600, 400), (1200, 0)

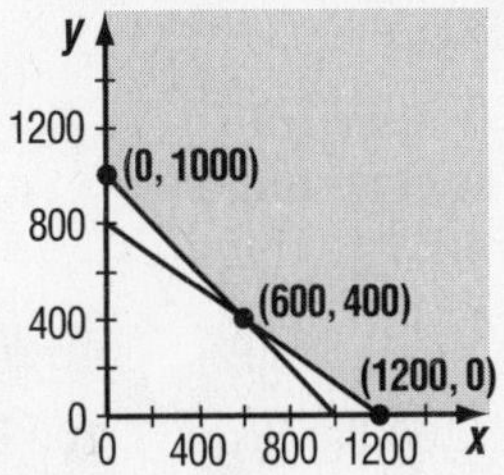

$f(x, y) = 3x + 4y$

(x, y)	3x + 4y	f(x, y)
(0, 1000)	3(0) + 4(1000)	4000
(600, 400)	3(600) + 4(400)	3400
(1200, 0)	3(1200) + 4(0)	3600

minimum: \$3400; maximum: unbounded

41. Let x = burger cost, y = fries cost, and z = cola cost.

$$2x + y + 2z = 6.35$$
$$x + 2y + 2z = 5.45$$
$$3x + 3y + 3z = 11.01$$

$$\begin{array}{ll} 2x + y + 2z = 6.35 \rightarrow & 2x + y + 2z = 6.35 \\ x + 2y + 2z = 5.45 \rightarrow & (+)\ -2x - 4y - 4z = -10.90 \\ \hline & -3y - 2z = -4.55 \end{array}$$

$$\begin{array}{ll} x + 2y + 2z = 5.45 \rightarrow & -3x - 6y - 6z = -16.35 \\ 3x + 3y + 3z = 11.01 \rightarrow & (+)\ 3x + 3y + 3z = 11.01 \\ \hline & -3y - 3z = -5.34 \end{array}$$

$$\begin{array}{r} -3y - 2z = -4.55 \\ (-)\ -3y - 3z = -5.34 \\ \hline z = 0.79 \end{array} \qquad \begin{array}{r} -3y - 2z = -4.55 \\ -3y - 2(0.79) = -4.55 \\ -3y - 1.58 = -4.55 \\ -3y = -2.97 \\ y = 0.99 \end{array}$$

$$\begin{array}{r} x + 2y + 2z = 5.45 \\ x + 2(0.99) + 2(0.79) = 5.45 \\ x + 1.98 + 1.58 = 5.45 \\ x = 1.89 \end{array}$$

burger, \$1.89; fries, \$0.99; cola, \$0.79

42. $0.40x + 0.30y + 0.10z = 131$
$0.40x + 0.90y + 0.80z = 291$
$0.30x + 0.70y + 0.70z = 232$

$$\begin{array}{l} 0.40x + 0.30y + 0.10z = 131 \rightarrow \\ \quad -3.2x - 2.4y - 0.80z = -1048 \\ \quad (+)\ 0.40x + 0.90y + 0.80z = 291 \\ \hline \quad -2.8x - 1.5y = -757 \end{array}$$

$$\begin{array}{l} 0.40x + 0.30y + 0.10z = 131 \rightarrow \\ \quad -2.8x - 2.1y - 0.70z = -917 \\ \quad 0.30x + 0.70y + 0.70z = 232 \\ \hline \quad -2.5x - 1.4y = -685 \end{array}$$

$$\begin{array}{ll} -2.8x - 1.5y = -757 \rightarrow & 3.92x + 2.1y = 1059.8 \\ -2.5x - 1.4y = -685 \rightarrow & (+)\ -3.75x - 2.1y = -1027.5 \\ \hline & 0.17x = 32.3 \\ & x = 190 \end{array}$$

$$\begin{array}{r} -2.8x - 1.5y = -757 \\ 2.8(190) - 1.5y = -757 \\ -532 - 1.5y = -757 \\ -1.5y = -225 \\ y = 150 \end{array}$$

$$\begin{array}{r} 0.40x + 0.30y + 0.10z = 131 \\ 0.40(190) + 0.30(150) + 0.10z = 131 \\ 76 + 45 + 0.10z = 131 \\ 0.10z = 10 \\ z = 100 \end{array}$$

Booth 1, 190 lb; Booth 2, 150 lb.; Booth 3, 100 lb.

Page 179 Alternative Assessment; Thinking Critically

- Sample answer: $x + y + z = 2$, $x - y - z = 2$, $x + y - z = 0$

$$\begin{array}{r} x - y + z = 2 \\ (+)\ x + y - z = 0 \\ \hline 2x = 2 \\ x = 1 \end{array} \qquad \begin{array}{r} x + y + z = 2 \\ (+)\ x - y + z = 2 \\ \hline 2x + 2z = 4 \\ x + z = 2 \end{array}$$

$$\begin{array}{r} x + z = 2 \\ 1 + z = 2 \\ z = 1 \end{array} \qquad \begin{array}{r} x + y + z = 2 \\ 1 + y + 1 = 2 \\ y + 2 = 2 \\ y = 0 \end{array}$$

(1, 0, 1)
When the system of equations is solved, one ordered triple results.

- Sample answer: $x + y + z = 1$, $x + y + z = 2$, $x + y + z = 3$

$$\begin{array}{r} x + y + z = 1 \\ (-)\ x + y + z = 2 \\ \hline 0 = -1 \end{array}$$

When an attempt to solve the system of equations, an incorrect statement results.

- Sample answer: $x + y + z = 2$, $2x + 2y + 2z = 4$, $3x + 3y + 3z - 6$

$$\begin{array}{ll} x + y + z = 2 \rightarrow & 2x + 2y + 2z = 4 \\ 2x + 2y + 2z = 4 \rightarrow & (-)\ 2x + 2y + 2z = -4 \\ \hline & 0 = 0 \end{array}$$

When the system is solved, a true statement results. In this case, all points are on the plane represented by $x + y + z = 2$ satisfy all three equations.

Chapter 4 Using Matrices

4-1A Graphing Technology: Matrices

Page 185 Exercises

Enter matrices: MATRX ▶ ▶ ENTER 3 ENTER 3 ENTER 2 ENTER 1 ENTER 4 ENTER 0 ENTER 1 ENTER (–) 1 ENTER 4 ENTER 2 ENTER 3 ENTER MATRX ▶ ▶ ▼ ENTER 2 ENTER 3 ENTER 6 ENTER (–) 2 ENTER 5 ENTER 0 ENTER 7 ENTER (–) 1 ENTER MATRX ▶ ▶ ▼ ▼ ENTER 3 ENTER 2 ENTER 1 ENTER 4 ENTER (–) 3 ENTER 6 ENTER 7 ENTER (–) 2 ENTER 2nd QUIT

1. (–) MATRX 3 ENTER $\begin{bmatrix} -1 & -4 \\ 3 & -6 \\ -7 & 2 \end{bmatrix}$
2. 4 MATRX 2 ENTER $\begin{bmatrix} 24 & -8 & 20 \\ 0 & 28 & -4 \end{bmatrix}$
3. MATRX ▶ ENTER MATRX ENTER ENTER -10
4. (–) 2 MATRX ENTER ENTER $\begin{bmatrix} -4 & -2 & -8 \\ 0 & -2 & 2 \\ -8 & -4 & -6 \end{bmatrix}$
5. MATRX ENTER x^{-1} $\begin{bmatrix} -0.5 & -0.5 & 0.5 \\ 0.4 & 1 & -0.2 \\ 0.4 & 0 & -0.2 \end{bmatrix}$
6. MATRX 3 MATRX 2 ENTER $\begin{bmatrix} 6 & 26 & 1 \\ -18 & 48 & -21 \\ 42 & -28 & 37 \end{bmatrix}$
7. MATRX 2 MATRX 3 ENTER $\begin{bmatrix} 47 & 2 \\ -28 & 44 \end{bmatrix}$
8. MATRX ▶ ENTER MATRX 2 MATRX 3 ENTER
   2124
9. MATRX 2 MATRX ENTER ENTER $\begin{bmatrix} 32 & 14 & 41 \\ -4 & 5 & -10 \end{bmatrix}$
10. MATRX 3 MATRX 2 – MATRX ENTER ENTER
    $\begin{bmatrix} 4 & 25 & -3 \\ -18 & 47 & -20 \\ 38 & -30 & 34 \end{bmatrix}$
11. MATRX ▶ ENTER MATRX 3 MATRX 2 ENTER
    0
12. MATRX ENTER + MATRX 3 MATRX 2 ENTER
    $\begin{bmatrix} 8 & 27 & 5 \\ -18 & 49 & -22 \\ 46 & -26 & 40 \end{bmatrix}$
13. (MATRX 2 MATRX 3) x^{-1}
    $\begin{bmatrix} 0.0207156309 & -9.416195857\text{ E }^{-4} \\ 0.0131826742 & 0.0221280603 \end{bmatrix}$
14. MATRX ENTER x^2 ENTER $\begin{bmatrix} 20 & 11 & 19 \\ -4 & -1 & -4 \\ 20 & 12 & 23 \end{bmatrix}$
15. (MATRX 2 MATRX 3) x^2 ENTER
    $\begin{bmatrix} 2153 & 182 \\ -2548 & 1880 \end{bmatrix}$
16. MATRX 2 + MATRX 2 MATRX ENTER ENTER
    $\begin{bmatrix} 38 & 12 & 46 \\ -4 & 12 & -11 \end{bmatrix}$
17. MATRX 2 MATRX ENTER MATRX 3 ENTER
    $\begin{bmatrix} 277 & 130 \\ -89 & 34 \end{bmatrix}$
18. MATRX 3 MATRX 2 MATRX ENTER ENTER
    $\begin{bmatrix} 16 & 34 & 1 \\ -120 & -12 & -183 \\ 232 & 88 & 307 \end{bmatrix}$

4-1 An Introduction to Matrices

Pages 190–191 Check for Understanding

1. Sample answer: a rectangular array of numbers in rows and columns
2. See students' work.
3. b; -1 is in row one, 3 is in row two
4. $\begin{bmatrix} 1 & 2 & -4 \\ 4 & -3 & -4 \end{bmatrix}$
5. Sample answer: an enlargement or reduction
6. Sample answer: When the matrix is multiplied by a number greater than 1, the figure is enlarged; when the matrix is multiplied by a number between 0 and 1, the figure is reduced. See students' work for drawings.
7. $-2[7\ \ 3\ \ -1] = [-14\ \ -6\ \ 2]$
8. $4\begin{bmatrix} -1 & 0 \\ 3 & -2 \end{bmatrix} = \begin{bmatrix} -4 & 0 \\ 12 & -8 \end{bmatrix}$
9. $[2x\ \ 3\ \ 3z] = [5\ \ 3y\ \ 9]$

   $2x = 5$, $x = 2.5$; $3 = 3y$, $1 = y$; $3z = 9$, $z = 3$

10. $\begin{bmatrix} 6x \\ y \end{bmatrix} = \begin{bmatrix} 62 + 8y \\ 6-2x \end{bmatrix}$

    $6x = 62 + 8y$
    $6x = 62 + 8(6-2x)$
    $6x = 62 + 48-16x$
    $22x = 110$
    $x = 5$

    $y = 6 - 2x$
    $= 6 - 2(5)$
    $= 6 - 10$
    $= -4$

11.

	plain	cheese
turkey	15	12
ham	8	10
roast beef	8	11

12a. $\begin{bmatrix} 4 & -3 & 1 \\ 5 & -2 & -4 \end{bmatrix}$

12b. $\frac{1}{2}\begin{bmatrix} 4 & -3 & 1 \\ 5 & -2 & -4 \end{bmatrix} = \begin{bmatrix} 2 & -1.5 & 0.5 \\ 2.5 & -1 & -2 \end{bmatrix}$

12c.

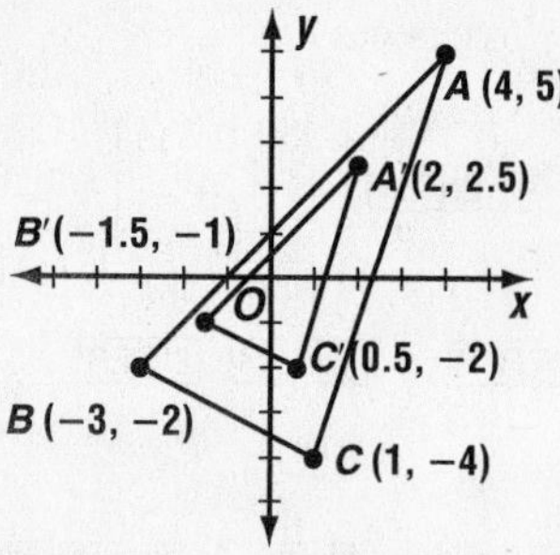

Pages 191–193 Exercises

13. $3\begin{bmatrix} 5 & -2 & 7 \\ -3 & 8 & 4 \end{bmatrix} = \begin{bmatrix} 15 & -6 & 21 \\ -9 & 24 & 12 \end{bmatrix}$

14. $-2\begin{bmatrix} 6 & -4 \\ -2 & 4 \end{bmatrix} = \begin{bmatrix} -12 & 8 \\ 4 & -8 \end{bmatrix}$

15. $\frac{1}{3}\begin{bmatrix} 6 & -5 \end{bmatrix} = \begin{bmatrix} 2 & -\frac{5}{3} \end{bmatrix}$

16. $0.2\begin{bmatrix} 10.50 \\ 8.75 \end{bmatrix} = \begin{bmatrix} 2.1 \\ 1.75 \end{bmatrix}$

17. $-5\begin{bmatrix} 1.3 & 0 & 5.1 \\ 0.4 & 1.0 & 2.5 \end{bmatrix} = \begin{bmatrix} -6.5 & 0 & -25.5 \\ -2 & -5 & -12.5 \end{bmatrix}$

18. $-0.3[8.95 \quad 7.50] = [-2.685 \quad -2.25]$

19. $[4x \quad 3y] = [12 \quad -1]$

$4x = 12 \qquad 3y = -1$
$x = 3 \qquad y = -\frac{1}{3}$

20. $\begin{bmatrix} 2x + y \\ x - 3y \end{bmatrix} = \begin{bmatrix} 5 \\ 13 \end{bmatrix}$

$x - 3y = 13 \qquad 2x + y = 5$
$x = 3y + 13 \qquad 2(3y + 13) + y = 5$
$x - 3y = 13 \qquad 6y + 26 + y = 5$
$x - 3(-3) = 13 \qquad 7y + 26 = 5$
$x + 9 = 13 \qquad 7y = -21$
$x = 4 \qquad y = -3$

21. $x\begin{bmatrix} 4 & y \\ 7 & 2 \end{bmatrix} = \begin{bmatrix} 12 & -15 \\ 21 & z \end{bmatrix}$

$\begin{bmatrix} 4x & xy \\ 7x & 2x \end{bmatrix} = \begin{bmatrix} 12 & -15 \\ 21 & z \end{bmatrix}$

$4x = 12 \qquad xy = -15 \qquad 2x = z \qquad 7x = 21$
$x = 3 \qquad 3y = -15 \qquad 2(3) = z \qquad x = 3$
$y = -5 \qquad 6 = z$

22. $4\begin{bmatrix} x & y-1 \\ 3 & z \end{bmatrix} = \begin{bmatrix} 20 & 8 \\ 6z & x+y \end{bmatrix}$

$\begin{bmatrix} 4x & 4y-4 \\ 12 & 4z \end{bmatrix} = \begin{bmatrix} 20 & 8 \\ 6z & x+y \end{bmatrix}$

$4x = 20 \qquad 4y - 4 = 8 \qquad 12 = 6z \qquad 4z = x + y$
$x = 5 \qquad 4y = 12 \qquad 2 = z \qquad 4(2) \stackrel{?}{=} 5 + 3$
$y = 3 \qquad 8 = 8$

23. $\begin{bmatrix} x^2 & 7 & 9 \\ 5 & 12 & 6 \end{bmatrix} = \begin{bmatrix} 25 & 7 & y \\ 5 & 2z & 6 \end{bmatrix}$

$x^2 = 25 \qquad 9 = y \qquad 12 = 2z$
$x = \pm 5 \qquad 6 = z$

24. $\begin{bmatrix} x + 3y \\ 3x + y \end{bmatrix} = \begin{bmatrix} -13 \\ 1 \end{bmatrix}$

$x + 3y = -13 \rightarrow \qquad \rightarrow x + 3y = -13$
$3x + y = 1 \rightarrow \text{Multiply by } -3 \rightarrow \underline{(+)\ -9x - 3y = -3}$
$-8x = -16$
$x = 2$

$3x + y = 1$
$3(2) + y = 1$
$6 + y = 1$
$y = -5$

25. $\frac{1}{4}\begin{bmatrix} 0 & 0 & 5 \\ 0 & 12 & 0 \end{bmatrix} = \begin{bmatrix} 0 & 0 & 1.25 \\ 0 & 3 & 0 \end{bmatrix}$; (0, 0), (0, 3), (1.25, 0)

26a.

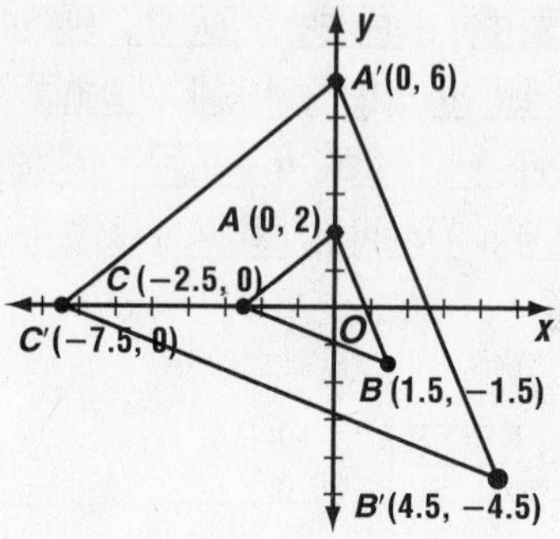

26b. $\begin{bmatrix} 0 & 4.5 & -7.5 \\ 6 & -4.5 & 0 \end{bmatrix}$

27. The perimeter is one-half the original perimeter; the triangle is rotated 180°. See students' work for drawing.

28. $\begin{bmatrix} r^2 - 24 & 17 \\ 7 & t^3 \end{bmatrix} = \begin{bmatrix} 1 & 2y + 3 \\ z^2 - 12 & 27 \end{bmatrix}$

$r^2 - 24 = 1 \qquad 17 = 2y + 3 \qquad 7 = z^2 - 12 \qquad t^3 = 27$
$r^2 = 25 \qquad 14 = 2y \qquad 19 = z^2 \qquad t = 3$
$r = \pm 5 \qquad 7 = y \qquad \pm\sqrt{19} = z$

29. $\begin{bmatrix} 5x - 7 & 11 \\ 5 & 23 \end{bmatrix} = \begin{bmatrix} 8 & 21 - m \\ r^3 - 3 & 4y + x \end{bmatrix}$

$5x - 7 = 8 \qquad 11 = 21 - m$
$5x = 15 \qquad -10 = -m$
$x = 3 \qquad 10 = m$

$5 = r^3 - 3 \qquad 23 = 4y + x$
$8 = r^3 \qquad 23 = 4y + 3$
$2 = r \qquad 20 = 4y$
$5 = y$

30. $\begin{bmatrix} 13 - 7y & a \\ 1 & 2b - 38 \end{bmatrix} = \begin{bmatrix} 5x & 2 - 6b \\ 2x + 3y & 5a \end{bmatrix}$

$13 - 7y = 5x \rightarrow 5x + 7y = 13 \rightarrow \qquad 10x + 14y = 26$
$1 = 2x + 3y \rightarrow 2x + 3y = 1 \rightarrow \underline{(+)\ -10x - 15y = -5}$
$-y = 21$
$y = -21$

$2x + 3y = 1$
$2x + 3(-21) = 1$
$2x - 63 = 1$
$2x = 64$
$x = 32$

$a = 2 - 6b \rightarrow a + 6b = 2 \rightarrow \qquad -5a - 30b = -10$
$2b - 38 = 5a \rightarrow 5a - 2b = -38 \rightarrow \underline{(+)\ 5a - 2b = -38}$
$-32b = -48$
$b = 1.5$

(Continued next column)

$a = 2 - 6b$
$= 2 - 6(1.5)$
$= 2 - 9$
$= -7$

31. No; see students' work for graph.

32.

	Mary	Carrie	Terri
Fred	x	x	✓
Ted	✓	x	x
Ed	x	✓	x

Mary is not Ed's date, they are brother and sister. Ed is not Terri's date, he is taller than her date. Therefore, Ed is Carrie's date and Carrie doesn't date Fred or Ted. Fred's date lives on State Street; Mary lives on Fifth Avenue, so Fred's date must be Terri. Ted, therefore, dates Mary.

33.

	Male	Female
Exercise Walking	21%	38%
Swimming	27%	28%
Bicycle Riding	25%	22%
Camping	23%	18%
Bowling	20%	18%
Fishing	25%	11%
Exercising with Equipment	17%	17%
Basketball	18%	6%
Aerobic Exercising	5%	19%
Golf	17%	5%

34. $3x + 6y - 8z = 24$

$3x + 6(0) - 8(0) = 24$
$3x = 24$
$x = 8$

$3(0) + 6y - 8(0) = 24$
$6y = 24$
$y = 4$

$3(0) + 6(0) - 8z = 24$
$-8z = 24$
$z = -3$

35. Let x = adult tickets and y = student tickets.
$x + y \leq 150$ $y \geq 50$ $x \geq 0$
vertices: (0, 50), (0, 150), (100, 50)

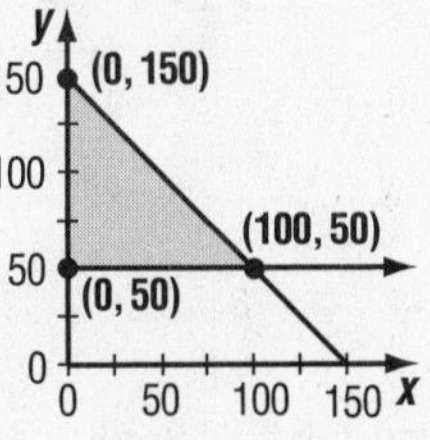

$f(x, y) = 2x + y$

(x, y)	$2x + y$	$f(x, y)$
(0, 50)	2(0) + 50	50
(0, 150)	2(0) + 150	150
(100, 50)	2(100) + 50	250

maximum: $f(100, 50) = 250$
100 adult and 50 student tickets should be sold.

36. $x + y < 8$
$y < -x + 8$

$x + y > 5$
$y > -x + 5$

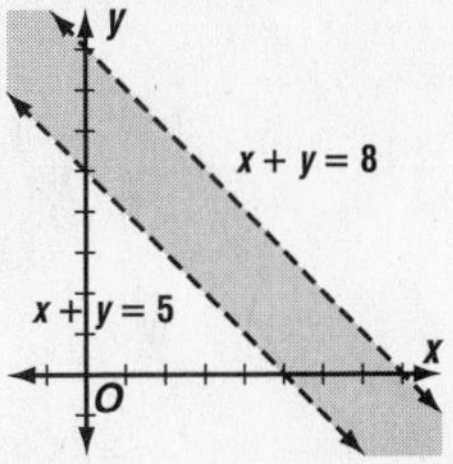

37. $f(x) = x^2 - 4$
$f(-2) = (-2)^2 - 4$
$= 4 - 4$
$= 0$

38. $|9 - 3t| > 5$
$9 - 3t > 5$ or $9 - 3t < -5$
$-3t > -4$ $-3t < -14$
$t < \frac{4}{3}$ $t > \frac{14}{3}$
$\left\{t \mid t < \frac{4}{3} \text{ or } t > \frac{14}{3}\right\}$

39a. 30; 26; $\frac{42 + 37 + 35 + 32 + 30 + 29 + 26 + 26 + 17}{9} = \frac{274}{9} = 30.\overline{4}$

39b. They are all located in the southwestern U.S.

4-2 Adding and Subtracting Matrices

Pages 196–197 Check for Understanding

1. They must have the same dimensions.
2. A dilation changes the size but not the shape of a figure. A translation moves a figure, but does not change its orientation, size, or shape.
3. Triangle ABC $\begin{bmatrix} 0 & 1 & 1 \\ 1 & 3 & 0 \end{bmatrix}$ Triangle $A'B'C'$ $\begin{bmatrix} 2 & 3 & 3 \\ 1 & 3 & 0 \end{bmatrix}$
   translation of x-coordinate: $0 + x = 2$
   $x = 2$
   translation of y-coordinate: $1 + y = 1$
   $y = 0$
   translation matrix: $\begin{bmatrix} 2 & 2 & 2 \\ 0 & 0 & 0 \end{bmatrix}$
4. The statement is true because you are adding pairs of real numbers. Since addition of real numbers is commutative and associative, so is matrix addition.
5. $\begin{bmatrix} 3 & 7 \\ -2 & 1 \end{bmatrix} - \begin{bmatrix} 2 & -3 \\ 5 & -4 \end{bmatrix} = \begin{bmatrix} 1 & 10 \\ -7 & 5 \end{bmatrix}$
6. $\begin{bmatrix} 4 \\ 1 \\ -3 \end{bmatrix} + \begin{bmatrix} 6 \\ -5 \\ 8 \end{bmatrix} = \begin{bmatrix} 10 \\ -4 \\ 5 \end{bmatrix}$
7. $2[3 \ \ -1] + 3[5 \ \ 0] = [6 \ \ -2] + [15 \ \ 0] = [21 \ \ -2]$
8. $\begin{bmatrix} 3293 \\ 1841 \\ 1332 \\ 978 \\ 726 \end{bmatrix} - \begin{bmatrix} 216 \\ 877 \\ 587 \\ 217 \\ 118 \end{bmatrix} = \begin{bmatrix} 3077 \\ 964 \\ 745 \\ 761 \\ 608 \end{bmatrix}$

9a.

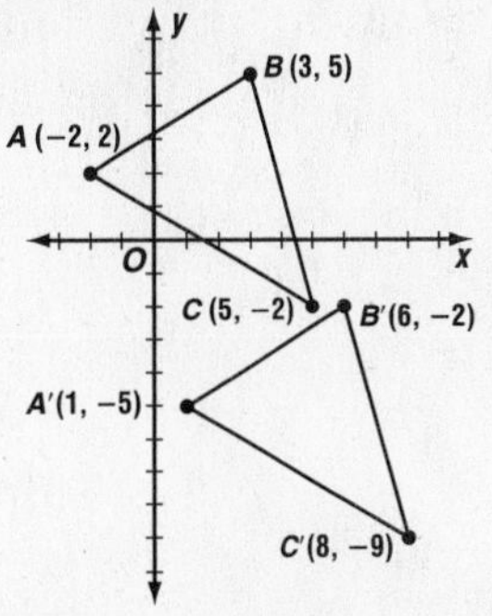

9b. x: $-2 + x = 1$

$x = 3$

y: $2 + y = -5$

$y = -7$

translation matrix: $\begin{bmatrix} 3 & 3 & 3 \\ -7 & -7 & -7 \end{bmatrix}$

9c. $\begin{bmatrix} 1 & 6 & 8 \\ -5 & -2 & -9 \end{bmatrix}$

Pages 197–198 Exercises

10. $\begin{bmatrix} 3 & -9 \\ 4 & 2 \end{bmatrix} + \begin{bmatrix} -8 & -4 \\ 3 & 10 \end{bmatrix} = \begin{bmatrix} -5 & -13 \\ 7 & 12 \end{bmatrix}$

11. $[5\ 8\ -4] + [-1\ 12\ 5] = [4\ 20\ 1]$

12. $4\begin{bmatrix} 2 & 7 \\ -3 & 6 \end{bmatrix} + 5\begin{bmatrix} -6 & -4 \\ 3 & 0 \end{bmatrix} = \begin{bmatrix} 8 & 28 \\ -12 & 24 \end{bmatrix} + \begin{bmatrix} -30 & -20 \\ 15 & 0 \end{bmatrix}$

$= \begin{bmatrix} -22 & 8 \\ 3 & 24 \end{bmatrix}$

13. $\frac{1}{2}\begin{bmatrix} 4 & 6 \\ 3 & 0 \end{bmatrix} - \frac{2}{3}\begin{bmatrix} 9 & 27 \\ 0 & 3 \end{bmatrix} = \begin{bmatrix} 2 & 3 \\ 1.5 & 0 \end{bmatrix} - \begin{bmatrix} 6 & 18 \\ 0 & 2 \end{bmatrix}$

$= \begin{bmatrix} -4 & -15 \\ 1.5 & -2 \end{bmatrix}$

14. $5\begin{bmatrix} 1 \\ -1 \\ -3 \end{bmatrix} + 6\begin{bmatrix} -4 \\ 3 \\ 5 \end{bmatrix} - 2\begin{bmatrix} -3 \\ 8 \\ -4 \end{bmatrix} = \begin{bmatrix} 5 \\ -5 \\ -15 \end{bmatrix} + \begin{bmatrix} -24 \\ 18 \\ 30 \end{bmatrix} - \begin{bmatrix} -6 \\ 16 \\ -8 \end{bmatrix}$

$= \begin{bmatrix} -13 \\ -3 \\ 23 \end{bmatrix}$

15. $2\begin{bmatrix} -2 & 4 \\ 1 & -1 \\ 3 & 0 \end{bmatrix} - 3\begin{bmatrix} 5 & 3 \\ -3 & 2 \\ 8 & -9 \end{bmatrix} + \begin{bmatrix} 0 & -5 \\ 9 & -3 \\ -2 & 7 \end{bmatrix}$

$= \begin{bmatrix} -4 & 8 \\ 2 & -2 \\ 6 & 0 \end{bmatrix} - \begin{bmatrix} 15 & 9 \\ -9 & 6 \\ 24 & -27 \end{bmatrix} + \begin{bmatrix} 0 & -5 \\ 9 & -3 \\ -2 & 7 \end{bmatrix}$

$= \begin{bmatrix} -19 & -6 \\ 20 & -11 \\ -20 & 34 \end{bmatrix}$

16a.

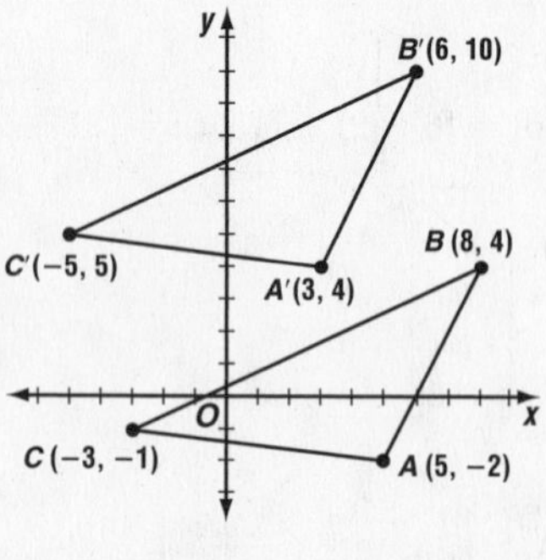

16b. $\begin{bmatrix} 3 & 6 & -5 \\ 4 & 10 & 5 \end{bmatrix}$

17a. x: $-1 + x = 3$ y: $4 + y = 2$ $\begin{bmatrix} 4 & 4 & 4 & 4 \\ -2 & -2 & -2 & -2 \end{bmatrix}$

$x = 4$ $y = -2$

17b. $\begin{bmatrix} 6 & 3 & -1 & -3 \\ 1 & 5 & 4 & -5 \end{bmatrix} + \begin{bmatrix} 4 & 4 & 4 & 4 \\ -2 & -2 & -2 & -2 \end{bmatrix} = \begin{bmatrix} 10 & 7 & 3 & 1 \\ -1 & 3 & 2 & -7 \end{bmatrix}$

B' (10, −1), U' (7, 3), T' (1, −7)

18. $\frac{1}{2}\begin{bmatrix} -6 & -2 & 4 \\ 2 & 8 & -5 \end{bmatrix} = \begin{bmatrix} -3 & -1 & 2 \\ 1 & 4 & -2.5 \end{bmatrix}$

x: $-3 + x = 2$ y: $1 + y = 2$ $\begin{bmatrix} 5 & 5 & 5 \\ 1 & 1 & 1 \end{bmatrix}$

$x = 5$ $y = 1$

$\begin{bmatrix} -3 & -1 & 2 \\ 1 & 4 & -2.5 \end{bmatrix} + \begin{bmatrix} 5 & 5 & 5 \\ 1 & 1 & 1 \end{bmatrix} = \begin{bmatrix} 2 & 4 & 7 \\ 2 & 5 & -1.5 \end{bmatrix}$

Y' (4, 5), Z' (7, −1.5)

19. $\begin{bmatrix} x \\ 7z \\ 2y \end{bmatrix} - \begin{bmatrix} 4z \\ -3y \\ 3x \end{bmatrix} + \begin{bmatrix} -2y \\ 2x \\ -5z \end{bmatrix} = \begin{bmatrix} -4 \\ 11 \\ 18 \end{bmatrix}$

$\begin{bmatrix} x - 4z - 2y \\ 7z + 3y + 2x \\ 2y - 3x - 5z \end{bmatrix} = \begin{bmatrix} -4 \\ 11 \\ 18 \end{bmatrix}$

$x - 4z - 2y = -4 \rightarrow x - 2y - 4z = -4$

$7z + 3y + 2x = 11 \rightarrow 2x + 3y + 7z = 11$

$2y - 3x - 5z = 18 \rightarrow -3x + 2y - 5z = 18$

$x - 2y - 4z = -4 \rightarrow$ $-2x + 4y + 8z = 8$

$2x + 3y + 7z = 11 \rightarrow$ $(+)\ 2x + 3y + 7z = 11$

$7y + 15z = 19$

$x - 2y - 4z = -4 \rightarrow$ $3x - 6y - 12z = -12$

$-3x + 2y - 5z = 18 \rightarrow$ $(+)\ -3x + 2y - 5z = 18$

$-4y - 17z = 6$

$7y + 15z = 19 \rightarrow$ $28y + 60z = 76$

$-4y - 17z = 6 \rightarrow$ $(+)\ -28y - 119z = 42$

$-59z = 118$

$z = -2$

$7y + 15z = 19$ $x - 2y - 4z = -4$

$7y + 15(-2) = 19$ $x - 2(7) - 4(-2) = -4$

$7y - 30 = 19$ $x - 14 + 8 = -4$

$7y = 49$ $x = 2$

$y = 7$

20. x: $5 + x = 0$ y: $-3 + y = 0$

$x = -5$ $y = 3$

translation matrix: $\begin{bmatrix} -5 & -5 & -5 & -5 \\ 3 & 3 & 3 & 3 \end{bmatrix}$

$\begin{bmatrix} 5 & 2 & -3 & -5 \\ -3 & 7 & 3 & 1 \end{bmatrix} + \begin{bmatrix} -5 & -5 & -5 & -5 \\ 3 & 3 & 3 & 3 \end{bmatrix} = \begin{bmatrix} 0 & -3 & -8 & -10 \\ 0 & 10 & 6 & 4 \end{bmatrix}$

$M(0, 0)$, $N(-3, 10)$, $P(-8, 6)$, $Q(-10, 4)$

21a. Sample answer: No; births and deaths are opposite occurrences.

21b. Yes; $B - D$ represents the population increase for 1992.

21c. Find $0.99D$.

22a. $F = \begin{bmatrix} 120 & 97 & 64 & 75 \\ 80 & 59 & 36 & 60 \\ 72 & 84 & 29 & 48 \end{bmatrix}$ $S = \begin{bmatrix} 112 & 87 & 56 & 74 \\ 84 & 65 & 39 & 70 \\ 88 & 98 & 43 & 60 \end{bmatrix}$

$T = \begin{bmatrix} 120 & 97 & 64 & 75 \\ 80 & 59 & 36 & 60 \\ 72 & 84 & 29 & 48 \end{bmatrix} + \begin{bmatrix} 112 & 87 & 56 & 74 \\ 84 & 65 & 39 & 70 \\ 88 & 98 & 43 & 60 \end{bmatrix}$

$= \begin{bmatrix} 232 & 184 & 120 & 149 \\ 164 & 124 & 75 & 130 \\ 160 & 182 & 72 & 108 \end{bmatrix}$

22b. $232 + 164 + 160 + 184 + 124 + 182 + 120 + 75 + 72 + 149 + 130 + 108 = 1700$
$1700 \div 4 = 425$ (425 cups of flour)
$425 \div 4 = 106.25$, 106.25 pounds

23. $4\begin{bmatrix} -7 & 5 & -11 \\ 2 & -4 & 9 \end{bmatrix} = \begin{bmatrix} -28 & 20 & -44 \\ 8 & -16 & 36 \end{bmatrix}$

24. 2

25. $y > x + 4$

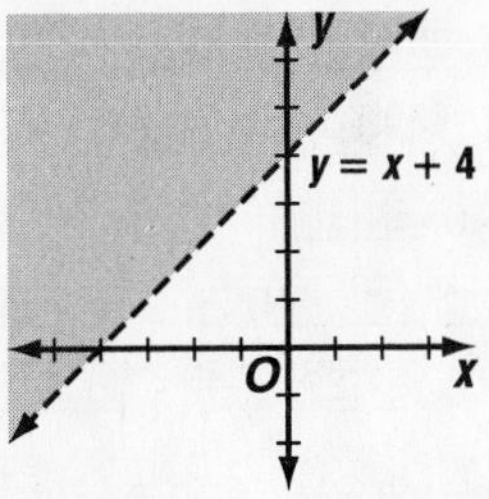

26. no; x is squared

27. $\frac{3}{4}t + 1 = 10$

$\frac{3}{4}t = 9$

$t = 12$

4-3 Multiplying Matrices

Page 202 Check for Understanding

1. The first matrix has the same number of columns as the second matrix has rows.
2. 3×4
3. The statement is false. Sample answer: $A_{2 \times 3} \cdot B_{3 \times 3} = (AB)_{2 \times 3}$, but BA is not defined.
4. Sample answer: $M_{2 \times 3}$ and $N_{3 \times 2}$
5. Dolores; Sample answer: $A_{2 \times 3}$ and $B_{2 \times 3}$ can be added, but not multiplied.
6. Sample:

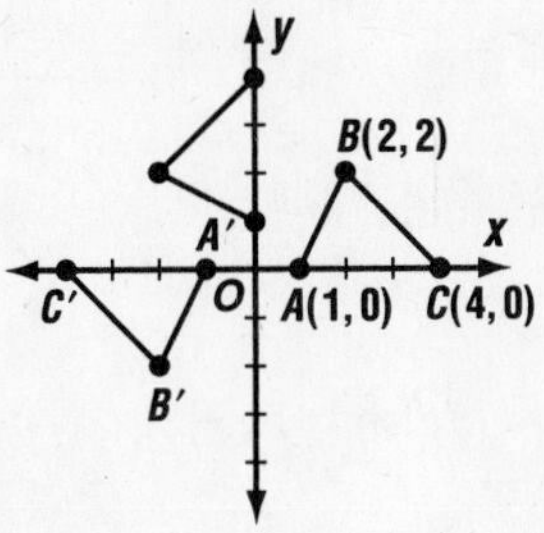

$A(1, 0)$, $B(2, 2)$, $C(4, 0)$
$A'(-1, 0)$, $B'(-2, -2)$, $C'(-4, 0)$
It rotates the figure 180°.

7. 3×2
8. 2×4
9. $\begin{bmatrix} 4 & -2 & -7 \\ 6 & 3 & 5 \end{bmatrix} \cdot \begin{bmatrix} -2 \\ 5 \\ 3 \end{bmatrix} = \begin{bmatrix} 4(-2) + (-2)5 + (-7)3 \\ 6(-2) + 3(5) + 5(3) \end{bmatrix}$

$= \begin{bmatrix} -8 - 10 - 21 \\ -12 + 15 + 15 \end{bmatrix}$

$= \begin{bmatrix} -39 \\ 18 \end{bmatrix}$

10. not possible to evaluate
11.

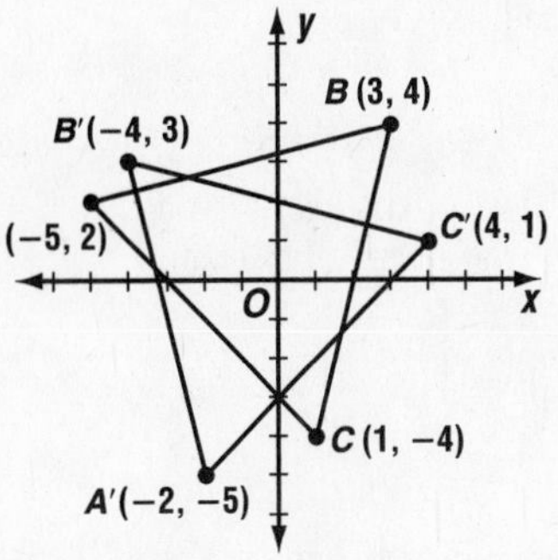

$A'(-2, -5)$, $B'(-4, 3)$, $C'(4, 1)$

Pages 202–204 Exercises

12. 5×5
13. not defined
14. 2×4
15. 3×1
16. 1×1
17. not defined
18. $[2 \ \ -1] \cdot \begin{bmatrix} 5 \\ 3 \end{bmatrix} = [2(5) + (-1)3]$

$= [10 - 3]$

$= [7]$

19. $\begin{bmatrix} 2 & -1 \\ 3 & 4 \end{bmatrix} \cdot \begin{bmatrix} 3 & -9 & -2 \\ 5 & 7 & -6 \end{bmatrix}$

$= \begin{bmatrix} 2(3) + (-1)5 & 2(-9) + (-1)7 & 2(-2) + (-1)(-6) \\ 3(3) + 4(5) & 3(-9) + 4(7) & 3(-2) + 4(-6) \end{bmatrix}$

$= \begin{bmatrix} 6 - 5 & -18 - 7 & -4 + 6 \\ 9 + 20 & -27 + 28 & -6 - 24 \end{bmatrix}$

$= \begin{bmatrix} 1 & -25 & 2 \\ 29 & 1 & -30 \end{bmatrix}$

20. $\begin{bmatrix} 4 & -1 \\ 3 & 5 \end{bmatrix} \cdot \begin{bmatrix} 7 \\ 4 \end{bmatrix} = \begin{bmatrix} 4(7) + (-1)4 \\ 3(7) + 5(4) \end{bmatrix}$

$= \begin{bmatrix} 28 - 4 \\ 21 + 20 \end{bmatrix}$

$= \begin{bmatrix} 24 \\ 41 \end{bmatrix}$

21. not possible to evaluate
22. $3\begin{bmatrix} 5 & 7 \\ 1 & -2 \end{bmatrix} + 2\begin{bmatrix} -3 & 0 \\ -4 & 2 \end{bmatrix} = \begin{bmatrix} 15 & 21 \\ 3 & -6 \end{bmatrix} + \begin{bmatrix} -6 & 0 \\ -8 & 4 \end{bmatrix}$

$= \begin{bmatrix} 9 & 21 \\ -5 & -2 \end{bmatrix}$

23. $\begin{bmatrix} 0 & 8 \\ 3 & 1 \\ -1 & 5 \end{bmatrix} \cdot \begin{bmatrix} 3 & 1 & -2 \\ 0 & 8 & -5 \end{bmatrix}$

$= \begin{bmatrix} 0(3)+8(0) & 0(1)+8(8) & 0(-2)+8(-5) \\ 3(3)+1(0) & 3(1)+1(8) & 3(-2)+1(-5) \\ -1(3)+5(0) & -1(1)+5(8) & -1(-2)+5(-5) \end{bmatrix}$

$= \begin{bmatrix} 0+0 & 0+64 & 0-40 \\ 9+0 & 3+8 & -6-5 \\ -3+0 & -1+40 & 2-25 \end{bmatrix}$

$= \begin{bmatrix} 0 & 64 & -40 \\ 9 & 11 & -11 \\ -3 & 39 & -23 \end{bmatrix}$

24. $\begin{bmatrix} 0 & -1 \\ 1 & 0 \end{bmatrix} \cdot \begin{bmatrix} 3 & 6 & 0 \\ 4 & 5 & 0 \end{bmatrix}$

$= \begin{bmatrix} 0(3)+(-1)4 & 0(6)+(-1)5 & 0(0)+(-1)0 \\ 1(3)+0(4) & 1(6)+0(5) & 1(0)+0(0) \end{bmatrix}$

$= \begin{bmatrix} 0-4 & 0-5 & 0+0 \\ 3+0 & 6+0 & 0+0 \end{bmatrix}$

$= \begin{bmatrix} -4 & -5 & 0 \\ 3 & 6 & 0 \end{bmatrix}$

$A'(-4, 3)$, $B'(-5, 6)$, $C'(0, 0)$

25. No; multiplication is not commutative.

26. $\begin{bmatrix} 3 & -1 \\ 2 & 4 \end{bmatrix} \cdot \begin{bmatrix} 4 & 0 & -3 \\ 7 & -5 & 9 \end{bmatrix} + \begin{bmatrix} 4 & 0 & -3 \\ 7 & -5 & 9 \end{bmatrix}$

$= \begin{bmatrix} 3(4)+(-1)7 & 3(0)+(-1)(-5) & 3(-3)+(-1)9 \\ 2(4)+4(7) & 2(0)+4(-5) & 2(-3)+4(9) \end{bmatrix}$

$+ \begin{bmatrix} 4 & 0 & -3 \\ 7 & -5 & 9 \end{bmatrix}$

$= \begin{bmatrix} 12-7 & 0+5 & -9-9 \\ 8+28 & 0-20 & -6+36 \end{bmatrix} + \begin{bmatrix} 4 & 0 & -3 \\ 7 & -5 & 9 \end{bmatrix}$

$= \begin{bmatrix} 5 & 5 & -18 \\ 36 & -20 & 30 \end{bmatrix} + \begin{bmatrix} 4 & 0 & -3 \\ 7 & -5 & 9 \end{bmatrix}$

$= \begin{bmatrix} 9 & 5 & -21 \\ 43 & -25 & 39 \end{bmatrix}$

27. $C_{3 \times 2} \cdot B_{2 \times 3} = (CB)_{3 \times 3}$; $(CB)_{3 \times 3} + B_{2 \times 3}$ is not defined.

28. $A_{2 \times 3} \cdot D_{2 \times 2} = (AD)_{2 \times 2}$; $C_{3 \times 2} \cdot B_{2 \times 3} = (CB)_{3 \times 3}$; $(AD)_{2 \times 2} + (CB)_{3 \times 3}$ is undefined

29. $\begin{bmatrix} 3 & -1 \\ 2 & 4 \end{bmatrix} \cdot \begin{bmatrix} -1 & 0 \\ 3 & 7 \end{bmatrix} + \begin{bmatrix} 4 & 0 & -3 \\ 7 & -5 & 9 \end{bmatrix} \cdot \begin{bmatrix} -6 & 4 \\ -2 & 8 \\ 3 & 0 \end{bmatrix}$

$= \begin{bmatrix} 3(-1)+(-1)3 & 3(0)+(-1)7 \\ 2(-1)+4(3) & 2(0)+4(7) \end{bmatrix} +$

$\begin{bmatrix} 4(-6)+0(-2)+(-3)3 & 4(4)+0(8)+(-3)0 \\ 7(-6)+(-5)(-2)+9(3) & 7(4)+(-5)8+9(0) \end{bmatrix}$

$= \begin{bmatrix} -3-3 & 0-7 \\ -2+12 & 0+28 \end{bmatrix} + \begin{bmatrix} -24+0-9 & 16+0+0 \\ -42+10+27 & 28-40+0 \end{bmatrix}$

$= \begin{bmatrix} -6 & -7 \\ 10 & 28 \end{bmatrix} + \begin{bmatrix} -33 & 16 \\ -5 & -12 \end{bmatrix}$

$= \begin{bmatrix} -39 & 9 \\ 5 & 16 \end{bmatrix}$

30. $\begin{bmatrix} 0 & -1 \\ 1 & 0 \end{bmatrix} \cdot \begin{bmatrix} a & b & c \\ d & e & f \end{bmatrix} = \begin{bmatrix} -3 & -2 & 1 \\ -5 & 7 & 4 \end{bmatrix}$

$0(a) + (-1)d = -3$
$0 - d = -3$
$-d = -3$
$d = 3$

$0(b) + (-1)(e) = -2$
$0 - e = -2$
$-e = -2$
$e = 2$

$0(c) + (-1)f = 1$
$0 - f = 1$
$-f = 1$
$f = -1$

$1(a) + 0(d) = -5$
$a + 0 = -5$
$a = -5$

$1(b) + 0(e) = 7$
$b + 0 = 7$
$b = 7$

$1(c) + 0(f) = 4$
$c + 0 = 4$
$c = 4$

$(-5, 3)$, $(7, 2)$, $(4, -1)$

31–34. enter matrices: MATRX ▶ ▶ ENTER 2 ENTER 4 ENTER 0 ENTER 1 ENTER 1 ENTER 0 ENTER 0 ENTER 0 ENTER 1 ENTER 1 ENTER MATRX ▶ ▶ ▼ ENTER 2 ENTER 2 ENTER (–) 1 ENTER 0 ENTER 0 ENTER (–) 1 ENTER MATRX ▶ ▶ ▼ ▼ ENTER 2 ENTER 2 ENTER 1 ENTER 0 ENTER 0 ENTER (–) 1 ENTER MATRX ▶ ▶ ▼ ▼ ▼ ENTER 2 ENTER 2 ENTER (–) 1 ENTER 0 ENTER 0 ENTER 1 ENTER MATRX ▶ ▶ ▼ ▼ ▼ ▼ ENTER 2 ENTER 2 ENTER 0 ENTER 1 ENTER 1 ENTER 0 ENTER 2nd QUIT

31. MATRX 2 MATRX 1 ENTER $\begin{bmatrix} 0 & -1 & -1 & 0 \\ 0 & 0 & -1 & -1 \end{bmatrix}$
rotates 180°

32. MATRX 3 MATRX 1 ENTER $\begin{bmatrix} 0 & 1 & 1 & 0 \\ 0 & 0 & -1 & -1 \end{bmatrix}$
reflects over x-axis

33. MATRX 4 MATRX 1 ENTER $\begin{bmatrix} 0 & -1 & -1 & 0 \\ 0 & 0 & 1 & 1 \end{bmatrix}$
reflects over y-axis

34. MATRX 5 MATRX 1 ENTER $\begin{bmatrix} 0 & 0 & 1 & 1 \\ 0 & 1 & 1 & 0 \end{bmatrix}$
reflects over $y = x$

35. $\begin{bmatrix} 1 & 2 \\ 3 & 4 \end{bmatrix} \cdot \begin{bmatrix} w & x \\ y & z \end{bmatrix} = \begin{bmatrix} 1 & 2 \\ 3 & 4 \end{bmatrix}$

$\begin{bmatrix} 1w+2y & 1x+2z \\ 3w+4y & 3x+4z \end{bmatrix} = \begin{bmatrix} 1 & 2 \\ 3 & 4 \end{bmatrix}$

$w + 2y = 1 \rightarrow$ Multiply by -2 $\rightarrow -2w - 4y = -2$
$3w + 4y = 3 \rightarrow$ $\rightarrow (+)\ 3w + 4y = 3$
$w = 1$

$w + 2y = 1$
$1 + 2y = 1$
$2y = 0$
$y = 0$

$x + 2z = 2 \rightarrow$ Multiply by -2 $\rightarrow -2x - 4z = -4$
$3x + 4z = 4 \rightarrow$ $\rightarrow (+)\ 3x + 4z = 4$
$x = 0$

$x + 2z = 2$
$0 + 2z = 2$
$2z = 2$
$z = 1$ the original matrix

36. $\begin{bmatrix} 4 & 10 & 6 \\ 7 & 6 & 9 \\ 8 & 3 & 4 \end{bmatrix} \cdot \begin{bmatrix} 5 \\ 3 \\ 1 \end{bmatrix} = \begin{bmatrix} 4(5) + 10(3) + 6(1) \\ 7(5) + 6(3) + 9(1) \\ 8(5) + 3(3) + 4(1) \end{bmatrix}$

$= \begin{bmatrix} 20 + 30 + 6 \\ 35 + 18 + 9 \\ 40 + 9 + 4 \end{bmatrix}$

$= \begin{bmatrix} 56 \\ 62 \\ 53 \end{bmatrix}$

Blendon: 56, Walnut Springs: 62, Heritage: 53

37. $R = \begin{bmatrix} 0.5 & 0.5 \\ 0.3 & 0.7 \end{bmatrix}$ $\quad P = [0.8 \ \ 0.2]$

Tuesday:

$PR = [0.8 \ \ 0.2] \cdot \begin{bmatrix} 0.5 & 0.5 \\ 0.3 & 0.7 \end{bmatrix}$

$= [0.8(0.5) + 0.2(0.3) \ \ 0.8(0.5) + 0.2(0.7)]$

$= [0.4 + 0.06 \ \ 0.4 + 0.14]$

$= [0.46 \ \ 0.54]$

Wednesday:

$PR = [0.46 \ \ 0.54] \cdot \begin{bmatrix} 0.5 & 0.5 \\ 0.3 & 0.7 \end{bmatrix}$

$= [0.46(0.5) + 0.54(0.3) \ \ 0.46(0.5) + 0.54(0.7)]$

$= [0.23 + 0.162 \ \ 0.23 + 0.378]$

$= [0.392 \ \ 0.608]$

about 39%

38a.

	well	sick
today	0.7	0.3
tomorrow	0.5	0.5

38b. $[0.8 \ \ 0.2] \cdot \begin{bmatrix} 0.7 & 0.3 \\ 0.5 & 0.5 \end{bmatrix}$

$= [0.8(0.7) + 0.2(0.5) \ \ 0.8(0.3) + 0.2(0.5)]$

$= [0.56 + 0.1 \ \ 0.24 + 0.1]$

$= [0.66 \ \ 0.34]$; 34%

39a. $[150 \ \ 100 \ \ 200] \cdot \begin{bmatrix} 54 \\ 60 \\ 43.50 \end{bmatrix}$

$= [150(54) + 100(60) + 200(43.50)]$

$= [8100 + 6000 + 8700]$

$= [22{,}800]$; \$22,800

39b. $55.25 - 54 = 1.25$, $61 - 60 = 1$, $41.75 - 43.50 = -1.75$;

$[150 \ \ 100 \ \ 200] \cdot \begin{bmatrix} 1.25 \\ 1 \\ -1.75 \end{bmatrix}$

$= [150(1.25) + 100(1) + 200(-1.75)]$

$= [187.5 + 100 - 350]$

$= [-62.50]$

\$22,800 − 62.50 = \$22,737.50 sold; \$62.50 lost

40. $[4 \ \ 1 \ \ -3] + [6 \ \ -5 \ \ 8] = [10 \ \ -4 \ \ 5]$

41. $-6\begin{bmatrix} 2 & -1 \\ -5 & 7 \end{bmatrix} = \begin{bmatrix} -12 & 6 \\ 30 & -42 \end{bmatrix}$

42. Let x = short answer question, y = essay question.

$x + y \le 20$ $\quad 2x + 12y \le 60$ $\quad x \ge 0$;

$y \le -x + 20$ $\quad 12y \le -2x + 60$ $\quad y \ge 0$

$y \le -\frac{1}{6}x + 5$

vertices: (0, 0), (0, 5), (18, 2), (20, 0)

$f(x, y) = 5x + 15y$

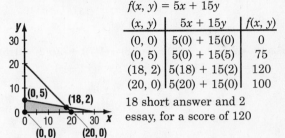

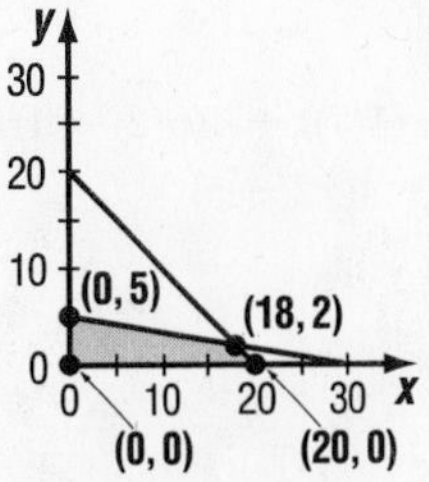

(x, y)	$5x + 15y$	$f(x, y)$
(0, 0)	5(0) + 15(0)	0
(0, 5)	5(0) + 15(5)	75
(18, 2)	5(18) + 15(2)	120
(20, 0)	5(20) + 15(0)	100

18 short answer and 2 essay, for a score of 120

43. $\begin{aligned} 3x - 6y &= 15 \\ (+)\ -3x + 5y &= -8 \\ \hline -y &= 7 \\ y &= -7 \end{aligned}$ $\quad \begin{aligned} 3x - 6y &= 15 \\ 3x - 6(-7) &= 15 \\ 3x + 42 &= 15 \\ 3x &= -27 \\ x &= -9 \end{aligned}$ $\quad (-9, -7)$

44. $y - y_1 = m(x - x_1)$

$y - 1 = -2(x - 3)$

$y - 1 = -2x + 6$

$y = -2x + 7$

45. y: $3x - 12y = 24$

$3(0) - 12y = 24$

$-12y = 24$

$y = -2$; $(0, -2)$

x: $3x - 12y = 24$

$3x - 12(0) = 24$

$3x = 24$

$x = 8$; $(8, 0)$

46. $12 - 3 = 9$

$y = 0.96x + 3.38$

$= 0.96(9) + 3.38$

$= 8.64 + 3.38$

$= 12.02$; \$12.02

4-4 Matrices and Determinants

Pages 208–209 Check for Understanding

1. $\begin{vmatrix} 7 & 8 \\ 3 & -2 \end{vmatrix}$ is a real number; $\begin{bmatrix} 7 & 8 \\ 3 & -2 \end{bmatrix}$ is a matrix.

2. Cross out the row containing 8. Cross out the column containing 8. The four remaining elements are the minor of 8.

3. square matrix

4. $\frac{1}{2}\begin{vmatrix} -2 & 3 & 1 \\ 1 & 2 & 1 \\ 4 & 4 & 1 \end{vmatrix}$

5. no; not square

6. yes; $\begin{vmatrix} -8 & 0 \\ 5 & -4 \end{vmatrix} = -8(-4) - 5(0)$

$= 32 - 0$

$= 32$

7. yes; $\begin{vmatrix} 1 & 0 & 0 \\ 0 & 1 & 0 \\ 0 & 0 & 1 \end{vmatrix} = 1\begin{vmatrix} 1 & 0 \\ 0 & 1 \end{vmatrix} - 0\begin{vmatrix} 0 & 0 \\ 0 & 1 \end{vmatrix} + 0\begin{vmatrix} 0 & 1 \\ 0 & 0 \end{vmatrix}$

$= 1(1 - 0) - 0(0 - 0) + 0(0 - 0)$
$= 1(1) - 0 + 0$
$= 1$

8. $\begin{vmatrix} 2 & 3 & 4 \\ 6 & 5 & 7 \\ 1 & 2 & 8 \end{vmatrix} = 2\begin{vmatrix} 5 & 7 \\ 2 & 8 \end{vmatrix} - 3\begin{vmatrix} 6 & 7 \\ 1 & 8 \end{vmatrix} + 4\begin{vmatrix} 6 & 5 \\ 1 & 2 \end{vmatrix}$

$= 2(5(8) - 2(7)) - 3(6(8) - 1(7)) + 4(6(2) - 1(5))$
$= 2(40 - 14) - 3(48 - 7) + 4(12 - 5)$
$= 2(26) - 3(41) + 4(7)$
$= 52 - 123 + 28$
$= -43$

9. $\begin{vmatrix} -1 & 4 & 0 \\ 3 & -2 & -5 \\ -3 & -1 & 2 \end{vmatrix} \to \begin{vmatrix} -1 & 4 & 0 \\ 3 & -2 & -5 \\ -3 & -1 & 2 \end{vmatrix}\begin{matrix} -1 & 4 \\ 3 & -2 \\ -3 & -1 \end{matrix}$

$= (-1)(-2)2 + 4(-5)(-3) + 0 \cdot 3(-1) -$
$(-3)(-2)0 - (-1)(-5)(-1) - 2 \cdot 3 \cdot 4$
$= 4 + 60 + 0 - 0 - (-5) - 24 = 45$

10. $A = \frac{1}{2}\begin{vmatrix} -2 & 3 & 1 \\ 5 & 8 & 1 \\ 1 & 2 & 1 \end{vmatrix} \to \frac{1}{2}\begin{vmatrix} -2 & 3 & 1 \\ 5 & 8 & 1 \\ 1 & 2 & 1 \end{vmatrix}\begin{matrix} -2 & 3 \\ 5 & 8 \\ 1 & 2 \end{matrix}$

$= \frac{1}{2}[(-2 \cdot 8 \cdot 1) + (3 \cdot 1 \cdot 1) + (1 \cdot 5 \cdot 2) -$
$(1 \cdot 8 \cdot 1) - (2 \cdot 1 \cdot (-2)) - (1 \cdot 5 \cdot 3)]$
$= \frac{1}{2}[-16 + 3 + 10 - 8 + 4 - 15]$
$= \frac{1}{2}(-22)$
$= -11$; 11 square units

Pages 209–211 Exercises

11. yes; $\begin{vmatrix} -3 & 5 \\ 6 & -10 \end{vmatrix} = -3(-10) - 6(5)$

$= 30 - 30$
$= 0$

12. no, not square

13. no, not square

14. yes; $\begin{vmatrix} -5 & 8 \\ 3 & 0 \end{vmatrix} = -5(0) - 3(8)$

$= 0 - 24$
$= -24$

15. yes; $\begin{vmatrix} -2 & 0 & 1 \\ 1 & 2 & 0 \\ 4 & -1 & 1 \end{vmatrix}\begin{matrix} -2 & 0 \\ 1 & 2 \\ 4 & -1 \end{matrix}$

$= (-2)2 \cdot 1 + 0 \cdot 0 \cdot 4 + 1 \cdot 1(-1) - 4 \cdot 2 \cdot 1 -$
$(-1)0(-2) - 1 \cdot 1 \cdot 0$
$= -4 + 0 - 1 - 8 - 0 - 0$
$= -13$

16. yes; $\begin{vmatrix} 5 & 7 & -2 \\ 3 & -2 & 6 \\ 1 & -4 & 3 \end{vmatrix}\begin{matrix} 5 & 7 \\ 3 & -2 \\ 1 & -4 \end{matrix}$

$= 5(-2)3 + 7 \cdot 6 \cdot 1 + (-2)3(-4) - 1(-2)(-2) -$
$(-4)6 \cdot 5 - 3 \cdot 3 \cdot 7$
$= -30 + 42 + 24 - 4 + 120 - 63$
$= 89$

17. $A = \frac{1}{2}\begin{vmatrix} 0 & 0 & 1 \\ 8 & 0 & 1 \\ 9 & 4 & 1 \end{vmatrix}$

$= \frac{1}{2}\left[0\begin{vmatrix} 0 & 1 \\ 4 & 1 \end{vmatrix} - 0\begin{vmatrix} 8 & 1 \\ 9 & 1 \end{vmatrix} + 1\begin{vmatrix} 8 & 0 \\ 9 & 4 \end{vmatrix}\right]$
$= \frac{1}{2}[0 - 0 + 1(8 \cdot 4 - 9 \cdot 0)]$
$= \frac{1}{2}[1(32)]$
$= \frac{1}{2}(32)$
$= 16$; 16 square units

$A = \frac{1}{2}bh$
$= \frac{1}{2}(8)(4)$
$= 16$; 16 square units

18. $\begin{vmatrix} -3 & 0 & 6 \\ 6 & 5 & -2 \\ 1 & 4 & 2 \end{vmatrix} = -3\begin{vmatrix} 5 & -2 \\ 4 & 2 \end{vmatrix} - 0\begin{vmatrix} 6 & -2 \\ 1 & 2 \end{vmatrix} + 6\begin{vmatrix} 6 & 5 \\ 1 & 4 \end{vmatrix}$

$= -3(10 - (-8)) - 0 + 6(24 - 5)$
$= -3(18) + 6(19)$
$= -54 + 114$
$= 60$

19. $\begin{vmatrix} 0 & -4 & 0 \\ 3 & -2 & 5 \\ 2 & -1 & 1 \end{vmatrix} = 0\begin{vmatrix} -2 & 5 \\ -1 & 1 \end{vmatrix} - (-4)\begin{vmatrix} 3 & 5 \\ 2 & 1 \end{vmatrix} + 0\begin{vmatrix} 3 & 5 \\ 2 & 1 \end{vmatrix}$

$= 0 + 4(3 - 10) + 0$
$= 4(-7)$
$= -28$

20. $\begin{vmatrix} -2 & 7 & -2 \\ 4 & 6 & 2 \\ 1 & 0 & -1 \end{vmatrix} = -2\begin{vmatrix} 6 & 2 \\ 0 & -1 \end{vmatrix} - 7\begin{vmatrix} 4 & 2 \\ 1 & -1 \end{vmatrix} + (-2)\begin{vmatrix} 4 & 6 \\ 1 & 0 \end{vmatrix}$

$= -2(-6 - 0) - 7(-4 - 2) - 2(0 - 6)$
$= -2(-6) - 7(-6) - 2(-6)$
$= 12 + 42 + 12$
$= 66$

21. $\begin{vmatrix} 1 & 6 & 4 \\ -2 & 3 & 1 \\ 1 & 6 & 4 \end{vmatrix}\begin{matrix} 1 & 6 \\ -2 & 3 \\ 1 & 6 \end{matrix} = 1 \cdot 3 \cdot 4 + 6 \cdot 1 \cdot 1 + 4(-2)6 -$

$1 \cdot 3 \cdot 4 - 6 \cdot 1 \cdot 1 - 4(-2)6$
$= 12 + 6 - 48 - 12 - 6 + 48$
$= 0$

22. $\begin{vmatrix} 1 & -1 & 1 \\ 3 & 3 & 1 \\ 0 & 5 & 2 \end{vmatrix}\begin{matrix} 1 & -1 \\ 3 & 3 \\ 0 & 5 \end{matrix} = 1 \cdot 3 \cdot 2 + (-1)1(0) + 1 \cdot 3 \cdot 5 -$

$0 \cdot 3 \cdot 1 - 5 \cdot 1 \cdot 1 - 2 \cdot 3(-1)$
$= 6 + 0 + 15 - 0 - 5 + 6$
$= 22$

23. $\begin{vmatrix} 2 & -3 & 4 \\ -2 & 1 & 5 \\ 5 & 3 & -2 \end{vmatrix}\begin{matrix} 2 & -3 \\ -2 & 1 \\ 5 & 3 \end{matrix} = 2 \cdot 1(-2) + (-3)5 \cdot 5 +$

$4(-2)3 - 5 \cdot 1 \cdot 4 -$
$3 \cdot 5 \cdot 2 - (-2)(-2)(-3)$
$= -4 - 75 - 24 - 20 - 30 + 12$
$= -141$

24. $A = \frac{1}{2}\begin{vmatrix} 0 & 0 & 1 \\ -1 & 6 & 1 \\ 2 & 4 & 1 \end{vmatrix} = \frac{1}{2}\left[0\begin{vmatrix} 6 & 1 \\ 4 & 1 \end{vmatrix} - 0\begin{vmatrix} -1 & 1 \\ 2 & 1 \end{vmatrix} + 1\begin{vmatrix} -1 & 6 \\ 2 & 4 \end{vmatrix}\right]$

$= \frac{1}{2}[0 - 0 + 1(-1 \cdot 4 - 2 \cdot 6)]$

$= \frac{1}{2}[-4 - 12]$

$= \frac{1}{2}[-16]$

$= -8$; 8 square units

25. $A = \frac{1}{2}\begin{vmatrix} 3 & 0 & 1 \\ 2 & 4 & 1 \\ -2 & -2 & 1 \end{vmatrix}$

$= \frac{1}{2}\left[3\begin{vmatrix} 4 & 1 \\ -2 & 1 \end{vmatrix} - 0\begin{vmatrix} 2 & 1 \\ -2 & 1 \end{vmatrix} + 1\begin{vmatrix} 2 & 4 \\ -2 & -2 \end{vmatrix}\right]$

$= \frac{1}{2}[3(4 + 2) - 0 + 1(-4 + 8)]$

$= \frac{1}{2}[3(6) + 1(4)]$

$= \frac{1}{2}[18 + 4]$

$= \frac{1}{2}[22]$

$= 11$; 11 square units

26. $A = \frac{1}{2}\begin{vmatrix} -3 & 1 & 1 \\ 4 & -4 & 1 \\ 3 & 4 & 1 \end{vmatrix} \rightarrow \frac{1}{2}\left|\begin{matrix} -3 & 1 & 1 \\ 4 & -4 & 1 \\ 3 & 4 & 1 \end{matrix}\right|\begin{matrix} -3 & 1 \\ 4 & -4 \\ 3 & 4 \end{matrix}$

$= \frac{1}{2}((-3)(-4)1 + 1 \cdot 1 \cdot 3 + 1 \cdot 4 \cdot 4 -$
$3(-4)1 - 4 \cdot 1(-3) - 1 \cdot 4 \cdot 1)$

$= \frac{1}{2}(12 + 3 + 16 + 12 + 12 - 4)$

$= \frac{1}{2}(51)$

$= 25.5$; 25.5 square units

27. $\begin{vmatrix} 2 & x \\ 5 & -3 \end{vmatrix} = 24$

$2(-3) - 5x = 24$

$-6 - 5x = 24$

$-5x = 30$

$x = -6$

28. $\begin{vmatrix} 4 & x & -2 \\ -x & -3 & 1 \\ -6 & 2 & 3 \end{vmatrix} = -3 \rightarrow \left|\begin{matrix} 4 & x & -2 \\ -x & -3 & 1 \\ -6 & 2 & 3 \end{matrix}\right|\begin{matrix} 4 & x \\ -x & -3 \\ -6 & 2 \end{matrix} = -3$

$4(-3)3 + x \cdot 1(-6) + (-2)(-x)2 -$
$(-6)(-3)(-2) - 2 \cdot 1 \cdot 4 - 3(-x)x = -3$

$-36 - 6x + 4x + 36 - 8 + 3x^2 = -3$

$3x^2 - 2x - 8 = -3$

$3x^2 - 2x - 5 = 0$

$(3x - 5)(x + 1) = 0$

$3x - 5 = 0$ or $x + 1 = 0$

$3x = 5$ $\quad x = -1$

$x = \frac{5}{3}$

29. $A = \frac{1}{2}\begin{vmatrix} 0 & 0 & 1 \\ 6 & 7 & 1 \\ 1 & 6 & 1 \end{vmatrix} = \frac{1}{2}\left(0\begin{vmatrix} 7 & 1 \\ 6 & 1 \end{vmatrix} - 0\begin{vmatrix} 6 & 1 \\ 1 & 1 \end{vmatrix} + 1\begin{vmatrix} 6 & 7 \\ 1 & 6 \end{vmatrix}\right)$

$= \frac{1}{2}(0 - 0 + 6 \cdot 6 - 1 \cdot 7)$

$= \frac{1}{2}(36 - 7)$

$= \frac{1}{2}(29)$

$= 14.5$

$A = \frac{1}{2}\begin{vmatrix} 0 & 0 & 1 \\ 5 & 1 & 1 \\ 6 & 7 & 1 \end{vmatrix} = \frac{1}{2}\left(0\begin{vmatrix} 1 & 1 \\ 7 & 1 \end{vmatrix} - 0\begin{vmatrix} 5 & 1 \\ 6 & 1 \end{vmatrix} + 1\begin{vmatrix} 5 & 1 \\ 6 & 7 \end{vmatrix}\right)$

$= \frac{1}{2}(0 - 0 + 5 \cdot 7 - 6 \cdot 1)$

$= \frac{1}{2}(35 - 6)$

$= \frac{1}{2}(29)$

$= 14.5$; $14.5 + 14.5 = 29$ square units

30. $A = \frac{1}{2}\begin{vmatrix} 2 & 2 & 1 \\ 4 & 5 & 1 \\ -2 & 2 & 1 \end{vmatrix} = \frac{1}{2}\left(2\begin{vmatrix} 5 & 1 \\ 2 & 1 \end{vmatrix} - 2\begin{vmatrix} 4 & 1 \\ -2 & 1 \end{vmatrix} + 1\begin{vmatrix} 4 & 5 \\ -2 & 2 \end{vmatrix}\right)$

$= \frac{1}{2}(2(5 - 2) - 2(4 + 2) + 1(8 + 10))$

$= \frac{1}{2}(2(3) - 2(6) + 1(18))$

$= \frac{1}{2}(6 - 12 + 18)$

$= \frac{1}{2}(12)$

$= 6$

$A = \frac{1}{2}\begin{vmatrix} 2 & 2 & 1 \\ 4 & 5 & 1 \\ 5 & -2 & 1 \end{vmatrix} = \frac{1}{2}\left(2\begin{vmatrix} 5 & 1 \\ -2 & 1 \end{vmatrix} - 2\begin{vmatrix} 4 & 1 \\ 5 & 1 \end{vmatrix} + 1\begin{vmatrix} 4 & 5 \\ 5 & -2 \end{vmatrix}\right)$

$= \frac{1}{2}(2(5 + 2) - 2(4 - 5) + 1(-8 - 25))$

$= \frac{1}{2}(2(7) - 2(-1) + 1(-33))$

$= \frac{1}{2}(14 + 2 - 33)$

$= \frac{1}{2}(-17)$

$= -8.5$; $|-8.5| = 8.5$

$8.5 + 6 = 14.5$ square units

31. $30 = \frac{1}{2}\begin{vmatrix} 6 & 5 & 1 \\ 8 & 2 & 1 \\ x & 11 & 1 \end{vmatrix}$

$30 = \frac{1}{2}\left(6\begin{vmatrix} 2 & 1 \\ 11 & 1 \end{vmatrix} - 5\begin{vmatrix} 8 & 1 \\ x & 1 \end{vmatrix} + 1\begin{vmatrix} 8 & 2 \\ x & 11 \end{vmatrix}\right)$

$30 = \frac{1}{2}(6(2 - 11) - 5(8 - x) + 1(88 - 2x))$

$30 = \frac{1}{2}(6(-9) - 5(8 - x) + 88 - 2x)$

$60 = -54 - 40 + 5x + 88 - 2x$

$60 = -6 + 3x$

$66 = 3x$

$22 = x$

32. Sample answer: $\begin{bmatrix} 1 & 1 & 0 \\ 1 & 0 & 1 \\ 1 & 1 & 1 \end{bmatrix}$ and $\begin{bmatrix} 1 & 1 & -1 \\ 1 & 0 & -1 \\ 1 & 1 & 1 \end{bmatrix}$

33. Sample answer: $\begin{bmatrix} 1 & 1 & 1 \\ 1 & 1 & 1 \\ 1 & 1 & 1 \end{bmatrix}$

34. Sample answer: Place a coordinate grid over the map so that Midway is on the y-axis and Easter Island is on the x-axis. Then use the scale to estimate the coordinates of the vertices. Finally, use a determinant to estimate the area.

35. $A = \frac{1}{2}\begin{vmatrix} 0 & 0 & 1 \\ 6 & 3.5 & 1 \\ 21 & -10.5 & 1 \end{vmatrix}$

$= \frac{1}{2}\left(0\begin{vmatrix} 3.5 & 1 \\ -10.5 & 1 \end{vmatrix} - 0\begin{vmatrix} 6 & 1 \\ 21 & 1 \end{vmatrix} + 1\begin{vmatrix} 6 & 3.5 \\ 21 & -10.5 \end{vmatrix}\right)$

$= \frac{1}{2}(0 - 0 + 1(-63 - 73.5))$

$= \frac{1}{2}(-136.5)$

$= -68.25$; $|-68.25| = 68.25$

about 68 square miles

36. not possible due to dimensions

37. $\begin{bmatrix} 2 & x \\ y & 5 \end{bmatrix} = \begin{bmatrix} 2 & 1 \\ 3 & z \end{bmatrix}$ $\quad x = 1, y = 3, z = 5$

38. $f(x, y) = 12x - 8y$

$f(-2, -4) = 12(-2) - 8(-4)$

$= -24 + 32$

$= 8$

39. $x = \dfrac{\begin{vmatrix} 7 & -1 \\ 7 & 3 \end{vmatrix}}{\begin{vmatrix} 2 & -1 \\ 1 & 3 \end{vmatrix}}$ $\qquad y = \dfrac{\begin{vmatrix} 2 & 7 \\ 1 & 7 \end{vmatrix}}{\begin{vmatrix} 2 & -1 \\ 1 & 3 \end{vmatrix}}$

$= \frac{21 + 7}{6 + 1}$ $\qquad = \frac{14 - 7}{6 + 1}$

$= \frac{28}{7}$ $\qquad = \frac{7}{7}$

$= 4$ $\qquad = 1$ $\qquad (4, 1)$

40. $f(x) = |x - 3|$

x	$f(x)$
0	3
1	2
2	1
3	0
4	1

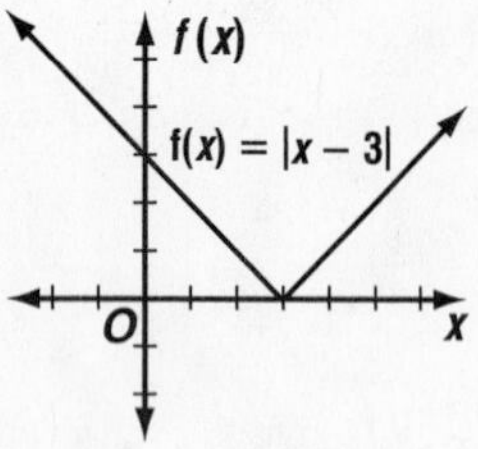

41. $f(x) = \frac{x}{3.5}$

$f(20) = \frac{20}{3.5}$

≈ 5.7; about 5.7 trees

42. distributive

Page 211 Self Test

1. $\begin{bmatrix} \text{Wife} & \text{Husband} \\ \text{Sue}(x + 200) & ? \\ \text{Tamara}(x) & ? \\ \text{Elisa}(x + 400) & ? \end{bmatrix}$

$x + 200 + x + x + 400 = 2400$

$3x + 600 = 2400$

$3x = 1800$

$x = 600$

$\begin{bmatrix} \text{Wife} & \text{Husband} \\ \text{Sue (800)} & ? \\ \text{Tamara (600)} & ? \\ \text{Elisa (1000)} & ? \end{bmatrix}$

$5400 - 2400 = 3000$

Use guess and check to match husbands with wives so that the husbands' investments total $3000.

$\begin{bmatrix} \text{Sue (800)} & \text{Lou (400)} \\ \text{Tamara (600)} & \text{Bob (600)} \\ \text{Elisa (1000)} & \text{Matea (2000)} \end{bmatrix}$

$400 + 600 + 2000 \stackrel{?}{=} 3000$

$3000 = 3000$

2. 3×3

3. $\begin{bmatrix} -2 & 1.5 \\ 3 & -0.25 \end{bmatrix} - \begin{bmatrix} -6 & 2 \\ 3 & 1.25 \end{bmatrix} = \begin{bmatrix} 4 & -0.5 \\ 0 & -1.5 \end{bmatrix}$

4. not possible, not same dimensions

5. $2\begin{bmatrix} 5 & 4 \\ -1 & 6 \end{bmatrix} - 3\begin{bmatrix} -3 & 0 \\ -2 & 0 \end{bmatrix} = \begin{bmatrix} 10 & 8 \\ -2 & 12 \end{bmatrix} - \begin{bmatrix} -9 & 0 \\ -6 & 0 \end{bmatrix}$

$= \begin{bmatrix} 19 & 8 \\ 4 & 12 \end{bmatrix}$

6. $-4\begin{bmatrix} -1 & -0.25 \\ 0 & 2 \\ 0.5 & 4 \end{bmatrix} = \begin{bmatrix} 4 & 1 \\ 0 & -8 \\ -2 & -16 \end{bmatrix}$

7. $\begin{bmatrix} -2 & 3 \\ 1 & 10 \\ 0 & -6 \end{bmatrix} \cdot \begin{bmatrix} 9 & 3 \\ 1 & 4 \end{bmatrix} = \begin{bmatrix} -2(9) + 3(1) & -2(3) + 3(4) \\ 1(9) + 10(1) & 1(3) + 10(4) \\ 0(9) + (-6)1 & 0(3) + (-6)4 \end{bmatrix}$

$= \begin{bmatrix} -18 + 3 & -6 + 12 \\ 9 + 10 & 3 + 40 \\ 0 - 6 & 0 - 24 \end{bmatrix}$

$= \begin{bmatrix} -15 & 6 \\ 19 & 43 \\ -6 & -24 \end{bmatrix}$

8. not possible due to dimensions

9. $\begin{vmatrix} -1 & 3 & 4 \\ 0 & 5 & 1 \\ 6 & -2 & 3 \end{vmatrix} = -1\begin{vmatrix} 5 & 1 \\ -2 & 3 \end{vmatrix} - 3\begin{vmatrix} 0 & 1 \\ 6 & 3 \end{vmatrix} + 4\begin{vmatrix} 0 & 5 \\ 6 & -2 \end{vmatrix}$

$= -1(15 + 2) - 3(0 - 6) + 4(0 - 30)$

$= -1(17) - 3(-6) + 4(-30)$

$= -17 + 18 - 120$

$= -119$

10. $A = \frac{1}{2}\begin{vmatrix} -1 & -2 & 1 \\ 5 & 3 & 1 \\ 2 & 6 & 1 \end{vmatrix}$

$= \frac{1}{2}\left(-1\begin{vmatrix} 3 & 1 \\ 6 & 1 \end{vmatrix} + 2\begin{vmatrix} 5 & 1 \\ 2 & 1 \end{vmatrix} + 1\begin{vmatrix} 5 & 3 \\ 2 & 6 \end{vmatrix}\right)$

$= \frac{1}{2}(-1(3 - 6) + 2(5 - 2) + 1(30 - 6))$

$= \frac{1}{2}(-1(-3) + 2(3) + 24)$

$= \frac{1}{2}(3 + 6 + 24)$

$= \frac{1}{2}(33)$

$= 16.5$; 16.5 square units

4-5 Identity and Inverse Matrices

Pages 216 Check for Understanding

1. With real numbers, the product of any number, except 0, and its inverse is the identity. With matrices, the product of any square matrix, except one with a determinant of 0, and its inverse is the identity matrix.

2. $\begin{bmatrix} 1 & 0 & 0 & 0 \\ 0 & 1 & 0 & 0 \\ 0 & 0 & 1 & 0 \\ 0 & 0 & 0 & 1 \end{bmatrix}$

3. $M^{-1} = \frac{1}{2(4) - 3(2)}\begin{bmatrix} 4 & -2 \\ -3 & 2 \end{bmatrix}$

$= \frac{1}{2}\begin{bmatrix} 4 & -2 \\ -3 & 2 \end{bmatrix}$

$= \begin{bmatrix} 2 & -1 \\ -\frac{3}{2} & 1 \end{bmatrix}$; c

4. Sample answer: $\begin{bmatrix} 1 & 2 \\ 3 & 6 \end{bmatrix}$

5. Miyoki; multiplication with the identity matrix is commutative and $\begin{bmatrix} 1 \\ 4 \end{bmatrix} \cdot \begin{bmatrix} 1 & 0 \\ 0 & 1 \end{bmatrix}$ is not defined.

6. $M^{-1} = \frac{1}{3(2) - 5(1)}\begin{bmatrix} 2 & -1 \\ -5 & 3 \end{bmatrix}$

$= \frac{1}{1}\begin{bmatrix} 2 & -1 \\ -5 & 3 \end{bmatrix}$

$= \begin{bmatrix} 2 & -1 \\ -5 & 3 \end{bmatrix}$

7. does not exist, not square

8. $6(4) - 8(3) = 0$
does not exist, determinant $= 0$

9. $M^{-1} = \frac{1}{(-5)(4) - 7(1)}\begin{bmatrix} 4 & -1 \\ -7 & -5 \end{bmatrix}$

$= -\frac{1}{27}\begin{bmatrix} 4 & -1 \\ -7 & -5 \end{bmatrix}$

10. $\begin{bmatrix} E & M \\ Y & U \end{bmatrix} = \begin{bmatrix} 5 & 13 \\ 25 & 21 \end{bmatrix}$

$C^{-1} = \begin{bmatrix} -1 & 1 \\ 1 & 0 \end{bmatrix}$

$\begin{bmatrix} -1 & 1 \\ 1 & 0 \end{bmatrix} \cdot \begin{bmatrix} 5 & 13 \\ 25 & 21 \end{bmatrix} = \begin{bmatrix} -1(5) + 1(25) & -1(13) + 1(21) \\ 1(5) + 0(25) & 1(13) + 0(21) \end{bmatrix}$

$= \begin{bmatrix} 20 & 8 \\ 5 & 13 \end{bmatrix}$ or $\begin{bmatrix} T & H \\ E & M \end{bmatrix}$

THEM

Pages 217–218 Exercises

11. $M^{-1} = \frac{1}{5(1) - 0(0)}\begin{bmatrix} 1 & 0 \\ 0 & 5 \end{bmatrix}$

$= \frac{1}{5}\begin{bmatrix} 1 & 0 \\ 0 & 5 \end{bmatrix}$

12. $M^{-1} = \frac{1}{8(2) - (-3)(-5)}\begin{bmatrix} 2 & 5 \\ 3 & 8 \end{bmatrix}$

$= \frac{1}{1}\begin{bmatrix} 2 & 5 \\ 3 & 8 \end{bmatrix}$

$= \begin{bmatrix} 2 & 5 \\ 3 & 8 \end{bmatrix}$

13. no inverse; det $= 0$

14. no inverse; not square

15. $M^{-1} = \frac{1}{4(7) - 2(-3)}\begin{bmatrix} 7 & 3 \\ -2 & 4 \end{bmatrix}$

$= \frac{1}{34}\begin{bmatrix} 7 & 3 \\ -2 & 4 \end{bmatrix}$

16. no inverse; not square

17. $M^{-1} = \frac{1}{2(1) - 6(-5)}\begin{bmatrix} 1 & 5 \\ -6 & 2 \end{bmatrix}$

$= \frac{1}{32}\begin{bmatrix} 1 & 5 \\ -6 & 2 \end{bmatrix}$

18. no inverse; determinant $= 0$

19. $M^{-1} = \frac{1}{-2(6) - 5(0)}\begin{bmatrix} 6 & 0 \\ -5 & -2 \end{bmatrix}$

$= \frac{1}{-12}\begin{bmatrix} 6 & 0 \\ -5 & -2 \end{bmatrix}$

$= -\frac{1}{12}\begin{bmatrix} 6 & 0 \\ -5 & -2 \end{bmatrix}$

20. $\begin{bmatrix} 0 & 1 \\ 1 & 1 \end{bmatrix} \cdot \begin{bmatrix} -1 & 1 \\ 1 & 0 \end{bmatrix} \stackrel{?}{=} I$

$\begin{bmatrix} 0(-1) + 1(1) & 0(1) + 1(0) \\ 1(-1) + 1(1) & 1(1) + 1(0) \end{bmatrix} \stackrel{?}{=} I$

$\begin{bmatrix} 1 & 0 \\ 0 & 1 \end{bmatrix} = I$; true

21. true; any matrix $\cdot\ I =$ itself

22. $\begin{bmatrix} \frac{1}{3} & -\frac{2}{3} \\ \frac{2}{3} & -\frac{1}{3} \end{bmatrix} \cdot \begin{bmatrix} 1 & 2 \\ 2 & 1 \end{bmatrix} \stackrel{?}{=} I$

$\begin{bmatrix} \frac{1}{3}(1) - \frac{2}{3}(2) & \frac{1}{3}(2) - \frac{2}{3}(1) \\ \frac{2}{3}(1) - \frac{1}{3}(2) & \frac{2}{3}(2) - \frac{1}{3}(1) \end{bmatrix} \stackrel{?}{=} I$

$\begin{bmatrix} -1 & 0 \\ 0 & 1 \end{bmatrix} \neq I$; false

23. $\begin{bmatrix} 1 & 5 \\ 1 & -2 \end{bmatrix} \cdot \begin{bmatrix} \frac{2}{7} & \frac{5}{7} \\ \frac{1}{7} & -\frac{1}{7} \end{bmatrix} \stackrel{?}{=} I$

$\begin{bmatrix} 1\left(\frac{2}{7}\right) + 5\left(\frac{1}{7}\right) & 1\left(\frac{5}{7}\right) + 5\left(-\frac{1}{7}\right) \\ 1\left(\frac{2}{7}\right) - 2\left(\frac{1}{7}\right) & 1\left(\frac{5}{7}\right) - 2\left(-\frac{1}{7}\right) \end{bmatrix} \stackrel{?}{=} I$

$\begin{bmatrix} 1 & 0 \\ 0 & 1 \end{bmatrix} = I$; true

24. $\begin{bmatrix} 3 & 1 & 2 \\ -2 & 0 & 4 \\ 3 & 5 & 2 \end{bmatrix} \cdot \left(-\frac{1}{64}\right) \begin{bmatrix} -20 & 8 & 4 \\ 16 & 0 & -16 \\ -10 & -12 & 2 \end{bmatrix} \stackrel{?}{=} I$

$\begin{bmatrix} 3 & 1 & 2 \\ -2 & 0 & 4 \\ 3 & 5 & 2 \end{bmatrix} \cdot \begin{bmatrix} \frac{5}{16} & -\frac{1}{8} & -\frac{1}{16} \\ -\frac{1}{4} & 0 & \frac{1}{4} \\ \frac{5}{32} & \frac{3}{16} & -\frac{1}{32} \end{bmatrix} \stackrel{?}{=} I$

$\begin{bmatrix} 3\left(\frac{5}{16}\right) + \left(-\frac{1}{4}\right) + 2\left(\frac{5}{32}\right) & 3\left(-\frac{1}{8}\right) + 2\left(\frac{3}{16}\right) & 3\left(-\frac{1}{16}\right) + \frac{1}{4} + 2\left(-\frac{1}{32}\right) \\ -2\left(\frac{5}{16}\right) + 4\left(\frac{5}{32}\right) & -2\left(-\frac{1}{8}\right) + 4\left(\frac{3}{16}\right) & -2\left(-\frac{1}{16}\right) + 4\left(-\frac{1}{32}\right) \\ 3\left(\frac{5}{16}\right) + 5\left(-\frac{1}{4}\right) + 2\left(\frac{5}{32}\right) & 3\left(-\frac{1}{8}\right) + 2\left(\frac{3}{16}\right) & 3\left(-\frac{1}{16}\right) + 5\left(\frac{1}{4}\right) + 2\left(-\frac{1}{32}\right) \end{bmatrix} \stackrel{?}{=} I$

$\begin{bmatrix} 1 & 0 & 0 \\ 0 & 1 & 0 \\ 0 & 0 & 1 \end{bmatrix} = I$; true

25. true **26.** true **27.** true

28. false **29.** true

30. The determinant is 0, so the matrix has no inverse.

31. Let $\begin{bmatrix} a & b \\ c & d \end{bmatrix}$ represent A and let $\begin{bmatrix} 1 & 0 \\ 0 & 1 \end{bmatrix}$ represent I.

$\begin{bmatrix} a & b \\ c & d \end{bmatrix} \cdot \begin{bmatrix} 1 & 0 \\ 0 & 1 \end{bmatrix} = \begin{bmatrix} a(1) + b(0) & a(0) + b(1) \\ c(1) + d(0) & c(0) + d(1) \end{bmatrix} = \begin{bmatrix} a & b \\ c & d \end{bmatrix}$

$\begin{bmatrix} 1 & 0 \\ 0 & 1 \end{bmatrix} \cdot \begin{bmatrix} a & b \\ c & d \end{bmatrix} = \begin{bmatrix} 1(a) + 0(c) & 1(b) + 0(d) \\ 0(a) + 1(c) & 0(b) + 1(d) \end{bmatrix} = \begin{bmatrix} a & b \\ c & d \end{bmatrix}$

Therefore, $A \cdot I = I \cdot A = A$.

32a. $M^{-1} = \frac{1}{0 \cdot 0 - 1(-1)} \begin{bmatrix} 0 & 1 \\ -1 & 0 \end{bmatrix}$

$= \frac{1}{1} \begin{bmatrix} 0 & 1 \\ -1 & 0 \end{bmatrix}$

$= \begin{bmatrix} 0 & 1 \\ -1 & 0 \end{bmatrix}$

32b. Sample answer: rotate figure 90° clockwise

32c. $\begin{bmatrix} 0 & 1 \\ -1 & 0 \end{bmatrix} \begin{bmatrix} 0 & 3 & 4 \\ 0 & 5 & 2 \end{bmatrix} = \begin{bmatrix} 0+0 & 0+5 & 0+2 \\ 0+0 & -3+0 & -4+0 \end{bmatrix} = \begin{bmatrix} 0 & 5 & 2 \\ 0 & -3 & -4 \end{bmatrix}$

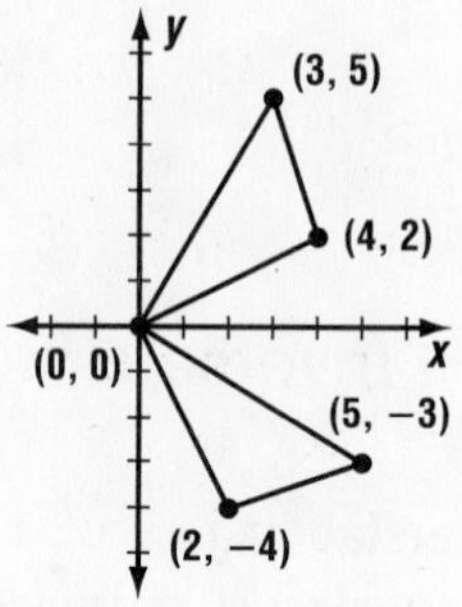

33a. $\begin{bmatrix} L & A \\ M & M \end{bmatrix} = \begin{bmatrix} 12 & 1 \\ 13 & 13 \end{bmatrix}$; $C^{-1} = \begin{bmatrix} -1 & 1 \\ 1 & 0 \end{bmatrix}$

$\begin{bmatrix} -1 & 1 \\ 1 & 0 \end{bmatrix} \cdot \begin{bmatrix} 12 & 1 \\ 13 & 13 \end{bmatrix} = \begin{bmatrix} -1(12) + 1(13) & -1(1) + 1(13) \\ 1(12) + 0(13) & 1(1) + 0(13) \end{bmatrix}$

$= \begin{bmatrix} 1 & 12 \\ 12 & 1 \end{bmatrix}$ or $\begin{bmatrix} A & L \\ L & A \end{bmatrix}$

$\begin{bmatrix} I & X \\ C & Q \end{bmatrix} = \begin{bmatrix} 9 & 24 \\ 3 & 17 \end{bmatrix}$

$\begin{bmatrix} -1 & 1 \\ 1 & 0 \end{bmatrix} \cdot \begin{bmatrix} 9 & 24 \\ 3 & 17 \end{bmatrix} = \begin{bmatrix} -1(9) + 1(3) & -1(24) + 1(17) \\ 1(9) + 0(3) & 1(24) + 0(17) \end{bmatrix}$

$= \begin{bmatrix} -6 & -7 \\ 9 & 24 \end{bmatrix}$ or $\begin{bmatrix} T & S \\ I & X \end{bmatrix}$

ALLATSIX

33b. MEET ME AT THE MALL AT SIX

33c. See students' work.

34. $\begin{vmatrix} 4 & -a \\ 7 & 3a \end{vmatrix} = 57$

$4(3a) - 7(-a) = 57$

$12a + 7a = 57$

$19a = 57$

$a = 3$

35. Let x = shorter leg, y = longer leg, and z = hypotenuse.

$x + y + z = 24$

$3y - 2x = z + 2$

$-2x + 3y - z = 2$

$x = \frac{1}{2}z + 1$

$x - \frac{1}{2}z = 1$

$2x - z = 2$

$x + y + z = 24 \rightarrow$ Multiply by 3 $\rightarrow 3x + 3y + 3z = 72$

$-2x + 3y - z = 2 \rightarrow \quad \rightarrow (-)\ -2x + 3y - z = 2$

$5x + 4z = 70$

$5x + 4z = 70 \rightarrow \quad \rightarrow 5x + 4z = 70$

$2x - z = 2 \rightarrow$ Multiply by 4 $\rightarrow (+)\ 8x - 4z = 8$

$13x = 78$

$x = 6$

$2x - z = 2$

$2(6) - z = 2$

$12 - z = 2$

$-z = -10$

$z = 10$

$x + y + z = 24$

$6 + y + 10 = 24$

$y + 16 = 24$

$y = 8$

6 centimeters, 8 centimeters, 10 centimeters

36. $3x + y = 3$

$y = -3x + 3$

$3x - 2y = -3$

$3x - 2(-3x + 3) = -3$

$3x + 6x - 6 = -3$

$9x - 6 = -3$

$9x = 3$

$x = \frac{1}{3}$

$3x + y = 3$

$3\left(\frac{1}{3}\right) + y = 3$

$1 + y = 3$

$y = 2$

$\left(\frac{1}{3}, 2\right)$

37. $g(x) = \frac{26 - x}{2}$

$g(12) = \frac{26 - 12}{2}$

$= \frac{14}{2}$

$= 7$

38. $5 < 2x - 9 < 11$

$14 < 2x < 20$

$7 < x < 10$

$\{x \mid 7 < x < 10\}$

39. $|a + 5| + 5 = 3$

$|a + 5| = -2$

no solution

Page 218 Mathematics and Society

1. Sample answer: The greatest integer function; $\left[3\frac{1}{2}\right] = x$ is easy to solve, by $[x] = 3$ is virtually impossible.
2. only top executives in each branch
3. Advantage: The messages are kept secret until authorized personnel translate them. Disadvantages: Messages cannot be translated unless the code is available. If the code is broken or stolen, important secrets would be known.

4-6 Using Matrices to Solve Systems of Equations

Page 223 Check for Understanding

1. $\begin{bmatrix} 2 & -8 \\ 7 & -2 \end{bmatrix} \cdot \begin{bmatrix} x \\ y \end{bmatrix} = \begin{bmatrix} 3 \\ 5 \end{bmatrix}$

2. $2r - 5s = 2$

$3r + 8s = 9$

3. Find the inverse of the coefficient matrix and multiply both sides of the matrix equation by the inverse.

4. Sample answer: $2x + 3y = 5$

$4x + 6y = 10$

5. $\begin{bmatrix} 4 & -7 \\ 3 & 5 \end{bmatrix} \cdot \begin{bmatrix} x \\ y \end{bmatrix} = \begin{bmatrix} 2 \\ 9 \end{bmatrix}$

6. $\begin{bmatrix} 2 & 3 & -5 \\ 7 & 0 & 3 \\ 3 & -6 & 1 \end{bmatrix} \cdot \begin{bmatrix} a \\ b \\ c \end{bmatrix} = \begin{bmatrix} 1 \\ 7 \\ -5 \end{bmatrix}$

7. $y = 3x$

$-3x + y = 0$

$\begin{bmatrix} -3 & 1 \\ 1 & 2 \end{bmatrix} \cdot \begin{bmatrix} x \\ y \end{bmatrix} = \begin{bmatrix} 0 \\ -21 \end{bmatrix}$

8. $\begin{bmatrix} 4 & 8 \\ 2 & -3 \end{bmatrix} \cdot \begin{bmatrix} x \\ y \end{bmatrix} = \begin{bmatrix} 7 \\ 0 \end{bmatrix}$

$-\frac{1}{28}\begin{bmatrix} -3 & -8 \\ -2 & 4 \end{bmatrix} \cdot \begin{bmatrix} 4 & 8 \\ 2 & -3 \end{bmatrix} \cdot \begin{bmatrix} x \\ y \end{bmatrix} = -\frac{1}{28}\begin{bmatrix} -3 & -8 \\ -2 & 4 \end{bmatrix} \cdot \begin{bmatrix} 7 \\ 0 \end{bmatrix}$

$-\frac{1}{28}\begin{bmatrix} -3(4) - 8(2) & -3(8) - 8(-3) \\ -2(4) + 4(2) & -2(8) + 4(-3) \end{bmatrix} \cdot \begin{bmatrix} x \\ y \end{bmatrix} = -\frac{1}{28}\begin{bmatrix} -3(7) - 8(0) \\ -2(7) + 4(0) \end{bmatrix}$

$-\frac{1}{28}\begin{bmatrix} -28 & 0 \\ 0 & -28 \end{bmatrix} \cdot \begin{bmatrix} x \\ y \end{bmatrix} = -\frac{1}{28}\begin{bmatrix} -21 \\ -14 \end{bmatrix}$

$\begin{bmatrix} x \\ y \end{bmatrix} = \begin{bmatrix} \frac{3}{4} \\ \frac{1}{2} \end{bmatrix}; \left(\frac{3}{4}, \frac{1}{2}\right)$

9. $\begin{bmatrix} 1 & 2 \\ 3 & 2 \end{bmatrix} \cdot \begin{bmatrix} x \\ y \end{bmatrix} = \begin{bmatrix} 8 \\ 6 \end{bmatrix}; M^{-1} = \frac{1}{1(2) - 3(2)}\begin{bmatrix} 2 & -2 \\ -3 & 1 \end{bmatrix}$

$= -\frac{1}{4}\begin{bmatrix} 2 & -2 \\ -3 & 1 \end{bmatrix}$

$-\frac{1}{4}\begin{bmatrix} 2 & -2 \\ -3 & 1 \end{bmatrix} \cdot \begin{bmatrix} 1 & 2 \\ 3 & 2 \end{bmatrix} \cdot \begin{bmatrix} x \\ y \end{bmatrix} = -\frac{1}{4}\begin{bmatrix} 2 & -2 \\ -3 & 1 \end{bmatrix} \cdot \begin{bmatrix} 8 \\ 6 \end{bmatrix}$

$\begin{bmatrix} x \\ y \end{bmatrix} = -\frac{1}{4}\begin{bmatrix} 16 - 12 \\ -24 + 6 \end{bmatrix}$

$\begin{bmatrix} x \\ y \end{bmatrix} = \begin{bmatrix} -1 \\ \frac{9}{2} \end{bmatrix}; \left(-1, \frac{9}{2}\right)$

10. $3s = -4 + 4t$

$3s - 4t = -4$

$\begin{bmatrix} 5 & 4 \\ 3 & -4 \end{bmatrix} \cdot \begin{bmatrix} s \\ t \end{bmatrix} = \begin{bmatrix} 12 \\ -4 \end{bmatrix}; M^{-1} = \frac{1}{5(-4) - 3(4)}\begin{bmatrix} -4 & -4 \\ -3 & 5 \end{bmatrix}$

$= -\frac{1}{32}\begin{bmatrix} -4 & -4 \\ -3 & 5 \end{bmatrix}$

$-\frac{1}{32}\begin{bmatrix} -4 & -4 \\ -3 & 5 \end{bmatrix} \cdot \begin{bmatrix} 5 & 4 \\ 3 & -4 \end{bmatrix} \cdot \begin{bmatrix} s \\ t \end{bmatrix} = -\frac{1}{32}\begin{bmatrix} -4 & -4 \\ -3 & 5 \end{bmatrix} \cdot \begin{bmatrix} 12 \\ -4 \end{bmatrix}$

$\begin{bmatrix} s \\ t \end{bmatrix} = -\frac{1}{32}\begin{bmatrix} -48 + 16 \\ -36 - 20 \end{bmatrix}$

$\begin{bmatrix} s \\ t \end{bmatrix} = \begin{bmatrix} 1 \\ 1.75 \end{bmatrix}; (1, 1.75)$

11. $3x - 15 = -6y$

$3x + 6y = 15$

$\begin{vmatrix} 1 & 2 \\ 3 & 6 \end{vmatrix} = 1(6) - 3(2)$

$= 0$; there is no unique solution

$x + 2y = 5$

$2y = -x + 5$

$y = -\frac{1}{2}x + \frac{5}{2}$

$3x - 15 = -6y$

$-\frac{1}{2}x + \frac{5}{2} = y$

The equations are the same; infinitely many.

Pages 224–225 Exercises

12. $\begin{bmatrix} 5 & -6 \\ 3 & 2 \end{bmatrix} \cdot \begin{bmatrix} a \\ b \end{bmatrix} = \begin{bmatrix} -47 \\ -17 \end{bmatrix}$ **13.** $\begin{bmatrix} 3 & -7 \\ 6 & 5 \end{bmatrix} \cdot \begin{bmatrix} m \\ n \end{bmatrix} = \begin{bmatrix} -43 \\ -10 \end{bmatrix}$

14. $s = r - 4$
$-r + s = -4$ $\begin{bmatrix} 2 & 3 \\ -1 & 1 \end{bmatrix} \cdot \begin{bmatrix} r \\ s \end{bmatrix} = \begin{bmatrix} -17 \\ -4 \end{bmatrix}$

15. $y = -x$ $y = 2x$
$-x - y = 0$ $2x - y = 0$ $\begin{bmatrix} -1 & -1 \\ 2 & -1 \end{bmatrix} \cdot \begin{bmatrix} x \\ y \end{bmatrix} = \begin{bmatrix} 0 \\ 0 \end{bmatrix}$

16. $y = x + 3$ $3y + x = 5$
$-x + y = 3$ $x + 3y = 5$
$x - y = -3$ $\begin{bmatrix} 1 & -1 \\ 1 & 3 \end{bmatrix} \cdot \begin{bmatrix} x \\ y \end{bmatrix} = \begin{bmatrix} -3 \\ 5 \end{bmatrix}$

17. $2x = 3y$ $y = 4x - 5$
$2x - 3y = 0$ $-4x + y = -5$
$4x - y = 5$ $\begin{bmatrix} 2 & -3 \\ 4 & -1 \end{bmatrix} \cdot \begin{bmatrix} x \\ y \end{bmatrix} = \begin{bmatrix} 0 \\ 5 \end{bmatrix}$

18. $-\frac{1}{10}\begin{bmatrix} -2 & -1 \\ -4 & 3 \end{bmatrix} \cdot \begin{bmatrix} 3 & 1 \\ 4 & -2 \end{bmatrix} \cdot \begin{bmatrix} x \\ y \end{bmatrix} = -\frac{1}{10}\begin{bmatrix} -2 & -1 \\ -4 & 3 \end{bmatrix} \cdot \begin{bmatrix} 13 \\ 24 \end{bmatrix}$

$\begin{bmatrix} x \\ y \end{bmatrix} = -\frac{1}{10}\begin{bmatrix} -26 - 24 \\ -52 + 72 \end{bmatrix}$

$\begin{bmatrix} x \\ y \end{bmatrix} = \begin{bmatrix} 5 \\ -2 \end{bmatrix}$; $(5, -2)$

19. $-\frac{1}{9}\begin{bmatrix} 1 & -1 & -2 \\ 21 & -12 & -15 \\ -33 & 15 & 21 \end{bmatrix} \cdot \begin{bmatrix} 3 & 1 & 1 \\ -6 & 5 & 3 \\ 9 & -2 & -1 \end{bmatrix}\begin{bmatrix} x \\ y \\ z \end{bmatrix}$

$= -\frac{1}{9}\begin{bmatrix} 1 & -1 & -2 \\ 21 & -12 & -15 \\ -33 & 15 & 21 \end{bmatrix} \cdot \begin{bmatrix} -1 \\ -9 \\ 5 \end{bmatrix}$

$\begin{bmatrix} x \\ y \\ z \end{bmatrix} = -\frac{1}{9}\begin{bmatrix} -1 + 9 - 10 \\ -21 + 108 - 75 \\ 33 - 135 + 105 \end{bmatrix}$

$\begin{bmatrix} x \\ y \\ z \end{bmatrix} = \begin{bmatrix} \frac{2}{9} \\ -\frac{4}{3} \\ -\frac{1}{3} \end{bmatrix}$; $\left(\frac{2}{9}, -\frac{4}{3}, -\frac{1}{3}\right)$

20. $-\frac{1}{9}\begin{bmatrix} -1 & -10 & 4 \\ -3 & -3 & 3 \\ -1 & 8 & -5 \end{bmatrix} \cdot \begin{bmatrix} 1 & 2 & 2 \\ 2 & -1 & 1 \\ 3 & -2 & 3 \end{bmatrix} \cdot \begin{bmatrix} a \\ b \\ c \end{bmatrix}$

$= -\frac{1}{9}\begin{bmatrix} -1 & -10 & 4 \\ -3 & -3 & 3 \\ -1 & 8 & -5 \end{bmatrix} \cdot \begin{bmatrix} 0 \\ -1 \\ -4 \end{bmatrix}$

$\begin{bmatrix} a \\ b \\ c \end{bmatrix} = -\frac{1}{9}\begin{bmatrix} 0 + 10 - 16 \\ 0 + 3 - 12 \\ 0 - 8 + 20 \end{bmatrix}$

$\begin{bmatrix} a \\ b \\ c \end{bmatrix} = \begin{bmatrix} \frac{2}{3} \\ 1 \\ -\frac{4}{3} \end{bmatrix}$; $\left(\frac{2}{3}, 1, -\frac{4}{3}\right)$

21. $M^{-1} = \frac{1}{2(-3) - 4(6)}\begin{bmatrix} -3 & -6 \\ -4 & 2 \end{bmatrix} = -\frac{1}{30}\begin{bmatrix} -3 & -6 \\ -4 & 2 \end{bmatrix}$

$-\frac{1}{30}\begin{bmatrix} -3 & -6 \\ -4 & 2 \end{bmatrix} \cdot \begin{bmatrix} 2 & 6 \\ 4 & -3 \end{bmatrix} \cdot \begin{bmatrix} x \\ y \end{bmatrix} = -\frac{1}{30}\begin{bmatrix} -3 & -6 \\ -4 & 2 \end{bmatrix} \cdot \begin{bmatrix} 3 \\ 1 \end{bmatrix}$

$\begin{bmatrix} x \\ y \end{bmatrix} = -\frac{1}{30}\begin{bmatrix} -9 - 6 \\ -12 + 2 \end{bmatrix}$

$\begin{bmatrix} x \\ y \end{bmatrix} = \begin{bmatrix} \frac{1}{2} \\ \frac{1}{3} \end{bmatrix}$; $\left(\frac{1}{2}, \frac{1}{3}\right)$

22. $M^{-1} = \frac{1}{8(3) - 2(-1)}\begin{bmatrix} 3 & 1 \\ -2 & 8 \end{bmatrix} = \frac{1}{26}\begin{bmatrix} 3 & 1 \\ -2 & 8 \end{bmatrix}$

$\frac{1}{26}\begin{bmatrix} 3 & 1 \\ -2 & 8 \end{bmatrix} \cdot \begin{bmatrix} 8 & -1 \\ 2 & 3 \end{bmatrix} \cdot \begin{bmatrix} a \\ b \end{bmatrix} = \frac{1}{26}\begin{bmatrix} 3 & 1 \\ -2 & 8 \end{bmatrix} \cdot \begin{bmatrix} 16 \\ -9 \end{bmatrix}$

$\begin{bmatrix} a \\ b \end{bmatrix} = \frac{1}{26}\begin{bmatrix} 48 - 9 \\ -32 - 72 \end{bmatrix}$

$\begin{bmatrix} a \\ b \end{bmatrix} = \begin{bmatrix} 1.5 \\ -4 \end{bmatrix}$; $(1.5, -4)$

23. $M^{-1} = \frac{1}{5(5) - 8(-3)}\begin{bmatrix} 5 & 3 \\ -8 & 5 \end{bmatrix} = \frac{1}{49}\begin{bmatrix} 5 & 3 \\ -8 & 5 \end{bmatrix}$

$\frac{1}{49}\begin{bmatrix} 5 & 3 \\ -8 & 5 \end{bmatrix} \cdot \begin{bmatrix} 5 & -3 \\ 8 & 5 \end{bmatrix} \cdot \begin{bmatrix} a \\ b \end{bmatrix} = \frac{1}{49}\begin{bmatrix} 5 & 3 \\ -8 & 5 \end{bmatrix} \cdot \begin{bmatrix} -30 \\ 1 \end{bmatrix}$

$\begin{bmatrix} a \\ b \end{bmatrix} = \frac{1}{49}\begin{bmatrix} -150 + 3 \\ 240 + 5 \end{bmatrix}$

$\begin{bmatrix} a \\ b \end{bmatrix} = \begin{bmatrix} -3 \\ 5 \end{bmatrix}$; $(-3, 5)$

24. $3x = 13 - y$
$3x + y = 13$ $\begin{bmatrix} 3 & 1 \\ 2 & -1 \end{bmatrix} \cdot \begin{bmatrix} x \\ y \end{bmatrix} = \begin{bmatrix} 13 \\ 2 \end{bmatrix}$

$M^{-1} = \frac{1}{3(-1) - 2(1)}\begin{bmatrix} -1 & -1 \\ -2 & 3 \end{bmatrix} = -\frac{1}{5}\begin{bmatrix} -1 & -1 \\ -2 & 3 \end{bmatrix}$

$-\frac{1}{5}\begin{bmatrix} -1 & -1 \\ -2 & 3 \end{bmatrix} \cdot \begin{bmatrix} 3 & 1 \\ 2 & -1 \end{bmatrix} \cdot \begin{bmatrix} x \\ y \end{bmatrix} = -\frac{1}{5}\begin{bmatrix} -1 & -1 \\ -2 & 3 \end{bmatrix} \cdot \begin{bmatrix} 13 \\ 2 \end{bmatrix}$

$\begin{bmatrix} x \\ y \end{bmatrix} = -\frac{1}{5}\begin{bmatrix} -13 - 2 \\ -26 + 6 \end{bmatrix}$

$\begin{bmatrix} x \\ y \end{bmatrix} = \begin{bmatrix} 3 \\ 4 \end{bmatrix}$; $(3, 4)$

25. $3a = 8b + 1$
$3a - 8b = 1$ $\begin{bmatrix} 6 & 2 \\ 3 & -8 \end{bmatrix} \cdot \begin{bmatrix} a \\ b \end{bmatrix} = \begin{bmatrix} 11 \\ 1 \end{bmatrix}$

$M^{-1} = \frac{1}{6(-8) - 3(2)}\begin{bmatrix} -8 & -2 \\ -3 & 6 \end{bmatrix} = -\frac{1}{54}\begin{bmatrix} -8 & -2 \\ -3 & 6 \end{bmatrix}$

$-\frac{1}{54}\begin{bmatrix} -8 & -2 \\ -3 & 6 \end{bmatrix} \cdot \begin{bmatrix} 6 & 2 \\ 3 & -8 \end{bmatrix} \cdot \begin{bmatrix} a \\ b \end{bmatrix} = -\frac{1}{54}\begin{bmatrix} -8 & -2 \\ -3 & 6 \end{bmatrix} \cdot \begin{bmatrix} 11 \\ 1 \end{bmatrix}$

$\begin{bmatrix} a \\ b \end{bmatrix} = -\frac{1}{54}\begin{bmatrix} -88 - 2 \\ -33 + 6 \end{bmatrix}$

$\begin{bmatrix} a \\ b \end{bmatrix} = \begin{bmatrix} \frac{5}{3} \\ \frac{1}{2} \end{bmatrix}$; $\left(\frac{5}{3}, \frac{1}{2}\right)$

26. $4x = -3y + 5 \qquad 8x = 9y$

$4x + 3y = 5 \qquad 8x - 9y = 0$

$$\begin{bmatrix} 4 & 3 \\ 8 & -9 \end{bmatrix} \cdot \begin{bmatrix} x \\ y \end{bmatrix} = \begin{bmatrix} 5 \\ 0 \end{bmatrix}$$

$$M^{-1} = \frac{1}{4(-9) - 8(3)} \begin{bmatrix} -9 & -3 \\ -8 & 4 \end{bmatrix} = -\frac{1}{60}\begin{bmatrix} -9 & -3 \\ -8 & 4 \end{bmatrix}$$

$$-\frac{1}{60}\begin{bmatrix} -9 & -3 \\ -8 & 4 \end{bmatrix} \cdot \begin{bmatrix} 4 & 3 \\ 8 & -9 \end{bmatrix} \cdot \begin{bmatrix} x \\ y \end{bmatrix} = -\frac{1}{60}\begin{bmatrix} -9 & -3 \\ -8 & 4 \end{bmatrix} \cdot \begin{bmatrix} 5 \\ 0 \end{bmatrix}$$

$$\begin{bmatrix} x \\ y \end{bmatrix} = -\frac{1}{60}\begin{bmatrix} -45 + 0 \\ -40 + 0 \end{bmatrix}$$

$$\begin{bmatrix} x \\ y \end{bmatrix} = \begin{bmatrix} \frac{3}{4} \\ \frac{2}{3} \end{bmatrix}; \left(\frac{3}{4}, \frac{2}{3}\right)$$

27. $\begin{vmatrix} 3 & -1 \\ 6 & 2 \end{vmatrix} = 3(2) - 6(-1) = 12;$

There is one unique solution.

$$\begin{bmatrix} 3 & -1 \\ 6 & 2 \end{bmatrix} \cdot \begin{bmatrix} x \\ y \end{bmatrix} = \begin{bmatrix} 4 \\ -8 \end{bmatrix};$$

$$M^{-1} = \frac{1}{3(2) - 6(-1)} \begin{bmatrix} 2 & 1 \\ -6 & 3 \end{bmatrix} = \frac{1}{12}\begin{bmatrix} 2 & 1 \\ -6 & 3 \end{bmatrix}$$

$$\frac{1}{12}\begin{bmatrix} 2 & 1 \\ -6 & 3 \end{bmatrix} \cdot \begin{bmatrix} 3 & -1 \\ 6 & 2 \end{bmatrix} \cdot \begin{bmatrix} x \\ y \end{bmatrix} = \frac{1}{12}\begin{bmatrix} 2 & 1 \\ -6 & 3 \end{bmatrix} \cdot \begin{bmatrix} 4 \\ -8 \end{bmatrix}$$

$$\begin{bmatrix} x \\ y \end{bmatrix} = \frac{1}{12}\begin{bmatrix} 8 - 8 \\ -24 - 24 \end{bmatrix}$$

$$\begin{bmatrix} x \\ y \end{bmatrix} = \begin{bmatrix} 0 \\ -4 \end{bmatrix}; (0, -4)$$

28. $3x - 18 = -9y$

$3x + 9y = 18$

$\begin{vmatrix} 1 & 3 \\ 3 & 9 \end{vmatrix} = 1(9) - 3(3) = 0;$ no unique solution

$x + 3y = 6$

$3y = -x + 6$

$y = -\frac{1}{3}x + 2$

$3x - 18 = -9y$

$-\frac{1}{3}x + 2 = y$

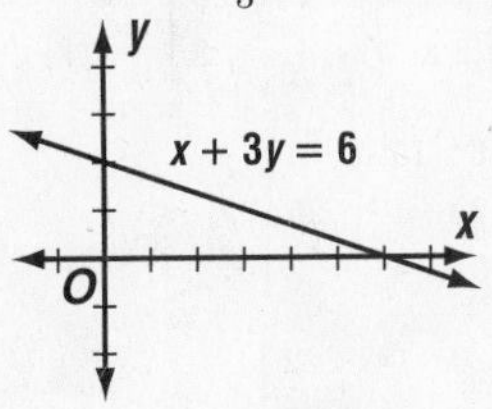

infinitely many

29. $6x - 42 = 16y$

$6x - 16y = 42$

$\begin{vmatrix} 3 & -8 \\ 6 & -16 \end{vmatrix} = 3(-16) - 6(-8) = 0;$ no unique solution

$3x - 8y = 4$

$-8y = -3x + 4$

$y = \frac{3}{8}x - \frac{1}{2}$

$6x - 42 = 16y$

$\frac{3}{8}x - \frac{21}{8} = y$

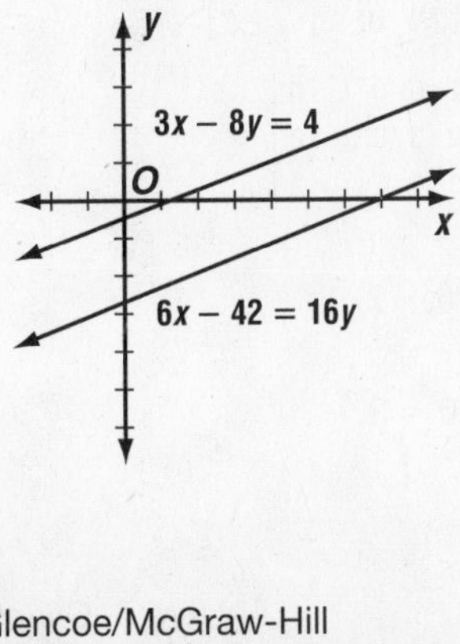

no solution

30. $5x + y = 1$
$9x + 3y = 1$ $\rightarrow \begin{bmatrix} 5 & 1 \\ 9 & 3 \end{bmatrix} \cdot \begin{bmatrix} x \\ y \end{bmatrix} = \begin{bmatrix} 1 \\ 1 \end{bmatrix}$

MATRX ▶ ▶ ENTER 2 ENTER 2 ENTER 5 ENTER 1 ENTER 9 ENTER 3 ENTER MATRX ▶ ▶ ▼ ENTER 2 ENTER 1 ENTER 1 ENTER 1 ENTER 2nd QUIT MATRX ENTER x^{-1} ENTER × MATRX ▼ ENTER ENTER $\begin{bmatrix} .3333333333 \\ -.6666666667 \end{bmatrix}$;

$\left(\frac{1}{3}, -\frac{2}{3}\right)$

31. $1.8x + 5y = 19.5$
$5.2x - 2.9y = 4.3$ $\rightarrow \begin{bmatrix} 1.8 & 5 \\ 5.2 & -2.9 \end{bmatrix} \cdot \begin{bmatrix} x \\ y \end{bmatrix} = \begin{bmatrix} 19.5 \\ 4.3 \end{bmatrix}$

MATRX ▶ ▶ ENTER 2 ENTER 2 ENTER 1.8 ENTER 5 ENTER 5.2 ENTER (−) 2.9 ENTER MATRX ▶ ▶ ▼ ENTER 2 ENTER 1 ENTER 19.5 ENTER 4.3 ENTER 2nd QUIT MATRX ENTER x^{-1} ENTER × MATRX ▼ ENTER ENTER $\begin{bmatrix} 2.5 \\ 3 \end{bmatrix}$; (2.5, 3)

32. $ax + by + cz = r$

$dx + ey + fz = s$

$gx + hy + iz = t$

$$x = \frac{\begin{vmatrix} r & b & c \\ s & e & f \\ t & h & i \end{vmatrix}}{\begin{vmatrix} a & b & c \\ d & e & f \\ g & h & i \end{vmatrix}}, \; y = \frac{\begin{vmatrix} a & r & c \\ d & s & f \\ g & t & i \end{vmatrix}}{\begin{vmatrix} a & b & c \\ d & e & f \\ g & h & i \end{vmatrix}}, \; z = \frac{\begin{vmatrix} a & b & r \\ d & e & s \\ g & h & t \end{vmatrix}}{\begin{vmatrix} a & b & c \\ d & e & f \\ g & h & i \end{vmatrix}}$$

33. Let x = amount of 60% solution and y = amount of 40% solution.

$x + y = 200$

$0.60x + 0.40y = 0.48(x + y)$

$0.60x + 0.40y = 0.48x + 0.48y$

$0.12x - 0.08y = 0$

$x + y = 200$
$0.12x - 0.08y = 0$ $\rightarrow \begin{bmatrix} 1 & 1 \\ 0.12 & -0.08 \end{bmatrix} \cdot \begin{bmatrix} x \\ y \end{bmatrix} = \begin{bmatrix} 200 \\ 0 \end{bmatrix}$

$$M^{-1} = \frac{1}{-0.08 - 0.12} \begin{bmatrix} -0.08 & -1 \\ -0.12 & 1 \end{bmatrix} = -\frac{1}{0.2}\begin{bmatrix} -0.08 & -1 \\ -0.12 & 1 \end{bmatrix}$$

$$-\frac{1}{0.2}\begin{bmatrix} -0.08 & -1 \\ -0.12 & 1 \end{bmatrix} \cdot \begin{bmatrix} 1 & 1 \\ 0.12 & -0.08 \end{bmatrix} \cdot \begin{bmatrix} x \\ y \end{bmatrix}$$

$$= -\frac{1}{0.2}\begin{bmatrix} -0.08 & -1 \\ -0.12 & 1 \end{bmatrix} \cdot \begin{bmatrix} 200 \\ 0 \end{bmatrix}$$

$$\begin{bmatrix} x \\ y \end{bmatrix} = -\frac{1}{0.2}\begin{bmatrix} -16 + 0 \\ -24 + 0 \end{bmatrix}$$

$$\begin{bmatrix} x \\ y \end{bmatrix} = \begin{bmatrix} 80 \\ 120 \end{bmatrix}$$

80 milliliters of 60% solution, 120 milliliters of 40% solution

34. Let x = number of hamburgers and y = number of chicken sandwiches.

$$\begin{matrix} 5x + 7y = 42 \\ 2x + 1y = 15 \end{matrix} \rightarrow \begin{bmatrix} 5 & 7 \\ 2 & 1 \end{bmatrix} \cdot \begin{bmatrix} x \\ y \end{bmatrix} = \begin{bmatrix} 42 \\ 15 \end{bmatrix}$$

$$M^{-1} = \frac{1}{5 - 14}\begin{bmatrix} 1 & -7 \\ -2 & 5 \end{bmatrix} = -\frac{1}{9}\begin{bmatrix} 1 & -7 \\ -2 & 5 \end{bmatrix}$$

$$-\frac{1}{9}\begin{bmatrix} 1 & -7 \\ -2 & 5 \end{bmatrix} \cdot \begin{bmatrix} 5 & 7 \\ 2 & 1 \end{bmatrix} \cdot \begin{bmatrix} x \\ y \end{bmatrix} = -\frac{1}{9}\begin{bmatrix} 1 & -7 \\ -2 & 5 \end{bmatrix} \cdot \begin{bmatrix} 42 \\ 15 \end{bmatrix}$$

$$\begin{bmatrix} x \\ y \end{bmatrix} = -\frac{1}{9}\begin{bmatrix} 42 - 105 \\ -84 + 75 \end{bmatrix}$$

$$\begin{bmatrix} x \\ y \end{bmatrix} = \begin{bmatrix} 7 \\ 1 \end{bmatrix}$$

7 hamburgers, 1 chicken sandwich

35. $$\begin{bmatrix} \frac{9}{2} & \frac{1}{2} \\ 4 & \frac{2}{3} \end{bmatrix} \cdot \begin{bmatrix} \frac{2}{3} & -\frac{1}{2} \\ -4 & \frac{9}{2} \end{bmatrix} \stackrel{?}{=} I$$

$$\begin{bmatrix} \frac{9}{2}\left(\frac{2}{3}\right) + \frac{1}{2}(-4) & \frac{9}{2}\left(-\frac{1}{2}\right) + \frac{1}{2}\left(\frac{9}{2}\right) \\ 4\left(\frac{2}{3}\right) + \frac{2}{3}(-4) & 4\left(-\frac{1}{2}\right) + \frac{2}{3}\left(\frac{9}{2}\right) \end{bmatrix} \stackrel{?}{=} I$$

$$\begin{bmatrix} 1 & 0 \\ 0 & 1 \end{bmatrix} = I\text{; true}$$

36. $$\begin{bmatrix} 2 \\ 9 \\ 0 \end{bmatrix} + 4\begin{bmatrix} -1 \\ 3 \\ 5 \end{bmatrix} + 3\begin{bmatrix} -6 \\ -3 \\ -1 \end{bmatrix} = \begin{bmatrix} 2 \\ 9 \\ 0 \end{bmatrix} + \begin{bmatrix} -4 \\ 12 \\ 20 \end{bmatrix} + \begin{bmatrix} -18 \\ -9 \\ -3 \end{bmatrix}$$

$$= \begin{bmatrix} -20 \\ 12 \\ 17 \end{bmatrix}$$

37. $y < 0$ or $x < 0$

38. $3x + 4y = 8$
$4y = -3x + 8$
$y = -\frac{3}{4}x + 2$

$6y - 8x = 12$
$6y = 8x + 12$
$y = \frac{4}{3}x + 2$

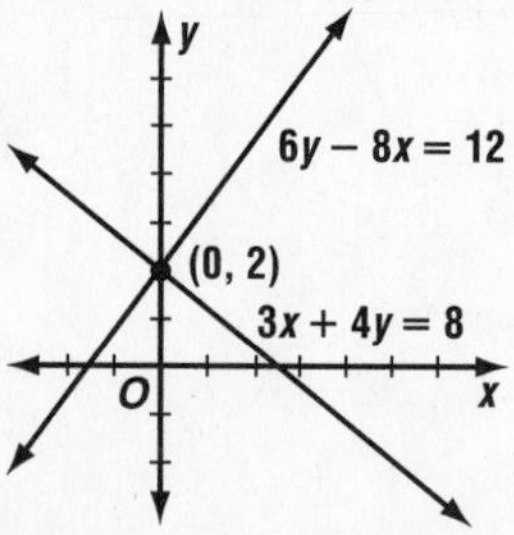

39. $f(x) = 1.15x$
$f(6.8) = 1.15(6.8)$
$= 7.82$; 7.82 tons per square inch

40. Let x = original price.
Sale price = $0.75x$.
Sale price = $x - 41$
$x - 41 = 0.75x$
$-41 = -0.25x$
$164 = x$

Sale price $= x - 41$
$= 164 - 41$
$= 123$

original price, $164; sale price, $123

4-7 Using Augmented Matrices

Pages 229–230 Check for Understanding

1. Advantage: can be used to solve equations with many variables; Disadvantage: requires many computations

2. $$\left[\begin{array}{ccc|c} 1 & 0 & 3 & 5 \\ 2 & 1 & 0 & 5 \\ -2 & 3 & -1 & 8 \end{array}\right]$$

3. Sample answer: Multiply row 1 by 4 and add to row 2, then divide by 19. The resulting row is 1 0 −3. Multiply this row by −3 and add to row 2, then divide by 4. The resulting row is 0 1 7.

4. c; row operations can only be performed on rows

5a. $x = 5, y = -2, z = 8$; $(5, -2, 8)$

5b. in row 2, $0 = 7$; no solution

5c. $x - 2z = 5$
$x = 5 + 2z$

$2y + z = 6$
$2y = 6 - z$
$y = 3 - 0.5z$

$(5 - 2z, 3 - 0.5z, z)$

6. See students' work.

7. $3x - 5y = 25$
$2x + 4y = 24$

8. $3x - 5y + 2z = 9$
$x - 7y + 3z = 11$
$4x - 3z = -1$

9. $$\begin{matrix} 4m - 7n = -19 \\ 3m + 2n = 22 \end{matrix} \rightarrow \left[\begin{array}{cc|c} 4 & -7 & -19 \\ 3 & 2 & 22 \end{array}\right]$$

$$\left[\begin{array}{cc|c} 4 & -7 & -19 \\ 3 & 2 & 22 \end{array}\right] = \left[\begin{array}{cc|c} 16 & -28 & -76 \\ 3 & 2 & 22 \end{array}\right] = \left[\begin{array}{cc|c} 58 & 0 & 232 \\ 3 & 2 & 22 \end{array}\right]$$

$$= \left[\begin{array}{cc|c} 1 & 0 & 4 \\ 3 & 2 & 22 \end{array}\right] = \left[\begin{array}{cc|c} 1 & 0 & 4 \\ 0 & 2 & 10 \end{array}\right] = \left[\begin{array}{cc|c} 1 & 0 & 4 \\ 0 & 1 & 5 \end{array}\right]; (4, 5)$$

10. $$\begin{matrix} 3a - b + 5c = -1 \\ a + 3b - c = 25 \\ 2a + 4c = 2 \end{matrix} \rightarrow \left[\begin{array}{ccc|c} 3 & -1 & 5 & -1 \\ 1 & 3 & -1 & 25 \\ 2 & 0 & 4 & 2 \end{array}\right]$$

$$\left[\begin{array}{ccc|c} 3 & -1 & 5 & -1 \\ 1 & 3 & -1 & 25 \\ 2 & 0 & 4 & 2 \end{array}\right] = \left[\begin{array}{ccc|c} 9 & -3 & 15 & -3 \\ 1 & 3 & -1 & 25 \\ 2 & 0 & 4 & 2 \end{array}\right]$$

$$= \left[\begin{array}{ccc|c} 10 & 0 & 14 & 22 \\ 1 & 3 & -1 & 25 \\ 2 & 0 & 4 & 2 \end{array}\right] = \left[\begin{array}{ccc|c} 10 & 0 & 14 & 22 \\ 1 & 3 & -1 & 25 \\ 10 & 0 & 20 & 10 \end{array}\right]$$

$$= \left[\begin{array}{ccc|c} 10 & 0 & 14 & 22 \\ 1 & 3 & -1 & 25 \\ 0 & 0 & 6 & -12 \end{array}\right] = \left[\begin{array}{ccc|c} 10 & 0 & 14 & 22 \\ 1 & 3 & -1 & 25 \\ 0 & 0 & 1 & -2 \end{array}\right]$$

$$= \left[\begin{array}{ccc|c} 10 & 0 & 0 & 50 \\ 1 & 3 & -1 & 25 \\ 0 & 0 & 1 & -2 \end{array}\right] = \left[\begin{array}{ccc|c} 1 & 0 & 0 & 5 \\ 1 & 3 & -1 & 25 \\ 0 & 0 & 1 & -2 \end{array}\right]$$

$$= \left[\begin{array}{ccc|c} 1 & 0 & 0 & 5 \\ 1 & 3 & 0 & 23 \\ 0 & 0 & 1 & -2 \end{array}\right] = \left[\begin{array}{ccc|c} 1 & 0 & 0 & 5 \\ 0 & 3 & 0 & 18 \\ 0 & 0 & 1 & -2 \end{array}\right]$$

$$= \left[\begin{array}{ccc|c} 1 & 0 & 0 & 5 \\ 0 & 1 & 0 & 6 \\ 0 & 0 & 1 & -2 \end{array}\right]; (5, 6, -2)$$

11. no solution; row 3: $0 = 3$

Pages 230–231 Exercises

12. $\left[\begin{array}{cc|c} 3 & 2 & 7 \\ 1 & -3 & 17 \end{array}\right] = \left[\begin{array}{cc|c} 1 & 8 & -27 \\ 1 & -3 & 17 \end{array}\right] = \left[\begin{array}{cc|c} 1 & 8 & -27 \\ 0 & 11 & -44 \end{array}\right]$

$= \left[\begin{array}{cc|c} 1 & 8 & -27 \\ 0 & 1 & -4 \end{array}\right] = \left[\begin{array}{cc|c} 1 & 0 & 5 \\ 0 & 1 & -4 \end{array}\right]$ (5, −4)

13. $\left[\begin{array}{cc|c} 4 & -3 & 5 \\ 2 & 9 & 6 \end{array}\right] = \left[\begin{array}{cc|c} 4 & -3 & 5 \\ 14 & 0 & 21 \end{array}\right] = \left[\begin{array}{cc|c} 4 & -3 & 5 \\ 2 & 0 & 3 \end{array}\right]$

$= \left[\begin{array}{cc|c} 0 & -3 & -1 \\ 2 & 0 & 3 \end{array}\right] = \left[\begin{array}{cc|c} 0 & 1 & \frac{1}{3} \\ 1 & 0 & \frac{2}{3} \end{array}\right]; \left(\frac{3}{2}, \frac{1}{3}\right)$

14. $2m = -5n$

$2m + 5n = 0$

$\left[\begin{array}{cc|c} 7 & -3 & 41 \\ 2 & 5 & 0 \end{array}\right] = \left[\begin{array}{cc|c} 7 & -3 & 41 \\ 14 & 35 & 0 \end{array}\right]$

$= \left[\begin{array}{cc|c} 7 & -3 & 41 \\ 0 & 41 & -82 \end{array}\right] = \left[\begin{array}{cc|c} 7 & -3 & 41 \\ 0 & 1 & -2 \end{array}\right] = \left[\begin{array}{cc|c} 7 & 0 & 35 \\ 0 & 1 & -2 \end{array}\right]$

$= \left[\begin{array}{cc|c} 1 & 0 & 5 \\ 0 & 1 & -2 \end{array}\right]$; (5, −2)

15. $\left[\begin{array}{ccc|c} 2 & -1 & 4 & 6 \\ 1 & 5 & -2 & -6 \\ 3 & -2 & 6 & 8 \end{array}\right] = \left[\begin{array}{ccc|c} 1 & -6 & 6 & 12 \\ 1 & 5 & -2 & -6 \\ 3 & -2 & 6 & 8 \end{array}\right]$

$= \left[\begin{array}{ccc|c} 1 & -6 & 6 & 12 \\ 2 & -1 & 4 & 6 \\ 3 & -2 & 6 & 8 \end{array}\right] = \left[\begin{array}{ccc|c} 1 & -6 & 6 & 12 \\ -2 & 1 & -4 & -6 \\ 3 & -2 & 6 & 8 \end{array}\right]$

$= \left[\begin{array}{ccc|c} 1 & -6 & 6 & 12 \\ -2 & 1 & -4 & -6 \\ 0 & 16 & -12 & -28 \end{array}\right] = \left[\begin{array}{ccc|c} 1 & -6 & 6 & 12 \\ -2 & 1 & -4 & -6 \\ 0 & 4 & -3 & -7 \end{array}\right]$

$= \left[\begin{array}{ccc|c} 1 & -6 & 6 & 12 \\ 0 & -11 & 8 & 18 \\ 0 & 4 & -3 & -7 \end{array}\right] = \left[\begin{array}{ccc|c} 1 & -6 & 6 & 12 \\ 0 & 1 & -1 & -3 \\ 0 & 4 & -3 & -7 \end{array}\right]$

$= \left[\begin{array}{ccc|c} 1 & -6 & 6 & 12 \\ 0 & 1 & -1 & -3 \\ 0 & 0 & 1 & 5 \end{array}\right] = \left[\begin{array}{ccc|c} 1 & -6 & 6 & 12 \\ 0 & 1 & 0 & 2 \\ 0 & 0 & 1 & 5 \end{array}\right]$

$= \left[\begin{array}{ccc|c} 1 & 0 & 6 & 24 \\ 0 & 1 & 0 & 2 \\ 0 & 0 & 1 & 5 \end{array}\right] = \left[\begin{array}{ccc|c} 1 & 0 & 0 & -6 \\ 0 & 1 & 0 & 2 \\ 0 & 0 & 1 & 5 \end{array}\right]$; (−6, 2, 5)

16. $\left[\begin{array}{ccc|c} 3 & -5 & 2 & 22 \\ 2 & 3 & -1 & -9 \\ 4 & 3 & 3 & 1 \end{array}\right] = \left[\begin{array}{ccc|c} 7 & 1 & 0 & 4 \\ 2 & 3 & -1 & -9 \\ 4 & 3 & 3 & 1 \end{array}\right]$

$= \left[\begin{array}{ccc|c} 7 & 1 & 0 & 4 \\ 2 & 3 & -1 & -9 \\ 8 & 9 & 1 & -17 \end{array}\right] = \left[\begin{array}{ccc|c} 7 & 1 & 0 & 4 \\ 10 & 12 & 0 & -26 \\ 8 & 9 & 1 & -17 \end{array}\right]$

$= \left[\begin{array}{ccc|c} 7 & 1 & 0 & 4 \\ 10 & 12 & 0 & -26 \\ -55 & 0 & 1 & -53 \end{array}\right] = \left[\begin{array}{ccc|c} 7 & 1 & 0 & 4 \\ -67 & 1 & 0 & -70 \\ -55 & 0 & 1 & -53 \end{array}\right]$

$= \left[\begin{array}{ccc|c} 74 & 0 & 0 & 74 \\ -67 & 1 & 0 & -70 \\ -55 & 0 & 1 & -53 \end{array}\right] = \left[\begin{array}{ccc|c} 1 & 0 & 0 & 1 \\ -67 & 1 & 0 & -70 \\ -55 & 0 & 1 & -53 \end{array}\right]$

$= \left[\begin{array}{ccc|c} 1 & 0 & 0 & 1 \\ 0 & 1 & 0 & -3 \\ -55 & 0 & 1 & -53 \end{array}\right] = \left[\begin{array}{ccc|c} 1 & 0 & 0 & 1 \\ 0 & 1 & 0 & -3 \\ 0 & 0 & 1 & 2 \end{array}\right]$; (1, −3, 2)

17. $\left[\begin{array}{ccc|c} 2 & 1 & 1 & 2 \\ -1 & -1 & 2 & 7 \\ -3 & 2 & 3 & 7 \end{array}\right] = \left[\begin{array}{ccc|c} 1 & 0 & 3 & 9 \\ -1 & -1 & 2 & 7 \\ -3 & 2 & 3 & 7 \end{array}\right]$

$= \left[\begin{array}{ccc|c} 1 & 0 & 3 & 9 \\ 0 & -1 & 5 & 16 \\ -3 & 2 & 3 & 7 \end{array}\right] = \left[\begin{array}{ccc|c} 1 & 0 & 3 & 9 \\ 0 & 1 & -5 & -16 \\ -3 & 2 & 3 & 7 \end{array}\right]$

$= \left[\begin{array}{ccc|c} 1 & 0 & 3 & 9 \\ 0 & 1 & -5 & -16 \\ 0 & 2 & 12 & 34 \end{array}\right] = \left[\begin{array}{ccc|c} 1 & 0 & 3 & 9 \\ 0 & 1 & -5 & -16 \\ 0 & 0 & 22 & 66 \end{array}\right]$

$= \left[\begin{array}{ccc|c} 1 & 0 & 3 & 9 \\ 0 & 1 & -5 & -16 \\ 0 & 0 & 1 & 3 \end{array}\right] = \left[\begin{array}{ccc|c} 1 & 0 & 3 & 9 \\ 0 & 1 & 0 & -1 \\ 0 & 0 & 1 & 3 \end{array}\right]$

$= \left[\begin{array}{ccc|c} 1 & 0 & 0 & 0 \\ 0 & 1 & 0 & -1 \\ 0 & 0 & 1 & 3 \end{array}\right]$; (0, −1, 3)

18. $3x = 6$ $\quad 2y = -8$

$x = 2$ $\quad y = -4$; (2, −4)

19. $4x + z = 4$ $\quad y - 2z = 5$

$4x = -z + 4$ $\quad y = 2z + 5$

$x = -\frac{1}{4}z + 1$ $\quad \left(-\frac{1}{4}z + 1, 2z + 5, z\right)$

20. $4x = -8$ $\quad z = 3$ $\quad 2y = 5$

$x = -2$ $\quad y = \frac{5}{2}$ $\quad \left(-2, \frac{5}{2}, 3\right)$

21. 3rd row: 0 = 2; no solution

22. $\left[\begin{array}{cc|c} 6 & 5 & -12 \\ 12 & 10 & -20 \end{array}\right] = \left[\begin{array}{cc|c} 6 & 5 & -12 \\ 0 & 0 & 44 \end{array}\right]$ 2nd row: 0 = 44; no solution

23. $3r = -2s$

$3r + 2s = 0$

$\left[\begin{array}{cc|c} 6 & 1 & 9 \\ 3 & 2 & 0 \end{array}\right] = \left[\begin{array}{cc|c} -12 & -2 & -18 \\ 3 & 2 & 0 \end{array}\right] = \left[\begin{array}{cc|c} -9 & 0 & -18 \\ 3 & 2 & 0 \end{array}\right]$

$= \left[\begin{array}{cc|c} 1 & 0 & 2 \\ 3 & 2 & 0 \end{array}\right] = \left[\begin{array}{cc|c} 1 & 0 & 2 \\ 0 & 2 & -6 \end{array}\right] = \left[\begin{array}{cc|c} 1 & 0 & 2 \\ 0 & 1 & -3 \end{array}\right]$; (2, −3)

24. $\left[\begin{array}{ccc|c} 4 & 2 & 5 & 24 \\ 3 & 5 & -1 & -13 \\ 1 & 7 & 3 & 33 \end{array}\right] = \left[\begin{array}{ccc|c} 4 & 2 & 5 & 24 \\ 3 & 5 & -1 & -13 \\ 7 & 17 & 1 & 7 \end{array}\right]$

$= \left[\begin{array}{ccc|c} 19 & 27 & 0 & -41 \\ 3 & 5 & -1 & -13 \\ 7 & 17 & 1 & 7 \end{array}\right] = \left[\begin{array}{ccc|c} 19 & 27 & 0 & -41 \\ 10 & 22 & 0 & -6 \\ 7 & 17 & 1 & 7 \end{array}\right]$

$= \left[\begin{array}{ccc|c} -1 & -17 & 0 & -29 \\ 10 & 22 & 0 & -6 \\ 7 & 17 & 1 & 7 \end{array}\right] = \left[\begin{array}{ccc|c} -1 & -17 & 0 & -29 \\ 10 & 22 & 0 & -6 \\ 6 & 0 & 1 & -22 \end{array}\right]$

$= \left[\begin{array}{ccc|c} 1 & 17 & 0 & 29 \\ 10 & 22 & 0 & -6 \\ 6 & 0 & 1 & -22 \end{array}\right] = \left[\begin{array}{ccc|c} 1 & 17 & 0 & 29 \\ 5 & 11 & 0 & -6 \\ 6 & 0 & 1 & -22 \end{array}\right]$

$= \left[\begin{array}{ccc|c} 1 & 17 & 0 & 29 \\ 0 & -74 & 0 & -148 \\ 6 & 0 & 1 & -22 \end{array}\right] = \left[\begin{array}{ccc|c} 1 & 17 & 0 & 29 \\ 0 & 1 & 0 & 2 \\ 6 & 0 & 1 & -22 \end{array}\right]$

$= \left[\begin{array}{ccc|c} 1 & 0 & 0 & -5 \\ 0 & 1 & 0 & 2 \\ 6 & 0 & 1 & -22 \end{array}\right] = \left[\begin{array}{ccc|c} 1 & 0 & 0 & -5 \\ 0 & 1 & 0 & 2 \\ 0 & 0 & 1 & 8 \end{array}\right]$; (−5, 2, 8)

25. $\left[\begin{array}{ccc|c} 6 & 2 & -6 & 4 \\ 3 & -5 & -3 & -1 \\ 2 & 4 & 1 & 1 \end{array}\right] = \left[\begin{array}{ccc|c} 6 & 2 & -6 & 4 \\ 9 & 7 & 0 & 2 \\ 2 & 4 & 1 & 1 \end{array}\right]$

$= \left[\begin{array}{ccc|c} 18 & 26 & 0 & 10 \\ 9 & 7 & 0 & 2 \\ 2 & 4 & 1 & 1 \end{array}\right] = \left[\begin{array}{ccc|c} 18 & 26 & 0 & 10 \\ 0 & -6 & 0 & -3 \\ 2 & 4 & 1 & 1 \end{array}\right]$

$= \left[\begin{array}{ccc|c} 9 & 13 & 0 & 5 \\ 0 & -6 & 0 & -3 \\ 2 & 4 & 1 & 1 \end{array}\right] = \left[\begin{array}{ccc|c} 9 & 13 & 0 & 5 \\ 0 & -6 & 0 & -3 \\ 6 & 12 & 3 & 3 \end{array}\right]$

$= \left[\begin{array}{ccc|c} 9 & 13 & 0 & 5 \\ 0 & -6 & 0 & -3 \\ 6 & 0 & 3 & -3 \end{array}\right] = \left[\begin{array}{ccc|c} 9 & 13 & 0 & 5 \\ 0 & -6 & 0 & -3 \\ 2 & 0 & 1 & -1 \end{array}\right] = \left[\begin{array}{ccc|c} 9 & 13 & 0 & 5 \\ 0 & 1 & 0 & \frac{1}{2} \\ 2 & 0 & 1 & -1 \end{array}\right]$

$= \left[\begin{array}{ccc|c} 9 & 0 & 0 & -\frac{3}{2} \\ 0 & 1 & 0 & \frac{1}{2} \\ 2 & 0 & 1 & -1 \end{array}\right] = \left[\begin{array}{ccc|c} 1 & 0 & 0 & -\frac{1}{6} \\ 0 & 1 & 0 & \frac{1}{2} \\ 2 & 0 & 1 & -1 \end{array}\right] = \left[\begin{array}{ccc|c} 1 & 0 & 0 & -\frac{1}{6} \\ 0 & 1 & 0 & \frac{1}{2} \\ 0 & 0 & 1 & -\frac{2}{3} \end{array}\right]$;

$\left(-\frac{1}{6}, \frac{1}{2}, -\frac{2}{3}\right)$

26. $\left[\begin{array}{ccc|c} 2 & -3 & 1 & -2 \\ 1 & 1 & -2 & 1 \\ 4 & 4 & -8 & 4 \end{array}\right] = \left[\begin{array}{ccc|c} 2 & -3 & 1 & -2 \\ 1 & 1 & -2 & 1 \\ 0 & 0 & 0 & 0 \end{array}\right] =$

$= \left[\begin{array}{ccc|c} 1 & -4 & 3 & -3 \\ 1 & 1 & -2 & 1 \\ 0 & 0 & 0 & 0 \end{array}\right] = \left[\begin{array}{ccc|c} 1 & -4 & 3 & -3 \\ 0 & 5 & -5 & 4 \\ 0 & 0 & 0 & 0 \end{array}\right]$

$= \left[\begin{array}{ccc|c} 1 & 1 & -2 & 1 \\ 0 & 5 & -5 & 4 \\ 0 & 0 & 0 & 0 \end{array}\right]$

$x + y - 2z = 1$ $5y - 5z = 4$

$x = -y + 2z + 1$ $5y = 5z + 4$

$y = z + \frac{4}{5}$

$\left(-y + 2z + 1, z + \frac{4}{5}, z\right)$

27. $\left[\begin{array}{ccc|c} 2 & -1 & -1 & 3 \\ 1 & 1 & -3 & 5 \\ 4 & -2 & -2 & -2 \end{array}\right] = \left[\begin{array}{ccc|c} 2 & -1 & -1 & 3 \\ 1 & 1 & -3 & 5 \\ 0 & 0 & 0 & 8 \end{array}\right]$

3rd row: $0 = 8$; no solution

28. Let a = measure of $\angle A$, b = measure of $\angle B$, and c = measure of $\angle C$.

$a + b + c = 180$ $a + b + c = 180$

$a = 2b$ $\rightarrow$ $a - 2b = 0$

$c = 4b + 12$ $-4b + c = 12$

$\left[\begin{array}{ccc|c} 1 & 1 & 1 & 180 \\ 1 & -2 & 0 & 0 \\ 0 & -4 & 1 & 12 \end{array}\right] = \left[\begin{array}{ccc|c} 1 & 5 & 0 & 168 \\ 1 & -2 & 0 & 0 \\ 0 & -4 & 1 & 12 \end{array}\right]$

$= \left[\begin{array}{ccc|c} 1 & 5 & 0 & 168 \\ 0 & -7 & 0 & -168 \\ 0 & -4 & 1 & 12 \end{array}\right] = \left[\begin{array}{ccc|c} 1 & 5 & 0 & 168 \\ 0 & 1 & 0 & 24 \\ 0 & -4 & 1 & 12 \end{array}\right]$

$= \left[\begin{array}{ccc|c} 1 & 0 & 0 & 48 \\ 0 & 1 & 0 & 24 \\ 0 & -4 & 1 & 12 \end{array}\right] = \left[\begin{array}{ccc|c} 1 & 0 & 0 & 48 \\ 0 & 1 & 0 & 24 \\ 0 & 0 & 1 & 108 \end{array}\right]$ 48°, 24°, 108°

29. a plane

30. Let x = shortest side, y = second side, and z = longest side.

$x + y + z = 83$ $\rightarrow x + y + z = 83$

$z = 3x$ $\rightarrow \; -3x + z = 0$

$z = \frac{1}{2}(x + y) + 17 \rightarrow 2z = x + y + 34 \rightarrow$

$-x - y + 2z = 34$

$\left[\begin{array}{ccc|c} 1 & 1 & 1 & 83 \\ -3 & 0 & 1 & 0 \\ -1 & -1 & 2 & 34 \end{array}\right] = \left[\begin{array}{ccc|c} 1 & 1 & 1 & 83 \\ -3 & 0 & 1 & 0 \\ 0 & 0 & 3 & 117 \end{array}\right]$

$= \left[\begin{array}{ccc|c} 1 & 1 & 1 & 83 \\ -3 & 0 & 1 & 0 \\ 0 & 0 & 1 & 39 \end{array}\right] = \left[\begin{array}{ccc|c} 1 & 1 & 1 & 83 \\ -4 & -1 & 0 & -83 \\ 0 & 0 & 1 & 39 \end{array}\right]$

$= \left[\begin{array}{ccc|c} 1 & 1 & 1 & 83 \\ 4 & 1 & 0 & 83 \\ 0 & 0 & 1 & 39 \end{array}\right] = \left[\begin{array}{ccc|c} 1 & 1 & 0 & 44 \\ 4 & 1 & 0 & 83 \\ 0 & 0 & 1 & 39 \end{array}\right] = \left[\begin{array}{ccc|c} -3 & 0 & 0 & -39 \\ 4 & 1 & 0 & 83 \\ 0 & 0 & 1 & 39 \end{array}\right]$

$= \left[\begin{array}{ccc|c} 1 & 0 & 0 & 13 \\ 4 & 1 & 0 & 83 \\ 0 & 0 & 1 & 39 \end{array}\right] = \left[\begin{array}{ccc|c} 1 & 0 & 0 & 13 \\ 0 & 1 & 0 & 31 \\ 0 & 0 & 1 & 39 \end{array}\right]$;

13 inches, 31 inches, 39 inches

31. Let x = small, y = medium, and z = large.

$0.89x + 1.19y + 1.39z = 58.98$

$\rightarrow \; 89x + 119y + 139z = 5898$

$x + y + z = 52$ $\rightarrow \; x + y + z = 52$

$y = 2z + 2$ $\rightarrow \; y - 2z = 2$

$\left[\begin{array}{ccc|c} 89 & 119 & 139 & 5898 \\ 1 & 1 & 1 & 52 \\ 0 & 1 & -2 & 2 \end{array}\right] = \left[\begin{array}{ccc|c} 89 & 119 & 139 & 5898 \\ 1 & 0 & 3 & 50 \\ 0 & 1 & -2 & 2 \end{array}\right]$

$= \left[\begin{array}{ccc|c} 0 & 119 & -128 & 1448 \\ 1 & 0 & 3 & 50 \\ 0 & 1 & -2 & 2 \end{array}\right] = \left[\begin{array}{ccc|c} 0 & 0 & 110 & 1210 \\ 1 & 0 & 3 & 50 \\ 0 & 1 & -2 & 2 \end{array}\right]$

$= \left[\begin{array}{ccc|c} 0 & 0 & 1 & 11 \\ 1 & 0 & 3 & 50 \\ 0 & 1 & -2 & 2 \end{array}\right] = \left[\begin{array}{ccc|c} 0 & 0 & 1 & 11 \\ 1 & 0 & 0 & 17 \\ 0 & 1 & -2 & 2 \end{array}\right]$

$= \left[\begin{array}{ccc|c} 0 & 0 & 1 & 11 \\ 1 & 0 & 0 & 17 \\ 0 & 1 & 0 & 24 \end{array}\right]$; 17 small, 24 medium, 11 large

32. $\begin{bmatrix} 3 & 2 \\ -1 & -7 \end{bmatrix} \cdot \begin{bmatrix} a \\ b \end{bmatrix} = \begin{bmatrix} 7 \\ 23 \end{bmatrix}$

$M^{-1} = \frac{1}{-21 + 2}\begin{bmatrix} -7 & -2 \\ 1 & 3 \end{bmatrix} = -\frac{1}{19}\begin{bmatrix} -7 & -2 \\ 1 & 3 \end{bmatrix}$

$-\frac{1}{19}\begin{bmatrix} -7 & -2 \\ 1 & 3 \end{bmatrix} \cdot \begin{bmatrix} 3 & 2 \\ -1 & -7 \end{bmatrix} \cdot \begin{bmatrix} a \\ b \end{bmatrix} = -\frac{1}{19}\begin{bmatrix} -7 & -2 \\ 1 & 3 \end{bmatrix}\begin{bmatrix} 7 \\ 23 \end{bmatrix}$

$\begin{bmatrix} a \\ b \end{bmatrix} = -\frac{1}{19}\begin{bmatrix} -49 - 46 \\ 7 + 69 \end{bmatrix}$

$\begin{bmatrix} a \\ b \end{bmatrix} = \begin{bmatrix} 5 \\ -4 \end{bmatrix}$ $(5, -4)$

33. $M^{-1} = \frac{1}{-4 + 10}\begin{bmatrix} -1 & 5 \\ -2 & 4 \end{bmatrix}$

$= \frac{1}{6}\begin{bmatrix} -1 & 5 \\ -2 & 4 \end{bmatrix}$

34. $\begin{vmatrix} -2 & 0 \\ 7 & -6 \end{vmatrix} = -2(-6) - 7(0)$

$= 12$

35. step function

36. $5 = 5x$

$1 = x$

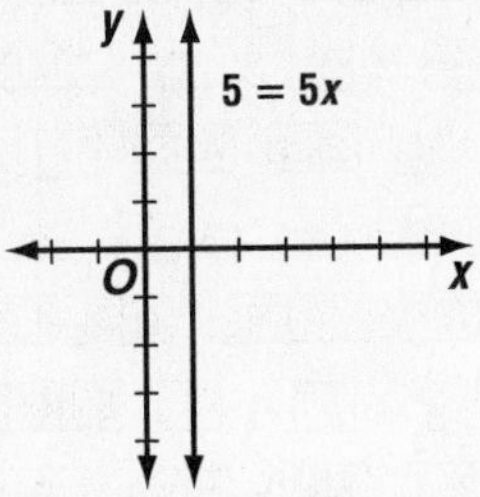

37. $\dfrac{3ab^2 - c^3}{a + c} = \dfrac{3(3)(7)^2 - (-2)^3}{3 + (-2)}$

$= \dfrac{3(3)(49) - (-8)}{1}$

$= \dfrac{441 + 8}{1}$

$= 449$

4-7B Graphing Technology: Matrix Row Operations

Page 234 Exercises

1. $\left[\begin{array}{cc|c} 3 & 2 & -2 \\ 2 & 3 & 7 \end{array}\right]$; [MATRX] [▶] [▶] [ENTER] 2 [ENTER] 3 [ENTER] 3 [ENTER] 2 [ENTER] [(–)] 2 [ENTER] 2 [ENTER] 3 [ENTER] 7 [ENTER] [2nd] [QUIT] [MATRX] [▶] 0 [(–)] 3 [,] [MATRX] 1 [,] 1 [)] [ENTER] [MATRX] [▶] [ALPHA] [A] 2 [,] [2nd] [ANS] [,] 2 [,] 1 [)] [ENTER] [MATRX] [▶] 0 [(–)] 5 [x^{-1}] [,] [2nd] [ANS] [,] 1 [)] [MATRX] [▶] [ALPHA] [A] [(–)] 2 [,] [2nd] [ANS] [,] 1 [,] 2 [)] [ENTER] [MATRX] [▶] 0 3 [x^{-1}] [,] [2nd] [ANS] [,] 2 [)] [ENTER]

$\begin{bmatrix} 1 & 0 & -4 \\ 0 & 1 & 5 \end{bmatrix}$; $(-4, 5)$

2. $\left[\begin{array}{cc|c} 1 & -3 & 5 \\ 2 & 1 & 1 \end{array}\right]$; [MATRX] [▶] [▶] [ENTER] 2 [ENTER] 3 [ENTER] 1 [ENTER] [(–)] 3 [ENTER] 5 [ENTER] 2 [ENTER] 1 [ENTER] 1 [ENTER] [2nd] [QUIT] [MATRX] [▶] [ALPHA] [A] [(–)] 2 [,] [MATRX] 1 [,] 1 [,] 2 [)] [ENTER] [MATRX] [▶] 0 7 [,] [2nd] [ANS] [,] 1 [)] [ENTER] [MATRX] [▶] [ALPHA] [A] 3 [,] [2nd] [ANS] [,] 2 [,] 1 [)] [ENTER] $\begin{bmatrix} 7 & 0 & 8 \\ 0 & 7 & -9 \end{bmatrix}$;

$7x = 8$ | $7y = -9$
$x = \frac{8}{7}$ | $y = -\frac{9}{7}$ | $\left(\frac{8}{7}, -\frac{9}{7}\right)$

3. $\left[\begin{array}{cc|c} 3 & -1 & 0 \\ 2 & -3 & 1 \end{array}\right]$; [MATRX] [▶] [▶] [ENTER] 2 [ENTER] 3 [ENTER] 3 [ENTER] [(–)] 1 [ENTER] 0 [ENTER] 2 [ENTER] [(–)] 3 [ENTER] 1 [ENTER] [2nd] [QUIT] [MATRX] [▶] 0 [(–)] 3 [,] [MATRX] 1 [,] 1 [)] [ENTER] [MATRX] [▶] 9 [2nd] [ANS] [,] 2 [,] 1 [)] [ENTER] [MATRX] [▶] 0 7 [,] [2nd] [ANS] [,] 2 [)] [ENTER] [MATRX] [▶] [ALPHA] [A] 2 [,] [2nd] [ANS] [,] 1 [,] 2 [)] [ENTER] [MATRX] [▶] 0 3 [x^{-1}] [,] [2nd] [ANS] [,] 2 [)] [ENTER] $\begin{bmatrix} -7 & 0 & 1 \\ 0 & -7 & 3 \end{bmatrix}$;

$-7x = 1$ | $-7y = 3$
$x = -\frac{1}{7}$ | $y = -\frac{3}{7}$ | $\left(-\frac{1}{7}, -\frac{3}{7}\right)$

4. $\left[\begin{array}{cc|c} 2 & 1 & 5 \\ 2 & -3 & 1 \end{array}\right]$; [MATRX] [▶] [▶] [ENTER] 2 [ENTER] 3 [ENTER] 2 [ENTER] 1 [ENTER] 5 [ENTER] 2 [ENTER] [(–)] 3 [ENTER] 1 [ENTER] [2nd] [QUIT] [MATRX] [▶] [ALPHA] [A] [(–)] 1 [,] [MATRX] 1 [,] 1 [,] 2 [)] [ENTER] [MATRX] [▶] 0 [(–)] 4 [x^{-1}] [,] [2nd] [ANS] [,] 2 [)] [ENTER] [MATRX] [▶] [ALPHA] [A] [(–)] 1 [,] [2nd] [ANS] [,] 2 [,] 1 [)] [ENTER] [MATRX] [▶] 0 2 [x^{-1}] [,] [2nd] [ANS] [,] 1 [)] [ENTER] $\begin{bmatrix} 1 & 0 & 2 \\ 0 & 1 & 1 \end{bmatrix}$; $(2, 1)$

5. $\left[\begin{array}{ccc|c} 1 & -1 & 1 & 2 \\ 1 & 0 & -1 & 1 \\ 0 & 1 & 2 & 0 \end{array}\right]$; [MATRX] [▶] [▶] [ENTER] 3 [ENTER] 4 [ENTER] 1 [ENTER] [(–)] 1 [ENTER] 1 [ENTER] 2 [ENTER] 1 [ENTER] 0 [ENTER] [(–)] 1 [ENTER] 1 [ENTER] 0 [ENTER] 1 [ENTER] 2 [ENTER] 0 [ENTER] [2nd] [QUIT] [MATRX] [▶] 9 [MATRX] 1 [,] 3 [,] 1 [)] [ENTER] [MATRX] [▶] [ALPHA] [A] [(–)] 1 [,] [2nd] [ANS] [,] 1 [,] 2 [)] [ENTER] [MATRX] [▶] 9 [2nd] [ANS] [,] 3 [,] 2 [)] [ENTER] [MATRX] [▶] [ALPHA] [A] [(–)] 1 [,] [2nd] [ANS] [,] 2 [,] 3 [)] [ENTER] [MATRX] [▶] [ALPHA] [A] 2 [x^{-1}] [,] [2nd] [ANS] [,] 3 [,] 2 [)] [ENTER] [MATRX] [▶] 0 4 [x^{-1}] [,] [2nd] [ANS] [,] 3 [)] [ENTER] [MATRX] [▶] [ALPHA] [A] [(–)] 3 [,] [2nd] [ANS] [,] 3 [,] 1 [)] [ENTER]

$\begin{bmatrix} 1 & 0 & 0 & 1.25 \\ 0 & 1 & 0 & -.5 \\ 0 & 0 & 1 & 1.25 \end{bmatrix}$; $(1.25, -0.5, 0.25)$ or $\left(\frac{5}{4}, -\frac{1}{2}, \frac{1}{4}\right)$

6. $\left[\begin{array}{rrr|r} 3 & -2 & 1 & -2 \\ 1 & -1 & 3 & 5 \\ -1 & 1 & 1 & -1 \end{array}\right]$; [MATRX] [▶] [▶] [ENTER] 3 [ENTER] 4 [ENTER] 3 [ENTER] [(–)] 2 [ENTER] 1 [ENTER] [(–)] 2 [ENTER] 1 [ENTER] [(–)] 1 [ENTER] 3 [ENTER] 5 [ENTER] [(–)] 1 [ENTER] 1 [ENTER] 1 [ENTER] [(–)] 1 [ENTER] [2nd] [QUIT] [MATRX] [▶] 9 [MATRX] 1 [,] 2 [,] 3 [)] [ENTER] [MATRX] [▶] [ALPHA] [A] [(–)] 2 [,] [2nd] [ANS] [,] 2 [,] 1 [)] [ENTER] [MATRX] [▶] 0 4 [x^{-1}] [,] [2nd] [ANS] [,] 3 [)] [ENTER] [MATRX] [▶] [ALPHA] [A] [(–)] 1 [,] [2nd] [ANS] [,] 1 [,] 2 [)] [ENTER] [MATRX] [▶] [ALPHA] [A] 5 [,] [2nd] [ANS] [,] 3 [,] 1 [)] [ENTER] [MATRX] [▶] [ALPHA] [A] [(–)] 8 [,] [2nd] [ANS] [,] 3 [,] 2 [)] [ENTER] [MATRX] [▶] [(–)] 1 [,] [2nd] [ANS] [,] 2 [)] [ENTER]

$\left[\begin{array}{rrrr} 1 & 0 & 0 & -7 \\ 0 & 1 & 0 & -9 \\ 0 & 0 & 1 & 1 \end{array}\right]$; (−7, −9, 1)

7. $\left[\begin{array}{rrr|r} 3 & 1 & 3 & 2 \\ 2 & 1 & 2 & 1 \\ 4 & 2 & 5 & 5 \end{array}\right]$; [MATRX] [▶] [▶] [ENTER] 3 [ENTER] 4 [ENTER] 3 [ENTER] 1 [ENTER] 3 [ENTER] 2 [ENTER] 2 [ENTER] 1 [ENTER] 2 [ENTER] 1 [ENTER] 4 [ENTER] 2 [ENTER] 5 [ENTER] 5 [ENTER] [2nd] [QUIT] [MATRX] [▶] [ALPHA] [A] [(–)] 1 [,] [MATRX] 1 [,] 2 [,] 1 [)] [ENTER] [MATRX] [▶] [ALPHA] [A] [(–)] 2 [,] [2nd] [ANS] [,] 2 [,] 3 [)] [ENTER] [MATRX] [▶] [ALPHA] [A] [(–)] 1 [,] [2nd] [ANS] [,] 3 [,] 1 [)] [ENTER] [MATRX] [▶] [ALPHA] [A] [(–)] 2 [,] [2nd] [ANS] [,] 1 [,] 2 [)] [ENTER] [MATRX] [▶] [ALPHA] [A] [(–)] 2 [,] [2nd] [ANS] [,] 3 [,] 2 [)] [ENTER]

$\left[\begin{array}{rrrr} 1 & 0 & 0 & -2 \\ 0 & 1 & 0 & -1 \\ 0 & 0 & 1 & 3 \end{array}\right]$; (−2, −1, 3)

8. $\left[\begin{array}{rrr|r} -3 & 1 & -2 & -7 \\ 2 & -1 & -3 & 1 \\ 1 & 2 & 1 & -2 \end{array}\right]$; [MATRX] [▶] [▶] [ENTER] 3 [ENTER] 4 [ENTER] [(–)] 3 [ENTER] 1 [ENTER] [(–)] 2 [ENTER] [(–)] 7 [ENTER] 2 [ENTER] [(–)] 1 [ENTER] [(–)] 3 [ENTER] 1 [ENTER] 1 [ENTER] 2 [ENTER] 1 [ENTER] [(–)] 2 [ENTER] [2nd] [QUIT] [MATRX] [▶] 9 [MATRX] 1 [,] 2 [,] 1 [)] [ENTER] [MATRX] [▶] 9 [2nd] [ANS] [,] 1 [,] 3 [)] [ENTER] [MATRX] [▶] [ALPHA] [A] 2 [,] [2nd] [ANS] [,] 1 [,] 2 [)]

(Continued next column)

[ENTER] [MATRX] [▶] [ALPHA] [A] 2 [,] [2nd] [ANS] [,] 2 [,] 3 [)] [ENTER] [MATRX] [▶] 0 [(–)] 30 [x^{-1}] [,] [2nd] [ANS] [,] 3 [)] [ENTER] [MATRX] [▶] [ALPHA] [A] 13 [,] [2nd] [ANS] [,] 3 [,] 2 [)] [ENTER] [MATRX] [▶] [ALPHA] [A] 5 [,] [2nd] [ANS] [,] 3 [,] 1 [)] [ENTER] [MATRX] [▶] 0 [(–)] 1 [,] [2nd] [ANS] [,] 1 [)] [ENTER] [MATRX] [▶] 0 [(–)] 1 [,] [2nd] [ANS] [,] 2 [)] [ENTER]

$\left[\begin{array}{rrrr} 1 & 0 & 0 & 1 \\ 0 & 1 & 0 & -2 \\ 0 & 0 & 1 & 1 \end{array}\right]$; (1, −2, 1)

9. $\left[\begin{array}{rrr|r} -2 & 1 & 1 & 4 \\ 4 & -3 & -2 & -2 \\ -3 & 1 & 1 & 5 \end{array}\right]$; [MATRX] [▶] [▶] [ENTER] 3 [ENTER] 4 [ENTER] [(–)] 2 [ENTER] 1 [ENTER] 1 [ENTER] 4 [ENTER] 4 [ENTER] [(–)] 3 [ENTER] [(–)] 2 [ENTER] [(–)] 2 [ENTER] [(–)] 3 [ENTER] 1 [ENTER] 1 [ENTER] 5 [ENTER] [2nd] [QUIT] [MATRX] [▶] [ALPHA] [A] [(–)] 1 [,] [MATRX] 1 [,] 3 [,] 1 [)] [ENTER] [MATRX] [▶] [ALPHA] [A] 3 [,] [2nd] [ANS] [,] 1 [,] 3 [)] [ENTER] [MATRX] [▶] [ALPHA] [A] 2 [,] [2nd] [ANS] [,] 3 [,] 2 [)] [ENTER] [MATRX] [▶] [ALPHA] [A] [(–)] 4 [,] [2nd] [ANS] [,] 1 [,] 2 [)] [ENTER] [MATRX] [▶] 9 [2nd] [ANS] [,] 2 [,] 3 [)] [ENTER] [MATRX] [▶] 0 [(–)] 1 [,] [2nd] [ANS] [,] 2 [)] [ENTER]

$\left[\begin{array}{rrrr} 1 & 0 & 0 & -1 \\ 0 & 1 & 0 & -6 \\ 0 & 0 & 1 & 8 \end{array}\right]$; (−1, −6, 8)

4-8 Integration: Statistics Box-and-Whisker Plots

Pages 240–241 Check for Understanding

1. See students' work.
2. Sample answer: quartiles, range, outliers
3. See students' work.
4. 1.5(72.5 − 52.5) = 1.5(20) or 30. Any item of data greater than 72.5 + 30 or less than 52.5 − 30 is an outlier.
5. Sample answer: Data is clustered around the median.
6. Mei; The data may be unevenly distributed around the median.

7a. 30 − 10 = 20 **7b.** 26
7c. 25% **7d.** 21 and 28

8. 1, 12, 14, 15, 19, 19, 20

range = 20 − 1 = 19; Q_2 is 4th value, 15; Q_1 is 2nd value, 12; Q_3 is 6th value, 19; IR = 19 − 12 = 7; outliers: below 12 − 1.5(7) = 1.5 or above 19 + 1.5(7) = 29.5, outlier = 1

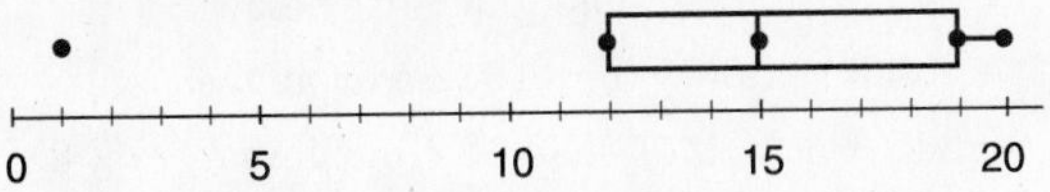

9. 21, 23, 24, 26, 31, 32, 33, 37, 38, 38, 39, 40

range = 40 − 21 = 19; Q_2 is between the 6th and 7th values, $\frac{32 + 33}{2}$ = 32.5; Q_1 is between the 3rd and 4th values, $\frac{24 + 26}{2}$ = 25; Q_3 is between the 9th and 10th values, $\frac{38 + 38}{2}$ = 38; IR = 38 − 25 = 13; outliers: below 25 − 1.5(13) = 5.5 or above 38 + 1.5(13) = 57.5, no outliers

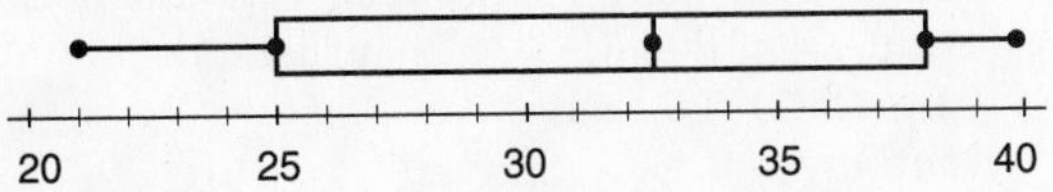

10. 10, 11, 16, 22, 24, 24, 153, 1416, 5832

10a. the 5th value, 24; Mars or Earth

10b. 24 hours

10c. Q_1 is between the 2nd and 3rd values, $\frac{11 + 16}{2}$ = 13.5; Q_3 is between the 7th and 8th values, $\frac{153 + 1416}{2}$ = 784.5

50% of the data lie between 13.5 and 784.5.

10d. See students' work; outliers: below 13.5 − 1.5(784.5 − 13.5) = −1143 or above 784.5 + 1.5(784.5 − 13.5) = 1941, outlier = 5832

10e. Extreme variability of data makes it difficult to put all values on a number line.

Page 241–244 Exercises

11a. 50% **11b.** 75%

11c. 50%

11d. The least value and the lower quartile are the same number.

12a. 700 − 490 = 210 **12b.** 670, 700

12c. 50% **12d.** 75%

13. 25, 29, 31, 39, 43, 46, 48, 53, 59, 64, 68

range = 68 − 25 = 43; Q_2 is the 6th value, 46; Q_1 is the 3rd value, 31; Q_3 is the 9th value, 59; IR = 59 − 31 = 28; outliers: below 31 − 1.5(28) = −11 or above 59 + 1.5(28) = 101, no outliers

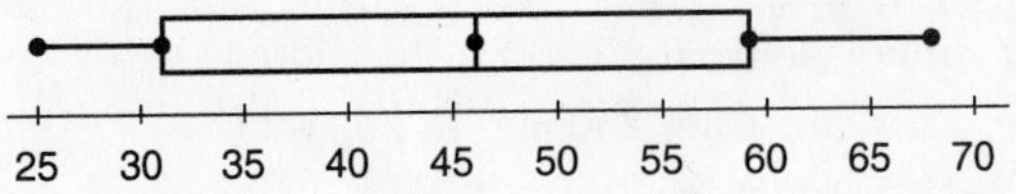

14. 17, 21, 25, 29, 29, 32, 36, 43, 47, 51

range = 51 − 17 = 34; Q_2 is between 5th and 6th values, $\frac{29 + 32}{2}$ = 30.5; Q_1 is the 3rd value, 25; Q_3 is the 8th value, 43; IR = 43 − 25 = 18; outliers: below 25 − 1.5(18) = −2 or above 43 + 1.5(18) = 70, no outliers

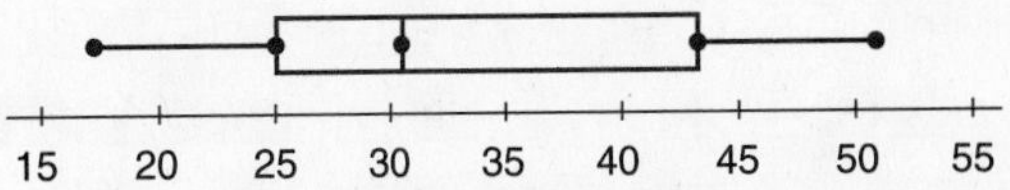

15. 23, 27, 39, 46, 46, 51, 53, 54, 55, 60, 69, 81

range = 81 − 23 = 58; Q_2 is between 6th and 7th values, $\frac{51 + 53}{2}$ = 52; Q_1 is between 3rd and 4th values, $\frac{39 + 46}{2}$ = 42.5; Q_3 is between 9th and 10th values, $\frac{55 + 60}{2}$ = 57.5; IR = 57.5 − 42.5 = 15; outliers: below 42.5 − 1.5(15) = 20 or above 57.5 + 1.5(15) = 80, outlier = 81

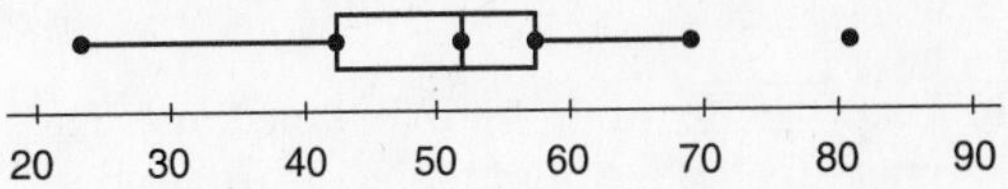

16. 88, 88, 88, 110, 110, 110, 110, 110, 110, 147, 150, 165, 165, 165, 200, 200, 330, 390, 440, 536

range = 536 − 88 = 448; Q_2 is between 10th and 11th values, $\frac{147 + 150}{2}$ = 148.5; Q_1 is between 5th and 6th values, 110; Q_3 is between 15th and 16th values, 200; IR = 200 − 110 = 90; outliers: below 110 − 1.5(90) = −25 or above 200 + 1.5(90) = 335, outliers = 390, 440, 536

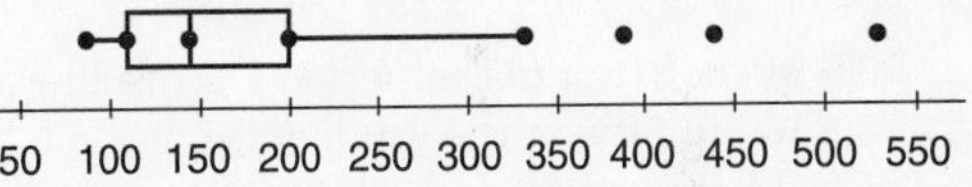

17. 13.6, 13.8, 14.1, 14.3, 14.9, 15.1, 15.7, 16.0, 16.3

range = 16.3 − 13.6 = 2.7; Q_2 is 5th value, 14.9; Q_1 is between 2nd and 3rd values, $\frac{13.8 + 14.1}{2}$ = 13.95; Q_3 is between 7th and 8th values, $\frac{15.7 + 16.0}{2}$ = 15.85; IR = 15.85 − 13.95 = 1.9; outliers: below 13.95 − 1.5(1.9) = 11.1 or above 15.85 + 1.5(1.9) = 18.7, no outliers

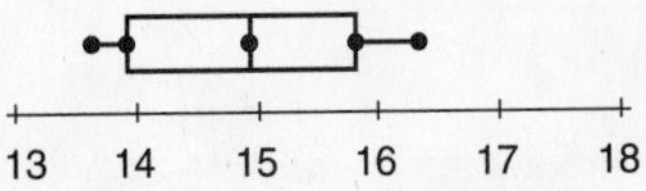

18. 5.8, 6.2, 7.6, 8.5, 8.5, 8.8, 9.0, 10.5, 11.5, 15.1

range = 15.1 − 5.8 = 9.3; Q_2 is between 5th and 6th values, $\frac{8.5 + 8.8}{2}$ = 8.65; Q_1 is 3rd value, 7.6; Q_3 is 8th value, 10.5; IR = 10.5 − 7.6 = 2.9; outliers: below 7.6 − 1.5(2.9) = 3.25 or above 10.5 + 1.5(2.9) = 14.85, outlier = 15.1

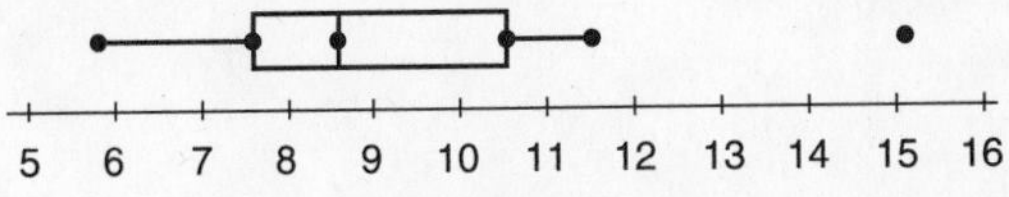

19a. [STAT] [ENTER] 41 [ENTER] 48 [ENTER] 57 [ENTER] 69 [ENTER] 72 [ENTER] 82 [ENTER] 89 [ENTER] 88 [ENTER] 80 [ENTER] 70 [ENTER] 59 [ENTER] 45 [ENTER] [▶] 59 [ENTER] 61 [ENTER] 61 [ENTER] 62 [ENTER] 65 [ENTER] 69 [ENTER] 69 [ENTER] 70 [ENTER] 72 [ENTER] 70 [ENTER] 61 [ENTER] 58 [ENTER] [2nd] [STAT PLOT] [ENTER] [▼] [▶] [▶] [ENTER] [▼] [ENTER] [▼] [ENTER] [2nd] [STAT PLOT] [▼] [ENTER] [ENTER] [▼] [▶] [▶] [ENTER] [▼] [▶] [ENTER] [▼] [ENTER] [WINDOW] [▼] 40 [ENTER] 90 [ENTER] 10 [ENTER] 0 [ENTER] 10 [ENTER] 0 [ENTER] [GRAPH]

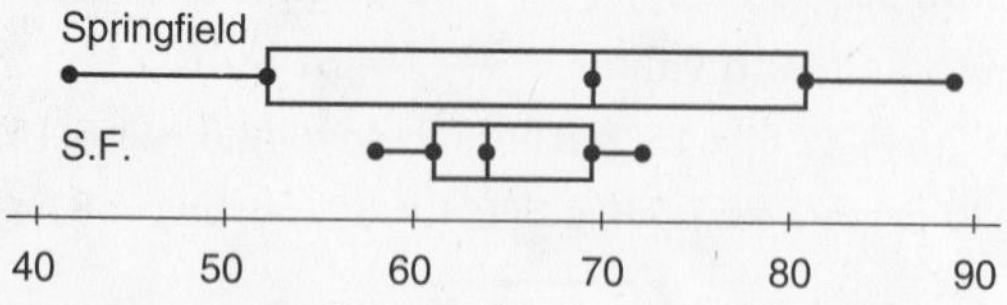

19b. Use [TRACE] and [▼] to find medians. The median average high temperature for San Francisco is 63.5°; the median average high temperature for Springfield is 69.5°.

19c. See students' work.

20. The data are clustered around the median with some extreme values.

21. Sample answer: {1, 4, 4, 4, 5, 5, 5, 6, 6, 15}; the data is clustered around the median with an extreme value at each end.

22a. period 1 **22b.** They are equal.

22c. period 2 **22d.** period 1

22e. 50% of the students in period 1 scored between 75 and 90; 50% of the students in period 2 scored between 60 and 85.

23a. Q_2 is between 18th and 19th values, $\frac{67 + 68}{2} = 67.5$; Q_1 is between 9th and 10th values, $\frac{60 + 63}{2} = 61.5$; Q_3 is between 27th and 28th values, 78; IR = 78 − 61.5 = 16.5; outliers: below 61.5 − 1.5(16.5) = 36.75 or above 78 + 1.5(16.5) = 102.75, no outliers

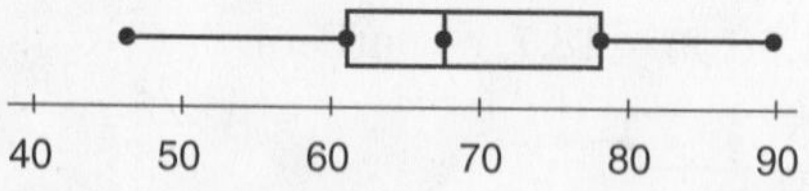

23b. Stem-and-leaf: advantage – all data are shown; disadvantage – difficult to see how data are dispersed. Box-and-whisker: advantage – easy to see range, median, and so on; disadvantage – data are lost.

24a. 125, 200, 211, 220, 239, 240, 240, 250, 327

Q_2 is the 5th value, 239; Q_1 is between 2nd and 3rd values, $\frac{200 + 211}{2} = 205.5$; Q_3 is between 7th and 8th values, $\frac{240 + 250}{2} = 245$; IR = 245 − 205.5 = 39.5; outliers: below 205.5 − 1.5(39.5) = 164.25 or above 245 + 1.5(39.5) = 304.25, outliers = 125, 327

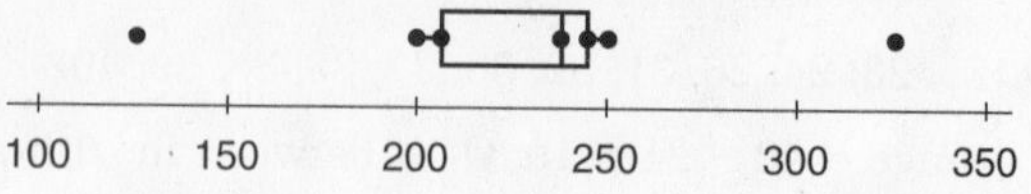

24b. The least and greatest values are both outliers.

25a. 1, 1, 1, 2, 2, 2, 2, 2, 2, 2, 3, 3, 3, 3, 3, 3, 3, 4, 4, 4, 4, 4, 4, 4, 4, 4, 5, 5, 5, 5, 5, 5, 5, 5, 5, 6, 6, 6, 7, 7, 8, 8, 8, 9

Q_2 is the 23rd value, 4; Q_1 is between 11th and 12th values, 3; Q_3 is between 34th and 35th values, 5; IR = 5 − 3 = 2; outliers: below 3 − 1.5(2) = 0 or above 5 − 1.5(2) = 8, outliers = 9

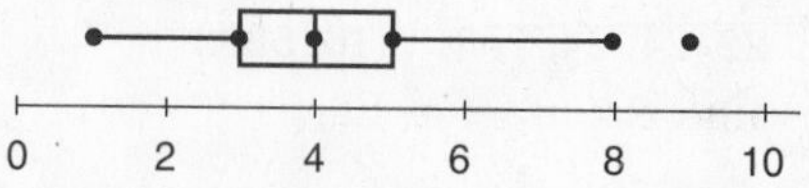

25b. See students' work.

25c. See students' work.

26a. 2000: 6, 8, 21, 35, 39, 77, 99, 117, 127, 153, 424, 681, 4906

Q_2 is the 7th value, 99; Q_1 is betweem 3rd and 4th value, $\frac{21 + 35}{2} = 28$; Q_3 is between 10th and 11th values, $\frac{153 + 424}{2} = 288.5$; IR = 288.5 − 28 = 260.5; outliers: below 28 − 1.5(260.5) = −362.75 or above 288.5 + 1.5(260.5) = 679.25, outliers = 681, 4906

2010: 9, 12, 31, 56, 59, 122, 148, 166, 204, 238, 635, 746, 7169

Q_2 is the 7th value, 148; Q_1 is between 3rd and 4th value, $\frac{31 + 56}{2} = 43.5$; Q_3 is between 10th and 11th values, $\frac{238 + 635}{2} = 436.5$; IR = 436.5 − 43.5 = 393; outliers: below 43.5 − 1.5(393) = −546 or above 436.5 + 1.5(393) = 1026, outliers = 7169

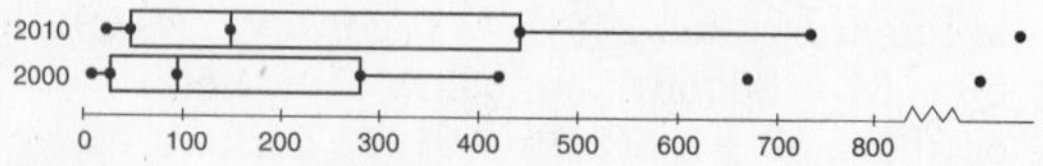

26b. increase from 99,000 to 148,000

26c. increase from 260,500 to 393,000

26d. See students' work.

27a. Calories: 270, 286, 320, 350, 360, 363, 380, 492, 500, 588, 1221

Q_2 is the 6th value, 363; Q_1 is the 3rd value, 320, Q_3 is the 9th value, 500; IR = 500 − 320 = 180; outliers: below 320 − 1.5(180) = 50 or above 500 + 1.5(180) = 770, outlier = 1221

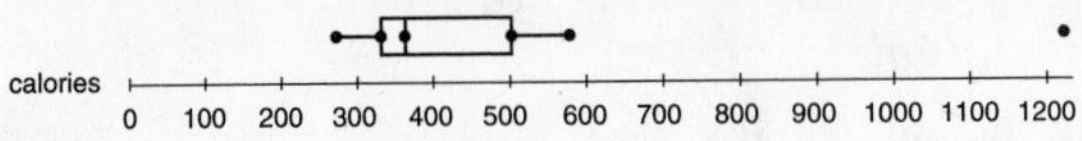

Fat: 2, 5, 9, 10, 16, 20, 21, 21, 22, 33, 97

Q_2 is the 6th value, 20; Q_1 is the 3rd value, 9; Q_3 is the 9th value, 22; IR = 22 − 9 = 13; outliers: below 9 − 1.5(13) = −10.5 or above 22 + 1.5(13) = 41.5, outlies = 97

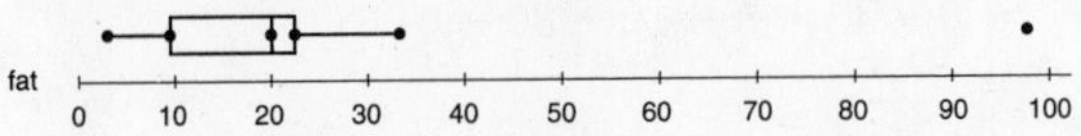

27b. Calories: 180, 270, 286, 320, 350, 360, 363, 380, 492, 500, 588, 901, 1221

Q_2 is the 7th value, 363; Q_1 is between 3rd and 4th values, $\frac{286 + 320}{2} = 303$; Q_3 is between 10th and 11th values, $\frac{500 + 588}{2} = 544$; IR = 544 − 303 = 241; outliers: below 303 − 1.5(241) = −58.5 or above 544 + 1.5(241) = 905.5, outliers = 1221

Fat: 1, 2, 5, 9, 10, 16, 20, 21, 21, 22, 33, 60, 97

Q_2 is the 7th value, 20; Q_1 is between 3rd and 4th values, $\frac{5 + 9}{2} = 7$; Q_3 is between 10th and 11th values, $\frac{22 + 33}{2} = 27.5$; IR = 27.5 − 7 = 20.5; outliers: below 7 − 1.5(20.5) = −23.75 or above 27.5 + 1.5(20.5) = 58.25, outliers 60, 97

Median is the same, box is longer.

27c. plain air−popped popcorn, Skittles

28. $$\left[\begin{array}{ccc|c} 2 & 1 & 1 & 0 \\ 3 & -2 & -3 & -21 \\ 4 & 5 & 3 & -2 \end{array}\right] = \left[\begin{array}{ccc|c} 2 & 1 & 1 & 0 \\ 3 & -2 & -3 & -21 \\ 0 & 3 & 1 & -2 \end{array}\right]$$

$$= \left[\begin{array}{ccc|c} 2 & 1 & 1 & 0 \\ 9 & 1 & 0 & -21 \\ 0 & 3 & 1 & -2 \end{array}\right] = \left[\begin{array}{ccc|c} 2 & -2 & 0 & 2 \\ 9 & 1 & 0 & -21 \\ 0 & 3 & 1 & -2 \end{array}\right] = \left[\begin{array}{ccc|c} 20 & 0 & 0 & -40 \\ 9 & 1 & 0 & -21 \\ 0 & 3 & 1 & -2 \end{array}\right]$$

$$= \left[\begin{array}{ccc|c} 1 & 0 & 0 & -2 \\ 9 & 1 & 0 & -21 \\ 0 & 3 & 1 & -2 \end{array}\right] = \left[\begin{array}{ccc|c} 1 & 0 & 0 & -2 \\ 0 & 1 & 0 & -3 \\ 0 & 3 & 1 & -2 \end{array}\right] = \left[\begin{array}{ccc|c} 1 & 0 & 0 & -2 \\ 0 & 1 & 0 & -3 \\ 0 & 0 & 1 & 7 \end{array}\right];$$

(−2, −3, 7)

29. $$[2\ -6\ 3] \cdot \begin{bmatrix} 3 & -3 \\ 9 & 0 \\ -2 & 4 \end{bmatrix}$$

$= [2(3) + (-6)9 + 3(-2) \quad 2(-3) + (-6)0 + 3(4)]$

$= [-54\ \ 6]$

30. $f(m, y) = 5280m + 3y$

$f(26, 385) = 5280(26) + 3(385)$

$= 137{,}280 + 1155$

$= 138{,}435$; 138,435 feet

31. $m = \frac{2-4}{2-5}$

$= \frac{-2}{-3}$

$= \frac{2}{3}$

32. I, R

33. $I = prt$

$= 6000(0.12)(2)$

$= 1440$; \$1440

Chapter 4 Highlights

Page 245 Understanding and Using the Vocabulary

1. identity matrix
2. reduced matrix
3. Scalar multiplication
4. rotation
5. determinant
6. augmented matrix
7. dimensions
8. translation
9. equal matrices
10. dilation

Chapter 4 Study Guide and Assessment

Pages 246–248 Skills and Concepts

11. $3\begin{bmatrix} 8 & -3 & 2 \\ 4 & 1 & 7 \end{bmatrix} = \begin{bmatrix} 24 & -9 & 6 \\ 12 & 3 & 21 \end{bmatrix}$

12. $-5\begin{bmatrix} -3 & 2 \\ 6 & 4 \end{bmatrix} = \begin{bmatrix} 15 & -10 \\ -30 & -20 \end{bmatrix}$

13. $\frac{2}{3}\begin{bmatrix} 3 & \frac{3}{4} & -6 \end{bmatrix} = \begin{bmatrix} 2 & \frac{1}{2} & -4 \end{bmatrix}$

14. $1.2\begin{bmatrix} -2 \\ 0.3 \\ 1 \end{bmatrix} = \begin{bmatrix} -2.4 \\ 0.36 \\ 1.2 \end{bmatrix}$

15. $4\begin{bmatrix} 1.3 & 5.1 \\ -2 & -3.7 \\ -2.8 & 4.5 \end{bmatrix} = \begin{bmatrix} 5.2 & 20.4 \\ -8 & -14.8 \\ -11.2 & 18 \end{bmatrix}$

16. $-\frac{1}{2}\begin{bmatrix} -2 & 4 \\ -8 & 2 \end{bmatrix} = \begin{bmatrix} 1 & -2 \\ 4 & -1 \end{bmatrix}$

17. $\begin{bmatrix} 2y - x \\ x \end{bmatrix} = \begin{bmatrix} 3 \\ 4y - 1 \end{bmatrix}$

$2y - x = 3$
$x = 4y - 1$

$2y - (4y - 1) = 3$
$2y - 4y + 1 = 3$
$-2y + 1 = 3$
$-2y = 2$
$y = -1$

$x = 4y - 1$
$= 4(-1) - 1$
$= -4 - 1$
$= -5$

18. $\begin{bmatrix} 7x \\ x + y \end{bmatrix} = \begin{bmatrix} 5 + 2y \\ 11 \end{bmatrix}$

$7x = 5 + 2y$
$x + y = 11$
$y = 11 - x$

$7x = 5 + 2(11 - x)$
$7x = 5 + 22 - 2x$
$9x = 5 + 22$
$9x = 27$
$x = 3$

$x + y = 11$
$3 + y = 11$
$y = 8$

19. $\begin{bmatrix} 3x + y \\ x - 3y \end{bmatrix} = \begin{bmatrix} -3 \\ -1 \end{bmatrix}$

$3x + y = -3 \rightarrow$ Multiply by 3 $\rightarrow 9x + 3y = -9$

$x - 3y = -1 \rightarrow \qquad \rightarrow (+)x - 3y = -1$

$10x = -10$

$x = -1$

$3x + y = -3$

$3(-1) + y = -3$

$-3 + y = -3$

$y = 0$

20. $\begin{bmatrix} 2x - y \\ 6x - y \end{bmatrix} = \begin{bmatrix} 2 \\ 22 \end{bmatrix}$

$2x - y = 2$

$(-)6x - y = 22$

$-4x = -20$

$x = 5$

$2x - y = 2$

$2(5) - y = 2$

$10 - y = 2$

$-y = -8$

$y = 8$

21. $\begin{bmatrix} -4 & 3 \\ -5 & 2 \end{bmatrix} + \begin{bmatrix} 1 & -3 \\ 3 & -8 \end{bmatrix} = \begin{bmatrix} -3 & 0 \\ -2 & -6 \end{bmatrix}$

22. $[0.2 \ \ 1.3 \ \ -0.4] - [2 \ \ 1.7 \ \ 2.6] = [-1.8 \ \ -0.4 \ \ -3]$

23. $\begin{bmatrix} 1 & -5 \\ -2 & 3 \end{bmatrix} + \frac{3}{4}\begin{bmatrix} 0 & 4 \\ -16 & 8 \end{bmatrix} = \begin{bmatrix} 1 & -5 \\ -2 & 3 \end{bmatrix} + \begin{bmatrix} 0 & 3 \\ -12 & 6 \end{bmatrix}$

$= \begin{bmatrix} 1 & -2 \\ -14 & 9 \end{bmatrix}$

24. $\begin{bmatrix} 1 & 0 & -3 \\ 4 & -5 & 2 \end{bmatrix} - 2\begin{bmatrix} -2 & 3 & 5 \\ -3 & -1 & 2 \end{bmatrix}$

$= \begin{bmatrix} 1 & 0 & -3 \\ 4 & -5 & 2 \end{bmatrix} + \begin{bmatrix} 4 & -6 & -10 \\ 6 & 2 & -4 \end{bmatrix}$

$= \begin{bmatrix} 5 & -6 & -13 \\ 10 & -3 & -2 \end{bmatrix}$

25. $[2 \ \ 7] \cdot \begin{bmatrix} 5 \\ -4 \end{bmatrix} = [10 - 28]$

$= [-18]$

26. $\begin{bmatrix} 8 & -3 \\ 6 & 1 \end{bmatrix} \cdot \begin{bmatrix} 2 & -3 \\ 1 & -5 \end{bmatrix} = \begin{bmatrix} 16 - 3 & -24 + 15 \\ 12 + 1 & -18 - 5 \end{bmatrix}$

$= \begin{bmatrix} 13 & -9 \\ 13 & -23 \end{bmatrix}$

27. not possible to evaluate due to dimensions

28. yes; $\begin{vmatrix} 4 & 11 \\ -7 & 8 \end{vmatrix} = 32 + 77$

$= 109$

29. yes; $\begin{vmatrix} 7 & -4 & 5 \\ 1 & 3 & -6 \\ 5 & -1 & -2 \end{vmatrix} \begin{matrix} 7 & -4 \\ 1 & 3 \\ 5 & -1 \end{matrix}$

$= 7 \cdot 3(-2) + (-4)(-6)5 + 5 \cdot 1(-1) - 5 \cdot 3 \cdot 5 - (-1)(-6)7 - (-2)1(-4)$

$= -42 + 120 - 5 - 75 - 42 - 8$

$= -52$

30. yes; $\begin{vmatrix} 5 & -1 & 2 \\ -6 & -7 & 3 \\ 7 & 0 & 4 \end{vmatrix} \begin{matrix} 5 & -1 \\ -6 & -7 \\ 7 & 0 \end{matrix}$

$= 5(-7)4 + (-1)3 \cdot 7 + 2(-6)0 - 7(-7)2 - 0 \cdot 3 \cdot 5 - 4(-6)(-1)$

$= -140 - 21 + 0 + 98 - 0 - 24$

$= -87$

31. yes; $\begin{vmatrix} 2 & -3 & 1 \\ 0 & 7 & 8 \\ 2 & 1 & 3 \end{vmatrix} \begin{matrix} 2 & -3 \\ 0 & 7 \\ 2 & 1 \end{matrix}$

$= 2 \cdot 7 \cdot 3 + (-3)8 \cdot 2 + 1 \cdot 0 \cdot 1 - 2 \cdot 7 \cdot 1 - 1 \cdot 8 \cdot 2 - 3 \cdot 0(-3)$

$= 42 - 48 + 0 - 14 - 16 + 0$

$= -36$

32. no; not square

33. yes; $\begin{vmatrix} 6 & 3 & -2 \\ -4 & 2 & 5 \\ -3 & -1 & 0 \end{vmatrix} \begin{matrix} 6 & 3 \\ -4 & 2 \\ -3 & -1 \end{matrix}$

$= 6 \cdot 2 \cdot 0 + 3 \cdot 5(-3) + (-2)(-4)(-1) - (-3)2(-2) - (-1)5 \cdot 6 - 0(-4)3$

$= 0 - 45 - 8 - 12 + 30 - 0$

$= -35$

34. $M^{-1} = \frac{1}{-6 - 8}\begin{bmatrix} -2 & -2 \\ -4 & 3 \end{bmatrix}$

$= -\frac{1}{14}\begin{bmatrix} -2 & -2 \\ -4 & 3 \end{bmatrix}$ or $\frac{1}{14}\begin{bmatrix} 2 & 2 \\ 4 & -3 \end{bmatrix}$

35. $M^{-1} = \frac{1}{56 - 54}\begin{bmatrix} 7 & -6 \\ -9 & 8 \end{bmatrix}$

$= \frac{1}{2}\begin{bmatrix} 7 & -6 \\ -9 & 8 \end{bmatrix}$

36. not possible; $\begin{vmatrix} 2 & -4 \\ -3 & 6 \end{vmatrix} = 0$

37. $M^{-1} = \frac{1}{-6 - 6}\begin{bmatrix} 1 & -2 \\ -3 & -6 \end{bmatrix}$

$= -\frac{1}{12}\begin{bmatrix} 1 & -2 \\ -3 & -6 \end{bmatrix}$ or $\frac{1}{12}\begin{bmatrix} -1 & 2 \\ 3 & 6 \end{bmatrix}$

38. $M^{-1} = \frac{1}{0 - 10}\begin{bmatrix} -4 & -2 \\ -5 & 0 \end{bmatrix}$

$= -\frac{1}{10}\begin{bmatrix} -4 & -2 \\ -5 & 0 \end{bmatrix}$ or $\frac{1}{10}\begin{bmatrix} 4 & 2 \\ 5 & 0 \end{bmatrix}$

39. not possible; not square

40. $M^{-1} = \frac{1}{15 + 2}\begin{bmatrix} 3 & 2 \\ -1 & 5 \end{bmatrix}$

$= \frac{1}{17}\begin{bmatrix} 3 & 2 \\ -1 & 5 \end{bmatrix}$

$\frac{1}{17}\begin{bmatrix} 3 & 2 \\ -1 & 5 \end{bmatrix} \cdot \begin{bmatrix} 5 & -2 \\ 1 & 3 \end{bmatrix} \cdot \begin{bmatrix} x \\ y \end{bmatrix} = \frac{1}{17}\begin{bmatrix} 3 & 2 \\ -1 & 5 \end{bmatrix} \cdot \begin{bmatrix} 16 \\ 10 \end{bmatrix}$

$\begin{bmatrix} x \\ y \end{bmatrix} = \frac{1}{17}\begin{bmatrix} 48 + 20 \\ -16 + 50 \end{bmatrix}$

$\begin{bmatrix} x \\ y \end{bmatrix} = \begin{bmatrix} 4 \\ 2 \end{bmatrix}$; (4, 2)

41. $M^{-1} = \frac{1}{-8 - 3}\begin{bmatrix} -2 & -1 \\ -3 & 4 \end{bmatrix}$

$= -\frac{1}{11}\begin{bmatrix} -2 & -1 \\ -3 & 4 \end{bmatrix}$

(Continued on next page)

$$-\frac{1}{11}\begin{bmatrix}-2&-1\\-3&4\end{bmatrix}\cdot\begin{bmatrix}4&1\\3&-2\end{bmatrix}\cdot\begin{bmatrix}a\\b\end{bmatrix}=-\frac{1}{11}\begin{bmatrix}-2&-1\\-3&4\end{bmatrix}\cdot\begin{bmatrix}9\\4\end{bmatrix}$$

$$\begin{bmatrix}a\\b\end{bmatrix}=-\frac{1}{11}\begin{bmatrix}-18-4\\-27+16\end{bmatrix}$$

$$\begin{bmatrix}a\\b\end{bmatrix}=\begin{bmatrix}2\\1\end{bmatrix};\ (2, 1)$$

42. $3x + 8 = -y$
$3x + y = -8$
$4x - 2y = -14$

$$\begin{bmatrix}3&1\\4&-2\end{bmatrix}\cdot\begin{bmatrix}x\\y\end{bmatrix}=\begin{bmatrix}-8\\-14\end{bmatrix}$$

$$M^{-1}=\frac{1}{-6-4}\begin{bmatrix}-2&-1\\-4&3\end{bmatrix}$$

$$=-\frac{1}{10}\begin{bmatrix}-2&-1\\-4&3\end{bmatrix}$$

$$-\frac{1}{10}\begin{bmatrix}-2&-1\\-4&3\end{bmatrix}\cdot\begin{bmatrix}3&1\\4&-2\end{bmatrix}\cdot\begin{bmatrix}x\\y\end{bmatrix}=-\frac{1}{10}\begin{bmatrix}-2&-1\\-4&3\end{bmatrix}\cdot\begin{bmatrix}-8\\-14\end{bmatrix}$$

$$\begin{bmatrix}x\\y\end{bmatrix}=-\frac{1}{10}\begin{bmatrix}16+14\\32-42\end{bmatrix}$$

$$\begin{bmatrix}x\\y\end{bmatrix}=\begin{bmatrix}-3\\1\end{bmatrix};\ (-3, 1)$$

43. $3x - 5y = -13$
$4x + 3y = 2$

$$\begin{bmatrix}3&-5\\4&3\end{bmatrix}\cdot\begin{bmatrix}x\\y\end{bmatrix}=\begin{bmatrix}-13\\2\end{bmatrix}$$

$$M^{-1}=\frac{1}{9+20}\begin{bmatrix}3&5\\-4&3\end{bmatrix}$$

$$=\frac{1}{29}\begin{bmatrix}3&5\\-4&3\end{bmatrix}$$

$$\frac{1}{29}\begin{bmatrix}3&5\\-4&3\end{bmatrix}\cdot\begin{bmatrix}3&-5\\4&3\end{bmatrix}\cdot\begin{bmatrix}x\\y\end{bmatrix}=\frac{1}{29}\begin{bmatrix}3&5\\-4&3\end{bmatrix}\cdot\begin{bmatrix}-13\\2\end{bmatrix}$$

$$\begin{bmatrix}x\\y\end{bmatrix}=\frac{1}{29}\begin{bmatrix}-39+10\\52+6\end{bmatrix}$$

$$\begin{bmatrix}x\\y\end{bmatrix}=\begin{bmatrix}-1\\2\end{bmatrix};\ (-1, 2)$$

44. $$\left[\begin{array}{cc|c}9&-1&1\\3&2&12\end{array}\right]=\left[\begin{array}{cc|c}9&-1&1\\12&1&13\end{array}\right]=\left[\begin{array}{cc|c}21&0&14\\12&1&13\end{array}\right]$$

$$=\left[\begin{array}{cc|c}3&0&2\\12&1&13\end{array}\right]=\left[\begin{array}{cc|c}3&0&2\\0&1&5\end{array}\right]=\left[\begin{array}{cc|c}1&0&\frac{2}{3}\\0&1&5\end{array}\right];\ \left(\frac{2}{3}, 5\right)$$

45. $$\left[\begin{array}{cc|c}1&5&14\\-2&6&4\end{array}\right]=\left[\begin{array}{cc|c}1&5&14\\0&16&32\end{array}\right]=\left[\begin{array}{cc|c}1&5&14\\0&1&2\end{array}\right]$$

$$=\left[\begin{array}{cc|c}1&0&4\\0&1&2\end{array}\right];\ (4, 2)$$

46. $$\left[\begin{array}{ccc|c}6&0&-7&13\\0&8&2&14\\7&0&1&6\end{array}\right]=\left[\begin{array}{ccc|c}55&0&0&55\\0&8&2&14\\7&0&1&6\end{array}\right]=\left[\begin{array}{ccc|c}1&0&0&1\\0&8&2&14\\7&0&1&6\end{array}\right]$$

$$=\left[\begin{array}{ccc|c}1&0&0&1\\0&8&2&14\\0&0&1&-1\end{array}\right]=\left[\begin{array}{ccc|c}1&0&0&1\\0&8&0&16\\0&0&1&-1\end{array}\right]=\left[\begin{array}{ccc|c}1&0&0&1\\0&1&0&2\\0&0&1&-1\end{array}\right];$$

(1, 2 −1)

47. $$\left[\begin{array}{ccc|c}2&-1&-3&-20\\4&2&1&6\\2&1&-1&-6\end{array}\right]=\left[\begin{array}{ccc|c}14&5&0&-2\\4&2&1&6\\2&1&-1&-6\end{array}\right]$$

$$=\left[\begin{array}{ccc|c}14&5&0&-2\\6&3&0&0\\2&1&-1&-6\end{array}\right]=\left[\begin{array}{ccc|c}14&5&0&-2\\6&3&0&0\\-6&-3&3&18\end{array}\right]$$

$$=\left[\begin{array}{ccc|c}14&5&0&-2\\6&3&0&0\\0&0&3&18\end{array}\right]=\left[\begin{array}{ccc|c}14&5&0&-2\\6&3&0&0\\0&0&1&6\end{array}\right]$$

$$=\left[\begin{array}{ccc|c}14&5&0&-2\\-84&-42&0&0\\0&0&1&6\end{array}\right]=\left[\begin{array}{ccc|c}84&30&0&-12\\-84&-42&0&0\\0&0&1&6\end{array}\right]$$

$$=\left[\begin{array}{ccc|c}84&30&0&-12\\0&-12&0&-12\\0&0&1&6\end{array}\right]=\left[\begin{array}{ccc|c}84&30&0&-12\\0&1&0&1\\0&0&1&6\end{array}\right]$$

$$=\left[\begin{array}{ccc|c}84&0&0&-42\\0&1&0&1\\0&0&1&6\end{array}\right]=\left[\begin{array}{ccc|c}1&0&0&-\frac{1}{2}\\0&1&0&1\\0&0&1&6\end{array}\right];\ \left(-\frac{1}{2}, 1, 6\right)$$

48. 78, 79, 84, 85, 86 88, 89, 90, 92, 93

range = 93 − 78 = 15; Q_2 is between 5th and 6th values, $\frac{86+88}{2}$ = 87; Q_1 is the 3rd value, 84; Q_3 is the 8th value, 90; IR = 90 − 84 = 6; outliers: below 84 − 1.5(6) = 75 or above 90 + 1.5(6) = 99, no outliers

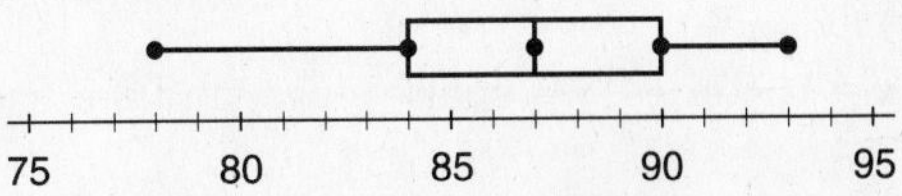

49. 0, 10, 40, 40, 50, 50, 60, 90, 90

range = 90 − 0 = 90; Q_2 is the 5th value, 50; Q_1 is between the 2nd and 3rd values, $\frac{10+40}{2}$ = 25; Q_3 is between the 7th and 8th values, $\frac{60+90}{2}$ = 75; IR = 75 − 25 = 50; outliers: below 25 − 1.5(50) = −50 or above 75 + 1.5(50) = 150, no outliers

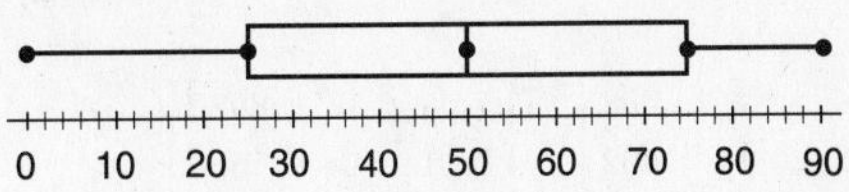

50. 0.1, 0.2, 0.2, 0.3, 0.4, 0.4, 0.4, 0.5, 0.5, 0.5, 0.6, 0.7, 0.8, 0.9, 1.9

range = 1.9 − 0.1 = 1.8; Q_2 is the 8th value, 0.5; Q_1 is the 4th value, 0.3; Q_3 is the 12th value, 0.7; IR = 0.7 − 0.3 = 0.4; outliers: below 0.3 − 1.5(0.4) = −0.3 or above 0.7 + 1.5(0.4) = 1.3, outlier = 1.9

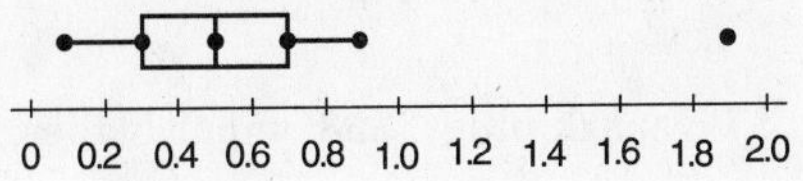

51. 975, 1005, 1025, 1055, 1075, 1075, 1095, 1100, 1125, 1125, 1145

range = 1145 − 975 = 170; Q_2 is the 6th value, 1075; Q_1 is the 3rd value, 1025; Q_3 is the 9th value, 1125; IR = 1125 − 1025 = 100; outliers: below 1025 − 1.5(100) = 875 or above 1125 + 1.5(100) = 1275, no outliers

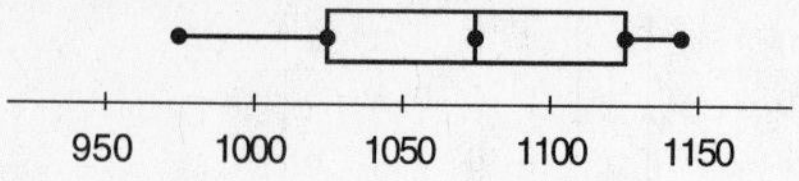

Page 248 Applications and Problem Solving

52. $A = \frac{1}{2}\begin{vmatrix} a & b & 1 \\ c & d & 1 \\ e & f & 1 \end{vmatrix}$

$25 = \frac{1}{2}\begin{vmatrix} -2 & 4 & 1 \\ 3 & -5 & 1 \\ 3 & f & 1 \end{vmatrix}$

$25 = \frac{1}{2}\left|\begin{array}{ccc|cc} -2 & 4 & 1 & -2 & 4 \\ 3 & -5 & 1 & 3 & -5 \\ 3 & f & 1 & 3 & f \end{array}\right.$

$25 = \frac{1}{2}((-2)(-5)1 + 4 \cdot 1 \cdot 3 + 1 \cdot 3 \cdot f - 3(-5)1 - f \cdot 1(-2) - 1 \cdot 3 \cdot 4)$

$25 = \frac{1}{2}(10 + 12 + 3f + 15 + 2f - 12)$

$50 = 5f + 25$

$25 = 5f$

$5 = f$

53. Let x = batteries, y = spark plugs, and z = wiper blades.

$6x + 5y + 2z = 830 \qquad 6x + 5y + 2z = 830$

$3x + 7y + 4z = 820 \quad \rightarrow \quad 3x + 7y + 4z = 820$

$x = 2z - 22 \qquad x - 2z = -22$

$\left[\begin{array}{ccc|c} 6 & 5 & 2 & 830 \\ 3 & 7 & 4 & 820 \\ 1 & 0 & -2 & -22 \end{array}\right] = \left[\begin{array}{ccc|c} 6 & 5 & 2 & 830 \\ -9 & -3 & 0 & -840 \\ 1 & 0 & -2 & -22 \end{array}\right]$

$= \left[\begin{array}{ccc|c} 7 & 5 & 0 & 808 \\ -9 & -3 & 0 & -840 \\ 1 & 0 & -2 & -22 \end{array}\right] = \left[\begin{array}{ccc|c} 7 & 5 & 0 & 808 \\ -63 & -21 & 0 & -5880 \\ 1 & 0 & -2 & -22 \end{array}\right]$

$= \left[\begin{array}{ccc|c} 7 & 5 & 0 & 808 \\ 0 & 24 & 0 & 1392 \\ 1 & 0 & -2 & -22 \end{array}\right] = \left[\begin{array}{ccc|c} 7 & 5 & 0 & 808 \\ 0 & 1 & 0 & 58 \\ 1 & 0 & -2 & -22 \end{array}\right]$

$= \left[\begin{array}{ccc|c} 7 & 0 & 0 & 518 \\ 0 & 1 & 0 & 58 \\ 1 & 0 & -2 & -22 \end{array}\right] = \left[\begin{array}{ccc|c} 1 & 0 & 0 & 74 \\ 0 & 1 & 0 & 58 \\ 1 & 0 & -2 & -22 \end{array}\right]$

$= \left[\begin{array}{ccc|c} 1 & 0 & 0 & 74 \\ 0 & 1 & 0 & 58 \\ 0 & 0 & -2 & -96 \end{array}\right] = \left[\begin{array}{ccc|c} 1 & 0 & 0 & 74 \\ 0 & 1 & 0 & 58 \\ 0 & 0 & 1 & 48 \end{array}\right];$

batteries, $74; spark plugs, $58; wiper blades, $48

Page 249 Alternative Assessment; Thinking Critically

- Matrix $ROSE = \begin{bmatrix} -2 & 3 & 2 & -1 \\ -1 & 0 & 2 & 2 \end{bmatrix}$

$\begin{bmatrix} 0 & -1 \\ 1 & 0 \end{bmatrix} \cdot \begin{bmatrix} -2 & 3 & 2 & -1 \\ -1 & 0 & 2 & 2 \end{bmatrix} = \begin{bmatrix} 0+1 & 0+0 & 0-2 & 0-2 \\ -2+0 & 3+0 & 2+0 & -1+0 \end{bmatrix}$

$= \begin{bmatrix} 1 & 0 & -2 & -2 \\ -2 & 3 & 2 & -1 \end{bmatrix}$

$\begin{bmatrix} 0 & -1 \\ 1 & 0 \end{bmatrix} \cdot \begin{bmatrix} 1 & 0 & -2 & -2 \\ -2 & 3 & 2 & -1 \end{bmatrix} = \begin{bmatrix} 0+2 & 0-3 & 0-2 & 0+1 \\ 1+0 & 0+0 & -2+0 & -2+0 \end{bmatrix}$

$= \begin{bmatrix} 2 & -3 & -2 & 1 \\ 1 & 0 & -2 & -2 \end{bmatrix};$

$R'(2, 1)$, $O'(-3, 0)$, $S'(-2, -2)$, $E'(1, -2)$

The new coordinates have opposite signs compared to the original coordinates. The result is a 180° rotation.

- No, when the determinant of the coefficient matrix is 0, the inverse matrix would be $\frac{1}{0}\begin{bmatrix} d & -b \\ -c & a \end{bmatrix}$ and $\frac{1}{0}$ is undefined. The system of equations has no unique solution.

College Entrance Exam Practice, Chapters 1–4

Pages 250–251

1. D = {9, 3, 12, 1, −11, 0}

g is not a function; C

2. $\left[\begin{array}{cc|c} 1 & 5 & 1 \\ 2 & -3 & 15 \end{array}\right] = \left[\begin{array}{cc|c} 1 & 5 & 1 \\ 0 & -13 & 13 \end{array}\right] = \left[\begin{array}{cc|c} 1 & 5 & 1 \\ 0 & 1 & -1 \end{array}\right]$

$= \left[\begin{array}{cc|c} 1 & 0 & 6 \\ 0 & 1 & -1 \end{array}\right]$; A

3. $2(x + 5) \le 18$; C

4. B

5. $3x - 2y = 8$

$-2y = -3x + 8$

$y = \frac{3}{2}x - 4$

$m = -\frac{2}{3}$

$y = mx + b$

$-4 = -\frac{2}{3}(1) + b$

$-4 = -\frac{2}{3} + b$

$-\frac{10}{3} = b$

$y = -\frac{2}{3}x - \frac{10}{3}$; A

6.

(x, y)	$x + 3y$	$f(x, y)$
(0, 0)	0 + 3(0)	0
(4, 0)	4 + 3(0)	4
(5, 5)	5 + 3(5)	20
(0, 8)	0 + 3(8)	24

maximum: $f(0, 8) = 24$

minimum: $f(0, 0) = 0$; A

7. D

8. $6x + y = 4$

$y = -6x + 4$

$a = \frac{1}{6}$; B

9. Answers may vary.

10. $\left|x - \frac{7}{3}\right| = 6$

$x - \frac{7}{3} = 6$ or $x - \frac{7}{3} = -6$

$x = \frac{25}{3}$ $\quad x = -\frac{11}{3}$

11. $3\begin{bmatrix} 5 & -2 \\ -3 & 4 \\ -2 & -3 \end{bmatrix} = \begin{bmatrix} 15 & -6 \\ -9 & 12 \\ -6 & -9 \end{bmatrix}$

$A'(15, -6)$, $B'(-9, 12)$, $C'(-6, -9)$

12. $r + t = 24$ $\quad 0.19r + 0.29t = 5.46$

$r = 24 - t$ $\quad 0.19(24 - t) + 0.29t = 5.46$

$4.56 - 0.19t + 0.29t = 5.46$

$0.10t = 0.9$

$t = 9$

$r + t = 24$

$r + 9 = 24$

$r = 15$

13. Let h = price of a hot dog and s = price of a soft drink.

$48h + 72s = 264 \rightarrow 2592h + 3888s = 14{,}256$

$54h + 117s = 387 \rightarrow (-)2592h + 5616s = 18{,}576$

$-1728s = -4320$

$s = 2.5$

$48h + 72s = 264$

$48h + 72(2.5) = 264$

$48h + 180 = 264$

$48h = 84$

$h = 1.75$

hot dog, $1.75; soft drink, $2.50

14. Let s = Maria's pay and h = hours worked.

$s = 5.5h - 10$

$s = 5.5(32) - 10$

$= 176 - 10$

$= 166$; $166

15. $\frac{1}{2}\begin{vmatrix} -5 & 2 & 1 \\ -3 & 7 & 1 \\ 3 & 8 & 1 \end{vmatrix} = \frac{1}{2}(-35 + 6 - 24 - 21 + 40 + 6)$

$= \frac{1}{2}(-28)$

$= -14$

$\frac{1}{2}\begin{vmatrix} 3 & 8 & 1 \\ 4 & -1 & 1 \\ -5 & 2 & 1 \end{vmatrix} = \frac{1}{2}(-3 - 40 + 8 - 5 - 6 - 32)$

$= \frac{1}{2}(-78)$

$= -39$

$14 + 39 = 53$ square units

16. $\begin{vmatrix} 3 & -2 & x \\ x & 1 & -5 \\ 2 & 0 & -1 \end{vmatrix} = 1$

$-3 + 20 + 0 - 2x + 0 - 2x = 1$

$-4x + 17 = 1$

$-4x = -16$

$x = 4$

$x + y + 3z = 7$

$(+)2x - 2y - 3z = 2$

$3x - y = 9$

$2x - 2y - 3z = 2 \rightarrow 4x - 4y - 6z = 4$

$3x - y - 2z = 1 \rightarrow (-)9x - 3y - 6z = 3$

$-5x - y = 1$

$3x - y = 9 \rightarrow 15x - 5y = 45$

$-5x - y = 1 \rightarrow (+)-15x - 3y = 3$

$-8y = 48$

$y = -6$

$4 > -6$; A

17. $5a + 4b = -1 \rightarrow 10a + 8b = -2$

$2a - b = 10 \rightarrow (-)10a - 5b = 50$

$13b = -52$

$b = -4$

$\begin{vmatrix} -4 & 6 \\ -13 & 24 \end{vmatrix} = -4(24) - (-13)(6) = -18$

$-4 > -18$; A

18. $t + 10 > 9$

$t > -1$

$3t - 2$ $\quad -t + 2(t + 3) = -t + 2t + 6$

$= t + 6$

Try $t = 3$.

$3t - 2 = 3(3) - 2$ $\quad t + 6 = 3 + 6$

$= 9 - 2$ $\quad = 9$

$= 7$

$7 < 9$

Try $t = 4$.

$3t - 2 = 3(4) - 2$ $\quad t + 6 = 4 + 6$

$= 12 - 2$ $\quad = 10$

$= 10$

$10 = 10$

Try $t = 5$.

$3t - 2 = 3(5) - 2$ $\quad t + 6 = 5 + 6$

$= 15 - 2$ $\quad = 11$

$= 13$

$13 > 11$; D

19. The mean cannot be determined from the box-and-whisker plot. D

20. $2x + 3y = 7 \rightarrow 8x + 12y = 28$

$3x - 4y = 2 \rightarrow (+)9x - 12y = 6$

$17x = 34$

$x = 2$

$2x + 3y = 7$

$2(2) + 3y = 7$

$4 + 3y = 7$ $\quad 2 > 1$; A

$3y = 3$

$y = 1$

Chapter 5 Exploring Polynomials and Radical Expressions

5-1 Monomials

Pages 258–259 Check for Understanding

1. You cannot divide by 0.
2. No, $(4x)^2 = (4x)(4x)$ or $16x^2$
3. Negative; a negative to an odd power is negative.
4. No, it should not contain parentheses; $2x^6y^3$ is in simplest form.
5. $3wz^{-4} = 3w \cdot \frac{1}{z^4} = \frac{3w}{z^4}$
6. $y^5 \cdot y^7 = y^{5+7}$
   $= y^{12}$
7. $(3a)^4 = 3^4 \cdot a^4$
   $= 81a^4$
8. $(m^2)^2(m^{-2})^2 = m^{2 \cdot 2}\, m^{-2 \cdot 2}$
   $= m^4 \cdot m^{-4}$
   $= m^{4-4}$
   $= m^0$
   $= 1$
9. $\frac{40x^4}{-5x^2} = \frac{40}{-5} \cdot x^{4-2}$
   $= -8x^2$
10. $\frac{-2c^3d^6}{24c^2d^2} = -\frac{2}{24} \cdot c^{3-2} \cdot d^{6-2}$
    $= -\frac{1}{12}cd^4$
    $= -\frac{cd^4}{12}$
11. $\frac{16s^6t^5}{(2s^2t)^2} = \frac{16s^6t^5}{2^2s^{2 \cdot 2}t^2}$
    $= \frac{16s^6t^5}{4s^4t^2}$
    $= \frac{16}{4} \cdot s^{6-2} \cdot t^{5-2}$
    $= 4s^4t^3$
12. $\left(\frac{1}{x^3y^2}\right)^4 = \frac{1^4}{(x^3y^2)^4}$
    $= \frac{1}{x^{3 \cdot 4}y^{2 \cdot 4}}$
    $= \frac{1}{x^{12}y^8}$
13. $\left(\frac{bc}{2}\right)^{-3} = \left(\frac{2}{bc}\right)^3$
    $= \frac{2^3}{(bc)^3}$
    $= \frac{8}{b^3c^3}$
14. $\left(\frac{-6y^5}{3y^2}\right)^{-2} = \left(\frac{3y^2}{-6y^5}\right)^2$
    $= \frac{(3y^2)^2}{(-6y^5)^2}$
    $= \frac{3^2y^{2 \cdot 2}}{(-6)^2y^{5 \cdot 2}}$
    $= \frac{9y^4}{36y^{10}}$
    $= \frac{1}{4y^{10-4}}$
    $= \frac{1}{4y^6}$
15. $386{,}000 = 3.86 \times 100{,}000$
    $= 3.86 \times 10^5$
16. $0.000346 = 3.46 \times 0.0001$
    $= 3.46 \times 10^{-4}$
17. $\frac{8 \times 10^{-1}}{16 \times 10^{-2}} = 0.5 \times 10^{-1-(-2)}$
    $= 0.5 \times 10^1$
    $= 5 \times 10^0$
    $5 \times 10^0 = 5 \times 1$
    $= 5$
18. $(3.42 \times 10^8)(1.1 \times 10^{-5}) = (3.42 \times 1.1)(10^8 \times 10^{-5})$
    $= 3.762 \times 10^3$
    $3.762 \times 10^3 = 3.762 \times 1000$
    $= 3762$

Pages 259–260 Exercises

19. $b^3 \cdot b^5 = b^{3+5}$
    $= b^8$
20. $x^2 \cdot x \cdot x^3 = x^{2+1+3}$
    $= x^6$
21. $(m^3)^3 = m^{3 \cdot 3}$
    $= m^9$
22. $(-3y)^3 = (-3)^3(y)^3$
    $= -27y^3$
23. $\frac{an^6}{n^5} = an^{6-5}$
    $= an$
24. $\frac{-x^6y^6}{x^3y^4} = -x^{6-3}y^{6-4}$
    $= -x^3y^2$
25. $(a^3b^3)(ab)^{-2} = (a^3b^3)\left(\frac{1}{ab}\right)^2$
    $= (a^3b^3)\left(\frac{1^2}{a^2b^2}\right)$
    $= \frac{a^3b^3}{a^2b^2}$
    $= a^{3-2}b^{3-2}$
    $= ab$
26. $(4x^3y^{-4})(7xy^2) = 4 \cdot 7 \cdot x^3 \cdot x \cdot y^{-4} \cdot y^2$
    $= 28x^{3+1}y^{-4+2}$
    $= 28x^4y^{-2}$
    $= \frac{28x^4}{y^2}$
27. $(-3r^2s)^2(2rs^3) = (-3)^2r^{2 \cdot 2}s^2(2rs^3)$
    $= 9r^4s^2 \cdot 2rs^3$
    $= 9 \cdot 2 \cdot r^4 \cdot r \cdot s^2 \cdot s^3$
    $= 18r^{4+1}s^{2+3}$
    $= 18r^5s^5$
28. $(3a^3b)(-5a^2b^2) = 3 \cdot (-5) \cdot a^3 \cdot a^2 \cdot b \cdot b^2$
    $= -15a^{3+2}b^{1+2}$
    $= -15a^5b^3$
29. $(2mn^2)(5m^2n) = 2 \cdot 5 \cdot m \cdot m^2 \cdot n^2 \cdot n$
    $= 10m^{1+2} \cdot n^{2+1}$
    $= 10m^3n^3$
30. $(-5x^2y)(-2x^4y^7) = (-5)(-2)x^2 \cdot x^4 \cdot y \cdot y^7$
    $= 10x^{2+4}y^{1+7}$
    $= 10x^6y^8$
31. $(-\frac{3}{4}m^2n^3)(\frac{8}{9}mn^4) = (-\frac{3}{4})\frac{8}{9} \cdot m^2 \cdot m \cdot n^3 \cdot n^4$
    $= -\frac{2}{3}m^{2+1}n^{2+4}$
    $= -\frac{2}{3}m^3n^7$
32. $2b^2(2ab)^3 = 2b^2(2)^3(a)^3(b)^3$
    $= 2 \cdot b^2 \cdot 8 \cdot a^3 \cdot b^3$
    $= 2 \cdot 8 \cdot a^3 \cdot b^2 \cdot b^3$
    $= 16a^3b^{2+3}$
    $= 16a^3b^5$
33. $4x(-3x)^3 = 4x \cdot (-3)^3(x)^3$
    $= 4x(-27)x^3$
    $= 4(-27)\,x \cdot x^3$
    $= -108x^{1+3}$
    $= -108x^4$

34. $4a^2(3b^3)(2a^2b) = 4 \cdot 3 \cdot 2 \cdot a^2 \cdot a^2 \cdot b^3 \cdot b$
$= 24a^{2+2}\,b^{3+1}$
$= 24a^4b^4$

35. $5mn^2(m^3n)(-3p^2) = 5 \cdot (-3) \cdot m \cdot m^3 \cdot n^2 \cdot n \cdot p^2$
$= -15m^{1+3}\,n^{2+1}\,p^2$
$= -15m^4n^3p^2$

36. $5x(6x^2y)(3xy^3) = 5 \cdot 6 \cdot 3 \cdot x \cdot x^2 \cdot x \cdot y \cdot y^3$
$= 90x^{1+2+1}\,y^{1+3}$
$= 90x^4y^4$

37. $\frac{-6x^2y^3z^3}{24x^2y^7z^3} = \frac{-6}{24} \cdot x^{2-2} \cdot y^{3-7} \cdot z^{3-3}$
$= \frac{-1}{4}\,x^0\,y^{-4}\,z^0$
$= \frac{-1}{4y^4}$

38. $\frac{2x^5y^3z^3}{8x^3y^7z} = \frac{2}{8} \cdot x^{5-3} \cdot y^{3-7} \cdot z^{3-1}$
$= \frac{1}{4}\,x^2\,y^{-4}\,z^2$
$= \frac{x^2z^2}{4y^4}$

39. $\frac{-15m^5n^8(m^3n^2)}{45m^4n} = \frac{-15m^{5+3} \cdot n^{8+2}}{45m^4n}$
$= \frac{-15m^8n^{10}}{45m^4n}$
$= \frac{-15}{45}\,m^{8-4}\,n^{10-1}$
$= -\frac{1}{3}m^4n^9$
$= -\frac{m^4n^9}{3}$

40. $\frac{2a^3b}{(-2ab^3)^{-2}} = 2a^3b(-2ab^3)^2$
$= 2a^3b(-2)^2a^2 \cdot b^{3 \cdot 2}$
$= 2a^3b \cdot 4 \cdot a^2 \cdot b^6$
$= 8a^{3+2}\,b^{1+6}$
$= 8a^5b^7$

41. $\left(\frac{5a^3b}{10a^2b^2}\right)^4 = \frac{5^4 \cdot (a^3)^4 \cdot b^4}{10^4(a^2)^4(b^2)^4}$
$= \frac{625a^{12}b^4}{10{,}000a^8b^8}$
$= \frac{625}{10{,}000}\,a^{12-8}\,b^{4-8}$
$= \frac{1}{16}a^4b^{-4}$
$= \frac{a^4}{16b^4}$

42. $\left(\frac{a}{b^{-1}}\right)^{-2} = \left(\frac{b^{-1}}{a}\right)^2$
$= \frac{(b^{-1})^2}{a^2}$
$= \frac{b^{-2}}{a^2}$
$= \frac{1}{a^2b^2}$

43. $\frac{40a^{-1}b^{-7}}{20a^{-5}b^{-9}} = \frac{40}{20}\,a^{-1-(-5)}\,b^{-7-(-9)}$
$= 2a^4b^2$

44. $\frac{5^{2x}}{5^{2x+2}} = 5^{2x-(2x+2)}$
$= 5^{2x-2x-2}$
$= 5^{-2}$
$= \frac{1}{5^2}$
$= \frac{1}{25}$

45. $\frac{8}{m^0+n^0} = \frac{8}{1+1}$
$= \frac{8}{2}$
$= 4$

46. $810.4 = 8.104 \times 100$
$= 8.104 \times 10^2$

47. $786{,}500{,}000 = 7.865 \times 100{,}000{,}000$
$= 7.865 \times 10^8$

48. $0.0008742 = 8.742 \times 0.0001$
$= 8.742 \times 10^{-4}$

49. $0.001250 = 1.25 \times 0.001$
$= 1.25 \times 10^{-3}$

50. $901{,}010{,}000 = 9.0101 \times 100{,}000{,}000$
$= 9.0101 \times 10^8$

51. $0.03331 = 3.331 \times 0.01$
$= 3.331 \times 10^{-2}$

52. $(6.23 \times 10^4)(2.0 \times 10^5) = (6.23 \times 2.0)(10^4 \times 10^5)$
$= 12.46 \times 10^{4+5}$
$= 1.246 \times 10^1 \times 10^9$
$= 1.246 \times 10^{1+9}$
$= 1.246 \times 10^{10}$

$1.246 \times 10^{10} = 1.246 \times 10{,}000{,}000{,}000$
$= 12{,}460{,}000{,}000$

53. $(2 \times 10^{-3})(2.01 \times 10^{-2}) = (2 \times 2.01)(10^{-3} \times 10^{-2})$
$= 4.02 \times 10^{-3+(-2)}$
$= 4.02 \times 10^{-5}$

$4.02 \times 10^{-5} = 4.02 \times 0.00001$
$= 0.0000402$

54. $(45{,}000)(0.0025) = (4.5 \times 10^4)(2.5 \times 10^{-3})$
$= (4.5 \times 2.5)(10^4 \times 10^{-3})$
$= 11.25 \times 10^{4+(-3)}$
$= 1.125 \times 10^1 \times 10^1$
$= 1.125 \times 10^{1+1}$
$= 1.125 \times 10^2$

$1.125 \times 10^2 = 1.125 \times 100$
$= 112.5$

55. $(9.5 \times 10^3)^2 = (9.5)^2 \times (10^3)^2$
$= 90.25 \times 10^{3 \cdot 2}$
$= 9.025 \times 10^1 \times 10^6$
$= 9.025 \times 10^{1+6}$
$= 9.025 \times 10^7$

$9.025 \times 10^7 = 9.025 \times 10{,}000{,}000$
$= 90{,}250{,}000$

56. $(6.9 \times 10^3)(1.4 \times 10^3)^{-1} = \frac{6.9 \times 10^3}{1.4 \times 10^3}$
$\approx 4.93 \times 10^{3-3}$
$\approx 4.93 \times 10^0$

$4.93 \times 10^0 = 4.93$

57. $\frac{(93{,}000{,}000)\,(0.005)}{0.0015} = \frac{(9.3 \times 10^7)(5.0 \times 10^{-3})}{1.5 \times 10^{-3}}$
$= \frac{(9.3 \times 5.0)(10^7 \times 10^{-3})}{1.5 \times 10^{-3}}$
$= \frac{46.5 \times 10^{7+(-3)}}{1.5 \times 10^{-3}}$
$= \frac{46.5 \times 10^4}{1.5 \times 10^{-3}}$
$= 31 \times 10^{4-(-3)}$
$= 3.1 \times 10^1 \times 10^7$
$= 3.1 \times 10^8$

$3.1 \times 10^8 = 3.1 \times 100{,}000{,}000$
$= 310{,}000{,}000$

58. $y^{28} = y^{3r} \cdot y^7$
$y^{28} = y^{3r+7}$
$28 = 3r + 7$
$21 = 3r$
$7 = r$

59. $2^{r+5} = 2^{2r-1}$
$r + 5 = 2r - 1$
$5 = r - 1$
$6 = r$

60. $2^{2r+1} = 32$
$2^{2r+1} = 2^5$
$2r + 1 = 5$
$2r = 4$
$r = 2$

61. $(x^3 \cdot x^r)^5 = x^{30}$
$(x^{3+r})^5 = x^{30}$
$x^{(3+r)\cdot 5} = x^{30}$
$(3 + r)5 = 30$
$15 + 5r = 30$
$5r = 15$
$r = 3$

62. $\frac{x^{2r}}{x^{-3r}} = x^{15}$
$x^{2r-(-3r)} = x^{15}$
$2r - (-3r) = 15$
$5r = 15$
$r = 3$

63. $\frac{m^r}{m^{15}} = (m^3)^{r+2}$
$m^{r-15} = m^{3(r+2)}$
$r - 15 = 3(r + 2)$
$r - 15 = 3r + 6$
$-15 = 2r + 6$
$-21 = 2r$
$-\frac{21}{2} = r$

64. $100^{10} = (10^2)^{10}$ or 10^{20} and $10^{100} > 10^{20}$, so $10^{100} > 100^{10}$.

65. $\frac{x + x^2 + x^3 + x^4 + x^5 + x^6 + x^7}{x^{-3} + x^{-4} + x^{-5} + x^{-6} + x^{-7} + x^{-8} + x^{-9}}$

Simplify the denominator:
Denominator
$= \left(\frac{x^{-3}}{x^{-10}} + \frac{x^{-4}}{x^{-10}} + \frac{x^{-5}}{x^{-10}} + \frac{x^{-6}}{x^{-10}} + \frac{x^{-7}}{x^{-10}} + \frac{x^{-8}}{x^{-10}} + \frac{x^{-9}}{x^{-10}}\right)(x^{-10})$
$= (x^{-3-(-10)} + x^{-4-(-10)} + x^{-5-(-10)} + x^{-6-(-10)} + x^{-7-(-10)} + x^{-8-(-10)} + x^{-9-(-10)})(x^{-10})$
$= (x^7 + x^6 + x^5 + x^4 + x^3 + x^2 + x)(x^{-10})$
Substitute into expression:
$\frac{x + x^2 + x^3 + x^4 + x^5 + x^6 + x^7}{(x^7 + x^6 + x^5 + x^4 + x^3 + x^2 + x)(x^{-10})} = \frac{1}{x^{-10}}$
$= x^{10}$

66. $\frac{468{,}000{,}000{,}000}{250{,}000{,}000} = \frac{4.68 \times 10^{11}}{2.5 \times 10^8}$
$= 1.872 \times 10^{11-8}$
$= 1.872 \times 10^3$
$= 1872$; \$1872

67. $t = \frac{r}{d}$
$= \frac{4.58 \times 10^9}{3.00 \times 10^5}$
$\approx 1.53 \times 10^{9-5}$
$\approx 1.53 \times 10^4$
1.53×10^4 seconds or:
$1.53 \times 10^4 = 15300$
$15300 \div 60 = 255$
$255 \div 60 = 4.25$
4.25 hours

68a. 16, 16, 16, 17, 18, 18, 18, 18, 18, 18, 18, 18, 19, 20, 20, 22, 24, 26
Q_2 is between 9th and 10th values, $\frac{18 + 18}{2} = 18$; Q_1 is the 5th value, 18; Q_3 is the 14th value, 20; IR = 20 − 18 = 2; outliers: below 18 − 1.5(2) = 15 or above 20 + 1.5(2) = 23, outliers = 24, 26

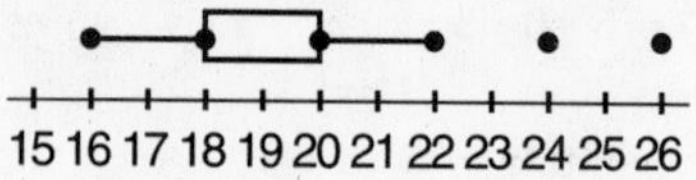

68b. See students' work.

69. $\begin{bmatrix} 3 & 6 & 1 \\ 2 & -1 & 0 \end{bmatrix} \cdot M = \begin{bmatrix} 3 & 6 & 1 \\ 2 & -1 & 0 \end{bmatrix}$; M is an identity matrix.
It must have 3 rows in order to multiply.
$M = \begin{bmatrix} 1 & 0 & 0 \\ 0 & 1 & 0 \\ 0 & 0 & 1 \end{bmatrix}$

70. $\begin{vmatrix} 5a & 3 \\ a & 5 \end{vmatrix} = 7$
$25a - 3a = 7$
$22a = 7$
$a = \frac{7}{22}$

71. $y\begin{bmatrix} 3 & -4 \\ 2 & x \end{bmatrix} = \begin{bmatrix} 15 & -20 \\ z & 5 \end{bmatrix}$
$\begin{bmatrix} 3y & -4y \\ 2y & xy \end{bmatrix} = \begin{bmatrix} 15 & -20 \\ z & 5 \end{bmatrix}$

$3y = 15$, $y = 5$ | $-4y = -20$, $y = 5$ | $2y = z$, $2(5) = z$, $10 = z$ | $xy = 5$, $x(5) = 5$, $x = 1$

72. $8a - 3b + c = 7 \rightarrow$
$-2a + b - c = 0 \rightarrow$

$8a - 3b + c = 7$
$(+)-8a + 4b - 4c = 0$
$b - 3c = 7$

$-2a + b - c = 0$
$(+)2a - 3b + 9c = -1$
$-2b + 8c = -1$

$b - 3c = 7 \rightarrow$
$-2b + 8c = -1 \rightarrow$

$2b - 6c = 14$
$(+)-2b + 8c = -1$
$2c = 13$
$c = \frac{13}{2}$

$-2b + 8c = -1$
$-2b + 8\left(\frac{13}{2}\right) = -1$
$-2b + 52 = -1$
$-2b = -53$
$b = \frac{53}{2}$

$-2a + b - c = 0$
$-2a + \frac{53}{2} - \frac{13}{2} = 0$
$-2a + 20 = 0$
$-2a = -20$
$a = 10$

$\left(10, \frac{53}{2}, \frac{13}{2}\right)$

73. $x + y < 9$
$y < -x + 9$
$x - y < 3$
$-y < -x + 3$
$y > x - 3$
$y - x > 4$
$y > x + 4$

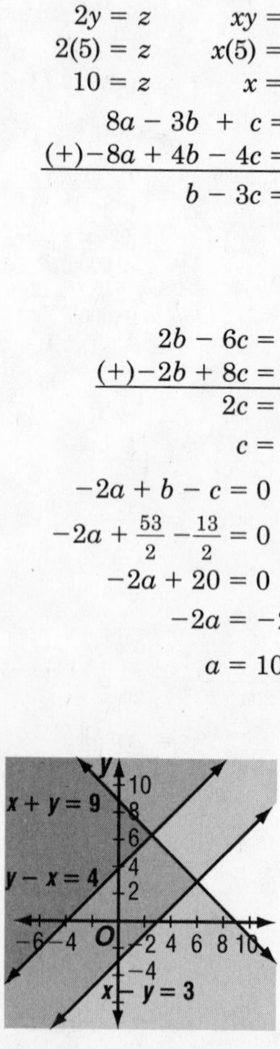

74. They are the same line.

75. $4x - y + 3 = 0$
$-y + 3 = -4x$
$-y = -4x - 3$
$y = 4x - 3$; parallel slope = 4
$y - y_1 = m(x - x_1)$
$y - 2 = 4(x - 2)$
$y - 2 = 4x - 8$
$y = 4x - 6$

76. $f(x) = 13x + 26$
$0 = 13x + 26$
$-26 = 13x$
$-2 = x$

$f(x) = 13x + 26$
$y = 13(0) + 26$
$y = 0 + 26$
$y = 26$

77. $x - 3y = -3$
$-3y = -x - 3$
$y = \frac{1}{3}x + 1$

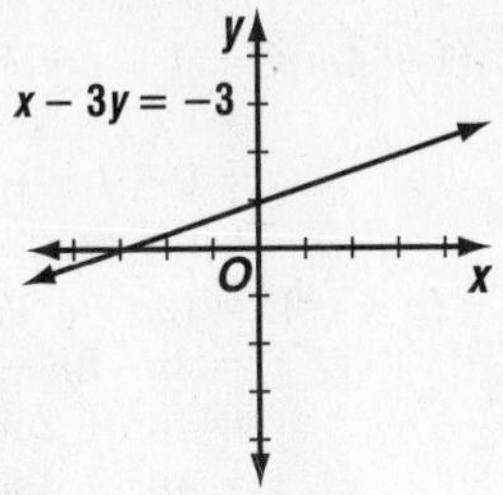

78. $-2(4 - 3x) > 4$
$-8 + 6x > 4$
$6x > 12$
$x > 2$
$\{x \mid x > 2\}$

79. $15 - 3(2) \div 8 - 11 = 15 - 6 \div 8 - 11$
$= 15 - \frac{3}{4} - 11$
$= 14\frac{1}{4} - 11$
$= 3\frac{1}{4}$

5-2 Polynomials

Pages 263–264 Check for Understanding

1. F:$3a(a)$ or $3a^2$, O:$3a(-b)$ or $-3ab$, I: $4b(a)$ or $4ab$, L: $4b(-b)$ or $-4b^2$; $3a^2 - 3ab + 4ab - 4b^2 = 3a^2 + ab - 4b^2$

2. $(k^2 + 3k + 9)(k + 3)$
$= (k^2 + 3k + 9)k + (k^2 + 3k + 9)3$
$= k^2 \cdot k + 3k \cdot k + 9 \cdot k + k^2 \cdot 3 + 3k \cdot 3 + 9 \cdot 3$
$= k^3 + 3k^2 + 9k + 3k^2 + 9k + 27$
$= k^3 + 6k^2 + 18k + 27$

3. Sample answer: $3x^4y^2 + x^3y^2 - 5xy + 20$

4. Sample answer:

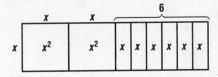

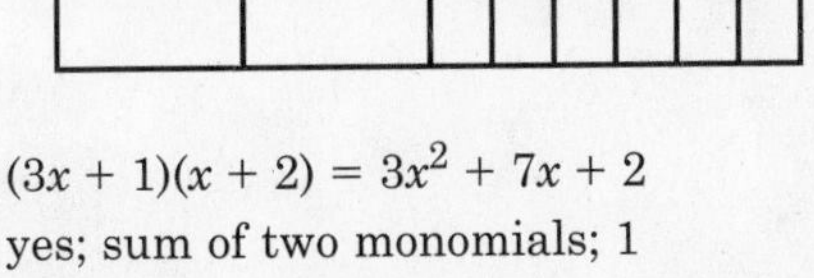

5. $(3x + 1)(x + 2) = 3x^2 + 7x + 2$

6. yes; sum of two monomials; 1

7. yes; difference of two monomials; 3

8. no; a variable may not be in the denominator

9. $(5x - 7y) + (6x + 8y) = 5x + 6x - 7y + 8y$
$= 11x + y$

10. $(-2y^2 - 4y + 7) - (2y^2 + 4y - 7)$
$= -2y^2 - 4y + 7 - 2y^2 - 4y + 7$
$= -2y^2 - 2y^2 - 4y - 4y + 7 + 7$
$= -4y^2 - 8y + 14$

11. $3y(2x + 6) = 3y(2x) + 3y(6)$
$= 6xy + 18y$

12. $2m^2n(5mn - 3m^3n^2 + 4mn^4)$
$= 2m^2n(5mn) + 2m^2n(-3m^3n^2) + 2m^2n(4mn^4)$
$= 10m^3n^2 - 6m^5n^3 + 8m^3n^5$

13. $(x + 6)(x + 3) = x \cdot x + x \cdot 3 + 6 \cdot x + 6 \cdot 3$
$= x^2 + 3x + 6x + 18$
$= x^2 + 9x + 18$

14. $(y - 10)(y + 7) = y \cdot y + y \cdot 7 + (-10)y + (-10)7$
$= y^2 + 7y - 10y - 70$
$= y^2 - 3y - 70$

15. $(3m - 1)(3m + 1)$
$= 3m \cdot 3m + 3m \cdot 1 + (-1)3m + (-1)1$
$= 9m^2 + 3m - 3m - 1$
$= 9m^2 - 1$

16. $(2p - 3s)^2$
$= (2p - 3s)(2p - 3s)$
$= 2p \cdot 2p + 2p(-3s) + (-3s)2p + (-3s)(-3s)$
$= 4p^2 - 6ps - 6ps + 9s^2$
$= 4p^2 - 12ps + 9s^2$

17a. $P = (a + 2c) + (a - 3c) + (a + 2c) + (a - 3c)$
$= a + a + a + a + 2c - 3c + 2c - 3c$
$= 4a - 2c$; $(4a - 2c)$ yards

17b. $A = (a + 2c)(a + c)$
$= a \cdot a + a \cdot c + 2c \cdot a + 2c \cdot c$
$= a^2 + ac + 2ac + 2c^2$
$= a^2 + 3ac + 2c^2$;
$(a^2 + 3ac + 2c^2)$ square yards

Pages 264–266 Exercises

18. yes; sum of 3 monomials; 2

19. yes; sum of 2 monomials; 3

20. no; $\sqrt{s}$ does not represent monomial

21. yes; sum of 2 monomials; 7

22. no; variables may not be in denominator

23. yes; sum of 2 monomials; 6

24. $(3r + s) - (r - s) - (r + 3s)$
$= 3r + s - r + s - r - 3s$
$= 3r - r - r + s + s - 3s$
$= r - s$

25. $(z^2 - 6z - 10) + (2z^2 + 4z - 11)$
$= z^2 + 2z^2 - 6z + 4z - 10 - 11$
$= 3z^2 - 2z - 21$

26. $(-12y - 6y^2) + (-7y + 6y^2)$
$= -12y - 7y - 6y^2 + 6y^2$
$= -19y$

27. $(3m^2 + 5m - 6) + (7m^2 - 9)$
$= 3m^2 + 7m^2 + 5m - 6 - 9$
$= 10m^2 + 5m - 15$

28. $(10x^2 - 3xy + 4y^2) - (3x^2 + 5xy)$
$= 10x^2 - 3xy + 4y^2 - 3x^2 - 5xy$
$= 10x^2 - 3x^2 - 3xy - 5xy + 4y^2$
$= 7x^2 - 8xy + 4y^2$

29. $(8r^2 + 5r + 14) - (7r^2 + 6r + 8)$
$= 8r^2 + 5r + 14 - 7r^2 - 6r - 8$
$= 8r^2 - 7r^2 + 5r - 6r + 14 - 8$
$= r^2 - r + 6$

30. $4a(3a^2b) = 12a^3b$

31. $4f(gf - bh) = 4f(gf) + 4f(-bh)$
$= 4gf^2 - 4fbh$

32. $\frac{2}{3}x^2(6x + 9y - 12xy^2)$
$= \frac{2}{3}x^2(6x) + \frac{2}{3}x^2(9y) + \frac{2}{3}x^2(-12xy^2)$
$= 4x^3 + 6x^2y - 8x^3y^2$

33. $-5mn^2(-3m^2n + 6m^3n - 3m^4n^4)$
$= -5mn^2(-3m^2n) - 5mn^2(6m^3n) -$
$5mn^2(-3m^4n^4)$
$= 15m^3n^3 - 30m^4n^3 + 15m^5n^6$

34. $(c^2 - 6cd - 2d^2) + (7c^2 - cd + 8d^2) -$
$(-c^2 + 5cd - d^2)$
$= c^2 - 6cd - 2d^2 + 7c^2 - cd + 8d^2 + c^2 - 5cd +$
d^2
$= c^2 + 7c^2 + c^2 - 6cd - cd - 5cd - 2d^2 + 8d^2 +$
d^2
$= 9c^2 - 12cd + 7d^2$

35. $(4x^2 - 3y^2 + 5xy) - (8xy + 6x^2 + 3y^2)$
$= 4x^2 - 3y^2 + 5xy - 8xy - 6x^2 - 3y^2$
$= 4x^2 - 6x^2 + 5xy - 8xy - 3y^2 - 3y^2$
$= -2x^2 - 3xy - 6y^2$

36. $P = (3y - 2) + y + (3y + 5)$
$= 3y + y + 3y - 2 + 5$
$= 7y + 3$; $(7y + 3)$ meters

37. $P = 4(7m - 3n)$
$= 4(7m) + 4(-3n)$
$= 28m - 12n$; $(28m - 12n)$ feet

38. $P = 3 + 4z + 2 + 3x + (2 + 3) + (4z + 3x)$
$= 4z + 4z + 3x + 3x + 3 + 2 + 2 + 3$
$= 8z + 6x + 10$; $(8z + 6x + 10)$ inches

39. $(q - 7)(q + 5) = q \cdot q + q \cdot 5 + (-7)q + (-7)5$
$= q^2 + 5q - 7q - 35$
$= q^2 - 2q - 35$

40. $(m + 7)(m + 2) = m \cdot m + m \cdot 2 + 7 \cdot m + 7 \cdot 2$
$= m^2 + 2m + 7m + 14$
$= m^2 + 9m + 14$

41. $(5 - r)(5 + r) = 5 \cdot 5 + 5 \cdot r + (-r)5 + (-r)r$
$= 25 + 5r - 5r - r^2$
$= 25 - r^2$

42. $(2x + 7)(3x + 5) = 2x \cdot 3x + 2x \cdot 5 + 7 \cdot 3x + 7 \cdot 5$
$= 6x^2 + 10x + 21x + 35$
$= 6x^2 + 31x + 35$

43. $(3y - 8)(2y + 7)$
$= 3y \cdot 2y + 3y \cdot 7 + (-8)2y + (-8)7$
$= 6y^2 + 21y - 16y - 56$
$= 6y^2 + 5y - 56$

44. $(x^3 - y)(x^3 + y) = x^3 \cdot x^3 + x^3 \cdot y + (-y)x^3 + (-y)y$
$= x^6 + x^3y - x^3y - y^2$
$= x^6 - y^2$

45. $g^{-3}(g^5 - 2g^3 + g^{-1})$
$= g^{-3}(g^5) + g^{-3}(-2g^3) + g^{-3}(g^{-1})$
$= g^2 - 2g^0 + g^{-4}$
$= g^2 - 2 + \frac{1}{g^4}$

46. $x^{-3}y^2(yx^4 + y^{-1}x^3 + y^{-2}x^2)$
$= x^{-3}y^2(yx^4) + x^{-3}y^2(y^{-1}x^3) + x^{-3}y^2(y^{-2}x^2)$
$= x^1y^3 + x^0y^1 + x^{-1}y^0$
$= xy^3 + y + \frac{1}{x}$

47. $(y - 3x)^2 = (y - 3x)(y - 3x)$
$= y \cdot y + y(-3x) + (-3x)y + (-3x)(-3x)$
$= y^2 - 3xy - 3xy + 9x^2$
$= y^2 - 6xy + 9x^2$

48. $(1 + 4m)^2 = (1 + 4m)(1 + 4m)$
$= 1 \cdot 1 + 1 \cdot 4m + 4m \cdot 1 + 4m \cdot 4m$
$= 1 + 4m + 4m + 16m^2$
$= 1 + 8m + 16m^2$

49. $(2p + q^3)^2 = (2p + q^3)(2p + q^3)$
$= 2p \cdot 2p + 2p \cdot q^3 + q^3 \cdot 2p + q^3 \cdot q^3$
$= 4p^2 + 2pq^3 + 2pq^2 + q^6$
$= 4p^2 + 4pq^3 + q^6$

50. $(w^2 - 5)(2w^2 + 3)$
$= w^2 \cdot 2w^2 + w^2 \cdot 3 + (-5)2w^2 + (-5)3$
$= 2w^4 + 3w^2 - 10w^2 - 15$
$= 2w^4 - 7w^2 - 15$

51. $A = \frac{1}{2}(5y + 3)(4y)$
$= \frac{1}{2}(5y \cdot 4y + 3 \cdot 4y)$
$= \frac{1}{2}(20y^2 + 12y)$
$= \frac{1}{2}(20y^2) + \frac{1}{2}(12y)$
$= 10y^2 + 6y$; $(10y^2 + 6y)$ square feet

52. $A = (8x - 2y)(8x + 2y)$
$= 8x \cdot 8x + 8x \cdot 2y + (-2y)8x + (-2y)(2y)$
$= 64x^2 + 16xy - 16xy - 4y^2$
$= 64x^2 - 4y^2$; $(64x^2 - 4y^2)$ square centimeters

53. $A = \frac{1}{2}(y^2)((3x + y) + (6x - y))$
$= \frac{y^2}{2}(3x + 6x + y - y)$
$= \frac{y^2}{2}(9x)$
$= \frac{9xy^2}{2}$; $\frac{9xy^2}{2}$ square meters

54. $(3y + 1)(3y - 1)(y + 2)$
$= (3y \cdot 3y + 3y(-1) + 1 \cdot 3y + 1(-1))(y + 2)$
$= (9y^2 - 3y + 3y - 1)(y + 2)$
$= (9y^2 - 1)(y + 2)$
$= 9y^2 \cdot y + 9y^2 \cdot 2 + (-1)y + (-1)2$
$= 9y^3 + 18y^2 - y - 2$

55. $(x^2 + xy + y^2)(x - y)$
$= x^2(x - y) + xy(x - y) + y^2(x - y)$
$= x^2 \cdot x + x^2(-y) + xy \cdot x + xy(-y) + y^2 \cdot x +$
$y^2(-y)$
$= x^3 - x^2y + x^2y - xy^2 + xy^2 - y^3$
$= x^3 - y^3$

56. $(2q + 1)(q - 2)^2$
$= (2q + 1)(q - 2)(q - 2)$
$= (2q \cdot q + 2q(-2) + 1 \cdot q + 1(-2))\,(q - 2)$
$= (2q^2 - 4q + q - 2)(q - 2)$
$= (2q^2 - 3q - 2)(q - 2)$
$= 2q^2(q - 2) - 3q(q - 2) - 2(q - 2)$
$= 2q^2 \cdot q + 2q^2(-2) - 3q \cdot q - 3q(-2) - 2 \cdot q - 2(-2)$
$= 2q^3 - 4q^2 - 3q^2 + 6q - 2q + 4$
$= 2q^3 - 7q^2 + 4q + 4$

57. $(x - 2)(x + 2)(x^2 + 5)$
$= (x \cdot x + x \cdot 2 + (-2)x + (-2)2)(x^2 + 5)$
$= (x^2 + 2x - 2x - 4)(x^2 + 5)$
$= (x^2 - 4)(x^2 + 5)$
$= x^2 \cdot x^2 + x^2 \cdot 5 + (-4)x^2 + (-4)5$
$= x^4 + 5x^2 - 4x^2 - 20$
$= x^4 + x^2 - 20$

58. $(3b - c)^3$
$= (3b - c)(3b - c)(3b - c)$
$= (3b \cdot 3b + 3b(-c) + (-c)3b + (-c)(-c))(3b - c)$
$= (9b^2 - 3bc - 3bc + c^2)(3b - c)$
$= (9b^2 - 6bc + c^2)(3b - c)$
$= 9b^2(3b - c) - 6bc(3b - c) + c^2(3b - c)$
$= 9b^2 \cdot 3b + 9b^2(-c) - 6bc \cdot 3b - 6bc(-c) +$
$c^2 \cdot 3b + c^2(-c)$
$= 27b^3 - 9b^2c - 18b^2c + 6bc^2 + 3bc^2 - c^3$
$= 27b^3 - 27b^2c + 9bc^2 - c^3$

59. $(y + x)^2(y - x)^2$
$= (y + x)(y + x)(y - x)(y - x)$
$= (y \cdot y + y \cdot x + x \cdot y + x \cdot x)(y \cdot y + y(-x) +$
$(-x)y + (-x)(-x))$
$= (y^2 + xy + xy + x^2)(y^2 - xy - xy + x^2)$
$= (y^2 + 2xy + x^2)(y^2 - 2xy + x^2)$
$= y^2(y^2 - 2xy + x^2) + 2xy(y^2 - 2xy + x^2) +$
$x^2(y^2 - 2xy + x^2)$
$= y^2 \cdot y^2 + y^2(-2xy) + y^2 \cdot x^2 + 2xy(y^2) +$
$2xy(-2xy) + 2xy \cdot x^2 + x^2 \cdot y^2 + x^2(-2xy) +$
$x^2 \cdot x^2$
$= y^4 - 2xy^3 + x^2y^2 + 2xy^3 - 4x^2y^2 + 2x^3y + x^2y^2 -$
$2x^3y + x^4$
$= y^4 + 2x^3y - 2x^3y + x^2y^2 - 4x^2y^2 + x^2y^2 - 2xy^2 +$
$2xy^3 + x^4$
$= y^4 - 2x^2y^2 + x^4$

60. Begin with a square with side = x. Cut out a 3 by 3 square from the corner. The small rectangle at the right has dimensions $(x - 3)$ and 3. Cut and move it to fit on bottom of square. The resulting rectangle has dimensions $(x - 3)$ and $(x + 3)$.

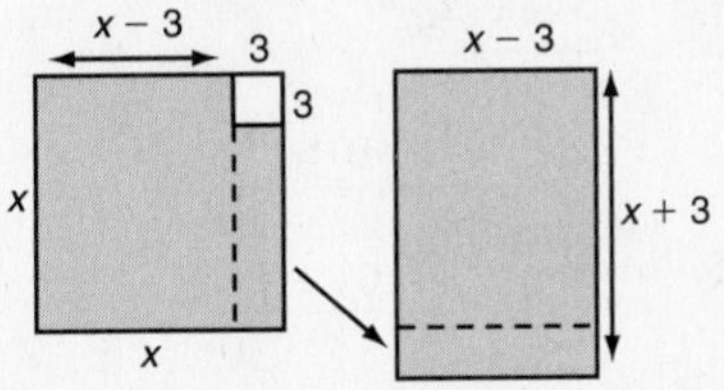

61a. $(a + b + c)^2$; $a^2 + 2ab + b^2 + 2ac + 2bc + c^2$

61b. $P = (a + b + c) + (a + b + c) + (a + b + c) +$
$(a + b + c)$
$= a + a + a + a + b + b + b + b + c + c + c + c$
$= 4a + 4b + 4c$

62a. Sample answer: Let x = amount invested at 6% and \$1500 − x = amount invested at 7%. The return can be expressed as $0.06x + 0.07(1500 - x)$.

62b.
$100 = 0.06x + 0.07(1500 - x)$
$100 = 0.06x + 105 - 0.07x$
$100 = -0.01x + 105$
$-5 = -0.01x$
$500 = x$
$1500 - x = 1500 - 500 = 1000$
\$1000 at 7%, \$500 at 6%

63a. $m\angle B$
$= \frac{1}{2}m\,\widehat{ADC}$
$= \frac{1}{2}(3x - 8 + 6x + 6)$
$= \frac{1}{2}(9x - 2)$

$m\angle A$
$= \frac{1}{2}m\,\widehat{BCD}$
$= \frac{1}{2}(4x + 8 + 6x + 6)$
$= \frac{1}{2}(10x + 14)$

ratio: $\dfrac{\frac{1}{2}(10x + 14)}{\frac{1}{2}(9x - 2)} = \dfrac{10x + 14}{9x - 2}$

63b.
$m\widehat{AB} + m\widehat{BC} + m\widehat{CD} + m\widehat{AD} = 360°$
$(6x + 2) + (4x + 8) + (6x + 6) + (3x - 8) = 360$
$6x + 4x + 6x + 3x + 2 + 8 + 6 - 8 = 360$
$19x + 8 = 360$
$19x = 352$
$x \approx 18.5$;
about 18.5°

64.

	x	x	y	y	y
x	x^2	x^2	xy	xy	xy
1	x	x	y	y	y
1	x	x	y	y	y
1	x	x	y	y	y
1	x	x	y	y	y
1	x	x	y	y	y

$2x^2 + 10x + 3xy + 15y$

65. $(p + q)^2 = \left(\frac{3}{4} + \frac{1}{4}\right)^2$

$p^2 = \left(\frac{3}{4}\right)^2 = \frac{9}{16}$ $\quad 2pq = 2\left(\frac{3}{4}\right)\left(\frac{1}{4}\right) = \frac{6}{16}$ $\quad q^2 = \left(\frac{1}{4}\right)^2 = \frac{1}{16}$

9 out of 16, RR; 6 out of 16, Rr; 1 out of 16, rr

66. $2(rk)^2(5rt^2) - k(2rk)(2rt)^2$
$= 2r^2k^2(5rt^2) - k(2rk)(4r^2t^2)$
$= 10k^2r^3t^2 - 8k^2r^3t^2$
$= 2k^2r^3t^2$

67.
$$\left[\begin{array}{ccc|c} 4 & -1 & 1 & 6 \\ 2 & 1 & 2 & 3 \\ 3 & -2 & 1 & 3 \end{array}\right] = \left[\begin{array}{ccc|c} 4 & -1 & 1 & 6 \\ -4 & 5 & 0 & -3 \\ 3 & -2 & 1 & 3 \end{array}\right]$$
$$= \left[\begin{array}{ccc|c} 1 & 1 & 0 & 3 \\ -4 & 5 & 0 & -3 \\ 3 & -2 & 1 & 3 \end{array}\right] = \left[\begin{array}{ccc|c} 1 & 1 & 0 & 3 \\ 0 & 9 & 0 & 9 \\ 3 & -2 & 1 & 3 \end{array}\right]$$
$$= \left[\begin{array}{ccc|c} 1 & 1 & 0 & 3 \\ 0 & 1 & 0 & 1 \\ 3 & -2 & 1 & 3 \end{array}\right] = \left[\begin{array}{ccc|c} 1 & 0 & 0 & 2 \\ 0 & 1 & 0 & 1 \\ 3 & -2 & 1 & 3 \end{array}\right]$$
$$= \left[\begin{array}{ccc|c} 1 & 0 & 0 & 2 \\ 0 & 1 & 0 & 1 \\ 0 & -2 & 1 & -3 \end{array}\right] = \left[\begin{array}{ccc|c} 1 & 0 & 0 & 2 \\ 0 & 1 & 0 & 1 \\ 0 & 0 & 1 & -1 \end{array}\right]; (2, 1, -1)$$

68. $\begin{bmatrix} 3 & -1 \\ 2 & 33 \end{bmatrix} \cdot \begin{bmatrix} x \\ y \end{bmatrix} = \begin{bmatrix} 5 \\ 29 \end{bmatrix}$

69. $\begin{bmatrix} 2 & -3 \\ 1 & 4 \end{bmatrix} \cdot \begin{bmatrix} -4 & 0 \\ 2 & 5 \end{bmatrix} = \begin{bmatrix} -8 + (-6) & 0 + (-15) \\ -4 + 8 & 0 + 20 \end{bmatrix}$

$= \begin{bmatrix} -14 & -15 \\ 4 & 20 \end{bmatrix}$

70. Let x = adults and y = students.

$x + y \le 150$ $\quad y \ge \frac{1}{2}x$ $\quad x \ge 0$ $\quad y \ge 0$

$y \le -x + 150$

vertices: (0, 0), (0, 150), (100, 50)

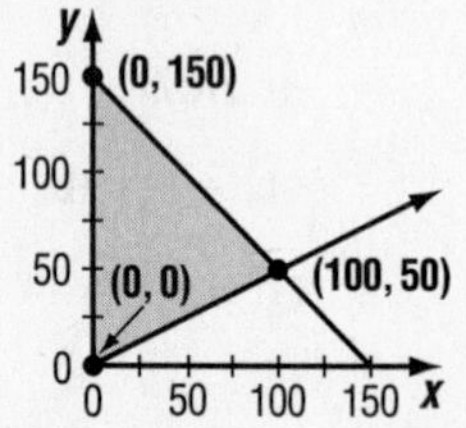

$f(x, y) = 2x + y$

(x, y)	$2x + y$	$f(x, y)$
(0, 0)	2(0) + 0	0
(0, 150)	2(0) + 150	150
(100, 50)	2(100) + 50	250

100 adults and 50 students

71. $x - 7y = -2$ $\quad 6x + 4y = 80$ $\quad x - 7y = -2$

$x = 7y - 2$ $\quad 6(7y - 2) + 4y = 80$ $\quad x - 7(2) = -2$

$42y - 12 + 4y = 80$ $\quad x - 14 = -2$

$46y - 12 = 80$ $\quad x = 12$

$46y = 92$ $\quad (12, 2)$

$y = 2$

72. $2x + 2y = -12$

$2y = -2x - 12$

$y = -x - 6$

$3x - 2y = -3$

$-2y = -3x - 3$

$y = \frac{3}{2}x + \frac{3}{2}$

$(-3, -3)$

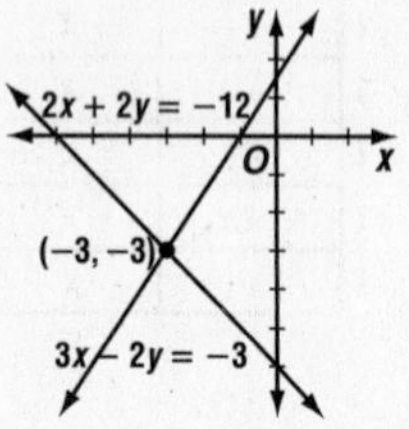

73. $4x - |y| \le 12$ $\qquad 4x - |y| \le 12$

$4(0) - |0| \overset{?}{\le} 12$ $\qquad 4(-1) - |-3| \overset{?}{\le} 12$

$0 - 0 \overset{?}{\le} 12$ $\qquad -4 - 3 \overset{?}{\le} 12$

$0 \le 12$; true $\qquad -7 \le 12$; true

$4x - |y| \le 12$

$4(4) - |0| \overset{?}{\le} 12$

$16 - 0 \overset{?}{\le} 12$

$16 \not\le 12$; false

(0, 0), (−1, −3)

74. $h(x) = \frac{3 + x}{4}$

$h(-7) = \frac{3 + (-7)}{4}$

$= \frac{-4}{4}$

$= -1$

75. 39, 39, 40, 41, 42, 44, 45, 46, 49

$\frac{39 + 39 + 40 + 41 + 42 + 44 + 45 + 46 + 49}{9} = \frac{385}{9}$

≈ 42.778; the 5th value is 42; 39

76. $I = prt$

$= (7500)(0.072)(5)$

$= 2700$; \$2700

5-3 Dividing Polynomials

Pages 270–271 Check for Understanding

1. $\underline{-1}\rfloor$ 5 1 0 −7

2. Each position in synthetic division represents a power of the variable. If you do not put in zeros, then an expression like $x^4 + x^2 + 2$ is written as 1 1 2. This represents $x^2 + x + 2$.

3. Jocelyn is correct. Because $(4x + 8) \div (x + 2) = 4$, regardless of the value of x.

4. See students' work.

5. $\frac{5xy^2 - 4xy + 7x^2y}{xy} = \frac{5xy^2}{xy} - \frac{4xy}{xy} + \frac{7x^2y}{xy}$

$= 5y - 4 + 7x$

6. $(6xy^2 - 3xy + 2x^2y)(xy)^{-1} = \frac{6xy^2 - 3xy + 2x^2y}{xy}$

$= \frac{6xy^2}{xy} - \frac{3xy}{xy} + \frac{2x^2y}{xy}$

$= 6y - 3 + 2x$

7. Quotient: $a - 12$

$a + 2\overline{)a^2 - 10a - 24}$

$\underline{a^2 + 2a}$

$-12a - 24$

$\underline{-12a - 24}$

0

8. Quotient: $3b + 5$

$3b - 2\overline{)9b^2 + 9b - 10}$

$\underline{9b^2 - 6b}$

$15b - 10$

$\underline{15b - 10}$

0

9. Quotient: $a^2 - ba + b^2$

$a + b\overline{)a^3 + 0a^2 + 0a + b^3}$

$\underline{a^3 + ba^2}$

$-ba^2 + 0a$

$\underline{-ba^2 - b^2a}$

$b^2a + b^3$

$\underline{b^2a + b^3}$

0

10. Quotient: $y^4 + 2y^3 + 4y^2 + 5y + 10$

$y - 2\overline{)y^5 + 0y^4 + 0y^3 - 3y^2 + 0y - 20}$

$\underline{y^5 - 2y^4}$

$2y^4 + 0y^3$

$\underline{2y^4 - 4y^3}$

$4y^3 - 3y^2$

$\underline{4y^3 - 8y^2}$

$5y^2 + 0y$

$\underline{5y^2 - 10y}$

$10y - 20$

$\underline{10y - 20}$

0

11. $\underline{-1}\rfloor$

3	−6	−2	1	−6	
	−3	9	−7	6	
3	−9	7	−6	0	$3x^3 - 9x^2 + 7x - 6$

12. $\underline{2}\rfloor$

1	−2	1	−3	2	
	2	0	2	−2	
1	0	1	−1	0	$t^3 + t - 1$

13. $(12x^2 + 36x + 15) \div (6x + 3) = \frac{12x^2 + 36x + 15}{6x + 3}$

$$= \frac{(12x^2 + 36x + 15) \div 6}{(6x + 3) \div 6}$$

$$= \frac{2x^2 + 6x + \frac{5}{2}}{x + \frac{1}{2}}$$

$$\begin{array}{r|rrr} -\frac{1}{2} & 2 & 6 & \frac{5}{2} \\ & & -1 & -\frac{5}{2} \\ \hline & 2 & 5 & 0 \end{array} \qquad 2x + 5$$

14.
$$\begin{array}{r|rrrr} -2 & 1 & 13 & -12 & -8 \\ & & -2 & -22 & 68 \\ \hline & 1 & 11 & -34 & 60 \end{array} \qquad x^2 + 11x - 34 + \frac{60}{x + 2}$$

Pages 271–273 Exercises

15. $\frac{8x^2y^3 - 28x^3y^2}{4xy^2} = \frac{8x^2y^3}{4xy^2} - \frac{28x^3y^2}{4xy^2}$

$= 2xy - 7x^2$

16. $\frac{2mn^3 + 4m^2 - 9m^3n^2}{mn} = \frac{2mn^3}{mn} + \frac{4m^2}{mn} - \frac{9m^3n^2}{mn}$

$= 2n^2 + \frac{4m}{n} - 9m^2n$

17. $(12rs^3 + 9r^2s^2 - 15r^2s) \div 3rs = \frac{12rs^3}{3rs} + \frac{9r^2s^2}{3rs} - \frac{15r^2s}{3rs}$

$= 4s^2 + 3rs - 5r$

18. $(28k^3p - 42kp^2 + 56kp^3) \div 14kp$

$= \frac{28k^3p}{14kp} - \frac{42kp^2}{14kp} + \frac{56kp^3}{14kp}$

$= 2k^2 - 3p + 4p^2$

19. $(a^3b^2 - a^2b + 2a)(-ab)^{-1} = \frac{a^3b^2}{-ab} - \frac{a^2b}{-ab} + \frac{2a}{-ab}$

$= -a^2b + a - \frac{2}{b}$

20.
$$\begin{array}{r l} & b^2 + 10b \\ b - 2 \,) & b^3 + 8b^2 - 20b \\ & \underline{b^3 - 2b^2} \\ & 10b^2 - 20b \\ & \underline{10b^2 - 20b} \\ & 0 \end{array}$$

21.
$$\begin{array}{r l} & x - 15 \\ x + 3 \,) & x^2 - 12x - 45 \\ & \underline{x^2 + 3x} \\ & -15x - 45 \\ & \underline{-15x - 45} \\ & 0 \end{array}$$

22.
$$\begin{array}{r l} & n^2 - 2n + 3 \\ n + 4 \,) & n^3 + 2n^2 - 5n + 12 \\ & \underline{n^3 + 4n^2} \\ & -2n^2 - 5n \\ & \underline{-2n^2 - 8n} \\ & 3n + 12 \\ & \underline{3n + 12} \\ & 0 \end{array}$$

23.
$$\begin{array}{r l} & g + 5 \\ g + 3 \,) & g^2 + 8g + 15 \\ & \underline{g^2 + 3g} \\ & 5g + 15 \\ & \underline{5g + 15} \\ & 0 \end{array}$$

24.
$$\begin{array}{r l} & 2b^2 - b - 1 + \frac{4}{b+1} \\ b + 1 \,) & 2b^3 + b^2 - 2b + 3 \\ & \underline{2b^3 + 2b^2} \\ & -b^2 - 2b \\ & \underline{-b^2 - b} \\ & -b + 3 \\ & \underline{-b - 1} \\ & 4 \end{array}$$

25.
$$\begin{array}{r l} & 3t^2 - 2t + 3 \\ 2t + 3 \,) & 6t^3 + 5t^2 + 0t + 9 \\ & \underline{6t^3 + 9t^2} \\ & -4t^2 + 0t \\ & \underline{-4t^2 - 6t} \\ & 6t + 9 \\ & \underline{6t + 9} \\ & 0 \end{array}$$

26.
$$\begin{array}{r l} & 5a - 7b \\ 10a + 14b \,) & 50a^2 + 0ab - 98b^2 \\ & \underline{50a^2 + 70ab} \\ & -70ab - 98b^2 \\ & \underline{-70ab - 98b^2} \\ & 0 \end{array}$$

27.
$$\begin{array}{r l} & 5y^2 - 4y + 4 - \frac{11}{y + 1} \\ y + 1 \,) & 5y^3 + y^2 + 0y - 7 \\ & \underline{5y^3 + 5y^2} \\ & -4y^2 + 0y \\ & \underline{-4y^2 - 4y} \\ & 4y - 7 \\ & \underline{4y + 4} \\ & -11 \end{array}$$

28.
$$\begin{array}{r l} & h^2 - 4h + 17 \\ 2h + 3 \,) & 2h^3 - 5h^2 + 22h + 51 \\ & \underline{2h^3 + 3h^2} \\ & -8h^2 + 22h \\ & \underline{-8h^2 - 12h} \\ & 34h + 51 \\ & \underline{34h + 51} \\ & 0 \end{array}$$

29.
$$\begin{array}{r l} & 2y + 7 + \frac{5}{y - 3} \\ y - 3 \,) & 2y^2 + y - 16 \\ & \underline{2y^2 - 6y} \\ & 7y - 16 \\ & \underline{7y - 21} \\ & 5 \end{array}$$

30.
$$\begin{array}{r l} & x^2 \\ x - 4 \,) & x^3 - 4x^2 \\ & \underline{x^3 - 4x^2} \\ & 0 \end{array}$$

31.
$$\begin{array}{r l} & x^2 + 3x + 9 \\ x - 3 \,) & x^3 + 0x^2 + 0x - 27 \\ & \underline{x^3 - 3x^2} \\ & 3x^2 + 0x \\ & \underline{3x^2 - 9x} \\ & 9x - 27 \\ & \underline{9x - 27} \\ & 0 \end{array}$$

32.
$$\begin{array}{r} 4x^2+2x+1 \\ 2x-1\overline{)8x^3+0x^2+0x-1} \\ \underline{8x^3-4x^2} \\ 4x^2+0x \\ \underline{4x^2-2x} \\ 2x-1 \\ \underline{2x-1} \\ 0 \end{array}$$

33. $\frac{9d^3+5d-8}{3d-2} = \frac{(9d^3+5d-8)\div 3}{(3d-2)\div 3}$

$= \frac{3d^3+\frac{5}{3}d-\frac{8}{3}}{d-\frac{2}{3}}$

$$\begin{array}{r|rrrr} \frac{2}{3} & 3 & 0 & \frac{5}{3} & -\frac{8}{3} \\ & & 2 & \frac{4}{3} & 2 \\ \hline & 3 & 2 & 3 & -\frac{2}{3} \end{array}$$

$\frac{-\frac{2}{3}}{d-\frac{2}{3}} = \frac{-2}{3d-2}$ $\quad 3d^2+2d+3-\frac{2}{3d-2}$

34. $\frac{m^3-7m+3m^2-21}{m+3} = \frac{m^3+3m^2-7m-21}{m+3}$

$$\begin{array}{r|rrrr} -3 & 1 & 3 & -7 & -21 \\ & & -3 & 0 & 21 \\ \hline & 1 & 0 & -7 & 0 \end{array}$$

m^2-7

35.
$$\begin{array}{r|rrrr} 2 & 2 & -3 & 3 & -4 \\ & & 4 & 2 & 10 \\ \hline & 2 & 1 & 5 & 6 \end{array}$$

$2c^2+c+5+\frac{6}{c-2}$

36. $(2x^3-x^2+5x-12)\div(2x-3)$

$= \frac{2x^3-x^2+5x-12}{2x-3}$

$= \frac{(2x^3-x^2+5x-12)\div 2}{(2x-3)\div 2}$

$= \frac{x^3-\frac{1}{2}x^2+\frac{5}{2}x-6}{x-\frac{3}{2}}$

$$\begin{array}{r|rrrr} \frac{3}{2} & 1 & -\frac{1}{2} & \frac{5}{2} & -6 \\ & & \frac{3}{2} & \frac{3}{2} & 6 \\ \hline & 1 & 1 & 4 & 0 \end{array}$$

x^2+x+4

37. $(w^2-w^3)(w-1)^{-1} = (-w^3+w^2)\div(w-1)$

$$\begin{array}{r|rrrr} 1 & -1 & 1 & 0 & 0 \\ & & -1 & 0 & 0 \\ \hline & -1 & 0 & 0 & 0 \end{array}$$

$-w^2$

38.
$$\begin{array}{r|rrrrrr} 2 & 6 & 0 & 0 & -18 & 0 & -120 \\ & & 12 & 24 & 48 & 60 & 120 \\ \hline & 6 & 12 & 24 & 30 & 60 & 0 \end{array}$$

$6w^4+12w^3+24w^2+30w+60$

39.
$$\begin{array}{r|rrrrr} 3 & 2 & -5 & 0 & -10 & 8 \\ & & 6 & 3 & 9 & -3 \\ \hline & 2 & 1 & 3 & -1 & 5 \end{array}$$

$2m^3+1m^2+3m-1+\frac{5}{m-3}$

40.
$$\begin{array}{r|rrrrr} -1 & 1 & -5 & -13 & 53 & 60 \\ & & -1 & 6 & 7 & -60 \\ \hline & 1 & -6 & -7 & 60 & 0 \end{array}$$

$a^3-6a^2-7a+60$

41.
$$\begin{array}{r|rrrrrr} -2 & 1 & 0 & 0 & 0 & 0 & 32 \\ & & -2 & 4 & -8 & 16 & -32 \\ \hline & 1 & -2 & 4 & -8 & 16 & 0 \end{array}$$

$y^4-2y^3+4y^2-8y+16$

42.
$$\begin{array}{r|rrrrrr} 2 & 1 & 0 & 0 & -3 & 0 & -20 \\ & & 2 & 4 & 8 & 10 & 20 \\ \hline & 1 & 2 & 4 & 5 & 10 & 0 \end{array}$$

$t^4+2t^3+4t^2+5t+10$

43. $(b+1)y = 2b^3+b^2-2b+3$

$y = \frac{2b^3+b^2-2b+3}{b+1}$

$$\begin{array}{r|rrrr} -1 & 2 & 1 & -2 & 3 \\ & & -2 & 1 & 1 \\ \hline & 2 & -1 & -1 & 4 \end{array}$$

$2b^2-b-1+\frac{4}{b+1}$

44a.
$$\begin{array}{r|rrrr} 2 & 3 & 0 & -5 & -2 \\ & & 6 & 12 & 14 \\ \hline & 3 & 6 & 7 & 12 \end{array}$$

$3x^2+6x+7+\frac{12}{x-2}$

$3x^3-5x-2 = 3(2)^3-5(2)-2$
$= 3(8)-10-2$
$= 24-10-2$
$= 12$

44b.
$$\begin{array}{r|rrrrr} -1 & 2 & 0 & -3 & 0 & 1 \\ & & -2 & 2 & 1 & -1 \\ \hline & 2 & -2 & -1 & 1 & 0 \end{array}$$

$2x^3-2x^2-x+1$

$2x^4-3x^2+1 = 2(-1)^4-3(-1)^2+1$
$= 2(1)-3(1)+1$
$= 2-3+1$
$= 0$

44c. $f(r)$ = the remainder

45. $(r-3)(r^2-6r+9)-1$
$= r(r^2-6r+9)-3(r^2-6r+9)-1$
$= r^3-6r^2+9r-3r^2+18r-27-1$
$= r^3-9r^2+27r-28$
$r^3-9r^2+27r-28$ and $r-3$

46a. execute program: 5 [ENTER] [(–)] 1 [ENTER] 2 [ENTER] 3 [ENTER] [(–)] 6 [ENTER] 6 [ENTER] [(–)] 8 [ENTER] 3 [ENTER]

$2x^4+x^3-7x^2+13x-21+\frac{24}{x+1}$

46b. execute program: 4 [ENTER] 3 [ENTER] 1 [ENTER] 2 [ENTER] [(–)] 7 [ENTER] 2 [ENTER] [(–)] 8 [ENTER]

$a^3+5a^2+8a+26+\frac{70}{a-3}$

46c. execute program: 5 ENTER 2 ENTER 1 ENTER 0 ENTER 0 ENTER (−) 3 ENTER 0 ENTER (−) 20 ENTER

$x^4 + 2x^3 + 4x^2 + 5x + 10$

47.
$$A = \ell \cdot w$$
$$32x^2 + x = (8x)\left(\frac{x}{2} + x + x + x + \frac{x}{2} + s\right)$$
$$32x^2 + x = (8x)(4x + s)$$
$$32x^2 + x = 8x \cdot 4x + 8x \cdot s$$
$$32x^2 + x = 32x^2 + 8xs$$
$$x = 8xs$$
$$\frac{x}{8x} = s$$
$$\frac{1}{8} = s; \frac{1}{8} \text{ inch}$$

48a.
$$\begin{array}{r} 170 - \frac{170}{t^2+1} \\ t^2 + 1\overline{)170t^2 + \quad 0} \\ \underline{170t^2 + 170} \\ -170 \end{array}$$

48b.
$$n = \frac{170t^2}{t^2+1}$$
$$= \frac{170(1)^2}{1^2+1}$$
$$= \frac{170}{2} = 85; \text{ 85 people}$$

48c.

Let $t = 5$.	Let $t = 10$.	Let $t = 100$.
$n = \frac{170t^2}{t^2+1}$	$n = \frac{170t^2}{t^2+1}$	$n = \frac{170t^2}{t^2+1}$
$= \frac{170(5)^2}{5^2+1}$	$= \frac{170(10)^2}{10^2+1}$	$= \frac{170(100)^2}{100^2+1}$
$= \frac{4250}{26}$	$= \frac{17000}{101}$	$= \frac{1{,}700{,}000}{10{,}001}$
≈ 163.46	≈ 168.32	≈ 169.98

It approaches 170.

49.
$$(a - b)^2 = (a - b)(a - b)$$
$$= a \cdot a + a(-b) + (-b)a + (-b)(-b)$$
$$= a^2 - ab - ab + b^2$$
$$= a^2 - 2ab + b^2$$

50.
$$t = \frac{d}{r}$$
$$= \frac{1.496 \times 10^8}{3 \times 10^5}$$
$$\approx 0.499 \times 10^3$$
$$\approx 4.99 \times 10^{-1} \times 10^3$$
$$\approx 4.99 \times 10^2$$

$$4.99 \times 10^2 = 499$$
$$499 \div 60 = 8.31\overline{6}$$
$$0.31\overline{6} \times 60 = 19$$

4.99×10^2 seconds or about 8 minutes 19 seconds

51.
$$\left[\begin{array}{ccc|c} 1 & 1 & 1 & -2 \\ 2 & -3 & 1 & -11 \\ -1 & 2 & -1 & 8 \end{array}\right] = \left[\begin{array}{ccc|c} 0 & 3 & 0 & 6 \\ 2 & -3 & 1 & -11 \\ -1 & 2 & -1 & 8 \end{array}\right]$$
$$= \left[\begin{array}{ccc|c} 0 & 3 & 0 & 6 \\ 1 & -1 & 0 & -3 \\ -1 & 2 & -1 & 8 \end{array}\right] = \left[\begin{array}{ccc|c} 3 & 0 & 0 & -3 \\ 1 & -1 & 0 & -3 \\ -1 & 2 & -1 & 8 \end{array}\right]$$
$$= \left[\begin{array}{ccc|c} 1 & 0 & 0 & -1 \\ 1 & -1 & 0 & -3 \\ -1 & 2 & -1 & 8 \end{array}\right] = \left[\begin{array}{ccc|c} 1 & 0 & 0 & -1 \\ 0 & -1 & 0 & -2 \\ -1 & 2 & -1 & 8 \end{array}\right]$$
$$= \left[\begin{array}{ccc|c} 1 & 0 & 0 & -1 \\ 0 & 1 & 0 & 2 \\ -1 & 2 & -1 & 8 \end{array}\right] = \left[\begin{array}{ccc|c} 1 & 0 & 0 & -1 \\ 0 & 1 & 0 & 2 \\ 0 & 2 & -1 & 7 \end{array}\right]$$
$$= \left[\begin{array}{ccc|c} 1 & 0 & 0 & -1 \\ 0 & 1 & 0 & 2 \\ 0 & 0 & -1 & 3 \end{array}\right] = \left[\begin{array}{ccc|c} 1 & 0 & 0 & -1 \\ 0 & 1 & 0 & 2 \\ 0 & 0 & 1 & -3 \end{array}\right]; (-1, 2, -3)$$

52.
$$\begin{bmatrix} -2 & 1 \\ 3 & -6 \\ 4 & 5 \end{bmatrix} \cdot \begin{bmatrix} 1 & 2 & -3 & 7 \\ -3 & 2 & 9 & -1 \end{bmatrix}$$
$$= \begin{bmatrix} -2 + (-3) & -4 + 2 & 6 + 9 & -14 + (-1) \\ 3 + 18 & 6 + (-12) & -9 + (-54) & 21 + 6 \\ 4 + (-15) & 8 + 10 & -12 + 45 & 28 + (-5) \end{bmatrix}$$
$$= \begin{bmatrix} -5 & -2 & 15 & -15 \\ 21 & -6 & -63 & 27 \\ -11 & 18 & 33 & 23 \end{bmatrix}$$

53.
$$f(x, y) = 5x - 2y$$
$$f(4, 1) = 5(4) - 2(1)$$
$$= 20 - 2$$
$$= 18$$

54.
$$2w = \ell + 2$$
$$2w - 2 = \ell$$

$$86 = 2\ell + 2w$$
$$86 = 2(2w - 2) + 2w$$
$$86 = 4w - 4 + 2w$$
$$86 = 6w - 4$$
$$90 = 6w$$
$$15 = w$$

$$2w - 2 = \ell$$
$$2(15) - 2 = \ell$$
$$30 - 2 = \ell$$
$$28 = \ell$$

15 inches by 28 inches

55.
$$h(x) = [\![3x + 7]\!]$$
$$h\left(-\frac{1}{2}\right) = \left[\!\left[3\left(-\frac{1}{2}\right) + 7\right]\!\right]$$
$$= \left[\!\left[-\frac{3}{2} + 7\right]\!\right]$$
$$= \left[\!\left[5\frac{1}{2}\right]\!\right]$$
$$= 5$$

56.
$$y - y_1 = m(x - x_1)$$
$$y - (-3) = -2(x - 5)$$
$$y + 3 = -2x + 10$$
$$y = -2x + 7$$

57. $|x - 7| = 13$

$x - 7 = 13$ or $x - 7 = -13$

$x = 20$ $\qquad x = -6$

5-4 Factoring

Page 278 Check for Understanding

1. $12x^2 - 8x - 15$
   $(6x + 5)(2x - 3)$; c
2. 1, 4, 9, 16, 25, 36, 49, 64, 81, 100; 1, 8, 27, 64, 125, 216, 343, 512, 729, 1000; Factoring patterns frequently involve squared or cubed numbers.
3. First factor the GCF: $2(x^2 - 3x - 10)$.
   Then factor the trinomial: $2(x - 5)(x + 2)$
4. $(b^3 + 4b) - (3b^2 + 12) = b(b^2 + 4) - 3(b^2 + 4)$
   $= (b^2 + 4)(b - 3)$; yes

5. $a^6 - b^6 = (a^2 - b^2)(a^4 + a^2b^2 + b^4)$
$= (a - b)(a + b)(a^2 + ab + b^2)(a^2 - ab + b^2)$
The factoring technique for difference of two squares results in two binomials, which are easier to factor.

6.

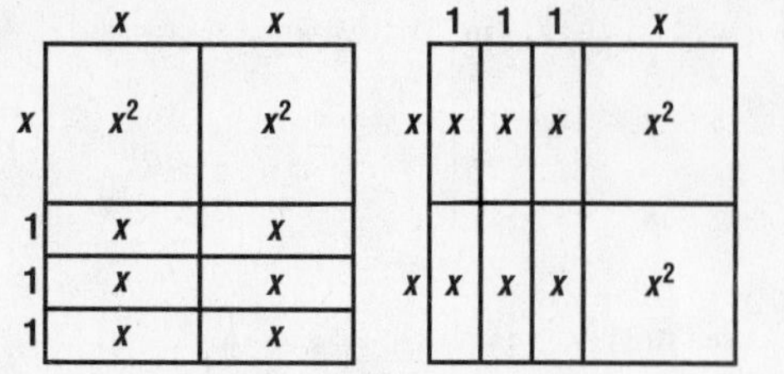

6a. distributive

6b. $2x(x + 3)$

7. $-15x^2 - 5x = -5x(3x + 1)$

8. $m^2 - 6m + 8 = (m - 4)(m - 2)$

9. $x^2 + xy + 3x = x(x + y + 3)$

10. $16r^2 - 169 = (4r + 13)(4r - 13)$

11. $y^2 - 3y - 10 = (y - 5)(y + 2)$

12. $a^2 + 5a + 6 = (a + 3)(a + 2)$

13. $3h^2 - 48 = 3(h^2 - 16)$
$= 3(h - 4)(h + 4)$

14. $2r^3 - 16s^3 = 2(r^3 - 8s^3)$
$= 2(r - 2s)(r^2 + 2rs + 4s^2)$

15. $g^3 + 8000 = (g + 20)(g^2 - 20g + 400)$

16. $21 - 7y + 3x - xy = (21 - 7y) + (3x - xy)$
$= 7(3 - y) + x(3 - y)$
$= (3 - y)(7 + x)$

17.
$$\begin{array}{r}
2y^2 + y - 1 \\
3y - 2\,\overline{)\,6y^3 - y^2 - 5y + 2} \\
\underline{6y^3 - 4y^2} \qquad\qquad \\
3y^2 - 5y \qquad \\
\underline{3y^2 - 2y} \qquad \\
-3y + 2 \\
\underline{-3y + 2} \\
0
\end{array}$$

yes, $2y^2 + y - 1$ or $(2y - 1)(y + 1)$

Pages 279–280 Exercises

18. prime

19. $10a^3b - 12a^2b^2 = 2a^2b(5a - 6b)$

20. $w^2 + 10w + 9 = (w + 1)(w + 9)$

21. prime

22. $3x^2 - 3y^2 = 3(x^2 - y^2)$
$= 3(x + y)(x - y)$

23. $y^2 - 12y + 20 = (y - 10)(y - 2)$

24. $12ab^3 - 8a^2b^2 + 10a^5b^3 = 2ab^2(6b - 4a + 5a^4b)$

25. $y^2 + 7y + 6 = (y + 6)(y + 1)$

26. $x^2 - 5x + 4 = (x - 4)(x - 1)$

27. $x^4 - y^2 = (x^2 + y)(x^2 - y)$

28. $6m^2 + 13m + 6 = (2m + 3)(3m + 2)$

29. $3n^2 + 21n - 24 = 3(n^2 + 7n - 8)$
$= 3(n + 8)(n - 1)$

30. $3ay^2 + 9a = 3a(y^2 + 3)$

31. $3a^2 - 27b^2 = 3(a^2 - 9b^2)$
$= 3(a - 3b)(a + 3b)$

32. $a^2 + 8ab + 16b^2 = (a + 4b)^2$

33. $5x - 14 + x^2 = x^2 + 5x - 14$
$= (x + 7)(x - 2)$

34. $2x^2 + 3x + 1 = (x + 1)(2x + 1)$

35. $5x^2 + 15x - 10 = 5(x^2 + 3x - 2)$

36. $2a^2 + 13a - 7 = (a + 7)(2a - 1)$

37. $3a^2 + 24a + 45 = 3(a^2 + 8a + 15)$
$= 3(a + 3)(a + 5)$

38. $12z^2 - z - 6 = (4z - 3)(3z + 2)$

39. prime

40. $8ax - 6x - 12a + 9 = (8ax - 6x) - (12a - 9)$
$= 2x(4a - 3) - 3(4a - 3)$
$= (4a - 3)(2x - 3)$

41. $4ax + 14ay - 10bx - 35by$
$= (4ax + 14ay) - (10bx + 35by)$
$= 2a(2x + 7y) - 5b(2x + 7y)$
$= (2x + 7y)(2a - 5b)$

42. $10w^2 - 14wv - 15w + 21v$
$= (10w^2 - 15w) - (14wv - 21v)$
$= 5w(2w - 3) - 7v(2w - 3)$
$= (2w - 3)(5w - 7v)$

43. $81y^2 - 49 = (9y + 7)(9y - 7)$

44. $6a^2 + 27a - 15 = 3(2a^2 + 9a - 5)$
$= 3(2a - 1)(a + 5)$

45. $2x^4 + 4x^3 + 2x^2 = 2x^2(x^2 + 2x + 1)$
$= 2x^2(x + 1)^2$

46. $m^4 - 1 = (m^2 + 1)(m^2 - 1)$
$= (m^2 + 1)(m + 1)(m - 1)$

47. $y^4 - 16 = (y^2 + 4)(y^2 - 4)$
$= (y^2 + 4)(y + 2)(y - 2)$

48. $7mx^2 + 2nx^2 - 7my^2 - 2ny^2$
$= (7mx^2 + 2nx^2) - (7my^2 + 2ny^2)$
$= x^2(7m + 2n) - y^2(7m + 2n)$
$= (7m + 2n)(x^2 - y^2)$
$= (7m + 2n)(x + y)(x - y)$

49. $8a^2 + 8ab + 8ac + 3a + 3b + 3c$
$= (8a^2 + 8ab + 8ac) + (3a + 3b + 3c)$
$= 8a(a + b + c) + 3(a + b + c)$
$= (a + b + c)(8a + 3)$

50. $5a^2x + 4aby + 3acz - 5abx - 4b^2y - 3bcz$
$= (5a^2x + 4aby + 3acz) - (5abx + 4b^2y + 3bcz)$
$= a(5ax + 4by + 3cz) - b(5ax + 4by + 3cz)$
$= (5ax + 4by + 3cz)(a - b)$

51. $3x^3 + 2x^2 - 5x + 9x^2y + 6xy - 15y$
$= (3x^3 + 2x^2 - 5x) + (9x^2y + 6xy - 15y)$
$= x(3x^2 + 2x - 5) + 3y(3x^2 + 2x - 5y)$
$= (3x^2 + 2x - 5)(x + 3y)$
$= (3x + 5)(x - 1)(x + 3y)$

52.
$$\begin{array}{r}
x + 12 \\
x - 4\,\overline{)\,x^2 + 8x + k} \\
\underline{x^2 - 4x} \qquad \\
12x + k \\
\underline{12x - 48} \\
k + 48
\end{array}$$

$k + 48 = 0$
$k = -48$

53. $\left(\frac{n^2+2n-15}{n^2+3n-10}\right)\cdot\left(\frac{n^2-9}{n^2-9n+14}\right)^{-1}$

$= \frac{n^2+2n-15}{n^2+3n-10}\cdot\frac{n^2-9n+14}{n^2-9}$

$= \frac{(n+5)(n-3)}{(n+5)(n-2)}\cdot\frac{(n-7)(n-2)}{(n-3)(n+3)}$

$= \frac{n-7}{n+3}$

54.

$$\begin{array}{rl}
 & m \quad + \quad k-3 \\
m-k+3 \,\big) & m^2 + 0mk + 0m - k^2 + 6k - 9 \\
 & \underline{m^2 - mk + 3m} \\
 & \quad mk - 3m - k^2 + 6k \\
 & \quad \underline{mk \qquad - k^2 + 3k} \\
 & \qquad -3m \quad + 3k - 9 \\
 & \qquad \underline{-3m \quad + 3k - 9} \\
 & \qquad\qquad\qquad 0
\end{array}$$

55. [Y=] [X,T,θ,n] [x²] [+] 6 [X,T,θ,n] [+] 9 [ENTER] [(] [X,T,θ,n] [+] 3 [)] [(] [X,T,θ,n] [+] 3 [)] [ZOOM] 6

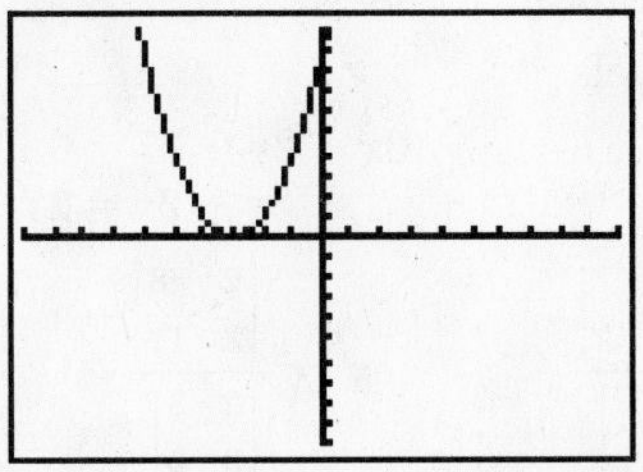

correct

56. [Y=] 3 [X,T,θ,n] [x²] [+] 5 [X,T,θ,n] [+] 2 [ENTER] [(] 3 [X,T,θ,n] [+] 2 [)] [(] [X,T,θ,n] [+] 1 [)] [ZOOM] 6

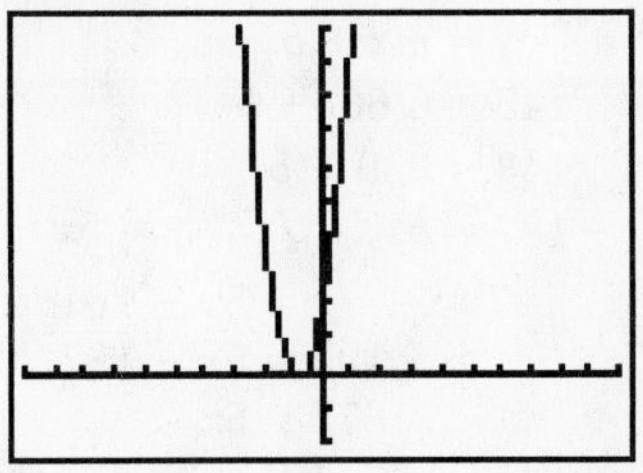

correct

57. [Y=] [X,T,θ,n] [^] 3 [+] 8 [ENTER] [(] [X,T,θ,n] [+] 2 [)] [(] [X,T,θ,n] [x²] [−] [X,T,θ,n] [+] 4 [)] [WINDOW] [▼] [(−)] 5 [ENTER] 5 [ENTER] 1 [ENTER] [(−)] 5 [ENTER] 20 [ENTER] 1 [GRAPH]

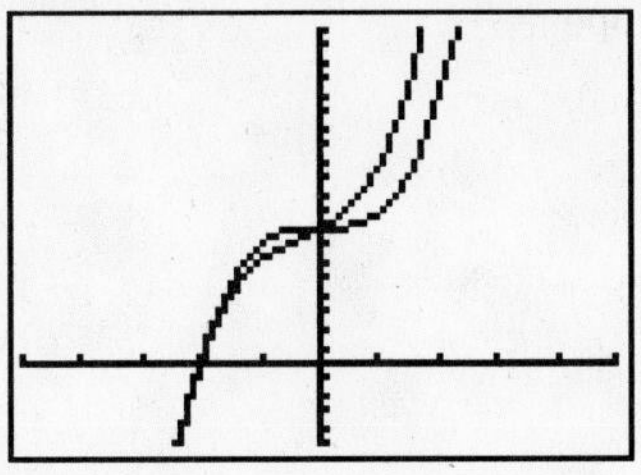

(Continued next column)

incorrect; $x^3 + 8 = (x+2)(x^2 - 2x + 4)$

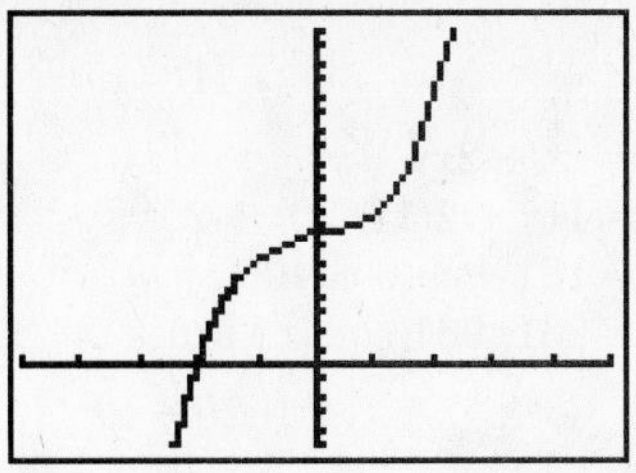

58. [Y=] 3 [X,T,θ,n] [x²] [−] 48 [ENTER] 3 [(] [X,T,θ,n] [+] 4 [)] [(] [X,T,θ,n] [−] 4 [)] [WINDOW] [▼] [(−)] 10 [ENTER] 10 [ENTER] 1 [ENTER] [(−)] 50 [ENTER] 5 [ENTER] 5 [GRAPH]

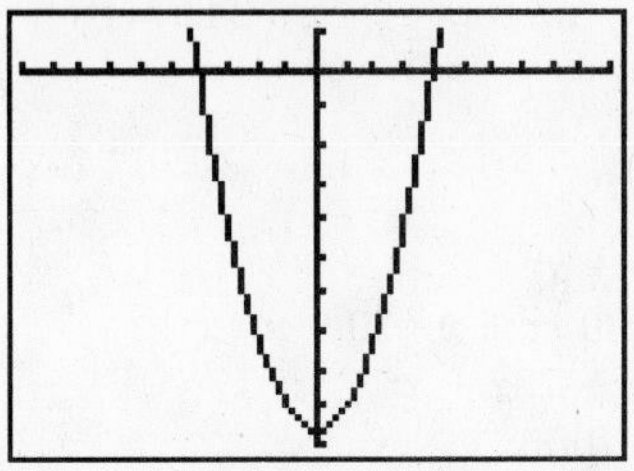

correct

59. [Y=] 2 [X,T,θ,n] [x²] [−] 5 [X,T,θ,n] [−] 3 [ENTER] [(] [X,T,θ,n] [−] 1 [)] [(] 2 [X,T,θ,n] [+] 3 [)] [WINDOW] [▼] [(−)] 5 [ENTER] 10 [ENTER] 1 [ENTER] [(−)] 10 [ENTER] 10 [ENTER] 1 [GRAPH]

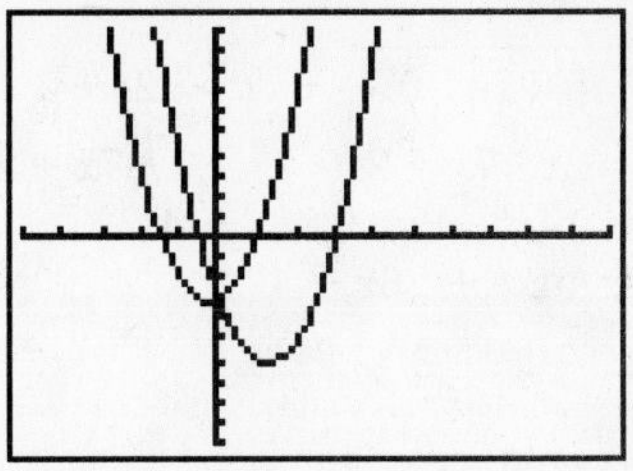

incorrect; $2x^2 - 5x - 3 = (2x+1)(x-3)$

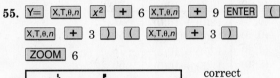

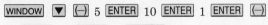

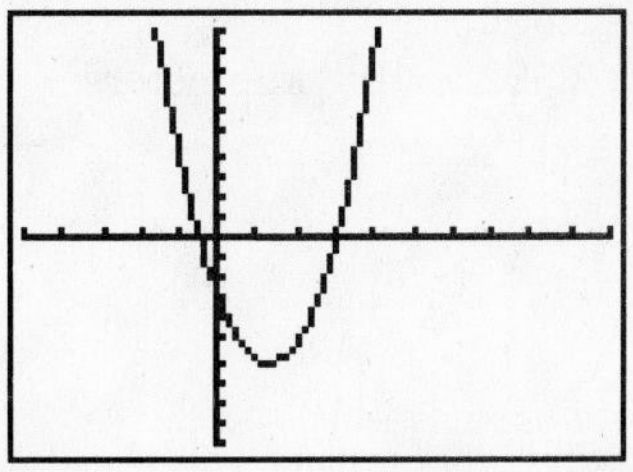

60. $49p^{2n} + 14p^n + 1 = (7p^n + 1)(7p^n + 1)$
$= (7p^n + 1)^2$

61a. square I: $A = s^2$; $y^2 = s^2$; $y = s$ square II: $P = 4s$; $4x = 4s$; $x = s$

square III: side = $x + y$

$A = (x+y)^2$
$= (x+y)(x+y)$
$= x \cdot x + x \cdot y + y \cdot x + y \cdot y$
$= x^2 + xy + xy + y^2$
$= x^2 + 2xy + y^2$;
$(x^2 + 2xy + y^2)$ square units

61b. square I: $A = y^2$; $400 = y^2$; $20 = y$

square II: $P = 4x$; $44 = 4x$; $11 = x$

square III: $A = x^2 + 2xy + y^2$
$= 11^2 + 2(11)(20) + 20^2$
$= 121 + 440 + 400$
$= 961$; 961 square units

62a. $A = b \cdot h$
$= 100 \cdot 70$
$= 7000$;
7000 square meters

$P = 2b + 2h$
$= 2(100) + 2(70)$
$= 200 + 140$
$= 340$; 340 meters

62b. $b = 100 + 1$
$= 101$
$h = 70 + 1$
$= 71$

$A = b \cdot h$
$= 101 \cdot 71$
$= 7171$;
7171 square meters

$P = 2b + 2h$
$= 2(101) + 2(71)$
$= 202 + 142$
$= 344$;
344 meters

62c. $b = 100 + x$
$h = 70 + x$
$A = b \cdot h$
$= (100 + x)(70 + x)$
$= 100 \cdot 70 + 100 \cdot x + x \cdot 70 + x \cdot x$
$= 7000 + 100x + 70x + x^2$
$= x^2 + 170x + 7000$;
$(x^2 + 170x + 7000)$ square meters

$P = 2b + 2h$
$= 2(100 + x) + 2(70 + x)$
$= 200 + 2x + 140 + 2x$
$= 340 + 4x$; $(340 + 4x)$ meters

63.
$$\begin{array}{r|rrrr} -2 & 1 & 0 & -3 & 2 \\ & & -2 & 4 & -2 \\ \hline & 1 & -2 & 1 & 0 \end{array} \qquad t^2 - 2t + 1$$

64. $(2x + 4)(7x - 1) = 2x \cdot 7x + 2x(-1) + 4 \cdot 7x + 4(-1)$
$= 14x^2 - 2x + 28x - 4$
$= 14x^2 + 26x - 4$

65. $\frac{300{,}000 \text{ km}}{\text{sec}} \times \frac{60 \text{ sec}}{\text{min}} \times \frac{60 \text{ min}}{\text{hr}} \times \frac{24 \text{ hr}}{\text{day}}$
$= 25{,}920{,}000{,}000$ km/day
$25{,}920{,}000{,}000 = 2.592 \times 10{,}000{,}000{,}000$
$= 2.592 \times 10^{10}$;
2.592×10^{10} kilometers

66. $\begin{bmatrix} 5 & 4 \\ 3 & -5 \end{bmatrix} \cdot \begin{bmatrix} x \\ y \end{bmatrix} = \begin{bmatrix} -3 \\ -24 \end{bmatrix}$

$\begin{bmatrix} 5x + 4y \\ 3x - 5y \end{bmatrix} = \begin{bmatrix} -3 \\ -24 \end{bmatrix}$

$5x + 4y = -3$
$3x - 5y = -24$

67. $-2\begin{bmatrix} \frac{1}{2} & 3 \\ 5 & 7 \end{bmatrix} + \begin{bmatrix} 1 & 2 \\ 3 & 4 \end{bmatrix} = \begin{bmatrix} -1 & -6 \\ -10 & -14 \end{bmatrix} + \begin{bmatrix} 1 & 2 \\ 3 & 4 \end{bmatrix}$
$= \begin{bmatrix} 0 & -4 \\ -7 & -10 \end{bmatrix}$

68. Let x = rockers and y = swivels.

$2x + 4y \le 20$
$4y \le -2x + 20$
$y \le -\frac{1}{2}x + 5$

$3x + y \le 15$
$y \le -3x + 15$

$x \ge 0$
$y \ge 0$

vertices: (0, 0), (0, 5), (4, 3), (5, 0)

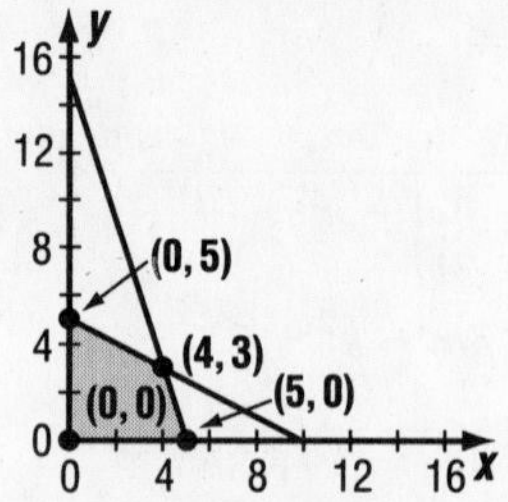

$f(x, y) = 12x + 10y$

(x, y)	$12x + 10y$	$f(x, y)$
(0, 0)	12(0) + 10(0)	0
(0, 5)	12(0) + 10(5)	50
(4, 3)	12(4) + 10(3)	78
(5, 0)	12(5) + 10(0)	60

4 rockers, 3 swivels

69. $2x + 3y - 8 = 0$
$2x + 3y = 8$

$3x + 2y - 17 = 0$
$3x + 2y = 17$

$x = \dfrac{\begin{vmatrix} 8 & 3 \\ 17 & 2 \end{vmatrix}}{\begin{vmatrix} 2 & 3 \\ 3 & 2 \end{vmatrix}} = \dfrac{16 - 51}{4 - 9} = \dfrac{-35}{-5} = 7$

$y = \dfrac{\begin{vmatrix} 2 & 8 \\ 3 & 17 \end{vmatrix}}{\begin{vmatrix} 2 & 3 \\ 3 & 2 \end{vmatrix}} = \dfrac{34 - 24}{4 - 9} = \dfrac{10}{-5} = -2$

(7, −2)

70a. $m = \frac{143 - 153}{66 - 68}$
$= \frac{-10}{-2}$
$= 5$

$y = mx + b$
$143 = 5(66) + b$
$143 = 330 + b$
$-187 = b$

$y = 5x - 187$

70b. $y = 5x - 187$
$= 5(71) - 187$
$= 355 - 187$
$= 168$; 168 pounds

70c. $y = 5x - 187$
$190 = 5x - 187$
$377 = 5x$
$75.4 = x$; 75.4 inches

71. $2x + 3y - 1 = 4$
$2x + 3y = 5$
$3y = -2x + 5$
$y = -\frac{2}{3}x + \frac{5}{3}$

perpendicular slope $= \frac{3}{2}$

$y - y_1 = m(x - x_1)$
$y - 2 = \frac{3}{2}(x - 2)$
$y - 2 = \frac{3}{2}x - 3$
$y = \frac{3}{2}x - 1$

72. $a + 5a^2$

73. distributive

5-5 Roots of Real Numbers

Pages 284–285 Check for Understanding

1. An absolute value is not necessary if the root is a positive number, regardless of the value of the variable.
2. Taking the nth root and raising to the nth power are inverse operations.
3. The index is odd and the radicand is less than 0; there is one negative root: -2.

4a. No, if $x < 0$, then $\sqrt[4]{(-x)^4} = -x$.

4b. No, if $x < 0$, then $\sqrt[5]{(-x)^5} = -x$.

5. See table below.

6. $\sqrt{99} \approx 9.950$

7. $-\sqrt[3]{23} \approx -2.844$

8. $\sqrt[4]{64} \approx 2.828$

9. $\sqrt{(-3)^2} = \sqrt{9}$
$= \sqrt{3^2}$
$= 3$

10. $\sqrt[3]{27} = \sqrt[3]{3^3}$
$= 3$

11. $\sqrt[5]{-32} = \sqrt[5]{(-2)^5}$
$= -2$

12. $\sqrt[4]{-10{,}000}$
no real roots

13. $\sqrt[3]{m^3} = m$

14. $\sqrt[4]{x^4} = |x|$

15. $-\sqrt{25x^6} = -\sqrt{(5x^3)^2}$
$= -5|x^3|$

16. $\sqrt{25x^2y^4} = \sqrt{(5xy^2)^2}$
$= 5|x|y^2$

17. $\sqrt{(3m - 2n)^2} = |3m - 20|$

18. $\sqrt[5]{32} = \sqrt[5]{2^5}$
$= 2$

19. $\sqrt[3]{-125} = \sqrt[3]{(-5)^3}$
$= -5$

Pages 285–287 Exercises

20. $\sqrt{121} = 11$

21. $-\sqrt{144} = -12$

22. $\sqrt[3]{65} \approx 4.021$

23. $\sqrt{0.81} = 0.9$

24. $\sqrt[3]{-670} \approx -8.750$

25. $\sqrt[4]{625} = 5$

26. $\sqrt[7]{82{,}567} \approx 5.040$

27. $\sqrt[6]{(345)^3} \approx 18.574$

28. $\sqrt[4]{(3600)^2} = 60$

29. $\sqrt{16} = \sqrt{4^2}$
$= 4$

30. $\pm\sqrt{121} = \pm\sqrt{11^2}$
$= \pm 11$

31. $\sqrt{196} = \sqrt{14^2}$
$= 14$

32. $\sqrt{-(-6)^2} = \sqrt{-36}$
no real roots

33. $\sqrt[4]{81} = \sqrt[4]{3^4}$
$= 3$

34. $-\sqrt{121} = -\sqrt{11^2}$
$= -11$

35. $\sqrt[4]{\left(-\frac{1}{2}\right)^4} = \sqrt[4]{\frac{1}{16}}$
$= \sqrt[4]{\left(\frac{1}{2}\right)^4}$
$= \frac{1}{2}$

36. $\sqrt[3]{-27} = \sqrt[3]{(-3)^3}$
$= -3$

37. $\sqrt[3]{1000} = \sqrt[3]{10^3}$
$= 10$

38. $\sqrt{0.36} = \sqrt{0.6^2}$
$= 0.6$

39. $\sqrt[3]{-0.125} = \sqrt[3]{(-0.5)^3}$
$= -0.5$

40. $\sqrt[7]{-1} = \sqrt[7]{(-1)^7}$
$= -1$

41. $\sqrt[3]{y^3} = y$

42. $\sqrt[4]{t^8} = \sqrt[4]{(t^2)^4}$
$= t^2$

43. $-\sqrt[4]{x^4} = -|x|$

44. $\sqrt{(5f)^4} = \sqrt{625f^4}$
$= \sqrt{(25f^2)^2}$
$= 25f^2$

45. $\sqrt{36g^6} = \sqrt{(6g^3)^2}$
$= 6|g^3|$

46. $\sqrt{64h^8} = \sqrt{(8h^4)^2}$
$= 8h^4$

47. $\sqrt[3]{m^6n^9z^{12}} = \sqrt[3]{(m^2n^3z^4)^3}$
$= m^2n^3z^4$

48. $\sqrt[3]{8b^3c^3} = \sqrt[3]{(2bc)^3}$
$= 2bc$

49. $\sqrt[3]{-27a^9b^{12}} = \sqrt[3]{(-3a^3b^4)^3}$
$= -3a^3b^4$

50. $\pm\sqrt{(a^3 + 2)^2} = \pm|a^3 + 2|$

51. $\sqrt[3]{(s + t)^3} = s + t$

52. $\sqrt{(3x + y)^2} = |3x + y|$

53. $-\sqrt{x^2 + 2x + 1} = -\sqrt{(x + 1)^2}$
$= -|x + 1|$

5. (From above)

Powers	In words	Roots	In words
$2^3 = 2 \cdot 2 \cdot 2 = 8$	2 cubed is 8.	$\sqrt[3]{8} = \sqrt[3]{2 \cdot 2 \cdot 2} = 2$	The cube root of 8 is 2.
$8^4 = 4096$	8 to the fourth power is 4096.	$\sqrt[4]{4096} = 8$	A fourth root of 4096 is 8.
$7^5 = 16{,}807$	7 to the fifth power is 16,807.	$\sqrt[5]{16{,}807} = 7$	The fifth root of 16,807 is 7.
$3^6 = 729$	3 to the sixth power is 729.	$\sqrt[6]{729} = 3$	A sixth root of 729 is 3.
$a^n = b$	a to the nth power is b.	$\sqrt[n]{b} = a$	An nth root of b is a.

54. $\sqrt{x^2 + 6x + 9} = \sqrt{(x + 3)^2}$
$= |x + 3|$

55. $\pm\sqrt{s^2 - 2st + t^2} = \pm\sqrt{(s - t)^2}$
$= \pm|s - t|$

56. $\sqrt[5]{-(2m - 3n)^5} = -(2m - 3n)$

57. $\sqrt{-4y^2 - 12y - 9} = \sqrt{-1(4y^2 + 12y + 9)}$
no real roots

58. $\pm\sqrt{16m^2 - 24mn + 9n^2} = \pm\sqrt{(4m - 3n)^2}$
$= \pm|4m - 3n|$

59. $\sqrt{x^2 + y^2} = x + y$
$x^2 + y^2 = (x + y)^2$
$x^2 + y^2 = (x + y)(x + y)$
$x^2 + y^2 = x^2 + 2xy + y^2$
$0 = 2xy$
$0 = xy$
$0 = x$ or $0 = y$

60. $9.8 \div 2 = 4.9$
$N = \frac{1}{2\pi}\sqrt{\frac{a}{r}}$
$= \frac{1}{2\pi}\sqrt{\frac{4.9}{25}}$
$= \frac{1}{2\pi}\sqrt{0.196}$
$\approx \frac{1}{2\pi}(0.443)$
≈ 0.07 rot/sec
$0.07 \times 60 = 4.2$
4.2 rotations per minute

61. $c = \sqrt{a^2 + b^2}$
$= \sqrt{90^2 + 90^2}$
$= \sqrt{8100 + 8100}$
$= \sqrt{16{,}200}$
≈ 127.3; 127.3 feet

62. $25 - 5 = 20$
$t = \sqrt{\frac{2d}{g}}$
$= \sqrt{\frac{2(20)}{32.2}}$
$= \sqrt{\frac{40}{32.2}}$
$\approx \sqrt{1.242}$
≈ 1.11; 1.11 seconds

63. $\sqrt{(5b)^4} = \sqrt{625b^4}$
$= \sqrt{(25b^2)^2}$
$= 25b^2$

64. $(2p + q^3)^2 = (2p + q^3)(2p + q^3)$
$= 2p \cdot 2p + 2p \cdot q^3 + q^3 \cdot 2p + q^3 \cdot q^3$
$= 4p^2 + 2pq^3 + 2pq^3 + q^6$
$= 4p^2 + 4pq^3 + q^6$

65. $y^2x^{-3}(yx^4 + y^{-1}x^3 + y^{-2}x^2)$
$= y^2x^{-3} \cdot yx^4 + y^2x^{-3} \cdot y^{-1}x^3 + y^2x^{-3} \cdot y^{-2}x^2$
$= xy^3 + y + \frac{1}{x}$

66. $1.28(3 \times 10^5) = (1.28 \times 3) \times 10^5$
$= 3.48 \times 10^5$; 3.48×10^5 kilometers

67. $\begin{vmatrix} 5 & 7 \\ -2 & 2x \end{vmatrix} = 54$
$10x + 14 = 54$
$10x = 40$
$x = 4$

68. $\begin{bmatrix} 5 & -2 \\ \frac{1}{2} & -3 \end{bmatrix} \cdot \begin{bmatrix} 2 \\ 1 \end{bmatrix} = \begin{bmatrix} 10 + (-2) \\ 1 + (-3) \end{bmatrix}$
$= \begin{bmatrix} 8 \\ -2 \end{bmatrix}$

69. $y \geq x \quad y \leq x + 5 \quad x \geq -3 \quad y + 2x \leq 5$
$y \leq -2x + 5$
vertices: $(-3, -3)$, $(-3, 2)$, $(0, 5)$, $\left(\frac{5}{3}, \frac{5}{3}\right)$

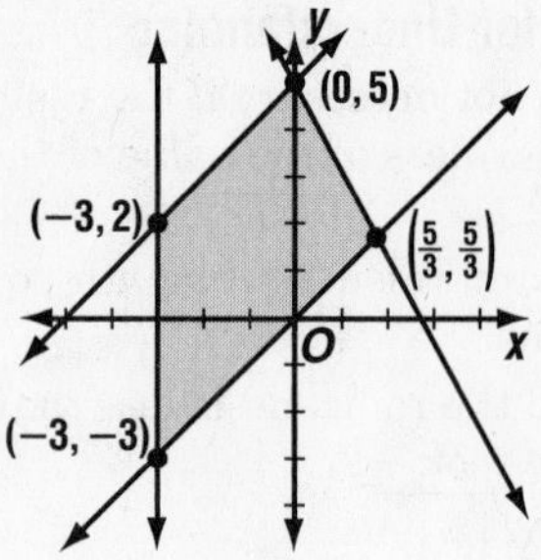

$f(x, y) = x - 2y$

(x, y)	$x - 2y$	$f(x, y)$
$(-3, -3)$	$-3 - 2(-3)$	3
$(-3, 2)$	$-3 - 2(2)$	-7
$(0, 5)$	$0 - 2(5)$	-10
$\left(\frac{5}{3}, \frac{5}{3}\right)$	$\frac{5}{3} - 2\left(\frac{5}{3}\right)$	$-\frac{5}{3}$

max: $f(-3, -3) = 3$
min: $f(0, 5) = -10$

70. $2x + 3y = -16$
$3y = -2x - 16$
$y = -\frac{2}{3}x - \frac{16}{3}$
$2y = 4x$
$y = 2x$

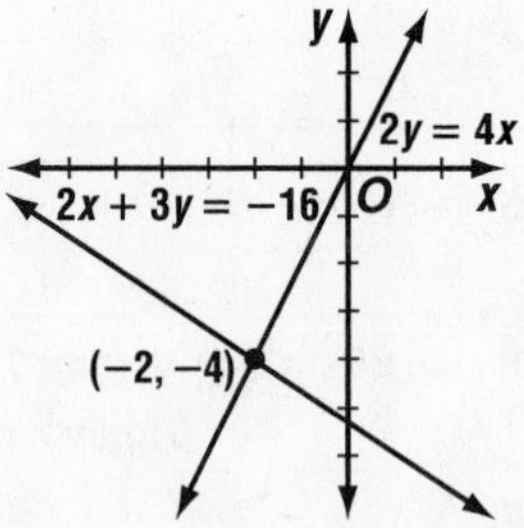

71. $b = 2[a] - 3$

a	$2[a] - 3$	b
0	$2[0] - 3$	-3
$\frac{1}{2}$	$2\left[\frac{1}{2}\right] - 3$	-3
1	$2[1] - 3$	-1
$1\frac{1}{2}$	$2\left[1\frac{1}{2}\right] - 3$	-1
2	$2[2] - 3$	1

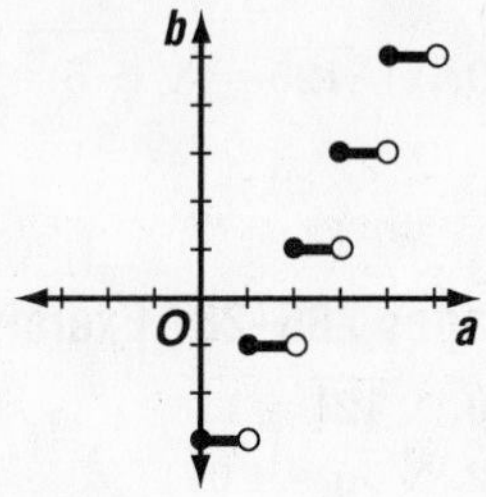

72. $b = 2a - 3$
$b = 2(0) - 3$
$b = -3$
$(0, 3)$

$b = 2a - 3$
$0 = 2a - 3$
$3 = 2a$
$\frac{3}{2} = a$
$\left(\frac{3}{2}, 0\right)$

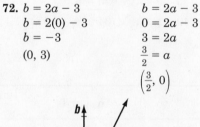

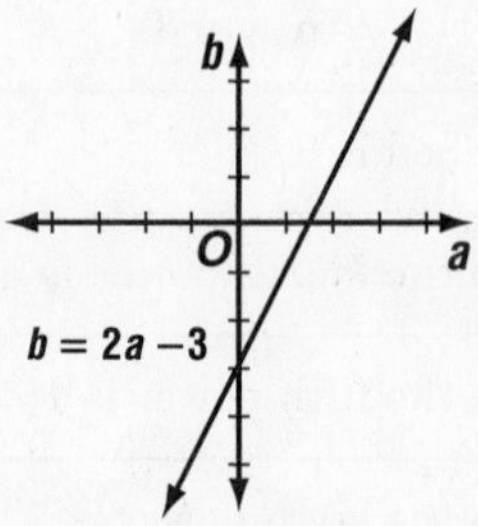

73a. 12–17 years: 0.3, 0.6, 0.8, 1.3, 3.3, 4.4, 8.1, 17.7, 62.6

$\frac{0.3 + 0.6 + 0.8 + 1.3 + 3.3 + 4.4 + 8.1 + 17.7 + 62.6}{9}$

$= \frac{99.1}{9} \approx 11.0$; middle value is 5th value, 3.3

18–29 years: 0.3, 0.4, 0.7, 1.8, 1.9, 7.5, 7.8, 14.2, 55.9

$\frac{0.3 + 0.4 + 0.7 + 1.8 + 1.9 + 7.5 + 7.8 + 14.2 + 55.9}{9}$

$= \frac{90.5}{9} \approx 10.1$; middle value is 5th value, 1.9

73b. 12–17 years: 1.9, 2.2, 2.8, 3.1, 6.4, 18.1

$\frac{1.9 + 2.2 + 2.8 + 3.1 + 6.4 + 18.1}{6} = \frac{34.5}{6} \approx 5.8$;

middle value between 3rd and 4th values,

$\frac{2.8 + 3.1}{2} \approx 3.0$

18–29 years: 1.2, 3.2, 3.4, 4.1, 6.8, 29.0;

$\frac{1.2 + 3.2 + 3.4 + 4.1 + 6.8 + 29.0}{6} = \frac{47.7}{6} \approx 8.0$;

middle value between 3rd and 4th values,

$\frac{3.4 + 4.1}{2} \approx 3.8$

73c. Sample answer: Teens have more leisure time than adults.

Page 287 Self Test

1. $93{,}000{,}000 = 9.3 \times 10{,}000{,}000$
$= 9.3 \times 10^7$; 9.3×10^7 miles

2. $8mn^{-5} = 8m \cdot \frac{1}{n^5}$
$= \frac{8m}{n^5}$

3. $(-3x^2y)^3(2x)^2 = (-3)^3(x^2)^3(y)^3(2)^2(x)^2$
$= -27 \cdot x^{2 \cdot 3} \cdot y^3 \cdot 4 \cdot x^2$
$= -27 \cdot 4 \cdot x^6 \cdot x^2 \cdot y^3$
$= -108x^{6+2}y^3$
$= -108\,x^8y^3$

4. $(9x + 2y) - (7x - 3y) = 9x + 2y - 7x + 3y$
$= 9x - 7x + 2y + 3y$
$= 2x + 5y$

5. $(n + 2)(n^2 - 3n + 1)$
$= n(n^2 - 3n + 1) + 2(n^2 - 3n + 1)$
$= n \cdot n^2 + n(-3n) + n \cdot 1 + 2 \cdot n^2 + 2(-3n) + 2 \cdot 1$
$= n^3 - 3n^2 + n + 2n^2 - 6n + 2$
$= n^3 - 3n^2 + 2n^2 + n - 6n + 2$
$= n^3 - n^2 - 5n + 2$

6.

$$
\begin{array}{r}
d^2 + d - 3 \\
2d^2 - 3\overline{)2d^4 + 2d^3 - 9d^2 - 3d + 9} \\
\underline{2d^4 \qquad - 3d^2} \qquad\qquad \\
2d^3 - 6d^2 - 3d \qquad \\
\underline{2d^3 \qquad - 3d} \qquad \\
-6d^2 \qquad + 9 \\
\underline{-6d^2 \qquad + 9} \\
0
\end{array}
$$

7.

$$
\begin{array}{r|rrrr}
4 & 1 & -4 & -3 & -7 \\
 & & 4 & 0 & -12 \\
\hline
 & 1 & 0 & -3 & -19
\end{array}
\qquad m^2 - 3 - \frac{19}{m - 4}
$$

8. $ax^2 + 6ax + 9a = a(x^2 + 6x + 9)$
$= a(x + 3)^2$

9. $8r^3 - 64s^6 = 8(r^3 - 8s^6)$
$= 8(r - 2s^2)(r^2 + 2rs^2 + 4s^4)$

10. $\sqrt[3]{-64a^6b^9} = \sqrt[3]{(-4a^2b^3)^3}$
$= -4a^2b^3$

11. $\sqrt{4n^2 + 12n + 9} = \sqrt{(2n + 3)^2}$
$= |2n + 3|$

5-6 Radical Expressions

Pages 292–293 Check for Understanding

1. Multiply by $\frac{\sqrt[3]{ac^2}}{\sqrt[3]{ac^2}}$

2. The first and second terms do not have the same index. The second and third terms do not have the same radicand. The first and third terms do not have the same index or radicand.

3. Answers will vary.

4. The product of two conjugates yields the difference of two squares. Each square would produce a rational number and the difference of two rationals is a rational.

5. If a and b were allowed to be negative when n is even, they would have no real roots. a and b may be negative when n is odd because negative radicands can have real roots if n is odd.

6. Use = because if c ≠ 0, then $\sqrt[n]{\frac{1}{c}} = \frac{\sqrt[n]{1}}{\sqrt[n]{c}} = \frac{1}{\sqrt[n]{c}}$.

7a. $a^2 + b^2 = c^2$
$1^2 + 3^2 = c^2$
$10 = c^2$
$\sqrt{10} = c$

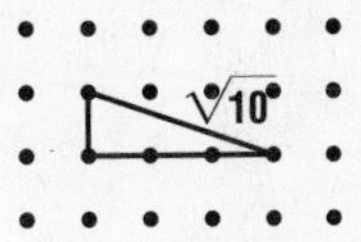

7b. $a^2 + b^2 = c^2$
$2^2 + 3^2 = c^2$
$13 = c^2$
$\sqrt{13} = c$

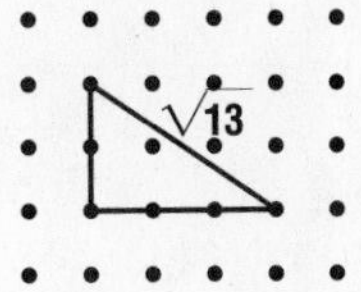

7c. $a^2 + b^2 = c^2$
$1^2 + 4^2 = c^2$
$17 = c^2$
$\sqrt{17} = c$

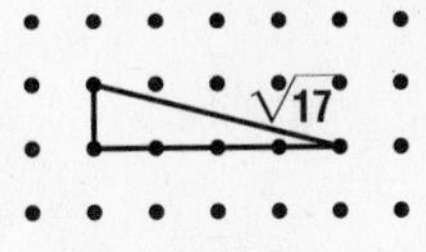

7d. $a^2 + b^2 = c^2$
$2^2 + 5^2 = c^2$
$29 = c^2$
$\sqrt{29} = c$

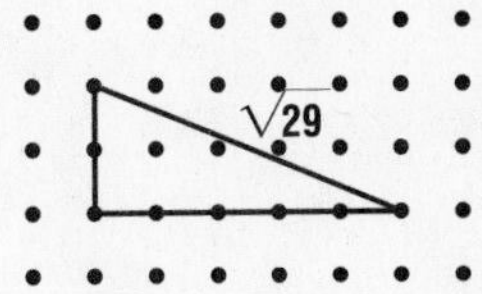

8. First use dot paper to create segments that have lengths $\sqrt{5}$ and $\sqrt{10}$. Then use a compass to copy these two lengths end to end to create a segment $(\sqrt{5} + \sqrt{10})$ units long. See student's work for drawing.

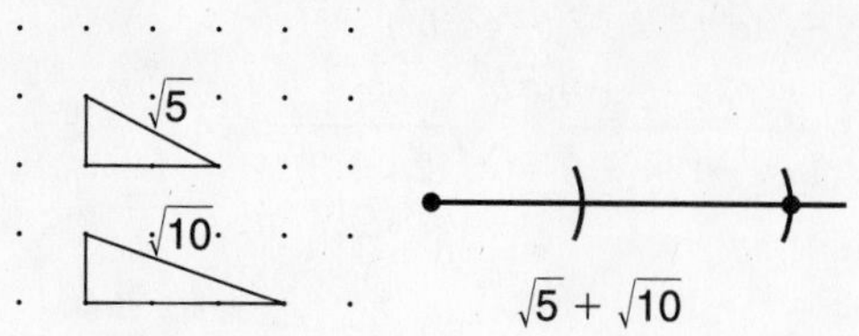

9. $\sqrt{80} = \sqrt{4^2 \cdot 5}$
$= \sqrt{4^2} \cdot \sqrt{5}$
$= 4\sqrt{5}$

10. $4\sqrt{54} = 4\sqrt{3^2 \cdot 6}$
$= 4\sqrt{3^2} \cdot \sqrt{6}$
$= 4 \cdot 3 \cdot \sqrt{6}$
$= 12\sqrt{6}$

11. $\sqrt[3]{64x^6y^3} = \sqrt[3]{(4x^2y)^3}$
$= 4x^2y$

12. $\sqrt[4]{81m^4n^5} = \sqrt[4]{(3mn)^4 \cdot n}$
$= \sqrt[4]{(3mn)^4} \cdot \sqrt[4]{n}$
$= 3|m|n\sqrt[4]{n}$

13. $(7\sqrt{6})(-3\sqrt{10}) = 7(-3) \cdot \sqrt{6 \cdot 10}$
$= -21\sqrt{2^2 \cdot 15}$
$= -21 \cdot \sqrt{2^2} \cdot \sqrt{15}$
$= -21 \cdot 2 \cdot \sqrt{15}$
$= -42\sqrt{15}$

14. $\sqrt{3x^2z^3} \cdot \sqrt{15x^2z} = \sqrt{3 \cdot 15 \cdot (x^2)^2 \cdot z^4}$
$= \sqrt{3^2 \cdot 5 \cdot (x^2)^2 \cdot (z^2)^2}$
$= 3x^2z^2\sqrt{5}$

15. $\dfrac{\sqrt[3]{81}}{\sqrt[3]{9}} = \sqrt[3]{\dfrac{81}{9}}$
$= \sqrt[3]{9}$

16. $\sqrt{\dfrac{5}{12a}} = \dfrac{\sqrt{5}}{\sqrt{12a}}$
$= \dfrac{\sqrt{5}}{\sqrt{2^2 \cdot 3a}}$
$= \dfrac{\sqrt{5}}{2\sqrt{3a}}$
$= \dfrac{\sqrt{5} \cdot \sqrt{3a}}{2\sqrt{3a} \cdot \sqrt{3a}}$
$= \dfrac{\sqrt{15a}}{2 \cdot 3a}$
$= \dfrac{\sqrt{15a}}{6a}$

17. $\sqrt{\dfrac{y^2}{y-3}} = \dfrac{\sqrt{y^2}}{\sqrt{y-3}}$
$= \dfrac{|y|}{\sqrt{y-3}}$
$= \dfrac{|y| \cdot \sqrt{y-3}}{\sqrt{y-3} \cdot \sqrt{y-3}}$
$= \dfrac{|y|\sqrt{y-3}}{\sqrt{(y-3)^2}}$
$= \left|\dfrac{y}{y-3}\right|\sqrt{y-3}$

18. $\sqrt{2} + 5\sqrt[3]{2} + 7\sqrt{2} - 4\sqrt[3]{2}$
$= \sqrt{2} + 7\sqrt{2} + 5\sqrt[3]{2} - 4\sqrt[3]{2}$
$= 8\sqrt{2} + \sqrt[3]{2}$

19. $5\sqrt[3]{135} - 2\sqrt[3]{81} = 5\sqrt[3]{3^3 \cdot 5} - 2\sqrt[3]{3^3 \cdot 3}$
$= 5 \cdot \sqrt[3]{3^3} \cdot \sqrt[3]{5} - 2\sqrt[3]{3^3} \cdot \sqrt[3]{3}$
$= 5 \cdot 3\sqrt[3]{5} - 2 \cdot 3\sqrt[3]{3}$
$= 15\sqrt[3]{5} - 6\sqrt[3]{3}$

20. $(5 + \sqrt{3})(2 - \sqrt{2})$
$= 5 \cdot 2 + 5(-\sqrt{2}) + \sqrt{3} \cdot 2 + \sqrt{3}(-\sqrt{2})$
$= 10 - 5\sqrt{2} + 2\sqrt{3} - \sqrt{6}$

21. $(7 + \sqrt{11y})(7 - \sqrt{11y})$
$= 7 \cdot 7 + 7(-\sqrt{11y}) + \sqrt{11y} \cdot 7 + \sqrt{11y}(-\sqrt{11y})$
$= 49 - 7\sqrt{11y} + 7\sqrt{11y} - \sqrt{(11y)^2}$
$= 49 - 11y$

22. $P = 2b + 2h$
$= 2(3 + 6\sqrt{2}) + 2(\sqrt{8})$
$= 2 \cdot 3 + 2 \cdot 6\sqrt{2} + 2\sqrt{8}$
$= 6 + 12\sqrt{2} + 2\sqrt{2^2 \cdot 2}$
$= 6 + 12\sqrt{2} + 2 \cdot \sqrt{2^2} \cdot \sqrt{2}$
$= 6 + 12\sqrt{2} + 2 \cdot 2\sqrt{2}$
$= 6 + 12\sqrt{2} + 4\sqrt{2}$
$= 6 + 16\sqrt{2}$; $(6 + 16\sqrt{2})$ yards

$A = b \cdot h$
$= (3 + 6\sqrt{2})(\sqrt{8})$
$= 3 \cdot \sqrt{8} + 6\sqrt{2}(\sqrt{8})$
$= 3\sqrt{2^2 \cdot 2} + 6\sqrt{2 \cdot 8}$
$= 3\sqrt{2^2} \cdot \sqrt{2} + 6\sqrt{16}$
$= 3 \cdot 2\sqrt{2} + 6\sqrt{4^2}$
$= 6\sqrt{2} + 6 \cdot 4$
$= 6\sqrt{2} + 24$; $(6\sqrt{2} + 24)$ square yards

Pages 293–295 Exercises

23. $\sqrt{32} = \sqrt{4^2 \cdot 2}$
$= \sqrt{4^2} \cdot \sqrt{2}$
$= 4\sqrt{2}$

24. $5\sqrt{50} = 5\sqrt{5^2 \cdot 2}$
$= 5\sqrt{5^2} \cdot \sqrt{2}$
$= 5 \cdot 5\sqrt{2}$
$= 25\sqrt{2}$

25. $\sqrt[3]{16} = \sqrt[3]{2^3 \cdot 2}$
$= \sqrt[3]{2^3} \cdot \sqrt[3]{2}$
$= 2\sqrt[3]{2}$

26. $\sqrt{98y^4} = \sqrt{7^2 \cdot 2 \cdot (y^2)^2}$
$= \sqrt{7^2} \cdot \sqrt{2} \cdot \sqrt{(y^2)^2}$
$= 7y^2\sqrt{2}$

27. $\sqrt[3]{32} = \sqrt[3]{2^3 \cdot 4}$
$= \sqrt[3]{2^3} \cdot \sqrt[3]{4}$
$= 2\sqrt[3]{4}$

28. $\sqrt[4]{48} = \sqrt[4]{2^4 \cdot 3}$
$= \sqrt[4]{2^4} \cdot \sqrt[4]{3}$
$= 2\sqrt[4]{3}$

29. $\sqrt{y^3} = \sqrt{y^2 \cdot y}$
$= \sqrt{y^2} \cdot \sqrt{y}$
$= y\sqrt{y}$

30. $\sqrt{8a^2b^3} = \sqrt{2^2 \cdot 2 \cdot a^2 \cdot b^2 \cdot b}$
$= \sqrt{2^2} \cdot \sqrt{2} \cdot \sqrt{a^2} \cdot \sqrt{b^2} \cdot \sqrt{b}$
$= 2|a|b\sqrt{2b}$

31. $5\sqrt{3} - 4\sqrt{3} = \sqrt{3}$

32. $8\sqrt[3]{6} + 3\sqrt[3]{6} = 11\sqrt[3]{6}$

33. $\sqrt{90x^3y^4} = \sqrt{3^2 \cdot 10 \cdot x^2 \cdot x \cdot (y^2)^2}$
$= \sqrt{3^2} \cdot \sqrt{10} \cdot \sqrt{x^2} \cdot \sqrt{x} \cdot \sqrt{(y^2)^2}$
$= 3xy^2\sqrt{10x}$

34. $3\sqrt[3]{56a^6b^3} = 3\sqrt[3]{2^3 \cdot 7(a^2)^3 \cdot b^3}$
$= 3 \cdot \sqrt[3]{2^3} \cdot \sqrt[3]{7} \cdot \sqrt[3]{(a^2)^3} \cdot \sqrt[3]{b^3}$
$= 3 \cdot 2 \cdot a^2 \cdot b \cdot \sqrt[3]{7}$
$= 6a^2b\sqrt[3]{7}$

35. $(-3\sqrt{24})(5\sqrt{20}) = -3 \cdot 5 \cdot \sqrt{24 \cdot 20}$
$= -15\sqrt{2^2 \cdot 6 \cdot 2^2 \cdot 5}$
$= -15 \cdot \sqrt{2^2} \cdot \sqrt{6} \cdot \sqrt{2^2} \cdot \sqrt{5}$
$= -15 \cdot 2 \cdot \sqrt{6} \cdot 2 \cdot \sqrt{5}$
$= -60\sqrt{30}$

36. $\sqrt{26} \cdot \sqrt{39} \cdot \sqrt{14} = \sqrt{26 \cdot 39 \cdot 14}$
$= \sqrt{2^2 \cdot 13^2 \cdot 3 \cdot 7}$
$= \sqrt{2^2} \cdot \sqrt{13^2} \cdot \sqrt{3} \cdot \sqrt{7}$
$= 2 \cdot 13 \cdot \sqrt{3 \cdot 7}$
$= 26\sqrt{21}$

37. $(4\sqrt{18})(2\sqrt{14}) = 4 \cdot 2 \cdot \sqrt{18 \cdot 14}$
$= 8\sqrt{3^2 \cdot 2^2 \cdot 7}$
$= 8 \cdot \sqrt{3^2} \cdot \sqrt{2^2} \cdot \sqrt{7}$
$= 8 \cdot 3 \cdot 2 \cdot \sqrt{7}$
$= 48\sqrt{7}$

38. $8\sqrt{y^2} + 7\sqrt{y} - 4\sqrt{y} = 8y + 3\sqrt{y}$

39. $\sqrt[3]{40} - 2\sqrt[3]{5} = \sqrt[3]{2^3 \cdot 5} - 2\sqrt[3]{5}$
$= \sqrt[3]{2^3} \cdot \sqrt[3]{5} - 2\sqrt[3]{5}$
$= 2\sqrt[3]{5} - 2\sqrt[3]{5}$
$= 0$

40. $(\sqrt{10} - \sqrt{6})(\sqrt{5} + \sqrt{3})$
$= \sqrt{10} \cdot \sqrt{5} + \sqrt{10} \cdot \sqrt{3} - \sqrt{6} \cdot \sqrt{5} - \sqrt{6} \cdot \sqrt{3}$
$= \sqrt{50} + \sqrt{30} - \sqrt{30} - \sqrt{18}$
$= \sqrt{5^2 \cdot 2} - \sqrt{3^2 \cdot 2}$
$= \sqrt{5^2} \cdot \sqrt{2} - \sqrt{3^2} \cdot \sqrt{2}$
$= 5\sqrt{2} - 3\sqrt{2}$
$= 2\sqrt{2}$

41. $-3\sqrt{7}(2\sqrt{14} + 5\sqrt{2})$
$= -3\sqrt{7}(2\sqrt{14}) - 3\sqrt{7}(5\sqrt{2})$
$= -3 \cdot 2 \cdot \sqrt{7 \cdot 14} - 3 \cdot 5 \cdot \sqrt{7 \cdot 2}$
$= -6\sqrt{7^2 \cdot 2} - 15\sqrt{14}$
$= -6\sqrt{7^2}\sqrt{2} - 15\sqrt{14}$
$= -6 \cdot 7\sqrt{2} - 15\sqrt{14}$
$= -42\sqrt{2} - 15\sqrt{14}$

42. $\sqrt{a}(\sqrt{b} + \sqrt{ab}) = \sqrt{a} \cdot \sqrt{b} + \sqrt{a} \cdot \sqrt{ab}$
$= \sqrt{ab} + \sqrt{a^2b}$
$= \sqrt{ab} + \sqrt{a^2} \cdot \sqrt{b}$
$= \sqrt{ab} + a\sqrt{b}$

43. $8\sqrt[3]{2x} + 3\sqrt[3]{2x} - 8\sqrt[3]{2x} = 3\sqrt[3]{2x}$

44. $5\sqrt{20} + \sqrt{24} - \sqrt{180} + 7\sqrt{54}$
$= 5\sqrt{2^2 \cdot 5} + \sqrt{2^2 \cdot 6} - \sqrt{6^2 \cdot 5} + 7\sqrt{3^2 \cdot 6}$
$= 5\sqrt{2^2} \cdot \sqrt{5} + \sqrt{2^2} \cdot \sqrt{6} - \sqrt{6^2} \cdot \sqrt{5} +$
$7\sqrt{3^2} \cdot \sqrt{6}$
$= 5 \cdot 2\sqrt{5} + 2\sqrt{6} - 6\sqrt{5} + 7 \cdot 3\sqrt{6}$
$= 10\sqrt{5} + 2\sqrt{6} - 6\sqrt{5} + 21\sqrt{6}$
$= 4\sqrt{5} + 23\sqrt{6}$

45. $(6 - \sqrt{2})(6 + \sqrt{2})$
$= 6 \cdot 6 + 6 \cdot \sqrt{2} - \sqrt{2} \cdot 6 - \sqrt{2} \cdot \sqrt{2}$
$= 36 + 6\sqrt{2} - 6\sqrt{2} - \sqrt{2^2}$
$= 36 - 2 = 34$

46. $(5 + \sqrt{6})(5 - \sqrt{2})$
$= 5 \cdot 5 + 5(-\sqrt{2}) + \sqrt{6} \cdot 5 + \sqrt{6}(-\sqrt{2})$
$= 25 - 5\sqrt{2} + 5\sqrt{6} - \sqrt{2^2 \cdot 3}$
$= 25 - 5\sqrt{2} + 5\sqrt{6} - \sqrt{2^2} \cdot \sqrt{3}$
$= 25 - 5\sqrt{2} + 5\sqrt{6} - 2\sqrt{3}$

47. $(\sqrt{3} - \sqrt{5})^2$
$= (\sqrt{3} - \sqrt{5})(\sqrt{3} - \sqrt{5})$
$= \sqrt{3} \cdot \sqrt{3} + \sqrt{3}(-\sqrt{5}) - \sqrt{5}(\sqrt{3}) - \sqrt{5}(-\sqrt{5})$
$= \sqrt{3^2} - \sqrt{15} - \sqrt{15} + \sqrt{5^2}$
$= 3 - 2\sqrt{15} + 5$
$= 8 - 2\sqrt{15}$

48. $(x + \sqrt{y})^2 = (x + \sqrt{y})(x + \sqrt{y})$
$= x \cdot x + x \cdot \sqrt{y} + \sqrt{y} \cdot x + \sqrt{y} \cdot \sqrt{y}$
$= x^2 + x\sqrt{y} + x\sqrt{y} + \sqrt{y^2}$
$= x^2 + 2x\sqrt{y} + y$

49. $\sqrt{98} - \sqrt{72} + \sqrt{32}$
$= \sqrt{7^2 \cdot 2} - \sqrt{6^2 \cdot 2} + \sqrt{4^2 \cdot 2}$
$= \sqrt{7^2} \cdot \sqrt{2} - \sqrt{6^2} \cdot \sqrt{2} + \sqrt{4^2} \cdot \sqrt{2}$
$= 7\sqrt{2} - 6\sqrt{2} + 4\sqrt{2}$
$= 5\sqrt{2}$

50. $\sqrt[4]{a^2} + \sqrt[4]{a^6} = \sqrt[4]{a^2} + \sqrt[4]{a^4 \cdot a^2}$
$= \sqrt[4]{a^2} + \sqrt[4]{a^4} \cdot \sqrt[4]{a^2}$
$= \sqrt[4]{a^2} + |a|\sqrt[4]{a^2}$
$= (1 + |a|)\sqrt[4]{a^2}$

51. $\sqrt{\frac{a^4}{b^3}} = \frac{\sqrt{a^4}}{\sqrt{b^3}}$
$= \frac{\sqrt{(a^2)^2}}{\sqrt{b^2 \cdot b}}$
$= \frac{a^2}{b\sqrt{b}}$
$= \frac{a^2 \cdot \sqrt{b}}{b\sqrt{b} \cdot \sqrt{b}}$
$= \frac{a^2\sqrt{b}}{b \cdot \sqrt{b^2}}$
$= \frac{a^2\sqrt{b}}{b \cdot b}$
$= \frac{a^2\sqrt{b}}{b^2}$

52. $\sqrt[4]{\frac{2}{3}} = \frac{\sqrt[4]{2}}{\sqrt[4]{3}}$
$= \frac{\sqrt[4]{2}\sqrt[4]{27}}{\sqrt[4]{3} \cdot \sqrt[4]{27}}$
$= \frac{\sqrt[4]{54}}{\sqrt[4]{3^4}}$
$= \frac{\sqrt[4]{54}}{3}$

53. $\sqrt{\frac{2}{5}} + \sqrt{40} + \sqrt{10} = \frac{\sqrt{2}}{\sqrt{5}} + \sqrt{2^2 \cdot 10} + \sqrt{10}$
$= \frac{\sqrt{2} \cdot \sqrt{5}}{\sqrt{5} \cdot \sqrt{5}} + \sqrt{2^2} \cdot \sqrt{10} + \sqrt{10}$
$= \frac{\sqrt{10}}{\sqrt{5^2}} + 2\sqrt{10} + \sqrt{10}$
$= \frac{\sqrt{10}}{5} + 2\sqrt{10} + \sqrt{10}$
$= \frac{\sqrt{10}}{5} + \frac{10\sqrt{10}}{5} + \frac{5\sqrt{10}}{5}$
$= \frac{16\sqrt{10}}{5}$

54. $\frac{7}{4 - \sqrt{3}} = \frac{7 \cdot (4 + \sqrt{3})}{(4 - \sqrt{3})(4 + \sqrt{3})}$
$= \frac{7 \cdot 4 + 7 \cdot \sqrt{3}}{4 \cdot 4 + 4 \cdot \sqrt{3} - \sqrt{3} \cdot 4 - \sqrt{3} \cdot \sqrt{3}}$
$= \frac{28 + 7\sqrt{3}}{16 + 4\sqrt{3} - 4\sqrt{3} - \sqrt{3^2}}$
$= \frac{28 + 7\sqrt{3}}{16 - 3}$
$= \frac{28 + 7\sqrt{3}}{13}$

55. $\frac{\sqrt{6}}{5 + \sqrt{3}} = \frac{\sqrt{6} \cdot (5 - \sqrt{3})}{(5 + \sqrt{3})(5 - \sqrt{3})}$
$= \frac{\sqrt{6} \cdot 5 + \sqrt{6}(-\sqrt{3})}{5 \cdot 5 + 5(-\sqrt{3}) + \sqrt{3} \cdot 5 + \sqrt{3}(-\sqrt{3})}$
$= \frac{5\sqrt{6} - \sqrt{3^2 \cdot 2}}{25 - 5\sqrt{3} + 5\sqrt{3} - \sqrt{3^2}}$
$= \frac{5\sqrt{6} - 3\sqrt{2}}{25 - 3}$
$= \frac{5\sqrt{6} - 3\sqrt{2}}{22}$

56. $\frac{2 + \sqrt{6}}{2 - \sqrt{6}} = \frac{(2 + \sqrt{6})(2 + \sqrt{6})}{(2 - \sqrt{6})(2 + \sqrt{6})}$
$= \frac{2 \cdot 2 + 2 \cdot \sqrt{6} + \sqrt{6} \cdot 2 + \sqrt{6} \cdot \sqrt{6}}{2 \cdot 2 + 2 \cdot \sqrt{6} - \sqrt{6} \cdot 2 - \sqrt{6} \cdot \sqrt{6}}$
$= \frac{4 + 2\sqrt{6} + 2\sqrt{6} + \sqrt{6^2}}{4 + 2\sqrt{6} - 2\sqrt{6} - \sqrt{6^2}}$
$= \frac{4 + 4\sqrt{6} + 6}{4 - 6}$
$= \frac{10 + 4\sqrt{6}}{-2}$
$= -5 - 2\sqrt{6}$

57. $\frac{\sqrt{x+1}}{\sqrt{x-1}} = \frac{(\sqrt{x+1})(\sqrt{x-1})}{(\sqrt{x-1})(\sqrt{x-1})}$
$= \frac{\sqrt{(x+1)(x-1)}}{\sqrt{(x-1)^2}}$
$= \frac{\sqrt{x \cdot x \cdot + x(-1) + 1 \cdot x + 1(-1)}}{|x - 1|}$
$= \frac{\sqrt{x^2 - x + x - 1}}{|x - 1|}$
$= \frac{\sqrt{x^2 - 1}}{|x - 1|}$

58. $\frac{1}{\sqrt{x^2 - 1}} = \frac{1 \cdot \sqrt{x^2 - 1}}{\sqrt{x^2 - 1} \cdot \sqrt{x^2 - 1}}$
$= \frac{\sqrt{x^2 - 1}}{\sqrt{(x^2 - 1)^2}}$
$= \frac{\sqrt{x^2 - 1}}{x^2 - 1}$

59. $\sqrt[4]{x^4} + \sqrt[3]{x^6} + \sqrt{x^8} = |x| + \sqrt[3]{(x^2)^3} + \sqrt{(x^4)^2}$
$= |x| + x^2 + x^4$

60. $(4\sqrt{5} - 3\sqrt{2})(2\sqrt{5} + 2\sqrt{2})$
$= 4\sqrt{5} \cdot 2\sqrt{5} + 4\sqrt{5} \cdot 2\sqrt{2} - 3\sqrt{2} \cdot 2\sqrt{5} -$
$3\sqrt{2} \cdot 2\sqrt{2}$
$= 8\sqrt{5^2} + 8\sqrt{10} - 6\sqrt{10} - 6\sqrt{2^2}$
$= 8 \cdot 5 + 2\sqrt{10} - 6 \cdot 2$
$= 28 + 2\sqrt{10}$

61. $a^2 + b^2 = c^2$
$(6y^2\sqrt{7})^2 + (2y^2\sqrt{7})^2 = c^2$
$6^2 \cdot (y^2)^2 \cdot (\sqrt{7})^2 + 2^2 \cdot (y^2)^2 \cdot (\sqrt{7})^2 = c^2$
$36y^4 \cdot 7 + 4y^4 \cdot 7 = c^2$
$252y^4 + 28y^4 = c^2$
$280y^4 = c^2$
$\sqrt{280y^4} = c$
$\sqrt{2^2 \cdot 70 \cdot (y^2)^2} = c$
$\sqrt{2^2} \cdot \sqrt{70} \cdot \sqrt{(y^2)^2} = c$
$2y^2\sqrt{70} = c;$
$2y^2\sqrt{70}$ inches

62. $r = \frac{1}{2}\sqrt{\frac{s}{\pi}}$
$= \frac{1}{2}\sqrt{\frac{2464}{\pi}}$
$\approx \frac{1}{2}\sqrt{784.32}$
$\approx \frac{1}{2}(28.01)$
≈ 14.0; about 14 inches

63. when x and y are not negative

64. when n is even and $x > 0$, or when n is any number and $x = 0$

65a. Akikta: $W = \frac{w}{\sqrt[3]{b - 35}}$
$= \frac{190}{\sqrt[3]{70 - 35}}$
$= \frac{190}{\sqrt[3]{35}}$
$\approx \frac{190}{3.27}$
≈ 58.09

Francisco: $W = \frac{w}{\sqrt[3]{b - 35}}$
$= \frac{240}{\sqrt[3]{110 - 35}}$
$= \frac{240}{\sqrt[3]{75}}$
$\approx \frac{240}{4.22}$
≈ 56.91

65b. Akikta

66. $T = 2\pi\sqrt{\frac{L}{384}}$

$= 2\pi\sqrt{\frac{10}{384}}$

$\approx 2\pi\sqrt{0.026} \approx 1.01$; about 1 second

67. $v = \sqrt{\frac{F_c r}{100}}$

$= \sqrt{\frac{2000 \cdot 320}{100}}$

$= \sqrt{6400}$

$= 80$; 80ft/s or

$\frac{80 \text{ ft}}{\text{s}} \cdot \frac{1 \text{ m}}{5280 \text{ ft}} \cdot \frac{60 \text{ s}}{\text{min}} \cdot \frac{60 \text{ min}}{\text{hr}} \approx 55$ mph

68. $\sqrt{(y+2)^2} = |y+2|$

69. $a + b + 3a^2 - 3b^2 = (a+b) + (3a^2 - 3b^2)$

$= (a+b) + 3(a^2 - b^2)$

$= (a+b) + 3(a+b)(a-b)$

$= (a+b)(1 + 3(a-b))$

$= (a+b)(1 + 3a - 3b)$

70.

5⌋	1	−8	0	54	105
		5	−15	−75	−105
	1	−3	−15	−21	0

$n^3 - 3n^2 - 15n - 21$

71. $(x^3 - 3x^2y + 4xy^2 + y^3) - (7x^3 + x^2y - 9xy^2 + y^3)$

$= x^3 - 3x^2y + 4xy^2 + y^3 - 7x^3 - x^2y + 9xy^2 - y^3$

$= x^3 - 7x^3 - 3x^2y - x^2y + 4xy^2 + 9xy^2 + y^3 - y^3$

$= -6x^3 - 4x^2y + 13xy^2$

72. 1 meter = 100 centimeters

$\frac{100}{5085.8 \times 10^{-8}} = \frac{10^2}{5085.8 \times 10^{-8}}$

$= \frac{1}{5085.8} \times 10^{2-(-8)}$

$\approx 1.9663 \times 10^{-4} \times 10^{10}$

$\approx 1.9663 \times 10^{6}$;

1.9663×10^{6} wavelengths

73. $\frac{2}{3}\begin{bmatrix} 9 & 0 \\ 12 & 15 \end{bmatrix} + \begin{bmatrix} -2 & 3 \\ -7 & -7 \end{bmatrix} = \begin{bmatrix} 6 & 0 \\ 8 & 10 \end{bmatrix} + \begin{bmatrix} -2 & 3 \\ -7 & -7 \end{bmatrix}$

$= \begin{bmatrix} 4 & 3 \\ 1 & 3 \end{bmatrix}$

74. $2y = 4$
$y = 2$

$2y + 3z = 16$
$2(2) + 3z = 16$
$4 + 3z = 16$
$3z = 12$
$z = 4$

$x - 2y + z = -9$
$x - 2(2) + 4 = -9$
$x - 4 + 4 = -9$
$x = -9$
$(-9, 2, 4)$

75. $s = \frac{\begin{vmatrix} 5 & 1 \\ 3 & -1 \end{vmatrix}}{\begin{vmatrix} 1 & 1 \\ 3 & -1 \end{vmatrix}}$ $\quad t = \frac{\begin{vmatrix} 1 & 5 \\ 3 & 3 \end{vmatrix}}{\begin{vmatrix} 1 & 1 \\ 3 & -1 \end{vmatrix}}$

$= \frac{-5-3}{-1-3}$ $\quad = \frac{3-15}{-1-3}$

$= \frac{-8}{-4}$ $\quad = \frac{-12}{-4}$

$= 2$ $\quad = 3$ $\quad (2, 3)$

76. $y + 3x > -1$

$y > -3x - 1$

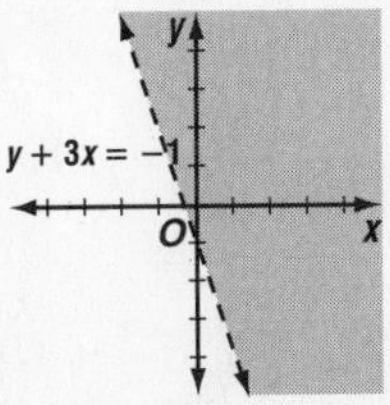

77. $f(x) = x^2 - 3x - 9$

$f(-3) = (-3)^2 - 3(-3) - 9$

$= 9 + 9 - 9$

$= 9$

78. $f(x) = 0.50(x-1) + 1.50$

$4.50 = 0.50(x-1) + 1.50$

$4.50 = 0.50x - 0.50 + 1.50$

$4.50 = 0.50x + 1$

$3.50 = 0.50x$

$7 = x$; 7 hours

79. $\frac{3ab}{cd} = \frac{3(3)(7)}{(-2)(0.5)}$

$= \frac{63}{-1}$

$= -63$

Page 295 Mathematics and Society

1. See students' work.

2a.

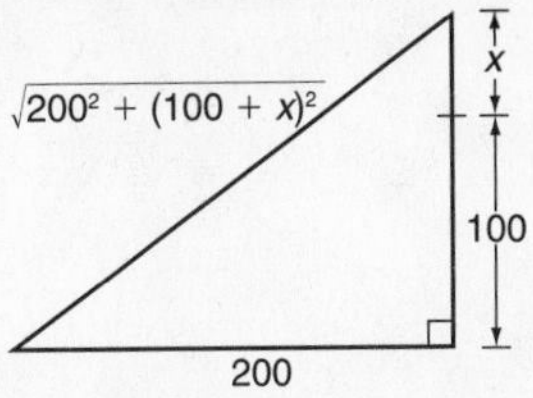

1st monkey: $100 + 200 = 300$

2nd monkey: $x + \sqrt{200^2 + (100+x)^2}$

$x + \sqrt{200^2 + (100+x)^2} = 300$

$\sqrt{40{,}000 + 10{,}000 + 200x + x^2} = 300 - x$

$50{,}000 + 200x + x^2 = 90{,}000 - 600x + x^2$

$800x = 40{,}000$

$x = 50$; 50 cubits

2b. Let x = flock.

$10\sqrt{x} + \frac{1}{8}x + 2(3) = x$

$10\sqrt{x} = \frac{7}{8}x - 6$

$(10\sqrt{x})^2 = \left(\frac{7}{8}x - 6\right)^2$

$100x = \frac{49}{64}x^2 - \frac{84}{8}x + 36$

$6400x = 49x^2 - 672x + 2304$

$0 = 49x^2 - 7072x + 2304$

$0 = (49x + 16)(x - 144)$

$49x + 16 = 0$ or $x - 144 = 0$

$x = -\frac{16}{49}$ $\quad x = 144$

144 geese

5-7 Rational Exponents

Page 300 Check for Understanding

1. Answers will vary.
2. No, because $\sqrt[6]{2916} = (3^6 \cdot 2^2)^{\frac{1}{6}} = 3 \cdot 2^{\frac{1}{3}}$ or $3\sqrt[3]{2}$.
3. The radical form $\sqrt[4]{-81}$ has an even index and negative radicand.
4. To rationalize a denominator like $\frac{1}{x^{\frac{n}{m}}}$, multiply by 1 in the form $\frac{x^{\frac{m-n}{m}}}{x^{\frac{m-n}{m}}}$.

5. See students' work.

6. $\sqrt{14} = 14^{\frac{1}{2}}$

7. $\sqrt[4]{27} = 27^{\frac{1}{4}}$

8. $\sqrt[6]{b^3} = b^{\frac{3}{6}}$ or $b^{\frac{1}{2}}$

9. $\sqrt[3]{16a^5b^7} = 16^{\frac{1}{3}}a^{\frac{5}{3}}b^{\frac{7}{3}}$

10. $16^{\frac{1}{4}} = \sqrt[4]{16}$
$= \sqrt[4]{2^4}$
$= 2$

11. $8^{-\frac{1}{3}} = \frac{1}{8^{\frac{1}{3}}}$
$= \frac{1}{\sqrt[3]{8}}$
$= \frac{1}{\sqrt[3]{2^3}}$
$= \frac{1}{2}$

12. $64^{\frac{2}{3}} = (\sqrt[3]{64})^2$
$= \left(\sqrt[3]{(2^2)^3}\right)^2$
$= (2^2)^2$
$= 4^2$
$= 16$

13. $\frac{16}{4^{\frac{3}{2}}} = \frac{16}{(\sqrt{4})^3}$
$= \frac{16}{(\sqrt{2^2})^3}$
$= \frac{16}{2^3}$
$= \frac{16}{8}$
$= 2$

14. $\sqrt[6]{9x^3} = \sqrt[6]{3^2x^3}$
$= 3^{\frac{2}{6}}x^{\frac{3}{6}}$
$= 3^{\frac{1}{3}}x^{\frac{1}{2}}$
$= \sqrt[3]{3}\sqrt{x}$

15. $x^{\frac{3}{2}}y^{\frac{7}{3}}z^{\frac{9}{6}} = x^{\frac{9}{6}} \cdot y^{\frac{14}{6}} \cdot z^{\frac{9}{6}}$
$= \sqrt[6]{x^9y^{14}z^9}$
$= \sqrt[6]{x^6 \cdot x^3 \cdot (y^2)^6 \cdot y^2 \cdot z^6 \cdot z^3}$
$= xy^2z\sqrt[6]{x^3y^2z^3}$

16. $\frac{\sqrt[4]{125}}{\sqrt[4]{5}} = \sqrt[4]{\frac{125}{5}}$
$= \sqrt[4]{25}$
$= \sqrt[4]{5^2}$
$= 5^{\frac{2}{4}}$
$= 5^{\frac{1}{2}}$
$= \sqrt{5}$

17. $\frac{1}{5x^{\frac{1}{3}}} = \frac{1 \cdot x^{\frac{2}{3}}}{5x^{\frac{1}{3}} \cdot x^{\frac{2}{3}}}$
$= \frac{x^{\frac{2}{3}}}{5x^{\frac{3}{3}}}$
$= \frac{x^{\frac{2}{3}}}{5x}$

18. $(x^2y)^{-\frac{1}{3}} = \frac{1}{(x^2y)^{\frac{1}{3}}}$
$= \frac{1}{x^{\frac{2}{3}}y^{\frac{1}{3}}}$
$= \frac{1\left(x^{\frac{1}{3}}y^{\frac{2}{3}}\right)}{x^{\frac{2}{3}}y^{\frac{1}{3}}\left(x^{\frac{1}{3}}y^{\frac{2}{3}}\right)}$
$= \frac{x^{\frac{1}{3}}y^{\frac{2}{3}}}{x^{\frac{3}{3}}y^{\frac{3}{3}}}$
$= \frac{x^{\frac{1}{3}}y^{\frac{2}{3}}}{xy}$

19. $c(a - 4b)^{-\frac{1}{2}} = \frac{c}{(a - 4b)^{\frac{1}{2}}}$
$= \frac{c \cdot (a - 4b)^{\frac{1}{2}}}{(a - 4b)^{\frac{1}{2}} \cdot (a - 4b)^{\frac{1}{2}}}$
$= \frac{c(a - 4b)^{\frac{1}{2}}}{a - 4b}$

20. $x^{\frac{1}{3}} \cdot x^{\frac{3}{4}} = x^{\frac{4}{12}} \cdot x^{\frac{9}{12}}$
$= x^{\frac{13}{12}}$

21. $\frac{y^{\frac{5}{6}}}{y^{\frac{1}{6}}} = y^{\frac{5}{6} - \frac{1}{6}}$
$= y^{\frac{4}{6}}$
$= y^{\frac{2}{3}}$

22. $\frac{x^3}{y^{\frac{1}{2}}} \cdot \frac{y}{x^{\frac{1}{3}}} = \frac{x^3y}{x^{\frac{1}{3}}y^{\frac{1}{2}}}$
$= x^{3 - \frac{1}{3}}y^{1 - \frac{1}{2}}$
$= x^{\frac{8}{3}}y^{\frac{1}{2}}$

23a. $4^x = 2$
$(2^2)^x = 2^1$
$2^{2x} = 2^1$
$2x = 1$
$x = \frac{1}{2}$

23b. $32^x = 8$
$(2^5)^x = 2^3$
$2^{5x} = 2^3$
$5x = 3$
$x = \frac{3}{5}$

23c. $(x^3)^y = x$
$x^{3y} = x^1$
$3y = 1$
$y = \frac{1}{3}$

Pages 300–302 Exercises

24. $125^{\frac{1}{3}} = \sqrt[3]{125}$
$= \sqrt[3]{5^3}$
$= 5$

25. $100^{-\frac{1}{2}} = \frac{1}{100^{\frac{1}{2}}}$
$= \frac{1}{\sqrt{100}}$
$= \frac{1}{\sqrt{10^2}}$
$= \frac{1}{10}$

26. $16^{-\frac{3}{4}} = \frac{1}{16^{\frac{3}{4}}}$
$= \frac{1}{(2^4)^{\frac{3}{4}}}$
$= \frac{1}{2^3}$
$= \frac{1}{8}$

27. $81^{\frac{2}{3}} \cdot 81^{\frac{3}{2}} = 81^{\frac{2}{3} + \frac{3}{2}}$
$= 81^{\frac{4}{6} + \frac{9}{6}}$
$= 81^{\frac{13}{6}}$ or
$= (9^2)^{\frac{13}{6}}$
$= 9^{\frac{13}{3}}$ or
$= (3^2)^{\frac{13}{3}}$
$= 3^{\frac{26}{3}}$

28. $9^{\frac{5}{2}} \cdot 9^{\frac{3}{2}} = 9^{\frac{5}{2} + \frac{3}{2}}$
$= 9^{\frac{8}{2}}$
$= 9^4$
$= 6561$

29. $(-64)^{-\frac{2}{3}} = \dfrac{1}{(-64)^{\frac{2}{3}}}$

$= \dfrac{1}{\sqrt[3]{(-64)^2}}$

$= \dfrac{1}{\sqrt[3]{4096}}$

$= \dfrac{1}{\sqrt[3]{16^3}}$

$= \dfrac{1}{16}$

30. $\left(\dfrac{16}{81}\right)^{\frac{1}{4}} = \dfrac{16^{\frac{1}{4}}}{81^{\frac{1}{4}}}$

$= \dfrac{(2^4)^{\frac{1}{4}}}{(3^4)^{\frac{1}{4}}}$

$= \dfrac{2}{3}$

31. $\left(\dfrac{1}{32}\right)^{-\frac{3}{5}} = (32)^{\frac{3}{5}}$

$= (2^5)^{\frac{3}{5}}$

$= 2^3$

$= 8$

32. $\left(\dfrac{27}{64}\right)^{-\frac{1}{3}} = \left(\dfrac{64}{27}\right)^{\frac{1}{3}}$

$= \dfrac{64^{\frac{1}{3}}}{27^{\frac{1}{3}}}$

$= \dfrac{(4^3)^{\frac{1}{3}}}{(3^3)^{\frac{1}{3}}}$

$= \dfrac{4}{3}$

33. $\dfrac{24}{6^{\frac{2}{3}}} = \dfrac{24 \cdot 6^{\frac{1}{3}}}{6^{\frac{2}{3}} \cdot 6^{\frac{1}{3}}}$

$= \dfrac{4 \cdot 6 \cdot 6^{\frac{1}{3}}}{6^{\frac{3}{3}}}$

$= \dfrac{4 \cdot 6 \cdot 6^{\frac{1}{3}}}{6}$

$= 4 \cdot 6^{\frac{1}{3}}$

34. $\dfrac{21}{7^{\frac{2}{3}}} = \dfrac{21 \cdot 7^{\frac{1}{3}}}{7^{\frac{2}{3}} \cdot 7^{\frac{1}{3}}}$

$= \dfrac{3 \cdot 7 \cdot 7^{\frac{1}{3}}}{7^{\frac{3}{3}}}$

$= \dfrac{3 \cdot 7 \cdot 7^{\frac{1}{3}}}{7}$

$= 3 \cdot 7^{\frac{1}{3}}$

35. $\dfrac{8}{3^{\frac{1}{2}}} = \dfrac{8 \cdot 3^{\frac{1}{2}}}{3^{\frac{1}{2}} \cdot 3^{\frac{1}{2}}}$

$= \dfrac{8 \cdot 3^{\frac{1}{2}}}{3^{\frac{2}{2}}}$

$= \dfrac{8 \cdot 3^{\frac{1}{2}}}{3}$

36. $2^{\frac{5}{3}} \cdot a^{\frac{7}{3}} = \sqrt[3]{2^5 a^7}$

$= \sqrt[3]{2^3 \cdot 2^2 \cdot (a^2)^3 \cdot a}$

$= 2a^2\sqrt[3]{2^2 a}$

$= 2a^2\sqrt[3]{4a}$

37. $(2m)^{\frac{1}{2}} m^{\frac{1}{2}} = 2^{\frac{1}{2}} m^{\frac{1}{2}} m^{\frac{1}{2}}$

$= 2^{\frac{1}{2}} m$

$= m\sqrt{2}$

38. $11^{\frac{1}{3}} p^{\frac{7}{3}} q^{\frac{2}{3}} = \sqrt[3]{11p^7q^2}$

$= \sqrt[3]{11(p^2)^3 pq^2}$

$= p^2\sqrt[3]{11pq^2}$

39. $\dfrac{1}{w^{\frac{4}{5}}} = \dfrac{1 \cdot w^{\frac{1}{5}}}{w^{\frac{4}{5}} \cdot w^{\frac{1}{5}}}$

$= \dfrac{w^{\frac{1}{5}}}{w^{\frac{5}{5}}}$

$= \dfrac{w^{\frac{1}{5}}}{w}$

40. $\dfrac{1}{(u-v)^{\frac{1}{3}}} = \dfrac{1(u-v)^{\frac{2}{3}}}{(u-v)^{\frac{1}{3}}(u-v)^{\frac{2}{3}}}$

$= \dfrac{1(u-v)^{\frac{2}{3}}}{(u-v)^{\frac{3}{3}}}$

$= \dfrac{(u-v)^{\frac{2}{3}}}{u-v}$

41. $x^{-\frac{5}{6}} = \dfrac{1}{x^{\frac{5}{6}}}$

$= \dfrac{1 \cdot x^{\frac{1}{6}}}{x^{\frac{5}{6}} \cdot x^{\frac{1}{6}}}$

$= \dfrac{x^{\frac{1}{6}}}{x^{\frac{6}{6}}}$

$= \dfrac{x^{\frac{1}{6}}}{x}$

42. $\dfrac{1}{b^{\frac{1}{2}} + 1} = \dfrac{1\left(b^{\frac{1}{2}} - 1\right)}{\left(b^{\frac{1}{2}} + 1\right)\left(b^{\frac{1}{2}} - 1\right)}$

$= \dfrac{b^{\frac{1}{2}} - 1}{b - b^{\frac{1}{2}} + b^{\frac{1}{2}} - 1}$

$= \dfrac{b^{\frac{1}{2}} - 1}{b - 1}$

43. $\dfrac{b^{-\frac{1}{2}}}{8b^{\frac{1}{3}} \cdot b^{-\frac{1}{4}}} = \dfrac{b^{-\frac{6}{12}}}{8b^{\frac{4}{12}} \cdot b^{-\frac{3}{12}}}$

$= \dfrac{b^{-\frac{6}{12}}}{8b^{\frac{1}{12}}}$

$= \dfrac{1}{8b^{\frac{1}{12}} \cdot b^{\frac{6}{12}}}$

$= \dfrac{1}{8b^{\frac{7}{12}}}$

$= \dfrac{1 \cdot b^{\frac{5}{12}}}{8b^{\frac{7}{12}} \cdot b^{\frac{5}{12}}}$

$= \dfrac{b^{\frac{5}{12}}}{8b^{\frac{12}{12}}}$

$= \dfrac{b^{\frac{5}{12}}}{8b}$

44. $\dfrac{g^{\frac{3}{2}} + 3g^{-\frac{1}{2}}}{g^{\frac{1}{2}}} = \dfrac{g^{\frac{3}{2}}}{g^{\frac{1}{2}}} + \dfrac{3g^{-\frac{1}{2}}}{g^{\frac{1}{2}}}$

$= g^{\frac{3}{2} - \frac{1}{2}} + \dfrac{3}{g^{\frac{1}{2}}g^{\frac{1}{2}}}$

$= g + \dfrac{3}{g}$

$= \dfrac{g^2}{g} + \dfrac{3}{g}$

$= \dfrac{g^2 + 3}{g}$

45. $\dfrac{3x^{-\frac{1}{3}} + x^{\frac{5}{3}}y}{x^{\frac{2}{3}}} = \dfrac{3x^{-\frac{1}{3}}}{x^{\frac{2}{3}}} + \dfrac{x^{\frac{5}{3}}y}{x^{\frac{2}{3}}}$

$= \dfrac{3}{x^{\frac{2}{3}}x^{\frac{1}{3}}} + x^{\frac{5}{3} - \frac{2}{3}}y$

$= \dfrac{3}{x} + xy$

$= \dfrac{3}{x} + \dfrac{x^2y}{x}$

$= \dfrac{3 + x^2y}{x}$

46. $\dfrac{2a^{\frac{1}{2}} + a^{\frac{3}{2}}}{a^{\frac{1}{2}}} = \dfrac{2a^{\frac{1}{2}}}{a^{\frac{1}{2}}} + \dfrac{a^{\frac{3}{2}}}{a^{\frac{1}{2}}}$

$= 2 + a$

47. $\dfrac{pq}{\sqrt[3]{r}} = \dfrac{pq}{r^{\frac{1}{3}}}$

$= \dfrac{pq \cdot r^{\frac{2}{3}}}{r^{\frac{1}{3}} \cdot r^{\frac{2}{3}}}$

$= \dfrac{pqr^{\frac{2}{3}}}{r^{\frac{3}{3}}}$

$= \dfrac{pqr^{\frac{2}{3}}}{r}$

48. $\left(m^{-\frac{2}{3}}\right)^{-\frac{1}{6}} = m^{\left(-\frac{2}{3}\right)\left(-\frac{1}{6}\right)}$

$= m^{\frac{1}{9}}$

49. $b^{-\frac{1}{3}} - b^{\frac{1}{3}} = \dfrac{1}{b^{\frac{1}{3}}} - b^{\frac{1}{3}}$

$= \dfrac{1 \cdot b^{\frac{2}{3}}}{b^{\frac{1}{3}} \cdot b^{\frac{2}{3}}} - b^{\frac{1}{3}}$

$= \dfrac{b^{\frac{2}{3}}}{b^{\frac{3}{3}}} - b^{\frac{1}{3}}$

$= \dfrac{b^{\frac{2}{3}}}{b} - b^{\frac{1}{3}}$

50. $\dfrac{z^{\frac{3}{2}}}{z^{\frac{1}{2}} + 2} = \dfrac{z^{\frac{3}{2}}\left(z^{\frac{1}{2}} - 2\right)}{\left(z^{\frac{1}{2}} + 2\right)\left(z^{\frac{1}{2}} - 2\right)}$

$= \dfrac{z^2 - 2z^{\frac{3}{2}}}{z - 2z^{\frac{1}{2}} + 2z^{\frac{1}{2}} - 4}$

$= \dfrac{z^2 - 2z^{\frac{3}{2}}}{z - 4}$

51. $\left(\dfrac{m^{-2}n^{-6}}{121}\right)^{-\frac{1}{2}} = \left(\dfrac{1}{121m^2n^6}\right)^{-\frac{1}{2}}$

$= (121m^2n^6)^{\frac{1}{2}}$

$= \sqrt{121m^2n^6}$

$= \sqrt{(11mn^3)^2}$

$= 11mn^3$

52. $\dfrac{8^{\frac{1}{6}} - 9^{\frac{1}{4}}}{\sqrt{3} + \sqrt{2}} = \dfrac{(2^3)^{\frac{1}{6}} - (3^2)^{\frac{1}{4}}}{\sqrt{3} + \sqrt{2}}$

$= \dfrac{2^{\frac{3}{6}} - 3^{\frac{2}{4}}}{\sqrt{3} + \sqrt{2}}$

$= \dfrac{2^{\frac{1}{2}} - 3^{\frac{1}{2}}}{\sqrt{3} + \sqrt{2}}$

$= \dfrac{\sqrt{2} - \sqrt{3}}{\sqrt{3} + \sqrt{2}}$

$= \dfrac{(\sqrt{2} - \sqrt{3})(\sqrt{3} - \sqrt{2})}{(\sqrt{3} + \sqrt{2})(\sqrt{3} - \sqrt{2})}$

$= \dfrac{\sqrt{6} - \sqrt{4} - \sqrt{9} + \sqrt{6}}{\sqrt{9} - \sqrt{6} + \sqrt{6} - \sqrt{4}}$

$= \dfrac{2\sqrt{6} - 2 - 3}{3 - 2}$

$= 2\sqrt{6} - 5$

53. $\dfrac{a^{\frac{5}{3}} - a^{\frac{1}{3}}b^{\frac{4}{3}}}{a^{\frac{2}{3}} + b^{\frac{2}{3}}} = \dfrac{\left(a^{\frac{5}{3}} - a^{\frac{1}{3}}b^{\frac{4}{3}}\right)\left(a^{\frac{2}{3}} - b^{\frac{2}{3}}\right)}{\left(a^{\frac{2}{3}} + b^{\frac{2}{3}}\right)\left(a^{\frac{2}{3}} - b^{\frac{2}{3}}\right)}$

$= \dfrac{a^{\frac{1}{3}}\left(a^{\frac{4}{3}} - b^{\frac{4}{3}}\right)\left(a^{\frac{2}{3}} - b^{\frac{2}{3}}\right)}{a^{\frac{4}{3}} - a^{\frac{2}{3}}b^{\frac{2}{3}} + a^{\frac{2}{3}}b^{\frac{2}{3}} - b^{\frac{4}{3}}}$

$= \dfrac{a^{\frac{1}{3}}\left(a^{\frac{4}{3}} - b^{\frac{4}{3}}\right)\left(a^{\frac{2}{3}} - b^{\frac{2}{3}}\right)}{a^{\frac{4}{3}} - b^{\frac{4}{3}}}$

$= a^{\frac{1}{3}}\left(a^{\frac{2}{3}} - b^{\frac{2}{3}}\right)$

$= a - a^{\frac{1}{3}}b^{\frac{2}{3}}$

54. $\sqrt[4]{49} = \sqrt[4]{7^2}$

$= 7^{\frac{2}{4}}$

$= 7^{\frac{1}{2}}$

$= \sqrt{7}$

55. $r^{\frac{1}{2}}s^{\frac{1}{3}} = r^{\frac{3}{6}}s^{\frac{2}{6}}$

$= \sqrt[6]{r^3s^2}$

56. $\sqrt[6]{81p^4q^8} = \sqrt[6]{(9p^2q^4)^2}$

$= (9p^2q^4)^{\frac{2}{6}}$

$= (9p^2q^4)^{\frac{1}{3}}$

$= \sqrt[3]{9p^2q^4}$

57. $\sqrt{13} \cdot \sqrt[3]{13^2} = 13^{\frac{1}{2}} \cdot 13^{\frac{2}{3}}$
$= 13^{\frac{1}{2} + \frac{2}{3}}$
$= 13^{\frac{7}{6}}$
$= \sqrt[6]{13^7}$
$= \sqrt[6]{13^6 \cdot 13}$
$= 13\sqrt[6]{13}$

58. $a^{\frac{5}{6}}b^{\frac{7}{3}}c^{\frac{3}{2}} = a^{\frac{5}{6}}b^{\frac{14}{6}}c^{\frac{9}{6}}$
$= \sqrt[6]{a^5b^{14}c^9}$
$= \sqrt[6]{a^5(b^2)^6 \cdot b^2 \cdot c^6 \cdot c^3}$
$= b^2c\sqrt[6]{a^5b^2c^3}$

59. $\sqrt[3]{\sqrt{27}} = (\sqrt{27})^{\frac{1}{3}}$
$= (27^{\frac{1}{2}})^{\frac{1}{3}}$
$= 27^{\frac{1}{6}}$
$= (3^3)^{\frac{1}{6}}$
$= 3^{\frac{1}{2}}$
$= \sqrt{3}$

60. $f(x) = x^{-\frac{2}{3}} + x^{-3}$

$f(-8) = (-8)^{-\frac{2}{3}} + (-8)^{-3}$
$= \frac{1}{(-8)^{\frac{2}{3}}} + \frac{1}{(-8)^3}$
$= \frac{1}{(\sqrt[3]{-8})^2} + \frac{1}{-512}$
$= \frac{1}{\left(\sqrt[3]{(-2)^3}\right)^2} - \frac{1}{512}$
$= \frac{1}{(-2)^2} - \frac{1}{512}$
$= \frac{1}{4} - \frac{1}{512}$
$= \frac{128}{512} - \frac{1}{512}$
$= \frac{127}{512}$

61. $f(x) = x^{-\frac{2}{3}} + x^{-3}$

$f(1000) = 1000^{-\frac{2}{3}} + 1000^{-3}$
$= \frac{1}{1000^{\frac{2}{3}}} + \frac{1}{1000^3}$
$= \frac{1}{(\sqrt[3]{1000})^2} + \frac{1}{1,000,000,000}$
$= \frac{1}{\left(\sqrt[3]{10^3}\right)^2} + \frac{1}{1,000,000,000}$
$= \frac{1}{10^2} + \frac{1}{1,000,000,000}$
$= \frac{1}{100} + \frac{1}{1,000,000,000}$
$= 0.01 + 0.000000001$
$= 0.010000001$

62. $f(x) = x^{-\frac{2}{3}} + x^{-3}$

$f(0.001) = (0.001)^{-\frac{2}{3}} + (0.001)^{-3}$
$= \frac{1}{(0.001)^{\frac{2}{3}}} + \frac{1}{(0.001)^3}$
$= \frac{1}{(\sqrt[3]{0.001})^2} + \frac{1}{0.000000001}$
$= \frac{1}{\left(\sqrt[3]{0.1^3}\right)^2} + \frac{1}{0.000000001}$
$= \frac{1}{(0.1)^2} + \frac{1}{0.000000001}$
$= \frac{1}{0.01} + \frac{1}{0.000000001}$
$= 100 + 1,000,000,000$
$= 1,000,000,100$

63. $45^{0.33} \approx 3.51$ **64.** $2.75^{\frac{2}{3}} \approx 1.96$

65. $\left(4\frac{1}{2}\right)^{0.075} \approx 1.12$

66. Rewrite the equation so that the bases are the same on each side.

$9^x = 3^{x + \frac{1}{2}}$
$(3^2)^x = 3^{x + \frac{1}{2}}$
$3^{2x} = 3^{x + \frac{1}{2}}$

Since the bases are the same and this is an equation, the exponents must be equal. Solve $2x = x + \frac{1}{2}$. Thus $x = \frac{1}{2}$.

67a. $f_n = 440(\sqrt[12]{2})^{n-1}$
$f_{12} = 440(\sqrt[12]{2})^{12-1}$
$= 440(\sqrt[12]{2})^{11}$
$\approx 440(1.059)^{11}$
$\approx 440(1.89)$
≈ 831
831 vibrations per second

67b. $f_n = 440(\sqrt[12]{2})^{n-1}$
$f_{-9} = 440(\sqrt[12]{2})^{-9-1}$
$= 440(\sqrt[12]{2})^{-10}$
$\approx 440(1.059)^{-10}$
$\approx 440(0.561)$
≈ 247
247 vibrations per second

68a. $V = V_{max}\left[1 - \left(\frac{r}{r_0}\right)^2\right]$
$7 = 10\left[1 - \left(\frac{r}{25}\right)^2\right]$
$7 = 10\left[1 - \frac{r^2}{625}\right]$
$7 = 10 - \frac{10r^2}{625}$
$-3 = -\frac{10r^2}{625}$
$\frac{1875}{10} = r^2$
$\sqrt{\frac{1875}{10}} = r$
$\sqrt{187.5} = r$
$13.7 \approx r$; about 13.7 feet

68b. See students' work.

69. $4\sqrt{(x-5)^2} = 4(x-5)$
$= 4x - 20$

70. $\sqrt{\frac{9}{36}x^4} = \sqrt{\left(\frac{3}{6}x^2\right)^2}$
$= \frac{3}{6}x^2$
$= \frac{1}{2}x^2$

71. $a^3b^3 - 27 = (ab - 3)(a^2b^2 + 3ab + 9)$

72. $\frac{-15r^5s^2}{5r^5s^{-4}} = -\frac{15}{5} \cdot r^{5-5} \cdot s^{2-(-4)}$
$= -3r^0s^6$
$= -3s^6$

73. $\left[\begin{array}{cc|c} 2 & 1 & 0 \\ 3 & -4 & 22 \end{array}\right] = \left[\begin{array}{cc|c} 8 & 4 & 0 \\ 3 & -4 & 22 \end{array}\right] = \left[\begin{array}{cc|c} 11 & 0 & 22 \\ 3 & -4 & 22 \end{array}\right]$
$= \left[\begin{array}{cc|c} 1 & 0 & 2 \\ 3 & -4 & 22 \end{array}\right] = \left[\begin{array}{cc|c} 1 & 0 & 2 \\ 0 & -4 & 16 \end{array}\right] = \left[\begin{array}{cc|c} 1 & 0 & 2 \\ 0 & 1 & -4 \end{array}\right]$; (2, −4)

74. No; only square matrices have inverses.

75. Let x = 1st number, y = 2nd number, and z = 3rd number.
$x + y + z = 6$ $\quad$ $x + y + z = 6$
$x = 2y$ $\quad$ $2y + y + 3y = 6$
$z = 3y$ $\quad$ $6y = 6$
$y = 1$
$z = 3y$ $\quad$ $x = 2y$
$= 3(1)$ $\quad$ $= 2(1)$
$= 3$ $\quad$ $= 2$ $\quad$ 2, 1, 3

76. $ax + by = -10$
$a \cdot 2 + b \cdot 1 = -10$
Let $a = 6$.
$2a + b = -10$
$2(-6) + b = -10$
$-12 + b = -10$
$b = 2$; Sample answer: $a = -6$, $b = 2$

77. $t = 0.36s + 61.4$
$= 0.36(60) + 61.4$
$= 21.6 + 61.4$
$= 83$

78. $h(x) = \frac{x - 5}{7}$
$h(m - 2) = \frac{(m - 2) - 5}{7}$
$= \frac{m - 7}{7}$

79. $4 < 2x - 2 < 10$
$6 < 2x < 12$
$3 < x < 6$
$\{x \mid 3 < x < 6\}$

80. reflexive (=)

5-8 Solving Equations Containing Radicals

Page 307 Check for Understanding

1. Add $\sqrt{x + 3}$ to each side of the equation. Square each side of the equation. Then solve for x.
2. When the radical is isolated, squaring will remove it. If it is not isolated, squaring will simply produce another radical term in the equation.
3. While Pedro's method will always work in checking for extraneous solutions, Rochelle can save herself time by observing the equation. Since it is a fourth root, the principal value will always be positive. The equation states that the fourth root is negative. This is not possible.

4. $\sqrt{3d + 1} = 4$
$(\sqrt{3d + 1})^2 = 4^2$
$3d + 1 = 16$
$3d = 15$
$d = 5$

Check: $\sqrt{3d + 1} = 4$
$\sqrt{3(5) + 1} \stackrel{?}{=} 4$
$\sqrt{15 + 1} \stackrel{?}{=} 4$
$\sqrt{16} \stackrel{?}{=} 4$
$4 = 4$ ✓

5. $3 - (2 - y)^{\frac{1}{2}} = 0$
$-(2 - y)^{\frac{1}{2}} = -3$
$(2 - y)^{\frac{1}{2}} = 3$
$[(2 - y)^{\frac{1}{2}}]^2 = 3^2$
$2 - y = 9$
$-y = 7$
$y = -7$

Check: $3 - (2 - y)^{\frac{1}{2}} = 0$
$3 - (2 - (-7))^{\frac{1}{2}} \stackrel{?}{=} 0$
$3 - (9)^{\frac{1}{2}} \stackrel{?}{=} 0$
$3 - 3 \stackrel{?}{=} 0$
$0 = 0$ ✓

6. $1 + x\sqrt{2} = 0$
$x\sqrt{2} = -1$
$x = -\frac{1}{\sqrt{2}}$
$x = -\frac{1 \cdot \sqrt{2}}{\sqrt{2} \cdot \sqrt{2}}$
$x = -\frac{\sqrt{2}}{2}$

Check: $1 + x\sqrt{2} = 0$
$1 + \left(-\frac{\sqrt{2}}{2}\right)\sqrt{2} \stackrel{?}{=} 0$
$1 + \left(-\frac{\sqrt{4}}{2}\right) \stackrel{?}{=} 0$
$1 - \frac{2}{2} \stackrel{?}{=} 0$
$0 = 0$ ✓

7. $\sqrt{a - 4} - 3 = 0$
$\sqrt{a - 4} = 3$
$(\sqrt{a - 4})^2 = 3^2$
$a - 4 = 9$
$a = 13$

Check: $\sqrt{a - 4} - 3 = 0$
$\sqrt{13 - 4} - 3 \stackrel{?}{=} 0$
$\sqrt{9} - 3 \stackrel{?}{=} 0$
$3 - 3 \stackrel{?}{=} 0$
$0 = 0$ ✓

8. $\frac{2}{3} \cdot (4m)^{\frac{1}{3}} = 4$
$(4m)^{\frac{1}{3}} = 6$
$\left[(4m)^{\frac{1}{3}}\right]^3 = 6^3$
$4m = 216$
$m = 54$

Check: $\frac{2}{3} \cdot (4m)^{\frac{1}{3}} = 4$
$\frac{2}{3} \cdot (4 \cdot 54)^{\frac{1}{3}} \stackrel{?}{=} 4$
$\frac{2}{3}(216)^{\frac{1}{3}} \stackrel{?}{=} 4$
$\frac{2}{3} \cdot 6 \stackrel{?}{=} 4$
$4 = 4$ ✓

9. $\sqrt[3]{y + 1} = 2$
$(\sqrt[3]{y + 1})^3 = 2^3$
$y + 1 = 8$
$y = 7$

Check: $\sqrt[3]{y + 1} = 2$
$\sqrt[3]{7 + 1} \stackrel{?}{=} 2$
$\sqrt[3]{8} \stackrel{?}{=} 2$
$2 = 2$ ✓

10. $\sqrt[4]{2x + 3} - 4 = -5$
$\sqrt[4]{2x + 3} = -1$
no solution

11. $\sqrt{n + 12} - \sqrt{n} > 2$
$\sqrt{n + 12} > \sqrt{n} + 2$
$(\sqrt{n + 12})^2 > (\sqrt{n} + 2)^2$
$n + 12 > n + 2\sqrt{n} + 2\sqrt{n} + 4$
$n + 12 > n + 4\sqrt{n} + 4$
$12 > 4\sqrt{n} + 4$
$8 > 4\sqrt{n}$
$2 > \sqrt{n}$
$2^2 > (\sqrt{n})^2$
$4 > n \geq 0$

Check: $\sqrt{n + 12} - \sqrt{n} > 2$
$\sqrt{0 + 12} - \sqrt{0} \stackrel{?}{>} 2$
$\sqrt{12} - \sqrt{0} \stackrel{?}{>} 2$
$3.46 - 0 \stackrel{?}{>} 2$
$3.46 > 2$ ✓

12.
$$\begin{aligned}
\sqrt{x+9} &= 9-\sqrt{x}\\
(\sqrt{x+9})^2 &= (9-\sqrt{x})^2\\
x+9 &= 81-9\sqrt{x}-9\sqrt{x}+x\\
x+9 &= 81-18\sqrt{x}+x\\
9 &= 81-18\sqrt{x}\\
-72 &= -18\sqrt{x}\\
4 &= \sqrt{x}\\
4^2 &= (\sqrt{x})^2\\
16 &= x;\ \text{d}
\end{aligned}$$

$$\begin{aligned}
\text{Check: } \sqrt{x+9} &= 9-\sqrt{x}\\
\sqrt{16+9} &\stackrel{?}{=} 9-\sqrt{16}\\
\sqrt{25} &\stackrel{?}{=} 9-4\\
5 &= 5\ ✓
\end{aligned}$$

13.
$$\begin{aligned}
y &= \sqrt{r^2+s^2}\\
y^2 &= \left(\sqrt{r^2+s^2}\right)^2\\
y^2 &= r^2+s^2\\
y^2-s^2 &= r^2\\
\pm\sqrt{y^2-s^2} &= \sqrt{r^2}\\
\pm\sqrt{y^2-s^2} &= r
\end{aligned}$$

Pages 307–309 Exercises

14.
$$\begin{aligned}
\sqrt{x} &= 3\\
(\sqrt{x})^2 &= 3^2\\
x &= 9
\end{aligned}
\qquad
\begin{aligned}
\text{Check: } \sqrt{x} &= 3\\
\sqrt{9} &\stackrel{?}{=} 3\\
3 &= 3\ ✓
\end{aligned}$$

15.
$$\begin{aligned}
\sqrt{q}-8 &= 0\\
\sqrt{q} &= 8\\
(\sqrt{q})^2 &= 8^2\\
q &= 64
\end{aligned}
\qquad
\begin{aligned}
\text{Check: } \sqrt{q}-8 &= 0\\
\sqrt{64}-8 &\stackrel{?}{=} 0\\
8-8 &\stackrel{?}{=} 0\\
0 &= 0\ ✓
\end{aligned}$$

16.
$$\begin{aligned}
x^{\frac{1}{2}}+4 &= 0\\
x^{\frac{1}{2}} &= -4\\
\left(x^{\frac{1}{2}}\right)^2 &= (-4)^2\\
x &= 16
\end{aligned}
\qquad
\begin{aligned}
\text{Check: } x^{\frac{1}{2}}+4 &= 0\\
16^{\frac{1}{2}}+4 &\stackrel{?}{=} 0\\
4+4 &\stackrel{?}{=} 0\\
8 &\neq 0
\end{aligned}$$

no solution

17.
$$\begin{aligned}
7+6n\sqrt{5} &= 0\\
6n\sqrt{5} &= -7\\
n &= \frac{-7}{6\sqrt{5}}\\
n &= \frac{-7\cdot\sqrt{5}}{6\sqrt{5}\cdot\sqrt{5}}\\
n &= -\frac{7\sqrt{5}}{30}
\end{aligned}
\qquad
\begin{aligned}
\text{Check: } 7+6n\sqrt{5} &= 0\\
7+6\left(-\frac{7\sqrt{5}}{30}\right)\sqrt{5} &\stackrel{?}{=} 0\\
7-\frac{7\sqrt{25}}{5} &\stackrel{?}{=} 0\\
7-\frac{7\cdot 5}{5} &\stackrel{?}{=} 0\\
7-7 &\stackrel{?}{=} 0\\
0 &= 0\ ✓
\end{aligned}$$

18.
$$\begin{aligned}
\sqrt[3]{r-1} &= 3\\
(\sqrt[3]{r-1})^3 &= 3^3\\
r-1 &= 27\\
r &= 28
\end{aligned}
\qquad
\begin{aligned}
\text{Check: } \sqrt[3]{r-1} &= 3\\
\sqrt[3]{28-1} &\stackrel{?}{=} 3\\
\sqrt[3]{27} &\stackrel{?}{=} 3\\
3 &= 3\ ✓
\end{aligned}$$

19.
$$\begin{aligned}
\sqrt[3]{2p+1} &= 3\\
(\sqrt[3]{2p+1})^3 &= 3^3\\
2p+1 &= 27\\
2p &= 26\\
p &= 13
\end{aligned}
\qquad
\begin{aligned}
\text{Check: } \sqrt[3]{2p+1} &= 3\\
\sqrt[3]{2(13)+1} &\stackrel{?}{=} 3\\
\sqrt[3]{26+1} &\stackrel{?}{=} 3\\
\sqrt[3]{27} &\stackrel{?}{=} 3\\
3 &= 3\ ✓
\end{aligned}$$

20.
$$\begin{aligned}
\sqrt[4]{7+3z} &= 2\\
(\sqrt[4]{7+3z})^4 &= 2^4\\
7+3z &= 16\\
3z &= 9\\
z &= 3
\end{aligned}
\qquad
\begin{aligned}
\text{Check: } \sqrt[4]{7+3z} &= 2\\
\sqrt[4]{7+3(3)} &\stackrel{?}{=} 2\\
\sqrt[4]{7+9} &\stackrel{?}{=} 2\\
\sqrt[4]{16} &\stackrel{?}{=} 2\\
2 &= 2\ ✓
\end{aligned}$$

21.
$$\begin{aligned}
x\sqrt{x} &= 8\\
(x\sqrt{x})^2 &= 8^2\\
x^2\cdot x &= 64\\
x^3 &= 64\\
x &= 4
\end{aligned}
\qquad
\begin{aligned}
\text{Check: } x\sqrt{x} &= 8\\
4\sqrt{4} &\stackrel{?}{=} 8\\
4\cdot 2 &\stackrel{?}{=} 8\\
8 &= 8\ ✓
\end{aligned}$$

22.
$$\begin{aligned}
y\sqrt{3}-y &= 7\\
y(\sqrt{3}-1) &= 7\\
y &= \frac{7}{\sqrt{3}-1}\\
y &= \frac{7(\sqrt{3}+1)}{(\sqrt{3}-1)(\sqrt{3}+1)}\\
y &= \frac{7(\sqrt{3}+1)}{3+\sqrt{3}-\sqrt{3}-1}\\
y &= \frac{7(\sqrt{3}+1)}{2}\\
y &= \frac{7}{2}(\sqrt{3}+1)
\end{aligned}$$

$$\begin{aligned}
\text{Check: } y\sqrt{3}-y &= 7\\
\frac{7}{2}(\sqrt{3}+1)\sqrt{3}-\frac{7}{2}(\sqrt{3}+1) &\stackrel{?}{=} 7\\
\left(\frac{7\sqrt{3}}{2}+\frac{7}{2}\right)\sqrt{3}-\frac{7\sqrt{3}}{2}-\frac{7}{2} &\stackrel{?}{=} 7\\
\frac{7\cdot 3}{2}+\frac{7\sqrt{3}}{2}-\frac{7\sqrt{3}}{2}-\frac{7}{2} &\stackrel{?}{=} 7\\
\frac{21}{2}-\frac{7}{2} &\stackrel{?}{=} 7\\
\frac{14}{2} &\stackrel{?}{=} 7\\
7 &= 7\ ✓
\end{aligned}$$

23.
$$\begin{aligned}
\sqrt{2x-9} &= -\frac{1}{3}\\
(\sqrt{2x-9})^2 &= \left(-\frac{1}{3}\right)^2\\
2x-9 &= \frac{1}{9}\\
2x &= \frac{82}{9}\\
x &= \frac{41}{9}
\end{aligned}
\qquad
\begin{aligned}
\text{Check: } \sqrt{2x-9} &= -\frac{1}{3}\\
\sqrt{2\left(\frac{41}{9}\right)-9} &\stackrel{?}{=} -\frac{1}{3}\\
\sqrt{\frac{82}{9}-9} &\stackrel{?}{=} -\frac{1}{3}\\
\sqrt{\frac{1}{9}} &\stackrel{?}{=} -\frac{1}{3}\\
\frac{1}{3} &\neq -\frac{1}{3}
\end{aligned}$$

no solution

24.
$$\begin{aligned}
9+\sqrt{4x+8} &= 11\\
\sqrt{4x+8} &= 2\\
(\sqrt{4x+8})^2 &= 2^2\\
4x+8 &= 4\\
4x &= -4\\
x &= -1
\end{aligned}
\qquad
\begin{aligned}
\text{Check: } 9+\sqrt{4x+8} &= 11\\
9+\sqrt{4(-1)+8} &\stackrel{?}{=} 11\\
9+\sqrt{4} &\stackrel{?}{=} 11\\
9+2 &\stackrel{?}{=} 11\\
11 &= 11\ ✓
\end{aligned}$$

25.
$$\begin{aligned}
3+\sqrt{4n-5} &= 10\\
\sqrt{4n-5} &= 7\\
(\sqrt{4n-5})^2 &= 7^2\\
4n-5 &= 49\\
4n &= 54\\
n &= \frac{54}{4}
\end{aligned}
\qquad
\begin{aligned}
\text{Check: } 3+\sqrt{4n-5} &= 10\\
3+\sqrt{4\left(\frac{54}{4}\right)-5} &\stackrel{?}{=} 10\\
3+\sqrt{54-5} &\stackrel{?}{=} 10\\
3+\sqrt{49} &\stackrel{?}{=} 10\\
3+7 &\stackrel{?}{=} 10\\
10 &= 10\ ✓
\end{aligned}$$

26.
$$\begin{aligned}
6-\sqrt{2y+1} &< 3\\
-\sqrt{2y+1} &< -3\\
\sqrt{2y+1} &> 3\\
(\sqrt{2y+1})^2 &> 3^2\\
2y+1 &> 9\\
2y &> 8\\
y &> 4
\end{aligned}
\qquad
\begin{aligned}
\text{Check: } 6-\sqrt{2y+1} &< 3\\
6-\sqrt{2(12)+1} &\stackrel{?}{<} 3\\
6-\sqrt{25} &\stackrel{?}{<} 3\\
6-5 &\stackrel{?}{<} 3\\
1 &< 3\ ✓
\end{aligned}$$

27. $(7-5x)^{\frac{1}{2}} \geq 8$

$[(7-5x)^{\frac{1}{2}}]^2 \geq 8^2$

$7-5x \geq 64$

$-5x \geq 57$

$x \leq -\frac{57}{5}$

Check: $(7-5x)^{\frac{1}{2}} \geq 8$

$\left(7-5\left(-\frac{74}{5}\right)\right)^{\frac{1}{2}} \stackrel{?}{\geq} 8$

$(7+74)^{\frac{1}{2}} \stackrel{?}{\geq} 8$

$81^{\frac{1}{2}} \stackrel{?}{\geq} 8$

$9 \geq 8$ ✓

28. $13-3r = r\sqrt{5}$

$13 = 3r + r\sqrt{5}$

$13 = r(3+\sqrt{5})$

$\frac{13}{3+\sqrt{5}} = r$

$\frac{13(3-\sqrt{5})}{(3+\sqrt{5})(3-\sqrt{5})} = r$

$\frac{39-13\sqrt{5}}{9-3\sqrt{5}+3\sqrt{5}-5} = r$

$\frac{39-13\sqrt{5}}{4} = r$

Check: $13-3r = r\sqrt{5}$

$13-3\left(\frac{39-13\sqrt{5}}{4}\right) \stackrel{?}{=} \left(\frac{39-13\sqrt{5}}{4}\right)\sqrt{5}$

$13+\frac{-117+39\sqrt{5}}{4} \stackrel{?}{=} \frac{39\sqrt{5}-13\cdot 5}{4}$

$\frac{-65+39\sqrt{5}}{4} = \frac{39\sqrt{5}-65}{4}$ ✓

29. $3x+5 = x\sqrt{3}$

$5 = -3x + x\sqrt{3}$

$5 = x(-3+\sqrt{3})$

$\frac{5}{-3+\sqrt{3}} = x$

$\frac{5(-3-\sqrt{3})}{(-3+\sqrt{3})(-3-\sqrt{3})} = x$

$\frac{-15-5\sqrt{3}}{9+3\sqrt{3}-3\sqrt{3}-3} = x$

$\frac{-15-5\sqrt{3}}{6} = x$

Check: $3x+5 = x\sqrt{3}$

$3\left(\frac{-15-5\sqrt{3}}{6}\right)+5 \stackrel{?}{=} \left(\frac{-15-5\sqrt{3}}{6}\right)\sqrt{3}$

$\frac{-45-15\sqrt{3}}{6}+5 \stackrel{?}{=} \frac{-15\sqrt{3}-5\cdot 3}{6}$

$\frac{-15-15\sqrt{3}}{6} = \frac{-15\sqrt{3}-15}{6}$ ✓

30. $\sqrt{g-4} = \sqrt{2g-3}$

$(\sqrt{g-4})^2 = (\sqrt{2g-3})^2$

$g-4 = 2g-3$

$-4 = g-3$

$-1 = g$

Check: $\sqrt{g-4} = \sqrt{2g-3}$

$\sqrt{-1-4} \stackrel{?}{=} \sqrt{2(-1)-3}$

$\sqrt{-5} \stackrel{?}{=} \sqrt{-5}$

$\sqrt{-5}$ has no real solution.

no solution

31. $\sqrt{2r-6} = \sqrt{3+r}$

$(\sqrt{2r-6})^2 = (\sqrt{3+r})^2$

$2r-6 = 3+r$

$r-6 = 3$

$r = 9$

Check: $\sqrt{2r-6} = \sqrt{3+r}$

$\sqrt{2(9)-6} \stackrel{?}{=} \sqrt{3+9}$

$\sqrt{18-6} \stackrel{?}{=} \sqrt{12}$

$\sqrt{12} = \sqrt{12}$ ✓

32. $\sqrt{2}-\sqrt{x+6} \leq -\sqrt{x}$

$\sqrt{2}+\sqrt{x} \leq \sqrt{x+6}$

$(\sqrt{2}+\sqrt{x})^2 \leq (\sqrt{x+6})^2$

$2+\sqrt{2x}+\sqrt{2x}+x \leq x+6$

$2+2\sqrt{2x}+x \leq x+6$

$2\sqrt{2x} \leq 4$

$\sqrt{2x} \leq 2$

$(\sqrt{2x})^2 \leq 2^2$

$2x \leq 4$

$0 \leq x \leq 2$

Check: $\sqrt{2}-\sqrt{x+6} \leq -\sqrt{x}$

$\sqrt{2}-\sqrt{2+6} \stackrel{?}{\leq} -\sqrt{2}$

$\sqrt{2}-\sqrt{8} \stackrel{?}{\leq} -\sqrt{2}$

$1.41-2.65 \stackrel{?}{\leq} -\sqrt{2}$

$-1.24 \leq -\sqrt{2}$ ✓

33. $\sqrt{k+9}-\sqrt{k} > \sqrt{3}$

$\sqrt{k+9} > \sqrt{k}+\sqrt{3}$

$(\sqrt{k+9})^2 > (\sqrt{k}+\sqrt{3})^2$

$k+9 > k+\sqrt{3k}+\sqrt{3k}+3$

$k+9 > k+2\sqrt{3k}+3$

$6 > 2\sqrt{3k}$

$3 > \sqrt{3k}$

$3^2 > (\sqrt{3k})^2$

$9 > 3k$

$3 > k \geq 0$

Check: $\sqrt{k+9}-\sqrt{k} > \sqrt{3}$

$\sqrt{1+9}-\sqrt{1} \stackrel{?}{>} \sqrt{3}$

$\sqrt{10}-\sqrt{1} \stackrel{?}{>} \sqrt{3}$

$3.16-1 \stackrel{?}{>} \sqrt{3}$

$2.16 > \sqrt{3}$ ✓

34. $\sqrt{x-6} = 3+\sqrt{x}$

$(\sqrt{x-6})^2 = (3+\sqrt{x})^2$

$x-6 = 9+3\sqrt{x}+3\sqrt{x}+x$

$x-6 = 9+6\sqrt{x}+x$

$-15 = 6\sqrt{x}$

$-\frac{15}{6} = \sqrt{x}$

$\left(-\frac{15}{6}\right)^2 = (\sqrt{x})^2$

$\frac{225}{36} = x$

Check: $\sqrt{x-6} = 3+\sqrt{x}$

$\sqrt{\frac{225}{36}-6} \stackrel{?}{=} 3+\sqrt{\frac{225}{36}}$

$\sqrt{\frac{189}{36}} \stackrel{?}{=} 3+\frac{15}{6}$

$\frac{\sqrt{189}}{6} \neq \frac{33}{6}$

no solution

35. $\sqrt{h+3}+\sqrt{h-1} = 5$

$\sqrt{h+3} = 5-\sqrt{h-1}$

$(\sqrt{h+3})^2 = (5-\sqrt{h-1})^2$

$h+3 = 25-10\sqrt{h-1}+(h-1)$

$3 = 24-10\sqrt{h-1}$

$-21 = -10\sqrt{h-1}$

$\frac{21}{10} = \sqrt{h-1}$

$(2.1)^2 = (\sqrt{h-1})^2$

$4.41 = h-1$

$5.41 = h$

(Continued next page)

Check: $\sqrt{h+3} + \sqrt{h-1} = 5$
$\sqrt{5.41+3} + \sqrt{5.41-1} \stackrel{?}{=} 5$
$\sqrt{8.41} + \sqrt{4.41} \stackrel{?}{=} 5$
$2.9 + 2.1 \stackrel{?}{=} 5$
$5 = 5$ ✓

36. $\sqrt{x+21} - 1 = \sqrt{x+12}$
$(\sqrt{x+21} - 1)^2 = (\sqrt{x+12})^2$
$x + 21 - 2\sqrt{x+21} + 1 = x + 12$
$22 - 2\sqrt{x+21} = 12$
$-2\sqrt{x+21} = -10$
$\sqrt{x+21} = 5$
$(\sqrt{x+21})^2 = 5^2$
$x + 21 = 25$
$x = 4$
Check: $\sqrt{x+21} - 1 = \sqrt{x+12}$
$\sqrt{4+21} - 1 \stackrel{?}{=} \sqrt{4+12}$
$\sqrt{25} - 1 \stackrel{?}{=} \sqrt{16}$
$5 - 1 \stackrel{?}{=} 4$
$4 = 4$ ✓

37. $\sqrt{4x+1} = 3 + \sqrt{4x-2}$
$(\sqrt{4x+1})^2 = (3 + \sqrt{4x-2})^2$
$4x + 1 = 9 + 6\sqrt{4x-2} + (4x - 2)$
$1 = 7 + 6\sqrt{4x-2}$
$-6 = 6\sqrt{4x-2}$
$-1 = \sqrt{4x-2}$
$(-1)^2 = (\sqrt{4x-2})^2$
$1 = 4x - 2$
$3 = 4x$
$\frac{3}{4} = x$
Check: $\sqrt{4x+1} = 3 + \sqrt{4x-2}$
$\sqrt{4\left(\frac{3}{4}\right) + 1} \stackrel{?}{=} 3 + \sqrt{4\left(\frac{3}{4}\right) - 2}$
$\sqrt{4} \stackrel{?}{=} 3 + \sqrt{1}$
$2 \stackrel{?}{=} 3 + 1$
$2 \neq 4$
no solution

38. $(6g-5)^{\frac{1}{3}} + 2 = -3$
$(6g-5)^{\frac{1}{3}} = -5$
$[(6g-5)^{\frac{1}{3}}]^3 = (-5)^3$
$6g - 5 = -125$
$6g = -120$
$g = -20$

Check: $(6g-5)^{\frac{1}{3}} + 2 = -3$
$(6(-20) - 5)^{\frac{1}{3}} + 2 \stackrel{?}{=} -3$
$(-125)^{\frac{1}{3}} + 2 \stackrel{?}{=} -3$
$-5 + 2 \stackrel{?}{=} -3$
$-3 = -3$ ✓

39. $\sqrt{a+1} = \sqrt{a+6} - 1$
$(\sqrt{a+1})^2 = (\sqrt{a+6} - 1)^2$
$a + 1 = a + 6 - 2\sqrt{a+6} + 1$
$1 = 7 - 2\sqrt{a+6}$
$-6 = -2\sqrt{a+6}$
$3 = \sqrt{a+6}$
$3^2 = (\sqrt{a+6})^2$
$9 = \text{a} + 6$
$3 = a$
Check: $\sqrt{a+1} = \sqrt{a+6} - 1$
$\sqrt{3+1} \stackrel{?}{=} \sqrt{3+6} - 1$
$\sqrt{4} \stackrel{?}{=} \sqrt{9} - 1$
$2 \stackrel{?}{=} 3 - 1$
$2 = 2$ ✓

40. $\sqrt{b+5} + \sqrt{b+10} > 2$
$(\sqrt{b+5})^2 > (2 - \sqrt{b+10})^2$
$b + 5 > 4 - 4\sqrt{b+10} + b + 10$
$4\sqrt{b+10} > 9$
$(\sqrt{b+10})^2 > \left(\frac{9}{4}\right)^2$
$b + 10 > \frac{81}{16}$
$b > \frac{81}{16} - 10$
$b > \frac{81}{16} - \frac{160}{16}$
$b > \frac{-79}{16}$
$b > -4.9375$
Check: $\sqrt{b+5} + \sqrt{b+10} > 2$
$\sqrt{-1+5} + \sqrt{-1+10} \stackrel{?}{>} 2$
$\sqrt{4} + \sqrt{9} \stackrel{?}{>} 2$
$2 + 3 \stackrel{?}{>} 2$
$5 > 2$ ✓

41. $\sqrt{a-5} - \sqrt{a+7} \leq 4$
$\sqrt{a-5} \leq 4 + \sqrt{a+7}$
$a - 5 \leq 16 + 8\sqrt{a+7} + a + 7$
$\frac{-28}{8} \leq a + 7$
$\frac{-28}{8} - 7 \leq a$
$\frac{-28}{8} - \frac{56}{8} \leq a$
$\frac{-84}{8} \leq a$
$\frac{-21}{2} \leq a$
$-10\frac{1}{2} \leq a$
But $a - 5 \geq 0$, so $a \geq 5$.
Check: $\sqrt{a-5} - \sqrt{a+7} \leq 4$
$\sqrt{9-5} - \sqrt{9+7} \stackrel{?}{\leq} 4$
$\sqrt{4} - \sqrt{16} \stackrel{?}{\leq} 4$
$2 - 4 \stackrel{?}{\leq} 4$
$-2 \leq 4$ ✓

42. $x + \sqrt{x} - 30 = 0$
$25 + \sqrt{25} - 30 \stackrel{?}{=} 0$
$25 + 5 - 30 \stackrel{?}{=} 0$
$0 = 0$ ✓

$x + \sqrt{x} - 30 = 0$
$36 + \sqrt{36} - 30 \stackrel{?}{=} 0$
$36 + 6 - 30 \stackrel{?}{=} 0$
$12 \neq 0$

25 is an acceptable solution but 36 is not.

43. $T = 2\pi\sqrt{\frac{\ell}{g}}$

$\frac{T}{2\pi} = \sqrt{\frac{\ell}{g}}$

$\left(\frac{T}{2\pi}\right)^2 = \left(\sqrt{\frac{\ell}{g}}\right)^2$

$\frac{T^2}{4\pi^2} = \frac{\ell}{g}$

$g \cdot \frac{T^2}{4\pi^2} = \ell$

44. $t = \sqrt{\frac{2s}{g^2}}$

$t^2 = \left(\sqrt{\frac{2s}{g^2}}\right)^2$

$t^2 = \frac{2s}{g^2}$

$\frac{t^2g^2}{2} = s$

45. $m^2 = \sqrt[3]{\frac{rp}{g^2}}$

$(m^2)^3 = \left(\sqrt[3]{\frac{rp}{g^2}}\right)^3$

$m^6 = \frac{rp}{g^2}$

$\frac{m^6g^2}{r} = p$

46. $r = \sqrt[3]{\frac{2mM}{c}}$

$r^3 = \left(\sqrt[3]{\frac{2mM}{c}}\right)^3$

$r^3 = \frac{2mM}{c}$

$cr^3 = 2mM$

$c = \frac{2mM}{r^3}$

47a. $S = \pi r\sqrt{r^2 + h^2}$

$\frac{S}{\pi r} = \sqrt{r^2 + h^2}$

$\left(\frac{S}{\pi r}\right)^2 = \left(\sqrt{r^2 + h^2}\right)^2$

$\frac{S^2}{\pi^2 r^2} = r^2 + h^2$

$\frac{S^2}{\pi^2 r^2} - r^2 = h^2$

$\frac{S^2 - r^4\pi^2}{\pi^2 r^2} = h^2$

$\frac{\sqrt{S^2 - r^4\pi^2}}{\pi r} = h$

47b. $h = \frac{\sqrt{S^2 - r^4\pi^2}}{\pi r}$

$= \frac{\sqrt{225^2 - 5^4\pi^2}}{\pi \cdot 5}$

$\approx \frac{\sqrt{50{,}625 - 6168.5}}{15.71}$

$\approx \frac{210.85}{15.71}$

≈ 13.4

48. Yes, $\sqrt[n]{b^m} = (b^m)^{\frac{1}{n}} = b^{\frac{m}{n}} = (b^{\frac{1}{n}})^m = (\sqrt[n]{b})^m$

49. Yes, $\sqrt[k]{\sqrt[m]{b}} = (b^{\frac{1}{m}})^{\frac{1}{k}} = b^{\frac{1}{km}} = \sqrt[km]{b}$

50. $c = 100\sqrt[3]{n^2} + 1200$

$10{,}000 = 100\sqrt[3]{n^2} + 1200$

$8800 = 100\sqrt[3]{n^2}$

$88 = \sqrt[3]{n^2}$

$(88)^3 = \left(\sqrt[3]{n^2}\right)^3$

$681{,}472 = n^2$

$825.5 \approx n$; about 826 chips

51. $A = \pi r^2$

$250{,}000 = \pi r^2$

$79{,}577.47 \approx r^2$

$282.09 \approx r$

about 282 feet

52a. $\frac{T_a}{T_b} = \left(\frac{r_a}{r_b}\right)^{\frac{3}{2}}$

$\left(\frac{T_a}{T_b}\right)^{\frac{2}{3}} = \left[\left(\frac{r_a}{r_b}\right)^{\frac{3}{2}}\right]^{\frac{2}{3}}$

$\left(\frac{T_a}{T_b}\right)^{\frac{2}{3}} = \frac{r_a}{r_b}$

$r_b\left(\frac{T_a}{T_b}\right)^{\frac{2}{3}} = r_a$

52b. $r_a = r_b\left(\frac{T_a}{T_b}\right)^{\frac{2}{3}}$

$= 36{,}000{,}000\left(\frac{12 \cdot 365}{88}\right)^{\frac{2}{3}}$

$\approx 36{,}000{,}000(49.77)^{\frac{2}{3}}$

$\approx 36{,}000{,}000(13.53)$

$\approx 487{,}113{,}455.6$

about 487 million miles

53. $r = \sqrt[3]{\frac{GMt^2}{4\pi^2}}$

$r^3 = \left(\sqrt[3]{\frac{GMt^2}{4\pi^2}}\right)^3$

$r^3 = \frac{GMt^2}{4\pi^2}$

$\frac{4\pi^2r^3}{GM} = t^2$

$\sqrt{\frac{4\pi^2r^3}{GM}} = t$

$\frac{2\pi r\sqrt{r}}{\sqrt{GM}} = t$

$\frac{2\pi r\sqrt{r} \cdot \sqrt{GM}}{\sqrt{GM} \cdot \sqrt{GM}} = t$

$\frac{2\pi r\sqrt{GMr}}{GM} = t$

54. $\frac{1}{0.01} = \frac{x}{15}$

$15 = 0.01x$

$1500 = x$

1500 square centimeters

$s^2 = 1500$

$s = \sqrt{1500}$

$s = 10\sqrt{15}$

$s \approx 38.73$

$10\sqrt{15}$ or about 38.73 centimeters on each side.

55. $5^{\frac{3}{7}}$

56. $\sqrt{3}(\sqrt{6} - 2) = \sqrt{18} - 2\sqrt{3}$

$= \sqrt{3^2 \cdot 2} - 2\sqrt{3}$

$= 3\sqrt{2} - 2\sqrt{3}$

57. $\sqrt{x^2 + 10x + 25} = \sqrt{(x + 5)^2}$

$= |x + 5|$

58.

1	2	0	−2	−3
		2	2	0
	2	2	0	−3

$2t^2 + 2t - \frac{3}{t - 1}$

59. $(y^5)^2 = y^{5 \cdot 2}$

$= y^{10}$

60. $\left[\begin{array}{ccc|c} 1 & 5 & 2 & 10 \\ 3 & -3 & 2 & 2 \\ 2 & 4 & -1 & -15 \end{array}\right] = \left[\begin{array}{ccc|c} 1 & 5 & 2 & 10 \\ 3 & -3 & 2 & 2 \\ 4 & 8 & -2 & -30 \end{array}\right]$

$= \left[\begin{array}{ccc|c} 5 & 13 & 0 & -20 \\ 3 & -3 & 2 & 2 \\ 4 & 8 & -2 & -30 \end{array}\right] = \left[\begin{array}{ccc|c} 5 & 13 & 0 & -20 \\ 7 & 5 & 0 & -28 \\ 4 & 8 & -2 & -30 \end{array}\right]$

$= \left[\begin{array}{ccc|c} 5 & 13 & 0 & -20 \\ -35 & -25 & 0 & 140 \\ 4 & 8 & -2 & -30 \end{array}\right] = \left[\begin{array}{ccc|c} 5 & 13 & 0 & -20 \\ 0 & 66 & 0 & 0 \\ 4 & 8 & -2 & -30 \end{array}\right]$

$= \left[\begin{array}{ccc|c} 5 & 13 & 0 & -20 \\ 0 & 1 & 0 & 0 \\ 4 & 8 & -2 & -30 \end{array}\right] = \left[\begin{array}{ccc|c} 5 & 0 & 0 & -20 \\ 0 & 1 & 0 & 0 \\ 4 & 8 & -2 & -30 \end{array}\right]$

$= \left[\begin{array}{ccc|c} 1 & 0 & 0 & -4 \\ 0 & 1 & 0 & 0 \\ 4 & 8 & -2 & -30 \end{array}\right] = \left[\begin{array}{ccc|c} 1 & 0 & 0 & -4 \\ 0 & 1 & 0 & 0 \\ 0 & 8 & -2 & -14 \end{array}\right]$

$= \left[\begin{array}{ccc|c} 1 & 0 & 0 & -4 \\ 0 & 1 & 0 & 0 \\ 0 & 0 & -2 & -14 \end{array}\right] = \left[\begin{array}{ccc|c} 1 & 0 & 0 & -4 \\ 0 & 1 & 0 & 0 \\ 0 & 0 & 1 & 7 \end{array}\right]$; $(-4, 0, 7)$

61. $\begin{vmatrix} 4 & -2 \\ 3 & 7 \end{vmatrix} = 28 - (-6)$
$= 34$

62. Let one drum $= a$ and the other drum $= b$.

$a + b = 7$
$b = -a + 7$
$30a + 20b = 160$
$20b = -30a + 160$
$b = -\frac{3}{2}a + 8$
$(2, 5)$

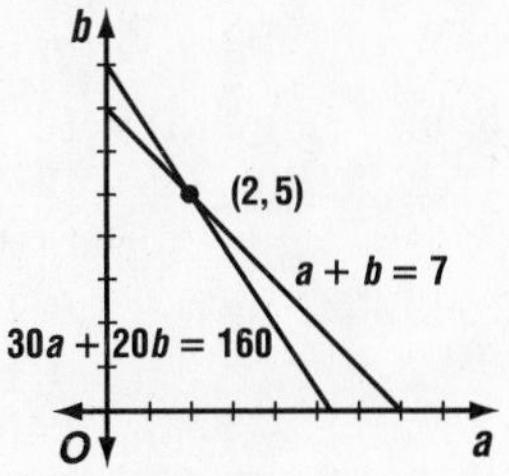

63a. $y = \frac{1}{4}(0.20x + 60)$
$= 0.05x + 15$

63b. $y = 0.05x + 15$
$= 0.05(42) + 15$
$= 2.1 + 15$
$= 17.10$; \$17.10

64.

Stem	Leaf
0	4 4 4 4 5 6 6 6 6 7 7 8 9 9
1	1 1 2 2 6 9 9 9
	1 | 1 = 11¢

5-9 Complex Numbers

Page 314 Check for Understanding

1a. true **1b.** true

2a. along the real axis (x-axis)

2b. along the imaginary axis (y-axis)

3. $\sqrt{-50} = \sqrt{5^2} \cdot \sqrt{2} \cdot \sqrt{-1}$
$= 5 \cdot \sqrt{2} \cdot i$
$= 5i\sqrt{2}$; c

4. $(-4 + 3i) + (5 + 2i) = 1 + 5i$

5.

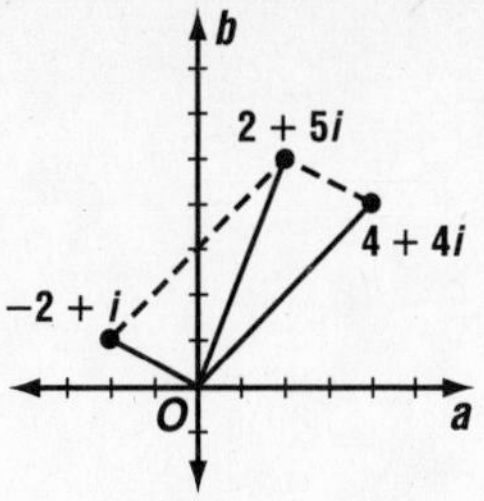

$2 + 5i$

6. $\sqrt{-64} = \sqrt{8^2} \cdot \sqrt{-1}$
$= 8i$

7. $\sqrt{-98m^2n^2} = \sqrt{7^2} \cdot \sqrt{2} \cdot \sqrt{m^2} \cdot \sqrt{n^2} \cdot \sqrt{-1}$
$= 7 \cdot \sqrt{2} \cdot |m| \cdot |n| \cdot i$
$= 7i|mn|\sqrt{2}$

8. $(4i)(-3i) = -12i^2$
$= -12(-1)$
$= 12$

9. $5\sqrt{-24} \cdot 3\sqrt{-18}$
$= 5 \cdot \sqrt{2^2} \cdot \sqrt{6} \cdot \sqrt{-1} \cdot 3 \cdot \sqrt{3^2} \cdot \sqrt{2} \cdot \sqrt{-1}$
$= 5 \cdot 2 \cdot \sqrt{6} \cdot i \cdot 3 \cdot 3 \cdot \sqrt{2} \cdot i$
$= 90i^2\sqrt{12}$
$= 90(-1)\sqrt{2^2} \cdot \sqrt{3}$
$= -90 \cdot 2\sqrt{3}$
$= -180\sqrt{3}$

10. $\sqrt{3} \cdot \sqrt{-27} = \sqrt{-81}$
$= \sqrt{9^2} \cdot \sqrt{-1}$
$= 9i$

11. $i^{16} = (i^2)^8$
$= (-1)^8$
$= 1$

12. $(15 + 10i) - (4 + 6i) = (15 - 4) + (10i - 6i)$
$= 11 + 4i$

13. $(4 + 2i) + (1 + 3i) = (4 + 1) + (2i + 3i)$
$= 5 + 5i$

14. $(4 - 3i)(5 + 7i) = 20 + 28i - 15i - 21i^2$
$= 20 + 13i - 21(-1)$
$= 41 + 13i$

15. $(3 + 2i)(3 - 2i) = 9 - 6i + 6i - 4i^2$
$= 9 - 4(-1)$
$= 13$

16. $(2 - 4i)(3 + 9i) = 6 + 18i - 12i - 36i^2$
$= 6 + 6i - 36(-1)$
$= 42 + 6i$

17. $5x^2 + 40 = 0$
$5x^2 = -40$
$x^2 = -8$
$x = \pm\sqrt{-8}$
$x = \pm 2i\sqrt{2}$

$5x^2 + 40 = 0$
$5(-2i\sqrt{2})^2 + 40 \stackrel{?}{=} 0$
$40i^2 + 40 \stackrel{?}{=} 0$
$40(-1) + 40 \stackrel{?}{=} 0$
$-40 + 40 \stackrel{?}{=} 0$
$0 = 0$

The other solution is $2i\sqrt{2}$.

18. $5x^2 + 30 = 5$
$5x^2 = -25$
$x^2 = -5$
$x = \pm\sqrt{-5}$
$x = \pm i\sqrt{5}$

19. $a^2 + 16 = 0$
$a^2 = -16$
$a = \pm\sqrt{-16}$
$a = \pm 4i$

Pages 314–316 Exercises

20. $\sqrt{-169} = \sqrt{13^2} \cdot \sqrt{-1}$
$= 13i$

21. $\sqrt{-\frac{4}{9}} = \sqrt{\frac{2^2}{3^2}} \cdot \sqrt{-1}$
$= \frac{2}{3}i$

22. $\sqrt{-49} = \sqrt{7^2} \cdot \sqrt{-1}$
$= 7i$

23. $\sqrt{-100k^4} = \sqrt{10^2} \cdot \sqrt{(k^2)^2} \cdot \sqrt{-1}$
$= 10k^2i$

24. $\sqrt{-36m^4n^2} = \sqrt{6^2} \cdot \sqrt{(m^2)^2} \cdot \sqrt{n^2} \cdot \sqrt{-1}$
$= 6m^2|n|i$

25. $\sqrt{-\frac{9x^3}{25y^8}} = \frac{\sqrt{3^2} \cdot \sqrt{x^2 \cdot x} \cdot \sqrt{-1}}{\sqrt{5^2} \cdot \sqrt{(y^4)^2}}$
$= \frac{3 \cdot |x| \cdot \sqrt{x} \cdot i}{5 \cdot y^4}$
$= \frac{3i|x|}{5y^4}\sqrt{x}$

26. $(2i)^2 = 2^2i^2$
$= 4(-1)$
$= -4$

27. $(-4i)(-5i)(3i) = 60i^2 \cdot i$
$= 60(-1)i$
$= -60i$

28. $5i(-2i)^2 = 5i(4i^2)$
$= 5i(-4)$
$= -20i$

29. $(\sqrt{-11})(\sqrt{-22}) = \sqrt{11} \cdot \sqrt{-1} \cdot \sqrt{22} \cdot \sqrt{-1}$
$= \sqrt{11} \cdot i \cdot \sqrt{22} \cdot i$
$= \sqrt{11} \cdot \sqrt{11} \cdot \sqrt{2} \cdot i^2$
$= 11 \cdot \sqrt{2} \cdot (-1)$
$= -11\sqrt{2}$

30. $(2\sqrt{-50})\left(\frac{1}{8}\sqrt{-2}\right)$
$= 2 \cdot \frac{1}{8} \cdot \sqrt{5^2} \cdot \sqrt{2} \cdot \sqrt{-1} \cdot \sqrt{2} \cdot \sqrt{-1}$
$= \frac{1}{4} \cdot 5 \cdot 2 \cdot i \cdot i$
$= \frac{5}{2}i^2$
$= -\frac{5}{2}$

31. $\sqrt{-8} \cdot \sqrt{-18}$
$= \sqrt{2^2} \cdot \sqrt{2} \cdot \sqrt{-1} \cdot \sqrt{3^2} \cdot \sqrt{2} \cdot \sqrt{-1}$
$= 2 \cdot 2 \cdot i \cdot 3 \cdot i$
$= 12i^2$
$= -12$

32. $\sqrt{-5} \cdot \sqrt{20} = \sqrt{5} \cdot \sqrt{-1} \cdot \sqrt{2^2} \cdot \sqrt{5}$
$= 5 \cdot i \cdot 2$
$= 10i$

33. $\sqrt{-8} \cdot \sqrt{6} = \sqrt{2^2} \cdot \sqrt{2} \cdot \sqrt{-1} \cdot \sqrt{2} \cdot \sqrt{3}$
$= 2 \cdot 2 \cdot i \cdot \sqrt{3}$
$= 4i\sqrt{3}$

34. $-2\sqrt{-x} \cdot -5\sqrt{-y}$
$= -2 \cdot \sqrt{x} \cdot \sqrt{-1} \cdot -5 \cdot \sqrt{y} \cdot \sqrt{-1}$
$= 10\sqrt{x} \cdot i \cdot \sqrt{y} \cdot i$
$= 10i^2\sqrt{xy}$
$= -10\sqrt{xy}$

35. $i^{17} = i \cdot i^{16}$
$= i \cdot (i^2)^8$
$= i \cdot (-1)^8$
$= i$

36. $i^{59} = i \cdot i^{58}$
$= i \cdot (i^2)^{29}$
$= i \cdot (-1)^{29}$
$= -i$

37. $i^{34} = (i^2)^{17}$
$= (-1)^{17}$
$= -1$

38. $2\sqrt{-18} + 3\sqrt{-2}$
$= 2\sqrt{3^2} \cdot \sqrt{2} \cdot \sqrt{-1} + 3 \cdot \sqrt{2} \cdot \sqrt{-1}$
$= 2 \cdot 3 \cdot \sqrt{2} \cdot i + 3\sqrt{2} \cdot i$
$= 6i\sqrt{2} + 3i\sqrt{2}$
$= 9i\sqrt{2}$

39. $(4 - i) + (3 + 3i) = (4 + 3) + (-i + 3i)$
$= 7 + 2i$

40. $(8 - 5i) - (2 + i) = (8 - 2) + (-5i - i)$
$= 6 - 6i$

41. $(7 - 6i) - (5 - 6i) = (7 - 5) + (-6i + 6i)$
$= 2$

42. $(2 - 4i) + (2 + 4i) = (2 + 2) + (-4i + 4i)$
$= 4$

43. $(11 - \sqrt{-3}) - (-4 + \sqrt{-5})$
$= (11 + 4) + (-\sqrt{-3} - \sqrt{-5})$
$= 15 - i\sqrt{3} - i\sqrt{5}$

44. $(4 + i)(4 - i) = 16 - 4i + 4i - i^2$
$= 16 - (-1)$
$= 17$

45. $(4 - i)(3 + 2i) = 12 + 8i - 3i - 2i^2$
$= 12 + 5i - 2(-1)$
$= 14 + 5i$

46. $(3 - 4i)^2 = 9 - 12i - 12i + 16i^2$
$= 9 - 24i + 16(-1)$
$= -7 - 24i$

47. $(2 - \sqrt{-3})(2 + \sqrt{-3}) = (2 - i\sqrt{3})(2 + i\sqrt{3})$
$= 4 + 2i\sqrt{3} - 2i\sqrt{3} - i^2 \cdot 3$
$= 4 - (-1)3$
$= 7$

48. $3(-5 - 2i) + 2(-3 + 2i) = (-15 - 6i) + (-6 + 4i)$
$= (-15 - 6) + (-6i + 4i)$
$= -21 - 2i$

49. $(3 + 2i)^2 + (3 + 4i)^2$
$= 9 + 6i + 6i + 4i^2 + 9 + 12i + 12i + 16i^2$
$= 9 + 12i + 4(-1) + 9 + 24i + 16(-1)$
$= -2 + 36i$

50. $-6x^2 - 30 = 0$
$-6x^2 = 30$
$x^2 = -5$
$x = \pm\sqrt{-5}$
$x = \pm i\sqrt{5}$

51. $5x^2 + 40 = 0$
$5x^2 = -40$
$x^2 = -8$
$x = \pm\sqrt{-8}$
$x = \pm 2i\sqrt{2}$

52. $3x^2 + 18 = 0$
$3x^2 = -18$
$x^2 = -6$
$x = \pm\sqrt{-6}$
$x = \pm i\sqrt{6}$

53. $7x^2 + 84 = 0$
$7x^2 = -84$
$x^2 = -12$
$x = \pm\sqrt{-12}$
$x = \pm 2i\sqrt{3}$

54. $\frac{2}{3}x^2 + 30 = 0$
$\frac{2}{3}x^2 = -30$
$x^2 = -45$
$x = \pm\sqrt{-45}$
$x = \pm 3i\sqrt{5}$

55. $4x^2 + 5 = 0$
$4x^2 = -5$
$x^2 = -\frac{5}{4}$
$x = \pm\sqrt{-\frac{5}{4}}$
$x = \pm i\frac{\sqrt{5}}{2}$

56. $(-6 + 2i)(7 - i)(4 + 3i)$
$= (-42 + 6i + 14i - 2i^2)(4 + 3i)$
$= (-42 + 20i + 2)(4 + 3i)$
$= (-40 + 20i)(4 + 3i)$
$= -160 - 120i + 80i + 60i^2$
$= -160 - 40i - 60$
$= -220 - 40i$

57. $(7 - 5i)(7 + 5i)(2 - 3i)$
$= (49 + 35i - 35i - 25i^2)(2 - 3i)$
$= (49 + 25)(2 - 3i)$
$= 74(2 - 3i)$
$= 148 - 222i$

58. $(7 - i)(4 + 2i)(5 + 2i) = (28 + 14i - 4i - 2i^2)(5 + 2i)$
$= (28 + 10i + 2)(5 + 2i)$
$= (30 + 10i)(5 + 2i)$
$= 150 + 60i + 50i + 20i^2$
$= 150 + 110i - 20$
$= 130 + 110i$

59. $(2 + i)(1 + 2i)(3 - 4i) = (2 + 4i + i + 2i^2)(3 - 4i)$
$= (2 + 5i - 2)(3 - 4i)$
$= 5i(3 - 4i)$
$= 15i - 20i^2$
$= 20 + 15i$

60. $18 + 7i = 3m + 2ni$
$18 = 3m \qquad 7i = 2ni$
$6 = m \qquad 3.5 = n$

61. $(2m + n) + (m - n)i = 7 - i$

$$\begin{array}{rl} 2m + n = & 7 \\ (+)\,m - n = & -1 \\ \hline 3m \quad = & 6 \\ m = & 2 \end{array} \qquad \begin{array}{r} m - n = -1 \\ 2 - n = -1 \\ -n = -3 \\ n = 3 \end{array}$$

62. $(m + 2n) + (2m - n)i = 5 + 5i$

$m + 2n = 5 \rightarrow \qquad \rightarrow \quad m + 2n = 5$
$2m - n = 5 \rightarrow$ Multiply by 2 $\rightarrow (+)4m - 2n = 10$

$$\begin{array}{rl} 5m & = 15 \\ m & = 3 \end{array}$$

$2m - n = 5$
$2(3) - n = 5$
$6 - n = 5$
$-n = -1$
$n = 1$

63. $(2m - 3n)i + (m + 4n) = 13 + 7i$

$m + 4n = 13$
$m = -4n + 13$

$2m - 3n = 7$
$2(-4n + 13) - 3n = 7$
$-8n + 26 - 3n = 7$
$-11n + 26 = 7$
$-11n = -19$
$n = \frac{19}{11}$

$m + 4n = 13$
$m + 4\left(\frac{19}{11}\right) = 13$
$m + \frac{76}{11} = 13$
$m = \frac{67}{11}$

64. Sample answer: $(2 + i)(2 - i) = 4 - i^2$ or 5

65a. $y = -6x^2 - 30 \qquad y = 5x^2 + 40$
$y = 3x^2 + 18 \qquad y = 7x^2 + 84$
$y = \frac{2}{3}x^2 + 30 \qquad y = 4x^2 + 5$

65b. [Y=] [(-)] 6 [X,T,θ,n] [x^2] [−] 30 [GRAPH]
(WINDOW [−10, 10] by [−80, 10])

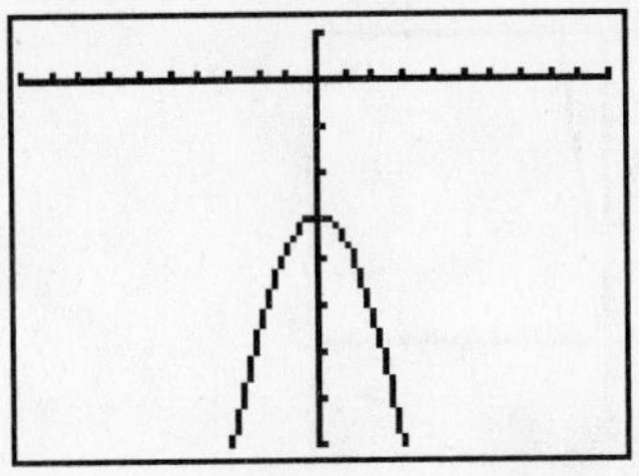

[Y=] 5 [X,T,θ,n] [x^2] [+] 40 [GRAPH]
(WINDOW [−10, 10] by [−10, 100])

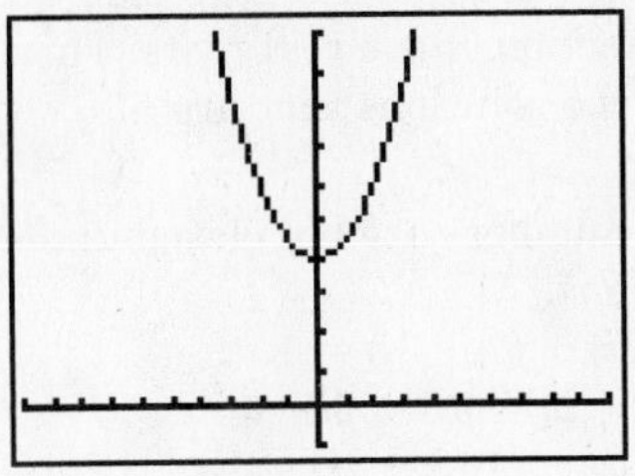

[Y=] 3 [X,T,θ,n] [x^2] [+] 18 [GRAPH]
(WINDOW [−10, 10] by [−5, 50])

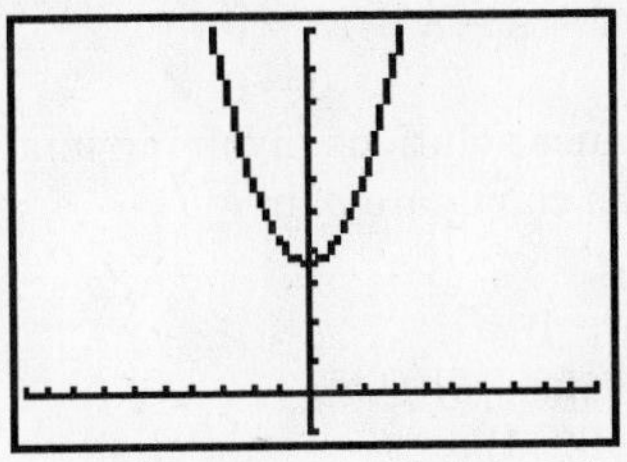

[Y=] 7 [X,T,θ,n] [x^2] [+] 84 [GRAPH]
(WINDOW [−10, 10] by [−5, 160])

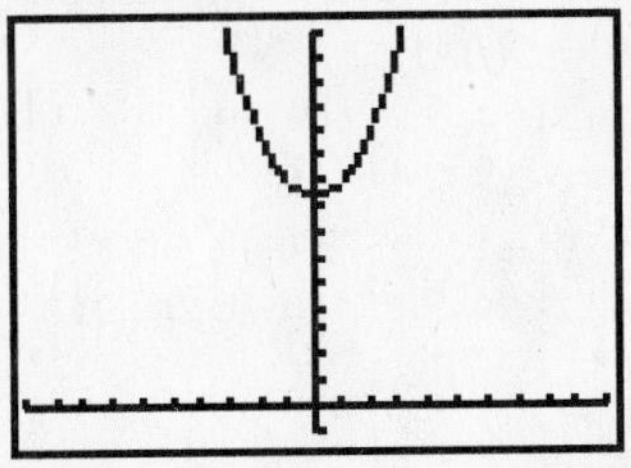

[Y=] [(] 2 [÷] 3 [)] [X,T,θ,n] [x^2] [+] 30
[GRAPH] (WINDOW [−10, 10] by [−10, 150])

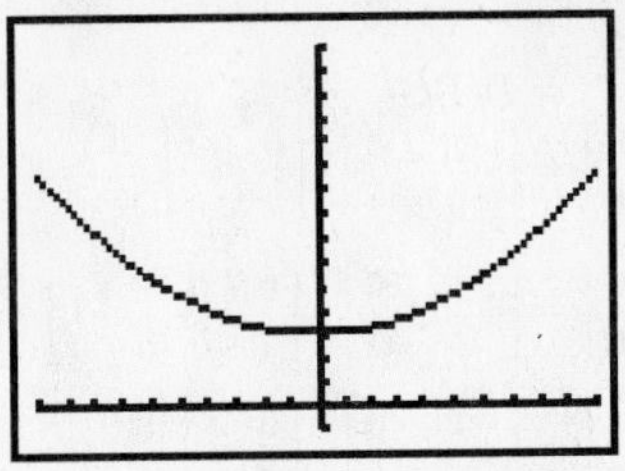

(Continued next page)

Y= 4 X,T,θ,n x² + 5 GRAPH

(WINDOW [−10, 10] by [−5, 15])

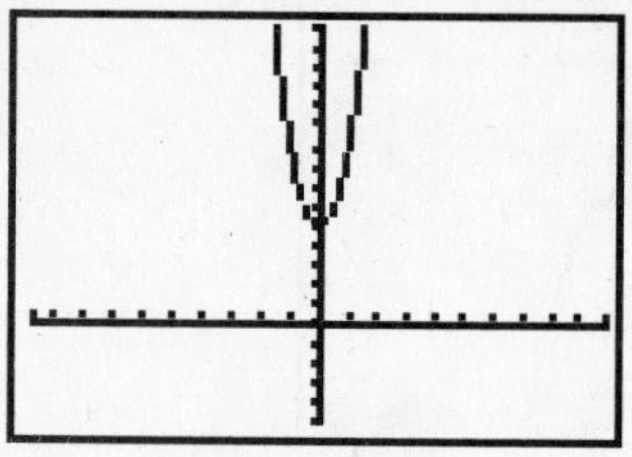

65c. Sample answers: None of the graphs intercept the x-axis. All of the graphs are parabolas.

65d. Since none of the graphs intercept the x-axis, none of the functions have real roots. This is confirmed by the solutions that are all imaginary.

66. The imaginary numbers are not closed under any of these operations.
Addition: $(2 + 3i) + (2 - 3i) = 4$
Subtraction: $(1 + 2i) - (3 + 2i) = -2$
Multiplication: $(3 + 2i)(3 - 2i) = 13$

67.
$$x^2 - 4x + 13 = 0$$
$$(2 - 3i)^2 - 4(2 - 3i) + 13 \stackrel{?}{=} 0$$
$$(4 - 12i + 9i^2) - 8 + 12i + 13 \stackrel{?}{=} 0$$
$$4 - 9 - 8 + 13 \stackrel{?}{=} 0$$
$$0 = 0 \checkmark$$

Yes, $2 + 3i$, because solutions involving imaginary numbers occur in conjugate pairs.

68a.
$$\begin{aligned} E &= I \cdot Z \\ &= (7 + 3j)(5 - j) \\ &= 35 - 7j + 15j - 3j^2 \\ &= 35 + 8j - 3(-1) \\ &= 38 + 8j \end{aligned}$$

68b.
$$\begin{aligned} (50 + 20j) - (10 + 5j) &= (50 - 10) + (20j - 5j) \\ &= 40 + 15j; \end{aligned}$$
$(40 + 15j)$ amps

69a.
$$AB = D(BA)$$
$$\begin{bmatrix} 0 & 1 \\ 1 & 0 \end{bmatrix} \cdot \begin{bmatrix} 0 & -i \\ i & 0 \end{bmatrix} \stackrel{?}{=} \begin{bmatrix} -1 & 0 \\ 0 & -1 \end{bmatrix} \left(\begin{bmatrix} 0 & -i \\ i & 0 \end{bmatrix} \cdot \begin{bmatrix} 0 & 1 \\ 1 & 0 \end{bmatrix} \right)$$
$$\begin{bmatrix} 0 + i & 0 + 0 \\ 0 + 0 & -i + 0 \end{bmatrix} \stackrel{?}{=} \begin{bmatrix} -1 & 0 \\ 0 & -1 \end{bmatrix} \cdot \begin{bmatrix} 0 - i & 0 + 0 \\ 0 + 0 & i + 0 \end{bmatrix}$$
$$\begin{bmatrix} i & 0 \\ 0 & -i \end{bmatrix} \stackrel{?}{=} \begin{bmatrix} -1 & 0 \\ 0 & -1 \end{bmatrix} \cdot \begin{bmatrix} -i & 0 \\ 0 & i \end{bmatrix}$$
$$\begin{bmatrix} i & 0 \\ 0 & -i \end{bmatrix} \stackrel{?}{=} \begin{bmatrix} i + 0 & 0 + 0 \\ 0 + 0 & 0 - i \end{bmatrix}$$
$$\begin{bmatrix} i & 0 \\ 0 & -i \end{bmatrix} = \begin{bmatrix} i & 0 \\ 0 & -i \end{bmatrix}$$

69b.
$$CB = D(BC)$$
$$\begin{bmatrix} 1 & 0 \\ 0 & -1 \end{bmatrix} \cdot \begin{bmatrix} 0 & -i \\ i & 0 \end{bmatrix} \stackrel{?}{=} \begin{bmatrix} -1 & 0 \\ 0 & -1 \end{bmatrix} \left(\begin{bmatrix} 0 & -i \\ i & 0 \end{bmatrix} \cdot \begin{bmatrix} 1 & 0 \\ 0 & -1 \end{bmatrix} \right)$$
$$\begin{bmatrix} 0 + 0 & -i + 0 \\ 0 - i & 0 + 0 \end{bmatrix} \stackrel{?}{=} \begin{bmatrix} -1 & 0 \\ 0 & -1 \end{bmatrix} \cdot \begin{bmatrix} 0 + 0 & 0 + i \\ i + 0 & 0 + 0 \end{bmatrix}$$
$$\begin{bmatrix} 0 & -i \\ -i & 0 \end{bmatrix} \stackrel{?}{=} \begin{bmatrix} -1 & 0 \\ 0 & -1 \end{bmatrix} \cdot \begin{bmatrix} 0 & i \\ i & 0 \end{bmatrix}$$
$$\begin{bmatrix} 0 & -i \\ -i & 0 \end{bmatrix} \stackrel{?}{=} \begin{bmatrix} 0 + 0 & -i + 0 \\ 0 - i & 0 + 0 \end{bmatrix}$$
$$\begin{bmatrix} 0 & -i \\ -i & 0 \end{bmatrix} = \begin{bmatrix} 0 & -i \\ -i & 0 \end{bmatrix}$$

70a. $i^0 = 1$, $i^1 = i$, $i^2 = -1$, $i^3 = (i^2 \cdot i) = -i$, $i^4 = (i^2 \cdot i^2) = 1$, $i^5 = (i^4 \cdot i) = i$, $i^6 = (i^4 \cdot i^2) = -1$, $i^7 = (i^6 \cdot i) = -i$, $i^8 = (i^4 \cdot i^4) = 1$, $i^9 = (i^8 \cdot i) = i$, $i^{10} = (i^8 \cdot i^2) = -1$, $i^{11} = (i^{10} \cdot i) = -i$, $i^{12} = (i^6 \cdot i^6) = 1$; They all equal 1, i, −1 or $-i$.

70b. Evaluate $(i^2)^{\frac{n}{2}}$.

70c.
(1) $\begin{aligned} i^{4k} &= (i^2)^{\frac{4k}{2}} \\ &= (-1)^{2k} \\ &= 1 \end{aligned}$

(2) $\begin{aligned} i^{4k+1} &= (i^2)^{\frac{4k+1}{2}} \\ &= \sqrt{-1^{4k+1}} \\ &= i \end{aligned}$

(3) $\begin{aligned} i^{4k+2} &= (i^2)^{\frac{4k+2}{2}} \\ &= (-1)^{2k+1} \\ &= -1 \end{aligned}$

(4) $\begin{aligned} i^{4k+3} &= i^{4k+2} \cdot i^1 \\ &= -1 \cdot i \\ &= -i \end{aligned}$

70d.
(1) $\begin{aligned} i^{784} &= (i^2)^{\frac{784}{2}} \\ &= (-1)^{392} \\ &= 1 \end{aligned}$

(2) $\begin{aligned} i^{503} &= (i^2)^{\frac{503}{2}} \\ &= \sqrt{(-1)^{503}} \\ &= \sqrt{-1} \\ &= i \end{aligned}$

(3) $\begin{aligned} i^{8,413,634} &= (i^2)^{\frac{8,413,634}{2}} \\ &= (-1)^{4,206,817} \\ &= -1 \end{aligned}$

71.
$$\sqrt{3y^2 + 11y - 5} = y\sqrt{3} + 1$$
$$\left(\sqrt{3y^2 + 11y - 5}\right)^2 = (y\sqrt{3} + 1)^2$$
$$3y^2 + 11y - 5 = 3y^2 + 2y\sqrt{3} + 1$$
$$11y - 5 = 2y\sqrt{3} + 1$$
$$11y - 2y\sqrt{3} = 6$$
$$y(11 - 2\sqrt{3}) = 6$$
$$y = \frac{6}{11 - 2\sqrt{3}}$$
$$y = \frac{6(11 + 2\sqrt{3})}{(11 - 2\sqrt{3})(11 + 2\sqrt{3})}$$
$$y = \frac{6(11 + 2\sqrt{3})}{121 + 22\sqrt{3} - 22\sqrt{3} - 12}$$
$$y = \frac{6(11 + 2\sqrt{3})}{109}$$

72. List perfect squares between 0 and 100: 1, 4, 9, 16, 25, 36, 49, 64, 81, 100;
total: 10
odd: 5
Fraction $= \frac{5}{10}$ or $\frac{1}{2}$

73.
$$\begin{aligned} t &= \tfrac{1}{4}\sqrt{d} \\ &= \tfrac{1}{4}\sqrt{150} \\ &\approx \tfrac{1}{4}(12.25) \\ &\approx 3.06; \text{ 3.06 seconds} \end{aligned}$$

74.
$$\begin{aligned} 3p(p^2 - 2p + 3) &= 3p(p^2) + 3p(-2p) + 3p(3) \\ &= 3p^3 - 6p^2 + 9p \end{aligned}$$

75. $\left[\begin{array}{rrr|r} 1 & 3 & -2 & 9 \\ -1 & 5 & 2 & 31 \\ 2 & 0 & 9 & -32 \end{array}\right] = \left[\begin{array}{rrr|r} 1 & 3 & -2 & 9 \\ 0 & 8 & 0 & 40 \\ 2 & 0 & -9 & -32 \end{array}\right]$

$= \left[\begin{array}{rrr|r} 1 & 3 & -2 & 9 \\ 0 & 1 & 0 & 5 \\ 2 & 0 & -9 & -32 \end{array}\right] = \left[\begin{array}{rrr|r} 1 & 0 & -2 & -6 \\ 0 & 1 & 0 & 5 \\ 2 & 0 & 9 & -32 \end{array}\right]$

$= \left[\begin{array}{rrr|r} 1 & 0 & -2 & -6 \\ 0 & 1 & 0 & 5 \\ 0 & 0 & -5 & -20 \end{array}\right] = \left[\begin{array}{rrr|r} 1 & 0 & -2 & -6 \\ 0 & 1 & 0 & 5 \\ 0 & 0 & 1 & 4 \end{array}\right]$

$= \left[\begin{array}{rrr|r} 1 & 0 & 0 & 2 \\ 0 & 1 & 0 & 5 \\ 0 & 0 & 1 & 4 \end{array}\right]$; (2, 5, 4)

76. $3\begin{bmatrix} 3 & -2 & 5 \\ 2 & 7 & -5 \end{bmatrix} + 2\begin{bmatrix} -1 & 3 & 4 \\ 2 & -3 & 0 \end{bmatrix} = \begin{bmatrix} 9 & -6 & 15 \\ 6 & 21 & -15 \end{bmatrix} + \begin{bmatrix} -2 & 6 & 8 \\ 4 & -6 & 0 \end{bmatrix}$

$= \begin{bmatrix} 7 & 0 & 23 \\ 10 & 15 & -15 \end{bmatrix}$

77. Let x = sofa, y = loveseat, and z = coffee table.

$x + y + z = 2100$ $\quad x + y + z = 2100$ $\quad x = 2y$

$x = 2y$ $\quad \underline{(-)x \quad + z = 1510}$ $\quad = 2(590)$

$x + z = 1510$ $\quad y \quad = 590$ $\quad = 1180$

$x + z = 1510$

$1180 + z = 1510$

$z = 330$

sofa, \$1180; loveseat, \$590; table, \$330

78. $3x - 2y = 7$ $\quad 3x - 2y = 7$

$\underline{(+)-3x + 9y = 14}$ $\quad 3x - 2(3) = 7$

$7y = 21$ $\quad 3x - 6 = 7$

$y = 3$ $\quad 3x = 13$

$x = \frac{13}{3}$ $\quad \left(\frac{13}{3}, 3\right)$

79. x-intercept: (6, 0) $\quad m = \frac{-5 - 0}{0 - 6}$

y-intercept: (0, −5) $\quad = \frac{-5}{-6}$

$= \frac{5}{6}$

$y - y_1 = m(x - x_1)$

$y - 0 = \frac{5}{6}(x - 6)$

$y = \frac{5}{6}x - 5$

$-\frac{5}{6}x + y = -5$

$5x - 6y = 30$

80. $2x + 3y = 12$

$2(0) + 3y = 12$ $\quad 2x + 3(0) = 12$

$3y = 12$ $\quad 2x = 12$

$y = 4$ $\quad x = 6$

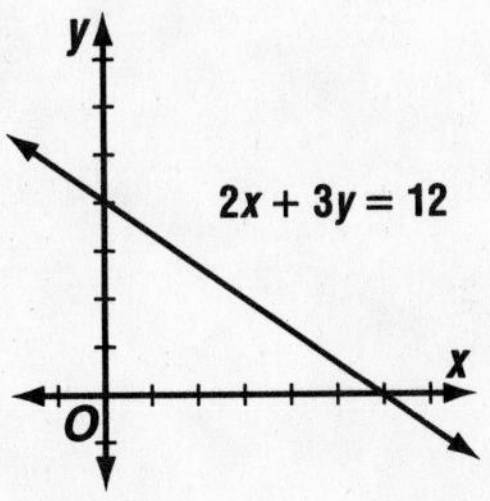

81. Let n = the number.

$n + 27 = 46$

$n = 19$

82. commutative (+)

5-10 Simplifying Expressions Containing Complex Numbers

Page 319 Check for Understanding

1. To rationalize the denominator, multiply 1 in the form of $\frac{a - bi}{a - bi}$.
2. The resulting product is a sum of two squares that are each real numbers.

3a. $z^2 = (1 + 2i)^2$

$= 1 + 2i + 2i + 4i^2$

$= 1 + 4i + 4(-1)$

$= -3 + 4i$

3b. $\frac{1}{z} = \frac{1}{1 + 2i}$

$= \frac{1(1 - 2i)}{(1 + 2i)(1 - 2i)}$

$= \frac{1 - 2i}{1 - 4i^2}$

$= \frac{1 - 2i}{5}$

3c. z or $1 + 2i$; $\quad z^2 \cdot \frac{1}{z} \stackrel{?}{=} z$

$(1 + 2i)^2 \cdot \left(\frac{1}{1 + 2i}\right) \stackrel{?}{=} 1 + 2i$

$\frac{(1 + 2i)(1 + 2i)}{(1 + 2i)} \stackrel{?}{=} 1 + 2i$

$1 + 2i = 1 + 2i$

4. All have additive inverses, but 0 does not have a multiplicative inverse.

5. $-7i$ $\qquad$ **6.** $3 - 5i$

7. $(-10i)(10i) = -100i^2$

$= 100$

8. $(12 + 5i)(12 - 5i) = 144 - 25i^2$

$= 144 - (-25)$

$= 169$

9. $\frac{7}{-2i} = \frac{7 \cdot i}{-2i \cdot i}$

$= \frac{7i}{-2i^2}$

$= \frac{7i}{2}$

10. $\frac{9 + 3i}{2i} = \frac{9 + 3i}{2i} \cdot \frac{i}{i}$

$= \frac{9i + 3i^2}{2i^2}$

$= \frac{9i - 3}{-2}$

$= \frac{3 - 9i}{2}$

11. $\frac{5}{2 + i} = \frac{5}{2 + i} \cdot \frac{2 - i}{2 - i}$

$= \frac{10 - 5i}{4 - i^2}$

$= \frac{10 - 5i}{5}$

$= 2 - i$

12. $\frac{5 + i}{1 + 2i} = \frac{5 + i}{1 + 2i} \cdot \frac{1 - 2i}{1 - 2i}$

$= \frac{5 - 10i + i - 2i^2}{1 - 4i^2}$

$= \frac{5 - 9i + 2}{1 + 4}$

$= \frac{7 - 9i}{5}$

13. $\frac{3 - 2i}{1 - i} = \frac{3 - 2i}{1 - i} \cdot \frac{1 + i}{1 + i}$

$= \frac{3 + 3i - 2i - 2i^2}{1 - i^2}$

$= \frac{3 - i + 2}{2}$

$= \frac{5 - i}{2}$

14. $\frac{7}{\sqrt{2}-3i} = \frac{7}{\sqrt{2}-3i} \cdot \frac{\sqrt{2}+3i}{\sqrt{2}+3i}$
$= \frac{7\sqrt{2}+21i}{2-9i^2}$
$= \frac{7\sqrt{2}+21i}{2+9}$
$= \frac{7\sqrt{2}+21i}{11}$

15. $\left(\frac{7+3i}{1}\right)\left(\frac{7-3i}{58}\right) = \frac{49-9i^2}{58}$
$= \frac{49+9}{58}$
$= \frac{58}{58}$
$= 1$

Pages 320–321 Exercises

16. $-10i$

17. $12 - i$

18. $15i$

19. $10 + 4i$

20. $7 - i\sqrt{5}$

21. $6 - i\sqrt{7}$

22. $(-2i)(2i) = -4i^2$
$= 4$

23. $(5 - 2i)(5 + 2i) = 25 - 4i^2$
$= 25 - (-4)$
$= 29$

24. $(4 + 6i)(4 - 6i) = 16 - 36i^2$
$= 16 - (-36)$
$= 52$

25. $(1 + i)(1 - i) = 1 - i^2$
$= 1 - (-1)$
$= 2$

26. $(3 + 5i\sqrt{2})(3 - 5i\sqrt{2}) = 9 - 25i^2 \cdot 2$
$= 9 - 50(-1)$
$= 59$

27. $(8 - 2i)(8 + 2i) = 64 - 4i^2$
$= 64 - (-4)$
$= 68$

28. $\frac{2+8i}{3i} = \frac{2+8i}{3i} \cdot \frac{i}{i}$
$= \frac{2i+8i^2}{3i^2}$
$= \frac{2i-8}{-3}$
$= \frac{8-2i}{3}$

29. $\frac{3+7i}{2i} = \frac{3+7i}{2i} \cdot \frac{i}{i}$
$= \frac{3i+7i^2}{2i^2}$
$= \frac{3i-7}{-2}$
$= \frac{7-3i}{2}$

30. $\frac{11+i}{2-i} = \frac{11+i}{2-i} \cdot \frac{2+i}{2+i}$
$= \frac{22+11i+2i+i^2}{4-i^2}$
$= \frac{22+13i-1}{4-(-1)}$
$= \frac{21+13i}{5}$

31. $\frac{3i}{2+i} = \frac{3i}{2+i} \cdot \frac{2-i}{2-i}$
$= \frac{6i-3i^2}{4-i^2}$
$= \frac{6i+3}{4+1}$
$= \frac{3+6i}{5}$

32. $\frac{-3i}{5+4i} = \frac{-3i}{5+4i} \cdot \frac{5-4i}{5-4i}$
$= \frac{-15i+12i^2}{25-16i^2}$
$= \frac{-15i-12}{25+16}$
$= \frac{-12-15i}{41}$

33. $\frac{3}{6+4i} = \frac{3}{6+4i} \cdot \frac{6-4i}{6-4i}$
$= \frac{18-12i}{36-16i^2}$
$= \frac{18-12i}{36+16}$
$= \frac{18-12i}{52}$
$= \frac{9-6i}{26}$

34. $\frac{3+5i}{1+i} = \frac{3+5i}{1+i} \cdot \frac{1-i}{1-i}$
$= \frac{3-3i+5i-5i^2}{1-i^2}$
$= \frac{3+2i+5}{1+1}$
$= \frac{8+2i}{2}$
$= 4 + i$

35. $\frac{2+i}{3-i} = \frac{2+i}{3-i} \cdot \frac{3+i}{3+i}$
$= \frac{6+2i+3i+i^2}{9-i^2}$
$= \frac{6+5i-1}{9+1}$
$= \frac{5+5i}{10}$
$= \frac{1+i}{2}$

36. $\frac{1-i}{4-5i} = \frac{1-i}{4-5i} \cdot \frac{4+5i}{4+5i}$
$= \frac{4+5i-4i-5i^2}{16-25i^2}$
$= \frac{4+i+5}{16+25}$
$= \frac{9+i}{41}$

37. $\frac{2+3i}{3-2i} = \frac{2+3i}{3-2i} \cdot \frac{3+2i}{3+2i}$
$= \frac{6+4i+9i+6i^2}{9-4i^2}$
$= \frac{6+13i-6}{9+4}$
$= \frac{13i}{13}$
$= i$

38. $\frac{5-6i}{-3i} = \frac{5-6i}{-3i} \cdot \frac{i}{i}$
$= \frac{5i-6i^2}{-3i^2}$
$= \frac{5i+6}{3}$
$= \frac{6+5i}{3}$

39. $\frac{3-9i}{4+2i} = \frac{3-9i}{4+2i} \cdot \frac{4-2i}{4-2i}$
$= \frac{12-6i-36i+18i^2}{16-4i^2}$
$= \frac{12-42i-18}{16+4}$
$= \frac{-6-42i}{20}$
$= -\frac{3-21i}{10}$

40. $\frac{8}{\sqrt{2}+i} = \frac{8}{\sqrt{2}+i} \cdot \frac{\sqrt{2}-i}{\sqrt{2}-i}$
$= \frac{8\sqrt{2}-8i}{2-i^2}$
$= \frac{8\sqrt{2}-8i}{2+1}$
$= \frac{8\sqrt{2}-8i}{3}$

41. $\frac{1}{3-i\sqrt{2}} = \frac{1}{3-i\sqrt{2}} \cdot \frac{3+i\sqrt{2}}{3+i\sqrt{2}}$
$= \frac{3+i\sqrt{2}}{9-2i^2}$
$= \frac{3+i\sqrt{2}}{9+2}$
$= \frac{3+i\sqrt{2}}{11}$

42. $\frac{4}{\sqrt{3}+2i} = \frac{4}{\sqrt{3}+2i} \cdot \frac{\sqrt{3}-2i}{\sqrt{3}-2i}$
$= \frac{4\sqrt{3}-8i}{3-4i^2}$
$= \frac{4\sqrt{3}-8i}{3+4}$
$= \frac{4\sqrt{3}-8i}{7}$

43. $\frac{1}{6-5i} = \frac{1}{6-5i} \cdot \frac{6+5i}{6+5i}$
$= \frac{6+5i}{36-25i^2}$
$= \frac{6+5i}{36+25}$
$= \frac{6+5i}{61}$

44. $\frac{3+5i}{-i} = \frac{3+5i}{-i} \cdot \frac{i}{i}$
$= \frac{3i+5i^2}{-i^2}$
$= \frac{3i-5}{1}$
$= -5+3i$

45. $\frac{1}{x+yi} = \frac{1}{x+yi} \cdot \frac{x-yi}{x-yi}$
$= \frac{x-yi}{x^2-y^2i^2}$
$= \frac{x-yi}{x^2+y^2}$

46. $f(x) = x^2 + 2$
$f(1+i) = (1+i)^2 + 2$
$= 1 + i + i + i^2 + 2$
$= 1 + 2i - 1 + 2$
$= 2 + 2i$
$f(2+2i) = (2+2i)^2 + 2$
$= 4 + 4i + 4i + 4i^2 + 2$
$= 4 + 8i - 4 + 2$
$= 2 + 8i$

47. $f(x) = 3x^2 + 2$
$f(1-i) = 3(1-i)^2 + 2$
$= 3(1 - i - i + i^2) + 2$
$= 3(1 - 2i - 1) + 2$
$= 3(-2i) + 2$
$= -6i + 2$
$= 2 - 6i$
$f(2-6i) = 3(2-6i)^2 + 2$
$= 3(4 - 12i - 12i + 36i^2) + 2$
$= 3(4 - 24i - 36) + 2$
$= 3(-32 - 24i) + 2$
$= -96 - 72i + 2$
$= -94 - 72i$

48. $f(x) = x^2 - x$
$f(i+3) = (i+3)^2 - (i+3)$
$= i^2 + 3i + 3i + 9 - i - 3$
$= -1 + 6i + 9 - i - 3$
$= 5 + 5i$
$f(5+5i) = (5+5i)^2 - (5+5i)$
$= 25 + 25i + 25i + 25i^2 - 5 - 5i$
$= 25 + 50i - 25 - 5 - 5i$
$= -5 + 45i$

49. $\frac{3-i\sqrt{5}}{3+i\sqrt{5}} = \frac{3-i\sqrt{5}}{3+i\sqrt{5}} \cdot \frac{3-i\sqrt{5}}{3-i\sqrt{5}}$
$= \frac{9-3i\sqrt{5}-3i\sqrt{5}+5i^2}{9-5i^2}$
$= \frac{9-6i\sqrt{5}-5}{9+5}$
$= \frac{4-6i\sqrt{5}}{14}$
$= \frac{2-3i\sqrt{5}}{7}$

50. $\frac{1+i\sqrt{3}}{1-i\sqrt{3}} = \frac{1+i\sqrt{3}}{1-i\sqrt{3}} \cdot \frac{1+i\sqrt{3}}{1+i\sqrt{3}}$
$= \frac{1+i\sqrt{3}+i\sqrt{3}+3i^2}{1-3i^2}$
$= \frac{1+2i\sqrt{3}-3}{1+3}$
$= \frac{-2+2i\sqrt{3}}{4}$
$= \frac{-1+i\sqrt{3}}{2}$

51. $\frac{1-i}{(1+i)^2} = \frac{1-i}{(1+i)(1+i)}$
$= \frac{1-i}{1+i+i+i^2}$
$= \frac{1-i}{1+2i-1}$
$= \frac{1-i}{2i}$
$= \frac{1-i}{2i} \cdot \frac{i}{i}$
$= \frac{i-i^2}{2i^2}$
$= \frac{i+1}{-2}$
$= \frac{-1-i}{2}$

52. $\left(\frac{\sqrt{3}}{2+3i}\right)^2 = \frac{3}{(2+3i)^2}$
$= \frac{3}{4+6i+6i+9i^2}$
$= \frac{3}{4+12i-9}$
$= \frac{3}{-5+12i}$
$= \frac{3}{-5+12i} \cdot \frac{-5-12i}{-5-12i}$
$= \frac{-15-36i}{25-144i^2}$
$= \frac{-15-36i}{25+144}$
$= \frac{-15-36i}{169}$

53. $\frac{(2+3i)^2}{(3+i)^2} = \frac{4+6i+6i+9i^2}{9+3i+3i+i^2}$
$= \frac{4+12i-9}{9+6i-1}$
$= \frac{-5+12i}{8+6i}$
$= \frac{-5+12i}{8+6i} \cdot \frac{8-6i}{8-6i}$
$= \frac{-40+30i+96i-72i^2}{64-36i^2}$
$= \frac{-40+126i+72}{64+36}$
$= \frac{32+126i}{100}$
$= \frac{16+63i}{50}$

54. $\dfrac{(4+3i)^2}{(3-4i)^2} = \dfrac{16+12i+12i+9i^2}{9-12i-12i+16i^2}$

$= \dfrac{16+24i-9}{9-24i-16}$

$= \dfrac{7+24i}{-7-24i}$

$= \dfrac{7+24i}{-1(7+24i)}$

$= \dfrac{1}{-1}$

$= -1$

55. $\overline{z \cdot w} = \overline{(a+bi)\cdot(c+di)}$

$= \overline{ac + adi + bci - bdi^2}$

$= \overline{(ac-bd) + (ad+bc)i}$

$= (ac-bd) - (ad+bc)i$

$= ac - adi - bd - bci$

$= ac - adi + bdi^2 - bci$

$= a(c-di) - bi(-di + c)$

$= (a-bi)(c-di)$

$= \overline{z} \cdot \overline{w}$

56. $\left(\dfrac{-1+i\sqrt{3}}{2}\right)^3 = \left(\dfrac{1-2i\sqrt{3}-3}{4}\right)\left(\dfrac{-1+i\sqrt{3}}{2}\right)$

$= \left(\dfrac{-1-i\sqrt{3}}{2}\right)\left(\dfrac{-1+i\sqrt{3}}{2}\right)$

$= \dfrac{1+3}{4}$ or 1

57a.

$E = IZ$

$60 + 112j = I(10+6j)$

$\dfrac{60+112j}{10+6j} = I$

$\dfrac{60+112j}{10+6j} \cdot \dfrac{10-6j}{10-6j} = I$

$\dfrac{600 - 360j + 1120j - 672j^2}{100 - 36j^2} = I$

$\dfrac{600 + 760j + 672}{100+36} = I$

$\dfrac{1272 + 760j}{136} = I$

$\dfrac{159 + 95j}{17} = I$

57b.

$E = IZ$

$85 + 110j = I(3-4j)$

$\dfrac{85+110j}{3-4j} = I$

$\dfrac{85+110j}{3-4j} \cdot \dfrac{3+4j}{3+4j} = I$

$\dfrac{255 + 340j + 330j + 440j^2}{9 - 16j^2} = I$

$\dfrac{255 + 670j - 440}{9+16} = I$

$\dfrac{-185 + 670j}{25} = I$

$\dfrac{-37 + 134j}{5} = I$

57c.

$E = IZ$

$-50 + 100j = (-6+2j)Z$

$\dfrac{-50+100j}{-6+2j} = Z$

$\dfrac{-50+100j}{-6+2j} \cdot \dfrac{-6-2j}{-6-2j} = Z$

$\dfrac{300 + 100j - 600j - 200j^2}{36 - 4j^2} = Z$

$\dfrac{300 - 500j + 200}{36+4} = Z$

$\dfrac{500 - 500j}{40} = Z$

$\dfrac{25 - 25j}{2} = Z$

57d.

$E = I \cdot Z$

$-70 + 240j = (-5+4j)Z$

$\dfrac{-70+240j}{-5+4j} = Z$

$\dfrac{-70+240j}{-5+4j} \cdot \dfrac{-5-4j}{-5-4j} = Z$

$\dfrac{350 + 280j - 1200j - 960j^2}{25 - 16j^2} = Z$

$\dfrac{350 - 920j + 960}{25+16} = Z$

$\dfrac{1310 - 920j}{41} = Z$

58a.

$E = IZ$

$5 = (1 + 2j\sqrt{2})Z$

$\dfrac{5}{1+2j\sqrt{2}} = Z$

$\dfrac{5}{1+2j\sqrt{2}} \cdot \dfrac{1-2j\sqrt{2}}{1-2j\sqrt{2}} = Z$

$\dfrac{5 - 10j\sqrt{2}}{1 - 4j^2 \cdot 2} = Z$

$\dfrac{5 - 10j\sqrt{2}}{1+8} = Z$

$\dfrac{5 - 10j\sqrt{2}}{9} = Z$

$\dfrac{5 - 10j\sqrt{2}}{9}$ ohms

58b.

$E = I \cdot Z$

$3 = I(2+3j)$

$\dfrac{3}{2+3j} = I$

$\dfrac{3}{2+3j} \cdot \dfrac{2-3j}{2-3j} = I$

$\dfrac{6-9j}{4-9j^2} = I$

$\dfrac{6-9j}{4+9} = I$

$\dfrac{6-9j}{13} = I$

$\dfrac{6-9j}{13}$ amps

59. $f(x) = x^2 - 1$

$$\begin{aligned} f(1 + i) &= (1 + i)^2 - 1 \\ &= 1 + i + i + i^2 - 1 \\ &= 2i - 1; -1 + 2i \end{aligned}$$

$(1 + i, -1 + 2i)$

$$\begin{aligned} f(-1 + 2i) &= (-1 + 2i)^2 - 1 \\ &= 1 - 2i - 2i + 4i^2 - 1 \\ &= -4i - 4; -4 - 4i \end{aligned}$$

$(-1 + 2i, -4 - 4i)$

$$\begin{aligned} f(-4 - 4i) &= (-4 - 4i)^2 - 1 \\ &= 16 + 16i + 16i + 16i^2 - 1 \\ &= 15 + 32i - 16 \\ &= -1 + 32i \end{aligned}$$

$(-4 - 4i, -1 + 32i)$

$$\begin{aligned} f(-1 + 32i) &= (-1 + 32i)^2 - 1 \\ &= 1 - 32i - 32i + 1024i^2 - 1 \\ &= -64i - 1024; -1024 - 64i \end{aligned}$$

$(-1 + 32i, -1024 - 64i)$

60.
$$\begin{aligned} 3a^2 + 24 &= 0 \\ 3a^2 &= -24 \\ a^2 &= -8 \\ a &= \pm\sqrt{-8} \\ a &= \pm\sqrt{2^2} \cdot \sqrt{2} \cdot \sqrt{-1} \\ a &= \pm 2i\sqrt{2} \end{aligned}$$

61.
$$\begin{aligned} 2x + 7 &= -x\sqrt{2} \\ 2x + x\sqrt{2} &= -7 \\ x(2 + \sqrt{2}) &= -7 \\ x &= \frac{-7}{2 + \sqrt{2}} \\ x &= \frac{-7}{2 + \sqrt{2}} \cdot \frac{(2 - \sqrt{2})}{(2 - \sqrt{2})} \\ x &= \frac{-14 + 7\sqrt{2}}{4 - 2} \\ x &= \frac{7\sqrt{2} - 14}{2} \end{aligned}$$

62. $(x + y)^2 - \frac{1}{4} = \left(x + y - \frac{1}{2}\right)\left(x + y + \frac{1}{2}\right)$

63.
$$\begin{aligned} V &= \ell \cdot w \cdot h \\ 4x^3 - 168x^2 + 1728x &= (48 - 2x) \cdot w \cdot (x) \\ 4x^2 - 168x + 1728 &= (48 - 2x)w \\ \frac{4x^2 - 168x + 1728}{48 - 2x} &= w \\ \frac{(2x - 48)(2x - 36)}{(-1)(2x - 48)} &= w \\ -1(2x - 36) &= w \\ -2x + 36 &= w; \text{ 36 inches} \end{aligned}$$

64.
$$\begin{aligned} M^{-1} &= \frac{1}{3 - (-4)}\begin{bmatrix} 1 & -1 \\ 4 & 3 \end{bmatrix} \\ &= \frac{1}{7}\begin{bmatrix} 1 & -1 \\ 4 & 3 \end{bmatrix} \end{aligned}$$

65.
$6x - 2y - 3z = -10 \rightarrow$ $18x - 6y - 9z = -30$
$-6x + y + 9z = 3 \rightarrow$ $(+)-6x + y + 9z = 3$

$$12x - 5y = -27$$

$8x - 3y = -16 \rightarrow$ $-40x + 15y = 80$
$12x - 5y = -27 \rightarrow$ $(+)36x - 15y = -81$

$$\begin{aligned} -4x &= -1 \\ x &= \frac{1}{4} \end{aligned}$$

(Continued next column)

$$\begin{aligned} 8x - 3y &= -16 \\ 8\left(\frac{1}{4}\right) - 3y &= -16 \\ 2 - 3y &= -16 \\ -3y &= -18 \\ y &= 6 \end{aligned}$$

$$\begin{aligned} -6x + y + 9z &= 3 \\ -6\left(\frac{1}{4}\right) + 6 + 9z &= 3 \\ -\frac{3}{2} + 6 + 9z &= 3 \\ \frac{9}{2} + 9z &= 3 \\ 9z &= -\frac{3}{2} \\ z &= -\frac{1}{6} \end{aligned}$$

$\left(\frac{1}{4}, 6, -\frac{1}{6}\right)$

66. $x > 1$
$y < -1$
$y < x$

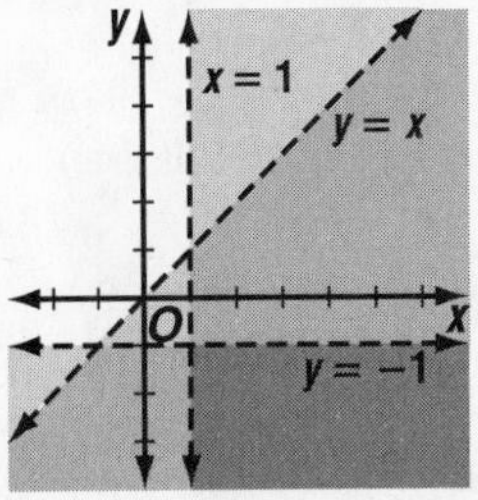

67. Yes, each element of the domain is paired with exactly one element of the range.

68.
$$\begin{aligned} 3(2m - 3) &\geq 9 \\ 6m - 9 &\geq 9 \\ 6m &\geq 18 \\ m &\geq 3 \end{aligned}$$

$\{m \mid m \geq 3\}$

69.
$$\begin{aligned} [(-8 + 3) \times 4 - 2] \div 6 &= [-5 \times 4 - 2] \div 6 \\ &= [-20 - 2] \div 6 \\ &= [-22] \div 6 \\ &= -\frac{11}{3} \end{aligned}$$

Chapter 5 Highlights

Page 323 Understanding and Using the Vocabulary

1. scientific notation
2. constants
3. Rationalizing the denominator
4. synthetic division
5. irrational numbers
6. FOIL method
7. coefficient
8. monomial
9. extraneous solution
10. Complex conjugates
11. square root
12. trinomial
13. degree of a polynomial
14. principal root
15. Fractals

Chapter 5 Study Guide and Assessment

Pages 324–326 Skills and Concepts

16.
$$\begin{aligned} m^3 \cdot m^5 &= m^{3 + 5} \\ &= m^8 \end{aligned}$$

17.
$$\begin{aligned} f^{-7} \cdot f^4 &= f^{-7 + 4} \\ &= f^{-3} \\ &= \frac{1}{f^3} \end{aligned}$$

18.
$$\begin{aligned} (3x^2)^3 &= 3^3 \cdot x^{2 \cdot 3} \\ &= 27x^6 \end{aligned}$$

19.
$$\begin{aligned} (2y)(4xy^3) &= 2 \cdot 4 \cdot x \cdot y \cdot y^3 \\ &= 8xy^{1 + 3} \\ &= 8xy^4 \end{aligned}$$

20. $\left(\frac{3}{5}c^2f\right)\left(\frac{4}{3}cd\right)^2 = \frac{3}{5}c^2f \cdot \frac{(4)^2}{(3)^2} \cdot (c)^2 \cdot (d)^2$
$= \frac{3}{5} \cdot \frac{16}{9} \cdot c^2 \cdot c^2 \cdot d^2 \cdot f$
$= \frac{16}{15}c^{2+2}d^2f$
$= \frac{16}{15}c^4d^2f$

21. $\frac{1}{x^0+y^0} - \frac{x^0+y^0}{1} = \frac{1}{1+1} - \frac{1+1}{1}$
$= \frac{1}{2} - \frac{2}{1}$
$= -\frac{3}{2}$

22. $3(ab)^3(4ac^2) + c(4ab)(5a^3b^2c)$
$= 3 \cdot a^3 \cdot b^3 \cdot 4 \cdot a \cdot c^2 + c \cdot 4 \cdot a \cdot b \cdot 5 \cdot a^3 \cdot b^2 \cdot c$
$= 12a^3 \cdot a \cdot b^3 \cdot c^2 + 20 \cdot a \cdot a^3 \cdot b \cdot b^2 \cdot c \cdot c$
$= 12a^{3+1}b^3c^2 + 20a^{1+3}b^{1+2}c^{1+1}$
$= 12a^4b^3c^2 + 20a^4b^3c^2$
$= 32a^4b^3c^2$

23. $(2000)(85{,}000) = (2 \times 1000)(8.5 \times 10{,}000)$
$= (2 \times 10^3)(8.5 \times 10^4)$
$= (2 \times 8.5)(10^3 \times 10^4)$
$= 17 \times 10^7$
$= 1.7 \times 10 \times 10^7$
$= 1.7 \times 10^8$
$1.7 \times 10^8 = 1.7 \times 100{,}000{,}000$
$= 170{,}000{,}000$

24. $(0.0014)^2 = (1.4 \times 0.001)(1.4 \times 0.001)$
$= (1.4 \times 1.4)(10^{-3} \times 10^{-3})$
$= 1.96 \times 10^{-6}$
$1.96 \times 10^{-6} = 1.96 \times 0.000001$
$= 0.00000196$

25. $5{,}400{,}000 \div 6000 = \frac{5.4 \times 1{,}000{,}000}{6.0 \times 1000}$
$= \frac{5.4 \times 10^6}{6 \times 10^3}$
$= 0.9 \times 10^3$
$= 9 \times 10^{-1} \times 10^3$
$= 9 \times 10^2$
$9 \times 10^2 = 9 \times 100$
$= 900$

26. $(4c - 5) - (c + 11) + (-6c + 17)$
$= 4c - 5 - c - 11 - 6c + 17$
$= 4c - c - 6c - 5 - 11 + 17$
$= -3c + 1$

27. $(11x^2 + 13x - 15) - (7x^2 - 9x + 19)$
$= 11x^2 + 13x - 15 - 7x^2 + 9x - 19$
$= 11x^2 - 7x^2 + 13x + 9x - 15 - 19$
$= 4x^2 + 22x - 34$

28. $-6m^2(3mn + 13m - 5n)$
$= -6m^2(3mn) - 6m^2(13m) - 6m^2(-5n)$
$= -18m^3n - 78m^3 + 30m^2n$

29. $(d - 5)(d + 3) = d \cdot d + d \cdot 3 - 5 \cdot d - 5 \cdot 3$
$= d^2 + 3d - 5d - 15$
$= d^2 - 2d - 15$

30. $x^{-8}y^{10}(x^{11}y^{-9} + x^{10}y^{-6})$
$= x^{-8}y^{10}(x^{11}y^{-9}) + x^{-8}y^{10}(x^{10}y^{-6})$
$= x^3y + x^2y^4$

31. $(2a^2 + 6)^2 = (2a^2 + 6)(2a^2 + 6)$
$= 2a^2(2a^2) + 2a^2(6) + 6(2a^2) + 6 \cdot 6)$
$= 4a^4 + 12a^2 + 12a^2 + 36$
$= 4a^4 + 24a^2 + 36$

32. $-5f^{12}(4f^3g + 2f) = -5f^{12}(4f^3g) - 5f^{12}(2f)$
$= -20f^{15}g - 10f^{13}$

33. $(2b - 3c)^3$
$= (2b - 3c)(2b - 3c)(2b - 3c)$
$= (2b \cdot 2b + 2b(-3c) - 3c(2b) - 3c(-3c))(2b - 3c)$
$= (4b^2 - 6bc - 6bc + 9c^2)(2b - 3c)$
$= (4b^2 - 12bc + 9c^2)(2b - 3c)$
$= 4b^2(2b - 3c) - 12bc(2b - 3c) + 9c^2(2b - 3c)$
$= 4b^2 \cdot 2b + 4b^2(-3c) - 12bc \cdot 2b - 12bc(-3c) +$
$9c^2 \cdot 2b + 9c^2(-3c)$
$= 8b^3 - 12b^2c - 24b^2c + 36bc^2 + 18bc^2 - 27c^3$
$= 8b^3 - 36b^2c + 54bc^2 - 27c^3$

34.
$$\begin{array}{r|rrrrr} 3 & 2 & -6 & 1 & -3 & -3 \\ & & 6 & 0 & 3 & 0 \\ \hline & 2 & 0 & 1 & 0 & |\,-3 \end{array}$$
$2x^3 + x - \frac{3}{x-3}$

35.
$$\begin{array}{r|rrrrr} -1 & 10 & 5 & 4 & 0 & -9 \\ & & -10 & 5 & -9 & 9 \\ \hline & 10 & -5 & 9 & -9 & |\,0 \end{array}$$
$10x^3 - 5x^2 + 9x - 9$

36.
$$\begin{array}{r|rrr} 1 & 1 & -5 & 4 \\ & & 1 & -4 \\ \hline & 1 & -4 & |\,0 \end{array}$$
$x - 4$

37.
$$\begin{array}{r} 5x^2 + 3x + 1 \\ x^2 + 3x \overline{)\,5x^4 + 18x^3 + 10x^2 + 3x} \\ \underline{5x^4 + 15x^3} \qquad\qquad\quad \\ 3x^3 + 10x^2 \qquad \\ \underline{3x^3 + 9x^2} \qquad \\ x^2 + 3x \\ \underline{x^2 + 3x} \\ 0 \end{array}$$

38. $200x^2 - 50 = 50(4x^2 - 1)$
$= 50(2x - 1)(2x + 1)$

39. $10a^3 - 20a^2 - 2a + 4 = 2(5a^3 - 10a^2 - a + 2)$
$= 2[(5a^3 - 10a^2) - (a - 2)]$
$= 2[5a^2(a - 2) - (a - 2)]$
$= 2(a - 2)(5a^2 - 1)$

40. $5w^3 - 20w^2 + 3w - 12 = (5w^3 - 20w^2) + (3w - 12)$
$= 5w^2(w - 4) + 3(w - 4)$
$= (w - 4)(5w^2 + 3)$

41. $s^3 + 512 = (s + 8)(s^2 - 8s + 64)$

42. prime

43. $\pm\sqrt{256} = \pm\sqrt{16^2}$
$= \pm 16$

44. $\sqrt[3]{-216} = \sqrt[3]{(-6)^3}$
$= -6$

45. $\sqrt{-(-8)^2} = \sqrt{-64}$
no real roots

46. $\sqrt[5]{c^5d^{15}} = \sqrt[5]{(cd^3)^5}$
$= cd^3$

47. $\pm\sqrt{(x^4 - 3)^2} = \pm x^4 - 3$

48. $\sqrt[3]{(512 + x^2)^3} = 512 + x^2$

49. $\sqrt[4]{16m^8} = \sqrt[4]{(2m^2)^4}$
$= 2m^2$

50. $\sqrt{a^2 - 10a + 25} = \sqrt{(a - 5)^2}$
$= |a - 5|$

51. $\sqrt[4]{64} = \sqrt[4]{2^4 \cdot 2^2}$
$= 2\sqrt[4]{2^2}$
$= 2 \cdot 2^{\frac{2}{4}}$
$= 2 \cdot 2^{\frac{1}{2}}$
$= 2\sqrt{2}$

52. $\sqrt{5} + \sqrt{20} = \sqrt{5} + \sqrt{2^2 \cdot 5}$
$= \sqrt{5} + 2\sqrt{5}$
$= 3\sqrt{5}$

53. $5\sqrt{12} - 3\sqrt{75} = 5\sqrt{2^2 \cdot 3} - 3\sqrt{5^2 \cdot 3}$
$= 5 \cdot 2\sqrt{3} - 3 \cdot 5\sqrt{3}$
$= 10\sqrt{3} - 15\sqrt{3}$
$= -5\sqrt{3}$

54. $6\sqrt[5]{11} - 8\sqrt[5]{11} = -2\sqrt[5]{11}$

55. $(\sqrt{8} + \sqrt{12})^2 = (\sqrt{8} + \sqrt{12})(\sqrt{8} + \sqrt{12})$
$= 8 + \sqrt{96} + \sqrt{96} + 12$
$= 20 + 2\sqrt{96}$
$= 20 + 2\sqrt{4^2 \cdot 6}$
$= 20 + 2 \cdot 4\sqrt{6}$
$= 20 + 8\sqrt{6}$

56. $\sqrt{8} \cdot \sqrt{15} \cdot \sqrt{21} = \sqrt{2^2 \cdot 2 \cdot 3 \cdot 5 \cdot 3 \cdot 7}$
$= 2 \cdot 3\sqrt{2 \cdot 5 \cdot 7}$
$= 6\sqrt{70}$

57. $\frac{1}{3 + \sqrt{5}} = \frac{1}{3 + \sqrt{5}} \cdot \frac{3 - \sqrt{5}}{3 - \sqrt{5}}$
$= \frac{3 - \sqrt{5}}{9 - 3\sqrt{5} + 3\sqrt{5} - 5}$
$= \frac{3 - \sqrt{5}}{9 - 5}$
$= \frac{3 - \sqrt{5}}{4}$

58. $\frac{\sqrt{10}}{4 + \sqrt{2}} = \frac{\sqrt{10}}{4 + \sqrt{2}} \cdot \frac{4 - \sqrt{2}}{4 - \sqrt{2}}$
$= \frac{4\sqrt{10} - \sqrt{20}}{16 - 4\sqrt{2} + 4\sqrt{2} - 2}$
$= \frac{4\sqrt{10} - 2\sqrt{5}}{14}$
$= \frac{2\sqrt{10} - \sqrt{5}}{7}$

59. $27^{-\frac{2}{3}} = \frac{1}{27^{\frac{2}{3}}}$
$= \frac{1}{(\sqrt[3]{27})^2}$
$= \frac{1}{3^2}$
$= \frac{1}{9}$

60. $9^{\frac{1}{3}} \cdot 9^{\frac{5}{3}} = 9^{\frac{6}{3}}$
$= 9^2$
$= 81$

61. $\left(\frac{8}{27}\right)^{-\frac{2}{3}} = \left(\frac{27}{8}\right)^{\frac{2}{3}}$
$= \left(\sqrt[3]{\frac{27}{8}}\right)^2$
$= \left(\frac{3}{2}\right)^2$
$= \frac{9}{4}$

62. $\frac{1}{y^{\frac{2}{5}}} = \frac{1 \cdot y^{\frac{3}{5}}}{y^{\frac{2}{5}} \cdot y^{\frac{3}{5}}}$
$= \frac{y^{\frac{3}{5}}}{y}$

63. $\frac{xy}{\sqrt[3]{z}} = \frac{xy}{z^{\frac{1}{3}}} \frac{xy}{\sqrt[3]{z}}$
$= \frac{xy \cdot z^{\frac{2}{3}}}{z^{\frac{1}{3}} \cdot z^{\frac{2}{3}}}$
$= \frac{xyz^{\frac{2}{3}}}{z}$

64. $\frac{3x + 4x^2}{x^{-\frac{2}{3}}} = (3x + 4x^2)x^{\frac{2}{3}}$
$= 3x^{\frac{5}{3}} + 4x^{\frac{8}{3}}$

65. $y^{\frac{1}{3}} - 7 = 0$
$y^{\frac{1}{3}} = 7$
$(y^{\frac{1}{3}})^3 = 7^3$
$y = 343$

Check: $y^{\frac{1}{3}} - 7 = 0$
$343^{\frac{1}{3}} - 7 \stackrel{?}{=} 0$
$7 - 7 \stackrel{?}{=} 0$
$0 = 0$ ✓

66. $(x - 2)^{\frac{3}{2}} = -8$
$[(x - 2)^{\frac{3}{2}}]^{\frac{2}{3}} = (-8)^{\frac{2}{3}}$
$x - 2 = (\sqrt[3]{-8})^2$
$x - 2 = (-2)^2$
$x - 2 = 4$
$x = 6$

Check: $(x - 2)^{\frac{3}{2}} = -8$
$(6 - 2)^{\frac{3}{2}} \stackrel{?}{=} -8$
$4^{\frac{3}{2}} \stackrel{?}{=} -8$
$(\sqrt{4})^3 \stackrel{?}{=} -8$
$2^3 \stackrel{?}{=} -8$
$8 \neq -8$
no solution

67. $6 + 2x\sqrt{3} = 0$
$2x\sqrt{3} = -6$
$x = \frac{-6}{2\sqrt{3}}$
$x = \frac{-3}{\sqrt{3}}$
$x = -\frac{3 \cdot \sqrt{3}}{\sqrt{3} \cdot \sqrt{3}}$
$x = -\frac{3\sqrt{3}}{3}$
$x = -\sqrt{3}$

Check: $6 + 2x\sqrt{3} = 0$
$6 + 2(-\sqrt{3})\sqrt{3} \stackrel{?}{=} 0$
$6 - 6 \stackrel{?}{=} 0$
$0 = 0$ ✓

68. $\sqrt{3t - 5} - 3 = 4$
$\sqrt{3t - 5} = 7$
$(\sqrt{3t - 5})^2 = 7^2$
$3t - 5 = 49$
$3t = 54$
$t = 18$

Check: $\sqrt{3t - 5} - 3 = 14$
$\sqrt{3(18) - 5} - 3 \stackrel{?}{=} 4$
$\sqrt{49} - 3 \stackrel{?}{=} 4$
$7 - 3 \stackrel{?}{=} 4$
$4 = 4$ ✓

69. $\sqrt{1 + 8v} - 2 = v$
$\sqrt{1 + 8v} = v + 2$
$(\sqrt{1 + 8v})^2 = (v + 2)^2$
$1 + 8v = v^2 + 4v + 4$
$0 = v^2 - 4v + 3$
$0 = (v - 3)(v - 1)$
$v - 3 = 0$ or $v - 1 = 0$
$v = 3$ $\quad v = 1$

Check: $\sqrt{1 + 8v} - 2 = v$
$\sqrt{1 + 8(3)} - 2 \stackrel{?}{=} 3$
$\sqrt{25} - 2 \stackrel{?}{=} 3$
$5 - 2 \stackrel{?}{=} 3$
$3 = 3$ ✓
$\sqrt{1 + 8(1)} - 2 \stackrel{?}{=} 1$
$\sqrt{9} - 2 \stackrel{?}{=} 1$
$3 - 2 \stackrel{?}{=} 1$
$1 = 1$ ✓

70. $\sqrt[4]{2x - 1} = 2$
$(\sqrt[4]{2x - 1})^4 = 2^4$
$2x - 1 = 16$
$2x = 17$
$x = 8.5$

Check: $\sqrt[4]{2x - 1} = 2$
$\sqrt[4]{2(8.5) - 1} \stackrel{?}{=} 2$
$\sqrt[4]{16} \stackrel{?}{=} 2$
$2 = 2$ ✓

71. $\sqrt{y+5} = \sqrt{2y-3}$ Check: $\sqrt{y+5} = \sqrt{2y-3}$
$(\sqrt{y+5})^2 = (\sqrt{2y-3})^2$ $\quad \sqrt{8+5} \stackrel{?}{=} \sqrt{2(8)-3}$
$y + 5 = 2y - 3$ $\quad \sqrt{13} = \sqrt{13}$ ✓
$8 = y$

72. $\sqrt{y+1} + \sqrt{y-3} = 5$
$\sqrt{y+1} = \sqrt{y-3} + 5$
$(\sqrt{y+1})^2 = (\sqrt{y-3}+5)^2$
$y + 1 = y - 3 + 10\sqrt{y-3} + 25$
$1 = 22 + 10\sqrt{y-3}$
$-21 = 10\sqrt{y-3}$
$-2.1 = \sqrt{y-3}$
$(-2.1)^2 = (\sqrt{y-3})^2$
$4.41 = y - 3$
$7.41 = y$
Check: $\sqrt{y+1} + \sqrt{y-3} = 5$
$\sqrt{7.41+1} + \sqrt{7.41-3} \stackrel{?}{=} 5$
$\sqrt{8.41} + \sqrt{4.41} \stackrel{?}{=} 5$
$2.9 + 2.1 \stackrel{?}{=} 5$
$5 = 5$ ✓

73. $\sqrt{-256} = \sqrt{16^2} \cdot \sqrt{-1}$
$= 16i$

74. $\sqrt[6]{-64m^{12}} = \sqrt[6]{2^6} \cdot \sqrt[6]{(m^2)^6} \cdot \sqrt[6]{-1}$
$= 2m^2i$

75. $(13i - 2)5i = (13i)(5i) - 2(5i)$
$= 65i^2 - 10i$
$= -65 - 10i$

76. $(7 - 4i) - (-3 + 6i) = (7 + 3) + (-4i - 6i)$
$= 10 - 10i$

77. $-6\sqrt{-a} \cdot 2\sqrt{-b} = -12 \cdot i\sqrt{a} \cdot i\sqrt{b}$
$= -12i^2\sqrt{ab}$
$= 12\sqrt{ab}$

78. $i^6 = (i^2)^3$
$= (-1)^3$
$= -1$

79. $i^{85} = i^{84} \cdot i$
$= (i^2)^{42} \cdot i$
$= 1 \cdot i$
$= i$

80. $(3 + 4i)(5 - 2i) = 3(5) + 3(-2i) + 4i(5) + 4i(-2i)$
$= 15 - 6i + 20i - 8i^2$
$= 15 + 14i + 8$
$= 23 + 14i$

81. $(\sqrt{6} + i)(\sqrt{6} - i) = \sqrt{6} \cdot \sqrt{6} - i\sqrt{6} + i\sqrt{6} - i^2$
$= 6 - (-1)$
$= 7$

82. $\frac{1+i}{1-i} = \frac{1+i}{1-i} \cdot \frac{1+i}{1+i}$
$= \frac{1+i+i+i^2}{1-i^2}$
$= \frac{1+2i-1}{1-(-1)}$
$= \frac{2i}{2}$
$= i$

83. $\frac{4-3i}{4+3i} = \frac{4-3i}{4+3i} \cdot \frac{4-3i}{4-3i}$
$= \frac{16-12i-12i+9i^2}{16-9i^2}$
$= \frac{16-24i-9}{16+9}$
$= \frac{7-24i}{25}$

84. $\frac{4}{4+5i} = \frac{4}{4+5i} \cdot \frac{4-5i}{4-5i}$
$= \frac{16-20i}{16-25i^2}$
$= \frac{16-20i}{16+25}$
$= \frac{16-20i}{41}$

85. $\frac{1+i\sqrt{2}}{1-i\sqrt{2}} = \frac{1+i\sqrt{2}}{1-i\sqrt{2}} \cdot \frac{1+i\sqrt{2}}{1+i\sqrt{2}}$
$= \frac{1+i\sqrt{2}+i\sqrt{2}+2i^2}{1-2i^2}$
$= \frac{1+2i\sqrt{2}-2}{1+2}$
$= \frac{-1+2i\sqrt{2}}{3}$

Page 326 Applications and Problem Solving

86. $N = \frac{1}{2\pi}\sqrt{\frac{a}{r}}$
$= \frac{1}{2\pi}\sqrt{\frac{4.9}{12.5}}$
$= \frac{1}{2\pi}\sqrt{0.392}$
$\approx \frac{1}{2\pi}(0.626)$
≈ 0.0996; 0.0996 rotations per second
$\frac{0.0996 \text{ rot}}{\text{s}} \cdot \frac{60\text{s}}{\text{min}} \approx 6$; 6 rotations per minute

87. $s = 2\sqrt{5\ell}$
$= 2\sqrt{5(120)}$
$= 2\sqrt{600}$
$\approx 2(24.49)$
≈ 48.99
No, she is not telling the truth. She was going approximately 49 mph.

88. $A = A_0(2.7)^{-\frac{3}{5}}$
$= 500(2.7)^{-\frac{3}{5}}$
$\approx 500(0.551)$
≈ 275.52; 276 milligrams

Page 327 Alternative Assessment; Thinking Critically

- No; performing all four operations can result in a rational number. Example: $\frac{2\pi}{\pi} = 2$

Chapter 6 Exploring Quadratic Functions and Inequalities

6-1A Graphing Technology: Quadratic Functions

Page 333 Exercises

1–6. Sample answers are given.

1. **Y=** 4 **X,T,θ,n** **x^2** **+** 11 **ZOOM** 6 WINDOW [−10, 10] by [−10, 40]
2. **Y=** 7.5 **X,T,θ,n** **x^2** **+** 9.5 **ZOOM** 6 WINDOW [−5, 5] by [−10, 40]
3. **Y=** 6 **X,T,θ,n** **x^2** **+** 250 **X,T,θ,n** **+** 725 **ZOOM** 6 WINDOW [−50, 10] by [−2000, 500]
4. **Y=** **X,T,θ,n** **x^2** **+** 4 **X,T,θ,n** **−** 15 **ZOOM** 6 WINDOW [−10, 10] by [−25, 10]
5. **Y=** **(−)** 2 **X,T,θ,n** **x^2** **−** **X,T,θ,n** **−** 15 **ZOOM** 6 WINDOW [−10, 10] by [−80, 5]
6. **Y=** **X,T,θ,n** **x^2** **+** 30 **X,T,θ,n** **+** 225 **ZOOM** 6 WINDOW [−50, 10] by [−100, 500]
7. **Y=** 4 **X,T,θ,n** **x^2** **+** 11 **GRAPH** (WINDOW [−10, 10] by [−10, 40]) no solution
8. **Y=** 7.5 **X,T,θ,n** **x^2** **+** 9.5 **GRAPH** (WINDOW [−5, 5] by [−10, 40]) no solution
9. **Y=** 6 **X,T,θ,n** **x^2** **+** 250 **X,T,θ,n** **+** 725 **GRAPH** (WINDOW [−50, 10] by [−2000, 500]) Use **TRACE** and **ZOOM** or **2nd** **CALC** 2 (root) to solve; −3.14, −38.53
10. **Y=** **X,T,θ,n** **x^2** **+** 4 **X,T,θ,n** **−** 15 **GRAPH** (WINDOW [−10, 10] by [−25, 10]) Use **TRACE** and **ZOOM** or **2nd** **CALC** 2 (root) to solve; −6.36, 2.36

6-1 Solving Quadratic Equations by Graphing

Page 338 Check for Understanding

1. No, because the degree of the equation is greater than 2.

2a. value that satisfies an equation

2b. solution to an equation

2c. x value of a function that makes the function equal to 0

2d. where the graph crosses the x-axis

All of these terms refer to the same values.

3a. Three possible solutions are: $b = 10, h = 5$; $b = 12, h = 7$; $b = 7, h = 2$.

3b. $\frac{1}{2}b^2 - \frac{5}{2}b = 0$

$\frac{1}{2}b(b - 5) = 0$

$\frac{1}{2}b = 0$ or $b - 5 = 0$

$b = 0$ $b = 5; b > 5$

4. A quadratic function is an equation that equals $f(x)$, whereas a quadratic equation equals 0.

5. The graph of its related function is a parabola and cannot cross the x-axis more than twice.

6. $x = 1$ and -4; these are the x-intercepts of the related quadratic function, $y = x^2 + 3x - 4$.

7. x^2; x; -4

8. $-4x^2, -8x, -9$

9. $g(x) = x^2 - 4x + 4$

x	$g(x)$
0	4
1	1
2	0
3	1
4	4

vertex: (2, 0)

axis of symmetry: $x = 2$

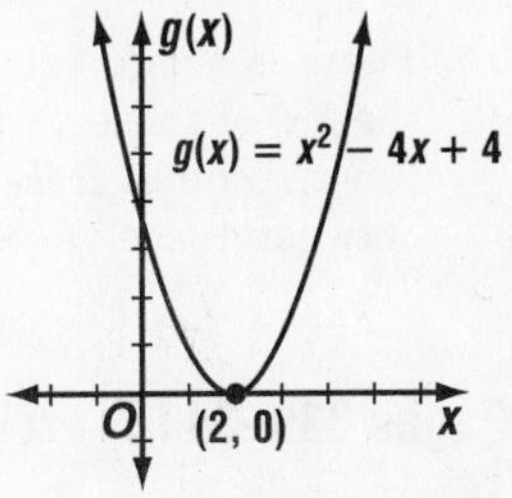

10. $f(x) = x^2 + 9$

x	$f(x)$
−2	13
−1	10
0	9
1	10
2	13

vertex: (0, 9)

axis of symmetry: $x = 0$

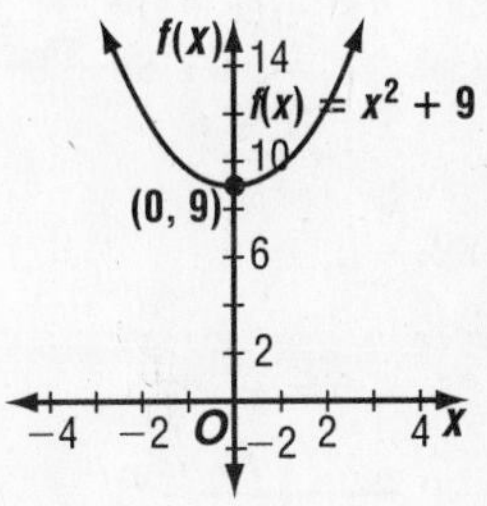

11. $h(x) = x^2 + 6x + 9$

x	$h(x)$
−4	1
−3	0
−2	1
−1	4

vertex: (−3, 0)

axis of symmetry: $x = -3$

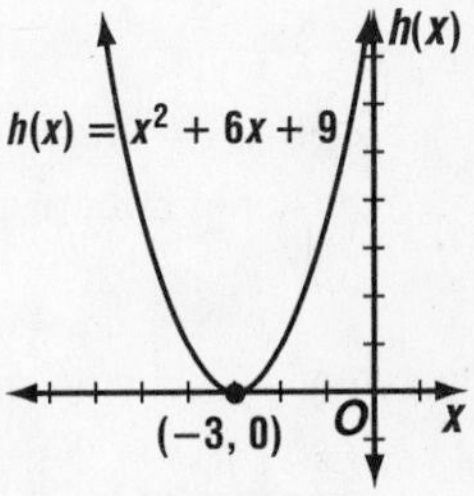

12. $d^2 + 5d + 6 = 0$

d	y
−3	0
−2	0
−1	2
0	6

−3, −2

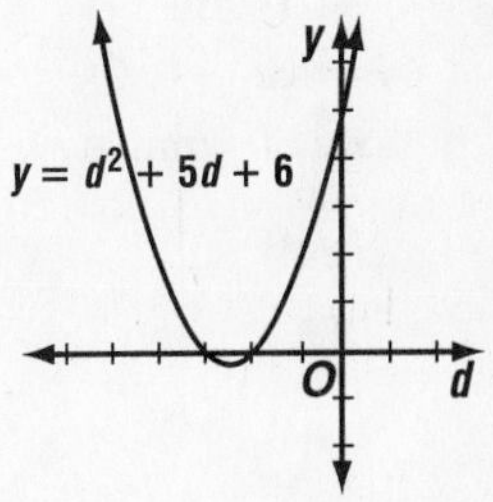

13. $a^2 - 4a + 4 = 0$

a	y
0	4
1	1
2	0
3	1

2

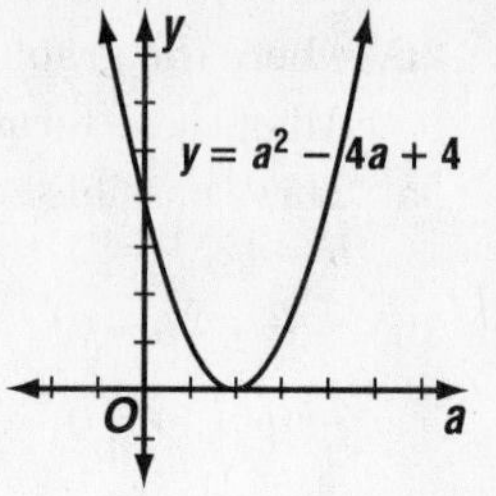

14. $2x^2 - x - 3 = 0$

x	y
−1	0
0	−3
1	−2
2	3

$-1, \frac{3}{2}$

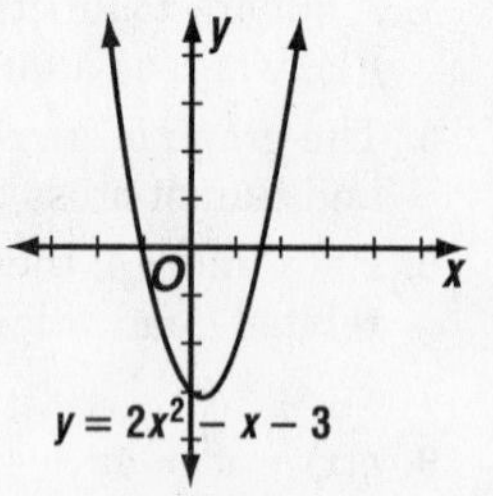

15. There is a zero between $x = 6$ and $x = 9$ because the $f(x)$ of those x's have opposite signs. The function must cross the x-axis at least once between those values.

Pages 339–340 Exercises

16. $5x^2$; $-7x$; 2

17. $3n^2$; 0; −1

18. $\frac{1}{3}n^2$; 0; 4

19. z^2; $3z$; 0

20. $f(x) = (x + 3)^2$
$= x^2 + 6x + 9$
x^2; $6x$; 9

21. $f(t) = (3t + 1)^2 - 8$
$= 9t^2 + 6t + 1 - 8$
$= 9t^2 + 6t - 7$
$9t^2$; $6t$; −7

22. −2, 1

23. −4

24. 0, 16

25. $f(x) = x^2$

x	$f(x)$
−2	4
−1	1
0	0
1	1

vertex: (0, 0)
axis of symmetry: $x = 0$

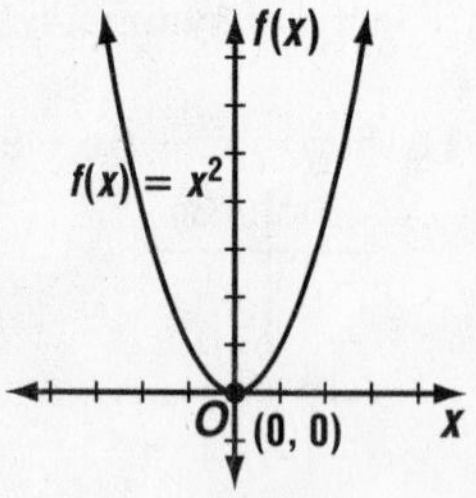

26. $f(x) = x^2 + 12x + 36$

x	$f(x)$
−8	4
−6	0
−4	4

vertex: (−6, 0)
axis of symmetry: $x = -6$

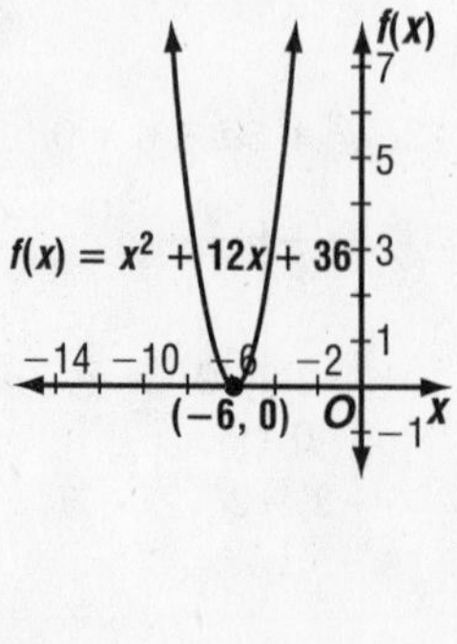

27. $g(x) = x^2 - 9x + 9$

x	$g(x)$
2	−5
3	−9
4	−11
$4\frac{1}{2}$	$-11\frac{1}{4}$
5	−11

vertex: $\left(4\frac{1}{2}, -11\frac{1}{4}\right)$
axis of symmetry: $x = 4\frac{1}{2}$

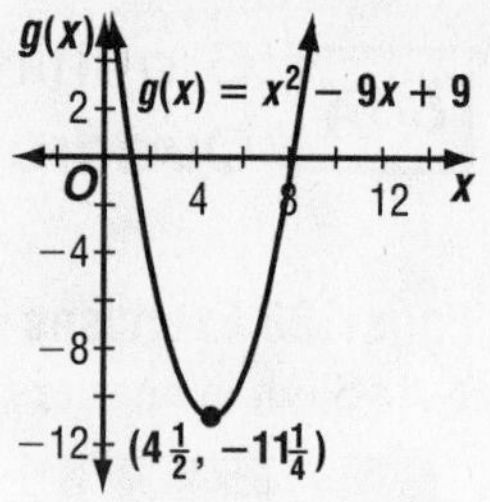

28. $h(x) = x^2 + 4$

x	$h(x)$
−2	8
−1	5
0	4
1	5

vertex: (0, 4)
axis of symmetry: $x = 0$

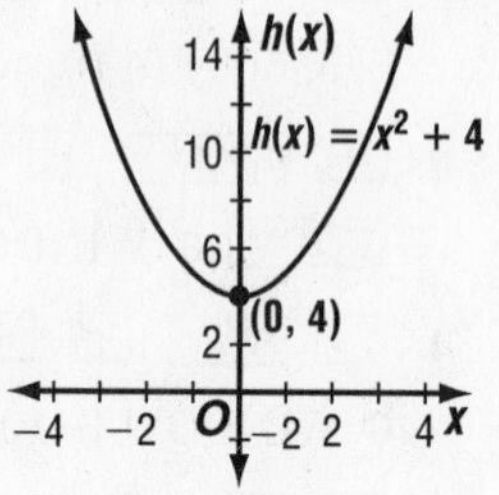

29. $f(x) = x^2 - 9$

x	$f(x)$
−2	−5
−1	−8
0	−9
1	−8

vertex: (0, −9)
axis of symmetry: $x = 0$

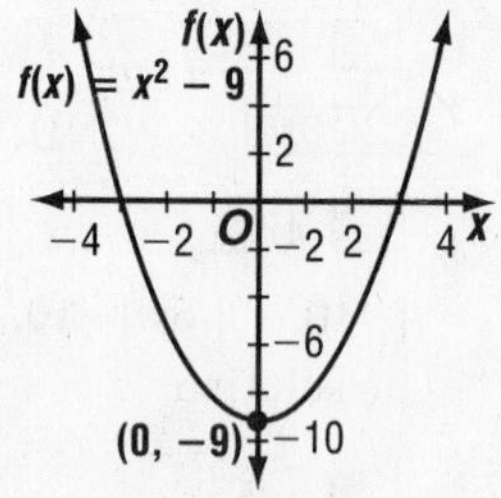

30. $h(x) = x^2 - 10x + 27$

x	$h(x)$
3	6
4	3
5	2
6	3

vertex: (5, 2)
axis of symmetry: $x = 5$

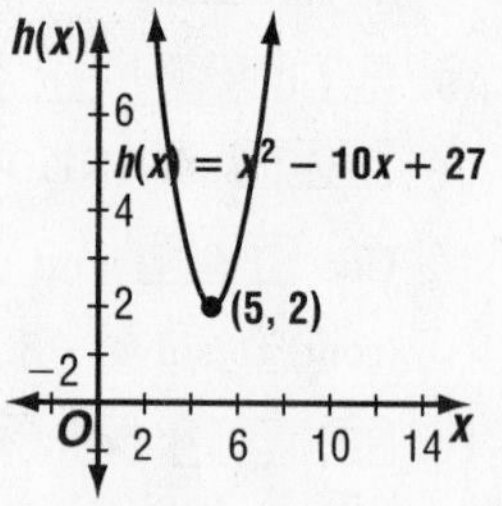

31. $f(x) = x^2 + 20x + 93$

x	$f(x)$
−14	9
−12	−3
−10	−7
−8	−3

vertex: (−10, −7)
axis of symmetry: $x = -10$

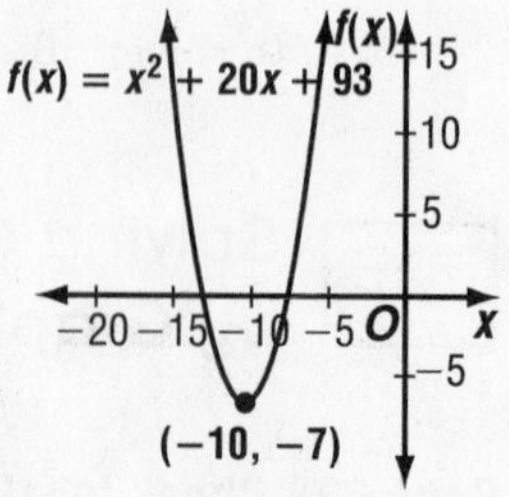

32. $g(x) = x^2 - \frac{2}{5}x + \frac{26}{25}$

x	$g(x)$
-1	2.44
0	1.04
$\frac{1}{5}$	1
1	1.64

vertex: $\left(\frac{1}{5}, 1\right)$

axis of symmetry: $x = \frac{1}{5}$

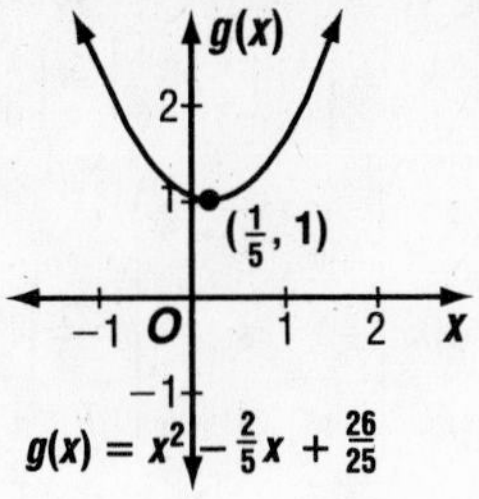

33. $f(x) = x^2 + 3x - 0.95$

x	$f(x)$
-4	3.05
-2	-2.95
$-1\frac{1}{2}$	-3.2
0	-0.95

vertex: $(-1\frac{1}{2}, -3\frac{1}{5})$

axis of symmetry: $x = -1\frac{1}{2}$

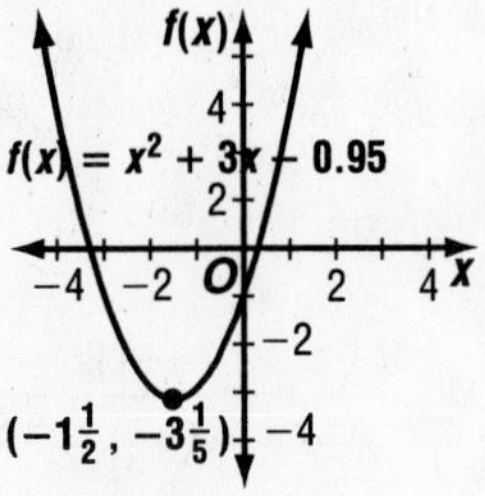

34. $m^2 + 3m = 28$

$m^2 + 3m - 28 = 0$

m	y
-8	12
-4	-24
0	-28
4	0

$-7, 4$

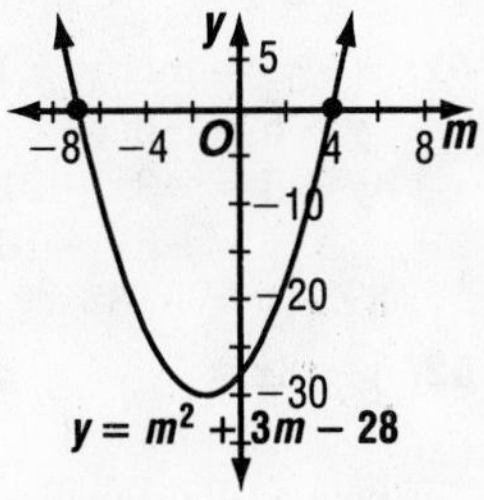

35. $p^2 - 2p - 24 = 0$

p	y
-4	0
0	-24
4	-16

$-4, 6$

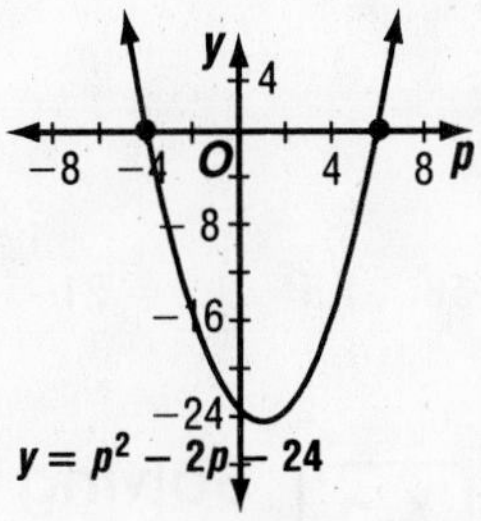

36. $4n^2 - 7n - 15 = 0$

n	y
-1	-4
1	-18
3	0

$-\frac{5}{4}, 3$

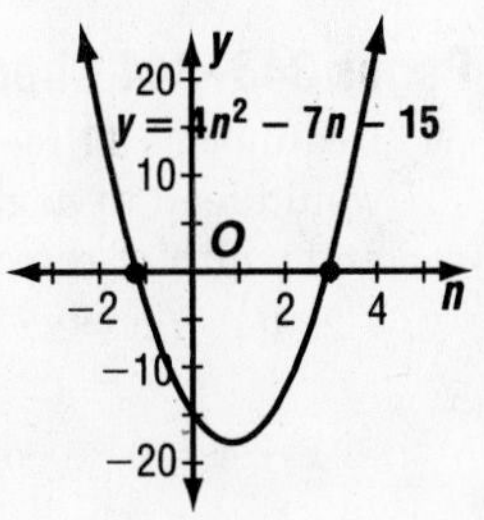

37. $c^2 + 4c + 4 = 0$

c	y
-3	1
-2	0
-1	1
0	4

-2

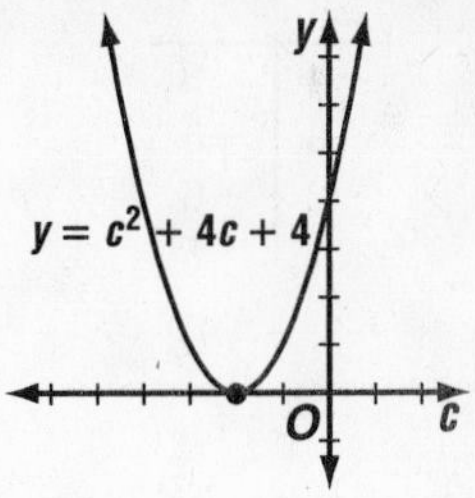

38. $n^2 - 3n = 0$

n	y
0	0
1	-2
2	-2
3	0

0, 3

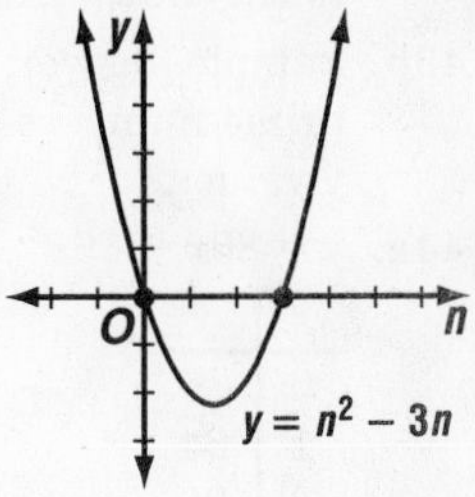

39. $2w^2 - 3w = 9$

$2w^2 - 3w - 9 = 0$

w	y
-2	5
0	-9
1	-10
3	0

$-1.5, 3$

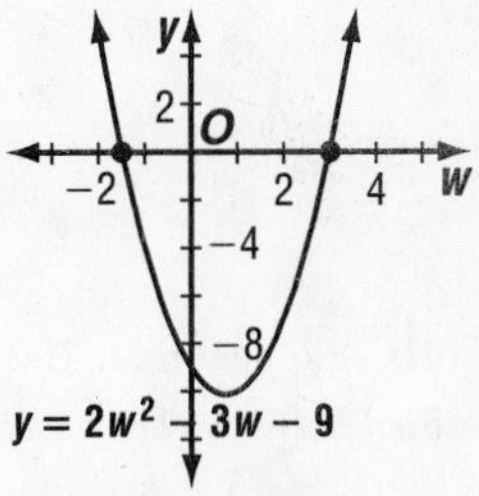

40. $4v^2 - 8v - 5 = 0$

v	y
-1	7
0	-5
1	-9
2	-5

$-\frac{1}{2}, \frac{5}{2}$

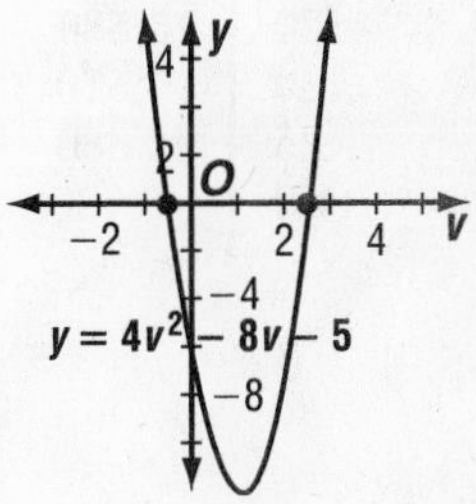

41. $2c^2 + 5c - 12 = 0$

c	y
-4	0
-2	-14
0	-12
2	6

$-4, \frac{3}{2}$

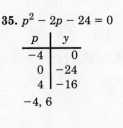

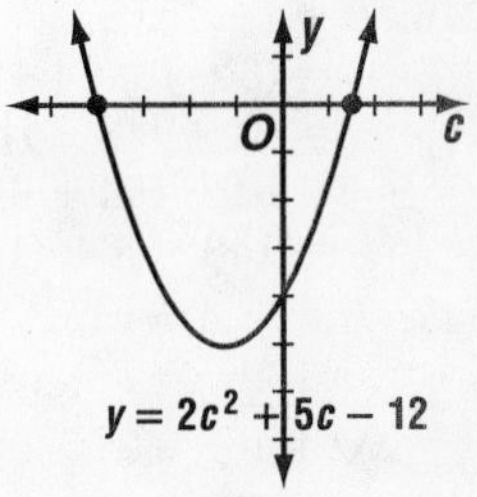

42. $(3x + 4)(2x + 7) = 0$

x	y
-4	8
-3	-5
-2	-6
-1	5

$-\frac{7}{2}, -\frac{4}{3}$

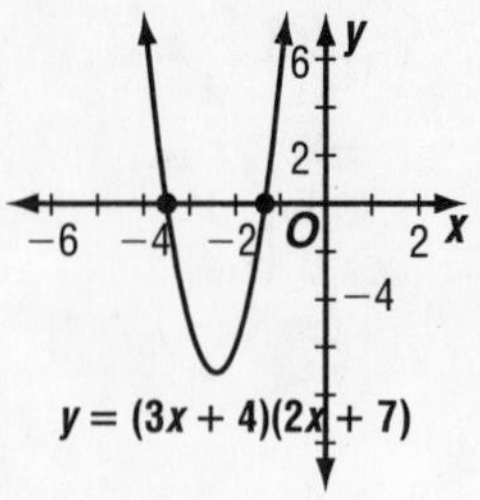

43a. There are no roots because the graph does not touch the x-axis.

43b. Sample answer: There cannot be any negative prime numbers since the graph has no negative y values.

44a. $y = 80x - 16x^2$

x	y
0	0
1	64
2	96
3	96
4	64
5	0

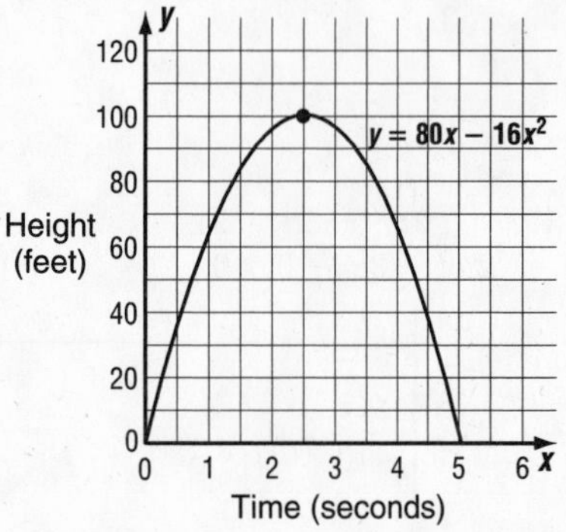

44b. 2.5 seconds, 100 feet

45a. $h(t) = -16t^2 + 21{,}980$

t	$h(t)$
0	21,980
10	20,380
20	15,580
30	7,580
35	2,380
40	−3,620

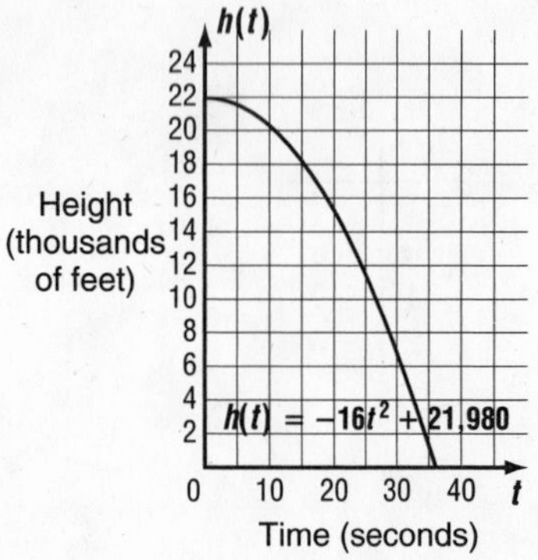

45b. about 37 seconds

46. $E = I \cdot Z$
$= (6 - j8)(14 + j8)$
$= 84 + j48 - j112 - j^2 64$
$= 84 - j64 + 64$
$= 148 - j64$; $(148 - j64)$ volts

47.
$A = s^2$
$169x^2 = s^2$
$\sqrt{169x^2} = s$
$13x = s$

$s - 14 = 77$
$13x - 14 = 77$
$13x = 91$
$x = 7$

48. $\left[\begin{array}{cc|c} 4 & 3 & 10 \\ 5 & -1 & 3 \end{array}\right] = \left[\begin{array}{cc|c} 4 & 3 & 10 \\ 15 & -3 & 9 \end{array}\right] = \left[\begin{array}{cc|c} 19 & 0 & 19 \\ 15 & -3 & 9 \end{array}\right] = \left[\begin{array}{cc|c} 1 & 0 & 1 \\ 15 & -3 & 9 \end{array}\right]$
$= \left[\begin{array}{cc|c} 1 & 0 & 1 \\ 0 & -3 & -6 \end{array}\right] = \left[\begin{array}{cc|c} 1 & 0 & 1 \\ 0 & 1 & 2 \end{array}\right]$; (1, 2)

49. $\begin{vmatrix} \frac{1}{2} & -1 & 3 \\ -3 & 5 & -2 \\ 3 & 2 & 4 \end{vmatrix} = \frac{1}{2}\begin{vmatrix} 5 & -2 \\ 2 & 4 \end{vmatrix} - (-1)\begin{vmatrix} -3 & -2 \\ 3 & 4 \end{vmatrix} + 3\begin{vmatrix} -3 & 5 \\ 3 & 2 \end{vmatrix}$
$= \frac{1}{2}(20 + 4) + (-12 + 6) + 3(-6 - 15)$
$= 12 - 6 - 63$
$= -57$

50. Let x = oldest son, y = middle son, and z = youngest son.

$x = 3z \rightarrow x - 3z = 0$
$y = \frac{1}{2}x \rightarrow -\frac{1}{2}x + y = 0$
$x + y + z = 42 - 9 \rightarrow x + y + z = 33$

$3x + 3y + 3z = 99$
$(+)x \quad - 3z = 0$
$4x + 3y \quad = 99$

$4x + 3y = 99$
$(+)-4x + 8y = 0$
$11y = 99$
$y = 9$

$y = \frac{1}{2}x$
$9 = \frac{1}{2}x$
$18 = x$

$x = 3z$
$18 = 3z$
$6 = z$

6, 9, 18

51. $y - y_1 = m(x - x_1)$
$y - 5 = -3(x - (-7))$
$y - 5 = -3x - 21$
$y = -3x - 16;$
$3x + y = -16$

52. $y - 3x = 1$
$y = 3x + 1$
perpendicular slope $= -\frac{1}{3}$

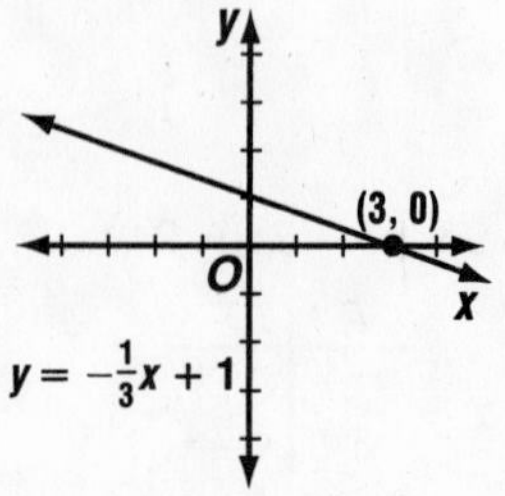

53. $31.5 \div 1.5 = 21$

6-2 Solving Quadratic Equations by Factoring

Pages 343–344 Check for Understanding

1. x cannot be 11 feet since $15 - 2x$ and $9 - 2x$ would lead to negative dimensions for the length and width of the carpet.
2. $-2, 4$; $f(x) = x^2 - 2x - 8$
$= (x - 4)(x + 2)$
$x - 4 = 0$ or $x + 2 = 0$
$x = 4$ $\quad x = -2$
3. Carmen is right. Chelsea didn't factor correctly. $x^2 - 13x + 36 = 0$ factors to $(x - 9)(x - 4) = 0$ and the solutions for x are 9 and 4.

4. $(y-8)(y+6)=0$

$y-8=0$ or $y+6=0$

$y=8$ $y=-6$

5. $(3y+7)(y+5)=0$

$3y+7=0$ or $y+5=0$

$3y=-7$ $y=-5$

$y=-\frac{7}{3}$

6. $q^2-5q-24=0$

$(q-8)(q+3)=0$

$q-8=0$ or $q+3=0$

$q=8$ $q=-3$

7. $r^2-16r+64=0$

$(r-8)(r-8)=0$

$r-8=0$ or $r-8=0$

$r=8$ $r=8$

8. $a^3=81a$

$a^3-81a=0$

$a(a^2-81)=0$

$a(a-9)(a+9)=0$

$a=0$ or $a-9=0$ or $a+9=0$

$a=9$ $a=-9$

9. $3y^2+y-14=0$

$(3y+7)(y-2)=0$

$3y+7=0$ or $y-2=0$

$3y=-7$ $y=2$

$y=-\frac{7}{3}$

10a. $t^2=1.23L$ $9.75 \div 12 = 0.8125$

$t^2=1.23(73.8125)$

$t^2=90.789375$

$t \approx 9.53$; 9.53 seconds

10b. $t^2=1.23L$

$t^2=1.23(6)$

$t^2=7.38$

$t \approx 2.72$; 2.72 seconds

10c. $60 \div 15 = 4$; 4 seconds

$t^2=1.23L$

$4^2=1.23L$

$16=1.23L$

$13.01 \approx L$; 13 feet

Pages 344–345 Exercises

11. $(a+4)(a+1)=0$

$a+4=0$ or $a+1=0$

$a=-4$ $a=-1$

12. $z(z-1)=0$

$z=0$ or $z-1=0$

$z=1$

13. $(2z+6)(x-3)=0$

$2x+6=0$ or $x-3=0$

$2x=-6$ $x=3$

$x=-3$

14. $(3y-5)(2y+7)=0$

$3y-5=0$ or $2y+7=0$

$3y=5$ $2y=-7$

$y=\frac{5}{3}$ $y=-\frac{7}{2}$

15. $x^2-x=12$

$x^2-x-12=0$

$(x-4)(x+3)=0$

$x-4=0$ or $x+3=0$

$x=4$ $x=-3$

16. $d^2-5d=0$

$d(d-5)=0$

$d=0$ or $d-5=0$

$d=5$

17. $z^2-12z+36=0$

$(z-6)(z-6)=0$

$z-6=0$ or $z-6=0$

$z=6$ $z=6$

18. $y^2+y-30=0$

$(y+6)(y-5)=0$

$y+6=0$ or $y-5=0$

$y=-6$ $y=5$

19. $r^2-3r=4$

$r^2-3r-4=0$

$(r-4)(r+1)=0$

$r-4=0$ or $r+1=0$

$r=4$ $r=-1$

20. $3c^2=5c$

$3c^2-5c=0$

$c(3c-5)=0$

$c=0$ or $3c-5=0$

$3c=5$

$c=\frac{5}{3}$

21. $18u^2-3u=1$

$18u^2-3u-1=0$

$(6u+1)(3u-1)=0$

$6u+1=0$ or $3u-1=0$

$6u=-1$ $3u=1$

$u=-\frac{1}{6}$ $u=\frac{1}{3}$

22. $4y^2=25$

$4y^2-25=0$

$(2y-5)(2y+5)=0$

$2y-5=0$ or $2y+5=0$

$2y=5$ $2y=-5$

$y=\frac{5}{2}$ $y=-\frac{5}{2}$

23. $9y^2+16=-24y$

$9y^2+24y+16=0$

$(3y+4)(3y+4)=0$

$3y+4=0$ or $3y+4=0$

$3y=-4$ $3y=-4$

$y=-\frac{4}{3}$ $y=-\frac{4}{3}$

24. $4x^2-13x=12$

$4x^2-13x-12=0$

$(4x+3)(x-4)=0$

$4x+3=0$ or $x-4=0$

$4x=-3$ $x=4$

$x=-\frac{3}{4}$

25. $b^2+3b=40$

$b^2+3b-40=0$

$(b+8)(b-5)=0$

$b+8=0$ or $b-5=0$

$b=-8$ $b=5$

26. $4a^2 - 17a + 4 = 0$

$(4a - 1)(a - 4) = 0$

$4a - 1 = 0$ or $a - 4 = 0$

$4a = 1$ $\quad a = 4$

$a = \frac{1}{4}$

27. $4s^2 - 11s = 3$

$4s^2 - 11s - 3 = 0$

$(4s + 1)(s - 3) = 0$

$4s + 1 = 0$ or $s - 3 = 0$

$4s = -1$ $\quad s = 3$

$s = -\frac{1}{4}$

28. $6r^2 + 7r = 3$

$6r^2 + 7r - 3 = 0$

$(3r - 1)(2r + 3) = 0$

$3r - 1 = 0$ or $2r + 3 = 0$

$3r = 1$ $\quad 2r = -3$

$r = \frac{1}{3}$ $\quad r = -\frac{3}{2}$

29. $12m^2 + 25m + 12 = 0$

$(4m + 3)(3m + 4) = 0$

$4m + 3 = 0$ or $3m + 4 = 0$

$4m = -3$ $\quad 3m = -4$

$m = -\frac{3}{4}$ $\quad m = -\frac{4}{3}$

30. $18n^2 - 3n = 15$

$18n^2 - 3n - 15 = 0$

$(3n - 3)(6n + 5) = 0$

$3n - 3 = 0$ or $6n + 5 = 0$

$3n = 3$ $\quad 6n = -5$

$n = 1$ $\quad n = -\frac{5}{6}$

31. $n^3 = 9n$

$n^3 - 9n = 0$

$n(n^2 - 9) = 0$

$n(n - 3)(n + 3) = 0$

$n = 0$ or $n - 3 = 0$ or $n + 3 = 0$

$n = 3$ $\quad n = -3$

32. $x^3 = 64x$

$x^3 - 64x = 0$

$x(x^2 - 64) = 0$

$x(x - 8)(x + 8) = 0$

$x = 0$ or $x - 8 = 0$ or $x + 8 = 0$

$x = 8$ $\quad x = -8$

33. $35z^3 + 16z^2 = 12z$

$35z^3 + 16z^2 - 12z = 0$

$z(35z^2 + 16z - 12) = 0$

$z(7z + 6)(5z - 2) = 0$

$z = 0$ or $7z + 6 = 0$ or $5z - 2 = 0$

$7z = -6$ $\quad 5z = 2$

$z = -\frac{6}{7}$ $\quad z = \frac{2}{5}$

34. $18r^3 + 16r = 34r^2$

$18r^3 - 34r^2 + 16r = 0$

$r(18r^2 - 34r + 16) = 0$

$r(9r - 8)(2r - 2) = 0$

$r = 0$ or $9r - 8 = 0$ or $2r - 2 = 0$

$9r = 8$ $\quad 2r = 2$

$r = \frac{8}{9}$ $\quad r = 1$

35. $(x + 8)(x - 4) = x^2 + 4x - 32$

y-intercept $= -8$, so multiply by $\frac{-8}{-32}$ or 0.25

$y = 0.25(x + 8)(x - 4)$ or $y = 0.25x^2 + x - 8$

36a. $(VM)^2 = 1.22A$

$(VM)^2 = 1.22(36{,}000)$

$(VM)^2 = 43{,}920$

$VM \approx 209.57$; 210 miles

36b. $(VM)^2 = 1.22A$

$(236)^2 = 1.22A$

$55{,}696 = 1.22A$

$45{,}652.46 \approx A$; 45,652 feet

36c. $(VM)^2 = 1.22A$

$(VM)^2 = 1.22(1454)$

$(VM)^2 = 1773.88$

$VM \approx 42.12$; 42 miles

37a. $y = 216t^2 - 5^3$

t	y
−1	91
0	−125
1	91

about 45 minutes

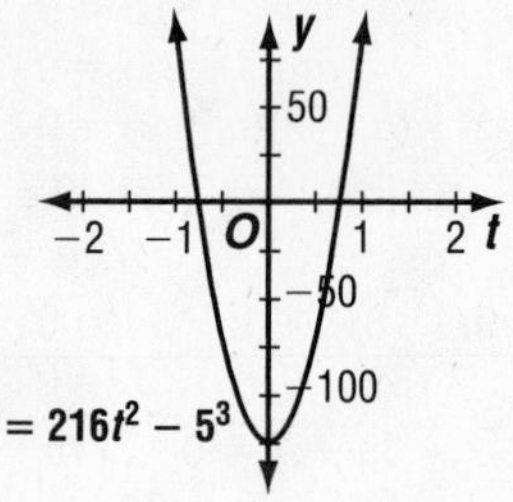

37b. $216t^2 = d^3$

$216t^2 = 5^3$

$216t^2 = 125$

$t^2 \approx 0.579$

$t \approx 0.76$; 0.76 hour

38. integers with sum of 15:

integers	product
1, 14	14
2, 13	26
3, 12	36
4, 11	44
5, 10	50
6, 9 ✓	54 ✓

6, 9

39. $p = \frac{1}{2}x^2 + \frac{1}{2}x + 1$

$37 = \frac{1}{2}x^2 + \frac{1}{2}x + 1$

$0 = \frac{1}{2}x^2 + \frac{1}{2}x - 36$

$0 = x^2 + x - 72$

$0 = (x + 9)(x - 8)$

$x + 9 = 0$ or $x - 8 = 0$

$x = -9$ $\quad x = 8$; 8 chords

40a. Let w = width. Then $\ell = w + 2$.

$A = w \cdot \ell$

$A = w(w + 2)$

w	A
−1	−1
0	0
1	3
2	8

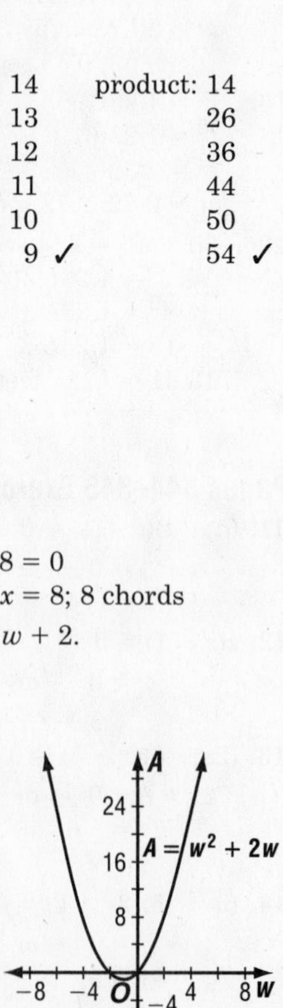

40b. 24cm^2; $A = 4(4 + 2) = 24$

41. $6y^2 = -96$

$y^2 = -16$

$y = \pm\sqrt{-16}$

$y = \pm 4\boldsymbol{i}$

42. $\dfrac{rs}{r^{\frac{1}{2}} + r^{\frac{3}{2}}} = \dfrac{rs \cdot r^{\frac{1}{2}}}{\left(r^{\frac{1}{2}} + r^{\frac{3}{2}}\right)r^{\frac{1}{2}}}$

$= \dfrac{rs \cdot r^{\frac{1}{2}}}{r^{\frac{1}{2}+\frac{1}{2}} + r^{\frac{3}{2}+\frac{1}{2}}}$

$= \dfrac{rs \cdot r^{\frac{1}{2}}}{r + r^2}$

$= \dfrac{rs \cdot r^{\frac{1}{2}}}{r(1 + r)}$

$= \dfrac{r^{\frac{1}{2}}s}{1 + r}$

43. $M^{-1} = \dfrac{1}{24 - 6}\begin{bmatrix} 6 & 2 \\ 3 & 4 \end{bmatrix}$

$= \dfrac{1}{18}\begin{bmatrix} 6 & 2 \\ 3 & 4 \end{bmatrix}$

44. $3x - 2y = 10$

$-2y = -3x + 10$

$y = \frac{3}{2}x - 5$

$y - x = -1$

$y = x - 1$

(8, 7)

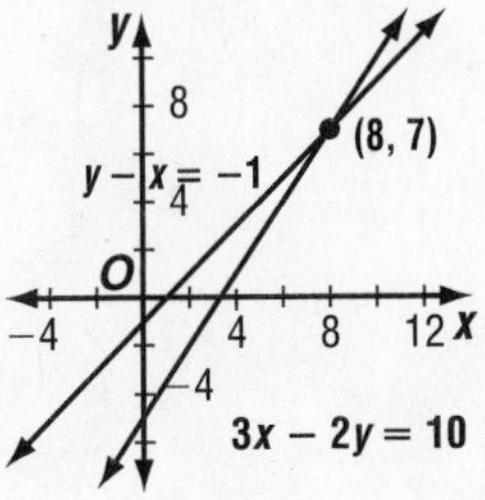

45. $3(2m + 9n) - (4 + 6m) = -5m$

$6m + 27n - 4 - 6m = -5m$

$27n - 4 = -5m$

$\dfrac{27n - 4}{-5} = m$

$\dfrac{-1(4 - 27n)}{-1(5)} = m$

$\dfrac{4 - 27n}{5} = m$

46. $\frac{2}{3}\left(\frac{1}{2}a + 3b\right) + \frac{1}{2}\left(\frac{2}{3}a + b\right)$

$= \frac{2}{3}\left(\frac{1}{2}a\right) + \frac{2}{3}(3b) + \frac{1}{2}\left(\frac{2}{3}a\right) + \frac{1}{2}(b)$

$= \frac{1}{3}a + 2b + \frac{1}{3}a + \frac{1}{2}b$

$= \frac{1}{3}a + \frac{1}{3}a + 2b + \frac{1}{2}b$

$= \frac{2}{3}a + \frac{5}{2}b$

6-3 Completing the Square

Page 350 Check for Understanding

1. Sample answer: Add 5 to each side of the equation, add $\left(\frac{21}{2}\right)^2$ to each side, factor the left side, take the square root of each side, and then isolate the variable x. The solution is $-10.5 \pm \sqrt{115.25}$.
2. The graph does not intersect the x-axis.
3. No, $\left(\frac{5}{2}\right)^2 \neq 23$.
4. See students' work.

5. $x^2 + 4x - 5 = 0$

$x^2 + 4x = 5$

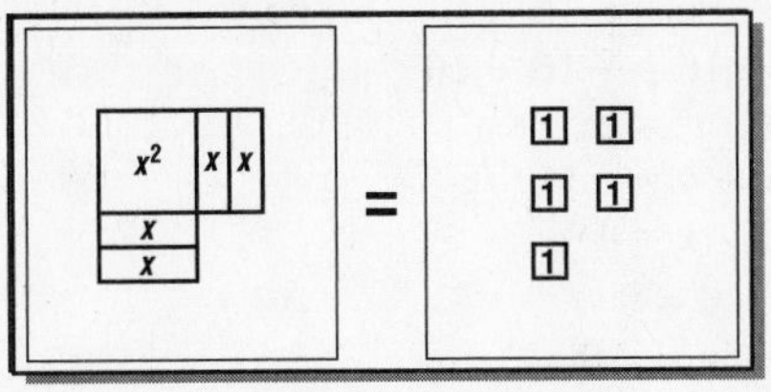

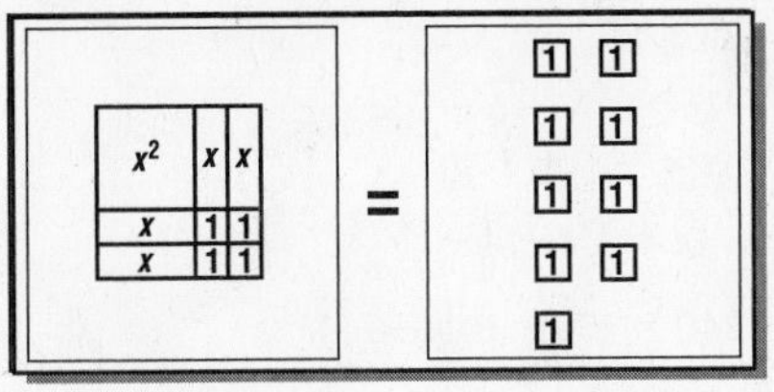

$(x + 2)^2 = 9$

$x + 2 = \pm 3$

$x + 2 = 3$ or $x + 2 = -3$

$x = 1$ $\quad$ $x = -5$

6. $c = \left(\frac{12}{2}\right)^2$

$= 6^2$

$= 36$

7. $c = \left(-\frac{7}{2}\right)^2$

$= \frac{49}{4}$

8. $x^2 + 8x = 20$

$x^2 + 8x + 16 = 20 + 16$

$(x + 4)^2 = 36$

$x + 4 = \pm 6$

$x + 4 = 6$ or $x + 4 = -6$

$x = 2$ $\quad$ $x = -10$

9. $12t^2 - 17t = 5$

$t^2 - \frac{17}{12}t = \frac{5}{12}$

$t^2 - \frac{17}{12}t + \frac{289}{576} = \frac{5}{12} + \frac{289}{576}$

$(t - \frac{17}{24})^2 = \frac{529}{576}$

$t - \frac{17}{24} = \pm\frac{23}{24}$

$t - \frac{17}{24} = \frac{23}{24}$ or $t - \frac{17}{24} = -\frac{23}{24}$

$t = \frac{40}{24}$ $\quad$ $t = -\frac{6}{24}$

$t = \frac{5}{3}$ $\quad$ $t = -\frac{1}{4}$

10. $r^2 + 14 = 8r$

$r^2 - 8r = -14$

$r^2 - 8r + 16 = -14 + 16$

$(r - 4)^2 = 2$

$r - 4 = \pm\sqrt{2}$

$r = 4 \pm \sqrt{2}$

11. $x^2 - 7x + 4 = 0$

$x^2 - 7x = -4$

$x^2 - 7x + \frac{49}{4} = -4 + \frac{49}{4}$

$\left(x - \frac{7}{2}\right)^2 = \frac{33}{4}$

$x - \frac{7}{2} = \pm\sqrt{\frac{33}{4}}$

$x = \frac{7}{2} \pm \frac{\sqrt{33}}{2}$

$x = \frac{7 \pm \sqrt{33}}{2}$

12. $\frac{1}{2}x^2 - 4x + 8 = 0$
$x^2 - 8x + 16 = 0$
$x^2 - 8x = -16$
$x^2 - 8x + 16 = -16 + 16$
$(x - 4)^2 = 0$
$x - 4 = 0$
$x = 4$

13. $x^2 + 2x + 6 = 0$
$x^2 + 2x = -6$
$x^2 + 2x + 1 = -6 + 1$
$(x + 1)^2 = -5$
$x + 1 = \pm\sqrt{-5}$
$x = -1 \pm i\sqrt{5}$

14. $s = V_i t + \frac{1}{2}at^2$
$240 = (60)t + \frac{1}{2}(-7\frac{1}{2})t^2$
$240 = 60t - \frac{15}{4}t^2$
$64 = 16t - t^2$
$t^2 - 16t = -64$
$t^2 - 16t + 64 = -64 + 64$
$(t - 8)^2 = 0$
$t - 8 = 0$
$t = 8$; 8 seconds

Pages 351–352 Exercises

15. $c = \left(\frac{2}{2}\right)^2 = 1^2 = 1$

16. $c = \left(\frac{18}{2}\right)^2 = 9^2 = 81$

17. $c = \left(\frac{40}{2}\right)^2 = 20^2 = 400$

18. $c = \left(-\frac{9}{2}\right)^2 = \frac{81}{4}$

19. $c = \left(-\frac{100}{2}\right)^2 = (-50)^2 = 2500$

20. $c = \left(\frac{15}{2}\right)^2 = \frac{225}{4}$

21. $x^2 + 3x - 18 = 0$
$x^2 + 3x = 18$
$x^2 + 3x + \frac{9}{4} = 18 + \frac{9}{4}$
$\left(x + \frac{3}{2}\right)^2 = \frac{81}{4}$
$x + \frac{3}{2} = \pm\frac{9}{2}$
$x + \frac{3}{2} = \frac{9}{2}$ or $x + \frac{3}{2} = -\frac{9}{2}$
$x = \frac{6}{2}$ or 3 $\quad x = -\frac{12}{2}$ or -6

22. $x^2 + 2x - 120 = 0$
$x^2 + 2x = 120$
$x^2 + 2x + 1 = 120 + 1$
$(x + 1)^2 = 121$
$x + 1 = \pm 11$
$x + 1 = 11$ or $x + 1 = -11$
$x = 10 \quad x = -12$

23. $x^2 - 8x + 11 = 0$
$x^2 - 8x = -11$
$x^2 - 8x + 16 = -11 + 16$
$(x - 4)^2 = 5$
$x - 4 = \pm\sqrt{5}$
$x = 4 \pm \sqrt{5}$

24. $x^2 + 7x - 17 = 0$
$x^2 + 7x = 17$
$x^2 + 7x + \frac{49}{4} = 17 + \frac{49}{4}$
$\left(x + \frac{7}{2}\right)^2 = \frac{117}{4}$
$x + \frac{7}{2} = \pm\frac{3\sqrt{13}}{2}$
$x = \frac{-7 \pm 3\sqrt{13}}{2}$

25. $x^2 + 9x + 20.25 = 0$
$x^2 + 9x = -20.25$
$x^2 + 9x + \frac{81}{4} = -20.25 + \frac{81}{4}$
$\left(x + \frac{9}{2}\right)^2 = 0$
$x + \frac{9}{2} = 0$
$x = -\frac{9}{2}$

26. $9x^2 + 96x + 256 = 0$
$x^2 + \frac{32}{3}x + \frac{256}{9} = 0$
$x^2 + \frac{32}{3}x = -\frac{256}{9}$
$x^2 + \frac{32}{3}x + \frac{1024}{36} = -\frac{256}{9} + \frac{1024}{36}$
$\left(x + \frac{16}{3}\right)^2 = 0$
$x + \frac{16}{3} = 0$
$x = -\frac{16}{3}$

27. $x^2 + 4x + 11 = 0$
$x^2 + 4x = -11$
$x^2 + 4x + 4 = -11 + 4$
$(x + 2)^2 = -7$
$x + 2 = \pm\sqrt{-7}$
$x = -2 \pm i\sqrt{7}$

28. $2x^2 - 7x + 12 = 0$
$x^2 - \frac{7}{2}x + 6 = 0$
$x^2 - \frac{7}{2}x = -6$
$x^2 - \frac{7}{2}x + \frac{49}{16} = -6 + \frac{49}{16}$
$\left(x - \frac{7}{4}\right)^2 = -\frac{47}{16}$
$x - \frac{7}{4} = \pm\frac{\sqrt{-47}}{4}$
$x = \frac{7 \pm i\sqrt{47}}{4}$

29. $3x^2 + 7x + 7 = 0$
$x^2 + \frac{7}{3}x + \frac{7}{3} = 0$
$x^2 + \frac{7}{3}x = -\frac{7}{3}$
$x^2 + \frac{7}{3}x + \frac{49}{36} = -\frac{7}{3} + \frac{49}{36}$
$\left(x + \frac{7}{6}\right)^2 = -\frac{35}{36}$
$x + \frac{7}{6} = \pm\frac{\sqrt{-35}}{6}$
$x = \frac{-7 \pm i\sqrt{35}}{6}$

30. $16x^2 + 9x + 20 = 0$
$x^2 + \frac{9}{16}x + \frac{5}{4} = 0$
$x^2 + \frac{9}{16}x = -\frac{5}{4}$
$x^2 + \frac{9}{16}x + \frac{81}{1024} = -\frac{5}{4} + \frac{81}{1024}$
$\left(x + \frac{9}{32}\right)^2 = -\frac{1199}{1024}$
$x + \frac{9}{32} = \pm\frac{\sqrt{-1199}}{32}$
$x = \frac{-9 \pm i\sqrt{1199}}{32}$

31. $x^2 - 3x - 20 = 0$

$$x^2 - 3x = 20$$
$$x^2 - 3x + \frac{9}{4} = 20 + \frac{9}{4}$$
$$\left(x - \frac{3}{2}\right)^2 = \frac{89}{4}$$
$$x - \frac{3}{2} = \pm\frac{\sqrt{89}}{2}$$
$$x = \frac{3 \pm \sqrt{89}}{2}$$

32. $2x^2 - x - 31 = 0$

$$x^2 - \frac{1}{2}x - \frac{31}{2} = 0$$
$$x^2 - \frac{1}{2}x = \frac{31}{2}$$
$$x^2 - \frac{1}{2}x + \frac{1}{16} = \frac{31}{2} + \frac{1}{16}$$
$$\left(x - \frac{1}{4}\right)^2 = \frac{249}{16}$$
$$x - \frac{1}{4} = \pm\frac{\sqrt{249}}{4}$$
$$x = \frac{1 \pm \sqrt{249}}{4}$$

33. $12x^2 - 13x - 35 = 0$

$$x^2 - \frac{13}{12}x - \frac{35}{12} = 0$$
$$x^2 - \frac{13}{12}x = \frac{35}{12}$$
$$x^2 - \frac{13}{12}x + \frac{169}{576} = \frac{35}{12} + \frac{169}{576}$$
$$\left(x - \frac{13}{24}\right)^2 = \frac{1849}{576}$$
$$x - \frac{13}{24} = \pm\frac{43}{24}$$

$x - \frac{13}{24} = \frac{43}{24}$ or $x - \frac{13}{24} = -\frac{43}{24}$

$x = \frac{56}{24}$ $\qquad$ $x = -\frac{30}{24}$

$x = \frac{7}{3}$ $\qquad$ $x = -\frac{5}{4}$

34. $x^2 + 19x - 12 = 0$

$$x^2 + 19x = 12$$
$$x^2 + 19x + \frac{361}{4} = 12 + \frac{361}{4}$$
$$\left(x + \frac{19}{2}\right)^2 = \frac{409}{4}$$
$$x + \frac{19}{2} = \pm\frac{\sqrt{409}}{2}$$
$$x = \frac{-19 \pm \sqrt{409}}{2}$$

35. $ax^2 + bx + c = 0$

$$x^2 + \frac{b}{a}x + \frac{c}{a} = 0$$
$$x^2 + \frac{b}{a}x = -\frac{c}{a}$$
$$x^2 + \frac{b}{a}x + \frac{b^2}{4a^2} = -\frac{c}{a} + \frac{b^2}{4a^2}$$
$$\left(x + \frac{b}{2a}\right)^2 = \frac{-4ac + b^2}{4a^2}$$
$$x + \frac{b}{2a} = \pm\frac{\sqrt{b^2 - 4ac}}{2a}$$
$$x = \frac{-b \pm \sqrt{b^2 - 4ac}}{2a}$$

36. $px^2 + rx + m = 0$

$$x^2 + \frac{r}{p}x + \frac{m}{p} = 0$$
$$x^2 + \frac{r}{p}x = -\frac{m}{p}$$
$$x^2 + \frac{r}{p}x + \frac{r^2}{4p^2} = -\frac{m}{p} + \frac{r^2}{4p^2}$$
$$\left(x + \frac{r}{2p}\right)^2 = \frac{-4pm + r^2}{4p^2}$$
$$x + \frac{r}{2p} = \pm\frac{\sqrt{r^2 - 4pm}}{2p}$$
$$x = \frac{-r \pm \sqrt{r^2 - 4pm}}{2p}$$

37. Enter program. Guess-and-check to find k.

37a. ± 16 **37b.** 49 **37c.** 9 **37d.** 25

37e. ± 4 **37f.** 25

38. $c = \left(\frac{m+5}{2}\right)^2$ $\qquad$ $c = 5m + 1$

$$= \frac{m^2 + 10m + 25}{4}$$
$$\frac{m^2 + 10m + 25}{4} = 5m + 1$$
$$m^2 + 10m + 25 = 20m + 4$$
$$m^2 - 10m + 21 = 0$$
$$(m - 7)(m - 3) = 0$$

$m - 7 = 0$ or $m - 3 = 0$

$m = 7$ $\qquad$ $m = 3$; 2 roots

39a. $I = 2(s)^2$

s	I
0	0
1	2
2	8
3	18
4	32

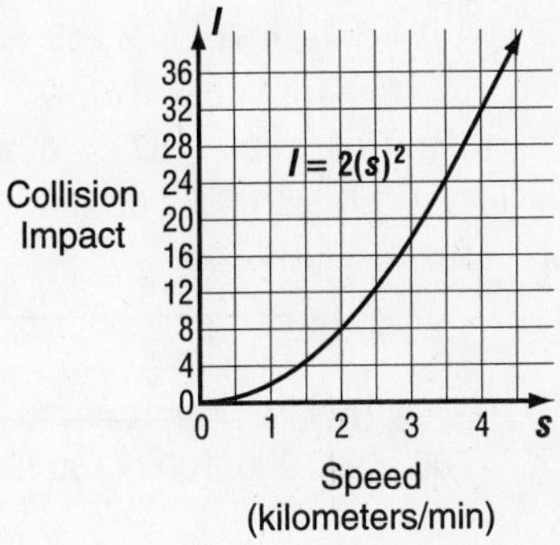

39b. 2; 8; 32

39c. The impact of the collision quadruples.

40. $\frac{s^2}{24} = d$

$$\frac{s^2}{24} = 50$$
$$s^2 = 1200$$

$s \approx 34.64$; about 35 miles per hour

41a. $h(t) = 56t - 16t^2$

$h(1) = 56(1) - 16(1)^2$

$= 40$; 40 feet

41b.

t	$h(t)$
1	40
2	48
3	24
4	−32

49 feet

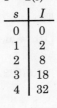

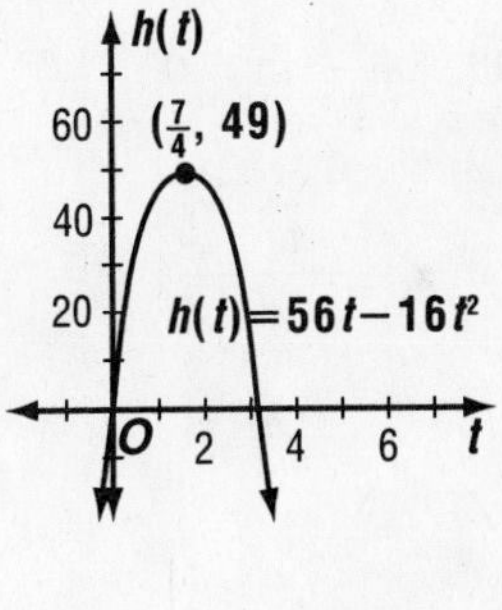

41c. 3.5 seconds

42.
$$V = 0.0027\,Ld^2 + 0.0027L\left(d + \frac{L}{A}\right)^2$$
$$150 = 0.0027(16)d^2 + 0.0027(16)\left(d + \frac{16}{8}\right)^2$$
$$150 = 0.0432d^2 + 0.0432(d + 2)^2$$
$$150 = 0.0432d^2 + 0.0432(d^2 + 4d + 4)$$
$$150 = 0.0432d^2 + 0.0432d^2 + 0.1728d + 0.1728$$
$$0 = 0.0864d^2 + 0.1728d - 149.8272$$
$$0 = d^2 + 2d - \frac{15{,}607}{9}$$
$$\frac{15{,}607}{9} = d^2 + 2d$$
$$\frac{15{,}607}{9} + 1 = d^2 + 2d + 1$$
$$\frac{15{,}616}{9} = (d + 1)^2$$
$$\pm\frac{\sqrt{15{,}616}}{3} = d + 1$$
$$\frac{-3 \pm \sqrt{15{,}616}}{3} = d$$
$d = 40.65$ or -42.65; about 41 inches

43. $\sqrt[4]{5m^3n^5} \cdot \sqrt[4]{125m^2n^3} = \sqrt[4]{625m^5n^8}$
$= \sqrt[4]{5^4m^4 \cdot m^1(n^2)^4}$
$= 5mn^2 \cdot \sqrt[4]{m}$

44. $2ab(c - d) + 10d(c - d) = (2ab + 10d)(c - d)$
$= 2(ab + 5d)(c - d)$

45. 775, 812, 819, 877, 890, 900, 949, 973, 1100, 1299, 1399, 1399, 1409, 1450

Q_2 is between 7th and 8th values; $\frac{949 + 973}{2} = 961$; Q_1 is the 4th value, 877; Q_3 is the 11th value, 1399; IR = 1399 − 877 = 522; outliers: below 877 − 1.5(522) = 94 or above 1399 + 1.5(522) = 2182; no outliers

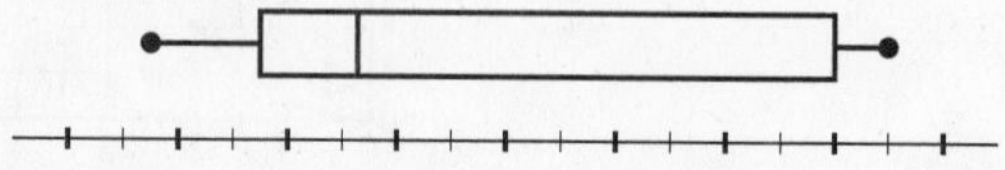

46. $y \le 7$ $y \ge -x + 6$ $y \le x + 4$ $x \le 5$
vertices: (1, 5), (3, 7), (5, 7), (5, 1)

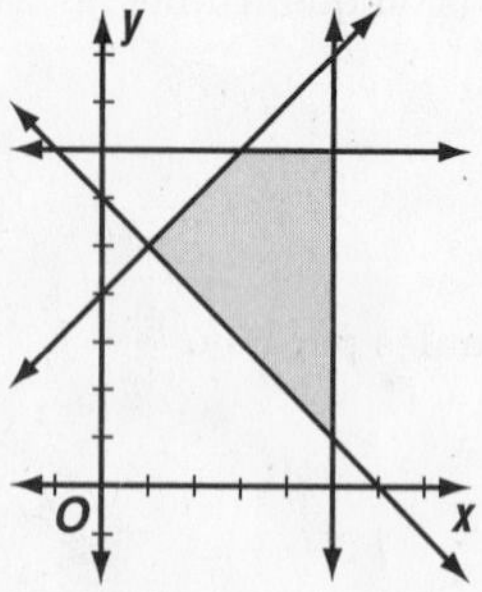

$f(x, y) = 2x - 3y$

(x, y)	$2x - 3y$	$f(x, y)$
(1, 5)	2(1) − 3(5)	−13
(3, 7)	2(3) − 3(7)	−15
(5, 7)	2(5) − 3(7)	−11
(5, 1)	2(5) − 3(1)	7

max: $f(5, 1) = 7$
min: $f(3, 7) = -15$

47. $3m - 4n = 0$ $n + 7 = -m$
$m + n = -7$

$$x = \frac{\begin{vmatrix} 0 & -4 \\ -7 & 1 \end{vmatrix}}{\begin{vmatrix} 3 & -4 \\ 1 & 1 \end{vmatrix}} = \frac{0 - 28}{3 + 4} = \frac{-28}{7} = -4$$

$$y = \frac{\begin{vmatrix} 3 & 0 \\ 1 & -7 \end{vmatrix}}{\begin{vmatrix} 3 & -4 \\ 1 & 1 \end{vmatrix}} = \frac{-21 - 0}{3 + 4} = \frac{-21}{7} = -3$$

(−4, −3)

48.

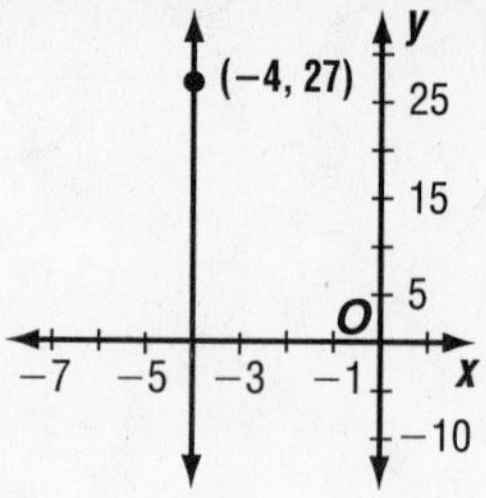

6-4 The Quadratic Formula and the Discriminant

Pages 356–357 Check for Understanding

1. The square root of a negative number is an imaginary number.
2. See students' work.
3. $b^2 - 4ac = 0^2 - 4(0.00012244898)(6)$
$= -0.0029387755$; This means that the cables do not touch the floor of the bridge, since the graph does not intersect the x-axis and the roots are imaginary.
4. The discriminant is 0; there is one real root.
5. See students' work. **6.** c
7. $3x^2 - 5x = 2$
$3x^2 - 5x - 2 = 0$; $a = 3$, $b = -5$, $c = -2$
$b^2 - 4ac = (-5)^2 - 4(3)(-2)$
$= 25 + 24$
$= 49$
8. $a = 1$, $b = -24$, $c = 144$
$b^2 - 4ac = (-24)^2 - 4(1)(144)$
$= 576 - 576$
$= 0$
9. $x^2 + 7 = -5x$
$x^2 + 5x + 7 = 0$; $a = 1$, $b = 5$, $c = 7$
$b^2 - 4ac = 5^2 - 4(1)(7)$
$= 25 - 28$
$= -3$

For Exercises 10–13, R = real, C = imaginary, Q = rational, and I = irrational.

10. $x^2 + 10x = -25$
$x^2 + 10x + 25 = 0$; $a = 1$, $b = 10$, $c = 25$
$b^2 - 4ac = 10^2 - 4(1)(25)$
$= 100 - 100$
$= 0$; 1R, Q
$x = \frac{-10 \pm \sqrt{0}}{2(1)}$
$= \frac{-10}{2}$
$= -5$
11. $2x^2 = 72$
$2x^2 - 72 = 0$; $a = 2$, $b = 0$, $c = -72$
$b^2 - 4ac = 0^2 - 4(2)(-72)$
$= 576$; 2R, Q
$x = \frac{-0 \pm \sqrt{576}}{2(2)}$
$= \frac{\pm 24}{4}$
$= \pm 6$

12. $x^2 + x - 5 = 0; a = 1, b = 1, c = -5$

$$b^2 - 4ac = 1^2 - 4(1)(-5) = 1 + 20 = 21; \text{2R, I}$$

$$x = \frac{-1 \pm \sqrt{21}}{2(1)} = \frac{-1 \pm \sqrt{21}}{2}; 1.79, -2.79$$

13. $x^2 + 5x + 10 = 0; a = 1, b = 5, c = 10$

$$b^2 - 4ac = 5^2 - 4(1)(10) = 25 - 40 = -15; \text{2C}$$

$$x = \frac{-5 \pm \sqrt{-15}}{2(1)} = \frac{-5 \pm i\sqrt{15}}{2}$$

14. The graph will cross the x-axis twice since 2025 is a positive square root.

15a. $x^2 + 2x - 5 = 0; a = 1, b = 2, c = -5$

$$b^2 - 4ac = 2^2 - 4(1)(-5) = 4 + 20 = 24; \text{2 roots}$$

$$x = \frac{-2 \pm \sqrt{24}}{2} = \frac{-2 \pm 2\sqrt{6}}{2} = -1 \pm \sqrt{6}; 1.4, -3.4$$

15b. 1.4 and -3.4

Pages 357–358 Exercises

For exercises 16–29, R = real, C = imaginary, Q = rational, and I = irrational.

16. $a = 1, b = 12, c = 32$

$$b^2 - 4ac = 12^2 - 4(1)(32) = 144 - 128 = 16; \text{2R, Q}$$

$$x = \frac{-12 \pm \sqrt{16}}{2(1)} = \frac{-12 \pm 4}{2}$$

$$x = \frac{-12 + 4}{2} \text{ or } -4 \text{ and } x = \frac{-12 - 4}{2} \text{ or } -8$$

17. $a = 2, b = -12, c = 18$

$$b^2 - 4ac = (-12)^2 - 4(2)(18) = 144 - 144 = 0; \text{1R, Q}$$

$$x = \frac{12 \pm \sqrt{0}}{2(2)} = \frac{12}{4} = 3$$

18. $a = 1, b = -4, c = 1$

$$b^2 - 4ac = (-4)^2 - 4(1)(1) = 16 - 4 = 12; \text{2R, I}$$

$$x = \frac{4 \pm \sqrt{12}}{2} = \frac{4 \pm 2\sqrt{3}}{2} = 2 \pm \sqrt{3}; 3.73, 0.27$$

19. $a = 3, b = 5, c = -2$

$$b^2 - 4ac = 5^2 - 4(3)(-2) = 25 + 24 = 49; \text{2R, Q}$$

$$x = \frac{-5 \pm \sqrt{49}}{2(3)} = \frac{-5 \pm 7}{6}$$

$$x = \frac{-5 + 7}{6} \text{ or } \frac{1}{3} \text{ and } x = \frac{-5 - 7}{6} \text{ or } -2$$

20. $a = 1, b = -2, c = 5$

$$b^2 - 4ac = (-2)^2 - 4(1)(5) = 4 - 20 = -16; \text{2C}$$

$$x = \frac{2 \pm \sqrt{-16}}{2(1)} = \frac{2 \pm 4i}{2} = 1 \pm 2i$$

21. $a = 3, b = 11, c = 4$

$$b^2 - 4ac = 11^2 - 4(3)(4) = 121 - 48 = 73; \text{2R, I}$$

$$x = \frac{-11 \pm \sqrt{73}}{2(3)} = \frac{-11 \pm \sqrt{73}}{6}; -0.41, -3.26$$

22. $a = 1, b = -12, c = 42$

$$b^2 - 4ac = (-12)^2 - 4(1)(42) = 144 - 168 = -24; \text{2C}$$

$$x = \frac{12 \pm \sqrt{-24}}{2(1)} = \frac{12 \pm 2i\sqrt{6}}{2} = 6 \pm i\sqrt{6}$$

23. $x^2 = 6x$

$x^2 - 6x = 0; a = 1, b = -6, c = 0$

$$b^2 - 4ac = (-6)^2 - 4(1)(0) = 36 - 0 = 36; \text{2R, Q}$$

$$x = \frac{6 \pm \sqrt{36}}{2(1)} = \frac{6 \pm 6}{2}$$

$$x = \frac{6 + 6}{2} \text{ or } 6 \text{ and } x = \frac{6 - 6}{2} \text{ or } 0$$

24. $a = 2, b = 7, c = -11$

$$b^2 - 4ac = 7^2 - 4(2)(-11) = 49 + 88 = 137; \text{2R, I}$$

$$x = \frac{-7 \pm \sqrt{137}}{2(2)} = \frac{-7 \pm \sqrt{137}}{4}; 1.18, -4.68$$

25. $a = 5, b = -8, c = 9$

$b^2 - 4ac = (-8)^2 - 4(5)(9)$
$= 64 - 180$
$= -116$; 2C

$x = \frac{8 \pm \sqrt{-116}}{2(5)}$
$= \frac{8 \pm 2i\sqrt{29}}{10}$
$= \frac{4 \pm i\sqrt{29}}{5}$

26. $0.4x^2 + x = 0.3$

$0.4x^2 + x - 0.3 = 0$; $a = 0.4, b = 1, c = -0.3$

$b^2 - 4ac = 1^2 - 4(0.4)(-0.3)$
$= 1 + 0.48$
$= 1.48$; 2R, I

$x = \frac{-1 \pm \sqrt{1.48}}{2(0.4)}$
$= \frac{-1 \pm \sqrt{1.48}}{0.8}$; 0.27, −2.77

27. $2x^2 - 13x = 7$

$2x^2 - 13x - 7 = 0$; $a = 2, b = -13, c = -7$

$b^2 - 4ac = (-13)^2 - 4(2)(-7)$
$= 169 + 56$
$= 225$; 2R, Q

$x = \frac{13 \pm \sqrt{225}}{2(2)}$
$= \frac{13 \pm 15}{4}$

$x = \frac{13 + 15}{4}$ or 7 and $x = \frac{13 - 15}{4}$ or $-\frac{1}{2}$

28. $a = 1, b = -16, c = 4$

$b^2 - 4ac = (-16)^2 - 4(1)(4)$
$= 256 - 16$
$= 240$; 2R, I

$x = \frac{16 \pm \sqrt{240}}{2(1)}$
$= \frac{16 \pm 4\sqrt{15}}{2}$
$= 8 \pm 2\sqrt{15}$; 15.75 or 0.25

29. $4x^2 - 9x = -7$

$4x^2 - 9x + 7 = 0$; $a = 4, b = -9, c = 7$

$b^2 - 4ac = (-9)^2 - 4(4)(7)$
$= 81 - 112$
$= -31$; 2c

$x = \frac{9 \pm \sqrt{-31}}{2(4)}$
$= \frac{9 \pm i\sqrt{31}}{8}$

30. $b^2 - 4ac < 0$

$6^2 - 4(1)c < 0$
$36 - 4c < 0$
$-4c < -36$
$c > 9$

If $c > 9$ for $b^2 - 4ac < 0$, then the values resulting in imaginary roots are 10, 11, and 12; which is $\frac{3}{12}$ or $\frac{1}{4}$ of the given values.

31a. $P = 0.01A^2 + 0.05A + 107$

A	P
0	107
10	108.5
20	112
30	117.5
40	125
50	134.5

$P = 0.006A^2 - 0.02A + 120$

A	P
0	120
10	120.4
20	122
30	124.8
40	128.8
50	134

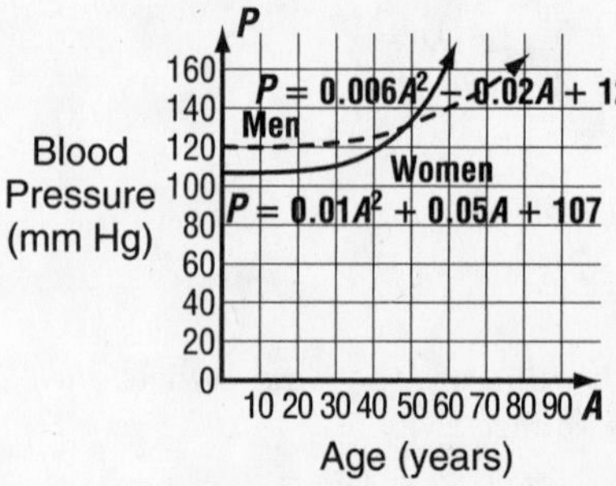

The graph representing the normal blood pressure of women is more narrow than the graph of men's blood pressure. Initially, women's blood pressure is lower than men's, but it increases at a faster rate.

31b. $P = 0.01A^2 + 0.05A + 107$
$= 0.01(35)^2 + 0.05(35) + 107$
$= 12.25 + 1.75 + 107$
$= 121$; 121 mm Hg

31c. $P = 0.006A^2 - 0.02A + 120$

$134 = 0.006A^2 - 0.02A + 120$
$0 = 0.006A^2 - 0.02A - 14$

$A = \frac{0.02 \pm \sqrt{(-0.02)^2 - 4(0.006)(-14)}}{2(0.006)}$
$= \frac{0.02 \pm \sqrt{0.0004 + 0.336}}{0.012}$
$= \frac{0.02 \pm 0.58}{0.012}$

$A = \frac{0.02 + 0.58}{0.012}$ or 50 and $A = \frac{0.02 - 0.58}{0.012}$ or $-46.\overline{6}$

50 years

32a. $R = -p^2 + 50p - 125$

p	R
0	−125
10	275
20	475
30	475
40	275
50	−125

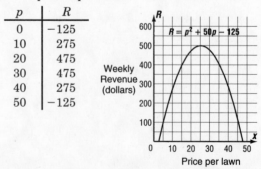

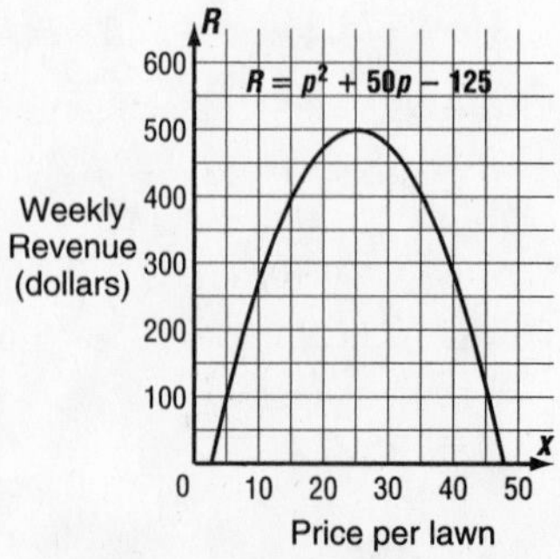

Bryan's profit is determined by the price he chooses to charge per lawn. If he chooses a price that is too high, not as many customers will be willing to pay, and the profit will decrease.

32b. Bryan could charge \$15 and cut more lawns or charge \$35 and cut fewer lawns.

32c. \$25, \$500

32d. $-p^2 + 50p - 125 = 600$

$-p^2 + 50p - 725 = 0$

$b^2 - 4ac = 50^2 - 4(-1)(-725)$

$= -400$

No, if the profit is \$600, the discriminant is -400, so there is no real number to satisfy the equation.

33. $A = s^2$ $\quad P = 4s \quad 4x^2 + 8x - 12 = 0$

$4x^2 = s^2 \quad = 4(2x) \quad 4(x^2 + 2x - 3) = 0$

$2x = s \quad = 8x \quad 4(x + 3)(x - 1) = 0$

$x + 3 = 0$ or $x - 1 = 0$

$x = -3 \qquad x = 1$

1

34. $3t^2 - 4t = 15$

$3t^2 + 4t + 15 = 0$

$(3t - 5)(t + 3) = 0$

$3t - 5 = 0$ or $t + 3 = 0$

$3t = 5 \qquad t = -3$

$t = \frac{5}{3}$

35. $\sqrt{x^2 + 6x + 9} = \sqrt{(x + 3)^2}$

$= |x + 3|$

36. $958{,}904{,}100 - 356{,}164{,}384 = 602{,}739{,}716$

$603{,}000{,}000 = 6.03 \times 100{,}000{,}000$

$= 6.03 \times 10^8$

37. $x - y = 10$

$-3x + 2y = -1$

$\begin{bmatrix} 1 & -1 \\ -3 & 2 \end{bmatrix} \cdot \begin{bmatrix} x \\ y \end{bmatrix} = \begin{bmatrix} 10 \\ -1 \end{bmatrix}; M^{-1} = \frac{1}{2-3}\begin{bmatrix} 2 & 1 \\ 3 & 1 \end{bmatrix}$

$= -1\begin{bmatrix} 2 & 1 \\ 3 & 1 \end{bmatrix}$

$-1\begin{bmatrix} 2 & 1 \\ 3 & 1 \end{bmatrix} \cdot \begin{bmatrix} 1 & -1 \\ -3 & 2 \end{bmatrix} \cdot \begin{bmatrix} x \\ y \end{bmatrix} = -1\begin{bmatrix} 2 & 1 \\ 3 & 1 \end{bmatrix} \cdot \begin{bmatrix} 10 \\ -1 \end{bmatrix}$

$\begin{bmatrix} x \\ y \end{bmatrix} = -1\begin{bmatrix} 20 - 1 \\ 30 - 1 \end{bmatrix}$

$\begin{bmatrix} x \\ y \end{bmatrix} = \begin{bmatrix} -19 \\ -29 \end{bmatrix}$

$(-19, -29)$

38. $|2x - 5| \le 9$

$-9 \le 2x - 5 \le 9$

$-4 \le \quad 2x \quad \le 14$

$-2 \le \quad x \quad \le 7; \{x \mid -2 \le x \le 7\}$

Page 358 Self Test

1. $z^2 + 4z + 3 = 0$

z	y
-4	3
-3	0
-2	-1
-1	0

$-3, -1$

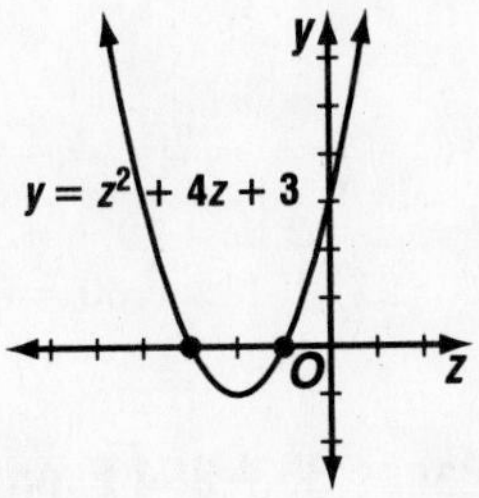

2. $m^2 + 6m = 27$

$m^2 + 6m - 27 = 0$

m	y
-9	0
-6	-27
-3	-36
0	-27
3	0

$-9, 3$

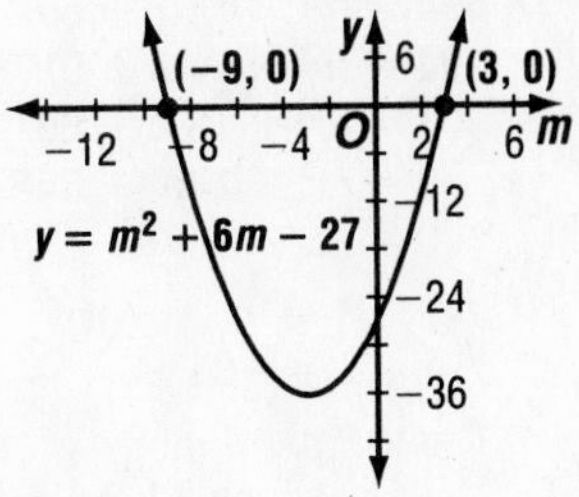

3. $x^2 + 5x - 36 = 0$

$(x + 9)(x - 4) = 0$

$x + 9 = 0$ or $x - 4 = 0$

$x = -9 \qquad x = 4$

4. $2x^2 + 7x = -3$

$2x^2 + 7x + 3 = 0$

$(2x + 1)(x + 3) = 0$

$2x + 1 = 0$ or $x + 3 = 0$

$2x = -1 \qquad x = -3$

$x = -\frac{1}{2}$

5. $x^2 + 6x = 55$

$x^2 + 6x + 9 = 55 + 9$

$(x + 3)^2 = 64$

$x + 3 = \pm 8$

$x + 3 = 8$ or $x + 3 = -8$

$x = 5 \qquad x = -11$

6. $x^2 - 7x + 21 = 0$

$x^2 - 7x = -21$

$x^2 - 7x + \frac{49}{4} = -21 + \frac{49}{4}$

$\left(x - \frac{7}{2}\right)^2 = \frac{-35}{4}$

$x - \frac{7}{2} = \pm \frac{i\sqrt{-35}}{2}$

$x = \frac{7 \pm i\sqrt{35}}{2}$

7. $a = 1, b = -8, c = 2$

$b^2 - 4ac = (-8)^2 - 4(1)(2)$

$= 64 - 8$

$= 56$; 2R, I

8. $a = 3, b = 5, c = -1$

$x = \frac{-5 \pm \sqrt{5^2 - 4(3)(-1)}}{2(3)}$

$= \frac{-5 \pm \sqrt{37}}{6}$

9. $a = 2, b = -25, c = 72$

$x = \frac{25 \pm \sqrt{(-25)^2 - 4(2)(72)}}{2(2)}$

$= \frac{25 \pm \sqrt{49}}{4}$

$= \frac{25 \pm 7}{4}$

$x = \frac{25 + 7}{4}$ and $x = \frac{25 - 7}{4}$

$= 8 \qquad = \frac{9}{2}$

10. Let w = width. Then $\ell = w + 5$.

$A = w \cdot \ell$
$594 = (w + 4)(w + 5 + 4)$
$594 = (w + 4)(w + 9)$
$594 = w^2 + 13w + 36$
$0 = w^2 + 13w - 558$
$0 = (w + 31)(w - 18)$
$w + 31 = 0$ or $w - 18 = 0$
$w = -31$ $\quad w = 18$
$\ell = w + 5$
$= 18 + 5$ or 23; 18 feet by 23 feet

6-5 Sum and Product of Roots

Page 362 Check for Understanding

1. $-\frac{b}{a}, \frac{c}{a}$
2. Set the sum of the roots equal to $\frac{-b}{a}$. Set the product of the roots equal to $\frac{c}{a}$. This will tell you the values of a, b, and c. Substitute the values of a, b, and c in $ax^2 + bx + c = 0$.
3. Set the sum of the roots equal to $\frac{-b}{a}$ and the product of the roots equal to $\frac{c}{a}$. Substitute this into $x^2 + \frac{-b}{a}x + \frac{c}{a} = 0$. Put this equation in standard form by multiplying both sides of the equation by a.
4. See students' work.
5. $-\frac{b}{a} = -\frac{-12}{1} = 12$
$\frac{c}{a} = \frac{22}{1} = 22$
6. $-\frac{b}{a} = -\frac{0}{1} = 0$
$\frac{c}{a} = \frac{-22}{1} = -22$
7. $-\frac{b}{a} = -\frac{0}{3} = 0$
$\frac{c}{a} = \frac{75}{3} = 25$
8. $2x^2 - \frac{1}{4}x = -\frac{8}{15}$
$2x^2 - \frac{1}{4}x + \frac{8}{15} = 0$
$-\frac{b}{a} = -\frac{-\frac{1}{4}}{2} = \frac{1}{8}$
$\frac{c}{a} = \frac{\frac{8}{15}}{2} = \frac{4}{15}$
9. $s_1 + s_2 = (4 + \sqrt{5}) + (4 - \sqrt{5})$
$= 8$
$s_1(s_2) = (4 + \sqrt{5})(4 - \sqrt{5})$
$= 16 - 5$
$= 11$
$-\frac{b}{a} = \frac{8}{1}; \frac{c}{a} = \frac{11}{1}$
$a = 1, b = -8, c = 11$
$x^2 - 8x + 11 = 0$
10. $s_1 + s_2 = (\sqrt{5} + 8i) + (\sqrt{5} - 8i)$
$= 2\sqrt{5}$
$s_1(s_2) = (\sqrt{5} + 8i)(\sqrt{5} - 8i)$
$= 5 - 64i^2$
$= 69$

(Continued next column)

$-\frac{b}{a} = \frac{2\sqrt{5}}{1}; \frac{c}{a} = \frac{69}{1}$
$a = 1, b = -2\sqrt{5}, c = 69$
$x^2 - 2\sqrt{5}x + 69 = 0$

11. $s_1 + s_2 = -7 + \frac{2}{3}$
$= \frac{-19}{3}$
$s_1(s_2) = (-7)\left(\frac{2}{3}\right)$
$= \frac{-14}{3}$
$-\frac{b}{a} = \frac{-19}{3}; \frac{c}{a} = \frac{-14}{3}$
$a = 3, b = 19, c = -14$
$3x^2 + 19x - 14 = 0$

12. $s_1 + s_2 = -\frac{3}{4} + \frac{5}{8}$
$= -\frac{1}{8}$ or $-\frac{4}{32}$
$s_1(s_2) = \left(-\frac{3}{4}\right)\left(\frac{5}{8}\right)$
$= -\frac{15}{32}$
$-\frac{b}{a} = -\frac{4}{32}; \frac{c}{a} = -\frac{15}{32}$
$a = 32, b = 4, c = -15$
$32x^2 + 4x - 15 = 0$

13. $x^2 - 49 = 0$
$(x - 7)(x + 7) = 0$
$x - 7 = 0$ or $x + 7 = 0$
$x = 7$ $\quad x = -7$
$-\frac{b}{a} = \frac{0}{1}$
$= 0$
$s_1 + s_2 = 7 + (-7)$
$= 0$ ✓
$\frac{c}{a} = \frac{-49}{1}$
$= -49$
$s_1(s_2) = 7(-7)$
$= -49$ ✓

14. $2x^2 + 15x = 27$
$2x^2 + 15x - 27 = 0$
$(2x - 3)(x + 9) = 0$
$2x - 3 = 0$ or $x + 9 = 0$
$2x = 3$ $\quad x = -9$
$x = \frac{3}{2}$
$-\frac{b}{a} = -\frac{15}{2}$
$s_1 + s_2 = \frac{3}{2} + (-9)$
$= -\frac{15}{2}$ ✓
$\frac{c}{a} = -\frac{27}{2}$
$s_1s_2 = \left(\frac{3}{2}\right)(-9)$
$= -\frac{27}{2}$

15. $16x^2 - 81 = 0$
$(4x - 9)(4x + 9) = 0$
$4x - 9 = 0$ or $4x + 9 = 0$
$4x = 9$ $\quad 4x = -9$
$x = \frac{9}{4}$ $\quad x = -\frac{9}{4}$
$-\frac{b}{a} = -\frac{0}{16}$
$= 0$
$s_1 + s_2 = \frac{9}{4} + \left(-\frac{9}{4}\right)$
$= 0$ ✓
$\frac{c}{a} = \frac{-81}{16}$
$s_1(s_2) = \left(\frac{9}{4}\right)\left(-\frac{9}{4}\right)$
$= \frac{-81}{16}$ ✓

16. $-\frac{b}{a} = -\frac{19}{2}; \frac{c}{a} = -30$ or $-\frac{60}{2}$
$a = 2, b = 19, c = -60$
$2x^2 + 19x - 60 = 0$

Pages 363–364 Exercises

17. $s_1 + s_2 = 6 + (-9)$
$= -3$
$s_1(s_2) = (6)(-9)$
$= -54$
$-\frac{b}{a} = -\frac{3}{1}; \frac{c}{a} = -\frac{54}{1}$
$a = 1, b = 3, c = -54$
$x^2 + 3x - 54 = 0$

18. $s_1 + s_2 = 5 + (-1)$
$= 4$
$s_1(s_2) = (5)(-1)$
$= -5$

$-\frac{b}{a} = \frac{4}{1}; \frac{c}{a} = -\frac{5}{1}$
$a = 1, b = -4, c = -5$
$x^2 - 4x - 5 = 0$

19. $s_1 + s_2 = 2 + \frac{5}{8}$
$= \frac{21}{8}$
$s_1(s_2) = 2\left(\frac{5}{8}\right)$
$= \frac{10}{8}$

$-\frac{b}{a} = \frac{21}{8}; \frac{c}{a} = \frac{10}{8}$
$a = 8, b = -21, c = 10$
$8x^2 - 21x + 10 = 0$

20. $s_1 + s_2 = 6 + 6$
$= 12$
$s_1(s_2) = 6 \cdot 6$
$= 36$

$-\frac{b}{a} = \frac{12}{1}; \frac{c}{a} = \frac{36}{1}$
$a = 1, b = -12, c = 36$
$x^2 - 12x + 36 = 0$

21. $s_1 + s_2 = \left(-\frac{2}{5}\right) + \left(\frac{2}{5}\right)$
$= 0 \text{ or } \frac{0}{25}$
$s_1(s_2) = \left(-\frac{2}{5}\right)\left(\frac{2}{5}\right)$
$= -\frac{4}{25}$

$-\frac{b}{a} = \frac{0}{25}; \frac{c}{a} = -\frac{4}{25}$
$a = 25, b = 0. c = -4$
$25x^2 - 4 = 0$

22. $s_1 + s_2 = \left(-\frac{2}{5}\right) + \left(\frac{2}{7}\right)$
$= -\frac{4}{35}$
$s_1(s_2) = \left(-\frac{2}{5}\right)\left(\frac{2}{7}\right)$
$= -\frac{4}{35}$

$-\frac{b}{a} = -\frac{4}{35}; \frac{c}{a} = -\frac{4}{35}$
$a = 35, b = 4, c = -4$
$35x^2 + 4x - 4 = 0$

23. $s_1 + s_2 = (-4) + \left(-\frac{2}{3}\right)$
$= -\frac{14}{3}$
$s_1(s_2) = (-4)\left(-\frac{2}{3}\right)$
$= \frac{8}{3}$

$-\frac{b}{a} = -\frac{14}{3}; \frac{c}{a} = \frac{8}{3}$
$a = 3, b = 14, c = 8$
$3x^2 + 14x + 8 = 0$

24. $s_1 + s_2 = \left(\frac{4}{3}\right) + \left(-\frac{1}{6}\right)$
$= \frac{7}{6} \text{ or } \frac{21}{18}$
$s_1(s_2) = \left(\frac{4}{3}\right)\left(-\frac{1}{6}\right)$
$= -\frac{4}{18}$

$-\frac{b}{a} = \frac{21}{18}; \frac{c}{a} = -\frac{4}{18}$
$a = 18, b = -21, c = -4$
$18x^2 - 21x - 4 = 0$

25. $s_1 + s_2 = (4 + \sqrt{3}) + (4 - \sqrt{3})$
$= 8$
$s_1(s_2) = (4 + \sqrt{3})(4 - \sqrt{3})$
$= 16 - 3$
$= 13$
$-\frac{b}{a} = \frac{8}{1}; \frac{c}{a} = \frac{13}{1}$
$a = 1, b = -8, c = 13$
$x^2 - 8x + 13 = 0$

26. $s_1 + s_2 = \left(\frac{3}{7} + 2i\right) + \left(\frac{3}{7} - 2i\right)$
$= \frac{6}{7} \text{ or } \frac{42}{49}$
$s_1 + s_2 = \left(\frac{3}{7} + 2i\right)\left(\frac{3}{7} - 2i\right)$
$= \frac{9}{49} - 4i^2$
$= \frac{205}{49}$
$-\frac{b}{a} = \frac{42}{49}; \frac{c}{a} = \frac{205}{49}$
$a = 49, b = -42, c = 205$
$49x^2 - 42x + 205 = 0$

27. $s_1 + s_2 = \left(\frac{-2 + 5i}{4}\right) + \left(\frac{-2 - 5i}{4}\right)$
$= -\frac{4}{4} \text{ or } -\frac{16}{16}$
$s_1(s_2) = \left(\frac{-2 + 5i}{4}\right) + \left(\frac{-2 - 5i}{4}\right)$
$= \frac{4 - 25i^2}{16}$
$= \frac{29}{16}$
$-\frac{b}{a} = -\frac{16}{16}; \frac{c}{a} = \frac{29}{16}$
$a = 16, b = 16, c = 29$
$16x^2 + 16x + 29 = 0$

28. $s_1 + s_2 = \left(\frac{-2 + 3\sqrt{5}}{7}\right)\left(\frac{-2 - 3\sqrt{5}}{7}\right)$
$= -\frac{4}{7} \text{ or } -\frac{28}{49}$
$s_1(s_2) = \left(\frac{-2 + 3\sqrt{5}}{7}\right)\left(\frac{-2 - 3\sqrt{5}}{7}\right)$
$= \frac{4 - 45}{49}$
$= -\frac{41}{49}$
$-\frac{b}{a} = -\frac{28}{49}; \frac{c}{a} = -\frac{41}{49}$
$a = 49, b = 28, c = -41$
$49x^2 + 28x - 41 = 0$

29. $-2x^2 - 11x - 12 = 0$
$x = \frac{11 \pm \sqrt{(-11)^2 - 4(-2)(-12)}}{2(-2)}$
$= \frac{11 \pm \sqrt{25}}{-4}$

$x = \frac{11 + 5}{-4}$ or $x = \frac{11 - 5}{-4}$
$= -4$ $= -\frac{3}{2}$

$-\frac{b}{a} = -\frac{(-11)}{(-2)}$
$= -\frac{11}{2}$
$\frac{c}{a} = \frac{-12}{-2}$
$= 6$

$s_1 + s_2 = (-4) + \left(-\frac{3}{2}\right)$
$= -\frac{11}{2}$ ✓
$s_1(s_2) = (-4)(-\frac{3}{2})$
$= 6$ ✓

30. $-3x^2 + 22x - 24 = 0$
$x = \frac{-22 \pm \sqrt{22^2 - 4(-3)(-24)}}{2(-3)}$
$= \frac{-22 \pm \sqrt{196}}{-6}$

$x = \frac{-22 + 14}{-6}$ or $x = \frac{-22 - 14}{-6}$
$= \frac{4}{3}$ $= 6$

$-\frac{b}{a} = -\frac{22}{(-3)}$
$= \frac{22}{3}$
$\frac{c}{a} = \frac{-24}{-3}$
$= 8$

$s_1 + s_2 = \frac{4}{3} + 6$
$= \frac{22}{3}$ ✓
$s_1(s_2) = \frac{4}{3} \cdot 6$
$= 8$ ✓

31. $x^2 - 8x = 0$
$x(x - 8) = 0$
$x = 0 \text{ or } x - 8 = 0$
$x = 8$

$-\frac{b}{a} = -\frac{(-8)}{1}$
$= 8$
$\frac{c}{a} = \frac{0}{1}$
$= 0$

$s_1 + s_2 = 0 + 8$
$= 8$ ✓
$s_1(s_2) = 0(8)$
$= 0$ ✓

32. $x^2 - 16 = 0$

$(x - 4)(x + 4) = 0$

$x - 4 = 0$ or $x + 4 = 0$

$x = 4$ $\quad x = -4$

$-\frac{b}{a} = -\frac{0}{1} = 0$ $\qquad s_1 + s_2 = 4 + (-4) = 0$ ✓

$\frac{c}{a} = -\frac{16}{1} = -16$ $\qquad s_1(s_2) = 4(-4) = -16$

33. $x^2 + \frac{1}{6}x - \frac{1}{3} = 0$

$6x^2 + x - 2 = 0$

$(2x - 1)(3x + 2) = 0$

$2x - 1 = 0$ or $3x + 2 = 0$

$2x = 1$ $\quad 3x = -2$

$x = \frac{1}{2}$ $\quad x = -\frac{2}{3}$

$-\frac{b}{a} = \frac{-\frac{1}{6}}{1} = -\frac{1}{6}$ $\qquad s_1 + s_2 = \frac{1}{2} + \left(-\frac{2}{3}\right) = -\frac{1}{6}$ ✓

$\frac{c}{a} = \frac{-\frac{1}{3}}{1} = -\frac{1}{3}$ $\qquad s_1 + s_2 = \left(\frac{1}{2}\right)\left(-\frac{2}{3}\right) = -\frac{1}{3}$ ✓

34. $\frac{1}{2}x^2 - \frac{13}{20}x - \frac{3}{20} = 0$

$10x^2 - 13x - 3 = 0$

$x = \frac{13 \pm \sqrt{13^2 - 4(10)(-3)}}{2(10)}$

$= \frac{13 \pm \sqrt{289}}{20}$

$x = \frac{13 + 17}{20}$ or $x = \frac{13 - 17}{20}$

$= \frac{3}{2}$ $\quad = -\frac{1}{5}$

$-\frac{b}{a} = -\frac{\left(-\frac{13}{20}\right)}{\frac{1}{2}} = \frac{13}{10}$ $\qquad s_1 + s_2 = \frac{3}{2} + \left(-\frac{1}{5}\right) = \frac{13}{10}$ ✓

$\frac{c}{a} = \frac{\left(\frac{-3}{20}\right)}{\frac{1}{2}} = -\frac{3}{10}$ $\qquad s_1(s_2) = \left(\frac{3}{2}\right)\left(-\frac{1}{5}\right) = -\frac{3}{10}$ ✓

35. $x^2 - 8x - 18 = 0$

$x = \frac{8 \pm \sqrt{(-8)^2 - 4(1)(-18)}}{2(1)}$

$= \frac{8 \pm \sqrt{136}}{2}$

$= \frac{8 \pm 2\sqrt{34}}{2}$

$= 4 \pm \sqrt{34}$

$-\frac{b}{a} = -\frac{(-8)}{1} = 8$ $\qquad s_1 + s_2 = (4 + \sqrt{34}) + (4 - \sqrt{34}) = 8$ ✓

$\frac{c}{a} = \frac{-18}{1} = -18$ $\qquad s_1(s_2) = (4 + \sqrt{34})(4 - \sqrt{34}) = 16 - 34 = -18$ ✓

36. $2x^2 + 10x = -10$

$2x^2 + 10x + 10 = 0$

$x = \frac{-10 \pm \sqrt{10^2 - 4(2)(10)}}{2(2)}$

$= \frac{-10 \pm \sqrt{20}}{4}$

$= \frac{-10 \pm 2\sqrt{5}}{4}$

$= \frac{-5 \pm \sqrt{5}}{2}$

$-\frac{b}{a} = -\frac{10}{2} = -5$ $\qquad s_1 + s_2 = \left(\frac{-5 + \sqrt{5}}{2}\right) + \left(\frac{-5 - \sqrt{5}}{2}\right) = \frac{-10}{2} = -5$ ✓

$\frac{c}{a} = \frac{10}{2} = 5$ $\qquad s_1(s_2) = \left(\frac{-5 + \sqrt{5}}{2}\right)\left(\frac{-5 - \sqrt{5}}{2}\right) = \frac{25 - 5}{4} = 5$ ✓

37. $4x^2 - 31x - 45 = 0$

$x = \frac{31 \pm \sqrt{(-31)^2 - 4(4)(-45)}}{2(4)}$

$= \frac{31 \pm \sqrt{1681}}{8}$

$x = \frac{31 + 41}{8}$ or $x = \frac{31 - 41}{8}$

$= 9$ $\quad = -\frac{5}{4}$

$-\frac{b}{a} = -\frac{(-31)}{4} = \frac{31}{4}$ $\qquad s_1 + s_2 = 9 + \left(-\frac{5}{4}\right) = \frac{31}{4}$ ✓

$\frac{c}{a} = -\frac{45}{4}$ $\qquad s_1(s_2) = 9\left(-\frac{5}{4}\right) = -\frac{45}{4}$ ✓

38. $3x + 17 = 0$

$x = \frac{0 \pm \sqrt{0^2 - 4(3)(17)}}{2(3)}$

$= \frac{\pm\sqrt{-204}}{6}$

$= \frac{\pm 2i\sqrt{51}}{6}$

$= \frac{\pm i\sqrt{51}}{3}$

$-\frac{b}{a} = -\frac{0}{3} = 0$ $\qquad s_1 + s_2 = \left(\frac{i\sqrt{51}}{3}\right) + \left(\frac{-i\sqrt{51}}{3}\right) = 0$ ✓

$\frac{c}{a} = \frac{17}{3}$ $\qquad s_1(s_2) = \left(\frac{i\sqrt{51}}{3}\right)\left(\frac{-i\sqrt{51}}{3}\right) = \frac{-51i^2}{9} = \frac{17}{3}$ ✓

39a. $-\frac{b}{a} = 4; = \frac{48}{12}$ $\qquad \frac{c}{a} = \frac{13}{12}$

$a = 12, b = -48, c = 13$

$12x^2 - 48x + 13 = 0$

39b. $-\frac{b}{a} = \frac{1}{6};$ $\qquad \frac{c}{a} = \frac{5}{21}$

$= \frac{7}{42} \qquad = \frac{10}{42}$

$a = 42,\ b = -7,\ c = 10$

$42x^2 - 7x + 10 = 0$

40. $2x^2 + kx - 21 = 0$

$2(3)^2 + k(3) - 21 = 0$

$18 - 3k - 21 = 0$

$-3k - 3 = 0$

$-3k = 3$

$k = -1$

41. $2x^2 + 11x = -k$

$2\left(\frac{1}{2}\right)^2 + 11\left(\frac{1}{2}\right) = -k$

$\frac{1}{2} + \frac{11}{2} = -k$

$6 = -k$

$-6 = k$

42. $\frac{c}{a} = s_1(s_2)$

$\frac{-24}{1} = s_1(s_2)$

$-24 = s_1(s_2)$

If s_1 and s_2 are integers, the possible solutions are 24, −1; −24, 1; 12, −2; −12, 2; 8 −3; −8, 3; 6, −4; −6, 4.

43. $h = v_it - \frac{1}{2}gt^2$

$0 = -\frac{1}{2}gt^2 + v_it - h$

$0 = -\frac{1}{2}(9.8)t^2 + v_it - h$

$0 = -4.9t^2 + v_it - h$

$s_1 + s_2 = -\frac{b}{a}$

$0 + 18 = -\frac{v_i}{(-4.9)}$

$18 = \frac{v_i}{4.9}$

$88.2 = v_i$; 88.2 meters per second

44a. *ABCD*: $\ell = 1 + x,\ w = 1;\ \frac{1+x}{1}$

EBCF: $\ell = 1,\ w = x;\ \frac{1}{x}$

44b. $\frac{1+x}{1} = \frac{1}{x}$

$x(1 + x) = 1$

$x + x^2 = 1$

$x^2 + x - 1 = 0$

$x = \frac{-1 \pm \sqrt{1^2 - 4(1)(-1)}}{2(1)}$

$= \frac{-1 \pm \sqrt{5}}{2}$; 0.618 or −1.618; 0.618

44c. $\frac{1+x}{1} = \frac{1 + 0.618}{1} \qquad \frac{1}{x} = \frac{1}{0.618}$

$= 1.618 \qquad \approx 1.68$

45. $x^2 - 2x - 35 = 0$

$x = \frac{2 \pm \sqrt{(-2)^2 - 4(1)(-35)}}{2(1)}$

$= \frac{2 \pm \sqrt{144}}{2}$

$x = \frac{2 + 12}{2}$ or $x = \frac{2 - 12}{2}$

$= 7 \qquad = -5$

46. $m^2 + 3m - 180 = 0$

$m^2 + 3m = 180$

$m^2 + 3m + \frac{9}{4} = 180 + \frac{9}{4}$

$\left(m + \frac{3}{2}\right)^2 = \frac{729}{4}$

$m + \frac{3}{2} = \pm\frac{27}{2}$

$m + \frac{3}{2} = \frac{27}{2}$ or $m + \frac{3}{2} = -\frac{27}{2}$

$m = \frac{24}{2} \qquad m = -\frac{30}{2}$

$m = 12 \qquad m = -15$

47. $f(x) = x^2 + 8x - 5$

x	$f(x)$
−6	−17
−4	−21
−2	−17
0	−5

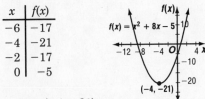

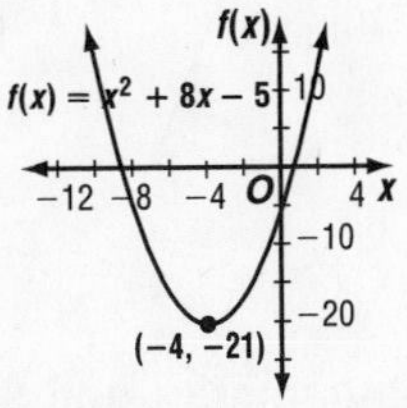

vertex: (−4, −21)

axis of symmetry: $x = -4$

48. $\sqrt{108} - \sqrt{48} + (\sqrt{3})^3$

$= \sqrt{6^2 \cdot 3} - \sqrt{4^2 \cdot 3} + (\sqrt{3} \cdot \sqrt{3} \cdot \sqrt{3})$

$= 6\sqrt{3} - 4\sqrt{3} + 3\sqrt{3}$

$= 5\sqrt{3}$

49. $4x^2 - 9 = (2x - 3)(2x + 3)$

50. $\left[\begin{array}{ccc|c} 3 & -1 & 2 & 7 \\ -1 & 4 & -1 & 3 \\ 1 & 4 & -1 & 1 \end{array}\right] = \left[\begin{array}{ccc|c} 3 & -1 & 2 & 7 \\ -1 & 4 & -1 & 3 \\ 0 & 8 & -2 & 4 \end{array}\right]$

$= \left[\begin{array}{ccc|c} 3 & -1 & 2 & 7 \\ -3 & 12 & -3 & 9 \\ 0 & 8 & -2 & 4 \end{array}\right] = \left[\begin{array}{ccc|c} 3 & -1 & 2 & 7 \\ 0 & 11 & -1 & 16 \\ 0 & 8 & -2 & 4 \end{array}\right]$

$= \left[\begin{array}{ccc|c} 3 & 7 & 0 & 11 \\ 0 & 11 & -1 & 16 \\ 0 & 8 & -2 & 4 \end{array}\right] = \left[\begin{array}{ccc|c} 3 & 7 & 0 & 11 \\ 0 & -22 & 2 & -32 \\ 0 & 8 & -2 & 4 \end{array}\right]$

$= \left[\begin{array}{ccc|c} 3 & 7 & 0 & 11 \\ 0 & -14 & 0 & -28 \\ 0 & 8 & -2 & 4 \end{array}\right] = \left[\begin{array}{ccc|c} 3 & 7 & 0 & 11 \\ 0 & 1 & 0 & 2 \\ 0 & 8 & -2 & 4 \end{array}\right]$

$= \left[\begin{array}{ccc|c} 3 & 0 & 0 & -3 \\ 0 & 1 & 0 & 2 \\ 0 & 8 & -2 & 4 \end{array}\right] = \left[\begin{array}{ccc|c} 1 & 0 & 0 & -1 \\ 0 & 1 & 0 & 2 \\ 0 & 8 & -2 & 4 \end{array}\right]$

$= \left[\begin{array}{ccc|c} 1 & 0 & 0 & -1 \\ 0 & 1 & 0 & 2 \\ 0 & 0 & -2 & -12 \end{array}\right] = \left[\begin{array}{ccc|c} 1 & 0 & 0 & -1 \\ 0 & 1 & 0 & 2 \\ 0 & 0 & 1 & 6 \end{array}\right]$; (−1, 2, 6)

51. $\begin{vmatrix} a & 2 & -1 \\ 4a & -7 & -1 \\ 2 & 2 & -2 \end{vmatrix} = 45$

$a\begin{vmatrix} -7 & -1 \\ 2 & -2 \end{vmatrix} - 2\begin{vmatrix} 4a & -1 \\ 2 & -2 \end{vmatrix} - 1\begin{vmatrix} 4a & -7 \\ 2 & 2 \end{vmatrix} = 45$

$a(14 + 2) - 2(-8a + 2) - 1(8a + 14) = 45$

$14a + 2a + 16a - 4 - 8a - 14 = 45$

$24a - 18 = 45$

$24a = 63$

$a = \frac{21}{8}$

52. $y = -|5x - 12| + 1$

x	$-\|5x - 12\| + 1$	y
0	$-\|5(0) - 12\| + 1$	-11
1	$-\|5(1) - 12\| + 1$	-6
2.5	$-\|5(2.5) - 12\| + 1$	0.5
4	$-\|5(4) - 12\| + 1$	-7

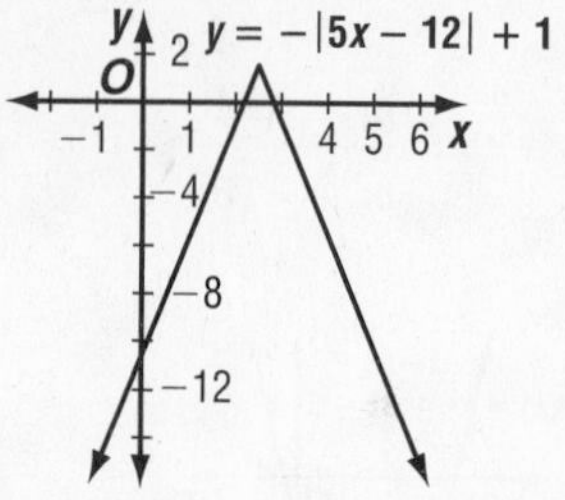

Page 364 Mathematics and Society

1. The paths of the objects being tossed are parabolas, quadratic equations.
2. Sample answer: how many objects are being thrown, how far apart the people are who are juggling, how heavy the objects are.
3. Answers will vary.

6-6A Graphing Technology: Families of Parabolas

Page 366 Exercises

1. The value of k determines the vertical position of the graph. As you change k, the graph will slide up or down the coordinate plane. Examples will vary.
2. The value of h determines the horizontal position of the graph. As you change the h, the graph will slide to the right or the left on the coordinate plane. Examples will vary.
3. Both graphs have the same shape and vertex, but the first graph opens upward and the second graph opens downward. Examples will vary.
4. [Y=] [X,T,θ,n] [x^2] [ENTER] [(] [X,T,θ,n] [+] 6 [)] [x^2] [ZOOM] 6

   Both graphs have the same shape, but the graph of $y = (x + 6)^2$ is 6 units to the left of the graph of $y = x^2$.
5. [Y=] [X,T,θ,n] [x^2] [ENTER] [(] [X,T,θ,n] [−] 8 [)] [x^2] [ZOOM] 6

   Both graphs have the same shape, but the graph of $y = (x - 8)^2$ is 8 units to the right of the graph of $y = x^2$.
6. [Y=] [X,T,θ,n] [x^2] [ENTER] [X,T,θ,n] [x^2] [+] 1.15 [ZOOM] 6

   Both graphs have the same shape, but the graph of $y = x^2 + 1.5$ is 1.5 units above the graph of $y = x^2$.
7. [Y=] [X,T,θ,n] [x^2] [ENTER] [X,T,θ,n] [x^2] [−] 11 [ZOOM] 6

   Both graphs have the same shape, but the graph of $y = x^2 - 11$ is 11 units below the graph of $y = x^2$.
8. [Y=] [(−)] [X,T,θ,n] [x^2] [ENTER] [(−)] 5 [X,T,θ,n] [x^2] [ZOOM] 6

   Both graphs open downward, but the graph of $y = -5x^2$ is more narrow than the graph of $y = -x^2$.
9. [Y=] [X,T,θ,n] [x^2] [ENTER] [(−)] 2 [X,T,θ,n] [x^2] [ZOOM] 6

   The graph of $y = -2x^2$ opens downward and is more narrow than the graph of $y = x^2$.
10. [Y=] [X,T,θ,n] [x^2] [ENTER] [−] [(] 1 [÷] 2 [)] [X,T,θ,n] [x^2] [+] 4 [ZOOM] 6

    The graph of $y = -\frac{1}{2}x^2 + 4$ opens downward, it is wider, and it is 4 units above the graph of $y = x^2$.
11. [Y=] [(−)] [(] 1 [÷] 3 [)] [X,T,θ,n] [x^2] [ENTER] [−] [(] 1 [÷] 3 [)] [X,T,θ,n] [x^2] [+] 2 [ZOOM] 6

    Both graphs have the same shape, but the graph of $y = -\frac{1}{3}x^2 + 2$ is 2 units above the graph of $y = -\frac{1}{3}x^2$.
12. [Y=] [X,T,θ,n] [x^2] [ENTER] [(−)] 6 [(] [X,T,θ,n] [+] 1 [)] [x^2] [−] 11 [GRAPH] (WINDOW [−10, 10] by [−20, 10])

    The graph of $y = -6(x + 1)^2 - 11$ opens downward, is more narrow than the graph of $y = x^2$, and it is 11 units down and 1 unit to the left.
13. [Y=] [(] [X,T,θ,n] [+] 2 [)] [x^2] [+] 1 [ENTER] [(] [X,T,θ,n] [+] 2 [)] [x^2] [−] 4 [ZOOM] 6

    Both graphs have the same shape, but the graph of $y = (x + 2)^2 - 4$ is 5 units below the graph of $y = (x + 2)^2 + 1$.
14. [Y=] 2 [(] [X,T,θ,n] [+] 3 [)] [x^2] [+] 1 [ENTER] 4 [(] [X,T,θ,n] [+] 3 [)] [x^2] [+] 1 [ZOOM] 6

    The graph of $y = 4(x + 3)^2 + 1$ is more narrow than the graph of $y = 2(x + 3)^2 + 1$.
15. [Y=] 2 [(] [X,T,θ,n] [−] 4 [)] [x^2] [+] 3 [ENTER] [(] 1 [÷] 2 [)] [(] [X,T,θ,n] [−] 4 [)] [x^2] [−] 5 [ZOOM] 6

    The graph of $y = \frac{1}{2}(x - 4)^2 - 5$ is 8 units below and is wider than the graph of $y = 2(x - 4)^2 + 3$.

6-6 Analyzing Graphs of Quadratic Functions

Page 372 Check for Understanding

1. The graph of each function has a vertex at $(-6, -2)$ and an axis of symmetry at $x = -6$. The graph of $y = 4(x + 6)^2 - 2$ is narrow and opens upward; the graph of $y = -\frac{1}{2}(x + 6)^2 - 2$ is wider and opens downward.
2. To find the equation of a parabola, you would need the vertex and one point, three points, or the vertex and the value of a.
3. Vertex $(-4, 7)$; axis of symmetry $x = -4$; graph opens downward and is wide.

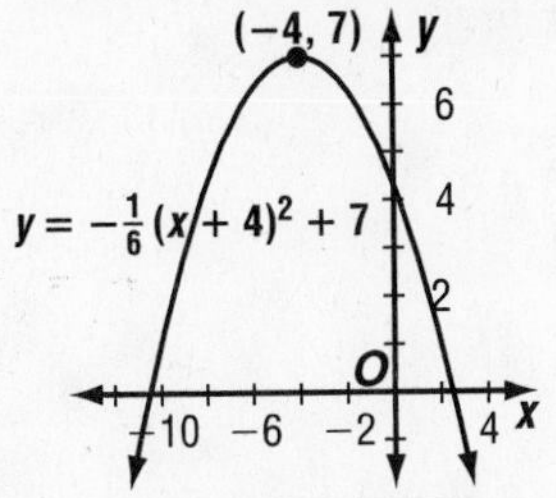

4. $y = 5(x - 1)^2 - 4$
5. Marisel is correct. To complete the square, Leticia should have subtracted 2(9) or 18, not 9.
6. $f(x) = -2(x + 3)^2$; $(-3, 0)$, $x = -3$, down
7. $f(x) = 5x^2 - 6$
   $= 5(x - 0)^2 - 6$; $(0, -6)$, $x = 0$, up
8. $f(x) = x^2 - 4x + 5$
   $= (x^2 - 4x) + 5$
   $= (x^2 - 4x + 4) + 5 - 4$
   $= (x - 2)^2 + 1$; $(2, 1)$, $x = 2$, up
9. $f(x) = -3x^2 + 12x$
   $= -3(x^2 - 4x)$
   $= -3(x^2 - 4x + 4) - (-3)(4)$
   $= -3(x - 2)^2 + 12$; $(2, 12)$, $x = 2$, down
10. $y = a(x - h)^2 + k$
    $-2 = a(1 - 0)^2 + 0$
    $-2 = a$
    $y = -2(x - 0)^2 + 0$
    $y = -2x^2$
11. $y = a(x - h)^2 + k$
    $-5 = a(0 - (-2))^2 + (-3)$
    $-5 = 4a - 3$
    $-2 = 4a$
    $-\frac{1}{2} = a$
    $y = -\frac{1}{2}(x + 2)^2 - 3$
12. $(0, 2) \rightarrow 2 = a(0)^2 + b(0) + c \rightarrow 2 = c$
    $(2, 2) \rightarrow 2 = a(2)^2 + b(2) + c \rightarrow 2 = 4a + 2b + c$
    $(3, 4) \rightarrow 4 = a(3)^2 + b(3) + c \rightarrow 4 = 9a + 3b + c$
    Substitute 2 for c:
    $2 = 4a + 2b + 2 \rightarrow 0 = 4a + 2b \rightarrow 0 = -12a - 6b$
    $4 = 9a + 3b + 2 \rightarrow 2 = 9a + 3b \rightarrow (+)4 = 18a + 6b$
    $4 = 6a$
    $\frac{2}{3} = a$

(Continued next column)

$2 = 9a + 3b$
$2 = 9\left(\frac{2}{3}\right) + 3b$
$2 = 6 + 3b$
$-4 = 3b$
$-\frac{4}{3} = b$ $y = \frac{2}{3}x^2 - \frac{4}{3}x + 2$

13. $(1, 6) \rightarrow 6 = a(1)^2 + b(1) + c \rightarrow 6 = a + b + c$
    $(-2, 27) \rightarrow 27 = a(-2)^2 + b(-2) + c \rightarrow 27 = 4a - 2b + c$
    $(2, 11) \rightarrow 11 = a(2)^2 + b(2) + c \rightarrow 11 = 4a + 2b + c$
    $27 = 4a - 2b + c$
    $(-)11 = 4a + 2b + c$
    $16 = -4b$
    $-4 = b$
    $6 = a + b + c$
    $(-)27 = 4a - 2b + c$
    $-21 = -3a + 3b$
    $-21 = -3a + 3(-4)$
    $-21 = -3a - 12$
    $-9 = -3a$
    $3 = a$
    $6 = a + b + c$
    $6 = 3 + (-4) + c$
    $7 = c$ $y = 3x^2 - 4x + 7$
14. $f(x) = 5(x + 3)^2 - 1$

x	$5(x + 3)^2 - 1$	$f(x)$
−4	$5(-4 + 3)^2 - 1$	4
−3	$5(-3 + 3)^2 - 1$	−1
−2	$5(-2 + 3)^2 - 1$	4
−1	$5(-1 + 3)^2 - 1$	19

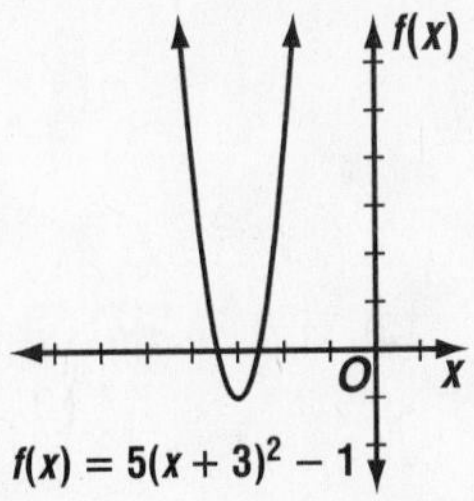

15. $f(x) = -4x^2 + 16x - 11$

x	$-4x^2 + 16x - 11$	$f(x)$
1	$-4(1)^2 + 16(1) - 11$	1
2	$-4(2)^2 + 16(2) - 11$	5
3	$-4(3)^2 + 16(3) - 11$	1
4	$-4(4)^2 + 16(4) - 11$	−11

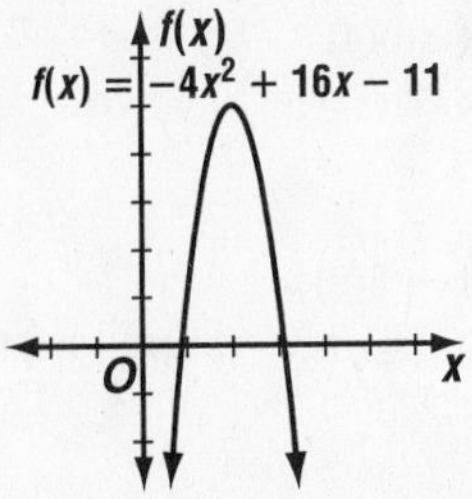

16. $f(x) = \frac{1}{3}(x-1)^2 + 2$

x	$\frac{1}{3}(x-1)^2 + 2$	$f(x)$
-1	$\frac{1}{3}((-1)-1)^2 + 2$	$\frac{10}{3}$
0	$\frac{1}{3}(0-1)^2 + 2$	$\frac{7}{3}$
1	$\frac{1}{3}(1-1)^2 + 2$	2
2	$\frac{1}{3}(2-1)^2 + 2$	$\frac{7}{3}$

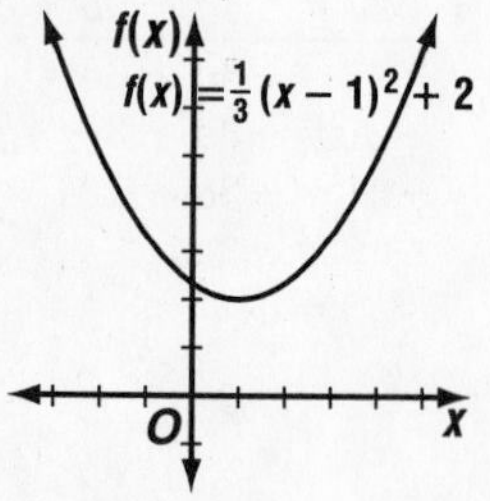

17. $f(x) = 3x^2 - 5$

Pages 373–375 Exercises

18. $(-3, 1)$, $x = -3$, up

19. $(-11, -6)$, $x = -11$, down

20. $(2, -2)$, $x = 2$, down

21. $\left(\frac{1}{2}, \frac{1}{4}\right)$, $x = \frac{1}{2}$, up

22.
$$\begin{aligned} f(x) &= x^2 + 6x - 3 \\ &= (x^2 + 6x + 9) - 3 - 9 \\ &= (x+3)^2 - 12;\ (-3, -12),\ x = -3,\ \text{up} \end{aligned}$$

23.
$$\begin{aligned} f(x) &= -x^2 - 4x + 8 \\ &= -1(x^2 + 4x) + 8 \\ &= -1(x^2 + 4x + 4) + 8 + 4 \\ &= -(x+2)^2 + 12;\ (-2, 12),\ x = -2,\ \text{down} \end{aligned}$$

24.
$$\begin{aligned} f(x) &= 4x^2 + 24x \\ &= 4(x^2 + 6x) \\ &= 4(x^2 + 6x + 9) - 4(9) \\ &= 4(x+3)^2 - 36;\ (-3, -36),\ x = -3,\ \text{up} \end{aligned}$$

25.
$$\begin{aligned} f(x) &= -6x^2 + 24x \\ &= -6(x^2 - 4x) \\ &= -6(x^2 - 4x + 4) - (-6)(4) \\ &= -6(x-2)^2 + 24;\ (2, 24),\ x = 2,\ \text{down} \end{aligned}$$

26.
$$\begin{aligned} f(x) &= 3x^2 - 18x + 11 \\ &= 3(x^2 - 6x) + 11 \\ &= 3(x^2 - 6x + 9) + 11 - 3(9) \\ &= 3(x-3)^2 - 16;\ (3, -16),\ x = 3,\ \text{up} \end{aligned}$$

27.
$$\begin{aligned} f(x) &= -2x^2 - 20x - 50 \\ &= -2(x^2 + 10x) - 50 \\ &= -2(x^2 + 10x + 25) - 50 - (-2)(25) \\ &= -2(x+5)^2;\ (-5, 0),\ x = -5,\ \text{down} \end{aligned}$$

28.
$$\begin{aligned} f(x) &= -\tfrac{1}{2}x^2 + 5x - \tfrac{27}{2} \\ &= -\tfrac{1}{2}(x^2 - 10x) - \tfrac{27}{2} \\ &= -\tfrac{1}{2}(x^2 - 10x + 25) - \tfrac{27}{2} - \left(-\tfrac{1}{2}\right)(25) \\ &= -\tfrac{1}{2}(x-5)^2 - 1;\ (5, -1),\ x = 5,\ \text{down} \end{aligned}$$

29.
$$\begin{aligned} f(x) &= \tfrac{1}{3}x^2 - 4x + 15 \\ &= \tfrac{1}{3}(x^2 - 12x) + 15 \\ &= \tfrac{1}{3}(x^2 - 12x + 36) + 15 - \left(\tfrac{1}{3}\right)(36) \\ &= \tfrac{1}{3}(x-6)^2 + 3;\ (6, 3),\ x = 6,\ \text{up} \end{aligned}$$

30.
$$\begin{aligned} y &= a(x-h)^2 + k \\ 4 &= a(1-2)^2 + 0 \\ 4 &= a;\ y = 4(x-2)^2 \end{aligned}$$

31.
$$\begin{aligned} y &= a(x-h)^2 + k \\ -2 &= a(2-4)^2 + 1 \\ -2 &= 4a + 1 \\ -3 &= 4a \\ -\tfrac{3}{4} &= a;\ y = -\tfrac{3}{4}(x-4)^2 + 1 \end{aligned}$$

32.
$$\begin{aligned} y &= a(x-h)^2 + k \\ 2 &= a(-5-(-3))^2 + 6 \\ 2 &= 4a + 6 \\ -4 &= 4a \\ -1 &= a;\ y = -(x+3)^2 + 6 \end{aligned}$$

33.
$$\begin{aligned} y &= a(x-h)^2 + k \\ 8 &= a(3-0)^2 + 5 \\ 8 &= 9a + 5 \\ 3 &= 9a \\ \tfrac{1}{3} &= a;\ y = \tfrac{1}{3}(x-0)^2 + 5 \text{ or } y = \tfrac{1}{3}x^2 + 5 \end{aligned}$$

34.
$$\begin{aligned} y &= a(x-h)^2 + k \\ 8 &= a(-1-(-3))^2 + (-2) \\ 8 &= 4a - 2 \\ 10 &= 4a \\ \tfrac{5}{2} &= a;\ y = \tfrac{5}{2}(x+3)^2 - 2 \end{aligned}$$

35.
$$\begin{aligned} y &= a(x-h)^2 + k \\ -8 &= a(7-5)^2 + 4 \\ -8 &= 4a + 4 \\ -12 &= 4a \\ -3 &= a;\ y = -3(x-5)^2 + 4 \end{aligned}$$

36.
$(0, 0) \to 0 = a(0)^2 + b(0) + c \quad \to 0 = c$

$(2, 6) \to 6 = a(2)^2 + b(2) + c \quad \to 6 = 4a + 2b + c$

$(-1, 3) \to 3 = a(-1)^2 + b(-1) + c \quad \to 3 = a - b + c$

Substitute 0 for c:

$6 = 4a + 2b + 0 \quad \to \quad 6 = 4a + 2b \qquad 3 = a - b$

$3 = a - b + 0 \quad \to \quad \underline{(+)6 = 2a - 2b} \qquad 3 = 2 - b$

$\qquad 12 = 6a \qquad 1 = -b$

$\qquad 2 = a \qquad -1 = b$

$y = 2x^2 - x$

37.
$(2, -3) \to -3 = a(2)^2 + b(2) + c \to$

$\qquad -3 = 4a + 2b + c$

$(0, -1) \to -1 = a(0)^2 + b(0) + c \quad \to -1 = c$

$\left(-1, \frac{3}{2}\right) \to \frac{3}{2} = a(-1)^2 + b(-1) + c \quad \to \frac{3}{2} = a - b + c$

Substitute -1 for c:

$-3 = 4a + 2b + (-1) \to -2 = 4a + 2b \to -2 = 4a + 2b$

$\frac{3}{2} = a - b + (-1) \to \frac{5}{2} = a - b \qquad \to \underline{(+)5 = 2a - 2b}$

$\qquad 3 = 6a$

$\qquad \frac{1}{2} = a$

$$\begin{aligned} -2 &= 4a + 2b \\ -2 &= 4\left(\tfrac{1}{2}\right) + 2b \\ -2 &= 2 + 2b \\ -4 &= 2b \\ -2 &= b \end{aligned} \qquad y = \tfrac{1}{2}x^2 - 2x - 1$$

38. $(1, 0) \to 0 = a(1)^2 + b(1) + c \quad \to \; 0 = a + b + c$

$(3, 38) \to 38 = a(3)^2 + b(3) + c \to 38 = 9a + 3b + c$

$(-2, 48) \to 48 = a(-2)^2 + b(-2) + c \to 48 = 4a - 2b + c$

$$\begin{aligned} 0 &= a + b + c \\ (-)38 &= 9a + 3b + c \\ \hline -38 &= -8a - 2b \end{aligned} \qquad \begin{aligned} 38 &= 9a + 3b + c \\ (-)48 &= 4a - 2b + c \\ \hline -10 &= 5a + 5b \end{aligned}$$

$$\begin{aligned} -38 &= -8a - 2b \to \\ -10 &= 5a + 5b \to \end{aligned} \qquad \begin{aligned} -190 &= -40a - 10b \\ (+)-20 &= 10a + 10b \\ \hline -210 &= -30a \\ 7 &= a \end{aligned}$$

$$\begin{aligned} -10 &= 5a + 5b \\ -10 &= 5(7) + 5b \\ -10 &= 35 + 5b \\ -45 &= 5b \\ -9 &= b \end{aligned} \qquad \begin{aligned} 0 &= a + b + c \\ 0 &= 7 + (-9) + c \\ 0 &= -2 + c \\ 2 &= c \\ y &= 7x^2 - 9x + 2 \end{aligned}$$

39. $(-1, -10) \to -10 = a(-1)^2 + b(-1) + c \to$
$-10 = a - b + c$

$(0, 6) \to 6 = a(0)^2 + b(0) + c \quad \to \; 6 = c$

$(2, 88) \to 88 = a(2)^2 + b(2) + c \to 88 = 4a + 2b + c$

Substitute 6 for c:

$-10 = a - b + 6 \to -16 = a - b \quad \to \quad -32 = 2a - 2b$

$88 = 4a + 2b + 6 \to 82 = 4a + 2b \to (+)\ 82 = 4a + 2b$

$$\begin{aligned} 50 &= 6a \\ \frac{25}{3} &= a \end{aligned}$$

$$\begin{aligned} -16 &= a - b \\ -16 &= \frac{25}{3} - b \\ -\frac{73}{3} &= -b \\ \frac{73}{3} &= b \end{aligned} \qquad y = \frac{25}{3}x^2 + \frac{73}{3}x + 6$$

40. $f(x) = 3(x + 3)^2$

x	$3(x + 3)^2$	$f(x)$
-4	$3(-4 + 3)^2$	3
-3	$3(-3 + 3)^2$	0
-2	$3(-2 + 3)^2$	3
-1	$3(-1 + 3)^2$	12

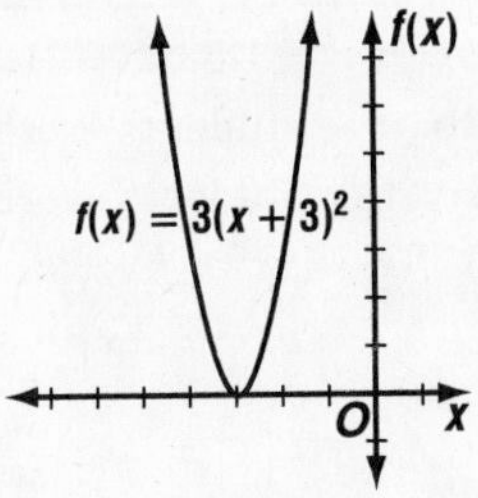

41. $f(x) = 2(x + 3)^2 - 5$

x	$2(x + 3)^2 - 5$	$f(x)$
-5	$2(-5 + 3)^2 - 5$	3
-4	$2(-4 + 3)^2 - 5$	-3
-3	$2(-3 + 3)^2 - 5$	-5
-2	$2(-2 + 3)^2 - 5$	-3

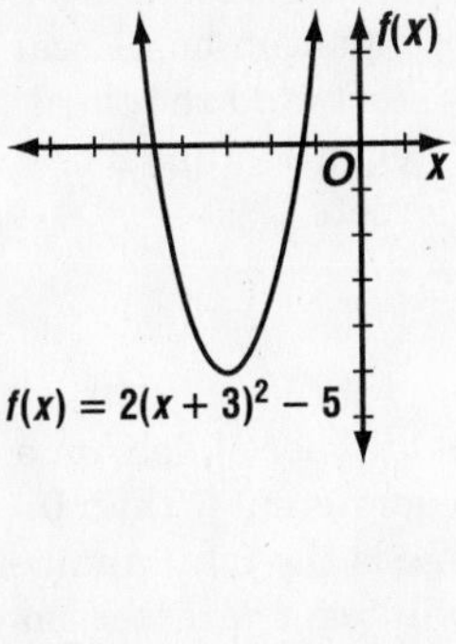

42. $f(x) = \frac{1}{2}(x + 3)^2 - 5$

x	$\frac{1}{2}(x + 3)^2 - 5$	$f(x)$
-7	$\frac{1}{2}(-7 + 3)^2 - 5$	3
-5	$\frac{1}{2}(-5+ 3)^2 - 5$	-3
-3	$\frac{1}{2}(-3 + 3)^2 - 5$	-5
-1	$\frac{1}{2}(-1 + 3)^2 - 5$	-3

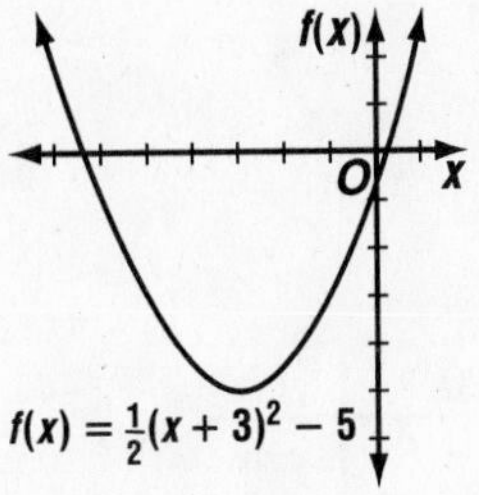

43. $f(x) = \frac{1}{3}(x - 1)^2 + 3$

x	$\frac{1}{3}(x - 1)^2 + 3$	$f(x)$
-1	$\frac{1}{3}(-1 - 1)^2 + 3$	$\frac{13}{3}$
0	$\frac{1}{3}(0 - 1)^2 + 3$	$\frac{10}{3}$
1	$\frac{1}{3}(1 - 1)^2 + 3$	3
2	$\frac{1}{3}(2 - 1)^2 + 3$	$\frac{10}{3}$
3	$\frac{1}{3}(3 - 1)^2 + 3$	$\frac{13}{3}$

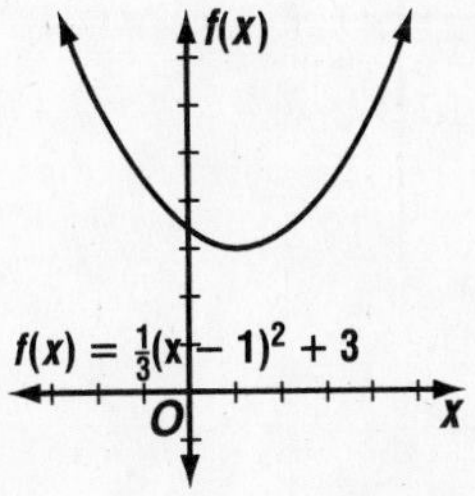

44. $f(x) = x^2 + 6x + 2$

x	$x^2 + 6x + 2$	$f(x)$
-7	$(-7)^2 + 6(-7) + 2$	9
-5	$(-5)^2 + 6(-5) + 2$	-3
-3	$(-3)^2 + 6(-3) + 2$	-7
-1	$(-1)^2 + 6(-1) + 2$	-3

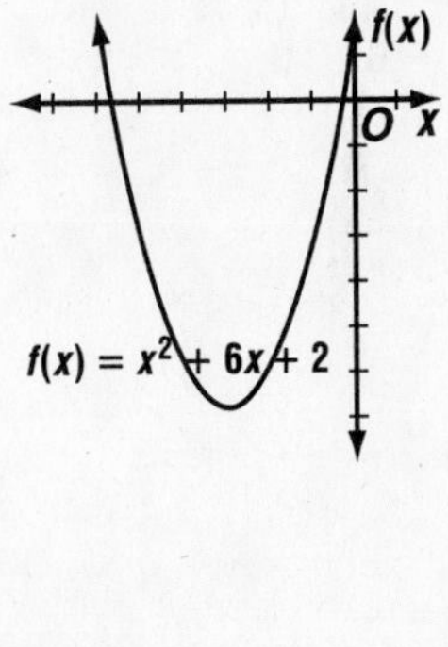

45. $f(x) = -2x^2 + 16x - 31$

x	$-2x^2 + 16x - 31$	$f(x)$
2	$-2(2)^2 + 16(2) - 31$	-7
3	$-2(3)^2 + 16(3) - 31$	-1
4	$-2(4)^2 + 16(4) - 31$	1
5	$-2(5)^2 + 16(5) - 31$	-1

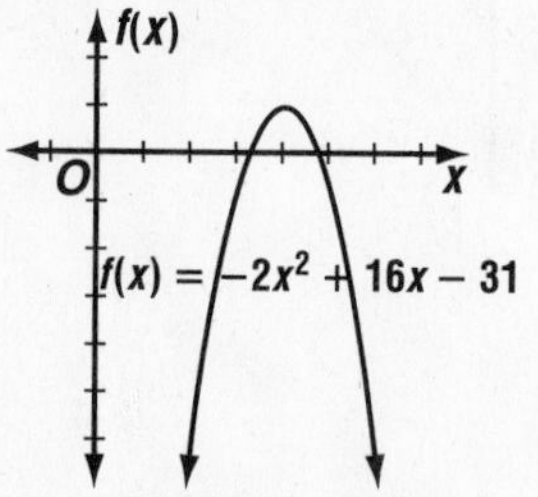

46. $f(x) = -5x^2 - 40x - 80$

x	$-5x^2 - 40x - 80$	$f(x)$
-5	$-5(-5)^2 - 40(-5) - 80$	-5
-4	$-5(-4)^2 - 40(-4) - 80$	0
-3	$-5(-3)^2 - 40(-3) - 80$	-5
-2	$-5(-2)^2 - 40(-2) - 80$	-20

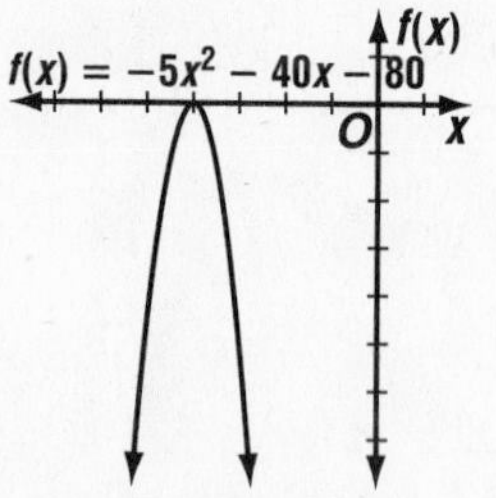

47. $f(x) = 2x^2 + 8x + 10$

x	$2x^2 + 8x + 10$	$f(x)$
-3	$2(-3)^2 + 8(-3) + 10$	4
-2	$2(-2)^2 + 8(-2) + 10$	2
-1	$2(-1)^2 + 8(-1) + 10$	4
0	$2(0)^2 + 8(0) + 10$	10

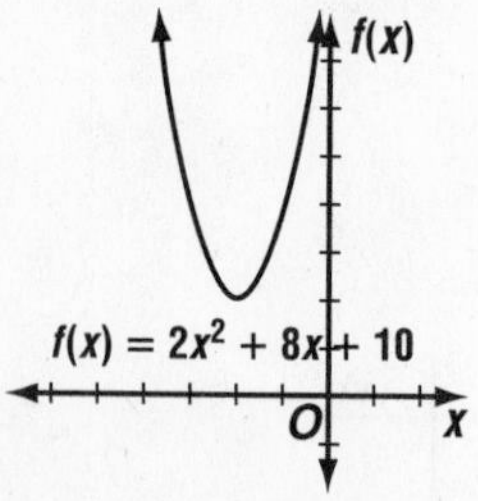

48. $f(x) = -9x^2 - 18x - 6$

x	$-9x^2 - 18x - 6$	$f(x)$
-2	$-9(-2)^2 - 18(-2) - 6$	-6
-1	$-9(-1)^2 - 18(-1) - 6$	3
0	$-9(0)^2 - 18(0) - 6$	-6

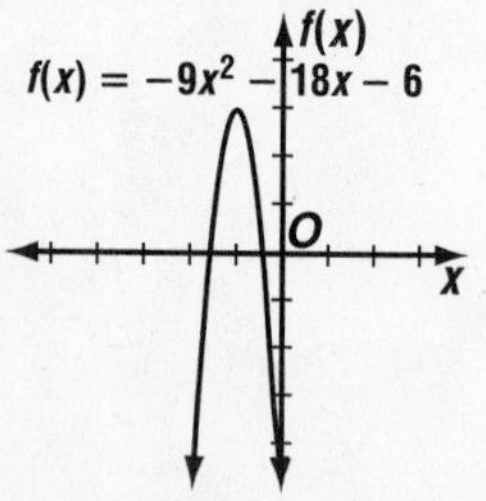

49. $f(x) = -0.25x^2 - 2.5x - 0.25$

x	$-0.25x^2 - 2.5x - 0.25$	$f(x)$
-10	$-0.25(-10)^2 - 2.5(-10) - 0.25$	-0.25
-6	$-0.25(-6)^2 - 2.5(-6) - 0.25$	5.75
-2	$-0.25(-2)^2 - 2.5(-2) - 0.25$	3.75
0	$-0.25(0)^2 - 2.5(0) - 0.25$	-0.25

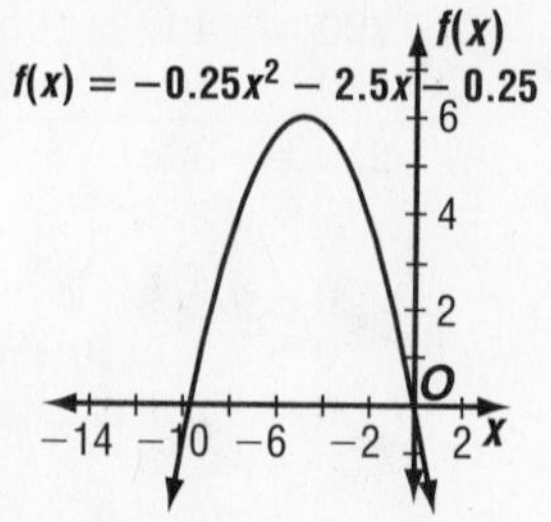

50. $(h, k) = (6, 1)$, $a = 9$; $y = 9(x - 6)^2 + 1$

51. $f(x) = -2(x - 2)^2 + 9$

52a. Number the months from 1–12. WINDOW [0, 13] by [0, 120] with Xscl of 1 and Yscl of 20. Clear any entries in L_1 and L_2.

[STAT] [ENTER] 1 [ENTER] 2 [ENTER] 3 [ENTER] 4 [ENTER] 5 [ENTER] 6 [ENTER] 7 [ENTER] 8 [ENTER] 9 [ENTER] 10 [ENTER] 11 [ENTER] 12 [ENTER] [▶] 65 [ENTER] 73 [ENTER] 81 [ENTER] 88 [ENTER] 100 [ENTER] 110 [ENTER] 116 [ENTER] 113 [ENTER] 106 [ENTER] 91 [ENTER] 75 [ENTER] 66 [ENTER] [2nd] [STAT PLOT] 1 [ENTER] [▼] [ENTER] [GRAPH] [STAT] [▶] 6 [2nd] [L1] [,] [2nd] [L2] [ENTER]

$y = -1.58x^2 + 21.30x + 37.23$

52b. See students' work.

52c. See students' work.

53. $f(x) = ax^2 + bx + c$

$$= a\left(x^2 + \frac{b}{a}x\right) + c$$

$$= a\left(x^2 + \frac{b}{a}x + \frac{b^2}{4a^2}\right) + c - a\left(\frac{b^2}{4a^2}\right)$$

$$= a\left(x + \frac{b}{2a}\right)^2 + \left(\frac{4a^2c - ab^2}{4a^2}\right)$$

$$= a\left(x + \frac{b}{2a}\right)^2 + \left(\frac{4ac - b^2}{4a}\right)$$

$$h = -\frac{b}{2a},\ k = \frac{4ac - b^2}{4a} \text{ or } c - \frac{b^2}{4a}$$

54.

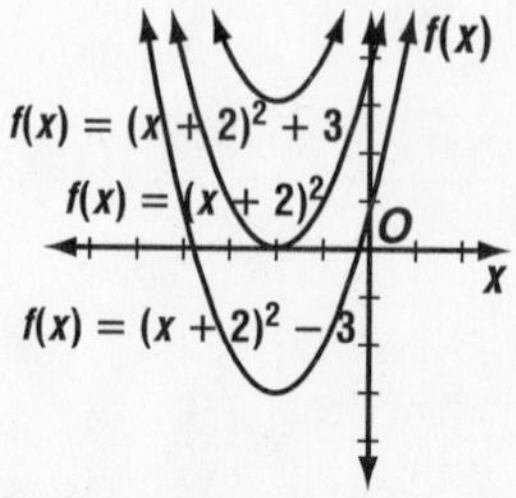

The first equation has 0 real roots, the second equation has 1 real root, and the third equation has 2 real roots.

55a. Since the domain is the number of dots on a side, it is the set of integers greater than 0. Likewise, since the range is the total number of dots, it is also the set of integers greater than 0.

55b. $(1, 1) \rightarrow 1 = a(1)^2 + b(1) + c \rightarrow 1 = a + b + c$
$(2, 3) \rightarrow 3 = a(2)^2 + b(2) + c \rightarrow 3 = 4a + 2b + c$
$(3, 6) \rightarrow 6 = a(3)^2 + b(3) + c \rightarrow 6 = 9a + 3b + c$

$$\begin{array}{rl} 1 = & a + b + c \\ (-)3 = & 4a + 2b + c \\ \hline -2 = & -3a - b \end{array} \qquad \begin{array}{rl} 6 = & 9a + 3b + c \\ (-)3 = & 4a + 2b + c \\ \hline 3 = & 5a + b \end{array}$$

$$\begin{array}{rl} -2 = & -3a - b \\ (+)3 = & 5a + b \\ \hline 1 = & 2a \\ \frac{1}{2} = & a \end{array}$$

$$\begin{array}{rl} -2 &= -3a - b \\ -2 &= -3\left(\frac{1}{2}\right) - b \\ -2 &= -\frac{3}{2} - b \\ -\frac{1}{2} &= -b \\ \frac{1}{2} &= b \end{array} \qquad \begin{array}{rl} 1 &= a + b + c \\ 1 &= \frac{1}{2} + \frac{1}{2} + c \\ 1 &= 1 + c \\ 0 &= c \end{array}$$

$f(x) = \frac{1}{2}x^2 + \frac{1}{2}x$ or $f(x) = \frac{1}{2}x(x + 1)$

55c.

x	$\frac{1}{2}x(x + 1)$	$f(x)$
-2	$\frac{1}{2}(-2)(-2 + 1)$	1
-1	$\frac{1}{2}(-1)(-1 + 1)$	0
0	$\frac{1}{2}(0)(0 + 1)$	0
1	$\frac{1}{2}(1)(1 + 1)$	1

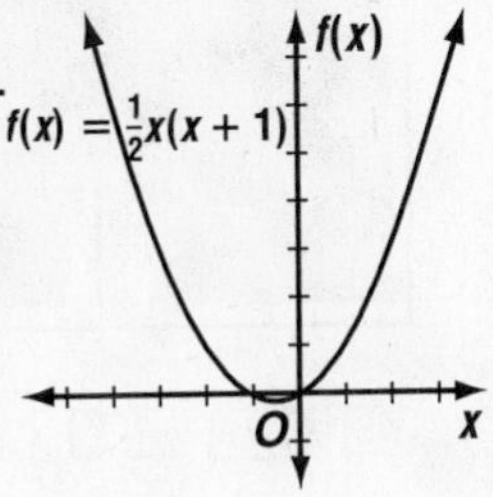

56a. (0, 14), (1, 10.5), (3, 6.5)

56b. $(0, 14) \rightarrow 14 = a(0)^2 + b(0) + c \rightarrow 14 = c$
$(1, 10.5) \rightarrow 10.5 = a(1)^2 + b(1) + c \rightarrow 10.5 = a + b + c$
$(3, 6.5) \rightarrow 6.5 = a(3)^2 + b(3) + c \rightarrow 6.5 = 9a + 3b + c$

Substitute 14 for c:
$10.5 = a + b + 14 \rightarrow -3.5 = a + b \rightarrow 10.5 = -3a - 3b$
$6.5 = 9a + 3b + 14 \rightarrow -7.5 = 9a + 3b \rightarrow$

$$\begin{array}{rl} (+)\ -7.5 = & 9a + 3b \\ \hline 3 = & 6a \\ \frac{1}{2} = & a \end{array}$$

$$\begin{array}{rl} -3.5 &= a + b \\ -3.5 &= \frac{1}{2} + b \\ -4 &= b \end{array}$$

$f(x) = \frac{1}{2}x^2 - 4x + 14$

56c.

x	$\frac{1}{2}x^2 - 4x + 14$	$f(x)$
0	$\frac{1}{2}(0)^2 - 4(0) + 14$	14
2	$\frac{1}{2}(2)^2 - 4(2) + 14$	8
4	$\frac{1}{2}(4)^2 - 4(4) + 14$	6
6	$\frac{1}{2}(6)^2 - 4(6) + 14$	8

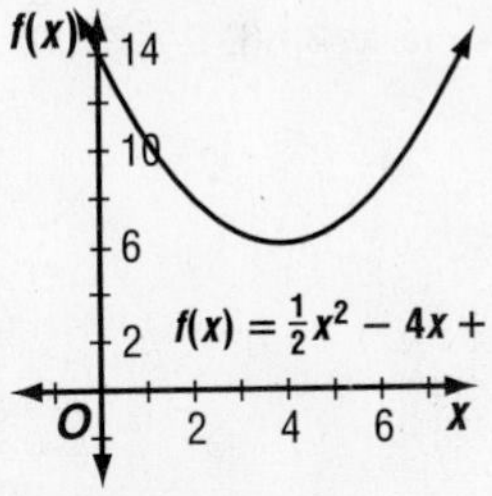

56d. 6 meters

57. $A = 25 \cdot 50$
$= 1250$

$$\begin{array}{rl} 1250 + 400 &= (x + 25)(x + 50) \\ 1650 &= x^2 + 75x + 1250 \\ 0 &= x^2 + 75x - 400 \\ 0 &= (x + 80)(x - 5) \end{array}$$

$x + 80 = 0$ or $x - 5 = 0$
$x = -80$ $\quad x = 5$

5 feet

58. $4x^2 - 8x + 13 = 0;\ a = 4,\ b = -8,\ c = 13$

$$\begin{aligned} x &= \frac{8 \pm \sqrt{(-8)^2 - 4(4)(13)}}{2(4)} \\ &= \frac{8 \pm \sqrt{-144}}{8} \\ &= \frac{8 \pm 12i}{8} \\ &= \frac{2 \pm 3i}{2} \end{aligned}$$

59. $h(x) = x^2 - 2x + 5$

x	$h(x)$
0	5
1	4
2	5
3	8

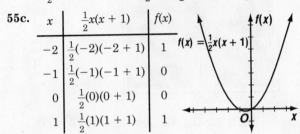

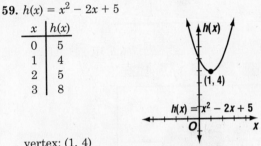

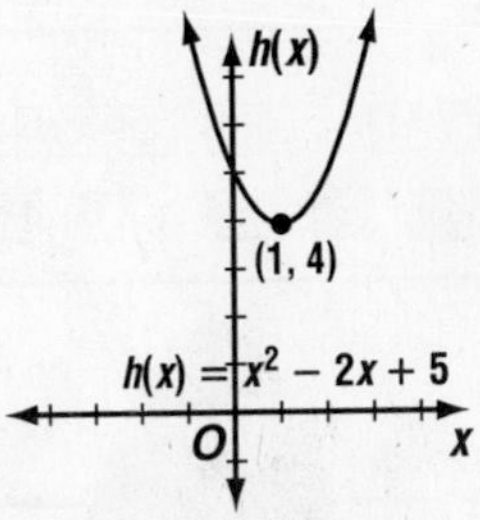

vertex: (1, 4)
axis of symmetry: $x = 1$

60. If x is your number, you can write the expression $\frac{3x + (x + 8)}{(x + 2)}$, which equals 4.

61. $(-x + 4)(-2 - 3x) = 2x + 3x^2 - 8 - 12x$
$= 3x^2 - 10x - 8$

62. $$\begin{bmatrix} -6 & 3 \\ 4 & 7 \end{bmatrix} \cdot \begin{bmatrix} 2 & -5 \\ -3 & 6 \end{bmatrix} = \begin{bmatrix} -12 - 9 & 30 + 18 \\ 8 - 21 & -20 + 42 \end{bmatrix} = \begin{bmatrix} -21 & 48 \\ -13 & 22 \end{bmatrix}$$

63. $$-2\begin{bmatrix} -3 & 0 & 12 \\ -7 & \frac{1}{3} & 4 \end{bmatrix} = \begin{bmatrix} 6 & 0 & -24 \\ 14 & -\frac{2}{3} & -8 \end{bmatrix}$$

64. $4z = 24$
$z = 6$

$x + 2y - 6 = -7 \rightarrow x + 2y = -1$
$3x + y + 6 = -12 \rightarrow 3x + y = -18$

$$\begin{array}{rl} x + 2y &= -1 \\ (+)-6x - 2y &= 36 \\ \hline -5x &= 35 \\ x &= -7 \end{array} \qquad \begin{array}{rl} 3(-7) + y &= -18 \\ -21 + y &= -18 \\ y &= 3 \end{array}$$

$(-7, 3, 6)$

65. perpendicular slope $= -\frac{3}{4}$; $(0, -2)$

$$\begin{aligned} y - y_1 &= m(x - x_1) \\ y - (-2) &= -\tfrac{3}{4}(x - 0) \\ y + 2 &= -\tfrac{3}{4}x \\ y &= -\tfrac{3}{4}x - 2 \\ \tfrac{3}{4}x + y &= -2 \\ 3x + 4y &= -8 \end{aligned}$$

66. $23x - 7 > 62$
$23x > 69$
$x > 3;\ \{x \mid x > 3\}$

6-7A Graphing Technology: Quadratic Inequalities

Page 377 Exercises

1. WINDOW: [−20, 5] by [−40, 10]; Xscl = 5, Yscl = 10

[2nd] [DRAW] 7 [X,T,θ,n] [x^2] [+] 11 [X,T,θ,n] [−] 3 [,] 10 [)] [ENTER]

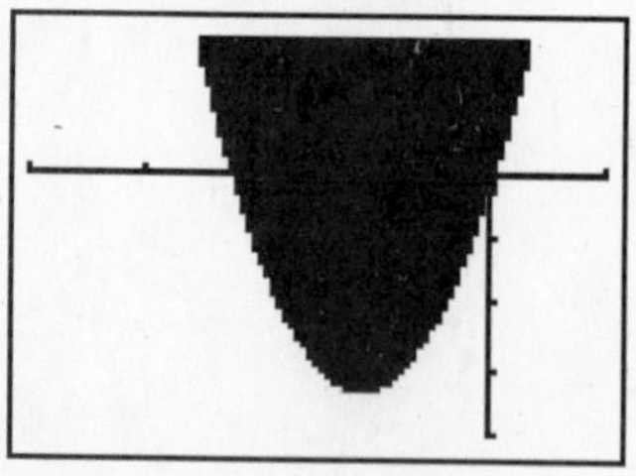

2. [ZOOM] 6 [2nd] [DRAW] 7 [(−)] 10 [,] [(−)] .5 [X,T,θ,n] [x^2] [+] 9 [)] [ENTER]

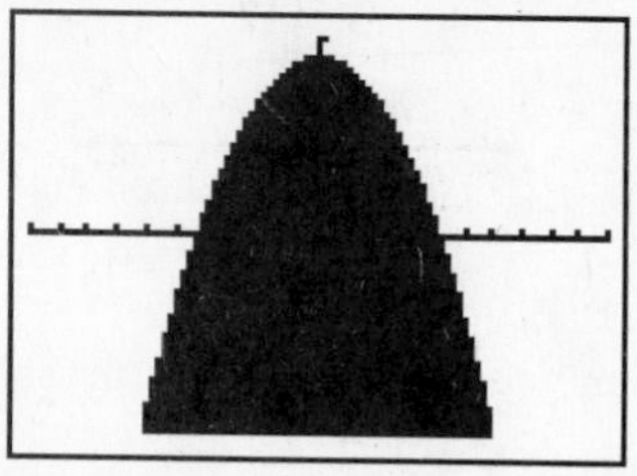

3. WINDOW: [−20, 10] by [−50, 10]; Xscl = 1, Yscl = 5

[2nd] [DRAW] 7 [(−)] 50 [,] 1.2 [X,T,θ,n] [x^2] [+] 15 [X,T,θ,n] [)] [ENTER]

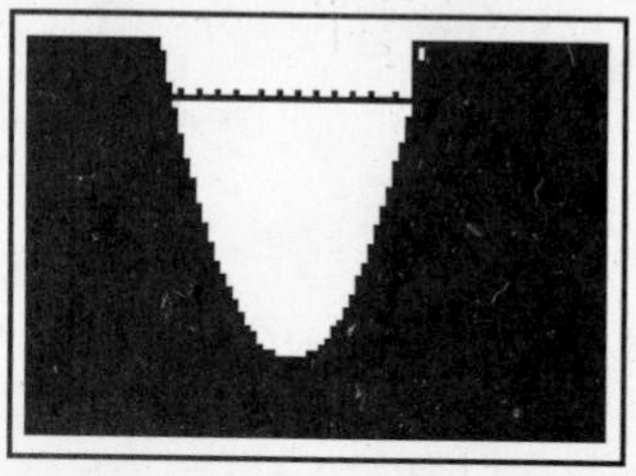

4. [ZOOM] 6 [2nd] [DRAW] 7 6 [X,T,θ,n] [x^2] [−] 15 [X,T,θ,n] [+] 7 [,] 10 [)] [ENTER]

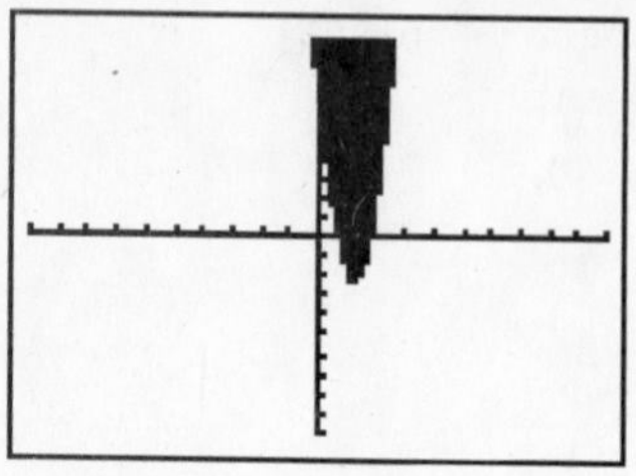

5. WINDOW: [−10, 10] by [−10, 20]; Xscl = 1, Yscl = 1

[2nd] [DRAW] 7 [(−)] [X,T,θ,n] [x^2] [+] 6 [X,T,θ,n] [+] 8 [,] 20 [)] [ENTER]

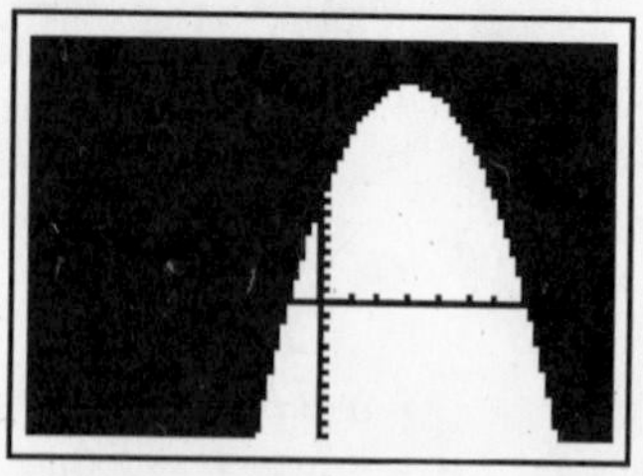

6. [ZOOM] 6 [2nd] [DRAW] 7 [(−)] 4 [X,T,θ,n] [x^2] [−] 3 [X,T,θ,n] [−] 6 [,] 10 [)] [ENTER]

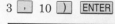

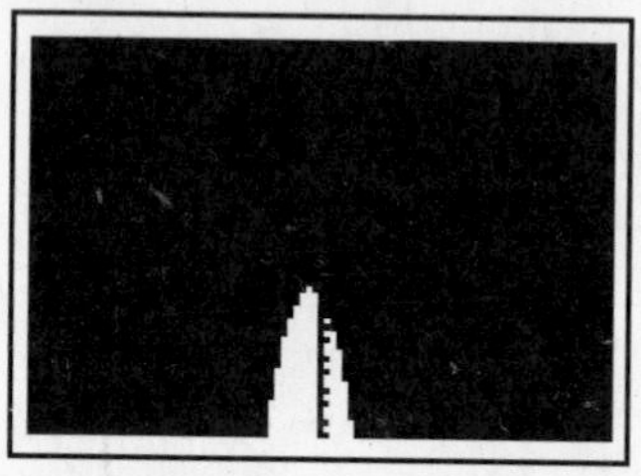

7. [Y=] [X,T,θ,n] [x^2] [+] 4 [X,T,θ,n] [−] 21 [ZOOM] 6; zoom in on intercepts; $\{x \mid x < -7 \text{ or } x > 3\}$

8. [Y=] 2 [X,T,θ,n] [x^2] [−] 4 [X,T,θ,n] [+] 1 [ZOOM] 6; zoom in on intercepts; $\{x \mid 0.29 \le x \le 1.71\}$

9. [Y=] [X,T,θ,n] [(] 2 [X,T,θ,n] [+] 1 [)] [ZOOM] 6; zoom in on intercepts; $\{x \mid x \le -0.5 \text{ or } x \ge 0\}$

10. [Y=] [X,T,θ,n] [x^2] [−] 3 [ZOOM] 6; zoom in on intercepts; $\{x \mid x < -1.73 \text{ or } x > 1.73\}$

11. $x^2 - 9x < 4$

$x^2 - 9x - 4 < 0$; [Y=] [X,T,θ,n] [x^2] [−] 9 [X,T,θ,n] [−] 4 [ZOOM] 6; zoom in on intercepts;

$\{x \mid -0.42 < x < 9.42\}$

12. $0.5x^2 > 1.8x$

$0.5x^2 - 1.8x > 0$; [Y=] .5 [X,T,θ,n] [x^2] [−] 1.8 [X,T,θ,n] [ZOOM] 6; zoom in on intercepts;

$\{x \mid x < 0 \text{ or } x > 3.60\}$

13. width = x, length = $w + 4$; $x(x + 4) \ge 28$

$x^2 + 4x - 28 \ge 0$

[Y=] [X,T,θ,n] [x^2] [+] 4 [X,T,θ,n] [−] 28 [ZOOM] 6; zoom in on intercepts; $x \le -7.66$ or $x \ge 3.66$; x cannot be negative; so $w \ge 3.66$, $\ell \ge 7.66$

6-7 Graphing and Solving Quadratic Inequalities

Pages 381–382 Check for Understanding

1a. Inside; the test point of (3, 0), which is inside the graph, gives a true statement.
$0 \geq 3^2 - 5(3) + 4$
$0 \geq -2$ ✓

1b. $0 = x^2 - 5x + 4$
$0 = (x - 4)(x - 1)$
$x - 4 = 0$ or $x - 1 = 0$
$x = 4$ $\quad x = 1$; $\{x \mid 1 \leq x \leq 4\}$

2. Sample answer: any number less than −2, one between −2 and 8, and one greater than 8.

3. Find the possible dimensions if the area of the rectangle is less than 216 square centimeters.

4. Sample answer: Factoring gives test points that can be used to find the solution.

5. See students' work.

6. $y < 2x^2 + 4$
$5 \overset{?}{<} 2(3)^2 + 4$
$5 < 22$; yes

7. $y \geq x^2 - 9$
$5 \overset{?}{\geq} 0^2 - 9$
$5 \geq -9$; yes

8. $y \leq 2x^2 - 3x + 1$
$4 \overset{?}{\leq} 2(-1)^2 - 3(-1) + 1$
$4 \leq 6$; yes

9. $y \geq 5x^2 + 2x - 3$
$-1 \overset{?}{\geq} 5(-1)^2 + 2(-1) - 3$
$-1 \ngeq 0$; no

10. $x^2 < x + 6$
$x^2 - x - 6 < 0$
$(x - 3)(x + 2) < 0$
$x - 3 < 0$ and $x + 2 > 0$ or $x - 3 > 0$ and $x + 2 < 0$
$x < 3$ $\quad x > -2$ $\quad x > 3$ $\quad x < -2$
$-2 < x < 3$; b $\quad \varnothing$

11. $y \leq x^2 + 4x + 4$
$y \leq (x + 2)^2$; vertex at $(-2, 0)$

x	$(x + 2)^2$	y
−3	$(-3 + 2)^2$	1
−1	$(-1 + 2)^2$	1
0	$(0 + 2)^2$	4

Test: (0, 0)
$y \leq x^2 + 4x + 4$
$0 \overset{?}{\leq} 0^2 + 4(0) + 4$
$0 \leq 4$; true

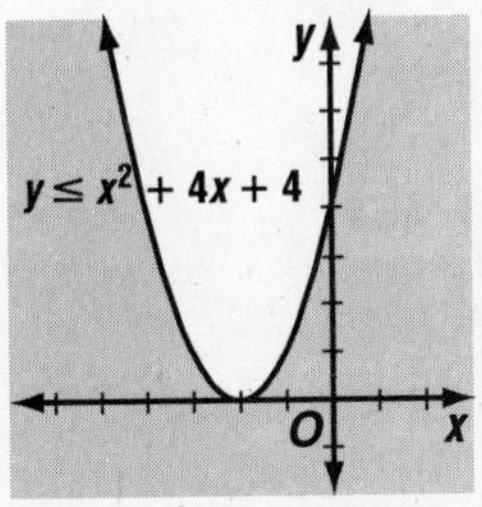

12. $y > x^2 - 36$
vertex at $(0, -36)$

x	$x^2 - 36$	y
−2	$(-2)^2 - 36$	−32
2	$2^2 - 36$	−32
4	$4^2 - 36$	−20

Test: (0, 0)
$y > x^2 - 36$
$0 \overset{?}{>} 0^2 - 36$
$0 > -36$; true

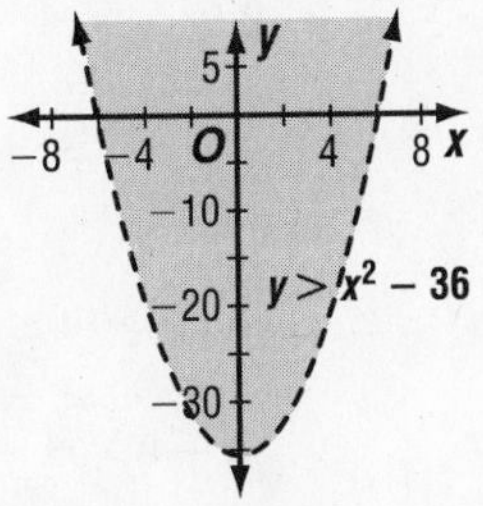

13. $y \leq -x^2 + 7x + 8$
$y \leq -1(x^2 - 7x) + 8$
$y \leq -1\left(x^2 - 7x + \frac{49}{4}\right) + 8 + \frac{49}{4}$
$y \leq -\left(x - \frac{7}{2}\right)^2 + \frac{81}{4}$; vertex at $\left(\frac{7}{2}, \frac{81}{4}\right)$

x	$-x^2 + 7x + 8$	y
0	$-0^2 + 7(0) + 8$	8
3	$-(3)^2 + 7(3) + 8$	20
6	$-(6)^2 + 7(6) + 8$	14

Test: (0, 0)
$y \leq -x^2 + 7x + 8$
$0 \overset{?}{\leq} -0^2 + 7(0) + 8$
$0 \leq 8$; true

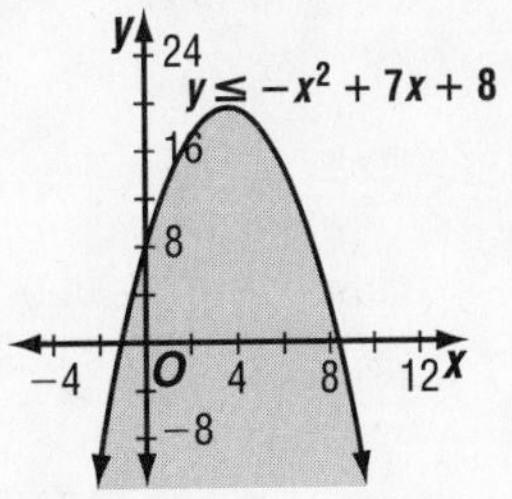

14. $y \leq -x^2 - 3x + 10$
$y \leq -1(x^2 + 3x) + 10$
$y \leq -1\left(x^2 + 3x + \frac{9}{4}\right) + 10 + \frac{9}{4}$
$y \leq -\left(x + \frac{3}{2}\right)^2 + \frac{49}{4}$; vertex at $\left(-\frac{3}{2}, \frac{49}{4}\right)$

x	$-x^2 - 3x + 10$	y
−4	$-(-4)^2 - 3(-4) + 10$	6
−2	$-(-2)^2 - 3(-2) + 10$	12
0	$-(0)^2 - 3(0) + 10$	10
2	$-(2)^2 - 3(2) + 10$	0

Test: (0, 0)
$y \leq -x^2 - 3x + 10$
$0 \overset{?}{\leq} -(0)^2 - 3(0) + 10$
$0 \leq 10$; true

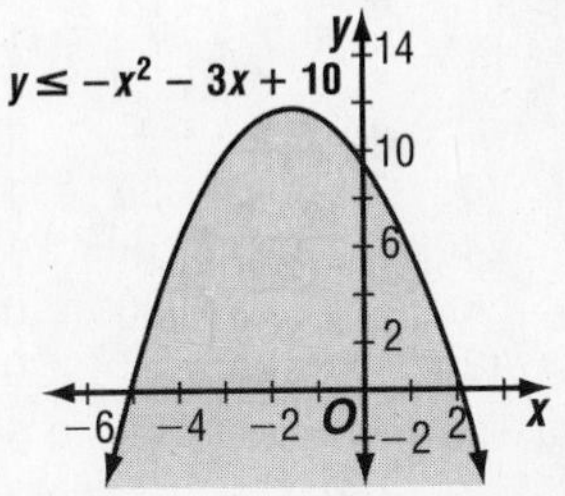

15. $-2 \leq x \leq 6$

16. $x < -3$ or $x > 3$

17. $x = 5$

18. $(x + 11)(x - 3) > 0$

$x + 11 > 0$ and $x - 3 > 0$ or $x + 11 < 0$ and $x - 3 < 0$

$x > -11 \quad x > 3 \quad x < -11 \quad x < 3$

$x > 3$ or $x < -11$

$\{x \mid x < -11 \text{ or } x > 3\}$

19. $(n - 2.5)(n + 3.8) \geq 0$

$n - 2.5 \geq 0$ and $n + 3.8 \geq 0$ or $n - 2.5 \leq 0$ and $n + 3.8 \leq 0$

$n \geq 2.5 \quad n \geq -3.8 \quad n \leq 2.5 \quad n \leq -3.8$

$n \geq 2.5$ or $n \leq -3.8$

$\{n \mid n \leq -3.8 \text{ or } n \geq 2.5\}$

20. $x^2 - 4x \leq 0$

$x(x - 4) \leq 0$

$x \leq 0$ and $x - 4 \geq 0$ or $x \geq 0$ and $x - 4 \leq 0$

$x \geq 4 \quad x \leq 4$

$\varnothing$ or $0 \leq x \leq 4$

$\{x \mid 0 \leq x \leq 4\}$

21. $b^2 \geq 10b - 25$

$b^2 - 10b + 25 \geq 0$

$(b - 5)(b - 5) \geq 0$

$b - 5 \geq 0$ and $b - 5 \geq 0$ or $b - 5 \leq 0$ and $b - 5 \leq 0$

$b \geq 5 \quad b \geq 5 \quad b \leq 5 \quad b \leq 5$

$b \geq 5$ or $b \leq 5$

{all reals}

22. $2x^2 > 25$

$2x^2 - 25 > 0$

$\left(x - \frac{5\sqrt{2}}{2}\right)\left(x + \frac{5\sqrt{2}}{2}\right) > 0$

$x - \frac{5\sqrt{2}}{2} > 0$ and $x + \frac{5\sqrt{2}}{2} > 0$ or

$x > \frac{5\sqrt{2}}{2} \quad x > -\frac{5\sqrt{2}}{2}$

$x - \frac{5\sqrt{2}}{2} < 0$ and $x + \frac{5\sqrt{2}}{2} < 0$

$x < \frac{5\sqrt{2}}{2} \quad x < -\frac{5\sqrt{2}}{2}$

$x > \frac{5\sqrt{2}}{2}$ or $x < -\frac{5\sqrt{2}}{2}$

$\left\{x \mid x < -\frac{5\sqrt{2}}{2} \text{ or } x > \frac{5\sqrt{2}}{2}\right\}$

23. $2b^2 - b < 6$

$2b^2 - b - 6 < 0$

$(2b + 3)(b - 2) < 0$

$2b + 3 < 0$ and $b - 2 > 0$ or $2b + 3 > 0$ and $b - 2 < 0$

$2b < -3 \quad b > 2 \quad 2b > -3 \quad b < 2$

$b < -\frac{3}{2}$ or $b > -\frac{3}{2}$

$\varnothing \quad -\frac{3}{2} < b < 2$

$\left\{b \mid -\frac{3}{2} < b < 2\right\}$

24a. $-1, 5$ **24b.** $x \leq -1$ or $x \geq 5$ **24c.** $-1 \leq x \leq 5$

25. $(60 - 2w)(40 - 2w) \geq 1500$

$2400 - 200w + 4w^2 \geq 1500$

$4w^2 - 200w + 900 \geq 0$

$(2w - 10)(2w - 90) \geq 0$

$2w - 10 \geq 0$ and $2w - 90 \geq 0$

$2w \geq 10 \quad 2w \geq 90$

$w \geq 5 \quad w \geq 45$

or $2w - 10 \leq 0$ and $2w - 90 \leq 0$

$2w \leq 10 \quad 2w \leq 90$

$w \leq 5 \quad w \leq 45$

$w \geq 45$ or $w \leq 5$

Sidewalk: $0 \leq w \leq 5$

Pages 382–383 Exercises

26. $y \geq x^2 - 10x + 25$

$y \geq (x^2 - 10x + 25) + 25 - 25$

$y \geq (x - 5)^2$; vertex at (5, 0)

x	$x^2 - 10x + 25$	y
3	$3^2 - 10(3) + 25$	4
4	$4^2 - 10(4) + 25$	1
6	$6^2 - 10(6) + 25$	1

Test: (5, 1)

$y \geq x^2 - 10x + 25$

$1 \overset{?}{\geq} 5^2 - 10(5) + 25$

$1 \geq 0$; true

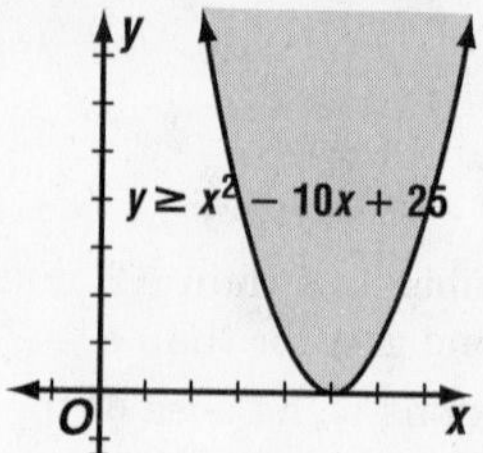

27. $y < x^2 - 16$; vertex at (0, −16)

x	$x^2 - 16$	y
−1	$(-1)^2 - 16$	−15
2	$2^2 - 16$	−12
4	$4^2 - 16$	0

Test: (0, −17)

$y < x^2 - 16$

$-17 \overset{?}{<} 0^2 - 16$

$-17 < -16$; true

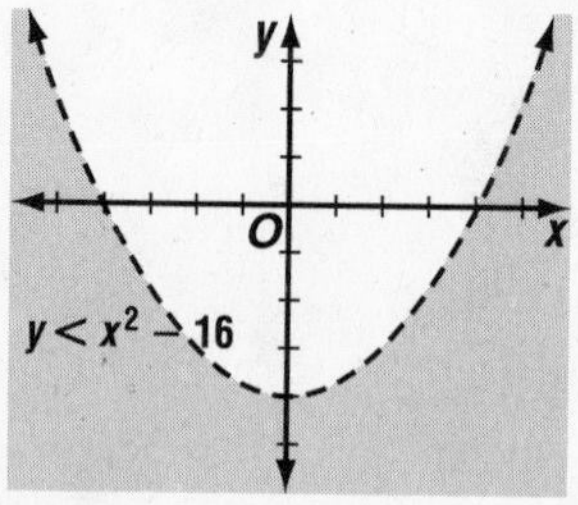

28. $y \leq x^2 - x - 20$

$y \leq \left(x^2 - x + \frac{1}{4}\right) - 20 - \frac{1}{4}$

$y \leq \left(x - \frac{1}{2}\right)^2 - \frac{81}{4}$; vertex at $\left(\frac{1}{2}, -\frac{81}{4}\right)$

x	$x^2 - x - 20$	y
−2	$(-2)^2 - (-2) - 20$	−14
2	$2^2 - 2 - 20$	−18
4	$4^2 - 4 - 20$	−8

Test: (0, −25)

$y \leq x^2 - x - 20$

$-25 \overset{?}{\leq} 0^2 - 0 - 20$

$-25 \leq -20$; true

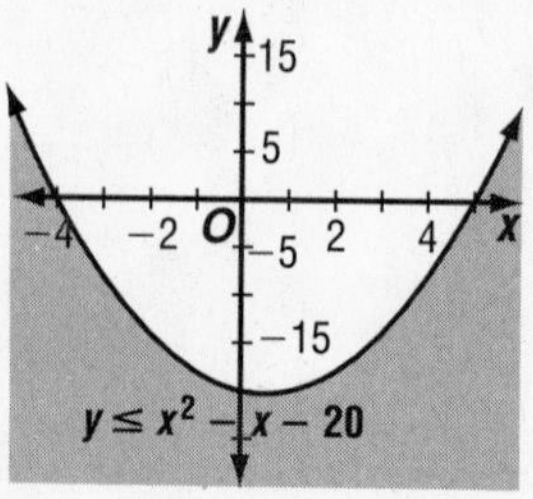

29. $y \le x^2 + 3x - 18$

$y \le \left(x^2 + 3x + \frac{9}{4}\right) - 18 - \frac{9}{4}$

$y \le \left(x + \frac{3}{2}\right)^2 - \frac{81}{4}$; vertex at $\left(-\frac{3}{2}, -\frac{81}{4}\right)$

x	$x^2 + 3x - 18$	y
-4	$(-4)^2 + 3(-4) - 18$	-14
0	$0^2 + 3(0) - 18$	-18
4	$4^2 + 3(4) - 18$	10

Test: $(0, -25)$

$y \le x^2 + 3x - 18$

$-25 \overset{?}{\le} 0^2 + 3(0) - 18$

$-25 \le -18$; true

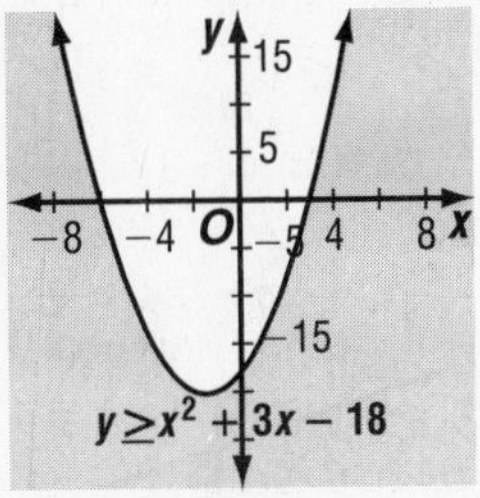

30. $y \ge 2x^2 + x - 3$

$y \ge 2\left(x^2 + \frac{1}{2}x + \frac{1}{16}\right) - 3 - 2\left(\frac{1}{16}\right)$

$y \ge 2\left(x + \frac{1}{4}\right)^2 - \frac{25}{8}$; vertex at $\left(-\frac{1}{4}, -\frac{25}{8}\right)$

x	$2x^2 + x - 3$	y
-2	$2(-2)^2 + (-2) - 3$	3
-1	$2(-1)^2 + (-1) - 3$	-2
1	$2(1)^2 + (1) - 3$	0

Test: $(0, 0)$

$y \ge 2x^2 + x - 3$

$0 \overset{?}{\ge} 2(0)^2 + 0 - 3$

$0 \ge -3$; true

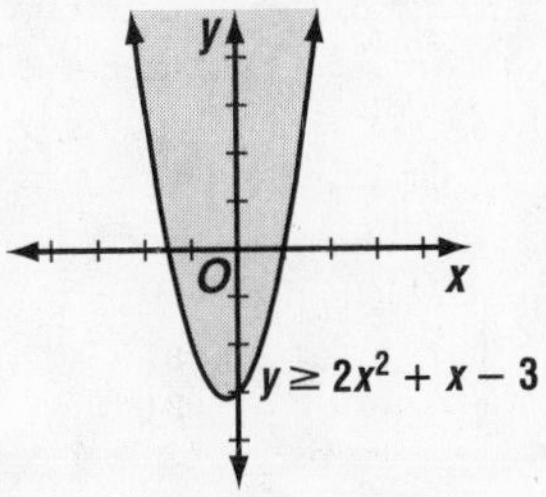

31. $y \le -x^2 + 5x + 6$

$y \le -1\left(x^2 - 5x + \frac{25}{4}\right) + 6 - (-1)\left(\frac{25}{4}\right)$

$y \le -\left(x - \frac{5}{2}\right)^2 + \frac{49}{4}$; vertex at $\left(\frac{5}{2}, \frac{49}{4}\right)$

x	$-x^2 + 5x + 6$	y
0	$-(0)^2 + 5(0) + 6$	6
3	$-(3)^2 + 5(3) + 6$	12
6	$-(6)^2 + 5(6) + 6$	0

Test: $(0, 0)$

$y \le -x^2 + 5x + 6$

$0 \overset{?}{\le} -(0)^2 + 5(0) + 6$

$0 \le 6$; true

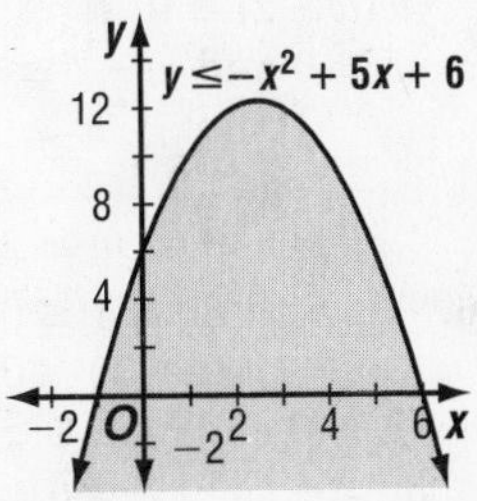

32. $y > 2x^2 + 3x - 5$

$y > 2\left(x^2 + \frac{3}{2}x + \frac{9}{16}\right) - 5 - 2\left(\frac{9}{16}\right)$

$y > 2\left(x + \frac{3}{4}\right)^2 - \frac{49}{8}$; vertex at $\left(-\frac{3}{4}, -\frac{49}{8}\right)$

x	$2x^2 + 3x - 5$	y
-2	$2(-2)^2 + 3(-2) - 5$	-3
0	$2(0)^2 + 3(0) - 5$	-5
1	$2(1)^2 + 3(1) - 5$	0

Test: $(0, 0)$

$y > 2x^2 + 3x - 5$

$0 \overset{?}{>} 2(0)^2 + 3(0) - 5$

$0 > -5$; true

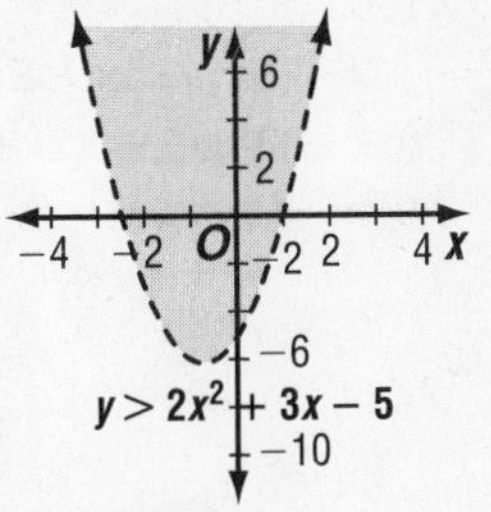

33. $y < -x^2 + 13x - 36$

$y < -1\left(x^2 - 13x + \frac{169}{4}\right) - 36 - (-1)\left(\frac{169}{4}\right)$

$y < -1\left(x - \frac{13}{2}\right)^2 + \frac{25}{4}$; vertex at $\left(\frac{13}{2}, \frac{25}{4}\right)$

x	$-x^2 + 13x - 36$	y
4	$-(4)^2 + 13(4) - 36$	0
6	$-(6)^2 + 13(6) - 36$	6
10	$-(10)^2 + 13(10) - 36$	-6

Test: $(6, 0)$

$y < -x^2 + 13x - 36$

$0 \overset{?}{<} -(6)^2 + 13(6) - 36$

$0 < 6$; true

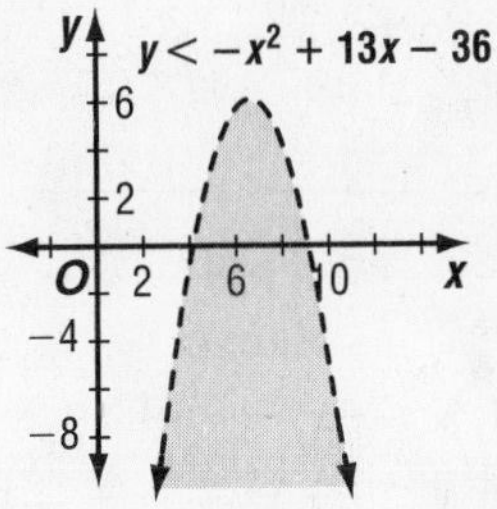

34. $y \le -x^2 + 5x + 14$

$y \le -1\left(x^2 - 5x + \frac{25}{4}\right) + 14 - (-1)\left(\frac{25}{4}\right)$

$y \le -\left(x - \frac{5}{2}\right)^2 + \frac{81}{4}$; vertex at $\left(\frac{5}{2}, \frac{81}{4}\right)$

x	$-x^2 + 5x + 14$	y
-2	$-(-2)^2 + 5(-2) + 14$	0
0	$-(0)^2 + 5(0) + 14$	14
4	$-(4)^2 + 5(4) + 14$	18

Test: $(0, 0)$

$y \le -x^2 + 5x + 14$

$0 \overset{?}{\le} -0^2 + 5(0) + 14$

$0 \le 14$; true

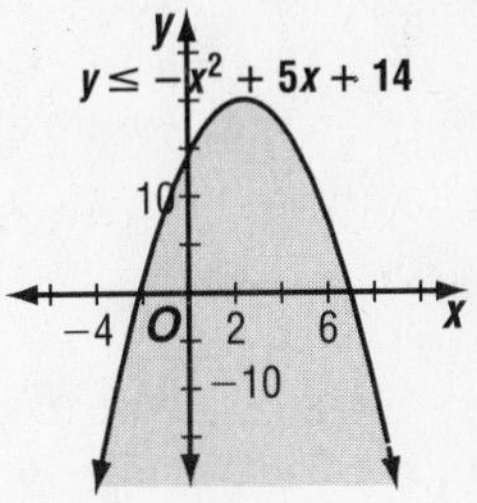

35. $y \geq -3x^2 + 5x + 2$

$y \geq -3\left(x^2 - \frac{5}{3}x + \frac{25}{36}\right) + 2 - (-3)\left(\frac{25}{36}\right)$

$y \geq -3\left(x - \frac{5}{6}\right)^2 + \frac{49}{12}$; vertex at $\left(\frac{5}{6}, \frac{49}{12}\right)$

x	$-3x^2 + 5x + 2$	y
-1	$-3(-1)^2 + 5(-1) + 2$	-6
0	$-3(0)^2 + 5(0) + 2$	2
2	$-3(2)^2 + 5(2) + 2$	0

Test: (3, 0)

$y \geq -3x^2 + 5x + 2$

$0 \overset{?}{\geq} -3(3)^2 + 5(3) + 2$

$0 \geq -10$; true

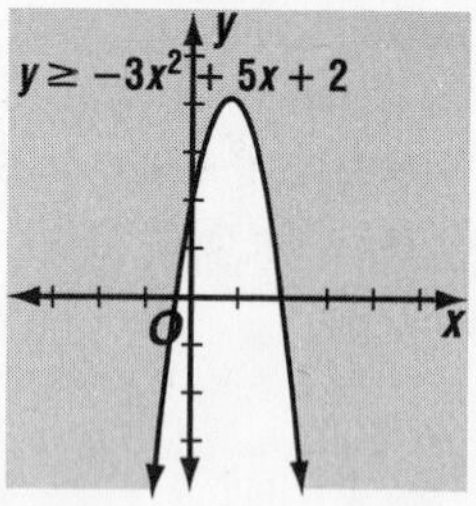

36. $y > 4x^2 - 8x + 3$

$y > 4(x^2 - 2x + 1) + 3 - 4(1)$

$y > 4(x - 1)^2 - 1$; vertex at $(1, -1)$

x	$4x^2 - 8x + 3$	y
0	$4(0)^2 - 8(0) + 3$	3
2	$4(2)^2 - 8(2) + 3$	3

Test: (1, 0)

$y > 4x^2 - 8x + 3$

$0 \overset{?}{>} 4(1)^2 - 8(1) + 3$

$0 > -1$; true

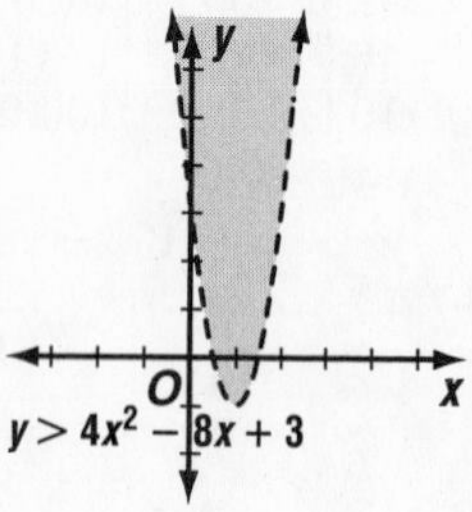

37. $y \leq -x^2 - 7x + 10$

$y \leq -1\left(x^2 + 7x + \frac{49}{4}\right) + 10 - (-1)\left(\frac{49}{4}\right)$

$y \leq -\left(x + \frac{7}{2}\right)^2 + \frac{89}{4}$; vertex at $\left(-\frac{7}{2}, \frac{89}{4}\right)$

x	$-x^2 - 7x + 10$	y
-8	$-(-8)^2 - 7(-8) + 10$	2
-4	$-(-4)^2 - 7(-4) + 10$	22
0	$-(0)^2 - 7(0) + 10$	10

Test: (0, 0)

$y \leq -x^2 - 7x + 10$

$0 \overset{?}{\leq} -0^2 - 7(0) + 10$

$0 \leq 10$; true

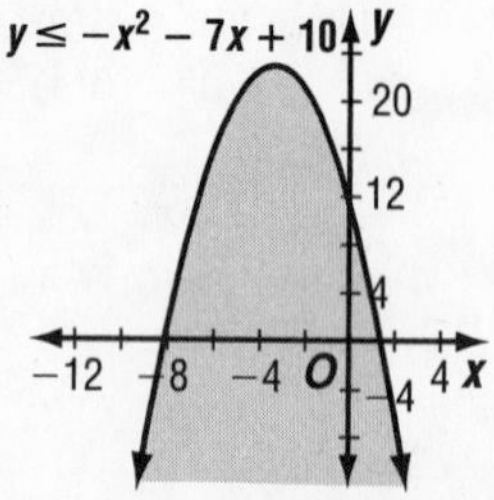

38. $(x - 4)(x + 7) < 0$

$x - 4 < 0$ and $x + 7 > 0$ or $x - 4 > 0$ and $x + 7 < 0$

$x < 4$ $\quad x > -7$ $\quad x > 4$ $\quad x < -7$

$-7 < x < 4$ $\quad$ or $\quad \varnothing$

$\{x \mid -7 < x < 4\}$

39. $x^2 - 3x - 18 > 0$

$(x - 6)(x + 3) > 0$

$x - 6 > 0$ and $x + 3 > 0$ or $x - 6 < 0$ and $x + 3 < 0$

$x > 6$ $\quad x > -3$ $\quad x < 6$ $\quad x < -3$

$x > 6$ $\quad$ or $\quad x < -3$

$\{x \mid x < -3$ or $x > 6\}$

40. $m^2 + m - 6 > 0$

$(m + 3)(m - 2) > 0$

$m + 3 > 0$ and $m - 2 > 0$ or $m + 3 < 0$ and $m - 2 < 0$

$m > -3$ $\quad m > 2$ $\quad m < -3$ $\quad m < 2$

$m > 2$ $\quad$ or $\quad m < -3$

$\{m \mid m < -3$ or $m > 2\}$

41. $q^2 + 2q \geq 24$

$q^2 + 2q - 24 \geq 0$

$(q + 6)(q - 4) \geq 0$

$q + 6 \geq 0$ and $q - 4 \geq 0$ or $q + 6 \leq 0$ and $q - 4 \leq 0$

$q \geq -6$ $\quad q \geq 4$ $\quad q \leq -6$ $\quad q \leq 4$

$q \geq 4$ $\quad$ or $\quad q \leq -6$

$\{q \mid q \leq -6$ or $q \geq 4\}$

42. $p^2 - 4p \leq 5$

$p^2 - 4p - 5 \leq 0$

$(p - 5)(p + 1) \leq 0$

$p - 5 \leq 0$ and $p + 1 \geq 0$ or $p - 5 \geq 0$ and $p + 1 \leq 0$

$p \leq 5$ $\quad p \geq -1$ $\quad p \geq 5$ $\quad p \leq -1$

$-1 \leq p \leq 5$ $\quad$ or $\quad \varnothing$

$\{p \mid -1 \leq p \leq 5\}$

43. $2x^2 + 5x - 12 \leq 0$

$(2x - 3)(x + 4) \leq 0$

$2x - 3 \leq 0$ and $x + 4 \geq 0$ or $2x - 3 \geq 0$ and $x + 4 \leq 0$

$2x \leq 3$ $\quad x \geq -4$ $\quad 2x \geq 3$ $\quad x \leq -4$

$x \leq \frac{3}{2}$ $\quad x \geq \frac{3}{2}$

$-4 \leq x \leq \frac{3}{2}$ $\quad$ or $\quad \varnothing$

$\left\{x \mid -4 \leq x \leq \frac{3}{2}\right\}$

44. $6s^2 + 5s > 4$

$6s^2 + 5s - 4 > 0$

$(3s + 4)(2s - 1) > 0$

$3s + 4 > 0$ and $2s - 1 > 0$ or $3s + 4 < 0$ and $2s - 1 < 0$

$3s > -4$ $\quad 2s > 1$ $\quad 3s < -4$ $\quad 2s < 1$

$s > -\frac{4}{3}$ $\quad s > \frac{1}{2}$ $\quad s < -\frac{4}{3}$ $\quad s < \frac{1}{2}$

$s > \frac{1}{2}$ $\quad$ or $\quad s < -\frac{4}{3}$

$\left\{s \mid s < -\frac{4}{3} \text{ or } s > \frac{1}{2}\right\}$

45. $w^2 \geq 2w$

$w^2 - 2w \geq 0$

$w(w - 2) \geq 0$

$w \geq 0$ and $w - 2 \geq 0$ or $w \leq 0$ and $w - 2 \leq 0$

$w \geq 2$ $\quad w \leq 2$

$w \geq 2$ $\quad$ or $\quad w \leq 0$

$\{w \mid w \leq 0$ or $w \geq 2\}$

46. $9v^2 - 6v + 1 \leq 0$

$(3v - 1)(3v - 1) \leq 0$

$3v - 1 \leq 0$ and $3v - 1 \geq 0$ or $3v - 1 \geq 0$ and $3v - 1 \leq 0$

$3v \leq 1$ $\quad 3v \geq 1$ $\quad 3v \geq 1$ $\quad 3v \leq 1$

$v \leq \frac{1}{3}$ $\quad v \geq \frac{1}{3}$ $\quad v \geq \frac{1}{3}$ $\quad v \leq \frac{1}{3}$

$v = \frac{1}{3}$ $\quad$ or $\quad v = \frac{1}{3}$

$\left\{v \mid v = \frac{1}{3}\right\}$

47. $2g^2 - 5g - 3 < 0$

$(2g + 1)(g - 3) < 0$

$2g + 1 < 0$ and $g - 3 > 0$ or $2g + 1 > 0$ and $g - 3 < 0$

$2g < -1$ $\quad g > 3 \quad$ $2g > -1$ $\quad g < 3$

$g < -\frac{1}{2}$ $\qquad$ $g > -\frac{1}{2}$

$\varnothing$ $\quad$ or $\quad$ $-\frac{1}{2} < g < 3$

$\left\{g \mid -\frac{1}{2} < g < 3\right\}$

48. $f^2 + 12f + 36 < 0$

$(f + 6)(f + 6) < 0$

$f + 6 < 0$ and $f + 6 > 0$ or $f + 6 > 0$ and $f + 6 < 0$

$f < -6 \quad f > -6 \quad f > -6 \quad f < -6$

$\varnothing$ $\quad$ or $\quad$ $\varnothing$

$\varnothing$

49. $n^2 \leq 3$

$n^2 - 3 \leq 0$

$(n - \sqrt{3})(n + \sqrt{3}) \leq 0$

$n - \sqrt{3} \leq 0$ and $n + \sqrt{3} \geq 0$ $\quad$ or

$n \leq \sqrt{3} \qquad n \geq -\sqrt{3}$

$n - \sqrt{3} \geq 0$ and $n + \sqrt{3} \leq 0$

$n \geq \sqrt{3} \qquad n \leq -\sqrt{3}$

$-\sqrt{3} \leq n \leq \sqrt{3}$ $\quad$ or $\quad$ $\varnothing$

$\{n \mid -\sqrt{3} \leq n \leq \sqrt{3}\}$

50. $8d + d^2 \geq -16$

$d^2 + 8d + 16 \geq 0$

$(d + 4)(d + 4) \geq 0$

$d + 4 \geq 0$ and $d + 4 \geq 0$ or $d + 4 \leq 0$ and $d + 4 \leq 0$

$d \geq -4 \quad d \geq -4 \quad d \leq -4 \quad d \leq -4$

$d \geq -4$ $\quad$ or $\quad$ $d \leq -4$

{all reals}

51. $4t^2 - 9 \leq -4t$

$4t^2 + 4t - 9 \leq 0$

$t = \frac{-4 \pm \sqrt{4^2 - 4(4)(-9)}}{2(4)}$

$= \frac{-4 \pm \sqrt{160}}{8}$

$= \frac{-1 \pm \sqrt{10}}{2}$

$\left(t - \frac{-1 + \sqrt{10}}{2}\right)\left(t - \frac{-1 - \sqrt{10}}{2}\right) \leq 0$

$t - \frac{-1 + \sqrt{10}}{2} \leq 0$ and $t - \frac{-1 - \sqrt{10}}{2} \geq 0$

$t \leq \frac{-1 + \sqrt{10}}{2} \qquad t \geq \frac{-1 - \sqrt{10}}{2}$

$\frac{-1 - \sqrt{10}}{2} \leq t \leq \frac{-1 + \sqrt{10}}{2}$

or

$t - \frac{-1 + \sqrt{10}}{2} \geq 0$ and $t - \frac{-1 - \sqrt{10}}{2} \leq 0$

$t \geq \frac{-1 + \sqrt{10}}{2} \qquad t \leq \frac{-1 - \sqrt{10}}{2}$

$\varnothing$

$\left\{t \mid \frac{-1 - \sqrt{10}}{2} \leq t \leq \frac{-1 + \sqrt{10}}{2}\right\}$

52. $(x - 1)(x + 4)(x - 3) > 0$

$x - 1 > 0$ and $x + 4 > 0$ and $x - 3 > 0$

$x > 1 \quad x > -4 \quad x > 3; x > 3$

or $x - 1 > 0$ and $x + 4 < 0$ and $x - 3 < 0$

$x > 1 \quad x < -4 \quad x < 3; \varnothing$

or $x - 1 < 0$ and $x + 4 > 0$ and $x - 3 < 0$

$x < 1 \quad x > -4 \quad x < 3;$

$-4 < x < 1$

or $x - 1 < 0$ and $x + 4 < 0$ and $x - 3 > 0$

$x < 1 \quad x < -4 \quad x > 3; \varnothing$

$\{x \mid -4 < x < 1 \text{ or } x > 3\}$

53. $(x + 2)(x + 4)(x - 8) \leq 0$

$x + 2 \leq 0$ and $x + 4 \leq 0$ and $x - 8 \leq 0$

$x \leq -2 \quad x \leq -4 \quad x \leq 8;$

$x \leq -4$

or $x + 2 \leq 0$ and $x + 4 \geq 0$ and $x - 8 \geq 0$

$x \leq -2 \quad x \geq -4 \quad x \geq 8; \varnothing$

or $x + 2 \geq 0$ and $x + 4 \leq 0$ and $x - 8 \geq 0$

$x \geq -2 \quad x \leq -4 \quad x \geq 8; \varnothing$

or $x + 2 \geq 0$ and $x + 4 \geq 0$ and $x - 8 \leq 0$

$x \geq -2 \quad x \geq -4 \quad x \leq 8;$

$-2 \leq x \leq 8$

$\{x \mid x \leq -4 \text{ or } -2 \leq x \leq 8\}$

54. $(x + 5)(x + 1)(x - 4)(x - 6) > 0$

$x + 5 > 0$ and $x + 1 > 0$ and $x - 4 > 0$ and $x - 6 > 0$

$x > -5 \quad x > -1 \quad x > 4 \quad x > 6;$

$x > 6$

or $x + 5 > 0$ and $x + 1 > 0$ and $x - 4 < 0$ and $x - 6 < 0$

$x > -5 \quad x > -1 \quad x < 4 \quad x < 6;$

$-1 < x < 4$

or $x + 5 > 0$ and $x + 1 < 0$ and $x - 4 > 0$ and $x - 6 < 0$

$x > -5 \quad x < -1 \quad x > 4 \quad x < 6;$

$\varnothing$

or $x + 5 > 0$ and $x + 1 < 0$ and $x - 4 < 0$ and $x - 6 > 0$

$x > -5 \quad x < -1 \quad x < 4 \quad x > 6;$

$\varnothing$

or $x + 5 < 0$ and $x + 1 > 0$ and $x - 4 > 0$ and $x - 6 < 0$

$x < -5 \quad x > -1 \quad x > 4 \quad x < 6;$

$\varnothing$

or $x + 5 < 0$ and $x + 1 > 0$ and $x - 4 < 0$ and $x - 6 > 0$

$x < -5 \quad x > -1 \quad x < 4 \quad x > 6;$

$\varnothing$

or $x + 5 < 0$ and $x + 1 < 0$ and $x - 4 > 0$ and $x - 6 > 0$

$x < -5 \quad x < -1 \quad x > 4 \quad x > 6;$

$\varnothing$

or $x + 5 < 0$ and $x + 1 < 0$ and $x - 4 < 0$ and $x - 6 < 0$

$x < -5 \quad x < -1 \quad x < 4 \quad x < 6;$

$x < -5$

$\{x \mid x < -5 \text{ or } -1 < x < 4 \text{ or } x > 6\}$

55. $(x-2)(x+2)(x-1)(x+3) \geq 0$

$x-2 \geq 0$ and $x+2 \geq 0$ and $x-1 \geq 0$ and $x+3 \geq 0$
$x \geq 2$ $\quad x \geq -2$ $\quad x \geq 1$ $\quad x \geq -3$;
$x \geq 2$

or $x-2 \geq 0$ and $x+2 \geq 0$ and $x-1 \leq 0$ and $x+3 \leq 0$
$x \geq 2$ $\quad x \geq -2$ $\quad x \leq -1$ $\quad x \leq -3$;
$\varnothing$

or $x-2 \geq 0$ and $x+2 \leq 0$ and $x-1 \geq 0$ and $x+3 \leq 0$
$x \geq 2$ $\quad x \leq -2$ $\quad x \geq 1$ $\quad x \leq -3$;
$\varnothing$

or $x-2 \geq 0$ and $x+2 \leq 0$ and $x-1 \leq 0$ and $x+3 \geq 0$
$x \geq 2$ $\quad x \leq -2$ $\quad x \leq 1$ $\quad x \geq -3$;
$\varnothing$

or $x-2 \leq 0$ and $x+2 \geq 0$ and $x-1 \geq 0$ and $x+3 \leq 0$
$x \leq 2$ $\quad x \geq -2$ $\quad x \geq 1$ $\quad x \leq -3$;
$\varnothing$

or $x-2 \leq 0$ and $x+2 \geq 0$ and $x-1 \leq 0$ and $x+3 \geq 0$
$x \leq 2$ $\quad x \geq -2$ $\quad x \leq 1$ $\quad x \geq -3$;
$-2 \leq x \leq 1$

or $x-2 \leq 0$ and $x+2 \leq 0$ and $x-1 \geq 0$ and $x+3 \geq 0$
$x \leq 2$ $\quad x \leq -2$ $\quad x \geq 1$ $\quad x \geq -3$;
$\varnothing$

or $x-2 \leq 0$ and $x+2 \leq 0$ and $x-1 \leq 0$ and $x+3 \leq 0$
$x \leq 2$ $\quad x \leq -2$ $\quad x \leq 1$ $\quad x \leq -3$;
$x \leq -3$

$\{x \mid x \leq -3$ or $-2 \leq x \leq 1$ or $x \geq 2\}$

56. $y \geq x^2 - 3$

x	$x^2 - 3$	y
−2	$(-2)^2 - 3$	1
0	$(0)^2 - 3$	−3
2	$(2)^2 - 3$	1
4	$(4)^2 - 3$	13

Test: (0, 0)
$0 \overset{?}{\geq} 0^2 - 3$
$0 \geq -3$; true

$y \leq x^2 + 3$

x	$x^2 + 3$	y
−2	$(-2)^2 + 3$	7
0	$(0)^2 + 3$	3
2	$(2)^2 + 3$	7
4	$(4)^2 + 3$	19

Test: (0, 0)
$0 \overset{?}{\leq} 0^2 + 3$
$0 \leq 3$; true

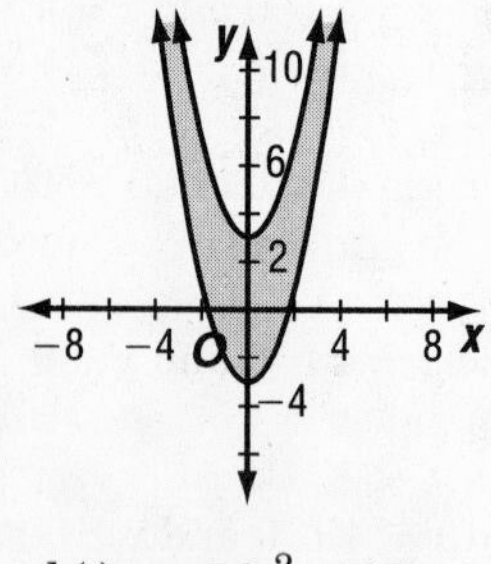

57a. $h(t) = -16t^2 + 65t$

$h(t) = -16\left(t^2 - \frac{65}{16}t + \frac{4225}{1024}\right) - (-16)\left(\frac{4225}{1024}\right)$

$h(t) \approx -16\left(t - \frac{65}{32}\right)^2 + 66.02$;

vertex at $\left(\frac{65}{32}, 66.02\right)$

No, the maximum height of the ball is about 66 feet.

57b. $90 = -16(3)^2 + v(3)$
$90 = -144 + 3v$
$234 = 3v$
$78 = v$; 78 feet per second

58. Let w = width. Then $\ell = w + 5$.
$w(w+5) > 104$
$w^2 + 5w - 104 > 0$
$(w+13)(w-8) > 0$

$w + 13 > 0$ and $w - 8 > 0$ or $w + 13 < 0$ and $w - 8 < 0$
$w > -13$ $\quad w > 8$ $\quad w < -13$ $\quad w < 8$
$w > 8$ or $w < -13$

The width is greater than 8 centimeters. The length is greater than $w + 5$ or 13 centimeters.

59. $(100 + 5x)(1.00 - 0.20x) > 66$
$100 - 15x - x^2 > 66$
$-x^2 - 15x + 34 > 0$
$x^2 + 15x - 34 < 0$
$(x + 17)(x - 2) < 0$

$x + 17 < 0$ and $x - 2 > 0$ or $x + 17 > 0$ and $x - 2 < 0$
$x < -17$ $\quad x > 2$ or $\quad x > -17$ $\quad x < 2$
$\varnothing$ $\quad -17 < x < 2$

1 decrease of \$0.20

60a.

t	$-16t^2 + 980t$	$h(t)$
0	$-16(0)^2 + 980(0)$	0
10	$-16(10)^2 + 980(10)$	8200
30	$-16(30)^2 + 980(30)$	15,000
50	$-16(50)^2 + 980(50)$	9000

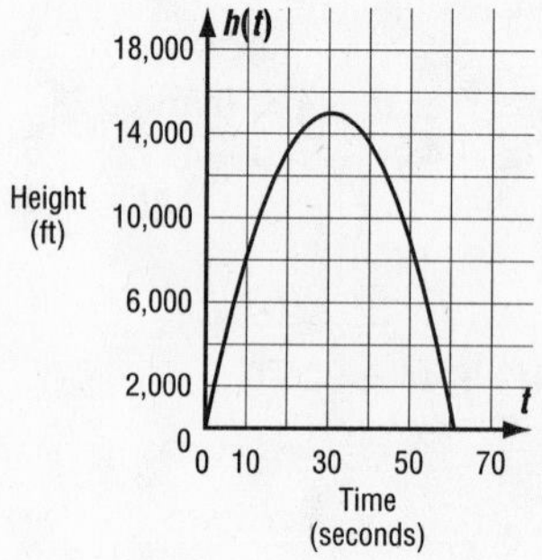

60b. Yes, the bullet reaches a height of approximately 15,006 feet.

61a. $f(x) = \frac{1}{315}(-2x^2 + 1260x)$
$= \frac{-2}{315}(x^2 - 630x + 99{,}225) - \left(-\frac{2}{315}\right)(99{,}225)$
$= -\frac{2}{315}(x - 315)^2 + 630$

61b. The arch will be tallest at $x = 315$;
$f(315) = -\frac{2}{315}(315 - 315)^2 + 630$
$= 630$; 630 feet

61c.

x	$\frac{1}{315}(-2x^2 + 1260x)$	y
0	$\frac{1}{315}(-2(0)^2 + 1260(0))$	0
200	$\frac{1}{315}(-2(200)^2 + 1260(200))$	546.03
400	$\frac{1}{315}(-2(400)^2 + 1260(400))$	584.13
600	$\frac{1}{315}(-2(600)^2 + 1260(600))$	114.29

(Continued on next page)

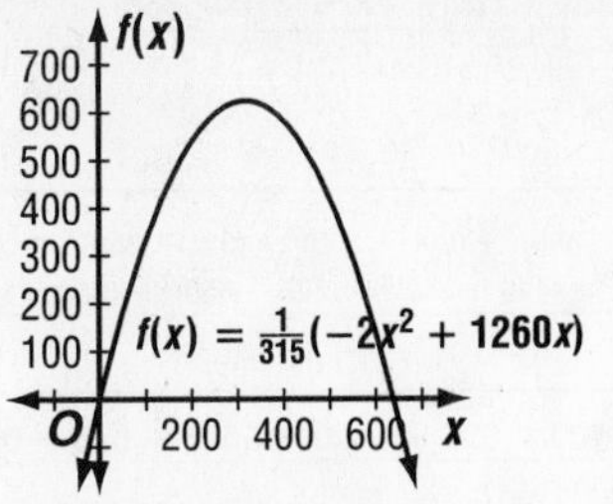

See students' work for comparison.

62. $x^2 + kx - 5 = 0$
$1^2 + k(1) - 5 = 0$
$1 + k - 5 = 0$
$k = 4$

63. $11m^2 - 12m = 10$
$11m^2 - 12m - 10 = 0$

$$m = \frac{12 \pm \sqrt{(-12)^2 - 4(11)(-10)}}{2(11)}$$
$$= \frac{12 \pm \sqrt{584}}{22}$$
$$= \frac{12 \pm 2\sqrt{146}}{22}$$
$$= \frac{6 \pm \sqrt{146}}{11}$$

64. $x^2 + bx + c = 0$
$$x^2 + bx = -c$$
$$x^2 + bx + \frac{b^2}{4} = -c + \frac{b^2}{4}$$
$$\left(x + \frac{b}{2}\right)^2 = \frac{-4c + b^2}{4}$$
$$x + \frac{b}{2} = \pm\frac{\sqrt{b^2 - 4c}}{2}$$
$$x = \frac{-b \pm \sqrt{b^2 - 4c}}{2}$$

65. $(5 + \sqrt{8})^2 = (5 + \sqrt{8})(5 + \sqrt{8})$
$= 25 + 5\sqrt{8} + 5\sqrt{8} + 8$
$= 33 + 10\sqrt{2^2 \cdot 2}$
$= 33 + 20\sqrt{2}$

66.

−3	1	3	0	1	−1
		−3	0	0	−3
	1	0	0	1	−4

$y^3 + 1 - \frac{4}{y + 3}$

67. $(5a - 3)(1 - 3a) = 5a - 15a^2 - 3 + 9a$
$= -15a^2 + 14a - 3$

68. $M^{-1} = \frac{1}{20 + 6}\begin{bmatrix} 5 & -6 \\ 1 & 4 \end{bmatrix}$
$= \frac{1}{26}\begin{bmatrix} 5 & -6 \\ 1 & 4 \end{bmatrix}$

69. $x = \frac{\begin{vmatrix} 10 & 7 \\ 20 & -4 \end{vmatrix}}{\begin{vmatrix} 6 & 7 \\ 3 & -4 \end{vmatrix}}$ $\quad y = \frac{\begin{vmatrix} 6 & 10 \\ 3 & 20 \end{vmatrix}}{\begin{vmatrix} 6 & 7 \\ 3 & -4 \end{vmatrix}}$

$= \frac{-40 - 140}{-24 - 21}$ $\quad = \frac{120 - 30}{-24 - 21}$

$= \frac{-180}{-45}$ $\quad = \frac{90}{-45}$

$= 4$ $\quad = -2$ $\quad (4, -2)$

70. $3x - 2y = 8$
$-2y = -3x + 8$
$y = \frac{3}{2}x - 4$ $\quad m = \frac{3}{2}$, y: -4
$0 = \frac{3}{2}x - 4$
$4 = \frac{3}{2}x$
$\frac{8}{3} = x$ $\quad$ x: $\frac{8}{3}$

71. $4x - (2x + 8) + 3x = 5x - 8$
$4x - 2x - 8 + 3x = 5x - 8$
$5x - 8 = 5x - 8$
$0 = 0$; all reals

6-8 Integration: Statistics Standard Deviation

Pages 388–389 Check for Understanding

1. See students' work.
2. \$30.88 + \$3.79 = \$34.67; \$30.88 − \$3.79 = \$27.09; 19 ticket prices; $\frac{19}{28} \approx 0.68$ or 68%
3. Answers will vary. Sample answer: floods along Mississippi River

4a. Variation is small.

4b. Variation is large.

5. $\bar{x} = \frac{110 + 70 + 20 + 40 + 10}{5} = \frac{250}{5} = 50$

$$SD = \sqrt{\frac{(110 - 50)^2 + (70 - 50)^2 + (20 - 50)^2 + (40 - 50)^2 + (10 - 50)^2}{5}}$$
$$= \sqrt{\frac{3600 + 400 + 900 + 100 + 1600}{5}}$$
$$= \sqrt{1320}$$
$$\approx 36.33$$

6. $\bar{x} = \frac{48 + 36 + 40 + 29 + 45 + 51 + 38 + 47 + 39 + 37}{10}$
$= \frac{410}{10} = 41$

$$SD = \sqrt{\frac{\left[\begin{array}{c}(48 - 41)^2 + (36 - 41)^2 + (40 - 41)^2 + (29 - 41)^2 + \\ (45 - 41)^2 + (51 - 41)^2 + (38 - 41)^2 + (47 - 41)^2 + \\ (39 - 41)^2 + (37 - 41)^2\end{array}\right]}{10}}$$
$$= \sqrt{\frac{49 + 25 + 1 + 144 + 16 + 100 + 9 + 36 + 4 + 16}{10}}$$
$$= \sqrt{40}$$
$$\approx 6.32$$

7. $\bar{x} = (43 + 56 + 78 + 81 + 47 + 42 + 34 + 22 + 78 + 98 + 38 + 46 + 54 + 67 + 58 + 92 + 55) \div 17$

$= 989 \div 17 \approx 58.18$

$$\text{SD} = \sqrt{\frac{\left[\begin{array}{c}(43 - 58.18)^2 + (56 - 58.18)^2 + (78 - 58.18)^2 + (81 - 58.18)^2 + \\ (47 - 58.18)^2 + (42 - 58.18)^2 + (34 - 58.18)^2 + (22 - 58.18)^2 + \\ (78 - 58.18)^2 + (98 - 58.18)^2 + (38 - 58.18)^2 + (46 - 58.18)^2 + \\ (54 - 58.18)^2 + (67 - 58.18)^2 + (58 - 58.18)^2 + (92 - 58.18)^2 + (55 - 58.18)^2\end{array}\right]}{17}}$$

$$= \sqrt{\frac{\left[\begin{array}{c}230.4324 + 4.7542 + 392.8324 + 520.7524 + \\ 124.9924 + 261.7924 + 584.6724 + 1308.9924 + \\ 392.8324 + 1585.6324 + 407.2324 + 148.3524 + \\ 17.4724 + 77.7924 + 0.0324 + 1143.7924 + 10.1124\end{array}\right]}{17}}$$

$\approx \sqrt{424.263}$

≈ 20.60

8. $\bar{x} = (4.3 + 4.5 + 4.6 + 4.8 + 5.2 + 5.4 + 5.5 + 5.6 + 6.1 + 6.2 + 6.4 + 6.5 + 6.5 + 6.6 + 6.7 + 6.7 + 6.7) \div 17 = 98.3 \div 17 \approx 5.78$

$$\text{SD} = \sqrt{\frac{\left[\begin{array}{c}(4.3 - 5.78)^2 + (4.5 - 5.78)^2 + (4.6 - 5.78)^2 + \\ (4.8 - 5.78)^2 + (5.2 - 5.78)^2 + (5.4 - 5.78)^2 + (5.5 - 5.78)^2 + \\ (5.6 - 5.78)^2 + (6.1 - 5.78)^2 + (6.2 - 5.78)^2 + \\ (6.4 - 5.75)^2 + 2(6.5 - 5.78)^2 + (6.6 - 5.78)^2 + 3(6.7 - 5.78)^2\end{array}\right]}{17}}$$

$$= \sqrt{\frac{\left[\begin{array}{c}2.1904 + 1.6384 + 1.3924 + 0.9604 + 0.3364 + \\ 0.1444 + 0.0784 + 0.0324 + 0.1024 + \\ 0.1764 + 0.3844 + 1.0368 + 0.6724 + 2.5392\end{array}\right]}{17}}$$

$\approx \sqrt{0.6873}$

≈ 0.83

9a. $\bar{x} = \dfrac{251 + 246 + 252 + 249 + 250 + 248 + 246 + 253 + 250 + 251}{10}$

$= \dfrac{2496}{10} = 249.6$

$$\text{SD} = \sqrt{\frac{\left[\begin{array}{c}(251 - 249.6)^2 + (246 - 249.6)^2 + (252 - 249.6)^2 + \\ (249 - 249.6)^2 + (250 - 249.6)^2 + (248 - 249.6)^2 + \\ (246 - 249.6)^2 + (253 - 249.6)^2 + (250 - 249.6)^2 + (251 - 249.6)^2\end{array}\right]}{10}}$$

$$= \sqrt{\frac{\left[\begin{array}{c}1.96 + 12.96 + 5.76 + 0.36 + \\ 0.16 + 2.56 + 12.96 + 11.56 + 0.16 + 1.96\end{array}\right]}{10}}$$

$= \sqrt{5.04}$

≈ 2.24

9b. small

9c. Answers will vary.

Pages 389–391 Exercises

10. $\bar{x} = \dfrac{45 + 65 + 145 + 85 + 25 + 25}{6} = \dfrac{390}{6} = 65$

$$\text{SD} = \sqrt{\frac{\left[\begin{array}{c}(45 - 65)^2 + (65 - 65)^2 + \\ (145 - 65)^2 + (85 - 65)^2 + 2(25 - 65)^2\end{array}\right]}{6}}$$

$$= \sqrt{\frac{400 + 0 + 6400 + 400 + 3200}{6}}$$

$= \sqrt{1733.\overline{3}}$

≈ 41.63

11. $\bar{x} = \dfrac{400 + 300 + 325 + 275 + 425 + 375 + 350}{7}$

$= \dfrac{2450}{7} = 350$

$$\text{SD} = \sqrt{\frac{\left[\begin{array}{c}(400 - 350)^2 + (300 - 350)^2 + (325 - 350)^2 + \\ (275 - 350)^2 + (425 - 350)^2 + (375 - 350)^2 + (350 - 350)^2\end{array}\right]}{7}}$$

$$= \sqrt{\frac{2500 + 2500 + 625 + 5625 + 5625 + 625 + 0}{7}}$$

$= \sqrt{2500}$

$= 50$

12. $\bar{x} = \dfrac{\left[\begin{array}{c}5 + 4 + 5 + 5 + 5 + 5 + 6 + 6 + \\ 6 + 6 + 7 + 7 + 7 + 7 + 8 + 9\end{array}\right]}{16} = \dfrac{98}{16} \approx 6.13$

$$\text{SD} = \sqrt{\frac{\left[\begin{array}{c}(4 - 6.13)^2 + 5(5 - 6.13)^2 + \\ 4(6 - 6.13)^2 + 4(7 - 6.13)^2 + (8 - 6.13)^2 + (9 - 6.13)^2\end{array}\right]}{16}}$$

$$= \sqrt{\frac{4.5369 + 6.3845 + 0.0676 + 3.0276 + 3.4969 + 8.2369}{16}}$$

$= \sqrt{1.6094}$

≈ 1.27

13. $\bar{x} = \dfrac{234 + 345 + 123 + 368 + 279 + 876 + 456 + 235 + 333 + 444}{10}$

$= \dfrac{3693}{10} = 369.30$

$$\text{SD} = \sqrt{\frac{\left[\begin{array}{c}(234 - 369.3)^2 + (345 - 369.3)^2 + (123 - 369.3)^2 + \\ (368 - 369.3)^2 + (279 - 369.3)^2 + (876 - 369.3)^2 + \\ (456 - 369.3)^2 + (235 - 369.3)^2 + (333 - 369.3)^2 + (444 - 369.3)^2\end{array}\right]}{10}}$$

$$= \sqrt{\frac{\left[\begin{array}{c}18{,}306.09 + 590.49 + 60{,}663.69 + 1.69 + 8154.09 + \\ 256{,}744.89 + 7516.89 + 18{,}036.49 + 1317.69 + 5580.09\end{array}\right]}{10}}$$

$= \sqrt{37{,}691.21}$

≈ 194.14

14. $\bar{x} = \dfrac{\left[\begin{array}{c}13 + 14 + 15 + 16 + 17 + 18 + 19 + \\ 20 + 21 + 23 + 67 + 56 + 34 + 99 + 44 + 55\end{array}\right]}{16}$

$= \dfrac{531}{16} \approx 33.19$

$$\text{SD} = \sqrt{\frac{\left[\begin{array}{c}(13 - 33.19)^2 + (14 - 33.19)^2 + (15 - 33.19)^2 + (16 - 33.19)^2 + \\ (17 - 33.19)^2 + (18 - 33.19)^2 + (19 - 33.19)^2 + (20 - 33.19)^2 + \\ (21 - 33.19)^2 + (23 - 33.19)^2 + (67 - 33.19)^2 + (56 - 33.19)^2 + \\ (34 - 33.19)^2 + (99 - 33.19)^2 + (44 - 33.19)^2 + (55 - 33.19)^2\end{array}\right]}{16}}$$

$$= \sqrt{\frac{\left[\begin{array}{c}407.6361 + 368.2561 + 330.8761 + 295.4961 + 262.1161 + \\ 230.7361 + 201.3561 + 173.9761 + 148.5961 + 103.8361 + \\ 1143.1161 + 520.2961 + 0.6561 + 4330.9561 + 116.8561 + 475.6761\end{array}\right]}{16}}$$

$\approx \sqrt{569.40}$

≈ 23.86

15. $\bar{x} = \dfrac{\left[\begin{array}{c}44 + 45 + 46 + 47 + 47 + 53 + 55 + \\ 56 + 57 + 58 + 59 + 67 + 67 + 68 + 69 + 69 + 69\end{array}\right]}{17}$

$= \frac{976}{17} \approx 57.41$

SD =

$$\sqrt{\dfrac{\left[\begin{array}{c}(44 - 57.41)^2 + (45 - 57.41)^2 + (46 - 57.41)^2 + 2(47 - 57.41)^2 + \\ (53 - 57.41)^2 + (55 - 57.41)^2 + (56 - 57.41)^2 + (57 - 57.41)^2 + \\ (58 - 57.41)^2 + (59 - 57.41)^2 + 2(67 - 57.41)^2 + (68 - 57.41)^2 + 3(69 - 57.41)^2\end{array}\right]}{17}}$$

$$= \sqrt{\dfrac{\left[\begin{array}{c}179.8281 + 154.0081 + 130.1881 + 216.7362 + \\ 19.4481 + 5.8081 + 1.9881 + 0.1681 + 0.3481 + \\ 2.5281 + 183.9362 + 112.1481 + 402.9843\end{array}\right]}{17}}$$

$= \sqrt{82.9481}$

≈ 9.11

16. $\bar{x} = \dfrac{\left[\begin{array}{c}3(5.7) + 5.8 + 5.9 + 6.3 + 6.4 + \\ 2(6.5) + 6.6 + 6.7 + 7.2 + 7.3 + 7.4 + 7.5 + 7.6\end{array}\right]}{16}$

$= \frac{104.8}{16}$ or 6.55

SD =

$$\sqrt{\dfrac{\left[\begin{array}{c}3(5.7 - 6.55)^2 + (5.8 - 6.55)^2 + (5.9 - 6.55)^2 + (6.3 - 6.55)^2 + \\ (6.4 - 6.55)^2 + 2(6.5 - 6.55)^2 + (6.6 - 6.55)^2 + (6.7 - 6.55)^2 + \\ (7.2 - 6.55)^2 + (7.3 + 6.55)^2 + (7.4 - 6.55)^2 + (7.5 - 6.55)^2 + (7.6 - 6.55)^2\end{array}\right]}{16}}$$

$$= \sqrt{\dfrac{\left[\begin{array}{c}2.1675 + 0.5625 + 0.4225 + 0.0625 + 0.0225 + 0.005 + \\ 0.0025 + 0.0225 + 0.4225 + 0.5625 + 0.7225 + 0.9025 + 1.1025\end{array}\right]}{16}}$$

$= \sqrt{0.43625}$

≈ 0.66

17. $\bar{x} = \dfrac{\left[\begin{array}{c}2(3.0) + 3.1 + 3.2 + 3.4 + 3.5 + 3(3.6) + 3.8 + \\ 3.9 + 2(4.1) + 4.3 + 2(4.4) + 2(4.5) + 4.6 + 4.7\end{array}\right]}{20}$

$= \frac{77.3}{20} \approx 3.87$

$$\text{SD} = \sqrt{\dfrac{\left[\begin{array}{c}2(3.0 - 3.87)^2 + (3.1 - 3.87)^2 + (3.2 - 3.87)^2 + \\ (3.4 - 3.87)^2 + (3.5 - 3.87)^2 + 3(3.6 - 3.87)^2 + (3.8 - 3.87)^2 + \\ (3.9 - 3.87)^2 + 2(4.1 - 3.87)^2 + (4.3 - 3.87)^2 + \\ 2(4.4 - 3.87)^2 + 2(4.5 - 3.87)^2 + (4.6 - 3.87)^2 + (4.7 - 3.87)^2\end{array}\right]}{20}}$$

$$= \sqrt{\dfrac{\left[\begin{array}{c}1.5138 + 0.5929 + 0.4489 + 0.2209 + \\ 0.1369 + 0.2187 + 0.0049 + 0.0009 + 0.1058 + \\ 0.1849 + 0.5618 + 0.7938 + 0.5329 + 0.6889\end{array}\right]}{20}}$$

$= \sqrt{0.3003}$

≈ 0.55

18. $\bar{x} = \dfrac{\left[\begin{array}{c}41 + 43 + 49 + 52 + 53 + 56 + \\ 59 + 64 + 64 + 65 + 67 + 68 + 72 + 74 + 77\end{array}\right]}{15}$

$= \frac{904}{15} \approx 60.27$

SD =

$$\sqrt{\dfrac{\left[\begin{array}{c}(41 - 60.27)^2 + (43 - 60.27)^2 + (49 - 60.27)^2 + \\ (52 - 60.27)^2 + (53 - 60.27)^2 + (56 - 60.27)^2 + \\ (59 - 60.27)^2 + 2(64 - 60.27)^2 + (65 - 60.27)^2 + (67 - 60.27)^2 + \\ (68 - 60.27)^2 + (72 - 60.27)^2 + (74 - 60.27)^2 + (77 - 60.27)^2\end{array}\right]}{15}}$$

$$= \sqrt{\dfrac{\left[\begin{array}{c}371.3329 + 298.2529 + 127.0129 + 68.3929 + \\ 52.8529 + 18.2329 + 1.6129 + 27.8258 + 22.3729 + \\ 45.2929 + 59.7529 + 137.5929 + 188.5129 + 279.8929\end{array}\right]}{15}}$$

$\approx \sqrt{113.2622}$

≈ 10.64

19. $\bar{x} = \dfrac{76 + 78 + 89 + 90 + 34 + 56 + 50}{7} = \dfrac{473}{7} \approx 67.57$

SD =

$$\sqrt{\dfrac{\left[\begin{array}{c}(76 - 67.57)^2 + (78 - 67.57)^2 + (89 - 67.57)^2 \\ (90 - 67.57)^2 + (34 - 67.57)^2 + (56 - 67.57)^2 + (50 - 67.57)^2\end{array}\right]}{7}}$$

$$= \sqrt{\dfrac{\left[\begin{array}{c}71.0649 + 108.7849 + 459.2449 + \\ 503.1049 + 1126.9449 + 133.8649 + 308.7049\end{array}\right]}{7}}$$

$\approx \sqrt{387.4020}$

≈ 19.68

20. $\bar{x} = \dfrac{\left[\begin{array}{c}321 + 322 + 323 + \\ 324 + 325 + 326 + 327 + 328 + 329 + 330\end{array}\right]}{10}$

$= \frac{3255}{10} = 325.50$

SD =

$$\sqrt{\dfrac{\left[\begin{array}{c}(321 - 325.5)^2 + (322 - 325.5)^2 + (323 - 325.5)^2 + \\ (324 - 325.5)^2 + (325 - 325.5)^2 + (326 - 325.5)^2 + \\ (327 - 325.5)^2 + (328 - 325.5)^2 + (329 - 325.5)^2 + (330 - 325.5)^2\end{array}\right]}{10}}$$

$$= \sqrt{\dfrac{\left[\begin{array}{c}20.25 + 12.25 + 6.25 + 2.25 + \\ 0.25 + 0.25 + 2.25 + 6.25 + 12.25 + 20.25\end{array}\right]}{10}}$$

$= \sqrt{8.25}$

≈ 2.87

21. 0; no variation from the mean

22a. $\bar{x} = \dfrac{150 + 145 + 120 + 168 + 175}{5} = \dfrac{758}{5} = 151.6$

$$\text{SD} = \sqrt{\dfrac{\left[\begin{array}{c}(150 - 151.6)^2 + (145 - 151.6)^2 + \\ (120 - 151.6)^2 + (168 - 151.6)^2 + (175 - 151.6)^2\end{array}\right]}{5}}$$

$$= \sqrt{\dfrac{2.56 + 43.56 + 998.56 + 268.96 + 547.56}{5}}$$

$= \sqrt{372.24}$

≈ 19.29

22b. $\bar{x} = \frac{124 + 157 + 195 + 205 + 177}{5} = \frac{858}{5} = 171.6$

$$SD = \sqrt{\frac{\left[\begin{array}{c}(124 - 171.6)^2 + (157 - 171.6)^2 + \\ (195 - 171.6)^2 + (205 - 171.6)^2 + (177 - 171.6)^2\end{array}\right]}{5}}$$

$$= \sqrt{\frac{2265.76 + 213.16 + 547.56 + 1115.56 + 29.16}{5}}$$

$$= \sqrt{834.24}$$

$$\approx 28.88$$

22c. $\bar{x} = \frac{146 + 155 + 176 + 186 + 199}{5} = \frac{862}{5} = 172.4$

$$SD = \sqrt{\frac{\left[\begin{array}{c}(146 - 172.4)^2 + (155 - 172.4)^2 + \\ (176 - 172.4)^2 + (186 - 172.4)^2 + (199 - 172.4)^2\end{array}\right]}{5}}$$

$$= \sqrt{\frac{696.96 + 302.76 + 12.96 + 184.96 + 707.56}{5}}$$

$$= \sqrt{381.04}$$

$$\approx 19.52$$

22d. Hillview; See students' work.

23a. $\bar{x} = \frac{\left[\begin{array}{c}88.7 + 84.8 + 83.0 + 80.5 + \\ 80.0 + 77.9 + 75.4 + 73.5 + 71.9\end{array}\right]}{9} = \frac{715.7}{9} \approx 79.52$

$$SD = \sqrt{\frac{\left[\begin{array}{c}(88.7 - 79.52)^2 + (84.8 - 79.52)^2 + (83.0 - 79.52)^2 + \\ (80.5 - 79.52)^2 + (80.0 - 79.52)^2 + (77.9 - 79.52)^2 + \\ (75.4 - 79.52)^2 + (73.5 - 79.52)^2 + (71.9 - 79.52)^2\end{array}\right]}{9}}$$

$$= \sqrt{\frac{\left[\begin{array}{c}84.2724 + 27.8784 + 12.1104 + 0.9604 + \\ 0.2304 + 2.6244 + 16.9744 + 36.2404 + 58.0644\end{array}\right]}{9}}$$

$$\approx \sqrt{26.595}$$

$$\approx 5.16$$

23b. $\bar{x} = \frac{\left[\begin{array}{c}0.29 + 0.68 + 1.09 + 0.64 + \\ 0.38 + 1.93 + 0.45 + 0.83 + 0.74\end{array}\right]}{9} = \frac{7.03}{9} \approx 0.78$

$$SD = \sqrt{\frac{\left[\begin{array}{c}(0.29 - 0.78)^2 + (0.68 - 0.78)^2 + (1.09 - 0.78)^2 + \\ (0.64 - 0.78)^2 + (0.38 - 0.78)^2 + (1.93 - 0.78)^2 + \\ (0.45 - 0.78)^2 + (0.83 - 0.78)^2 + (0.74 - 0.78)^2\end{array}\right]}{9}}$$

$$= \sqrt{\frac{\left[\begin{array}{c}0.2401 + 0.01 + 0.0961 + 0.0196 + \\ 0.16 + 1.3225 + 0.1089 + 0.0025 + 0.0016\end{array}\right]}{9}}$$

$$\approx \sqrt{0.2179}$$

$$\approx 0.47$$

23c. See students' work.

24a. $\bar{x} = \frac{20 + 17 + 31 + 15 + 23}{5} = \frac{106}{5} = 21.2$; \$21.20

$$SD = \sqrt{\frac{\left[\begin{array}{c}(20 - 21.2)^2 + (17 - 21.2)^2 + \\ (31 - 21.2)^2 + (15 - 21.2)^2 + (23 - 21.2)^2\end{array}\right]}{5}}$$

$$= \sqrt{\frac{1.44 + 17.64 + 96.04 + 38.44 + 3.24}{5}}$$

$$= \sqrt{31.36}$$

$= 5.6$; \$5.60

24b. $\bar{x} = \frac{19 + 26 + 48 + 21 + 30}{5} = \frac{144}{5} = 28.8$; \$28.80

$$SD = \sqrt{\frac{\left[\begin{array}{c}(19 - 28.8)^2 + (26 - 28.8)^2 + \\ (48 - 28.8)^2 + (21 - 28.8)^2 + (30 - 28.8)^2\end{array}\right]}{5}}$$

$$= \sqrt{\frac{96.04 + 7.84 + 368.64 + 60.84 + 1.44}{5}}$$

$$= \sqrt{106.96}$$

≈ 10.34; \$10.34

24c. women's jeans

24d. See students' work.

24e. The new standard deviation is the same as the original standard deviation since the prices of all the jeans are lowered by the same amount.

25a. $\bar{x} = \frac{14 + 20 + 18 + 20 + 23 + 12 + 21 + 23 + 13}{9}$

$= \frac{164}{9} \approx 18.22$; 18.22¢

$$SD = \sqrt{\frac{\left[\begin{array}{c}(14 - 18.22)^2 + 2(20 - 18.22)^2 + \\ (18 - 18.22)^2 + (23 - 18.22)^2 + (12 - 18.22)^2 + \\ (21 - 18.22)^2 + (23 - 18.22)^2 + (13 - 18.22)^2\end{array}\right]}{9}}$$

$$= \sqrt{\frac{\left[\begin{array}{c}17.8084 + 6.3368 + 0.0484 + \\ 22.8484 + 38.6884 + 7.7284 + 22.8484 + 27.2484\end{array}\right]}{9}}$$

$$\approx \sqrt{15.95}$$

≈ 3.99; 3.99¢

25b. $\bar{x} = \sqrt{\frac{\left[\begin{array}{c}2(25) + 12 + 2(17) + 5(21) + \\ 2(24) + 10 + 28 + 22 + 20 + 19\end{array}\right]}{17}}$

$= \frac{348}{17} \approx 20.47$; 20.47¢

$$SD = \sqrt{\frac{\left[\begin{array}{c}2(25 - 20.47)^2 + (12 - 20.47)^2 + 2(17 - 20.47)^2 + \\ 5(21 - 20.47)^2 + 2(24 - 20.47)^2 + (10 - 20.47)^2 + \\ (28 - 20.47)^2 + (22 - 20.47)^2 + (20 - 20.47)^2 + (19 - 20.47)^2\end{array}\right]}{17}}$$

$$= \sqrt{\frac{\left[\begin{array}{c}41.0418 + 71.7409 + 24.0818 + 1.4045 + \\ 24.9218 + 109.6209 + 56.7009 + 2.3409 + 0.2209 + 2.1609\end{array}\right]}{17}}$$

$$= \sqrt{19.6609}$$

$\approx$ 4.43; 4.43¢

26. $(3x - 9)(x + 12) < 0$

$3x - 9 < 0$ and $x + 12 > 0$ or $3x - 9 > 0$ and $x + 12 < 0$

$3x < 9$ $\quad x > -12 \quad$ $3x > 9$ $\quad x < -12$

$x < 3$ $\quad\quad\quad$ $x > 3$

$-12x < x < 3$ $\quad$ or $\quad \varnothing$

$\{x \mid -12 < x < 3\}$

27.
$$y = 0.00048x^2 + 18$$
$$48 = 0.00048x^2 + 18$$
$$30 = 0.00048x^2$$
$$62{,}500 = x^2$$
$\pm 250 = x$; 250 feet

28.

$$\begin{array}{r} r - 1 \\ 2r + 3\overline{)2r^2 + \ \ r - 3} \\ \underline{2r^2 + 3r} \quad\ \ \\ -2r - 3 \\ \underline{-2r - 3} \\ 0 \end{array}$$

29. $\left[\begin{array}{cc|c} 3 & 4 & 22 \\ 7 & -1 & 10 \end{array}\right] = \left[\begin{array}{cc|c} 31 & 0 & 62 \\ 7 & -1 & 10 \end{array}\right] = \left[\begin{array}{cc|c} 1 & 0 & 2 \\ 7 & -1 & 10 \end{array}\right]$

$= \left[\begin{array}{cc|c} 1 & 0 & 2 \\ 0 & -1 & -4 \end{array}\right] = \left[\begin{array}{cc|c} 1 & 0 & 2 \\ 0 & 1 & 4 \end{array}\right]$; (2, 4)

30. $f(x, y) = 6x - 3y$

$f(-5, 2) = 6(-5) - 3(2)$

$= -30 - 6$

$= -36$

6-9 Integration: Statistics The Normal Distribution

Page 395 Check for Understanding

1. Sample answer: The height of power forwards in basketball will fall within a certain range due to the fact that they have to be a certain height to play that position effectively. For the same reason, a histogram will approximate a normal curve. The mean, median and mode of data are very close to each other.

2.

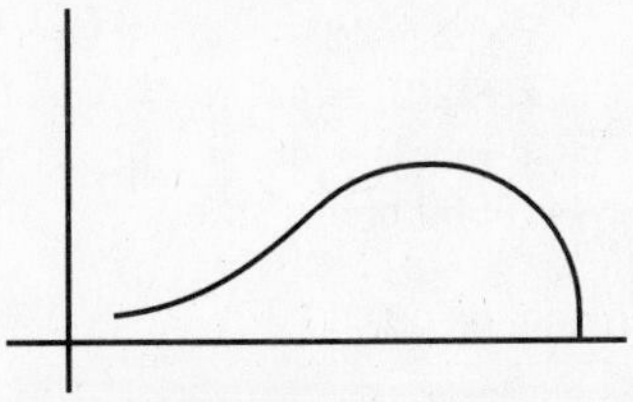

Sample answer: As the age increases, the average yearly income increases.

3. The means of the three graphs are the same, but the standard deviations of the three are different. The first graph has the least standard deviation, the middle graph's standard deviation will be slightly greater, and the last graph will have the greatest standard deviation.

4. See students' work.

5a. normally distributed

5b.

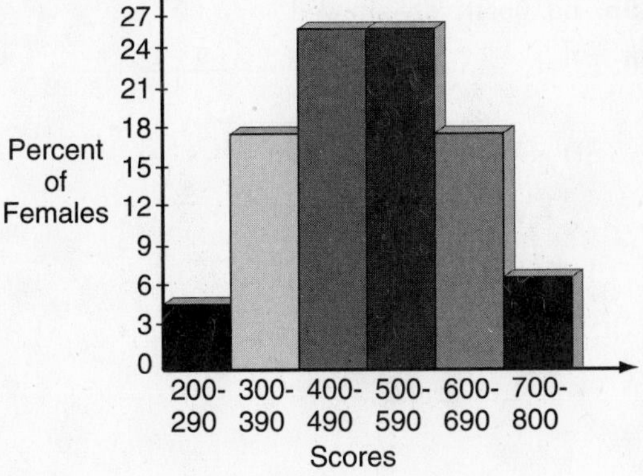

6. $\bar{x} - 3 = 82$ $\bar{x} + 3 = 88$

$\bar{x} - 2(3) = 79$ $\bar{x} + 2(3) = 91$

$\bar{x} - 3(3) = 76$ $\bar{x} + 3(3) = 94$

6a. 68%

6b. 13.5%

6c. 95%

7. $\bar{x} - 5000 = 25{,}000$ $\bar{x} + 5000 = 35{,}000$

$\bar{x} - 2(5000) = 20{,}000$ $\bar{x} + 2(5000) = 40{,}000$

$\bar{x} - 3(5000) = 15{,}000$ $\bar{x} + 3(5000) = 45{,}000$

7a. $10{,}000 \times 0.68 = 6800$; 6800 tires

7b. $10{,}000 \times 0.025 = 250$; 250 tires

7c. $10{,}000 \times 0.16 = 1600$; 1600 tires

7d. $2(34) + 13.5 = 81.5$; 81.5%

Pages 396–398 Exercises

8. positively skewed

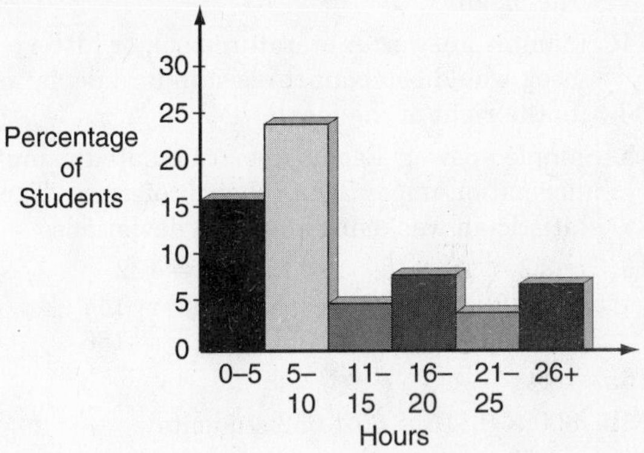

9. normally distributed

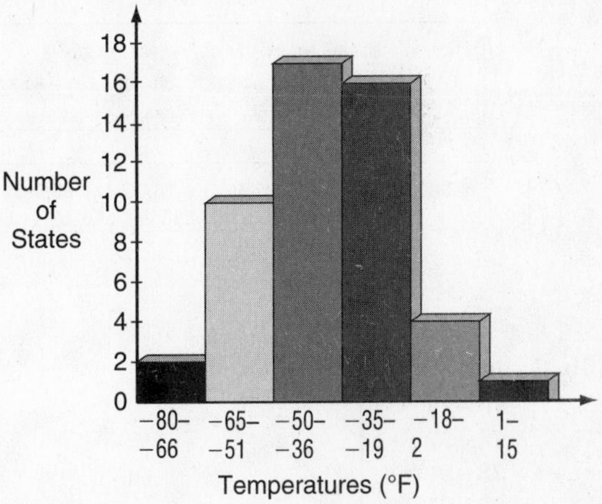

10. $\bar{x} - 3 = 9$ $\bar{x} + 3 = 15$

$\bar{x} - 2(3) = 6$ $\bar{x} + 2(3) = 18$

$\bar{x} - 3(3) = 3$ $\bar{x} + 3(3) = 21$

10a. 68%   **10b.** 34%

10c. 0.5%   **10d.** 16%

11. $\bar{x} - 0.2 = 5.8$ $\bar{x} + 0.2 = 6.2$

$\bar{x} - 2(0.2) = 5.6$ $\bar{x} + 2(0.2) = 6.4$

$\bar{x} - 3(0.2) = 5.4$ $\bar{x} + 3(0.2) = 6.8$

11a. 50%   **11b.** 50%

11c. 95%

12. $\bar{x} - 0.1 = 3.4$ $\quad \bar{x} + 0.1 = 3.6$
$\bar{x} - 2(0.1) = 3.3$ $\quad \bar{x} + 2(0.1) = 3.7$
$\bar{x} - 3(0.1) = 3.2$ $\quad \bar{x} + 3(0.1) = 3.8$

12a. 2.5%

12b. $1000 \times 0.815 = 815$; 815 disks

12c. $1000 \times 0.025 = 25$; 25 disks

13. $\bar{x} - 0.005 = 1.49$ $\quad \bar{x} + 0.005 = 1.5$
$\bar{x} - 2(0.005) = 1.485$ $\quad \bar{x} + 2(0.005) = 1.505$
$\bar{x} - 3(0.005) = 1.48$ $\quad \bar{x} + 3(0.005) = 1.51$

13a. $1000 \times 0.50 = 500$; 500 rods

13b. $1000 \times 0.815 = 815$; 815 rods

13c. $13.5 + 2 + 2(0.5) = 16.5$; 16.5%

13d. $100 - 16.5 = 83.5$; 83.5%

14a. Sample answer: The Algebra 2 textbook will be one standard deviation to the right of the mean.

14b. Sample answer: A paperback novel would be about three standard deviations to the left of the mean.

14c. Sample answer: A literature book or history book would be about three standard deviations to the right of the mean.

15. Sample answer: Each person calculated using information important to their profession. The statistician was using standard deviations.

16. $\bar{x} - 12 = 108$ $\quad \bar{x} + 12 = 132$
$\bar{x} - 2(12) = 96$ $\quad \bar{x} + 2(12) = 144$
$\bar{x} - 3(12) = 84$ $\quad \bar{x} + 3(12) = 156$

16a. 16%

16b. $800 \times 0.815 = 652$; 652 students

17a. $\bar{x} = (80 + 83 + 83 + 86 + 72 + 90 + 87 + 83 + 85 + 80 + 75 + 75 + 74 + 77 + 80 + 82) \div 16 = 1292 \div 16 = 80.75$

$$SD = \sqrt{\frac{\left[\begin{array}{l}3(80 - 80.75)^2 + 3(83 - 80.75)^2 + (86 - 80.75)^2 + \\ (72 - 80.75)^2 + (90 - 80.75)^2 + (87 - 80.75)^2 + (85 - 80.75)^2 + \\ 2(75 - 80.75)^2 + (74 - 80.75)^2 + (77 - 80.75)^2 + (82 - 80.75)^2\end{array}\right]}{16}}$$

$$= \sqrt{\frac{\left[\begin{array}{l}1.6875 + 15.1875 + 27.5625 + 76.5625 + 85.5625 + \\ 39.0625 + 18.0625 + 66.125 + 45.5625 + 14.0625 + 1.5625\end{array}\right]}{16}}$$

$$= \sqrt{24.4375}$$

$$\approx 4.94$$

17b.

Noise Levels	Frequency
70–73	1
74–77	4
78–81	3
82–85	5
86–89	2
90–93	1

(Continued next column)

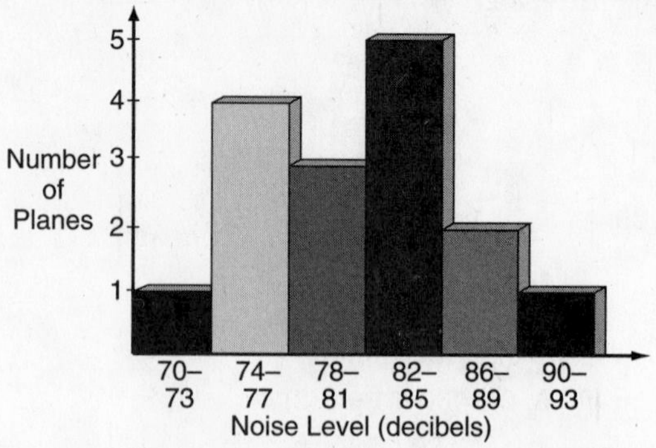

17c. Sample answer: The data do not appear to be normally distributed since they are not symmetrical about the mean.

18a.

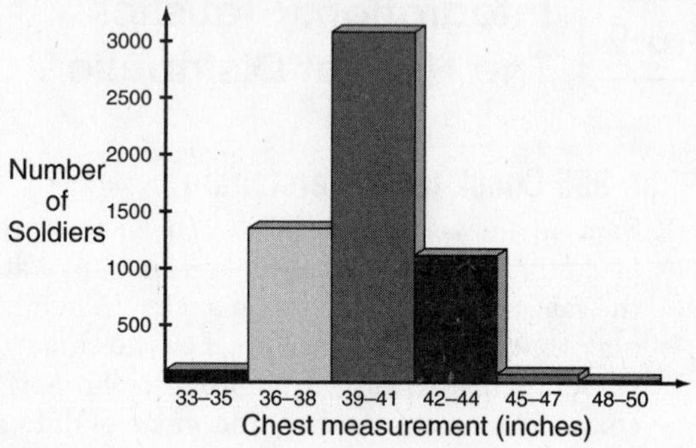

18b. 95%

18c. $\bar{x} - 2 = 38$ $\quad \bar{x} + 2 = 42$
$\bar{x} - 2(2) = 36$ $\quad \bar{x} + 2(2) = 44$
$\bar{x} - 3(2) = 34$ $\quad \bar{x} + 3(2) = 46$
Between 36 and 44: 5560 men
Total men: 5738
$5560 \div 5738 \approx 0.969$; 96.9%

19a.

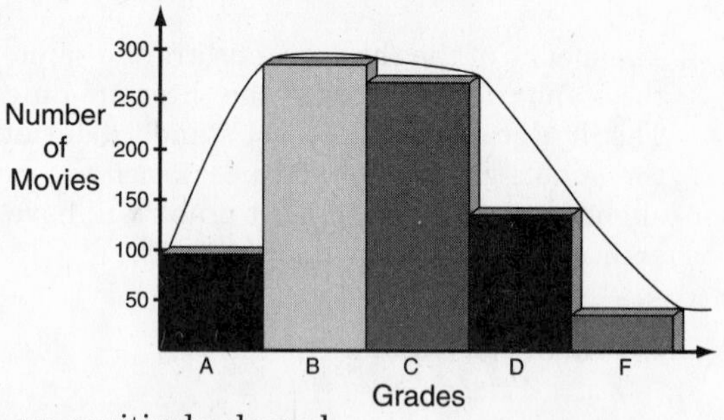

19b. no, positively skewed

20. $\bar{x} = \dfrac{7 + 16 + 9 + 4 + 12 + 3 + 9 + 4}{8} = \dfrac{64}{8} = 8$

$$SD = \sqrt{\frac{\left[\begin{array}{l}(7 - 8)^2 + (16 - 8)^2 + 2(9 - 8)^2 + \\ 2(4 - 8)^2 + (12 - 8)^2 + (3 - 8)^2\end{array}\right]}{8}}$$

$$= \sqrt{\frac{1 + 64 + 2 + 32 + 16 + 25}{8}}$$

$$= \sqrt{17.5}$$

$$\approx 4.18 \text{ or } 4.2$$

21a. $y = \frac{2}{5}x^2 - 6x + 32$
$= 0.4(x^2 - 15x) + 32$
$= 0.4(x^2 - 15x + 56.25) + 32 - (0.4)(56.25)$
$= 0.4(x - 7.5)^2 + 9.5$

x	$\frac{2}{5}x^2 - 6x + 32$	y
0	$\frac{2}{5}(0)^2 - 6(0) + 32$	32
5	$\frac{2}{5}(5)^2 - 6(5) + 32$	12
10	$\frac{2}{5}(10)^2 - 6(10) + 32$	12
15	$\frac{2}{5}(15)^2 - 6(15) + 32$	32

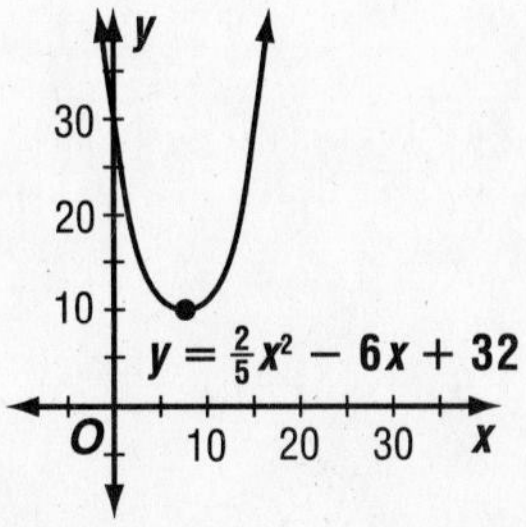

21b. $1995 - 1967 = 28$; $x = 1$ represents 1967 so
$x = 29$ represents 1995
$y = \frac{2}{5}x^2 - 6x + 32$
$= \frac{2}{5}(29)^2 - 6(29) + 32$
$= 194.4$; \$194.40

21c. $2001 - 1967 = 34$; $x = 1$ represents 1967 so
$x = 35$ represents 2001
$y = \frac{2}{5}x^2 - 6x + 32$
$= \frac{2}{5}(35)^2 - 6(35) + 32$
$= 312$; \$312

22. $s_1 + s_2 = (2 + \sqrt{3}) + (2 - \sqrt{3})$ $\quad -\frac{b}{a} = \frac{4}{1};\quad \frac{c}{a} = \frac{1}{1}$
$= 4$ $\quad a = 1, b = -4, c = 1$
$s_1(s_2) = (2 + \sqrt{3})(2 - \sqrt{3})$ $\quad x^2 - 4x + 1 = 0$
$= 4 - 3$
$= 1$

23. $(-x - 8)(3x + 4) = -3x^2 - 4x - 24x - 32$
$= -3x^2 - 28x - 32$

24. $6(3x - 5y) + (2 + 8x) = -11x$
$18x - 30y + 2 + 8x = -11x$
$37x - 30y + 2 = 0$
$37x = 30y - 2$
$x = \frac{30y - 2}{37}$

Chapter 6 Highlights

Page 399 Understanding and Using the Vocabulary

1. f	**2.** b	**3.** a	**4.** h
5. i	**6.** e	**7.** d	**8.** c
9. g	**10.** j		

Chapter 6 Study Guide and Assessment

Pages 400–402 Skills and Concepts

11. $x^2 + 6x - 40 = 0$

x	y
−8	−24
−4	−48
0	−40
4	0

−10, 4

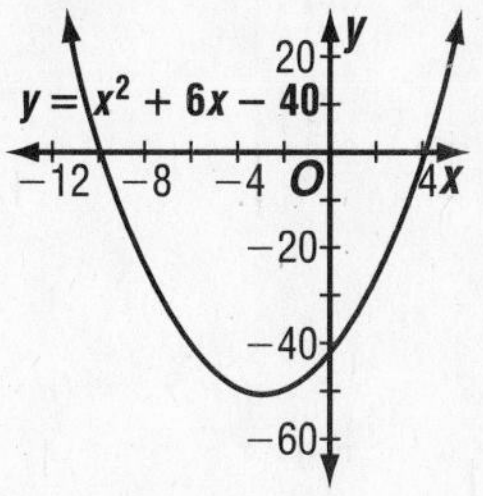

12. $x^2 - 2x - 15 = 0$

x	y
−2	−7
0	−15
2	−15
4	−7

−3, 5

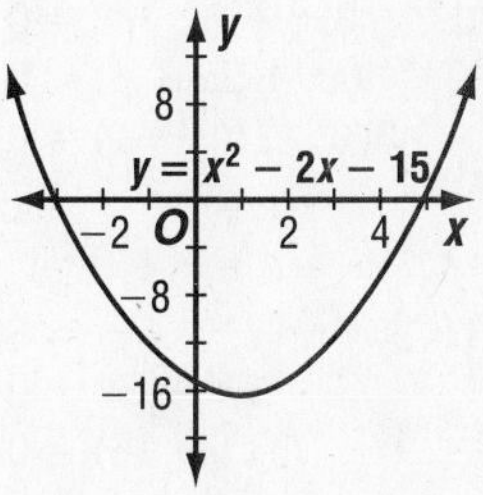

13. $a^2 - 8a - 20 = 0$

a	y
−2	0
0	−20
4	−36
8	−20

−2, 10

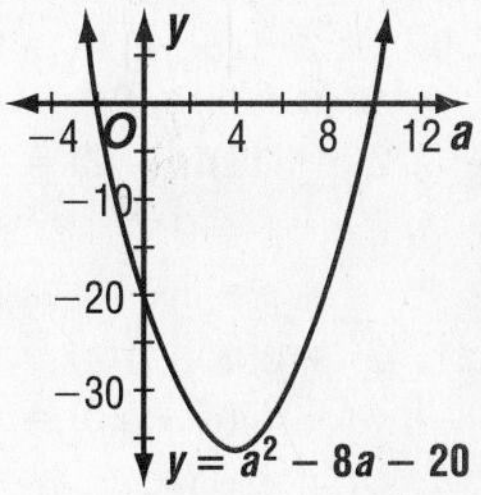

14. $3m^2 + 9m + 6 = 0$

m	y
−3	6
−2	0
−1	0
0	6

−2, −1

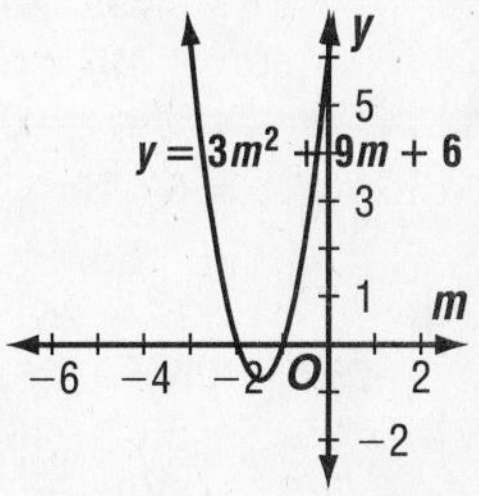

15. $x^2 + 12x + 35 = 0$

x	y
−8	3
−7	0
−6	−1
−5	0

−7, −5

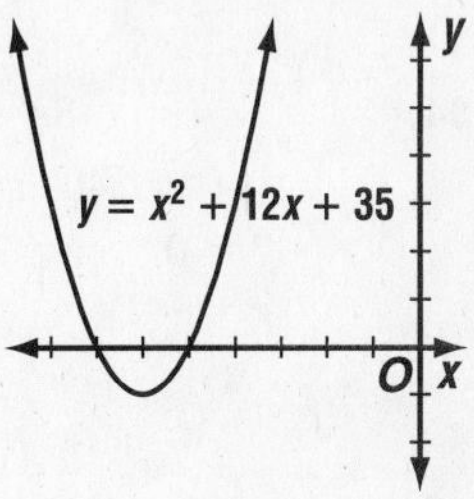

16. $0.5x^2 + 0.5x - 15 = 0$

x	y
−6	0
−2	−14
2	−12
6	6

−6, 5

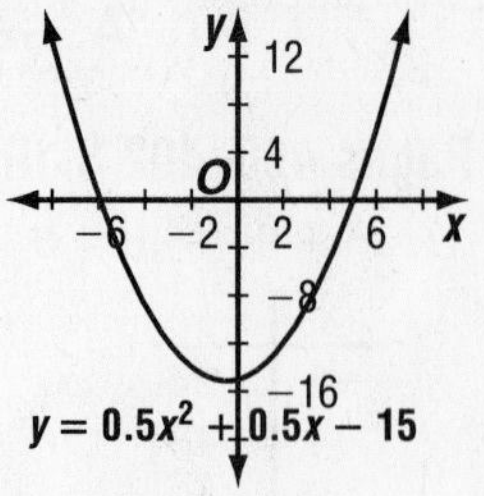

17. $x^2 - 4x - 32 = 0$
$(x + 4)(x - 8) = 0$
$x + 4 = 0$ or $x - 8 = 0$
$x = -4$ $\quad x = 8$

18. $3x^2 + 6x + 3 = 0$
$3(x^2 + 2x + 1) = 0$
$3(x + 1)(x + 1) = 0$
$x + 1 = 0$ or $x + 1 = 0$
$x = -1$ $\quad x = -1$

19. $5y^2 = 80$
$5y^2 - 80 = 0$
$5(y^2 - 16) = 0$
$5(y - 4)(y + 4) = 0$
$y - 4 = 0$ or $y + 4 = 0$
$y = 4$ $\quad y = -4$

20. $2c^2 + 18c - 44 = 0$
$2(c^2 + 9c - 22) = 0$
$2(c + 11)(c - 2) = 0$
$c + 11 = 0$ or $c - 2 = 0$
$c = -11$ $\quad c = 2$

21. $d^2 + 29d + 100 = 0$
$(d + 4)(d + 25) = 0$
$d + 4 = 0$ or $d + 25 = 0$
$d = -4$ $\quad d = -25$

22. $v^3 = 49v$
$v^3 - 49v = 0$
$v(v^2 - 49) = 0$
$v(v - 7)(v + 7) = 0$
$v = 0$ or $v - 7 = 0$ or $v + 7 = 0$
$v = 7$ $\quad v = -7$

23. $25x^3 - 25x^2 = 36x$
$25x^3 - 25x^2 - 36x = 0$
$x(25x^2 - 25x - 36) = 0$
$x(5x + 4)(5x - 9) = 0$
$x = 0$ or $5x + 4 = 0$ or $5x - 9 = 0$
$5x = -4$ $\quad 5x = 9$
$x = -\frac{4}{5}$ $\quad x = \frac{9}{5}$

24. $r^2 - 3r - 70 = 0$
$(r + 7)(r - 10) = 0$
$r + 7 = 0$ or $r - 10 = 0$
$r = -7$ $\quad r = 10$

25. $-5x^2 - 5x + 9 = 0$
$x^2 + x - \frac{9}{5} = 0$
$x^2 + x = \frac{9}{5}$
$x^2 + x + \frac{1}{4} = \frac{9}{5} + \frac{1}{4}$
$\left(x + \frac{1}{2}\right)^2 = \frac{41}{20}$
$x + \frac{1}{2} = \frac{\pm\sqrt{205}}{10}$
$x = -\frac{1}{2} \pm \frac{\sqrt{205}}{10}$

26. $k^2 + 6k - 4 = 0$
$k^2 + 6k = 4$
$k^2 + 6k + 9 = 4 + 9$
$(k + 3)^2 = 13$
$k + 3 = \pm\sqrt{13}$
$k = -3 \pm \sqrt{13}$

27. $b^2 + 4 = 6b$
$b^2 - 6b = -4$
$b^2 - 6b + 9 = -4 + 9$
$(b - 3)^2 = 5$
$b - 3 = \pm\sqrt{5}$
$b = 3 \pm \sqrt{5}$

28. $n^2 - 10n = 23$
$n^2 - 10n + 25 = 23 + 25$
$(n - 5)^2 = 48$
$n - 5 = \pm 4\sqrt{3}$
$n = 5 \pm 4\sqrt{3}$

29. $h^2 - 4h - 7 = 0$
$h^2 - 4h = 7$
$h^2 - 4h + 4 = 7 + 4$
$(h - 2)^2 = 11$
$h - 2 = \pm\sqrt{11}$
$h = 2 \pm \sqrt{11}$

30. $5x^2 - 15x - 9 = 2$
$5x^2 - 15x = 11$
$x^2 - 3x = \frac{11}{5}$
$x^2 - 3x + \frac{9}{4} = \frac{11}{5} + \frac{9}{4}$
$\left(x - \frac{3}{2}\right)^2 = \frac{89}{20}$
$x - \frac{3}{2} = \pm\frac{\sqrt{445}}{10}$
$x = \frac{3}{2} \pm \frac{\sqrt{445}}{10}$

31. $a = 1, b = 2, c = 7$
$x = \frac{-2 \pm \sqrt{2^2 - 4(1)(7)}}{2(1)}$
$= \frac{-2 \pm \sqrt{-24}}{2}$
$= \frac{-2 \pm 2i\sqrt{6}}{2}$
$= -1 \pm \sqrt{6}\boldsymbol{i}$

32. $x + 2x^2 + 1 = -1 - x$
$2x^2 + 2x + 2 = 0$
$a = 2, b = 2, c = 2$

$$x = \frac{-2 \pm \sqrt{2^2 - 4(2)(2)}}{2(2)}$$
$$= \frac{-2 \pm \sqrt{-12}}{4}$$
$$= \frac{-2 \pm 2i\sqrt{3}}{4}$$
$$= -\frac{1}{2} \pm \frac{\sqrt{3}}{2}i$$

33. $a = -1, b = 5, c = -9$

$$x = \frac{-5 \pm \sqrt{5^2 - 4(-1)(-9)}}{2(-1)}$$
$$= \frac{-5 \pm \sqrt{-11}}{-2}$$
$$= \frac{5}{2} \pm \frac{\sqrt{11}}{2}i$$

34. $a = -2, b = 12, c = -5$

$$x = \frac{-12 \pm \sqrt{12^2 - 4(-2)(-5)}}{2(-2)}$$
$$= \frac{-12 \pm \sqrt{104}}{-4}$$
$$= 3 \pm \frac{\sqrt{26}}{2}$$

35. $a = 3, b = 7, c = -2$

$$x = \frac{-7 \pm \sqrt{7^2 - 4(3)(-2)}}{2(3)}$$
$$= \frac{-7 \pm \sqrt{73}}{6}$$
$$= \frac{7}{6} \pm \frac{\sqrt{73}}{6}$$

36. $a = 8, b = -1, c = -15$

$$x = \frac{1 \pm \sqrt{(-1)^2 - 4(8)(-15)}}{2(8)}$$
$$= \frac{1 \pm \sqrt{481}}{16}$$
$$= \frac{1}{16} \pm \frac{\sqrt{481}}{16}$$

37. $s_1 + s_2 = 7 + (-6)$
$= 1$
$s_1(s_2) = 7(-6)$
$= -42$

$-\frac{b}{a} = \frac{1}{1}$; $\frac{c}{a} = \frac{-42}{1}$
$a = 1, b = -1, c = -42$
$x^2 - x - 42 = 0$

38. $s_1 + s_2 = 11 + 14$
$= 25$
$s_1(s_2) = 11(14)$
$= 154$

$-\frac{b}{a} = \frac{25}{1}$; $\frac{c}{a} = \frac{154}{1}$
$a = 1, b = -25, c = 154$
$x^2 - 25x + 154 = 0$

39. $s_1 + s_2 = -\frac{13}{2} + (-4)$
$= -\frac{21}{2}$
$s_1(s_2) = -\frac{13}{2}(-4)$
$= \frac{52}{2}$

$-\frac{b}{a} = -\frac{21}{2}$; $\frac{c}{a} = \frac{52}{2}$
$a = 2, b = 21, c = 52$
$2x^2 + 21x + 52 = 0$

40. $s_1 + s_2 = \frac{3}{4} + \frac{9}{2}$
$= \frac{21}{4}$ or $\frac{42}{8}$
$s_1(s_2) = \left(\frac{3}{4}\right)\left(\frac{9}{2}\right)$
$= \frac{27}{8}$

$-\frac{b}{a} = \frac{42}{8}$; $\frac{c}{a} = \frac{27}{8}$
$a = 8, b = -42, c = 27$
$8x^2 - 42x + 27 = 0$

41. $s_1 + s_2 = (-2.5) + 5.25$
$= 2.75$ or $\frac{11}{4}$ or $\frac{22}{8}$
$s_1(s_2) = (-2.5)(5.25)$
$= -13.125$ or $-13\frac{1}{8}$ or $\frac{105}{8}$

$-\frac{b}{a} = \frac{22}{8}$; $\frac{c}{a} = \frac{105}{8}$
$a = 8, b = -22,$
$c = 105$
$8x^2 - 22x + 105 = 0$

42. $s_1 + s_2 = (-0.25) + 0.25$
$= 0$ or $\frac{0}{16}$
$s_1(s_2) = (-0.25)(0.25)$
$= -0.0625$ or $-\frac{1}{16}$

$-\frac{b}{a} = \frac{0}{16}$, $\frac{c}{a} = -\frac{1}{16}$
$a = 16, b = 0, c = -1$
$16x^2 - 1 = 0$

43. $(-2, 3)$, $x = -2$, down

x	y
-3	-3
-1	-3

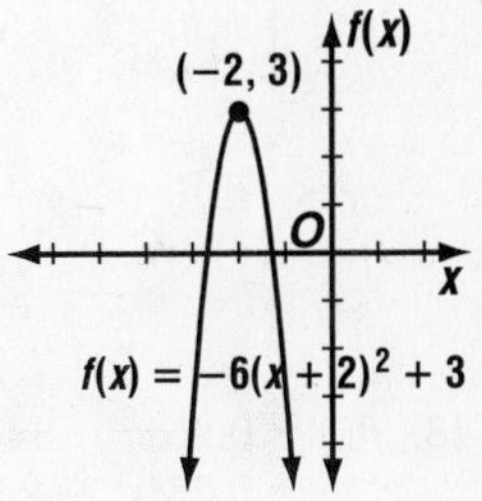

44. $(5, -7)$, $x = 5$, up

x	y
4	-3
6	-3

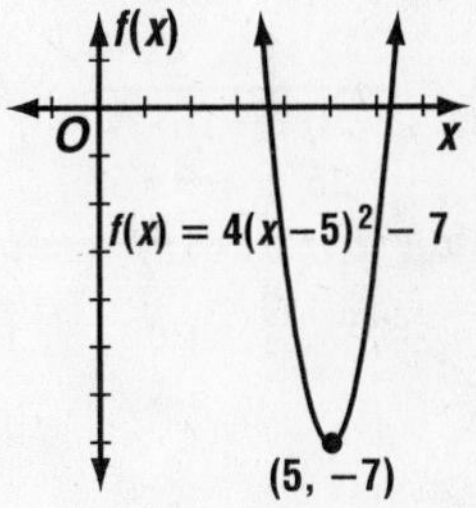

45. $f(x) = 5x^2 - 35x + 58$
$= 5\left(x^2 - 7x + \frac{49}{4}\right) + 58 - 5\left(\frac{49}{4}\right)$
$= 5\left(x - \frac{7}{2}\right)^2 - \frac{13}{4}$

$\left(\frac{7}{2}, -\frac{13}{4}\right)$, $x = \frac{7}{2}$, up

x	y
2	8
4	-2

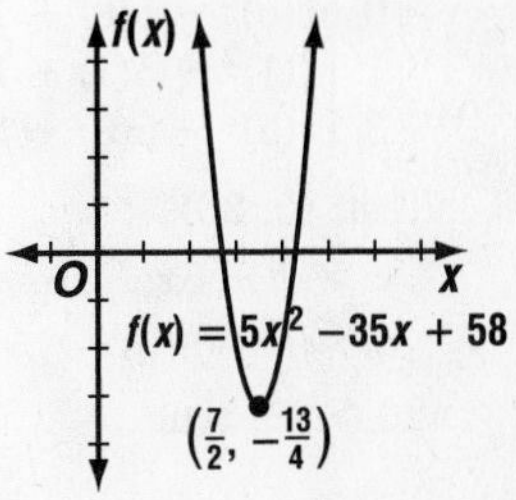

46. $f(x) = -9x^2 + 54x - 8$
$= -9(x^2 - 6x + 9) - 8 - (-9)(9)$
$= -9(x - 3)^2 + 73$
(3, 73), $x = 3$, down

x	y
1	37
5	37

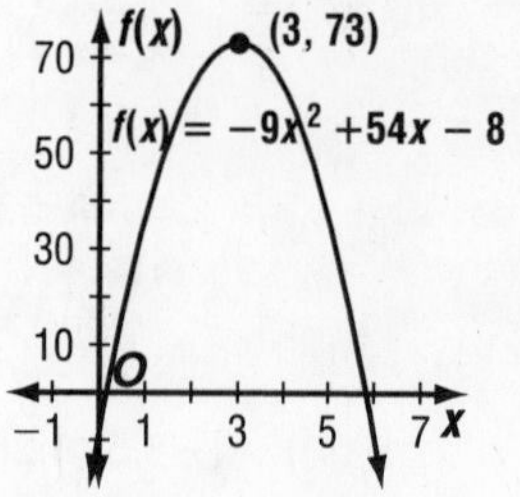

47. $f(x) = -\frac{1}{3}x^2 + 8x$
$= -\frac{1}{3}(x^2 - 24x + 144) - \left(-\frac{1}{3}\right)(144)$
$= -\frac{1}{3}(x - 12)^2 + 48$
(12, 48), $x = 12$, down

x	y
4	$26\frac{2}{3}$
20	$26\frac{2}{3}$

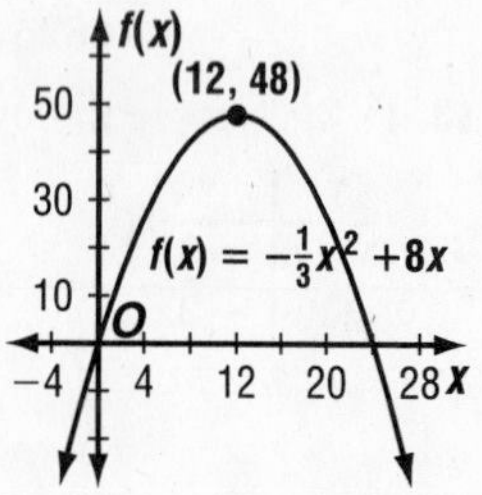

48. $f(x) = 0.25x^2 - 6x - 16$
$= 0.25(x^2 - 24x + 144) - 16 - (0.25)(144)$
$= 0.25(x - 12)^2 - 52$
(12, −52), $x = 12$, up

x	y
0	−16
25	−9.75

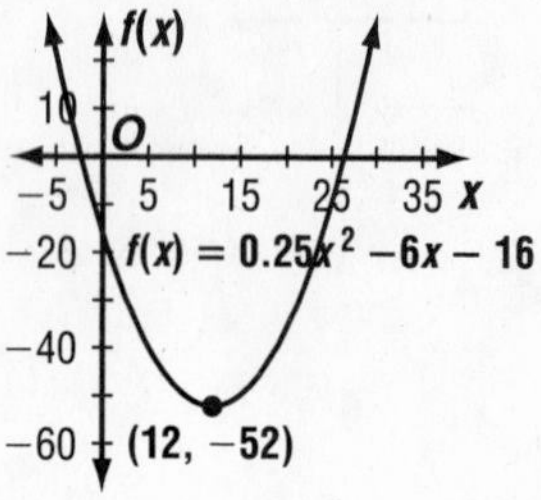

49. $y > x^2 - 5x + 15$
$y > \left(x^2 - 5x + \frac{25}{4}\right) + 15 - \frac{25}{4}$
$y > \left(x - \frac{5}{2}\right)^2 + \frac{35}{4}$; vertex at $\left(\frac{5}{2}, \frac{35}{4}\right)$

x	$x^2 - 5x + 15$	y
0	$(0)^2 - 5(0) + 15$	15
1	$(1)^2 - 5(1) + 15$	11
3	$(3)^2 - 5(3) + 15$	9

Test: (0, 20)
$y > x^2 - 5x + 15$
$20 \overset{?}{>} 0^2 - 5(0) + 15$
$20 > 15$; true

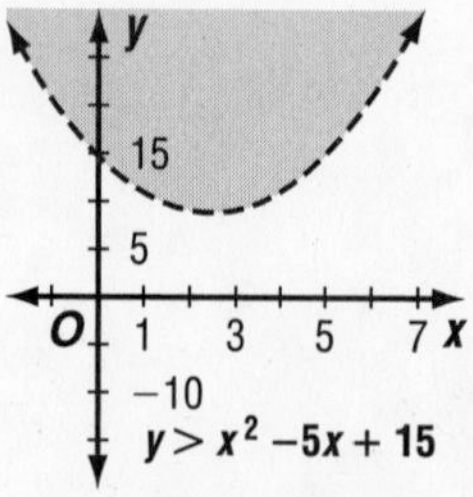

50. $y < -3x^2 + 48$; vertex at (0, 48)

x	$-3x^2 + 48$	y
−3	$-3(-3)^2 + 48$	21
−1	$-3(-1)^2 + 48$	45
1	$-3(1)^2 + 48$	45
3	$-3(3)^2 + 48$	21

Test: (0, 0)
$y < -3x^2 + 48$
$0 \overset{?}{<} -3(0)^2 + 48$
$0 < 48$; true

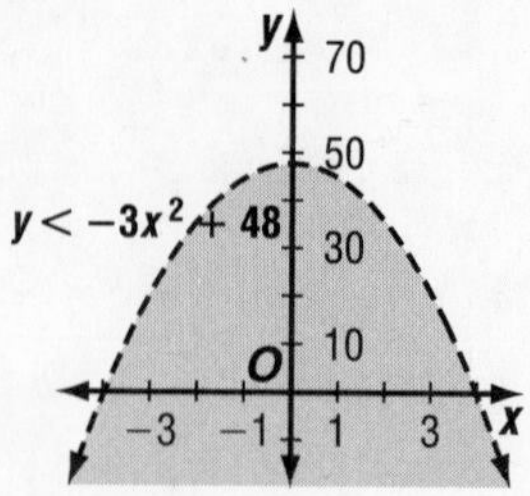

51. $y \le 4x^2 - 36x + 17$
$y \le 4\left(x^2 - 9x + \frac{81}{4}\right) + 17 - 4\left(\frac{81}{4}\right)$
$y \le 4\left(x - \frac{9}{2}\right)^2 - 64$; vertex at $\left(\frac{9}{2}, -64\right)$

x	$4x^2 - 36x + 17$	y
0	$4(0)^2 - 36(0) + 17$	17
2	$4(2)^2 - 36(2) + 17$	−39
6	$4(6)^2 - 36(6) + 17$	−55

Test: (0, −20)
$y \le 4x^2 - 36x + 17$
$-20 \overset{?}{\le} 4(0)^2 - 36(0) + 17$
$-20 \le 17$; true

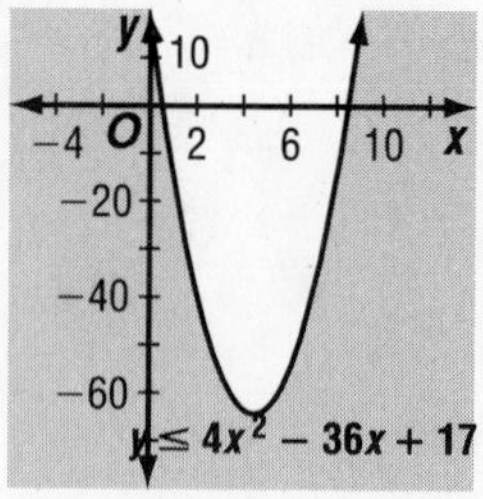

52. $y \ge -x^2 + 7x - 11$
$y \ge -\left(x^2 - 7x + \frac{49}{4}\right) - 11 - (-1)\left(\frac{49}{4}\right)$
$y \ge -\left(x - \frac{7}{2}\right)^2 + \frac{5}{4}$; vertex at $\left(\frac{7}{2}, \frac{5}{4}\right)$

x	$-x^2 + 7x - 11$	y
1	$-(1)^2 + 7(1) - 11$	−5
2	$-(2)^2 + 7(2) - 11$	−1
5	$-(5)^2 + 7(5) - 11$	−1

Test: (0, 0)
$y \ge -x^2 + 7x - 11$
$0 \overset{?}{\ge} -0^2 + 7(0) - 11$
$0 \ge -11$; true

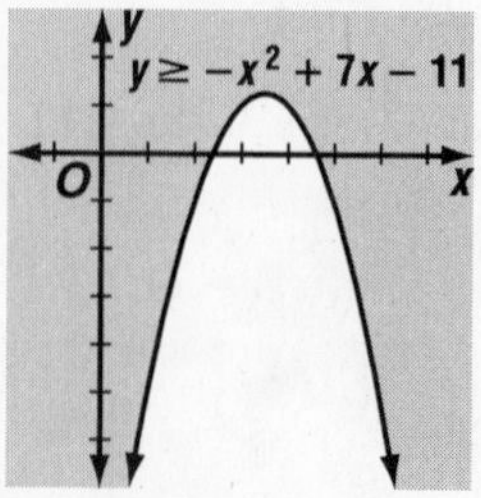

53. $y < x^2 + 5x + 6$

$y < \left(x^2 + 5x + \frac{25}{4}\right) + 6 - \frac{25}{4}$

$y < \left(x + \frac{5}{2}\right)^2 - \frac{1}{4}$; vertex at $\left(-\frac{5}{2}, -\frac{1}{4}\right)$

x	$x^2 + 5x + 6$	y
-4	$(-4)^2 + 5(-4) + 6$	2
-3	$(-3)^2 + 5(-3) + 6$	0
-1	$(-1)^2 + 5(-1) + 6$	2

Test: (0, 0)

$y < x^2 + 5x + 6$

$0 \overset{?}{<} 0^2 + 5(0) + 6$

$0 < 6$; true

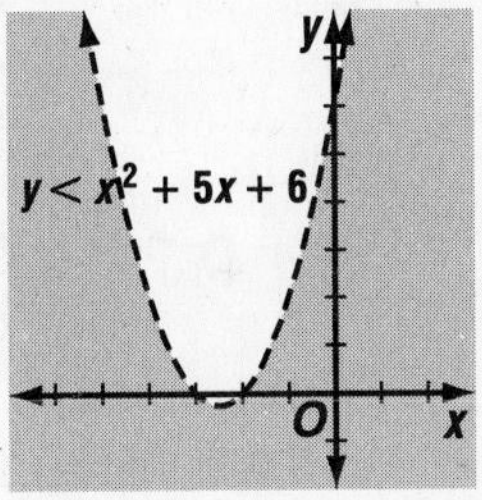

54. $y \geq 3x^2 - 15x + 22$

$y \geq 3\left(x^2 - 5x + \frac{25}{4}\right) + 22 - 3\left(\frac{25}{4}\right)$

$y \geq 3\left(x - \frac{5}{2}\right)^2 + \frac{13}{4}$; vertex at $\left(\frac{5}{2}, \frac{13}{4}\right)$

x	$3x^2 - 15x + 22$	y
1	$3(1)^2 - 15(1) + 22$	10
2	$3(2)^2 - 15(2) + 22$	4
3	$3(3)^2 - 15(3) + 22$	4

Test: (2, 6)

$y \geq 3x^2 - 15x + 22$

$6 \overset{?}{\geq} 3(2)^2 - 15(2) + 22$

$6 \geq 4$; true

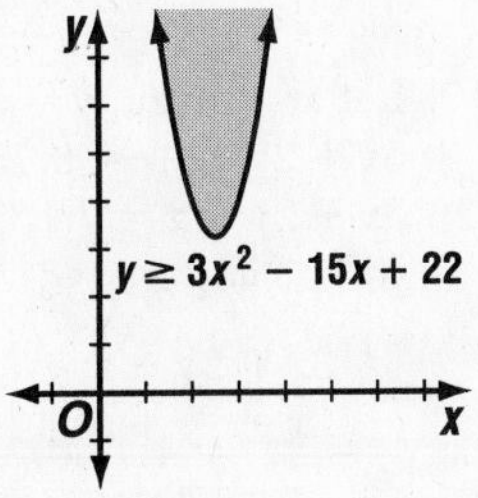

55. $\bar{x} = \frac{100 + 156 + 158 + 159 + 162 + 165 + 170 + 190}{8}$

$= \frac{1260}{8} = 157.5$

$$\text{SD} = \sqrt{\frac{\left[\begin{array}{c}(100 - 157.5)^2 + (156 - 157.5)^2 + \\ (158 - 157.5)^2 + (159 - 157.5)^2 + (162 - 157.5)^2 + \\ (165 - 157.5)^2 + (170 - 157.5)^2 + (190 - 157.5)^2\end{array}\right]}{8}}$$

$$= \sqrt{\frac{\left[\begin{array}{c}3306.25 + 2.25 + \\ 0.25 + 2.25 + 20.25 + 56.25 + 156.25 + 1056.25\end{array}\right]}{8}}$$

$= \sqrt{575}$

≈ 23.98

56. $\bar{x} = \frac{2(56) + 57 + 3(58) + 59 + 61}{8} = \frac{463}{8} \approx 57.88$

$$\text{SD} = \sqrt{\frac{\left[\begin{array}{c}2(56 - 57.88)^2 + (57 - 57.88)^2 + \\ 3(58 - 57.88)^2 + (59 - 57.88)^2 + (61 - 57.88)^2\end{array}\right]}{8}}$$

$$= \sqrt{\frac{7.0688 + 0.7744 + 0.0432 + 1.2544 + 9.7344}{8}}$$

$= \sqrt{2.3594}$

≈ 1.54

57. $\bar{x} = \frac{302 + 310 + 331 + 298 + 348 + 305 + 314 + 284 + 321 + 337}{10}$

$= \frac{3150}{10} = 315$

$$\text{SD} = \sqrt{\frac{\left[\begin{array}{c}(302 - 315)^2 + (310 - 315)^2 + (331 - 315)^2 + \\ (298 - 315)^2 + (348 - 315)^2 + (305 - 315)^2 + \\ (314 - 315)^2 + (284 - 315)^2 + (321 - 315)^2 + (337 - 315)^2\end{array}\right]}{10}}$$

$$= \sqrt{\frac{169 + 25 + 256 + 289 + 1089 + 100 + 1 + 961 + 36 + 484}{10}}$$

$= \sqrt{341}$

≈ 18.47

58. $\bar{x} = \frac{3.4 + 4.2 + 8.6 + 5.1 + 3.6 + 2.8 + 7.1 + 4.4 + 5.2 + 5.6}{10}$

$= \frac{50}{10} = 5$

$$\text{SD} = \sqrt{\frac{\left[\begin{array}{c}(3.4 - 5)^2 + (4.2 - 5)^2 + (8.6 - 5)^2 + (5.1 - 5)^2 + (3.6 - 5)^2 + \\ (2.8 - 5)^2 + (7.1 - 5)^2 + (4.4 - 5)^2 + (5.2 - 5)^2 + (5.6 - 5)^2\end{array}\right]}{10}}$$

$$= \sqrt{\frac{\left[\begin{array}{c}2.56 + 0.64 + 12.96 + 0.01 + \\ 1.96 + 4.84 + 4.41 + 0.36 + 0.04 + 0.36\end{array}\right]}{10}}$$

$= \sqrt{2.814}$

≈ 1.68

59. $\bar{x} - 6 = 72$ $\quad$ $\bar{x} + 6 = 84$

$\bar{x} - 2(6) = 66$ $\quad$ $\bar{x} + 2(6) = 90$

$\bar{x} - 3(6) = 60$ $\quad$ $\bar{x} + 3(6) = 96$

59a. 68% $\quad$ **59b.** 2%

59c. $30 \times 0.135 = 4.05$; 4 students

59d. 0.5%

59e. $30 \times 0.68 = 20.4$; 20 students

Page 402 Applications and Problem Solving

60.

$d(t) = v_i t + \frac{1}{2}at^2$

$7040 = 2760t + \frac{1}{2}(200)t^2$

$7040 = 100t^2 + 2760t$

$70.4 = t^2 + 27.6t$

$70.4 + 190.44 = t^2 + 27.6t + 190.44$

$260.84 = (t + 13.8)^2$

$\pm\sqrt{260.84} = t + 13.8$

$-13.8 \pm \sqrt{260.84} = t$

$t = -13.8 + \sqrt{260.84}$ or $t = -13.8 - \sqrt{260.84}$

≈ 2.35 $\quad$ ≈ -29.95

about 2.35 seconds

61. $h(t) = -16t^2 + 35t + 1250$

$0 = -16t^2 + 35t + 1250$

$0 = 16t^2 - 35t - 1250$

$0 = (t - 10)(16t + 125)$

$t - 10 = 0$ or $16t + 125 = 0$

$t = 10$ $\quad$ $16t = -125$

$t = -\frac{125}{16}$

10 seconds

62. $\bar{x} - 250 = 1000$ $\quad$ $\bar{x} + 250 = 1500$

$\bar{x} - 2(250) = 750$ $\quad$ $\bar{x} + 2(250) = 1750$

$\bar{x} - 3(250) = 500$ $\quad$ $\bar{x} + 3(250) = 2000$

62a. $10{,}000 \times 0.16 = 1600$; 1600 workers

62b. $10{,}000 \times 0.025 = 250$; 250 workers

62c. $2 + 13.5 + 34 + 34 + 13.5 = 97$; 97%

62d. $0.5 + 2 + 13.5 + 34 + 34 + 13.5 = 97.5$; 97.5%

Page 403 Alternative Assessment; Thinking Critically

a. $x^2 - 7x + k = 0; \quad a = 1, b = -7, c = k$

$$b^2 - 4ac > 0$$
$$(-7)^2 - 4(1)k > 0$$
$$49 - 4k > 0$$
$$-4k > -49$$
$$k < \frac{49}{4}$$

b. $kx^2 - 5x + 7 = 0; \quad a = k, b = -5, c = 7$

$$b^2 - 4ac < 0$$
$$(-5)^2 - 4(k)7 < 0$$
$$25 - 28k < 0$$
$$-28k < -25$$
$$k > \frac{25}{28}$$

c. $3x^2 - kx + 15 = 0; \quad a = 3, b = -k, c = 15$

$$b^2 - 4ac = 0$$
$$(-k)^2 - 4(3)(15) = 0$$
$$k^2 - 180 = 0$$
$$k^2 = 180$$
$$k = \pm 2\sqrt{45}$$

College Entrance Exam Practice, Chapters 1–6

Pages 404–405

1. $(4.5 \times 10^4)(3.33 \times 10^2) = (4.5 \times 3.33)(10^4 \times 10^2)$
$= 14.985 \times 10^{4+2}$
$= 1.4985 \times 10^1 \times 10^6$
$= 1.4985 \times 10^{1+6}$
$= 1.4985 \times 10^7$; 14,985,000

D

2. $\begin{bmatrix} 7 & 4 & -3 \\ -2 & 5 & 4 \end{bmatrix} + \begin{bmatrix} -5 & -5 & -5 \\ 1 & 1 & 1 \end{bmatrix} = \begin{bmatrix} 2 & -1 & -8 \\ -1 & 6 & 5 \end{bmatrix}$; B

3. $f(x) = 5x^2$; $f(x) = 5(x - 1)^2 - 8$; C

4. $A = \ell w$
$= (3\sqrt{3} - \sqrt{2})(\sqrt{3} + 3\sqrt{2})$
$= 9 + 9\sqrt{6} - \sqrt{6} - 6$
$= 3 + 8\sqrt{6}$; A

5. $4(5x + 2y) + 9(x - 2y) = 20x + 8y + 9x - 18y$
$= 29x - 10y$; B

6. $(-3, 0), (0, 3) \rightarrow m = \frac{3 - 0}{0 - (-3)} = \frac{3}{3} = 1$

$$y - y_1 = m(x - x_1)$$
$$y - 0 = 1(x - (-3))$$
$$y = x + 3;$$
$$y \le x + 3$$

(Continued on next column)

$(-3, 0), (0, -2) \rightarrow m = \frac{-2 - 0}{0 - (-3)} = -\frac{2}{3}$

$$y - y_1 = m(x - x_1)$$
$$y - 0 = -\frac{2}{3}(x - (-3))$$
$$y = -\frac{2}{3}x - 2;$$
$$y > -\frac{2}{3}x - 2$$

$(0, 3), (0, -2) \rightarrow m = \frac{-2 - 3}{0 - 0} = -\frac{5}{0}$, undefined

$x = 0;$

$x \le 0$

C

7. B

8. 2, 8, 18, 32, 50, 72
(differences: +6, +10, +14, +18, +22) D

9. $\bar{x} = \frac{\left[\begin{array}{c} 2(13.7) + 15.0 + 16.9 + \\ 13.6 + 14.3 + 2(14.8) + 15.1 + 15.4 + 14.9 \end{array}\right]}{11}$

$= \frac{162.2}{11} \approx 14.7$

$$\text{SD} = \sqrt{\frac{\left[\begin{array}{c} 2(13.7 - 14.7)^2 + (15.0 - 14.7)^2 + (16.9 - 14.7)^2 + \\ (13.6 - 14.7)^2 + (14.3 - 14.7)^2 + 2(14.8 - 14.7)^2 + \\ (15.1 - 14.7)^2 + (15.4 - 14.7)^2 + (14.9 - 14.7)^2 \end{array}\right]}{11}}$$

$$= \sqrt{\frac{2 + 0.09 + 4.84 + 1.21 + 0.16 + 0.02 + 0.16 + 0.49 + 0.04}{11}}$$

$\approx \sqrt{0.8191}$

≈ 0.9

10. Let x = pizza, y = salad, and z = soda.

$5x + 2y + 2z = 9.75 \rightarrow \quad 5x + 2y + 2z = 9.75$

$3x + 2y + z = 7.15 \rightarrow \quad (+) -6x - 4y - 2z = -14.30$

$2x + y + z = 4.35 \quad\quad -x - 2y = -4.55$

$3x + 2y + z = 7.15$
$(-) 2x + y + z = 4.35$
$x + y = 2.80$

$-x - 2y = -4.55$
$(+) x + y = 2.80$
$-y = -1.75$
$y = 1.75$

$x + y = 2.80$
$x + 1.75 = 2.80$
$x = 1.05$

$2x + y + z = 4.35$
$2(1.05) + 1.75 + z = 4.35$
$z = 0.50$

pizza: \$1.05; salad: \$1.75; soda: \$0.50

11. $\frac{(4 + 3i)^2}{(3 - i)^2} = \frac{(4 + 3i)(4 + 3i)}{(3 - i)(3 - i)}$

$= \frac{16 + 24i + 9i^2}{9 - 6i + i^2}$

$= \frac{7 + 24i}{8 - 6i}$

$= \frac{(7 + 24i)(8 + 6i)}{(8 - 6i)(8 + 6i)}$

$= \frac{56 + 234i + 144i^2}{64 - 36i^2}$

$= \frac{-88 + 234i}{100}$

$= \frac{-44 + 117i}{50}$

12. $m = \frac{5 - 0}{-3 - 2} = \frac{5}{-5} = -1$

13. $h(t) = -16t^2 + 80t + 200$
$= -16\left(t^2 - 5t + \frac{25}{4}\right) + 200 - (-16)\left(\frac{25}{4}\right)$
$= -16\left(t - \frac{5}{2}\right)^2 + 300$; vertex at $\left(\frac{5}{2}, 300\right)$
300 feet; 2.5 seconds

14. $A = P(1 + r)^t$
$= 1500(1 + 0.075)^{2.5}$
$\approx 1500(1.198)$
≈ 1797.27; \$1797.27

15. $77 - 41 = 36$; Q_2 is the 7th value, 59; Q_1 is between 3rd and 4th values, $\frac{49 + 52}{2} = 50.5$; Q_3 is between 10th and 11th values, $\frac{65 + 72}{2} = 68.5$; IR $= 68.5 - 50.5 = 18$; outliers: below $50.5 - 1.5(18) = 23.5$ or above $68.5 + 1.5(18) = 95.5$, no outliers;

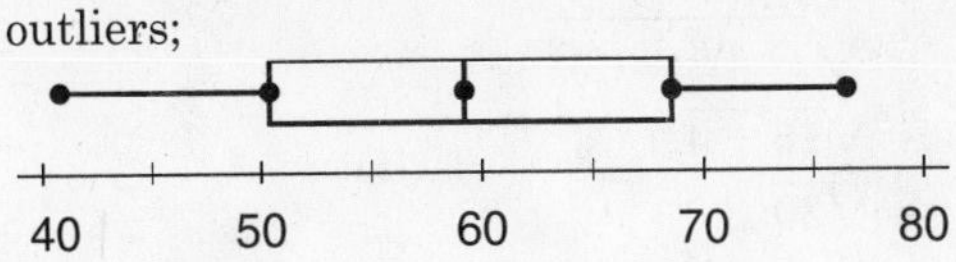

16. $(a - 10)(a - 3) \le 0$
$a - 10 \le 0$ and $a - 3 \ge 0$ or $a - 10 \ge 0$ and $a - 3 \le 0$
$a \le 10$ $\quad a \ge 3$ $\quad a \ge 10$ $\quad a \le 3$
$3 \le a \le 10$ or $\varnothing$
$a^2 + 4a - 21 < 0$
$(a + 7)(a - 3) < 0$
$a + 7 < 0$ and $a - 3 > 0$ or $a + 7 > 0$ and $a - 3 < 0$
$a < -7$ $\quad a > 3$ $\quad a > -7$ $\quad a < 3$
$\varnothing$ or $-7 < a < 3$

A

17. D

18. $\frac{2(3 + 7)^2}{2^3 + 3 \cdot 4} = \frac{2(10)^2}{8 + 12}$
$= \frac{200}{20}$
$= 10$
$(6 + 7 \cdot 2) - 10 - 8 \div 2 + 4 = (6 + 14) - 10 - 4 + 4$
$= 20 - 10 - 4 + 4$
$= 10$; C

19.

$$\begin{array}{r} m + 5 \\ m^2 + 2m + 7 \overline{)\, m^3 + 7m^2 + 17m + 35} \\ \underline{m^3 + 2m^2 + 7m} \phantom{{}+35} \\ 5m^2 + 10m + 35 \\ \underline{5m^2 + 10m + 35} \\ 0 \end{array}$$

$$\begin{array}{r} m - 2 \\ 3m^2 + 5m - 4 \overline{)\, 3m^3 - m^2 - 14m + 8} \\ \underline{3m^3 + 5m^2 - 4m} \phantom{{}+8} \\ -6m^2 - 10m + 8 \\ \underline{-6m^2 - 10m + 8} \\ 0 \end{array}$$

$m + 5 > m - 2$; A

20. $\sqrt[3]{2x + 1} = 3$
$(\sqrt[3]{2x + 1})^3 = 3^3$
$2x + 1 = 27$
$2x = 26$
$x = 13$

$\sqrt[3]{2}(3\sqrt[3]{4} + 2\sqrt[3]{32}) = x$
$\sqrt[3]{2}(3\sqrt[3]{4} + 4\sqrt[3]{4}) = x$
$\sqrt[3]{2}(7\sqrt[3]{4}) = x$
$7\sqrt[3]{8} = x$
$14 = x$

B

Chapter 7 Analyzing Conic Sections

7-1 Integration: Geometry The Distance and Midpoint Formulas

Page 411 Check for Understanding

1a. Substitute values into the midpoint formula and solve for the other endpoint.

1b.
$x = \frac{x_1 + x_2}{2}$ $\quad$ $y = \frac{y_1 + y_2}{2}$

$-4 = \frac{x_1 + 20}{2}$ $\quad$ $13 = \frac{y_1 + 31}{2}$

$-8 = x_1 + 20$ $\quad$ $26 = y_1 + 31$

$-28 = x_1$ $\quad$ $-5 = y_1$

The other endpoint is at $(-28, -5)$

2. any point on the perpendicular bisector of the segment, but not on the segment

3. $(x_2 - x_1)^2 = (x_1 - x_2)^2$ and $(y_2 - y_1)^2 = (y_1 - y_2)^2$

4. $d = \sqrt{(x_2 - x_1)^2 + (y_2 - y_1)^2}$
$= \sqrt{(-4 - 7)^2 + (9 - 8)^2}$
$= \sqrt{(-11)^2 + (1)^2}$
$= \sqrt{121 + 1}$
$= \sqrt{122}$; $\sqrt{122}$ units

5. $d = \sqrt{(x_2 - x_1)^2 + (y_2 - y_1)^2}$
$= \sqrt{(1.1 - 0.5)^2 + (2.9 - 1.4)^2}$
$= \sqrt{(0.6)^2 + (1.5)^2}$
$= \sqrt{0.36 + 2.25}$
$= \sqrt{2.61}$; $\sqrt{2.61}$ units

6. $d = \sqrt{(x_2 - x_1)^2 + (y_2 - y_1)^2}$
$= \sqrt{(-3\sqrt{3} - 2\sqrt{3})^2 + [9 - (-5)]^2}$
$= \sqrt{(-5\sqrt{3})^2 + (14)^2}$
$= \sqrt{75 + 196}$
$= \sqrt{271}$; $\sqrt{271}$ units

7. $(x, y) = \left(\frac{x_1 + x_2}{2}, \frac{y_1 + y_2}{2}\right)$
$= \left(\frac{8 + (-3)}{2}, \frac{9 + (-4.5)}{2}\right)$
$= \left(\frac{5}{2}, \frac{4.5}{2}\right)$
$= \left(\frac{5}{2}, \frac{9}{4}\right)$

8. $(x, y) = \left(\frac{x_1 + x_2}{2}, \frac{y_1 + y_2}{2}\right)$
$= \left(\frac{-3\sqrt{2} + 8\sqrt{2}}{2}, \frac{-4\sqrt{5} + 9\sqrt{5}}{2}\right)$
$= \left(\frac{5\sqrt{2}}{2}, \frac{5\sqrt{5}}{2}\right)$

9. $AB = \sqrt{[-3 - (-1)]^2 + (0 - 4)^2}$
$= \sqrt{(-2)^2 + (-4)^2}$
$= \sqrt{4 + 16}$
$= \sqrt{20}$
$= 2\sqrt{5}$

$BC = \sqrt{(-1 - 1)^2 + [4 - (-2)]^2}$
$= \sqrt{(-2)^2 + (6)^2}$
$= \sqrt{4 + 36}$
$= \sqrt{40}$
$= 2\sqrt{10}$

$AC = \sqrt{(-3 - 1)^2 + [0 - (-2)]^2}$
$= \sqrt{(-4)^2 + (2)^2}$
$= \sqrt{16 + 4}$
$= \sqrt{20}$
$= 2\sqrt{5}$

Since the length of $\overline{AB}$ and $\overline{AC}$ are the same, the triangle is isosceles.

10. midpoint of $\overline{MN} = \left(\frac{3 + (-2)}{2}, \frac{5 + 8}{2}\right)$
$= \left(\frac{1}{2}, \frac{13}{2}\right)$

midpoint of $\overline{NO} = \left(\frac{-2 + 7}{2}, \frac{8 + (-4)}{2}\right)$
$= \left(\frac{5}{2}, \frac{4}{2}\right)$
$= \left(\frac{5}{2}, 2\right)$

midpoint of $\overline{MO} = \left(\frac{3 + 7}{2}, \frac{5 + (-4)}{2}\right)$
$= \left(\frac{10}{2}, \frac{1}{2}\right)$
$= \left(5, \frac{1}{2}\right)$

Pages 411–414 Exercises

11. $d = \sqrt{(x_2 - x_1)^2 + (y_2 - y_1)^2}$
$= \sqrt{(-4 - 1)^2 + [9 - (-3)]^2}$
$= \sqrt{(-5)^2 + (12)^2}$
$= \sqrt{25 + 144}$
$= \sqrt{169}$
$= 13$; 13 units

12. $d = \sqrt{(x_2 - x_1)^2 + (y_2 - y_1)^2}$
$= \sqrt{[-4 - (-3)]^2 + [-10 - (-11)]^2}$
$= \sqrt{(-1)^2 + (1)^2}$
$= \sqrt{1 + 1}$
$= \sqrt{2}$; $\sqrt{2}$ units

13. $d = \sqrt{(x_2 - x_1)^2 + (y_2 - y_1)^2}$
$= \sqrt{(9 - 12)^2 + [-2 - (-14)]^2}$
$= \sqrt{(-3)^2 + (12)^2}$
$= \sqrt{9 + 144}$
$= \sqrt{153}$
$= 3\sqrt{17}$; $3\sqrt{17}$ units

14. $d = \sqrt{(x_2 - x_1)^2 + (y_2 - y_1)^2}$
$= \sqrt{(0.68 - 0.23)^2 + (-0.2 - 0.4)^2}$
$= \sqrt{(0.45)^2 + (-0.6)^2}$
$= \sqrt{0.2025 + 0.36}$
$= \sqrt{0.5625}$
$= 0.75$; 0.75 units

15. $d = \sqrt{(x_2 - x_1)^2 + (y_2 - y_1)^2}$
$= \sqrt{(2\sqrt{7} - 4\sqrt{7})^2 + (10 - 8)^2}$
$= \sqrt{(-6\sqrt{7})^2 + (2)^2}$
$= \sqrt{252 + 4}$
$= \sqrt{256}$
$= 16$; 16 units

16. $d = \sqrt{(x_2 - x_1)^2 + (y_2 - y_1)^2}$
$= \sqrt{(2\sqrt{3} - 2\sqrt{3})^2 + (-\sqrt{3} - 4\sqrt{3})^2}$
$= \sqrt{0^2 + (-5\sqrt{3})^2}$
$= \sqrt{75}$
$= 5\sqrt{3}$; $5\sqrt{3}$ units

17. $d = \sqrt{(x_2 - x_1)^2 + (y_2 - y_1)^2}$
$= \sqrt{(-3 - 5)^2 + \left(-\frac{2}{11} - \frac{9}{11}\right)^2}$
$= \sqrt{(-8)^2 + (-1)^2}$
$= \sqrt{64 + 1}$
$= \sqrt{65}$; $\sqrt{65}$ units

18. $d = \sqrt{(x_2 - x_1)^2 + (y_2 - y_1)^2}$
$= \sqrt{\left(\frac{-2\sqrt{3}}{3} - \frac{2\sqrt{3}}{3}\right)^2 + \left(\frac{\sqrt{5}}{4} - \frac{\sqrt{5}}{2}\right)^2}$
$= \sqrt{\left(\frac{-4\sqrt{3}}{3}\right)^2 + \left(\frac{-\sqrt{5}}{4}\right)^2}$
$= \sqrt{\frac{48}{9} + \frac{5}{16}}$
$= \sqrt{\frac{768}{144} + \frac{45}{144}}$
$= \sqrt{\frac{813}{144}}$
$= \frac{\sqrt{813}}{12}$; $\frac{\sqrt{813}}{12}$ units

19. $(x, y) = \left(\frac{x_1 + x_2}{2}, \frac{y_1 + y_2}{2}\right)$
$= \left(\frac{8 + 16}{2}, \frac{3 + 7}{2}\right)$
$= \left(\frac{24}{2}, \frac{10}{2}\right) = (12, 5)$

20. $(x, y) = \left(\frac{x_1 + x_2}{2}, \frac{y_1 + y_2}{2}\right)$
$= \left(\frac{5 + 12}{2}, \frac{9 + 18}{2}\right)$
$= \left(\frac{17}{2}, \frac{27}{2}\right)$

21. $(x, y) = \left(\frac{x_1 + x_2}{2}, \frac{y_1 + y_2}{2}\right)$
$= \left(\frac{-5 + (-3)}{2}, \frac{3 + (-7)}{2}\right)$
$= \left(\frac{-8}{2}, \frac{-4}{2}\right)$
$= (-4, -2)$

22. $(x, y) = \left(\frac{x_1 + x_2}{2}, \frac{y_1 + y_2}{2}\right)$
$= \left(\frac{6 + (-2)}{2}, \frac{-5 + (-7)}{2}\right)$
$= \left(\frac{4}{2}, \frac{-12}{2}\right)$
$= (2, -6)$

23. $(x, y) = \left(\frac{x_1 + x_2}{2}, \frac{y_1 + y_2}{2}\right)$
$= \left(\frac{0.45 + (-0.3)}{2}, \frac{7 + (-9)}{2}\right)$
$= \left(\frac{0.15}{2}, \frac{-2}{2}\right)$
$= (0.075, -1)$

24. $(x, y) = \left(\frac{x_1 + x_2}{2}, \frac{y_1 + y_2}{2}\right)$
$= \left(\frac{-3 + (-8)}{2}, \frac{-12 + 0.34}{2}\right)$
$= \left(\frac{-11}{2}, \frac{-11.66}{2}\right)$
$= (-5.5, -5.83)$

25. $d = \sqrt{(x_2 - x_1)^2 + (y_2 - y_1)^2}$
$10 = \sqrt{(-7 - a)^2 + (3 - 11)^2}$
$(10)^2 = \left(\sqrt{(-7 - a)^2 + (3 - 11)^2}\right)^2$
$100 = (-7 - a)^2 + (-8)^2$
$100 = a^2 + 14a + 49 + 64$
$100 = a^2 + 14a + 113$
$0 = a^2 + 14a + 13$
$0 = (a + 1)(a + 13)$
$a + 1 = 0$ or $a + 13 = 0$
$a = -1$ $\quad a = -13$

26. $d = \sqrt{(x_2 - x_1)^2 + (y_2 - y_1)^2}$
$10 = \sqrt{(-1 - 7)^2 + (a - 2)^2}$
$(10)^2 = \left(\sqrt{(-1 - 7)^2 + (a - 2)^2}\right)^2$
$100 = (-8)^2 + (a - 2)^2$
$100 = 64 + a^2 - 4a + 4$
$100 = a^2 - 4a + 68$
$0 = a^2 - 4a - 32$
$0 = (a - 8)(a + 4)$
$a - 8 = 0$ or $a + 4 = 0$
$a = 8$ $\quad a = -4$

27. $d = \sqrt{(x_2 - x_1)^2 + (y_2 - y_1)^2}$

$10 = \sqrt{(8-6)^2 + (a-3)^2}$

$(10)^2 = \left(\sqrt{(8-6)^2 + (a-3)^2}\right)^2$

$100 = (2)^2 + (a-3)^2$

$100 = 4 + a^2 - 6a + 9$

$100 = a^2 - 6a + 13$

$0 = a^2 - 6a - 87$

$a = \dfrac{-(-6) \pm \sqrt{(-6)^2 - 4(1)(-87)}}{2(1)}$

$= \dfrac{6 \pm \sqrt{384}}{2}$

$\approx \dfrac{6 \pm 19.6}{2}$

≈ 12.8 or -6.8

28. $d = \sqrt{(x_2 - x_1)^2 + (y_2 - y_1)^2}$

$10 = \sqrt{(-8 - a)^2 + (8 - 11)^2}$

$(10)^2 = \left(\sqrt{(-8 - a)^2 + (8 - 11)^2}\right)^2$

$100 = (-8 - a)^2 + (-3)^2$

$100 = a^2 + 16a + 64 + 9$

$100 = a^2 + 16a + 73$

$0 = a^2 + 16a + 27$

$a = \dfrac{-16 \pm \sqrt{(16)^2 - 4(1)(-27)}}{2(1)}$

$= \dfrac{-16 \pm \sqrt{364}}{2}$

$\approx \dfrac{-16 \pm 19}{2}$

≈ 1.5 or -17.5

29. $(x, y) = \left(\dfrac{x_1 + x_2}{2}, \dfrac{y_1 + y_2}{2}\right)$

$(4, 2) = \left(\dfrac{9 + x}{2}, \dfrac{3 + y}{2}\right)$

$4 = \dfrac{9 + x}{2}$ and $2 = \dfrac{3 + y}{2}$

$8 = 9 + x$ $\quad 4 = 3 + y$

$-1 = x$ $\quad 1 = y$

The coordinates of B are $(-1, 1)$.

30. $(x, y) = \left(\dfrac{x_1 + x_2}{2}, \dfrac{y_1 + y_2}{2}\right)$

$(-1, 7) = \left(\dfrac{2 + x}{2}, \dfrac{5 + y}{2}\right)$

$-1 = \dfrac{2 + x}{2}$ and $7 = \dfrac{5 + y}{2}$

$-2 = 2 + x$ $\quad 14 = 5 + y$

$-4 = x$ $\quad 9 = y$

The coordinates of A are $(-4, 9)$.

31. $(x, y) = \left(\dfrac{x_1 + x_2}{2}, \dfrac{y_1 + y_2}{2}\right)$

$(-0.8, 3.85) = \left(\dfrac{2.7 + x}{2}, \dfrac{4.9 + y}{2}\right)$

$-0.8 = \dfrac{2.7 + x}{2}$ and $3.85 = \dfrac{4.9 + y}{2}$

$-1.6 = 2.7 + x$ $\quad 7.7 = 4.9 + y$

$-4.3 = x$ $\quad 2.8 = y$

The coordinates of A are $(-4.3, 2.8)$

32. $(x, y) = \left(\dfrac{x_1 + x_2}{2}, \dfrac{y_1 + y_2}{2}\right)$

$\left(\dfrac{9}{16}, \dfrac{5}{4}\right) = \left(\dfrac{\frac{1}{4} + x}{2}, \dfrac{3 + y}{2}\right)$

$\dfrac{9}{16} = \dfrac{\frac{1}{4} + x}{2}$ and $\dfrac{5}{4} = \dfrac{3 + y}{2}$

$18 = 4 + 16x$ $\quad 10 = 12 + 4y$

$14 = 16x$ $\quad -2 = 4y$

$\dfrac{7}{8} = x$ $\quad -\dfrac{1}{2} = y$

The coordinates of B are $\left(\dfrac{7}{8}, -\dfrac{1}{2}\right)$.

33a. $m = \dfrac{y_2 - y_1}{x_2 - x_1}$

$= \dfrac{-2 - 0}{0 - (-5)}$

$= -\dfrac{2}{5}$

$y = mx + b$

$y = -\dfrac{2}{5}x - 2$

33b. $d = \sqrt{(x_2 - x_1)^2 + (y_2 - y_1)^2}$

$= \sqrt{(-5 - 0)^2 + [0 - (-2)]^2}$

$= \sqrt{(-5)^2 + (2)^2}$

$= \sqrt{25 + 4}$

$= \sqrt{29}$; $\sqrt{29}$ units

33c. $(x, y) = \left(\dfrac{x_1 + x_2}{2}, \dfrac{y_1 + y_2}{2}\right)$

$= \left(\dfrac{-5 + 0}{2}, \dfrac{0 + (-2)}{2}\right)$

$= \left(-\dfrac{5}{2}, -1\right)$

34a. midpoint of $\overline{AC} = \left(\dfrac{4 + 8}{2}, \dfrac{9 + (-9)}{2}\right)$

$= (6, 0)$

midpoint of $\overline{AT} = \left(\dfrac{8 + (-6)}{2}, \dfrac{-9 + 5}{2}\right)$

$= (1, -2)$

midpoint of $\overline{CT} = \left(\dfrac{4 + (-6)}{2}, \dfrac{9 + 5}{2}\right)$

$= (-1, 7)$

34b. $d = \sqrt{(4 - 1)^2 + [9 - (-2)]^2}$

$= \sqrt{(3)^2 + (11)^2}$

$= \sqrt{9 + 121}$

$= \sqrt{130}$; $\sqrt{130}$ units

34c. $\overline{CT} = \sqrt{(-6 - 4)^2 + (5 - 9)^2}$

$= \sqrt{(-10)^2 + (-4)^2}$

$= \sqrt{100 + 16}$

$= \sqrt{116}$

$= 2\sqrt{29}$

$\overline{CA} = \sqrt{(4 - 8)^2 + [9 - (-9)]^2}$

$= \sqrt{(-4)^2 + (18)^2}$

$= \sqrt{16 + 324}$

$= \sqrt{340}$

$= 2\sqrt{85}$

(Continued next page)

$$\overline{AT} = \sqrt{(-6-8)^2 + [5-(-9)]^2}$$
$$= \sqrt{(-14)^2 + (14)^2}$$
$$= \sqrt{196 + 196}$$
$$= \sqrt{392}$$
$$= 14\sqrt{2}$$

The perimeter of $\triangle CAT$ is $2\sqrt{29} + 14\sqrt{2} + 2\sqrt{85}$ units.

34d. $d = \sqrt{(6-1)^2 + [0-(-2)]^2}$
$$= \sqrt{5^2 + 2^2}$$
$$= \sqrt{25 + 4}$$
$$= \sqrt{29}$$
$$d = \sqrt{(-1-6)^2 + (7-0)^2}$$
$$= \sqrt{(-7)^2 + (7)^2}$$
$$= \sqrt{49 + 49}$$
$$= \sqrt{98}$$
$$= 7\sqrt{2}$$
$$d = \sqrt{(-1-1)^2 + [7-(-2)]^2}$$
$$= \sqrt{(-2)^2 + (9)^2}$$
$$= \sqrt{4 + 81}$$
$$= \sqrt{85}$$
perimeter $= \sqrt{29} + 7\sqrt{2} + \sqrt{85}$

34e. The perimeter in part c is twice the perimeter in part d.

35. $d = \sqrt{(-4-4)^2 + (6-5)^2}$
$$= \sqrt{(-8)^2 + (1)^2}$$
$$= \sqrt{64 + 1}$$
$$= \sqrt{65}$$
$$d = \sqrt{(4-6)^2 + (5-3)^2}$$
$$= \sqrt{(-2)^2 + (2)^2}$$
$$= \sqrt{4 + 4}$$
$$= \sqrt{8}$$
$$= 2\sqrt{2}$$
$$d = \sqrt{(5-6)^2 + (-8-3)^2}$$
$$= \sqrt{(-1)^2 + (-11)^2}$$
$$= \sqrt{1 + 121}$$
$$= \sqrt{122}$$
$$d = \sqrt{(-4-5)^2 + [6-(-8)]^2}$$
$$= \sqrt{(-9)^2 + (14)^2}$$
$$= \sqrt{81 + 196}$$
$$= \sqrt{277}$$

The perimeter is $\sqrt{65} + 2\sqrt{2} + \sqrt{122} + \sqrt{277}$ units.

36. $(x, y) = \left(\frac{9+11}{2}, \frac{0+(-14)}{2}\right)$
$$= \left(\frac{20}{2}, \frac{-14}{2}\right)$$
$$= (10, -7)$$

37a. $\overline{MT} = \sqrt{(16-2)^2 + (8-2)^2}$
$$= \sqrt{(14)^2 + (6)^2}$$
$$= \sqrt{196 + 36}$$
$$= \sqrt{232}$$
$$= 2\sqrt{58};\ 2\sqrt{58} \text{ units}$$
$$\overline{AH} = \sqrt{(12-6)^2 + (2-8)^2}$$
$$= \sqrt{(6)^2 + (-6)^2}$$
$$= \sqrt{36 + 36}$$
$$= \sqrt{72}$$
$$= 6\sqrt{2};\ 6\sqrt{2} \text{ units}$$

37b. $(x, y) = \left(\frac{2+16}{2}, \frac{2+8}{2}\right)$
$$= \left(\frac{18}{2}, \frac{10}{2}\right)$$
$$= (9, 5)$$

38a. $(x, y) = \left(\frac{-2+11}{2}, \frac{10+4}{2}\right)$
$$= \left(\frac{9}{2}, \frac{14}{2}\right)$$
$$= \left(\frac{9}{2}, 7\right)$$

The coordinates of Q are $\left(\frac{9}{2}, 7\right)$.

38b. $AY = \sqrt{[(-2)-(-2)]^2 + (10-4)^2}$
$$= \sqrt{(0^2) + (6)^2}$$
$$= \sqrt{36}$$
$$= 6$$
$$QY = \sqrt{\left[-2-\left(\frac{9}{2}\right)\right]^2 + (10-7)^2}$$
$$= \sqrt{\left(\frac{-13}{2}\right)^2 + (3)^2}$$
$$= \sqrt{\frac{169}{4} + 9}$$
$$= \sqrt{\frac{205}{4}}$$
$$= \frac{\sqrt{205}}{2}$$
$$AQ = \sqrt{\left[-2-\left(\frac{9}{2}\right)\right]^2 + (4-7)^2}$$
$$= \sqrt{\left(-\frac{13}{2}\right)^2 + (-3)^2}$$
$$= \sqrt{\frac{169}{4} + 9}$$
$$= \frac{\sqrt{205}}{2}$$

AQ and QY are the same length; therefore $\triangle AQY$ is isosceles.

38c. obtuse

39a. 5 units

39b. about 18.97 units

39c. :Clr Home
:Disp "X1 ="
:Input A
:Disp "Y1 ="
:Input B
:Disp "X2 ="
:Input C
:Disp "Y2 ="
:Input D
$:\frac{(A + C)}{2} \rightarrow X$
$:\frac{(B + D)}{2} \rightarrow Y$
:Disp " X VALUE OF MIDPOINT IS"
:Disp X
:Disp "Y VALUE OF MIDPOINT IS"
:Disp Y

39d. X VALUE OF MIDPOINT IS 3.5
Y VALUE OF MIDPOINT IS −1.5

40. $\left(\frac{-1+5}{2}, \frac{12+(-10)}{2}\right) = \left(\frac{4}{2}, \frac{2}{2}\right)$
$= (2, 1)$

The midpoint of PQ is (2, 1).
$\left(\frac{2+5}{2}, \frac{1+-10}{2}\right) = \left(\frac{7}{2}, -\frac{9}{2}\right)$
The coordinates of the point three-fourths of the way from P to Q is $\left(\frac{7}{2}, -\frac{9}{2}\right)$.

41a. Orlando, (4, 2); Tallahassee, (1, 5)
$d = \sqrt{(4-1)^2 + (2-5)^2}$
$= \sqrt{(3)^2 + (-3)^2}$
$= \sqrt{9+9}$
$= \sqrt{18}$
≈ 4.24
$4.24 \times 70 \approx 300$; about 300 miles

41b. $\frac{300}{180} \approx 1.6$; about 1.6 hours

42. 20 yards = 60 feet.
kick, $\left(60, 53\frac{1}{3}\right)$; midpoint of goal post, $(-30, 80)$

$$d = \sqrt{(60-(-30))^2 + \left(53\frac{1}{3} - 80\right)^2}$$
$$= \sqrt{(90)^2 + \left(-\frac{80}{3}\right)^2}$$
$$= \sqrt{8100 + \frac{6400}{9}}$$
$$= \sqrt{\frac{79{,}300}{9}}$$
≈ 93.87; about 93.87 feet

43a. Sample answer: Draw several lines across the U.S. One should go from the northeast corner to the southwest corner, another should go from the southeast corner to the northwest corner, another should go across the middle of the U.S. from east to west, etc. Find the centers of these lines. Find a point that represents all of the points.

43b. See students' work. **43c.** See students' work.

43d. Sample answer: Cut out Alaska and Hawaii and place them next to the continental U.S. Follow the procedure described in Exercise 43a.

43e. See students' work.

43f. Sample answer: Because certain sections of the U.S. are more populated, the geographical and population centers differ.

44a. $\bar{x} = \frac{5863 + 2866 + 3671 + 4730 + 4050 + 3268 + 4466 + 685}{8}$
$= \frac{29{,}599}{8}$
≈ 3700; 3700 acres

44b. $$\text{SD} = \sqrt{\frac{\left[\begin{array}{l}(3700-5863)^2 + (3700-2866)^2 + \\ (3700-3671)^2 + (3700-4730)^2 + (3700-4050)^2 + \\ (3700-3268)^2 + (3700-4466)^2 + (3700-685)^2\end{array}\right]}{8}}$$

$$= \sqrt{\frac{\left[\begin{array}{c}(2163)^2 + (834)^2 + \\ (29)^2 + (1030)^2 + (350)^2 + (432)^2 + (766)^2 + (3015)^2\end{array}\right]}{8}}$$

≈ 1432.7; 1432.7 acres

44c. Sample answer: large variation

45. $$\begin{array}{r|rrr} -2 & 1 & -3 & 2 \\ & & -2 & 10 \\ \hline & 1 & -5 & 12 \end{array}$$
$t - 5 + \frac{12}{t+2}$

46. $(s+3)^2 = (s)^2 + 2(3)(s) + (3)^2$
$= s^2 + 6s + 9$

47. $$\left[\begin{array}{rrr|r} 2 & -1 & 1 & 44 \\ -1 & 3 & -2 & -53 \\ 5 & -6 & -1 & 19 \end{array}\right] = \left[\begin{array}{rrr|r} -1 & 3 & -2 & -53 \\ 2 & -1 & 1 & 44 \\ 5 & -6 & -1 & 19 \end{array}\right]$$

$$= \left[\begin{array}{rrr|r} 1 & -3 & 2 & 53 \\ 2 & -1 & 1 & 44 \\ 5 & -6 & -1 & 19 \end{array}\right] = \left[\begin{array}{rrr|r} 1 & -3 & 2 & 53 \\ 0 & 5 & -3 & -62 \\ 5 & -6 & -1 & 19 \end{array}\right]$$

$$= \left[\begin{array}{rrr|r} 1 & -3 & 2 & 53 \\ 0 & 5 & -3 & -62 \\ 0 & 9 & -11 & -246 \end{array}\right] = \left[\begin{array}{rrr|r} 1 & -3 & 2 & 53 \\ 0 & 1 & -\frac{3}{5} & -\frac{62}{5} \\ 0 & 9 & -11 & -246 \end{array}\right]$$

$$= \left[\begin{array}{rrr|r} 1 & 0 & \frac{1}{5} & \frac{79}{5} \\ 0 & 1 & -\frac{3}{5} & -\frac{62}{5} \\ 0 & 9 & -11 & -246 \end{array}\right] = \left[\begin{array}{rrr|r} 1 & 0 & \frac{1}{5} & \frac{79}{7} \\ 0 & 1 & -\frac{3}{5} & -\frac{62}{5} \\ 0 & 0 & -\frac{28}{5} & -\frac{672}{5} \end{array}\right]$$

$$= \left[\begin{array}{rrr|r} 1 & 0 & \frac{1}{5} & \frac{79}{7} \\ 0 & 1 & -\frac{3}{5} & -\frac{62}{5} \\ 0 & 0 & 1 & 24 \end{array}\right] = \left[\begin{array}{rrr|r} 1 & 0 & 0 & 0 \\ 0 & 1 & -\frac{3}{5} & -\frac{62}{5} \\ 0 & 0 & 1 & 24 \end{array}\right]$$

$$= \left[\begin{array}{rrr|r} 1 & 0 & 0 & 11 \\ 0 & 1 & 0 & 2 \\ 0 & 0 & 0 & 24 \end{array}\right] \quad (11, 2, 24)$$

48. $$3\begin{bmatrix} 4 & -2 \\ 5 & 7 \end{bmatrix} + 2\begin{bmatrix} -3 & 5 \\ -4 & 3 \end{bmatrix} = \begin{bmatrix} 12 & -6 \\ 15 & 21 \end{bmatrix} + \begin{bmatrix} -6 & 10 \\ -8 & 6 \end{bmatrix}$$
$$= \begin{bmatrix} 6 & 4 \\ 7 & 27 \end{bmatrix}$$

49. Let ℓ = the length and w = the width.

$$2w = \ell + 2 \qquad 86 = 2\ell + 2w$$
$$2w - 2 = \ell \qquad 86 = 2(2w - 2) + 2w$$
$$86 = 4w - 4 + 2w$$
$$90 = 6w$$
$$15 = w$$

$$2w - 2 = \ell$$
$$2(15) - 2 = \ell$$
$$30 - 2 = \ell$$
$$28 = \ell$$

The dimensions of the picture are 15 inches by 28 inches.

50. $x + 3y = 14$

$$3y = -x + 14$$
$$y = -\frac{1}{3}x + \frac{14}{3}$$
$$m = -\frac{1}{3}$$

The slope of the line perpendicular to $x + 3y = 14$ is 3.

51. $2|-3x| - 9 = 2|-3(5)| - 9$

$$= 2|-15| - 9$$
$$= 2(15) - 9$$
$$= 30 - 9$$
$$= 21$$

7-2 Parabolas

Page 419 Check for Understanding

1. The axis of symmetry passes through the vertex and is perpendicular to the latus rectum and the directrix. The focus is also on the axis of symmetry. The latus rectum contains the focus, joins two points on the parabola, and is parallel to the directrix. The vertex is equidistant from the focus and the directrix.
2. Shanice; both $(x - 3)^2$ and $(3 - x)^2$ equal $x^2 - 6x + 9$.
3. The equation of a parabola opening up or down is $y = a(x - h)^2 + k$. The parabola opens upward if $a > 0$ and downward if $a < 0$. These equations are functions. The equation of a parabola opening right or left is $x = a(y - k)^2 + h$. The parabola opens to the right if $a > 0$ and to the left if $a < 0$. These equations are not functions.
4. The parabola with the focus 10 centimeters away will be wider than the other one.
5. $y = 2x^2 - 12x + 6$
$$= 2(x^2 - 6x) + 6$$
$$= 2(x^2 - 6x + 9) + 6 - 2(9)$$
$$= 2(x - 3)^2 - 12$$
6. $y = \frac{1}{2}x^2 + 12x - 8$
$$= \frac{1}{2}(x^2 + 24x) - 8$$
$$= \frac{1}{2}(x^2 + 24x + 144) - 8 - \frac{1}{2}(144)$$
$$= \frac{1}{2}(x + 12)^2 - 80$$
7. $x = 3y^2 + 5y - 9$
$$= 3\left(y^2 + \frac{5}{3}y\right) - 9$$
$$= 3\left(y^2 + \frac{5}{3}y + \frac{25}{36}\right) - 9 - 3\left(\frac{25}{36}\right)$$
$$= 3\left(y + \frac{5}{6}\right)^2 - 11\frac{1}{12}$$
8. $x = y^2 + 14y + 20$
$$= (y^2 + 14y + 49) + 20 - 49$$
$$= (y + 7)^2 - 29$$
9. $y = (x - 3)^2 - 4$

vertex: $(3, -4)$

focus: $\left(3, -4 + \frac{1}{4(1)}\right)$ or $\left(3, -3\frac{3}{4}\right)$

axis of symmetry: $x = 3$

directrix: $y = -4 - \frac{1}{4(1)}$ or $-4\frac{1}{4}$

direction of opening: upward, since $a > 0$

length of latus rectum: $\left|\frac{1}{1}\right|$ or 1 unit

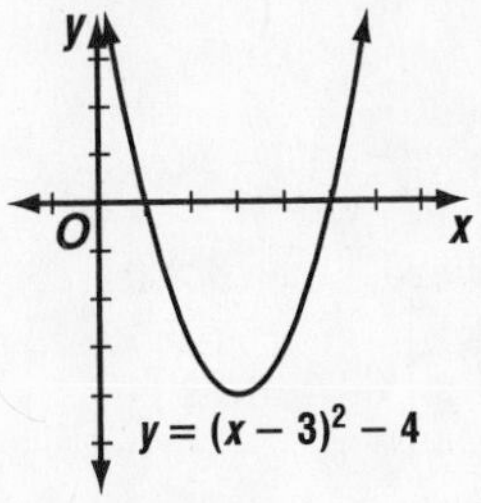

10. $y = 2(x + 7)^2 + 3$

vertex: $(-7, 3)$

focus: $\left(-7, 3 + \frac{1}{4(2)}\right)$ or $\left(-7, 3\frac{1}{8}\right)$

axis of symmetry: $x = -7$

directrix: $y = 3 - \frac{1}{4(2)}$ or $2\frac{7}{8}$

direction of opening: upward, since $a > 0$

length of latus rectum: $\left|\frac{1}{2}\right|$ or $\frac{1}{2}$ unit

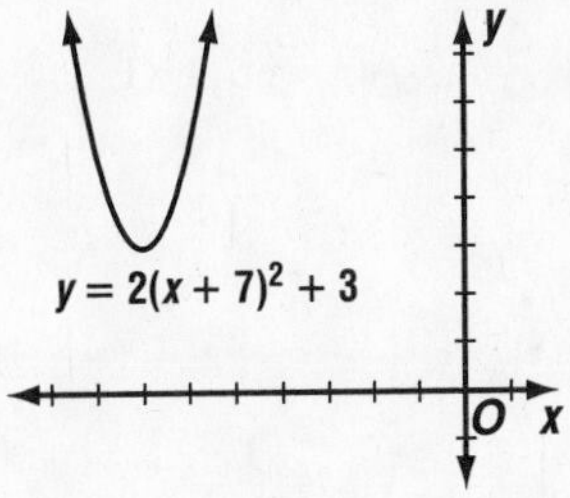

11. $y = 3x^2 - 8x + 6$
$$= 3\left(x^2 - \frac{8}{3}x\right) + 6$$
$$= 3\left(x^2 - \frac{8}{3}x + \frac{16}{9}\right) + 6 - 3\left(\frac{16}{9}\right)$$
$$= 3\left(x - \frac{4}{3}\right)^2 + \frac{2}{3}$$

vertex: $\left(\frac{4}{3}, \frac{2}{3}\right)$

focus: $\left(\frac{4}{3}, \frac{2}{3} + \frac{1}{4(3)}\right)$ or $\left(\frac{4}{3}, \frac{3}{4}\right)$

axis of symmetry: $x = \frac{4}{3}$

directrix: $y = \frac{2}{3} - \frac{1}{4(3)}$ or $\frac{7}{12}$

direction of opening: upward since $a > 0$

length of latus rectum: $\left|\frac{1}{3}\right|$ or $\frac{1}{3}$ unit

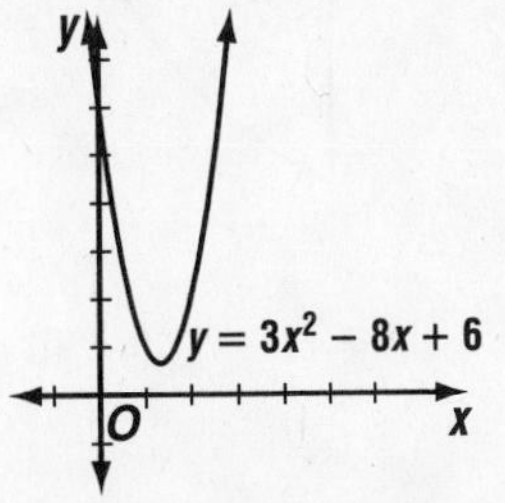

12. $y = \frac{2}{3}x^2 - 6x + 12$
$= \frac{2}{3}(x^2 - 9x) + 12$
$= \frac{2}{3}\left(x^2 - 9x + \frac{81}{4}\right) + 12 - \frac{2}{3}\left(\frac{81}{4}\right)$
$= \frac{2}{3}\left(x - \frac{9}{2}\right)^2 - \frac{3}{2}$

vertex: $\left(\frac{9}{2}, -\frac{3}{2}\right)$

focus: $\left(\frac{9}{2}, -\frac{3}{2} + \frac{1}{4\left(\frac{2}{3}\right)}\right)$ or $\left(\frac{9}{2}, -\frac{9}{8}\right)$

axis of symmetry: $x = \frac{9}{2}$

directrix: $y = -\frac{3}{2} - \frac{1}{4\left(\frac{2}{3}\right)}$ or $-\frac{15}{8}$

direction of opening: upward, since $a > 0$

length of latus rectum: $\left|\frac{1}{\frac{2}{3}}\right|$ or $\frac{3}{2}$ units

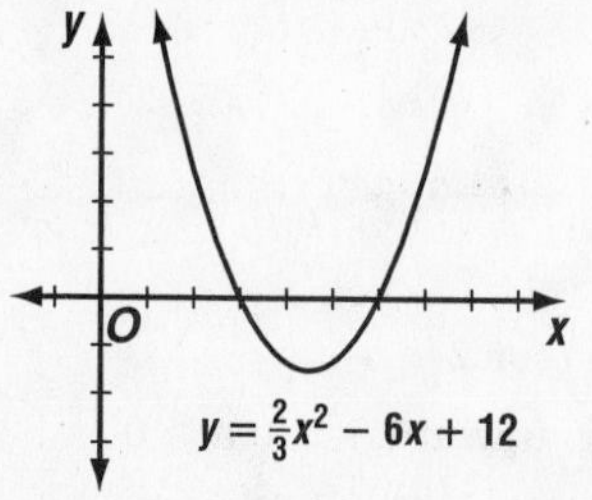

13. vertex: (0, 3)
$y = a(x - 0)^2 + 3$ passes through (1, 1)
$1 = a(1 - 0)^2 + 3$
$1 = a + 3$
$-2 = a$
$y = -2x^2 + 3$

14. vertex: (3, 6)
$y = a(x - 3)^2 + 6$
$6 + \frac{1}{4a} = 8$
$\frac{1}{4a} = 2$
$8a = 1$
$a = \frac{1}{8}$
$y = \frac{1}{8}(x - 3)^2 + 6$

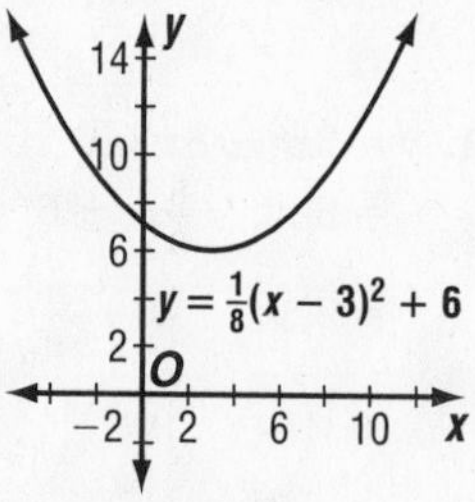

15. vertex: (5, −1)
$x = a(y + 1)^2 + 5$
$5 + \frac{1}{4a} = 3$
$\frac{1}{4a} = -2$
$-8a = 1$
$a = -\frac{1}{8}$
$x = -\frac{1}{8}(y + 1)^2 + 5$

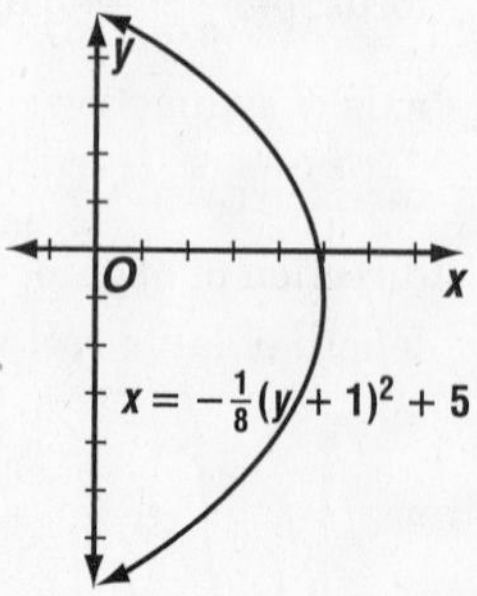

Pages 420–422 Exercises

16. $-6y = x^2$
$y = -\frac{1}{6}x^2$

vertex: (0, 0)

focus: $\left(0, 0 + \frac{1}{4\left(-\frac{1}{6}\right)}\right)$ or $\left(0, -\frac{3}{2}\right)$

axis of symmetry: $x = 0$

directrix: $y = 0 - \frac{1}{4\left(-\frac{1}{6}\right)}$ or $\frac{3}{2}$

direction of opening: downward, since $a < 0$

length of latus rectum: $\left|\frac{1}{-\frac{1}{6}}\right|$ or 6 units

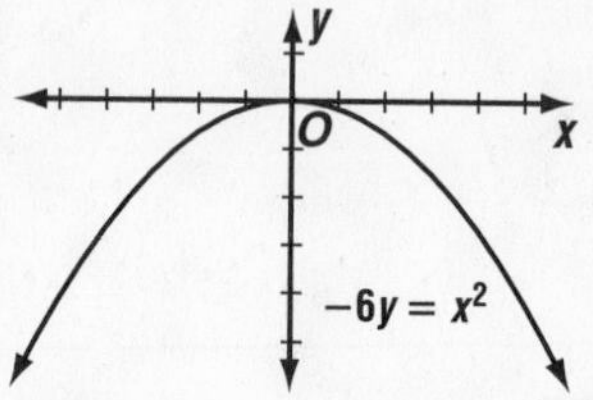

17. $3(y - 3) = (x + 6)^2$
$y - 3 = \frac{1}{3}(x + 6)^2$
$y = \frac{1}{3}(x + 6)^2 + 3$

vertex: (−6, 3)

focus: $\left(-6, 3 + \frac{1}{4\left(\frac{1}{3}\right)}\right)$ or $\left(-6, 3\frac{3}{4}\right)$

axis of symmetry: $x = -6$

directrix: $y = 3 - \frac{1}{4\left(\frac{1}{3}\right)}$ or $2\frac{1}{4}$

direction of opening: upward, since $a > 0$

length of latus rectum: $\left|\frac{1}{\frac{1}{3}}\right|$ or 3 units

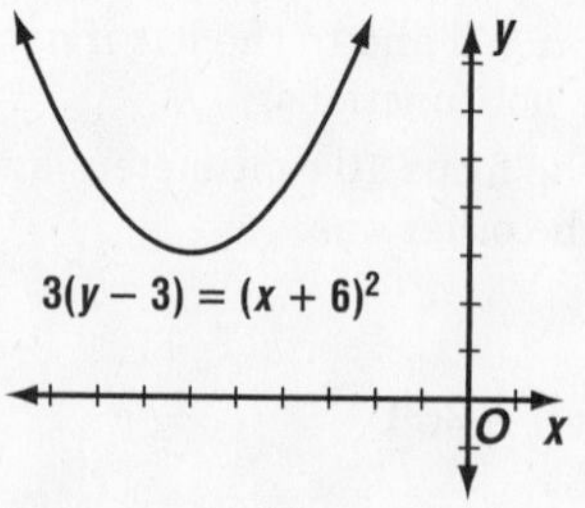

18. $-2(x - 4) = (y - 1)^2$
$x - 4 = -\frac{1}{2}(y - 1)^2$
$x = -\frac{1}{2}(y - 1)^2 + 4$

vertex: (4, 1)

focus: $\left(4 + \frac{1}{4\left(-\frac{1}{2}\right)}, 1\right)$ or $\left(3\frac{1}{2}, 1\right)$

axis of symmetry: $y = 1$

(Continued next page)

directrix: $x = 4 - \dfrac{1}{4\left(-\frac{1}{2}\right)}$ or $4\frac{1}{2}$

direction of opening: left, since $a < 0$

length of latus rectum: $\left|\dfrac{1}{-\frac{1}{2}}\right|$ or 2 units

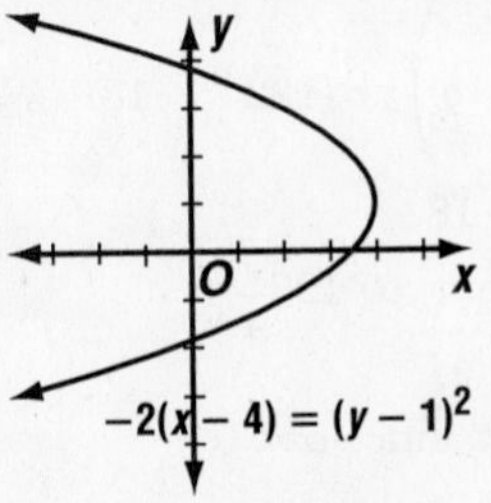

19. $4(x - 2) = (y + 3)^2$

$x - 2 = \frac{1}{4}(y + 3)^2$

$x = \frac{1}{4}(y + 3)^2 + 2$

vertex: $(2, -3)$

focus: $\left(2 + \dfrac{1}{4\left(\frac{1}{4}\right)}, -3\right)$ or $(3, -3)$

axis of symmetry: $y = -3$

directrix: $x = 2 - \dfrac{1}{4\left(\frac{1}{4}\right)}$ or 1

direction of opening: right, since $a > 0$

length of latus rectum: $\left|\dfrac{1}{\frac{1}{4}}\right|$ or 4 units

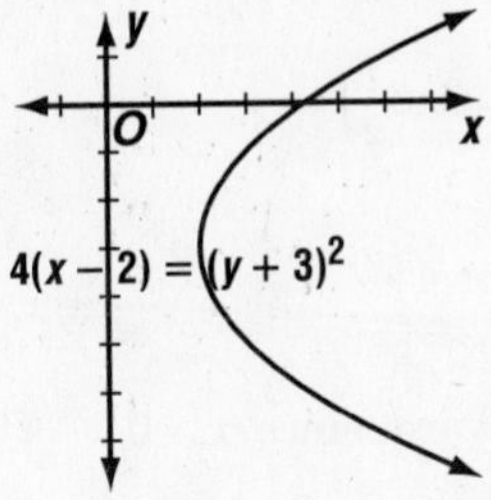

20. $(y - 8)^2 = -4(x - 4)$

$-\frac{1}{4}(y - 8)^2 = x - 4$

$-\frac{1}{4}(y - 8)^2 + 4 = x$

vertex: $(4, 8)$

focus: $\left(4 + \dfrac{1}{4\left(-\frac{1}{4}\right)}, 8\right)$ or $(3, 8)$

axis of symmetry: $y = 8$

directrix: $x = 4 - \dfrac{1}{4\left(-\frac{1}{4}\right)}$ or 5

direction of opening: left, since $a < 0$

length of latus rectum: $\left|\dfrac{1}{-\frac{1}{4}}\right|$ or 4 units

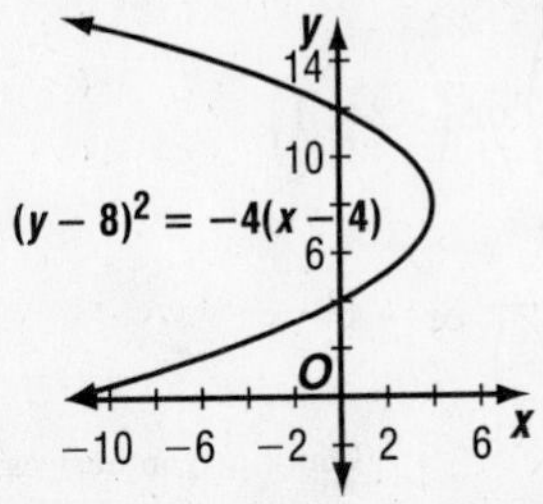

21. $y = x^2 - 12x + 20$

$= (x^2 - 12x + 36) + 20 - 36$

$= (x - 6)^2 - 16$

vertex: $(6, -16)$

focus: $\left(6, -16 + \frac{1}{4(1)}\right)$ or $\left(6, -15\frac{3}{4}\right)$

axis of symmetry: $x = 6$

directrix: $y = -16 - \frac{1}{4(1)}$ or $-16\frac{1}{4}$

direction of opening: upward, since $a > 0$

length of latus rectum: $\left|\frac{1}{1}\right|$ or 1 unit

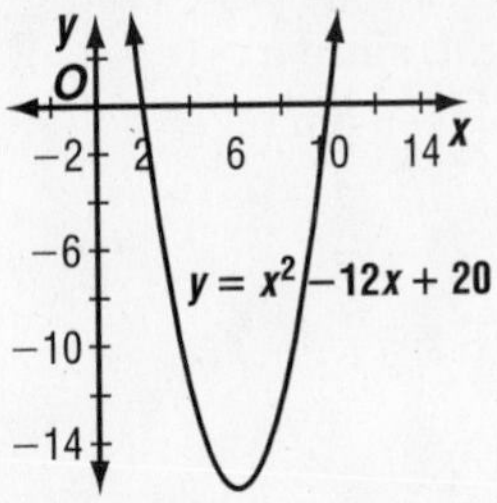

22. $x = y^2 - 14y + 25$

$= (y^2 - 14y + 49) + 25 - 49$

$= (y - 7)^2 - 24$

vertex: $(-24, 7)$

focus: $\left(-24 + \frac{1}{4(1)}, 7\right)$ or $\left(-23\frac{3}{4}, 7\right)$

axis of symmetry: $y = 7$

directrix: $x = -24 - \frac{1}{4(1)}$ or $-24\frac{1}{4}$

direction of opening: right, since $a > 0$

length of latus rectum $\left|\frac{1}{1}\right|$ or 1 unit

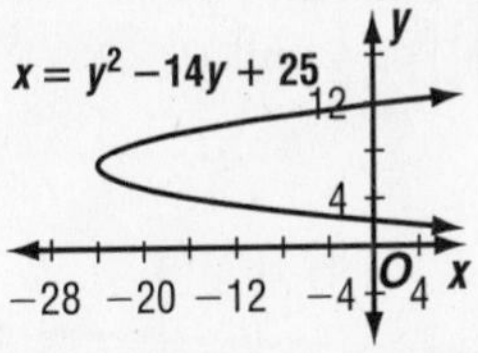

23. $y = -2x^2 + 5x - 10$

$= -2\left(x^2 - \frac{5}{2}x + \frac{25}{16}\right) - 10 + 2\left(\frac{25}{16}\right)$

$= -2\left(x - \frac{5}{4}\right)^2 - \frac{55}{8}$

vertex: $\left(\frac{5}{4}, -\frac{55}{8}\right)$

focus: $\left(\frac{5}{4}, -\frac{55}{8} + \frac{1}{4(-2)}\right)$ or $\left(\frac{5}{4}, -7\right)$

axis of symmetry: $x = \frac{5}{4}$

directrix: $y = -\frac{55}{8} - \frac{1}{4(-2)}$ or $\frac{-27}{4}$

direction of opening: downward, since $a < 0$

length of latus rectum: $\left|\frac{1}{-2}\right|$ or $\frac{1}{2}$ unit

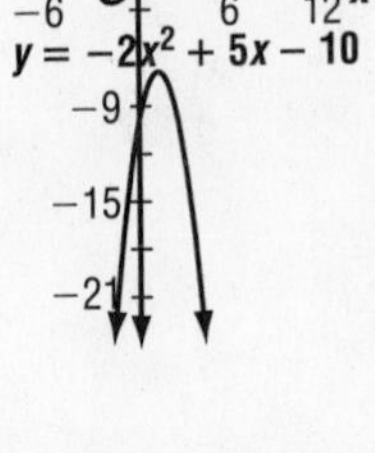

24. $x = 5y^2 - 25y + 60$
$= 5\left(y^2 - 5y + \frac{25}{4}\right) + 60 - 5\left(\frac{25}{4}\right)$
$= 5\left(y - \frac{5}{2}\right)^2 + \frac{115}{4}$
vertex: $\left(\frac{115}{4}, \frac{5}{2}\right)$
focus: $\left(\frac{115}{4} + \frac{1}{4(5)}, \frac{5}{2}\right)$ or $\left(28\frac{4}{5}, \frac{5}{2}\right)$
axis of symmetry: $y = \frac{5}{2}$
directrix: $x = \frac{115}{4} - \frac{1}{4(5)}$ or $28\frac{7}{10}$
direction of opening: right, since $a > 0$
length of latus rectum: $\left|\frac{1}{5}\right|$ or $\frac{1}{5}$ unit

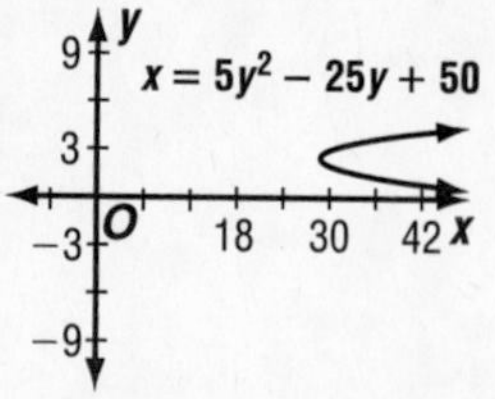

25. $y = 3x^2 - 24x + 50$
$= 3(x^2 - 8x + 16) + 50 - 3(16)$
$= 3(x - 4)^2 + 2$
vertex: (4, 2)
focus: $\left(4, 2 + \frac{1}{4(3)}\right)$ or $\left(4, \frac{25}{12}\right)$
axis of symmetry: $x = 4$
directrix: $y = 2 - \frac{1}{4(3)}$ or $\frac{23}{12}$
direction of opening: upward, since $a > 0$
length of latus rectum: $\left|\frac{1}{3}\right|$ or $\frac{1}{3}$ unit

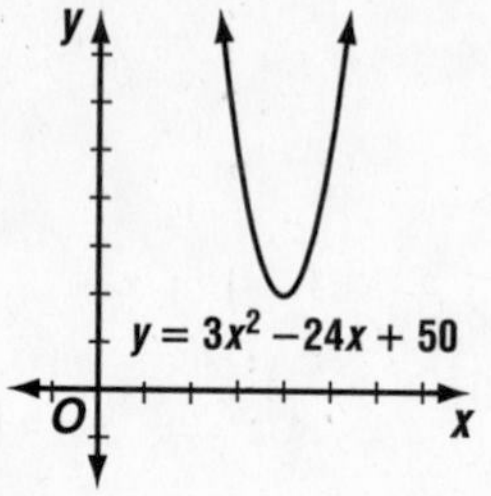

26. $\frac{1}{2}(y + 1) = (x - 8)^2$
$y + 1 = 2(x - 8)^2$
$y = 2(x - 8)^2 - 1$
vertex: (8, −1)
focus: $\left(8, -1 + \frac{1}{4(2)}\right)$ or $\left(8, -\frac{7}{8}\right)$
axis of symmetry: $x = 8$
directrix: $y = -1 - \frac{1}{4(2)}$ or $-\frac{9}{8}$
direction of opening: upward, since $a > 0$
length of latus rectum: $\left|\frac{1}{2}\right|$ or $\frac{1}{2}$ unit

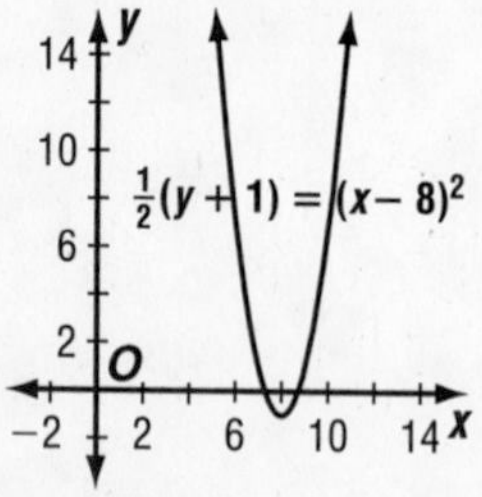

27. $x = -\frac{1}{3}y^2 - 12y + 15$
$= -\frac{1}{3}(y^2 + 36y + 324) + 15 + \frac{1}{3}(324)$
$= -\frac{1}{3}(y + 18) + 123$
vertex: (123, −18)
focus: $\left(123 + \frac{1}{4\left(\frac{1}{-3}\right)}, -18\right)$ or $(122\frac{1}{4}, -18)$
axis of symmetry: $y = -18$
directrix: $x = 123 - \frac{1}{4\left(-\frac{1}{3}\right)}$ or $123\frac{3}{4}$
direction of opening: left, since $a < 0$
length of latus rectum: $\left|\frac{1}{-\frac{1}{3}}\right|$ or 3 units

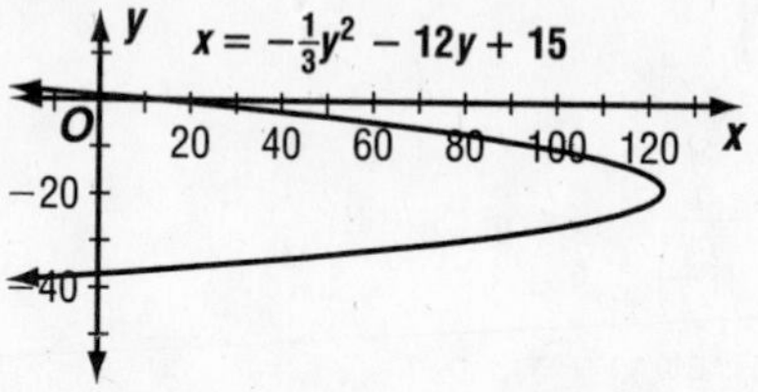

28. $y = \frac{1}{2}x^2 - 3x + \frac{19}{2}$
$= \frac{1}{2}(x^2 - 6x + 9) + \frac{19}{2} - \frac{1}{2}(9)$
$= \frac{1}{2}(x - 3)^2 + 5$
vertex: (3, 5)
focus: $\left(3, 5 + \frac{1}{4\left(\frac{1}{2}\right)}\right)$ or $\left(3, 5\frac{1}{2}\right)$
axis of symmetry: $x = 3$
directrix: $y = 5 - \frac{1}{4\left(\frac{1}{2}\right)}$ or $4\frac{1}{2}$
direction of opening: upward, since $a > 0$
length of latus rectum: $\left|\frac{1}{\frac{1}{2}}\right|$ or 2 units

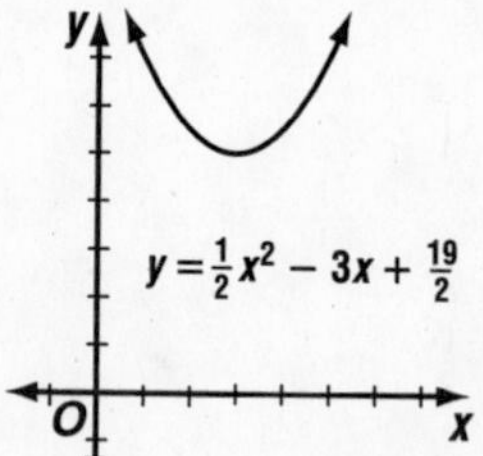

29. $x = \frac{1}{4}y^2 - \frac{1}{2}y - 3$
$x = \frac{1}{4}(y^2 - 2y + 1) - 3 - \frac{1}{4}(1)$
$x = \frac{1}{4}(y - 1)^2 - 3\frac{1}{4}$
vertex: $\left(-3\frac{1}{4}, 1\right)$
focus: $\left(-3\frac{1}{4} + \frac{1}{4\left(\frac{1}{4}\right)}, 1\right)$ or $\left(-2\frac{1}{4}, 1\right)$
axis of symmetry: $y = 1$
directrix: $x = -3\frac{1}{4} - \frac{1}{4\left(\frac{1}{4}\right)}$ or $-4\frac{1}{4}$

(Continued on next page)

direction of opening: right, since $a > 0$

length of latus rectum: $\left|\frac{1}{\frac{1}{4}}\right|$ or 4 units

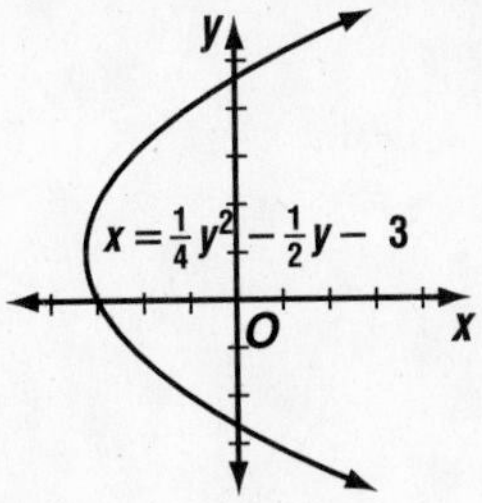

30. vertex: $(0, -2)$ passes through $(3, 0)$

$y = a(x - 0)^2 - 2$

$0 = a(3 - 0)^2 - 2$

$2 = 9a$

$\frac{2}{9} = a$

$y = \frac{2}{9}x^2 - 2$

31. vertex: $(1, 2)$, passes through $(3, 1)$

$x = a(y - 2)^2 + 1$

$3 = a(1 - 2)^2 + 1$

$2 = a$

$x = 2(y - 2)^2 + 1$

32. vertex: $\left(4, \frac{1}{2}\right)$

$k + \frac{1}{4a} = -3$

$\frac{1}{2} + \frac{1}{4a} = -3$

$\frac{1}{4a} = -\frac{7}{2}$

$-28a = 2$

$a = -\frac{1}{14}$

$y = -\frac{1}{14}(x - 4)^2 + \frac{1}{2}$

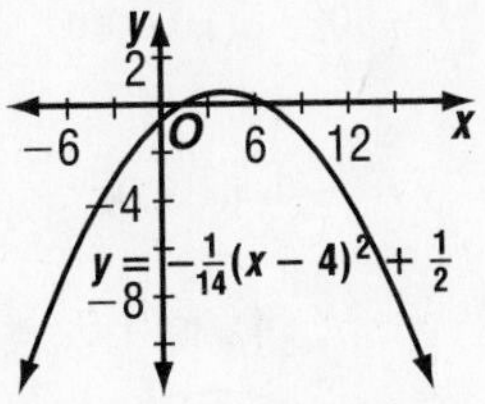

33. vertex: $(-3, -4)$

$k + \frac{1}{4a} = -2$

$-4 + \frac{1}{4a} = -2$

$\frac{1}{4a} = 2$

$8a = 1$

$a = \frac{1}{8}$

$y = \frac{1}{8}(x + 3)^2 - 4$

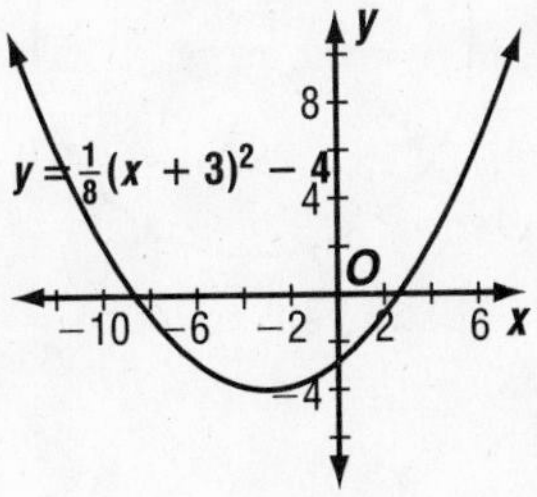

34. vertex: $\left(\frac{1}{2}, 0\right)$

$h + \frac{1}{4a} = 3$

$\frac{1}{2} + \frac{1}{4a} = 3$

$\frac{1}{4a} = \frac{5}{2}$

$20a = 2$

$a = \frac{1}{10}$

$x = \frac{1}{10}(y - 0)^2 + \frac{1}{2}$

or $x = \frac{1}{10}y^2 + \frac{1}{2}$

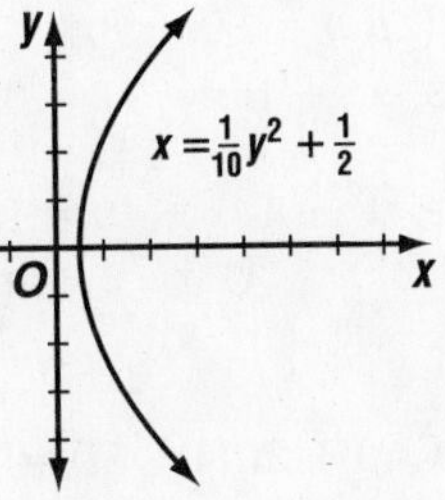

35. vertex: $\left(4, \frac{3}{2}\right)$

$k + \frac{1}{4a} = -3$

$\frac{3}{2} + \frac{1}{4a} = -3$

$\frac{1}{4a} = -\frac{9}{2}$

$-36a = 2$

$a = -\frac{1}{18}$

$y = -\frac{1}{18}(x - 4)^2 + \frac{3}{2}$

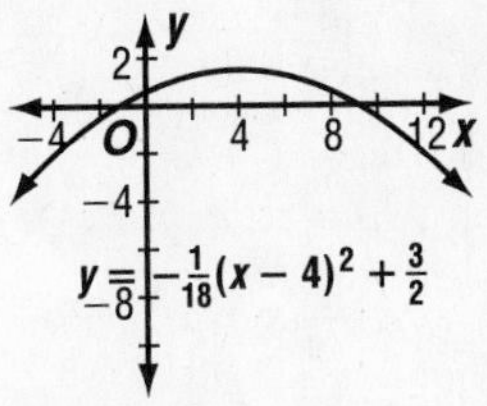

36. vertex: $\left(\frac{15}{2}, -4\right)$

$h + \frac{1}{4a} = 10$

$\frac{15}{2} + \frac{1}{4a} = 10$

$\frac{1}{4a} = \frac{5}{2}$

$20a = 2$

$a = \frac{1}{10}$

$x = \frac{1}{10}(y + 4)^2 + \frac{15}{2}$

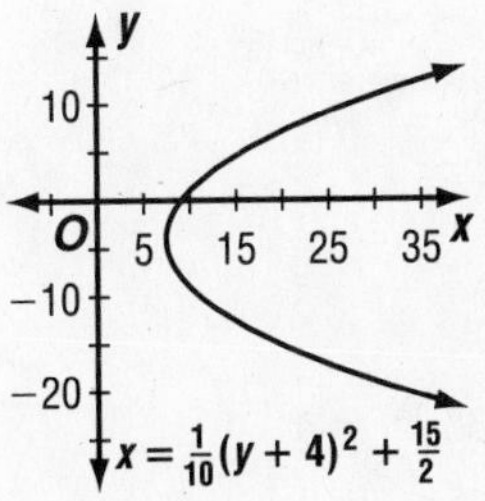

37. vertex: $(1, 0)$

$h + \frac{1}{4a} = 4$

$1 + \frac{1}{4a} = 4$

$\frac{1}{4a} = 3$

$12a = 1$

$a = \frac{1}{12}$

$x = \frac{1}{12}(y - 0)^2 + 1$

or $x = \frac{1}{2}y^2 + 1$

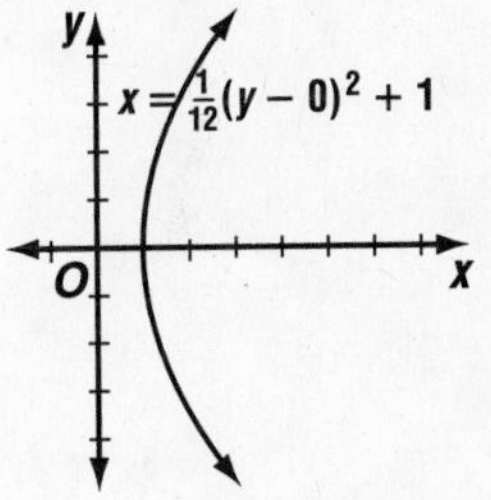

38. $k + \frac{1}{4a} = 5$

$1 + \frac{1}{4a} = 5$

$\frac{1}{4a} = 4$

$16a = 1$

$a = \frac{1}{16}$

$y = \frac{1}{16}(x - 0)^2 + 1$

or $y = \frac{1}{16}x^2 + 1$

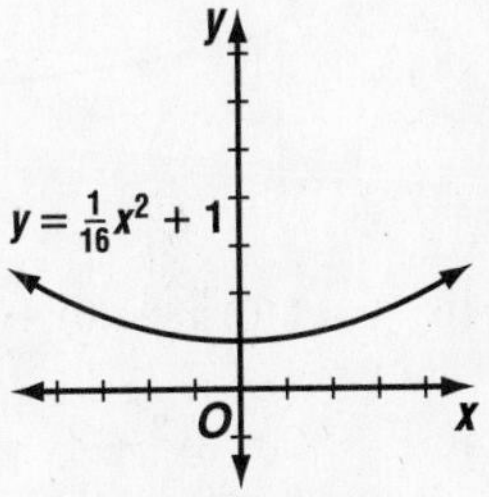

39. $h + \frac{1}{4a} = 2$

$8 + \frac{1}{4a} = 2$

$\frac{1}{4a} = -6$

$1 = -24a$

$-\frac{1}{24} = a$

$x = -\frac{1}{24}(y - 6)^2 + 8$

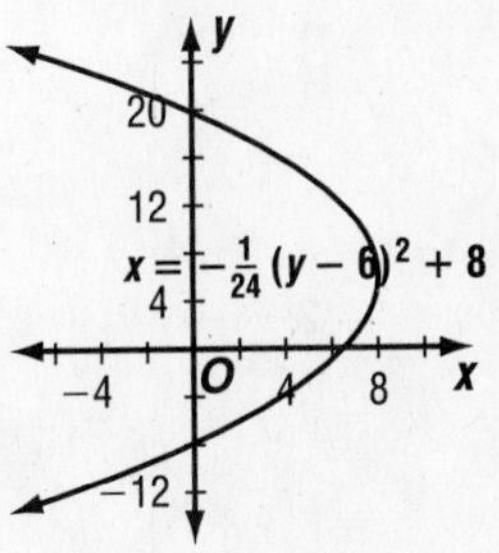

40. vertex: $(-6, -2)$

$-8 = h - \frac{1}{4a}$

$-8 = -6 - \frac{1}{4a}$

$-2 = -\frac{1}{4a}$

$8a = 1$

$a = \frac{1}{8}$

$x = \frac{1}{8}(y + 2)^2 - 6$

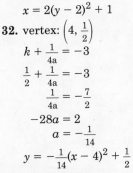

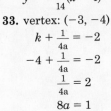

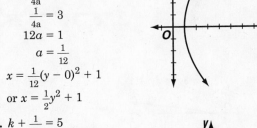

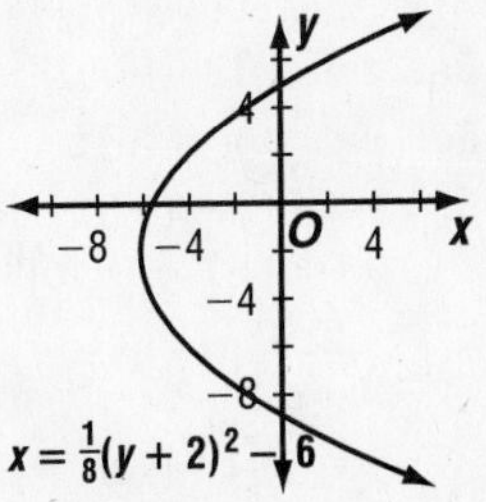

41. $3 = k - \frac{1}{4a}$

$3 = 7 - \frac{1}{4a}$

$-4 = -\frac{1}{4a}$

$16a = 1$

$a = \frac{1}{16}$

$y = \frac{1}{16}(x-1)^2 + 7$

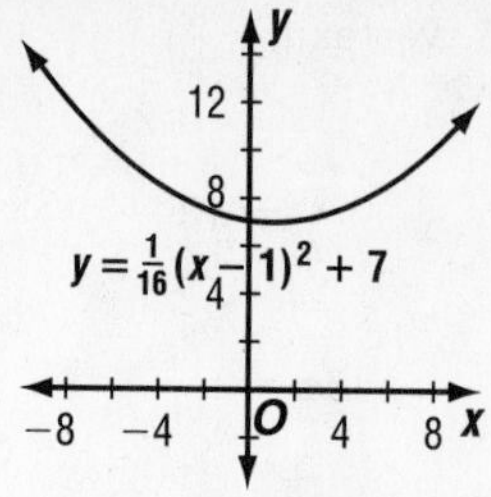

42. $\left|\frac{1}{a}\right| = 6$

$a = -\frac{1}{6}$

$y = -\frac{1}{6}(x+7)^2 + 4$

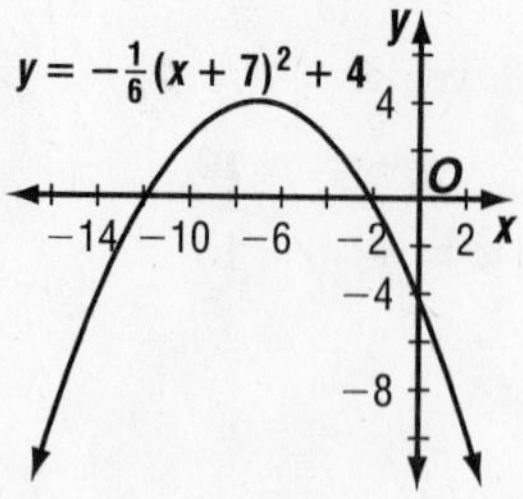

43. $\left|\frac{1}{a}\right| = 4$

$a = \frac{1}{4}$

$x = \frac{1}{4}(y-3)^2 + 4$

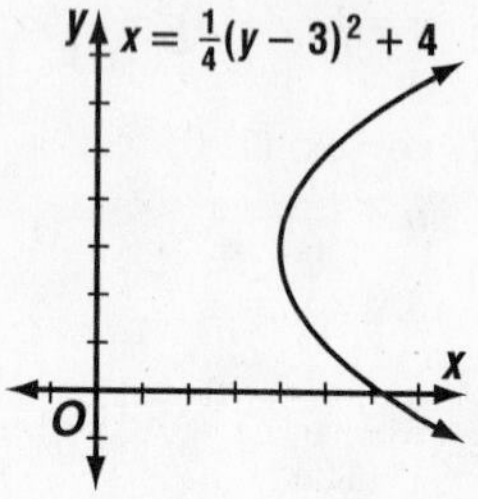

44a.

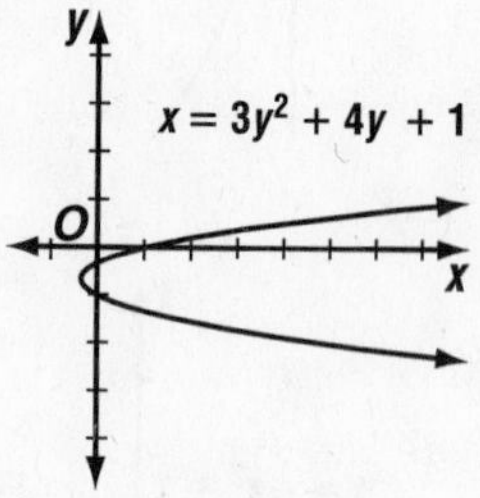

44b. $x = 3(0)^2 + 4(0) + 1$

$x = 1$

44c. $0 = 3y^2 + 4y + 1$

$0 = (3y+1)(y+1)$

$y + 1 = 0$ or $3y + 1 = 0$

$y = -1$ $\quad 3y = -1$

$y = -\frac{1}{3}$

44d. $y = -\frac{2}{3}$

44e. $x = 3y^2 + 4y + 1$

$= 3\left(y^2 + \frac{4}{3}y\right) + 1$

$= 3\left(y^2 + \frac{4}{3}y + \frac{4}{9}\right) + 1 - 3\left(\frac{4}{9}\right)$

$= 3\left(y + \frac{2}{3}\right)^2 - \frac{1}{3}$

vertex: $\left(-\frac{1}{3}, -\frac{2}{3}\right)$

45a. 4 and 12 **45b.** $4 < x < 12$

45c. $x < 4$ or $x > 12$

46. $y = a(x - (-3))^2 + 1$

$0 = a[-1 - (-3)]^2 + 1$

$-1 = 4a$

$-\frac{1}{4} = a$

$y = -\frac{1}{4}(x+3)^2 + 1$

$x = a(y-1)^2 + (-3)$

$-1 = a(0-1)^2 + (-3)$

$2 = a$

$x = 2(y-1)^2 - 3$

47. $k + \frac{1}{4}a = 0 + \frac{1}{4\left(\frac{1}{12}\right)}$

$= 0 + 3$

$= 3$; 3 units

48. focus: (0, 0); $a > 0$; vertex: (−6, 0);

latus rectum: 24

$\left|\frac{1}{a}\right| = 24$

$a = \frac{1}{24}$

$x = a(y-k)^2 + h$

$= \frac{1}{24}(y-0)^2 - 6$

$= \frac{1}{24}y^2 - 6$

49. vertex: (0, 6400 + 150) or (0, 6550); $a > 0$

$k + \frac{1}{4a} = 0$

$6550 + \frac{1}{4a} = 0$

$\frac{1}{4a} = -6550$

$a = -\frac{1}{26{,}200}$

$y = a(x-h)^2 + k$

$= -\frac{1}{26{,}200}(x-0)^2 + 6550$

$= -\frac{1}{26{,}200}x^2 + 6550$

50. focus: (0, 0); vertex: (0, 50);

passes through (100, 0)

$y = a(x-h)^2 + k$

$0 = a(100-0)^2 + 50$

$-50 = a(10{,}000)$

$-\frac{1}{200} = a$

$y = -\frac{1}{200}(x-0)^2 + 50$ or $y = -\frac{1}{200}x^2 + 50$

51.

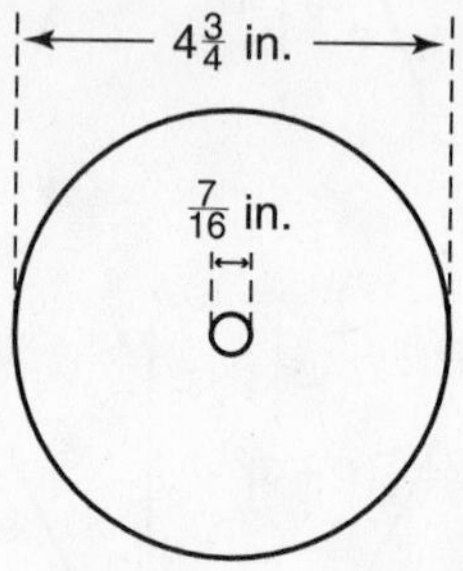

radius of hole $= \frac{1}{2}\left(\frac{7}{16}\right)$

$= \frac{7}{32}$

radius of disc $= \frac{1}{2}\left(4\frac{3}{4}\right)$

$= \frac{1}{2}\left(\frac{19}{4}\right)$

$= \frac{19}{8}$

distance from edge $= \frac{19}{8} - \frac{7}{32}$

$= \frac{76}{32} - \frac{7}{32}$

$= \frac{69}{32}$

$= 2\frac{5}{32}$; $2\frac{5}{32}$ inches

52. $f(x) = \quad (x-3)^2$

53. $x^2 + 14x - 12 = 0$

$x^2 + 14x = 12$

$x^2 + 14x + 49 = 12 + 49$

$(x+7)^2 = 61$

$x + 7 = \pm\sqrt{61}$

$x = -7 \pm \sqrt{61}$

54. $(3 + 2\boldsymbol{i})(4 + 5\boldsymbol{i}) = 12 + 15\boldsymbol{i} + 8\boldsymbol{i} + 10\boldsymbol{i}^2$

$= 12 + 23\boldsymbol{i} + 10(-1)$

$= 12 - 10 + 23\boldsymbol{i}$

$= 2 + 23\boldsymbol{i}$

55. $\frac{120 \text{ beats}}{1 \text{ minute}} \times \frac{2 \text{ hours}}{\text{day}} \times \frac{60 \text{ minutes}}{\text{hour}} \times 2 \text{ weeks} \times \frac{7 \text{ days}}{1\text{week}}$

$= 201{,}600$

$= 2.016 \times 100{,}000$

$= 2.016 \times 10^5$

56. $-3\begin{bmatrix} \frac{5}{6} & 3 \\ -2 & \frac{2}{9} \end{bmatrix} = \begin{bmatrix} -\frac{5}{2} & -9 \\ 6 & -\frac{2}{3} \end{bmatrix}$

57. $f(x, y) = -3y + 4x$
$f(-7 - 4) = -3(-4) + 4(-7)$
$= 12 + (-28)$
$= -16$

58. $C = 10\left(h - \frac{1}{2}\right) + 35$

59. $a^3b^2 + 4ac + 2d \geq 6c^2 - 4ab$
$(2)^3(-6)^2 + 4(2)(3) + 2d \geq 6(3)^2 - 4(2)(-6)$
$8(36) + 24 + 2d \geq 54 + 48$
$288 + 24 + 2d \geq 102$
$312 + 2d \geq 102$
$2d \geq -210$
$d \geq -105$

7-3 Circles

Pages 426–427 Check for Understanding

1. They have the same radius, 4 units, but different centers, (−3, 4) and (3, 2).
2. Answers will vary. Sample answer:
$(x - 2)^2 + (y - 3)^2 = 25$
$(x - 2)^2 + (y - 3)^2 = 36$

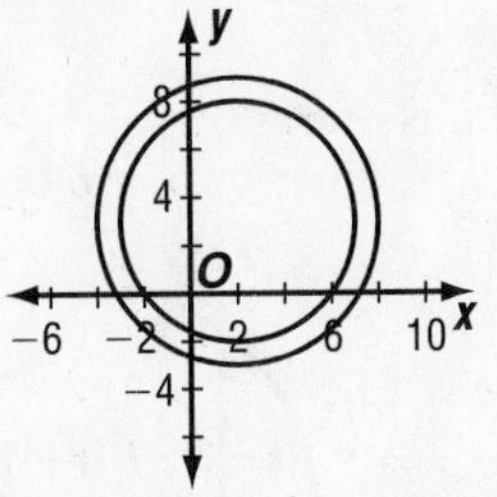

3. If the phrase is not included, the figure would be a sphere.
4. Marco; the square root of $(x - 2)^2 + (y + 3)^2$ is not $(x - 2) + (y + 3)$.
5. Infinite number; every line passing through the center of the circle is an axis of symmetry.
6. Quadrant I
$a > 0, b > 0,$
$a = b, r > 0$

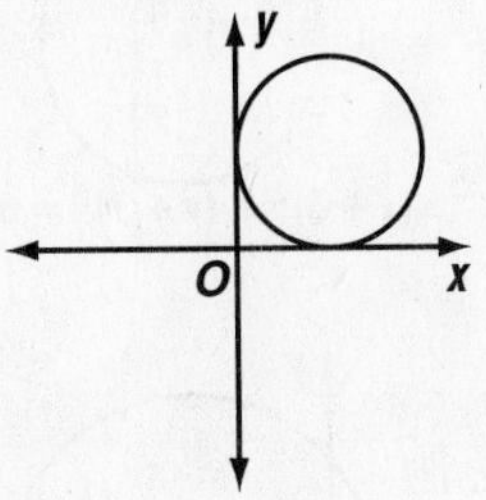

Quadrant II
$a < 0, b > 0,$
$a = -b, r > 0$

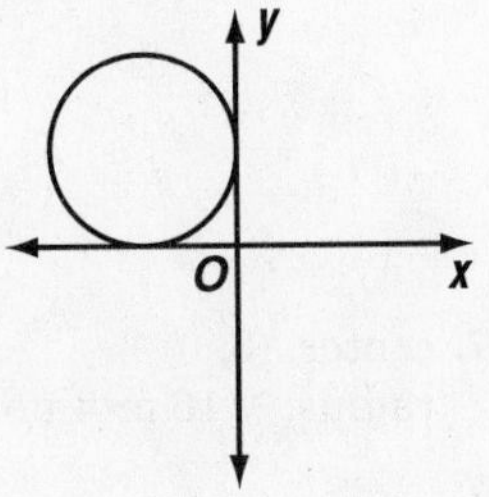

(Continued next column)

Quadrant III
$a < 0, b < 0$
$a = b, r > 0$

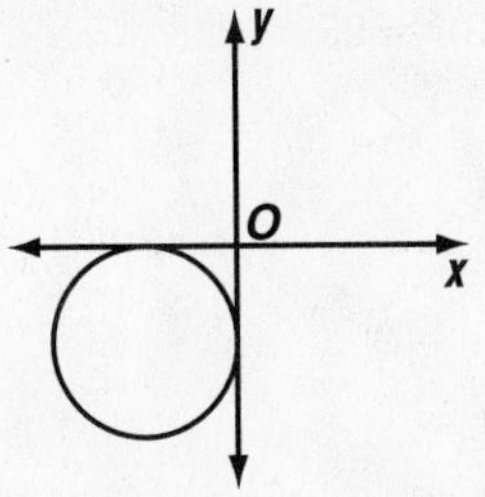

Quadrant IV
$a > 0, b < 0,$
$a = -b, r > 0$

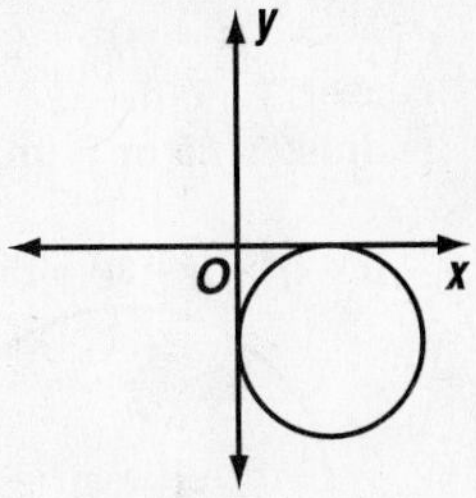

7. $(x - h)^2 + (y - k)^2 = r^2$
$[x - (-12)]^2 + (y - 0)^2 = (\sqrt{23})^2$
$(x + 12)^2 + y^2 = 23$

8. $(x - h)^2 + (y - k)^2 = r^2$
$(x - 8)^2 + [y - (-9.5)]^2 = \left(\frac{1}{2}\right)^2$
$(x - 8)^2 + (y + 9.5)^2 = \frac{1}{4}$

9. center: (4, 1)
radius: $\sqrt{9}$ or 3 units

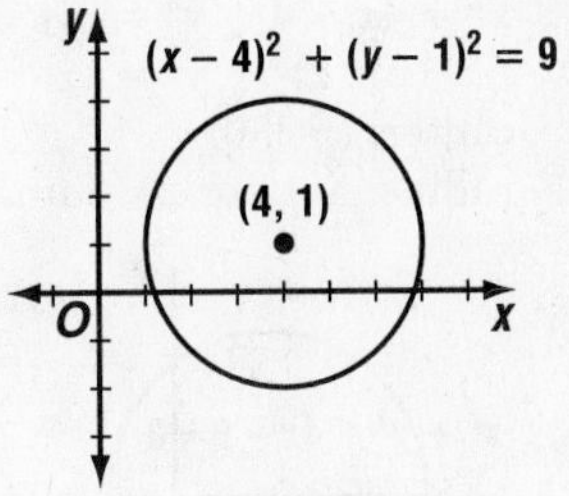

10. center: (0, 14)
radius: $\sqrt{34}$ units

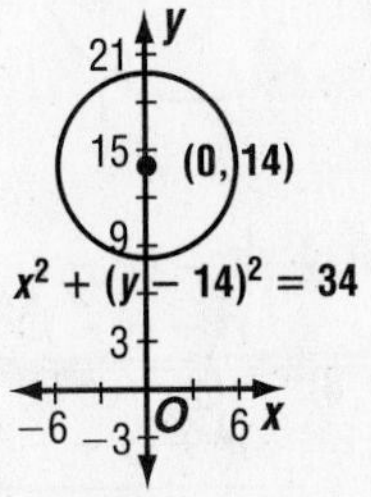

11. center: (4, 0)
radius: $\sqrt{\frac{16}{25}}$ or $\frac{4}{5}$ units

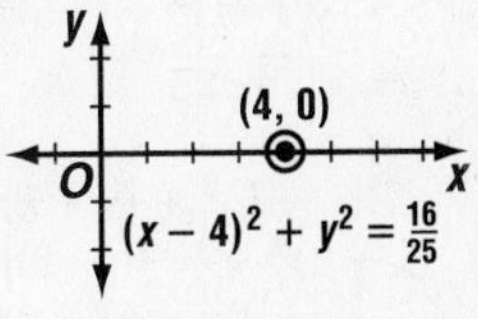

12. center: $\left(-\frac{2}{3}, \frac{1}{2}\right)$
radius: $\sqrt{\frac{8}{9}}$ or $\frac{2\sqrt{2}}{3}$ units

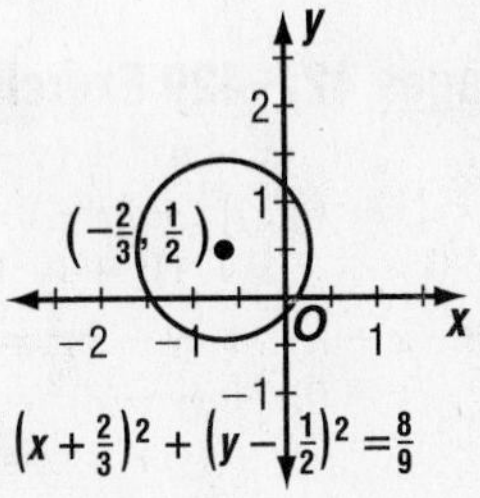

13. $x^2 + y^2 + 8x - 6y = 0$
$x^2 + 8x + y^2 - 6y = 0$
$x^2 + 8x + 16 + y^2 - 6y + 9 = 16 + 9$
$(x + 4)^2 + (y - 3)^2 = 25$
center: $(-4, 3)$
radius: $\sqrt{25}$ or 5 units

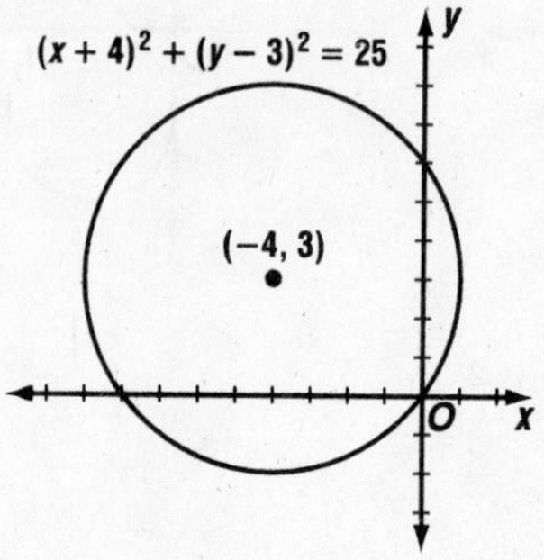

14. $x^2 + y^2 + 4x - 8 = 0$
$x^2 + 4x + y^2 = 8$
$x^2 + 4x + 4 + y^2 = 8 + 4$
$(x + 2)^2 + y^2 = 12$
center: $(-2, 0)$
radius: $\sqrt{12}$ or $2\sqrt{3}$ units

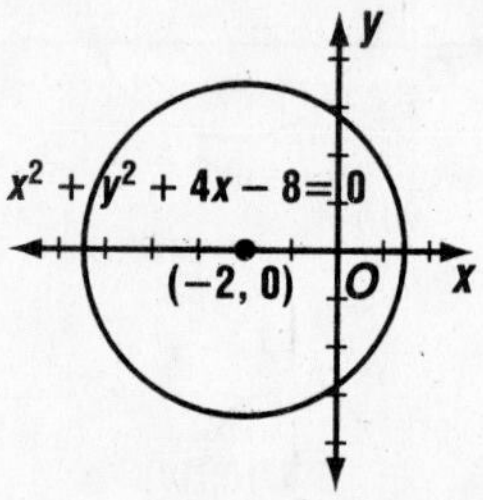

15. Center: $(3, -1)$; radius: 3 units
$(x - h)^2 + (y - k)^2 = r^2$
$(x - 3)^2 + [y - (-1)]^2 = (3)^2$
$(x - 3)^2 + (y + 1)^2 = 9$

16. $r = \sqrt{(4 - 5)^2 + (-2 - 3)^2}$
$= \sqrt{(-1)^2 + (-5)^2}$
$= \sqrt{1 + 25}$
$= \sqrt{26}$
$(x - h)^2 + (y - k)^2 = r^2$
$(x - 4)^2 + [y - (-2)]^2 = (\sqrt{26})^2$
$(x - 4)^2 + (y + 2)^2 = 26$

Pages 427–429 Exercises

17. $(x - h)^2 + (y - k)^2 = r^2$
$[x - (-1)]^2 + [y - (-5)]^2 = (2)^2$
$(x + 1)^2 + (y + 5)^2 = 4$

18. $(x - h)^2 + (y - k)^2 = r^2$
$(x - 0)^2 + (y - 3)^2 = (7)^2$
$x^2 + (y - 3)^2 = 49$

19. $(x - h)^2 + (y - k)^2 = r^2$
$[x - (-8)]^2 + (y - 7)^2 = \left(\frac{1}{2}\right)^2$
$(x + 8)^2 + (y - 7)^2 = \frac{1}{4}$

20. $(x - h)^2 + (y - k)^2 = r^2$
$[x - (-3)]^2 + [y - (-9)]^2 = \left(\frac{5}{6}\right)^2$
$(x + 3)^2 + (y + 9)^2 = \frac{25}{36}$

21. $(x - h)^2 + (y - k)^2 = r^2$
$(x - 0.5)^2 + (y - 0.7)^2 = (13.5)^2$
$(x - 0.5)^2 + (y - 0.7)^2 = 182.25$

22. $(x - h)^2 + (y - k)^2 = r^2$
$(x - \sqrt{2})^2 + (y - 3\sqrt{7})^2 = (0.25)^2$
$(x - \sqrt{2})^2 + (y - 3\sqrt{7})^2 = 0.0625$

23. center: $(0, -2)$
radius: $\sqrt{4}$ or 2 units

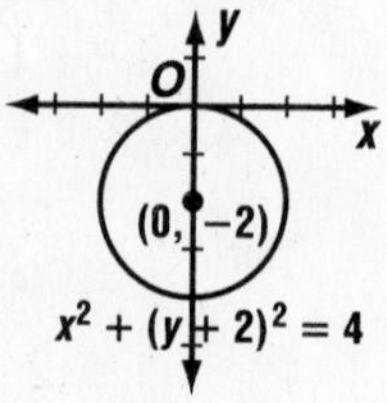

24. center: $(0, 0)$
radius: $\sqrt{144}$ or 12 units

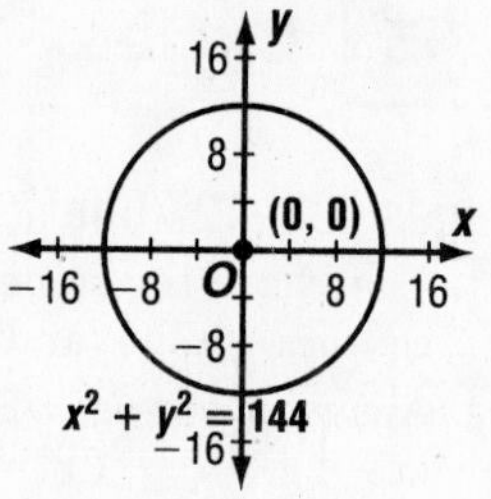

25. center: $(3, 1)$
radius: $\sqrt{25}$ or 5 units

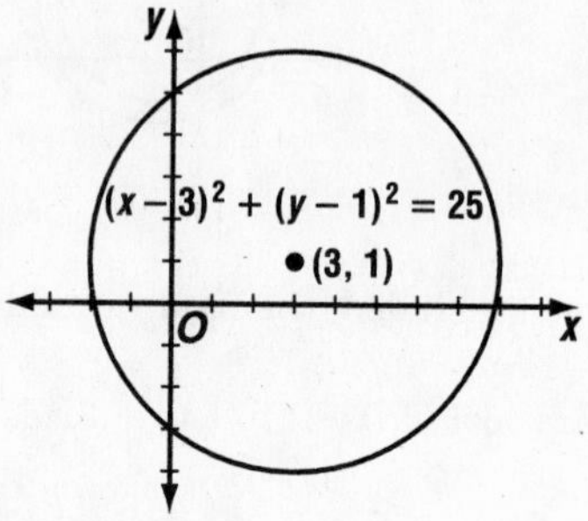

26. center: $(-3, -7)$
radius: $\sqrt{81}$ or 9 units

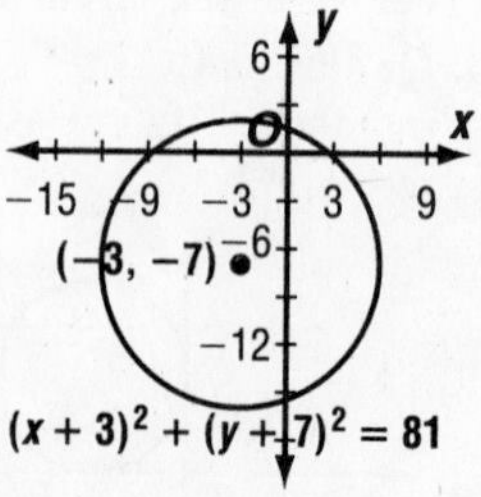

27. center: $(3, 0)$
radius: $\sqrt{16}$ or 4 units

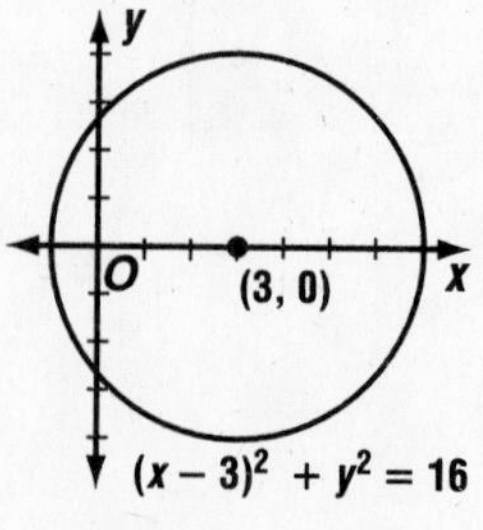

28. center: $(3, -7)$
radius: $\sqrt{50}$ or $5\sqrt{2}$ units

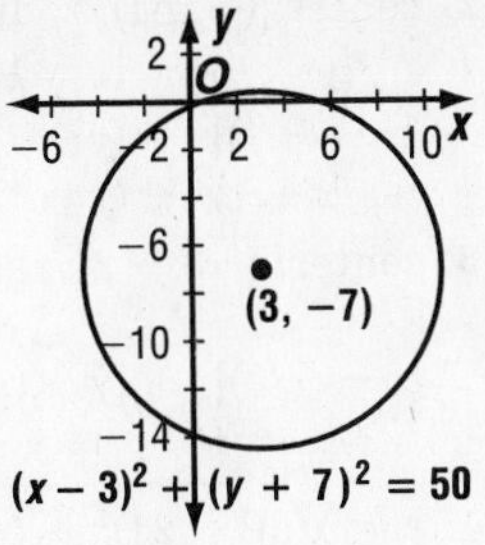

29.
$$(x + \sqrt{5})^2 + y^2 - 8y = 9$$
$$(x + \sqrt{5})^2 + y^2 - 8y + 16 = 9 + 16$$
$$(x + \sqrt{5})^2 + (y - 4)^2 = 25$$
center: $(-\sqrt{5}, 4)$
radius: $\sqrt{25}$ or 5 units

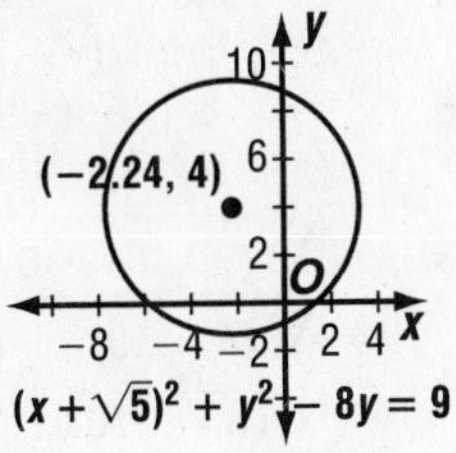

30.
$$x^2 + y^2 + 4x = 9$$
$$x^2 + 4x + y^2 = 9$$
$$x^2 + 4x + 4 + y^2 = 9 + 4$$
$$(x + 2)^2 + y^2 = 13$$
center: $(-2, 0)$
radius: $\sqrt{13}$

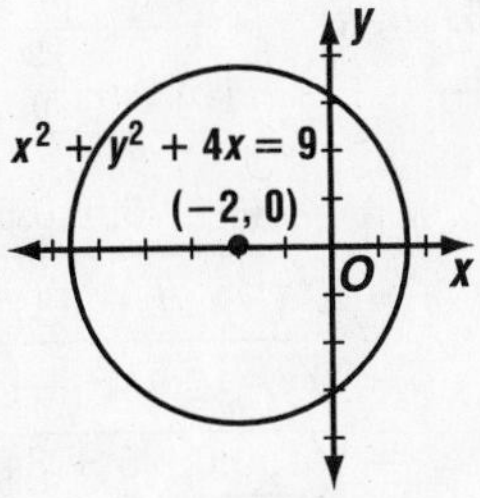

31.
$$x^2 + y^2 + 6y = -50 - 14x$$
$$x^2 + 14x + y^2 + 6y = -50$$
$$x^2 + 14x + 49 + y^2 + 6y + 9 = -50 + 49 + 9$$
$$(x + 7)^2 + (y + 3)^2 = 8$$
center: $(-7, -3)$
radius: $\sqrt{8}$ or $2\sqrt{2}$ units

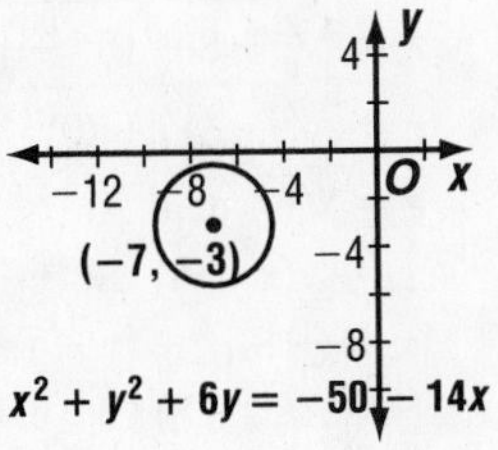

32. $x^2 + y^2 - 6y - 16 = 0$
$$x^2 + y^2 - 6y = 16$$
$$x^2 + y^2 - 6y + 9 = 16 + 9$$
$$x^2 + (y - 3)^2 = 25$$
center: $(0, 3)$
radius: $\sqrt{25}$ or
5 units

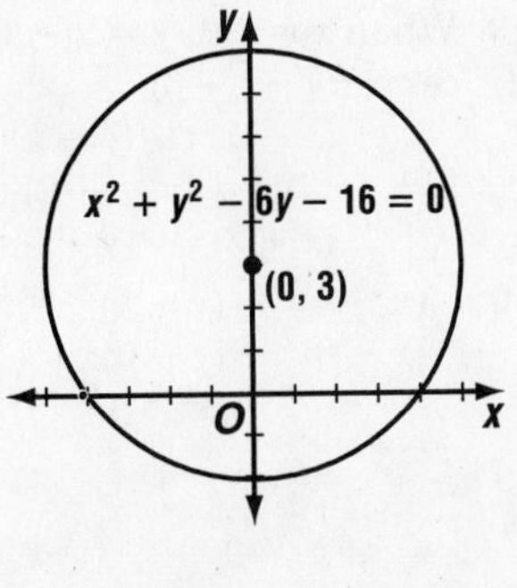

33. $x^2 + y^2 + 2x - 10 = 0$
$$x^2 + 2x + y^2 = 10$$
$$x^2 + 2x + 1 + y^2 = 10 + 1$$
$$(x + 1)^2 + y^2 = 11$$
center: $(-1, 0)$
radius: $\sqrt{11}$ units

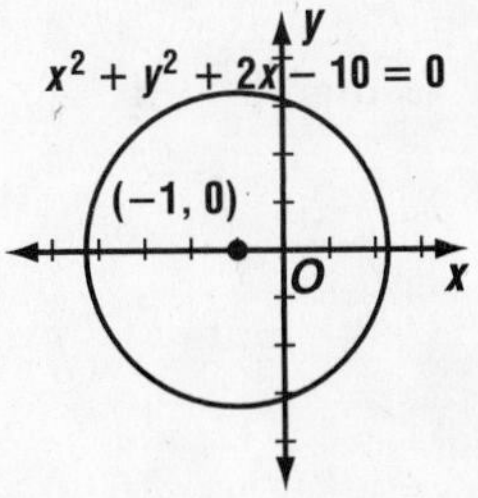

34.
$$x^2 + y^2 - 18x - 18y + 53 = 0$$
$$x^2 - 18x + y^2 - 18y = -53$$
$$x^2 - 18x + 81 + y^2 - 18y + 81 = -53 + 81 + 81$$
$$(x - 9)^2 + (y - 9)^2 = 109$$
center: $(9, 9)$
radius: $\sqrt{109}$ units

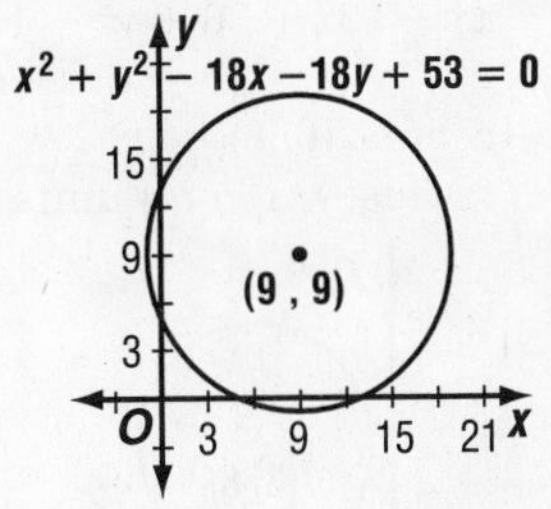

35. $4x^2 + 4y^2 + 36y + 5 = 0$
$$x^2 + y^2 + 9y = -\frac{5}{4}$$
$$x^2 + y^2 + 9y + \frac{81}{4} = -\frac{5}{4} + \frac{81}{4}$$
$$x^2 + \left(y + \frac{9}{2}\right)^2 = 19$$
center: $\left(0, -\frac{9}{2}\right)$
radius: $\sqrt{19}$ units

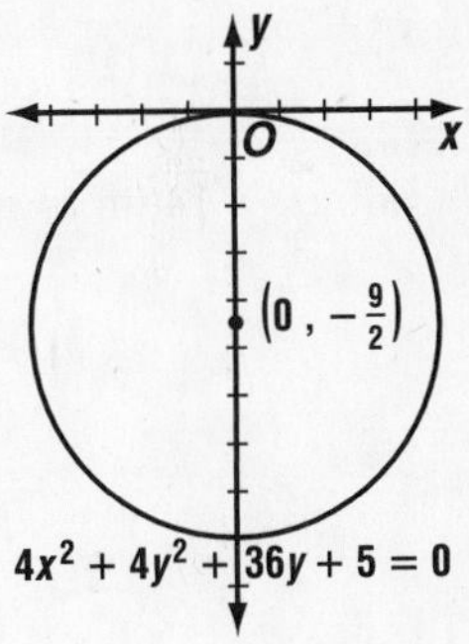

36.
$$x^2 + y^2 + 9x - 8y + 4 = 0$$
$$x^2 + 9x + y^2 - 8y = -4$$
$$x^2 + 9x + \frac{81}{4} + y^2 - 8y + 16 = -4 + \frac{81}{4} + 16$$
$$\left(x + \frac{9}{2}\right)^2 + (y - 4)^2 = \frac{129}{4}$$
center: $\left(-\frac{9}{2}, 4\right)$

radius: $\sqrt{\frac{129}{4}}$ or $\frac{\sqrt{129}}{2}$ units

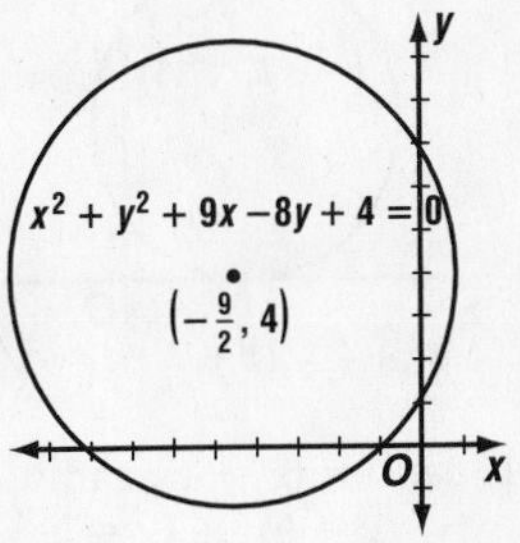

37.

$$x^2 + y^2 - 3x + 8y = 20$$
$$x^2 - 3x + y^2 + 8y = 20$$
$$x^2 - 3x + \frac{9}{4} + y^2 + 8y + 16 = 20 + \frac{9}{4} + 16$$
$$\left(x - \frac{3}{2}\right)^2 + (y + 4)^2 = \frac{153}{4}$$

center: $\left(\frac{3}{2}, -4\right)$

radius: $\sqrt{\frac{153}{4}}$ or $\frac{3\sqrt{17}}{2}$ units

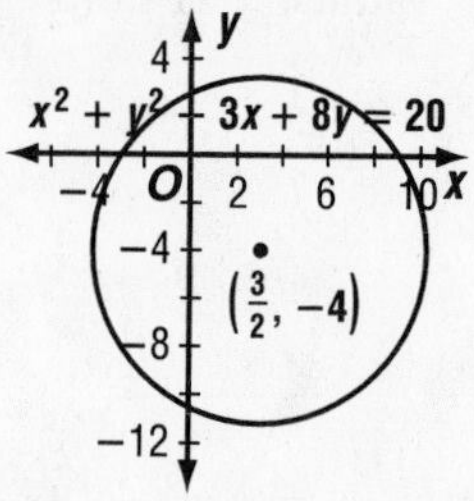

38.

$$x^2 - 12x + 84 = -y^2 + 16y$$
$$x^2 - 12x + y^2 - 16y = -84$$
$$x^2 - 12x + 36 + y^2 - 16y + 64 = -84 + 36 + 64$$
$$(x - 6)^2 + (y - 8)^2 = 16$$

center: (6, 8)
radius: $\sqrt{16}$ or 4 units

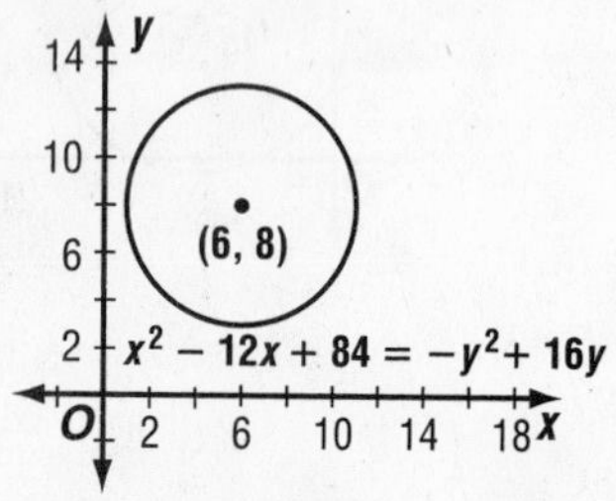

39.

$$x^2 + y^2 + 2x + 4y = 9$$
$$x^2 + 2x + y^2 + 4y = 9$$
$$x^2 + 2x + 1 + y^2 + 4y + 4 = 9 + 1 + 4$$
$$(x + 1)^2 + (y + 2)^2 = 14$$

center: (−1, −2)
radius: $\sqrt{14}$ units

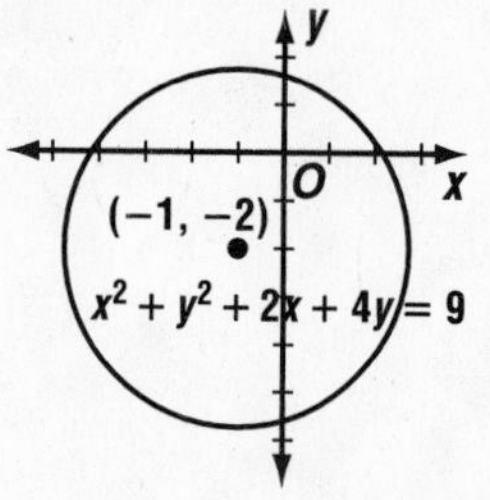

40. $x^2 + 2\sqrt{7}x + 7 + (y - \sqrt{11})^2 = 11$

$$(x + \sqrt{7})^2 + (y - \sqrt{11})^2 = 11$$

center: $(-\sqrt{7}, \sqrt{11})$
radius: $\sqrt{11}$ units

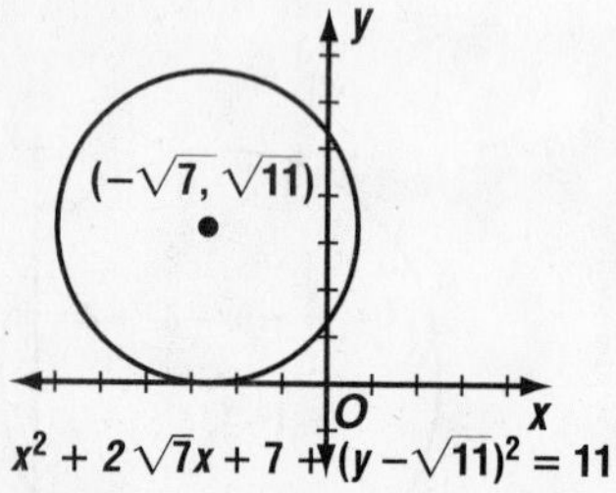

41. center: (2, −1); radius: 2 units

$$(x - h)^2 + (y - k)^2 = r^2$$
$$(x - 2)^2 + [y - (-1)]^2 = (2)^2$$
$$(x - 2)^2 + (y + 1)^2 = 4$$

42. center: (−1, 1); radius: 4 units

$$(x - h)^2 + (y - k)^2 = r^2$$
$$[x - (-1)]^2 + (y - 1)^2 = (4)^2$$
$$(x + 1)^2 + (y - 1)^2 = 16$$

43. center: (−3, −2); radius: 1 unit

$$(x - h)^2 + (y - k)^2 = r^2$$
$$[x - (-3)]^2 + [y - (-2)]^2 = (1)^2$$
$$(x + 3)^2 + (y + 2)^2 = 1$$

44. $r = \sqrt{(8 - 21)^2 + (-9 - 22)^2}$

$$= \sqrt{(-13)^2 + (-31)^2}$$
$$= \sqrt{169 + 961}$$
$$= \sqrt{1130}$$
$$(x - h)^2 + (y - k)^2 = r^2$$
$$(x - 8)^2 + [y - (-9)]^2 = (\sqrt{1130})^2$$
$$(x - 8)^2 + (y + 9)^2 = 1130$$

45. $r = \sqrt{(-\sqrt{13} - 0)^2 + (42 - 0)^2}$

$$= \sqrt{(-\sqrt{13})^2 + (42)^2}$$
$$= \sqrt{13 + 1764}$$
$$= \sqrt{1777}$$
$$(x - h)^2 + (y - k)^2 = r^2$$
$$[x - (-\sqrt{13})]^2 + (y - 42)^2 = (\sqrt{1777})^2$$
$$(x + \sqrt{13})^2 + (y - 42)^2 = 1777$$

46. $(h, k) = \left(\frac{x_1 + x_2}{2}, \frac{y_1 + y_2}{2}\right)$

$$= \left(\frac{11 + (-13.5)}{2}, \frac{18 + (-19)}{2}\right)$$
$$= (-1.25, -0.5)$$
$$r = \sqrt{(-1.25 - 11)^2 + (-0.5 - 18)^2}$$
$$= \sqrt{(-12.25)^2 + (-18.5)^2}$$
$$= \sqrt{150.0625 + 342.25}$$
$$= \sqrt{492.3125}$$
$$(x - h)^2 + (y - k)^2 = r^2$$
$$[x - (-1.25)]^2 + [y - (-0.5)]^2 = (\sqrt{492.3125})^2$$
$$(x + 1.25)^2 + (y + 0.5)^2 = 492.3125$$

47. center (−8, −7)

$$r = \sqrt{(-8 - 0)^2 + [-7 - (-7)]^2}$$
$$r = \sqrt{(-8)^2 + (0)^2}$$
$$r = \sqrt{64} \text{ or } 8$$
$$(x - h)^2 + (y - k)^2 = r^2$$
$$[x - (-8)]^2 + [y - (-7)]^2 = (8)^2$$
$$(x + 8)^2 + (y + 7)^2 = 64$$

48. radius: 4 units
center: (1, 4)

$$(x - h)^2 + (y - k)^2 = r^2$$
$$(x - 1)^2 + (y - 4)^2 = (4)^2$$
$$(x - 1)^2 + (y - 4)^2 = 16$$

49. When $x = -3$, $y = 2(-3)$ or $y = -6$.
center: (−3, −6)

$$(x - h)^2 + (y - k)^2 = r^2$$
$$[x - (-3)]^2 + [y - (-6)]^2 = (3)^2$$
$$(x + 3)^2 + (y + 6)^2 = 9$$

50a. $(x - h)^2 + (y - k)^2 = r^2$

$$(x - 0)^2 + (y - 0)^2 = (1)^2$$
$$x^2 + y^2 = 1$$

50b.

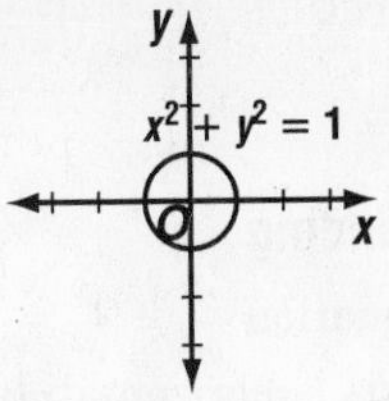

50c. $A = \pi r^2$
$= \pi(1)^2$
$= \pi$; π square units

50d. $C = 2\pi r$
$= 2\pi(1)$
$= 2\pi$; 2π units

51. $x^2 + 6x + y^2 + 4y + 9 = 0$
$x^2 + 6x + y^2 + 4y = -9$
$x^2 + 6x + 9 + y^2 + 4y + 4 = -9 + 9 + 4$
$(x + 3)^2 + (y + 2)^2 = 4$
center: $(-3, -2)$
radius: $\sqrt{4}$ or 2
$y = 0$

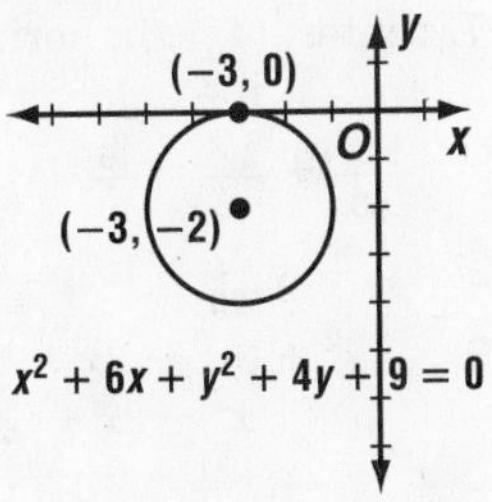

52a. (0, 5), (4, 3), (0, −5)

52b. Yes, the vertices of the triangle are on the circle and a diameter is on the y-axis.

53. $x^2 + y^2 = 4$
$y^2 = 4 - x^2$
$y = \pm\sqrt{4 - x^2}$
$y = \sqrt{4 - x^2}$, $y = -\sqrt{4 - x^2}$

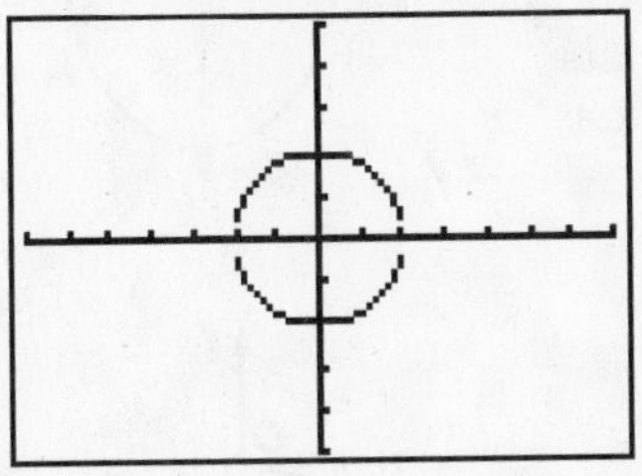

54. $(x + 3)^2 + (y - 1)^2 = 8$
$(y - 1)^2 = 8 - (x + 3)^2$
$y - 1 = \pm\sqrt{8 - (x + 3)^2}$
$y = 1 \pm \sqrt{8 - (x + 3)^2}$
$y = 1 + \sqrt{8 - (x + 3)^2}$, $y = 1 - \sqrt{8 - (x + 3)^2}$

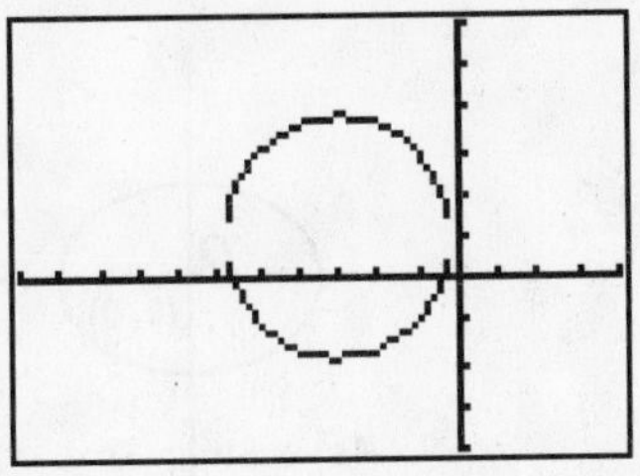

55. circles with a radius of 8 and centers on the graph of $x = 3$

56. $(x - h)^2 + (y - k)^2 = r^2$
$(x - 5)^2 + (y - 10)^2 = (20)^2$
$(x - 5)^2 + (y - 10)^2 = 400$

57a. radius: 25,000 + 4000 or 29,000 miles
$(x - h)^2 + (y - k)^2 = r^2$
$(x - 0)^2 + (y - 0)^2 = (29{,}000)^2$
$x^2 + y^2 = 841{,}000{,}000$

57b.

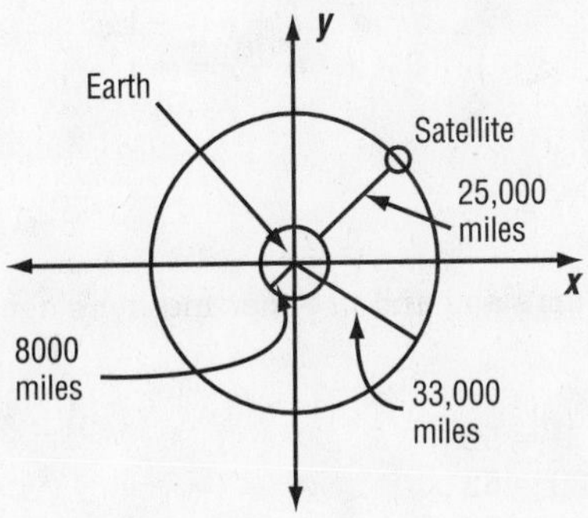

58a. $a^2 + b^2 = c^2$
$200^2 + b^2 = 340^2$
$b^2 = 75{,}600$
$b = 275$; center: $(200, -275)$
$(x - h)^2 + (y - k)^2 = r^2$
$(x - 200)^2 + [y - (-275)]^2 = (340)^2$
$(x - 200)^2 + (y + 275)^2 = 340^2$
$(y + 275)^2 = 340^2 - (x - 200)^2$
$y + 275 = \sqrt{340^2 - (x - 200)^2}$
$y = \sqrt{115{,}600 - (x^2 - 400x + 40{,}000)} - 275$
$y = \sqrt{-x^2 + 400x + 75{,}600} - 275$

58b. Using a coordinate plane with origin at point A, mark all the points that satisfy the equation from (0, 0) to (400, 0).

59. $y^2 = 6x$
$\frac{1}{6}y^2 = x$ or $x = \frac{1}{6}y^2$

60. $x^2 - 3x + 1 = 0$
$x = \frac{-(-3) \pm \sqrt{(-3)^2 - 4(1)(1)}}{2(1)}$
$= \frac{3 \pm \sqrt{5}}{2}$

Check:
$s_1 + s_2 = \frac{-b}{a} = 3$
$\frac{3 + \sqrt{5}}{2} + \frac{3 - \sqrt{5}}{2} = \frac{6}{2} = 3$ ✓
$s_1(s_2) = \frac{c}{a} = 1$
$\left(\frac{3 + \sqrt{5}}{2}\right)\left(\frac{3 + \sqrt{5}}{2}\right) = \frac{9 - 5}{4} = \frac{4}{4} = 1$ ✓

61. $\frac{3}{4 - i} = \left(\frac{3}{4 - i}\right)\left(\frac{4 + i}{4 + i}\right)$
$= \frac{12 + 3i}{16 - i^2}$
$= \frac{12 + 3i}{16 - (-1)}$
$= \frac{12 + 3i}{17}$

62. $23{,}450(1 + p)$; $23{,}450(1 + p)^3$

63. $\begin{vmatrix} x^2 & x \\ 3 & 1 \end{vmatrix} = 4$

$x^2 - 3x = 4$

$x^2 - 3x - 4 = 0$

$(x - 4)(x + 1) = 0$

$x - 4 = 0$ or $x + 1 = 0$

$x = 4$ $\quad$ $x = -1$

64. $5a = 15$

$a = 3$

$2a + b = 2$

$2(3) + b = 2$

$b = -4$

$a + b + c = -1$

$3 + (-4) + c = -1$

$c = 0$

$(3, -4, 0)$

65. Let k = Kari's age and m = her mother's age.

$k + m = 52$

$m = 20 + k$

$k + (20 + k) = 52$

$2k + 20 = 52$

$2k = 32$

$k = 16$

$m = 20 + 16$

$= 36$

Kari is 16 and her mother is 36 years old.

66. $m = \frac{y_2 - y_1}{x_2 - x_1}$

$= \frac{2 - 1}{8 - 5}$

$= \frac{1}{3}$

The slope is -3.

67. $r = 0.6(220 - a)$

$= 0.6(220 - 20)$

$= 0.6(200)$

$= 120$

68. $\sqrt{9} \div \sqrt{4} = 3 \div 2$

$= \frac{3}{2}$

7-4A Modeling Mathematics: Drawing Ellipses

Page 430 Exercises

1.

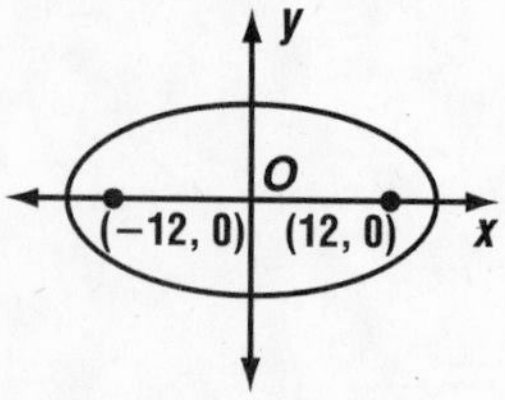

2.

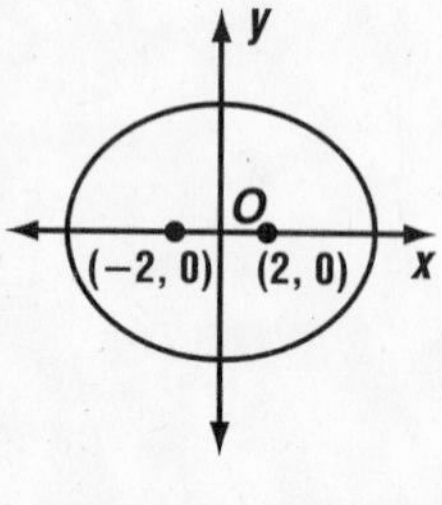

3.

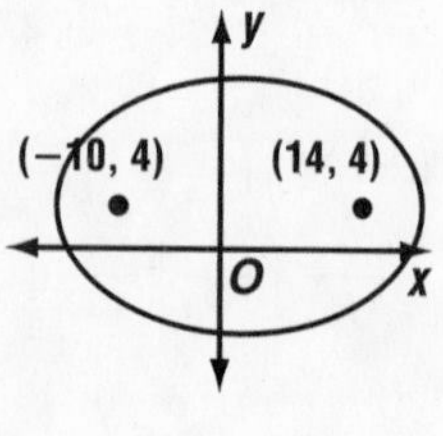

4a. As the thumbtacks are moved closer together, the ellipse looks more circular; as they move farther apart, the ellipse is wider.

4b. The ellipse is a circle.

4c. As the length of the piece of string is shortened, the ellipse is wider; as the length is increased, the ellipse is narrower.

7-4 Ellipses

Page 436 Check for Understanding

1. Sample answer: For the equation $\frac{x^2}{m^2} + \frac{y^2}{n^2} = 1$, if $m^2 > n^2$, then the major axis is horizontal. If $m^2 < n^2$, then the major axis is vertical.

2. If the major and minor axes are the same length, the ellipse is a circle.

3. The equation in this from allows easy determination of the length of the major and minor axes and the coordinates of the center.

4. The shortest distance from the center of the sun plus the longest distance from the center of the sun gives the major axis.

5. See students' work.

6. center: (0, 0), vertical

7. center: (4, −6); horizontal

8. $10x^2 + 2y^2 = 40$

$\frac{10x^2}{40} + \frac{2y^2}{40} = \frac{40}{40}$

$\frac{x^2}{4} + \frac{y^2}{20} = 1$

9. $x^2 + 6y^2 - 2x + 12y - 23 = 0$

$x^2 - 2x + 6y^2 + 12y = 23$

$x^2 - 2x + 1 + 6(y^2 + 2y + 1) = 23 + 1 + 6$

$(x - 1)^2 + 6(y + 1)^2 = 30$

$\frac{(x - 1)^2}{30} + \frac{(y + 1)^2}{5} = 1$

10. center: (0, 0)

foci: $b^2 = a^2 - c^2$

$9 = 18 - c^2$

$9 = c^2$

$\pm 3 = c$

$(0, \pm 3)$

length of major axis: $2(3\sqrt{2})$ or $6\sqrt{2}$ units

length of minor axis: $2(3)$ or 6 units

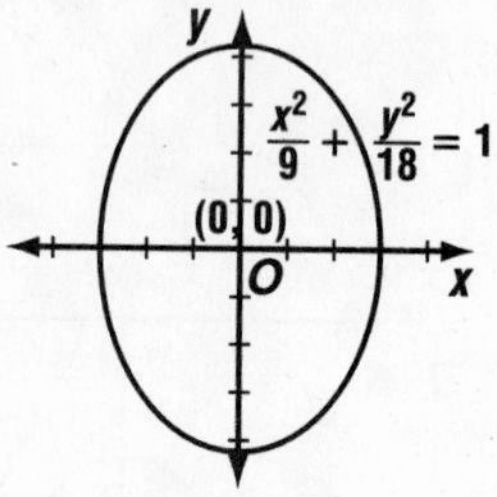

11. center: (1, −2)

foci: $b^2 = a^2 - c^2$

$4 = 20 - c^2$

$16 = c^2$

$\pm 4 = c$

$(1 \pm 4, -2)$ or $(5, -2)$ and $(-3, -2)$

length of major axis: $2(2\sqrt{5})$ or $4\sqrt{5}$ units

length of minor axis: $2(2)$ or 4 units

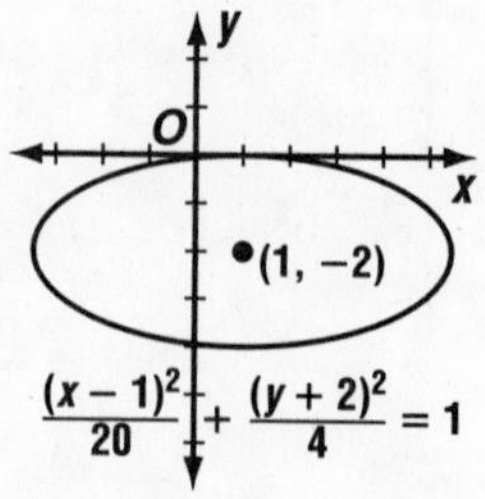

12. $4x^2 + 8y^2 = 32$

$\frac{x^2}{8} + \frac{y^2}{4} = 1$

center: (0, 0)

foci: $b^2 = a^2 - c^2$

$4 = 8 - c^2$

$4 = c^2$

$\pm 2 = c$

$(\pm 2, 0)$

length of major axis: $2(2\sqrt{2})$ or $4\sqrt{2}$ units

length of minor axis: $2(2)$ or 4 units

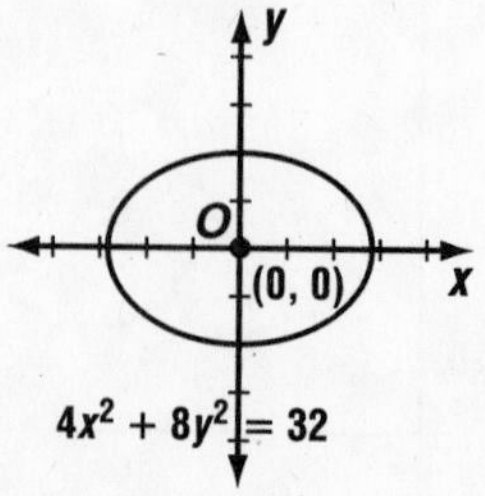

13. $x^2 + 25y^2 - 8x + 100y + 91 = 0$

$x^2 - 8x + 25y^2 + 100y = -91$

$x^2 - 8x + 16 + 25(y^2 + 4y + 4) = -91 + 16 + 100$

$(x - 4)^2 + 25(y + 2)^2 = 25$

$\frac{(x-4)^2}{25} + \frac{(y+2)^2}{1} = 1$

center: $(4, -2)$

foci: $b^2 = a^2 - c^2$

$1 = 25 - c^2$

$24 = c^2$

$\pm 2\sqrt{6} = c$

$(4 \pm 2\sqrt{6}, -2)$

length of major axis:

2(5) or 10 units

length of minor axis:

2(1) or 2 units

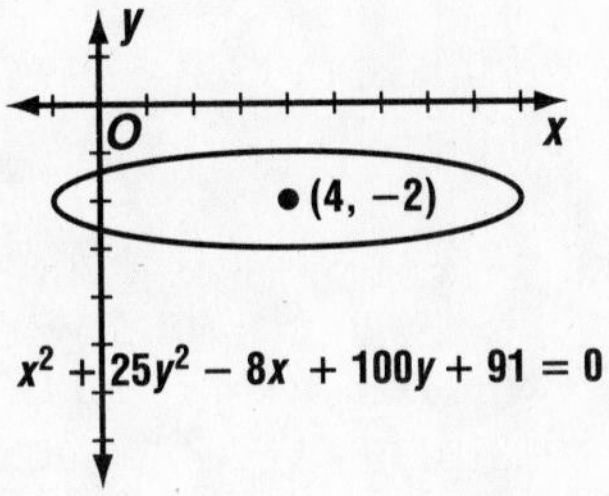

14. center: $(0, 0)$

length of major axis: 12 units

$2a = 12$

$a = 6$

foci: $(-4, 0)$, $(4, 0)$

$c = 4$

$b^2 = a^2 - c^2$

$b^2 = 36 - 16$

$b^2 = 20$

$\frac{x^2}{36} + \frac{y^2}{20} = 1$

15. center: $(0, 0)$

length of major axis: 20 units

$2a = 20$

$a = 10$

foci: $(0, -8)$, $(0, 8)$

$c = 8$

$b^2 = a^2 - c^2$

$b^2 = 100 - 64$

$b^2 = 36$

$\frac{x^2}{36} + \frac{y^2}{100} = 1$

Pages 437–439 Exercises

16. center: $(0, 0)$

length of major axis: 16 units

$2a = 16$

$a = 8$

foci: $(0, 5)$, $(0, -5)$

$c = 5$

$b^2 = a^2 - c^2$

$b^2 = 64 - 25$

$b^2 = 39$

$\frac{x^2}{39} + \frac{y^2}{64} = 1$

17. center: $(5, 4)$

length of major axis: 16 units

$2a = 16$

$a = 8$

foci: $(5 - \sqrt{55}, 4)$, $(5 + \sqrt{55}, 4)$

$c = \sqrt{55}$

$b^2 = a^2 - c^2$

$b^2 = 64 - 55$

$b^2 = 9$

$\frac{(x-5)^2}{64} + \frac{(y-4)^2}{9} = 1$

18. center: $(-2, 0)$

length of major axis: 8 units

$2a = 8$

$a = 4$

foci: $(-2, 2\sqrt{3})$, $(-2, -2\sqrt{3})$

$c = 2\sqrt{3}$

$b^2 = a^2 - c^2$

$b^2 = 16 - 12$

$b^2 = 4$

$\frac{(x+2)^2}{4} + \frac{y^2}{16} = 1$

19. center: $(0, 0)$

foci: $b^2 = a^2 - c^2$

$5 = 10 - c^2$

$5 = c^2$

$\pm\sqrt{5} = c$

$(0, \pm\sqrt{5})$

length of major axis:

$2(\sqrt{10})$ or $2\sqrt{10}$ units

length of minor axis:

$2(\sqrt{5})$ or $2\sqrt{5}$ units

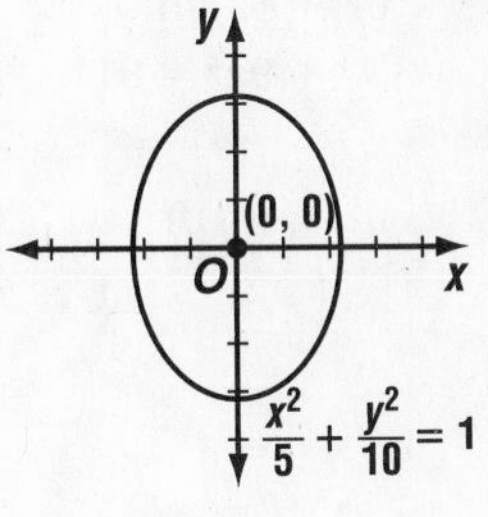

20. center: $(0, 0)$

foci: $b^2 = a^2 - c^2$

$9 = 25 - c^2$

$16 = c^2$

$\pm 4 = c$

$(\pm 4, 0)$

length of major axis:

2(5) or 10 units

length of minor axis:

2(3) or 6 units

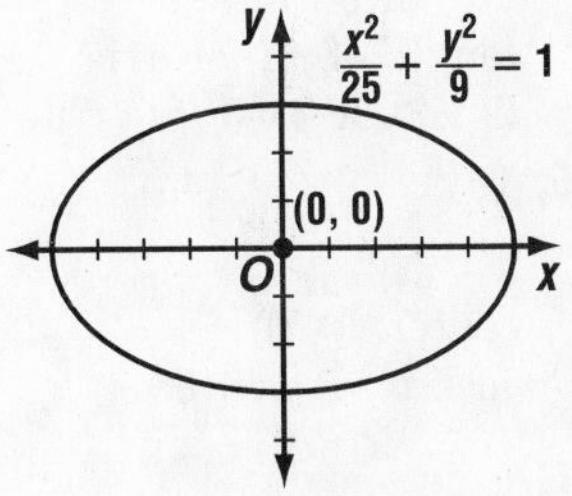

21. center: $(5, -11)$

foci: $b^2 = a^2 - c^2$

$121 = 144 - c^2$

$23 = c^2$

$\pm\sqrt{23} = c$

$(5, -11 \pm \sqrt{23})$

length of major axis:

2(12) or 24 units

length of minor axis:

2(11) or 22 units

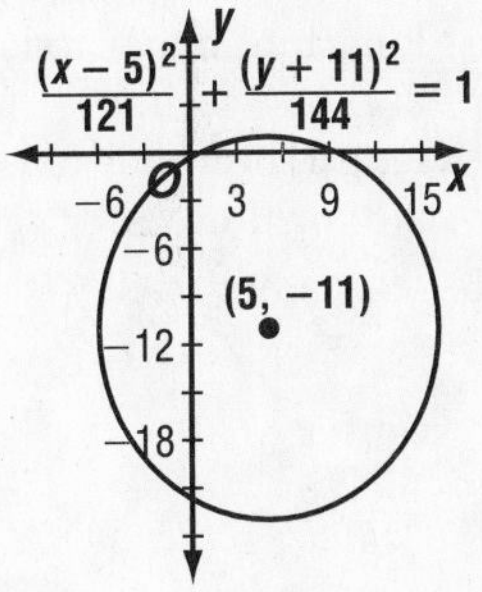

22. center: $(-8, 2)$

foci: $b^2 = a^2 - c^2$

$81 = 144 - c^2$

$63 = c^2$

$\pm 3\sqrt{7} = c$

$(-8 \pm 3\sqrt{7}, 2)$

length of major axis:

2(12) or 24 units

length of minor axis:

2(9) or 18 units

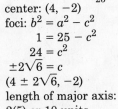

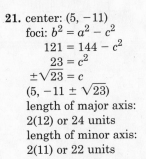

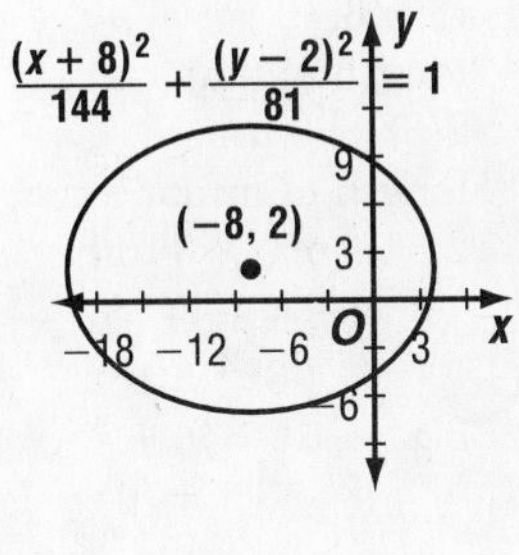

23. $36x^2 + 81y^2 = 2916$

$\frac{x^2}{81} + \frac{y^2}{36} = 1$

center: (0, 0)

foci: $b^2 = a^2 - c^2$

$36 = 81 - c^2$

$45 = c^2$

$\pm 3\sqrt{5} = c$

$(\pm 3\sqrt{5}, 0)$

length of major axis:

2(9) or 18 units

length of minor axis:

2(6) or 12 units

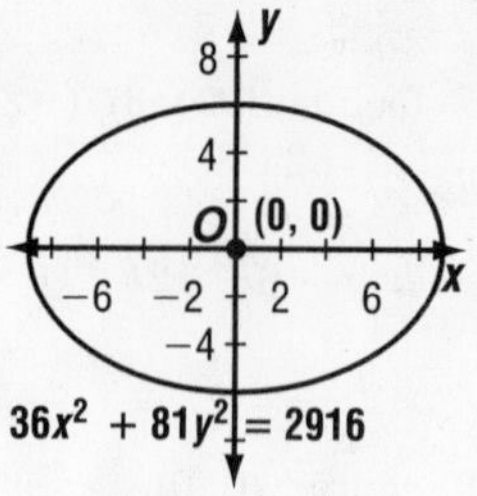

24. $27x^2 + 9y^2 = 81$

$\frac{x^2}{3} + \frac{y^2}{9} = 1$

center: (0, 0)

foci: $b^2 = a^2 - c^2$

$3 = 9 - c^2$

$6 = c^2$

$\pm\sqrt{6} = c$

$(0, \pm\sqrt{6})$

length of major axis:

2(3) or 6 units

length of minor axis:

$2(\sqrt{3})$ or $2\sqrt{3}$ units

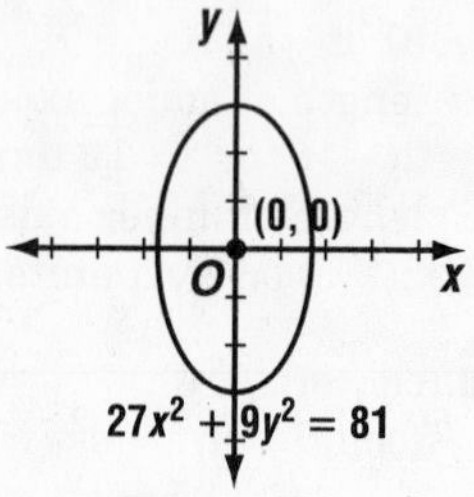

25. $16x^2 + 9y^2 = 144$

$\frac{x^2}{9} + \frac{y^2}{16} = 1$

center: (0, 0)

foci: $b^2 = a^2 - c^2$

$9 = 16 - c^2$

$7 = c^2$

$\pm\sqrt{7} = c$

$(0, \pm\sqrt{7})$

length of major axis:

2(4) or 8 units

length of minor axis:

2(3) or 6 units

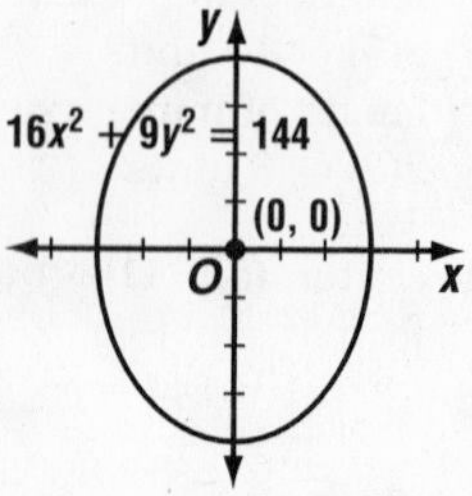

26. $3x^2 + 9y^2 = 27$

$\frac{x^2}{9} + \frac{y^2}{3} = 1$

center (0, 0)

foci: $b^2 = a^2 - c^2$

$3 = 9 - c^2$

$6 = c^2$

$\pm\sqrt{6} = c$

$(\pm\sqrt{6}, 0)$

length of major axis:

2(3) or 6 units

length of minor axis:

$2(\sqrt{3})$ or $2\sqrt{3}$ units

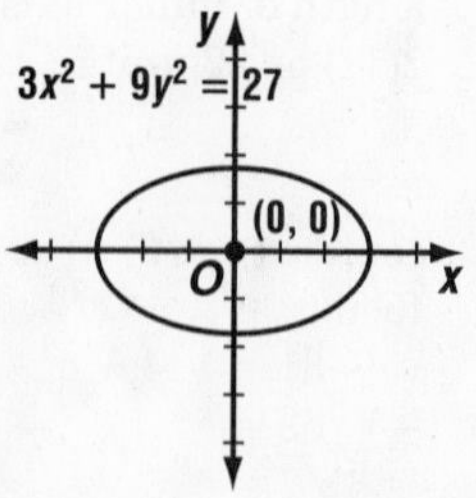

27. $3x^2 + y^2 + 18x - 2y + 4 = 0$

$3x^2 + 18x + y^2 - 2y = -4$

$3(x^2 + 6x + 9) + y^2 - 2y + 1 = -4 + 27 + 1$

$3(x + 3)^2 + (y - 1)^2 = 24$

$\frac{(x + 3)^2}{8} + \frac{(x - 1)^2}{24} = 1$

center: (−3, 1)

foci: $b^2 = a^2 - c^2$

$8 = 24 - c^2$

$16 = c^2$

$\pm 4 = c$

$(-3, 1 \pm 4)$ or $(-3, 5)$ and $(-3, -3)$

(Continued next column)

length of major axis:

$2(2\sqrt{6})$ or $4\sqrt{6}$ units

length of minor axis:

$2(2\sqrt{2})$ or $4\sqrt{2}$ units

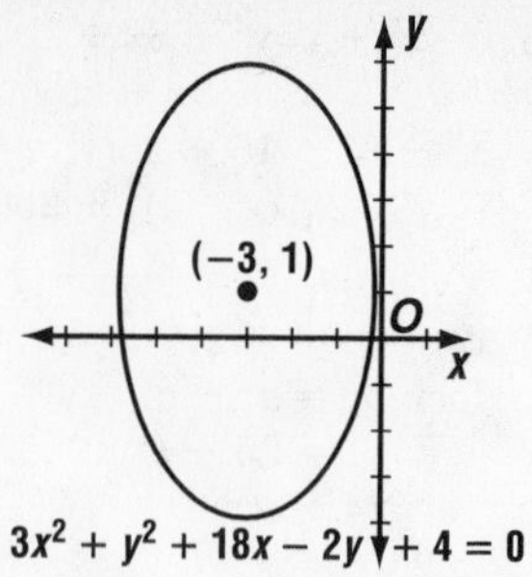

28. $x^2 + 5y^2 + 4x - 70y + 209 = 0$

$x^2 + 4x + 5y^2 - 70y = -209$

$x^2 + 4x + 4 + 5(y^2 - 14y + 49) = -209 + 4 + 245$

$(x + 2)^2 + 5(y - 7)^2 = 40$

$\frac{(x + 2)^2}{40} + \frac{(y - 7)^2}{8} = 1$

center: (−2, 7)

foci: $b^2 = a^2 - c^2$

$8 = 40 - c^2$

$32 = c^2$

$\pm 4\sqrt{2} = c$

$(-2 \pm 4\sqrt{2}, 7)$

length of major axis:

$2(2\sqrt{10})$ or $4\sqrt{10}$ units

length of minor axis:

$2(2\sqrt{2})$ or $4\sqrt{2}$ units

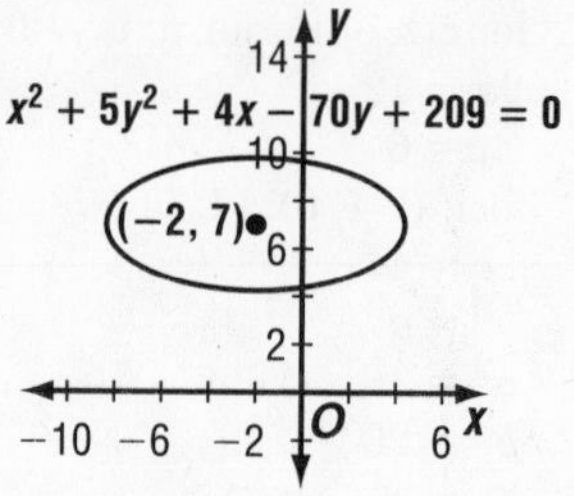

29. $7x^2 + 3y^2 - 28x - 12y = -19$

$7x^2 - 28x + 3y^2 - 12y = -19$

$7(x^2 - 4x + 4) + 3(y^2 - 4y + 4) = -19 + 28 + 12$

$7(x - 2)^2 + 3(y - 2)^2 = 21$

$\frac{(x - 2)^2}{3} + \frac{(y - 2)^2}{7} = 1$

center: (2, 2)

foci: $b^2 = a^2 - c^2$

$3 = 7 - c^2$

$4 = c^2$

$\pm 2 = c$

$(2, 2 \pm 2)$ or

(2, 0) and (2, 4)

length of major axis:

$2(\sqrt{7})$ or $2\sqrt{7}$ units

length of minor axis:

$2(\sqrt{3})$ or $2\sqrt{3}$ units

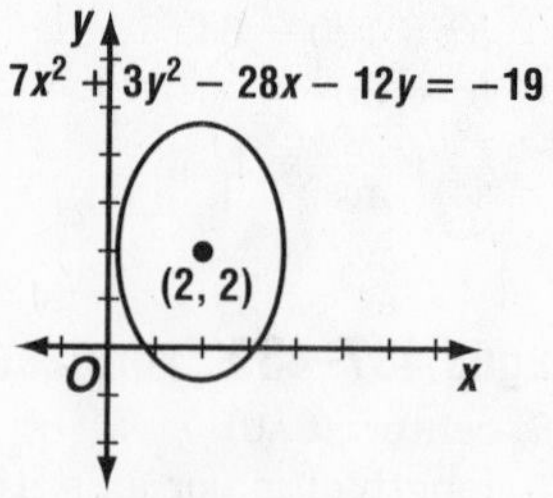

30. $16x^2 + 25y^2 + 32x - 150y = 159$

$16x^2 + 32x + 25y^2 - 150y = 159$

$16(x^2 + 2x + 1) + 25(y^2 - 6y + 9) = 159 + 16 + 225$

$16(x + 1)^2 + 25(y - 3)^2 = 400$

$\frac{(x + 1)^2}{25} + \frac{(y - 3)^2}{16} = 1$

center: (−1, 3)

foci: $b^2 = a^2 - c^2$

$16 = 25 - c^2$

$9 = c^2$

$\pm 3 = c$

$(-1 \pm 3, 3)$ or $(-4, 3)$

and (2, 3)

length of major axis:

2(5) or 10 units

length of minor axis:

2(4) or 8 units

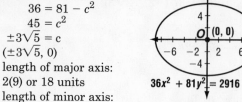

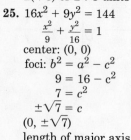

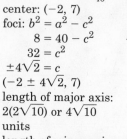

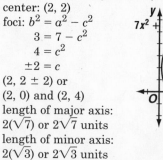

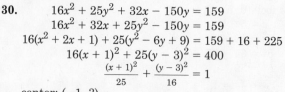

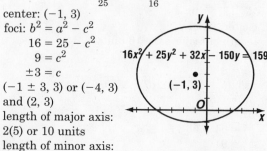

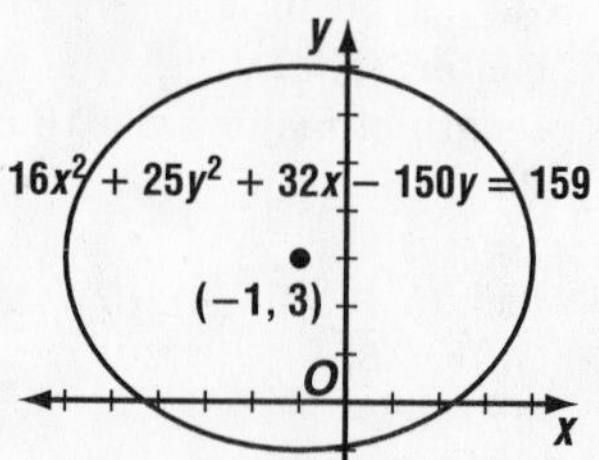

31. $9x^2 + 16y^2 - 18x + 64y = 71$
$9x^2 - 18x + 16y^2 + 64y = 71$
$9(x^2 - 2x + 1) + 16(y^2 + 4y + 4) = 71 + 9 + 64$
$9(x - 1)^2 + 16(y + 2)^2 = 144$
$\frac{(x-1)^2}{16} + \frac{(y+2)^2}{9} = 1$

center: $(1, -2)$
foci: $b^2 = a^2 - c^2$
$9 = 16 - c^2$
$7 = c^2$
$\pm\sqrt{7} = c$
$(1 \pm \sqrt{7}, -2)$
length of major axis:
2(4) or 8 units
length of minor axis:
2(3) or 6 units

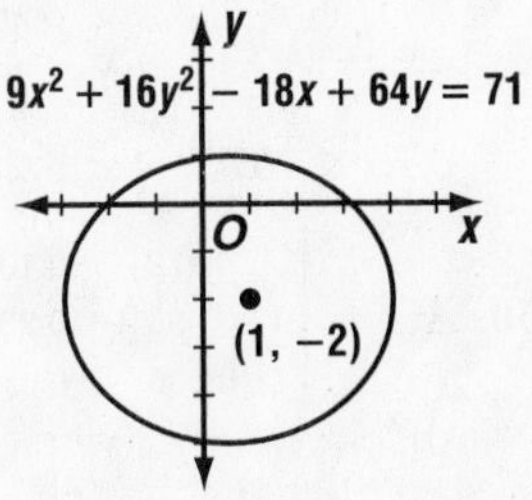

32. $4x^2 + 9y^2 + 16x - 18y - 11 = 0$
$4x^2 + 16x + 9y^2 - 18y = 11$
$4(x^2 + 4x + 4) + 9(y^2 - 2y + 1) = 11 + 16 + 9$
$4(x + 2)^2 + 9(y - 1)^2 = 36$
$\frac{(x+2)^2}{9} + \frac{(y-1)^2}{4} = 1$

center: $(-2, 1)$
foci: $b^2 = a^2 - c^2$
$4 = 9 - c^2$
$5 = c^2$
$\pm\sqrt{5} = c$
$(-2 \pm \sqrt{5}, 1)$
length of major axis:
2(3) or 6 units
length of minor axis:
2(2) or 4 units

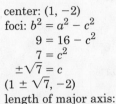

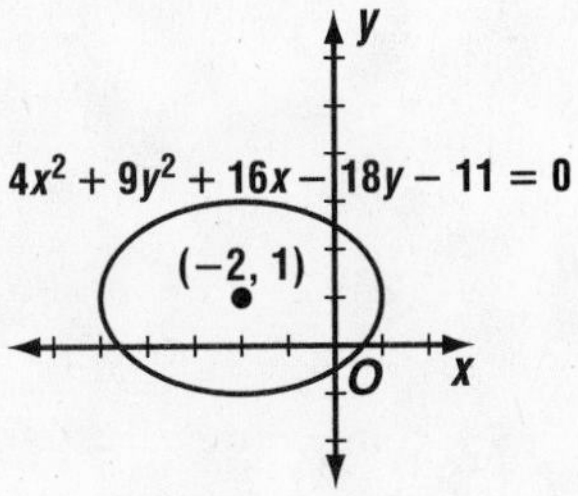

33. $(h, k) = \left(\frac{10 + (-8)}{2}, \frac{2+2}{2}\right)$
$= \left(\frac{2}{2}, \frac{4}{2}\right)$
$= (1, 2)$
length of major axis: 18 units
$2a = 18$
$a = 9$
foci: $(6, 2)$ and $(-4, 2)$
$c = 5$
$b^2 = a^2 - c^2$
$b^2 = 81 - 25$
$b^2 = 56$
$\frac{(x-1)^2}{81} + \frac{(y-2)^2}{56} = 1$

34. $2a = 20$
$a = 10$
$2b = 6$
$b = 3$
center: $(4, 2)$
$\frac{(x-4)^2}{9} + \frac{(y-2)^2}{100} = 1$

35. length of minor axis: 10 units
$2b = 10$
$b = 5$
foci: $(12, 0), (-12, 0)$
$c = 12$
$b^2 = a^2 - c^2$
$25 = a^2 - 144$
$169 = a^2$
center $(0, 0)$
$\frac{x^2}{169} + \frac{y^2}{25} = 1$

36. length of major axis: 18 units
$2a = 18$
$a = 9$
length of minor axis: 8 units
$2b = 8$
$b = 4$
$(h, k) = \left(\frac{-11 + 7}{2}, \frac{5+5}{2}\right)$
$= \left(\frac{-4}{2}, \frac{10}{2}\right)$
$= (-2, 5)$
$\frac{(x+2)^2}{81} + \frac{(y-5)^2}{16} = 1$

37. length of major axis: 16 units
$2a = 16$
$a = 8$
length of minor axis: 4 units
$2b = 4$
$b = 2$
$(h, k) = \left(\frac{2+2}{2}, \frac{12 + (-4)}{2}\right)$
$= \left(\frac{4}{2}, \frac{8}{2}\right)$
$= (2, 4)$
$\frac{(x+2)^2}{4} + \frac{(y-4)^2}{64} = 1$

38. $2a = 16$
$a = 8$
$2b = 9$
$b = \frac{9}{2}$
$\frac{(x-5)^2}{64} + \frac{(y-4)^2}{20.25} = 1$

39. See students' work.
As k increases, the length of the major axis increases, but the minor axis length stays the same.

40. See students' work
As k increases, the shape of the ellipse remains similar, and the size increases.

41. $2a = 40$
$a = 20$
$2b = 20$
$b = 10$
foci: $b^2 = a^2 - c^2$
$100 = 400 - c^2$
$300 = c^2$
$10\sqrt{3} = c$
The electrode should be placed $20\sqrt{3}$ centimeters or about 34.6 centimeters from the kidney stone.

42a. $2a = 96$
$a = 48$
$2b = 46$
$b = 23$
$\frac{x^2}{2304} + \frac{y^2}{529} = 1$

42b. foci: $b^2 = a^2 - c^2$
$529 = 2304 - c^2$
$1775 = c^2$
$42 \approx c$
The desk is at one focus; about 2(42) or 84 feet from Adams at the other.

43. length of major axis: 128,500,000 + 800,000 + 155,000,000 or 284,300,000 miles

$2a = 284{,}300{,}000$

$a = 142{,}150{,}000$

$c = 142{,}150{,}000 - 128{,}500{,}000$

$= 13{,}650{,}000$

$b^2 = a^2 - c^2$

$b^2 = (142{,}150{,}000)^2 - (13{,}650{,}000)^2$

$b^2 = 20{,}206{,}622{,}500{,}000{,}000 - 186{,}322{,}500{,}000{,}000$

$b^2 = 20{,}020{,}300{,}000{,}000{,}000$ or about 2.00×10^{16}

$a^2 = 20{,}206{,}622{,}500{,}000{,}000$ or about 2.02×10^{16}

about $\dfrac{x^2}{2.02 \times 10^{16}} + \dfrac{y^2}{2.00 \times 10^{16}} = 1$

44. $2a = 47$

$a = 23.5$

$2b = 18$

$b = 9$

$\dfrac{x^2}{552.25} + \dfrac{y^2}{81} = 1$

45a. length of major axis: 200 + 8000 + 100 or 8300 miles

$2a = 8300$

$a = 4150$

$c = 4150 - (4000 + 100)$

$= 50$

$b^2 = a^2 - c^2$

$b^2 = (4150)^2 - (50)^2$

$= 17{,}220{,}000$

$\dfrac{x^2}{17{,}222{,}500} + \dfrac{y^2}{17{,}220{,}000} = 1$

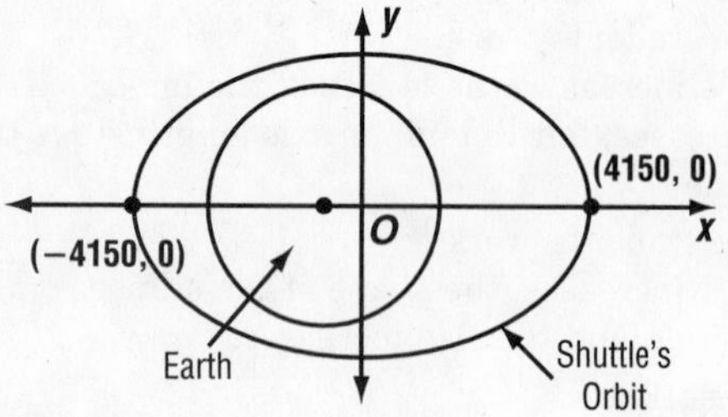

45b. center $(-50, 0)$

$\dfrac{(x + 50)^2}{17{,}222{,}500} + \dfrac{y^2}{17{,}220{,}000} = 1$

46. $(x - h)^2 + (y - k)^2 = r^2$

$(x - 6)^2 + (y - 2)^2 = 5^2$

$(x - 6)^2 + (y - 2)^2 = 25$

47. $y > x^2 - 7x + 10$

$y = x^2 - 7x + 10$

$= \left(x^2 - 7x + \frac{49}{4}\right) + 10 - \frac{49}{4}$

$= \left(x - \frac{7}{2}\right)^2 - \frac{9}{4}$

The boundary parabola opens upward with its vertex at $\left(\frac{7}{2}, -\frac{9}{4}\right)$.

Test: (3, 2)

$y \overset{?}{>} x^2 - 7x + 10$

$2 \overset{?}{>} (3)^2 - 7(3) + 10$

$2 \overset{?}{>} 9 - 21 + 10$

$2 > -2$; true

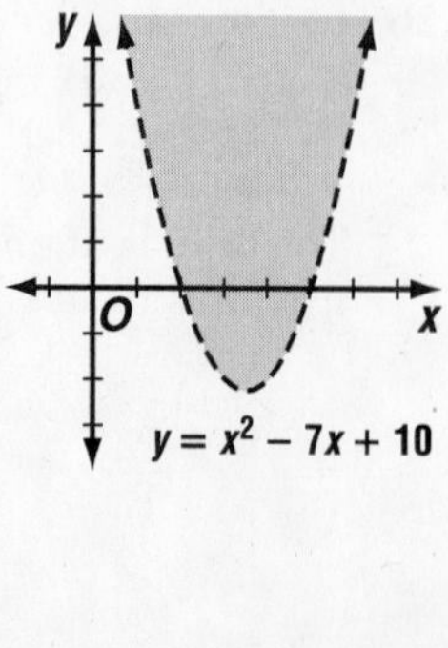

48. $(\sqrt[6]{5}\, a^{\frac{7}{4}} b^{-\frac{2}{3}})^{12} = (5^{\frac{1}{6}} a^{\frac{7}{4}} b^{-\frac{2}{3}})^{12}$

$= 5^2 a^{21} b^{-8}$

$= \dfrac{25a^{21}}{b^8}$

49. $\dfrac{1 \times 10^{-9}}{8} = \dfrac{x}{0.5}$

$\dfrac{0.5 \times 10^{-9}}{8} = x$

$6.25 \times 10^{-11} = x$; 6.25×10^{-11} seconds

50. $A^{-1} = \begin{bmatrix} 0.112 & -0.104 & 0.176 \\ -0.096 & 0.232 & -0.008 \\ -0.136 & -0.088 & 0.072 \end{bmatrix}$

$\begin{bmatrix} 2 & -1 & -5 \\ 1 & 4 & -2 \\ 5 & 3 & 2 \end{bmatrix} \begin{bmatrix} x \\ y \\ z \end{bmatrix} = \begin{bmatrix} 3 \\ 3 \\ 1 \end{bmatrix}$

$\begin{bmatrix} 0.112 & -0.104 & 0.176 \\ -0.096 & 0.232 & -0.008 \\ -0.136 & -0.088 & 0.072 \end{bmatrix} \begin{bmatrix} 2 & -1 & -5 \\ 1 & 4 & -2 \\ 5 & 3 & 2 \end{bmatrix} \begin{bmatrix} x \\ y \\ z \end{bmatrix} =$

$\begin{bmatrix} 0.112 & -0.104 & 0.176 \\ -0.096 & 0.232 & -0.008 \\ -0.136 & -0.088 & 0.072 \end{bmatrix} \begin{bmatrix} 3 \\ 3 \\ 1 \end{bmatrix}$

$\begin{bmatrix} x \\ y \\ z \end{bmatrix} = \begin{bmatrix} \frac{1}{5} \\ \frac{2}{5} \\ -\frac{3}{5} \end{bmatrix}$

$\left(\frac{1}{5}, \frac{2}{5}, -\frac{3}{5}\right)$

51. $a = \dfrac{\begin{vmatrix} -10.15 & 7 \\ 69.944 & -6 \end{vmatrix}}{\begin{vmatrix} 6 & 7 \\ 9.2 & -6 \end{vmatrix}}$ $\qquad b = \dfrac{\begin{vmatrix} 6 & -10.15 \\ 9.2 & 69.944 \end{vmatrix}}{\begin{vmatrix} 6 & 7 \\ 9.2 & -6 \end{vmatrix}}$

$= \dfrac{-10.15(-6) - (7)(69.944)}{6(-6) - 7(9.2)}$ $\qquad = \dfrac{6(69.944) - (-10.15)(9.2)}{6(-6) - 7(9.2)}$

$= \dfrac{-428.708}{-100.4}$ $\qquad = \dfrac{513.044}{-100.4}$

$= 4.27$ $\qquad = -5.11$

$(4.27, -5.11)$

52. $m = \dfrac{y_2 - y_1}{x_2 - x_1}$

$= \dfrac{-2 - 0}{4 - 0}$

$= \dfrac{-1}{2}$

The line perpendicular to the line has a slope of 2.

53. −7, 4, 5, 5, 5, 6, 7, 8, 12, 12, 12, 13, 13, 16, 16, 16, 16, 17, 17, 18, 18, 19, 20, 20, 22, 22, 23, 24, 24, 25, 25, 26, 26, 27, 27, 27, 29, 29, 29, 30, 31, 31, 31

median: 19°F; mode: 16°F;

mean:

$\dfrac{\begin{bmatrix} -7 + 4 + 5 + 5 + 5 + 6 + 7 + 8 + 12 + 12 + 12 + \\ 13 + 13 + 16 + 16 + 16 + 16 + 17 + 17 + 18 + 18 + \\ 19 + 20 + 20 + 22 + 22 + 23 + 24 + 24 + 25 + 25 + 26 + \\ 26 + 27 + 27 + 27 + 29 + 29 + 29 + 30 + 31 + 31 + 31 \end{bmatrix}}{43}$

$= \dfrac{796}{43}$

≈ 18.5°F

Page 439 Self Test

1. $d = \sqrt{(x_2 - x_1)^2 + (y_2 - y_1)^2}$

$= \sqrt{(4 - 9)^2 + (-7 - 5)^2}$

$= \sqrt{(-5)^2 + (-12)^2}$

$= \sqrt{25 + 144}$

$= \sqrt{169}$

$= 13$; 13 units

2. $d = \sqrt{(x_2 - x_1)^2 + (y_2 - y_1)^2}$

$= \sqrt{(10 - 0)^2 + [(-3) - (-5)]^2}$

$= \sqrt{(10)^2 + (2)^2}$

$= \sqrt{100 + 4}$

$= \sqrt{104}$

$= 2\sqrt{26}$; $2\sqrt{26}$ units

3. $(x, y) = \left(\frac{x_1 + x_2}{2}, \frac{y_1 + y_2}{2}\right)$

$= \left(\frac{8 + (-5)}{2}, \frac{0 + 12}{2}\right)$

$= \left(\frac{3}{2}, \frac{12}{2}\right)$

$= \left(\frac{3}{2}, 6\right)$

4. $(x, y) = \left(\frac{x_1 + x_2}{2}, \frac{y_1 + y_2}{2}\right)$

$= \left(\frac{5 + 3}{2}, \frac{-7 + (-1)}{2}\right)$

$= \left(\frac{8}{2}, \frac{-8}{2}\right)$

$= (4, -4)$

5. $y^2 = 6x$

$\frac{1}{6}y^2 = x$

vertex: (0, 0)

focus: $\left(0 + \frac{1}{4\left(\frac{1}{6}\right)}, 0\right)$ or $\left(\frac{3}{2}, 0\right)$

axis of symmetry: $y = 0$

directrix: $x = 0 - \frac{1}{4\left(\frac{1}{6}\right)}$ or $-\frac{3}{2}$

direction of opening: right, since $a > 0$

length of latus rectum: $\left|\frac{1}{\frac{1}{6}}\right|$ or 6 units

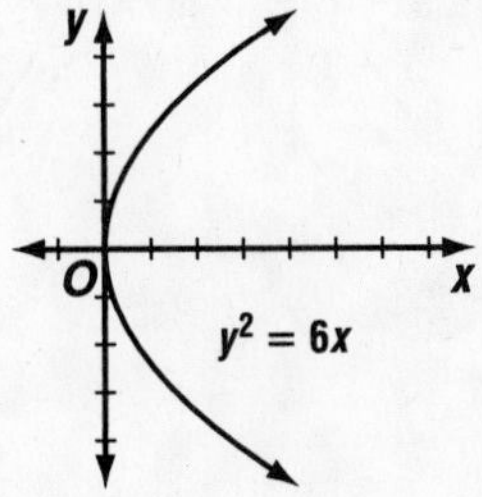

6. $y = x^2 + 8x + 20$

$= (x^2 + 8x + 16) + 20 - 16$

$= (x + 4)^2 + 4$

vertex: $(-4, 4)$

focus: $\left(-4, 4 + \frac{1}{4(1)}\right)$ or $\left(4, \frac{17}{4}\right)$

axis of symmetry: $x = -4$

(Continued next column)

directrix: $y = 4 - \frac{1}{4(1)}$ or $\frac{15}{4}$

direction of opening: upward, since $a > 0$

length of latus rectum: $\left|\frac{1}{1}\right|$ or 1 unit

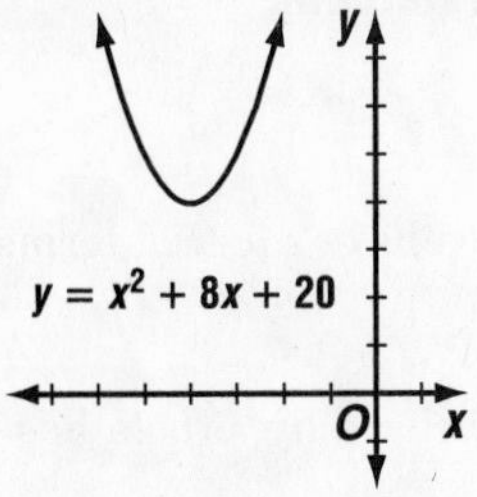

7. center: (0, 4)

radius: $\sqrt{49}$ or 7 units

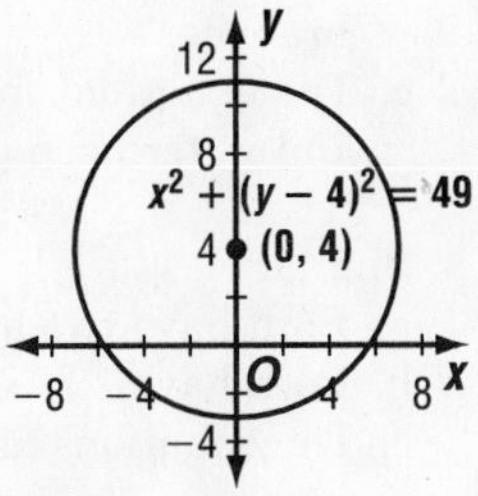

8.

$3x^2 + 3y^2 + 6y + 9x = 2$

$3x^2 + 9x + 3y^2 + 6y = 2$

$3\left(x^2 + 3x + \frac{9}{4}\right) + 3(y^2 + 2y + 1) = 2 + \frac{27}{4} + 3$

$3\left(x + \frac{3}{2}\right)^2 + 3(y + 1)^2 = \frac{47}{4}$

$\left(x + \frac{3}{2}\right)^2 + (y + 1)^2 = \frac{47}{12}$

center: $\left(-\frac{3}{2}, -1\right)$

radius: $\sqrt{\frac{47}{12}}$ or $\frac{\sqrt{141}}{6}$ units

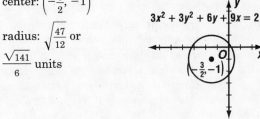

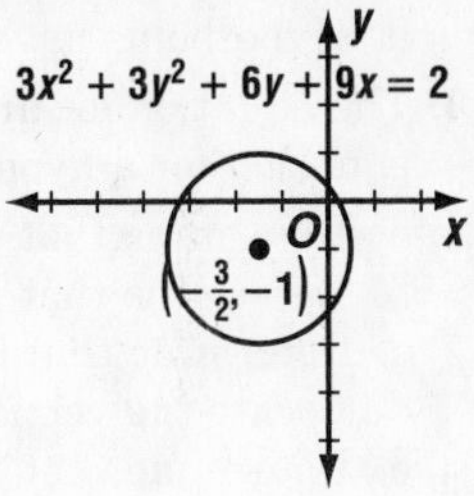

9.

$8x^2 + 4y^2 - 16x - 20y = 7$

$8x^2 - 16x + 4y^2 - 20y = 7$

$8(x^2 - 2x + 1) + 4\left(y^2 - 5y + \frac{25}{4}\right) = 7 + 8 + 25$

$8(x - 1)^2 + 4\left(y - \frac{5}{2}\right)^2 = 40$

$\frac{(x - 1)^2}{5} + \frac{(y - 2.5)^2}{10} = 1$

10. $2a = 18$

$a = 9$

$c = 7$

$b^2 = a^2 - c^2$

$b^2 = 81 - 49$

$b^2 = 32$

$(h, k) = \left(\frac{3 + 3}{2}, \frac{8 + (-6)}{2}\right)$

$= \left(\frac{6}{2}, \frac{2}{2}\right)$

$= (3, 1)$

$\frac{(x - 3)^2}{32} + \frac{(y - 1)^2}{81} = 1$

7-5 Hyperbolas

Page 445 Check for Understanding

1. Similarities
   a. Both have foci
   b. Both are curves.
   c. The equations for both have squared terms.
   d. Both are u-shaped.

   Differences
   a. A parabola has one focus; a hyperbola has 2 foci.
   b. A parabola is one curve; a hyperbola has 2 branches
   c. The equations for hyperbolas contain both x^2 and y^2 terms; a parabola has just one of these terms.
2. Similarities
   a. Both have two axes of symmetry.
   b. Both have 2 foci.
   c. The equations for both have two squared terms.

   Differences
   a. Standard equations for an ellipse contains addition; standard equation for a hyperbola contains subtraction.
   b. An ellipse is a closed figure; a hyperbola is not closed.
   c. For an ellipse, $b^2 = a^2 - c^2$; for a hyperbola, $c^2 = a^2 + b^2$.
   d. Hyperbolas have asymptotes; ellipses do not.
3. The equation for an ellipse contains addition; the equation for a hyperbola contains subtraction.
4. a. Determine that the center is at $(-2, 5)$.
   b. Determine that the transverse axis is vertical.
   c. Determine that the transverse axis is 12 units.
   d. Locate the vertices at $(-2, 11)$ and $(-2, -1)$.
   e. Determine that the conjugate axis is 6 units.
   f. Use a rectangle to draw the asymptotes.
   g. Sketch the graph.
5. hyperbola
6. ellipse
7. hyperbola
8. $6x^2 - 12y^2 = 108$

   $\frac{6x^2}{108} - \frac{12y^2}{108} = \frac{108}{108}$

   $\frac{x^2}{18} - \frac{y^2}{9} = 1$

9. $y^2 - 3x^2 + 6x + 6y = 18$

   $y^2 + 6y - 3x^2 + 6x = 18$

   $(y^2 + 6y + 9) - 3(x^2 - 2x + 1) = 18 + 9 - 3$

   $(y + 3)^2 - 3(x - 1)^2 = 24$

   $\frac{(y + 3)^2}{24} - \frac{(x - 1)^2}{8} = 1$

10. center: $(0, 0)$
    $a = \sqrt{18}$ or $3\sqrt{2}$, $b = \sqrt{20}$ or $2\sqrt{5}$
    vertices: $(0, \pm 3\sqrt{2})$
    foci: $c^2 = a^2 + b^2$
    $c^2 = 18 + 20$
    $c^2 = 38$
    $c = \pm\sqrt{38}$
    $(0, \pm\sqrt{38})$

(Continued next column)

    slopes of asymptotes: $\pm\frac{3\sqrt{2}}{2\sqrt{5}}$ or $\pm\frac{3\sqrt{10}}{10}$

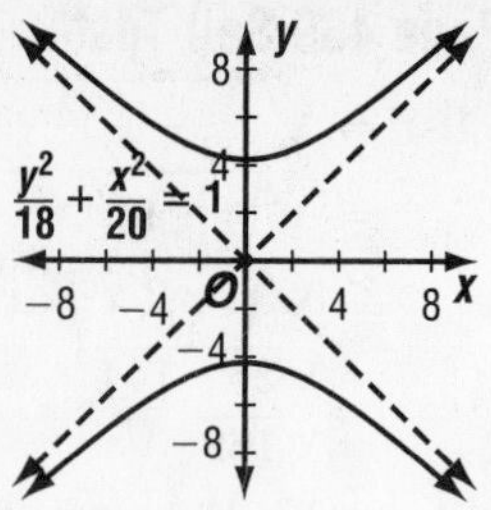

11. $x^2 - 36y^2 = 36$

    $\frac{x^2}{36} - \frac{y^2}{1} = 1$

    center: $(0, 0)$
    $a = \sqrt{36}$ or 6,
    $b = \sqrt{1}$ or 1
    vertices: $(\pm 6, 0)$
    foci: $c^2 = a^2 + b^2$
    $c^2 = 36 + 1$
    $c = \pm\sqrt{37}$
    $(\pm\sqrt{37}, 0)$
    slopes of asymptotes: $\pm\frac{1}{6}$

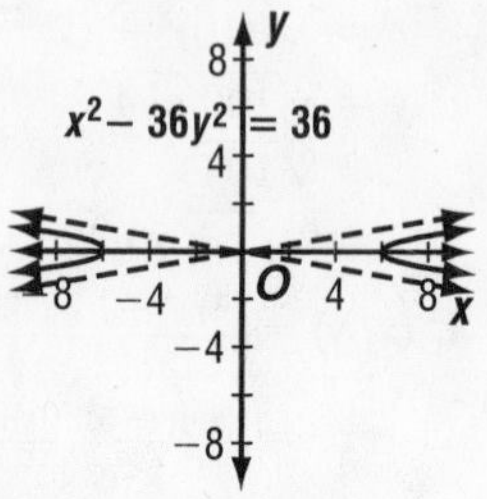

12. center: $(1, -6)$
    $a = \sqrt{20}$ or $2\sqrt{5}$,
    $b = \sqrt{25}$ or 5
    vertices: $(1, -6 \pm 2\sqrt{5})$
    foci: $c^2 = a^2 + b^2$
    $c^2 = 20 + 25$
    $c^2 = 45$
    $c = \pm 3\sqrt{5}$
    $(1, -6 \pm 3\sqrt{5})$
    slopes of asymptotes: $= \pm\frac{2\sqrt{5}}{5}$

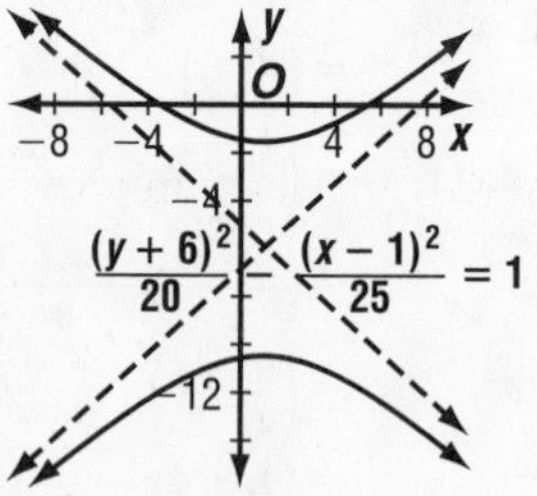

13. $5x^2 - 4y^2 - 40x - 16y = 36$

    $5x^2 - 40x - 4y^2 - 16y = 36$

    $5(x^2 - 8x + 16) - 4(y^2 + 4y + 4) = 36 + 80 - 16$

    $5(x - 4)^2 - 4(y + 2)^2 = 100$

    $\frac{(x - 4)^2}{20} - \frac{(y + 2)^2}{25} = 1$

    center: $(4, -2)$
    $a = \sqrt{20}$ or $2\sqrt{5}$,
    $b = \sqrt{25}$ or 5
    vertices: $(4 \pm 2\sqrt{5}, -2)$
    foci: $c^2 = a^2 + b^2$
    $c^2 = 20 + 25$
    $c^2 = 45$
    $c = \pm 3\sqrt{5}$
    $(4 \pm 3\sqrt{5}, -2)$
    slopes of asymptotes: $\pm\frac{5}{2\sqrt{5}}$ or $\pm\frac{\sqrt{5}}{2}$

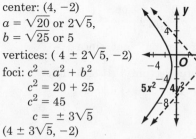

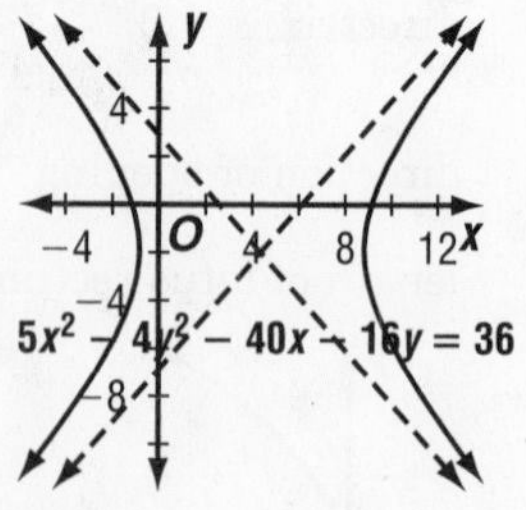

14. center: $(0, 0)$
    $a = 2$, $c = 5$
    $c^2 = a^2 + b^2$
    $25 = 4 + b^2$
    $21 = b^2$
    $\frac{y^2}{4} - \frac{x^2}{21} = 1$
15. center: $(0, 0)$
    $a = 1$, $b = 4$
    $\frac{x^2}{1} - \frac{y^2}{16} = 1$

Pages 445–447 Exercises

16. vertices: $(\pm 2, 0)$
foci: $(\pm 4, 0)$
$a = 2, c = 4$
$c^2 = a^2 + b^2$
$16 = 4 + b^2$
$12 = b^2$
$\frac{x^2}{4} - \frac{y^2}{12} = 1$

17. vertices: $(0, -3), (0, -8)$
$(h, k) = \left(\frac{0+0}{2}, \frac{-3+(-8)}{2}\right)$
$= \left(\frac{0}{2}, -\frac{11}{2}\right)$
$= (0, -5.5)$
$a = 2.5$
foci: $(0, -2)$ $(0, -9)$
$c = 3.5$
$c^2 = a^2 + b^2$
$12.25 = 6.25 + b^2$
$6 = b^2$
$\frac{(x+5.5)^2}{6.25} - \frac{x^2}{6} = 1$

18. slope of asymptotes: $\pm \frac{3}{2}$
$a = 2, b = 3$
center: $(3, -5)$
$\frac{(y-3)^2}{4} - \frac{(y+5)^2}{9} = 1$

19. center: $(0, 0)$
$a = \sqrt{81}$ or 9,
$b = \sqrt{49}$ or 7
vertices: $(\pm 9, 0)$
foci: $c^2 = a^2 + b^2$
$c^2 = 81 + 49$
$c^2 = 130$
$c = \pm\sqrt{130}$
$(\pm\sqrt{130}, 0)$
slopes of asymptotes: $\pm \frac{7}{9}$

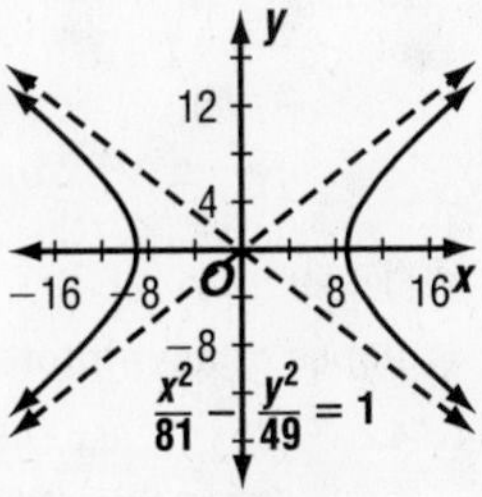

20. center: $(0, 0)$
$a = \sqrt{36}$ or 6;
$b = \sqrt{4}$ or 2
vertices: $(0, \pm 6)$
foci: $c^2 = a^2 + b^2$
$c^2 = 36 + 4$
$c^2 = 40$
$c = \pm\sqrt{40}$ or $\pm 2\sqrt{10}$
$(0, \pm 2\sqrt{10})$
slopes of asymptotes: $\pm \frac{6}{2}$ or ± 3

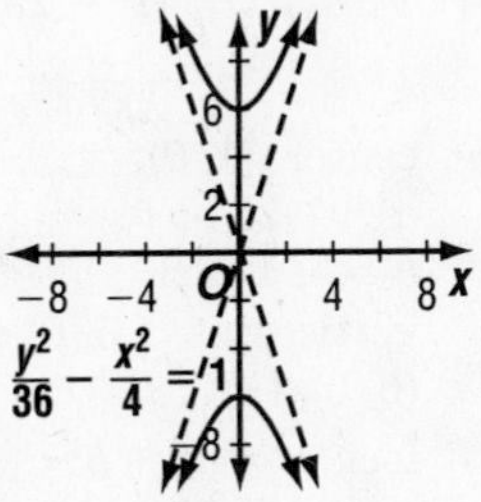

21. center: $(0, 0)$
$a = \sqrt{9}$ or 3,
$b = \sqrt{25}$ or 5
vertices: $(\pm 3, 0)$
foci: $c^2 = a^2 + b^2$
$c^2 = 9 + 25$
$c^2 = 34$
$c = \pm\sqrt{34}$
$(\pm\sqrt{34}, 0)$
slopes of asymptotes: $\pm \frac{5}{3}$

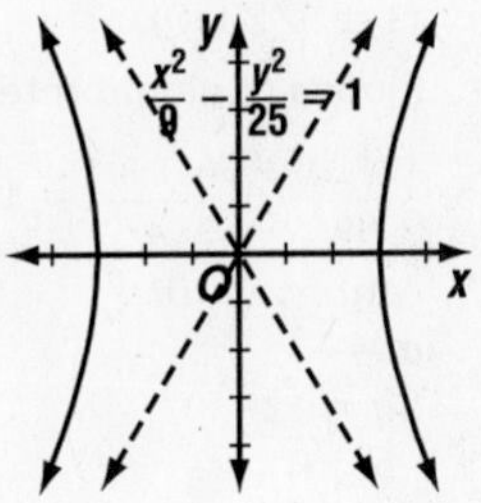

22. center: $(0, 0)$
$a = \pm\sqrt{16}$ or 4,
$b = \pm\sqrt{25}$ or 5
vertices: $(0, \pm 4)$
foci: $c^2 = a^2 + b^2$
$c^2 = 16 + 25$
$c^2 = 41$
$c = \pm\sqrt{41}$
$(0, \pm\sqrt{41})$
slopes of asymptotes: $\pm \frac{4}{5}$

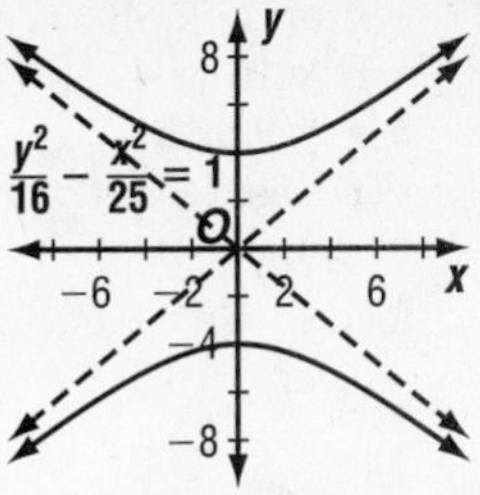

23. $x^2 - 2y^2 = 2$
$\frac{x^2}{2} - \frac{y^2}{1} = 1$
center: $(0, 0)$
$a = \sqrt{2}, b = 1$
vertices: $(\pm\sqrt{2}, 0)$
foci: $c^2 = a^2 + b^2$
$c^2 = 2 + 1$
$c^2 = 3$
$c = \pm\sqrt{3}$
$(\pm\sqrt{3}, 0)$
slopes of asymptotes:
$\pm \frac{1}{\sqrt{2}}$ or $\pm \frac{\sqrt{2}}{2}$

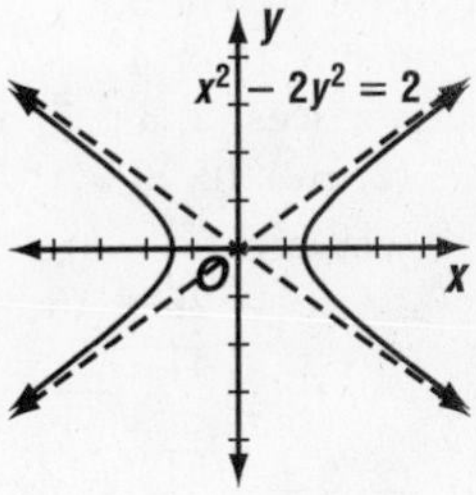

24. $y^2 = 36 + 4x^2$
$y^2 - 4x^2 = 36$
$\frac{y^2}{36} - \frac{x^2}{9} = 1$
center: $(0, 0)$
$a = \sqrt{36}$ or 6,
$b = \sqrt{9}$ or 3
vertices: $(0, \pm 6)$
foci: $c^2 = a^2 + b^2$
$c^2 = 36 + 9$
$c^2 = 45$
$c = \pm\sqrt{45}$ or $\pm 3\sqrt{5}$
$(0, \pm 3\sqrt{5})$
slopes of asymptotes: $\pm \frac{6}{3}$ or ± 2

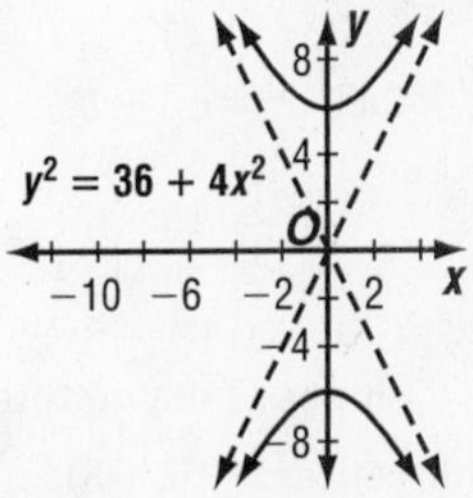

25. $x^2 - y^2 = 4$
$\frac{x^2}{4} - \frac{y^2}{4} = 1$
center: $(0, 0)$
$a = \sqrt{4}$ or 2, $b = \sqrt{4}$ or 2
vertices: $(\pm 2, 0)$
foci: $c^2 = a^2 + b^2$
$c^2 = 4 + 4$
$c^2 = 8$
$c = \pm\sqrt{8}$ or $\pm 2\sqrt{2}$
$(\pm 2\sqrt{2}, 0)$
slopes of asymptotes: $\pm \frac{2}{2}$ or ± 1

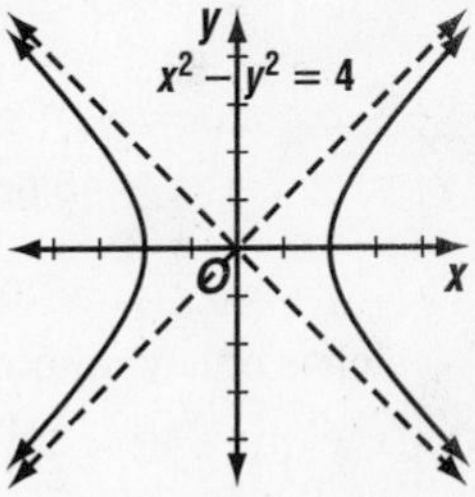

26. $2x^2 - 6y^2 = 12$
$\frac{x^2}{6} - \frac{y^2}{2} = 1$
center: $(0, 0)$
$a = \sqrt{6}, b = \sqrt{2}$
vertices: $(\pm\sqrt{6}, 0)$
foci: $c^2 = a^2 + b^2$
$c^2 = 6 + 2$
$c^2 = 8$
$c = \pm\sqrt{8}$ or $\pm 2\sqrt{2}$
$(\pm 2\sqrt{2}, 0)$
slopes of asymptotes: $\pm \frac{\sqrt{2}}{\sqrt{6}}$ or $\pm \frac{\sqrt{3}}{3}$

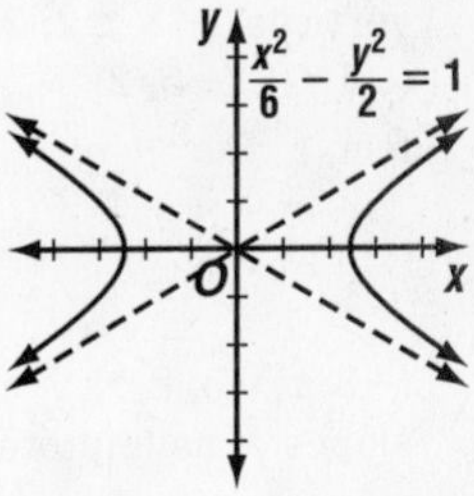

27. center: $(-2, 4)$
$a = \sqrt{16}$ or 4,
$b = \sqrt{9}$ or 3
vertices: $(-2, 4 \pm 4)$ or
$(-2, 0), (-2, 8)$
foci: $c^2 = a^2 + b^2$
$c^2 = 16 + 9$
$c^2 = 25$
$c = \pm 5$
$(-2, 4 \pm 5)$ or $(-2, -1), (-2, 9)$
slopes of asymptotes: $\pm \frac{4}{3}$

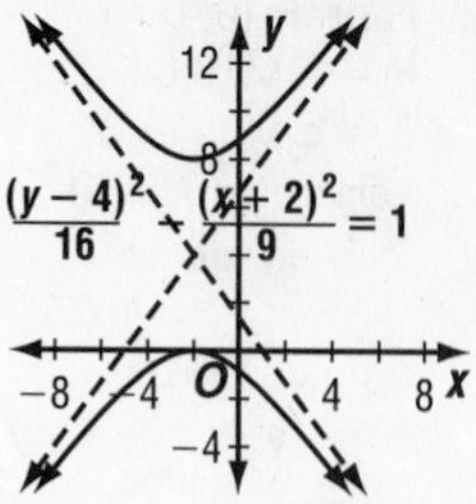

28. center: $(2, 3)$
$a = \sqrt{25}$ or 5,
$b = \sqrt{16}$ or 4
vertices $(2, 3 \pm 5)$ or
$(2, -2), (2, 8)$
foci: $c^2 = a^2 + b^2$
$c^2 = 25 + 16$
$c^2 = 41$
$c = \pm\sqrt{41}$
$(2, 3 \pm \sqrt{41})$
slopes of asymptotes: $\pm \frac{5}{4}$

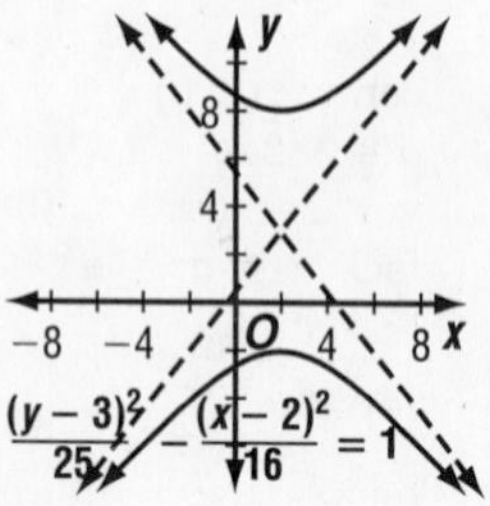

29. center: $(-1, -3)$
$a = \sqrt{4}$ or 2,
$b = \sqrt{9}$ or 3
vertices: $(-1 \pm 2, -3)$ or
$(-3, -3), (1, -3)$
foci: $c^2 = a^2 + b^2$
$c^2 = 4 + 9$
$c^2 = 13$
$c = \pm\sqrt{13}$
$(-1 \pm \sqrt{13}, -3)$
slopes of asymptotes: $\pm \frac{3}{2}$

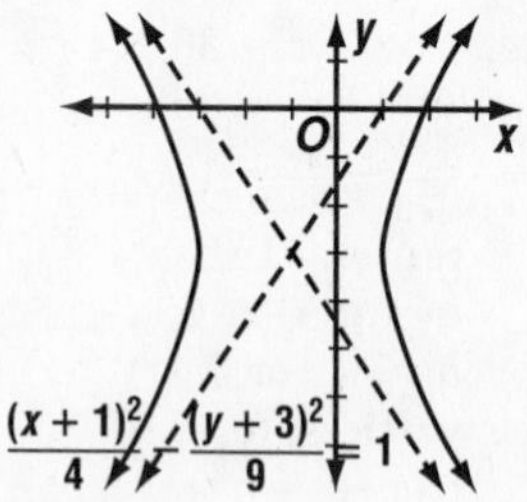

30. center: $(-6, -3)$
$a = \sqrt{36}$ or 6,
$b = \sqrt{9}$ or 3
vertices: $(-6 \pm 6, -3)$ or
$(-12, -3), (0, -3)$
foci: $c^2 = a^2 + b^2$
$c^2 = 36 + 9$
$c^2 = 45$
$c = \pm\sqrt{45}$ or
$\pm 3\sqrt{5}$
$(-6 \pm 3\sqrt{5}, -3)$
slopes of asymptotes: $\pm \frac{3}{6}$ or $\pm \frac{1}{2}$

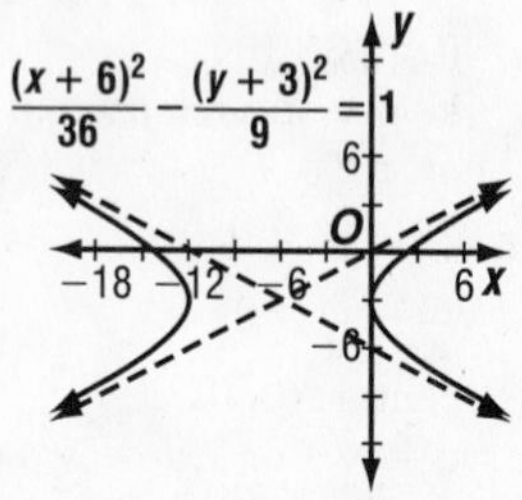

31. $(x + 3)^2 - 4(y - 2)^2 = 4$
$\frac{(x+3)^2}{4} - \frac{(y-2)^2}{1} = 1$
center: $(-3, 2)$
$a = \sqrt{4}$ or 2,
$b = \sqrt{1}$ or 1
vertices: $(-3 \pm 2, 2)$ or
$(-1, 2), (-5, 2)$
foci: $c^2 = a^2 + b^2$
$c^2 = 4 + 1$
$c^2 = 5$
$c = \pm\sqrt{5}$
$(-3 \pm \sqrt{5}, 2)$
slopes of asymptotes: $\pm \frac{1}{2}$

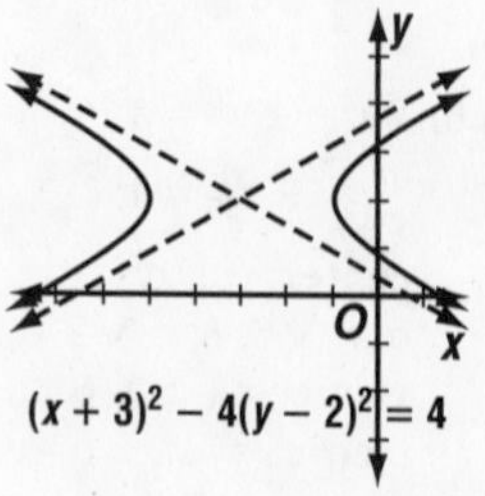

32. $9y^2 - 120x^2 - 54y = 999$
$9y^2 - 54y - 120x^2 = 999$
$9(y^2 - 6y + 9) - 120x^2 = 999 + 81$
$9(y - 3)^2 - 120x^2 = 1080$
$\frac{(y-3)^2}{120} - \frac{x^2}{9} = 1$
center: $(0, 3)$
$a = \sqrt{120}$ or $2\sqrt{30}$,
$b = \sqrt{9}$ or 3
vertices: $(0, 3 \pm 2\sqrt{3})$
foci: $c^2 = a^2 + b^2$
$c^2 = 120 + 9$
$c^2 = 129$
$c = \pm\sqrt{129}$
$(0, 3 \pm \sqrt{129})$
slopes of asymptotes: $\pm \frac{2\sqrt{30}}{3}$

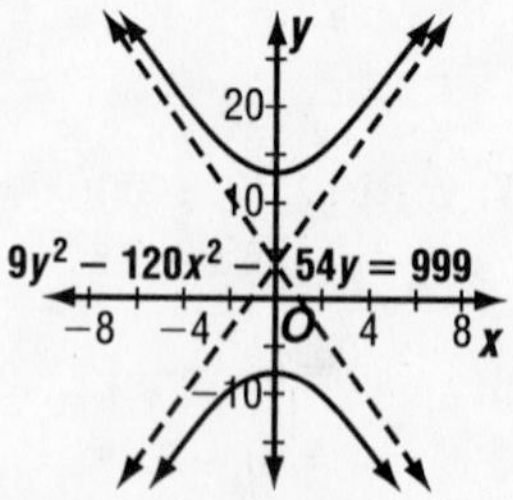

33. $y^2 - 3x^2 + 6y + 6x = 18$
$y^2 + 6y - 3x^2 + 6x = 18$
$(y^2 + 6y + 9) - 3(x^2 - 2x + 1) = 18 + 9 - 3$
$(y + 3)^2 - 3(x - 1)^2 = 24$
$\frac{(y+3)^2}{24} - \frac{(x-1)^2}{8} = 1$
center: $(1, -3)$
$a = \sqrt{24}$ or $2\sqrt{6}$,
$b = \sqrt{8}$ or $2\sqrt{2}$
vertices: $(1, -3 \pm 2\sqrt{6})$
foci: $c^2 = a^2 + b^2$
$c^2 = 24 + 8$
$c^2 = 32$
$c = \pm\sqrt{32}$ or
$\pm 4\sqrt{2}$
$(1, -3 \pm 4\sqrt{2})$
slopes of asymptotes: $\pm \frac{2\sqrt{6}}{2\sqrt{2}}$ or $\pm\sqrt{3}$

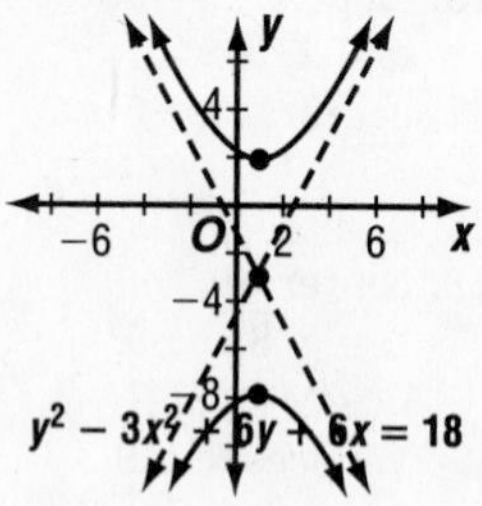

34. $4x^2 - 25y^2 - 8x - 96 = 0$
$4x^2 - 8x - 25y^2 = 96$
$4(x^2 - 2x + 1) - 25y^2 = 96 + 4$
$4(x - 1)^2 - 25y^2 = 100$
$\frac{(x-1)^2}{25} - \frac{y^2}{4} = 1$
center: $(1, 0)$
$a = \sqrt{25}$ or 5,
$b = \sqrt{4}$ or 2
vertices: $(1 \pm 5, 0)$ or
$(6, 0), (-4, 0)$
foci: $c^2 = a^2 + b^2$
$c^2 = 25 + 4$
$c^2 = 29$
$c = \pm\sqrt{29}$
$(1 \pm \sqrt{29}, 0)$
slopes of asymptotes: $\pm \frac{2}{5}$

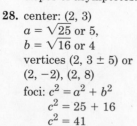

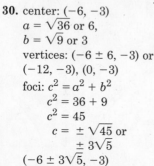

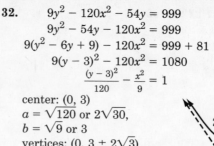

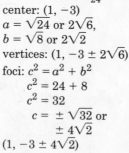

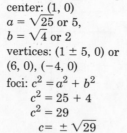

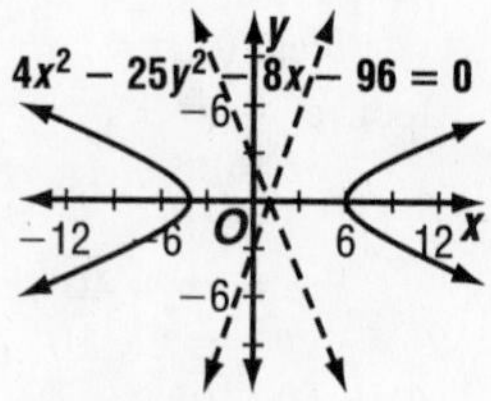

35. $\frac{(x-2)^2}{49} - \frac{(y+3)^2}{4} = 1$

36. $\frac{(y-5)^2}{16} - \frac{(x+4)^2}{81} = 1$

37. center: $(0, 0)$
$a = 5$
$2b = 12$
$b = 6$
$\frac{x^2}{25} - \frac{y^2}{36} = 1$

38. center: $(0, 0)$
$a = 4$
$2b = 14$
$b = 7$
$\frac{y^2}{16} - \frac{x^2}{49} = 1$

39.

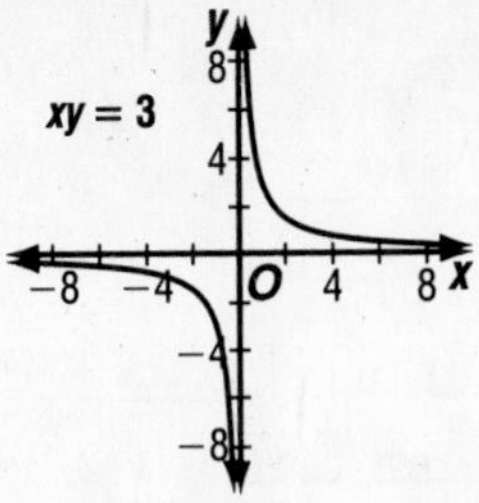

40.

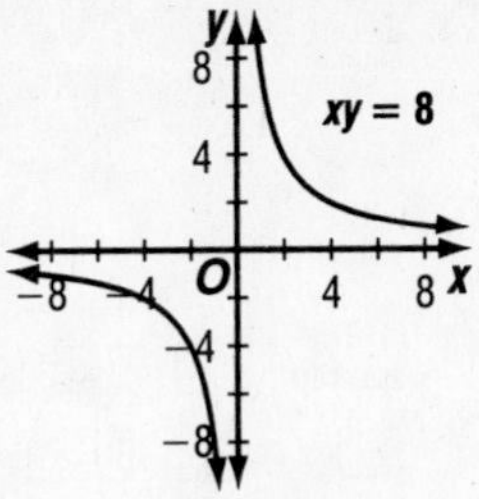

41.

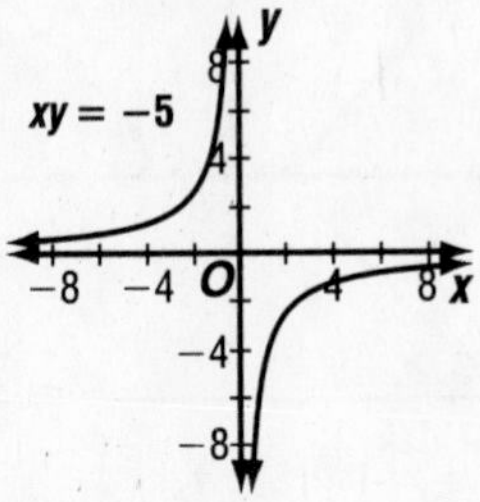

42.

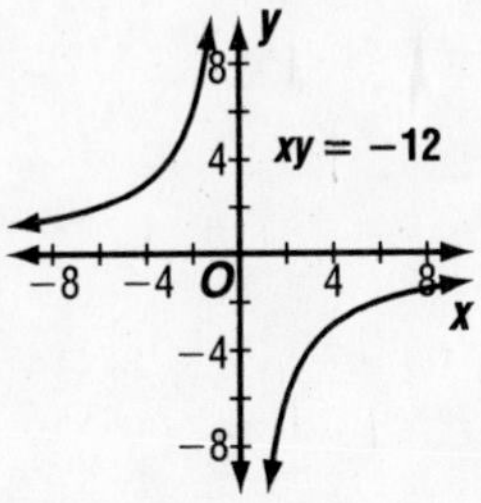

43. One branch is always in the first quadrant and the other is always in the third quadrant. As the value of c increases, the vertices move away from the origin.

44. One branch is always in the second quadrant and the other is always in the fourth quadrant. As the value of c decreases, the vertices move away from the origin.

45. The graph becomes the x- and y- axes.

46.

$$\begin{array}{rl} & y - x = 1 \\ (+) & y + x = 5 \\ \hline & 2y = 6 \\ & y = 3 \end{array} \qquad \begin{array}{l} y + x = 5 \\ 3 + x = 5 \\ x = 2 \end{array}$$

center: (2, 3)

slopes of asymptotes: $\pm$ 1

$a^2 = b^2$

$$\frac{(4-2)^2}{a^2} - \frac{(3-3)^2}{a^2} = 1$$

$$\frac{2^2}{a^2} - \frac{0}{a^2} = 1$$

$$\frac{4}{a^2} = 1$$

$$4 = a^2$$

$$\frac{(x-2)^2}{4} - \frac{(y-3)^2}{4} = 1$$

47. $PV = 22{,}500$

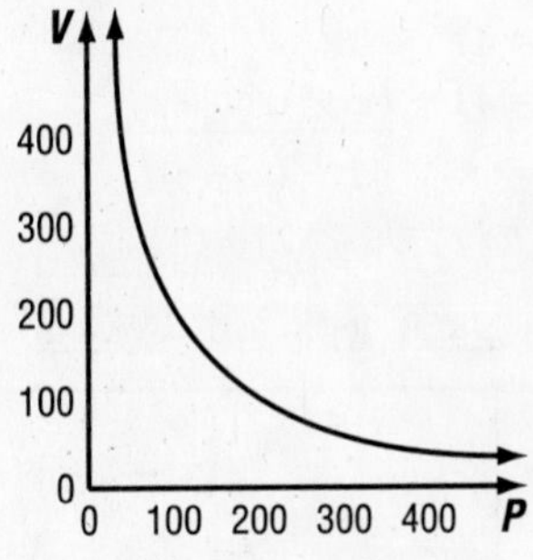

48a. center: (0, 0)

$a = 3(0.35) = 1.05$

vertices: $(\pm 1.05, 0)$

foci: $c^2 = a^2 + b^2 \quad c = \pm 3$

$(3)^2 = (1.05)^2 + b^2$

$9 = 1.1025 + b^2$

$7.8975 = b^2$

$$\frac{x^2}{1.1025} - \frac{y^2}{7.8975} = 1$$

48b.

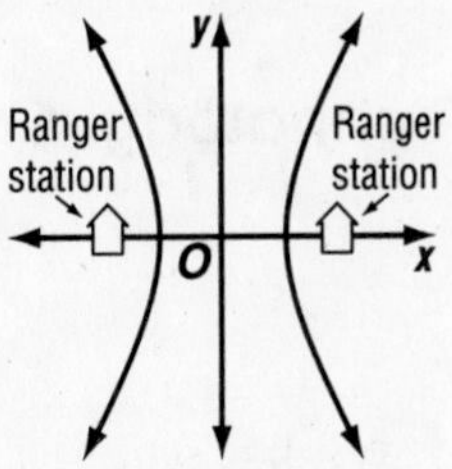

49. $(h, k) = \left(\frac{5 + (-3)}{2}, \frac{4 + 4}{2}\right)$

$= \left(\frac{2}{2}, \frac{8}{2}\right)$

$= (1, 4)$

$2a = 10$

$a = 5$

foci: $b^2 = a^2 - c^2$

$b^2 = 25 - 16$

$b^2 = 9$

$$\frac{(x-1)^2}{25} + \frac{(y-4)^2}{9} = 1$$

50. vertex: $(-2, 0)$

axis of symmetry: $x = -2$

51. $2q^2 + 11q = 21$

$2q^2 - 11q - 21 = 0$

$(2q - 3)(q + 7) = 0$

$2q - 3 = 0$ or $q + 7 = 0$

$2q = 3 \qquad q = -7$

$q = \frac{3}{2}$

52. $1.08 \times 10^8 = 0.108 \times 10^9$

$1.428 \times 10^9 - 0.108 \times 10^9 = 1.32 \times 10^9$

1.32×10^9 kilometers

53. 72.9, 73.2, 73.7, 74.0, 74.3, 75.0, 75.4, 75.6, 75.6, 75.9, 76.0, 76.0, 76.2, 76.8, 77.2, 77.2, 77.5, 77.5, 77.6, 78.4, 78.8, 79.5, 79.5, 79.6, 79.9

Q_2: the 13th value, 76.2; Q_1: mean of the 6th and 7th values, $\frac{75.0 + 75.4}{2} = \frac{150.4}{2} = 75.2$; Q_3: mean of the 19th and 20th values, $\frac{77.6 + 78.4}{2} = \frac{156.0}{2} = 78.0$; interquartile range: $78.0 - 75.2 = 2.8$; outliers: below $75.2 - 1.5(2.8) = 71.0$ or above $78.0 + 1.5(2.8) = 82.2$, no outliers

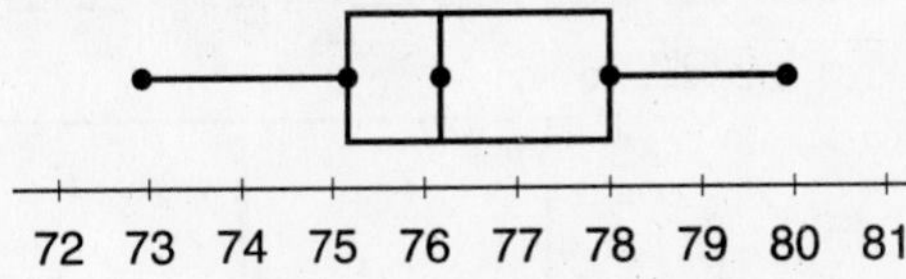

54.

$$\begin{array}{rl} & r + s + t = 15 \\ (-)r & \quad + t = 12 \\ \hline & s = 3 \end{array} \qquad \begin{array}{l} s + t = 10 \\ 3 + t = 10 \\ t = 7 \end{array} \qquad \begin{array}{l} r + t = 12 \\ r + 7 = 12 \\ r = 5 \end{array}$$

(5, 3, 7)

55. $h(x) = [5x - 4]$
$h(-1.5) = [5(-1.5) - 4]$
$= [-7.5 - 4]$
$= [-11.5]$
$= -12$

56. $C = 12 + 20t$
$52 = 12 + 20t$
$40 = 20t$
$2 = t$; 2 hours

57. $7x + 8y + 9y - 5x = 7x - 5x + 8y + 9y$
$= (7 - 5)x + (8 + 9)y$
$= 2x + 17y$

7-6A Graphing Technology: Conic Sections

Page 449 Exercises

1. Enter: [Y=] [X,T,θ,n] [x^2] [+] 9 [X,T,θ,n] [−] 12 [ENTER]

parabola

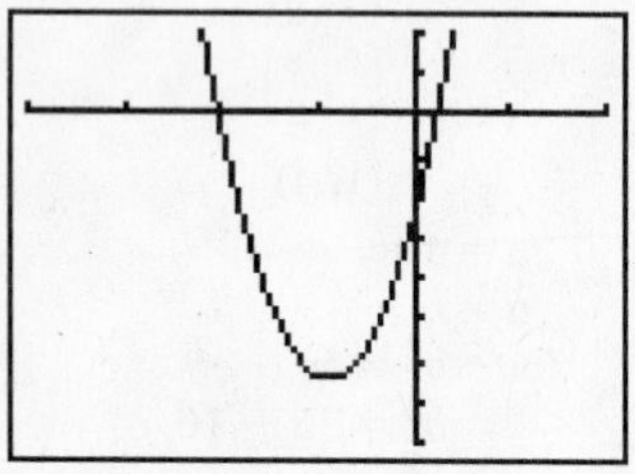

2. $(x - 3)^2 + y^2 = 25$
$y^2 = 25 - (x - 3)^2$
$y = \pm\sqrt{25 - (x - 3)^2}$

Enter: [Y=] [2nd] [√] [(] 25 [−] [(] [X,T,θ,n] [−] 3 [)] [x^2] [)] [ENTER] [(−)] [2nd] [√] [(] 25 [−] [(] [X,T,θ,n] [−] 3 [)] [x^2] [)] [ZOOM] 6

circle

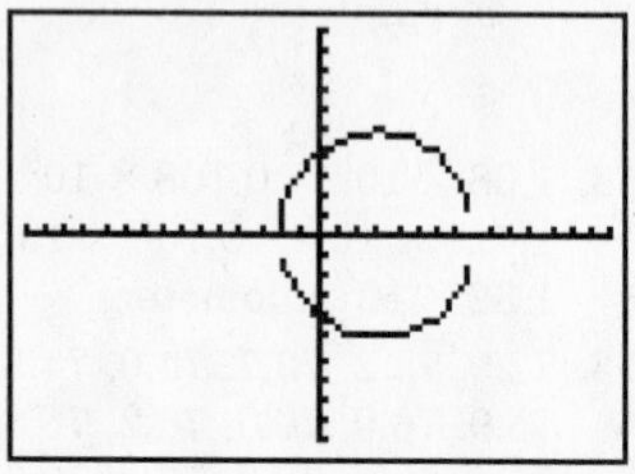

3. $16x^2 + 4y^2 = 48$
$4y^2 = 48 - 16x^2$
$y^2 = 12 - 4x^2$
$y = \pm\sqrt{12 - 4x^2}$

Enter: [Y=] [2nd] [√] [(] 12 [−] 4 [X,T,θ,n] [x^2] [)] [ENTER] [(−)] [2nd] [√] [(] 12 [−] 4 [X,T,θ,n] [x^2] [)] [ZOOM] 6

ellipse

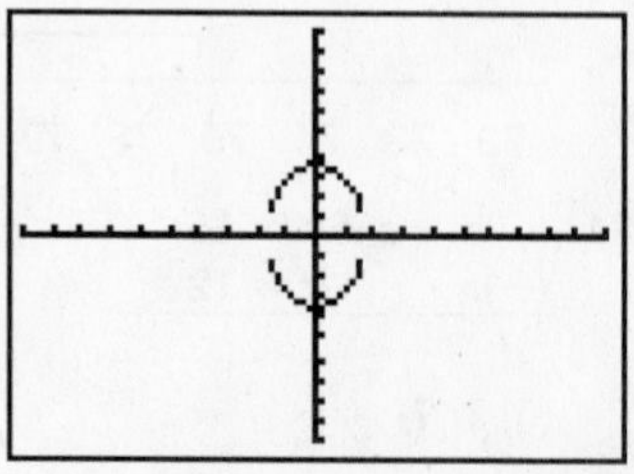

4. $10x^2 - 7y^2 - 70 = 0$
$-7y^2 = 70 - 10x^2$
$y^2 = \frac{10}{7}x^2 - 10$
$y = \pm\sqrt{\frac{10}{7}x^2 - 10}$

Enter: [Y=] [2nd] [√] [(] 10 [÷] 7 [X,T,θ,n] [x^2] [−] 10 [)] [ENTER] [(−)] [2nd] [Y-VARS] 1 1

hyperbola

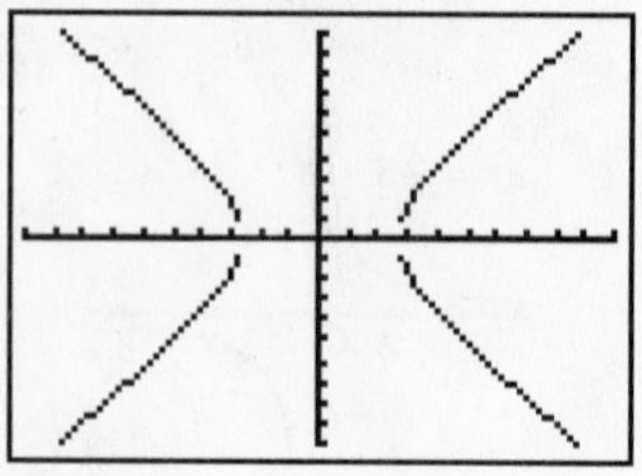

5. $25x^2 + 4y^2 - 24y = 64$
$25x^2 + 4(y^2 - 6y + 9) = 64 + 36$
$25x^2 + 4(y - 3)^2 = 100$
$4(y - 3)^2 = 100 - 25x^2$
$(y - 3)^2 = \frac{100 - 25x^2}{4}$
$y - 3 = \pm\sqrt{\frac{100 - 25x^2}{4}}$
$y = 3 \pm\sqrt{\frac{100 - 25x^2}{4}}$

Enter: [Y=] [2nd] [√] [(] [(] 100 [−] 25 [X,T,θ,n] [x^2] [)] [÷] 4 [)] [ENTER]
3 [+] [2nd] [Y-VARS] 1 1 [ENTER]
3 [−] [2nd] [Y-VARS] 1 1

ellipse

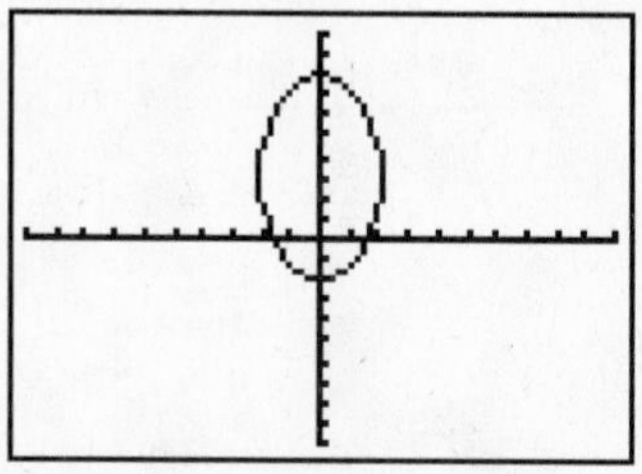

6. $x^2 - 8x + y^2 = 25$
$x^2 - 8x + 16 + y^2 = 25 + 16$
$(x - 4)^2 + y^2 = 41$
$y^2 = 41 - (x - 4)^2$
$y = \pm\sqrt{41 - (x - 4)^2}$

Enter: [Y=] [2nd] [√] [(] 41 [−] [(] [X,T,θ,n] [−] 4 [)] [x^2] [)] [ENTER] [(−)] [2nd] [Y-VARS] 1 1

circle

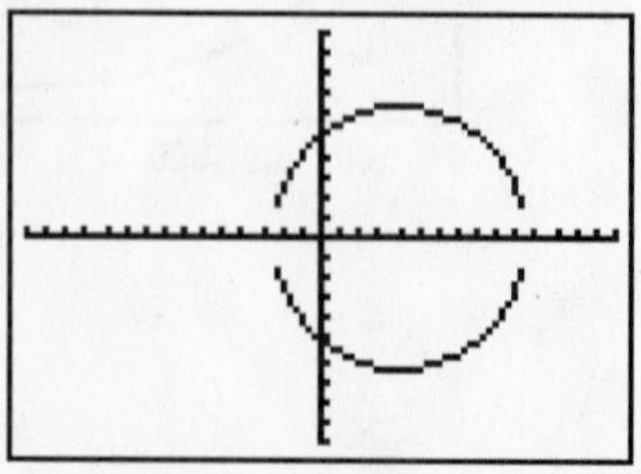

7. $4x^2 + y^2 - 100 = 0$

$$y^2 = 100 - 4x^2$$
$$y = \pm\sqrt{100 - 4x^2}$$

Enter: [Y=] [2nd] [√] [(] 100 [−] 4 [X,T,θ,n] [x²] [)] [ENTER] [(−)] [2nd] [Y-VARS] 1 1

ellipse

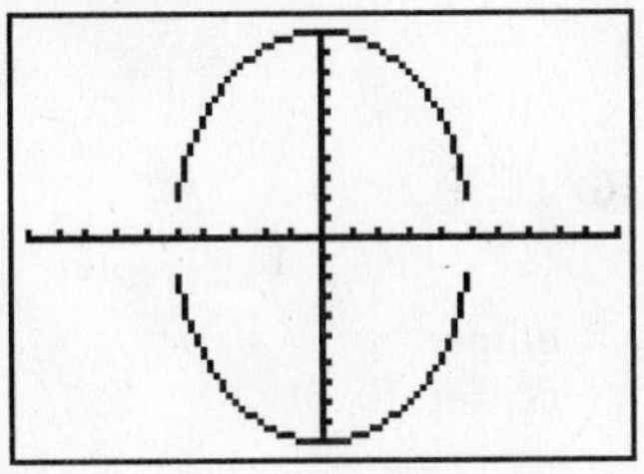

8.
$$y^2 + 5 = x^2 + 2y + 1$$
$$y^2 - 2y = x^2 - 4$$
$$y^2 - 2y + 1 = x^2 - 4 + 1$$
$$(y - 1)^2 = x^2 - 3$$
$$y - 1 = \pm\sqrt{x^2 - 3}$$
$$y = 1 \pm\sqrt{x^2 - 3}$$

Enter: [Y=] [2nd] [√] [(] [X,T,θ,n] [x²] [−] 3 [)] [ENTER] 1 [+] [2nd] [Y-VARS] 1 1 [ENTER] 1 [−] [2nd] [Y-VARS] 1 1

hyperbola

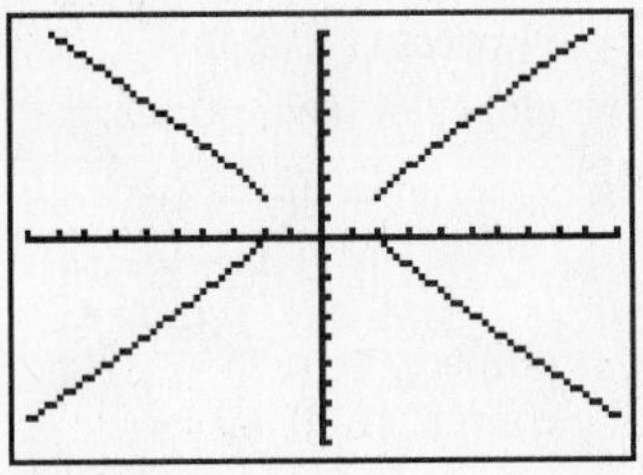

9. $y^2 - 12y - x + 25 = 0$

$$y^2 - 12y = x - 25$$
$$y^2 - 12y + 36 = x - 25 + 36$$
$$(y - 6)^2 = x + 11$$
$$y - 6 = \pm\sqrt{x + 11}$$
$$y = 6 \pm\sqrt{x + 11}$$

Enter: [Y=] [2nd] [√] [X,T,θ,n] [+] 11 [ENTER] 6 [+] [2nd] [Y-VARS] 1 1 [ENTER] 6 [−] [2nd] [Y-VARS] 1 1

parabola

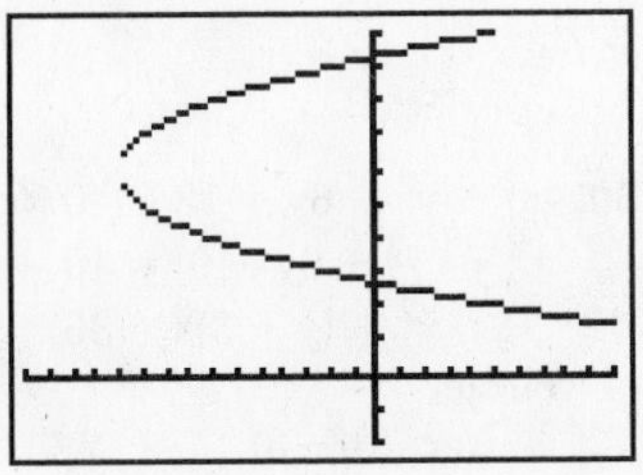

10. $(y + 1)^2 - x^2 - 4 = 0$

$$(y + 1)^2 = x^2 + 4$$
$$y + 1 = \pm\sqrt{x^2 + 4}$$
$$y = -1 \pm\sqrt{x^2 + 4}$$

Enter: [Y=] [2nd] [√] [X,T,θ,n] [x²] [+] 4 [ENTER] [(−)] 1 [+] [2nd] [Y-VARS] 1 1 [ENTER] [(−)] 1 [−] [2nd] [Y-VARS] 1 1

hyperbola

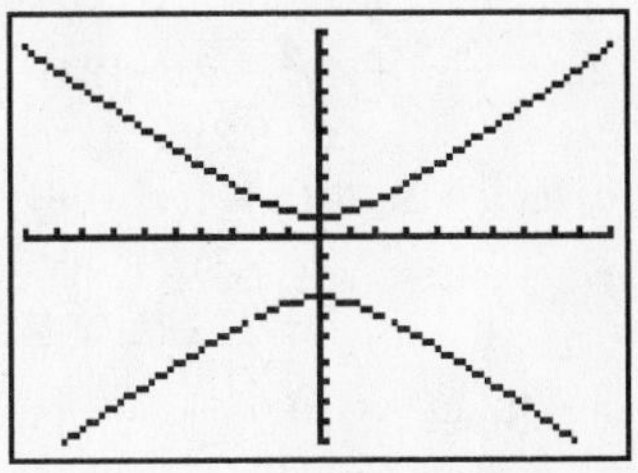

7-6 Conic Sections

Page 453 Check for Understanding

1. Slice the cone with a plane that is not perpendicular to the axis.
2. Slice the double cone with a plane that contains the axis.
3. a problem that is difficult or impossible to solve directly
4. See students' work.
5. circle
6. parabola
7. hyperbola
8. ellipse
9. $y = x^2 + 3x + 1$

$$= \left(x^2 + 3x + \frac{9}{4}\right) + 1 - \frac{9}{4}$$
$$= \left(x + \frac{3}{2}\right)^2 - \frac{5}{4}$$

parabola

vertex: $\left(-\frac{3}{2}, -\frac{5}{4}\right)$

opens upward

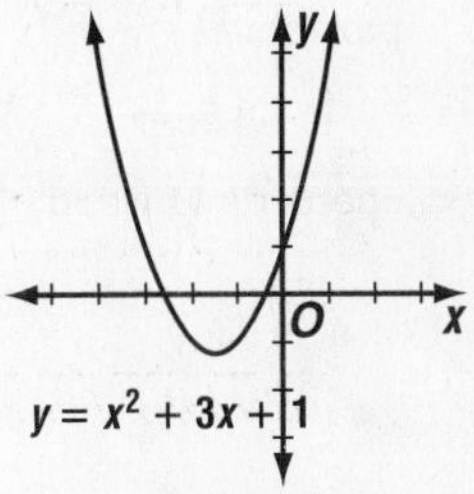

10. $y^2 - 2x^2 - 16 = 0$

$$y^2 - 2x^2 = 16$$
$$\frac{y^2}{16} - \frac{x^2}{8} = 1$$

hyperbola

center: (0, 0)

$a = \sqrt{16}$ or 4,

$b = \sqrt{8}$ or $2\sqrt{2}$

vertices: $(0, \pm 4)$

slopes of asymptotes: $\pm \frac{4}{2\sqrt{2}}$ or $\pm \sqrt{2}$

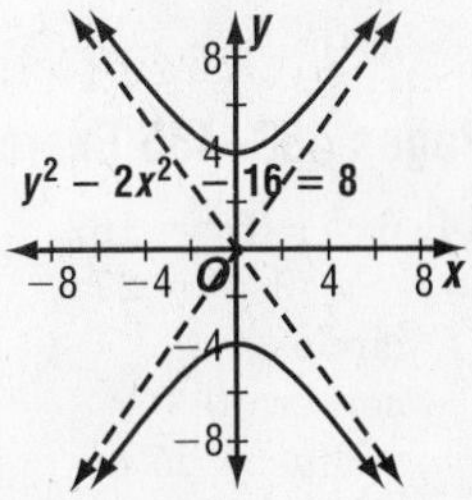

11. $x^2 + y^2 = x + 2$
$x^2 - x + y^2 = 2$
$x^2 - x + \frac{1}{4} + y^2 = 2 + \frac{1}{4}$
$\left(x - \frac{1}{2}\right)^2 + y^2 = \frac{9}{4}$
circle
center: $\left(\frac{1}{2}, 0\right)$
radius: $\sqrt{\frac{9}{4}}$ or $\frac{3}{2}$ units

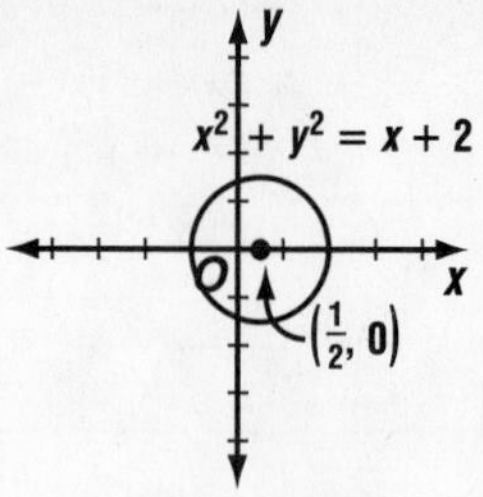

12. $x^2 + 4y^2 + 2x - 24y + 33 = 0$
$x^2 + 2x + 4y^2 - 24y = -33$
$(x^2 + 2x + 1) + 4(y^2 - 6y + 9) = -33 + 1 + 36$
$(x + 1)^2 + 4(y - 3)^2 = 4$
$\frac{(x+1)^2}{4} + \frac{(y-3)^2}{1} = 1$
ellipse
center: $(-1, 3)$

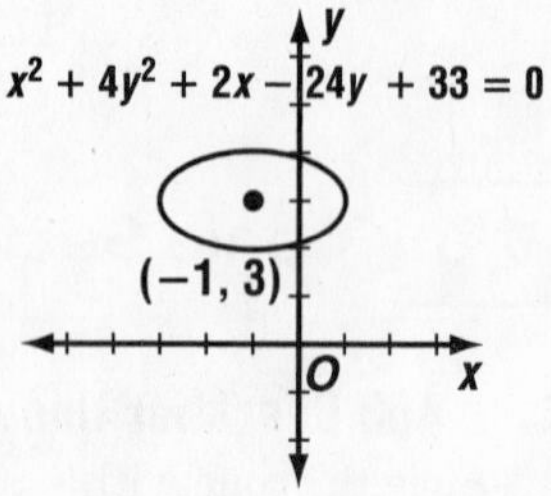

13. $x + 2 = x^2 + y$
$-y + 2 = x^2 - x$
$-y + 2 + \frac{1}{4} = x^2 - x + \frac{1}{4}$
$-y + \frac{9}{4} = \left(x - \frac{1}{2}\right)^2$
$-y = \left(x - \frac{1}{2}\right)^2 - \frac{9}{4}$
$y = -\left(x - \frac{1}{2}\right)^2 + \frac{9}{4}$
parabola
vertex: $\left(\frac{1}{2}, \frac{9}{4}\right)$
opens downward

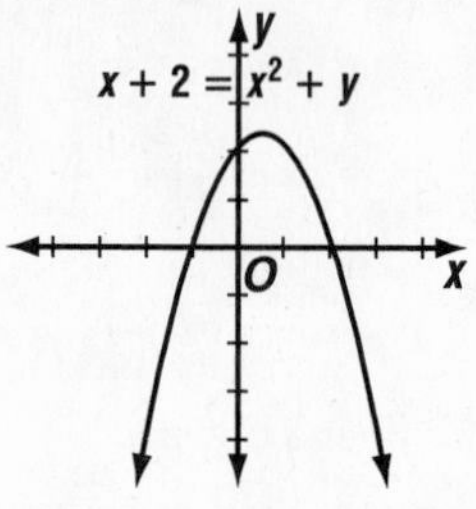

Pages 453–455 Exercises

14. $6x^2 + 6y^2 = 162$
$x^2 + y^2 = 27$
circle
center: $(0, 0)$
radius: $\sqrt{27}$ or $3\sqrt{3}$ units

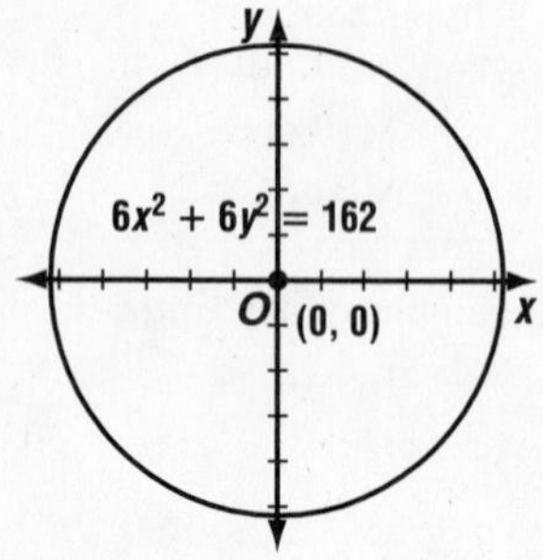

15. $x^2 = 8y$
$\frac{1}{8}x^2 = y$
parabola
vertex: $(0, 0)$
opens upward

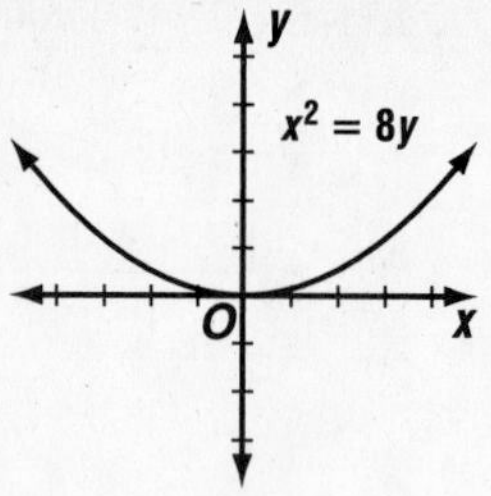

16. $4x^2 + 2y^2 = 8$
$\frac{x^2}{2} + \frac{y^2}{4} = 1$
ellipse
center: $(0, 0)$

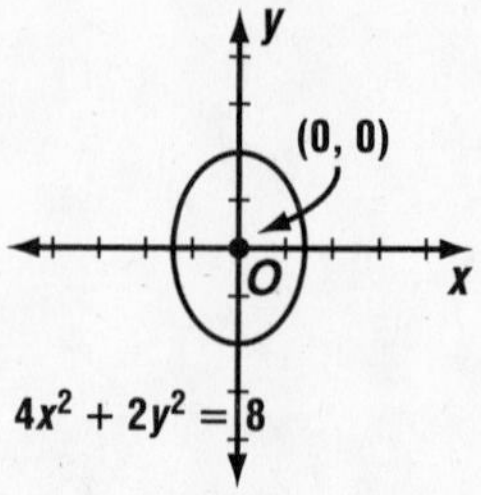

17. $4y^2 - x^2 + 4 = 0$
$4y^2 - x^2 = -4$
$-\frac{y^2}{1} + \frac{x^2}{4} = 1$
$\frac{x^2}{4} - \frac{y^2}{1} = 1$
hyperbola
center: $(0, 0)$
$a = \sqrt{4}$ or 2, $b = \sqrt{1}$ or 1
vertices: $(\pm 2, 0)$
slopes of asymptotes: $\pm \frac{1}{2}$

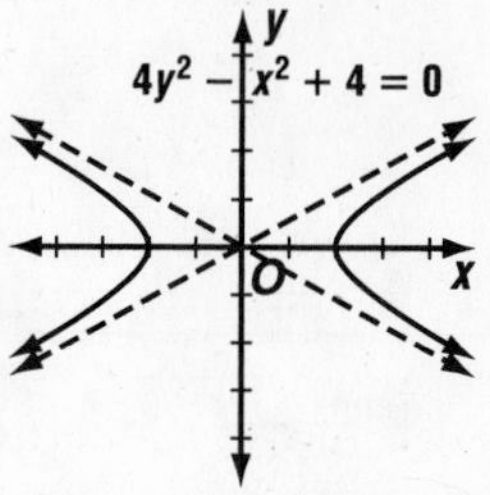

18. $(x - 1)^2 + 9(y - 4)^2 = 36$
$\frac{(x-1)^2}{36} + \frac{(y-4)^2}{4} = 1$
ellipse
center: $(1, 4)$

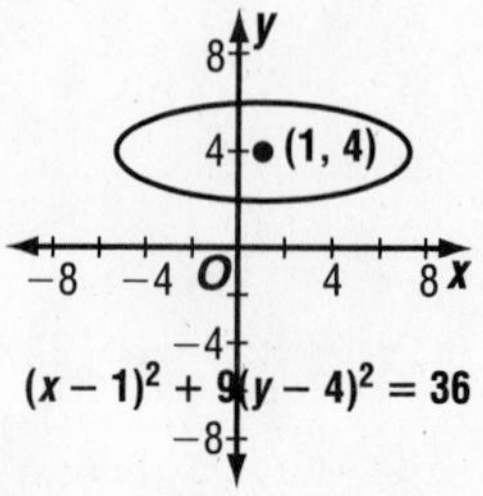

19. $y + 4 = (x - 2)^2$
$y = (x - 2)^2 - 4$
parabola
vertex: $(2, -4)$
opens upward

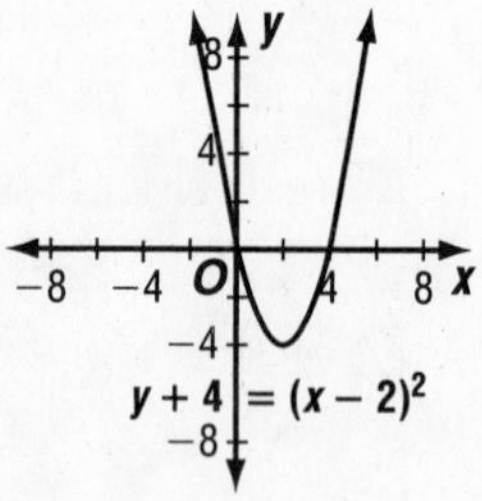

20. $x^2 + y^2 + 6y + 13 = 40$
$x^2 + (y^2 + 6y + 9) = 40 - 13 + 9$
$x^2 + (y + 3)^2 = 36$
circle
center: $(0, -3)$
radius: $\sqrt{36}$ or 6 units

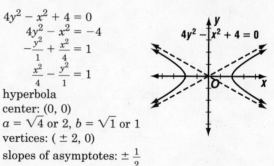

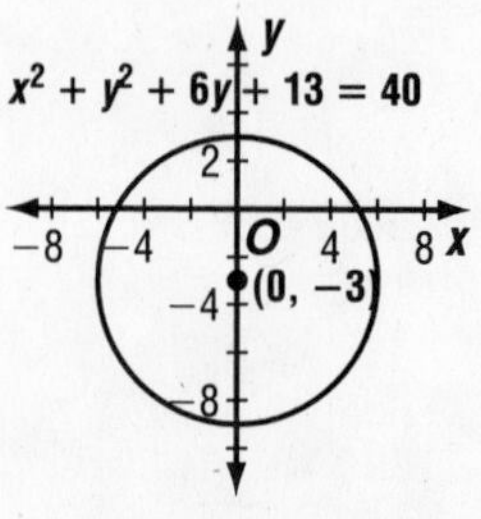

21. $x^2 - y^2 + 8x = 16$

$x^2 + 8x + 16 - y^2 = 16 + 16$

$(x + 4)^2 - y^2 = 32$

$\frac{(x+4)^2}{32} - \frac{y^2}{32} = 1$

hyperbola

center : $(-4, 0)$

$a = \sqrt{32}$ or $4\sqrt{2}$,

$b = \sqrt{32}$ or $4\sqrt{2}$

vertices: $(-4 \pm 4\sqrt{2}, 0)$

slopes of asymptotes: $\pm \frac{4\sqrt{2}}{4\sqrt{2}}$ or ± 1

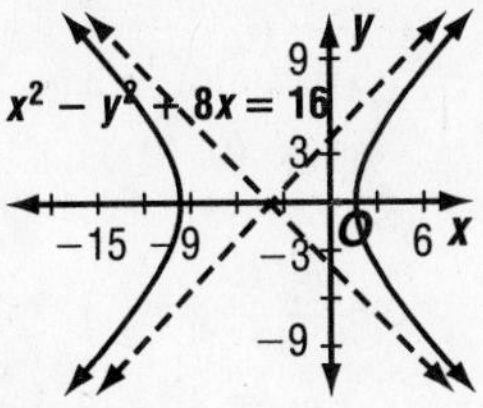

22. $x^2 + y^2 + 4x - 6y = -4$

$x^2 + 4x + 4 + y^2 - 6y + 9 = -4 + 4 + 9$

$(x + 2)^2 + (y - 3)^2 = 9$

circle

center: $(-2, 3)$

radius: $\sqrt{9}$ or 3 units

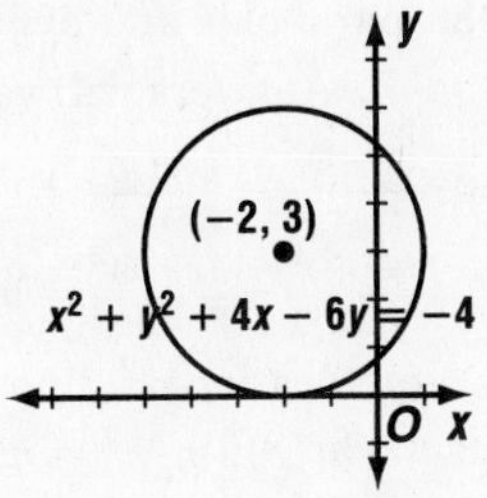

23. $y + x^2 = -(8x + 23)$

$y = -x^2 - 8x - 23$

$y = -(x^2 + 8x + 16) - 23 + 16$

$y = -(x + 4)^2 - 7$

parabola

vertex: $(-4, -7)$

opens downward

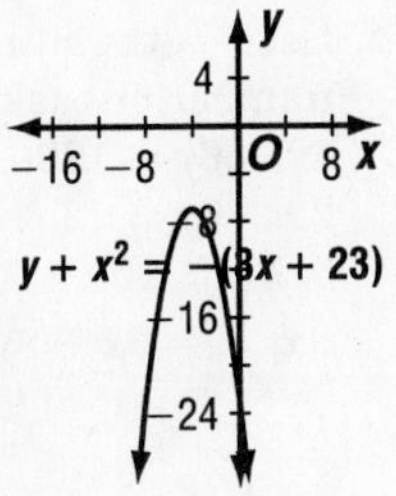

24. $3x^2 + 4y^2 + 8y = 8$

$3x^2 + 4(y^2 + 2y + 1) = 8 + 4$

$3x^2 + 4(y + 1)^2 = 12$

$\frac{x^2}{4} + \frac{(y+1)^2}{3} = 1$

elllipse

center: $(0, -1)$

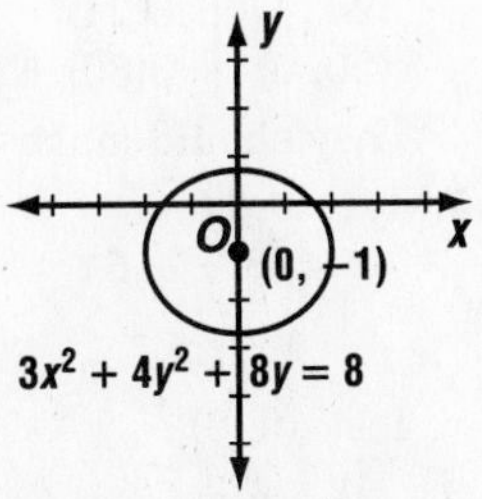

25. $(y - 4)^2 = 9(x - 4)$

$\frac{1}{9}(y - 4)^2 = x - 4$

$\frac{1}{9}(y - 4)^2 + 4 = x$

parabola

vertex: $(4, 4)$

opens right

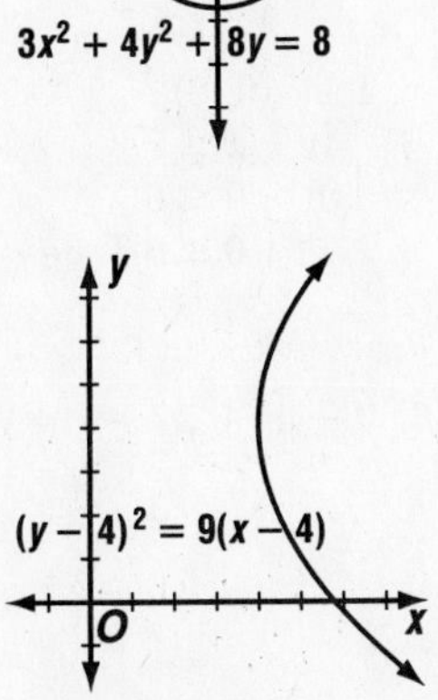

26. $x^2 - 8y + y^2 + 11 = 0$

$x^2 + y^2 - 8y + 16 = -11 + 16$

$x^2 + (y - 4)^2 = 5$

circle

center: $(0, 4)$

radius: $\sqrt{5}$ units

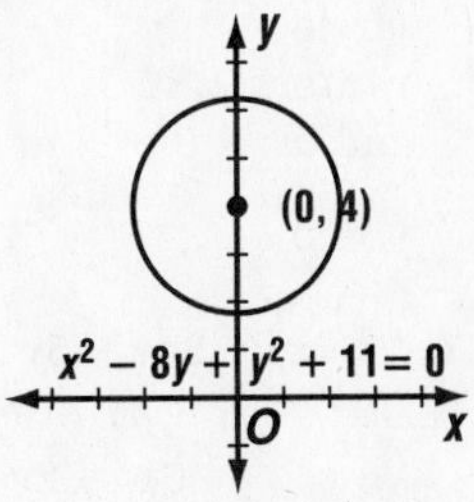

27. $25y^2 + 9x^2 - 50y - 54x = 119$

$9x^2 - 54x + 25y^2 - 50y = 119$

$9(x^2 - 6x + 9) + 25(y^2 - 2y + 1) = 119 + 81 + 25$

$9(x - 3)^2 + 25(y - 1)^2 = 225$

$\frac{(x-3)^2}{25} + \frac{(y-1)^2}{9} = 1$

ellipse

center: $(3, 1)$

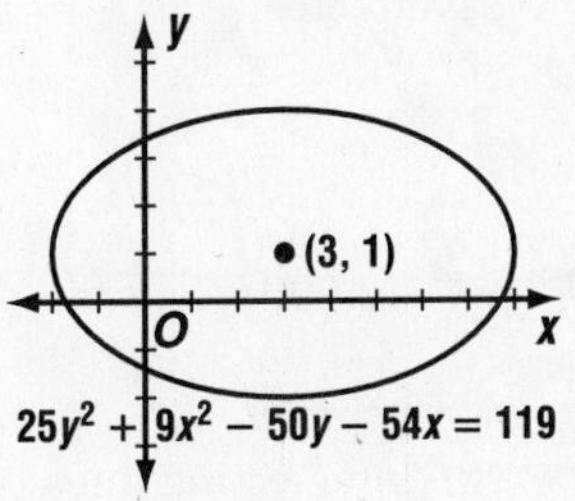

28. $x^2 + 4y^2 - 11 = 2(4y - x)$

$x^2 + 4y^2 - 11 = 8y - 2x$

$x^2 + 2x + 4y^2 - 8y = 11$

$(x^2 + 2x + 1) + 4(y^2 - 2y + 1) = 11 + 1 + 4$

$(x + 1)^2 + 4(y - 1)^2 = 16$

$\frac{(x+1)^2}{16} + \frac{(y-1)^2}{4} = 1$

ellipse

center: $(-1, 1)$

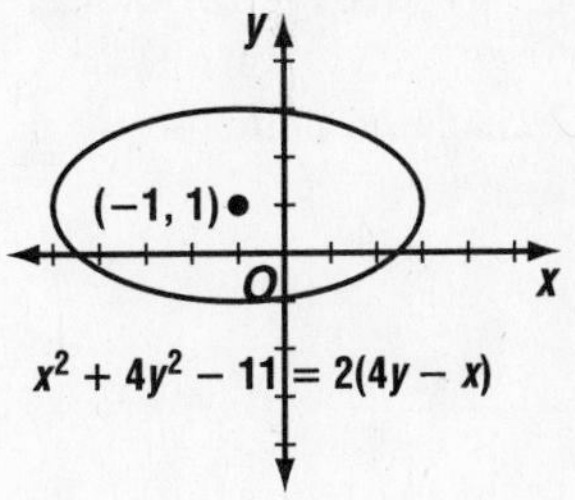

29. $9y^2 + 18y = 25x^2 + 216$

$9(y^2 + 2y + 1) - 25x^2 = 216 + 9$

$9(y + 1)^2 - 25x^2 = 225$

$\frac{(y+1)^2}{25} - \frac{x^2}{9} = 225$

hyperbola

center: $(0, -1)$

$a = \sqrt{25}$ or 5,

$b = \sqrt{9}$ or 3

vertices: $(0, -1 \pm 5)$ or

$(0, -6)$, $(0, 4)$

slopes of asymptotes: $\pm \frac{5}{3}$

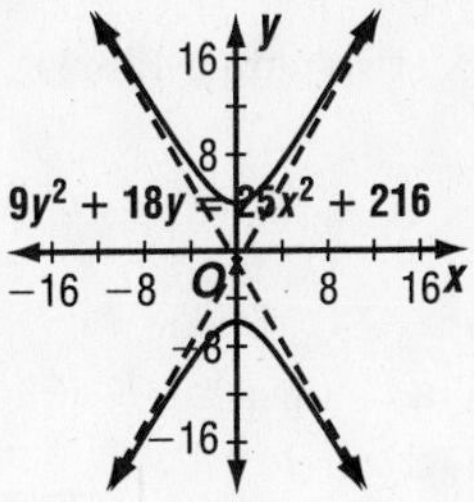

30. $x^2 + y^2 = 2x + 8$

$x^2 - 2x + y^2 = 8$

$x^2 - 2x + 1 + y^2 = 8 + 1$

$(x - 1)^2 + y^2 = 9$

circle

center: (1, 0)

radius: $\sqrt{9}$ or 3 units

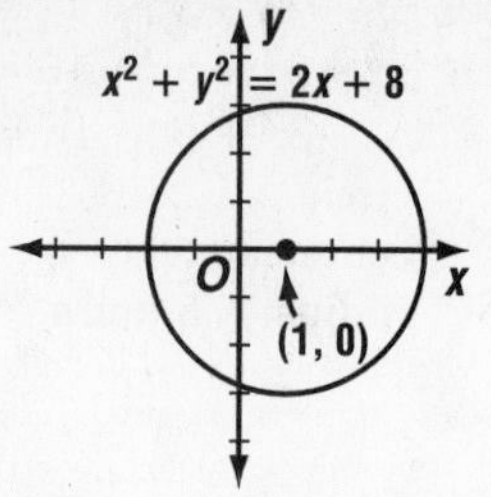

31. $6x^2 - 24x - 5y^2 - 10y - 11 = 0$

$6(x^2 - 4x + 4) - 5(y^2 - 2y + 1) = 11 + 24 - 5$

$6(x - 2)^2 - 5(y - 1)^2 = 30$

$\frac{(x-2)^2}{5} - \frac{(y-1)^2}{6} = 1$

hyperbola

center: (2, 1)

$a = \sqrt{5}$, $b = \sqrt{6}$

vertices: $(2 \pm \sqrt{5}, 1)$

slopes of asymptotes:

$\pm \frac{\sqrt{6}}{\sqrt{5}}$ or $\pm \frac{\sqrt{30}}{5}$

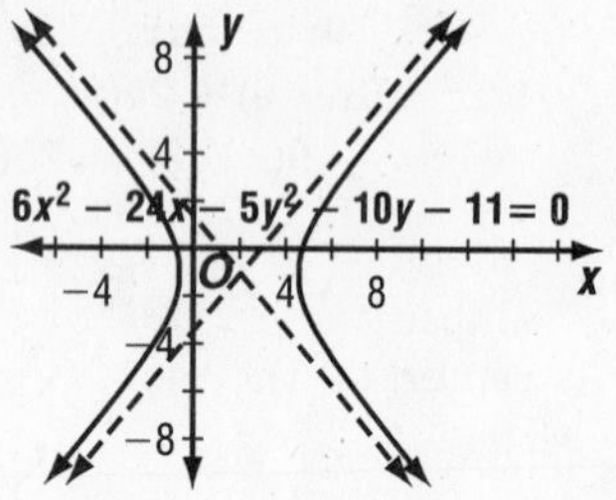

32. $4x^2 - y^2 = 0$

$4x^2 = y^2$

$\pm 2x = y$

two intersecting lines

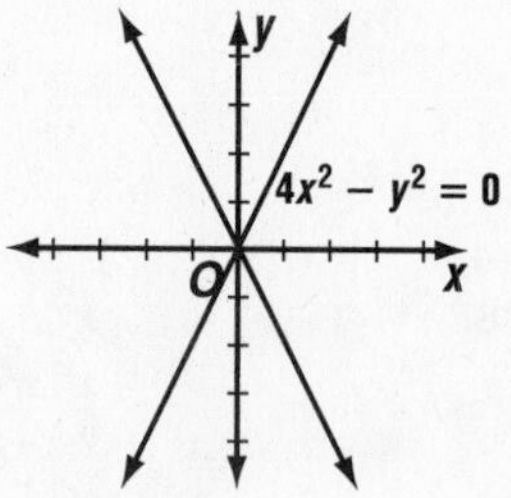

33. $4y^2 + 3x^2 + 32y - 6x = -67$

$4y^2 + 32y + 3x^2 - 6x = -67$

$4(y^2 + 8y + 16) + 3(x^2 - 2x + 1) = -67 + 64 + 3$

$4(y + 4)^2 + 3(x - 1)^2 = 0$

isolated point

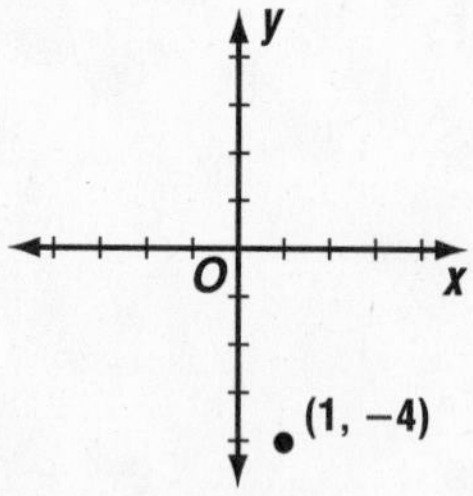

34. $x^2 - x = 0$

$x(x - 1) = 0$

$x = 0$ or $x - 1 = 0$

$x = 1$

two parallel lines

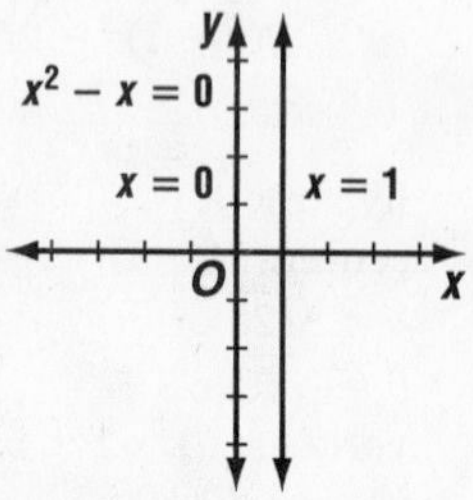

35a. ellipse **35b.** hyperbola

35c. circle **35d.** parabola

36a. The vertices move closer to the center.

36b. 2 intersecting lines

37. $\frac{x^2}{16} + \frac{y^2}{4} = 1$

$a = \sqrt{16}$ or 4, $b = \sqrt{4}$ or 2

focus: (0, 2)	or	focus: (0, −2)
directrix: $y = -2$		directrix: $y = 2$
vertex: (0, 0)		vertex: (0, 0)
$k + \frac{1}{4a} = 2$		$k + \frac{1}{4a} = -2$
$0 + \frac{1}{4a} = 2$		$0 + \frac{1}{4a} = -2$
$a = \frac{1}{8}$		$a = -\frac{1}{8}$
$y = a(x - h)^2 + k$		$y = a(x - h)^2 + k$
$y = \frac{1}{8}x^2$		$y = -\frac{1}{8}x$

$y = \pm \frac{1}{8}x^2$

38. parabolas and hyperbolas

39a–b. Answers will vary.

40. $\frac{(y-k)^2}{a^2} - \frac{(x-h)^2}{b^2} = 1$

$\frac{(y-4)^2}{36} - \frac{(x-5)^2}{16} = 1$

41. quadratic, $4x^2$; linear, $-8x$; constant, -2

42. $(m^5n^{-3})^2\, m^2n^7 = m^{10}n^{-6}m^2n^7$

$= m^{12}n$

43. $\begin{vmatrix} 4 & -7 & 2 \\ 3 & -3 & 3 \\ 2 & 7 & 5 \end{vmatrix} \begin{matrix} 4 & -7 \\ 3 & -3 \\ 2 & 7 \end{matrix}$

$-60 + (-42) + 42 - (-12) - (84) - (-105) = -27$

44. Let x = the number of footballs and y = the number of basketballs.

$4x + 6y \leq 120$

$2x + 6y \leq 72$

$0 \leq y \leq 10$

$f(x, y) = 3x + 2y$

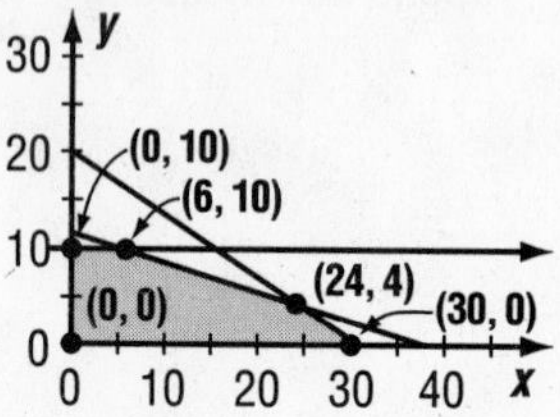

(x, y)	$3x + 2y$	$f(x, y)$
(0, 0)	3(0) + 2(0)	0
(0, 10)	3(0) + 2(10)	20
(6, 10)	3(6) + 2(10)	38
(24, 4)	3(24) + 2(4)	80
(30, 0)	3(30) + 2(0)	90

They should make 30 footballs and 0 basketballs.

45. $4y - x \leq 6$

$4y \leq x + 6$

$y \leq \frac{1}{4}x + \frac{3}{2}$

Test: (0, 0)

$4y - x \overset{?}{\leq} 6$

$4(0) - 0 \overset{?}{\leq} 6$

$0 \leq 6$ True

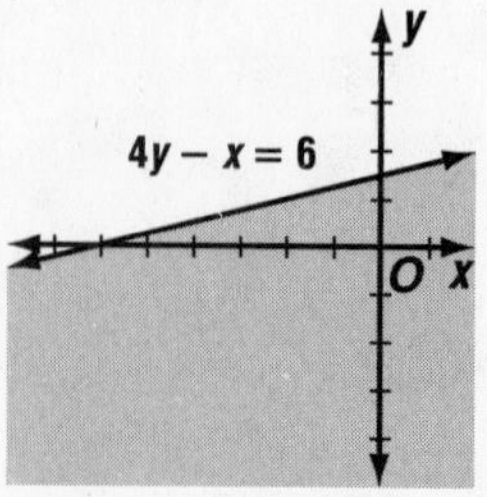

46. $7 - 4^2 + 27 - 1 = 7 - 16 + 27 - 1$

$= -9 + 27 - 1$

$= 18 - 1$

$= 17$

7-6B Modeling Mathematics: Conic Sections

Pages 457 Exercises

1. The points are equidistant from the focus and the directrix.
2. The ellipses become more circular; the ellipses become more oblong.
3. Each branch of the hyperbola becomes more narrow, and the vertices become farther apart. Each branch of the hyperbola becomes wider, and the vertices become closer.

7-7A Graphing Technology: Solving Quadratic Systems

Page 459 Exercises

1. $x^2 + y^2 = 16$ $\quad$ $y = 2x^2 - 2$
$y^2 = 16 - x^2$
$y = \pm\sqrt{16 - x^2}$
Enter: Y= 2nd √ (16 − X,T,θ,n x^2) ENTER (−) 2nd Y-VARS 1 1 ENTER 2 X,T,θ,n x^2 − 2 ENTER ZOOM 5
(±1.68, 3.63)

2. $9x^2 - 4y^2 = 36$ $\quad$ $x^2 + 4y^2 = 36$
$-4y^2 = 36 - 9x^2$ $\quad$ $4y^2 = 36 - x^2$
$y^2 = \frac{9x^2 - 36}{4}$ $\quad$ $y^2 = \frac{36 - x^2}{4}$
$y = \pm\sqrt{\frac{9x^2 - 36}{4}}$ $\quad$ $y = \pm\sqrt{\frac{36 - x^2}{4}}$
Enter: Y= 2nd √ ((9 X,T,θ,n x^2 − 36) ÷ 4) ENTER (−) 2nd Y-VARS 1 1 ENTER 2nd √ ((36 − X,T,θ,n x^2) ÷ 4) ENTER (−) 2nd Y-VARS 1 3 ZOOM 5
(±2.68, ±2.68)

3. $x^2 + 9y^2 = 9$ $\quad$ $y = x^2 - 1$
$9y^2 = 9 - x^2$
$y^2 = \frac{9 - x^2}{9}$
$y = \pm\sqrt{\frac{9 - x^2}{9}}$
Enter; Y= 2nd √ ((9 − X,T,θ,n x^2) ÷ 9) ENTER (−) 2nd Y-VARS 1 1 ENTER 1 X,T,θ,n x^2 − 1 ENTER ZOOM 5
(0, −1), (±1.36, 0.85)

4. $x^2 + y^2 = 64$ $\quad$ $9y^2 - 4x^2 = 1$
$y^2 = 64 - x^2$ $\quad$ $y^2 = \frac{4x^2 + 1}{9}$
$y = \pm\sqrt{64 - x^2}$ $\quad$ $y = \frac{\pm\sqrt{4x^2 + 1}}{3}$
Enter: Y= 2nd √ (64 − X,T,θ,n x^2) ENTER (−) 2nd Y-VARS 1 1 ENTER 2nd √ ((4 X,T,θ,n x^2 + 1) ÷ 9) ENTER (−) 2nd Y-VARS 1 3 ZOOM 5
(±6.65, ±4.45)

5. $(x - 1)^2 + y^2 = 9$ $\quad$ $x^2 + 64y^2 = 64$
$y^2 = 9 - (x - 1)^2$ $\quad$ $64y^2 = 64 - x^2$
$y = \pm\sqrt{9 - (x - 1)^2}$ $\quad$ $y^2 = \frac{64 - x^2}{64}$
$y = \pm\sqrt{\frac{64 - x^2}{64}}$
Enter: Y= 2nd √ (9 − (X,T,θ,n − 1) x^2) ENTER (−) 2nd Y-VARS 1 1 ENTER 2nd √ ((64 − X,T,θ,n x^2) ÷ 64) ENTER (−) 2nd Y-VARS 1 3 ZOOM 5
(±2.98, ±0.93)

6. $y = -x^2 + 7$ $\quad$ $y = x^2 - 7$
Enter: Y= (−) X,T,θ,n x^2 + 7 ENTER (−) 2nd Y-VARS 1 1 ENTER
(±2.65, 0)

7. $x = y^2 - 10y + 25$ $\quad$ $x^2 + y^2 = 25$
$x = (y - 5)^2$ $\quad$ $y^2 = 25 - x^2$
$\pm\sqrt{x} = y - 5$ $\quad$ $y = \pm\sqrt{25 - x^2}$
$5 \pm\sqrt{x} = y$
Enter: Y= 2nd √ X,T,θ,n ENTER 5 + 2nd Y-VARS 1 1 ENTER 5 − 2nd Y-VARS 1 1 ENTER 2nd √ (25 − X,T,θ,n x^2) ENTER (−) 2nd Y-VARS 1 3 ZOOM 5
(0, 5), (4, 3)

8. $x^2 + y^2 = 1$ $\quad$ $x^2 + y^2 = 45$
$y^2 = 1 - x^2$ $\quad$ $y^2 = 45 - x^2$
$y = \pm\sqrt{1 - x^2}$ $\quad$ $y = \pm\sqrt{45 - x^2}$
Enter: Y= 2nd √ (1 − X,T,θ,n x^2) ENTER (−) 2nd Y-VARS 1 1 ENTER 2nd √ (45 − X,T,θ,n x^2) ENTER (−) 2nd Y-VARS 1 3 ZOOM 5
no solution

7-7 Solving Quadratic Systems

Pages 464–465 Check for Understanding

1. Problems whose answers are not easily determined by looking at the graph; the graph helps to determine the number of answers and their approximate value.
2. There is no solution. You may get a complex solution when solving the system algebraically.
3. Sample answer: $y = x^2$

   $(x - 4)^2 + (y - 4)^2 = 4$

   $\frac{(x-6)^2}{16} + \frac{(y-4)^2}{4} = 1$
4. the solution of the system inequalities or the points that are solutions to both inequalities

5a. 0

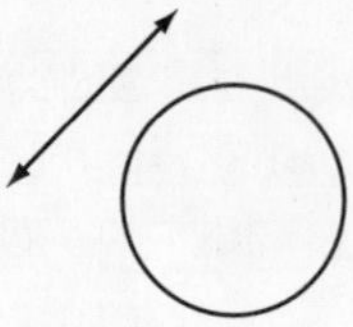

1

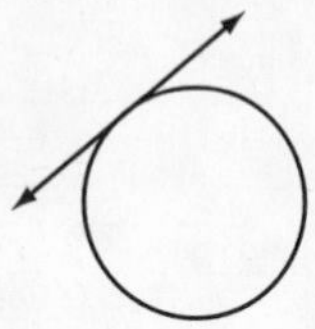

2

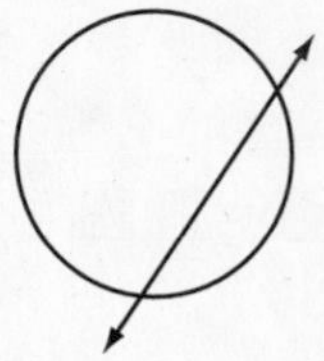

5b. 0

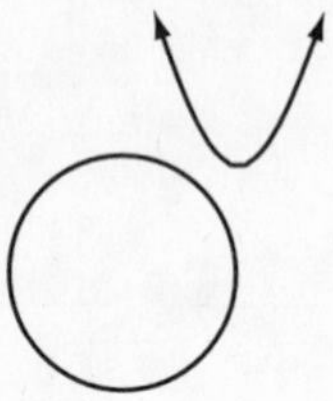

1

2

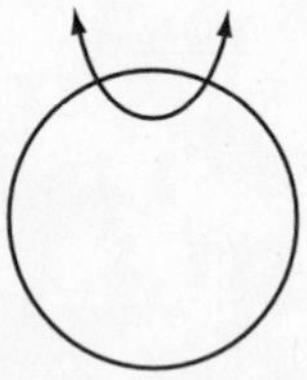

3

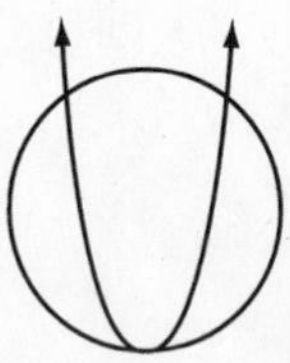

4

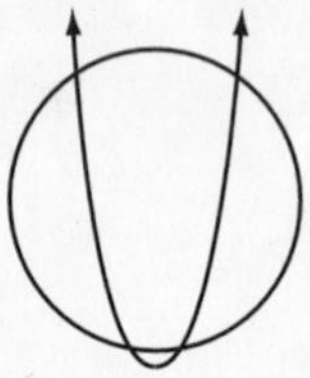

5c. 0

1

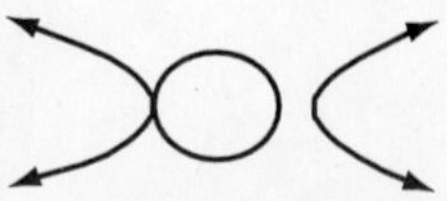

(Continued next column)

2

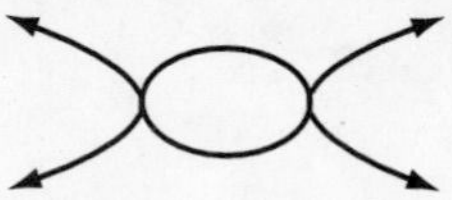

3

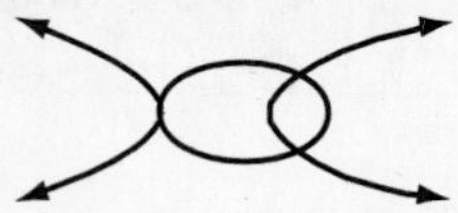

4

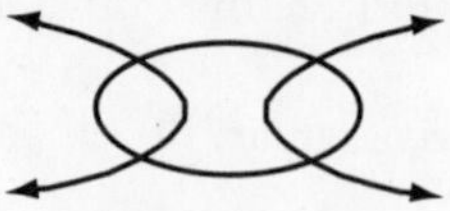

5d. 0

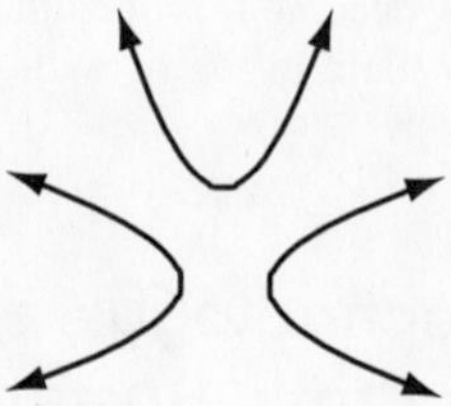

1

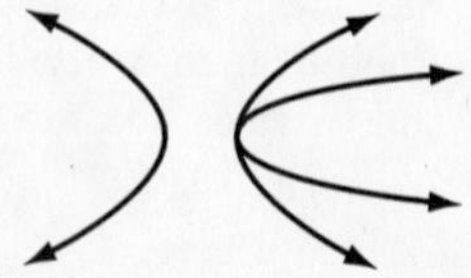

2

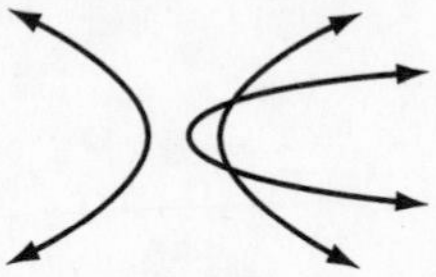

3

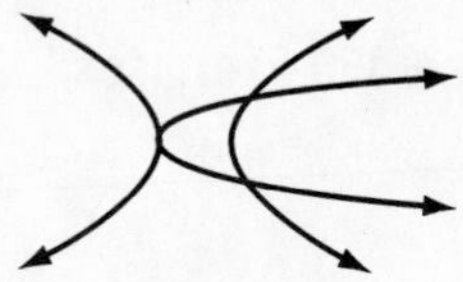

4

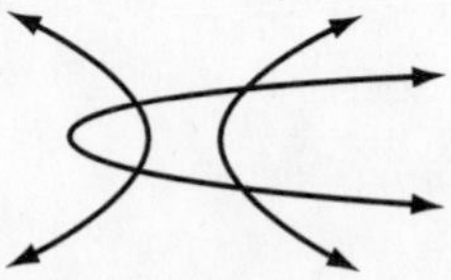

6. $x^2 + y^2 = 25$; circle

$y - x = 1$; line

$y = x + 1$

$x^2 + (x + 1)^2 = 25$

$x^2 + x^2 + 2x + 1 = 25$

$2x^2 + 2x + 1 = 25$

$2x^2 + 2x - 24 = 0$

$x^2 + x - 12 = 0$

$(x + 4)(x - 3) = 0$

$x + 4 = 0$ or $x - 3 = 0$

$x = -4$ $\quad$ $x = 3$

$y = x + 1$ $\quad$ $y = x + 1$

$= -4 + 1$ $\quad$ $= 3 + 1$

$= -3$ $\quad$ $= 4$

$(-4, -3), (3, 4)$

7. $x^2 + 3y^2 = 12$; ellipse

$x^2 - y^2 = 9$; hyperbola

$$\begin{array}{r} x^2 + 3y^2 = 12 \\ \underline{(-)x^2 \ - y^2 = \ 9} \\ 4x^2 \qquad = \ 3 \end{array}$$

$y^2 = \frac{3}{4}$

$y = \pm\sqrt{\frac{3}{4}}$ or $\pm\frac{\sqrt{3}}{2}$

(Continued next page)

$$x^2 - y^2 = 9$$
$$x^2 - \left(\frac{\sqrt{3}}{2}\right)^2 = 9$$
$$x^2 - \frac{3}{4} = 9$$
$$x^2 = \frac{39}{4}$$
$$x = \pm\sqrt{\frac{39}{4}} \text{ or } \pm\frac{\sqrt{39}}{2}$$

$$x^2 - y^2 = 9$$
$$x^2 - \left(-\frac{\sqrt{3}}{2}\right)^2 = 9$$
$$x^2 - \frac{3}{4} = 9$$
$$x^2 = \frac{39}{4}$$
$$x = \pm\sqrt{\frac{39}{4}} \text{ or } \pm\frac{\sqrt{39}}{2}$$

$\left(\pm\frac{\sqrt{39}}{2}, \pm\frac{\sqrt{3}}{2}\right)$

8. $2x^2 - 2y^2 = 72$; hyperbola
$4y^2 + x^2 = 25$; ellipse
$$\begin{aligned} 4x^2 - 4y^2 &= 144 \\ (+)\ x^2 + 4y^2 &= 25 \\ \hline 5x^2 &= 169 \end{aligned}$$
$$x^2 = \frac{169}{5}$$
$$x = \pm\sqrt{\frac{169}{5}} \text{ or } \pm\frac{13\sqrt{5}}{5}$$
$$2x^2 - 2y^2 = 72$$
$$2\left(\frac{13\sqrt{5}}{5}\right)^2 - 2y^2 = 72$$
$$2\left(\frac{169}{5}\right) - 2y^2 = 72$$
$$-2y^2 = 4.4$$
$$y^2 = -2.2$$
$$y = \pm\sqrt{-2.2}$$
no solution

9. $3x = 8y^2$; parabola
$8y^2 - 2x^2 = 16$; hyperbola
$(3x) - 2x^2 = 16$
$$0 = 2x^2 - 3x + 16$$
$$x = \frac{-(-3) \pm \sqrt{(-3)^2 - 4(2)(16)}}{2(2)}$$
$$= \frac{3 \pm \sqrt{-119}}{4}$$
no solution

10. $y = x + 2$
$y = x^2$
$$x^2 = x + 2$$
$$x^2 - x - 2 = 0$$
$$(x - 2)(x + 1) = 0$$
$x - 2 = 0$ or $x + 1 = 0$
$x = 2$ $\quad x = -1$
$y = x^2 = (2)^2 = 4$ $\quad y = x^2 = (-1)^2 = 1$
$(2, 4)\quad(-1, 1)$

11.
$$\begin{aligned} 5x^2 + y^2 &= 30 \\ (+)\ 9x^2 - y^2 &= -16 \\ \hline 14x^2 &= 14 \end{aligned}$$
$$x^2 = 1$$
$$x = \pm 1$$
$5x^2 + y^2 = 30$, $5(1)^2 + y^2 = 30$, $5 + y^2 = 30$, $y^2 = 25$, $y = \pm 5$
$5x^2 + y^2 = 30$, $5(-1)^2 + y^2 = 30$, $5 + y^2 = 30$, $y^2 = 25$, $y = \pm 5$
$(\pm 1, \pm 5)$

12. $x^2 + y^2 < 25$
center: (0, 0)
radius: $\sqrt{25}$ or 5 units
$4x^2 - 9y^2 < 36$
$\frac{x^2}{9} - \frac{y^2}{4} < 1$
center: (0, 0)
$a = \sqrt{9}$ or 3,
$b = \sqrt{4}$ or 2
vertices: $(\pm 3, 0)$
slopes of asymptotes: $\pm\frac{2}{3}$

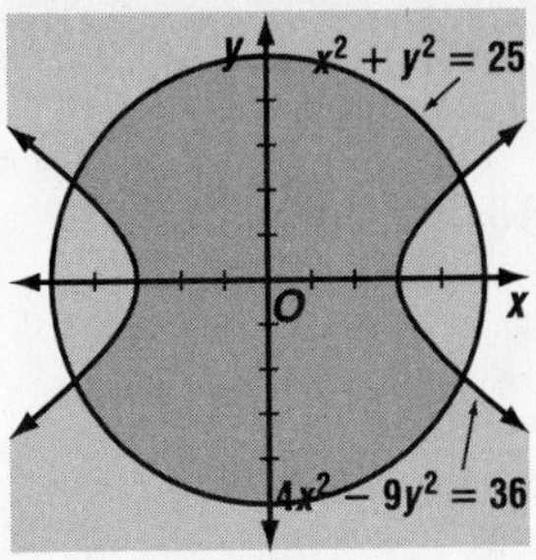

13. $y^2 < x$
vertex; (0, 0)
opens right
$x^2 - 4y^2 < 16$
$\frac{x^2}{16} - \frac{y^2}{4} < 1$
center: (0, 0)
$a = \sqrt{16}$ or 4,
$b = \sqrt{4}$ or 2
vertices: $(\pm 4, 0)$
slopes of asymptotes: $\pm\frac{2}{4}$ or $\pm\frac{1}{2}$

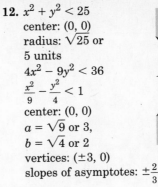

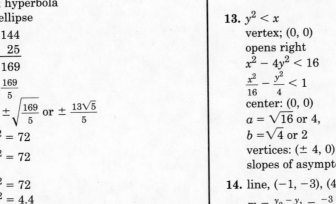

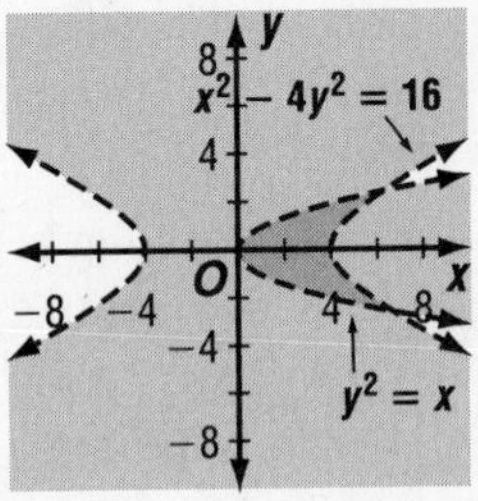

14. line, $(-1, -3)$, $(4, 12)$
$$m = \frac{y_2 - y_1}{x_2 - x_1} = \frac{-3 - 12}{-1 - 4} = \frac{-15}{-5} = 3$$
$y - y_1 = m(x - x_1)$
$y - 12 = 3(x - 4)$
$y - 12 = 3x - 12$
$y = 3x$
parabola, passes through (2, 0)
vertex: $(0, -4)$
$y = a(x - h)^2 + k$
$0 = a(2 - 0)^2 - 4$
$4 = 4a$
$1 = a$
$y = x^2 - 4$

Pages 465–467 Exercises

15. $y = 6$
$$y^2 = x^2 + 9$$
$$(6)^2 = x^2 + 9$$
$$36 = x^2 + 9$$
$$27 = x^2$$
$$\pm\sqrt{27} = x$$
$$\pm 3\sqrt{3} = x$$
$(\pm 3\sqrt{3}, 6)$

16. $y = 2x^2$
$y = x + 3$
$$2x^2 = x + 3$$
$$2x^2 - x - 3 = 0$$
$$(2x - 3)(x + 1) = 0$$
$2x - 3 = 0$ or $x + 1 = 0$
$x = \frac{3}{2}$ $\quad x = -1$
$y = x + 3 = \frac{3}{2} + 3 = \frac{9}{2}$ $\quad y = x + 3 = -1 + 3 = 2$
$\left(\frac{3}{2}, \frac{9}{2}\right), (-1, 2)$

17. $y^2 = x^2 - 25 \rightarrow -x^2 + y^2 = -25$
$x^2 - y^2 = 7 \rightarrow (+)x^2 - y^2 = 7$
$0 \neq 18$ no solution

18. $4x^2 + y^2 = 100$
$4x + y^2 = 20$
$y^2 = 20 - 4x$
$4x^2 + 20 - 4x = 100$
$4x^2 - 4x - 80 = 0$
$x^2 - x - 20 = 0$
$(x - 5)(x + 4) = 0$
$x - 5 = 0$ or $x + 4 = 0$
$x = 5$ $\quad x = -4$
$y^2 = 20 - 4x$ $\quad y^2 = 20 - 4x$
$y^2 = 20 - 4(5)$ $\quad y^2 = 20 - 4(-4)$
$y^2 = 0$ $\quad y^2 = 36$
$y = 0$ $\quad y = \pm 6$
$(5, 0), (-4, \pm 6)$

19. $x^2 + y^2 = 64$ $\quad x^2 + y^2 = 64$
$(-)x^2 + 64y^2 = 64$ $\quad x^2 + 0 = 64$
$-63y^2 = 0$ $\quad x^2 = 64$
$y^2 = 0$ $\quad x = \pm 8$
$y = 0$
$(\pm 8, 0)$

20. $x + 4 = (y - 1)^2$ $\quad (-y - 1) + 4 = (y - 1)^2$
$x + y + 1 = 0$ $\quad -y - 1 + 4 = y^2 - 2y + 1$
$x = -y - 1$ $\quad 0 = y^2 - y - 2$
$0 = (y - 2)(y + 1)$
$y - 2 = 0$ or $y + 1 = 0$
$y = 2$ $\quad y = -1$
$x = -y - 1$ $\quad x = -y - 1$
$= -2 - 1$ $\quad = -(-1) - 1$
$= -3$ $\quad = 0$
$(-3, 2), (0, -1)$

21. $y^2 = x^2 - 7 \rightarrow -x^2 + y^2 = -7$
$x^2 + y^2 = 25 \rightarrow (+)x^2 + y^2 = 25$
$2y^2 = 18$
$y^2 = 9$
$y = \pm 3$
$x^2 + y^2 = 25$ $\quad x^2 + y^2 = 25$
$x^2 + (-3)^2 = 25$ $\quad x^2 + 3^2 = 25$
$x^2 + 9 = 25$ $\quad x^2 + 9 = 25$
$x^2 = 16$ $\quad x^2 = 16$
$x = \pm 4$ $\quad x = \pm 4$
$(\pm 4, \pm 3)$

22. $y = 7 - x$
$y^2 + x^2 = 9$ $\quad (7 - x)^2 + x^2 = 9$
$49 - 14x + x^2 + x^2 = 9$
$2x^2 - 14x + 40 = 0$
$x^2 - 7x + 20 = 0$

$$x = \frac{-(-7) \pm \sqrt{(-7)^2 - 4(1)(20)}}{2(1)}$$
$$= \frac{7 \pm \sqrt{-31}}{2}$$
no solution

23. $x^2 + 2y^2 = 33$ $\quad x^2 + 2(-x^2 + 2x + 19) = 33$
$x^2 + y^2 - 19 = 2x$ $\quad x^2 - 2x^2 + 4x + 38 = 33$
$y^2 = -x^2 + 2x + 19$ $\quad -x^2 + 4x + 5 = 0$
$x^2 - 4x - 5 = 0$
$(x - 5)(x + 1) = 0$
$x - 5 = 0$ or $x + 1 = 0$
$x = 5$ $\quad x = -1$
$y^2 = -x^2 + 2x + 19$ $\quad y^2 = -x^2 + 2x + 19$
$y^2 = -(5)^2 + 2(5) + 19$ $\quad y^2 = -(-1)^2 + 2(-1) + 19$
$y^2 = -25 + 10 + 19$ $\quad y^2 = -1 - 2 + 19$
$y^2 = 4$ $\quad y^2 = 16$
$y = \pm 2$ $\quad y = \pm 4$
$(5, \pm 2), (-1, \pm 4)$

24. $x = (y - 3)^2 + 2$ $\quad 5 - y = (y - 3)^2 + 2$
$y + x = 5$ $\quad 5 - y = y^2 - 6y + 9 + 2$
$x = 5 - y$ $\quad 0 = y^2 - 5y + 6$
$0 = (y - 3)(y - 2)$
$y - 3 = 0$ or $y - 2 = 0$
$y = 3$ $\quad y = 2$
$x = 5 - y$ $\quad x = 5 - y$
$= 5 - 3$ $\quad = 5 - 2$
$= 2$ $\quad = 3$
$(2, 3), (3, 2)$

25. $\frac{x^2}{30} + \frac{y^2}{6} = 1$ $\quad \frac{x^2}{30} + \frac{x^2}{6} = 1$
$x = y$ $\quad x^2 + 5x^2 = 30$
$6x^2 = 30$
$x^2 = 5$ $\quad x = y$
$(\sqrt{5}, \sqrt{5}), (-\sqrt{5}, -\sqrt{5})$ $\quad x = \pm\sqrt{5}$ $\quad y = \pm\sqrt{5}$

26. $\frac{x^2}{36} - \frac{y^2}{4} = 1$ $\quad \frac{x^2}{36} - \frac{x^2}{4} = 1$
$x = y$ $\quad x^2 - 9x^2 = 36$
$-8x^2 = 36$
$x^2 = -\frac{36}{8}$
$x = \pm\frac{\sqrt{-9}}{2}$
no solution

27. $x^2 + y^2 = 36$ $\quad x^2 + (x + 2)^2 = 36$
$y = x + 2$ $\quad x^2 + x^2 + 4x + 4 = 36$
$2x^2 + 4x - 32 = 0$
$x^2 + 2x - 16 = 0$

$$x = \frac{-2 \pm \sqrt{2^2 - 4(1)(-16)}}{2(1)}$$
$$= \frac{-2 \pm \sqrt{68}}{2} \text{ or } -1 \pm \sqrt{17}$$
$y = x + 2$ $\quad y = x + 2$
$= (-1 + \sqrt{17}) + 2$ $\quad = (-1 - \sqrt{17}) + 2$
$= 1 + \sqrt{17}$ $\quad = 1 - \sqrt{17}$
$(-1 + \sqrt{17}, 1 + \sqrt{17}), (-1 - \sqrt{17}, 1 - \sqrt{17})$

28. $3x^2 - y^2 = 9 \rightarrow 3x^2 - y^2 = 9$
$x^2 + 2y^2 = 10 \rightarrow (+)-3x^2 - 6y^2 = -30$
$-7y^2 = -21$
$y^2 = 3$
$y = \pm\sqrt{3}$
$x^2 + 2y^2 = 10$ $\quad x^2 + 2y^2 = 10$
$x^2 + 2(\sqrt{3})^2 = 10$ $\quad x^2 + 2(\sqrt{-3})^2 = 10$
$x^2 + 6 = 10$ $\quad x^2 + 6 = 10$
$x^2 = 4$ $\quad x^2 = 4$
$x = \pm 2$ $\quad x = \pm 2$
$(\pm 2, \pm\sqrt{3})$

29. $x^2 + y^2 = 36$

$8y = x^2 - 79$

$8y + 79 = x^2$

$8y + 79 + y^2 = 36$

$y^2 + 8y + 43 = 0$

$y = \frac{-8 \pm \sqrt{64 - 172}}{2}$

$= \frac{-8 \pm \sqrt{-108}}{2}$

no solution

30. $y = -x^2 + 3$

$y - 3 = -x^2$

$-y + 3 = x^2$

$x^2 + 4y^2 = 36$

$-y + 3 + 4y^2 = 36$

$4y^2 - y - 33 = 0$

$(4y + 11)(y - 3) = 0$

$4y + 11 = 0$ or $y - 3 = 0$

$y = -2.75$ $\quad$ $y = 3$

$-y + 3 = x^2$ $\quad$ $-y + 3 = x^2$

$-(-2.75) + 3 = x^2$ $\quad$ $-3 + 3 = x^2$

$5.75 = x^2$ $\quad$ $0 = x^2$

$\pm 2.40 \approx x$ $\quad$ $0 = x$

$(0, 3), (\pm 2.40, -2.75)$

31. $x^2 + 2y^2 = 16 \rightarrow -2x^2 - 4y^2 = -32$

$y^2 + 2x^2 = 17 \rightarrow (+)\ 2x^2 + y^2 = 17$

$-3y^2 = -15$

$y^2 = 5$

$y = \pm\sqrt{5}$

$x^2 + 2y^2 = 16$ $\quad$ $x^2 + 2y^2 = 16$

$x^2 + 2(-\sqrt{5})^2 = 16$ $\quad$ $x^2 + 2(\sqrt{5})^2 = 16$

$x^2 + 10 = 16$ $\quad$ $x^2 + 10 = 16$

$x^2 = 6$ $\quad$ $x^2 = 6$

$x = \pm\sqrt{6}$ $\quad$ $x = \pm\sqrt{6}$

$(\pm\sqrt{6}, \pm\sqrt{5})$

32. $3x^2 - 20y^2 - 12x + 80y - 96 = 0$

$3x^2 + 20y^2 = 80y + 48$

$3x^2 + 20y^2 - 80y + 48 = 0$

$3x^2 - 20y^2 - 12x + 80y - 96 = 0$

$(+)\ 3x^2 + 20y^2 - 80y - 48 = 0$

$6x^2 - 12x - 144 = 0$

$x^2 - 2x - 24 = 0$

$(x - 6)(x + 4) = 0$

$x - 6 = 0$ $\quad$ $x + 4 = 0$

$x = 6$ $\quad$ $x = -4$

$3x^2 + 20y^2 = 80y + 48$

$3(6)^2 + 20y^2 = 80y + 48$

$108 + 20y^2 = 80y + 48$

$20y^2 - 80y + 108 - 48 = 0$

$20y^2 - 80y + 60 = 0$

$y^2 - 4y + 3 = 0$

$(y - 3)(y - 1) = 0$

$y - 3 = 0$ $\quad$ $y - 1 = 0$

$y = 3$ $\quad$ $y = 1$

$3x^2 + 20y^2 = 80y + 48$

$3(-4)^2 + 20y^2 = 80y + 48$

$48 + 20y^2 = 80y + 48$

$20y^2 - 80y = 0$

$20y(y - 4) = 0$

$20y = 0$ or $y - 4 = 0$

$y = 0$ $\quad$ $y = 4$

$(6, 3), (6, 1), (-4, 0)\ (-4, 4)$

33. $x^2 + y^2 \geq 4$

center: $(0, 0)$

radius: $\sqrt{4}$ or 2 units

$x^2 + y^2 \leq 36$

center: $(0, 0)$

radius: $\sqrt{36}$ or 6 units

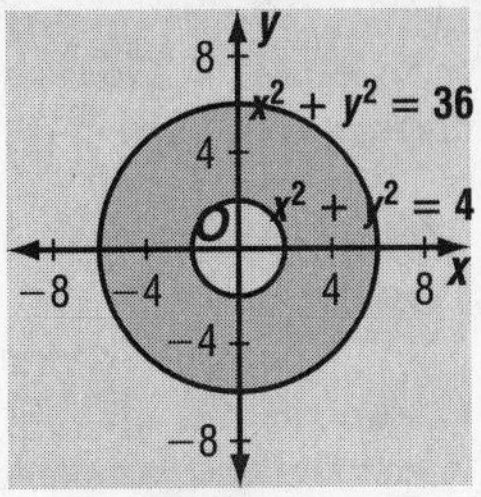

34. $x^2 + y^2 \leq 25$

center: $(0, 0)$

radius: $\sqrt{25}$ or 5 units

$x + 2y \geq 1$

$2y \geq -x + 1$

$y \geq -\frac{1}{2}x + \frac{1}{2}$

slope: $-\frac{1}{2}$

y-intercept: $\frac{1}{2}$

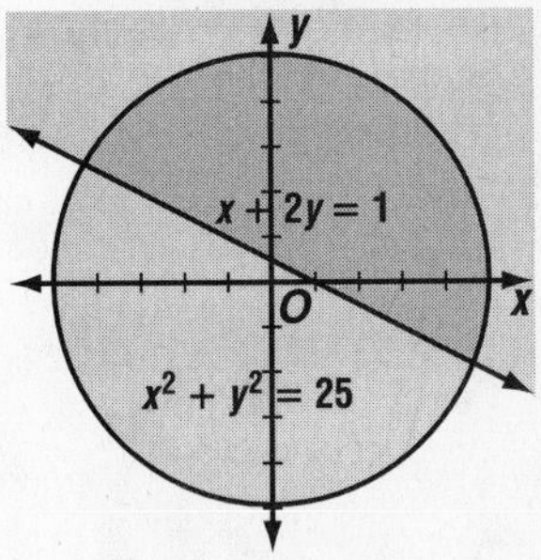

35. $x + y = 4$

$y = -x + 4$

slope: -1

y-intercept: 4

$9x^2 - 4y^2 \geq 36$

$\frac{x^2}{4} - \frac{y^2}{9} \geq 1$

center: $(0, 0)$

$a = \sqrt{4}$ or 2,

$b = \sqrt{9}$ or 3

vertices: $(\pm 2, 0)$

slope of asymptotes: $\pm\frac{3}{2}$

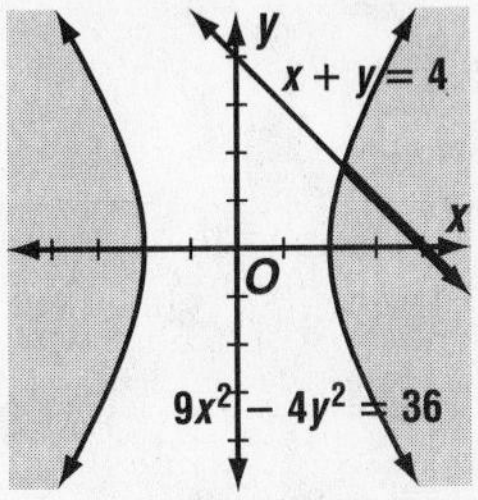

36. $4x^2 + 9y^2 \geq 36$

$\frac{x^2}{9} + \frac{y^2}{4} \geq 1$

center: $(0, 0)$

length of major axis: 6 units

length of minor axis: 4 units

horizontal transverse axis

$4y^2 + 9x^2 \leq 36$

$\frac{y^2}{9} + \frac{x^2}{4} \leq 1$

center: $(0, 0)$

length of major axis: 6 units

length of minor axis: 4 units

vertral transverse axis

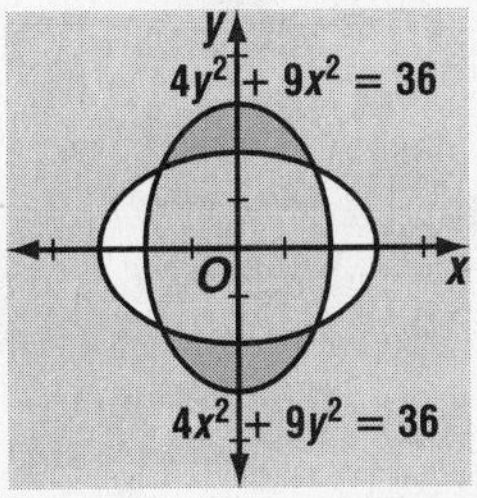

37. $(y - 3)^2 \geq x + 2$

$(y - 3)^2 - 2 \geq x$

vertex: $(-2, 3)$

opens right

$x^2 \leq y + 4$

$x^2 - 4 \leq y$

vertex: $(0, -4)$

opens upward

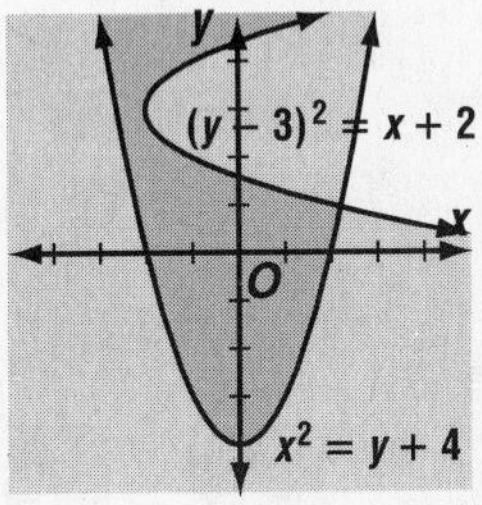

38. $(x+2)^2 + 16(y+3)^2 \geq 16$

$\frac{(x+2)^2}{16} + \frac{(y+3)^2}{1} \geq 1$

center: $(-2, -3)$
length of major axis: 8 units
length of minor axis: 2 units
horizontal transverse axis

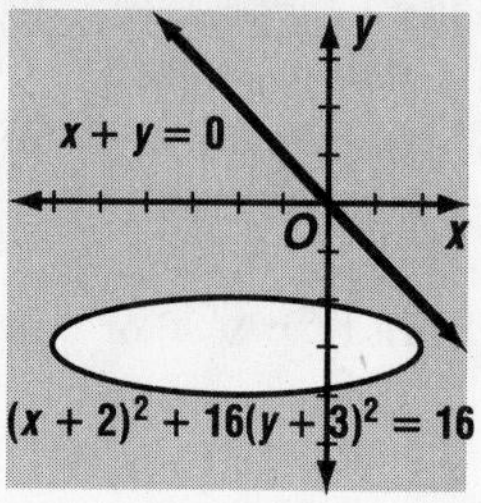

$x + y = 0$
$y = -x$
slope: -1
y-intercept: 0

39. line, $(-3, 2)$ $(0, -1)$

$m = \frac{y_2 - y_1}{x_2 - x_1}$
$= \frac{-1-2}{0-(-3)} =$
$= \frac{-3}{3}$
$= -1$
$y = mx + b$
$y = -x - 1$

parabola, vertex: $(-4, 1)$
passes through $(0, -1)$

$x = a(y-k)^2 + h$
$0 = a(-1-1)^2 - 4$
$4 = 4a$
$1 = a$
$x = (y-1)^2 - 4$

40. line, $(0, -3)$ $(1, 0)$

$m = \frac{y_2 - y_1}{x_2 - x_1}$
$= \frac{-3-0}{0-1}$
$= 3$
$y = mx + b$
$y = 3x - 3$

hyperbola, center: $(0, 0)$
vertices: $(0, \pm 4)$

slopes of asymptotes: $\pm\frac{2}{4}$
$a = 2, b = 4$
$\frac{x^2}{a^2} - \frac{y^2}{b^2} = 1$
$\frac{x^2}{16} - \frac{y^2}{4} = 1$

41. circle, center: $(0, 0)$
passes through $(-1, -2)$
$[0-(-1)]^2 + [0-(-2)]^2 = r^2$
$(1)^2 + (2)^2 = r^2$
$1 + 4 = r^2$
$5 = r^2$

$x^2 + y^2 = 5$
parabola, vertex: $(0, 0)$
passes through $(1, -2)$
opens downward
$y = a(x-h)^2 + k$
$-2 = a(1-0)^2$
$-2 = a$
$y = -2x^2$

42. circle, center: $(0, 0)$
radius: 3 units

$(x-h)^2 + (y-k)^2 = r^2$
$(x-0)^2 + (y-0)^2 = 3^2$
$x^2 + y^2 = 9$
$x^2 + y^2 \leq 9$

line, $(-2, 0)$ $(0, 1)$
$m = \frac{y_2 - y_1}{x_2 - x_1}$
$= \frac{0-1}{-2-0}$
$= \frac{1}{2}$
$y = mx + b$
$y = \frac{1}{2}x + 1$
$y \geq \frac{1}{2}x + 1$

43. circle, center: $(0, 0)$
radius: 5 units
$(x-h)^2 + (y-k)^2 = r^2$
$(x-0)^2 + (y-0)^2 = 5^2$
$x^2 + y^2 = 25$
$x^2 + y^2 \geq 25$

circle, center: $(0, 0)$
radius: 10 units
$(x-h)^2 + (y-k)^2 = r^2$
$(x-0)^2 + (y-0)^2 = 10^2$
$x^2 + y^2 = 100$
$x^2 + y^2 \leq 100$

44. circle, center: $(0, 0)$
radius: 4 units

$(x-h)^2 + (y-k)^2 = r^2$
$(x-0)^2 + (y-0)^2 = 4^2$
$x^2 + y^2 = 6$
$x^2 + y^2 = 6$
$x^2 + y^2 \geq 16$

line, $(0, 2)$, $(2, 0)$
$m = \frac{y_2 - y_1}{x_2 - x_1}$
$= \frac{2-0}{0-2}$
$= -1$
$y = mx + b$
$y = -x + 2$
$x + y = 2$

45. impossible

46. Sample answer: $y = x^2$
$x = (y-2)^2$

47. Sample answer: $x^2 + y^2 = 36$
$\frac{(x+2)^2}{16} - \frac{y^2}{4} = 1$

48. Sample answer: $x^2 + y^2 = 100$
$\frac{x^2}{16} + \frac{y^2}{4} = 1$

49. Sample answer: $x^2 + y^2 = 81$
$\frac{x^2}{4} + \frac{y^2}{100} = 1$

50. Sample answer: $\frac{x^2}{64} + \frac{y^2}{36} = 1$
$\frac{x^2}{64} - \frac{y^2}{16} = 1$

51a. $x + y^2 = 2$
$x = -y^2 + 2$
$2y - 2\sqrt{2} = x(\sqrt{2} + 2)$
$y = \frac{x(\sqrt{2}+2)}{2} + \sqrt{2}$
$x = -\left(\frac{x(\sqrt{2}+2)}{2} + \sqrt{2}\right)^2 + 2$
$x = -\frac{x^2(3+2\sqrt{2})}{2} - x(2+2\sqrt{2}) - 2 + 2$
$x = -\frac{x^2(3+2\sqrt{2})}{2} - x(2+2\sqrt{2})$
$0 = -\frac{x^2(3+2\sqrt{2})}{2} - x(3+2\sqrt{2})$
$0 = -x(3+2\sqrt{2})\left(\frac{x}{2} + 1\right)$

$-x = 0$ or $\frac{x}{2} + 1 = 0$
$x = 0$ $\quad$ $x = -2$
$y = \frac{0 \cdot (\sqrt{2}+2)}{2} + \sqrt{2}$ $\quad$ $y = \frac{-2(\sqrt{2}+2)}{2} + \sqrt{2}$
$= \sqrt{2}$ $\quad$ $= -2$
$(0, \sqrt{2})$, $(-2, -2)$

51b. $x^2 + y^2 = 1$
$y = 3x + 1$
$x^2 + (y+1)^2 = 4$
$x^2 + (3x+1)^2 = 1$
$x^2 + 9x^2 + 6x + 1 = 1$
$10x^2 + 6x = 0$
$2x(5x+3) = 0$

$x = 0$ or $x = -\frac{3}{5}$
$y = 3 \cdot 0 + 1$ $\quad$ $y = 3\left(-\frac{3}{5}\right) + 1$
$= 1$ $\quad$ $= -\frac{4}{5}$

$x^2 + (y+1)^2 = 4$
$0 + (1+1)^2 \stackrel{?}{=} 4$ or $\left(-\frac{3}{5}\right)^2 + \left(-\frac{4}{5} + 1\right)^2 \stackrel{?}{=} 4$
$4 = 4$ $\quad$ $\frac{9}{25} + \frac{1}{25} \stackrel{?}{=} 4$
$\frac{10}{25} \neq 4$

$(0, 1)$

52. Sample answer: $x^2 + y^2 \le 4$,

$\frac{x^2}{16} + \frac{y^2}{4} \ge 1$,

$x^2 + y^2 \le 16$

53.

$$x^2 + y^2 = 50^2 \rightarrow x^2 + y^2 = 2500$$
$$x^2 + (y - 30)^2 = 40^2 \rightarrow x^2 + (y - 30)^2 = 1600$$
$$(x - 35)^2 + (y - 18)^2 = 13^2 \rightarrow (x - 35)^2 + (y - 18)^2 = 169$$

$$\begin{aligned} x^2 \quad + y^2 &= 2500 \\ \underline{(-)x^2 + (y - 30)^2} &= \underline{1600} \\ y^2 - (y - 30)^2 &= 900 \\ y^2 - (y^2 - 60y + 900) &= 900 \\ 60y &= 1800 \\ y &= 30 \end{aligned}$$

$$\begin{aligned} x^2 + y^2 &= 2500 \\ x^2 + (30)^2 &= 2500 \\ x^2 + 900 &= 2500 \\ x^2 &= 1600 \\ x &= \pm 40 \end{aligned}$$

$$\begin{aligned} (x - 35)^2 + (y - 18)^2 &= 169 \\ (40 - 35)^2 + (30 - 18)^2 &\stackrel{?}{=} 169 \\ 5^2 + 12^2 &\stackrel{?}{=} 169 \\ 25 + 144 &\stackrel{?}{=} 169 \\ 169 &= 169 \end{aligned}$$

$$\begin{aligned} (-40 - 35)^2 + (30 - 18)^2 &\stackrel{?}{=} 169 \\ (-75)^2 + 12^2 &\stackrel{?}{=} 169 \\ 5625 + 144 &\stackrel{?}{=} 169 \\ 5769 &\ne 169 \end{aligned}$$

The epicenter of the earthquake was located at (40, 30).

54a. circle

54b.
$$\begin{aligned} y - x^2 &= 3x + 5 \\ y &= x^2 + 3x + 5 \\ &= \left(x^2 + 3x + \tfrac{9}{4}\right) + 5 - \tfrac{9}{4} \\ &= \left(x + \tfrac{3}{2}\right)^2 + \tfrac{11}{4}\text{; parabola} \end{aligned}$$

55. $\bar{x} = \frac{5.2 + 5.7 + 6.0 + 5.6 + 2.4}{5} = 4.98$

$$SD = \sqrt{\frac{\left[\begin{array}{c}(5.2 - 4.98)^2 + (5.7 - 4.98)^2 + \\ (6.0 - 4.98)^2 + (5.6 - 4.98)^2 + (2.4 - 4.98)^2\end{array}\right]}{5}}$$

$$= \sqrt{\frac{8.648}{5}}$$

$$\approx 1.3$$

56.
$$\begin{aligned} 2x^2 - x - 6 &< y \\ 2\left(x^2 - \tfrac{1}{2}x + \tfrac{1}{16}\right) - 6 - 2\left(\tfrac{1}{16}\right) &< y \\ 2\left(x - \tfrac{1}{4}\right)^2 - 6\tfrac{1}{8} &< y \end{aligned}$$

vertex: $\left(\frac{1}{4}, -6\frac{1}{8}\right)$

opens upward

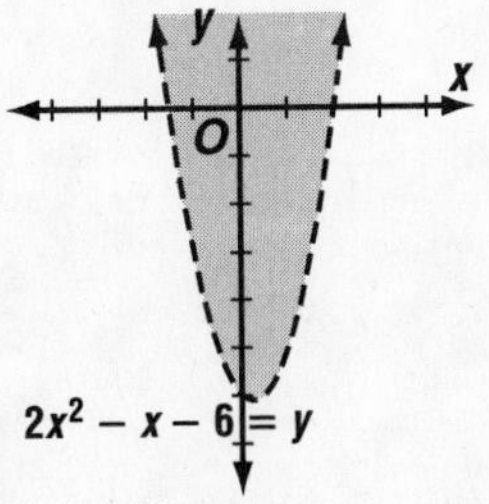

57. $\frac{5ab^2 - 4ab + 7a^2b}{ab} = \frac{5ab^2}{ab} - \frac{4ab}{ab} + \frac{7a^2b}{ab}$

$= 5b - 4 + 7a$

58. $[2 \ \ -5 \ \ 7] - [-3 \ \ 8 \ \ -1] = [5 \ \ -13 \ \ 8]$

59. $\frac{1}{2}x + \frac{1}{3}y = 2 \rightarrow \frac{3}{2}x + y = 6$

$x - y = -1 \rightarrow (+)x - y = -1$

$\frac{5}{2}x = 5$

$x = 2$

$$\begin{aligned} x - y &= -1 \\ 2 - y &= -1 \\ -y &= -3 \\ y &= 3 \end{aligned}$$

(2, 3)

60. Sample answer: $a = -4$, $b = 5$

61a.

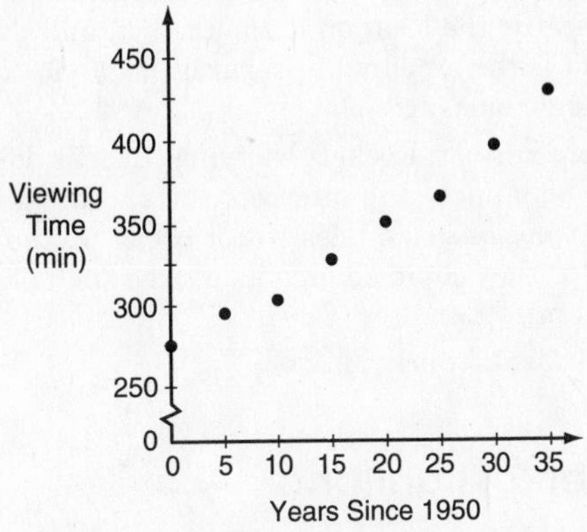

Sample answer: $y = 4.4x - 8305$

61b. Sample answer:
$$\begin{aligned} y &= 4.4x - 8305 \\ &= 4.4(2000) - 8305 \\ &= 8800 - 8305 \\ &= 495 \end{aligned}$$

495 minutes or 8 hours 15 minutes

62.
$$\begin{aligned} 3m + 2 &= 7n - 4 \\ 3m &= 7n - 6 \\ m &= \tfrac{7}{3}n - 2 \end{aligned}$$

63.
$$\begin{aligned} -\tfrac{16}{19}k &= 8 \\ \left(-\tfrac{19}{16}\right)\left(-\tfrac{16}{19}k\right) &= 8\left(-\tfrac{19}{16}\right) \\ k &= -\tfrac{19}{2} \end{aligned}$$

Page 467 Mathematics and Society

1. Sample answer: Use what they know about the trajectories of comets and asteroids in the solar system. Estimate or calculate the number of potentially dangerous bodies whose orbits cross that of Earth. Calculate the orbits of these bodies into the future to determine the percentage of them that would collide with or come close enough to Earth to cause damage.

2. Sample answer: Immediate damage would be similar to that of a nuclear blast. Everything near the impact site would be destroyed. In more outlying areas, fires would be started, buildings would be damaged, fuel and power supplies would be disrupted, and water supplies could be destroyed or contaminated. The impact could also trigger earthquakes, tidal waves, or forest fires. In the longer term, atmospheric dust raised by the impact could block the sunlight triggering widespread crop failure and starvation. Two major factors would affect the amount of damage. The first is the location of the impact, and the second is the amount of preparations and defensive measures.
3. Sample answer: Rockets carrying nuclear bombs could be launched to intercept the oncoming body. The explosions could destroy or break up the body, or they could change its course enough so it would miss Earth.
4. See students' work.

Chapter 7 Highlights

Page 469 Understanding and Using the Vocabulary

1. true
2. false
   The equation of a circle is $(x - h)^2 + (y - k)^2 = r^2$.
3. true
4. true
5. true
6. false
   A tangent line is a line that intersects a circle in exactly one point.
7. false
   A parabola is the set of all points that are the same distance from a given point called the focus and a given line called the directrix.
8. true
9. false
   The conjugate axis is the line segment perpendicular to the transverse axis.
10. true
11. false
    A hyperbola is the set of all points in a plane such that the absolute value of the difference of the distances from any point on the hyperbola to two given points is constant.
12. false
    An asymptote is a line that a curve approaches.
13. false
    The midpoint formula is given by the following: $\left(\frac{x_1 + x_2}{2}, \frac{y_1 + y_2}{2}\right)$.
14. true
15. true

Chapter 7 Study Guide and Assessment

Pages 470–472 Skills and Concepts

16. $$\begin{aligned} d &= \sqrt{(x_2 - x_1)^2 + (y_2 - y_1)^2} \\ &= \sqrt{[(-2) - (-2)]^2 + (10 - 13)^2} \\ &= \sqrt{0 + 9} \\ &= \sqrt{9} \\ &= 3 \end{aligned}$$

17. $$\begin{aligned} d &= \sqrt{(x_2 - x_1)^2 + (y_2 - y_1)^2} \\ &= \sqrt{(-9 - 8)^2 + (4 - 5)^2} \\ &= \sqrt{289 + 1} \\ &= \sqrt{290} \end{aligned}$$

18. $$\begin{aligned} d &= \sqrt{(x_2 - x_1)^2 + (y_2 - y_1)^2} \\ &= \sqrt{(-4\sqrt{3} - 3\sqrt{3})^2 + (-7\sqrt{3} - 5\sqrt{3})^2} \\ &= \sqrt{(-7\sqrt{3})^2 + (-12\sqrt{3})^2} \\ &= \sqrt{147 + 432} \\ &= \sqrt{579} \end{aligned}$$

19. $$\begin{aligned} d &= \sqrt{(x_2 - x_1)^2 + (y_2 - y_1)^2} \\ &= \sqrt{(7 - 1)^2 + (-3 - 2)^2} \\ &= \sqrt{36 + 25} \\ &= \sqrt{61} \end{aligned}$$

20. $$\begin{aligned} d &= \sqrt{(x_2 - x_1)^2 + (y_2 - y_1)^2} \\ &= \sqrt{(-13 - 5)^2 + [16 - (-8)]^2} \\ &= \sqrt{(-18)^2 + (24)^2} \\ &= \sqrt{900} \\ &= 30 \end{aligned}$$

21. $$\begin{aligned} \left(\frac{x_1 + x_2}{2}, \frac{y_1 + y_2}{2}\right) &= \left(\frac{1 + 4}{2}, \frac{2 + 6}{2}\right) \\ &= \left(\frac{5}{2}, \frac{8}{2}\right) \\ &= \left(\frac{5}{2}, 4\right) \end{aligned}$$

22. $$\begin{aligned} \left(\frac{x_1 + x_2}{2}, \frac{y_1 + y_2}{2}\right) &= \left(\frac{-8 + (-2)}{2}, \frac{0 + 3}{2}\right) \\ &= \left(\frac{-10}{2}, \frac{3}{2}\right) \\ &= \left(-5, \frac{3}{2}\right) \end{aligned}$$

23. $$\begin{aligned} \left(\frac{x_1 + x_2}{2}, \frac{y_1 + y_2}{2}\right) &= \left(\frac{7a + a}{2}, \frac{-5b + (-3b)}{2}\right) \\ &= \left(\frac{8a}{2}, \frac{-8b}{2}\right) \\ &= (4a, -4b) \end{aligned}$$

24. $$\begin{aligned} \left(\frac{x_1 + x_2}{2}, \frac{y_1 + y_2}{2}\right) &= \left(\frac{\frac{3}{5} + \frac{1}{4}}{2}, \frac{\frac{-7}{4} + \left(\frac{-2}{5}\right)}{2}\right) \\ &= \left(\frac{\frac{17}{20}}{2}, \frac{\frac{-43}{20}}{2}\right) \\ &= \left(\frac{17}{40}, -\frac{43}{40}\right) \end{aligned}$$

25. $(x-1)^2 = 12(y-1)$

$\frac{1}{12}(x-1)^2 = y - 1$

$\frac{1}{12}(x-1)^2 + 1 = y$

vertex: (1, 1)

focus: $\left(1, 1 + \frac{1}{4\left(\frac{1}{12}\right)}\right)$ or (1, 4)

axis of symmetry: $x = 1$

directrix: $y = 1 - \frac{1}{4\left(\frac{1}{12}\right)}$ or -2

direction of opening: upward, since $a > 0$

length of latus rectum: $\left|\frac{1}{\frac{1}{12}}\right|$ or 12 units

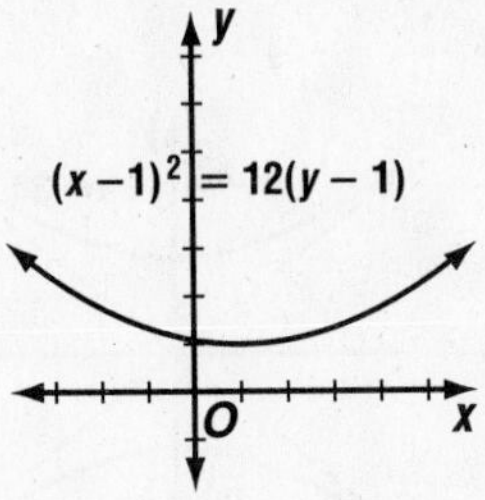

26. $(y+6) = 16(x-3)^2$

$y = 16(x-3)^2 - 6$

vertex: $(3, -6)$

focus: $\left(3, -6 + \frac{1}{4(16)}\right)$ or $\left(3, -5\frac{63}{64}\right)$

axis of symmetry: $x = 3$

directrix: $y = -6 - \frac{1}{4(16)}$ or $-6\frac{1}{64}$

direction of opening: upward, since $a > 0$

length of latus rectum: $\left|\frac{1}{16}\right|$ or $\frac{1}{16}$ unit

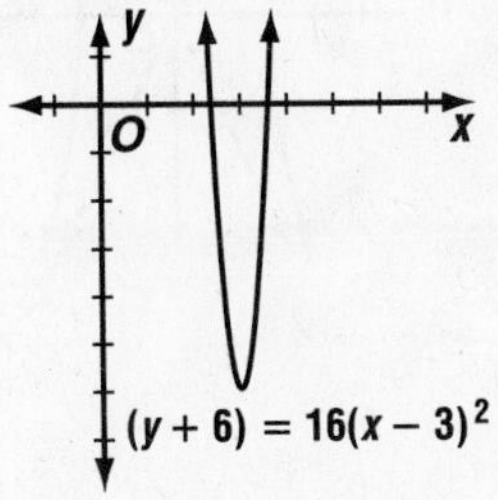

27. $x^2 - 8x + 8y + 32 = 0$

$x^2 - 8x + 32 = -8y$

$(x^2 - 8x + 16) + 32 - 16 = -8y$

$(x-4)^2 + 16 = -8y$

$-\frac{1}{8}(x-4)^2 - 2 = y$

vertex: $(4, -2)$

focus: $\left(4, -2 + \frac{1}{4\left(-\frac{1}{8}\right)}\right)$ or $(4, -4)$

axis of symmetry: $x = 4$

directrix: $y = -2 - \frac{1}{4\left(-\frac{1}{8}\right)}$ or 0

direction of opening: downward, since $a < 0$

length of latus rectum: $\left|\frac{1}{-\frac{1}{8}}\right|$ or 8 units

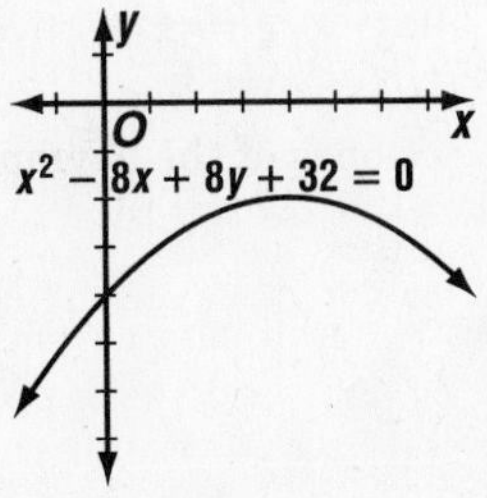

28. $x = 16y^2$

vertex: (0, 0)

focus: $\left(0 + \frac{1}{4(16)}, 0\right)$ or $\left(\frac{1}{64}, 0\right)$

axis of symmetry: $y = 0$

directrix: $x = 0 - \frac{1}{4(16)}$ or $-\frac{1}{64}$

direction of opening: right, since $a > 0$

length of latus rectum: $\left|\frac{1}{16}\right|$ or $\frac{1}{16}$ unit

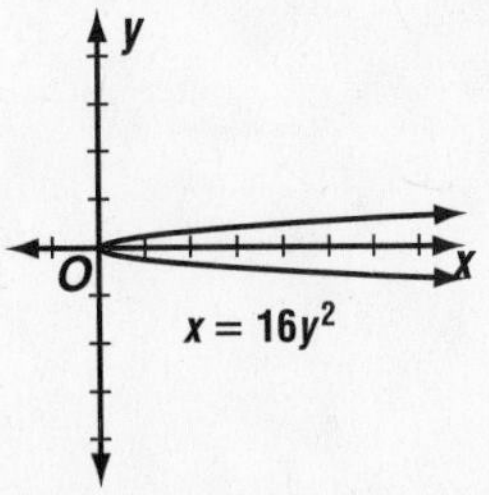

29. center: (0, 0)

radius: $\sqrt{169}$ or 13 units

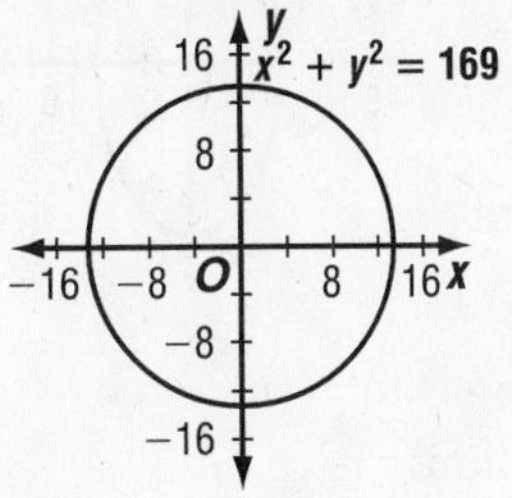

30. center: $(-5, 11)$

radius: $\sqrt{49}$ or 7 units

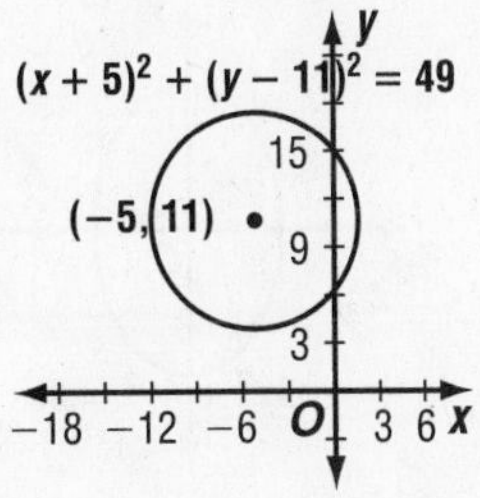

31. $x^2 + y^2 - 6x + 16y - 152 = 0$

$x^2 - 6x + 9 + y^2 + 16y + 64 = 152 + 9 + 64$

$(x-3)^2 + (y+8)^2 = 225$

center: $(3, -8)$

radius: $\sqrt{225}$ or 15 units

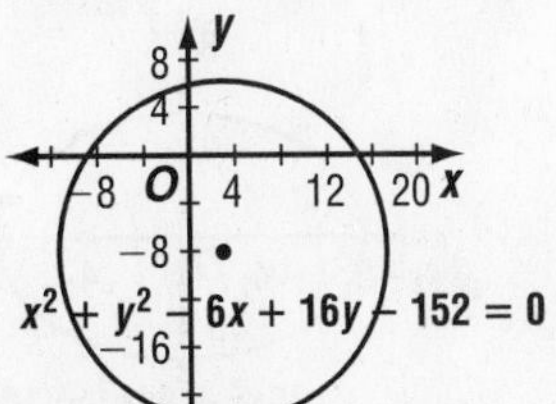

32. $x^2 + y^2 + 6x - 2y - 15 = 0$

$x^2 + 6x + 9 + y^2 - 2y + 1 = 15 + 9 + 1$

$(x + 3)^2 + (y - 1)^2 = 25$

center: $(-3, 1)$

radius: $\sqrt{25}$ or 5 units

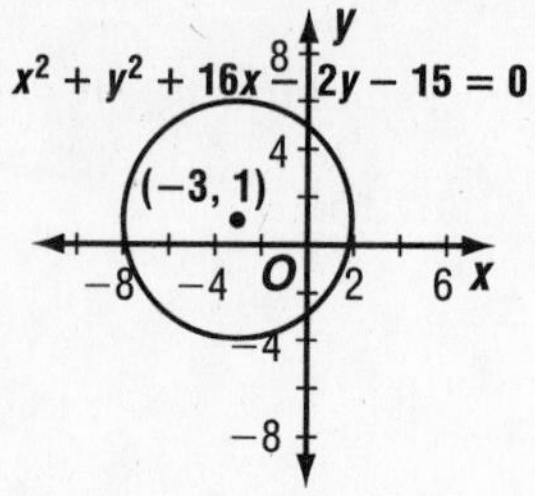

33. $49x^2 + 16y^2 = 784$

$\frac{x^2}{16} + \frac{y^2}{49} = 1$

center: $(0, 0)$

$a = \sqrt{49}$ or 7,

$b = \sqrt{16}$ or 4

foci: $b^2 = a^2 - c^2$

$16 = 49 - c^2$

$-33 = -c^2$

$\pm\sqrt{33} = c$

$(0, \pm\sqrt{33})$

length of major axis:

14 units

length of minor axis: 8 units

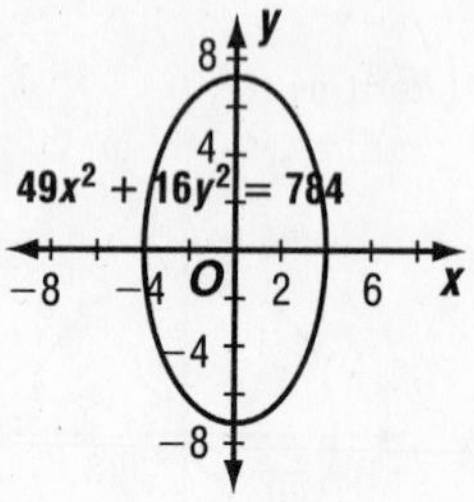

34. $9x^2 + 4y^2 = 36$

$\frac{x^2}{4} + \frac{y^2}{9} = 1$

center: $(0, 0)$

$a = \sqrt{9}$ or 3,

$b = \sqrt{4}$ or 2

foci: $b^2 = a^2 - c^2$

$4 = 9 - c^2$

$-5 = -c^2$

$\pm\sqrt{5} = c$

$(0, \pm\sqrt{5}$

length of major axis:

6 units

length of minor axis: 4 units

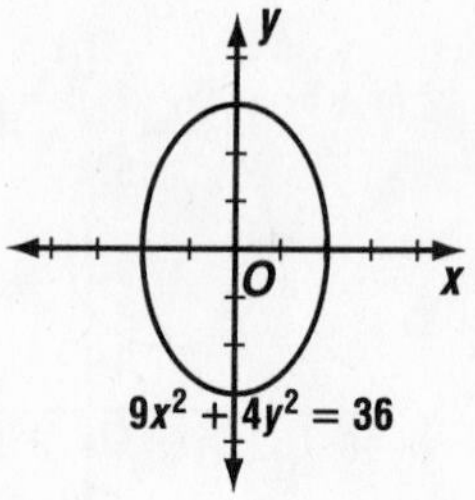

35. $25x^2 + 64y^2 = 1600$

$\frac{x^2}{64} + \frac{y^2}{25} = 1$

center: $(0, 0)$

$a = \sqrt{64}$ or 8,

$b = \sqrt{25}$ or 5

foci: $b^2 = a^2 - c^2$

$25 = 64 - c^2$

$-39 = -c^2$

$\pm\sqrt{39} = c$

$(\pm\sqrt{39}, 0)$

length of major axis:

16 units

length of minor axis: 10 units

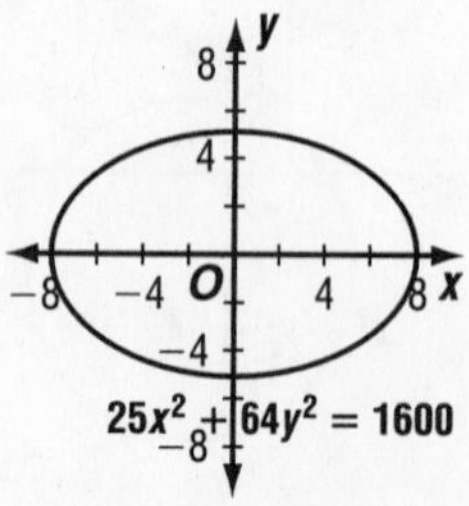

36. $\frac{x^2}{16} + \frac{y^2}{25} = 1$

center: $(0, 0)$

$a = \sqrt{25}$ or 5,

$b = \sqrt{16}$ or 4

foci: $b^2 = a^2 - c^2$

$16 = 25 - c^2$

$-9 = -c^2$

$\pm 3 = c$

$(0, \pm 3)$

length of major axis:

10 units

length of minor axis: 8 units

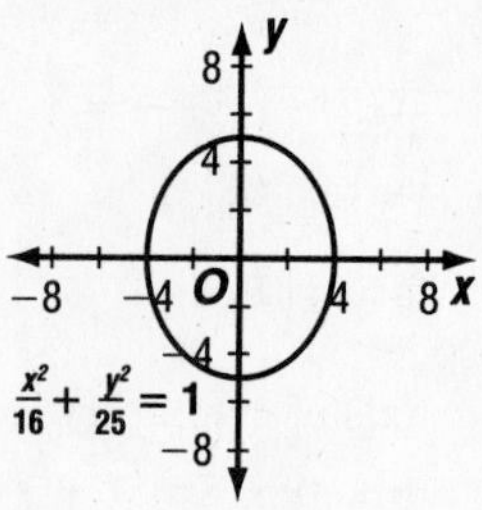

37. $9y^2 - 4x^2 = 36$

$\frac{y^2}{4} - \frac{x^2}{9} = 1$

center: $(0, 0)$

$a = \sqrt{4}$ or 2,

$b = \sqrt{9}$ or 3

vertices: $(0, \pm 2)$;

foci: $c^2 = a^2 + b^2$

$c^2 = 4 + 9$

$c^2 = 13$

$c = \pm\sqrt{13}$

$(0, \pm\sqrt{13})$

slopes of the asymptotes: $\pm\frac{2}{3}$

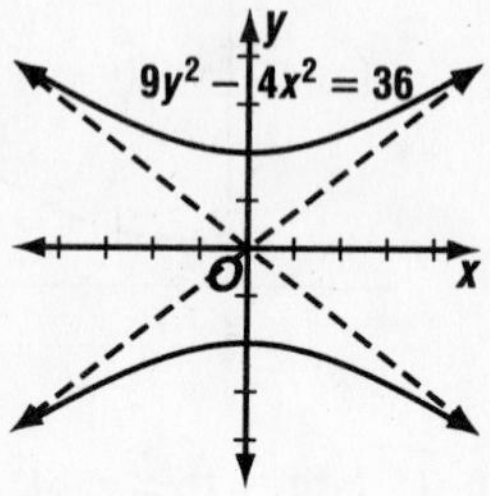

38. $25x^2 - 4y^2 = 100$

$\frac{x^2}{4} - \frac{y^2}{25} = 1$

center: $(0, 0)$

$a = \sqrt{4}$ or 2,

$b = \sqrt{25}$ or 5

vertices: $(\pm 2, 0)$

foci: $c^2 = a^2 + b^2$

$c^2 = 4 + 25$

$c^2 = 29$

$c = \pm\sqrt{29}$

$(\pm\sqrt{29}, 0)$

slopes of asymptotes: $\pm\frac{5}{2}$

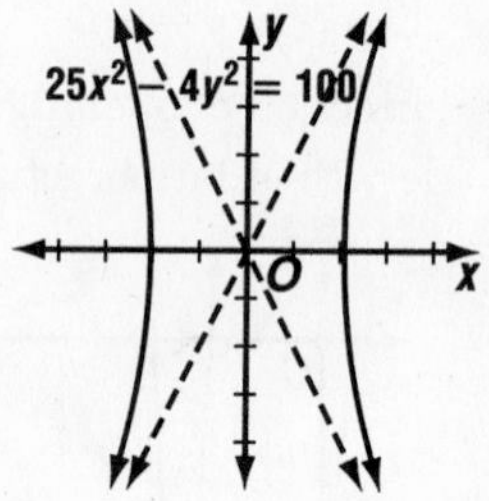

39. $9y^2 - 16x^2 = 144$

$\frac{y^2}{16} - \frac{x^2}{9} = 1$

center: $(0, 0)$

$a = \sqrt{16}$ or 4,

$b = \sqrt{9}$ or 3

vertices: $(0, \pm 4)$

foci: $c^2 = a^2 + b^2$

$c^2 = 16 + 9$

$c^2 = 25$

$c = \pm 5$

$(0, \pm 5)$

slopes of the asymptotes: $\pm\frac{4}{3}$

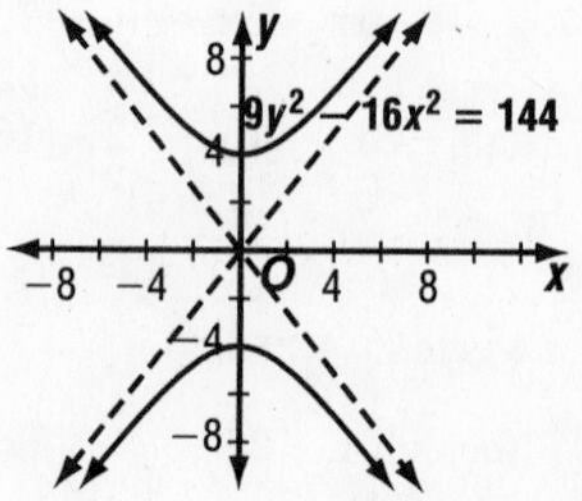

40. $x^2 - 25x^2 = 25$

$\frac{x^2}{25} - \frac{y^2}{1} = 1$

center: (0, 0)

$a = \sqrt{25}$ or 5,

$b = \sqrt{1}$ or 1

vertices: $(\pm 5, 0)$

foci: $c^2 = a^2 + b^2$

$c^2 = 25 + 1$

$c = \pm \sqrt{26}$

$(\pm \sqrt{26}, 0)$

slopes of the asymptotes: $\pm \frac{1}{5}$

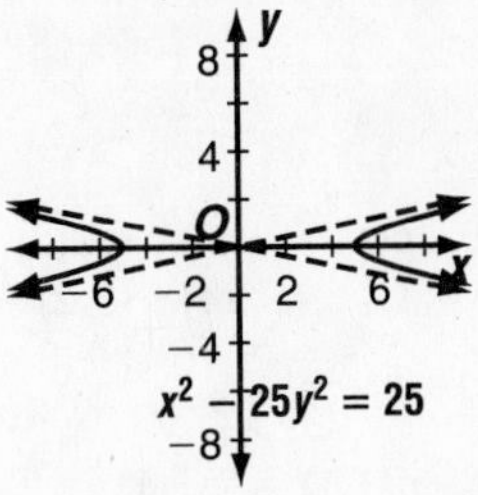

41. $7x^2 + 9y^2 = 63$

$\frac{x^2}{9} + \frac{y^2}{7} = 1$

ellipse

42. $11x^2 + 11y^2 = 55$

$x^2 + y^2 = 5$

circle

43. $(x - 4)^2 = 6y$

$\frac{1}{6}(x - 4)^2 = y$

parabola

44. $5y^2 - 13x^2 = 81$

$\frac{y^2}{\frac{81}{5}} - \frac{x^2}{\frac{81}{13}} = 1$

hyperbola

45. circle

46. $x^2 + y^2 - 18x + 24y + 200 = 0$

$4x + 3y = 0$

$3y = -4x$

$y = -\frac{4}{3}x$

$x^2 + \left(-\frac{4}{3}x\right)^2 - 18x + 24\left(-\frac{4}{3}x\right) + 200 = 0$

$x^2 + \frac{16}{9}x^2 - 18x - 32x + 200 = 0$

$\frac{25}{9}x^2 - 50x + 200 = 0$

$25x^2 - 450x + 1800 = 0$

$x^2 - 18x + 72 = 0$

$(x - 6)(x - 12) = 0$

$x - 6 = 0$ or $x - 12 = 0$

$x = 6$ $\quad$ $x = 12$

$y = -\frac{4}{3}x$ $\quad$ $y = -\frac{4}{3}x$

$= -\frac{4}{3}(6)$ $\quad$ $= -\frac{4}{3}(12)$

$= -8$ $\quad$ $= -16$

$(6, -8), (12, -16)$

47. $4x^2 + y^2 - 48x - 2y + 129 = 0$

$(-)x^2 + y^2 - 2x - 2y - 7 = 0$

$3x^2 - 46x + 136 = 0$

$(3x - 34)(x - 4) = 0$

$3x - 34 = 0$ or $x - 4 = 0$

$x = \frac{34}{3}$ $\quad$ $x = 4$

$x^2 + y^2 - 2x - 2y - 7 = 0$

$\left(\frac{34}{3}\right)^2 + y^2 - 2\left(\frac{34}{3}\right) - 2y - 7 = 0$

$\frac{1156}{9} + y^2 - \frac{68}{3} - 2y - 7 = 0$

$y^2 - 2y + \frac{889}{9} = 0$

$y = \frac{-(-2) \pm \sqrt{(-2)^2 - 4(1)\left(\frac{889}{9}\right)}}{2(1)}$

$\approx \frac{2 \pm \sqrt{-391}}{2}$; no solution

(Continued next column)

$x^2 + y^2 - 2x - 2y - 7 = 0$

$(4)^2 + y^2 - 2(4) - 2y - 7 = 0$

$y^2 - 2y + 1 = 0$

$(y - 1)^2 = 0$

$y - 1 = 0$

$y = 1$; (4, 1)

48. $y + x = 0$

$y = -x$

$x^2 + y^2 + 2x - 12y + 12 = 0$

$x^2 + (-x)^2 + 2x - 12(-x) + 12 = 0$

$x^2 + x^2 + 2x + 12x + 12 = 0$

$2x^2 + 14x + 12 = 0$

$x^2 + 7x + 6 = 0$

$(x + 6)(x + 1) = 0$

$x + 6 = 0$ or $x + 1 = 0$

$x = -6$ $\quad$ $x = -1$

$y = -x$ $\quad$ $y = -x$

$= -(-6)$ $\quad$ $= -(-1)$

$= 6$ $\quad$ $= 1$

$(-6, 6), (-1, 1)$

Page 472 Applications and Problem Solving

49. $a^2 + b^2 = c^2$

$45^2 + 60^2 = c^2$

$2025 + 3600 = c^2$

$5625 = c^2$

$75 = c$

75 miles

50. vertex: (0, 0)

focus: (0, 3)

$k + \frac{1}{4a} = 3$

$0 + \frac{1}{4a} = 3$

$12a = 1$

$a = \frac{1}{12}$

$y = a(x - h)^2 + k$

$= \frac{1}{12}(x - 0)^2 + 0$

$= \frac{1}{12}x^2$

51. center: (9, 23)

radius: 45 miles

$(x - h)^2 + (y - k)^2 = r^2$

$(x - 9)^2 + (y - 23)^2 = (45)^2$

$(x - 9)^2 + (y - 23)^2 = 2025$

Page 473 Alternative Assessment; Thinking Critically

- Sample answer: $y = x^2$, $y = -x^2 - 2$
- Sample answer: $y = (x - 2)^2 + 5$, $x = 2$
- Sample answer: for point (0, 3)

  $x^2 + y^2 = 9$

  $y = x^2 + 3$
- Sample answer: line: $m = \frac{-3 - 0}{0 - 3} = 1$

  $y = mx + b$

  $y = x - 3$

  parabola: vertex: (0, −3)

  passes through (3, 0)

  $y = a(x - h)^2 + k$

  $0 = a(3 - 0)^2 - 3$

  $3 = 9a$

  $\frac{1}{3} = a$

  $y = \frac{1}{3}x^2 - 3$

  circle: $x^2 + y^2 = 9$

Chapter 8 Exploring Polynomial Functions

8-1 Polynomial Functions

Pages 481–482 Check for Understanding

1. 4, 3, 2
2. Sample answer: Even-degree polynomial functions with positive leading coefficients have graphs whose leftmost points and rightmost points have positive values for $f(x)$. Odd-degree polynomial functions with positive leading coefficients have graphs whose leftmost points have negative values for $f(x)$ and whose rightmost points have positive values for $f(x)$.

3a. 4 **3b.** 1 **3c.** 2
3d. 5 **3e.** 3

4. Sample graph:

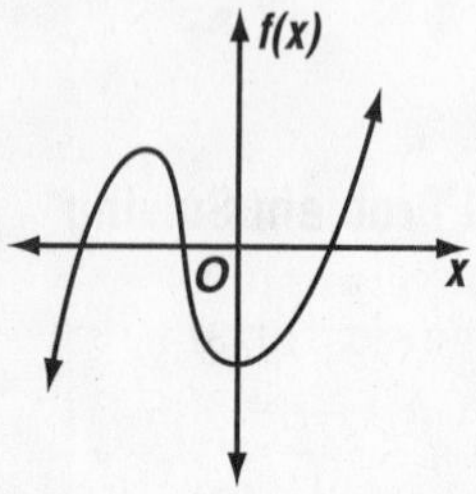

5. Zach is correct. For example, the graph of the function $y = x^2 + 4x + 4$ is tangent to the x-axis at one point, and the graph of the function $y = x^2 + 2$ does not intersect the x-axis at any point.
6. Sample answer: When the leading coefficient is positive, the graph's leftmost points go downward and the rightmost points go upward. When the leading coefficient is negative, the graph's leftmost points go upward and the rightmost points go downward. As the leading coefficient decreases, the graph stretches out and approaches the x-axis. As the leading coefficient increases, the graph narrows and approaches the y-axis.
7. 3
8. No, the polynomial contains two variables, a and b.
9. 5
10. cubic, 3, 3
11. quintic, 5, 5
12. linear, 1, 1
13. quartic, 4, 4

14. $p(5) = 3(5)^2 + 4(5) + 5$
$= 3(25) + 4(5) + 5$
$= 75 + 20 + 5$
$= 100$; b

15. $p(4) = (4)^4 - 7(4)^3 + 8(4) - 6$
$= 256 - 7(64) + 32 - 6$
$= 256 - 448 + 32 - 6$
$= -166$; a

16. $p(-2) = 7(-2)^2 - 9(-2) + 10$
$= 7(4) + 18 + 10$
$= 28 + 18 + 10$
$= 56$; d

17. $p(-4) = 4(-4)^3 - 2(-4)^2 - 6(-4) + 5$
$= -256 - 32 + 24 + 5$
$= -259$; c

18a. even **18b.** 3

19. $p(2) = 2(2)^2 + 6(2) - 8$
$= 2(4) + 6(2) - 8$
$= 8 + 12 - 8$
$= 12$

$p(-1) = 2(-1)^2 + 6(-1) - 8$
$= 2(1) + 6(-1) - 8$
$= 2 - 6 - 8$
$= -12$

20. $p(2) = -3(2)^4 + 1$
$= -3(16) + 1$
$= -48 + 1$
$= -47$

$p(-1) = -3(-1)^4 + 1$
$= -3(1) + 1$
$= -3 + 1$
$= -2$

21. $f(x + h) = 2(x + h) - 3$
$= 2x + 2h - 3$

22. $f(x + h) = 4(x + h)^2$
$= 4(x^2 + 2xh + h^2)$
$= 4x^2 + 8xh + 4h^2$

23. $P(25) = \frac{(25)^3}{1000}$
$= \frac{15,625}{1000}$
$= 15.625$; 15.625 units

Pages 483–484 Exercises

24. even, 4 **25.** odd, 2 **26.** even, 0

27. $p(3) = 5(3) + 6$
$= 15 + 6$
$= 21$

$p(-2) = 5(-2) + 6$
$= -10 + 6$
$= -4$

28. $p(3) = (3)^2 - 2(3) + 1$
$= 9 - 6 + 1$
$= 4$

$p(-2) = (-2)^2 - 2(-2) + 1$
$= 4 + 4 + 1$
$= 9$

29. $p(3) = 2(3)^3 - (3)^2 - 3(3) + 1$
$= 2(27) - 9 - 3(3) + 1$
$= 54 - 9 - 9 + 1$
$= 37$

$p(-2) = 2(-2)^3 - (-2)^2 - 3(-2) + 1$
$= 2(-8) - 4 - 3(-2) + 1$
$= -16 - 4 + 6 + 1$
$= -13$

30. $p(3) = (3)^5 - (3)^2$
$= 243 - 9$
$= 234$

$p(-2) = (-2)^5 - (-2)^2$
$= -32 - 4$
$= -36$

31. $p(3) = -(3)^4 + 53$
$= -81 + 53$
$= -28$

$p(-2) = -(-2)^4 + 53$
$= -16 + 53$
$= 37$

32. $p(3) = (3)^5 + 5(3)^4 - 15(3)^2 - 8$
$= 243 + 5(81) - 15(9) - 8$
$= 243 + 405 - 135 - 8$
$= 505$

$p(-2) = (-2)^5 + 5(-2)^4 - 15(-2)^2 - 8$
$= -32 + 5(16) - 15(4) - 8$
$= -32 + 80 - 60 - 8$
$= -20$

33. $f(x + h) = (x + h) + 2$
$= x + h + 2$

34. $f(x + h) = (x + h) - 4$
$= x + h - 4$

35. $f(x + h) = 5(x + h)^2$
$= 5(x^2 + 2xh + h^2)$
$= 5x^2 + 10xh + 5h^2$

36. $f(x + h) = (x + h)^2 - 2(x + h) + 5$
$= x^2 + 2hx + h^2 - 2x - 2h + 5$

37. $f(x + h) = 3(x + h)^2 + 7$
$= 3(x^2 + 2xh + h^2) + 7$
$= 3x^2 + 6xh + 3h^2 + 7$

38. $f(x + h) = (x + h)^3 + (x + h)$
$= x^3 + 3x^2h + 3xh^2 + h^3 + x + h$

39. $4[p(x)] = 4(x^2 + 5)$
$= 4x^2 + 20$

40. $4[p(x)] = 4[(6x^3 - 4x^2 + 2)$
$= 24x^3 - 16x^2 + 8$

41. $4[p(x)] = 4\left(\frac{x^3}{4} + \frac{x^2}{16} - 2\right)$
$= x^3 + \frac{x^2}{4} - 8$

42. $f(x) = (x + 1)(x - 2)^2$
$= (x + 1)(x^2 - 4x + 4)$
$= x^3 - 3x^2 + 4$

43. $f(x) = (x - 1)^2(x - 3)(x - 4)$
$= (x^2 - 2x + 1)(x^2 - 7x + 12)$
$= x^4 - 9x^3 + 27x^2 - 31x + 12$

44. $f(x) = x(x + 3)(x - 4)$
$= x(x^2 - x - 12)$
$= x^3 - x^2 - 12x$

45a. Sample graph:

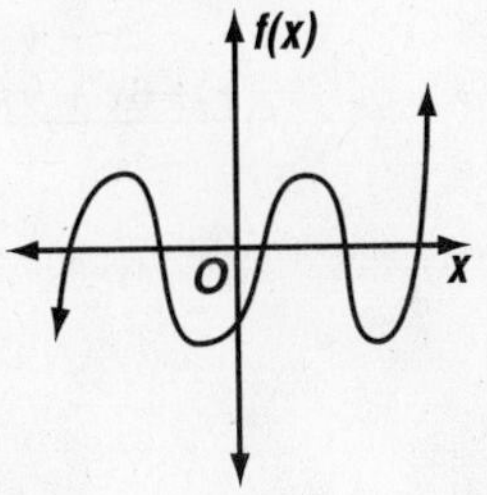

45b. Sample graph:

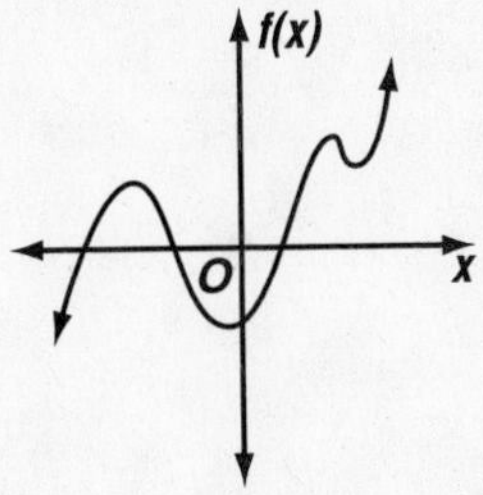

45c. Sample graph:

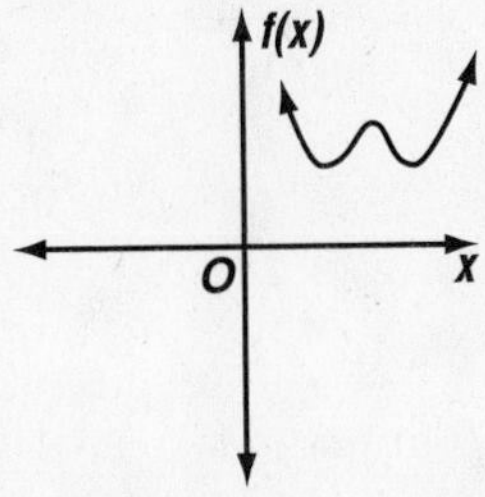

46. $2p(a) + p(a - 1) = 2[4(a) + 1] + [4(a - 1) + 1]$
$= 2(4a + 1) + [4a - 4 + 1]$
$= 8a + 2 + 4a - 3$
$= 12a - 1$

47. $2p(a) + p(a - 1) = 2[(a)^2 + 3] + [(a - 1)^2 + 3]$
$= 2(a^2 + 3) + [a^2 - 2a + 1 + 3]$
$= 2a^2 + 6 + a^2 - 2a + 4$
$= 3a^2 - 2a + 10$

48. $2p(a) + p(a - 1)$
$= 2[(a)^2 - 5(a) + 8] + [(a - 1)^2 - 5(a - 1) + 8]$
$= 2(a^2 - 5a + 8) + [a^2 - 2a + 1 - 5a + 5 + 8]$
$= 2a^2 - 10a + 16 + a^2 - 7a + 14$
$= 3a^2 - 17a + 30$

49. $2[f(x + 3)] = 2[2(x + 3) + 9]$
$= 2[2x + 6 + 9]$
$= 2(2x + 15)$
$= 4x + 30$

50. $2[f(x + 3)] = 2[(x + 3)^2 - 6]$
$= 2[x^2 + 6x + 9 - 6]$
$= 2[x^2 + 6x + 3]$
$= 2x^2 + 12x + 6$

51. $2[f(x + 3)] = 2[(x + 3)^2 + 3(x + 3) + 12]$
$= 2[x^2 + 6x + 9 + 3x + 9 + 12]$
$= 2[x^2 + 9x + 30]$
$= 2x^2 + 18x + 60$

52a. $f(x) = (x + 1)(x - 2)$
$= x^2 - x - 2$

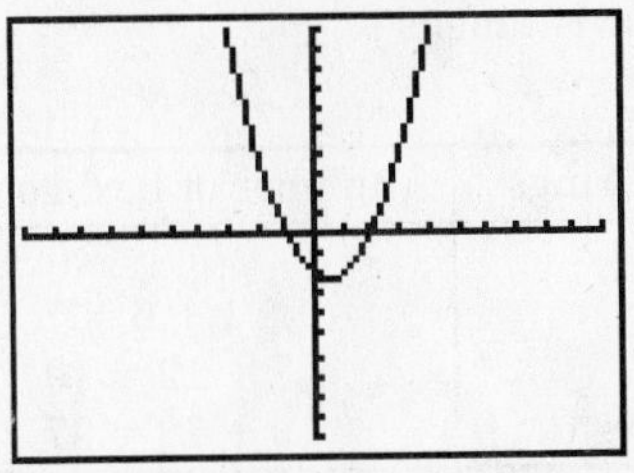

52b. $f(x) = (x + 2)(x + 1)\ (x - 2)$
$= x^3 + x^2 - 4x - 4$

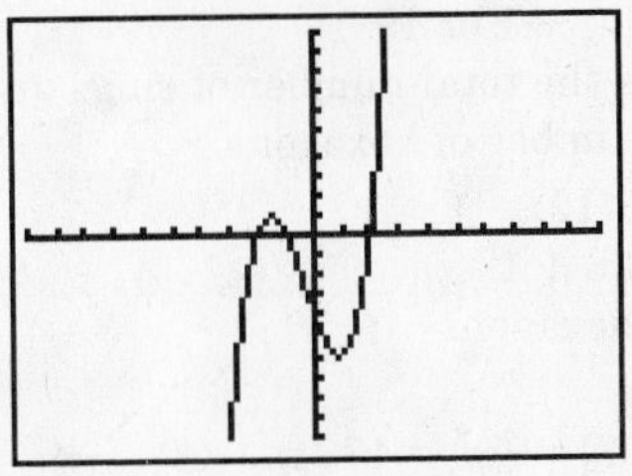

52c. $f(x) = (x + 2)(x + 1)(x - 1)(x - 2)$
$= x^4 - 5x^2 + 4$

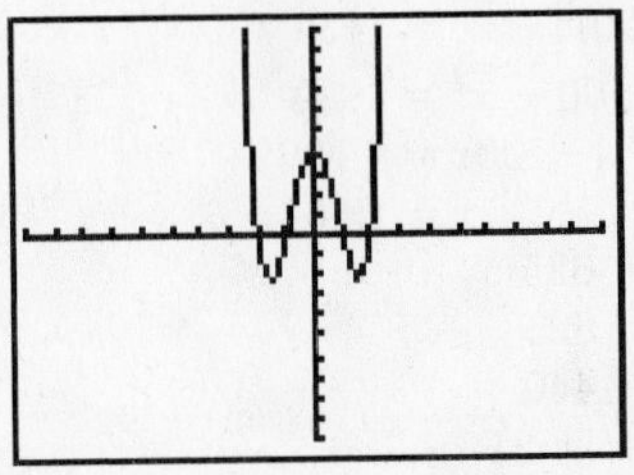

52d. $f(x) = (x + 2)(x + 1)(x)(x - 1)(x - 2)$
$= x^5 - 5x^3 + 4x$

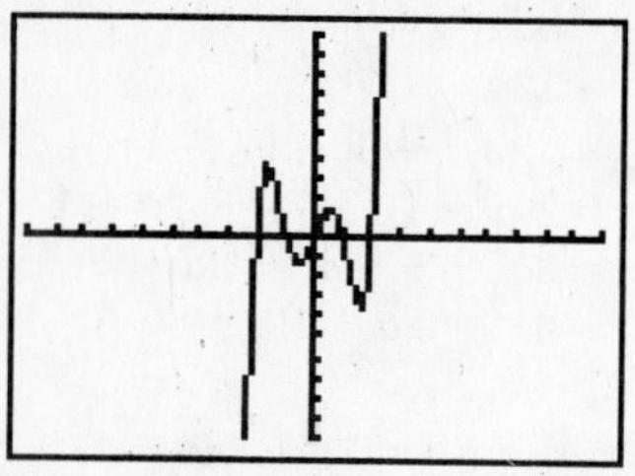

53. There is no real number x that can make the equation $0 = x^4 + x^2 + 1$ true.

54a. $f(x) = ax(x - 4)(x + 1)$
$15 = (a)(5)(5 - 4)(5 + 1)$
$15 = 30a$
$\frac{1}{2} = a$

54b.

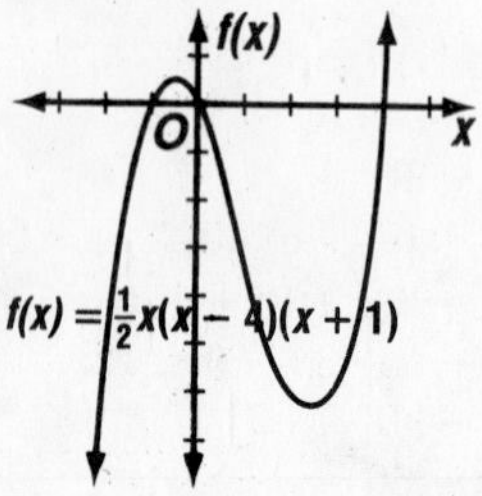

55. $L(30) = 10 + 0.3(30) + 0.4(30)^2 - 0.01(30)^3$
$= 10 + 9 + 360 - 270$
$= 109$; 109 lumens

56a. 18

56b.

number of rings	number of hexagons
1	1
2	1 + 6 = 7
3	7 + 12 = 19
4	19 + 18 = 37

56c. $h = 3(1)^2 - 3(1) + 1$ or 1
$h = 3(2)^2 - 3(2) + 1$ or 7
$h = 3(3)^2 - 3(3) + 1$ or 19
The domain is the total number of rings and the range is the number of hexagons.

56d. $h = 3(12)^2 - 3(12) + 1$
$= 3(144) - 36 + 1$
$= 397$; 397 hexagons

57. $x^2 + y^2 = 625$
$(x - 50)^2 + y^2 = 1764$

$$\begin{array}{rl} (x - 50)^2 + y^2 &= 1764 \\ (-) \quad x^2 + y^2 &= 625 \\ \hline (x - 50)^2 - x^2 &= 1139 \end{array}$$

$x^2 - 100x + 2500 - x^2 = 1139$
$-100x = -1361$
$x = 13.61$

$x^2 + y^2 = 625$
$(13.61)^2 + y^2 = 625$
$y^2 \approx 440$
$y \approx \pm 21$

Approximately (13.6, 21) or (13.6, −21); that is, the epicenter could have been 13.6 miles east and 21 miles north or south of the first station.

58. $x^2 + 4y^2 = 4$
$\frac{x^2}{4} + \frac{y^2}{1} = 1$
ellipse

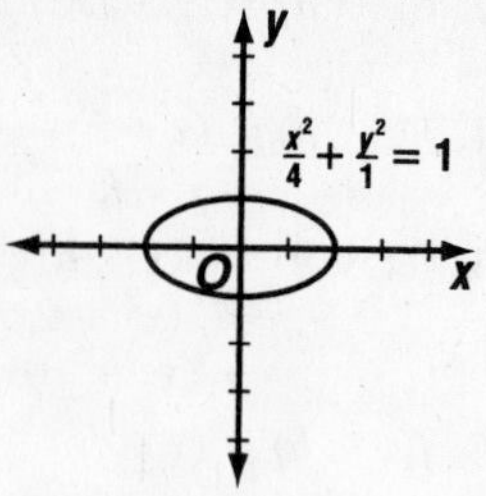

59. Let x = one number
and $-40 + x$ = the other number.
$x(-40 + x) = f(x)$
$x^2 - 40x = f(x)$
$x = \frac{-b}{2a} = \frac{40}{2}$ or 20
$-40 + x = -40 + 20$ or -20
The two numbers are 20 and −20.

60. $\sqrt{n + 12} - \sqrt{n} = 2$
$\sqrt{n + 12} = 2 + \sqrt{n}$
$(\sqrt{n + 12})^2 = (2 + \sqrt{n})^2$
$n + 12 = 4 + 4\sqrt{n} + n$
$8 = 4\sqrt{n}$
$2 = \sqrt{n}$
$(2)^2 = (\sqrt{n})^2$
$n = 4$

61. $1{,}600{,}000 = 1.6 \times 1{,}000{,}000$
$= 1.6 + 10^6$
$1{,}700{,}000 = 1.7 \times 1{,}000{,}000$
$= 1.7 \times 10^6$

62. 4×3

63. $\begin{bmatrix} -9 & 6 \\ 5 & 19 \end{bmatrix} - \begin{bmatrix} -3 & 18 \\ -4 & 12 \end{bmatrix} = \begin{bmatrix} -6 & -12 \\ 9 & 7 \end{bmatrix}$

64. 2

65. $2x - y = 36 \quad \rightarrow$
$3x - \frac{1}{2}y = 26 \quad \rightarrow$

$$\begin{array}{rl} 2x - y &= 36 \\ (+) -6x + y &= -52 \\ \hline -4x &= -16 \\ x &= 4 \end{array}$$

$2x - y = 36$
$2(4) - y = 36$
$8 - y = 36$
$y = -28$
$(4, -28)$

66. $2|-3x| - 9 = 2|-3(5)| - 9$
$= 2|-15| - 9$
$= 2(15) - 9$
$= 30 - 9$
$= 21$

8-2 The Remainder and Factor Theorems

Page 488 Check for Understanding

1. 0

2. Jack, the factor theorem states that if $x - a$ is a factor of $f(x)$, then $f(a) = 0$.

3a. $-4, 1, 4$

3b. The graph would be shifted up 100 units. It would have 1 real zero.

4a. 4, 3

4b. 5, 4

5. Sample answer: quadratic formula, synthetic substitution, guess-and-check factoring, completing the square.

6.
$$\begin{array}{r|rrrr} 4 & 1 & -4 & 2 & -6 \\ & & 4 & 0 & 8 \\ \hline & 1 & 0 & 2 & 2 \end{array}$$
$(x^3 - 4x^2 + 2x - 6) = (x^2 + 2)(x - 4) + 2$; no

7.
$$\begin{array}{r|rrrrr} 2 & 1 & 0 & 0 & 0 & -16 \\ & & 2 & 4 & 8 & 16 \\ \hline & 1 & 2 & 4 & 8 & 0 \end{array}$$
$(x^4 - 16) = (x^3 + 2x^2 + 4x + 8)(x - 2) + 0$; yes

8.
$$\begin{array}{r|rrrr} 2 & 1 & 0 & -5 & 2 \\ & & 2 & 4 & -2 \\ \hline & 1 & 2 & -1 & 0 \end{array}$$
$g(2) = 0$
$$\begin{array}{r|rrrr} -1 & 1 & 0 & -5 & 2 \\ & & -1 & 1 & 4 \\ \hline & 1 & -1 & -4 & 6 \end{array}$$
$g(-1) = 6$

9.
$$\begin{array}{r|rrrrr} 2 & 1 & 0 & 0 & -6 & -8 \\ & & 2 & 4 & 8 & 4 \\ \hline & 1 & 2 & 4 & 2 & -4 \end{array}$$
$g(2) = -4$
$$\begin{array}{r|rrrrr} -1 & 1 & 0 & 0 & -6 & -8 \\ & & -1 & 1 & -1 & 7 \\ \hline & 1 & -1 & 1 & -7 & -1 \end{array}$$
$g(-1) = -1$

10.
$$\begin{array}{r|rrrr} 1 & 1 & 2 & -1 & -2 \\ & & 1 & 3 & 2 \\ \hline & 1 & 3 & 2 & 0 \end{array}$$
$x^2 + 3x + 2 = (x + 2)(x + 1)$
$x + 1, x + 2$

11.
$$\begin{array}{r|rrrr} 2 & 1 & -6 & 11 & -6 \\ & & 2 & -8 & 6 \\ \hline & 1 & -4 & 3 & 0 \end{array}$$
$x^2 - 4x + 3 = (x - 3)(x - 1)$
$x - 3, x - 1$

12.
$$\begin{array}{r|rrrr} -7 & 2 & 7 & -53 & -28 \\ & & -14 & 49 & 28 \\ \hline & 2 & -7 & -4 & 0 \end{array}$$
$2x^2 - 7x - 4 = (2x + 1)(x - 4)$
$2x + 1, x - 4$

13.
$$\begin{array}{r|rrrrr} -1 & 1 & 2 & 2 & -2 & -3 \\ & & -1 & -1 & -1 & 3 \\ \hline & 1 & 1 & 1 & -3 & 0 \end{array}$$
$x^3 + x^2 + x - 3$
$$\begin{array}{r|rrrr} 1 & 1 & 1 & 1 & -3 \\ & & 1 & 2 & 3 \\ \hline & 1 & 2 & 3 & 0 \end{array}$$
$x^2 + 2x + 3$
$x - 1, x^2 + 2x + 3$

14.
$$\begin{array}{r|rrrrr} 2 & 1 & 0 & -3 & 0 & -4 \\ & & 2 & 4 & 2 & 4 \\ \hline & 1 & 2 & 1 & 2 & 0 \end{array}$$
$x^3 + 2x^2 + x + 2$
$$\begin{array}{r|rrrr} -2 & 1 & 2 & 1 & 2 \\ & & -2 & 0 & -2 \\ \hline & 1 & 0 & 1 & 0 \end{array}$$
$x^4 - 3x^2 - 4 = (x + 2)(x - 2)(x^2 + 1)$

15.
$$\begin{array}{r|rrrr} 8 & 1 & -4 & -29 & -24 \\ & & 8 & 32 & 24 \\ \hline & 1 & 4 & 3 & 0 \end{array}$$
$f(8) = 0$
$x^2 + 4x + 3 = (x + 3)(x + 1)$
$x + 1, x + 3$

Pages 489–490 Exercises

16.
$$\begin{array}{r|rrrr} 2 & 1 & -6 & 2 & -4 \\ & & 2 & -8 & -12 \\ \hline & 1 & -4 & -6 & -16 \end{array}$$
$(x^3 - 6x^2 + 2x - 4) = (x^2 - 4x - 6)(x - 2) - 16$; no

17.
$$\begin{array}{r|rrrr} 3 & 1 & -2 & -5 & 6 \\ & & 3 & 3 & -6 \\ \hline & 1 & 1 & -2 & 0 \end{array}$$
$(x^3 - 2x^2 - 5x + 6) = (x^2 + x - 2)(x - 3) + 0$; yes

18.
$$\begin{array}{r|rrrr} 2 & 2 & 8 & -3 & -1 \\ & & 4 & 24 & 42 \\ \hline & 2 & 12 & 21 & 41 \end{array}$$
$(2x^3 + 8x^2 - 3x - 1) = (2x^2 + 12x + 21)(x - 2) + 41$; no

19.
$$\begin{array}{r|rrrr} -3 & 1 & 0 & 0 & 27 \\ & & -3 & 9 & -27 \\ \hline & 1 & -3 & 9 & 0 \end{array}$$
$(x^3 + 27) = (x^2 - 3x + 9)(x + 3) + 0$; yes

20.
$$\begin{array}{r|rrrr} -4 & 2 & 1 & -8 & 16 \\ & & -8 & 28 & -80 \\ \hline & 2 & -7 & 20 & -64 \end{array}$$
$(2x^3 + x^2 - 8x + 16) = (2x^2 - 7x + 20)(x + 4) - 64$; no

21.
$$\begin{array}{r|rrrr} -2 & 6 & 9 & -6 & 2 \\ & & -12 & 6 & 0 \\ \hline & 6 & -3 & 0 & 2 \end{array}$$
$(6x^3 + 9x^2 - 6x + 2) = (6x^2 - 3x)(x + 2) + 2$; no

22.
$$\begin{array}{r|rrrr} 4 & 1 & 0 & 0 & -64 \\ & & 4 & 16 & 64 \\ \hline & 1 & 4 & 16 & 0 \end{array}$$
$(x^3 - 64) = (x^2 + 4x + 16)(x - 4) + 0$; yes

23. $$\begin{array}{r|rrrrr} 1 & 4 & 0 & -2 & 1 & 1 \\ & & 4 & 4 & 2 & 3 \\ \hline & 4 & 4 & 2 & 3 & 4 \end{array}$$

$(4x^4 - 2x^2 + x + 1)$
$= (4x^3 + 4x^2 + 2x + 3)(x - 1) + 4$; no

24. $$\begin{array}{r|rrrr} 2 & 1 & -2 & -1 & 1 \\ & & 2 & 0 & -2 \\ \hline & 1 & 0 & -1 & -1 \end{array}$$

$f(2) = -1$

$$\begin{array}{r|rrrr} -1 & 1 & -2 & -1 & 1 \\ & & -1 & 3 & -2 \\ \hline & 1 & -3 & 2 & -1 \end{array}$$

$f(-1) = -1$

25. $$\begin{array}{r|rrr} 2 & 2 & -8 & 6 \\ & & 4 & -8 \\ \hline & 2 & -4 & -2 \end{array} \qquad \begin{array}{r|rrr} -1 & 2 & -8 & 6 \\ & & -2 & 10 \\ \hline & 2 & -10 & 16 \end{array}$$

$f(2) = -2$ $\qquad$ $f(-1) = 16$

26. $$\begin{array}{r|rrrr} 2 & 1 & 2 & -3 & 1 \\ & & 2 & 8 & 10 \\ \hline & 1 & 4 & 5 & 11 \end{array}$$

$f(2) = 11$

$$\begin{array}{r|rrrr} -1 & 1 & 2 & -3 & 1 \\ & & -1 & -1 & 4 \\ \hline & 1 & 1 & -4 & 5 \end{array}$$

$f(-1) = 5$

27. $$\begin{array}{r|rrrr} 2 & 1 & -8 & -2 & 5 \\ & & 2 & -12 & -28 \\ \hline & 1 & -6 & -14 & -23 \end{array}$$

$f(2) = -23$

$$\begin{array}{r|rrrr} -1 & 1 & -8 & -2 & 5 \\ & & -1 & 9 & -7 \\ \hline & 1 & -9 & 7 & -2 \end{array}$$

$f(-1) = -2$

28. $$\begin{array}{r|rrrrr} 2 & 5 & 0 & -6 & 0 & 2 \\ & & 10 & 20 & 28 & 56 \\ \hline & 5 & 10 & 14 & 28 & 58 \end{array}$$

$f(2) = 58$

$$\begin{array}{r|rrrrr} -1 & 5 & 0 & -6 & 0 & 2 \\ & & -5 & 5 & 1 & -1 \\ \hline & 5 & -5 & -1 & 1 & 1 \end{array}$$

$f(-1) = 1$

29. $$\begin{array}{r|rrrrr} 2 & 3 & 1 & -2 & 1 & 12 \\ & & 6 & 14 & 24 & 50 \\ \hline & 3 & 7 & 12 & 25 & 62 \end{array}$$

$f(2) = 62$

$$\begin{array}{r|rrrrr} -1 & 3 & 1 & -2 & 1 & 12 \\ & & -3 & 2 & 0 & -1 \\ \hline & 3 & -2 & 0 & 1 & 11 \end{array}$$

$f(-1) = 11$

30. $$\begin{array}{r|rrrr} -1 & 1 & -1 & -5 & -3 \\ & & -1 & 2 & 3 \\ \hline & 1 & -2 & -3 & 0 \end{array}$$

$x^2 - 2x - 3 = (x - 3)(x + 1)$
$x + 1, x - 3$

31. $$\begin{array}{r|rrrr} 1 & 1 & 0 & -3 & 2 \\ & & 1 & 1 & -2 \\ \hline & 1 & 1 & -2 & 0 \end{array}$$

$x^2 + x - 2 = (x + 2)(x - 1)$
$x + 2, x - 1$

32. $$\begin{array}{r|rrrr} 4 & 1 & 1 & -16 & -16 \\ & & 4 & 20 & 16 \\ \hline & 1 & 5 & 4 & 0 \end{array}$$

$x^2 + 5x + 4 = (x + 4)(x + 1)$
$x + 4, x + 1$

33. $$\begin{array}{r|rrrr} \frac{2}{3} & 6 & -25 & 2 & 8 \\ & & 4 & -14 & -8 \\ \hline & 6 & -21 & -12 & 0 \end{array}$$

$2x^2 - 7x - 4 = (2x + 1)(x - 4)$
$2x + 1, x - 4$

34. $$\begin{array}{r|rrrr} -\frac{7}{2} & 2 & 17 & 23 & -42 \\ & & -7 & -35 & 42 \\ \hline & 2 & 10 & -12 & 0 \end{array}$$

$x^2 + 5x - 6 = (x + 6)(x - 1)$
$x + 6, x - 1$

35. $$\begin{array}{r|rrrrr} -2 & 1 & 2 & 0 & -8 & -16 \\ & & -2 & 0 & 0 & 16 \\ \hline & 1 & 0 & 0 & -8 & 0 \end{array}$$

$x^3 - 8$

$$\begin{array}{r|rrrr} 2 & 1 & 0 & 0 & -8 \\ & & 2 & 4 & 8 \\ \hline & 1 & 2 & 4 & 0 \end{array}$$

$x^2 + 2x + 4$
$x - 2, x^2 + 2x + 4$

36. $$\begin{array}{r|rrrrr} -\frac{1}{2} & 8 & 32 & 0 & 1 & 4 \\ & & -4 & -14 & 7 & -4 \\ \hline & 8 & 28 & -14 & 8 & 0 \end{array}$$

$4x^3 + 14x^2 - 7x + 4$

$$\begin{array}{r|rrrr} -4 & 4 & 14 & -7 & 4 \\ & & -16 & 8 & -4 \\ \hline & 4 & -2 & 1 & 0 \end{array}$$

$4x^2 - 2x + 1$
$x + 4, 4x^2 - 2x + 1$

37. $$\begin{array}{r|rrrrrr} 2 & 16 & -32 & 0 & 0 & -81 & 162 \\ & & 32 & 0 & 0 & 0 & -162 \\ \hline & 16 & 0 & 0 & 0 & -81 & 0 \end{array}$$

$16x^4 - 81$

$$\begin{array}{r|rrrrr} \frac{3}{2} & 16 & 0 & 0 & 0 & -81 \\ & & 24 & 36 & 54 & 81 \\ \hline & 16 & 24 & 36 & 54 & 0 \end{array}$$

$8x^3 + 12x^2 + 18x + 27$

$$\begin{array}{r|rrrr} -\frac{3}{2} & 8 & 12 & 18 & 27 \\ & & -12 & 0 & -27 \\ \hline & 8 & 0 & 18 & 0 \end{array}$$

$4x^2 + 9$
$2x - 3, 2x + 3, 4x^2 + 9$

38.

2	1	1	−3	−3	−4	−4
		2	6	6	6	4
	1	3	3	3	2	0

$x^4 + 3x^3 + 3x^2 + 3x + 2$

−2	1	3	3	3	2
		−2	−2	−2	−2
	1	1	1	1	0

$x^3 + x^2 + x + 1$

−1	1	1	1	1
		−1	0	−1
	1	0	1	0

$x^2 + 1$

$x^5 + x^4 - 3x^3 - 3x^2 - 4x - 4$
$= (x - 2)(x + 2)(x + 1)(x^2 + 1)$

39.

−4	1	7	15	13	4
		−4	−12	−12	−4
	1	3	3	1	0

$x^3 + 3x^2 + 3x + 1$

−1	1	3	3	1
		−1	−2	−1
	1	2	1	0

$x^2 + 2x + 1 = (x + 1)(x + 1)$
$x^4 + 7x^3 + 15x^2 + 13x + 4 = (x + 4)(x + 1)^3$

40.

1	1	−1	k
		1	0
	1	0	k

$k = 3$

41.

2	1	k	−17
		2	$2k + 4$
	1	$k + 2$	$2k - 13$

$2k - 13 = 3$
$2k = 16$
$k = 8$

42.

−2	1	4	1	k
		−2	−4	6
	1	2	−3	$k + 6$

$k + 6 = 3$
$k = -3$

43.

$-k$	1	5	7
		$-k$	$k^2 - 5k$
	1	$5 - k$	$k^2 - 5k + 7$

$k^2 - 5k + 7 = 3$
$k^2 - 5k + 4 = 0$
$(k - 4)(k - 1) = 0$

$k - 4 = 0$ or $k - 1 = 0$
$k = 4$ $\quad k = 1$

44a.

−4	1	2	−5	−6
		−4	8	−12
	1	−2	3	−18

$f(-4) = -18$

−2	1	2	−5	−6
		−2	0	10
	1	0	−5	4

$f(-2) = 4$

0	1	2	−5	−6
		0	0	0
	1	2	−5	−6

$f(0) = -6$

2	1	2	−5	−6
		2	8	6
	1	4	3	0

$f(2) = 0$

(Continued next column)

4	1	2	−5	−6
		4	24	76
	1	6	19	70

$f(4) = 70$

44b.

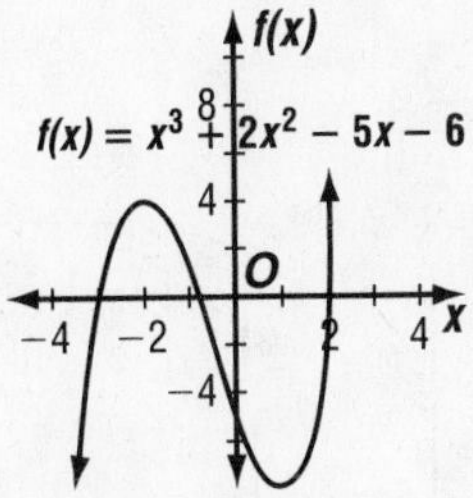

44c. 3 times, yes

45a.

1	−0.5	4	−12	16	0
		−0.5	3.5	−8.5	7.5
	−0.5	3.5	−8.5	7.5	7.5

$f(1) = 7.5$

2	−0.5	4	−12	16	0
		−1	6	−12	8
	−0.5	3	−6	4	8

$f(2) = 8$

3	−0.5	4	−12	16	0
		−1.5	7.5	−13.5	7.5
	−0.5	2.5	−4.5	2.5	7.5

$f(3) = 7.5$

45b.

4	−0.5	4	−12	16	0
		−2	8	−16	0
	−0.5	2	−4	0	0

$f(4) = 0$; The elevator is stopping or is stopped.

46.

9	0.03	−0.02	0.2	0.1
		0.27	2.25	22.05
	0.03	0.25	2.45	22.15

about $22 billion

47. $20{,}000(1.14)^2 + 35{,}000(1.14) = 65{,}892$; $65,892

48. $\frac{y^2}{81} - \frac{x^2}{25} = 1$
center: (0, 0)
$a = \sqrt{81}$ or 9, $b = \sqrt{25}$ or 5
vertices: $(0, \pm 9)$
foci: $c^2 = a^2 + b^2$
$c^2 = 81 + 25$
$c^2 = 106$
$c = \pm\sqrt{106}$
$(0, \pm\sqrt{106})$
slopes of the asymptotes: $\pm\frac{9}{5}$

49. $-y \leq -x^2 + 5x$
$-(-4) \overset{?}{\leq} -(4)^2 + 5(4)$
$4 \leq -16 + 20$
$4 \leq 4$; yes

50. $x = \frac{-(-5) \pm \sqrt{(-5)^2 - 4(2)(4)}}{2(2)}$
$= \frac{5 \pm \sqrt{-7}}{4}$
$= \frac{5 \pm i\sqrt{7}}{4}$

51.

$$\begin{array}{r} 2x^2 - 3x - 2 \\ 3x + 2\overline{)6x^3 - 5x^2 - 12x - 4} \\ (-)\underline{6x^3 + 4x^2} \\ -9x^2 - 12x \\ (-)\underline{-9x^2 - 6x} \\ -6x - 4 \\ (-)\underline{-6x - 4} \\ 0 \end{array}$$

$(6x^3 - 5x^2 - 12x - 4) \div (3x + 2) = 2x^2 - 3x - 2$

52. $7\begin{bmatrix} -1 & 4 \\ 8 & -6 \end{bmatrix} + 2\begin{bmatrix} 6 & -5 \\ 1 & 8 \end{bmatrix} = \begin{bmatrix} -7 & 28 \\ 56 & -42 \end{bmatrix} + \begin{bmatrix} 12 & -10 \\ 2 & 16 \end{bmatrix}$

$= \begin{bmatrix} 5 & 18 \\ 58 & -26 \end{bmatrix}$

53. $y + 1 = 3$ $\quad 2x = y$

$y = 2$ $\quad 2x = 2$

$x = 1$

(1, 2)

54.

$$\begin{aligned} -a^3b^2 + 2ab + 3d &\geq \tfrac{1}{2}c^3 \\ -(-1)^3(7)^2 + 2(-1)(7) + 3d &\geq \tfrac{1}{2}(4)^3 \\ 49 - 14 + 3d &\geq 32 \\ 35 + 3d &\geq 32 \\ 3d &\geq -3 \\ d &\geq -1 \end{aligned}$$

8-3A Graphing Technology: Polynomial Functions

Page 492 Exercises

1. Sample answer: viewing window: [−10, 10] by [−5, 25]

   Enter: 2 [X,T,θ,n] [^] 3 [−] 3 [X,T,θ,n] [^] 2 [−] 12 [X,T,θ,n] [+] 17

   3 real zeros
2. Sample answer: viewing window: [−10, 10] by [−125, 100]

   Enter: 3 [X,T,θ,n] [^] 4 [−] 8 [X,T,θ,n] [^] 3 [−] 35 [X,T,θ,n] [^] 2 [+] 72 [X,T,θ,n] [+] 47

   4 real zeros
3. Sample answer: viewing window: [−15, 10] by [−175, 75]

   Enter: 0.1 [X,T,θ,n] [^] 4 [+] 1 [X,T,θ,n] [^] 3 [−] 1 [X,T,θ,n] [^] 2 [+] 3 [X,T,θ,n] [+] 18

   2 real zeros
4. Sample answer: viewing window: [−10, 10] by [−40, 40]

   Enter: 1 [X,T,θ,n] [^] 5 [−] 4 [X,T,θ,n] [^] 4 [+] 2 [X,T,θ,n] [^] 3 [−] 7 [X,T,θ,n] [+] 15

   3 real zeros
5. Enter: 1 [X,T,θ,n] [^] 4 [−] 3 [X,T,θ,n] [^] 2 [−] 6 [X,T,θ,n] [−] 2

   zeros: −0.41, 2.41

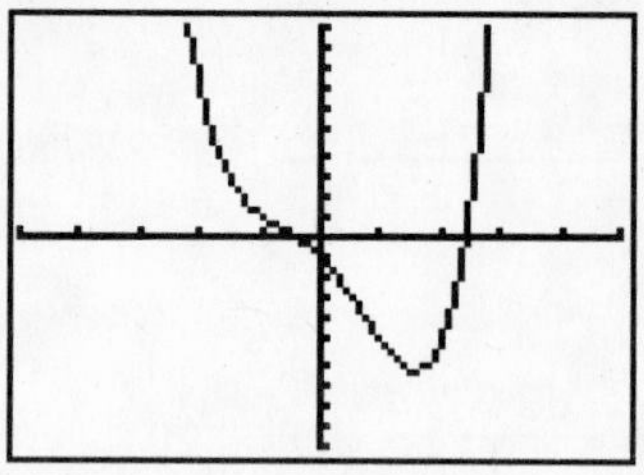

6. Enter: 2 [X,T,θ,n] [^] 5 [+] 3 [X,T,θ,n] [−] 2

   zeros: 0.61

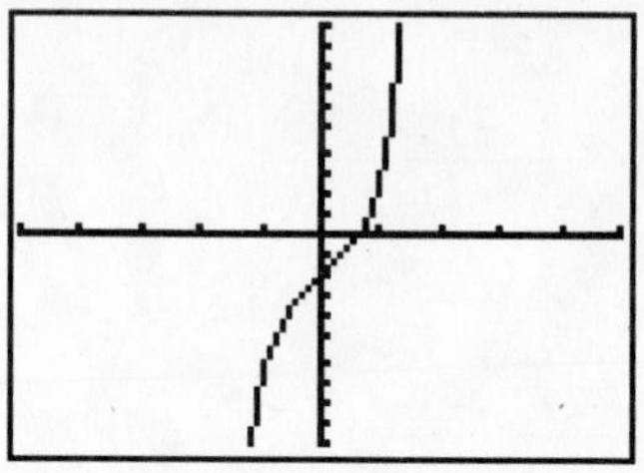

7. Enter; 3 [X,T,θ,n] [^] 13 [+] 4 [X,T,θ,n] [^] 3 [+] 2

   zeros: −0.78

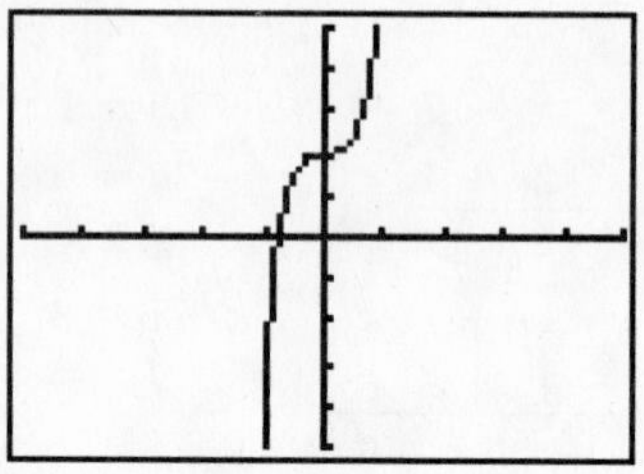

8. Enter: 2 [X,T,θ,n] [^] 8 [+] 4 [X,T,θ,n] [^] 2 [+] 1

   zeros: no real zeros

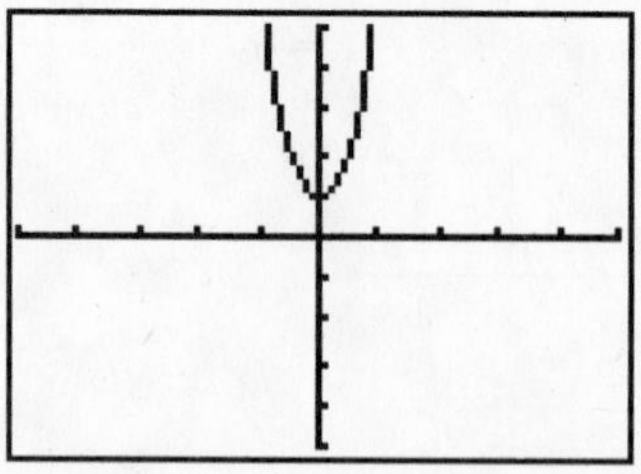

9. Enter: 8 [X,T,θ,n] [^] 5 [−] 20 [X,T,θ,n] [^] 3 [+] 73 [X,T,θ,n] [^] 2 [+] 28 [X,T,θ,n] [−] 4

   zeros: −2.38, −0.45, 0.11

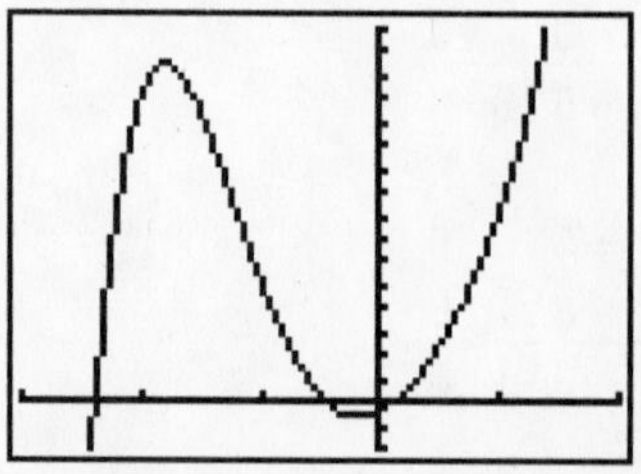

10. Enter: 1 [X,T,θ,n] [^] 5 [+] 1 [X,T,θ,n] [^] 4 [–] 8 [X,T,θ,n] [^] 3 [–] 10 [X,T,θ,n] [^] 2 [+] 7 [X,T,θ,n] [–] 4

zeros: 2.83

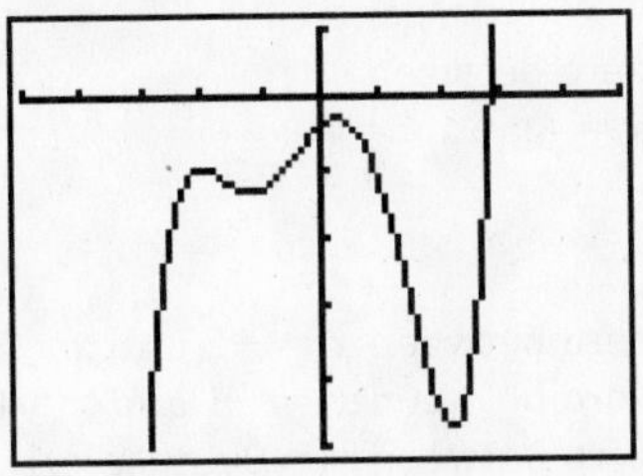

8-3 Graphing Polynomial Functions and Approximating Zeros

Page 497 Check for Understanding

1a. 1 **1b.** 1 **1c.** 2 **1d.** 1

2. Negative dimensions have no meaning.

3a. Sample answer:

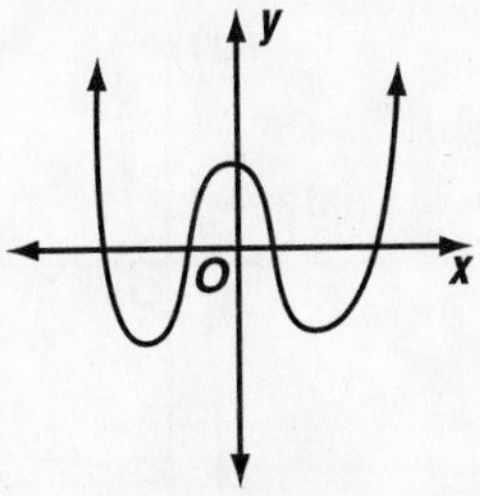

3b. Sample answer:

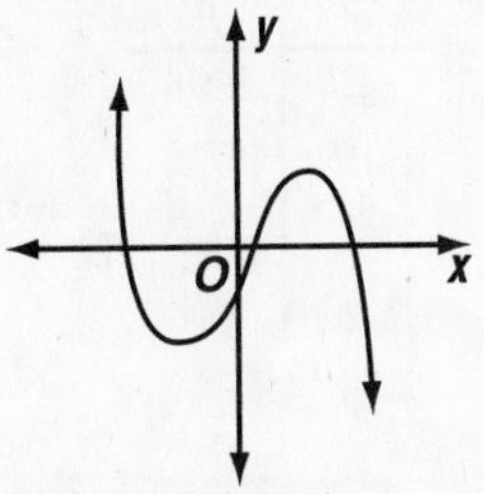

3c. Sample answer:

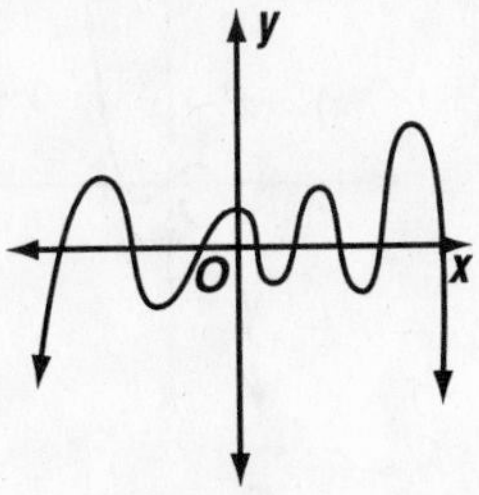

3d. Sample answer:

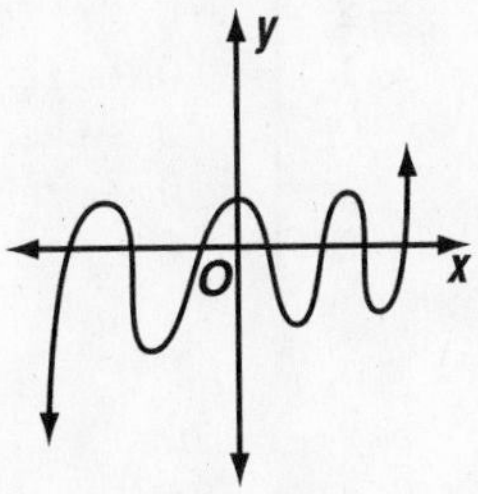

4a.

x	$f(x)$
−4	138
−3	19
−2	−6
−1	3
0	10
1	3
2	−6
3	19
4	138

4b. −3 and −2; −2.5
−2 and −1; −1.2
1 and 2; 1.2
2 and 3; 2.5

4c. negative between −2.5 and −1.2 and between 1.2 and 2.5; positive between −1.2 and 1.2, less than −2.5, and greater than 2.5

4d. min: (−2, −6), (2, −6)
max: (0, 10)

4e.

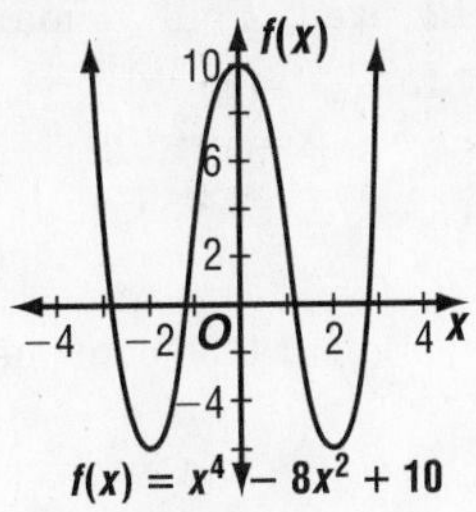

5.

x	$f(x)$	
−2	−11	
−1	−1	← zero between $x = -1$ and $x = 0$
0	1	
1	1	
2	5	

−0.8

6.

x	$g(x)$	
−4	59	← zero between $x = -4$ and $x = -3$
−3	−5	
−2	−13	
−1	−7	
0	−5	
1	−1	← zero between $x = 1$ and $x = 2$
2	35	

−3.2, 1.1

7.

x	$f(x)$	
−2	−8	
−1	−1	
0	0	← zero
1	1	
2	8	

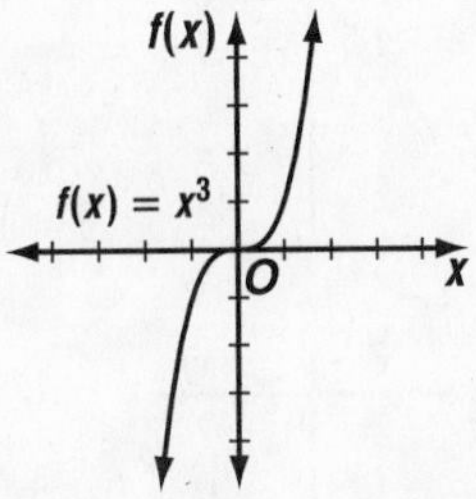

8.

x	$f(x)$	
−3	−20	
−2	0	← zero
−1	6	
0	4	
1	0	← zero
2	0	← zero
3	10	

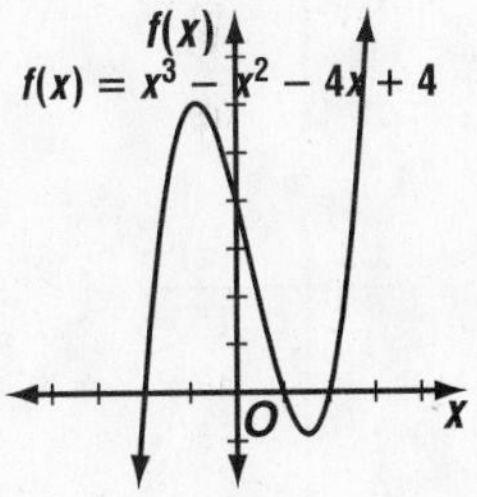

9.

x	$f(x)$	
−2	192	
−1	75	
0	16	← zero
1	−3	
2	0	← zero
3	7	
4	0	← zero

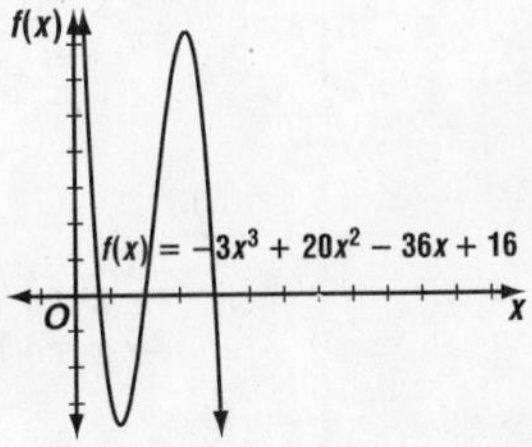

10.

x	$f(x)$	
−3	20	← zero
−2	−9	
−1	−2	← zero
0	5	
1	0	← zero
2	−5	← zero
3	26	

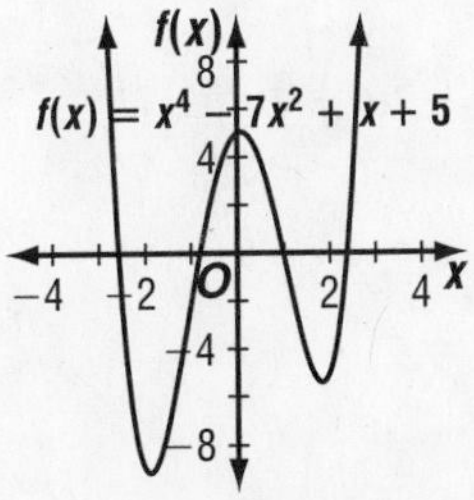

11. odd; 1 min, 1 max

12. even; 2 min, 1 max

13. even; 0 min, 1 max

14.
$V = \pi r^2 h$
$2 = \pi r^2(2)$
$\frac{1}{\pi} = r^2$
$0.56 \approx r$
about 0.56 centimeters

Pages 498–499 Exercises

15.

x	$f(x)$	
−2	−10	← zero between $x = -2$ and $x = -1$
−1	3	
0	6	
1	5	
2	6	

−1.3

16.

x	$h(x)$	
−2	−72	
−1	−7	
0	−2	← zero between $x = 0$ and $x = 1$
1	3	
2	68	

0.6

17.

x	$r(x)$	
−2	−38	
−1	−7	
0	−6	
1	−5	← zero between $x = 1$ and $x = 2$
2	26	

1.4

18.

x	$g(x)$	
−2	−7	
−1	0	← zero
0	1	
1	2	
2	9	

−1

19.

x	$f(x)$	
−3	15	← zero between $x = -3$ and $x = -2$
−2	−7	
−1	−5	
0	−3	
1	−1	← zero between $x = 1$ and $x = 2$
2	25	

−2.6, 1.1

20.

x	$p(x)$	
−3	−5	← zero between $x = -3$ and $x = -2$
−2	1	← zero between $x = -2$ and $x = -1$
−1	−1	
0	−5	
1	−5	← zero between $x = 1$ and $x = 2$
2	5	

−2.4, −1.3, 1.7

21.

x	$n(x)$	
−1	−25	← zero between $x = -1$ and $x = 0$
0	6	
1	5	← zero between $x = 1$ and $x = 2$
2	−10	
3	−21	
4	−10	← zero between $x = 4$ and $x = 5$
5	41	

−0.3, 1.4, 4.3

22.

x	$h(x)$	
−2	2	← zero between $x = -2$ and $x = -1$
−1	−1	← zero between $x = -1$ and $x = 0$
0	2	← zero between $x = 0$ and $x = 1$
1	−1	← zero between $x = 1$ and $x = 2$
2	2	

−1.8, −0.8, 0.8, 1.8

23.

x	$f(x)$	
−2	256	
−1	4	
0	0	← zero
1	4	
2	256	

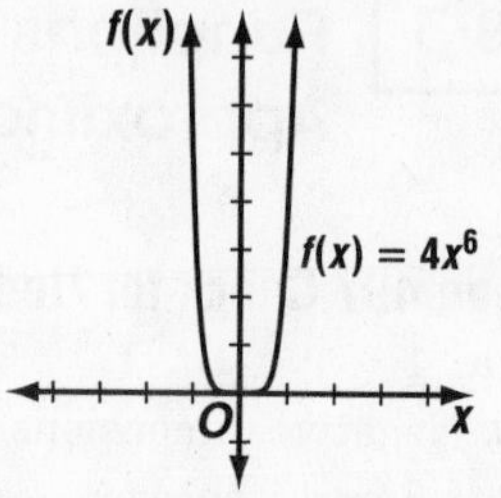

24.

x	$f(x)$	
−2	−96	
−1	−3	
0	0	← zero
1	3	
2	96	

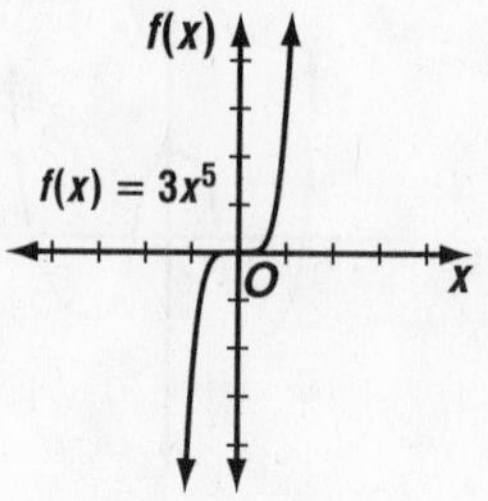

25.

x	$f(x)$	
−2	−6	
−1	0	← zero
0	0	← zero
1	0	← zero
2	6	

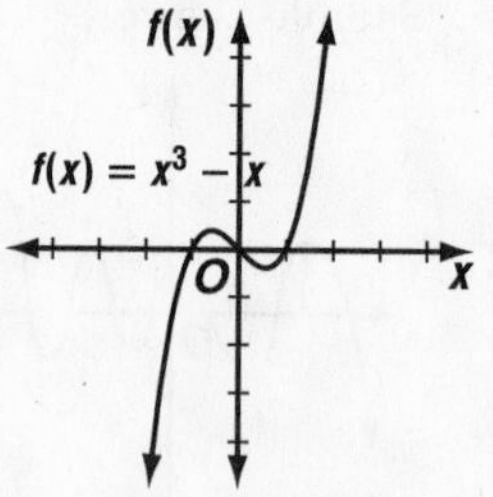

26.

x	$f(x)$	
−4	0	← zero
−3	−9	
−2	−8	
−1	−3	
0	0	← zero
1	−5	

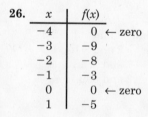

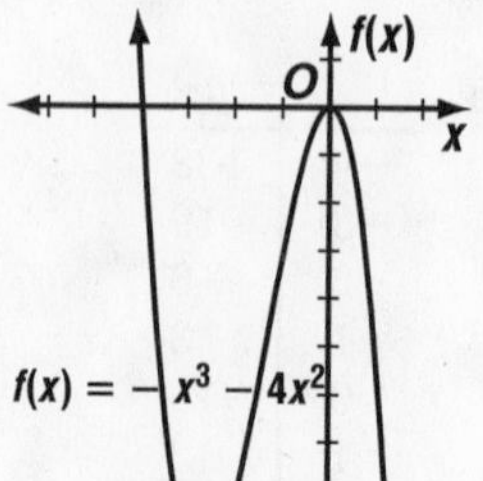

27.

x	$f(x)$	
-2	-3	← zero between $x = -2$ and $x = -1$
-1	4	
0	5	
1	6	
2	13	

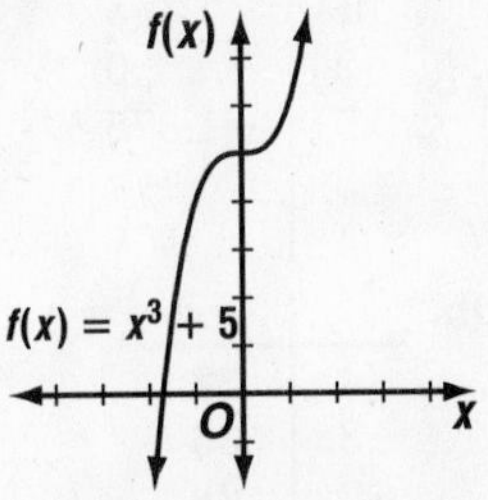

28.

x	$f(x)$	
-3	0	← zero
-2	-65	
-1	-80	
0	-81	
1	-80	
2	-65	
3	0	← zero

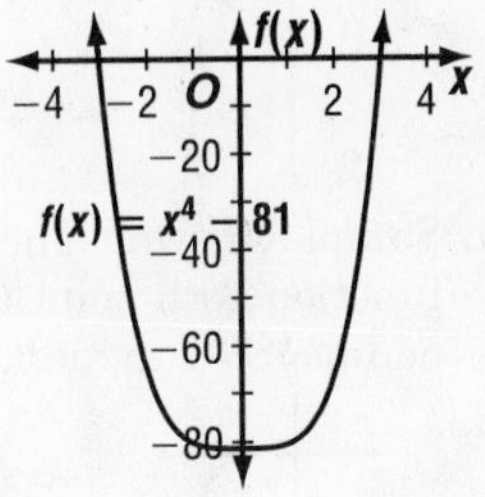

29.

x	$f(x)$	
-2	-180	
-1	-28	← zero between $x = -1$ and $x = 0$
0	2	← zero between $x = 0$ and $x = 0.5$
0.5	-0.625	
1	0	← zero
2	56	
3	260	

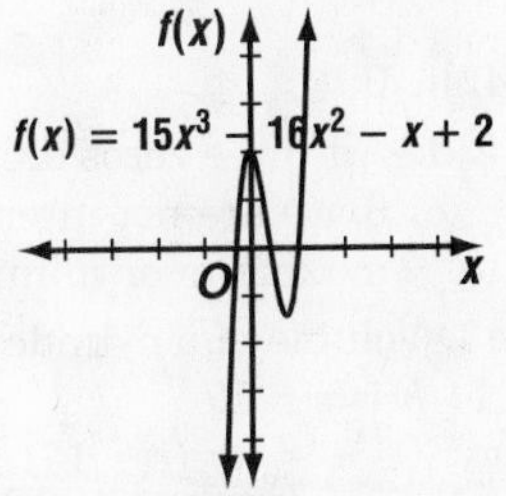

30.

x	$f(x)$	
-3	0	← zero
-2	-15	
-1	0	← zero
0	9	
1	0	← zero
2	-15	
3	0	← zero

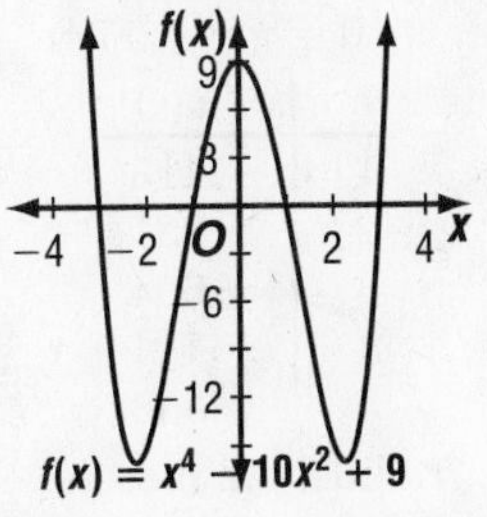

31.

x	$f(x)$	
-3	-39	← zero between $x = -3$ and $x = -2$
-2	5	
-1	3	← zero between $x = -1$ and $x = 0$
0	-3	← zero between $x = 0$ and $x = 1$
1	5	
2	21	
3	15	← zero between $x = 3$ and $x = 4$
4	-67	

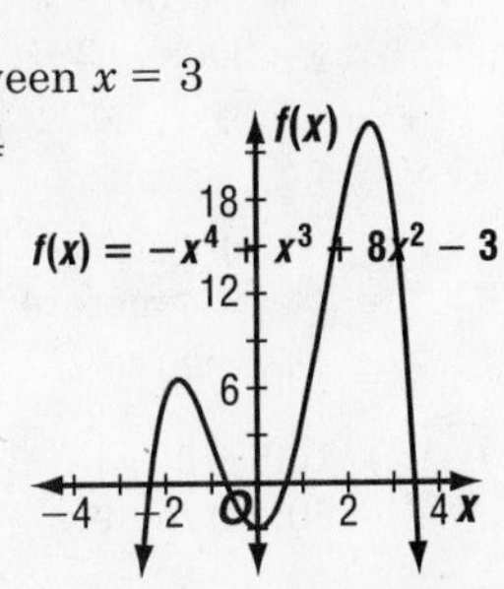

32.

x	$f(x)$	
-3	0	← zero
-2	16	
-1	18	
0	12	
1	4	
2	0	← zero

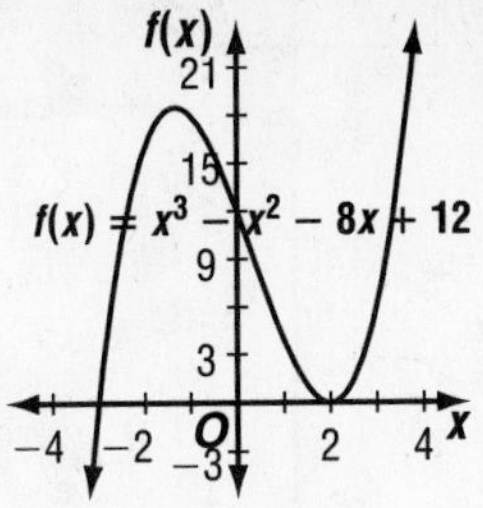

33.

x	$r(x)$	
-4	-77	← zero between $x = -4$ and $x = -3$
-3	30	
-2	7	← zero between $x = -2$ and $x = -1$
-1	-2	← zero between $x = -1$ and $x = 0$
0	3	← zero between $x = 0$ and $x = 1$
1	-2	← zero between $x = 1$ and $x = 2$
2	55	

$-3.6, -1.6, -0.7, 0.6, 1.3$

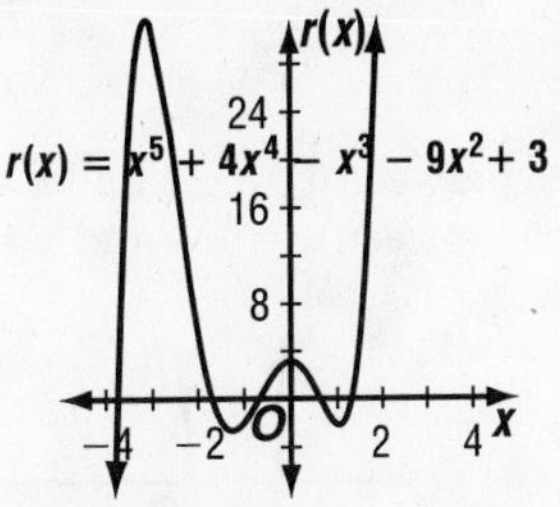

34.

x	$g(x)$	
-1	65	
0	6	← zero between $x = 0$ and $x = 1$
1	-1	← zero between $x = 1$ and $x = 2$
2	2	← zero between $x = 2$ and $x = 3$
3	-3	
4	-10	← zero between $x = 4$ and $x = 5$
5	11	

$0.4, 1.3, 2.6, 4.7$

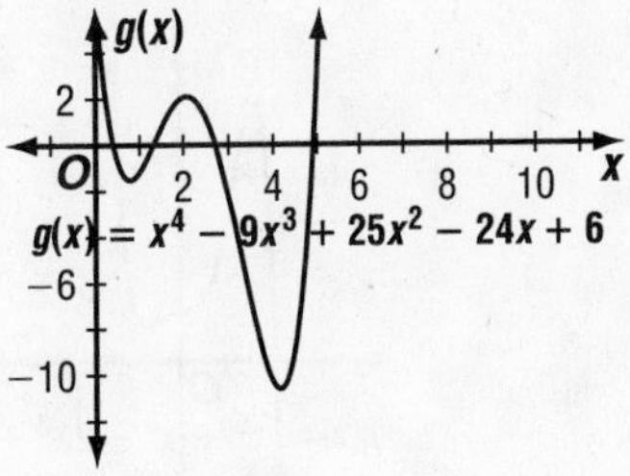

35.

x	$h(x)$	
-1	-2	← zero between $x = -1$ and $x = 0$
0	2	
1	0	← zero
2	-2	← zero between $x = 2$ and $x = 3$
3	2	

$-0.7, 1.0, 2.7$

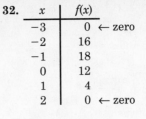

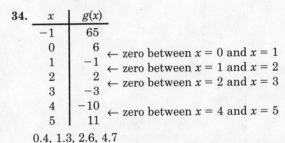

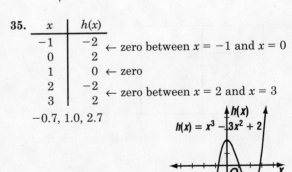

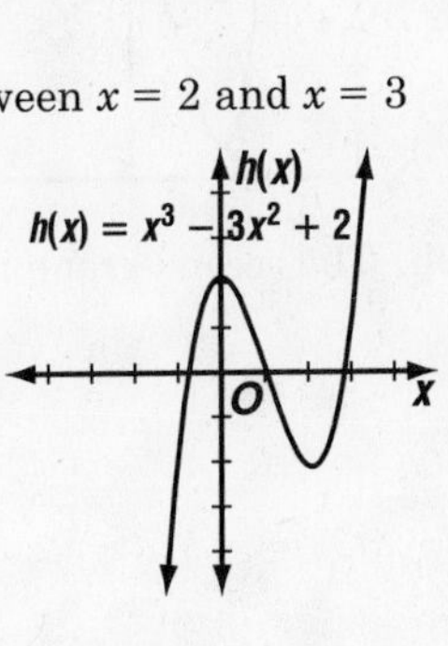

36.

x	$f(x)$	
−5	−9	← zero between $x = -5$ and $x = -4$
−4	7	
−3	9	
−2	3	← zero between $x = -2$ and $x = -1$
−1	−5	
0	−9	
1	−3	← zero between $x = 1$ and $x = 2$
2	19	

−4.6, −1.6, 1.2

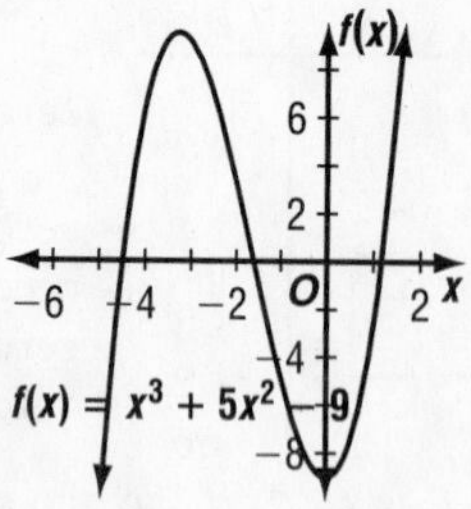

37.

x	$f(x)$	
−3	61	
−2	3	← zero between $x = -2$ and $x = -1$
−1	−5	← zero between $x = -1$ and $x = 0$
0	1	
1	9	

−1.9, −0.1

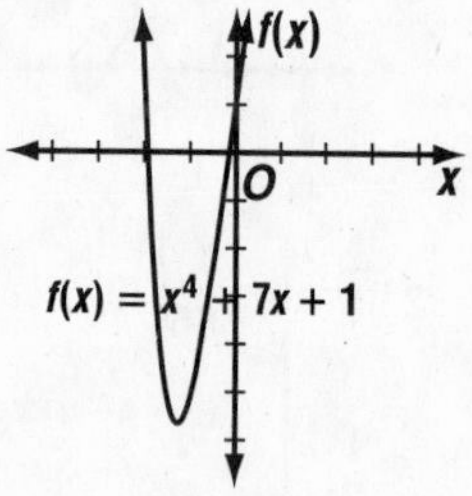

38.

x	$p(x)$	
−3	−107	← zero between $x = -3$ and $x = -2$
−2	1	
−1	3	
0	1	
1	1	
2	33	

−2.0

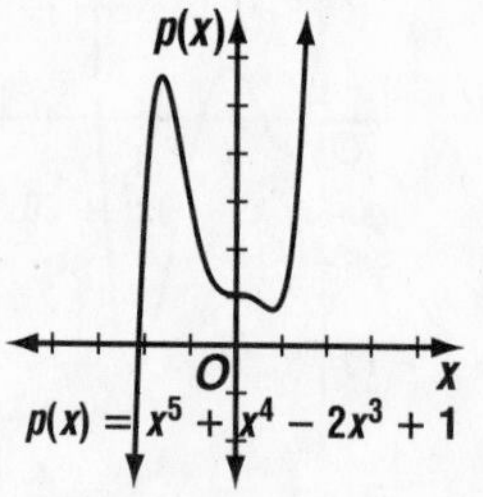

39a.

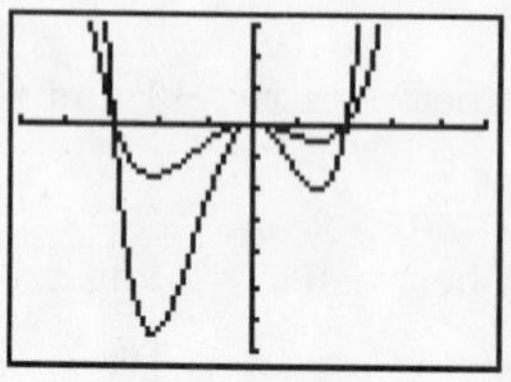

39b. The second graph is a vertical stretch of the first.

40a.

x	$f(x)$
−1	3
0	8
1	5
2	0
2.5	−1.375
3	−1
4	8

max: (0, 8)
min: (2.67, −1.48)

40b.

x	$f(x)$
−4	32
−3	36
−2	28
−1	14
0	1
1	−8
2	−4

max: (−3.24, 36.36)
min: (1.24, −8.36)

41. Sample answer: The ends of an even-degree function both point up or down and the ends of an odd-degree function point in opposite directions.

42a.

s	$V(s)$
−2	$-\frac{8}{3}$
−1	$-\frac{1}{3}$
0	0
1	$\frac{1}{3}$
2	$\frac{8}{3}$

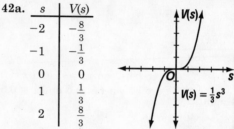

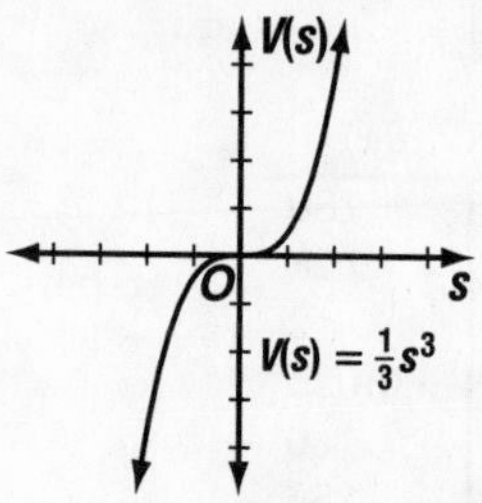

42b. 0

42c. There are none.

42d. All three zeros occur at 0. However, since $V(s) \neq 0$, we are not interested in zeros. There is no maximum or minimum volume for any value of s.

43. Volume of a cylinder = $\pi r^2 h$

$h = r + 17$

$v = \pi r^2(r + 17)$

$1170 = \pi r^3 + 17\pi r^2$

$0 = \pi r^3 + 17\pi r^2 - 1170$

r	$v(r)$	
1	−1113	
2	−931	
3	−604	
4	−114	← zero between $r = 4$ and $r = 5$
5	558	

radius: 4.2 meters
height: 4.2 + 17 or 21.2 meters

44. Perimeter $= 2\ell + 2\pi r$

$200 = 2\ell + 2\pi r$

$100 = \ell + \pi r$

$100 - \pi r = \ell$

Area $= 2r\ell$

$= 2r(100 - \pi r)$

$= 200r - 2\pi r^2$

$r = -\frac{b}{2a}$

$= \frac{-200}{2(-2\pi)}$

$= \frac{50}{\pi}; \left(\frac{50}{\pi}\right)$ meters

$\ell = 100 - \pi\left(\frac{50}{\pi}\right)$

$= 100 - 50$

$= 50$; 50 meters

45. $V = \ell wh$

$= (x - 1)(x + 3)(x - 2)$

$= x^3 - 7x + 6$

$(x^3 - 7x + 6) \div (x - 3)$

$$\begin{array}{r|rrr|r} 3 & 1 & 0 & -7 & 6 \\ & & 3 & 9 & 6 \\ \hline & 1 & 3 & 2 & 12 \end{array}$$

12 cubic centimeters would remain unbottled.

46. $\frac{x^2}{4} + \frac{y^2}{25} = 1$

center: (0, 0)

$a = \sqrt{25}$ or 5, $b = \sqrt{4}$ or 2

foci: $c^2 = a^2 - b^2$

$c^2 = 25 - 4$

$c^2 = 21$

$c = \pm\sqrt{21}$

$(0, \pm\sqrt{21})$

length of major axis: 2(5) or 10 units

length of minor axis: 2(2) or 4 units

47. $y = (x - 3)^2 - 11$

vertex: $(3, -11)$

axis of symmetry: $x = 3$

48. $x^2 - 20x = -75$

$x^2 - 20x + 75 = 0$

$(x - 5)(x - 15) = 0$

$x - 5 = 0$ or $x - 15 = 0$

$x = 5$ $\quad$ $x = 15$

49. $-3y^2 = 18$

$y^2 = -6$

$y = \pm\sqrt{-6}$

$y = \pm i\sqrt{6}$

50. $$\left[\begin{array}{ccc|c} 1 & \frac{1}{2} & -3 & 19 \\ \frac{1}{2} & -1 & 2 & -16 \\ 5 & 2 & -2 & 50 \end{array}\right] = \left[\begin{array}{ccc|c} 1 & \frac{1}{2} & -3 & 19 \\ 0 & -\frac{5}{4} & \frac{7}{2} & -\frac{51}{2} \\ 5 & 2 & -2 & 50 \end{array}\right]$$

$$= \left[\begin{array}{ccc|c} 1 & \frac{1}{2} & -3 & 19 \\ 0 & -\frac{5}{4} & \frac{7}{2} & -\frac{51}{2} \\ 0 & -\frac{1}{2} & 13 & -45 \end{array}\right] = \left[\begin{array}{ccc|c} 1 & \frac{1}{2} & -3 & 19 \\ 0 & 1 & -\frac{14}{5} & \frac{102}{5} \\ 0 & -\frac{1}{2} & 13 & -45 \end{array}\right]$$

$$= \left[\begin{array}{ccc|c} 1 & 0 & 10 & -26 \\ 0 & 1 & -\frac{14}{5} & \frac{102}{5} \\ 0 & -\frac{1}{2} & 13 & -45 \end{array}\right] = \left[\begin{array}{ccc|c} 1 & 0 & 10 & -26 \\ 0 & 1 & -\frac{14}{5} & \frac{102}{5} \\ 0 & 0 & \frac{58}{5} & -\frac{174}{5} \end{array}\right]$$

$$= \left[\begin{array}{ccc|c} 1 & 0 & 10 & -26 \\ 0 & 1 & -\frac{14}{5} & \frac{102}{5} \\ 0 & 0 & 1 & -3 \end{array}\right] = \left[\begin{array}{ccc|c} 1 & 0 & 0 & 4 \\ 0 & 1 & -\frac{14}{5} & \frac{102}{5} \\ 0 & 0 & 1 & -3 \end{array}\right]$$

$$= \left[\begin{array}{ccc|c} 1 & 0 & 0 & 4 \\ 0 & 1 & 0 & 12 \\ 0 & 0 & 1 & -3 \end{array}\right] \quad (4, 12, -3)$$

51. $5 + 3x = -2y$

$-\frac{5}{2} - \frac{3}{2}x = y$

$m = \frac{2}{3}, (-2, 1)$

$y - y_1 = m(x - x_1)$

$y - 1 = \frac{2}{3}[x - (-2)]$

$y - 1 = \frac{2}{3}x + \frac{4}{3}$

$y = \frac{2}{3}x + \frac{7}{3}$

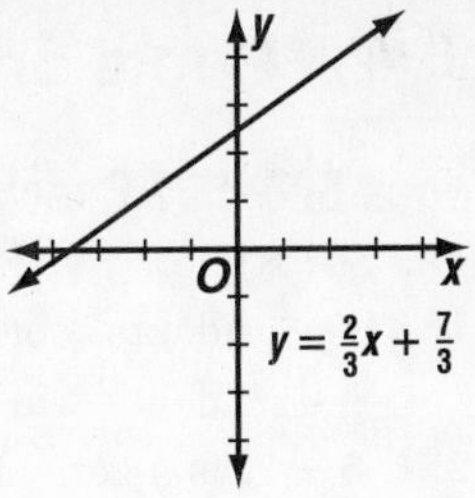

52. $\sqrt{64} \div \sqrt{4} = 8 \div 2$

$= 4$

8-3B Graphing Technology: Modeling Real-World Data

Page 501 Exercises

1. Sample answer:
[0, 15], Xscl = 3; [0, 11,000], Yscl = 1000

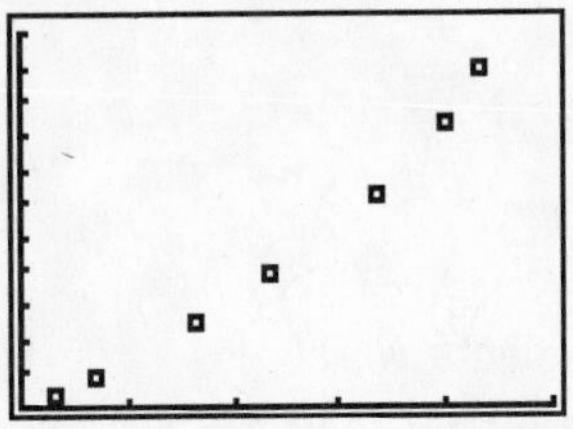

2. LinReg

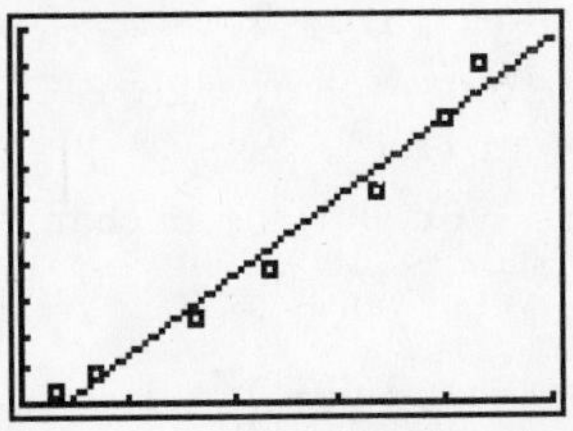

QuadReg

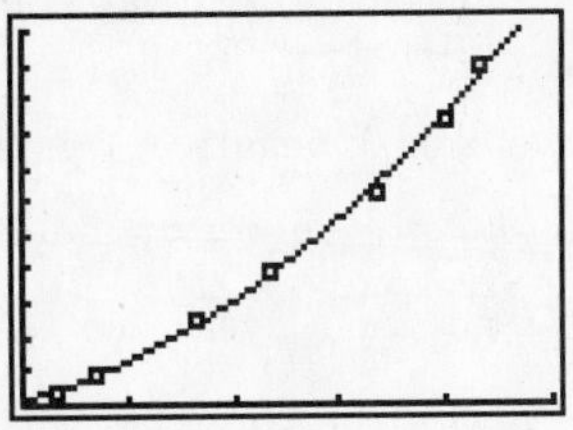

CubicReg

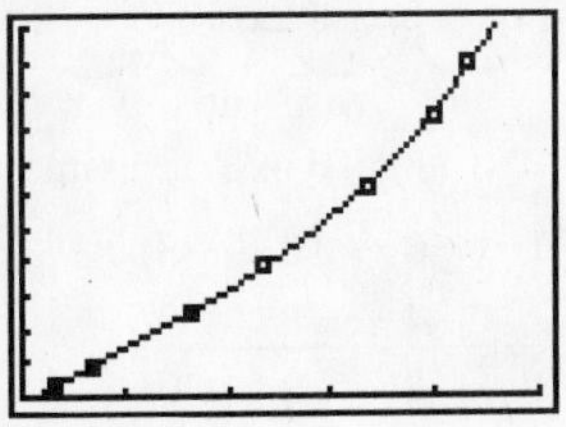

QuartReg

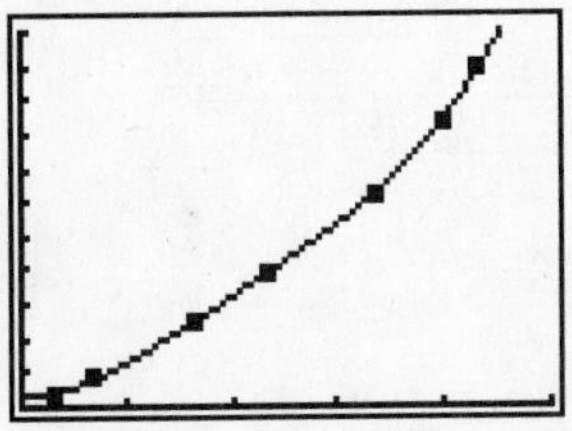

3. See students' work.

4. about 4981 miles; about 14,447 miles

8-4 Roots and Zeros

Pages 506–507 Check for Understanding

1a. See students' work.

1b. See students' work.

1c. See students' work.

2. If $6 + 7i$ is a zero of a polynomial function, then $6 - 7i$ is also a zero of the function.

3. $-6, 5 + i, 5 - i$

4a. See students' work.

4b. See students' work.

4c. See students' work.

5a. 1 real, 2 imaginary

5b.

$$\begin{array}{r|rrrr} 2 & 1 & 0 & 0 & -8 \\ & & 2 & 4 & 8 \\ \hline & 1 & 2 & 4 & \multicolumn{1}{|r}{0} \end{array}$$

$x^2 + 2x + 4 = 0$

$x = \frac{-2 \pm \sqrt{2^2 - 4(1)(4)}}{2}$

$= \frac{-2 \pm \sqrt{-12}}{2}$

$= -1 \pm i\sqrt{3}$

$2, -1 + i\sqrt{3}, -1 - i\sqrt{3}$

6. See students' work.

7. $f(-x) = 6(-x)^4 - 3(-x)^3 + 5(-x)^2 - (-x) + 2$
$= 6x^4 + 3x^3 + 5x^2 + x + 2$

8. $f(-x) = (-x)^7 - (-x)^3 + 2(-x) - 1$
$= -x^7 + x^3 - 2x - 1$

9. $f(x) = x^3 - 6x^2 + 1$; 2 sign changes
yes yes

$f(-x) = (-x)^3 - 6(-x)^2 + 1$
$= -x^3 - 6x^2 + 1$; 1 sign change
no yes

positive: 2 or 0; negative: 1; imaginary: 0 or 2

10. $f(x) = x^4 + 5x^3 + 2x^2 - 7x - 9$; 1 sign change
no no yes no

$f(-x) = (-x)^4 + 5(-x)^3 + 2(-x)^2 - 7(-x) - 9$
$= x^4 - 5x^3 + 2x^2 + 7x - 9$; 3 sign changes
yes yes no yes

positive: 1; negative: 3 or 1; imaginary: 0 or 2

11.

$$\begin{array}{r|rrrr} 4 & 1 & -6 & 10 & -8 \\ & & 4 & -8 & 8 \\ \hline & 1 & -2 & 2 & \multicolumn{1}{|r}{0} \end{array}$$

$x^2 - 2x + 2 = 0$

$x = \frac{-(-2) \pm \sqrt{(-2)^2 - 4(1)(2)}}{2(1)}$

$= \frac{2 \pm \sqrt{-4}}{2}$

$= \frac{2 \pm 2i}{2}$

$= 1 \pm i$

$4, 1 + i, 1 - i$

12.

$$\begin{array}{r|rrrr} -2 & 1 & 6 & 21 & 26 \\ & & -2 & -8 & -26 \\ \hline & 1 & 4 & 13 & \multicolumn{1}{|r}{0} \end{array}$$

$x^2 + 4x + 13 = 0$

$x = \frac{-4 \pm \sqrt{(4)^2 - 4(1)(13)}}{2(1)}$

$= \frac{-4 \pm \sqrt{-36}}{2}$

$= \frac{-4 \pm 6i}{2}$

$= -2 \pm 3i$

$-2, -2 + 3i, -2 - 3i$

13. $(x - 5i)(x + 5i) = x^2 + 25$

$$\begin{array}{r} x + 7 \\ x^2 + 25 \overline{)\, x^3 + 7x^2 + 25x + 175} \\ \underline{x^3 \qquad\quad + 25x \qquad} \\ 7x^2 \qquad\quad + 175 \\ \underline{7x^2 \qquad\quad + 175} \\ 0 \end{array}$$

$-5i, 5i, -7$

14. $[x - (3 - i)][x - (3 + i)] = x^2 - 6x + 9 - i^2$
$= x^2 - 6x + 10$

$$\begin{array}{r} x^2 - 3x - 4 \\ x^2 - 6x + 10 \overline{)\, x^4 - 9x^3 + 24x^2 - 6x - 40} \\ \underline{x^4 - 6x^3 + 10x^2 \qquad\qquad} \\ -3x^3 + 14x^2 - 6x \qquad \\ \underline{-3x^3 + 18x^2 - 30x \qquad} \\ -4x^2 + 24x - 40 \\ \underline{-4x^2 + 24x - 40} \\ 0 \end{array}$$

$x^2 - 3x - 4 = (x - 4)(x + 1)$

$x - 4 = 0$ or $x + 1 = 0$

$x = 4$ $\quad x = -1$

$3 + i, 3 - i, 4, -1$

15. $f(x) = (x + 4)(x - 1)(x - 5)$
$= x^3 - 2x^2 - 19x + 20$

16. $f(x) = (x - 9)(x - 1 - 2i)(x - 1 + 2i)$
$= x^3 - 11x^2 + 23x - 45$

17. $V = \ell wh$

$120 = (w + 3)(w)(w - 2)$

$120 = w(w^2 + w - 6)$

$0 = w^3 + w^2 - 6w - 120$

$$\begin{array}{r|rrrr} 5 & 1 & 1 & -6 & -120 \\ & & 5 & 30 & 120 \\ \hline & 1 & 6 & 24 & \multicolumn{1}{|r}{0} \end{array}$$

$w^2 + 6w + 24 = 0$

$w = \frac{-6 \pm \sqrt{36 - 4(1)(24)}}{2(1)}$

$= \frac{-6 \pm \sqrt{-60}}{2}$; no solution

$w = 5$ inches; $\ell = w + 3 = 5 + 3$ or 8 inches;
$h = w - 2 = 5 - 2$ or 3 inches

Pages 507–508 Exercises

18. $f(x) = 5x^3 + 8x^2 - 4x + 3$; 2 sign changes
no yes yes

$f(-x) = 5(-x)^3 + 8(-x)^2 - 4(-x) + 3$
$= -5x^3 + 8x^2 + 4x + 3$; 1 sign change
yes no no

positive: 2 or 0; negative: 1; imaginary: 2 or 0

19. $g(x) = x^4 + x^3 + 2x^2 - 3x - 1$; 1 sign change

no no yes no

$g(-x) = (-x)^4 + (-x)^3 + 2(-x)^2 - 3(-x) - 1$
$= x^4 - x^3 + 2x^2 + 3x - 1$; 3 sign changes

yes yes no yes

positive: 1, negative: 3 or 1, imaginary: 2 or 0

20. $h(x) = 4x^3 - 6x^2 + 8x - 5$; 3 sign changes

yes yes yes

$h(-x) = 4(-x)^3 - 6(-x)^2 + 8(-x) - 5$
$= -4x^3 - 6x^2 - 8x - 5$; 0 sign changes

no no no

positive: 3 or 1, negative: 0, imaginary: 2 or 0

21. $f(x) = x^4 - 9$; 1 sign change

yes

$f(-x) = (-x)^4 - 9$
$= x^4 - 9$; 1 sign change

yes

positive: 1, negative: 1, imaginary: 2

22. $r(x) = x^5 - x^3 - x + 1$; 2 sign changes

yes no yes

$r(-x) = (-x)^5 - (-x)^3 - (-x) + 1$
$= -x^5 + x^3 + x + 1$; 1 sign change

yes no no

positive: 2 or 0, negative: 1, imaginary: 4 or 2

23. $g(x) = x^{14} + x^{10} - x^9 + x - 1$; 3 sign changes

no yes yes yes

$g(-x) = (-x)^{14} + (-x)^{10} - (-x)^9 + (-x) - 1$
$= x^{14} + x^{10} + x^9 - x - 1$; 1 sign change

no no yes no

positive: 3 or 1, negative: 1, imaginary: 10 or 12

24. $p(x) = x^5 - 6x^4 - 3x^3 + 7x^2 - 8x + 1$; 4 sign changes

yes no yes yes yes

$p(-x) = (-x)^5 - 6(-x)^4 - 3(-x)^3 + 7(-x)^2 - 8(-x) + 1$
$= -x^5 - 6x^4 + 3x^3 + 7x^2 + 8x + 1$; 1 sign change

no yes no no no

positive: 4, 2, or 0; negative: 1; imaginary: 0, 2, or 4

25. $f(x) = x^{10} - x^8 + x^6 - x^4 + x^2 - 1$; 5 sign changes

yes yes yes yes yes

$f(-x) = (-x)^{10} - (-x)^8 + (-x)^6 - (-x)^4 + (-x)^2 - 1$
$= x^{10} - x^8 + x^6 - x^4 + x^2 - 1$; 5 sign changes

yes yes yes yes yes

positive: 5, 3, or 1; negative: 5, 3, or 1;
imaginary: 0, 2, 4, 6, or 8

26.
$$\begin{array}{r|rrrr} -4 & 1 & 2 & -3 & 20 \\ & & -4 & 8 & -20 \\ \hline & 1 & -2 & 5 & 0 \end{array}$$

$x^2 - 2x + 5 = 0$

$x = \frac{-(-2) \pm \sqrt{(-2)^2 - 4(1)(5)}}{2(1)}$

$= \frac{2 \pm \sqrt{-16}}{2}$

$= \frac{2 \pm 4i}{2}$

$= 1 \pm 2i$

$-4, 1 + 2i, 1 - 2i$

27.
$$\begin{array}{r|rrrr} 2 & 1 & -4 & 6 & -4 \\ & & 2 & -4 & 4 \\ \hline & 1 & -2 & 2 & 0 \end{array}$$

$x^2 - 2x + 2 = 0$

$x = \frac{-(-2) \pm \sqrt{(-2)^2 - 4(1)(2)}}{2(1)}$

$= \frac{2 \pm \sqrt{-4}}{2}$

$= \frac{2 \pm 2i}{2}$

$= 1 \pm i$

$2, 1 + i, 1 - i$

28. $(x - 2i)(x + 2i) = x^2 + 4$

$$\begin{array}{r} x - 3 \\ x^2 + 4 \overline{) x^3 - 3x^2 + 4x - 12} \\ \underline{x^3 \qquad + 4x} \\ -3x^2 \qquad - 12 \\ \underline{-3x^2 \qquad - 12} \\ 0 \end{array}$$

$3, 2i, -2i$

29. $(x - 2i)(x + 2i) = x^2 + 4$

$$\begin{array}{r} 4x^2 + 1 \\ x^2 + 4 \overline{) 4x^4 + 0x^3 + 17x^2 + 0x + 4} \\ \underline{4x^4 \qquad + 16x^2} \\ x^2 \qquad + 4 \\ \underline{x^2 \qquad + 4} \\ 0 \end{array}$$

$4x^2 + 1 = 0$

$4x^2 = -1$

$x^2 = -\frac{1}{4}$

$x = \pm\frac{1}{2}i$

$2i, -2i, \frac{1}{2}i, -\frac{1}{2}i$

30.
$$\begin{array}{r|rrrr} -\frac{3}{2} & 2 & -1 & 28 & 51 \\ & & -3 & 6 & -51 \\ \hline & 2 & -4 & 34 & 0 \end{array}$$

$2x^2 - 4x + 34 = 0$

$x^2 - 2x + 17 = 0$

$x = \frac{-(-2) \pm \sqrt{(-2)^2 - 4(1)(17)}}{2(1)}$

$= \frac{2 \pm \sqrt{-64}}{2}$

$= \frac{2 \pm 8i}{2}$

$= 1 \pm 4i$

$-\frac{3}{2}, 1 + 4i, 1 - 4i$

31.

$$\begin{array}{r|rrrr} \frac{1}{2} & 2 & -17 & 90 & -41 \\ & & 1 & -8 & 41 \\ \hline & 2 & -16 & 82 & 0 \end{array}$$

$$\begin{aligned} 2x^2 - 16x + 82 &= 0 \\ x^2 - 8x + 41 &= 0 \\ x &= \frac{-(-8) \pm \sqrt{(-8)^2 - 4(1)(41)}}{2(1)} \\ &= \frac{8 \pm \sqrt{-100}}{2} \\ &= \frac{8 \pm 10i}{2} \\ &= 4 \pm 5i \end{aligned}$$

$\frac{1}{2}$, $4 + 5i$, $4 - 5i$

32. $(x - 2 - 3i)(x - 2 + 3i) = x^2 - 4x + 4 - 9i^2$
$= x^2 - 4x + 13$

$$\begin{array}{r} x + 1 \\ x^2 - 4x + 13 \overline{\smash{)}\, x^3 - 3x^2 + 9x + 13} \\ \underline{x^3 - 4x^2 + 13x} \\ x^2 - 4x + 13 \\ \underline{x^2 - 4x + 13} \\ 0 \end{array}$$

-1, $2 + 3i$, $2 - 3i$

33. $(x - 3 - 2i)(x - 3 + 2i) = x^2 - 6x + 9 - 4i^2$
$= x^2 - 6x + 13$

$$\begin{array}{r} x^2 - 1 \\ x^2 - 6x + 13 \overline{\smash{)}\, x^4 - 6x^3 + 12x^2 + 6x - 13} \\ \underline{x^4 - 6x^3 + 13x^2} \\ -x^2 + 6x - 13 \\ \underline{-x^2 + 6x - 13} \\ 0 \end{array}$$

$x^2 - 1 = (x + 1)(x - 1)$

$x + 1 = 0$ or $x - 1 = 0$
$x = -1$ $\quad$ $x = 1$

-1, 1, $3 - 2i$, $3 + 2i$

34. $(x - 5 + i)(x - 5 - i) = x^2 - 10x + 25 - i^2$
$= x^2 - 10x + 26$

$$\begin{array}{r} x^2 - 5x - 6 \\ x^2 - 10x + 26 \overline{\smash{)}\, x^4 - 15x^3 + 70x^2 - 70x - 156} \\ \underline{x^4 - 10x^3 + 26x^2} \\ -5x^3 + 44x^2 - 70x \\ \underline{-5x^3 + 50x^2 - 130x} \\ -6x^2 + 60x - 156 \\ \underline{-6x^2 + 60x - 156} \\ 0 \end{array}$$

$x^2 - 5x - 6 = (x - 6)(x + 1)$

$x - 6 = 0$ or $x + 1 = 0$
$x = 6$ $\quad$ $x = -1$

$5 - i$, $5 + i$, 6, -1

35. $y = (x + 2)(x - 1)(x - 3)$
$= x^3 - 2x^2 - 5x + 6$

36. $y = (x - 2)(x - 4i)(x + 4i)$
$= x^3 - 2x^2 + 16x - 32$

37. $y = (x - 4i)(x + 4i)(x - 3)(x + 3)$
$= x^4 + 7x - 144$

38. $y = (x - 3)(x - 1 - i)(x - 1 + i)$
$= x^3 - 5x^2 + 8x - 6$

39. $y = (x - 2i)(x + 2i)(x - 3i)(x + 3i)(x - 1)$
$= x^5 - x^4 + 13x^3 - 13x^2 + 36x - 36$

40. $y = (x - 6)(x - 2 - 2i)(x - 2 + 2i)$
$= x^3 - 10x^2 + 32x - 48$

41. $(x + 2 + i)(x + 2 - i) = x^2 + 4x + 4 - i^2$
$= x^2 + 4x + 5$

$(x - 3)(x^2 + 4x + 5) = x^3 + x^2 - 7x - 15$

$k = 1$

42. Sample answer: The function could have two real roots, one of which must be a double root and it has two imaginary roots.

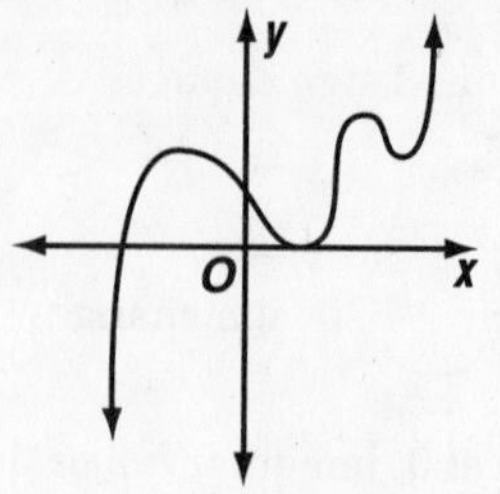

43a.

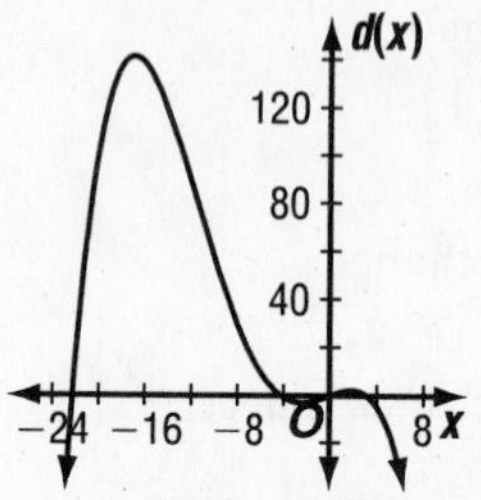

-22.3, -4.2, 0, 3.2

$$\begin{array}{r|rrrrr} -22.3 & -0.006 & -0.140 & -0.053 & 1.79 & 0 \\ & & 0.1338 & 0.13826 & -1.901 & 2.48 \\ \hline & -0.006 & -0.0062 & 0.08526 & -0.111 & 2.48 \end{array}$$

$$\begin{array}{r|rrrrr} -4.2 & -0.006 & -0.140 & -0.053 & 1.79 & 0 \\ & & 0.0252 & 0.482 & -1.806 & 0.0672 \\ \hline & -0.006 & -0.1148 & 0.429 & -0.016 & 0.0672 \end{array}$$

$$\begin{array}{r|rrrrr} 0 & -0.006 & -0.140 & -0.053 & 1.79 & 0 \\ & & 0 & 0 & 0 & 0 \\ \hline & -0.006 & -0.140 & -0.053 & 1.79 & 0 \end{array}$$

$$\begin{array}{r|rrrrr} 3.2 & -0.006 & -0.140 & -0.053 & 1.79 & 0 \\ & & -0.0192 & -0.509 & -1.80 & -0.03 \\ \hline & -0.006 & -0.1592 & -0.562 & -0.01 & -0.03 \end{array}$$

43b. 3.2, x represents the time in seconds and should be positive.

44.

$$\begin{array}{r|rrrr} 3 & -0.0374 & 0.1522 & 0.1729 & 0 \\ & & -0.1122 & 0.12 & 0.8787 \\ \hline & -0.0374 & 0.04 & 0.2929 & 0.8787 \end{array}$$

0.8787 liter

45.

x	$f(x)$
−3	−5
−2	9
−1	11
0	7
1	3
2	5

← zero between $x = -3$ and $x = -2$

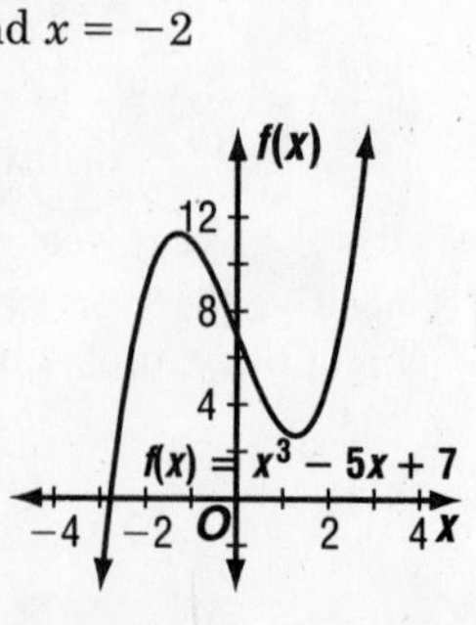

46. $x^2 + (y-3)^2 - 4x - 77 = 0$
$x^2 - 4x + 4 + (y-3)^2 = 77 + 4$
$(x-2)^2 + (y-3)^2 = 81$
center: (2, 3); radius: $\sqrt{81}$ or 9 units

47. $(x-3)(x+5) = x^2 + 2x - 15$

48. $\begin{bmatrix} -2 & \frac{2}{3} \\ -\frac{1}{4} & 3 \end{bmatrix} + \begin{bmatrix} 5 & \frac{4}{9} \\ \frac{1}{2} & -9 \end{bmatrix} = \begin{bmatrix} 3 & \frac{10}{9} \\ \frac{1}{4} & -6 \end{bmatrix}$

49.

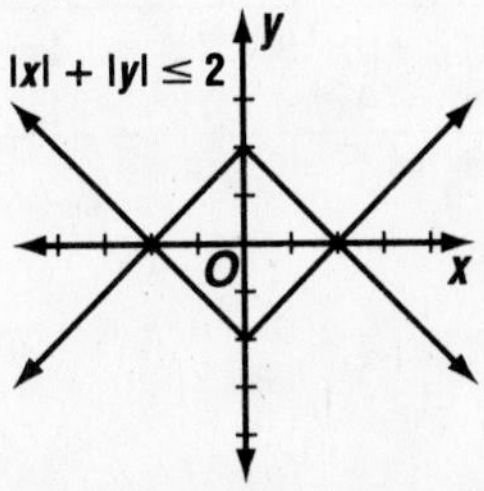

50.

ordered pair	$-2\lvert x\rvert - 5y < 3$	True or False
(7, −3)	$-2\lvert 7\rvert - 5(-3) < 3$	True
(−4, −1)	$-2\lvert -4\rvert - 5(-1) < 3$	True
(12, −6)	$-2\lvert 12\rvert - 5(-6) < 3$	False

(7, −3), (−4, −1)

51. $f(12) = \frac{19}{23-12}$
$= \frac{19}{11}$

52. $-4\lvert -5x\rvert + 17 = -4\lvert -5(2)\rvert + 17$
$= -4\lvert -10\rvert + 17$
$= -4(10) + 17$
$= -40 + 17$
$= -23$

Page 508 Self Test

1. $p(a^2) = 4(a^2)^3 - 3(a^2)^2 + 2(a^2) - 5$
$= 4a^6 - 3a^4 + 2a^2 - 5$

2. $p(x+1) = 4(x+1)^3 - 3(x+1)^2 + 2(x+1) - 5$
$= 4(x^3 + 3x^2 + 3x + 1) - 3(x^2 + 2x + 1) + 2x + 2 - 5$
$= 4x^3 + 12x^2 + 12x + 4 - 3x^2 - 6x - 3 + 2x + 2 - 5$
$= 4x^3 + 9x^2 + 8x - 2$

3.

3⌋	1	1	−24	36
		3	12	−36
	1	4	−12	0

$x^2 + 4x - 12 = 0$
$(x+6)(x-2) = 0$
$x + 6, x - 2$

4.

2⌋	2	13	1	−70
		4	34	70
	2	17	35	0

$2x^2 + 17x + 35 = 0$
$(2x+7)(x+5) = 0$
$2x + 7, x + 5$

5.

x	$g(x)$
−2	−37
−1	−6
0	−5
1	−4
2	27

← zero between $x = 1$ and $x = 2$

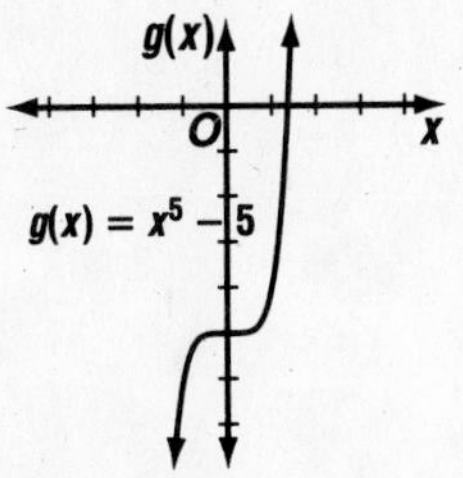

6.

x	$h(x)$
−2	−8
−1	2
0	4
1	4
2	8

← zero between $x = -2$ and $x = -1$

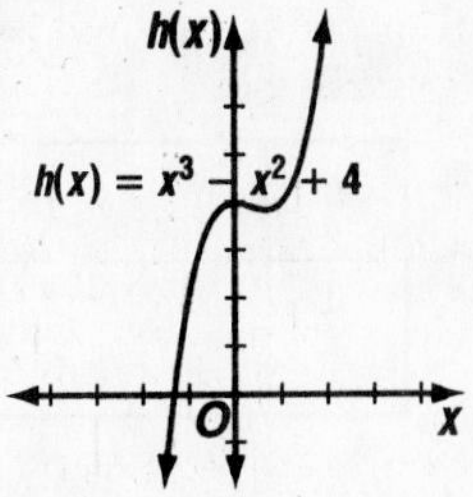

7. $f(x) = x^3 + 8x^2 - 7x + 10$; 2 sign changes
no yes yes

$f(-x) = (-x)^3 + 8(-x)^2 - 7(-x) + 10$
$= -x^3 + 8x^2 + 7x + 10$; 1 sign change
yes no no

positive: 2 or 0; negative: 1; imaginary: 0 or 2

8. $f(x) = 6x^4 + 18x^3 + 4x - 9$; 1 sign change
no no yes

$f(-x) = 6(-x)^4 + 18(-x)^3 + 4(-x) - 9$
$= 6x^4 - 18x^3 - 4x - 9$; 1 sign change
yes no no

positive: 1; negative: 1; imaginary: 2

9. even, 4

10. $V = \pi r^2 h$
$17.89 = \pi r^2(4r)$
$17.89 = 4r^3\pi$
$\frac{17.89}{4\pi} = r^3$
$1.125 \approx r$
$r \approx 1.125$ inches
$h = 4r \approx 4(1.125)$ or 4.5 inches

8-5 Rational Zero Theorem

Pages 512–513 Check for Understanding

1a. when leading coefficient is 1

1b. You limit the number of possible solutions.

2. Yes, if the length were 1, the width would be 1−1 or 0.

3. Sample answer: $f(x) = x^4 + 2x^3 - 3x^2 + 2x - 1$

4a. There are only 2 changes in sign for the coefficients of $p(x)$.

4b. There are no changes in sign for the coefficients of $p(x)$.

5. 1−10, 12, 14−15, 18, 20−21, 22, 24−25, 28, 30, 35, 36, 40, 42, 45, 50, 56, 60, 63, 70, 72, 75, 83, 84, 90 and 100.

6. Sample answer: $f(x) = 2x^2 + x + 3$

7. factors of p: ±1, ±2, ±3, ±6
factors of q: ±1
possible rational zeros: ±1, ±2, ±3, ±6

8. factors of p: $\pm1, \pm2$
factors of q: $\pm1, \pm2, \pm3, \pm6$
possible rational zeros: $\pm1, \pm2, \pm\frac{1}{2}, \pm\frac{1}{3}, \pm\frac{1}{6}, \pm\frac{2}{3}$

9. possible rational zeros: $\pm1, \pm2, \pm4, \pm7, \pm8, \pm14, \pm28, \pm56$

$\frac{p}{q}$	1	−1	−34	−56
−1	1	−2	−32	−24
−2	1	−3	−28	0 ← zero

$x^2 - 3x - 28 = 0$
$(x - 7)(x + 4) = 0$
$x - 7 = 0$ or $x + 4 = 0$
$x = 7$ $\quad x = -4$
$-2, -4, 7$

10. possible rational zeros: $\pm1, \pm2$

$\frac{p}{q}$	1	0	−3	−2
−1	1	−1	−2	0 ← zero

$x^2 - x - 2 = 0$
$(x - 2)(x + 1) = 0$
$x - 2 = 0$ or $x + 1 = 0$
$x = 2$ $\quad x = -1$
$-1, -1, 2$

11. possible rational zeros: $\pm1, \pm3$
$g(x) = x(x^3 - 3x^2 + x - 3)$
$x = 0$

$\frac{p}{q}$	1	−3	1	−3
1	1	−2	−1	−4
3	1	0	1	0 ← zero

$x^2 + 1 = 0$ no rational solutions
$0, 3$

12. possible rational zeros: $\pm1, \pm2, \pm\frac{1}{2}, \pm\frac{1}{3}, \pm\frac{1}{6}, \pm\frac{2}{3}$

$\frac{p}{q}$	6	11	−3	−2
−1	6	5	−8	6
−2	6	−1	−1	0 ← zero

$6x^2 - x - 1 = 0$
$(3x + 1)(2x - 1) = 0$
$3x + 1 = 0$ or $2x - 1 = 0$
$x = -\frac{1}{3}$ $\quad x = \frac{1}{2}$
$-\frac{1}{3}, \frac{1}{2}, -2$

13. possible rational zeros: $\pm1, \pm2, \pm3, \pm4, \pm6, \pm12, \pm\frac{4}{3}, \pm\frac{2}{3}, \pm\frac{1}{3}, \pm\frac{4}{9}, \pm\frac{2}{9}, \pm\frac{1}{9}$

$\frac{p}{q}$	9	0	−94	27	40	−12
1	9	9	−85	−58	−18	−30
2	9	18	−58	−89	−138	−288
3	9	27	−13	−12	4	0 ← zero
$\frac{2}{3}$	9	6	−90	−33	18	0 ← zero
$-\frac{2}{3}$	9	−6	−90	87	−18	0 ← zero

(Continued next column)

$$(x - 3)\left(x - \frac{2}{3}\right)\left(x + \frac{2}{3}\right) = (x - 3)\left(x^2 - \frac{4}{9}\right)$$
$$= x^3 - 3x^2 - \frac{4}{9}x + \frac{4}{3}$$

$$\begin{array}{r} 9x^2 + 27x - 9 \\ x^3 - 3x^2 - \frac{4}{9}x + \frac{4}{3}\overline{)\,9x^5 + 0x^4 - 94x^3 + 27x^2 + 40x - 12} \\ \underline{9x^5 - 27x^4 - 4x^3 + 12x^2} \\ 27x^4 - 90x^3 + 15x^2 + 40x \\ \underline{27x^4 - 81x^3 - 12x^2 + 36x} \\ -9x^3 + 27x^2 + 4x - 12 \\ \underline{-9x^3 + 27x^2 + 4x - 12} \\ 0 \end{array}$$

$9(x^2 + 3x - 1) = 0$
$$x = \frac{-3 \pm \sqrt{(3)^2 - 4(1)(-1)}}{2}$$
$$= \frac{-3 \pm \sqrt{13}}{2}$$
$3, \frac{2}{3}, -\frac{2}{3}, \frac{-3 \pm \sqrt{13}}{2}$

14. $f(x) = (x + 3)(x - 2)(x - 5)$
$= x^3 - 4x^2 - 11x + 30$

15. $V = \ell wh$
$384 = x(x + 4)(3x)$
$0 = 3x^3 + 12x^2 - 384$
$0 = x^3 + 4x^2 - 128$
possible rational zeros: $\pm1, \pm2, \pm4, \pm8, \pm16, \pm32, \pm64, \pm128$

$\frac{p}{q}$	1	4	0	−128
2	1	6	12	−104
4	1	8	32	0 ← zero

$x = 4$, $x + 4 = 4 + 4$ or 8, $3x = 3(4)$ or 12
12 centimeters by 8 centimeters by 4 centimeters

Pages 513–514 Exercises

16. factors of p: $\pm1, \pm2$
factors of q: ±1
possible rational zeros: $\pm1, \pm2$

17. factors of p: $\pm1, \pm2, \pm5, \pm10$
factors of q: ±1
possible rational zeros: $\pm1, \pm2, \pm5, \pm10$

18. factors of p: $\pm1, \pm2, \pm3, \pm6, \pm9, \pm18$
factors of q: ±1
possible rational zeros: $\pm1, \pm2, \pm3, \pm6, \pm9, \pm18$

19. factors of p: $\pm1, \pm3$
factors of q: $\pm1, \pm3$
possible rational zeros: $\pm1, \pm3, \pm\frac{1}{3}$

20. factors of p: $\pm1, \pm3, \pm5, \pm15$
factors of q: $\pm1, \pm3$
possible rational zeros: $\pm1, \pm3, \pm5, \pm15, \pm\frac{1}{3}, \pm\frac{5}{3}$

21. factors of p: $\pm1, \pm3, \pm9, \pm27$
factors of q: $\pm1, \pm3, \pm9$
possible rational zeros: $\pm1, \pm\frac{1}{3}, \pm\frac{1}{9}, \pm3, \pm9, \pm27$

22. possible rational zeros: ±1, ±2, ±4, ±7, ±8, ±14, ±28, ±56

$\frac{p}{q}$	1	−5	−22	56
1	1	−4	−26	30
2	1	−3	−28	0 ← zero

$x^2 - 3x - 28 = 0$
$(x - 7)(x + 4) = 0$
$x - 7 = 0$ or $x + 4 = 0$
$x = 7$ $\quad x = -4$
−4, 2, 7

23. possible rational zeros: ± 1, ± 2, ± 3, ± 4, ± 5, ± 6, ± 10, ± 12, ± 15, ± 20, ± 25, ± 30, ± 50, ± 60, ± 75, ± 100, ± 150, ± 300

$\frac{p}{q}$	1	1	−80	−300
5	1	6	−50	−550
10	1	11	30	0 ← zero

$x^2 + 11x + 30 = 0$
$(x + 5)(x + 6) = 0$
$x + 5 = 0$ or $x + 6 = 0$
$x = -5$ $\quad x = -6$
10, −5, −6

24. possible rational zeros: ± 1, ± 3, ± 9
$g(x) = x(x^3 - 3x^2 - 53x - 9)$
$x = 0$

$\frac{p}{q}$	1	−3	−53	−9
3	1	0	−53	−168
9	1	6	1	0 ← zero

$x^2 + 6x + 1 = 0$
not factorable, no rational zeros
0, 0, 9

25. possible rational zeros: ±1, ±3, ±9, $\pm\frac{9}{2}$, $\pm\frac{3}{2}$, $\pm\frac{1}{2}$

$\frac{p}{q}$	2	−11	12	9
1	2	−9	3	12
3	2	−5	−3	0 ← zero

$2x^2 - 5x - 3 = 0$
$(2x + 1)(x - 3) = 0$
$2x + 1 = 0$ or $x - 3 = 0$
$2x = -1$ $\quad x = 3$
$x = -\frac{1}{2}$
$-\frac{1}{2}$, 3, 3

26. possible rational zeros: ±1, $\pm\frac{1}{2}$

$\frac{p}{q}$	2	−1	0	0	−2	1
1	2	1	1	1	−1	0 ← zero
−1	2	−3	3	−3	1	0 ← zero
$\frac{1}{2}$	2	0	0	0	−2	0 ← zero
$-\frac{1}{2}$	2	−2	1	$-\frac{1}{2}$	$-\frac{7}{4}$	$\frac{15}{8}$

1, −1, $\frac{1}{2}$

27. possible rational zeros: ±1, ±2, ±4, ±8

$\frac{p}{q}$	1	10	33	38	8
−1	1	9	24	14	−6
−2	1	8	17	4	0 ← zero
−4	1	6	9	2	0 ← zero

$(x + 2)(x + 4) = x^2 + 6x + 8$

$$
\begin{array}{r}
x^2 + 4x + 1 \\
x^2 + 6x + 8\overline{)x^4 + 10x^3 + 33x^2 + 38x + 8} \\
\underline{x^4 + 6x^3 + 8x^2} \qquad\qquad \\
4x^3 + 25x^2 + 38x \quad\; \\
\underline{4x^3 + 24x^2 + 32x} \quad\; \\
x^2 + 6x + 8 \\
\underline{x^2 + 6x + 8} \\
0
\end{array}
$$

$x^2 + 4x + 1 = 0$
not factorable, no rational zeros
−2, −4

28. possible rational zeros: ±1, ±2

$\frac{p}{q}$	1	0	1	0	−2
1	1	1	2	2	0 ← zero
2	1	2	5	10	18
−1	1	−1	2	−2	0 ← zero

$(x + 1)(x - 1) = x^2 - 1$

$$
\begin{array}{r}
x^2 + 2 \qquad\quad \\
x^2 - 1\overline{)x^4 + 0x^3 + x^2 + 0x - 2} \\
\underline{x^4 \qquad\quad - x^2} \qquad\quad \\
2x^2 + 0x - 2 \\
\underline{2x^2 \qquad - 2} \\
0
\end{array}
$$

$x^2 + 2 = 0$
not factorable, no rational zeros
1, −1

29. possible rational zeros: ±1, ±2, ±3, ±4, ±6, ±9, ±12, ±18, ±36

$\frac{p}{q}$	1	0	−13	0	36
2	1	2	−9	−18	0 ← zero
3	1	3	−4	−12	0 ← zero

$(x - 2)(x - 3) = x^2 - 5x + 6$

$$
\begin{array}{r}
x^2 + 5x + 6 \\
x^2 - 5x + 6\overline{)x^4 + 0x^3 - 13x^2 + 0x + 36} \\
\underline{x^4 - 5x^3 + 6x^2} \qquad\qquad \\
5x^3 - 19x^2 \qquad\qquad \\
\underline{5x^3 - 25x^2 + 30x} \quad\; \\
6x^2 - 30x + 36 \\
\underline{6x^2 - 30x + 36} \\
0
\end{array}
$$

$x^2 + 5x + 6 = 0$
$(x + 2)(x + 3) = 0$
$x + 2 = 0$ or $x + 3 = 0$
$x = -2$ $\quad x = -3$
2, −2, 3, −3

30. possible rational zeros: $\pm 1, \pm 2, \pm 4$

$\frac{p}{q}$	1	−3	−5	3	4	
1	1	−2	−7	−4	0	← zero
−1	1	−4	−1	4	0	← zero

$(x+1)(x-1) = x^2 - 1$

$$\begin{array}{r} x^2 - 3x - 4 \\ x^2 - 1 \overline{) x^4 - 3x^3 - 5x^2 + 3x + 4} \\ \underline{x^4 \qquad\quad - x^2 \qquad\qquad} \\ -3x^3 - 4x^2 + 3x \quad \\ \underline{-3x^3 \qquad + 3x} \quad \\ -4x^2 + 4 \\ \underline{-4x^2 + 4} \\ 0 \end{array}$$

$x^2 - 3x - 4 = 0$

$(x-4)(x+1) = 0$

$x - 4 = 0$ or $x + 1 = 0$

$x = 4$ $\quad x = -1$

1, −1, −1, 4

31. possible rational zeros: $\pm 1, \pm 3, \pm 7, \pm 21$

$\frac{p}{q}$	1	3	−25	21	
1	1	4	−21	0	← zero

$x^2 + 4x - 21 = 0$

$(x+7)(x-3) = 0$

$x + 7 = 0$ or $x - 3 = 0$

$x = -7$ $\quad x = 3$

1, −7, 3

32. possible rational zeros: $\pm 1, \pm 2, \pm 4, \pm 8$

$f(x) = x(x^4 - 6x^2 + 8)$

$x = 0$

$\frac{p}{q}$	1	0	−6	0	8	
1	1	1	−5	−5	3	
2	1	2	−2	−4	0	← zero
−2	1	−2	−2	4	0	← zero

$(x+2)(x-2) = x^2 - 4$

$$\begin{array}{r} x^2 - 2 \qquad\qquad \\ x^2 - 4 \overline{) x^4 + 0x^3 - 6x^2 + 0x + 8} \\ \underline{x^4 \qquad\quad - 4x^2 \qquad\qquad} \\ -2x^2 \qquad + 8 \\ \underline{-2x^2 \qquad + 8} \\ 0 \end{array}$$

$x^2 - 2 = 0$

not factorable, no rational zeros

0, 2, −2

33. possible rational zeros: $\pm 1, \pm 3, \pm\frac{1}{2}, \pm\frac{1}{4}, \pm\frac{1}{6}, \pm\frac{1}{8}, \pm\frac{1}{12}, \pm\frac{1}{16}, \pm\frac{1}{24}, \pm\frac{1}{48}, \pm\frac{3}{2}, \pm\frac{3}{4}, \pm\frac{3}{8}, \pm\frac{3}{16}$

$\frac{p}{q}$	48	−52	0	13	−3	
1	48	−4	−4	9	6	
$\frac{1}{2}$	48	−28	−14	6	0	← zero
$\frac{1}{3}$	48	−36	−12	9	0	← zero

(Continued next column)

$(2x-1)(3x-1) = 6x^2 - 5x + 1$

$$\begin{array}{r} 8x^2 - 2x - 3 \\ 6x^2 - 5x + 1 \overline{) 48x^4 - 52x^3 + 0x^2 + 13x - 3} \\ \underline{48x^4 - 40x^3 + 8x^2 \qquad\qquad\quad} \\ -12x^3 - 8x^2 + 13x \quad\;\; \\ \underline{-12x^3 + 10x^2 - 2x} \quad\;\; \\ -18x^2 + 15x - 3 \\ \underline{-18x^2 + 15x - 3} \\ 0 \end{array}$$

$8x^2 - 2x - 3 = 0$

$(4x-3)(2x+1) = 0$

$4x - 3 = 0$ or $2x + 1 = 0$

$x = \frac{3}{4}$ $\quad x = -\frac{1}{2}$

$\frac{1}{2}, -\frac{1}{2}, \frac{1}{3}, \frac{3}{4}$

34. possible rational zeros: $\pm 1, \pm 2, \pm\frac{1}{2}, \pm\frac{1}{3}, \pm\frac{2}{3}, \pm\frac{1}{6}$

$\frac{p}{q}$	6	5	−9	2	
1	6	11	2	4	
$\frac{2}{3}$	6	9	−3	0	← zero

$6x^2 + 9x - 3 = 0$

$3(2x^2 + 3x - 1) = 0$

$x = \frac{-3 \pm \sqrt{(3)^2 - 4(2)(-1)}}{2(2)}$

$= \frac{-3 \pm \sqrt{17}}{4}$

$\frac{2}{3}, \frac{-3 \pm \sqrt{17}}{4}$

35. possible rational zeros: $\pm 1, \pm 2, \pm 5, \pm 8, \pm 10, \pm 20, \pm 40, \pm\frac{1}{2}, \pm\frac{1}{3}, \pm\frac{1}{6}, \pm\frac{2}{3}, \pm\frac{5}{2}, \pm\frac{5}{3}, \pm\frac{5}{6}, \pm\frac{8}{3}, \pm\frac{4}{3}, \pm\frac{10}{3}, \pm\frac{20}{3}, \pm\frac{40}{3}$

$\frac{p}{q}$	6	22	11	−38	−40	
−2	6	10	−9	−20	0	← zero
$\frac{4}{3}$	6	30	51	30	0	← zero

$(x+2)(3x-4) = 0$

$3x^2 + 2x - 8 = 0$

$$\begin{array}{r} 2x^2 + 6x + 5 \\ 3x^2 + 2x - 8 \overline{) 6x^4 + 22x^3 + 11x^2 - 38x - 40} \\ \underline{6x^4 + \;\, 4x^3 - 16x^2 \qquad\qquad\quad} \\ 18x^3 + 27x^2 - 38x \quad\;\; \\ \underline{18x^3 + 12x^2 - 48x} \quad\;\; \\ 15x^2 + 10x - 40 \\ \underline{15x^2 + 10x - 40} \\ 0 \end{array}$$

$2x^2 + 6x + 5 = 0$

$x = \frac{-6 \pm \sqrt{(6)^2 - 4(2)(5)}}{2(2)}$

$= \frac{-6 \pm \sqrt{-4}}{4}$

$= \frac{-6 \pm 2i}{4}$

$= \frac{-3 \pm i}{2}$

$-2, \frac{4}{3}, \frac{-3 \pm i}{2}$

36. possible rational zeros: $\pm1, \pm2, \pm4, \pm7, \pm14, \pm28, \pm\frac{1}{5}, \pm\frac{2}{5}, \pm\frac{4}{5}, \pm\frac{7}{5}, \pm\frac{14}{5}, \pm\frac{28}{5}$

$g(x) = x(5x^3 - 29x^2 + 55x - 28)$

$x = 0$

$\frac{p}{q}$	5	−29	55	−28
1	5	−24	31	3
$\frac{1}{5}$	5	−28	$\frac{247}{5}$	$-\frac{453}{25}$
$\frac{4}{5}$	5	−25	35	0 ← zero

$5x^2 - 25x + 35 = 0$

$5(x^2 - 5x + 7) = 0$

$x = \frac{-(-5) \pm \sqrt{(-5)^2 - 4(1)(7)}}{2(1)}$

$= \frac{5 \pm \sqrt{-3}}{2}$

$= \frac{5 \pm i\sqrt{3}}{2}$

$0, \frac{4}{5}, \frac{5 \pm i\sqrt{3}}{2}$

37. possible rational zeros: $\pm1, \pm2, \pm5, \pm10$

$\frac{p}{q}$	1	−2	−12	−12	−13	−10
−1	1	−3	−9	−3	−10	0 ← zero
−2	1	−4	−4	−4	−5	0 ← zero
2	1	0	−12	−36	−85	−180
5	1	3	3	3	2	0 ← zero

$(x + 1)(x + 2)(x - 5) = x^3 - 2x^2 - 13x - 10$

$$\begin{array}{r} x^2 + 1 \\ x^3 - 2x^2 - 13x - 10 \overline{)\, x^5 - 2x^4 - 12x^3 - 12x^2 - 13x - 10} \\ \underline{x^5 - 2x^4 - 13x^3 - 10x^2} \\ x^3 - 2x^2 - 13x - 10 \\ \underline{x^3 - 2x^2 - 13x - 10} \\ 0 \end{array}$$

$x^2 + 1 = 0$

$x^2 = -1$

$x = \pm i$

$-1, -2, 5, i, -i$

38.

	1	4	$9k$	−90
k	1	$4 + k$	$k^2 + 13k$	$k^3 + 13k^2 - 90 = 0$
$2k$	1	$4 + 2k$	$4k^2 + 17k$	$8k^3 + 34k^2 - 90 = 0$

$-8k^3 - 104k^2 + 720 = 0$

$\underline{(+)\ 8k^3 + 34k^2 - 90 = 0}$

$-70k^2 + 630 = 0$

$-70k^2 = -630$

$k^2 = 9$

$k = \pm 3; k = -3, k \neq 3$

$f(x) = x^3 + 4x^2 - 27x - 90$

−3	1	4	−27	−90
		−3	−3	90
	1	1	−30	0

$x^2 + x - 30 = 0$

$(x + 6)(x - 5) = 0$

$x + 6 = 0$ or $x - 5 = 0$

$x = -6$ $\quad x = 5$

$k = -3; -3, -6, 5$

39a. at 2:30 P.M. $x = 10$

10	−0.002	0.05	−0.3	−0.4	63
		−0.02	0.3	0	−4
	−0.002	0.03	0	−0.4	59

\$59

39b. They are the same.

40. $V = \frac{1}{3}\pi r^2 h$

$5.24 = \frac{1}{3}\pi r^2(r + 4)$

$0 = \frac{1}{3}\pi r^3 + \frac{4}{3}\pi r^2 - 5.24$

	$\frac{1}{3}\pi$	$\frac{4}{3}\pi$	0	−5.24
1	$\frac{\pi}{3}$	$\frac{5\pi}{3}$	$\frac{5\pi}{3}$	−0.004 ← zero
2	$\frac{\pi}{3}$	2π	4π	19.89

$r = 1$ inch, $h = 1 + 4$ or 5 inches

41a.

5	1	−6	23	−18	24
		5	−5	90	360
	1	−1	18	72	384

$\frac{384}{24} = 16$ regions

41b.

	1	−6	23	−18	24	
7	1	1	30	192	1368	÷ 24 = 57
8	1	2	39	294	2376	÷ 24 = 99

8 points

42. $f(x) = (x + 2)(x - 2 - 3i)(x - 2 + 3i)$

$= x^3 - 2x^2 + 5x + 26$

43. $2y^2 = 14x$

$\frac{1}{7}y^2 = x$

$x = \frac{1}{7}y^2$

44. $c^2 - 9c - 58 = -7c + 5$

$c^2 - 2c - 63 = 0$

$(c - 9)(c + 7) = 0$

$c - 9 = 0$ or $c + 7 = 0$

$c = 9$ $\quad c = -7$

45. $F_c = m\left(\frac{4\pi^2 r}{T^2}\right)$

$F_c T^2 = 4\pi^2 mr$

$T^2 = 4\pi^2 mr$

$\sqrt{T^2} = \sqrt{\frac{4\pi^2 mr}{F_c}}$

$T = \frac{2\pi\sqrt{mr}}{\sqrt{F_c}}$

$T = \frac{2\pi\sqrt{mrF_c}}{F_c}$

46. $\left[\begin{array}{ccc|c} 5 & -7 & 1 & 29 \\ -2 & -3 & 5 & 20 \\ 1 & -9 & 3 & 13 \end{array}\right] = \left[\begin{array}{ccc|c} 1 & -9 & 3 & 13 \\ -2 & -3 & 5 & 20 \\ 5 & -7 & 1 & 29 \end{array}\right]$

$= \left[\begin{array}{ccc|c} 1 & -9 & 3 & 13 \\ 0 & -21 & 11 & 46 \\ 5 & -7 & 1 & 29 \end{array}\right] = \left[\begin{array}{ccc|c} 1 & -9 & 3 & 13 \\ 0 & -21 & 11 & 46 \\ 0 & 38 & -14 & -36 \end{array}\right]$

$= \left[\begin{array}{ccc|c} 1 & -9 & 3 & 13 \\ 0 & 1 & -\frac{11}{21} & -\frac{46}{21} \\ 0 & 38 & -14 & -36 \end{array}\right] = \left[\begin{array}{ccc|c} 1 & 0 & -\frac{36}{21} & -\frac{141}{21} \\ 0 & 1 & -\frac{11}{21} & -\frac{46}{21} \\ 0 & 38 & -14 & -36 \end{array}\right]$

$= \left[\begin{array}{ccc|c} 1 & 0 & -\frac{36}{21} & -\frac{141}{21} \\ 0 & 1 & -\frac{11}{21} & -\frac{46}{21} \\ 0 & 0 & \frac{124}{21} & \frac{992}{21} \end{array}\right] = \left[\begin{array}{ccc|c} 1 & 0 & -\frac{36}{21} & -\frac{141}{21} \\ 0 & 1 & -\frac{11}{21} & -\frac{46}{21} \\ 0 & 0 & 1 & 8 \end{array}\right]$

$= \left[\begin{array}{ccc|c} 1 & 0 & -\frac{36}{21} & -\frac{141}{21} \\ 0 & 1 & 0 & 2 \\ 0 & 0 & 1 & 8 \end{array}\right] = \left[\begin{array}{ccc|c} 1 & 0 & 0 & 7 \\ 0 & 1 & 0 & 2 \\ 0 & 0 & 1 & 8 \end{array}\right]$ (7, 2, 8)

47. $-5x = 15y$ $9x + 4 = -31x$

$x = -3y$ $9(-3y) + 4 = -31y$

$-27y + 4 = -31y$ $x = -3y$

$4 = -4y$ $x = -3(-1)$

$-1 = y$ $x = 3$

(3, −1)

48. $f(-3, 7) = 9(-3) - 3(7)$

$= -27 - 21$

$= -48$

49. $\frac{y}{8} = \frac{1}{2}$

$2y = 8$

$y = 4$; 4 feet

50. Max: 17 years old
Margie: 6 + 17 or 23 years old
Moira: 23 − 19 or 4 years old

8-6 Using Quadratic Techniques to Solve Polynomial Equations

Pages 517–518 Check for Understanding

1. Only one root is real.
2. Sample answer: Square each side, write equation in quadratic form, and factor.
3. See students' work.
4. $x^4 - 3x^3 + 6x^2 = x^2(x^2 - 3x + 6)$
   quadratic factor: $x^2 - 3x + 6$
5. $2x^3 + 7x^2 - 8x = x(2x^2 + 7x - 8)$
   quadratic factor: $2x^2 + 7x - 8$
6. $4m^3 + 9m - 16m^2 = 4m^3 - 16m^2 + 9m$
   $= m(4m^2 - 16m + 9)$
   quadratic factor: $4m^2 - 16m + 9$
7. $y^3 - y^5 - 100y = -y^5 + y^3 - 100y$
   $= -y(y^4 - y^2 + 100)$
8. $x^7 + x^{\frac{7}{2}} + x^5 = x^7 + x^5 + x^{\frac{7}{2}}$
   $= x^5(x^2 + 1 + x^{\frac{-3}{2}})$
9. $x^3 - 729 = (x - 9)(x^2 + 9x + 81)$
   quadratic factor: $x^2 + 9x + 81$
10. $3(\sqrt{r})^2 + 7(\sqrt{r}) - 11 = 0$
11. $(a^4)^2 + 10(a^4) - 16 = 0$
12. $x - 16x^{\frac{1}{2}} = -64$

$(x^{\frac{1}{2}})^2 - 16(x^{\frac{1}{2}}) + 64 = 0$

$(x^{\frac{1}{2}} - 8)(x^{\frac{1}{2}} - 8) = 0$

$(x^{\frac{1}{2}} - 8)^2 = 0$

$x^{\frac{1}{2}} - 8 = 0$

$x^{\frac{1}{2}} = 8$

$(x^{\frac{1}{2}})^2 = (8)^2$

$x = 64$

13. $m^4 + 7m^3 + 12m^2 = 0$

$m^2(m^2 + 7m + 12) = 0$

$m^2(m + 3)(m + 4) = 0$

$m^2 = 0$ or $m + 3 = 0$ or $m + 4 = 0$

$m = 0$ $m = -3$ $m = -4$

14. $3m^{\frac{3}{2}} - 81 = 0$

$3(m^{\frac{3}{2}} - 27) = 0$

$m^{\frac{3}{2}} - 27 = 0$

$m^{\frac{3}{2}} = 27$

$(m^{\frac{3}{2}})^{\frac{2}{3}} = (27)^{\frac{2}{3}}$

$m = 9$

15. $y^3 = 26.6y - 3.2y^2$

$y^3 + 3.2y^2 - 26.6y = 0$

$y(y^2 + 3.2y - 26.6) = 0$

$y(y - 3.8)(y + 7) = 0$

$y = 0$ or $y - 3.8 = 0$ or $y + 7 = 0$

$y = 3.8$ $y = -7$

16. Let w = the width, then $h = w - 2$ and $\ell = w + 4$.

$V = \ell wh$

$8\ell = \ell wh$

$8(w + 4) = (w + 4)(w)(w - 2)$

$8w + 32 = w(w^2 + 2w - 8)$

$8w + 32 = w^3 + 2w^2 - 8w$

$0 = w^3 + 2w^2 - 16w - 32$

$0 = w^2(w + 2) - 16(w + 2)$

$0 = (w^2 - 16)(w + 2)$

$0 = (w + 4)(w - 4)(w + 2)$

$w + 4 = 0$ or $w - 4 = 0$ or $w + 2 = 0$

$w = -4$ $w = 4$ $w = -2$

w = 4 centimeters, h = 4 − 2 or 2 centimeters, ℓ = 4 + 4 or 8 centimeters

Pages 518–519 Exercises

17. $x^8 + 10x^4 + 13.2 = 0$

$(x^4)^2 + 10(x^4) + 13.2 = 0$

18. $11x^4 + 3x + 8 = 0$

impossible; $(x^4)^{\frac{1}{2}} \neq x$

19. $84n^4 - 62n^2 = 0$

$84(n^2)^2 - 62(n^2) = 0$

20. $7q + 8\sqrt{q} - 13 = 0$
$7(\sqrt{q})^2 + 8(\sqrt{q}) - 13 = 0$

21. $5y^4 + 7y - 8 = 0$
impossible; $(y^4)^{\frac{1}{2}} \neq y$

22. $11n^4 + 44n^2 = 0$
$11(n^2)^2 + 44(n^2) = 0$

23. $x^3 - 3x^2 - 10x = 0$
$x(x^2 - 3x - 10) = 0$
$x(x - 5)(x + 2) = 0$
$x = 0$ or $x - 5 = 0$ or $x + 2 = 0$
$x = 5$ $x = -2$

24. $n^3 + 12n^2 + 32n = 0$
$n(n^2 + 12n + 32) = 0$
$n(n + 4)(n + 8) = 0$
$n = 0$ or $n + 4 = 0$ or $n + 8 = 0$
$n = -4$ $n = -8$

25. $b^3 = 1331$
$b^3 - 1331 = 0$
$(b - 11)(b^2 + 11b + 121) = 0$
$b - 11 = 0$ or $b^2 + 11b + 121 = 0$
$b = 11$ $b = \frac{-11 \pm \sqrt{121 - 4(1)(121)}}{2(1)}$
$= \frac{-11 \pm \sqrt{-363}}{2}$
$= \frac{-11 \pm 11i\sqrt{3}}{2}$

26. $m^4 - 7m^2 + 12 = 0$
$(m^2)^2 - 7(m^2) + 12 = 0$
$(m^2 - 4)(m^2 - 3) = 0$
$(m + 2)(m - 2)(m^2 - 3) = 0$
$m + 2 = 0$ or $m - 2 = 0$ or $m^2 - 3 = 0$
$m = -2$ $m = 2$ $m^2 = 3$
$m = \pm\sqrt{3}$

27. $z - 8\sqrt{z} - 240 = 0$
$(\sqrt{z})^2 - 8(\sqrt{z}) - 240 = 0$
$(\sqrt{z} + 12)(\sqrt{z} - 20) = 0$
$\sqrt{z} + 12 = 0$ $\sqrt{z} - 20 = 0$
$\sqrt{z} = -12$ $\sqrt{z} = 20$
$(\sqrt{z})^2 = (-12)^2$ $(\sqrt{z})^2 = (20)^2$
$z = 144$ $z = 400$
check: $z - 8\sqrt{z} - 240 = 0$
$144 - 8\sqrt{144} - 240 \stackrel{?}{=} 0$
$144 - 96 - 240 \stackrel{?}{=} 0$
$-192 \neq 0$
$z - 8\sqrt{z} - 240 = 0$
$400 - 8\sqrt{400} - 240 \stackrel{?}{=} 0$
$400 - 160 - 240 \stackrel{?}{=} 0$
$0 = 0$ ✓

28. $y^3 - 729 = 0$
$(y - 9)(y^2 + 9y + 81) = 0$
$y - 9 = 0$ or $y^2 + 9y + 81 = 0$
$y = 9$ $y = \frac{-9 \pm \sqrt{(9)^2 - 4(1)(81)}}{2(1)}$
$= \frac{-9 \pm \sqrt{-243}}{2}$
$= \frac{-9 \pm 9i\sqrt{3}}{2}$

29. $y^{\frac{2}{3}} - 9y^{\frac{1}{3}} + 20 = 0$
$(y^{\frac{1}{3}})^2 - 9(y^{\frac{1}{3}}) + 20 = 0$
$(y^{\frac{1}{3}} - 5)(y^{\frac{1}{3}} - 4) = 0$
$y^{\frac{1}{3}} - 5 = 0$ or $y^{\frac{1}{3}} - 4 = 0$
$y^{\frac{1}{3}} = 5$ $y^{\frac{1}{3}} = 4$
$(y^{\frac{1}{3}})^3 = (5)^3$ $(y^{\frac{1}{3}})^3 = 4^3$
$y = 125$ $y = 64$

30. $r - 19r^{\frac{1}{2}} + 60 = 0$
$(r^{\frac{1}{2}})^2 - 19(r^{\frac{1}{2}}) + 60 = 0$
$(r^{\frac{1}{2}} - 15)(r^{\frac{1}{2}} - 4) = 0$
$r^{\frac{1}{2}} - 15 = 0$ or $r^{\frac{1}{2}} - 4 = 0$
$r^{\frac{1}{2}} = 15$ $r^{\frac{1}{2}} = 4$
$(r^{\frac{1}{2}})^2 = (15)^2$ $(r^{\frac{1}{2}})^2 = (4)^2$
$r = 225$ $r = 16$

31. $6.25m^3 - 12.25m = 0$
$m(6.25m^2 - 12.25) = 0$
$m = 0$ or $6.25m^2 = 12.25$
$m^2 = 1.96$
$\sqrt{m^2} = \pm\sqrt{1.96}$
$m = \pm 1.4$

32. $y^{\frac{1}{3}} = 7.5$
$(y^{\frac{1}{3}})^3 = (7.5)^3$
$y = 421.875$

33. $m^5 + 1.5m^4 = 15.04m^3$
$m^5 + 1.5m^4 - 15.04m^3 = 0$
$m^3(m^2 + 1.5m - 15.04) = 0$
$m^3(m - 3.2)(m + 4.7) = 0$
$m^3 = 0$ $m - 3.2 = 0$ $m + 4.7 = 0$
$m = 0$ $m = 3.2$ $m = -4.7$

34. $p^{\frac{2}{3}} + 11p^{\frac{1}{3}} + 28 = 0$
$(p^{\frac{1}{3}})^2 + 11(p^{\frac{1}{3}}) + 28 = 0$
$(p^{\frac{1}{3}} + 4)(p^{\frac{1}{3}} + 7) = 0$
$p^{\frac{1}{3}} + 4 = 0$ or $p^{\frac{1}{3}} + 7 = 0$
$p^{\frac{1}{3}} = -4$ $p^{\frac{1}{3}} = -7$
$(p^{\frac{1}{3}})^3 = (-4)^3$ $(p^{\frac{1}{3}})^3 = (-7)^3$
$p = -64$ $p = -343$
$-64, -343$

35. $x(x + 3)(x - 2) = 0$
$x(x^2 + x - 6) = 0$
$x^3 + x^2 - 6x = 0$

36. Sample answer: Write the equation in quadratic form, factor, use the zero product property to solve for a.
$(|a - 3|)^2 - 9(|a - 3|) + 8 = 0$
$(|a - 3| - 8)(|a - 3| - 1) = 0$
$|a - 3| - 8 = 0$ or $|a - 3| - 1 = 0$
$|a - 3| = 8$ $|a - 3| = 1$
$a - 3 = 8$ or $a - 3 = -8$ or $a - 3 = 1$ or $a - 3 = -1$
$a = 11$ $a = -5$ $a = 4$ $a = 2$

37. $A = \pi ab \qquad b = 2.3 + a$

$$8.85 = \pi(a)(2.3 + a)$$
$$0 = \pi a^2 + 2.3\pi a - 8.85$$
$$a = \frac{-2.3\pi \pm \sqrt{(2.3\pi)^2 - 4(\pi)(-8.85)}}{2\pi}$$
$$= \frac{-2.3\pi \pm \sqrt{163.42}}{2\pi}$$
$$= \frac{-2.3\pi \pm 12.78}{2\pi}$$

≈ 0.885; 0.885 inch

b $\approx 0.885 + 2.3$ or 3.185 inches

38a. Perimeter of a square = $4s$

Perimeter of an equilateral triangle = $3s$

$7s < 50$

$s < \frac{50}{7}$

1 inch, 2 inches, 3 inches, 4 inches, 5 inches, 6 inches, 7 inches

38b. 7(1) or 7 inches **38c.** 7(7) or 49 inches

39a.
$$(3960 + r)^2 = \frac{3960^2 \cdot 140}{120}$$
$$(3960 + r)^2 = 18295200$$
$$\sqrt{(3960 + r)^2} = \sqrt{18295200}$$
$$3960 + r \approx 4277.29$$
$r \approx 317.29$; 317.29 miles

39b.
$$(3960 + 99)^2 = \frac{3960^2 \cdot 125}{W_s}$$
$$16475481W_s = 1{,}960{,}200{,}000$$
$W_s \approx 119$; 119 pounds

40. Let s = the length of the base and $h = s + 3$.

$V = \ell wh$

$200 = s^2(s + 3)$

$200 = s^3 + 3s^2$

$0 = s^3 + 3s^2 - 200$

5	1	3	0	−200
		5	40	200
	1	8	40	0

$s = 5$, $h = 5 + 3$ or 8

5 inches by 5 inches by 8 inches

41.
$$d = \sqrt{(x_2 - x_1)^2 + (y_2 - y_1)^2}$$
$$5 = \sqrt{(7 - 3)^2 + (2 - c)^2}$$
$$25 = 4^2 + (2 - c)^2$$
$$25 = 16 + (2 - c)^2$$
$$9 = (2 - c)^2$$
$$\pm\sqrt{9} = \sqrt{(2 - c)^2}$$
$$\pm 3 = 2 - c$$
$$-2 \pm 3 = -c$$
$-2 + 3 = -c$ or $-2 - 3 = -c$

$1 = -c \qquad -5 = -c$

$-1 = c \qquad 5 = c$

42a.

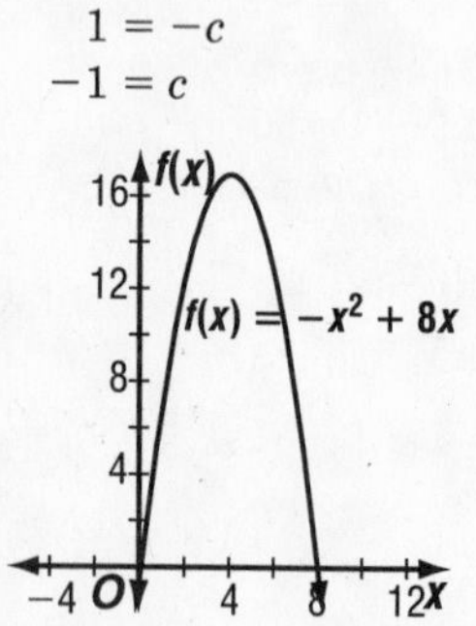

42b. $2 \le x \le 6$

42c. Sample answer: If few trees are planted, production will be low since there will be fewer trees producing apples. If many trees are planted, production might be low because there are more trees to maintain, with less time paid to production.

43.
$$t = \sqrt{\frac{2h}{g}}$$
$$= \sqrt{\frac{2 \cdot 64}{32}}$$
$= 4$ seconds

44.
$$\begin{bmatrix} -9 & 12 \\ 4 & -7 \end{bmatrix}\begin{bmatrix} 1 & 0 \\ 0 & 1 \end{bmatrix} = \begin{bmatrix} -9 & 12 \\ 4 & -7 \end{bmatrix}$$
$$m = \begin{bmatrix} 1 & 0 \\ 0 & 1 \end{bmatrix}$$

45.
$$x = \frac{\begin{vmatrix} \frac{7}{3} & -\frac{2}{3} \\ -50 & 4 \end{vmatrix}}{\begin{vmatrix} \frac{1}{2} & -\frac{2}{3} \\ 3 & 4 \end{vmatrix}} \qquad y = \frac{\begin{vmatrix} \frac{1}{2} & \frac{7}{3} \\ 3 & -50 \end{vmatrix}}{\begin{vmatrix} \frac{1}{2} & -\frac{2}{3} \\ 3 & 4 \end{vmatrix}}$$
$$= \frac{\frac{7}{3}(4) - (-50)\left(-\frac{2}{3}\right)}{\left(\frac{1}{2}\right)(4) - (3)\left(-\frac{2}{3}\right)} \qquad = \frac{\frac{1}{2}(-50) - (3)\left(\frac{7}{3}\right)}{\left(\frac{1}{2}\right)(4) - (3)\left(-\frac{2}{3}\right)}$$
$$= \frac{-24}{4} = -6 \qquad = \frac{-32}{4} = -8$$
$(-6, -8)$

46a.

Stem	Leaf
3	5
4	6
5	1 4
6	5
7	0 6
8	3 4 6 7

4 | 6 = 46

46b. 4 **46c.** 87% **46d.** 35%

8-7 Composition of Functions

Page 523 Check for Understanding

1. g of h of x **2.** 5, 12

3a. domain of g: 1, 17, 6

range of g: 28, 4, 9

domain of f: 28, 4, 9

range of f: 5, 2, 13

3b. $g = \{(1, 28), (17, 9), (6, 4)\}$

$f = \{(28, 5), (4, 2), (9, 13)\}$

3c. $[g \circ f]\,(x)$ does not exist because the range of f is not a subset of the domain of g.

4. quadratic

5.
$$[f \circ g]\,(x) = f[g(x)] \qquad [g \circ f](x) = g[f(x)]$$
$$= f[x - 4] \qquad = g[x^2]$$
$$= (x - 4)^2 \qquad = (x^2) - 4$$
$$= x^2 - 8x + 16 \qquad = x^2 - 4$$

6. Sample answer: $f(x) = x - 6$, $g(x) = x^2$

7. Use $f(1)$ to find $f(2)$ and use $f(2)$ to find $f(3)$.

8. See students' work.

9. $[f \circ g](2) = f[g(2)]$
$= f[2 - 3]$
$= f(-1)$
$= (-1) + 6$
$= 5$

$[g \circ f](2) = g[f(2)]$
$= g[2 + 6]$
$= g(8)$
$= 8 - 3$
$= 5$

10. $[f \circ g](2) = f[g(2)]$
$= f[2 + 1]$
$= f(3)$
$= (3)^2 + 3$
$= 12$

$[g \circ f](2) = g[f(2)]$
$= g[(2)^2 + 3]$
$= g(7)$
$= 7 + 1$
$= 8$

11. $g[h(x)] = g(2x-1)$
$= 4(2x - 1)$
$= 8x - 4$

$h[g(x)] = h(4x)$
$= 2(4x) - 1$
$= 8x - 1$

12. $g[h(x)] = g(x^2)$
$= (x^2) + 2$
$= x^2 + 2$

$h[g(x)] = h(x + 2)$
$= (x + 2)^2$
$= x^2 + 4x + 4$

13. $f[g(1)] = f[3(1)]$
$= f(3)$
$= (3)^2$
$= 9$

14. $[f \circ h](4) = f[h(4)]$
$= f[(4) + 2]$
$= f(6)$
$= (6)^2$
$= 36$

15. $h[f(x)] = h[x^2]$
$= (x^2) + 2$
$= x^2 + 2$

16. $f(0) = 1$
$f(1) = f(1 - 1) + 3 = f(0) + 3 = 4$
$f(2) = f(2 - 1) + 3 = f(1) + 3 = 7$
$f(3) = f(3 - 1) + 3 = f(2) + 3 = 10$
$f(4) = f(4 - 1) + 3 = f(3) + 3 = 13$

17. $f(1) = 3$
$f(2) = 2f(2 - 1) = 2f(1) = 6$
$f(3) = 2f(3 - 1) = 2f(2) = 12$
$f(4) = 2f(4 - 1) = 2f(3) = 24$
$f(5) = 2f(5 - 1) = 2f(4) = 48$

18a. $h[f(x)]$; You must subtract first.

18b. $h[f(400{,}000)] = h[400{,}000 - 275{,}000]$
$= h[125{,}000]$
$= 0.03(125{,}000)$
$= 3750$; \$3750

Pages 524–525 Exercises

19. $[f \circ g](3) = f[g(3)]$
$= f[-(3)]$
$= f(-3)$
$= -3$

$[g \circ f](3) = g[f(3)]$
$= g(3)$
$= -(3)$
$= -3$

20. $[f \circ g](3) = f[g(3)]$
$= f[(3)^3]$
$= f(27)$
$= (27)^2$
$= 729$

$[g \circ f](3) = g[f(3)]$
$= g[(3)^2]$
$= g(9)$
$= (9)^3$
$= 729$

21. $[f \circ g](3) = f[g(3)]$
$= f[(3)^2 + 6]$
$= f(15)$
$= 15 + 1$
$= 16$

$[g \circ f](3) = g[f(3)]$
$= g[(3) + 1]$
$= g(4)$
$= (4)^2 + 6$
$= 22$

22. $[f \circ g](3) = f[g(3)]$
$= f(1)$
$= -7$

$[g \circ f](3) = g[f(3)]$
$= g(0)$
$= 11$

23. $[f \circ g](3) = f[g(3)]$
$= f(-1)$
$= 9$

$[g \circ f](3) = g[f(3)]$
$= g(6)$
$= 12$

24. $[f \circ g](3) = f[g(3)]$
$= f[(3)^2 - 3(3) + 7]$
$= f(7)$
$= 7(7) - 5$
$= 44$

$[g \circ f](3) = g[f(3)]$
$= g[7(3) - 5]$
$= g(16)$
$= (16)^2 - 3(16) + 7$
$= 215$

25. $g[h(x)] = g[x + 4]$
$= (x + 4) + 7$
$= x + 11$

$h[g(x)] = h[x + 7]$
$= (x + 7) + 4$
$= x + 11$

26. $g[h(x)] = g(2x)$
$= 5(2x)$
$= 10x$

$h[g(x)] = h(5x)$
$= 2(5x)$
$= 10x$

27. $g[h(x)] = g(x^2)$
$= (x^2) - 2$
$= x^2 - 2$

$h[g(x)] = h(x - 2)$
$= (x - 2)^2$
$= x^2 - 4x + 4$

28. $g[h(x)] = g(-3x + 1)$
$= -2(-3x + 1)$
$= 6x - 2$

$h[g(x)] = h(-2x)$
$= -3(-2x) + 1$
$= 6x + 1$

29. $g[h(x)] = g(x^3)$
$= (x^3) + 1$
$= x^3 + 1$

$h[g(x)] = h(x + 1)$
$= (x + 1)^3$
$= x^3 + 3x^2 + 3x + 1$

30. $g[h(x)] = g(x - 3)$
$= |x - 3|$

$h[g(x)] = h(|x|)$
$= |x| - 3$

31. $h[g(2)] = h[4(2)]$
$= h(8)$
$= (8) - 1$
$= 7$

32. $[f \circ g](4) = f[g(4)]$
$= f[4(4)]$
$= f(16)$
$= (16)^2$
$= 256$

33. $[h \circ f](3) = h[f(3)]$
$= h[(3)^2]$
$= h(9)$
$= (9) - 1$
$= 8$

34. $[f \circ h](-3) = f[h(-3)]$
$= f[(-3) - 1]$
$= f(-4)$
$= (-4)^2$
$= 16$

35. $h[g(-2)] = h[4(-2)]$
$= h(-8)$
$= (-8) - 1$
$= -9$

36. $h[f(-4)] = h[(-4)^2]$
$= h(16)$
$= (16) - 1$
$= 15$

37. $g[f(x)] = g(x^2)$
$= 4(x^2)$
$= 4x^2$

38. $[f \circ g](x) = f[g(x)]$
$= f(4x)$
$= (4x)^2$
$= 16x^2$

39. $[f \circ (g \circ h)](x) = f[g[h(x)]]$
$= f[g(x - 1)]$
$= f[4(x - 1)]$
$= f(4x - 4)$
$= (4x - 4)^2$
$= 16x^2 - 32x + 16$

40. $f(0) = 4$
$f(1) = f(1 - 1) - 5 = f(0) - 5 = -1$
$f(2) = f(2 - 1) - 5 = f(1) - 5 = -6$
$f(3) = f(3 - 1) - 5 = f(2) - 5 = -11$
$f(4) = f(4 - 1) - 5 = f(3) - 5 = -16$

41. $f(1) = 2$
$f(2) = 3f(2 - 1) = 3f(1) = 6$
$f(3) = 3f(3 - 1) = 3f(2) = 18$
$f(4) = 3f(4 - 1) = 3f(3) = 54$
$f(5) = 3f(5 - 1) = 3f(4) = 162$

42. $f(1) = 3$
$f(2) = f(2 - 1) + 4(2) = f(1) + 8 = 11$
$f(3) = f(3 - 1) + 4(3) = f(2) + 12 = 23$
$f(4) = f(4 - 1) + 4(4) = f(3) + 16 = 39$
$f(5) = f(5 - 1) + 4(5) = f(4) + 20 = 59$

43. $f(0) = 0.2$
$f(1) = 1[f(1 - 1)] = 1[f(0)] = 0.2$
$f(2) = 2[f(2 - 1)] = 2[f(1)] = 0.4$
$f(3) = 3[f(3 - 1)] = 3[f(2)] = 1.2$
$f(4) = 4[f(4 - 1)] = 4[f(3)] = 4.8$

44. $f(0) = -2$
$f(1) = 3f(1 - 1) - 2(1) = 3f(0) - 2 = -8$
$f(2) = 3f(2 - 1) - 2(2) = 3f(1) - 4 = -28$
$f(3) = 3f(3 - 1) - 2(3) = 3f(2) - 6 = -90$
$f(4) = 3f(4 - 1) - 2(4) = 3f(3) - 8 = -278$

45. $f(0) = 6$
$f(1) = 4f(1 - 1) + (1)^2 = 4f(0) + 1 = 25$
$f(2) = 4f(2 - 1) + (2)^2 = 4f(1) + 4 = 104$
$f(3) = 4f(3 - 1) + (3)^2 = 4f(2) + 9 = 425$
$f(4) = 4f(4 - 1) + (4)^2 = 4f(3) + 16 = 1716$

46. $f \circ g = \{(1, -3), (-3, 1), (2, 1)\}$
$g \circ f = \{(1, 0), (0, 1)\}$

47. $f \circ g$ does not exist
$g \circ f = \{(3, 6), (4, 4), (6, 6), (7, 8)\}$

48. Sample answer: $f(x) = x$, $g(x) = -x$

49. $f(0) = 4$
$f(0 + 1) = 3f(0) - 2$
$f(1) = 12 - 2 = 10$
$f(1 + 1) = 3f(1) - 2$
$f(2) = 28$
$f(2 + 1) = 3f(2) - 2$
$f(3) = 82$
$f(3 + 1) = 3f(3) - 2$
$f(4) = 244$

50a. $B[A(x)] = 0.9733(0.6252x)$
$= 0.6085x$
It represents converting American dollars to Irish punts.

50b. $0.6085(500) \approx 304.25$; 304.25 punts

51a. $r(x) = x - 5$,
$p(x) = x - 0.25x$

51b. $r[p(38)] = r[(38) - 0.25(38)]$
$= r[28.5]$
$= (28.5) - 5$
$= 23.5$; \$23.50; taking the discount first

51c. $p[r(38)] = p[(38) - 5]$
$= p(33)$
$= (33) - 0.25(33)$
$= 24.75$; \$24.75; taking the rebate first

52. $f(1) = 450$
$f(2) = f(2 - 1) + 0.014f(2 - 1) - 30 = f(1) - 0.014f(1) - 30 = \$426.30$
$f(3) = f(3 - 1) + 0.014f(3 - 1) - 30 = f(2) - 0.014f(2) - 30 = \$402.27$
$f(4) = f(4 - 1) + 0.014f(4 - 1) - 30 = f(3) - 0.014f(3) - 30 = \$377.90$
$f(5) = f(5 - 1) + 0.014f(5 - 1) - 30 = f(4) - 0.014f(4) - 30 = \$353.19$

53. $(x^3)^2 + 3(x^3) - 10 = 0$

54. $y^2 = 6x$
$\frac{1}{6}y^2 = x$
$x = \frac{1}{6}y^2$

55. $$\text{mean} = \frac{11.20 + 11.17 + 10.92 + 11.06 + 11.19 + 10.97 + 11.09 + 11.05 + 11.22 + 11.03}{10}$$
$$= \frac{110.9}{10} = 11.09; \text{ 11.09 minutes}$$

$$\text{SD} = \sqrt{\frac{\left[\begin{array}{l}(11.20 - 11.09)^2 + (11.17 - 11.09)^2 + (10.92 - 11.09)^2 + \\ (11.06 - 11.09)^2 + (11.19 - 11.09)^2 + (10.97 - 11.09)^2 + (11.09 - \\ 11.09)^2 + (11.05 - 11.09)^2 + (11.22 - 11.09)^2 + (11.03 - 11.09)^2\end{array}\right]}{10}}$$

$$= \sqrt{\frac{\left[\begin{array}{l}0.0121 + 0.0064 + 0.0289 + 0.0009 + \\ 0.01 + 0.0144 + 0 + 0.0016 + 0.0169 + 0.0036\end{array}\right]}{10}}$$

$$= \sqrt{\frac{0.0948}{10}} = \sqrt{0.00948} \approx 0.097; \text{ 0.097 minutes}$$

56. $(m + 7)^2 = (m)^2 + 2(m)(7) + (7)^2$
$= m^2 + 14m + 49$

57. $$\begin{bmatrix} 4 & 5 \\ -2 & 9 \\ -1 & 4 \end{bmatrix} \begin{bmatrix} 5 & 3 & -6 & 0 \\ -2 & 1 & 4 & -1 \end{bmatrix}$$

$$= \begin{bmatrix} (4)(5) + (5)(-2) & (4)(3) + (5)(1) & (4)(-6) + (5)(4) & (4)(0) + (5)(-1) \\ (-2)(5) + (9)(-2) & (-2)(3) + 9(1) & (-2)(-6) + 9(4) & (-2)(0) + 9(-1) \\ (-1)(5) + (4)(-2) & (-1)(5) + (4)(1) & (-1)(-6) + (4)(4) & (-1)(0) + 4(-1) \end{bmatrix}$$

$$= \begin{bmatrix} 10 & 17 & -4 & -5 \\ -28 & 3 & 48 & -9 \\ -13 & 1 & 22 & -4 \end{bmatrix}$$

58. $y \geq -\frac{\sqrt{5}}{2}$
$y \leq -\frac{\sqrt{5}}{2}x + \frac{\sqrt{5}}{2}$
$y \leq \frac{\sqrt{5}}{2}x + \frac{\sqrt{5}}{2}$

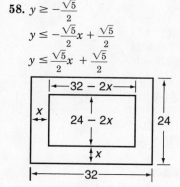

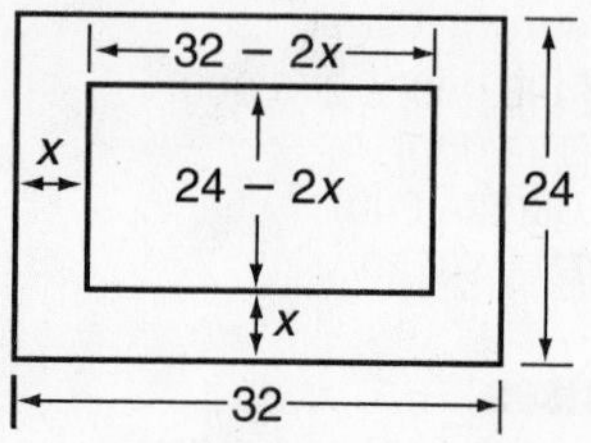

59. b

60. $x - 2y = 18$
$-2y = -x + 18$
$y = \frac{1}{2}x - 9$
slope of the line perpendicular is -2
$b = -2$

61. $-4(3a + 2b) - 3(-7a - 6b)$
$= (-4)(3a) + (-4)(2b) + (-3)(-7a) + (-3)(-6b)$
$= -12a - 8b + 21a + 18b$
$= 9a + 10b$

8-7B Modeling Mathematics: Exploring Iteration

Page 527 Exercises

1. $g(x_0) = g(0.2)$
$= 5(0.2)$
$= 1$
$g(x_1) = g(1)$
$= 5(1)$
$= 5$
$g(x_2) = g(5)$
$= 5(5)$
$= 25$

2. $g(x_0) = g(-0.5)$
$= -2(-0.5) + 1$
$= 2$
$g(x_1) = g(2)$
$= -2(2) + 1$
$= -3$
$g(x_2) = g(-3)$
$= -2(-3) + 1$
$= 7$

3. $g(x_0) = g(-4)$
$= 3 - 0.4(-4)$
$= 4.6$
$g(x_1) = g(4.6)$
$= 3 - 0.4(4.6)$
$= 1.16$
$g(x_2) = g(1.16)$
$= 3 - 0.4(1.16)$
≈ 2.54

4. $g(x_0) = g(1)$
$= 3(1) - 0.5(1)^2$
$= 2.5$
$g(x_1) = g(2.5)$
$= 3(2.5) - 0.5(2.5)^2$
≈ 4.38
$g(x_2) = g(4.38)$
$= 3(4.38) - 0.5(4.38)^2$
≈ 3.55

5. 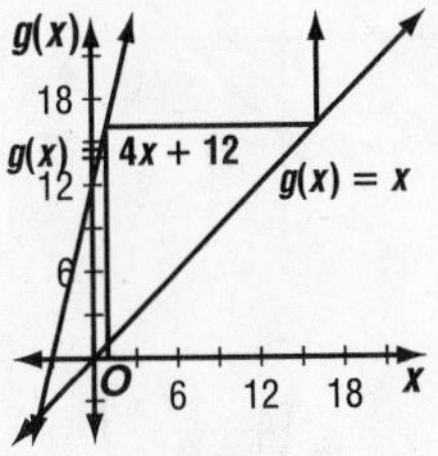

slope: 4; staircase out

6. 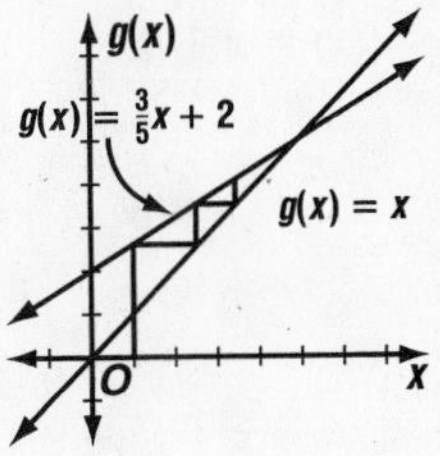

slope: $\frac{3}{5}$; staircase in

7. 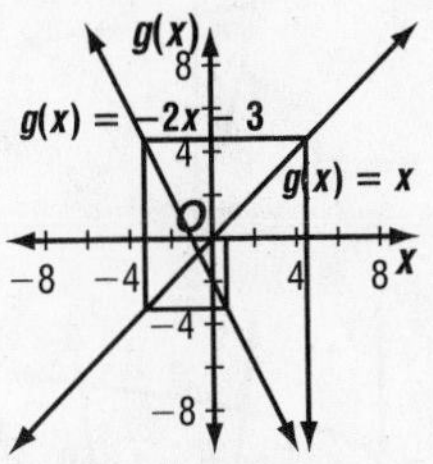

slope: −2; spiral out

8. 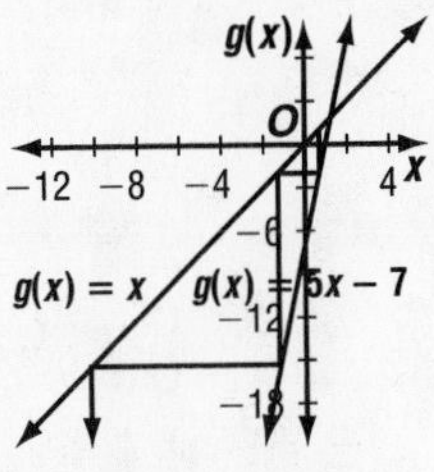

slope: 5; staircase out

9. 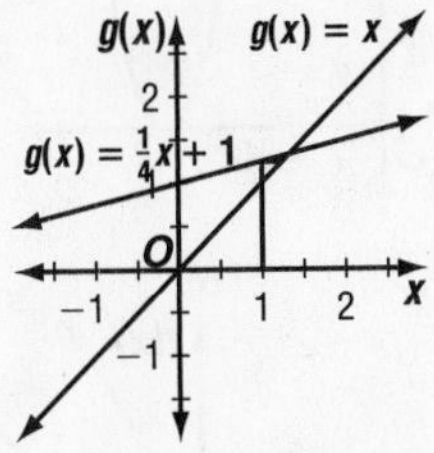

slope: $\frac{1}{4}$; staircase in

10. 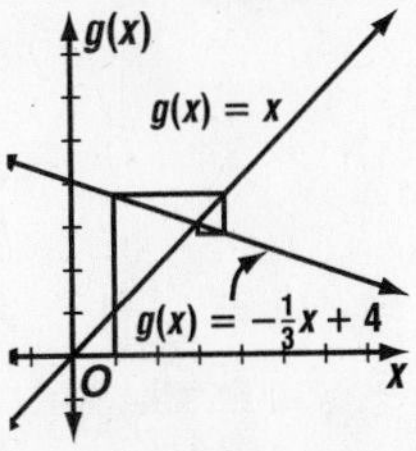

slope: $\frac{1}{3}$; spiral in

11. Sample answer: Functions whose slopes are positive form staircase paths; functions whose slopes are negative form spiral paths.
12. It initially forms a staircase pattern, then settles into a cyclical pattern.

8-8 Inverse Functions and Relations

Pages 531–532 Check for Understanding

1. Inverse functions have both their compositions equal to the identity function. Inverse relations contain ordered pairs such that the coordinates of one relation are in reverse order of the coordinates of the other. Inverse functions are also inverse relations, but inverse relations are not always functions.
2. Switch x and y in the equation and solve for y.
3. The graph does not pass the vertical line test for functions.
4. The graphs are reflections of each other over the line of symmetry, $y = x$.
5. The inverse is a function because it passes the vertical line test.
6. $y = \frac{1}{2}x^2 - 3$
$x = \frac{1}{2}y^2 - 3$
$x + 3 = \frac{1}{2}y^2$
$2x + 6 = y^2$
$\pm\sqrt{2x + 6} = y$
$f^{-1}(x) = \pm\sqrt{2x + 6}$
See students' work.

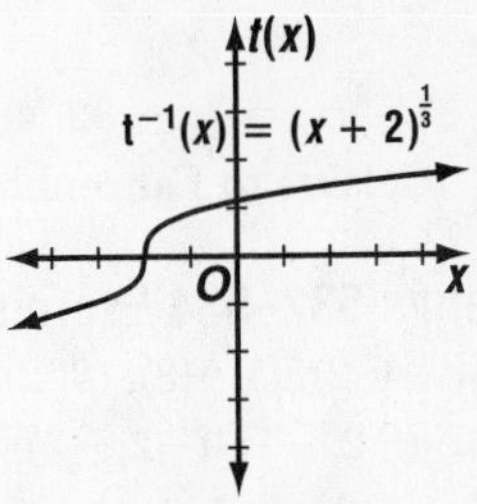

7. {(2, 3), (2, 4)}, no
8. {(8, 3), (−2, 4), (−3, 5)}, yes
9. $y = 7x$
$x = 7y$
$\frac{x}{7} = y$
$y^{-1} = \frac{x}{7}$

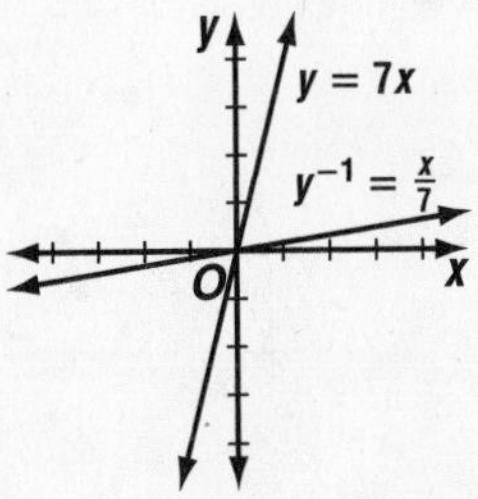

10. $y = x$
$y^{-1} = x$

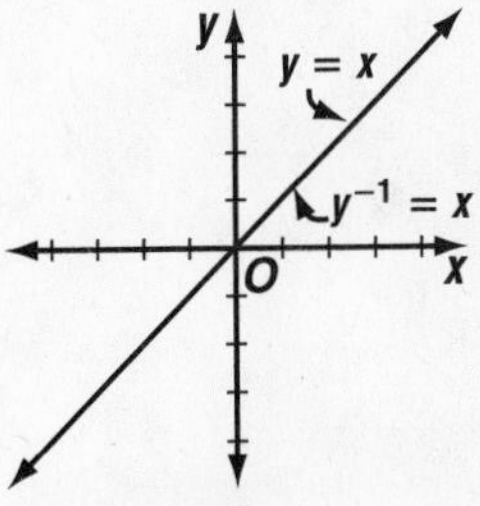

11. $y = x - 6$
$x = y - 6$
$x + 6 = y$
$f^{-1}(x) = x + 6$

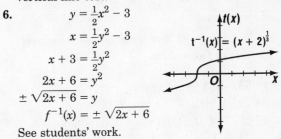

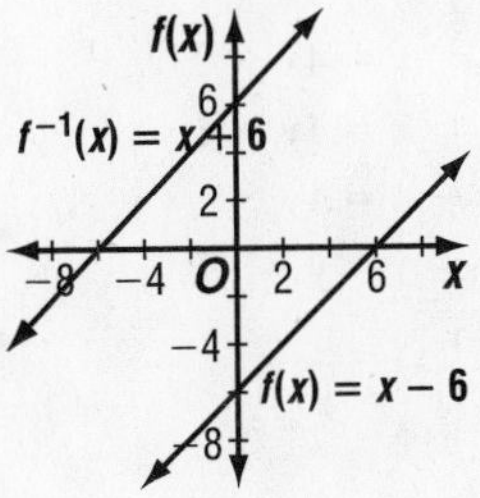

12. $y = -2x - 1$
$x = -2y - 1$
$x + 1 = -2y$
$-\frac{x-1}{2} = y$
$y^{-1} = -\frac{x-1}{2}$

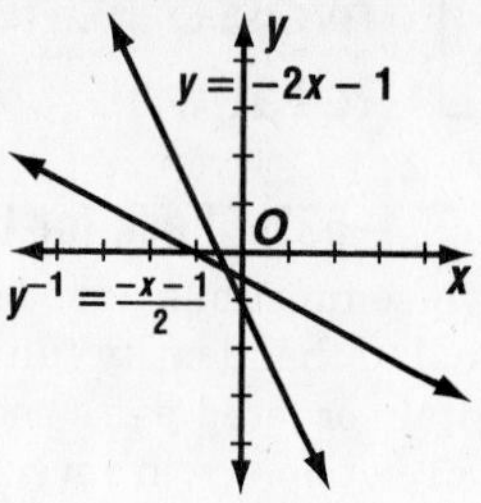

13. $f[g(x)] = f\left[\frac{x+2}{6}\right]$
$= 6\left(\frac{x+2}{6}\right) + 2$
$= x + 4$

$g[f(x)] = g[6x + 2]$
$= \frac{(6x+2)+2}{6}$
$= \frac{6x+4}{6}$

no

14. $y = \frac{5}{9}(x - 32)$
$x = \frac{5}{9}(y - 32)$
$\frac{9}{5}x = y - 32$
$\frac{9}{5}x + 32 = y$
$C^{-1}(x) = \frac{9}{5}x + 32$, and it can be used to convert Celsius to Fahrenheit.

Pages 532–534 Exercises

15. {(4, 2), (1, −3), (8, 2)}, yes
16. {(−2, −1), (−2, −3), (−4, −1), (6, 0)}, no
17. {(3, 1), (−1, 1), (−3, 1), (1, 1)}, yes
18. {(11, 6), (7, −2), (3, 0), (3, −5)}, no
19. $y = 6$
$x = 6$

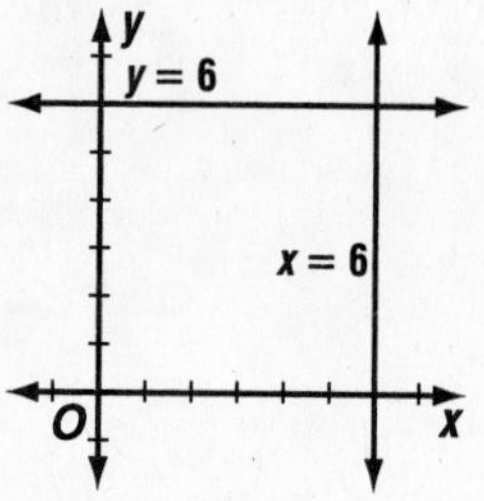

20. $y = 4x$
$x = 4y$
$\frac{x}{4} = y$
$y^{-1} = \frac{x}{4}$

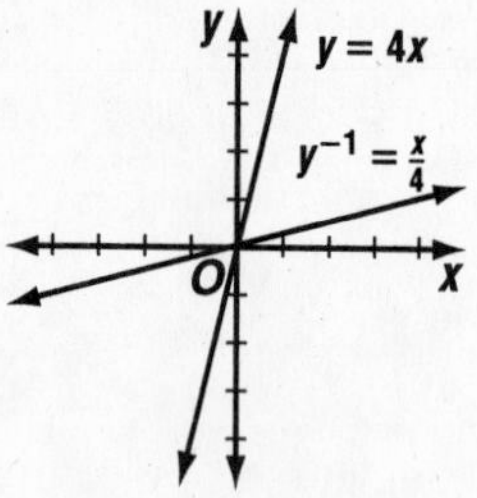

21. $f(x) = 4x + 4$
$y = 4x + 4$
$x = 4y + 4$
$x - 4 = 4y$
$\frac{1}{4}x - 1 = y$
$f^{-1}(x) = \frac{1}{4}x - 1$

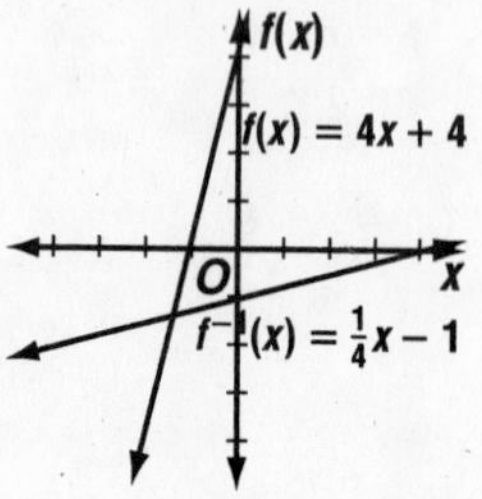

22. $g(x) = \frac{1}{2}x + 2$
$y = \frac{1}{2}x + 2$
$x = \frac{1}{2}y + 2$
$x - 2 = \frac{1}{2}y$
$2x - 4 = y$
$g^{-1}(x) = 2x - 4$

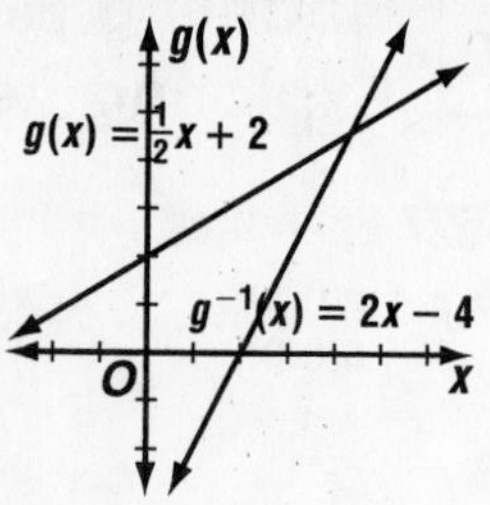

23. $f(x) = -x$
$y = -x$
$x = -y$
$-x = y$
$f^{-1}(x) = -x$

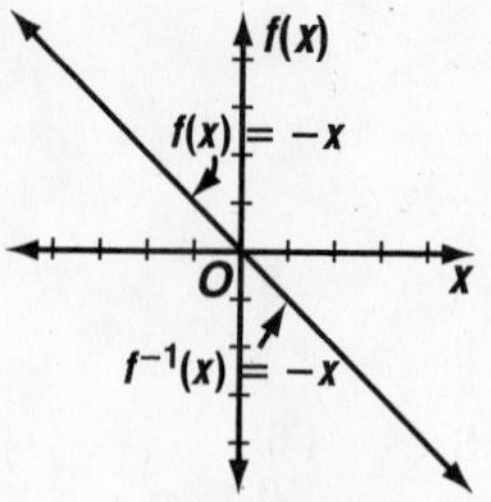

24. $g(x) = x - 2$
$y = x - 2$
$x = y - 2$
$x + 2 = y$
$g^{-1}(x) = x + 2$

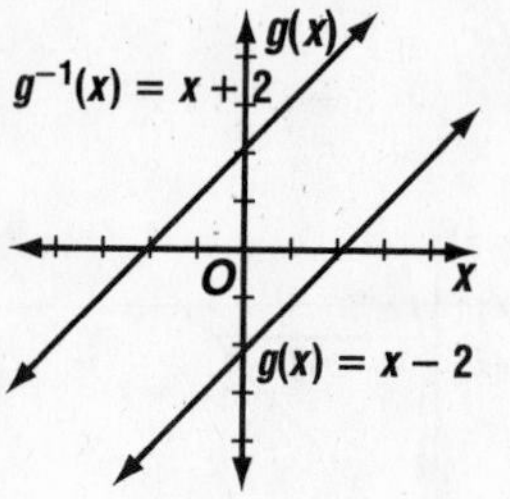

25. $y = x^2 - 9$
$x = y^2 - 9$
$x + 9 = y^2$
$\pm\sqrt{x+9} = y$
$y^{-1} = \pm\sqrt{x+9}$

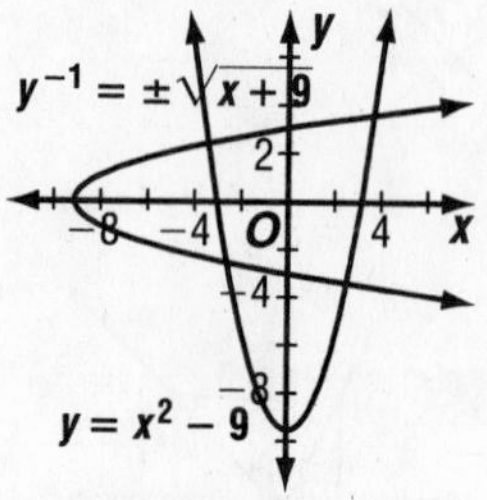

26. $y = (x - 9)^2$
$x = (y - 9)^2$
$\pm\sqrt{x} = y - 9$
$\pm\sqrt{x} + 9 = y$
$y^{-1} = \pm\sqrt{x} + 9$

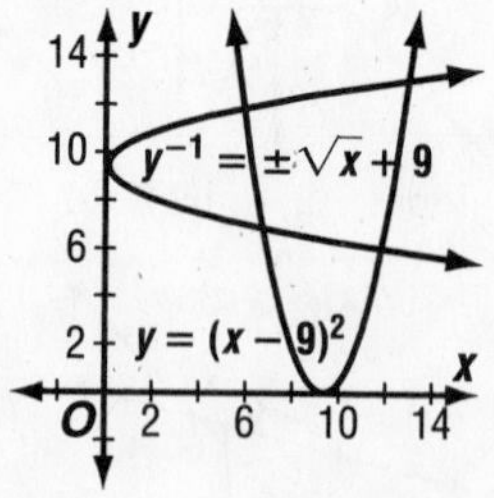

27. $f(x) = \frac{2x-1}{3}$
$y = \frac{2x-1}{3}$
$x = \frac{2y-1}{3}$
$3x = 2y - 1$
$3x + 1 = 2y$
$\frac{3x+1}{2} = y$
$f^{-1}(x) = \frac{3x+1}{2}$

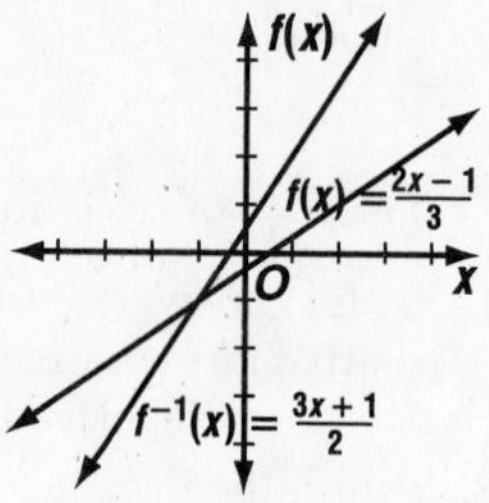

28.
$$y = x^2 + 1$$
$$x = y^2 + 1$$
$$x - 1 = y^2$$
$$\pm\sqrt{x - 1} = y$$
$$y^{-1} = \pm\sqrt{x - 1}$$

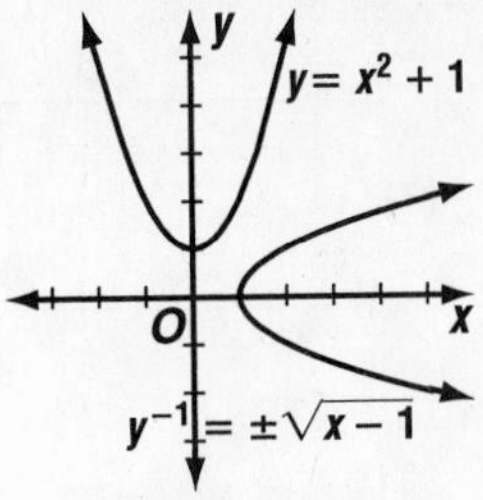

29.
$$y = (x - 4)^2$$
$$x = (y - 4)^2$$
$$\pm\sqrt{x} = y - 4$$
$$\pm\sqrt{x} + 4 = y$$
$$y^{-1} = \pm\sqrt{x} + 4$$

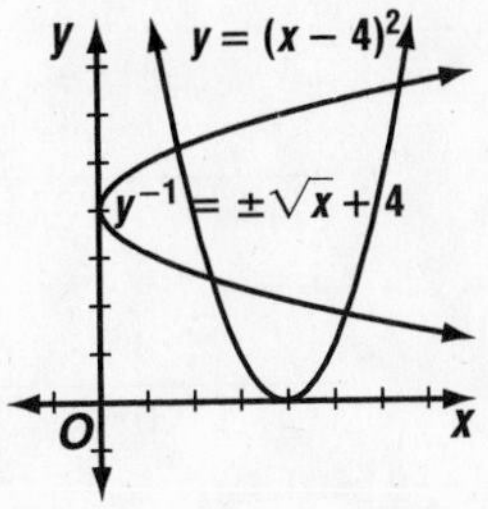

30.
$$y = (x + 2)^2 - 3$$
$$x = (y + 2)^2 - 3$$
$$x + 3 = (y + 2)^2$$
$$\pm\sqrt{x + 3} = y + 2$$
$$\pm\sqrt{x + 3} - 2 = y$$
$$y^{-1} = \pm\sqrt{x + 3} - 2$$

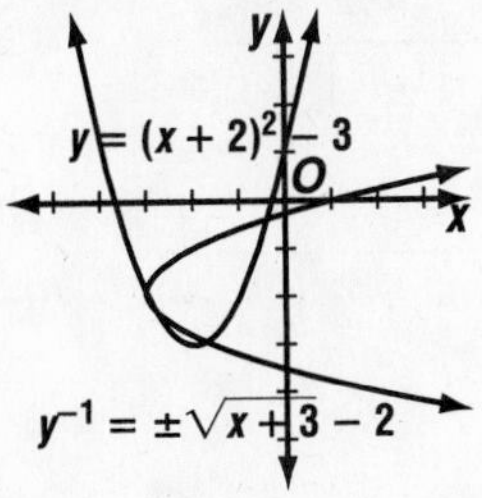

31. $f[g(x)] = f(x - 7)$ $= (x - 7) + 7$ $= x$ $\quad g[f(x)] = g(x + 7)$ $= (x + 7) - 7$ $= x$

yes

32. $h[g(x)] = h(2x - 3)$ $= -2(2x - 3) + 3$ $= -4x + 9$ $\quad g[h(x)] = g(-2x + 3)$ $= 2(-2x + 3) - 3$ $= -4x + 3$

no

33. $f[g(x)] = f(3x - 2)$ $= \frac{(3x - 2) - 2}{3}$ $= \frac{3x - 4}{3}$ $\quad g[f(x)] = g\left[\frac{x - 2}{3}\right]$ $= 3\left(\frac{x - 2}{3}\right) - 2$ $= x - 4$

no

34. $f[g(x)] = f(2x + 1)$ $= \frac{(2x + 1) - 1}{2}$ $= x$ $\quad g[f(x)] = g\left(\frac{x - 1}{2}\right)$ $= 2\left(\frac{x - 1}{2}\right) + 1$ $= x$

yes

35. yes

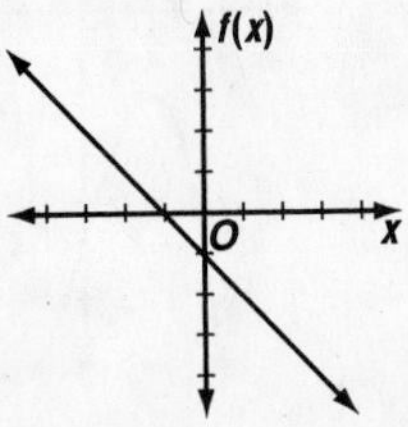

36. no

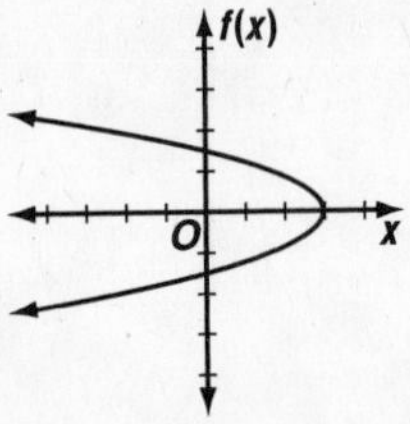

37. no

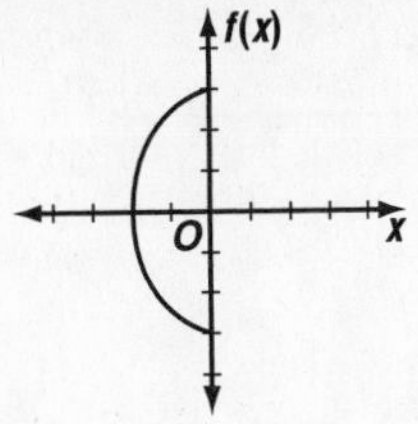

38a.

x	$f[g(x)]$	$g[f(x)]$
0	0	0
1	1	1
2	2	2

yes

38b.

x	$f[g(x)]$	$g[f(x)]$
0	36	16
1	54	17
2	76	20

no

38c.

x	$g[h(x)]$	$h[g(x)]$
0	0	0
1	1	1
2	2	2

yes

39. Sample answer: $f(x) = x$ and $f^{-1}(x) = x$ or $f(x) = -x$ and $f^{-1}(x) = -x$.

40. Let x = the regular price.
$$x - 0.25x - 40 = 522.50$$
$$0.75x = 562.50$$
$$x = 750;\ \$750$$

41. final number: 35
$35 \times 2 = 70$
$70 + 6 = 76$
$76 \div 4 = 19$
$19 - 7 = 12$
original number: 12

42.
$$I(m) = 320 + 0.04m$$
$$500 = 320 + 0.04m$$
$$180 = 0.04m$$
$$4500 = m;\ \$4500$$

43.
$$C = \frac{5}{9}(59 - 32)$$
$$= \frac{5}{9}(27)$$
$$= 15$$
$$K = 273 + C$$
$$= 273 + 15$$
$$= 288;\ 288°K$$

44.
$$6 = k - \frac{1}{4a}$$
$$6 = 5 - \frac{1}{4a}$$
$$1 = -\frac{1}{4a}$$
$$-4a = 1$$
$$a = -\frac{1}{4}$$
$$y = -\frac{1}{4}(x - 2)^2 + 5$$

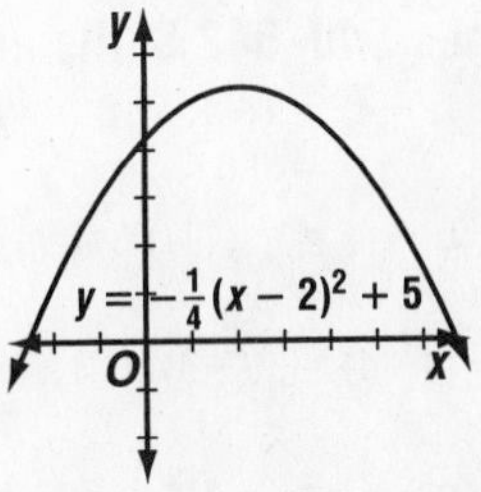

45.
$$h(t) = -16t^2 + 80t + 200$$
$$= -16\left(t^2 + 5t + \frac{25}{4}\right) + 200 + 16\left(\frac{25}{4}\right)$$
$$= -16\left(t + \frac{5}{2}\right)^2 + 300$$

maximum height: 300 feet at 2.5 seconds

46.

-1	1	-1	4	6
		-1	2	-6
	1	-2	6	0

$n^2 - 2n + 6$

47. $-2\begin{bmatrix} 0 & 3 \\ -5 & 3 \end{bmatrix} + \begin{bmatrix} 5 & 3 \\ -3 & 9 \end{bmatrix} = \begin{bmatrix} 0 & -6 \\ 10 & -6 \end{bmatrix} + \begin{bmatrix} 5 & 3 \\ -3 & 9 \end{bmatrix}$

$= \begin{bmatrix} 5 & -3 \\ 7 & 3 \end{bmatrix}$

48.

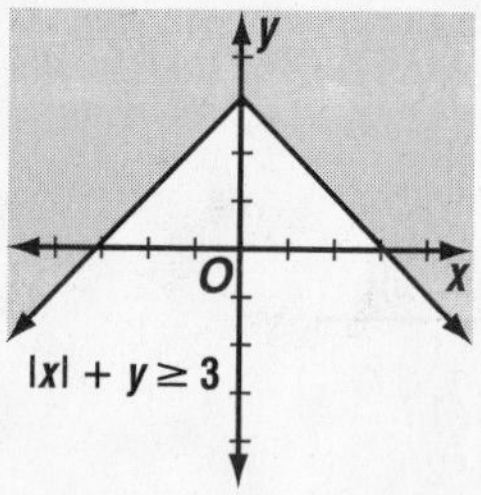

49. D = {−11, 0, 1, 3, 9, 12}
R = {−6, −4, −3, 0, 1, 7, 8}
no

50. $10 - 0.001 \le d \le 10 + 0.001$
$9.999 \le d \le 10.001$

8-8B Square Root Functions and Relations

See page 525 for solutions.

Chapter 8 Highlights

Page 539 Understanding and Using the Vocabulary

1. h **2.** e **3.** a **4.** c
5. g **6.** b **7.** f **8.** d

Chapter 8 Study Guide and Assessment

Pages 540–542 Skills and Concepts

9. $p(-4) = (-4) - 2 = -6$ $\quad p(x + h) = (x + h) - 2 = x + h - 2$

10. $p(-4) = -(-4) + 4 = 8$ $\quad p(x + h) = -(x + h) + 4 = -x - h + 4$

11. $p(-4) = 6(-4) + 3 = -21$ $\quad p(x + h) = 6(x + h) + 3 = 6x + 6h + 3$

12. $p(-4) = (-4)^2 + 5 = 21$ $\quad p(x + h) = (x + h)^2 + 5 = x^2 + 2hx + h^2 + 5$

13. $p(-4) = (-4)^2 - (-4) = 16 + 4 = 20$ $\quad p(x + h) = (x + h)^2 - (x + h) = x^2 + 2hx + h^2 - x - h$

14. $p(-4) = 2(-4)^3 - 1 = -129$ $\quad p(x + h) = 2(x + h)^3 - 1 = 2(x^3 + 3x^2h + 3xh^2 + h^3) - 1 = 2x^3 + 6x^2h + 6xh^2 + 2h^3 - 1$

15.

3	1	0	-5	$f(3) = 4$
		3	9	
	1	3	4	
-2	1	0	-5	$f(-2) = -1$
		-2	4	
	1	-2	-1	

16.

3	1	-4	4	$f(3) = 1$
		3	-3	
	1	-1	1	
-2	1	-4	4	$f(-2) = 16$
		-2	12	
	1	-6	16	

17.

3	1	-3	4	8	$f(3) = 20$
		3	0	12	
	1	0	4	20	
-2	1	-3	4	8	$f(-2) = -20$
		-2	10	-28	
	1	-5	14	-20	

18.

3	1	0	0	-5	2	$f(3) = 68$
		3	9	27	66	
	1	3	9	22	68	
-2	1	0	0	-5	2	$f(-2) = 28$
		-2	4	-8	26	
	1	-2	4	-13	28	

19.

-1	1	5	8	4
		-1	-4	-4
	1	4	4	0

$x^2 + 4x + 4 = (x + 2)^2$
$x + 2, x + 2$

20.

-2	1	4	7	6
		-2	-4	-6
	1	2	3	0

$x^2 + 2x + 3$

21.

-2	1	-1	-4	4
		-2	6	-4
	1	-3	2	0

$x^2 - 3x + 2 = (x - 2)(x - 1)$
$x - 2, x - 1$

22.

-1	1	-6	0	22	15
		-1	7	-7	-15
	1	-7	7	15	0
3	1	-7	7	15	
		3	-12	-15	
	1	-4	-5	0	

$x^2 - 4x - 5 = (x + 1)(x - 5)$
$x - 3, x + 1, x - 5$

23.

x	$h(x)$
-2	-5
-1	-4
0	-9
1	-14
2	-13
3	0 ← zero

3.0

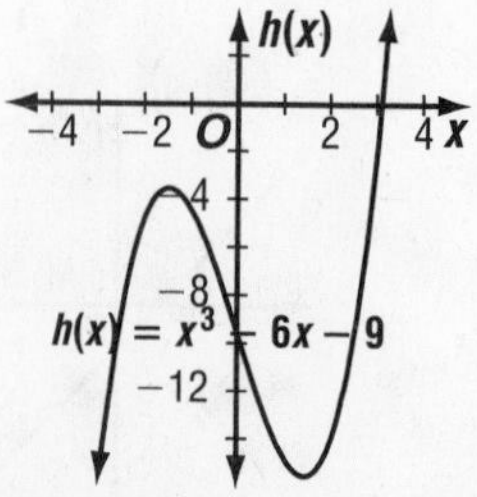

24.

x	$f(x)$
-2	3
-1	-5
0	1
1	9

← zero between $x = -2$ and $x = -1$
← zero between $x = -1$ and $x = 0$

$-1.9, -0.1$

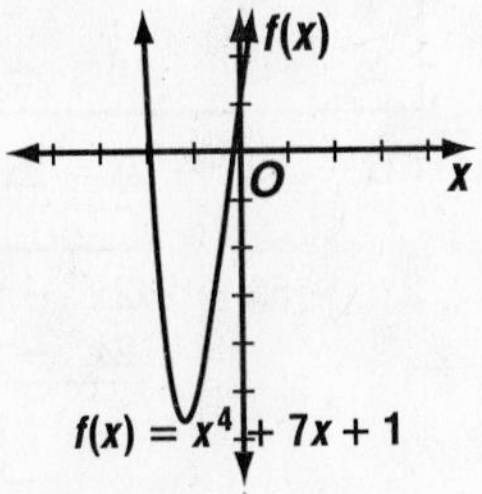

25.

x	$p(x)$
-3	-107
-2	1
-1	3
0	1
1	1

← zero between $x = -3$ and $x = -2$

-2.0

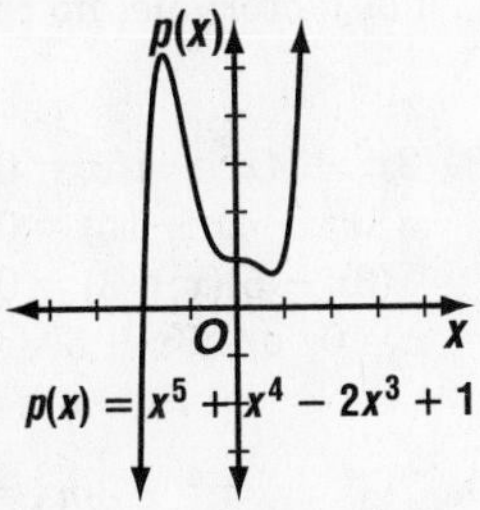

26.

x	$g(x)$
-2	-11
-1	-1
0	1
1	1
2	5

← zero between $x = -1$ and $x = 0$

-0.8

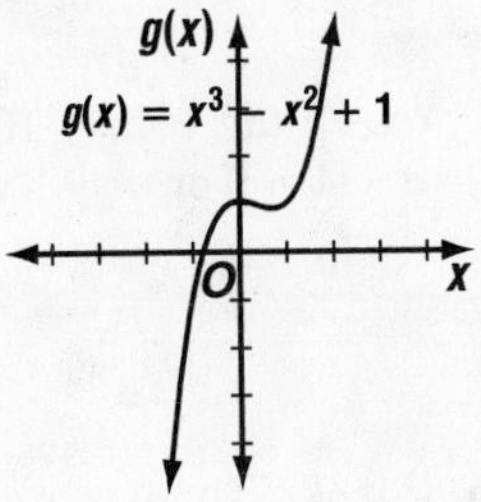

27.

x	$r(x)$
-2	-3
-1	11
0	3
1	-3
2	17

← zero between $x = -2$ and $x = -1$
← zero between $x = 0$ and $x = 1$
← zero between $x = 1$ and $x = 2$

$-1.9, 0.3, 1.4$

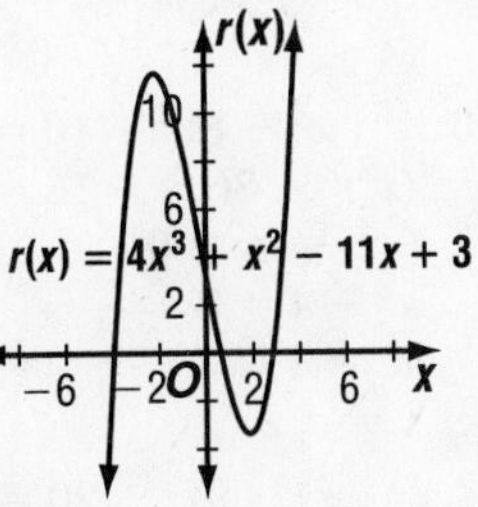

28.

x	$f(x)$
-4	-6
-3	4
-2	4
-1	0
0	-2
1	4

← zero between $x = -4$ and $x = -3$
← zero
← zero between $x = 0$ and $x = 1$

$-3.6, -1, 0.6$

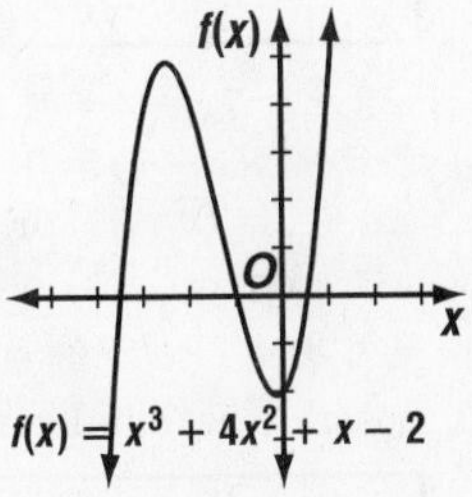

29. $f(x) = 2x^4 - x^3 + 5x^2 + 3x - 9$; 3 sign changes

yes yes no yes

$f(-x) = 2(-x)^4 - (-x)^3 + 5(-x)^2 + 3(-x) - 9$
$= 2x^4 + x^3 + 5x^2 - 3x - 9$; 1 sign change

no no yes no

positive: 3 or 1; negative: 1; imaginary: 2 or 0

30. $f(x) = 7x^3 + 5x - 1$; 1 sign change

no yes

$f(-x) = 7(-x)^3 + 5(-x) - 1$
$= -7x^3 - 5x - 1$; 0 sign changes

no no

positive: 1; negative: 0; imaginary: 2

31. $f(x) = -4x^4 - x^2 - x - 1$; 0 sign changes

no no no

$f(-x) = -4(-x)^4 - (-x)^2 - (-x) - 1$
$= -4x^4 - x^2 + x - 1$; 2 sign changes

no yes yes

positive: 0; negative: 2 or 0; imaginary: 2 or 4

32. $f(x) = 3x^4 - x^3 + 8x^2 + x - 7$; 3 sign changes

yes yes no yes

$f(-x) = 3(-x)^4 - (-x)^3 + 8(-x)^2 + (-x) - 7$
$= 3x^4 + x^3 + 8x^2 - x - 7$; 1 sign change

no no yes no

positive: 3 or 1; negative: 1; imaginary: 0 or 2

33. $f(x) = x^4 + x^3 - 7x + 1$; 2 sign changes

no yes yes

$f(-x) = (-x)^4 + (-x)^3 - 7(-x) + 1$
$= x^4 - x^3 + 7x + 1$; 2 sign changes

yes yes no

positive: 2 or 0; negative: 2 or 0; imaginary: 4, 2, or 0

34. possible rational zeros: $\pm 1, \pm 2, \pm 3, \pm 4, \pm 6, \pm 12$
$\pm \frac{1}{2}, \pm \frac{3}{2}$

$\frac{p}{q}$	2	−13	17	12
1	2	−11	6	18
2	2	−9	−1	10
3	2	−7	−4	0 ← zero

$2x^2 - 7x - 4 = 0$
$(2x + 1)(x - 4) = 0$
$2x + 1 = 0$ or $x - 4 = 0$
$x = -\frac{1}{2}$ $\quad x = 4$
$-\frac{1}{2}, 3, 4$

35. possible rational zeros: $\pm 1, \pm 2, \pm 4, \pm 8$

$\frac{p}{q}$	1	5	15	19	8
−1	1	4	11	8	0 ← zero
−2	1	3	9	1	6

$$x^2 + 2x + 1 \overline{\smash{)}x^4 + 5x^3 + 15x^2 + 19x + 8} \quad \text{quotient: } x^2 + 3x + 8$$
$\underline{x^4 + 2x^3 + x^2}$
$3x^3 + 14x^2 + 19x$
$\underline{3x^3 + 6x^2 + 3x}$
$8x^2 + 16x + 8$
$\underline{8x^2 + 16x + 8}$
0

$x^2 + 3x + 8 = 0$
not factorable, no rational solutions
$-1, -1$

36. possible rational zeros: $\pm 1, \pm 2, \pm 3, \pm 4, \pm 6, \pm 8,$
$\pm 12, \pm 24$

$\frac{p}{q}$	1	−3	−10	24
1	1	−2	−12	12
2	1	−1	−12	0 ← zero

$x^2 - x - 12 = 0$
$(x - 4)(x + 3) = 0$
$x - 4 = 0$ or $x + 3 = 0$
$x = 4$ $\quad x = -3$
$-3, 2, 4$

37. possible rational zeros: $\pm 1, \pm 3, \pm 5, \pm 15, \pm \frac{1}{2}, \pm \frac{3}{2},$
$\pm \frac{5}{2}, \pm \frac{15}{2}$

$\frac{p}{q}$	2	−5	−28	15
−1	2	−7	−21	36
−3	2	−11	5	0 ← zero

$2x^2 - 11x + 5 = 0$
$(2x - 1)(x - 5) = 0$
$2x - 1 = 0$ or $x - 5 = 0$
$x = \frac{1}{2}$ $\quad x = 5$
$-3, \frac{1}{2}, 5$

38. possible rational zeros: $\pm 1, \pm 2, \pm 5, \pm 10, \pm \frac{1}{2}, \pm \frac{5}{2}$

$\frac{p}{q}$	2	−9	2	21	−10
$\frac{1}{2}$	2	−8	−2	20	0 ← zero
1	2	−7	−5	16	6
2	2	−5	−8	5	0 ← zero

$(2x - 1)(x - 2) = 2x^2 - 5x + 2$

$$2x^2 - 5x + 2 \overline{\smash{)}2x^4 - 9x^3 + 2x^2 + 21x - 10} \quad \text{quotient: } x^2 - 2x - 5$$
$\underline{2x^4 - 5x^3 + 2x^2}$
$-4x^3 + 21x$
$\underline{-4x^3 + 10x^2 - 4x}$
$-10x^2 + 25x - 10$
$\underline{-10x^2 + 25x - 10}$

$x^2 - 2x - 5 = 0;$
not factorable, no rational solutions
$\frac{1}{2}, 2$

39. $3x^3 + 4x^2 - 15x = 0$
$x(3x^2 + 4x - 15) = 0$
$x(3x - 5)(x + 3) = 0$
$x = 0$ or $3x - 5 = 0$ or $x + 3 = 0$
$x = \frac{5}{3}$ $\quad x = -3$

40. $m^4 + 3m^3 = 40m^2$
$m^4 + 3m^3 - 40m^2 = 0$
$m^2(m^2 + 3m - 40) = 0$
$m^2(m + 8)(m - 5) = 0$
$m^2 = 0$ or $m + 8 = 0$ or $m - 5 = 0$
$m = 0$ $\quad m = -8$ $\quad m = 5$

41. $a^3 - 64 = 0$
$(a - 4)(a^2 + 4a + 16) = 0$
$a - 4 = 0$ or $a^2 + 4a + 16 = 0$
$a = 4$ $\quad a = \frac{-4 \pm \sqrt{(4)^2 - 4(1)(16)}}{2(1)}$
$= \frac{-4 \pm \sqrt{-48}}{2}$
$= -2 \pm 2i\sqrt{3}$

42. $r + 9\sqrt{r} = -8$
$r + 9\sqrt{r} + 8 = 0$
$(\sqrt{r})^2 + 9(\sqrt{r}) + 8 = 0$
$(\sqrt{r} + 8)(\sqrt{r} + 1) = 0$
$\sqrt{r} + 8 = 0$ or $\sqrt{r} + 1 = 0$
$\sqrt{r} = -8$ $\quad \sqrt{r} = -1$
$(\sqrt{r})^2 = (-8)^2$ $\quad (\sqrt{r})^2 = (-1)^2$
~~$r = 64$~~ $\quad$ ~~$r = 1$~~
$\varnothing$

check: $64 + 9\sqrt{64} = -8$
$64 + 72 \stackrel{?}{=} -8$
$136 \neq -8$
$1 + 9\sqrt{1} = -8$
$1 + 9 \stackrel{?}{=} -8$
$10 \neq -8$

43. $x^4 - 8x^2 + 16 = 0$
$(x^2)^2 - 8(x^2) + 16 = 0$
$(x^2 - 4)^2 = 0$
$x^2 - 4 = 0$
$x^2 = 4$
$x = \pm 2$

44. $x^{\frac{2}{3}} - 9x^{\frac{1}{3}} + 20 = 0$
$(x^{\frac{1}{3}})^2 - 9(x^{\frac{1}{3}}) + 20 = 0$
$(x^{\frac{1}{3}} - 4)(x^{\frac{1}{3}} - 5) = 0$
$x^{\frac{1}{3}} - 4 = 0$ or $x^{\frac{1}{3}} - 5 = 0$
$x^{\frac{1}{3}} = 4$ $\quad x^{\frac{1}{3}} = 5$
$(x^{\frac{1}{3}})^3 = (4)^3$ $\quad (x^{\frac{1}{3}})^3 = (5)^3$
$x = 64$ $\quad x = 125$

45. $g[h(x)] = 3(2x - 1) + 4$ $\quad h[g(x)] = 2(3x + 4) - 1$
$= (6x - 3) + 4$ $\quad = (6x + 8) - 1$
$= 6x + 1$ $\quad = 6x + 7$

46. $g[h(x)] = (x^2 + 2) - 3$ $\quad h[g(x)] = (x - 3)^2 + 2$
$= x^2 - 1$ $\quad = (x^2 - 6x + 9) + 2$
$\quad = x^2 - 6x + 11$

47. $g[h(x)] = -2(x^2 + 1) + 1$ $\quad h[g(x)] = (-2x + 1)^2 + 1$
$= (-2x^2 - 2) + 1$ $\quad = (4x^2 - 4x + 1) + 1$
$= -2x^2 - 1$ $\quad = 4x^2 - 4x + 2$

48. $g[h(x)] = 3(-5x) - 5$ $\quad h[g(x)] = -5(3x - 5)$
$= -15x - 5$ $\quad = -15x + 25$

49. $g[h(x)] = (x^3) - 2$ $\quad h[g(x)] = (x - 2)^3$
$= x^3 - 2$ $\quad = x^3 - 6x^2 + 12x - 8$

50. $g[h(x)] = |x + 4|$ $\quad h[g(x)] = |x| + 4$

51. $f(x) = 3x - 4$
$y = 3x - 4$
$x = 3y - 4$
$x + 4 = 3y$
$\frac{x + 4}{3} = y$
$f^{-1}(x) = \frac{x + 4}{3}$

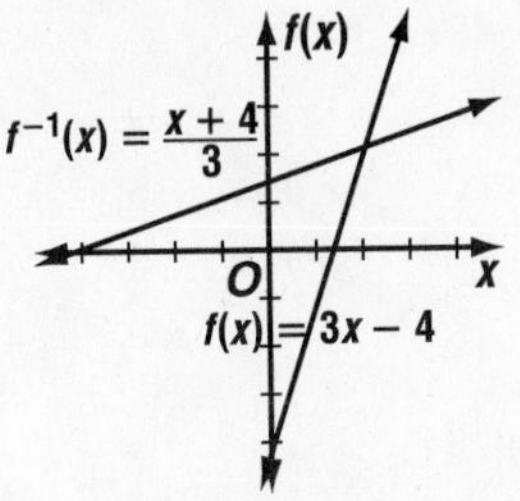

52. $f(x) = -2x - 3$
$y = -2x - 3$
$x = -2y - 3$
$x + 3 = -2y$
$\frac{-x - 3}{2} = y$
$f^{-1}(x) = \frac{-x - 3}{2}$

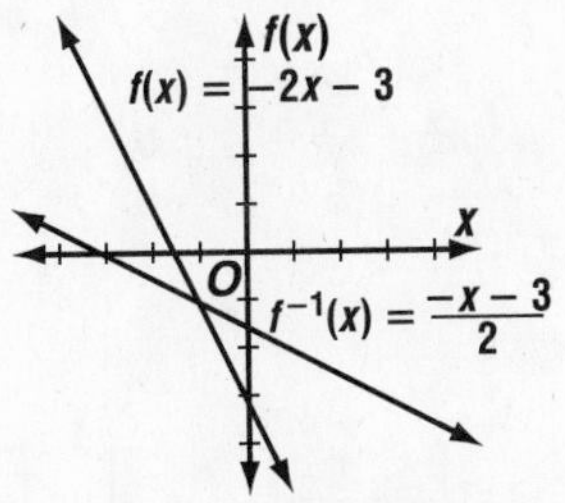

53. $g(x) = \frac{1}{3}x + 2$
$y = \frac{1}{3}x + 2$
$x = \frac{1}{3}y + 2$
$x - 2 = \frac{1}{3}y$
$3x - 6 = y$
$g^{-1}(x) = 3x - 6$

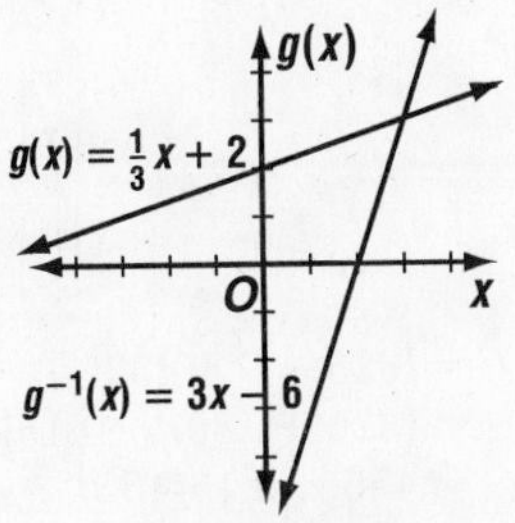

54. $f(x) = \frac{-3x + 1}{2}$
$y = \frac{-3x + 1}{2}$
$x = \frac{-3y + 1}{2}$
$2x = -3y + 1$
$2x - 1 = -3y$
$\frac{2x - 1}{-3} = y$
$f^{-1}(x) = \frac{2x - 1}{-3}$

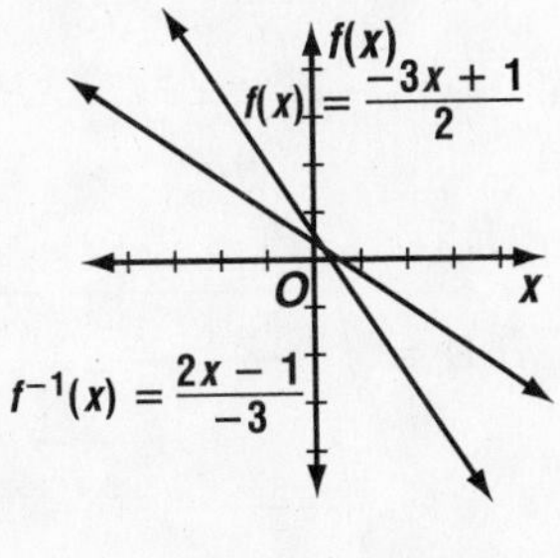

55. $y = x^2$
$x = y^2$
$\pm\sqrt{x} = y$
$y^{-1} = \pm\sqrt{x}$

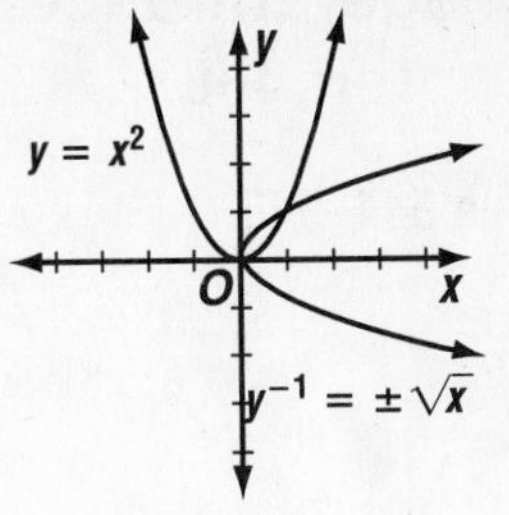

56. $y = (2x + 3)^2$
$x = (2y + 3)^2$
$\pm\sqrt{x} = 2y + 3$
$\pm\sqrt{x} - 3 = 2y$
$\frac{\pm\sqrt{x} - 3}{2} = y$
$y^{-1} = \pm\frac{\sqrt{x} - 3}{2}$

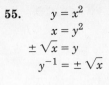

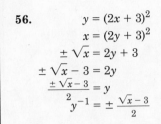

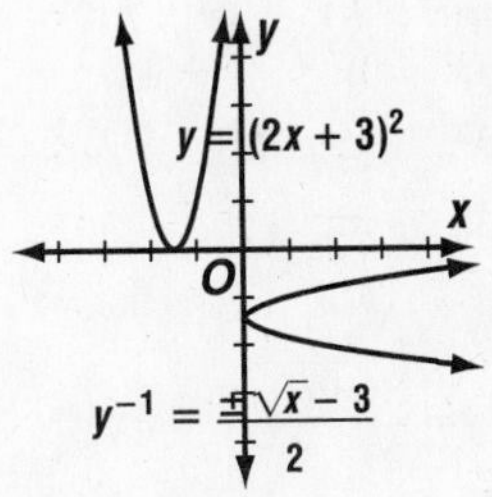

Page 542 Applications and Problem Solving

57a. $A = 1000(1 + r)^6 + 1000(1 + r)^5 + 1000(1 + r)^4 + 1200(1 + r)^3 + 1200(1 + r)^2 + 2000(1 + r)$

57b. $A = 1000(1 + 0.6)^6 + 1000(1 + 0.6)^5 + 1000(1 + 0.6)^4 + 1200(1 + 0.6)^3 + 1200(1 + 0.6)^2 + 2000(1 + 0.6)$
≈ 8916.76; \$8916.76

58. $V = \frac{1}{3}\pi r^2 h$ $\quad d = h$
$7.07 = \frac{1}{3}\pi r^2(2r)$ $\quad d = 2r$
$7.07 = \frac{2}{3}\pi r^3$ $\quad h = 2r$
$3.38 \approx r^3$
$1.5 \approx r$
diameter: 2(1.5) or 3 inches
height: 3 inches

59. Let x = the wholesale price.
$(x + x) - 0.20(x + x) = 12$
$2x - 0.20(2x) = 12$
$2x - 0.40x = 12$
$1.60x = 12$
$x = 7.5$; \$7.50

Page 543 Alternative Assessment; Thinking Critically

- By the complex conjugates theorem all imaginary roots are in conjugate pairs, therefore an odd number minus an even number is at least one real root.
  Examples: $x^3 - 1 = 0$
  $(x - 1)(x^2 + x + 1) = 0$
  Roots are 1 and $\frac{-1 \pm i\sqrt{3}}{2}$
  $x^5 + x^4 + 5x^3 + 5x^2 + 4x + 4 = 0$
  $(x + 1)(x^2 + 1)(x^2 + 4) = 0$
  Roots are -1, i, $-i$, $-2i$, and $2i$

College Entrance Exam Practice Chapters 1–8

Pages 544–545

1. $\dfrac{2[15 - 9 \div 3 + 2]}{(7 + 5) \div 4} = \dfrac{2[15 - 3 + 2]}{12 \div 4}$
$= \dfrac{2[14]}{3}$
$= \dfrac{28}{3}$; A

2. $(x - h)^2 + (y - k)^2 = r^2$
$(x - 3)^2 + (y - 11)^2 = 7^2$
$(x - 3)^2 + (y - 11)^2 = 49$; B

3. D

4. $t = \sqrt{\dfrac{2h}{g}}$
$= \sqrt{\dfrac{2(112)}{32}}$
$= \sqrt{\dfrac{224}{32}}$
$= \sqrt{7}$ $\quad 2(\sqrt{7}) = 2\sqrt{7}$; A

5. $g(-2) = (-2)^2 - (-2) + 5$
$= 4 + 2 + 5$
$= 11$
$2[g(a - 1)] = 2[(a - 1)^2 - (a - 1) + 5]$
$= 2[a^2 - 2a + 1 - a + 1 + 5]$
$= 2[a^2 - 3a + 7]$
$= 2a^2 - 6a + 14$
$g(h + 3) = (h + 3)^2 - (h + 3) + 5$
$= h^2 + 6h + 9 - h - 3 + 5$
$= h^2 + 5h + 11$
$g(b) - g(2b) = (b)^2 - (b) + 5 - [(2b)^2 - (2b) + 5]$
$= b^2 - b + 5 - [4b^2 - 2b + 5]$
$= b^2 - b + 5 - 4b^2 + 2b - 5$
$= -3b^2 + b$
C

6. B

7. $d = \sqrt{(x_2 - x_1)^2 + (y_2 - y_1)^2}$
$= \sqrt{(-4 - 3)^2 + [-2 - (-5)]^2}$; D

8. $y = \dfrac{\begin{vmatrix} 2 & 2 \\ 3 & -5 \end{vmatrix}}{\begin{vmatrix} 2 & -6 \\ 3 & 4 \end{vmatrix}}$ $\quad y = \dfrac{\begin{vmatrix} a & e \\ c & f \end{vmatrix}}{\begin{vmatrix} a & b \\ c & d \end{vmatrix}}$ $\quad$ for $ax + by = e$, $cx + dy = f$
$2x - 6y = 2$
$3x + 5y = -5$; C

9. $(24 - 2x)(32 - 2x) = 425$
$768 - 112x + 4x^2 = 425$
$4x^2 - 112x + 343 = 0$
$(2x - 49)(2x - 7) = 0$

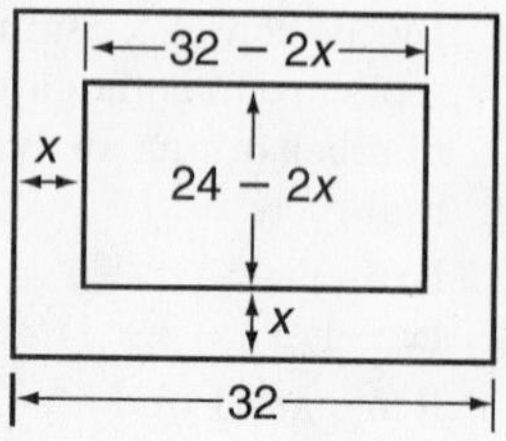

$2x - 49 = 0$ or $2x - 7 = 0$
~~$x = \dfrac{49}{2}$~~ $\quad x = \dfrac{7}{2}$
The walkway is 3.5 meters wide.

10. $4x^2 + 9y^2 = 36 \qquad 4x^2 - 9y^2 = 36$
$\dfrac{x^2}{9} + \dfrac{y^2}{4} = 1 \qquad \dfrac{x^2}{9} - \dfrac{y^2}{4} = 1$

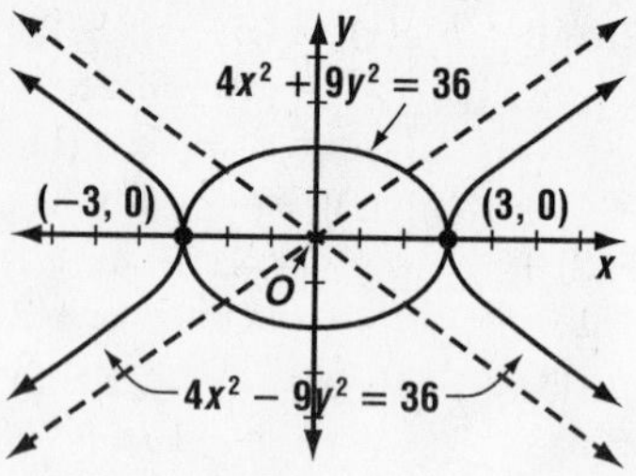

11. $x + 2y = 5 \rightarrow \quad x + 2y = 5 \qquad x + 2y = 5$
$2x - y = 5 \rightarrow \quad (+)4x - 2y = 10 \qquad 3 + 2y = 5$
$5x = 15 \qquad 2y = 2$
$x = 3 \qquad y = 1$

12. $6x^2 - 24x - 5y^2 - 10y = 11$
$6(x^2 - 4x + 4) - 5(y^2 + 2y + 1) = 11 + 24 - 5$
$6(x - 2)^2 - 5(y + 1)^2 = 30$
$\dfrac{(x - 2)^2}{5} - \dfrac{(y + 1)^2}{6} = 1$: hyperbola

13.

k	1	5	7
		k	$k^2 + 5k$
	1	$5 + k$	$k^2 + 5k + 7$

$k^2 + 5k + 7 = 3$
$k^2 + 5k + 4 = 0$
$(k + 4)(k + 1) = 0$
$k = 1$ or 4

14. $\begin{bmatrix} 3 & 2 \\ 1 & -2 \end{bmatrix}\begin{bmatrix} x \\ y \end{bmatrix} = \begin{bmatrix} 9 \\ 11 \end{bmatrix} \quad M^{-1} = -\dfrac{1}{8}\begin{bmatrix} -2 & -2 \\ -1 & 3 \end{bmatrix}$
$-\dfrac{1}{8}\begin{bmatrix} -2 & -2 \\ -1 & 3 \end{bmatrix}\begin{bmatrix} 3 & 2 \\ 1 & -2 \end{bmatrix}\begin{bmatrix} x \\ y \end{bmatrix} = -\dfrac{1}{8}\begin{bmatrix} -2 & -2 \\ -1 & 3 \end{bmatrix}\begin{bmatrix} 9 \\ 11 \end{bmatrix}$
$\begin{bmatrix} x \\ y \end{bmatrix} = -\dfrac{1}{8}\begin{bmatrix} -40 \\ 24 \end{bmatrix}$
$\begin{bmatrix} x \\ y \end{bmatrix} = \begin{bmatrix} 5 \\ -3 \end{bmatrix}$ $\quad (5, -3)$

15. $C = [325 + 0.40(325)] - 0.15[325 + 0.40(325)]$
$= (325 + 130) - 0.15[325 + 130]$
$= 455 - 0.15(455)$
$= 455 - 68.25$
$= 386.75$; \$386.75

16. mean $= \dfrac{2(5) + 7 + 3(3) + 8(4) + 2}{15} = \dfrac{10 + 7 + 9 + 32 + 2}{15} =$
$= \dfrac{60}{15} = 4$
$\text{SD} = \sqrt{\dfrac{2(5 - 4)^2 + (7 - 4)^2 + 3(3 - 4)^2 + 8(4 - 4)^2 + (2 - 4)^2}{15}}$
$= \sqrt{\dfrac{2 + 9 + 3 + 0 + 4}{15}} = \sqrt{\dfrac{18}{15}} \approx 1.1$
$g(-3) = \dfrac{(-3)^2}{2} - 3$
$= \dfrac{9}{2} - 3$
$= 1.5$ $\qquad$ B

17. $x = 6$ $\quad [9\ 4\ 2]\begin{bmatrix} 2 \\ 6 \\ 11 \end{bmatrix} = [64]$

x-intercept is 6

B

18. If $x < 0$, $x^2 > 0$ and $x^3 < 0$.

A

19. A to C

$$d = \sqrt{(3-5)^2 + (-2-5)^2}$$
$$= \sqrt{(-2)^2 + (-7)^2}$$
$$= \sqrt{4 + 49}$$
$$= \sqrt{53}$$

B to C

$$d = \sqrt{(-2-5)^2 + (1-5)^2}$$
$$= \sqrt{(-7)^2 + (-4)^2}$$
$$= \sqrt{49 + 16}$$
$$= \sqrt{65}$$

B

20. $\sqrt[3]{-8000} = -20$ $\quad -\sqrt[4]{256} = -4$

B

Chapter 9 Exploring Rational Expressions

9-1A Graphing Technology: Rational Functions

Page 549 Exercises

1. [Y=] 2 [÷] [(] [X,T,θ,n] [−] 4 [)] [ZOOM] 6

Vertical asymptote: $x = 4$

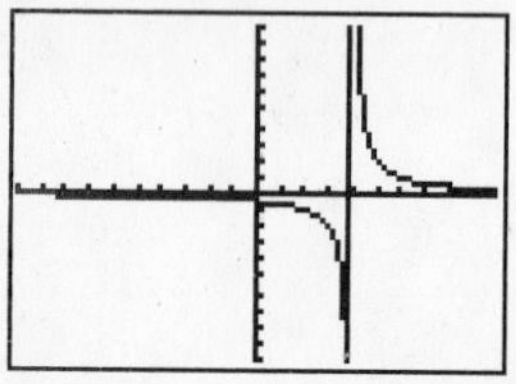

2. [Y=] [X,T,θ,n] [÷] [(] [X,T,θ,n] [+] 2 [)]
[ZOOM] 6

Vertical asymptote: $x = -2$

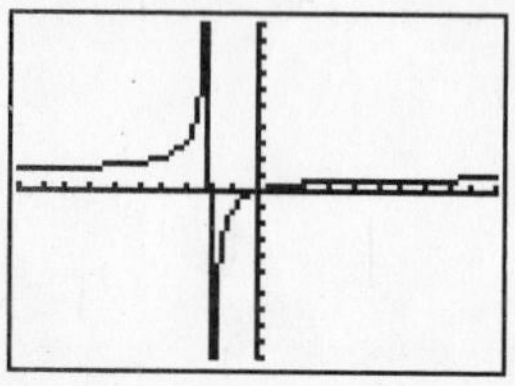

3. [Y=] 8 [÷] [(] [(] [X,T,θ,n] [+] 3 [)] [(]
[X,T,θ,n] [−] 5 [)] [)] [ZOOM] 6

WINDOW: $[-10, 10]$ by $[-5, 5]$

Vertical asymptotes: $x = -3, 5$

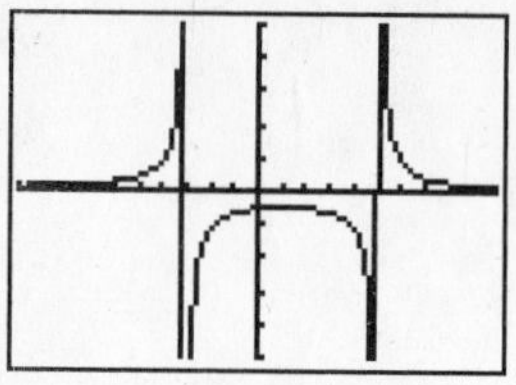

4. [Y=] 2 [X,T,θ,n] [÷] [(] 3 [X,T,θ,n] [−] 6 [)]
[ZOOM] 6

Vertical asymptote: $x = 2$

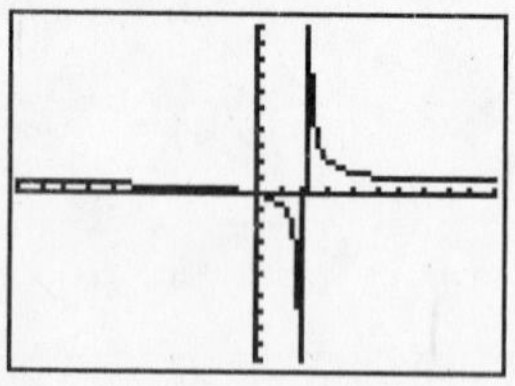

5. [Y=] [(] [X,T,θ,n] [x^2] [−] 16 [)] [÷] [(]
[X,T,θ,n] [−] 4 [)] [ZOOM] 6

Point of discontinuity: $x = 4$

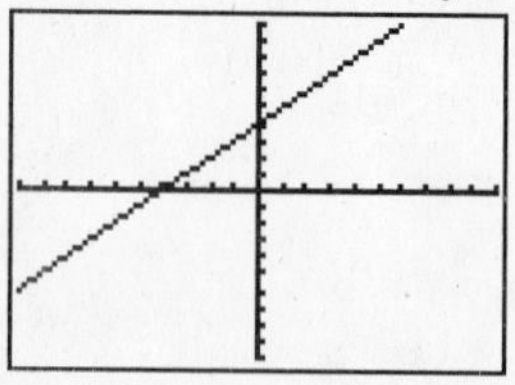

6. [Y=] [(−)] [(] 2 [X,T,θ,n] [+] 7 [)] [÷] [(] [(]
[X,T,θ,n] [+] 7 [)] [(] [X,T,θ,n] [+] 2 [)] [)]
[ZOOM] 6

WINDOW: $[-10, 10]$ by $[-5, 5]$

Vertical asymptotes: $x = -7, -2$

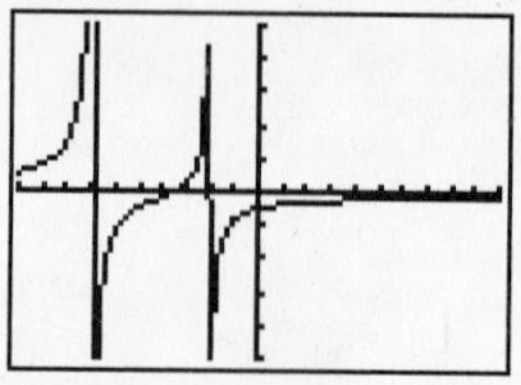

7. [Y=] 7 [÷] [X,T,θ,n]

Horizontal asymptote: $y = 0$

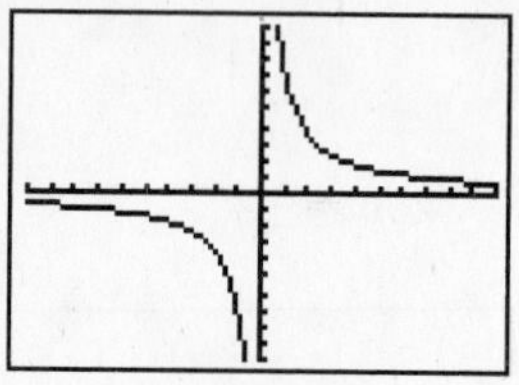

8. [Y=] [(] [X,T,θ,n] [x^2] [−] 3 [X,T,θ,n] [+] 2 [)]
[÷] [(] [X,T,θ,n] [x^2] [+] [X,T,θ,n] [−] 6 [)]
[ZOOM] 6

Horizontal asymptote: $y = 1$

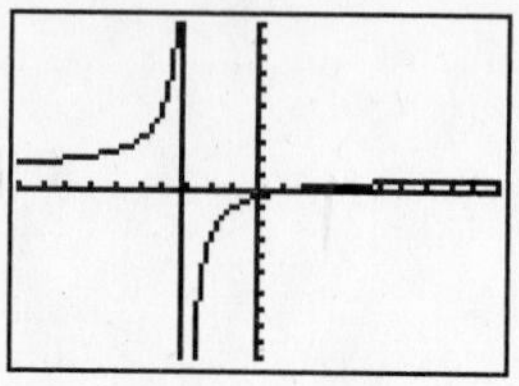

9. [Y=] [(] 8 [X,T,θ,n] [−] 5 [)] [÷] 2 [X,T,θ,n]
[ZOOM] 6

Horizontal asymptote: $y = 4$

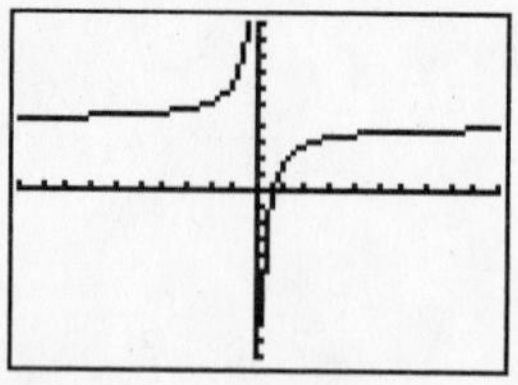

10. [Y=] [(] [X,T,θ,n] [−] 9 [)] [÷] [(] 9 [+] 2
[X,T,θ,n] [)] [ZOOM] 6

Horizontal asymptote: $y = \frac{1}{2}$

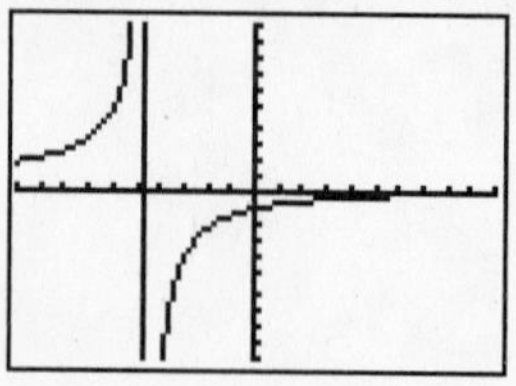

9-1 Graphing Rational Functions

Pages 553–554 Check for Understanding

1a. $x - 3 \neq 0$

$x \neq 3$

D: all real numbers except 3;

R: all real numbers except 0

1b. $x = 3$ **1c.** $y = 0$; See students' work for table.

2. The graph of the first function has a vertical asymptote at $x = -2$. The graph of the second function has point discontinuity at $x = -2$.

3. $x = 2$, $f(x) = 0$

4. $x - 2 = 0$ $y = 0$

$x = 2$

5. $(x - 1)(x + 3) = 0$

$x - 1 = 0$ or $x + 3 = 0$

$x = 1$ $x = -3$

$y = 0$

6.

x	$f(x)$
−10	−0.1
−5	−0.2
−2	−0.5
−1	−1
$-\frac{1}{2}$	−2
$-\frac{1}{10}$	−10

x	$f(x)$
0	undefined
$\frac{1}{10}$	10
$\frac{1}{2}$	2
1	1
2	0.5
5	0.2

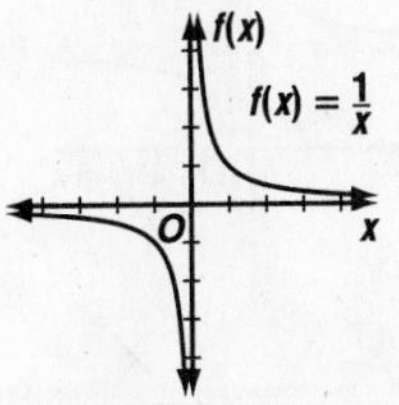

7.

x	$g(x)$
−10	0.67
−5	0.5
0	0
2	−0.67
4	−4

x	$g(x)$
5	undefined
6	6
8	2.67
10	2
15	1.5

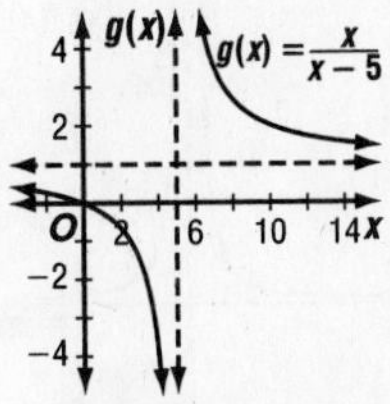

8.

x	$f(x)$
−10	1.67
−8	1.86
−4	3
−2	7
−1	undefined

x	$f(x)$
0	−5
2	−1
4	−0.2
8	0.3
10	0.45

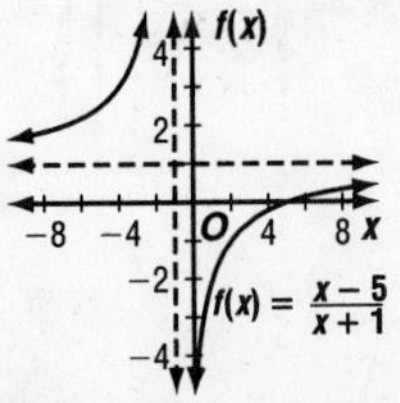

9.

x	$g(x)$
−2	0.5
0	0.25
1	0
3	−2
3.5	−5

x	$g(x)$
4	undefined
5	4
6	2.5
7	2
8	1.75

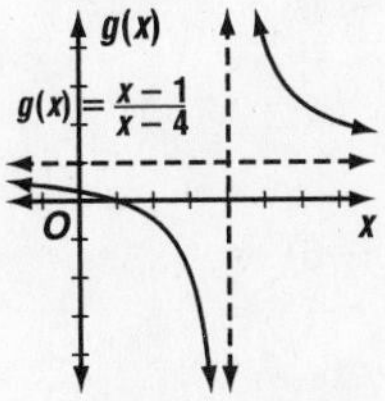

10.

x	$f(x)$
−6	0.0625
−4	0.25
−3	1
−2.5	4
−2	undefined

x	$f(x)$
−1.5	4
−1	1
0	0.25
1	0.11
2	0.0625

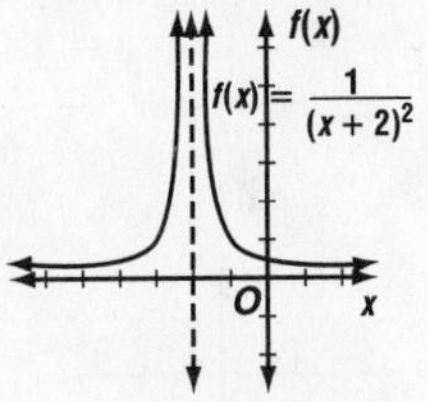

11.

x	$h(x)$
−6	0.38
−4	1.6
−3.5	3.56
−3	undefined
−2.5	−4.57

x	$h(x)$
−1	−2
0.5	−4.57
1	undefined
1.5	3.56
3	0.67

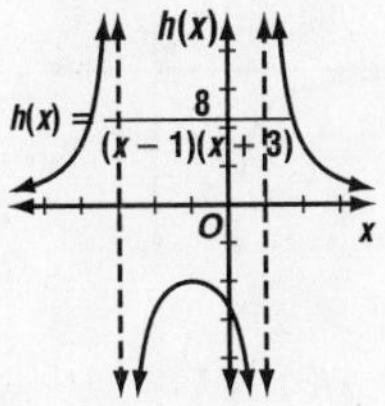

12a. $V = \frac{V_1t_1 + V_2t_2}{t_1 + t_2}$

$V = \frac{60t_1 + 320}{t_1 + 8}$

t_1	V
−40	65
−20	73.3
−10	140
−8	undefined

t_1	V
−5	6.67
0	40
10	51.11
20	54.29

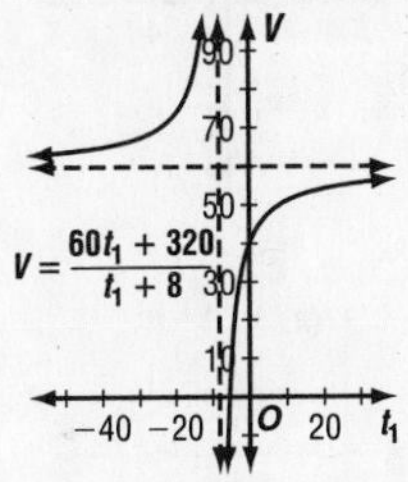

12b. $V = \frac{60t_1 + 320}{t_1 + 8}$

$= \frac{60(9) + 320}{9 + 8}$

$= \frac{860}{17}$

≈ 50.59; about 50.59 mph

Pages 554–555 Exercises

13. $x - 4 = 0$
$x = 4$
$y = 1$

14. $(x - 6)^2 = 0$
$x - 6 = 0$
$x = 6$
$y = 0$

15. $(x - 1)(x + 5) = 0$
$x - 1 = 0$ or $x + 5 = 0$
$x = 1$ $x = -5$
$y = 0$

16. $3x = 0$
$x = 0$
$y = 0$

17. $x - 3 = 0$
$x = 3$
$y = 1$

18. $x - 7 = 0$
$x = 7$
$y = 1$

19.

x	$f(x)$
−4	−0.75
−2	−1.5
−1	−3
0	undefined
1	3
2	1.5
4	0.75

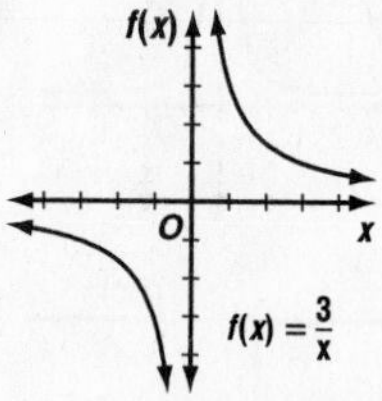

20.

x	$f(x)$
−6	−0.25
−4	−0.5
−2.5	−2
−2	undefined
−1.5	2
0	0.5
2	0.25

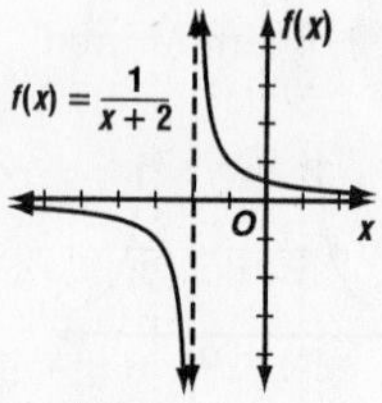

21.

x	$f(x)$
−1	0.25
1	−0.5
2.5	−5
3	undefined
3.5	7
5	2.5
7	1.75

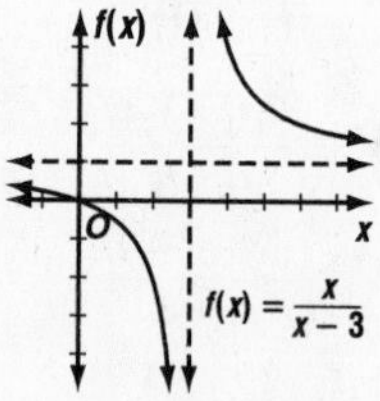

22.

x	$f(x)$
−8	0.44
−4	0
0	−4
1	undefined
2	6
4	2.67
8	1.7

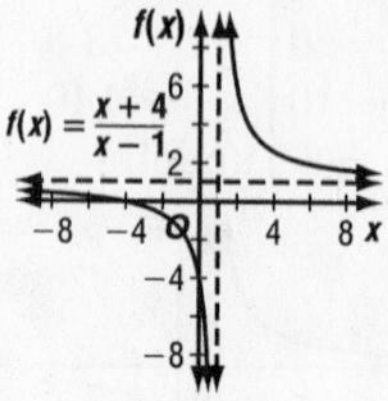

23.

x	$f(x)$
−1	0.5
1	0
2.5	−3
3	undefined
3.5	5
5	2
7	1.5

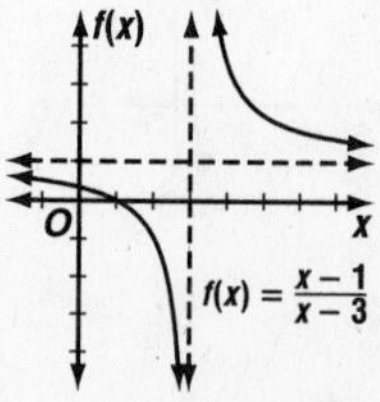

24.

x	$f(x)$
−8	0.71
−4	1.67
−2	5
−1	undefined
−0.5	−10
4	−1
8	−0.56

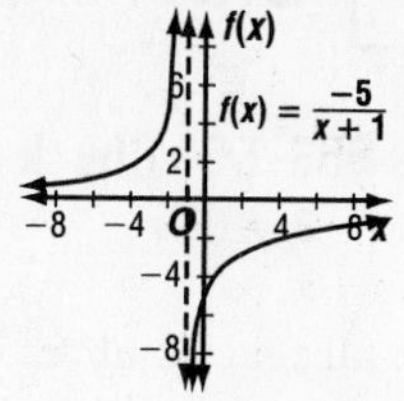

25.

x	$f(x)$
−8	−14
−6	undefined
0	−6
4	−2

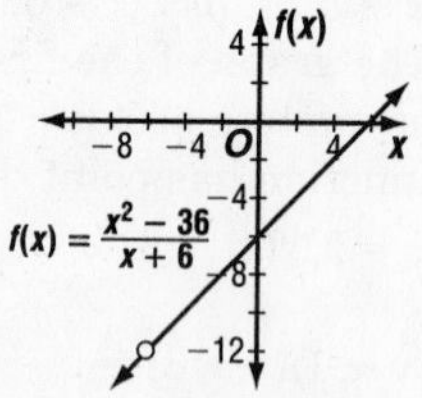

26.

x	$f(x)$
−2	−0.1875
0	−0.75
1	−3
2	undefined
2.5	−12
4	−0.75
6	−0.1875

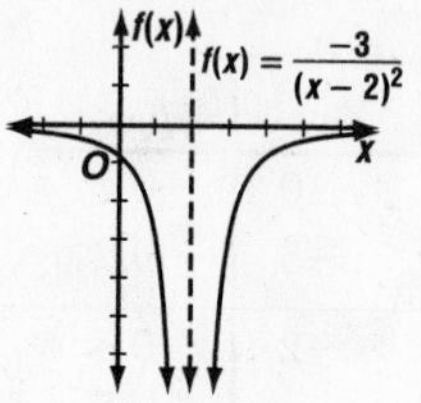

27.

x	$f(x)$
−8	5.71
−4	6.67
−2	10
−1	undefined
0	0
4	4
8	4.44

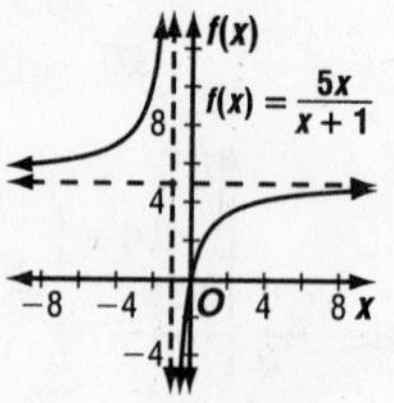

28.

x	$f(x)$
−3	−2
−1	0
1	undefined
3	4

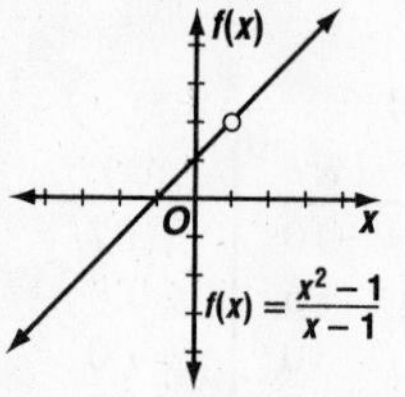

29.

x	$f(x)$
−6	0.11
−4	1
−3.5	4
−3	undefined
−2.5	4
−1	0.25
1	0.0625

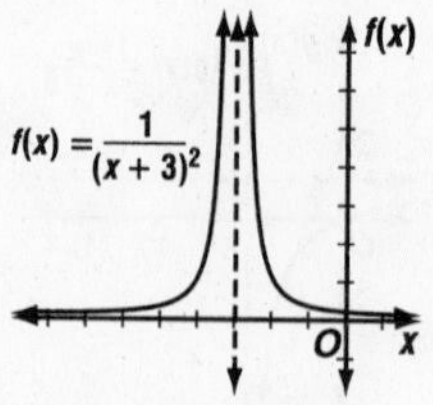

30.

x	$f(x)$
−7	0.1875
−5.5	0.92
−5	undefined
−4.5	−1.1
−3	−0.75
0.5	−1.1
1	undefined
1.5	0.92
2	0.43

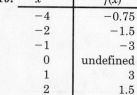

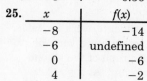

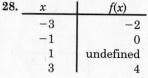

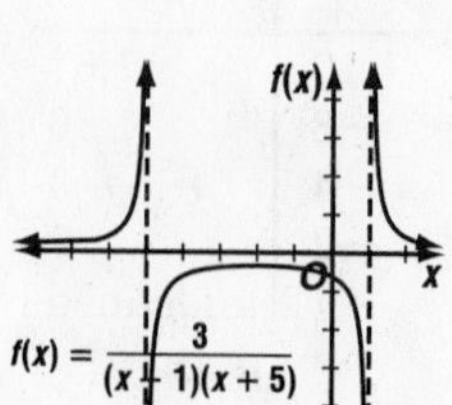

31.

x	$f(x)$
−4	−0.07
−2.5	−0.36
−2	undefined
−1.5	0.44
0	0.17
2.5	0.44
3	undefined
3.5	−0.36
5	−0.07

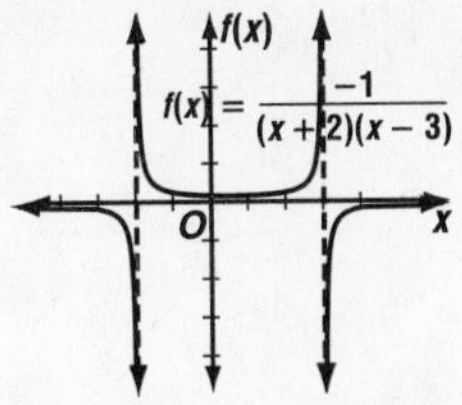

32.

x	$f(x)$
−5	−0.2
−2	−0.67
−1.5	−1.2
−1	undefined
−0.5	0.67
0	0
0.5	−0.67
1	undefined
1.5	1.2
4	0.27

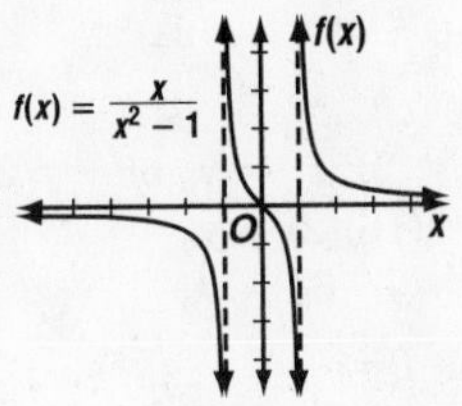

33.

x	$f(x)$
−5	−0.29
−2.5	−1.56
−2	undefined
−1.5	1.43
0	0.25
1.5	−0.29
2	undefined
2.5	0.67
4	0.25

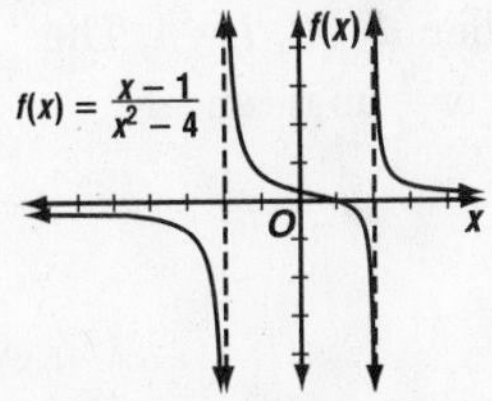

34a. The first graph has a vertical asymptote at $x = 0$ and a horizontal asymptote at $y = 0$. The second graph is translated 7 units up and has a vertical asymptote at $x = 0$ and a horizontal asymptote at $y = 7$.

34b. Both graphs have a vertical asymptote at $x = 0$ and a horizontal asymptote at $y = 0$. The second graph is stretched by a factor of 4.

34c. The first graph has a vertical asymptote at $x = 0$ and a horizontal asymptote at $y = 0$. The second graph is translated 5 units to the left and has a vertical asymptote at $x = -5$ and a horizontal asymptote at $y = 0$.

34d.

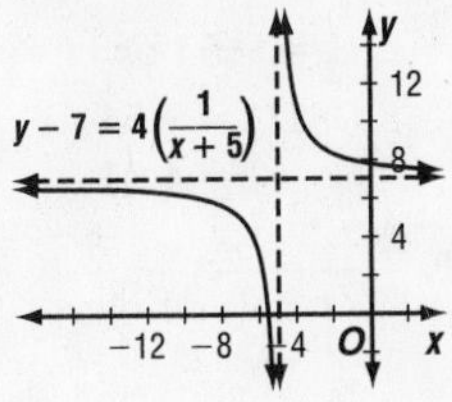

35a. $C = \frac{y}{y + 12} \cdot D$

$= \frac{8}{8 + 12} \cdot 250$

$= 100$; 100 milligrams

35b.

y	C
−16	4
−13	13
−12	undefined
−11	−11
0	0
16	0.57

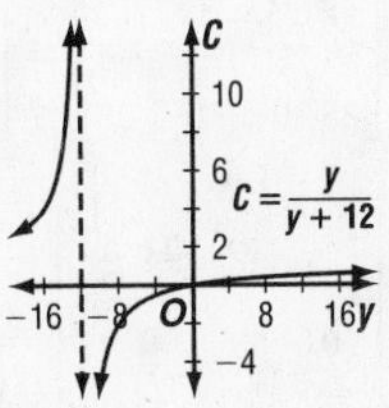

The graph has a vertical asymptote at $y = -12$ and a horizontal asymptote at $C = 1$.

36a. $V_f = \frac{m_1 - m_2}{m_1 + m_2} v_i$

$= \frac{m_1 - 7}{m_1 + 7} \cdot 5$

m_1	V_f
−24	9.1
−8	75
−7	undefined
−6	−65
0	−5
12	1.3

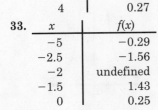

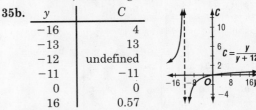

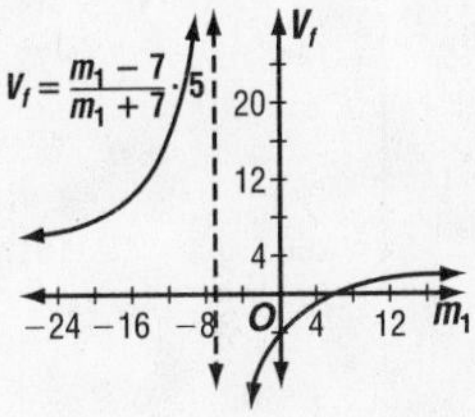

36b. $V_f = \frac{m_1 - 7}{m_1 + 7} \cdot 5$

$= \frac{5 - 7}{5 + 7} \cdot 5$

≈ -0.83; −0.83 m/s

37. $[f \circ g](x) = f(-x)$
$= -x$

$[g \circ f](x) = g(x)$
$= -x$; no

38.

x	$g(x)$
0	6
1	−1
2	2
3	−3
4	−106
5	11

x	$g(x)$
0.3	0.8151
0.4	−0.1504
1.2	−0.2784
1.3	0.1331
2.6	0.1136
2.7	−0.5529

x	$g(x)$
4.7	−0.9889
4.8	2.3136

0.4, 1.3, 2.6, 4.7

39. $6y^2 - 34x^2 = 204$

$\frac{y^2}{34} - \frac{x^2}{6} = 1$

40. $\bar{x} - 40 = 260$ $\quad\bar{x} + 40 = 340$

$\bar{x} - 2(40) = 220$ $\quad\bar{x} + 2(40) = 380$

$\bar{x} - 3(40) = 180$ $\quad\bar{x} + 3(40) = 420$

40a. 10,000(0.68) = 6800 **40b.** 10,000(0.95) = 9500

40c. 10,000(0.50) = 5000 **40d.** 10,000(0.50) = 5000

40e. 10,000(0.025) = 250 **40f.** 10,000(0.005) = 50

41. $b^2 - 4ac = (-10)^2 - 4(1)(25)$

$= 0$; 1R, Q

$x = \frac{10 \pm \sqrt{0}}{2(1)}$

$= 5$

42. $$\begin{bmatrix} 8 & -3 & -4 & 6 \\ 4 & 9 & -2 & -4 \\ 6 & 12 & 5 & -1 \end{bmatrix} = \begin{bmatrix} 8 & -3 & -4 & 6 \\ 4 & 9 & -2 & -4 \\ 38 & 0 & -11 & 23 \end{bmatrix} = \begin{bmatrix} 24 & -9 & -12 & 18 \\ 4 & 9 & -2 & -4 \\ 38 & 0 & 11 & 23 \end{bmatrix}$$

$$= \begin{bmatrix} 28 & 0 & -14 & 14 \\ 4 & 9 & -2 & -4 \\ 38 & 0 & -11 & 23 \end{bmatrix} = \begin{bmatrix} 28 & 0 & -14 & 14 \\ -28 & -63 & 14 & 28 \\ 38 & 0 & -11 & 23 \end{bmatrix}$$

$$= \begin{bmatrix} 28 & 0 & -14 & 14 \\ 0 & -63 & 0 & 42 \\ 38 & 0 & -11 & 23 \end{bmatrix} = \begin{bmatrix} 28 & 0 & -14 & 14 \\ 0 & 1 & 0 & -\frac{2}{3} \\ 38 & 0 & -11 & 23 \end{bmatrix}$$

$$= \begin{bmatrix} 14 & 0 & -7 & 7 \\ 0 & 1 & 0 & -\frac{2}{3} \\ 38 & 0 & -11 & 23 \end{bmatrix} = \begin{bmatrix} -154 & 0 & 77 & -77 \\ 0 & 1 & 0 & -\frac{2}{3} \\ 38 & 0 & -11 & 23 \end{bmatrix}$$

$$= \begin{bmatrix} -154 & 0 & 77 & -77 \\ 0 & 1 & 0 & -\frac{2}{3} \\ 266 & 0 & -77 & 161 \end{bmatrix} = \begin{bmatrix} 112 & 0 & 0 & 84 \\ 0 & 1 & 0 & -\frac{2}{3} \\ 266 & 0 & -77 & 161 \end{bmatrix}$$

$$= \begin{bmatrix} 1 & 0 & 0 & \frac{3}{4} \\ 0 & 1 & 0 & -\frac{2}{3} \\ 266 & 0 & -77 & 161 \end{bmatrix} = \begin{bmatrix} 1 & 0 & 0 & \frac{3}{4} \\ 0 & 1 & 0 & -\frac{2}{3} \\ 0 & 0 & -77 & -38.5 \end{bmatrix}$$

$$= \begin{bmatrix} 1 & 0 & 0 & \frac{3}{4} \\ 0 & 1 & 0 & -\frac{2}{3} \\ 0 & 0 & 1 & \frac{1}{2} \end{bmatrix}; \left(\frac{3}{4}, -\frac{2}{3}, \frac{1}{2}\right)$$

43. $3x - 2y = 12$
$3(0) - 2y = 12$
$-2y = 12$
$y = -6$

$3x - 2y = 12$
$3x - 2(0) = 12$
$3x = 12$
$x = 4$

9-2 Direct, Inverse, and Joint Variation

Page 559 Check for Understanding

1. x increases if $k > 0$ and decreases if $k < 0$.
2. k is constant and never varies.
3. Direct; as the value of x increases, the value of y increases.
4. Sample answer: direct variation, wages and hours worked; inverse variation, distance traveled and amount of gas in car.
5. inverse, – 5
6. joint, 2
7. $\frac{x}{y} = 3$
$x = 3y$
$\frac{1}{3}x = y$; direct, $\frac{1}{3}$

8. $\frac{x_1}{y_2} = \frac{x_2}{y_1}$
$\frac{10}{y_2} = \frac{x_2}{5}$
$y_2x_2 = 50$
$y_2 = \frac{50}{x_2}$ or $y = \frac{50}{x}$
$y_2 = \frac{50}{2}$
$y_2 = 25$

9. $\frac{y_1}{x_1} = \frac{y_2}{x_2}$
$\frac{15}{3} = \frac{y_2}{x_2}$
$15x_2 = 3y_2$
$5x_2 = y_2$ or $y = 5x$
$5(12) = y_2$
$60 = y_2$

10. $\frac{y_1}{x_1z_1} = \frac{y^2}{x_2z_2}$
$\frac{80}{(5)(8)} = \frac{y_2}{x_2z_2}$
$2 = \frac{y_2}{x_2z_2}$
$2x_2z_2 = y_2$ or $y = 2xz$
$2(16)(2) = y_2$
$64 = y_2$

11a. $I = \frac{k}{d^2}$

11b. $I = \frac{16}{d^2}$

d	I
−4	1
−1	16
0	undefined
1	16
4	1

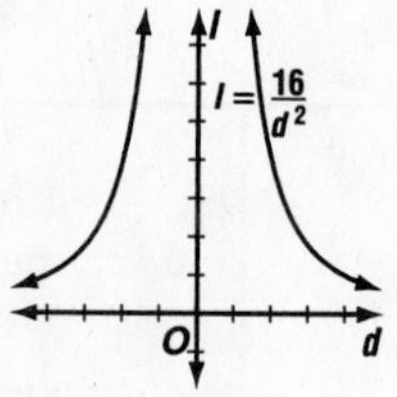

11c. When $d = 1$, $I = 16$; when $d = 2$, $I = 4$. The sound will be heard $\frac{4}{16}$ or $\frac{1}{4}$ as intensely.

Pages 559–561 Exercises

12. direct, $\frac{1}{5}$

13. $\frac{x}{y} = -7$
$x = -7y$
$-\frac{1}{7}x = y$; direct, $-\frac{1}{7}$

14. $x = 4y$
$\frac{1}{4}x = y$; direct, $\frac{1}{4}$

15. $x = \frac{1}{y}$
$y = \frac{1}{x}$; inverse, 1

16. joint, $\frac{1}{2}$

17. $\frac{2}{3}a = -\frac{1}{2}b$
$-\frac{4}{3}a = b$; direct, $-\frac{4}{3}$

18. $\frac{y_1}{x_1} = \frac{y_2}{x_2}$
$\frac{12}{3} = \frac{y_2}{x_2}$
$4x_2 = y_2$ or $y = 4x$
$4(16) = y_2$
$64 = y_2$

19. $\frac{t_1}{r_2} = \frac{t_2}{r_1}$
$\frac{-3}{r_2} = \frac{t_2}{18}$
$r_2t_2 = -54$ or $rt = -54$
$r_2(-11) = -54$
$r_2 \approx 4.91$

20. $\frac{y_1}{x_1} = \frac{y_2}{x_2}$
$\frac{0.5}{6} = \frac{y_2}{x_2}$
$0.5x_2 = 6y_2$
$\frac{1}{12}x_2 = y_2$ or $y = \frac{x}{12}$
$\frac{1}{12}(10) = y_2$
$0.8\overline{3} = y$

21. $\frac{x_1}{y_2} = \frac{x_2}{y_1}$
$\frac{25}{y_2} = \frac{x_2}{2}$
$x_2y_2 = 50$ or $xy = 50$
$x_2(40) = 50$
$x_2 = 1.25$

22. $\frac{y_1}{x_1 z_1} = \frac{y_2}{x_2 z_2}$

$\frac{16}{(2)(5)} = \frac{y_2}{(8)(3)}$

$1.6 = \frac{y_2}{24}$

$38.4 = y_2$

23. $\frac{A_1}{b_1 h_1} = \frac{A_2}{b_2 h_2}$

$\frac{180}{(15)(12)} = \frac{1615}{(42.5)h_2}$

$1 = \frac{1615}{42.5h_2}$

$42.5h_2 = 1615$

$h_2 = 38$; 38 meters

24. $A = kbh$

$100 = k(25)(8)$

$\frac{1}{2} = k$

$A = \frac{1}{2}bh$

25. $\frac{y_1}{x_1} = \frac{y_2}{x_2}$

$\frac{1}{5} = \frac{y_2}{22}$

$22 = 5y_2$

$\frac{22}{5} = y_2$

26. $\frac{x_1}{y_2} = \frac{x_2}{y_1}$

$\frac{14}{2} = \frac{x_2}{7}$

$49 = x_2$

27. $\frac{y_1}{x_1} = \frac{y_2}{x_2}$

$\frac{\frac{2}{5}}{\frac{1}{20}} = \frac{y_2}{\frac{1}{2}}$

$\frac{1}{5} = \frac{1}{20}y_2$

$4 = y_2$

28. $\frac{x_1}{y_2} = \frac{x_2}{y_1}$

$\frac{16}{y_2} = \frac{\frac{2}{3}}{\frac{1}{8}}$

$\frac{2}{3}y_2 = 2$

$y_2 = 3$

29a. $C = 2\pi r$; directly

29b. 2π

30a. $V = \frac{4}{3}\pi r^3$; directly

30b. $\frac{4}{3}\pi$

31a. $P = \frac{4.3}{10}d$

$= 0.43d$

31b. $P = 0.43(60)$

$= 25.8$; 25.8 psi

31c. $65 = 0.43d$

$150 \approx d$; about 150 feet

31d.

d	P
0	0
1	0.43
2	0.86
3	1.29

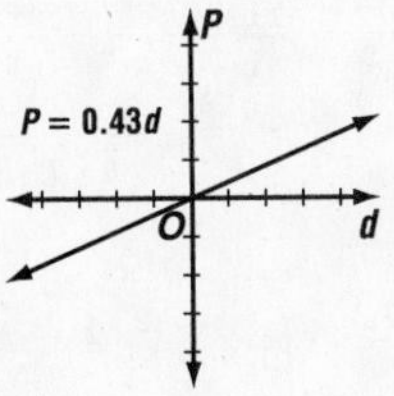

32. $30{,}000 \cdot \frac{1}{6} = 5000$; approximately 5000 pounds

33a. like one third of a month

33b. like 5 weeks

33c. $\frac{30}{5} = 6$; 6×10 min $= 60$ min or like 1 hour

34a. $C = \frac{kP_1P_2}{d^2}$

$29{,}000 = \frac{k(966{,}000)(490{,}000)}{575^2}$

$29{,}000 \approx 1{,}431{,}652.17k$

$0.02 \approx k$; $C = \frac{0.02P_1P_2}{d^2}$

34b. $C = \frac{0.02(610{,}000)(490{,}000)}{399^2}$

$\approx 37{,}550.02$; 37,550 calls

34c. $112{,}451 = \frac{0.02(610{,}000)(2{,}768{,}000)}{d^2}$

$112{,}451d^2 = 33{,}769{,}600{,}000$

$d^2 \approx 300{,}305.02$

$d \approx 548$; 548 miles

34d. No, $d \neq 0$.

35. $\frac{500}{10} = \frac{x}{30}$

$15000 = 10x$

$1500 = x$; 1500 BTU/h

36.

x	$f(x)$
−5	1.25
−2	2
−1.5	3
−1	undefined
−0.5	−1
0	0
3	0.75

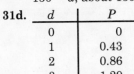

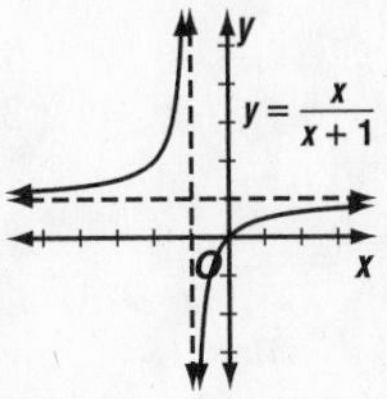

37. $g[h(x)] = g(-x)$
$= -(-x)$
$= x$

$h[g(x)] = h(-x)$
$= -(-x)$
$= x$

38.

2⌋	3	0	8	0	−1
		6	12	40	80
	3	6	20	40	79

−1⌋	3	0	8	0	−1
		−3	3	−11	11
	3	−3	11	−11	10

39. $2a = 12$
$a = 6$

$2b = 8$
$b = 4$

$\frac{(x + 2)^2}{16} + \frac{(y - 3)^2}{36} = 1$

40. $d^2 \geq 3d + 28$

$d^2 - 3d - 28 \geq 0$

$(d - 7)(d + 4) \geq 0$

$d - 7 \geq 0$ and $d + 4 \geq 0$ or $d - 7 \leq 0$ and $d + 4 \leq 0$

$d \geq 7$ $\quad d \geq -4$ $\quad d \leq 7$ $\quad d \leq -4$

$d \geq 7$ or $d \leq -4$

$\{d \mid d \leq -4$ or $d \geq 7\}$

41. Let x = the number of passengers over 100.
Then $5 - 0.02x$ = the new price.
And $100 + x$ = number of passengers.

$I = (100 + x)(5 - 0.02x)$
$= 500 + 3x - 0.02x^2$
$= -0.02(x^2 - 150x + 75^2) + 500 + 112.5$
$= -0.02(x - 75)^2 + 612.5$

The vertex is (75, 612.5). The profit is maximized when $x = 75$. So, $100 + x$ is 175.
175 passengers will produce a maximum profit.

42a. $|w - 7.32| \leq 0.002$

$-0.002 \leq w - 7.32 \leq 0.002$

$7.318 \leq w \leq 7.322$

maximum: 7.322 centimeters
minimum: 7.318 centimeters

42b. $5.24 - 5.18 = 0.06$

$\frac{0.06}{2} = 0.03$; 0.03 centimeters

9-3 Multiplying and Dividing Rational Expressions

Pages 565–566 Check for Understanding

1. No. For example, $\frac{x^2-4}{2x^2+12x+18} = \frac{(x-2)(x+2)}{2(x+3)(x+3)}$. There are no common factors, so the expression is in simplest form.
2. When the denominator equals 0.
3. $\frac{13b}{9a}$
4. $ab - bc = b(a-c)$; $3xy + 4tr$; 1
5. GCF: $6x$

$$\frac{30xy}{12x^2} = \frac{5y \cdot 6x}{2x \cdot 6x} = \frac{5y}{2x}$$

6. GCF: $3xy^2$

$$\frac{-3xy^4}{21x^2y^2} = \frac{-y^2 \cdot 3xy^2}{7x \cdot 3xy^2} = \frac{-y^2}{7x}$$

7. GCF $= c + 5$

$$\frac{c+5}{2c+10} = \frac{1(c+5)}{2(c+5)} = \frac{1}{2}$$

8. $$\frac{m^3}{3n} \div \left(-\frac{m^4}{9n^2}\right) = \frac{m^3}{3n} \cdot \left(-\frac{9n^2}{m^4}\right) = -\frac{9m^3n^2}{3m^4n} = -\frac{3n}{m}$$

9. $$\frac{3ab}{4ac} \cdot \frac{6a^2}{3b^2} = \frac{18a^3b}{12ab^2c} = \frac{3a^2}{2bc}$$

10. $$-\frac{-3}{5a} \div \left(-\frac{9}{15ab}\right) = -\frac{-3}{5a} \cdot \left(-\frac{15ab}{9}\right) = \frac{-45ab}{45a} = -b$$

11. $$\left(\frac{3a^2}{a+2}\right)\left(\frac{a+2}{a^2}\right) = \frac{3a^2(a+2)}{a^2(a+2)} = 3$$

12. $$\frac{5}{m-3} \div \frac{10}{m-3} = \frac{5}{m-3} \cdot \frac{m-3}{10} = \frac{5(m-3)}{10(m-3)} = \frac{1}{2}$$

13. $$\left(\frac{4a+4}{3}\right)\left(\frac{1}{a+1}\right) = \frac{4a+4}{3(a+1)} = \frac{4(a+1)}{3(a+1)} = \frac{4}{3}$$

14. $$\frac{w^2-11w+24}{w^2-18w+80} \cdot \frac{w^2-15w+50}{w^2-9w+20} = \frac{(w-8)(w-3)}{(w-10)(w-8)} \cdot \frac{(w-10)(w-5)}{(w-5)(w-4)} = \frac{w-3}{w-4}$$

15. $$\frac{\frac{2y}{y^2-4}}{\frac{3}{y^2-4y+4}} = \frac{2y}{y^2-4} \div \frac{3}{y^2-4y+4} = \frac{2y}{y^2-4} \cdot \frac{y^2-4y+4}{3} = \frac{2y}{(y-2)(y+2)} \cdot \frac{(y-2)(y-2)}{3} = \frac{2y(y-2)}{3(y+2)}$$

16. $$A = \frac{1}{2}b \cdot h$$
$$4x^2 - 2x - 6 = \frac{1}{2}b(x+1)$$
$$\frac{4x^2-2x-6}{x+1} = \frac{1}{2}b$$
$$\frac{2(4x^2-2x-6)}{x+1} = b$$
$$\frac{2 \cdot 2(x+1)(2x-3)}{x+1} = b$$
$$4(2x-3) = b$$
$8x - 12 = b$; $(8x - 12)$ meters

Pages 566–568 Exercises

17. $$\frac{45xy^3}{20y^7} = \frac{9x \cdot 5y^3}{4y^4 \cdot 5y^3} = \frac{9x}{4y^4}$$

18. $$\frac{(-3x^2y)^3}{9x^2y^2} = \frac{-27x^6y^3}{9x^2y^2} = \frac{-3x^4y \cdot 9x^2y^2}{1 \cdot 9x^2y^2} = -3x^4y$$

19. $$\frac{5x-5}{x^2-1} = \frac{5(x-1)}{(x-1)(x+1)} = \frac{5}{x+1}$$

20. $$\frac{p^3}{2q} \div \frac{-p^2}{4q} = \frac{p^3}{2q} \cdot \frac{4q}{-p^2} = \frac{4p^3q}{-2p^2q} = -2p$$

21. $$\frac{y^2}{x+2} \div \frac{y}{x+2} = \frac{y^2}{x+2} \cdot \frac{x+2}{y} = \frac{y^2(x+2)}{y(x+2)} = y$$

22. $$\frac{3h}{h+1}\left(\frac{1}{h-2}\right) = \frac{3h}{(h+1)(h-2)}$$

23. $$\frac{2a^2}{5b^2c} \cdot \frac{3bc^2}{8a^2} = \frac{2 \cdot 3 \cdot a^2bc^2}{5 \cdot 2 \cdot 4 \cdot a^2b^2c} = \frac{3c}{20b}$$

24. $$\frac{35}{16x^2} \div \frac{21}{4x} = \frac{35}{16x^2} \cdot \frac{4x}{21} = \frac{4 \cdot 7 \cdot 5 \cdot x}{4 \cdot 4 \cdot 7 \cdot 3 \cdot x^2} = \frac{5}{12x}$$

25. $$\frac{2x^3y}{z^5} \div \left(-\frac{4xy}{z^3}\right)^2 = \frac{2x^3y}{z^5} \cdot \left(-\frac{z^3}{4xy}\right)^2 = \frac{2x^3y}{z^5} \cdot \frac{z^6}{16x^2y^2} = \frac{2 \cdot x^3yz^6}{2 \cdot 8x^2y^2z^5} = \frac{xz}{8y}$$

26. $$\frac{(ab)^2}{c} \cdot \frac{cx^2}{xa^3b} = \frac{a^2b^2cx^2}{a^3bcx} = \frac{bx}{a}$$

27. $$\left(\frac{2x}{y}\right)^2 \cdot \frac{5}{6x} = \frac{4x^2}{y^2} \cdot \frac{5}{6x} = \frac{2 \cdot 2 \cdot 5x^2}{2 \cdot 3xy^2} = \frac{10x}{3y^2}$$

28. $$\frac{t+3}{t-1} \cdot \frac{t-1}{t} = \frac{(t+3)(t+1)}{t(t+1)} = \frac{t+3}{t}$$

29. $$\frac{(xy)}{a^3} \div \frac{x^2y^3}{(ab)^3} = \frac{xy}{a^3} \cdot \frac{a^3b^3}{x^2y^3} = \frac{a^3b^3xy}{a^3x^2y^3} = \frac{b^3}{xy^2}$$

30. $\dfrac{4a^3b}{7c^2d^3} \cdot \dfrac{21c^3d}{16abc^2} = \dfrac{4 \cdot 3 \cdot 7a^3bc^3d}{4 \cdot 4 \cdot 7abc^4d^3}$

$= \dfrac{3a^2}{4cd^2}$

31. $\dfrac{9x^2y^3}{(5xyz)^2} \div \dfrac{(3xy)^3}{20x^2y} = \dfrac{9x^2y^3}{25x^2y^2z^2} \cdot \dfrac{20x^2y}{27x^3y^3}$

$= \dfrac{9 \cdot 4 \cdot 5x^4y^4}{9 \cdot 3 \cdot 5 \cdot 5 \cdot x^5y^5z^2}$

$= \dfrac{4}{15xyz^2}$

32. $\dfrac{3x+6}{7x-7} \cdot \dfrac{14x-14}{5x+10} = \dfrac{3(x+2)}{7(x-1)} \cdot \dfrac{14(x-1)}{5(x+2)}$

$= \dfrac{3 \cdot 7 \cdot 2(x+2)(x-1)}{7 \cdot 5(x+2)(x-1)}$

$= \dfrac{6}{5}$

33. $\dfrac{3x^2-3}{2x^2+8x+6} \div \dfrac{5x^2-10x+5}{4x+12}$

$= \dfrac{3x^2-3}{2x^2+8x+6} \cdot \dfrac{4x+12}{5x^2-10x+5}$

$= \dfrac{3(x-1)(x+1)}{2(x+3)(x+1)} \cdot \dfrac{4(x+3)}{5(x-1)(x+1)}$

$= \dfrac{3 \cdot 2 \cdot 2(x-1)(x+1)(x+3)}{5 \cdot 2(x-1)(x+1)(x+3)(x-1)}$

$= \dfrac{6}{5(x-1)}$

34. $\dfrac{4x^2-4}{9(x+1)^2} \cdot \dfrac{3x+3}{2x-2} = \dfrac{4(x-1)(x+1)}{9(x+1)(x+1)} \cdot \dfrac{3(x+1)}{2(x-1)}$

$= \dfrac{2 \cdot 2 \cdot 3(x-1)(x+1)(x+1)}{2 \cdot 3 \cdot 3(x-1)(x+1)(x+1)}$

$= \dfrac{2}{3}$

35. $\dfrac{12x+6}{21x^2-21} \div \dfrac{6x^2+9x+3}{7x^3-7x^2}$

$= \dfrac{12x+6}{21x^2-21} \cdot \dfrac{7x^3-7x^2}{6x^2+9x+3}$

$= \dfrac{6(2x+1)}{21(x-1)(x+1)} \cdot \dfrac{7x^2(x-1)}{3(2x+1)(x+1)}$

$= \dfrac{2 \cdot 3 \cdot 7x^2(2x+1)(x-1)}{3 \cdot 3 \cdot 7(2x+1)(x-1)(x+1)(x+1)}$

$= \dfrac{2x^2}{3(x+1)(x+1)}$ or $\dfrac{2x^2}{3(x+1)^2}$

36. $\dfrac{12x^2+6x-6}{4(x+1)^2} \div \dfrac{6x-3}{2x+10} = \dfrac{12x^2+6x-6}{4(x+1)^2} \cdot \dfrac{2x+10}{6x-3}$

$= \dfrac{6(2x-1)(x+1)}{4(x+1)(x+1)} \cdot \dfrac{2(x+5)}{3(2x-1)}$

$= \dfrac{2 \cdot 2 \cdot 3(2x-1)(x+1)(x+5)}{2 \cdot 2 \cdot 3(2x-1)(x+1)(x+1)}$

$= \dfrac{x+5}{x+1}$

37. $\dfrac{5x^2+10x-75}{4x^2-24x-28} \cdot \dfrac{2x^2-10x-28}{x^2+7x+10}$

$= \dfrac{5(x+5)(x-3)}{4(x-7)(x+1)} \cdot \dfrac{2(x-7)(x+2)}{(x+5)(x+2)}$

$= \dfrac{5 \cdot 2(x+5)(x-7)(x+2)(x-3)}{2 \cdot 2(x+5)(x-7)(x+2)(x+1)}$

$= \dfrac{5(x-3)}{2(x+1)}$

38. $\dfrac{\frac{x+y}{2x-y}}{\frac{x+y}{2x+y}} = \dfrac{x+y}{2x-y} \div \dfrac{x+y}{2x+y}$

$= \dfrac{x+y}{2x-y} \cdot \dfrac{2x+y}{x+y}$

$= \dfrac{2x+y}{2x-y}$

39. $\dfrac{\frac{m+n}{5}}{\frac{m^2+n^2}{15}} = \dfrac{m+n}{5} \div \dfrac{m^2+n^2}{15}$

$= \dfrac{m+n}{5} \cdot \dfrac{15}{m^2+n^2}$

$= \dfrac{3(m+n)}{m^2+n^2}$

40. $\dfrac{\frac{6y^2-6}{8y^2+8y}}{\frac{3y-3}{4y^2+4y}} = \dfrac{6y^2-6}{8y^2+8y} \div \dfrac{3y-3}{4y^2+4y}$

$= \dfrac{6y^2-6}{8y^2+8y} \cdot \dfrac{4y^2+4y}{3y-3}$

$= \dfrac{6(y-1)(y+1)}{8y(y+1)} \cdot \dfrac{4y(y+1)}{3(y-1)}$

$= \dfrac{2 \cdot 2 \cdot 2 \cdot 3(y-1)(y+1)(y+1)}{2 \cdot 2 \cdot 2 \cdot 3(y-1)(y+1)}$

$= y+1$

41. $\dfrac{\frac{5x^2-5x-30}{45-15x}}{\frac{6+x-x^2}{4x-12}} = \dfrac{5x^2-5x-30}{45-15x} \div \dfrac{6+x-x^2}{4x-12}$

$= \dfrac{5x^2-5x-30}{45-15x} \cdot \dfrac{4x-12}{6+x-x^2}$

$= \dfrac{5(x-3)(x+2)}{-15(-3+x)} \cdot \dfrac{4(x-3)}{-1(x-3)(x+2)}$

$= \dfrac{5 \cdot 4(x-3)(x-3)(x+2)}{5 \cdot 3(x-3)(x-3)(x+2)}$

$= \dfrac{4}{3}$

42. $\dfrac{x^{-1}+y^{-1}}{x^{-1}-y^{-1}} = \dfrac{\frac{1}{x}+\frac{1}{y}}{\frac{1}{x}-\frac{1}{y}}$

$= \dfrac{\frac{y+x}{xy}}{\frac{y-x}{xy}}$

$= \dfrac{y+x}{xy} \div \dfrac{y-x}{xy}$

$= \dfrac{y+x}{xy} \cdot \dfrac{xy}{y-x}$

$= \dfrac{y+x}{y-x}$

43. Parallelogram A: $A = bh$

$12x^2 + 2x - 2 = b(2x-5)$

$\dfrac{12x^2+2x-2}{2x-5} = b$

$\dfrac{2(3x-1)(2x+1)}{2x-5} = b$

Parallelogram B: $A = bh$

$2x^2 - 3x - 5 = b(3x-1)$

$\dfrac{2x^2-3x-5}{3x-1} = b$

$\dfrac{(2x-5)(x+1)}{3x-1} = b$

Rectangle C: $A = \ell w$

$= \left(\dfrac{2(3x-1)(2x+1)}{2x-5}\right)\left(\dfrac{(2x-5)(x+1)}{3x-1}\right)$

$= 2(2x+1)(x+1)$

$= 4x^2 + 6x + 2$;

$(4x^2 + 6x + 2)$ square feet

44.
$$c^2 = a^2 + b^2$$
$$(x + 10)^2 = (x + 2)^2 + (x + 9)^2$$
$$x^2 + 20x + 100 = x^2 + 4x + 4 + x^2 + 18x + 81$$
$$0 = x^2 + 2x - 15$$
$$0 = (x - 3)(x + 5)$$
$x - 3 = 0$ or $x + 5 = 0$
$x = 3$ $\quad x = -5$
$x + 2 = 3 + 2 = 5$ $\quad x + 9 = 3 + 9 = 12$ $\quad x + 10 = 3 + 10 = 13$
5 inches, 12 inches, 13 inches

45. $P_1V_1 = P_2V_2$
$1(16) = (0.75)V_2$
$21\frac{1}{3} = V_2$; $21\frac{1}{3}$ cubic meters

46. $x^4 + 5x^3 + 6x^2 = 0$
$x^2(x^2 + 5x + 6) = 0$
$x^2(x + 3)(x + 2) = 0$
$x^2 = 0$ or $x + 3 = 0$ or $x + 2 = 0$
$x = 0$ $\quad x = -3$ $\quad x = -2$; 0, 0, −3, −2

47.
$$f(x) = x^2 - \frac{1}{2}x$$
$$f(x + h) = (x + h)^2 - \frac{1}{2}(x + h)$$
$$= x^2 + 2xh + h^2 - \frac{1}{2}x - \frac{1}{2}h$$

48.
$$(x + 2)^2 + (y - 1)^2 = 81$$
$$(x - (-2))^2 + (y - 1)^2 = 9^2$$
center: (−2, 1)
radius: 9 units

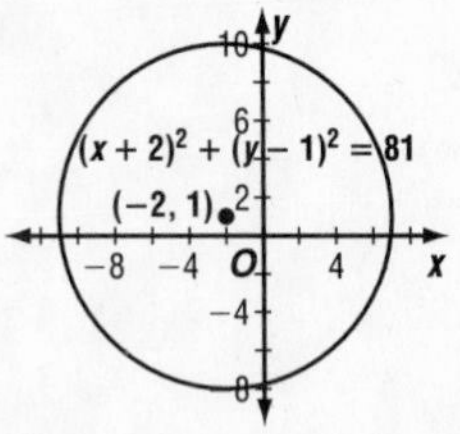

49a.
$$\bar{x} = \frac{\left[3(22) + 2(14) + 33 + 2(11) + 25 + 2(36) + 35 + 28 + 20 + 15 + 21 + 12 + 10\right]}{18}$$
$$= \frac{387}{18}$$
$$= 21.5$$

$$SD = \sqrt{\frac{\left[3(22 - 21.5)^2 + 2(14 - 21.5)^2 + (33 - 21.5)^2 + 2(11 - 21.5)^2 + (25 - 21.5)^2 + 2(36 - 21.5)^2 + (35 - 21.5)^2 + (28 - 21.5)^2 + (20 - 21.5)^2 + (15 - 21.5)^2 + (21 - 21.5)^2 + (12 - 21.5)^2 + (10 - 21.5)^2\right]}{18}}$$
$$= \sqrt{\frac{\left[0.75 + 112.5 + 132.25 + 220.5 + 12.25 + 420.5 + 182.25 + 42.25 + 2.25 + 42.25 + 0.25 + 90.25 + 132.25\right]}{18}}$$
$$\approx \sqrt{77.264}$$
$$\approx 8.8$$

49b.
$$\bar{x} = \frac{\left[32 + 16 + 22 + 3(24) + 2(23) + 13 + 31 + 15 + 2(21) + 27 + 30 + 12\right]}{16}$$
$$= \frac{358}{16}$$
$$\approx 22.38$$

(Continued next column)

$$SD = \sqrt{\frac{\left[(32 - 22.38)^2 + (16 - 22.38)^2 + (22 - 22.38)^2 + 3(24 - 22.38)^2 + 2(23 - 22.38)^2 + (13 - 22.38)^2 + (31 - 22.38)^2 + (15 - 22.38)^2 + 2(21 - 22.38)^2 + (27 - 22.38)^2 + (30 - 22.38)^2 + (12 - 22.38)^2\right]}{16}}$$
$$= \sqrt{\frac{\left[92.5444 + 40.7044 + 0.1444 + 7.8732 + 0.7688 + 87.9844 + 74.3044 + 54.4644 + 3.8088 + 21.3444 + 58.0644 + 107.7444\right]}{16}}$$
$$= \sqrt{34.3594}$$
$$\approx 5.9$$

49c. $\bar{x} = (23 + 2(28) + 2(16) + 2(30) + 2(12) + 22 + 11 + 33 + 3(25) + 21 + 29 + 18 + 24 + 13) \div 20 = 441 \div 20 = 22.05$

$$SD = \sqrt{\frac{\left[(23 - 22.05)^2 + 2(28 - 22.05)^2 + 2(16 - 22.05)^2 + 2(30 - 22.05)^2 + 2(12 - 22.05)^2 + (22 - 22.05)^2 + (11 - 22.05)^2 + (33 - 22.05)^2 + 3(25 - 22.05)^2 + (21 - 22.05)^2 + (29 - 22.05)^2 + (18 - 22.05)^2 + (24 - 22.05)^2 + (13 - 22.05)^2\right]}{20}}$$
$$= \sqrt{\frac{\left[0.9025 + 70.805 + 73.205 + 126.405 + 202.005 + 0.0025 + 122.1025 + 119.9025 + 26.1075 + 1.1025 + 48.3025 + 16.4025 + 3.8025 + 81.9025\right]}{20}}$$
$$= \sqrt{44.6475}$$
$$\approx 6.7$$

49d. Fitright Shoes

50a. $(30 + x)(20 + x) = 2(30 \cdot 20)$
$600 + 50x + x^2 = 1200$
$x^2 + 50x - 600 = 0$
$(x + 60)(x - 10) = 0$
$x + 60 = 0$ or $x - 10 = 0$
$x = -60$ $\quad x = 10$; 10 meters

50b. $30 + x = 30 + 10 = 40$ $\quad 20 + x = 20 + 10 = 30$
40 meters by 30 meters

51.
$$\begin{vmatrix} 2 & -1 & -6 \\ 5 & 0 & 3 \\ -3 & 2 & 11 \end{vmatrix} = 2\begin{vmatrix} 0 & 3 \\ 2 & 11 \end{vmatrix} + 1\begin{vmatrix} 5 & 3 \\ -3 & 11 \end{vmatrix} - 6\begin{vmatrix} 5 & 0 \\ -3 & 2 \end{vmatrix}$$
$$= 2(-6) + 64 - 6(10)$$
$$= -8$$

52. Let x = amount in savings and y = amount in CD.
$x + y = 4000$
$0.065x + 0.08y = 297.50$
$$x = \frac{\begin{vmatrix} 4000 & 1 \\ 297.50 & 0.08 \end{vmatrix}}{\begin{vmatrix} 1 & 1 \\ 0.065 & 0.08 \end{vmatrix}} \qquad y = \frac{\begin{vmatrix} 1 & 4000 \\ 0.065 & 297.50 \end{vmatrix}}{\begin{vmatrix} 1 & 1 \\ 0.065 & 0.08 \end{vmatrix}}$$
$$= \frac{22.5}{0.015} \qquad = \frac{37.5}{0.015}$$
$$= 1500 \qquad = 2500$$
\$2500, CD; \$1500, savings

Page 568 Self Test

1. $x = 4$, $y = 0$
2. $x = -3$, $y = 2$

3.

x	$f(x)$
−6	−0.75
−4	−1.5
−2.5	−6
−2	undefined
−1.5	6
0	1.5
2	0.75

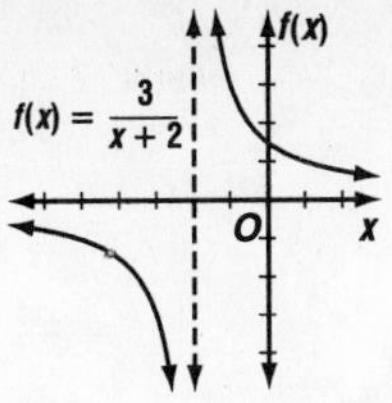

4.

x	$f(x)$
−1	−0.125
1	−0.5
2.5	−8
3	undefined
3.5	−8
5	−0.5
7	−0.125

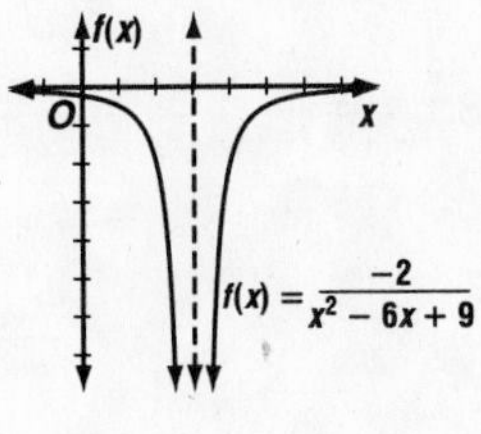

5. $\frac{y_1}{x_1} = \frac{y_2}{x_2}$

$\frac{\frac{1}{5}}{11} = \frac{\frac{2}{5}}{x_2}$

$\frac{1}{5}x_2 = \frac{22}{5}$

$x_2 = 22$

6. $\frac{m_1}{n_2} = \frac{m_2}{n_1}$

$\frac{-8}{\frac{2}{3}} = \frac{m_2}{-2}$

$\frac{2}{3}m_2 = 16$

$m_2 = 24$

7. $\frac{\frac{1}{2}}{640} = \frac{2}{x}$ $\qquad$ $\frac{\frac{3}{2}}{1920} = \frac{2}{x}$

$\frac{1}{2}x = 1280$ $\qquad$ $\frac{3}{2}x = 3840$

$x = 2560$ $\qquad$ $x = 2560$; \$2560

8. $\frac{4xy}{2yz} \cdot \frac{11x^2y}{5y^2} = \frac{2 \cdot 2 \cdot 11x^3y^2}{2 \cdot 5 \cdot y^3 \cdot z}$

$= \frac{22x^3}{5yz}$

9. $\frac{48}{6a + 42} \cdot \frac{7a + 49}{16} = \frac{16 \cdot 3}{6(a + 7)} \cdot \frac{7(a + 7)}{16}$

$= \frac{16 \cdot 3 \cdot 7(a + 7)}{16 \cdot 3 \cdot 2(a + 7)}$

$= \frac{7}{2}$

10. $\frac{w^2 + 5w + 4}{6} \div \frac{w + 1}{18w + 24} = \frac{w^2 + 5w + 4}{6} \cdot \frac{18w + 24}{w + 1}$

$= \frac{(w + 4)(w + 1)}{6} \cdot \frac{6(3w + 4)}{(w + 1)}$

$= \frac{6(w + 1)(w + 4)(3w + 4)}{6(w + 1)}$

$= (w + 4)(3w + 4)$

9-4 Adding and Subtracting Rational Expressions

Pages 572–573 Check for Understanding

1. $x^2 + 5x + 6 = (x + 3)(x + 2)$;
$x^2 + x - 2 = (x - 1)(x + 2)$

1a. $(x + 3)(x + 2)(x - 1)$

1b. $(x + 2)$

2. $\frac{3y}{5} - \frac{4}{5}$

3. The denominators have to be the same to add the numerators.

4. Sample answer: One way to find the LCD is to factor each rational expression. The LCD must contain each factor of each denominator raised to the highest power that occurs in either denominator. It is necessary to find the LCD when adding or subtracting rational expressions.

5. $10x^2 = 2 \cdot 5 \cdot x \cdot x$

$70x^2y^2 = 2 \cdot 5 \cdot 7 \cdot x \cdot x \cdot y \cdot y$

$\text{LCD} = 2 \cdot 5 \cdot 7 \cdot x \cdot x \cdot y \cdot y$

$= 70x^2y^2$

6. $x(x - 2)$

$x^2 - 4 = (x - 2)(x + 2)$

$\text{LCD} = x(x - 2)(x + 2)$

7. $\frac{6}{ab} + \frac{8}{a} = \frac{6}{ab} + \frac{8(b)}{a(b)}$

$= \frac{6 + 8b}{ab}$

8. $\frac{2}{x^2y} - \frac{1}{xy} = \frac{2}{x^2y} - \frac{1(x)}{xy(x)}$

$= \frac{2 - x}{x^2y}$

9. $\frac{1}{x + 1} + 2 = \frac{1}{x + 1} + \frac{2(x + 1)}{(x + 1)}$

$= \frac{1}{x + 1} + \frac{2x + 2}{x + 1}$

$= \frac{2x + 3}{x + 1}$

10. $\frac{7}{y - 8} - \frac{6}{8 - y} = \frac{7}{y - 8} - \frac{6(-1)}{(8 - y)(-1)}$

$= \frac{7}{y - 8} - \frac{-6}{y - 8}$

$= \frac{13}{y - 8}$

11. $\frac{6}{x^2 + 4x + 4} + \frac{5}{x + 2} = \frac{6}{(x + 2)(x + 2)} + \frac{5}{x + 2}$

$= \frac{6}{(x + 2)(x + 2)} + \frac{5(x + 2)}{(x + 2)(x + 2)}$

$= \frac{6 + 5x + 10}{(x + 2)(x + 2)}$

$= \frac{5x + 16}{(x + 2)^2}$

12. $\frac{x}{x - y} + \frac{y}{y^2 - x^2} + \frac{2x}{x + y}$

$= \frac{x}{x - y} - \frac{y}{x^2 - y^2} + \frac{2x}{x + y}$

$= \frac{x}{x - y} - \frac{y}{(x - y)(x + y)} + \frac{2x}{x + y}$

$= \frac{x(x + y)}{(x - y)(x + y)} - \frac{y}{(x - y)(x + y)} + \frac{2x(x - y)}{(x - y)(x + y)}$

$= \frac{x^2 + xy - y + 2x^2 - 2xy}{(x - y)(x + y)}$

$= \frac{3x^2 - xy - y}{(x - y)(x + y)}$

13. $\frac{1}{p} + \frac{1}{q} = \frac{q}{pq} + \frac{p}{pq}$

$= \frac{q + p}{pq}$

Pages 573–575 Exercises

14. $12y^2 = 2 \cdot 2 \cdot 3 \cdot y \cdot y$

$6x^2 = 2 \cdot 3 \cdot x \cdot x$

$\text{LCD} = 2 \cdot 2 \cdot 3 \cdot x \cdot x \cdot y \cdot y$

$= 12x^2y^2$

15. $4w - 12 = 2 \cdot 2(w - 3)$

$2w - 6 = 2(w - 3)$

$\text{LCD} = 2 \cdot 2 \cdot (w - 3)$

$= 4w - 12$

16. $36x^2y = 2 \cdot 2 \cdot 3 \cdot 3 \cdot x \cdot x \cdot y$
$20xyz = 2 \cdot 2 \cdot 5 \cdot x \cdot y \cdot z$
$\text{LCD} = 2 \cdot 2 \cdot 3 \cdot 3 \cdot 5 \cdot x \cdot x \cdot y \cdot z$
$= 180x^2yz$

17. $x^2 - y^2 = (x - y)(x + y)$
$x^2(x + y)$
$\text{LCD} = x^2(x - y)(x + y)$

18. $(x + 2)(x + 1)$
$x^2 - 1 = (x + 1)(x - 1)$
$\text{LCD} = (x + 2)(x + 1)(x - 1)$

19. $2x - 10 = 2(x - 5)$
$2x^2 - 4x - 30 = 2(x - 5)(x + 3)$
$\text{LCD} = 2(x - 5)(x + 3)$

20. $\frac{3m + 2}{m + n} + \frac{4}{2m + 2n} = \frac{3m + 2}{m + n} + \frac{4}{2(m + n)}$
$= \frac{2(3m + 2)}{2(m + n)} + \frac{4}{2(m + n)}$
$= \frac{6m + 4 + 4}{2(m + n)}$
$= \frac{6m + 8}{2(m + n)}$
$= \frac{2(3m + 4)}{2(m + n)}$
$= \frac{3m + 4}{m + n}$

21. $5 + \frac{x - 3}{x + 2} = \frac{5(x + 2)}{(x + 2)} + \frac{x - 3}{x + 2}$
$= \frac{5x + 10 + x - 3}{x + 2}$
$= \frac{6x + 7}{x + 2}$

22. $\frac{5}{3a} - \frac{2}{7a} - \frac{1}{2a} = \frac{5(14)}{3a(14)} - \frac{2(6)}{7a(6)} - \frac{1(21)}{2a(21)}$
$= \frac{70}{42a} - \frac{12}{42a} - \frac{21}{42a}$
$= \frac{37}{42a}$

23. $\frac{y}{y - 4} - \frac{3}{4 - y} = \frac{y}{y - 4} - \frac{3(-1)}{(4 - y)(-1)}$
$= \frac{y}{y - 4} - \frac{-3}{y - 4}$
$= \frac{y + 3}{y - 4}$

24. $\frac{m}{m^2 - 4} + \frac{2}{3m + 6} = \frac{m}{(m - 2)(m + 2)} + \frac{2}{3(m + 2)}$
$= \frac{3m}{3(m - 2)(m + 2)} + \frac{2(m - 2)}{3(m - 2)(m + 2)}$
$= \frac{3m + 2m - 4}{3(m - 2)(m + 2)}$
$= \frac{5m - 4}{3(m - 2)(m + 2)}$

25. $y - 3 + \frac{1}{y - 3} = \frac{y(y - 3)}{y - 3} - \frac{3(y - 3)}{y - 3} + \frac{1}{y - 3}$
$= \frac{y^2 - 3y - 3y + 9 + 1}{y - 3}$
$= \frac{y^2 - 6y + 10}{y - 3}$

26. $x + 1 + \frac{1}{x + 1} = \frac{x(x + 1)}{x + 1} + \frac{1(x + 1)}{x + 1} + \frac{1}{x + 1}$
$= \frac{x^2 + x + x + 1 + 1}{x + 1}$
$= \frac{x^2 + 2x + 2}{x + 1}$

27. $\frac{x}{x + 3} - \frac{6x}{x^2 - 9} = \frac{x}{x + 3} - \frac{6x}{(x + 3)(x - 3)}$
$= \frac{x(x - 3)}{(x + 3)(x - 3)} - \frac{6x}{(x + 3)(x - 3)}$
$= \frac{x^2 - 3x - 6x}{(x + 3)(x - 3)}$
$= \frac{x^2 - 9x}{(x + 3)(x - 3)}$
$= \frac{x(x - 9)}{(x + 3)(x - 3)}$

28. $\frac{5}{x + 3} - \frac{2}{x - 2} = \frac{5(x - 2)}{(x + 3)(x - 2)} - \frac{2(x + 3)}{(x + 3)(x - 2)}$
$= \frac{5x - 10 - 2x - 6}{(x + 3)(x - 2)}$
$= \frac{3x - 16}{(x + 3)(x - 2)}$

29. $\frac{m}{m^2 - m - 20} + \frac{2}{m + 4} = \frac{m}{(m - 5)(m + 4)} + \frac{2}{m + 4}$
$= \frac{m}{(m - 5)(m + 4)} + \frac{2(m - 5)}{(m - 5)(m + 4)}$
$= \frac{m + 2m - 10}{(m - 5)(m + 4)}$
$= \frac{3m - 10}{(m - 5)(m + 4)}$

30. $\frac{5}{x^2 - 3x - 28} + \frac{7}{2x - 14} = \frac{5}{(x - 7)(x + 4)} + \frac{7}{2(x - 7)}$
$= \frac{5 \cdot 2}{2(x - 7)(x + 4)} + \frac{7(x + 4)}{2(x - 7)(x + 4)}$
$= \frac{10 + 7x + 28}{2(x - 7)(x + 4)}$
$= \frac{7x + 38}{2(x - 7)(x + 4)}$

31. $\frac{x}{x^2 + 2x + 1} - \frac{x + 2}{x + 1} - \frac{3x}{x + 1}$
$= \frac{x}{(x + 1)(x + 1)} - \frac{x + 2}{x + 1} - \frac{3x}{x + 1}$
$= \frac{x}{(x + 1)(x + 1)} - \frac{(x + 2)(x + 1)}{(x + 1)(x + 1)} - \frac{3x(x + 1)}{(x + 1)(x + 1)}$
$= \frac{x - (x^2 + 3x + 2) - (3x^2 + 3x)}{(x + 1)(x + 1)}$
$= \frac{x - x^2 - 3x - 2 - 3x^2 - 3x}{(x + 1)(x + 1)}$
$= \frac{-4x^2 - 5x - 2}{(x + 1)^2}$

32. $\frac{1}{x^2 - 9x + 20} - \frac{5}{x^2 - 10x + 25}$
$= \frac{1}{(x - 4)(x - 5)} - \frac{5}{(x - 5)(x - 5)}$
$= \frac{1(x - 5)}{(x - 4)(x - 5)(x - 5)} - \frac{5(x - 4)}{(x - 4)(x - 5)(x - 5)}$
$= \frac{x - 5 - (5x - 20)}{(x - 4)(x - 5)(x - 5)}$
$= \frac{x - 5 - 5x + 20}{(x - 4)(x - 5)(x - 5)}$
$= \frac{-4x + 15}{(x - 4)(x - 5)(x - 5)}$

33. $\frac{-18}{9xy} + \frac{7}{2x} - \frac{2}{3x^2} = \frac{-18(2x)}{9xy(2x)} + \frac{7(9xy)}{2x(9xy)} - \frac{2(6y)}{3x^2(6y)}$

$= \frac{-36x}{18x^2y} + \frac{63xy}{18x^2y} - \frac{12y}{18x^2y}$

$= \frac{-36x + 63xy - 12y}{18x^2y}$

$= \frac{3(-12x + 21xy - 4y)}{3(6x^2y)}$

$= \frac{-12x + 21xy - 4y}{6x^2y}$

34. $\frac{m^2 + n^2}{m^2 - n^2} + \frac{m}{n - m} + \frac{n}{m + n}$

$= \frac{m^2 + n^2}{(m + n)(m - n)} + \frac{m(-1)}{(n - m)(-1)} + \frac{n}{m + n}$

$= \frac{m^2 + n^2}{(m + n)(m - n)} + \frac{-m(m + n)}{(m + n)(m - n)} + \frac{n(m - n)}{(m + n)(m - n)}$

$= \frac{m^2 + n^2 - m^2 - mn + mn - n^2}{(m + n)(m - n)}$

$= \frac{0}{(m + n)(m - n)}$

$= 0$

35. $3 + \frac{x}{x + 2} - \frac{2}{x^2 - 4}$

$= \frac{3}{1} + \frac{x}{x + 2} - \frac{2}{(x + 2)(x - 2)}$

$= \frac{3(x + 2)(x - 2)}{(x + 2)(x - 2)} + \frac{x(x - 2)}{(x + 2)(x - 2)} - \frac{2}{(x + 2)(x - 2)}$

$= \frac{3x^2 - 12 + x^2 - 2x - 2}{(x + 2)(x - 2)}$

$= \frac{4x^2 - 2x - 14}{x^2 - 4}$

36. $\frac{x - 4}{x^2 + 2x - 8} - \frac{x + 2}{x^2 - 16}$

$= \frac{x - 4}{(x + 4)(x - 2)} - \frac{x + 2}{(x - 4)(x + 4)}$

$= \frac{(x - 4)(x - 4)}{(x - 4)(x + 4)(x - 2)} - \frac{(x + 2)(x - 2)}{(x - 4)(x + 4)(x - 2)}$

$= \frac{x^2 - 8x + 16 - (x^2 - 4)}{(x - 4)(x + 4)(x - 2)}$

$= \frac{x^2 - 8x + 16 - x^2 + 4}{(x - 4)(x + 4)(x - 2)}$

$= \frac{-8x + 20}{(x - 4)(x + 4)(x - 2)}$

37. $\frac{x + 1}{x - 1} + \frac{x + 2}{x - 2} + \frac{x}{x^2 - 3x + 2}$

$= \frac{x + 1}{x - 1} + \frac{x + 2}{x - 2} + \frac{x}{(x - 1)(x - 2)}$

$= \frac{(x + 1)(x - 2)}{(x - 1)(x - 2)} + \frac{(x + 2)(x - 1)}{(x - 1)(x - 2)} + \frac{x}{(x - 1)(x - 2)}$

$= \frac{x^2 - x - 2 + x^2 + x - 2 + x}{(x - 1)(x - 2)}$

$= \frac{2x^2 + x - 4}{(x - 1)(x - 2)}$

38. $\frac{(x + y)\left(\frac{1}{x} - \frac{1}{y}\right)}{(x - y)\left(\frac{1}{x} + \frac{1}{y}\right)} = \frac{(x + y)\left(\frac{y}{xy} - \frac{x}{xy}\right)}{(x - y)\left(\frac{y}{xy} + \frac{x}{xy}\right)}$

$= (x + y)\left(\frac{y - x}{xy}\right) \div (x - y)\left(\frac{y + x}{xy}\right)$

$= \frac{(x + y)(-1)(y - x)}{xy} \cdot \frac{xy}{(x - y)(y + x)}$

$= -1$

39. $\frac{\frac{1}{x + 2} + \frac{1}{x - 5}}{\frac{2x^2 - x - 3}{x^2 - 3x - 10}} = \frac{\frac{x - 5}{(x + 2)(x - 5)} + \frac{x + 2}{(x + 2)(x - 5)}}{\frac{(2x - 3)(x + 1)}{(x - 5)(x + 2)}}$

$= \frac{x - 5 + x + 2}{(x + 2)(x - 5)} \div \frac{(2x - 3)(x + 1)}{(x - 5)(x + 2)}$

$= \frac{2x - 3}{(x + 2)(x - 5)} \cdot \frac{(x - 5)(x + 2)}{(2x - 3)(x + 1)}$

$= \frac{1}{x + 1}$

40. enter program

40a. Execute program ENTER 41 ENTER 3 ENTER 1; 123

40b. Execute program ENTER 1078 ENTER 1547 ENTER 7; 238,238

40c. Execute program ENTER 199 ENTER 24 ENTER 1; 4776

40d. Execute program ENTER 187 ENTER 221 ENTER 17; 2431

40e. Execute program ENTER 182 ENTER 1690 ENTER 26; 11,830

40f. Execute program ENTER 766 ENTER 424 ENTER 2; 162,392

41. Sample answer: 2, 4; LCM = 4, GCF = 2; $4 \times 2 = 8$

42. $\frac{1}{R} = \frac{1}{R_1} + \frac{1}{R_2}$

$= \frac{1}{30} + \frac{1}{20}$

$= \frac{2}{30(2)} + \frac{3}{20(3)}$

$= \frac{2}{60} + \frac{3}{60}$

$= \frac{5}{60}$

$= \frac{1}{12}$

$\frac{1}{R} = \frac{1}{12}$

$R = 12$; 12 ohms

43a. $A = -\frac{20.4t}{t^2 + 36} + 6.5$

t	A
0	6.5
6	4.8
12	5.14
18	5.48
30	5.85
42	6.024
54	6.13

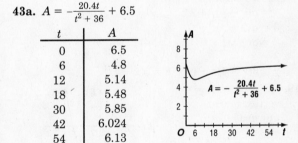

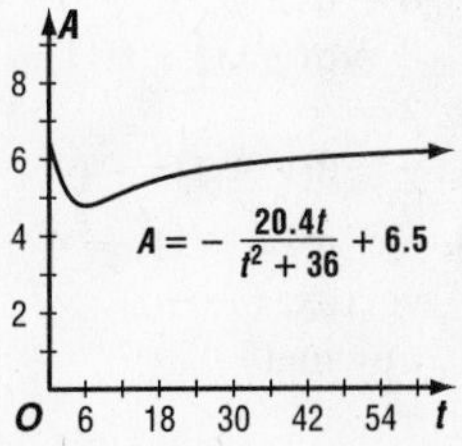

43b. 5.8

43c. It quickly drops below normal and then slowly rises back to normal.

43d. after 6 minutes

44. $-\frac{x^2 - y^2}{x + y} \cdot \frac{1}{x - y} = -\frac{(x - y)(x + y)}{x + y} \cdot \frac{1}{x - y}$

$= -1$

45. Synthetic division:

$$\begin{array}{r|rrrr} -\frac{1}{2} & 8 & -36 & 22 & 21 \\ & & -4 & 20 & -21 \\ \hline \frac{3}{2} & 8 & -40 & 42 & 0 \\ & & 12 & -42 & \\ \hline \frac{7}{2} & 8 & -28 & 0 & \\ & & 28 & & \\ \hline & 8 & 0 & & \end{array} \quad -\frac{1}{2}, \frac{3}{2}, \frac{7}{2}$$

46a. circle

46b.
$$x^2 + 5x = y^2 - 6y - 1$$
$$x^2 + 5x - (y^2 - 6y) = -1$$
$$\left(x^2 + 5x + \frac{25}{4}\right) - (y^2 - 6y + 9) = -1 + \frac{25}{4} - 9$$
$$\left(x + \frac{5}{2}\right)^2 - (y - 3)^2 = -\frac{15}{4}$$
$$(y - 3)^2 - \left(x + \frac{5}{2}\right)^2 = \frac{15}{4}$$
$$\frac{(y-3)^2}{\frac{15}{4}} - \frac{\left(x + \frac{5}{2}\right)^2}{\frac{15}{4}} = 1$$

hyperbola

46c.
$$x^2 + y^2 - 4x = 9$$
$$x^2 - 4x + y^2 = 9$$
$$(x^2 - 4x + 4) + y^2 = 9 + 4$$
$$(x - 2)^2 + y^2 = 13$$

circle

47.
$$\sqrt{(x - 11)^2 + (y + 1)^2} = \sqrt{(x - x)^2 + (y - 2)^2}$$
$$(x - 11)^2 + (y + 1)^2 = (x - x)^2 + (y - 2)^2$$
$$(x - 11)^2 + y^2 + 2y + 1 = y^2 - 4y + 4$$
$$(x - 11)^2 = -6y + 3$$
$$(x - 11)^2 - 3 = -6y$$
$$-\frac{1}{6}(x - 11)^2 + \frac{1}{2} = y$$

48. vertex: (1, 0)
passes through (0, 3)
$y = a(x - h)^2 + k$
$3 = a(0 - 1)^2 + 0$
$3 = a(-1)^2 + 0$
$3 = a$
$y = 3(x - 1)^2 + 0$ or $y = 3(x - 1)^2$

49. $f(x) = (x - 1)^2 - 4$
vertex: (1, −4)
upward
−1, 3

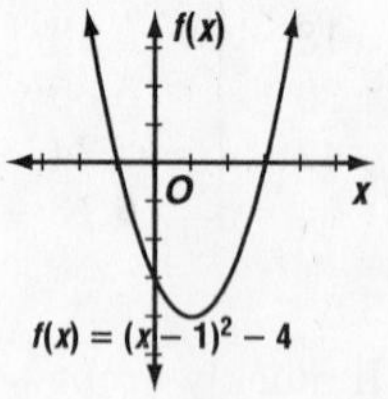

50.
$$v = \sqrt{2gh}$$
$$72 = \sqrt{2(32)h}$$
$$5184 = 64h$$
$$81 = h; \text{ yes}$$

51.
$$\frac{5}{6}x - 15 = 20y$$
$$\frac{5}{6}x = 20y + 15$$
$$x = (20y + 15)\frac{6}{5}$$
$$x = 24y + 18$$

9-5 Solving Rational Equations

Page 581 Check for Understanding

1. If you subtract $\frac{1}{x-1}$ from each side, you get $x = 1$.

But $x \neq 1$ because it gives 0 in the denominator.

2. because you multiply by quantities that may be positive or negative

3a. $(x - 3)(3)$

3b. $x - 3 \neq 3$
$x \neq 3$

4. Janine is correct; another solution is −3. To avoid losing a solution to an equation when you divide each side by an expression that involves a variable, check any numbers that make the divisor zero.

5. Sample answer: Use graphs or tables.

6. $5(y + 4);\ y + 4 \neq 0$
$y \neq -4$
$$\frac{2}{y+4} + y = \frac{1}{5}$$
$$5(y + 4)\left(\frac{2}{y+4} + y\right) = 5(y + 4)\left(\frac{1}{5}\right)$$
$$5(y + 4)\left(\frac{2}{y+4}\right) + 5(y + 4)y = 5(y + 4)\left(\frac{1}{5}\right)$$
$$10 + 5y^2 + 20y = y + 4$$
$$5y^2 + 19y + 6 = 0$$
$$y = \frac{-19 \pm \sqrt{19^2 - 4(5)(6)}}{2(5)}$$
$$= \frac{-19 \pm \sqrt{241}}{10}$$
$$\approx -0.35 \text{ or } -3.45$$

7. $(m - 4)(m - 2);\ m - 4 \neq 0,\quad m - 2 \neq 0$
$m \neq 4,\quad m \neq 2$
$$\frac{1}{m-4} = \frac{2}{m-2}$$
$$(m - 4)(m - 2)\left(\frac{1}{m-4}\right) = (m - 4)(m - 2)\left(\frac{2}{m-2}\right)$$
$$m - 2 = 2(m - 4)$$
$$m - 2 = 2m - 8$$
$$6 = m$$

8.
$$\frac{y}{y+1} = \frac{2}{3}$$
$$3(y + 1)\left(\frac{y}{y+1}\right) = 3(y + 1)\left(\frac{2}{3}\right)$$
$$3y = 2(y + 1)$$
$$3y = 2y + 2$$
$$y = 2$$

9.
$$\frac{x}{3} - \frac{2}{5} = 1$$
$$15\left(\frac{x}{3} - \frac{2}{5}\right) = 15(1)$$
$$15\left(\frac{x}{3}\right) - 15\left(\frac{2}{5}\right) = 15$$
$$5x - 6 = 15$$
$$5x = 21$$
$$x = \frac{21}{5}$$

10. $b^2 + \frac{17b}{6} = \frac{1}{2}$

$6\left(b^2 + \frac{17b}{6}\right) = 6\left(\frac{1}{2}\right)$

$6(b^2) + 6\left(\frac{17b}{6}\right) = 3$

$6b^2 + 17b = 3$

$6b^2 + 17b - 3 = 0$

$(6b - 1)(b + 3) = 0$

$6b - 1 = 0$ or $b + 3 = 0$

$6b = 1$ $\quad b = -3$

$b = \frac{1}{6}$

11. $\frac{2x}{3} - \frac{x+3}{6} > 2$

$6\left(\frac{2x}{3} - \frac{x+3}{6}\right) > 6(2)$

$6\left(\frac{2x}{3}\right) - 6\left(\frac{x+3}{6}\right) > 12$

$4x - (x + 3) > 12$

$4x - x - 3 > 12$

$3x > 15$

$x > 5$

12. Bricklayer A can complete $\frac{1}{5}$ of the wall/day; or $\frac{t}{5}$ in t days.

Bricklayer B can complete $\frac{1}{4}$ of the wall/day; or $\frac{t}{4}$ in t days.

$\frac{t}{5} + \frac{t}{4} = 1$

$20\left(\frac{t}{5} + \frac{t}{4}\right) = 20(1)$

$4t + 5t = 20$

$9t = 20$

$t = \frac{20}{9}$ or $2\frac{2}{9}$

$2\frac{2}{9}$ days

Pages 582–583 Exercises

13. 4; none

$\frac{x+2}{2} - \frac{3}{4} = x$

$4\left(\frac{x+2}{2} - \frac{3}{4}\right) = 4(x)$

$2(x + 2) - 3 = 4x$

$2x + 4 - 3 = 4x$

$1 = 2x$

$\frac{1}{2} = x$

14. $2a$; $a \neq 0$

$\frac{1}{a} + \frac{1}{2} = \frac{2}{a}$

$2a\left(\frac{1}{a} + \frac{1}{2}\right) = 2a\left(\frac{2}{a}\right)$

$2 + a = 4$

$a = 2$

15. m^2; $m \neq 0$

$\frac{6}{m} = \frac{9}{m^2}$

$m^2\left(\frac{6}{m}\right) = m^2\left(\frac{9}{m^2}\right)$

$6m = 9$

$m = \frac{3}{2}$

16. $3(x - 3)$; $x - 3 \neq 0$

$x \neq 3$

$\frac{x}{x-3} + \frac{1}{3} = 1$

$3(x - 3)\left(\frac{x}{x-3} + \frac{1}{3}\right) = 3(x - 3)(1)$

$3x + x - 3 = 3(x - 3)$

$4x - 3 = 3x - 9$

$x = -6$

17. $(a - 6)(a - 2)$; $a - 6 \neq 0$, $\quad a - 2 \neq 0$

$a \neq 6$, $\quad a \neq 2$

$\frac{3}{a-6} - \frac{1}{a-2} = 3$

$(a - 6)(a - 2)\left(\frac{3}{a-6} - \frac{1}{a-2}\right) = (a - 6)(a - 2)(3)$

$3(a - 2) - (a - 6) = (a^2 - 8a + 12)(3)$

$3a - 6 - a + 6 = 3a^2 - 24a + 36$

$0 = 3a^2 - 26a + 36$

$a = \frac{26 \pm \sqrt{(-26)^2 - 4(3)(36)}}{2(3)}$

$= \frac{26 \pm \sqrt{244}}{6}$

≈ 6.94 or 1.73

18. $7(2 + y)$; $2 + y \neq 0$

$y \neq -2$

$\frac{3y}{2+y} - \frac{5}{7} = 4$

$7(2 + y)\left(\frac{3y}{2+y} - \frac{5}{7}\right) = 7(2 + y)(4)$

$21y - 5(2 + y) = (14 + 7y)(4)$

$21y - 10 - 5y = 56 + 28y$

$16y - 10 = 56 + 28y$

$-12y = 66$

$y = -\frac{11}{2}$

19. $\frac{x+1}{3} + \frac{x-1}{3} = \frac{4}{3}$

$3\left(\frac{x+1}{3} + \frac{x-1}{3}\right) = 3\left(\frac{4}{3}\right)$

$x + 1 + x - 1 = 4$

$2x = 4$

$x = 2$

20. $\frac{5+7z}{8} - \frac{15+3z}{10} < 2$

$40\left(\frac{5+7z}{8} - \frac{15+3z}{10}\right) < 40(2)$

$5(5 + 7z) - 4(15 + 3z) < 80$

$25 + 35z - 60 - 12z < 80$

$23z - 35 < 80$

$23z < 115$

$z < 5$

21. $y + 5 \leq \frac{6}{y}$

$y(y + 5) \leq y\left(\frac{6}{y}\right)$

$y^2 + 5y \leq 6$

$y^2 + 5y - 6 \leq 0$

$(y + 6)(y - 1) \leq 0$

$y + 6 \leq 0$ or $y - 1 \leq 0$

$y \leq -6$ $\quad y \leq 1$ $\quad$ So $y \leq -6$.

22. $\frac{1}{t-1} + \frac{1}{t+2} = \frac{1}{2}$

$2(t - 1)(t + 2)\left(\frac{1}{t-1} + \frac{1}{t+2}\right) = 2(t - 1)(t + 2)\left(\frac{1}{2}\right)$

$2(t + 2) + 2(t - 1) = (t - 1)(t + 2)$

$2t + 4 + 2t - 2 = t^2 + t - 2$

$0 = t^2 - 3t - 4$

$0 = (t - 4)(t + 1)$

$t - 4 = 0$ or $t + 1 = 0$

$t = 4$ $\quad t = -1$

23. $\frac{1}{m+2} - \frac{1}{3-m} = -\frac{1}{6}$

$6(m+2)(3-m)\left(\frac{1}{m+2} - \frac{1}{3-m}\right)$
$= 6(m+2)(3-m)\left(-\frac{1}{6}\right)$

$6(3-m) - 6(m+2) = (m+2)(3-m)(-1)$

$18 - 6m - 6m - 12 = (3m - m^2 + 6 - 2m)(-1)$

$6 - 12m = m^2 - m - 6$

$0 = m^2 + 11m - 12$

$0 = (m+12)(m-1)$

$m + 12 = 0$ or $m - 1 = 0$

$m = -12$ $\quad m = 1$

24. $\frac{1}{2y+1} + \frac{1}{y+1} \geq \frac{8}{15}$

$15(2y+1)(y+1)\left(\frac{1}{2y+1} + \frac{1}{y+1}\right) \geq 15(2y+1)(y+1)\left(\frac{8}{15}\right)$

$15(y+1) + 15(2y+1) \geq (2y+1)(y+1)(8)$

$15y + 15 + 30y + 15 \geq (2y^2 + 3y + 1)(8)$

$45y + 30 \geq 16y^2 + 24y + 8$

$0 \geq 16y^2 - 21y - 22$

$0 \geq (16y + 11)(y - 2)$

$16y + 11 \geq 0$ or $y - 2 \leq 0$

$16y \geq -11$ $\quad y \leq 2$

$y \geq -\frac{11}{16}$

25. $\frac{1}{9} + \frac{1}{2a} = \frac{1}{a^2}$

$18a^2\left(\frac{1}{9} + \frac{1}{2a}\right) = 18a^2\left(\frac{1}{a^2}\right)$

$2a^2 + 9a = 18$

$2a^2 + 9a - 18 = 0$

$(2a - 3)(a + 6) = 0$

$2a - 3 = 0$ or $a + 6 = 0$

$2a = 3$ $\quad a = -6$

$a = \frac{3}{2}$

26. $\frac{1}{1-x} = 1 - \frac{x}{x-1}$

$(x-1)(1-x)\left(\frac{1}{1-x}\right) = (x-1)(1-x)\left(1 - \frac{x}{x-1}\right)$

$x - 1 = (x-1)(1-x) - (1-x)(x)$

$x - 1 = -x^2 + 2x - 1 - x + x^2$

$x - 1 = x - 1;\ \{x \mid x \neq 1\}$

27. $\frac{3}{x^2 + 3x} + \frac{x+2}{x+3} = \frac{1}{x}$

$x(x+3)\left(\frac{3}{x^2+3x} + \frac{x+2}{x+3}\right) = x(x+3)\left(\frac{1}{x}\right)$

$3 + x(x+2) = x + 3$

$3 + x^2 + 2x = x + 3$

$x^2 + x = 0$

$x(x+1) = 0$

$x = 0$ or $x + 1 = 0$

But, $x \neq 0$ $\quad x = -1$

28. $\frac{6}{y^2 + 2y} - \frac{y+1}{y+2} = \frac{2}{y}$

$y(y+2)\left(\frac{6}{y^2+2y} - \frac{y+1}{y+2}\right) = y(y+2)\left(\frac{2}{y}\right)$

$6 - y(y+1) = (y+2)(2)$

$6 - y^2 - y = 2y + 4$

$0 = y^2 + 3y - 2$

$y = \frac{-3 \pm \sqrt{3^2 - 4(1)(-2)}}{2(1)}$

$= \frac{-3 \pm \sqrt{17}}{2}$

29. $\frac{1}{x+4} = \frac{2}{x^2 + 3x - 4} - \frac{1}{1-x}$

$\frac{1}{x+4} = \frac{2}{(x-1)(x+4)} - \frac{1}{1-x}$

$(x-1)(x+4)(1-x)\left(\frac{1}{x+4}\right)$
$= (x-1)(x+4)(1-x)$
$\left(\frac{2}{(x-1)(x+4)} - \frac{1}{1-x}\right)$

$(x-1)(1-x) = (1-x)(2) - (x-1)(x+4)$

$-x^2 + 2x - 1 = 2 - 2x - (x^2 + 3x - 4)$

$-x^2 + 2x - 1 = 2 - 2x - x^2 - 3x + 4$

$7x = 7$

$x = 1$; But, $x \neq 1$, so $\varnothing$.

30. $\frac{3}{b^2 + 5b + 6} + \frac{b-1}{b+2} = \frac{7}{b+3}$

$\frac{3}{(b+3)(b+2)} + \frac{b-1}{b+2} = \frac{7}{b+3}$

$(b+3)(b+2)\left(\frac{3}{(b+3)(b+2)} + \frac{b-1}{b+2}\right)$
$= (b+3)(b+2)\left(\frac{7}{b+3}\right)$

$3 + (b+3)(b-1) = (b+2)7$

$3 + b^2 + 2b - 3 = 7b + 14$

$b^2 - 5b - 14 = 0$

$(b - 7)(b + 2) = 0$

$b - 7 = 0$ or $b + 2 = 0$

$b = 7$ $\quad b = -2$; But $b \neq -2$.

31. $\frac{1}{a} - \frac{1}{b} = c$

$ab\left(\frac{1}{a} - \frac{1}{b}\right) = ab(c)$

$b - a = abc$

$b = abc + a$

$b = a(bc + 1)$

$\frac{b}{bc+1} = a$

32. $\frac{A}{z+2} + \frac{B}{2z-3} = \frac{5z - 11}{2z^2 + z - 6}$

$(2z-3)(z+2)\left(\frac{A}{z+2} + \frac{B}{2z-3}\right)$
$= (2z-3)(z+2)\left(\frac{5z-11}{(2z-3)(z+2)}\right)$

$A(2z - 3) + B(z + 2) = 5z - 11$

$2Az - 3A + Bz + 2B = 5z - 11$

$2Az + Bz - 3A + 2B = 5z - 11$

$(2A + B)z - (3A - 2B) = 5z - 11$

$2A + B = 5$	$4A + 2B = 10$	$2A + B = 5$
$3A - 2B = 11 \rightarrow$	$(+)3A - 2B = 11$	$2(3) + B = 5$
	$7A \quad = 21$	$6 + B = 5$
	$A = 3$	$B = -1$

33a. $\frac{x+11}{x+20} \geq 0.70$

33b. $(x+20)\left(\frac{x+11}{x+20}\right) \geq (x+20)(0.70)$

$x + 11 \geq 0.70x + 14$

$0.3x \geq 3$

$x \geq 10$; 10 free throws

33c. Selena needs at least 10 consecutive free throws.

34a. $\frac{1}{2}\left(\frac{1}{y} + \frac{1}{z}\right) = \frac{1}{x}$

$\frac{1}{2y} + \frac{1}{2z} = \frac{1}{x}$

$\frac{1}{2y} + \frac{1}{2(20)} = \frac{1}{8}$

$40y\left(\frac{1}{2y} + \frac{1}{40}\right) = 40y\left(\frac{1}{8}\right)$

$20 + y = 5y$

$20 = 4y$

$5 = y$

34b. $\frac{1}{2y} + \frac{1}{2z} = \frac{1}{x}$

$\frac{1}{2(5)} + \frac{1}{2(8)} = \frac{1}{x}$

$\frac{1}{10} + \frac{1}{16} = \frac{1}{x}$

$80x\left(\frac{1}{10} + \frac{1}{16}\right) = 80x\left(\frac{1}{x}\right)$

$8x + 5x = 80$

$13x = 80$

$x \approx 6.15$

35. $\frac{1}{4}$ of trip: 40 mph; $\frac{3}{4}$ of trip: 65 mph

$$\text{Average} = \frac{40 + 65 + 65 + 65}{4}$$
$$= \frac{235}{4}$$
$$= 58.75;\ 58.75 \text{ mph}$$

36. Let x = the time it would take 1st artist to do job alone. Artist A worked 20 weeks and artist B worked 8 weeks.

$$\frac{20}{x} + \frac{8}{24} = 1$$
$$24x\left(\frac{20}{x} + \frac{8}{24}\right) = 24x\,(1)$$
$$480 + 8x = 24x$$
$$480 = 16x$$
$$30 = x;\ 30 \text{ weeks}$$

37. Let x = the number.

$$\frac{x - 8}{28 + x} = \frac{2}{5}$$
$$5(28 + x)\left(\frac{x - 8}{28 + x}\right) = 5(28 + x)\left(\frac{2}{5}\right)$$
$$5(x - 8) = (28 + x)(2)$$
$$5x - 40 = 56 + 2x$$
$$3x = 96$$
$$x = 32$$

38.
$$\frac{3}{a - 2} + \frac{2}{a - 3} = \frac{3(a - 3)}{(a - 2)(a - 3)} + \frac{2(a - 2)}{(a - 2)(a - 3)}$$
$$= \frac{3a - 9 + 2a - 4}{(a - 2)(a - 3)}$$
$$= \frac{5a - 13}{(a - 2)(a - 3)}$$

39. $f(x) = x^3 + 1$

0 positive real zeros

$f(-x) = (-x)^3 + 1$

$= -x^3 + 1$

1 negative real zero

2 imaginary zeros

40. $x + y + 7 = 0$

$$y = -7 - x$$
$$x^2 + y^2 = 25$$
$$x^2 + (-7 - x)^2 = 25$$
$$x^2 + 49 + 14x + x^2 = 25$$
$$2x^2 + 14x + 24 = 0$$
$$2(x + 4)(x + 3) = 0$$

$x + 4 = 0$ or $x + 3 = 0$

$x + 4 = 0$	or	$x + 3 = 0$
$x = -4$		$x = -3$
$y = -7 - (-4)$		$y = -7 - (-3)$
$y = -3$		$y = -4$
$(-4, -3)$		$(-3, -4)$

41.
$$d = \sqrt{(x_2 - x_1)^2 + (y_2 - y_1)^2}$$
$$= \sqrt{(-2.2 - (-0.5))^2 + (-0.3 - 1)^2}$$
$$= \sqrt{2.89 + 1.69}$$
$$= \sqrt{4.58};\ \sqrt{4.58} \text{ units}$$

42. $s_1 + s_2 = 3 + \frac{1}{2}$ $\qquad -\frac{b}{a} = \frac{7}{2};\ \frac{c}{a} = \frac{3}{2}$

$= \frac{7}{2}$ $\qquad a = 2,\ b = -7,\ c = 3$

$s_1(s_2) = 3\left(\frac{1}{2}\right)$ $\qquad 2x^2 - 7x + 3 = 0$

$= \frac{3}{2}$

43.
$$r = \sqrt[3]{\frac{3V}{4\pi}}$$
$$= \sqrt[3]{\frac{3(175)}{4\pi}}$$
$$\approx \sqrt[3]{41.78}$$
$$\approx 3.5;\ 3.5 \text{ inches}$$

diameter: 7 inches

about 7 inches by 7 inches by 7 inches

44.

$4x + 3 < -9$	or	$7 < 2x - 11$
$4x < -12$	or	$18 < 2x$
$x < -3$	or	$9 < x$; $\{x \mid x < -3 \text{ or } x > 9\}$

Page 583 Mathematics and Society

1. See students' work.
2. Sample answer: advances in computer processing power
3. See students' work.

Chapter 9 Highlights

Page 585 Understanding and Using the Vocabulary

1. false, point discontinuity
2. true
3. true
4. false, rational
5. false, asymptote
6. true
7. false, $x = -2$
8. false, joint

Chapter 9 Study Guide and Assessment

Pages 586–588 Skills and Concepts

9. $x - 2 = 0$

$x = 2;\ y = 0$

x	$f(x)$
−2	−1
1	−4
1.5	−8
2	undefined
2.5	8
4	2
6	1

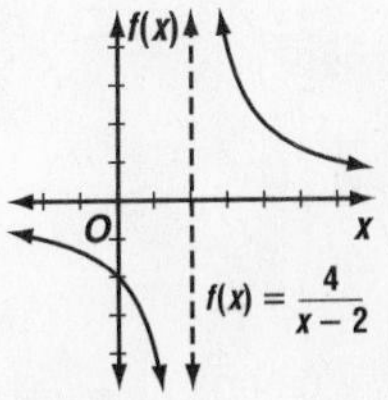

10. $x + 3 = 0$

$x = -3;\ y = 1$

x	$f(x)$
−7	1.75
−5	2.5
−3.5	7
−3	undefined
−2.5	−5
−1	−0.5
1	0.25

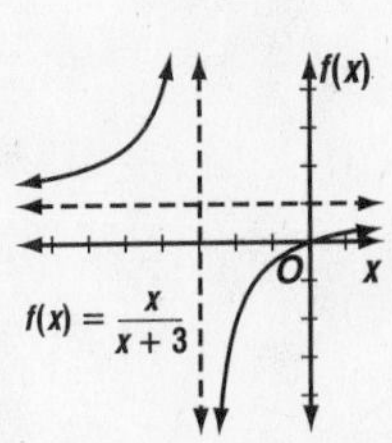

11. $x = 0$; $y = 0$

x	$f(x)$
-4	-0.5
-1	-2
-0.5	-4
0	undefined
0.5	4
2	1
4	0.5

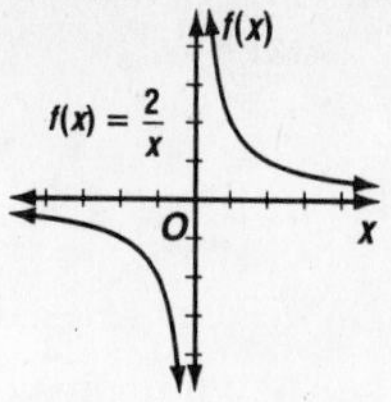

12. $x + 3 = 0$

$x = -3$; $y = 1$

x	$f(x)$
-12	1.78
-8	2.4
-4	8
-3	undefined
-2	-6
0	-1.3
4	0

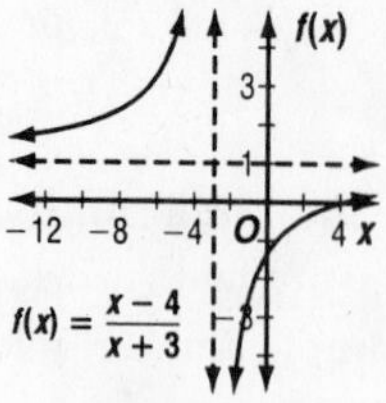

13. $x + 1 = 0$, $x = -1$ $\qquad$ $x - 3 = 0$, $x = 3$; $y = 0$

x	$f(x)$
-3	0.42
-2	0.5
-1.5	2.2
-1	undefined
-0.5	-2.86

x	$f(x)$
1	-1.25
2.5	-2.86
3	undefined
3.5	2.2
7	0.16

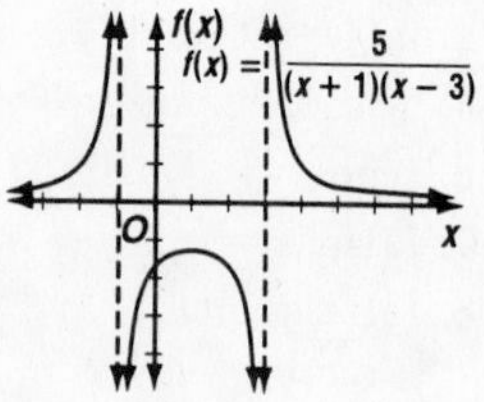

14. $\frac{y_1}{x_1} = \frac{y_2}{x_2}$

$\frac{21}{7} = \frac{y_2}{x_2}$

$21x_2 = 7y_2$

$3x_2 = y_2$ or $y = 3x$

$3x_2 = -5$

$x_2 = -\frac{5}{3}$

15. $\frac{x_1}{y_2} = \frac{x_2}{y_1}$

$\frac{2.5}{y_2} = \frac{x_2}{9}$

$y_2x_2 = 22.5$ or $xy = 22.5$

$y_2(-0.6) = 22.5$

$y_2 = -37.5$

16. $\frac{x_1}{y_2} = \frac{x_2}{y_1}$

$\frac{28}{y_2} = \frac{x_2}{18}$

$y_2x_2 = 504$ or $xy = 504$

$63x_2 = 504$

$x_2 = 8$

17. $\frac{y_1}{x_1} = \frac{y_2}{x_2}$

$\frac{18}{28} = \frac{y_2}{x_2}$

$18x_2 = 28y_2$

$\frac{9}{14}x_2 = y_2$ or $y = \frac{9}{14}x$

$\frac{9}{14}x_2 = 63$

$x_2 = 98$

18. $\frac{y_1}{x_1z_1} = \frac{y_2}{x_2z_2}$

$\frac{16}{(2)(4)} = \frac{y_2}{x_2z_2}$

$2 = \frac{y_2}{x_2z_2}$

$2x_2z_2 = y_2$ or $y = 2xz$

$2(5)(8) = y_2$

$80 = y_2$

19. $\frac{y_1}{x_1z_1} = \frac{y_2}{x_2z_2}$

$\frac{25}{(4)(2)} = \frac{y_2}{x_2z_2}$

$\frac{25}{8} = \frac{y_2}{x_2z_2}$

$\frac{25}{8}x_2z_2 = y_2$ or $y = \frac{25}{8}xz$

$\frac{25}{8}x_2(20) = 12$

$\frac{125}{2}x_2 = 12$

$x_2 = 0.192$

20. $\frac{-4ab}{21c} \cdot \frac{14c^2}{22a^2} = \frac{-2 \cdot 2 \cdot 2 \cdot 7 \cdot a \cdot b \cdot c^2}{2 \cdot 11 \cdot 3 \cdot 7 \cdot a^2 \cdot c}$

$= \frac{-4bc}{33a}$

21. $\frac{y-2}{a-3} \cdot (a-3) = \frac{(y-2)(a-3)}{(a-3)}$

$= y - 2$

22. $\frac{a^2 - b^2}{6b} \div \frac{a+b}{36b^2} = \frac{a^2 - b^2}{6b} \cdot \frac{36b^2}{a+b}$

$= \frac{(a-b)(a+b) \cdot 6 \cdot 6 \cdot b^2}{6 \cdot b \cdot (a+b)}$

$= 6b(a - b)$

23. $\frac{5x(x+y)}{a} \div \frac{25x^3(x+y)}{a^2} = \frac{5x(x+y)}{a} \cdot \frac{a^2}{25x^3(x+y)}$

$= \frac{5x(x+y) \cdot a^2}{5 \cdot 5x^3(x+y) \cdot a}$

$= \frac{a}{5x^2}$

24. $\frac{y^2 - y - 12}{y+2} \div \frac{y-4}{y^2 - 4y - 12} = \frac{y^2 - y - 12}{y+2} \cdot \frac{y^2 - 4y - 12}{y-4}$

$= \frac{(y-4)(y+3)}{y+2} \cdot \frac{(y-6)(y-2)}{y-4}$

$= (y+3)(y-6)$

25. $\frac{x^2 + 3x - 10}{x^2 + 8x + 15} \cdot \frac{x^2 + 5x + 6}{x^2 + 4x + 4} = \frac{(x+5)(x-2)}{(x+5)(x+3)} \cdot \frac{(x+3)(x+2)}{(x+2)(x+2)}$

$= \frac{x-2}{x+2}$

26. $\frac{\frac{1}{x}}{\frac{2x}{17}} = \frac{1}{x} \div \frac{2x}{17}$

$= \frac{1}{x} \cdot \frac{17}{2x}$

$= \frac{17}{2x^2}$

27. $\frac{\frac{1}{n^2 - 6n + 9}}{\frac{n+3}{2n^2 - 18}} = \frac{1}{n^2 - 6n + 9} \div \frac{n+3}{2n^2 - 18}$

$= \frac{1}{n^2 - 6n + 9} \cdot \frac{2n^2 - 18}{n+3}$

$= \frac{1}{(n-3)(n-3)} \cdot \frac{2(n-3)(n+3)}{n+3}$

$= \frac{2}{n-3}$

28. $\dfrac{\dfrac{x^2+7x+10}{x+2}}{\dfrac{x^2+2x-15}{x+2}} = \dfrac{x^2+7x+10}{x+2} \div \dfrac{x^2+2x-15}{x+2}$

$= \dfrac{x^2+7x+10}{x+2} \cdot \dfrac{x+2}{x^2+2x-15}$

$= \dfrac{(x+5)(x+2)}{x+2} \cdot \dfrac{x+2}{(x+5)(x-3)}$

$= \dfrac{x+2}{x-3}$

29. $\dfrac{-9}{4a} + \dfrac{7}{3b} = \dfrac{-9(3b)}{4a(3b)} + \dfrac{7(4a)}{3b(4a)}$

$= \dfrac{-27b}{12ab} + \dfrac{28a}{12ab}$

$= \dfrac{28a-27b}{12ab}$

30. $\dfrac{x+2}{x-5} + 6 = \dfrac{x+2}{x-5} + \dfrac{6(x-5)}{x-5}$

$= \dfrac{x+2+6x-30}{x-5}$

$= \dfrac{7x-28}{x-5}$

$= \dfrac{7(x-4)}{x-5}$

31. $\dfrac{x-1}{x^2-1} + \dfrac{2}{5x+5} = \dfrac{x-1}{(x-1)(x+1)} + \dfrac{2}{5(x+1)}$

$= \dfrac{(x-1)5}{(x-1)(x+1)5} + \dfrac{2(x-1)}{5(x+1)(x-1)}$

$= \dfrac{5x-5+2x-2}{5(x-1)(x+1)}$

$= \dfrac{7x-7}{5(x-1)(x+1)}$

$= \dfrac{7(x-1)}{5(x-1)(x+1)}$

$= \dfrac{7}{5(x+1)}$

32. $\dfrac{7}{y} - \dfrac{2}{3y} = \dfrac{7\cdot 3}{y\cdot 3} - \dfrac{2}{3y}$

$= \dfrac{21-2}{3y}$

$= \dfrac{19}{3y}$

33. $\dfrac{7}{y-2} - \dfrac{11}{2-y} = \dfrac{7}{y-2} + \dfrac{11}{y-2}$

$= \dfrac{18}{y-2}$

34. $\dfrac{3}{4b} - \dfrac{2}{5b} - \dfrac{1}{2b} = \dfrac{3\cdot 5}{4b\cdot 5} - \dfrac{2\cdot 4}{5b\cdot 4} - \dfrac{1\cdot 10}{2b\cdot 10}$

$= \dfrac{15}{20b} - \dfrac{8}{20b} - \dfrac{10}{20b}$

$= \dfrac{-3}{20b}$

35. $\dfrac{m+3}{m^2-6m+9} - \dfrac{8m-24}{9-m^2}$

$= \dfrac{m+3}{(m-3)(m-3)} + \dfrac{8m-24}{m^2-9}$

$= \dfrac{m+3}{(m-3)(m-3)} + \dfrac{8m-24}{(m-3)(m+3)}$

$= \dfrac{(m+3)(m+3)}{(m-3)(m-3)(m+3)} + \dfrac{(8m-24)(m-3)}{(m-3)(m-3)(m+3)}$

$= \dfrac{m^2+6m+9+8m^2-48m+72}{(m-3)(m-3)(m+3)}$

$= \dfrac{9m^2-42m+81}{(m-3)^2(m+3)}$

$= \dfrac{3(3m^2+14m+27)}{(m-3)^2(m+3)}$

36. $\dfrac{3}{y} + \dfrac{7}{y} = 9$

$y\left(\dfrac{3}{y} + \dfrac{7}{y}\right) = y(9)$

$3 + 7 = 9y$

$10 = 9y$

$\dfrac{10}{9} = y$

37. $1 + \dfrac{5}{y-1} = \dfrac{7}{6}$

$6(y-1)\left(1 + \dfrac{5}{y-1}\right) = 6(y-1)\left(\dfrac{7}{6}\right)$

$6(y-1) + 6(5) = 7(y-1)$

$6y - 6 + 30 = 7y - 7$

$31 = y$

38. $\dfrac{3x+2}{4} = \dfrac{9}{4} - \dfrac{3-2x}{6}$

$12\left(\dfrac{3x+2}{4}\right) = 12\left(\dfrac{9}{4} - \dfrac{3-2x}{6}\right)$

$3(3x+2) = 3(9) - 2(3-2x)$

$9x + 6 = 27 - 6 + 4x$

$5x = 15$

$x = 3$

39. $\dfrac{1}{r^2-1} = \dfrac{2}{r^2+r-2}$

$\dfrac{1}{(r-1)(r+1)} = \dfrac{2}{(r+2)(r-1)}$

$(r-1)(r+1)(r+2)\left(\dfrac{1}{(r-1)(r+1)}\right)$

$= (r-1)(r+1)(r+2)\left(\dfrac{2}{(r+2)(r-1)}\right)$

$r + 2 = 2(r+1)$

$r + 2 = 2r + 2$

$0 = r$

40. $\frac{x}{x^2-1} + \frac{2}{x+1} = 1 + \frac{1}{2x-2}$

$\frac{x}{(x-1)(x+1)} + \frac{2}{x+1} = 1 + \frac{1}{2(x-1)}$

$2(x-1)(x+1)\left(\frac{x}{(x-1)(x+1)} + \frac{2}{x+1}\right)$

$= 2(x-1)(x+1)\left(1 + \frac{1}{2(x-1)}\right)$

$2x + 2(x-1)(2) = 2(x-1)(x+1) + (x+1)$

$2x + 4x - 4 = 2x^2 - 2 + x + 1$

$0 = 2x^2 - 5x + 3$

$0 = (2x-3)(x-1)$

$2x - 3 = 0$ or $x - 1 = 0$

$2x = 3$ $x = 1$

$x = \frac{3}{2}$ But, $x \neq 1$.

Page 588 Applications and Problem Solving

41a. $\frac{R_1}{I_2} = \frac{R_2}{I_1}$

$\frac{0.5}{I_2} = \frac{R_2}{12}$

$I_2R_2 = 6$

$I_2 = \frac{6}{R_2}$ or $I = \frac{6}{R}$

41b. 6

42. Let x = numerator, then fraction = $\frac{x}{2x-1}$.

$\frac{x+7}{2x-1+7} = \frac{7}{10}$

$\frac{x+7}{2x+6} = \frac{7}{10}$

$\frac{x+7}{2(x+3)} = \frac{7}{10}$

$10(x+3)\left(\frac{x+7}{2(x+3)}\right) = 10(x+3)\left(\frac{7}{10}\right)$

$5(x+7) = 7(x+3)$

$5x + 35 = 7x + 21$

$14 = 2x$

$7 = x$; fraction = $\frac{7}{2(7)-1} = \frac{7}{13}$

43. $\frac{x_1}{y_2} = \frac{x_2}{y_1}$

$\frac{140}{100} = \frac{x_2}{30}$

$100x_2 = 4200$

$x_2 = 42$; 42 lb/in^2

Page 589 Alternative Assessment, Thinking Critically

- If $x = 0$ or $z = 0$, then $y = kxz$ would become $y = 0$ which does not show variation.
- $4x = 7x$ is a simplified form of $\frac{1}{4x} = \frac{1}{7x}$.

However, $4x = 7x$ has no restrictions in the domain. In the equation $\frac{1}{4x} = \frac{1}{7x}$; $x \neq 0$.

$\frac{1}{4x} = \frac{1}{7x}$

$28x\left(\frac{1}{4x}\right) = 28x\left(\frac{1}{7x}\right)$

$7 = 4$

This is not a true equation; $\varnothing$.
Solve: $4x = 7x$

$0 = 3x$

$0 = x$

This is a correct solution of the second equation but it would be the restricted value of the first equation.

Chapter 10 Exploring Exponential and Logarithmic Functions

10-1A Graphing Technology: Exponential and Logarithmic Functions

Page 595 Exercises

1. WINDOW: [−5, 5] by [−5, 5]; [Y=] 10 [^] [X,T,θ,n] [GRAPH]

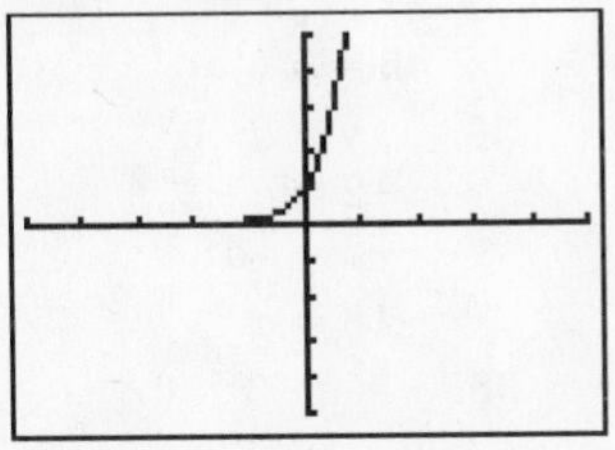

2. WINDOW: [−5, 5] by [−5, 5]; [Y=] 3.5 [^] [X,T,θ,n] [GRAPH]

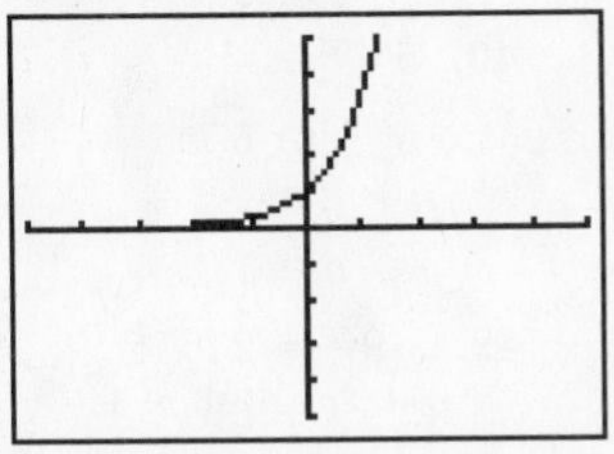

3. WINDOW: [−5, 5] by [−5, 5]; [Y=] 0.1 [^] [X,T,θ,n] [GRAPH]

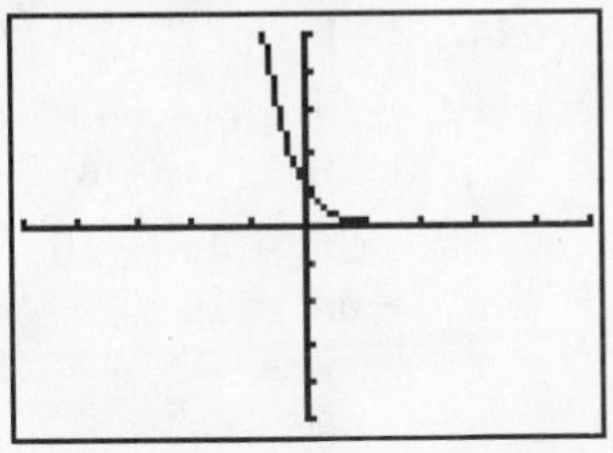

4. WINDOW: [−5, 5] by [−5, 5]; [Y=] 0.05 [^] [X,T,θ,n] [GRAPH]

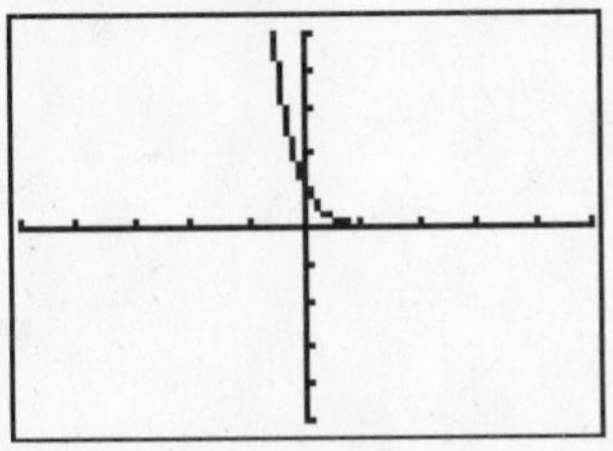

5. WINDOW: [−5, 5] by [−5, 5]; [Y=] [LOG] [X,T,θ,n] [÷] [LOG] 4 [GRAPH]

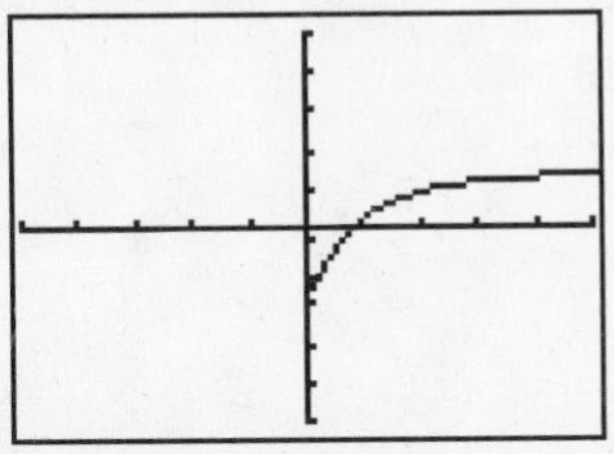

6. WINDOW: [−5, 5] by [−5, 5]; [Y=] [LOG] [X,T,θ,n] [÷] [LOG] 0.3 [GRAPH]

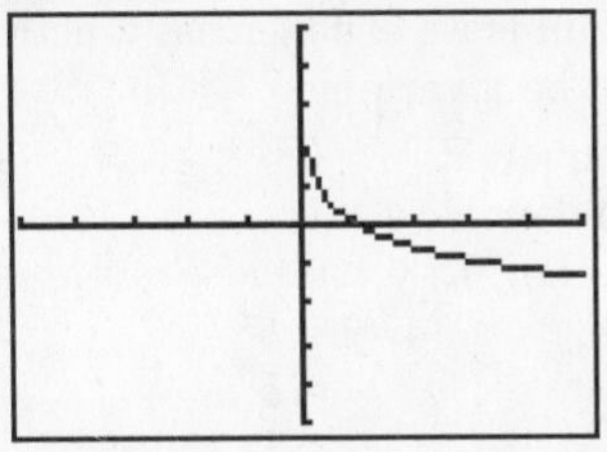

7. [Y=] 4 [^] [X,T,θ,n] [ENTER] 8 [ZOOM] 6; use ZOOM−IN or INTERSECT to solve; 1.50
8. [Y=] 3.2 [^] [X,T,θ,n] [ENTER] 52.5 [GRAPH] ; use ZOOM−IN or INTERSECT to solve; 3.41 (WINDOW: [−10, 10] by [−10, 60])
9. [Y=] 2.1 [^] [(] [X,T,θ,n] [−] 5 [)] [ENTER] 9.7 [ZOOM] 6; use ZOOM−IN or INTERSECT to solve; 8.06
10. [Y=] 0.65 [^] [(] [X,T,θ,n] [+] 3 [)] [ENTER] 3 [^] [(] 2 [X,T,θ,n] [−] 1 [)] [ZOOM] 6; use ZOOM−IN or INTERSECT to solve; −0.07
11. [Y=] 2 [^] [X,T,θ,n] [ENTER] [X,T,θ,n] [x^2] [ZOOM] 6; use ZOOM−IN or INTERSECT to solve; −0.77, 2, 4
12. [Y=] 1.5 [^] [X,T,θ,n] [ENTER] 2500 [GRAPH] ; use ZOOM−IN or INTERSECT to solve; 19.30 (WINDOW: [−10, 20] by [−10, 3000])
13. [Y=] [LOG] [X,T,θ,n] [ENTER] 0.23 [GRAPH] ; use ZOOM−IN or INTERSECT to solve; 1.70 (WINDOW: [−3, 3] by [−3, 3])
14. [Y=] [LOG] [(] [X,T,θ,n] [+] 2 [)] [÷] [LOG] 2 [ENTER] [LOG] 2 [÷] [LOG] 0.5 [ZOOM] 6; use ZOOM−IN or INTERSECT to solve; −1.50
15. [Y=] [LOG] [(] [X,T,θ,n] [+] 4 [)] [÷] [LOG] 9 [ENTER] [LOG] [X,T,θ,n] [÷] [LOG] 2 [ZOOM] 6; use ZOOM−IN or INTERSECT to solve; 1.73
16. [Y=] 3 [^] [(] 4 [X,T,θ,n] [−] 7 [)] [ENTER] 4 [^] [(] 2 [X,T,θ,n] [+] 3 [)] [ZOOM] 6; use INTERSECT to solve; 7.30

10-1 Real Exponents and Exponential Functions

Pages 599–600 Check for Understanding

1. Juan; if the equation is an exponential function, the exponent must be a variable.

2a. D: x is a real number; R: $y > 0$

2b. D: x is a real number; R: $y > 0$

2c. D: x is a real number; R: $y < 0$

3. They are the same.

4. $y = b^x$
$= b^0$
$= 1$

5. $1^{x_1} = 1^{x_2}$ for any x_1 and x_2.

6. Sample answer: Find 2.3^x for each possible value of x to determine which expression is about 3; b.

7. 4.7

8. 2.3

9. $5^{\sqrt{2}} \cdot 5^{3\sqrt{2}} = 5^{\sqrt{2}+3\sqrt{2}}$
$= 5^{4\sqrt{2}}$

10. $(3^{\sqrt{5}})^{\sqrt{5}} = 3^{\sqrt{5}\cdot\sqrt{5}}$
$= 3^5$ or 243

11. $27^{\sqrt{5}} \div 3^{\sqrt{5}} = (3^3)^{\sqrt{5}} \div 3^{\sqrt{5}}$
$= 3^{3\sqrt{5}} \div 3^{\sqrt{5}}$
$= 3^{3\sqrt{5}-\sqrt{5}}$
$= 3^{2\sqrt{5}}$

12. $y = a \cdot 2^x$
$12 = a \cdot 2^2$
$12 = 4a$
$3 = a$

13. $y = a \cdot 2^x$
$-16 = a \cdot 2^3$
$-16 = 8a$
$-2 = a$

14. $3^n = 81$
$3^n = 3^4$
$n = 4$

15. $2^{2n} = \frac{1}{16}$
$2^{2n} = 2^{-4}$
$2n = -4$
$n = -2$

16. $\left(\frac{1}{7}\right)^{b-3} = 343$
$\left(\frac{1}{7}\right)^{b-3} = \left(\frac{1}{7}\right)^{-3}$
$b - 3 = -3$
$b = 0$

17.

Start	15 min	30 min	45 min	60 min
1	2	4	8	16

16 cells

Pages 600–602 Exercises

18. 3.2

19. 0.7

20. 2.7

21. 0.5

22. 3.0

23. 0.5

24. $(2^{\sqrt{2}})^{\sqrt{8}} = 2^{\sqrt{2}\cdot\sqrt{8}}$
$= 2^{\sqrt{16}}$
$= 2^4$ or 16

25. $4^{\sqrt{2}} \cdot 4^{2\sqrt{2}} = 4^{\sqrt{2}+2\sqrt{2}}$
$= 4^{3\sqrt{2}}$

26. $7^{3\sqrt{2}} \div 7^{\sqrt{2}} = 7^{3\sqrt{2}-\sqrt{2}}$
$= 7^{2\sqrt{2}}$

27. $(y^{\sqrt{3}})^{\sqrt{12}} = y^{\sqrt{3}\cdot\sqrt{12}}$
$= y^{\sqrt{36}}$
$= y^6$

28. $5^{\sqrt{3}} \cdot 5^{\sqrt{27}} = 5^{\sqrt{3}+3\sqrt{3}}$
$= 5^{4\sqrt{3}}$

29. $64^{\sqrt{7}} \div 2^{\sqrt{7}} = 2^{6\sqrt{7}} \div 2^{\sqrt{7}}$
$= 2^{6\sqrt{7}-\sqrt{7}}$
$= 2^{5\sqrt{7}}$

30. $2(3^{\sqrt{2}})(3^{-\sqrt{2}}) = 2(3^{\sqrt{2}+(-\sqrt{2})})$
$= 2(3^0)$
$= 2$

31. $(a^{\sqrt{5}})^{\sqrt{20}} = a^{\sqrt{5}\cdot\sqrt{20}}$
$= a^{\sqrt{100}}$
$= a^{10}$

32. $(m^{\sqrt{3}} + n^{\sqrt{2}})^2 = (m^{\sqrt{3}} + n^{\sqrt{2}})(m^{\sqrt{3}} + n^{\sqrt{2}})$
$= m^{2\sqrt{3}} + 2m^{\sqrt{3}}n^{\sqrt{2}} + n^{2\sqrt{2}}$

33. $y = a \cdot 3^x$
$36 = a \cdot 3^2$
$36 = 9a$
$4 = a$

34. $y = a \cdot 3^x$
$15 = a \cdot 3^{-1}$
$15 = \frac{1}{3}a$
$45 = a$

35. $y = a \cdot 3^x$
$-81 = a \cdot 3^4$
$-81 = 81a$
$-1 = a$

36. $y = a \cdot 3^x$
$-2 = a \cdot 3^{-2}$
$-2 = \frac{1}{9}a$
$-18 = a$

37. $y = a \cdot 3^x$
$27 = a \cdot 3^5$
$27 = 243a$
$\frac{1}{9} = a$

38. $y = a \cdot 3^x$
$\frac{1}{9} = a \cdot 3^{-3}$
$\frac{1}{9} = \frac{1}{27}a$
$3 = a$

39. $3^{4x} = 3^{3-x}$
$4x = 3 - x$
$5x = 3$
$x = \frac{3}{5}$

40. $5^{n-3} \geq \frac{1}{25}$
$5^{n-3} \geq 5^{-2}$
$n - 3 \geq -2$
$n \geq 1$

41. $\frac{1}{32} = 2^{1-m}$
$2^{-5} = 2^{1-m}$
$-5 = 1 - m$
$-6 = -m$
$6 = m$

42. $9^{2p} = 27^{p-1}$
$(3^2)^{2p} = (3^3)^{p-1}$
$3^{4p} = 3^{3p-3}$
$4p = 3p - 3$
$p = -3$

43. $16^n > 8^{n+1}$
$(2^4)^n > (2^3)^{n+1}$
$2^{4n} > 2^{3n+3}$
$4n > 3n + 3$
$n > 3$

44. $\left(\frac{1}{9}\right)^m = 81^{m+4}$
$(3^{-2})^m = (3^4)^{m+4}$
$3^{-2m} = 3^{4m+16}$
$-2m = 4m + 16$
$-6m = 16$
$m = -\frac{8}{3}$

45. $2^x \cdot 4^{x+5} = 4^{2x-1}$
$2^x \cdot (2^2)^{x+5} = (2^2)^{2x-1}$
$2^x \cdot 2^{2x+10} = 2^{4x-2}$
$2^{3x+10} = 2^{4x-2}$
$3x + 10 = 4x - 2$
$12 = x$

46. $2^{5x} \cdot 16^{1-x} = 4^{x-3}$
$2^{5x} \cdot (2^4)^{1-x} = (2^2)^{x-3}$
$2^{5x} \cdot 2^{4-4x} = 2^{2x-6}$
$2^{4+x} = 2^{2x-6}$
$4 + x = 2x - 6$
$10 = x$

47. $25^x = 5^{x^2-15}$
$(5^2)^x = 5^{x^2-15}$
$5^{2x} = 5^{x^2-15}$
$2x = x^2 - 15$
$0 = x^2 - 2x - 15$
$0 = (x - 5)(x + 3)$
$x - 5 = 0$ or $x + 3 = 0$
$x = 5$ $\quad x = -3$

48. $y = 4^x$

x	y
−4	0.004
0	1
1	4

$y = -(4)^x$

x	y
−4	−0.004
0	−1
1	−4

$y = \left(\frac{1}{4}\right)^x$

x	y
−1	4
0	1
4	0.004

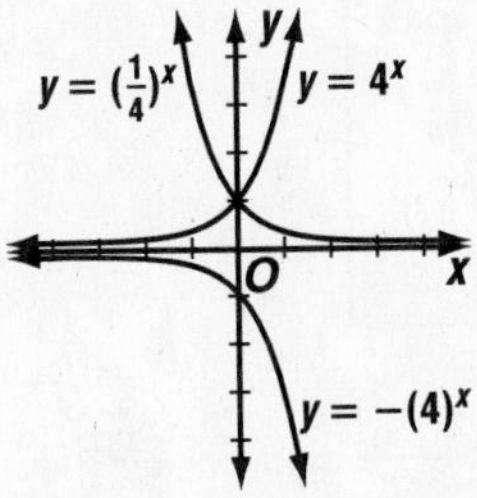

The graph of $y = -(4)^x$ is the reflection of the graph of $y = 4^x$ over the x-axis. The graph of $y = \left(\frac{1}{4}\right)^x$ is the reflection of the graph of $y = 4^x$ over the y-axis.

49. [Y=] 2.1 [^] [X,T,θ,n] [GRAPH] ; WINDOW: [−5, 5] by [−5, 5]

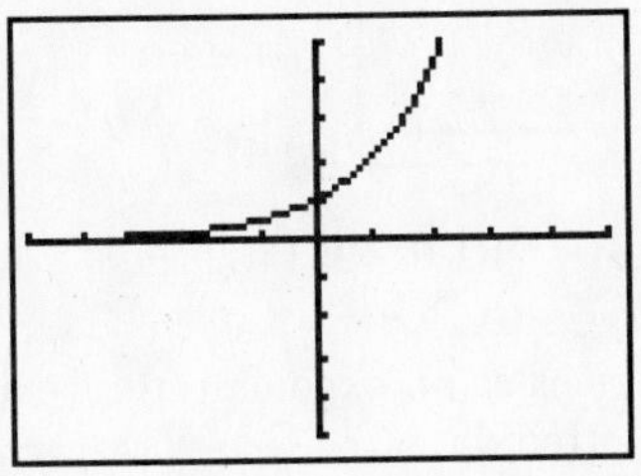

50. [Y=] 0.5 [(] 2.1 [)] [^] [X,T,θ,n] [GRAPH] ; WINDOW: [−5, 5] by [−5, 5]

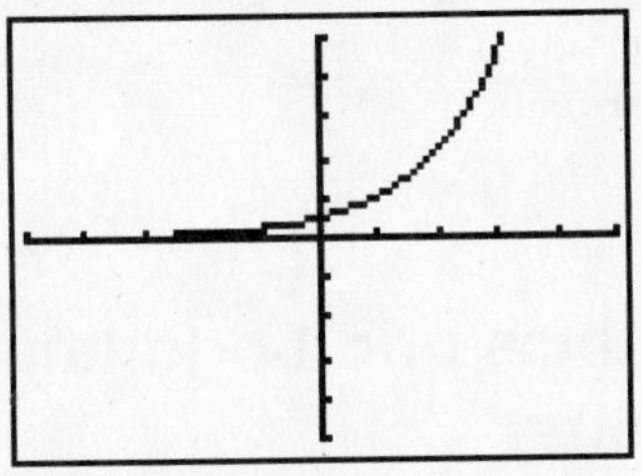

51. [Y=] [(−)] 0.2 [(] 2.1 [)] [^] [X,T,θ,n] [GRAPH] ; WINDOW: [−5, 5] by [−5, 5]

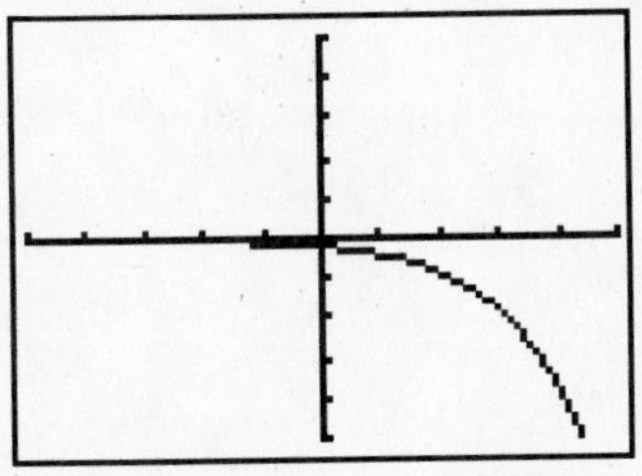

52. If $x = 1$, $2.3^1 = 2.3$; so x must be less than 1. Test decimals less than 1; 0.8.

53a. 2, 4, 8, 16

53b. $y = 2^x$

53c. $y = 0.003(2)^x$

53d. $y = 0.003(2)^x$
$= 0.003(2)^{30}$
$\approx 3{,}221{,}225.47$; about 3,221,225.47 inches

54a. $a = kw^{1.31}$
$170 = k \cdot 45^{1.31}$
$1.16 \approx k$
$a = 1.16w^{1.31}$

54b. $a = 1.16w^{1.31}$
$= 1.16(430)^{1.31}$
≈ 3268; about 3268 square yards

55a. $P = 14.7(10)^{-0.02h}$
$= 14.7(10)^{-0.02 \cdot 0}$
≈ 14.7; about 14.7 psi

55b. $P = 14.7(10)^{-0.02h}$
$= 14.7(10)^{-0.02(1)}$
≈ 14.0; about 14.0 psi

55c. $P = 14.7(10)^{-0.02h}$
$= 14.7(10)^{-0.02(5.5)}$
≈ 11.4; about 11.4 psi

55d. $P = 14.7(10)^{-0.02h}$
$= 14.7(10)^{-0.02(-1.9)}$
≈ 16.0; about 16.0 psi

55e.

h	P
−40	92.8
−20	36.9
0	14.7
20	5.9

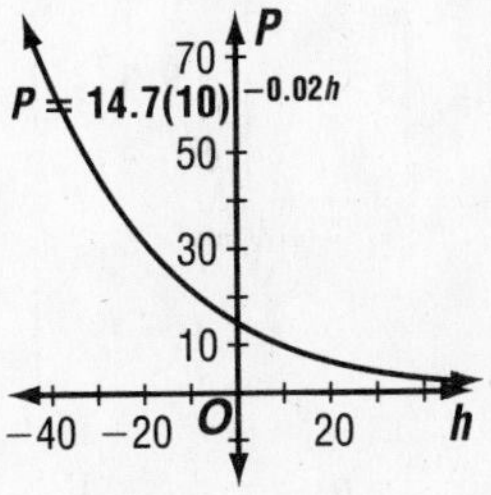

They represent the atmospheric pressure for places below sea level.

56. $2000 - 1990 = 10$; $P = 164{,}693(2.7)^{0.007t}$
$= 164{,}693(2.7)^{0.007(10)}$
≈ 176551.17; about 176,552

57a. $d = kh^{\frac{3}{2}}$
$19.1 = k(6)^{\frac{3}{2}}$
$1.30 \approx k$
$d = 1.30h^{\frac{3}{2}}$

57b. $d = 1.30h^{\frac{3}{2}}$
$= 1.30(83.8)^{\frac{3}{2}}$
≈ 997
about 997 centimeters

58. $\frac{6}{a-7} = \frac{a-49}{a^2-7a} + \frac{1}{a}$
$a(a-7)\left(\frac{6}{a-7}\right) = a(a-7)\left(\frac{a-49}{a^2-7a} + \frac{1}{a}\right)$
$6a = a - 49 + a - 7$
$4a = -56$
$a = -14$

59. $f(x) = -x^4 - x^2 - x - 1$; 0 positive
$f(-x) = -x^4 - x^2 + x - 1$; 2 or 0 negative
2 or 4 imaginary

60. focus: (0, 0)
vertex: (−5, 0)
measure of latus rectum: 20
$20 = \left|\frac{1}{a}\right|$
$\frac{1}{20} = a$
$x = a(y - k)^2 + h$
$x = \frac{1}{20}y^2 - 5$

61. $d = \sqrt{(x_2 - x_1)^2 + (y_2 - y_1)^2}$

$= \sqrt{(12 - 9)^2 + (5 - 3)^2}$

$= \sqrt{9 + 4}$

$= \sqrt{13}$

≈ 3.61; $3.61 \times 10 = 36.1$ or 36 miles

62. $x^2 + 14x - 12 = 0$

$x^2 + 14x = 12$

$x^2 + 14x + 49 = 12 + 49$

$(x + 7)^2 = 61$

$x + 7 = \pm\sqrt{61}$

$x = -7 \pm \sqrt{61}$

63. $\frac{1}{3 - 4i} = \frac{1(3 + 4i)}{(3 - 4i)(3 + 4i)}$

$= \frac{3 + 4i}{9 - 16i^2}$

$= \frac{3 + 4i}{25}$

64. $\frac{(3 + \sqrt{5})}{(1 + \sqrt{2})} = \frac{(3 + \sqrt{5})(1 - \sqrt{2})}{(1 + \sqrt{2})(1 - \sqrt{2})}$

$= \frac{3 - 3\sqrt{2} + \sqrt{5} - \sqrt{10}}{1 - 2}$

$= \frac{3 - 3\sqrt{2} + \sqrt{5} - \sqrt{10}}{-1}$

$= -3 + 3\sqrt{2} - \sqrt{5} + \sqrt{10}$

65. $\begin{bmatrix} -2 & 3 \\ 1 & 10 \\ 0 & -6 \end{bmatrix} \cdot \begin{bmatrix} 9 & 3 \\ 1 & 4 \end{bmatrix} = \begin{bmatrix} -18 + 3 & -6 + 12 \\ 9 + 10 & 3 + 40 \\ 0 - 6 & 0 - 24 \end{bmatrix}$

$= \begin{bmatrix} -15 & 6 \\ 19 & 43 \\ -6 & -24 \end{bmatrix}$

66. $\begin{array}{rl} r + s + t &= 15 \\ (-)r \quad + t &= 12 \\ \hline s &= 3 \end{array}$ $\qquad$ $\begin{array}{rl} r + s + t &= 15 \\ (-) \quad s + t &= 10 \\ \hline r &= 5 \end{array}$

$s + t = 10$

$3 + t = 10$

$t = 7$; (5, 3, 7)

67. no

68. associative property of addition

10-1B Graphing Technology: Curve Fitting with Real-World Data

Page 604 Exercises

1. [STAT] [ENTER] 1970 [ENTER] 1800 [ENTER] 1810 [ENTER] 1820 [ENTER] 1830 [ENTER] 1840 [ENTER] 1850 [ENTER] 1860 [ENTER] 1870 [ENTER] 1880 [ENTER] 1890 [ENTER] 1900 [ENTER] 1910 [ENTER] 1920 [ENTER] 1930 [ENTER] 1940 [ENTER] 1950 [ENTER] 1960 [ENTER] 1970 [ENTER] 1980 [ENTER] [▶] ([▲] to $L_2(1)$ if necessary) 4.5 [ENTER] 6.1 [ENTER] 4.3 [ENTER] 5.5 [ENTER] 7.4 [ENTER] 9.8 [ENTER] 7.9 [ENTER] 10.6 [ENTER] 10.9 [ENTER] 14.2 [ENTER] 17.8 [ENTER] 21.5 [ENTER] 26.0 [ENTER] 29.9 [ENTER] 34.7 [ENTER] 37.2 [ENTER] 42.6

(Continued next column)

[ENTER] 50.6 [ENTER] 57.5 [ENTER] 64.0 [ENTER] [WINDOW] [▼] 1780 [ENTER] 1990 [ENTER] 10 [ENTER] 0 [ENTER] 70 [ENTER] 5 [ENTER] [GRAPH]

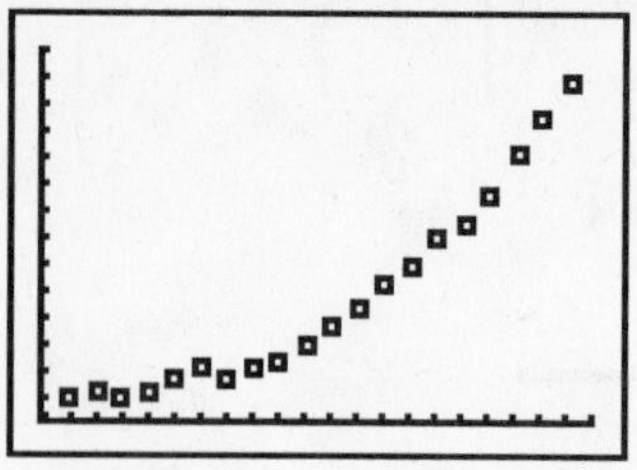

[STAT] [▶] [ALPHA] A [2nd] L_1 [,] [2nd] L_2 [ENTER]; $y = (1.159105 \times 10^{-11})(1.014951462)^x$; $r = 0.9901350318$

[Y=] [VARS] 5 [▶] [▶] 7 [GRAPH]

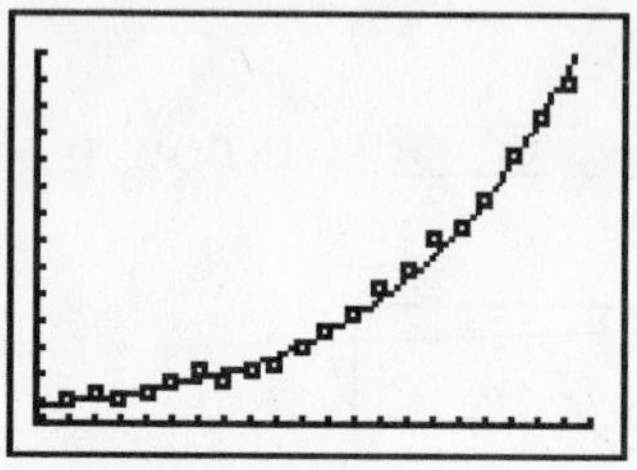

2. $y = (1.159105 \times 10^{-11})(1.014951462)^x$; $r = 0.9901350318$
   The best-fit line rises at an exponential rate and closely fits the plotted data.
3. [WINDOW] [▼] [▼] 2010 [ENTER] [GRAPH] [2nd] [CALC] [ENTER] 2000 [ENTER] ; about 90.088
4. A quadratic equation might be a good model for this example because the shape is close to a portion of the parabola.
5. Louisiana Purchase

10-2 Logarithms and Logarithmic Functions

Page 608 Check for Understanding

1. the logarithm base 2 of x
2. Sample answer: $y = \log_2 x$
3. all real numbers
4. all real numbers
5.

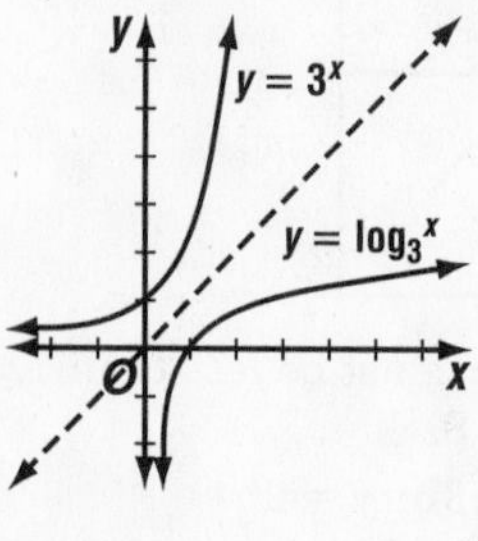

6. $\log_3 27 = 3$
7. $\log_2 32 = 5$
8. $\log_4 \frac{1}{16} = -2$
9. $5^3 = 125$

10. $8^{\frac{2}{3}} = 4$

11. $10^{-3} = 0.001$

12. $\log_3 \frac{1}{27} = x$
$3^x = \frac{1}{27}$
$3^x = 3^{-3}$
$x = -3$

13. $\log_{16} 4 = x$
$16^x = 4$
$(2^4)^x = 2^2$
$2^{4x} = 2^2$
$4x = 2$
$x = \frac{1}{2}$

14. $5^{\log_5 25} = 25$

15. $\log_7 y = -2$
$7^{-2} = y$
$\frac{1}{49} = y$

16. $\log_b 64 = 3$
$b^3 = 64$
$b^3 = 4^3$
$b = 4$

17. $\log_{\frac{1}{3}} 27 = x$
$\left(\frac{1}{3}\right)^x = 27$
$\left(\frac{1}{3}\right)^x = \left(\frac{1}{3}\right)^{-3}$
$x = -3$

18. $\log_5 (2x - 3) = \log_5 (x + 2)$
$2x - 3 = x + 2$
$x = 5$

19. $\log_{10} (x^2 + 36) = \log_{10} 100$
$x^2 + 36 = 100$
$x^2 = 64$
$x = \pm 8$

20. $\log_3 3^{(2x-1)} = 7$
$3^7 = 3^{(2x-1)}$
$7 = 2x - 1$
$8 = 2x$
$4 = x$

21. $7 - 4 = 3$
10^3 or 1000 times stronger

Pages 609–610 Exercises

22. $\log_{10} 1000 = x$
$10^x = 1000$
$x = 3$

23. $\log_5 25 = x$
$5^x = 25$
$x = 2$

24. $\log_{14} 196 = x$
$14^x = 196$
$14^x = 14^2$
$x = 2$

25. $\log_3 \frac{1}{81} = x$
$3^x = \frac{1}{81}$
$3^x = 3^{-4}$
$x = -4$

26. $\log_2 \frac{1}{128} = x$
$2^x = \frac{1}{128}$
$2^x = 2^{-7}$
$x = -7$

27. $\log_{36} 6 = x$
$36^x = 6$
$(6^2)^x = 6$
$6^{2x} = 6$
$2x = 1$
$x = \frac{1}{2}$

28. $\log_8 8^4 = x$
$8^x = 8^4$
$x = 4$

29. $3^{\log_3 243} = 243$

30. $7^{\log_7 (x+3)} = x + 3$

31. $\log_2 x = 5$
$2^5 = x$
$32 = x$

32. $\log_3 27 = y$
$3^y = 27$
$3^y = 3^3$
$y = 3$

33. $\log_b 9 = 2$
$b^2 = 9$
$b^2 = 3^2$
$b = 3$

34. $\log_5 \sqrt{5} = y$
$5^y = \sqrt{5}$
$5^y = 5^{\frac{1}{2}}$
$y = \frac{1}{2}$

35. $\log_{25} x = \frac{3}{2}$
$25^{\frac{3}{2}} = x$
$125 = x$

36. $\log_b 0.01 = -2$
$b^{-2} = 0.01$
$b^{-2} = 10^{-2}$
$b = 10$

37. $\log_{\frac{1}{10}} x = -3$
$\frac{1}{10}^{-3} = x$
$1000 = x$

38. $\log_{3x} 125 = 3$
$(3x)^3 = 125$
$27x^3 = 125$
$x^3 = \frac{125}{27}$
$x^3 = \frac{5^3}{3^3}$
$x^3 = \left(\frac{5}{3}\right)^3$
$x = \frac{5}{3}$

39. $\log_{x+2} 16 = 2$
$(x + 2)^2 = 16$
$x^2 + 4x + 4 = 16$
$x^2 + 4x - 12 = 0$
$(x + 6)(x - 2) = 0$
$x + 6 = 0$ or $x - 2 = 0$
$x = -6$ $\quad x = 2$
$b > 0$ so $x \neq -6$

40. $\log_8 (3x - 1) = \log_8 (2x^2)$
$3x - 1 = 2x^2$
$0 = 2x^2 - 3x + 1$
$0 = (2x - 1)(x - 1)$
$2x - 1 = 0$ or $x - 1 = 0$
$2x = 1$ $\quad x = 1$
$x = \frac{1}{2}$

41. $\log_2 (4x + 10) - \log_2 (x + 1) < 3$
$\log_2 \left(\frac{(4x + 10)}{(x + 1)}\right) < 3$
$2^3 < \frac{(4x + 10)}{(x + 1)}$
$8 < \frac{(4x + 10)}{(x + 1)}$
$8(x + 1) < (4x + 10)$
$8x + 8 < 4x + 10$
$4x < 2$
$x < \frac{1}{2}$

42. $\log_{10} (x^2 + 16) = \log_{10} 80$
$x^2 + 16 = 80$
$x^2 = 64$
$x = \pm 8$

43. $4^{\log_4(x-1)} = -0.5$
$x - 1 = -0.5$
$x = 0.5$
The value $\log_4(x - 1)$ is undefined if $x = 0.5$, so there is no solution.

44. $\log_2 2^{(3x + 2)} = 14$
$2^{14} = 2^{(3x + 2)}$
$14 = 3x + 2$
$12 = 3x$
$4 = x$

45. $3^{\log_3 10} = x$
$10 = x$

46. $\log_{10} (\log_8 8) = x$
$10^x = \log_8 8$
$10^x = 1$
$x = 0$

47. $\log_4 (\log_2 16) = y$
$4^y = \log_2 16$
$4^y = 4$
$y = 1$

48. $y = \log_5 x$ $\quad y = 5^x$

x	y
$\frac{1}{5}$	-1
1	0
5	1

x	y
-2	$\frac{1}{25}$
0	1
1	5

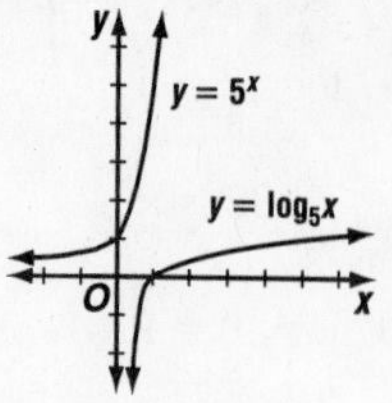

49. $y = \log_{\frac{1}{3}} x$ $\quad y = \left(\frac{1}{3}\right)^x$

x	y
$\frac{1}{9}$	2
1	0
3	-1

x	y
-1	3
0	1
2	$\frac{1}{9}$

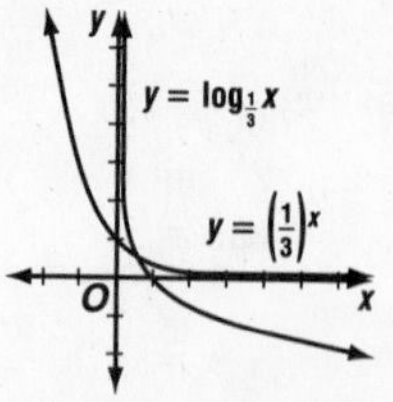

50. The graphs are reflections of each other along the line $x = y$.

51. If the parent graph is $\log_{10}x$, the following is true. (1) All graphs go through (1, 0) and $\log x$ is defined only for $x > 0$. (2) When $b > 1$ in $\log_b x$, the graphs curve upward to the right. As b increases, the graph of $\log x$ stays closer to the x-axis. (3) When $b < 1$ in $\log_b x$, the graphs curve downward to the right. As b decreases, the graph of $\log x$ stays closer to the x-axis.

52. $\log_4 4 + \log_4 16 \stackrel{?}{=} \log_4 64$
$1 + 2 \stackrel{?}{=} 3$
$3 = 3$

53. $\log_4 16 \stackrel{?}{=} 2 \log_4 4$
$2 \stackrel{?}{=} 2(1)$
$2 = 2$

54. $\log_2 8 \cdot \log_8 2 \stackrel{?}{=} 1$
$3 \cdot \frac{1}{3} \stackrel{?}{=} 1$
$1 = 1$

55. $\log_{10} [\log_3 (\log_4 64)] \stackrel{?}{=} 0$
$\log_{10} [\log_3 3] \stackrel{?}{=} 0$
$\log_{10} 1 \stackrel{?}{=} 0$
$0 = 0$

56. 3 and 4; 2460 is between 1000 or 10^3 and 10,000 or 10^4.

57. 1989: $10^{7.1} = x$; $7.1 = \log_{10} x$
1965: $10^{7.0} = y$; $7.0 = \log_{10} y$
$\frac{x}{y} = \frac{10^{7.1}}{10^{7.0}}$
$= 10^{0.1}$
≈ 1.26; about 1.26 times greater

58. $7 = \log_{10} x$ $\qquad \frac{x}{y} = \frac{10^7}{10^{4.2}}$
$4.2 = \log_{10} y$ $\qquad = 10^{2.8}$
≈ 630; about 630 times more acidic

59. $11^{\sqrt{5}} \cdot 11^{\sqrt{45}} = 11^{\sqrt{5}} \cdot 11^{3\sqrt{5}}$
$= 11^{4\sqrt{5}}$

60. $\frac{x_1}{y_2} = \frac{x_2}{y_1}$
$\frac{3.4}{101.3} = \frac{x_2}{120}$
$101.3x_2 = 408$
$x_2 = 4.03$
about 4.03 cubic decimeters

61. $f \circ g$ does not exist since the range of g is not a subset of the domain of f.
$g \circ f = \{(2, 5), (-1, -1), (2, 2)\}$

62. center: $(3, -5)$
$2a = 4$
$a = 2$
Asymptotes have equations $y = \pm \frac{3}{2}x$. Since $a = 2$ and $y = \pm \frac{b}{a}x$, $b = 3$.
$\frac{(x-3)^2}{4} - \frac{(y+5)^2}{9} = 1$

63. $s_1 + s_2 = 6 + (-6)$
$= 0$
$s_1(s_2) = 6(-6)$
$= -36$
$0 = -\frac{b}{a}$; $-36 = \frac{c}{a}$
$a = 1, b = 0, c = -36$
$x^2 - 36 = 0$

64. $x^2 + 6x = -9$
$x^2 + 6x + 9 = 0$
$(x + 3)(x + 3) = 0$
$x + 3 = 0$ or $x + 3 = 0$
$x = -3$ $\qquad x = -3$

65. $t = \frac{1}{4}\sqrt{5}$
$= \frac{1}{4}\sqrt{200}$
≈ 3.54; about 3.54 seconds

66. $\begin{vmatrix} 6 & 5 & -2 \\ -3 & 0 & 6 \\ 1 & 4 & 2 \end{vmatrix} = 6\begin{vmatrix} 0 & 6 \\ 4 & 2 \end{vmatrix} - 5\begin{vmatrix} -3 & 6 \\ 1 & 2 \end{vmatrix} - 2\begin{vmatrix} -3 & 0 \\ 1 & 4 \end{vmatrix}$
$= 6(-24) - 5(-12) - 2(-12)$
$= -60$

67. $y - x \leq 3$
$y \leq x + 3$
$y \geq x - 2$

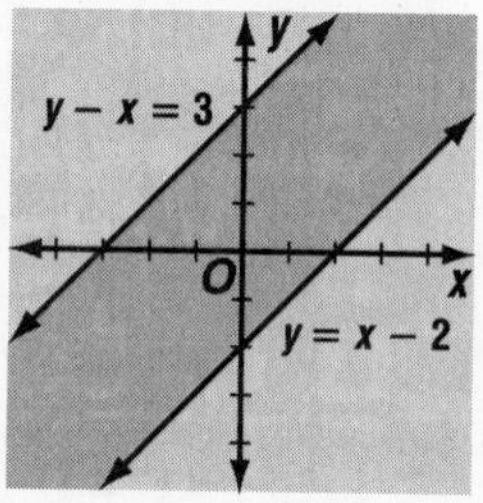

68. $3x + 5y = 30$
$3(0) + 5y = 30$
$5y = 30$
$y = 6$
$3x + 5y = 30$
$3x + 5(0) = 30$
$3x = 30$
$x = 10$

69. $8x + 5 < 7x - 3$
$x + 5 < -3$
$x < -8$

Page 610 Mathematics and Society

1. logarithmic with base 10
2. Sample answer: Problems arise trying to devise a scale that is simpler and easier to understand and yet can take into account the huge differences in magnitude that need to be measured.
3. See students' work.

10-3 Properties of Logarithms

Page 614 Check for Understanding

1. The pH of a solution indicates its acidity. The pH level is actually an exponent to the power of 10, so it is a logarithm to the base 10.
2. properties of exponents

3. Sample answer:

Let $b^x = m$, then $\log_b m = x$.

$(b^x)^p = m^p$

$b^{xp} = m^p$ Multiplying exponents

$\log_b b^{xp} = \log_b m^p$ Property of equality for logarithmic functions

$xp = \log_b m^p$ Definition of inverse function

$p \log_b m = \log_b m^p$ Substitution property

4. multiplying exponents → product property of logarithms

dividing exponents → quotient property of logarithms

power of powers → power property of logarithms

See students' work.

5. $\log_4 x^2 y = \log_4 x^2 + \log_4 y$
$= 2 \log_4 x + \log_4 y$

6. $\log_3 (xy)^3 = \log_3 x^3y^3$
$= \log_3 x^3 + \log_3 y^3$
$= 3\log_3 x + 3\log_3 y$

7. $\log_5 \frac{ac}{b} = \log_5 ac - \log_5 b$
$= \log_5 a + \log_5 c - \log_5 b$

8. $\log_2 r^{\frac{1}{3}} t = \log_2 r^{\frac{1}{3}} + \log_2 t$
$= \frac{1}{3} \log_2 r + \log_2 t$

9. $\log_2 \frac{7}{3} = \log_2 7 - \log_2 3$
$= 2.807 - 1.585$
$= 1.222$

10. $\log_2 36 = \log_2 (4 \cdot 9)$
$= \log_2 2^2 + \log_2 3^2$
$= 2 + 2 \log_2 3$
$= 2 + 2(1.585)$
$= 5.170$

11. $\log_2 0.75 = \log_2 \frac{3}{4}$
$= \log_2 3 - \log_2 2^2$
$= 1.585 - 2$
$= -0.415$

12. $\log_2 5 + \log_2 x = \log_2 15$
$\log_2 5x = \log_2 15$
$5x = 15$
$x = 3$

13. $\log_5 16 - \log_5 2t = \log_5 2$
$\log_5 \frac{16}{2t} = \log_5 2$
$\log5 \frac{8}{t} = \log_5 2$
$\frac{8}{t} = 2$
$8 = 2t$
$4 = t$

14. $\log_{10} 7 + \log_{10} (n - 2) = \log_{10} 6n$
$\log_{10} 7(n - 2) = \log_{10} 6n$
$7(n \cdot 2) = 6n$
$7n - 14 = 6n$
$n = 14$

15. $\log_2 (y + 2) - 1 = \log_2 (y - 2)$
$\log_2 (y + 2) - \log_2 (y - 2) = 1$
$\log_2 \frac{y+2}{y-2} = 1$
$2^1 = \frac{y+2}{y-2}$
$2(y - 2) = y + 2$
$2y - 4 = y + 2$
$y = 6$

16. $10^{8.5-4.1} = 10^{4.4}$
$\approx 25{,}119$; about 25,119 times more acidic

Pages 615–616 Exercises

17. $\log_3 4 = \log_3 2^2$
$= 2 \log_3 2$
$= 2(0.6310)$
$= 1.262$

18. $\log_3 49 = \log_3 7^2$
$= 2 \log_3 7$
$= 2(1.7712)$
$= 3.5424$

19. $\log_3 \frac{7}{2} = \log_3 7 - \log_3 2$
$= 1.7712 - 0.6310$
$= 1.1402$

20. $\log_3 18 = \log_3 (3^2 \cdot 2)$
$= \log_3 3^2 + \log_3 2$
$= 2 + 0.6310$
$= 2.6310$

21. $\log_3 \frac{2}{3} = \log_3 2 - \log_3 3$
$= 0.6310 - 1$
$= -0.3690$

22. $\log_3 54 = \log_3 (3^3 \cdot 2)$
$= \log_3 3^3 + \log_3 2$
$= 3 + 0.6310$
$= 3.6310$

23. $\log_3 108 = \log_3 (3^3 \cdot 2^2)$
$= \log_3 3^3 + \log_3 2^2$
$= 3 + 2 \log_3 2$
$= 3 + 2(0.6310)$
$= 4.2620$

24. $\log_3 \frac{18}{49} = \log_3 18 - \log_3 49$
$= \log_3 (3^2 \cdot 2) - \log_3 7^2$
$= \log_3 3^2 + \log_3 2 - 2 \log_3 7$
$= 2 + 0.6310 - 2(1.7712)$
$= -0.9114$

25. $\log_3 \frac{7}{9} = \log_3 7 - \log_3 3^2$
$= 1.7712 - 2$
$= -0.2288$

26. $\log_3 2 + \log_3 7 = \log_3 x$
$\log_3 14 = \log_3 x$
$14 = x$

27. $\log_5 42 - \log_5 6 = \log_5 k$
$\log_5 \frac{42}{6} = \log_5 k$
$\frac{42}{6} = k$
$7 = k$

28. $\log_5 m = \frac{1}{3} \log_5 125$
$\log_5 m = \log_5 125^{\frac{1}{3}}$
$m = 125^{\frac{1}{3}}$
$m = 5$

29. $\log_{10} y = \frac{1}{4} \log_{10} 16 + \frac{1}{2} \log_{10} 49$
$\log_{10} y = \log_{10} 16^{\frac{1}{4}} + \log_{10} 49^{\frac{1}{2}}$
$\log_{10} y = \log_{10} 2 + \log_{10} 7$
$\log_{10} y = \log_{10} 14$
$y = 14$

30. $\log_9 5 + \log_9 (n + 1) = \log_9 6n$
$\log_9 5(n + 1) = \log_9 6n$
$5(n + 1) = 6n$
$5n + 5 = 6n$
$5 = n$

31. $3\log_5 x - \log_5 4 = \log_5 16$
$\log_5 x^3 - \log_5 4 = \log_5 16$
$\log_5 \frac{x^3}{4} = \log_5 16$
$\frac{x^3}{4} = 16$
$x^3 = 64$
$x = 4$

32. $2\log_3 y + \log_3 0.1 = \log_3 5 + \log_3 2$
$\log_3 y^2 + \log_3 0.1 = \log_3 5 + \log_3 2$
$\log_3 0.1y^2 = \log_3 10$
$0.1y^2 = 10$
$y^2 = 100$
$y = 10$

33. $\log_{10} a + \log_{10} (a + 21) = 2$
$\log_{10} a(a + 21) = 2$
$10^2 = a(a + 21)$
$100 = a^2 + 21a$
$0 = a^2 + 21a - 100$
$0 = (a + 25)(a - 4)$
$a + 25 = 0$ or $a - 4 = 0$
$a = -25$ $a = 4$
Since log is not defined for negative numbers, −25 is not an acceptable solution.

34. $\log_6 48 - \log_6 \frac{16}{5} + \log_6 5 = \log_6 5x$
$\log_6 (48 \div \frac{16}{5} \cdot 5) = \log_6 5x$
$\log_6 75 = \log_6 5x$
$75 = 5x$
$15 = x$

35. $\log_3 64 - \log_3 \frac{8}{3} + \log_3 2 = \log_3 4r$
$\log_3 (64 \div \frac{8}{3} \cdot 2) = \log_3 4r$
$\log_3 48 = \log_3 4r$
$48 = 4r$
$12 = r$

36. $\log_6 (b^2 + 2) + \log_6 2 = 2$
$\log_6 2(b^2 + 2) = 2$
$6^2 = 2(b^2 + 2)$
$36 = 2b^2 + 4$
$32 = 2b^2$
$16 = b^2$
$\pm 4 = b$

37. $\log_3 (5z + 5) - \log_3 (z^2 - 1) = 0$
$\log_3 \frac{5z + 5}{z^2 - 1} = 0$
$3^0 = \frac{5z + 5}{z^2 - 1}$
$1 = \frac{5z + 5}{z^2 - 1}$
$z^2 - 1 = 5z + 5$
$z^2 - 5z - 6 = 0$
$(z - 6)(z + 1) = 0$
$z - 6 = 0$ or $z + 1 = 0$
$z = 6$ $z = -1$
$z = -1$ is not an acceptable solution because the resulting equation would be $\log_3 0 - \log_3 0 = 0$.

38. $\log_n a = \log_n (y + 3) - \log_n 3$
$\log_n a = \log_n \frac{y + 3}{3}$
$a = \frac{y + 3}{3}$
$a = \frac{y}{3} + 1$

39. $\log_b 2a - \log_b x^3 = \log_b x$
$\log_b \frac{2a}{x^3} = \log_b x$
$\frac{2a}{x^3} = x$
$2a = x^4$
$a = \frac{x^4}{2}$

40. $\log_x a^2 + 5\log_x y = \log_x a$
$\log_x a^2 + \log_x y^5 = \log_x a$
$\log_x a^2y^5 = \log_x a$
$a^2y^5 = a$
$ay^5 = 1$
$a = \frac{1}{y^5}$

41. $\log_b 4 + 2\log_b a = 2\log_b (n + 1)$
$\log_b 4 + \log_b a^2 = \log_b (n + 1)^2$
$\log_b 4a^2 = \log_b (n + 1)^2$
$4a^2 = (n + 1)^2$
$a^2 = \frac{(n + 1)^2}{4}$
$a = \frac{n + 1}{2}$ or $\frac{1}{2}(n + 1)$

42. $2\log_b x + \frac{1}{3}\log_b (x + 2) - 4\log_b (x - 3)$
$= \log_b x^2 + \log_b (x + 2)^{\frac{1}{3}} - \log_b (x - 3)^4$
$= \log_b \left[x^2 \cdot \frac{\sqrt[3]{x + 2}}{(x - 3)^4}\right]$

43. $\log_b (xy)^2 + 2\log_b \frac{x}{y} - 3\log_b (yx^{\frac{2}{3}})$
$= \log_b (xy^2) + \log_b \left(\frac{x}{y}\right)^2 - \log_b (yx^{\frac{2}{3}})^3$
$= \log_b (xy^2) + \log_b \left(\frac{x^2}{y^2}\right) - \log_b (y^3x^2)$
$= \log_b \frac{xy^2 \cdot \frac{x^2}{y^2}}{y^3x^2}$
$= \log_b \frac{x}{y^3}$

44. $\log_m y = \log_m a - \log_m b - \log_m c$
$\log_m y = \log_m \frac{a}{bc}$
$y = \frac{a}{bc}$

45a. $\text{pH} = 6.1 + \log_{10} \frac{B}{C}$
$= 6.1 + \log_{10} B - \log_{10} C$

45b. a very weak base

45c. $\text{pH} = 6.1 + \log_{10} \frac{B}{C}$
$= 6.1 + \log_{10} \frac{25}{2}$
$= 6.1 + \log_{10} 12.5$
≈ 7.197

46a. $E = 1.4 (\log_{10} C_2 - \log_{10} C_1)$
$= 1.4 \log_{10} \frac{C_2}{C_1}$
$= \log_{10} \left(\frac{C_2}{C_1}\right)^{1.4}$

46b. Let $C_1 = x$, then $C_2 = 3x$.
$E = \log_{10} \left(\frac{3x}{x}\right)^{1.4}$
$= \log_{10} (3)^{1.4}$
≈ 0.668; about 0.668 kilocalories per gram

47. $\log_3 243 = y$
$3^y = 243$
$3^y = 3^5$
$y = 5$

48. $\frac{x+2}{x+3} \div \frac{x^2+x-12}{x^2-9} = \frac{x+2}{x+3} \cdot \frac{x^2-9}{x^2+x-12}$
$= \frac{x+2}{x+3} \cdot \frac{(x-3)(x+3)}{(x+4)(x-3)}$
$= \frac{x+2}{x+4}$

49. $p(a+1) = 4(a+1) - (a+1)^2 - 4$
$= 4a + 4 - (a^2 + 2a + 1) - 4$
$= 4a + 4 - a^2 - 2a - 1 - 4$
$= -a^2 + 2a - 1$

50. $(x,y) = \left(\frac{x_1+x_2}{2}, \frac{y_1+y_2}{2}\right)$
$= \left(\frac{5+6}{2}, \frac{5+(-7)}{2}\right)$
$= (5.5, -1)$

51. $x^2 + 8x + 64; \left(\frac{8}{2}\right)^2 = 16$; no

52. $A = \pi r^2$
$\frac{18}{0.01} = \pi r^2$
$1800 = \pi r^2$
$572.96 \approx r^2$
$23.94 \approx r$; about 23.94 centimeters

53. $x^3 + 2x^2 - 35x = x(x^2 + 2x - 35)$
$= x(x+7)(x-5)$

54. $2x + 3y = 2 \rightarrow 8x + 12y = 8$
$3x - 4y = -14 \rightarrow (+)9x - 12y = -42$
$17x = -34$
$x = -2$

$2x + 3y = 2$
$2(-2) + 3y = 2$
$-4 + 3y = 2$
$3y = 6$
$y = 2$; $(-2, 2)$

10-4 Common Logarithms

Pages 619–620 Check for Understanding

1. raising 10 to this power: antilog $x = 10^x$
2. 10; common logarithms
3. characteristic

4a. Adding or subtracting logarithms and then finding the antilogarithm of the sum or difference was easier than multiplying or dividing some numbers.

4b. Multiplication and division can be accomplished more quickly with a calculator than with logarithms.

4c. Sample answers: Richter scale, pH levels, decibel levels

5. 2 6. 0.9420 7. 1.1367; 0.1367; 1

8. -1.2518; $(-1.2518 + 10) - 10 = 8.7482 - 10$; 0.7482; $8 - 10 = -2$

9. 2.8662 10. 0.0071

11. $M = m + 5 + 5 \log p$
$= 5.3 + 5 + 5 \log 0.018$
$\approx 5.3 + 5 - 8.7236$
≈ 1.58

Pages 620–621 Exercises

12. 0.8129 13. 3 14. 6500 15. 0.8129
16. 6500 17. 0.8129 18. 1.8109; 0.8109; 1
19. 2.9544; 0.9544; 2
20. -1.3279; $(-1.3279 + 10) - 10 = 8.6721 - 10$; 0.6721; $8 - 10 = -2$
21. 0.8046; 0.8046; 0
22. -2.4559; $(-2.4559 + 10) - 10 = 7.5441 - 10$; 0.5441; $7 - 10 = -3$
23. -3.1549; $(-3.1549 + 10) - 10 = 6.8451 - 10$; 0.8451; $6 - 10 = -4$
24. 2.0616 25. 141.0912 26. 0.5476
27. 0.0153 28. 0.0037 29. 0.0014

30. Since calculators use logarithms, finding $(-3)^3$ would proceed as follows.
$x = (-3)^3$
$\log x = \log (-3)^3$
$\log x = 3 \log (-3)$
Since the logarithm of -3 is undefined, the calculator sends an error message.

31a. $L = 10 \log \frac{I}{I_0}$
$85 = 10 \log \frac{I}{1}$
$8.5 = \log I$
$316{,}227{,}766 = I$; about 316,227,766 times

31b. $L = 10 \log \frac{I}{I_0}$
$73 = 10 \log \frac{I}{1}$
$7.3 = \log I$
$19{,}952{,}623 \approx I$; about 19,952,623 times

31c. $316{,}227{,}766 - 19{,}952{,}623 = 296{,}275{,}143$
$296{,}275{,}143 \div 316{,}227{,}766 \approx 0.937$ or about 93.7%

32a. $10^{5.3} \approx 199{,}526.23$; about 199,526 times

32b. $10^{7.1-4.3} = 10^{2.8}$
≈ 630.96; about 631 times

33. $2 \log_6 3 + 3 \log_6 2 = \log_6 x$
$\log_6 3^2 + \log_6 2^3 = \log_6 x$
$\log_6 9 \cdot 8 = \log_6 x$
$72 = x$

34. $[f \circ g](x) = f[g(x)]$
$= f(2x+1)$
$= \frac{2x+1-1}{2}$
$= \frac{2x}{2}$
$= x$

$[g \circ f](x) = g[f(x)]$
$= g\left(\frac{x-1}{2}\right)$
$= 2\left(\frac{x-1}{2}\right) + 1$
$= x - 1 + 1$
$= x$

yes

35. $y = a(x-h)^2 + k$
$2 = a(3-4)^2 - 1$
$2 = a(-1)^2 - 1$
$2 = a - 1$
$3 = a$
$y = 3(x-4)^2 - 1$

36. $2(1.08 \times 10^9) = (2 \times 1.08) \times 10^9$
$= 2.16 \times 10^9$; 2.16×10^9 kilometers

37. $3\begin{bmatrix}4\\1\\7\end{bmatrix}+2\begin{bmatrix}3\\-2\\6\end{bmatrix}-5\begin{bmatrix}-2\\3\\6\end{bmatrix}=\begin{bmatrix}12\\3\\21\end{bmatrix}+\begin{bmatrix}6\\-4\\12\end{bmatrix}-\begin{bmatrix}-10\\15\\30\end{bmatrix}$

$=\begin{bmatrix}28\\-16\\3\end{bmatrix}$

38. Let x = number of jackets and y = number of jeans.

$x + 2y \le 40$
$2y \le -x + 40$
$y \le -\frac{1}{2}x + 20$
$4x + 2y \le 52$
$2y \le -4x + 52$
$y \le -2x + 26$
$x \ge 0$
$y \ge 0$

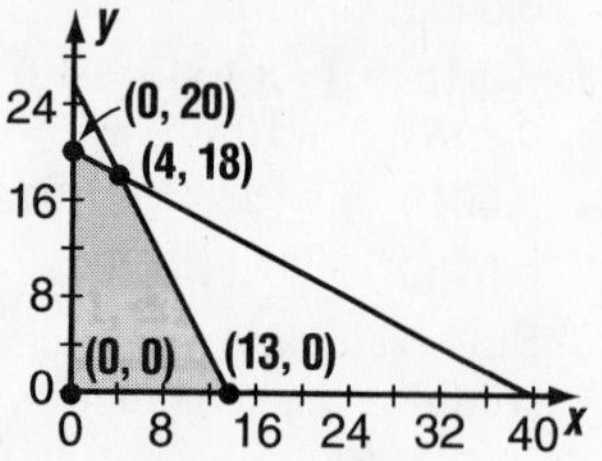

vertices: (0, 0), (0, 20), (4, 18), (13, 0)
$P(x, y) = 14x + 18y$

(x, y)	$14x + 18y$	$P(x, y)$
(0, 0)	14(0) + 18(0)	0
(0, 20)	14(0) + 18(20)	360
(4, 18)	14(4) + 18(18)	380
(13, 0)	14(13) + 18(0)	182

4 pair jeans, 18 jackets

Page 621 Self Test

1. $5^{3y+4} = 5^y$
$3y + 4 = y$
$2y = -4$
$y = -2$

2. $2^{x+3} = \frac{1}{16}$
$2^{x+3} = 2^{-4}$
$x + 3 = -4$
$x = -7$

3. $\log_{10} 10{,}000 = x$
$10^x = 10{,}000$
$10^x = 10^4$
$x = 4$

4. $\log_3 \frac{1}{243} = x$
$3^x = \frac{1}{243}$
$3^x = 3^{-5}$
$x = -5$

5. $\log_{25} 5 = x$
$25^x = 5$
$(5^2)^x = 5$
$5^{2x} = 5$
$2x = 1$
$x = \frac{1}{2}$

6. $10^{6.4-5.6} = 10^{0.8}$
≈ 6.31
about 6.3 times more intense

7. $2 \log_6 4 - \frac{1}{3}\log_6 8 = \log_6 y$
$\log_6 4^2 - \log_6 8^{\frac{1}{3}} = \log_6 y$
$\log_6 \frac{16}{2} = \log_6 y$
$8 = y$

8. $\log_2 (9t + 5) - \log_2(t^2 - 1) = 2$
$\log_2 \frac{9t+5}{t^2-1} = 2$
$2^2 = \frac{9t+5}{t^2-1}$
$4(t^2 - 1) = 9t + 5$
$4t^2 - 4 = 9t + 5$
$4t^2 - 9t - 9 = 0$
$(4t + 3)(t - 3) = 0$
$4t + 3 = 0$ or $t - 3 = 0$
$4t = -3$ $\quad t = 3$
$t = -\frac{3}{4}$

(Continued next column)

Since log is not defined for negative numbers, and $-\frac{3}{4}$ would result in negative values, $-\frac{3}{4}$ is not an acceptable solution.

9. 2.7786; 0.7786; 2

10. −0.7235; (−0.7235 + 10) − 10 = 9.2765 − 10; 0.2765; 9 − 10 = −1

10-5 Natural Logarithms

Pages 623–624 Check for Understanding

1. the number e
2. Natural logarithms are used when the base of the exponent is e.
3. Sample answer: $2500 is invested at 8% annual interest.

4. 1.1378	5. −3.1011	6. −0.2588
7. 1.2961	8. 7.5195	9. 0.2066

10. $A = Pe^{rt}$
$A = (1000)e^{(0.065)(16)}$
$A = 1000e^{1.04}$
$\ln A = \ln (1000e^{1.04})$
$\ln A = \ln 1000 + (1.04)\ln e$
$\ln A = \ln 1000 + 1.04$
$\ln A \approx 7.9478$
$A \approx 2829.22$
Yes; she has $2829.22 in her account.

Pages 624–625 Exercises

11. 2.0732	12. 0.2927	13. 4.0483	14. −0.0429
15. 1.0000	16. 9.2103	17. −5.2983	18. 0.0020
19. −4.6052	20. 2.1858	21. 1.0000	22. 13.5299
23. 0.8940	24. 0.0104	25. 2.7319	26. 0.1349
27. 4.7115	28. 0.1866		

29. $y = \ln x$

x	y
$\frac{1}{5}$	−1.61
1	0
5	1.61

$y = e^x$

x	y
−2	0.14
0	1
2	7.39

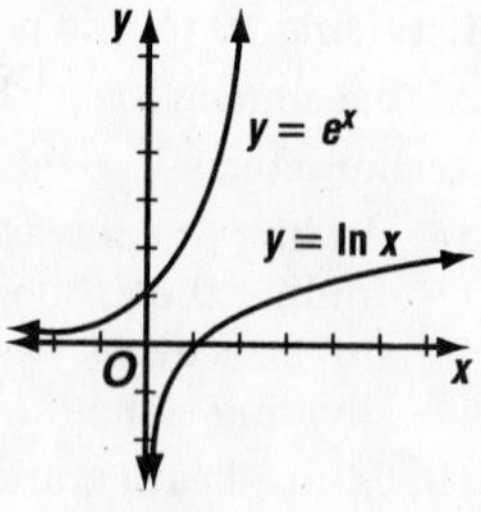

30. $y = \log x$

x	y
$\frac{1}{5}$	−0.70
1	0
5	0.70

$y = \ln x$

x	y
$\frac{1}{5}$	−1.61
1	0
5	1.61

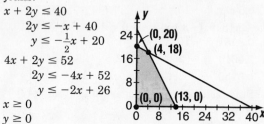

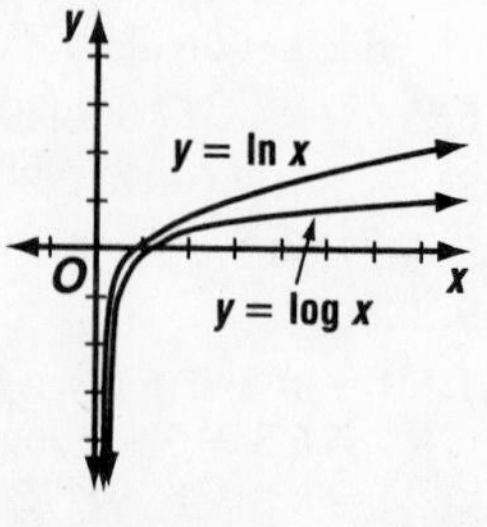

31. The graphs of $y = \ln x$ and $y = e^x$ are reflections of each other along the line $x = y$.

32. Both graphs pass through (1, 0). Where $y > 0$, the rise of the graph of $y = \ln x$ is steeper than the rise of the graph of $y = \log x$. Where $y < 0$, the rise of the graph of $y = \log x$ is steeper than the rise of the graph of $y = \ln x$.

33a. $1 + \frac{1}{1} + \frac{1}{1 \cdot 2} + \frac{1}{1 \cdot 2 \cdot 3} + \frac{1}{1 \cdot 2 \cdot 3 \cdot 4} + \frac{1}{1 \cdot 2 \cdot 3 \cdot 4 \cdot 5}$

$= 1 + 1 + \frac{1}{2} + \frac{1}{6} + \frac{1}{24} + \frac{1}{120}$

$\approx 1 + 1 + 0.5 + 0.1667 + 0.0417 + 0.0083$

≈ 2.7167

33b. $1 + \frac{1}{1} + \frac{1}{1 \cdot 2} + \frac{1}{1 \cdot 2 \cdot 3} + \frac{1}{1 \cdot 2 \cdot 3 \cdot 4} + \frac{1}{1 \cdot 2 \cdot 3 \cdot 4 \cdot 5} + \frac{1}{1 \cdot 2 \cdot 3 \cdot 4 \cdot 5 \cdot 6} + \frac{1}{1 \cdot 2 \cdot 3 \cdot 4 \cdot 5 \cdot 6 \cdot 7}$

$= 1 + 1 + \frac{1}{2} + \frac{1}{6} + \frac{1}{24} + \frac{1}{120} + \frac{1}{720} + \frac{1}{5040}$

$\approx 1 + 1 + 0.5 + 0.1667 + 0.0417 + 0.0083 + 0.0014 + 0.0002$

≈ 2.7183

33c. the second one

33d. $2.7183 - 2.7167 = 0.0016$
$0.0016 \div 2.7183 \approx 0.0006$ or about 0.06%

34.
$$\begin{aligned}
A &= Pe^{rt} \\
3000 &= Pe^{(0.0725)(5)} \\
3000 &= Pe^{0.3625} \\
\ln 3000 &= \ln (Pe^{0.3625}) \\
\ln 3000 &= \ln P + (0.3625)\ln e \\
\ln 3000 &= \ln P + 0.3625 \\
7.6439 &\approx \ln P \\
\text{antiln } 7.6439 &\approx \text{antiln } (\ln P) \\
2087.80 &\approx P\text{; about \$2088}
\end{aligned}$$

35a. $2000 - 1988 = 12$
$$\begin{aligned}
S &= 75{,}000e^{0.83t} \\
S &= 75{,}000e^{0.83(12)} \\
S &= 75{,}000e^{9.96} \\
\ln S &= \ln (75{,}000e^{9.96}) \\
\ln S &= \ln 75{,}000 + (9.96) \ln e \\
\ln S &= \ln 75{,}000 + 9.96 \\
\ln S &\approx 21.1852 \\
\text{antiln } (\ln S) &\approx \text{antiln } 21.1852 \\
S &\approx 1{,}587{,}209{,}679
\end{aligned}$$
about 1,587,209,679 drives

35b. $S = 75{,}000e^{0.83t}$

t	S
1	171,998.9
2	394,448.3
3	904,595.7
4	2,074,526.3

Sample answer: Both graphs show the sales increasing more and more each year.

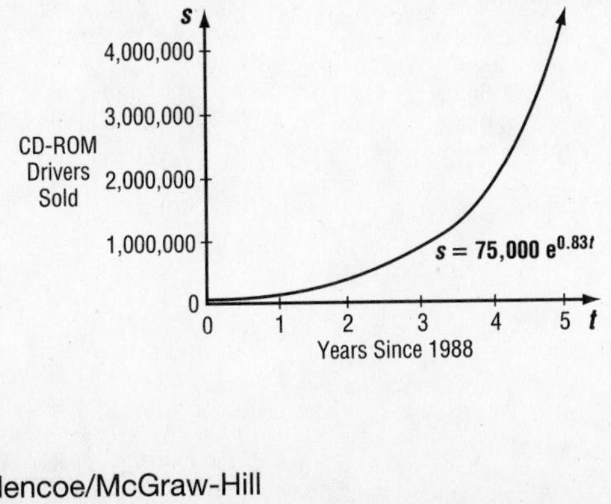

36. $\frac{I_0}{I} = 2$

$\ln 2 = 0.014d$

$\frac{\ln 2}{0.014} = d$

$49.5 \approx d$; about 49.5 centimeters

37a. 1.8882 **37b.** −2.2518

37c. 3603.2965 **37d.** 0.0006

38.
$$\begin{aligned}
\frac{\frac{x^2}{x^2 - 25y^2}}{\frac{x}{5y - x}} &= \frac{x^2}{x^2 - 25y^2} \div \frac{x}{5y - x} \\
&= \frac{x^2}{x^2 - 25y^2} \cdot \frac{5y - x}{x} \\
&= \frac{x^2}{(x - 5y)(x + 5y)} \cdot \frac{-1(x - 5y)}{x} \\
&= \frac{-x}{x + 5y}
\end{aligned}$$

39.

1⌋	1	1	0	0	−1	−1
		1	2	2	2	1
−1⌋	1	2	2	2	1	0
		−1	−1	−1	−1	
−1⌋	1	1	1	1	0	
		−1	0	−1		
	1	0	1	0		

$(x^2 + 1)(x - 1)(x + 1)^2$

40. $510 - 4 = 506$ $\quad 510 + 4 = 514$
$510 - 2(4) = 502$ $\quad 510 + 2(4) = 518$
$510 - 3(4) = 498$ $\quad 510 + 3(4) = 522$

40a. $1000 \cdot 50\% = 500$; 500 boxes

40b. $1000 \cdot 81.5\% = 815$; 815 boxes

40c. $1000 \cdot 0.5\% = 5$; 5 boxes

40d. $1000 \cdot 2.5\%; = 25$; 25 boxes

41. $A = 4 \cdot 6 = 24$; Let x = amount added to length and width.

$(4 + x)(6 + x) = 24 \cdot 5$
$24 + 10x + x^2 = 120$
$x^2 + 10x - 96 = 0$
$(x + 16)(x - 6) = 0$

$x + 16 = 0$ or $x - 6 = 0$
$x = -16$ $\quad x = 6$
$4 + x = 4 + 6$ $\quad 6 + x = 6 + 6$
$= 10$ $\quad = 12$

10 inches by 12 inches

42.
$$\begin{vmatrix} x & 5 & 2 \\ -6 & 4 & 1 \\ 3 & 1 & x \end{vmatrix} = x^2 + 22x - 1$$

$$x\begin{vmatrix} 4 & 1 \\ 1 & x \end{vmatrix} - 5\begin{vmatrix} -6 & 1 \\ 3 & x \end{vmatrix} + 2\begin{vmatrix} -6 & 4 \\ 3 & 1 \end{vmatrix} = x^2 + 22x - 1$$

$$\begin{aligned}
x(4x - 1) - 5(-6x - 3) + 2(-18) &= x^2 + 22x - 1 \\
4x^2 - x + 30x + 15 - 36 &= x^2 + 22x - 1 \\
3x^2 + 7x - 20 &= 0 \\
(3x - 5)(x + 4) &= 0
\end{aligned}$$

$3x - 5 = 0$ or $x + 4 = 0$
$3x = 5$ $\quad x = -4$
$x = \frac{5}{3}$

43. $x \geq 0$
$y \geq 0$
$y \leq 3 - x$
$3x + y \leq 6$
$y \leq -3x + 6$
vertices: (0, 0), (0, 3), (1.5, 1.5), (2, 0)

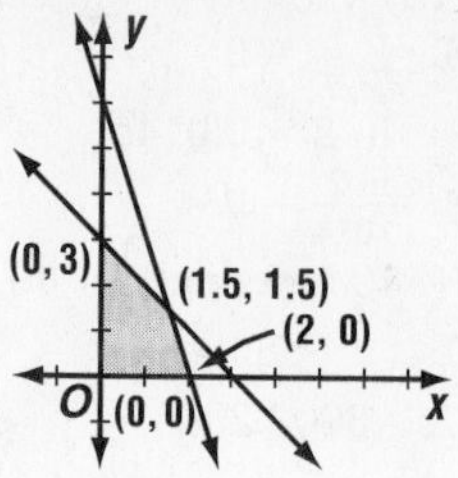

(x, y)	$2x + 4y$	$f(x + y)$
(0, 0)	2(0) + 4(0)	0
(0, 3)	2(0) + 4(3)	12
(1.5, 1.5)	2(1.5) + 4(1.5)	9
(2, 0)	2(2) + 4(0)	4

max: $f(0, 3) = 12$
min: $f(0, 0) = 0$

10-6 Solving Exponential Equations

Page 628 Check for Understanding

1. Tisha; in exponential equations, the unknown is an exponent. To solve $36 = x^5$, Karen must find $36^{\frac{1}{5}}$.
2. Sample answer: when finding logarithms of different bases on the calculator
3. Yes; use the change of base formula using $a = e$, $b = 10$, and $n =$ the number.

4. $\log_4 22 = \frac{\log 22}{\log 4}$
≈ 2.230

5. $\log_{12} 95 = \frac{\log 95}{\log 12}$
≈ 1.833

6.
$$\begin{aligned} 5^x &= 52 \\ \log 5^x &= \log 52 \\ x \log 5 &= \log 52 \\ x &= \frac{\log 52}{\log 5} \\ x &\approx \frac{1.7160}{0.6990} \\ x &\approx 2.455 \end{aligned}$$

7.
$$\begin{aligned} 8^{2a} &= 124 \\ \log 8^{2a} &= \log 124 \\ 2a \log 8 &= \log 124 \\ 2a &= \frac{\log 124}{\log 8} \\ 2a &\approx \frac{2.0934}{0.9031} \\ 2a &\approx 2.3180 \\ a &\approx 1.159 \end{aligned}$$

8.
$$\begin{aligned} 2.1^{t-5} &= 9.32 \\ \log 2.1^{t-5} &= \log 9.32 \\ (t-5) \log 2.1 &= \log 9.32 \\ t - 5 &= \frac{\log 9.32}{\log 2.1} \\ t - 5 &\approx \frac{0.9694}{0.3222} \\ t - 5 &\approx 3.0087 \\ t &\approx 8.009 \end{aligned}$$

9.
$$\begin{aligned} y &= \log_4 125 \\ 4^y &= 125 \\ \log 4^y &= \log 125 \\ y \cdot \log 4 &= \log 125 \\ y &= \frac{\log 125}{\log 4} \\ y &\approx \frac{2.0969}{0.6021} \\ y &\approx 3.483 \end{aligned}$$

10.
$$\begin{aligned} 2^{2x+3} &= 3^{3x} \\ \log 2^{2x+3} &= \log 3^{3x} \\ (2x+3) \log 2 &= 3x \log 3 \\ 2x \log 2 + 3 \log 2 &= 3x \log 3 \\ 2x \log 2 - 3x \log 3 &= -3 \log 2 \\ x(2 \log 2 - 3 \log 3) &= -3 \log 2 \\ x &= \frac{-3 \log 2}{2 \log 2 - 3 \log 3} \\ x &\approx \frac{-3(0.3010)}{2(0.3010) - 3(0.4771)} \\ x &\approx 1.089 \end{aligned}$$

11.
$$\begin{aligned} 2^n &= \sqrt{3^{n-2}} \\ 2^n &= (3^{n-2})^{\frac{1}{2}} \\ \log 2^n &= \log 3^{\frac{1}{2}n-1} \\ n \log 2 &= \left(\frac{1}{2}n - 1\right) \log 3 \\ n \log 2 &= \frac{1}{2}n \log 3 - \log 3 \\ n(\log 2 - \frac{1}{2} \log 3) &= -\log 3 \\ n &= \frac{-\log 3}{\log 2 - \frac{1}{2} \log 3} \\ n &\approx \frac{-0.4771}{0.3010 - \frac{1}{2}(0.4771)} \\ n &\approx -7.638 \end{aligned}$$

12. $1500 \times 2 = 3000$
$$\begin{aligned} A &= Pe^{rt} \\ 3000 &= 1500\, e^{(0.065)t} \\ \frac{3000}{1500} &= e^{0.065t} \\ \ln 2 &= \ln e^{0.065t} \\ 0.6931 &\approx 0.065t \end{aligned}$$
$10.66 \approx t$; about 10.7 years

Pages 629–630 Exercises

13. $\log_5 16 = \frac{\log 16}{\log 5}$
$\approx \frac{1.2041}{0.6989}$
≈ 1.723

14. $\log_6 82 = \frac{\log 82}{\log 6}$
$\approx \frac{1.9138}{0.7782}$
≈ 2.459

15. $\log_3 125 = \frac{\log 125}{\log 3}$
$\approx \frac{2.0969}{0.4771}$
≈ 4.395

16. $\log_2 100 = \frac{\log 100}{\log 2}$
$\approx \frac{2}{0.3010}$
≈ 6.644

17. $\log_{12} 25 = \frac{\log 25}{\log 12}$
$\approx \frac{1.3979}{1.0792}$
≈ 1.295

18. $\log_4 48 = \frac{\log 48}{\log 4}$
$\approx \frac{1.6812}{0.6021}$
≈ 2.792

19.
$$\begin{aligned} 9^b &= 45 \\ \log 9^b &= \log 45 \\ b \log 9 &= \log 45 \\ b &= \frac{\log 45}{\log 9} \\ b &\approx \frac{1.6532}{0.9542} \\ b &\approx 1.732 \end{aligned}$$

20.
$$\begin{aligned} 2^x &= 30 \\ \log 2^x &= \log 30 \\ x \log 2 &= \log 30 \\ x &= \frac{\log 30}{\log 2} \\ x &\approx \frac{1.4771}{0.3010} \\ x &\approx 4.907 \end{aligned}$$

21.
$$5^p = 34$$
$$\log 5^p = \log 34$$
$$p \log 5 = \log 34$$
$$p = \frac{\log 34}{\log 5}$$
$$p \approx \frac{1.5315}{0.6990}$$
$$p \approx 2.191$$

22.
$$3.1^{a-3} = 9.42$$
$$\log 3.1^{a-3} = \log 9.42$$
$$(a-3) \log 3.1 = \log 9.42$$
$$a \log 3.1 - 3 \log 3.1 = \log 9.42$$
$$a \log 3.1 = \log 9.42 + 3 \log 3.1$$
$$a = \frac{\log 9.42 + 3 \log 3.1}{\log 3.1}$$
$$a \approx \frac{0.9741 + 3(0.4914)}{0.4914}$$
$$a \approx 4.982$$

23.
$$6^{x+2} = 17.2$$
$$\log 6^{x+2} = \log 17.2$$
$$(x+2) \log 6 = \log 17.2$$
$$x \log 6 + 2 \log 6 = \log 17.2$$
$$x \log 6 = \log 17.2 - 2 \log 6$$
$$x = \frac{\log 17.2 - 2 \log 6}{\log 6}$$
$$x \approx \frac{1.2355 - 2(0.7782)}{0.7782}$$
$$x \approx -0.412$$

24.
$$8.2^{n-3} = 42.5$$
$$\log 8.2^{n-3} = \log 42.5$$
$$(n-3) \log 8.2 = \log 42.5$$
$$n \log 8.2 - 3 \log 8.2 = \log 42.5$$
$$n \log 8.2 = \log 42.5 + 3 \log 8.2$$
$$n = \frac{\log 42.5 + 3 \log 8.2}{\log 8.2}$$
$$n \approx \frac{1.6284 + 3(0.9138)}{0.9138}$$
$$n \approx 4.782$$

25.
$$x = \log_5 61.4$$
$$5^x = 61.4$$
$$\log 5^x = \log 61.4$$
$$x \log 5 = \log 61.4$$
$$x = \frac{\log 61.4}{\log 5}$$
$$x \approx \frac{1.7882}{0.6990}$$
$$x \approx 2.558$$

26.
$$8^{y-2} = 7.28$$
$$\log 8^{y-2} = \log 7.28$$
$$(y-2) \log 8 = \log 7.28$$
$$y \log 8 - 2 \log 8 = \log 7.28$$
$$y \log 8 = \log 7.28 + 2 \log 8$$
$$y = \frac{\log 7.28 + 2 \log 8}{\log 8}$$
$$y \approx \frac{0.8621 + 2(0.9031)}{0.9031}$$
$$y \approx 2.955$$

27.
$$t = \log_8 200$$
$$8^t = 200$$
$$\log 8^t = \log 200$$
$$t \log 8 = \log 200$$
$$t = \frac{\log 200}{\log 8}$$
$$t \approx \frac{2.3010}{0.9031}$$
$$t \approx 2.548$$

28.
$$5^{s+2} = 15.3$$
$$\log 5^{s+2} = \log 15.3$$
$$(s+2) \log 5 = \log 15.3$$
$$s \log 5 + 2 \log 5 = \log 15.3$$
$$s \log 5 = \log 15.3 - 2 \log 5$$
$$s = \frac{\log 15.3 - 2 \log 5}{\log 5}$$
$$s \approx \frac{1.1847 - 2(0.6990)}{0.6990}$$
$$s \approx -0.305$$

29.
$$9^{z-4} = 6.28$$
$$\log 9^{z-4} = \log 6.28$$
$$(z-4) \log 9 = \log 6.28$$
$$z \log 9 - 4 \log 9 = \log 6.28$$
$$z \log 9 = \log 6.28 + 4 \log 9$$
$$z = \frac{\log 6.28 + 4 \log 9}{\log 9}$$
$$z \approx \frac{0.7980 + 4(0.9542)}{0.9542}$$
$$z \approx 4.836$$

30.
$$7.6^{a-2} = 41.7$$
$$\log 7.6^{a-2} = \log 41.7$$
$$(a-2) \log 7.6 = \log 41.7$$
$$a \log 7.6 - 2 \log 7.6 = \log 41.7$$
$$a \log 7.6 = \log 41.7 + 2 \log 7.6$$
$$a = \frac{\log 41.7 + 2 \log 7.6}{\log 7.6}$$
$$a \approx \frac{1.6201 + 2(0.8808)}{0.8808}$$
$$a \approx 3.839$$

31.
$$3.5^{3x+1} = 65.4$$
$$\log 3.5^{3x+1} = \log 65.4$$
$$(3x+1) \log 3.5 = \log 65.4$$
$$3x \log 3.5 + \log 3.5 = \log 65.4$$
$$3x \log 3.5 = \log 65.4 - \log 3.5$$
$$x = \frac{\log 65.4 - \log 3.5}{3 \log 3.5}$$
$$x \approx \frac{1.8156 - 0.5441}{3(0.5441)}$$
$$x \approx 0.779$$

32.
$$20^{x^2} = 70$$
$$\log 20^{x^2} = \log 70$$
$$x^2 \log 20 = \log 70$$
$$x^2 = \frac{\log 70}{\log 20}$$
$$x^2 \approx \frac{1.8451}{1.3010}$$
$$x^2 \approx 1.4182$$
$$x \approx \pm 1.191$$

33.
$$\begin{aligned} 8^{x^2-2} &= 32 \\ \log 8^{x^2-2} &= \log 32 \\ (x^2-2)\log 8 &= \log 32 \\ x^2 \log 8 - 2\log 8 &= \log 32 \\ x^2 \log 8 &= \log 32 + 2\log 8 \\ x^2 &= \frac{\log 32 + 2\log 8}{\log 8} \\ x^2 &\approx \frac{1.5051 + 2(0.9031)}{0.9031} \\ x^2 &\approx 3.6666 \\ x &\approx \pm 1.915 \end{aligned}$$

34.
$$\begin{aligned} 5.8^{x^2-3} &= 82.9 \\ \log 5.8^{x^2-3} &= \log 82.9 \\ (x^2-3)\log 5.8 &= \log 82.9 \\ x^2 \log 5.8 - 3\log 5.8 &= \log 82.9 \\ x^2 \log 5.8 &= \log 82.9 + 3\log 5.8 \\ x^2 &= \frac{\log 82.9 + 3\log 5.8}{\log 5.8} \\ x^2 &\approx \frac{1.9186 + 3(0.7634)}{0.7634} \\ x^2 &\approx 5.5132 \\ x &\approx \pm 2.348 \end{aligned}$$

35.
$$\begin{aligned} 9^a &= 2^a \\ \log 9^a &= \log 2^a \\ a\log 9 &= a\log 2 \\ a\log 9 - a\log 2 &= 0 \\ a(\log 9 - \log 2) &= 0 \\ a &= \frac{0}{\log 9 - \log 2} \\ a &= 0 \end{aligned}$$

36.
$$\begin{aligned} 5^{x-1} &= 3^x \\ \log 5^{x-1} &= \log 3^x \\ (x-1)\log 5 &= x\log 3 \\ x\log 5 - \log 5 &= x\log 3 \\ x\log 5 - x\log 3 &= \log 5 \\ x(\log 5 - \log 3) &= \log 5 \\ x &= \frac{\log 5}{\log 5 - \log 3} \\ x &\approx \frac{0.6990}{0.6990 - 0.4771} \\ x &\approx 3.151 \end{aligned}$$

37.
$$\begin{aligned} 7^{t-2} &= 5^t \\ \log 7^{t-2} &= \log 5^t \\ (t-2)\log 7 &= t\log 5 \\ t\log 7 - 2\log 7 &= t\log 5 \\ t\log 7 - t\log 5 &= 2\log 7 \\ t(\log 7 - \log 5) &= 2\log 7 \\ t &= \frac{2\log 7}{\log 7 - \log 5} \\ t &\approx \frac{2(0.8451)}{0.8451 - 0.6990} \\ t &\approx 11.567 \end{aligned}$$

38.
$$\begin{aligned} 16^{d-4} &= 3^{3-d} \\ \log 16^{d-4} &= \log 3^{3-d} \\ (d-4)\log 16 &= (3-d)\log 3 \\ d\log 16 - 4\log 16 &= 3\log 3 - d\log 3 \\ d\log 16 + d\log 3 &= 3\log 3 + 4\log 16 \\ d(\log 16 + \log 3) &= 3\log 3 + 4\log 16 \\ d &= \frac{3\log 3 + 4\log 16}{\log 16 + \log 3} \\ d &\approx \frac{3(0.4771) + 4(1.2041)}{1.2041 + 0.4771} \\ d &\approx 3.716 \end{aligned}$$

39.
$$\begin{aligned} 8^{x-2} &= 5^x \\ \log 8^{x-2} &= \log 5^x \\ (x-2)\log 8 &= x\log 5 \\ x\log 8 - 2\log 8 &= x\log 5 \\ x\log 8 - x\log 5 &= 2\log 8 \\ x(\log 8 - \log 5) &= 2\log 8 \\ x &= \frac{2\log 8}{\log 8 - \log 5} \\ x &\approx \frac{2(0.9031)}{0.9031 - 0.6990} \\ x &\approx 8.849 \end{aligned}$$

40.
$$\begin{aligned} 5^{3y} &= 8^{y-1} \\ \log 5^{3y} &= \log 8^{y-1} \\ 3y\log 5 &= (y-1)\log 8 \\ 3y\log 5 &= y\log 8 - \log 8 \\ 3y\log 5 - y\log 8 &= -\log 8 \\ y(3\log 5 - \log 8) &= -\log 8 \\ y &= \frac{-\log 8}{3\log 5 - \log 8} \\ y &\approx \frac{-0.9031}{3(0.6990) - 0.9031} \\ y &\approx -0.756 \end{aligned}$$

41.
$$\begin{aligned} 5^{5a-2} &= 2^{2a+1} \\ \log 5^{5a-2} &= \log 2^{2a+1} \\ (5a-2)\log 5 &= (2a+1)\log 2 \\ 5a\log 5 - 2\log 5 &= 2a\log 2 + \log 2 \\ 5a\log 5 - 2\log 2 &= \log 2 + 2\log 5 \\ a(5\log 5 - 2\log 2) &= \log 2 + 2\log 5 \\ a &= \frac{\log 2 + 2\log 5}{5\log 5 - 2\log 2} \\ a &\approx \frac{0.3010 + 2(0.6990)}{5(0.6990) - 2(0.3010)} \\ a &\approx 0.587 \end{aligned}$$

42.
$$\begin{aligned} 8^{2y} &= 52^{4y+3} \\ \log 8^{2y} &= \log 52^{4y+3} \\ 2y\log 8 &= (4y+3)\log 52 \\ 2y\log 8 &= 4y\log 52 + 3\log 52 \\ 2y\log 8 - 4y\log 52 &= 3\log 52 \\ y(2\log 8 - 4\log 52) &= 3\log 52 \\ y &= \frac{3\log 52}{2\log 8 - 4\log 52} \\ y &\approx \frac{3(1.7160)}{2(0.9031) - 4(1.7160)} \\ y &\approx -1.018 \end{aligned}$$

43.
$$\begin{aligned} 40^{3x} &= 5^{2x+1} \\ \log 40^{3x} &= \log 5^{2x+1} \\ 3x\log 40 &= (2x+1)\log 5 \\ 3x\log 4 &= 2x\log 5 + \log 5 \\ 3x\log 40 - 2x\log 5 &= \log 5 \\ x(3\log 40 - 2\log 5) &= \log 5 \\ x &= \frac{\log 5}{3\log 40 - 2\log 5} \\ x &\approx \frac{0.6990}{3(1.6021) - 2(0.6990)} \\ x &\approx 0.205 \end{aligned}$$

44.

$$4^n = \sqrt{5^{n-2}}$$
$$4^n = 5^{(n-2)\frac{1}{2}}$$
$$\log 4^n = \log 5^{\frac{1}{2}n-1}$$
$$n \log 4 = \left(\frac{1}{2}n - 1\right) \log 5$$
$$n \log 4 = \frac{1}{2}n \log 5 - \log 5$$
$$n \log 4 - \frac{1}{2}n \log 5 = -\log 5$$
$$n(\log 4 - \frac{1}{2} \log 5) = -\log 5$$
$$n = \frac{-\log 5}{\log 4 - \frac{1}{2}\log 5}$$
$$n \approx \frac{-0.6990}{0.6021 - \frac{1}{2}(0.6990)}$$
$$n \approx -2.767$$

45.

$$\sqrt[3]{2^{x-1}} = 8^{x-2}$$
$$2^{(x-1)\frac{1}{3}} = 8^{x-2}$$
$$\log 2^{\frac{1}{3}x-\frac{1}{3}} = \log 8^{x-2}$$
$$\left(\frac{1}{3}x - \frac{1}{3}\right) \log 2 = (x-2) \log 8$$
$$\frac{1}{3}x \log 2 - \frac{1}{3} \log 2 = x \log 8 - 2 \log 8$$
$$\frac{1}{3}x \log 2 - x \log 8 = -2 \log 8 + \frac{1}{3} \log 2$$
$$x\left(\frac{1}{3} \log 2 - \log 8\right) = -2 \log 8 + \frac{1}{3} \log 2$$
$$x = \frac{-2 \log 8 + \frac{1}{3} \log 2}{\frac{1}{3} \log 2 - \log 8}$$
$$x \approx \frac{-2(0.9031) + \frac{1}{3}(0.3010)}{\frac{1}{3}(0.3010) - 0.9031}$$
$$x \approx 2.125$$

46.

$$x = \log_a n$$
$$a^x = a^{\log_a n}$$
$$a^x = n$$
$$\log_b a^x = \log_b n$$
$$x \log_b a = \log_b n$$
$$x = \frac{\log_b n}{\log_b a}$$

47. $2500 \cdot 2 = 5000$

$$P(t) = P_0 e^{kt}$$
$$5000 = 2500\, e^{(0.03)t}$$
$$2 = e^{0.03t}$$
$$\ln 2 = \ln e^{0.03t}$$
$$0.6931 \approx 0.03t$$
$$23 \approx t;\text{ about 23 years}$$

48a.

$$E = 42e^{kt}$$
$$350 = 42e^{0.019t}$$
$$\frac{350}{42} = e^{0.019t}$$
$$\ln \frac{350}{42} = \ln e^{0.019t}$$
$$\ln 350 - \ln 42 = 0.019t$$
$$5.8579 - 3.7377 \approx 0.019t$$
$$2.1202 \approx 0.019t$$
$$111.6 \approx t$$

111.6 years or by the 2008 Summer Olympics

48b. $E = 42e^{0.019t}$

t	E
0	42
50	108.6
100	280.8

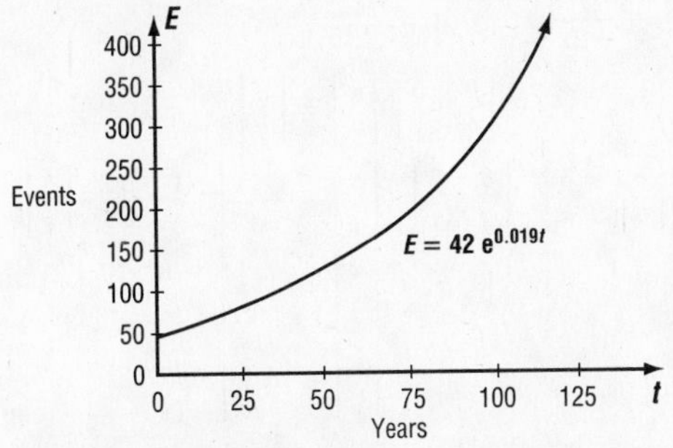

Sample answer: Both show that the number of events is increasing more and more at each Olympics.

49. 0.0023

50. Let x = the time it would take the painter to do the job alone.

$$\frac{16}{x} + \frac{6}{30} = 1$$
$$5x\left(\frac{16}{x} + \frac{1}{5}\right) = 5x(1)$$
$$80 + x = 5x$$
$$-4x = -80$$
$$x = 20;\ 20\text{ days}$$

51.

$$b^4 - 5b^2 + 4 = 0$$
$$(b^2)^2 - 5(b^2) + 4 = 0$$
$$(b^2 - 4)(b^2 - 1) = 0$$
$$(b-2)(b+2)(b-1)(b+1) = 0$$
$$b - 2 = 0 \text{ or } b + 2 = 0 \text{ or } b - 1 = 0 \text{ or } b + 1 = 0$$
$$b = 2 \qquad b = -2 \qquad b = 1 \qquad b = -1$$

52.

$$4y^2 - x^2 - 24y + 6x = 11$$
$$4y^2 - 24y - x^2 + 6x = 11$$
$$4(y^2 - 6y) - (x^2 - 6x) = 11$$
$$4(y^2 - 6y + 9) - (x^2 - 6x + 9) = 11 + 4(9) - 9$$
$$4(y-3)^2 - (x-3)^2 = 38$$
$$\frac{(y-3)^2}{9.5} - \frac{(x-3)^2}{38} = 1;\text{ hyperbola}$$

53. $(x + 2)(x + 9) > 0$

$$x + 2 > 0 \text{ and } x + 9 > 0 \text{ or } x + 2 < 0 \text{ and } x + 9 < 0$$
$$x > -2 \qquad x > -9 \qquad x < -2 \qquad x < -9$$
$$x > -2 \qquad \text{or} \qquad x < -9$$
$$\{x \mid x > -2 \text{ or } x < -9\}$$

54. Let x = width, then length $= \frac{1}{2}(6 - 2x)$ or $3 - x$

$$A = x(3 - x)$$
$$A = 3x - x^2$$

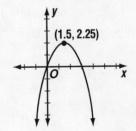

x	A
0	0
1	2
2	2
3	0

Maximum area is at $x = 1.5$.
1.5 feet by 1.5 feet

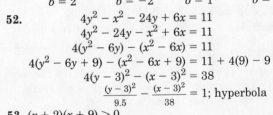

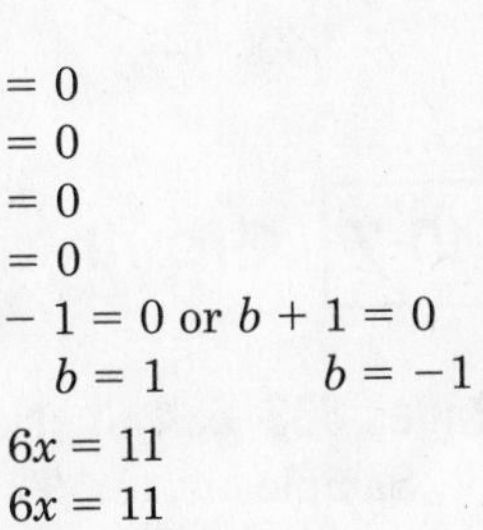

55. $2x + 5yi = 4 + 15i$

$2x = 4 \qquad 5yi = 15i$

$x = 2 \qquad y = 3$

56. $M^{-1} = \frac{1}{-6-15}\begin{bmatrix} -1 & -5 \\ -3 & 6 \end{bmatrix}$

$= \frac{1}{-21}\begin{bmatrix} -1 & -5 \\ -3 & 6 \end{bmatrix}$

$\begin{bmatrix} 6 & 5 \\ 3 & -1 \end{bmatrix} \begin{bmatrix} x \\ y \end{bmatrix} = \begin{bmatrix} 8 \\ 7 \end{bmatrix}$

$-\frac{1}{21}\begin{bmatrix} -1 & -5 \\ -3 & 6 \end{bmatrix} \cdot \begin{bmatrix} 6 & 5 \\ 3 & -1 \end{bmatrix} \cdot \begin{bmatrix} x \\ y \end{bmatrix} = -\frac{1}{21}\begin{bmatrix} -1 & -5 \\ -3 & 6 \end{bmatrix} \cdot \begin{bmatrix} 8 \\ 7 \end{bmatrix}$

$\begin{bmatrix} x \\ y \end{bmatrix} = -\frac{1}{21}\begin{bmatrix} -8 & -35 \\ -24 & 42 \end{bmatrix}$

$\begin{bmatrix} x \\ y \end{bmatrix} = -\frac{1}{21}\begin{bmatrix} -43 \\ 18 \end{bmatrix}$

$\begin{bmatrix} x \\ y \end{bmatrix} = \begin{bmatrix} \frac{43}{21} \\ -\frac{6}{7} \end{bmatrix}; \left(\frac{43}{21}, -\frac{6}{7}\right)$

57. perpendicular slope $= -\frac{3}{2}$

$y - y_1 = m(x - x_1)$

$y - 6 = -\frac{3}{2}(x - 4)$

$y - 6 = -\frac{3}{2}x + 6$

$y = -\frac{3}{2}x + 12$

$\frac{3}{2}x + y = 12$

$3x + 2y = 24$

10-7 Growth and Decay

Pages 633–634 Check for Understanding

1. Sample answer: The constant is positive when growth is depicted such as in the case of bacteria growth. The constant is negative when decay is depicted such as in radioactive decay. If k is zero, then the population is not growing or decaying and the function is a constant function.

2. Example 1 is dealing with e, and Examples 2 and 3 are dealing with base 10 numbers; yes; yes; You can take the logarithm of each side of an equation as long as you use the same base on both sides. Therefore, you can use natural logarithms or common logarithms in any problem.

3a. $y = 88(1.0137)^x$

$= 88(1.0137)^{3.5}$

≈ 92.3; about 92.3 megahertz

3b. $y = 88(1.0137)^x$

$100 = 88(1.0137)^x$

$\log 100 = \log 88 + x \log 1.0137$

$\log 100 - \log 88 = x \log 1.0137$

$\frac{\log 100 - \log 88}{\log 1.0137} = x$

$9.4 \approx x$; about 9.4 cm from the left side

4. $V_n = P(1 + r)^n$

$2000 = 4600(1 - 0.20)^n$

$0.4348 \approx 0.8^n$

$\log 0.4348 = \log 0.8^n$

$\log 0.4348 = n \log 0.8$

$\frac{\log 0.4348}{\log 0.8} = n$

$3.7 \approx n$; about 3.7 years

5a. $y = n\,e^{kt}$

$1 = 2\,e^{k(1620)}$

$0.5 = e^{1620k}$

$\ln 0.5 = \ln e^{1620k}$

$-0.6931 \approx 1620k$

$-0.00043 \approx k$; about -0.00043

5b. $y = n\,e^{-0.00043t}$

5c. $y = n\,e^{-0.00043t}$

$= 20e^{-0.00043(5000)}$

$= 20e^{-2.15}$

≈ 2.33; about 2.33 grams

5d. $y = n\,e^{-0.00043t}$

$1 = 4e^{-0.00043t}$

$0.25 = e^{-0.00043t}$

$\ln 0.25 = \ln e^{-0.00043t}$

$-1.3863 \approx -0.00043t$

$3224 \approx t$; in about 3224 years

5e. Never; the amount left will always be half of the amount that existed 1620 years ago.

Pages 634–636 Exercises

6. $V_n = P(1 + r)^n$

$V_n = 75{,}000(1 + 0.06)^5$

$V_n = 75{,}000(1.06)^5$

$V_n \approx 100{,}367$; about \$100,367

7. $y = n\,e^{-0.0856t}$

$1 = 2\,e^{-0.0856t}$

$0.5 = e^{-0.0856t}$

$\ln 0.5 = \ln e^{-0.0856t}$

$-0.6931 \approx -0.0856t$

$8.1 \approx t$; about 8.1 days

8a. Let x = the distance from the left side and y = the frequency. Since 535 Kilohertz is 0 centimeters from the left side and 1705 Kilohertz is 15 centimeters from the left side, the ordered pairs (0, 535) and (15, 1705) are solutions to the function $y = ab^x$.

$y = ab^x \qquad y = ab^x$

$535 = ab^0 \qquad 1705 = 535b^{15}$

$535 = a \qquad \log 1705 = \log(535b^{15})$

$\log 1705 = \log 535 + 15 \log b$

$\log 1705 - \log 535 = 15 \log b$

$\frac{\log 1705 - \log 535}{15} = \log b$

$0.0336 \approx \log b$

$\text{antilog } 0.0336 \approx \text{antilog}(\log b)$

$1.0803 \approx b$

about $y = 535(1.0803)^x$

8b. $y = 535(1.0803)^x$

$= 535(1.0803)^{4.5}$

≈ 757; about 757 Kilohertz

8c. $$y = 535(1.0803)^x$$
$$1000 = 535(1.0803)^x$$
$$\log 1000 = \log 535 + x \log 1.0803$$
$$\log 1000 - \log 535 = x \log 1.0803$$
$$\frac{\log 1000 - \log 535}{\log 1.0803} = x$$
$$8.1 \approx x$$
about 8.1 centimeters from the left side

9a. $$y = ne^{kt}$$
$$585{,}960 = 546{,}488e^{k(1990-1980)}$$
$$1.0722 \approx e^{10k}$$
$$\ln 1.0722 \approx \ln e^{10k}$$
$$0.06971 \approx 10k$$
$$0.0070 \approx k;\ y = 546{,}488e^{0.0070t}$$

9b. $2010 - 1980 = 30$
$$y = 546{,}488e^{0.0070t}$$
$$= 546{,}488e^{0.0070(30)}$$
$\approx 674{,}190.26$; about 674,190 people

9c. Sample answer: If the economy of a city is doing well, more people than expected may move into the area. If the economy is not doing well, people may lose their jobs and move out of the area.

10a. $$P = 50e^{-\frac{t}{250}}$$
$$= 50e^{-\frac{100}{250}}$$
≈ 33.5; about 33.5 watts

10b. $$P = 50e^{-\frac{t}{250}}$$
$$10 = 50e^{-\frac{t}{250}}$$
$$0.2 = e^{-\frac{t}{250}}$$
$$\ln 0.2 = \ln e^{-\frac{t}{250}}$$
$$-1.6094 \approx -\frac{t}{250}$$
$402 \approx t$; about 402 days

11. $$y = ne^{-0.00012t}$$
$$1 = 10e^{-0.00012t}$$
$$0.1 = e^{-0.00012t}$$
$$\ln 0.1 = \ln e^{-0.00012t}$$
$$-2.3026 \approx -0.00012t$$
$$19{,}188.21 \approx t$$
No; the bone is only about 19,000 years old and dinosaurs died out about 63,000,000 years ago.

12. $$V_n = P(1 + r)^n$$
$$140{,}000 = 80{,}000(1 + r)^{10}$$
$$1.75 = (1 + r)^{10}$$
$$\log 1.75 = 10 \log (1 + r)$$
$$\frac{\log 1.75}{10} = \log (1 + r)$$
$$0.0243 \approx \log (1 + r)$$
$$\text{antilog } 0.0243 \approx \text{antilog } (\log (1 + r))$$
$$1.0576 \approx 1 + r$$
$0.0575 \approx r$; about 5.75%

13a.
$$t = an^b \qquad t = an^b \qquad \frac{7}{4 \cdot 2^b} = \frac{3}{4^b}$$
$$1\tfrac{3}{4} = a2^b \qquad 3 = a4^b \qquad 7 \cdot 4^b = 3 \cdot 4 \cdot 2^b$$
$$\frac{7}{4} = a2^b \qquad \frac{3}{4^b} = a \qquad \frac{4^b}{2^b} = \frac{3 \cdot 4}{7}$$
$$\frac{7}{4 \cdot 2^b} = a \qquad \frac{2^{2b}}{2^b} = \frac{12}{7}$$
$$2^b = \frac{12}{7}$$
$$2^b \approx 1.7143$$
$$\log 2^b \approx \log 1.7143$$
$$b \log 2 \approx \log 1.7143$$
$$b \approx \frac{\log 1.7143}{\log 2}$$
$$b \approx 0.7776$$
$$a = \frac{3}{4^b} = \frac{3}{4^{0.7776}} \approx 1.0208;$$
about $t = 1.0208n^{0.7776}$

13b. $$t = 1.0208n^{0.7776}$$
$$= 1.0208(3)^{0.7776}$$
≈ 2.4; about 2.4 minutes

$$t = 1.0208n^{0.7776}$$
$$= 1.0208(5)^{0.7776}$$
≈ 3.6; about 3.6 minutes

14. $$H = \frac{P}{1 + (P - S)e^{-0.4t}}$$
$$800 = \frac{1600}{1 + (1600 - 2)e^{-0.4t}}$$
$$800(1 + 1598e^{-0.4t}) = 1600$$
$$1 + 1598e^{-0.4t} = 2$$
$$1598e^{-0.4t} = 1$$
$$e^{-0.4t} = \frac{1}{1598}$$
$$\ln e^{-0.4t} = \ln\left(\frac{1}{1598}\right)$$
$$-0.4t = \ln 1 - \ln 1598$$
$$t = \frac{\ln 1 - \ln 1598}{-0.4}$$
$t \approx 18.4$; about 18.4 minutes

15. enter program

15a. execute program ENTER 4000 ENTER 300 ENTER .09 ENTER 2 ENTER; 11

15b. execute program ENTER 7500 ENTER 400 ENTER .085 ENTER 4 ENTER; 16

15c. execute program ENTER 8995 ENTER 156 ENTER .0925 ENTER 12 ENTER; 48

15d. execute program ENTER 14600 ENTER 195 ENTER .0875 ENTER 12 ENTER; 60

15e. execute program ENTER 96000 ENTER 850 ENTER .0965 ENTER 12 ENTER; 81

15f. execute program ENTER 90000 ENTER 425 ENTER .0965 ENTER 26 ENTER; 157

16. The compound interest formula is actually a special case of the growth rate.

17. $$7^{x-2} = 5^{3-x}$$
$$\log 7^{x-2} = \log 5^{3-x}$$
$$(x - 2) \log 7 = (3 - x) \log 5$$
$$x \log 7 - 2 \log 7 = 3 \log 5 - x \log 5$$
$$x \log 7 + x \log 5 = 3 \log 5 + 2 \log 7$$
$$x(\log 7 + \log 5) = 3 \log 5 + 2 \log 7$$
$$x = \frac{3 \log 5 + 2 \log 7}{\log 7 + \log 5}$$
$$x \approx \frac{3(0.6990) + 2(0.8451)}{0.8451 + 0.6990}$$
$$x \approx 2.45$$

18. $2a = 8$ $\qquad$ $2b = 4$
$a = 4$ $\qquad$ $b = 2$
$$\frac{x^2}{2^2} + \frac{y^2}{4^2} = 1$$
$$\frac{x^2}{4} + \frac{y^2}{16} = 1$$
$$b^2 = a^2 - c^2$$
$$4 = 16 - c^2$$
$$c^2 = 12$$
$c = \pm 2\sqrt{3}$; $(0, \pm 2\sqrt{3})$

19a.
$$
\begin{aligned}
s &= v_i t + \tfrac{1}{2}at^2\\
100 &= 24t + \tfrac{1}{2}(8)t^2\\
100 &= 24t + 4t^2\\
100 &= 4t^2 + 24t\\
25 &= t^2 + 6t\\
25 + 9 &= t^2 + 6t + 9\\
34 &= (t + 3)^2\\
\pm\sqrt{34} &= t + 3
\end{aligned}
$$
$t + 3 = \sqrt{34}$ or $t + 3 = -\sqrt{34}$

$t \approx 2.8$ $\qquad$ $t \approx -8.8$

about 2.8 seconds

19b.
$$
\begin{aligned}
s &= v_i t + \tfrac{1}{2}at^2\\
200 &= 24t + \tfrac{1}{2}(8)t^2\\
200 &= 24t + 4t^2\\
200 &= 4t^2 + 24t\\
50 &= t^2 + 6t\\
50 + 9 &= t^2 + 6t + 9\\
59 &= (t + 3)^2\\
\pm\sqrt{59} &= t + 3
\end{aligned}
$$
$t + 3 = \sqrt{59}$ or $t + 3 = -\sqrt{59}$

$t \approx 4.7$ $\qquad$ $t \approx -10.7$

about 4.7 seconds

19c.
$$
\begin{aligned}
s &= v_i t + \tfrac{1}{2}at^2\\
300 &= 24t + \tfrac{1}{2}(8)t^2\\
300 &= 24t + 4t^2\\
300 &= 4t^2 + 24t\\
75 &= t^2 + 6t\\
75 + 9 &= t^2 + 6t + 9\\
84 &= (t + 3)^2\\
\pm\sqrt{84} &= t + 3
\end{aligned}
$$
$t + 3 = \sqrt{84}$ or $t + 3 = -\sqrt{84}$

$t \approx 6.2$ $\qquad$ $t = -12.2$

about 6.2s

19d. No, the formula is not a direct variation.

20a. 76,100 − 34,142 = 41,958

20b. Q_2 is between the 14th and 15th values; $\frac{52{,}952 + 53{,}192}{2} = 53{,}072$; Q_1 is between the 7th and 8th values; $\frac{47{,}313 + 48{,}000}{2} = 47{,}656.5$; Q_3 is between the 21st and 22nd values; $\frac{57{,}545 + 58{,}727}{2} = 58{,}136$

20c. IR = 58,136 − 47,656.5 = 10,479.5

20d. 47,656.5 − 1.5(10,479.5) = 31,937.25
58,136 + 1.5(10,479.5) = 73, 855.25
76,100 is an outlier.

20e.

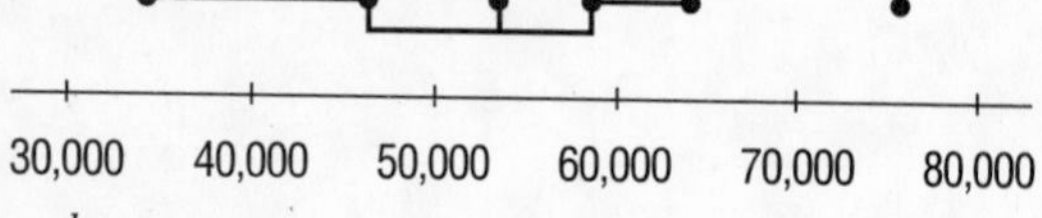

21.
$$
\begin{aligned}
A &= \tfrac{h}{2}(b_1 + b_2)\\
&= \tfrac{8}{2}(12 + 20)\\
&= 4(32)\\
&= 128;\ 128 \text{ square centimeters}
\end{aligned}
$$

Chapter 10 Highlights

Pages 637 Understanding and Using the Vocabulary

1. h
2. log 6500 ≈ 3.8129, log 6.5 ≈ 0.8129; d
3. b $\qquad$ **4a.** e $\qquad$ **4b.** f $\qquad$ **4c.** i
5. log 0.28 ≈ −0.5528, log $\frac{3}{4}$ ≈ −0.1249; a
6. c $\qquad$ **7.** g

Chapter 10 Study Guide and Assessment

Pages 638–640 Skills and Concepts

8. $3^{\sqrt{2}} \cdot 3^{\sqrt{2}} = 3^{\sqrt{2}+\sqrt{2}} = 3^{2\sqrt{2}}$

9. $(x^{\sqrt{5}})^{\sqrt{20}} = x^{\sqrt{5}\cdot\sqrt{20}} = x^{\sqrt{100}} = x^{10}$

10.
$$
\begin{aligned}
\frac{49^{\sqrt{2}}}{7^{\sqrt{12}}} &= \frac{(7^2)^{\sqrt{2}}}{7^{\sqrt{12}}}\\
&= 7^{2\sqrt{2}} \div 7^{2\sqrt{3}}\\
&= 7^{2\sqrt{2} - 2\sqrt{3}}
\end{aligned}
$$

11. $(8^{\sqrt{3}})(8^{-2\sqrt{3}})(8^{4\sqrt{3}}) = 8^{\sqrt{3}-2\sqrt{3}+4\sqrt{3}} = 8^{3\sqrt{3}}$

12.
$$
\begin{aligned}
2^{6x} &= 4^{5x+2}\\
2^{6x} &= (2^2)^{5x+2}\\
2^{6x} &= 2^{10x+4}\\
6x &= 10x + 4\\
-4x &= 4\\
x &= -1
\end{aligned}
$$

13.
$$
\begin{aligned}
49^{3p+1} &= 7^{2p-5}\\
(7^2)^{3p+1} &= 7^{2p-5}\\
7^{6p+2} &= 7^{2p-5}\\
6p + 2 &= 2p - 5\\
4p &= -7\\
p &= -\tfrac{7}{4}
\end{aligned}
$$

14.
$$
\begin{aligned}
9^{x^2} &= 27^{x^2-2}\\
(3^2)^{x^2} &= (3^3)^{x^2-2}\\
3^{2x^2} &= 3^{3x^2-6}\\
2x^2 &= 3x^2 - 6\\
6 &= x^2\\
\pm\sqrt{6} &= x
\end{aligned}
$$

15. $9^x = \frac{1}{81}$; $9^x = 9^{-2}$; $x = -2$

16. $7^3 = 343$; $\log_7 343 = 3$

17. $5^{-2} = \frac{1}{25}$; $\log_5 \frac{1}{25} = -2$

18. $4^0 = 1$; $\log_4 1 = 0$

19. $4^{\frac{3}{2}} = 8$; $\log_4 8 = \frac{3}{2}$

20. $\log_4 64 = 3$; $4^3 = 64$

21. $\log_8 2 = \frac{1}{3}$; $8^{\frac{1}{3}} = 2$

22. $\log_6 \frac{1}{36} = -2$; $6^{-2} = \frac{1}{36}$

23. $\log_6 1 = 0$; $6^0 = 1$

24. $6^{\log_6 7} = 7$

25. $\log_{10} 10^{-3} = x$; $10^x = 10^{-3}$; $x = -3$

26.
$$
\begin{aligned}
\log_{64} 8 &= x\\
64^x &= 8\\
(8^2)^x &= 8\\
8^{2x} &= 8\\
2x &= 1\\
x &= \tfrac{1}{2}
\end{aligned}
$$

27.
$$
\begin{aligned}
\log_{12} 144 &= x\\
12^x &= 144\\
12^x &= 12^2\\
x &= 2
\end{aligned}
$$

28.
$$
\begin{aligned}
\log_b 9 &= 2\\
b^2 &= 9\\
b^2 &= 3^2\\
b &= 3
\end{aligned}
$$

29. $\log_4 x = \frac{1}{2}$
$4^{\frac{1}{2}} = x$
$2 = x$

30. $\log_3 x = -3$
$3^{-3} = x$
$\frac{1}{27} = x$

31. $\log_7 2401 = x$
$7^x = 2401$
$7^x = 7^4$
$x = 4$

32. $\log_7 (x^2 + x) = \log_7 12$
$x^2 + x = 12$
$x^2 + x - 12 = 0$
$(x + 4)(x - 3) = 0$
$x + 4 = 0$ or $x - 3 = 0$
$x = -4$ $\quad x = 3$

33. $\log_6 12 = \log_6(5x - 3)$
$12 = 5x - 3$
$15 = 5x$
$3 = x$

34. $\log_8 (3y - 1) = \log_8 (y + 4)$
$3y - 1 = y + 4$
$2y = 5$
$y = 2.5$

35. $\log_2 (x^2 + 6x) = \log_2 (x - 4)$
$x^2 + 6x = x - 4$
$x^2 + 5x + 4 = 0$
$(x + 4)(x + 1) = 0$
$x + 4 = 0$ or $x + 1 = 0$
$x = -4$ $\quad x = -1$
Since log is not defined for negative numbers, there is no solution.

36. $\log_9 28 = \log_9 (7 \cdot 4)$
$= \log_9 7 + \log_9 4$
$= 0.8856 + 0.6309$
$= 1.5165$

37. $\log_9 49 = \log_9 7^2$
$= 2 \log_9 7$
$= 2(0.8856)$
$= 1.7712$

38. $\log_9 144 = \log_9(9 \times 16)$
$= \log_9 9 + \log_9 16$
$= \log_9 9 + \log_9 4^2$
$= \log_9 9 + 2\log_9 4$
$= 1 + 2(0.6309)$
$= 1 + 1.2618$
$= 2.2618$

39. $\log_9 15.75 = \log_9 \frac{63}{4}$
$= \log_9 63 - \log_9 4$
$= \log_9 9 + \log_9 7 - \log_9 4$
$= 1 + 0.8856 - 0.6309$
$= 1.2547$

40. $\log_3 x - \log_3 4 = \log_3 12$
$\log_3 x = \log_3 12 + \log_3 4$
$\log_3 x = \log_3 48$
$x = 48$

41. $\log_2 y = \frac{1}{3} \log_2 27$
$\log_2 y = \log_2 27^{\frac{1}{3}}$
$\log_2 y = \log_2 3$
$y = 3$

42. $\log_5 7 + \frac{1}{2} \log_5 4 = \log_5 x$
$\log_5 7 + \log_5 4^{\frac{1}{2}} = \log_5 x$
$\log_5 (7 \cdot 2) = \log_5 x$
$14 = x$

43. $2 \log_2 x - \log_2(x + 3) = 2$
$\log_2 x^2 - \log_2(x + 3) = 2$
$\log_2 \frac{x^2}{x + 3} = 2$
$2^2 = \frac{x^2}{x + 3}$
$4x + 12 = x^2$
$0 = x^2 - 4x - 12$
$0 = (x - 6)(x + 2)$
$x - 6 = 0$ or $x + 2 = 0$
$x = 6$ $\quad x = -2$
-2 is not an acceptable solution.

44. $\log_7 m = \frac{1}{3}\log_7 64 + \frac{1}{2}\log_7 121$
$\log_7 m = \log_7 64^{\frac{1}{3}} + \log_7 121^{\frac{1}{2}}$
$\log_7 m = \log_7 (4 \cdot 11)$
$m = 44$

45. 1.6680 **46.** 2.8313
47. −2.3298 **48.** −0.7375
49. 562.3413 **50.** 99.7700
51. 0.2710 **52.** 0.0003
53. 0.8329 **54.** 2.2246
55. 3.9120 **56.** −2.9957
57. 7.2102 **58.** 9.4499
59. 0.6132 **60.** 0.0111

61. $\log_5 15 = \frac{\log 15}{\log 5}$
$\approx \frac{1.1761}{0.6990}$
≈ 1.683

62. $\log_4 100 = \frac{\log 100}{\log 4}$
$\approx \frac{2}{0.6021}$
≈ 3.322

63. $\log_{12} 15 = \frac{\log 15}{\log 12}$
$\approx \frac{1.1761}{1.0792}$
≈ 1.090

64. $\log_2 36 = \frac{\log 36}{\log 2}$
$\approx \frac{1.5563}{0.3010}$
≈ 5.170

65. $\log_9 108 = \frac{\log 108}{\log 9}$
$\approx \frac{2.0334}{0.9542}$
≈ 2.131

66. $\log_{11} 104 = \frac{\log 104}{\log 11}$
$\approx \frac{2.0170}{1.0414}$
≈ 1.937

67. $2^x = 53$
$\log 2^x = \log 53$
$x \log 2 = \log 53$
$x = \frac{\log 53}{\log 2}$
$x \approx \frac{1.7243}{0.3010}$
$x \approx 5.7286$

68. $\log_4 11.2 = x$
$4^x = 11.2$
$\log 4^x = \log 11.2$
$x \log 4 = \log 11.2$
$x = \frac{\log 11.2}{\log 4}$
$x \approx \frac{1.0492}{0.6021}$
$x \approx 1.7427$

69. $2.3^{x^2} = 66.6$
$\log 2.3^{x^2} = \log 66.6$
$x^2 \log 2.3 = \log 66.6$
$x^2 = \frac{\log 66.6}{\log 2.3}$
$x^2 \approx \frac{1.8235}{0.3617}$
$x^2 \approx 5.0411$
$x \approx \pm 2.2452$

70. $$3^{4x-7} = 4^{2x+3}$$
$$\log 3^{4x-7} = \log 4^{2x+3}$$
$$(4x-7)\log 3 = (2x+3)\log 4$$
$$4x\log 3 - 7\log 3 = 2x\log 4 + 3\log 4$$
$$4x\log 3 - 2x\log 4 = 3\log 4 + 7\log 3$$
$$x(4\log 3 - 2\log 4) = 3\log 4 + 7\log 3$$
$$x = \frac{3\log 4 + 7\log 3}{4\log 3 - 2\log 4}$$
$$x \approx \frac{3(0.6021) + 7(0.4771)}{4(0.4771) - 2(0.6021)}$$
$$x \approx 7.3059$$

71. $$6^{3y} = 8^{y-3}$$
$$\log 6^{3y} = \log 8^{y-3}$$
$$3y\log 6 = (y-3)\log 8$$
$$3y\log 6 = y\log 8 - 3\log 8$$
$$3y\log 6 - y\log 8 = -3\log 8$$
$$y(3\log 6 - \log 8) = -3\log 8$$
$$y = \frac{-3\log 8}{3\log 6 - \log 8}$$
$$y \approx \frac{-3(0.9031)}{3(0.7782) - (0.9031)}$$
$$y \approx -1.8928$$

72. $$x = \log_{20} 1000$$
$$20^x = 1000$$
$$\log 20^x = \log 1000$$
$$x\log 20 = \log 1000$$
$$x = \frac{\log 1000}{\log 20}$$
$$x \approx \frac{3}{1.3010}$$
$$x \approx 2.3059$$

73. $$12^{x-4} = 4^{2-x}$$
$$\log 12^{x-4} = \log 4^{2-x}$$
$$(x-4)\log 12 = (2-x)\log 4$$
$$x\log 12 - 4\log 12 = 2\log 4 - x\log 4$$
$$x\log 12 + x\log 4 = 2\log 4 + 4\log 12$$
$$x(\log 12 + \log 4) = 2\log 4 + 4\log 12$$
$$x = \frac{2\log 4 + 4\log 12}{\log 12 + \log 4}$$
$$x \approx \frac{2(0.6021) + 4(1.0792)}{1.0792 + 0.6021}$$
$$x \approx 3.2838$$

74. $$2.1^{x-5} = 9.32$$
$$\log 2.1^{x-5} = \log 9.32$$
$$(x-5)\log 2.1 = \log 9.32$$
$$x\log 2.1 - 5\log 2.1 = \log 9.32$$
$$x\log 2.1 = \log 9.32 + 5\log 2.1$$
$$x = \frac{\log 9.32 + 5\log 2.1}{\log 2.1}$$
$$x \approx \frac{0.9694 + 5(0.3222)}{0.3222}$$
$$x \approx 8.0086$$

Page 640 Applications and Problem Solving

75. $P = 14.7\,(10)^{-0.02h}$
$= 14.7\,(10)^{-0.02(3)}$
≈ 12.8; about 12.8 psi

76a. $A = Pe^{rt}$
$= 500e^{0.065(7)}$
≈ 788.09; \$788.09

76b. $$A = Pe^{rt}$$
$$3(500) = 500e^{0.065t}$$
$$3 = e^{0.065t}$$
$$\ln 3 = \ln e^{0.065t}$$
$$\ln 3 = 0.065t$$
$$\frac{\ln 3}{0.065} = t$$
$16.9 \approx t$; 16.9 years

77. $$y = ne^{kt}$$
$$738 = 9e^{0.872t}$$
$$82 = e^{0.872t}$$
$$\ln 82 = \ln e^{0.872t}$$
$$\ln 82 = 0.872t$$
$$\frac{\ln 82}{0.872} = t$$
$5.05 \approx t$; 5.05 days

78. $$y = ne^{kt}$$
$$1 = 2e^{k(1800)}$$
$$0.5 = e^{1800k}$$
$$\ln 0.5 = \ln e^{1800k}$$
$$-0.6931 \approx 1800k$$
$-0.000385 \approx k$; about -0.000385

Page 641 Alternative Assessment; Thinking Critically

- Algebraically:

$f(g(x)) = f(b^x)$
$= \log_b b^x$
$= x$

$g(f(x)) = g(\log_b x)$
$= b^{\log_b x}$
$= x$

Graphically:

$0 < b < 1$

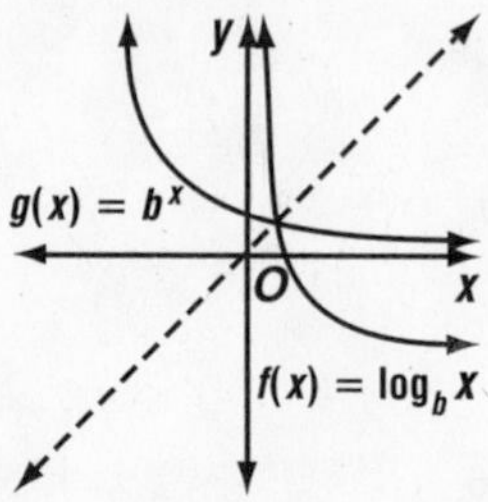

$b > 1$

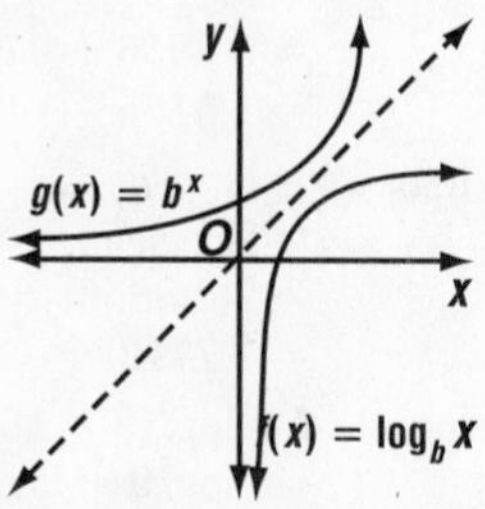

- Since $\log x$ and 10^x are inverses, they are usually found on the same key position. Other inverse functions are x^2 and $\sqrt{\ }$; ln and e^x.

College Entrance Exam Practice

Pages 642–643

1. C

2. $\frac{1}{x} + \frac{2}{x-2} + \frac{3}{x} + \frac{4}{x-2} + \frac{x}{x-2}$
$= \frac{x-2}{x(x-2)} + \frac{2x}{x(x-2)} + \frac{3(x-2)}{x(x-2)} + \frac{4x}{x(x-2)} + \frac{x^2}{x(x-2)}$
$= \frac{x - 2 + 2x + 3x - 6 + 4x + x^2}{x(x-2)}$
$= \frac{x^2 + 10x - 8}{x(x-2)}$; B

3. $4(2) + 3(0) = 8$; $4(-1) + 3(8) = 20$;
$4(-2) + 3(-5) = -23$
[8 20 −23]; C

4. $A = (2x + 5y)(3x + y)$
$= 6x^2 + 17xy + 5y^2$; B

5. $30 \div 10 = 3$
$3^3 = 27$; D

6. B

7. 6 hr at 55 mph = 330 miles traveled.
396 miles − 330 miles = 66 miles remaining.
8 hours − 6 hours − 0.5 hours = 1.5 hours left.
66 miles ÷ 1.5 hours = 44 mph; C

8. Let w = width and $\ell = 2w + 7$

$$P = 2\ell + 2w$$
$$152 = 2(2w + 7) + 2w$$
$$152 = 4w + 14 + 2w$$
$$138 = 6w$$
$$23 = w$$

$$\ell = 2w + 7 = 2(23) + 7 = 53;\ \text{A}$$

9. $\log_3 27 + \log_3 3 \stackrel{?}{=} \log_3 81$
$3 + 1 \stackrel{?}{=} 4$
$4 = 4$

10. $2y + x = 6$
$2y = -x + 6$
$y = -\frac{1}{2}x + 3$
$y = 2x + 3$

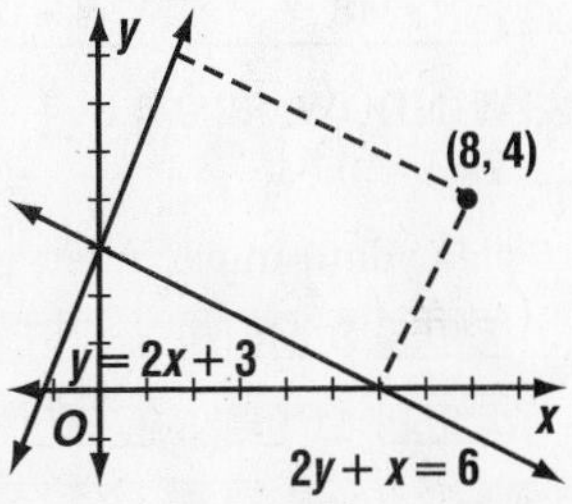

11. $6t^2 + 28t - 10 = 0$
$(6t - 2)(t + 5) = 0$
$6t - 2 = 0$ or $t + 5 = 0$
$6t = 2$ $\quad t = -5$
$t = \frac{1}{3}$

$s_1 + s_2 = \frac{1}{3} + (-5) = -\frac{14}{3}$

$s_1(s_2) = \frac{1}{3}(-5) = -\frac{5}{3}$

12. $$\frac{\dfrac{3 + 10t^2 - 17t}{5t^2 + 4t - 1}}{\dfrac{4t^2 - 9}{3 + 5t + 2t^2}} = \frac{10t^2 - 17t + 3}{5t^2 + 4t - 1} \cdot \frac{2t^2 + 5t + 3}{4t^2 - 9}$$
$$= \frac{(5t - 1)(2t - 3)}{(5t - 1)(t + 1)} \cdot \frac{(2t + 3)(t + 1)}{(2t - 3)(2t + 3)}$$
$$= \frac{1}{1} \text{ or } 1$$

13. $2x - 7 = 3y$
$\frac{2}{3}x - \frac{7}{3} = y$
$x - y = 5$
$x - 5 = y$
(8, 3); consistent, independent

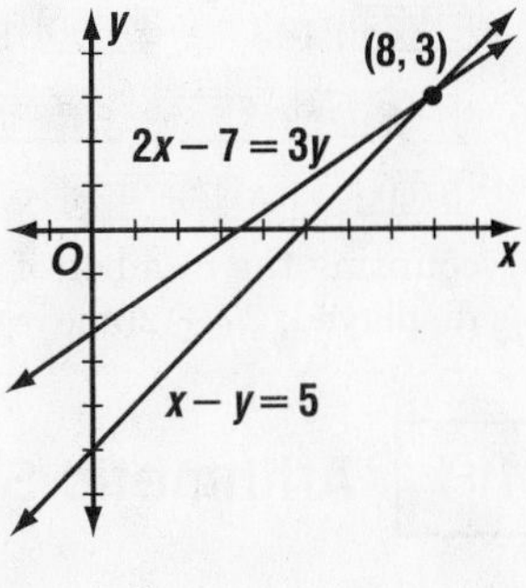

14. $$F_c = \frac{mv^2}{r}$$
$$F_c r = mv^2$$
$$\frac{F_c r}{m} = v^2$$
$$\sqrt{\frac{F_c r}{m}} = v$$
$$\frac{\sqrt{F_c rm}}{m} = v$$

15. $b^2 - 4ac = 1^2 - 4(2)(-3)$
$= 1 + 24$
$= 25$
2 rational roots

16. $2x + y = -3$
$y = -2x - 3$

$3x + 4y = -7$
$3x + 4(-2x - 3) = -7$
$3x - 8x - 12 = -7$
$-5x = 5$
$x = -1$

$y = -2x - 3$
$= -2(-1) - 3$
$= -1$; $(-1, -1)$

17. $$A = Pe^{rt}$$
$$6230 = 150e^{0.05t}$$
$$\frac{6230}{150} = e^{0.05t}$$
$$\ln \frac{6230}{150} = \ln e^{0.05t}$$
$$\ln 6230 - \ln 150 = 0.05t$$
$$\frac{8.7371 - 5.0106}{0.05} \approx t$$
$75 \approx t$; 75 years ago

18. $\log_4 (x + 3) + \log_4 (x - 3) = 2$
$\log_4 (x + 3)(x - 3) = 2$
$4^2 = (x + 3)(x - 3)$
$16 = x^2 - 9$
$25 = x^2$
$\pm 5 = x$
−5 is not an acceptable solution.

19. $x^2 = 100$
$x = \pm 10$

$y^2 = 36$
$y = \pm 6$; D

20. antiln $0.288 = 1.3338$

$$2000 = 5^{0.045x}$$
$$\log 2000 = \log 5^{0.045x}$$
$$\log 2000 = 0.045x \log 5$$
$$\frac{\log 2000}{\log 5} = 0.045x$$
$$\frac{3.3010}{0.6990} \approx 0.045x$$
$104.95 \approx x$; B

21. $f[g(x)] = f(x + 9)$
$= x + 9 + 4$
$= x + 13$

$g[f(x)] = g(x + 4)$
$= x + 4 + 9$
$= x + 13$

C

22. $\frac{1}{3} \approx 0.33$

$\frac{1}{3\sqrt{3}} \approx \frac{1}{5.196}$
≈ 0.19; A

23. $$\frac{2y - 5}{6} - \frac{y - 5}{4} = \frac{3}{4}$$
$$12\left(\frac{2y - 5}{6}\right) - 12\left(\frac{y - 5}{4}\right) = 12\left(\frac{3}{4}\right)$$
$$4y - 10 - 3y + 15 = 9$$
$$y = 4$$
$$\frac{x - 4}{x - 2} = \frac{x - 2}{x + 2} + \frac{1}{x - 2}$$
$$(x - 2)(x + 2)\left(\frac{x - 4}{x - 2}\right) = (x - 2)(x + 2)\left(\frac{x - 2}{x + 2}\right) + (x - 2)(x + 2)\left(\frac{1}{x - 2}\right)$$
$$(x + 2)(x - 4) = (x - 2)(x - 2) + (x + 2)$$
$$x^2 - 2x - 8 = x^2 - 4x + 4 + x + 2$$
$$-2x - 8 = -3x + 6$$
$x = 14$; B

Chapter 11 Investigating Sequences and Series

11-1A Graphing Technology: Arithmetic Sequences

Page 647 Exercises

1. 47 STO▸ X,T,θ,n ENTER X,T,θ,n + 7 STO▸ X,T,θ,n ENTER, press ENTER 9 more times; 117
2. 4.5 STO▸ X,T,θ,n ENTER X,T,θ,n − 0.75 STO▸ X,T,θ,n ENTER, press ENTER 9 more times; −3
3. 2.132 STO▸ X,T,θ,n ENTER X,T,θ,n + 0.998 STO▸ X,T,θ,n ENTER, press ENTER 9 more times; 12.112
4. (−) 57 STO▸ X,T,θ,n ENTER X,T,θ,n − 2.5 STO▸ X,T,θ,n ENTER, press ENTER 9 more times; −82

For 5-8, from the MODE menu, select DOT. Clear L_1, L_2, and Y=. All STAT PLOT graphs should be off.

5. WINDOW: [0, 94] by [−40, 60] with Xscl = 10, Yscl = 5.
   STAT ENTER 1 ENTER 2 ENTER 3 ENTER 4 ENTER 5 ENTER ▶ (−) 20 ENTER (−) 16 ENTER (−) 12 ENTER (−) 8 ENTER (−) 4 ENTER STAT ▶ 5 2nd L1 , 2nd L2 ENTER Y= VARS 5 ▶ ▶ 7 GRAPH use TRACE to find the 18th term; 48

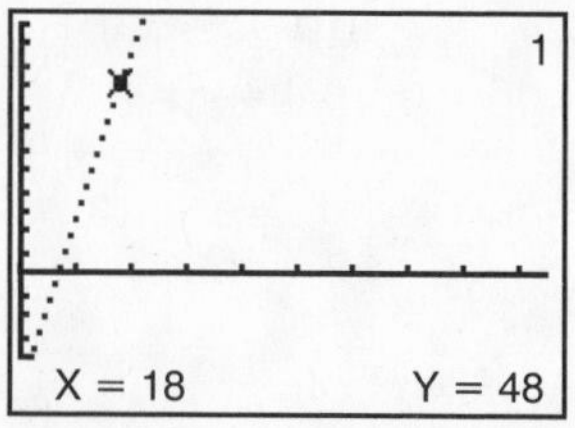

6. WINDOW: [0, 94] by [−20, 20] with Xscl = 10, Yscl = 2.
   STAT ENTER 1 ENTER 2 ENTER 3 ENTER 4 ENTER 5 ENTER ▶ (▲ to $L_{2(1)}$ if necessary) (−) 0.8 ENTER 0 ENTER 0.8 ENTER 1.6 ENTER 2.4 ENTER STAT ▶ 5 2nd L1 , 2nd L2 ENTER Y= VARS 5 ▶ ▶ 7 GRAPH use TRACE to find the 18th term; 12.8

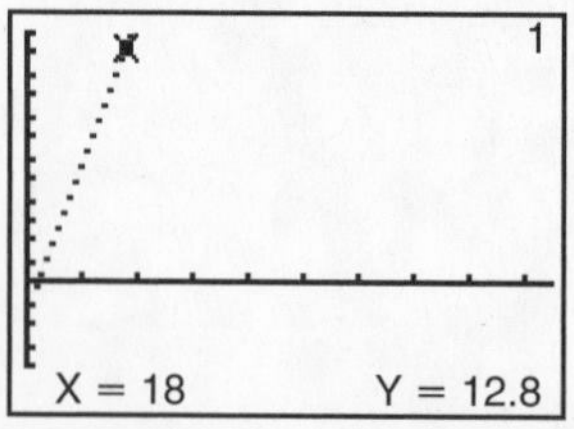

7. WINDOW: [0, 94] by [−150, 50] with Xscl = 10, Yscl = 10.
   STAT ENTER 1 ENTER 2 ENTER 3 ENTER 4 ENTER 5 ENTER ▶ (▲ $L_{2(1)}$ if necessary) 27 ENTER 18 ENTER 9 ENTER 0 ENTER (−) 9 ENTER STAT ▶ 5 2nd L1 , 2nd L2 ENTER Y= VARS 5 ▶ ▶ 7 GRAPH use TRACE to find the 18th term; −126

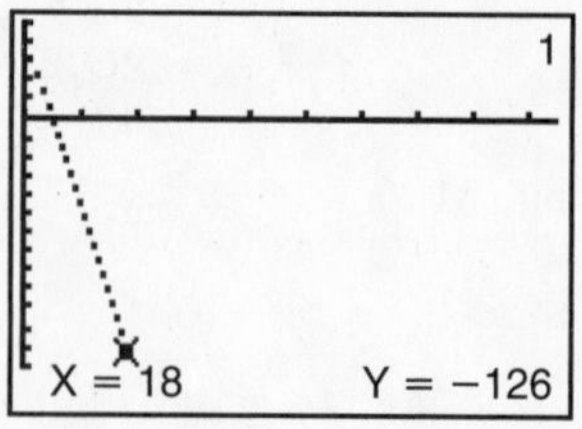

8. WINDOW: [0, 94] by [−6, 4] with Xscl = 10, Yscl = 0.5.
   clear data in each list; STAT ENTER 1 ENTER 2 ENTER 3 ENTER 4 ENTER ▶ 3 ENTER 13 ÷ 5 ENTER 11 ÷ 5 ENTER 9 ÷ 5 ENTER STAT ▶ 5 2nd L1 , 2nd L2 ENTER Y= VARS 5 ▶ ▶ 7 GRAPH use TRACE to find the 18th term; −3.8

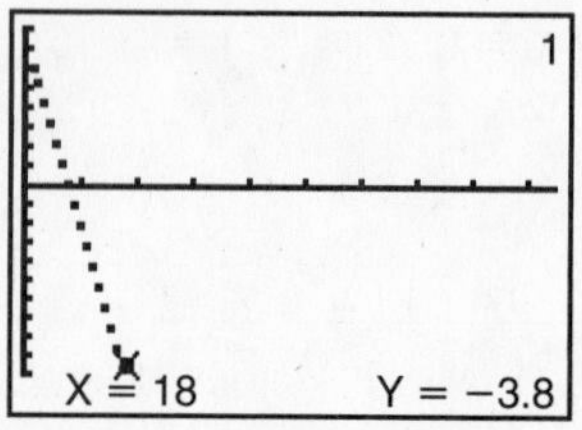

9. 148 STO▸ X,T,θ,n ENTER X,T,θ,n − 1.17 STO▸ X,T,θ,n ENTER ENTER ENTER; 144.49; ENTER; 143.32; ENTER 142.15
10. 17 STO▸ X,T,θ,n ENTER X,T,θ,n + 3.5 STO▸ X,T,θ,n ENTER continue pressing ENTER, counting the number of times until 115 is displayed; 27 + 2(above) = 29

11-1 Arithmetic Sequences

Pages 651–652 Check for Understanding

1. Consider three consecutive terms of the sequence and find whether the same number is added to each term to get the next.
2. $a_n = 5 + (n - 1)2$
   $24 = 5 + (n - 1)2$
   $24 = 5 + 2n - 2$
   $21 = 2n$
   $10.5 = n$; No, 10.5 is not in the domain of this function.

3a. −4, −2, 0, 2, 4

3b. The domain is made up of distinct values.

3c. $a_n = -4$ and $d = -2 - (-4) = 2$

$a_n = a_1 + (n-1)d$
$= -4 + (n-1)2$
$= -4 + 2n - 2$
$= 2n - 6$

3d. 2; The slope is the common difference of the sequence.

4. $a_n = 16 - (n-1)12$
$220 = 16 - (12n - 12)$
$220 = 28 - 12n$
$192 = -12n$
$-16 = n$; Janice is correct; $n = -16$ is not in the domain since it is not a positive integer.

5. $d = 16 - 12 = 4$; $20 + 4 = 24$, $24 + 4 = 28$, $28 + 4 = 32$, $32 + 4 = 36$;
24, 28, 32, 36

6. $d = 1 - 3 = -2$; $-1 + (-2) = -3$, $-3 + (-2) = -5$, $-5 + (-2) = -7$, $-7 + (-2) = -9$;
−3, −5, −7, −9

7. $5 + 3 = 8$, $8 + 3 = 11$, $11 + 3 = 14$, $14 + 3 = 17$;
5, 8, 11, 14, 17

8. $14 + (-2) = 12$, $12 + (-2) = 10$, $10 + (-2) = 8$, $8 + (-2) = 6$;
14, 12, 10, 8, 6

9. $a_n = a_1 + (n-1)d$
$a_{24} = 3 + (24-1)(-5)$
$= 3 - 115$
$= -112$

10. $a_n = a_1 + (n-1)d$
$a_{13} = -5 + (13-1)7$
$= -5 + 84$
$= 79$

11. $d = 3 - (-2) = 5$
$a_n = a + (n-1)d$
$68 = -2 + (n-1)5$
$68 = -2 + 5n - 5$
$75 = 5n$
$15 = n$

12. $d = -12 - (-17) = 5$
$a_n = a + (n-1)d$
$a_{13} = -17 + (13-1)5$
$= -17 + 60$
$= 43$

13a. $a_1 = 44$, $n = 5$, $a_5 = 92$
$a_n = a + (n-1)d$
$92 = 44 + (5-1)d$
$48 = 4d$
$12 = d$

13b. $44 + 12 = 56$, $56 + 12 = 68$, $68 + 12 = 80$;
56, 68, 80

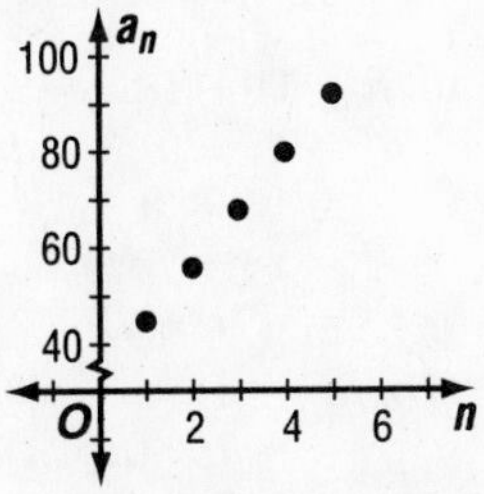

14. $a_1 = -26$, $d = -15 - (-26) = 11$
$a_n = a + (n-1)d$
$= -26 + (n-1)11$
$= -26 + 11n - 11$
$= 11n - 37$

15. $a_1 = 361$, $d = 322 - 361 = -39$, $n = 8$
$a_n = a + (n-1)d$
$a_8 = 361 + (8-1)(-39)$
$= 361 - 273$
$= 88$; \$88

Pages 652–655 Exercises

16. $d = 16 - 9 = 7$; $23 + 7 = 30$, $30 + 7 = 37$, $37 + 7 = 44$, $44 + 7 = 51$;
30, 37, 44, 51

17. $d = 24 - 31 = -7$; $17 + (-7) = 10$, $10 + (-7) = 3$, $3 + (-7) = -4$, $-4 + (-7) = -11$;
10, 3, −4, −11

18. $d = \frac{3}{4} - \frac{1}{4} = \frac{2}{4}$; $\frac{5}{4} + \frac{2}{4} = \frac{7}{4}$, $\frac{7}{4} + \frac{2}{4} = \frac{9}{4}$, $\frac{9}{4} + \frac{2}{4} = \frac{11}{4}$, $\frac{11}{4} + \frac{2}{4} = \frac{13}{4}$;
$\frac{7}{4}, \frac{9}{4}, \frac{11}{4}, \frac{13}{4}$

19. $d = -3.8 - (-7.8) = 4$; $0.2 + 4 = 4.2$, $4.2 + 4 = 8.2$, $8.2 + 4 = 12.2$, $12.4 + 4 = 16.2$;
4.2, 8.2, 12.2, 16.2

20. $12 + (-3) = 9$, $9 + (-3) = 6$, $6 + (-3) = 3$, $3 + (-3) = 0$;
12, 9, 6, 3, 0

21. $41 + 5 = 46$, $46 + 5 = 51$, $51 + 5 = 56$, $56 + 5 = 61$;
41, 46, 51, 56, 61

22. $\frac{4}{3} + \left(-\frac{1}{3}\right) = 1$, $1 + \left(-\frac{1}{3}\right) = \frac{2}{3}$, $\frac{2}{3} + \left(-\frac{1}{3}\right) = \frac{1}{3}$, $\frac{1}{3} + \left(-\frac{1}{3}\right) = 0$;
$\frac{4}{3}, 1, \frac{2}{3}, \frac{1}{3}, 0$

23. $\frac{5}{8} + \frac{3}{8} = 1$, $1 + \frac{3}{8} = \frac{11}{8}$, $\frac{11}{8} + \frac{3}{8} = \frac{14}{8}$, $\frac{14}{8} + \frac{3}{8} = \frac{17}{8}$;
$\frac{5}{8}, 1, \frac{11}{8}, \frac{14}{8}, \frac{17}{8}$

24. $a_n = a_1 + (n-1)d$
$a_{14} = 3 + (14-1)7$
$= 3 + 91$
$= 94$

25. $a_n = a_1 + (n-1)d$
$a_{20} = -4 + (20-1)(-9)$
$= -4 + (-171)$
$= -175$

26. $a_n = a_1 + (n-1)d$
$a_{12} = 5 + (12-1)\frac{1}{3}$
$= 5 + \frac{11}{3}$
$= \frac{26}{3}$ or $8\frac{2}{3}$

27. $a_n = a_1 + (n-1)d$
$a_{11} = \frac{5}{2} + (11-1)\left(-\frac{3}{2}\right)$
$= \frac{5}{2} - \frac{30}{2}$
$= -\frac{25}{2}$ or $-12\frac{1}{2}$

28. $a_n = a_1 + (n-1)d$
$a_{101} = 35\ (101-1)3$
$= 35 + 300$
$= 335$

29. $a_n = a_1 + (n-1)d$
$a_{81} = 20 + (81-1)4$
$= 20 + 320$
$= 340$

30. $a_1 = -4$, $d = 2 - (-4) = 6$
$a_n = a_1 + (n-1)d$
$170 = -4 + (n-1)6$
$174 = 6n - 6$
$180 = 6n$
$30 = n$

31. $a_1 = -2$, $d = 5 - (-2) = 7$
$a_n = a_1 + (n-1)d$
$124 = -2 + (n-1)7$
$126 = 7n - 7$
$133 = 7n$
$19 = n$

32. $a_1 = 2\frac{1}{5}$, $d = 2 - 2\frac{1}{5} = -\frac{1}{5}$

$$a_n = a_1 + (n-1)d$$
$$-14 = 2\frac{1}{5} + (n-1)\left(-\frac{1}{5}\right)$$
$$-16\frac{1}{5} = -\frac{1}{5}n + \frac{1}{5}$$
$$-16\frac{2}{5} = -\frac{1}{5}n$$
$$-\frac{82}{5} = -\frac{1}{5}n$$
$$82 = n$$

33. $a_1 = -17$, d $= -13 - (-17) = 4$

$$a_n = a_1 + (n-1)d$$
$$a_{12} = -17 + (12-1)4$$
$$= -17 + 44$$
$$= 27$$

34. $a_1 = 121$, $d = 118 - 121 = -3$

$$a_n = a_1 + (n-1)d$$
$$a_{21} = 121 + (21-1)(-3)$$
$$= 121 - 60$$
$$= 61$$

35. $a_1 = 5$, $d = 9 - 5 = 4$

$$a_n = a_1 + (n-1)d$$
$$a_{43} = 5 + (43-1)4$$
$$= 5 + 168$$
$$= 173$$

36. $a_1 = 8$, $d = 3 - 8 = -5$

$$a_n = a_1 + (n-1)d$$
$$a_{12} = 8 + (12-1)(-5)$$
$$= 8 - 55$$
$$= -47$$

37. $a_1 = 55$, $n = 5$, $a_5 = 115$

$$a_n = a_1 + (n-1)d$$
$$115 = 55 + (5-1)d$$
$$60 = 4d$$
$$15 = d$$

$55 + 15 = 70$, $70 + 15 = 85$, $85 + 15 = 100$; 70, 85, 100

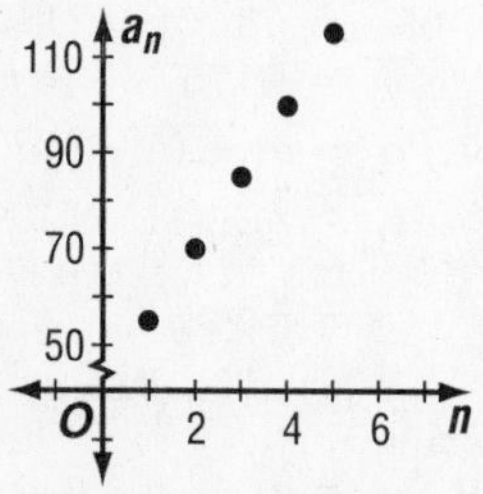

38. $a_1 = 10$, $n = 4$, $a_4 = -8$

$$a_n = a_1 + (n-1)d$$
$$-8 = 10 + (4-1)d$$
$$-18 = 3d$$
$$-6 = d$$

$10 + (-6) = 4$, $4 + (-6) = -2$; 4, −2

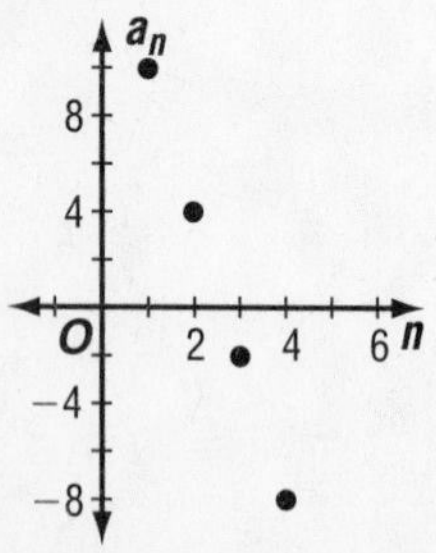

39. $a_1 = -5$, $n = 4$, $a_4 = 4$

$$a_n = a_1 + (n-1)d$$
$$4 = -5 + (4-1)d$$
$$9 = 3d$$
$$3 = d$$

$-5 - 3 = -8$, $-5 + 3 = -2$,
$-2 + 3 = 1$, $4 + 3 = 7$;
−8, −5, −2, 1, 4, 7

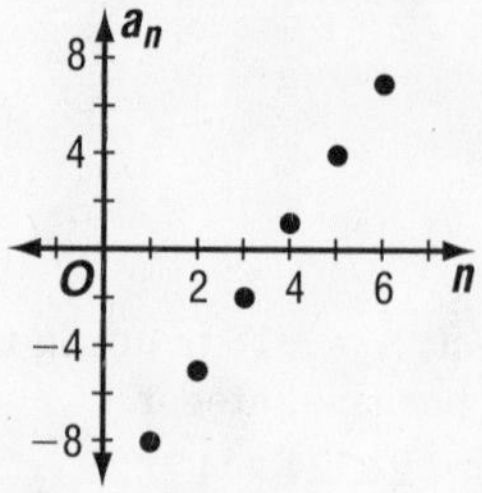

40. $a_1 = 3$, $n = 7$, $a_7 = 27$

$$a_n = a_1 + (n-1)d$$
$$27 = 3 + (7-1)d$$
$$24 = 6d$$
$$4 = d$$

$3 + 4 = 7$, $7 + 4 = 11$, $11 + 4 = 15$,
$15 + 4 = 19$, $19 + 4 = 23$;
7, 11, 15, 19, 23

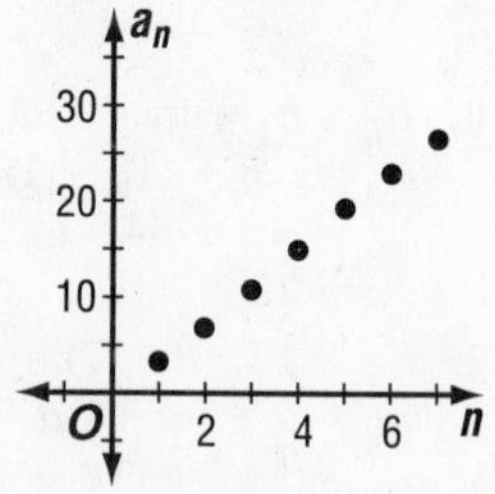

41. $d = 2 - (-4) = 6$

$$8 + 6 = 14$$
$$14 = 3y + 5$$
$$9 = 3y$$
$$3 = y$$

42. $d = 9 - 5 = 4$

$$9 + 4 = 13$$
$$13 = 2y - 1$$
$$14 = 2y$$
$$7 = y$$

43. $d = 6 - (y + 2)$

$$= 4 - y$$
$$6 + (4 - y) = y$$
$$10 - y = y$$
$$10 = 2y$$
$$5 = y$$

44. $d = (4y + 6) - (y + 8)$

$$= 3y - 2$$
$$4y + 6 + (3y - 2) = 3y$$
$$7y + 4 = 3y$$
$$4y = -4$$
$$y = -1$$

45. $d = 16 - 7 = 9$

$$a_n = a_1 + (n-1)d$$
$$= 7 + (n-1)9$$
$$= 7 + 9n - 9$$
$$= 9n - 2$$

46. $d = 11 - 18 = -7$

$$a_n = a_1 + (n-1)d$$
$$= 18 + (n-1)(-7)$$
$$= 18 - 7n + 7$$
$$= -7n + 25$$

47a. $a_n = a_1 + (n-1)d$

$$= 7 + (8-1)4$$
$$= 35$$

47b. $a_n = a_1 + (n-1)d$

$$= 7 + (n-1)4$$
$$= 7 + 4n - 4$$
$$= 4n + 3$$

48a.

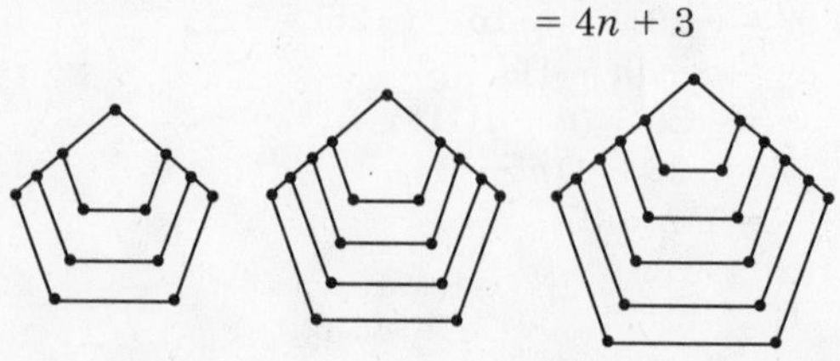

13, 17, 21

48b. yes; $d = 9 - 5 = 4$; $a_n = a_1 + (n - 1)d$
$= 1 + (n - 1)4$
$= 1 + 4n - 4$
$= 4n - 3$

48c. 4

48d. $a_n = a_1 + (n - 1)d$
$397 = 1 + (n - 1)4$
$397 = 1 + 4n - 4$
$400 = 4n$
$100 = n$; Yes, it's the 100th term.

49. If $a_1 = 19$, then $a_7 = 43$. $a_{11} = 43$ and $d = 4$
$a_n = a_1 + (n - 1)d$
$43 = 19 + (7 - 1)d$
$24 = 6d$
$4 = d$

$a_n = a_1 + (n - 1)d$
$43 = a_1 + (11 - 1)4$
$43 = a_1 + 40$
$3 = a_1$
$a_{87} = a_1 + (n - 1)d$
$= 3 + (87 - 1)4$
$= 347$

50. Let x = 1st number. Then
$x + d$ = 2nd number, and
$x + 2d$ = 3rd number.
$x + x + d + x + 2d = 36$
$3x + 3d = 36$
$x + d = 12$
$d = 12 - x$
$x(x + d)(x + 2d) = 276$
$x(x^2 + 3dx + 2d^2) = 276$
$x^3 + 3dx^2 + 2d^2x = 276$
$x^3 + 3(12 - x)x^2 + 2(12 - x)^2x = 276$
$x^3 + 36x^2 - 3x^3 + 2(144 - 24x + x^2)x = 276$
$x^3 + 36x^2 - 3x^3 + 288x - 48x^2 + 2x^3 = 276$
$-12x^2 + 288x - 276 = 0$
$x^2 - 24x + 23 = 0$
$(x - 1)(x - 23) = 0$

$x - 1 = 0$ or $x - 23 = 0$
$x = 1$ $x = 23$
$d = 12 - 1$ $d = 12 - 23$
$= 11$ $= -11$

1, 12, 23

51. Clear L_1, L_2, and Y=. From MODE menu, select DOT.
WINDOW: [0, 94] by [−50, 60] with Xscl = 10, Yscl = 10.

Use Edit option on STAT menu to enter 1, 2, 3, 4 into L_1 and −31, −24, −17, −10 into L_2. STAT ▶ 5 2nd L1 , 2nd L2 ENTER Y= VARS 5 ▶ ▶ 7 GRAPH
Use TRACE to find 12th term; 46

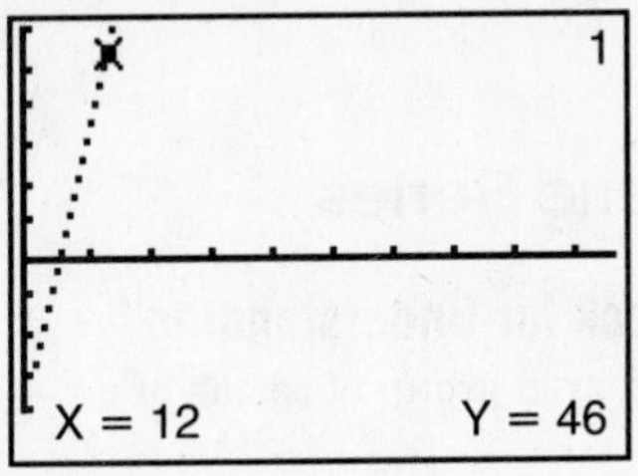

52. Clear L_1, L_2, and Y=. From MODE menu, select DOT.
WINDOW: [0, 94] by [−60, 400] with Xscl = 10, Yscl = 20.

Use EDIT option on STAT menu to enter 1, 2, 3, 4 into L_1 and 317, 313, 309, 305 into L_2. STAT ▶ 5 2nd L1 , 2nd L2 ENTER Y= VARS 5 ▶ ▶ 7 GRAPH ; use TRACE to find 12th term; 273

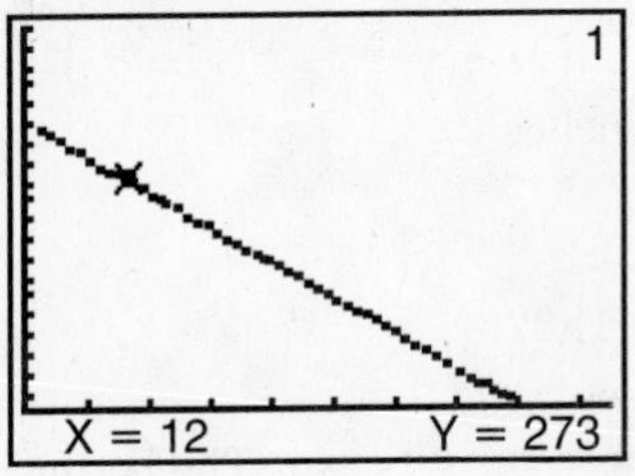

53. Clear L_1, L_2, and Y=. From MODE menu, select DOT.
Window: [0, 94] by [−50, 100] with Xscl = 10, Yscl = 10.

Use EDIT option on STAT menu to enter 1, 2, 3, 4 into L_1 and −16, −13, −10, −7 into L_2. STAT ▶ 5 2nd L1 , 2nd L2 ENTER Y= VARS 5 ▶ ▶ 7 GRAPH ; use TRACE to find 12th term; 17

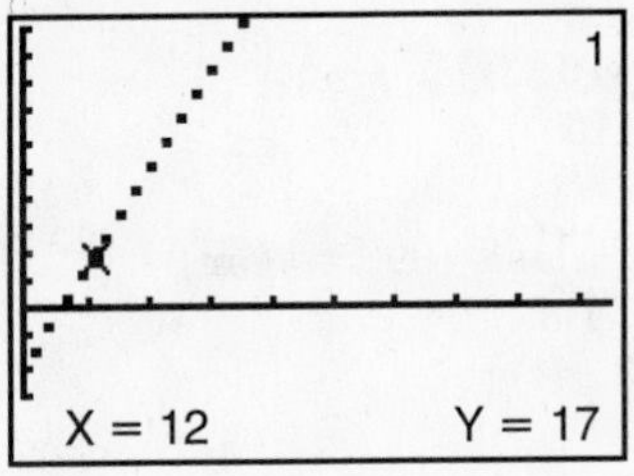

54. Clear L_1, L_2, and Y=. From MODE menu, select DOT.
WINDOW: [0, 94] by [−20, 100] with Xscl = 10, Yscl = 10.
Use EDIT option on STAT menu to enter 1, 2, 3, 4, 5 into L_1 and 23, 29, 35, 41, 47 into L_2.

STAT ▶ 5 2nd L1 , 2nd L2 ENTER Y= VARS 5 ▶ ▶ 7 GRAPH ; use TRACE to find 12th term; 89

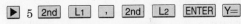

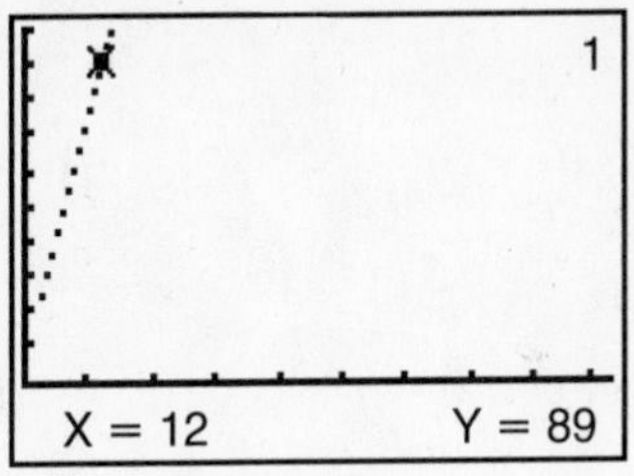

55. least multiple = 42
greatest multiple = 385
$a_n = a_1 + (n - 1)d$
$385 = 42 + (n - 1)7$
$385 = 42 + 7n - 7$
$350 = 7n$
$50 = n$

56. $d = v - u$
1st term = u
2nd term = $u + (v - u)$ or v
3rd term = $v + (v - u)$ or $2v - u$

57. $a_n = a_1 + (n - 1)d$
$a_{50} = 0.75 + (50 - 1)(0.75)$
$= 37.5$; 37.5 inches

58. $d = 48 - 16 = 32$
$a_n = a_1 + (n - 1)d$
$a_{10} = 16 + (10 - 1)(32)$
$= 304$; 304 feet

59a. 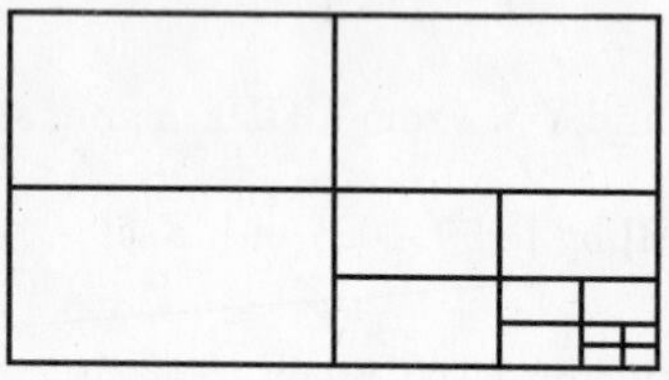

The bottom right box is divided into 4 parts.

59b. 9

59c. 19, 29

59d. $d = 19 - 9 = 10$
$a_n = a_1 + (n - 1)d$
$a_{50} = 9 + (50 - 1)10$
$= 499$

59e. $a_n = a_1 + (n - 1)d$
$= 9 + (n - 1)10$
$= 9 + 10n - 10$
$= 10n - 1$

60a. Let 1964 = year 1 and 1996 = year 33.
$a_n = a_1 + (n - 1)d$
$574 = 254 + (33 - 1)d$
$320 = 32d$
$10 = d$
Let 1938 = year 1 and 1964 = year 26.
$a_n = a_1 + (n - 1)d$
$254 = a_1 + (26 - 1)10$
$4 = a_1$; 4 cards

60b. $d = 10$; 10 cards

60c. $2010 - 1938 = 72$
$a_n = a_1 + (n - 1)d$
$a_{72} = 4 + (72 - 1)10$
$= 714$; 714 cards

61. $y = ne^{kt}$
$4000 = 500e^{k(1.5)}$
$8 = e^{1.5k}$
$\ln 8 = \ln e^{1.5k}$
$2.0794 \approx 1.5k$
$1.3863 \approx k$

62. $\log_3 729 = x$
$3^x = 729$
$3^x = 3^6$
$x = 6$

63. $\frac{y^2 - y}{w^2 - y^2} + \frac{y^2 - 2y + 1}{1 - y}$
$= \frac{y(y - 1)}{(w - y)(w + y)} + \frac{(y - 1)(y - 1)}{(1 - y)}$
$= \frac{y(y - 1)}{(w - y)(w + y)} + (-1)(y - 1)$
$= \frac{y(y - 1)}{(w - y)(w + y)} + \frac{-1(y - 1)(w - y)(w + y)}{(w - y)(w + y)}$
$= \frac{y^2 - y + (-y + 1)(w^2 - y^2)}{w^2 - y^2}$
$= \frac{y^2 - y - w^2y + y^3 + w^2 - y^2}{w^2 - y^2}$
$= \frac{y^3 - w^2y - y + w^2}{w^2 - y^2}$

64. $f[g(x)] = f(x - 1)$
$= 3(x - 1)$
$= 3x - 3$

65. parabola

66. $(4, 5) \rightarrow (-4, 6)$: $d = \sqrt{(-4 - 4)^2 + (6 - 5)^2}$
$= \sqrt{64 + 1}$
$= \sqrt{65}$
$(-4, 6) \rightarrow (-5, -8)$: $d = \sqrt{(-5 - (-4))^2 + (-8 - 6)^2}$
$= \sqrt{1 + 196}$
$= \sqrt{197}$
$(-5, -8) \rightarrow (6, 3)$: $d = \sqrt{(6 - (-5)^2 + (3 - (-8)^2}$
$= \sqrt{121 + 121}$
$= \sqrt{242}$ or $11\sqrt{2}$
$(6, 3) \rightarrow (4, 5)$: $d = \sqrt{(4 - 6)^2 + (5 - 3)^2}$
$= \sqrt{4 + 4}$
$= \sqrt{8}$ or $2\sqrt{2}$
perimeter $= \sqrt{65} + \sqrt{197} + 11\sqrt{2} + 2\sqrt{2}$
$= 13\sqrt{2} + \sqrt{65} + \sqrt{197}$ units

67. (9, 0); $x = 9$; downward

68. $\sqrt[3]{x + 5} + 6 = 4$
$\sqrt[3]{x + 5} = -2$
$x + 5 = -8$
$x = -13$

69. $A^{-1} = \frac{1}{12 - 5}\begin{bmatrix} -4 & -5 \\ -1 & -3 \end{bmatrix}$
$= \frac{1}{7}\begin{bmatrix} -4 & -5 \\ -1 & -3 \end{bmatrix}$

70. $m = \frac{-5 - (-3)}{0 - 1}$
$= \frac{-2}{-1}$
$= 2$

71. $4 + |2x| > 0$
$|2x| > -4$
$2x > -4$ or $2x < 4$
$x > -2$ $\quad$ $x < 2$
all reals

11-2 Arithmetic Series

Pages 659–660 Check for Understanding

1. The sum of a specified group of terms of a sequence.
2. It tells which terms to add and how many.
3. Sample answer: To find terms of a series when the sum is known, but not the last term.

4. 7; 1 − 7 = −6; −11; 4

5. 6; 7.4 − 6 = 1.4; 11.6; 5

6. $d = 38 - 35 = 3$, $35 - 3 = 32$; 3; 44; 5

7. $d = -6 - 12 = -18$, $12 - (-18) = 30$; −18; $-60 + (-18) = -78$; 7

8. $S_n = \frac{n}{2}(a_1 + a_n)$
$= \frac{25}{2}(4 + 100)$
$= 1300$

9. $S_n = \frac{n}{2}[2a_1 + (n-1)d]$
$= \frac{20}{2}[2(40) + (20-1)(-3)]$
$= 10[23]$
$= 230$

10. $a_n = a_1 + (n-1)d$
$52 = 132 + (n-1)(-4)$
$-80 = -4n + 4$
$-84 = -4n$
$21 = n$
$S_{21} = \frac{21}{2}(132 + 52)$
$= 1932$

11. $a_n = a_1 + (n-1)d$
$72 = a_1 + (16-1)5$
$72 = a_1 + 75$
$-3 = a_1$
$S_{16} = \frac{16}{2}(-3 + 72)$
$= 552$

12. $d = 11 - 5 = 6$
$a_n = a_1 + (n-1)d$
$95 = 5 + (n-1)6$
$90 = 6n - 6$
$96 = 6n$
$16 = n$
$S_{16} = \frac{16}{2}(5 + 95)$
$= 800$

13. $d = 35 - 38 = -3$
$a_n = a_1 + (n-1)d$
$2 = 38 + (n-1)(-3)$
$-36 = -3n + 3$
$-39 = -3n$
$13 = n$
$S_{13} = \frac{13}{2}(38 + 2)$
$= 260$

14. 2(1) = 2, 2(2) = 4, 2(3) = 6, 2(4) = 8, 2(5) = 10, 2(6) = 12, 2(7) = 14;
2 + 4 + 6 + 8 + 10 + 12 + 14 = 56

15a. $a_1 = 2$, $a_2 = 4$, $d = 4 - 2 = 2$, $n = 1000$
$S_{1000} = \frac{1000}{2}[2(2) + (1000 - 1)2]$
$= 500[2002]$
$= 1{,}001{,}000$

15b. $a_1 = 3$, $a_2 = 6$, $d = 6 - 3 = 3$, $n = \frac{999}{3} = 333$
$S_{333} = \frac{333}{2}[2(3) + (333 - 1)3]$
$= \frac{333}{2}[1002]$
$= 166{,}833$

Pages 660–661 Exercises

16. $S_8 = \frac{8}{2}(7 + 79)$
$= 344$

17. $S_{26} = \frac{26}{2}(58 + (-7))$
$= 663$

18. $S_{19} = \frac{19}{2}(43 + 115)$
$= 1501$

19. $S_{21} = \frac{21}{2}(76 + 176)$
$= 2646$

20. $S_9 = \frac{9}{2}[2(7) + (9-1)(-2)]$
$= \frac{9}{2}[-2]$
$= -9$

21. $S_8 = \frac{8}{2}(3 + (-38))$
$= -140$

22. $S_{13} = \frac{13}{2}\left[2(5) + (13-1)\frac{1}{2}\right]$
$= \frac{13}{2}[16]$
$= 104$

23. $S_{13} = \frac{13}{2}\left[2(12) + (13-1)\frac{1}{3}\right]$
$= \frac{13}{2}[28]$
$= 182$

24. $a_n = a_1 + (n-1)d$
$15 = 91 + (n-1)(-4)$
$-76 = -4n + 4$
$-80 = -4n$
$20 = n$
$S_{20} = \frac{20}{2}(91 + 15)$
$= 1060$

25. $a_n = a_1 + (n-1)d$
$72 = a_1 + (18-1)7$
$72 = a_1 + 119$
$-47 = a_1$
$S_{18} = \frac{18}{2}(-47 + 72)$
$= 225$

26. $a_n = a_1 + (n-1)d$
$-64 = a_1 + (21-1)(-3)$
$-64 = a_1 - 60$
$-4 = a_1$
$S_{21} = \frac{21}{2}(-4 + (-64))$
$= -714$

27. $a_n = a_1 + (n-1)d$
$9 = -2 + (n-1)\frac{1}{3}$
$11 = \frac{1}{3}n - \frac{1}{3}$
$\frac{34}{3} = \frac{1}{3}n$
$34 = n$
$S_{34} = \frac{34}{2}(-2 + 9)$
$= 119$

28. $d = 13 - 6 = 7$
$a_n = a_1 + (n-1)d$
$97 = 6 + (n-1)7$
$91 = 7n - 7$
$98 = 7n$
$14 = n$
$S_{14} = \frac{14}{2}(6 + 97)$
$= 721$

29. $d = 14 - 7 = 7$
$a_n = a_1 + (n-1)d$
$98 = 7 + (n-1)7$
$91 = 7n - 7$
$98 = 7n$
$14 = n$
$S_{14} = \frac{14}{2}(7 + 98)$
$= 735$

30. $d = 30 - 34 = -4$
$a_n = a_1 + (n-1)d$
$2 = 34 + (n-1)(-4)$
$-32 = -4n + 4$
$-36 = -4n$
$9 = n$
$S_9 = \frac{9}{2}(34 + 2)$
$= 162$

31. $d = 10 - 16 = -6$
$a_n = a_1 + (n-1)d$
$-50 = 16 + (n-1)(-6)$
$-66 = -6n + 6$
$-72 = -6n$
$12 = n$
$S_{12} = \frac{12}{2}(16 + (-50))$
$= -204$

32. $2(1) + 11 = 13$, $2(2) + 11 = 15$, $2(3) + 11 = 17$, $2(4) + 11 = 19$, $2(5) + 11 = 21$, $2(6) + 11 = 23$; $13 + 15 + 17 + 19 + 21 + 23 = 108$

33. $5(19) - 3 = 92$, $5(20) - 3 = 97$, $5(21) - 3 = 102$, $5(22) - 3 = 107$, $5(23) - 3 = 112$; $92 + 97 + 102 + 107 + 112 = 510$

34. $42 - 9(7) = -21$, $42 - 9(8) = -30$, $42 - 9(9) = -39$, $42 - 9(10) = -48$, $42 - 9(11) = -57$; $-21 - 30 - 39 - 48 - 57 = -195$

35.

$S_n = \frac{n}{2}(a_1 + a_n)$	$a_n = a_1 + (n-1)d$
$2247 = \frac{n}{2}(17 + 197)$	$197 = 17 + (21 - 1)d$
$2247 = 107n$	$180 = 20d$
$21 = n$	$9 = d$

$a_2 = 17 + 9$ or 26, $a_3 = 26 + 9$ or 35; 17, 26, 35

36.

$S_n = \frac{n}{2}(a_1 + a_n)$	$a_n = a_1 + (n-1)d$
$1102 = \frac{19}{2}(a_1 + 103)$	$103 = 13 + (19 - 1)d$
$1102 = \frac{19}{2}a_1 + \frac{1957}{2}$	$90 = 18d$
$\frac{247}{2} = \frac{19}{2}a_1$	$5 = d$
$13 = a_1$	

$a_2 = 13 + 5$ or 18, $a_3 = 18 + 5$ or 23; 13, 18, 23

37.

$S_n = \frac{n}{2}(a_1 + a_n)$	$a_n = a_1 + (n-1)d$
$1023 = \frac{31}{2}(a_1 + 78)$	$78 = -12 + (31 - 1)d$
$1023 = \frac{31}{2}a_1 + 1209$	$90 = 30d$
$-186 = \frac{31}{2}a_1$	$3 = d$
$-12 = a_1$	

$a_2 = -12 + 3 = -9$, $a_3 = -9 + 3 = -6$; $-12, -9, -6$

38.

$S_n = \frac{n}{2}(a_1 + a_n)$	$a_n = a_1 + (n-1)d$
$18{,}423 = \frac{n}{2}(-13 + 427)$	$427 = -13 + (89 - 1)d$
$18{,}423 = 207n$	$440 = 88d$
$89 = n$	$5 = d$

$a_2 = -13 + 5 = -8$, $a_3 = -8 + 5 = -3$; $-13, -8, -3$

39. $d = \frac{2}{5} - \frac{1}{5} = \frac{1}{5}$

$a_n = a_1 + (n-1)d$

$\frac{12}{5} = \frac{1}{5} + (n-1)\frac{1}{5}$

$\frac{11}{5} = \frac{1}{5}n - \frac{1}{5}$

$\frac{12}{5} - \frac{1}{5}n$

$12 = n$

$a_n = a_1 + (n-1)d$

$= \frac{1}{5} + (n-1)\frac{1}{5}$

$= \frac{1}{5}n$

$S_n = \frac{12}{2}\left(\frac{1}{5} + \frac{12}{5}\right)$

$= 6\left(\frac{13}{5}\right)$

$= \frac{78}{5}$

$\sum_{n=1}^{12} \frac{1}{5}n$

40. [2nd] [LIST] [▶] 5 [2nd] [LIST] 5 2 [ALPHA] [N] [+] 5 [,] [ALPHA] [N] [,] 21 [,] 75 [,] 1 [)] [ENTER]; 5555

41. [2nd] [LIST] [▶] 5 [2nd] [LIST] 5 3 [ALPHA] [N] [−] 1 [,] [ALPHA] [N] [,] 10 [,] 50 [,] 1 [)] [ENTER]; 3649

42a. $(3 - 2)^2 = 1$, $(4 - 2)^2 = 4$, $(5 - 2)^2 = 9$, $(6 - 2)^2 = 16$; $1 + 4 + 9 + 16 = 30$

$1^2 = 1$, $2^2 = 4$, $3^2 = 9$, $4^2 = 16$;

$1 + 4 + 9 + 16 = 30$

42b. They describe the same series.

42c. The summation of a series can be expressed in different ways.

43. $65{,}600 = 5000 + 5000 + 5000 + 5000 + [5000 + 5200 + 5400 + \ldots]$

$45{,}600 = 5000 + 5200 + 5400 + \ldots$

$45{,}600 = \frac{n}{2}[2(5000) + (n-1)200]$

$45{,}600 = \frac{n}{2}[10{,}000 + 200n - 200]$

$45{,}600 = \frac{n}{2}[9800 + 200n]$

$45{,}600 = 4900n + 100n^2$

$0 = 100(n^2 + 49n - 456)$

$0 = (n + 57)(n - 8)$

$n + 57 = 0$ or $n - 8 = 0$

$n = -57$ $\quad n = 8$; n cannot be negative

$n = 8 + 4 = 12$; 12 days

44. $a_1 = 20$, $d = 1$, $n = 24$

$S_n = \frac{24}{2}[2(20) + (24 - 1)1]$

$= 12[63]$

$= 756$; 756 seats

45. $d = 60 - 20 = 40$

$a_n = 20 + (20 - 1)40$

$= 780$; 780 feet

46. $4.3^{3x+1} = 78.5$

$\log 4.3^{3x+1} = \log 78.5$

$(3x + 1) \log 4.3 = \log 78.5$

$3x + 1 = \frac{\log 78.5}{\log 4.3}$

$3x + 1 \approx \frac{1.8949}{0.6335}$

$3x \approx 1.9913$

$x \approx 0.6638$

47. -2.8824

48. $\frac{x}{15} + \frac{x}{20} = 1$

$60\left(\frac{x}{15} + \frac{x}{20}\right) = 60(1)$

$4x + 3x = 60$

$7x = 60$

$x = \frac{60}{7}$ or $8\frac{4}{7}$; $8\frac{4}{7}$ hours

49. even; 2

50. $x - y = -2$

$x + 2 = y$

$\frac{(x-2)^2}{16} + \frac{y^2}{16} = 1$

$(x - 2)^2 + y^2 = 16$

$(x - 2)^2 + (x + 2)^2 = 16$

$x^2 - 4x + 4 + x^2 + 4x + 4 = 16$

$2x^2 - 8 = 0$

$2x^2 = 8$

$x^2 = 4$

$x = \pm 2$

$x + 2 = y$, $2 + 2 = y$, $4 = y$; (2, 4)

$x + 2 = y$, $-2 + 2 = y$, $0 = y$; $(-2, 0)$

51. $f(x) = (x + 2)^2 - 6$

$= x^2 + 4x + 4 - 6$

$= x^2 + 4x - 2$; x^2; $4x$; -2

52a. 0.3, 0.5, 0.6, 0.6, 0.6, 0.6, 0.8, 0.8, 1.0, 1.0, 2.0, 2.3, 3.7; $3.7 - 0.3 = 3.4$

52b. Q_2 is the 7th value = 0.8; Q_1 is between 3rd and 4th values, $\frac{0.6 + 0.6}{2} = 0.6$; Q_3 is between 10th and 11th values, $\frac{1.0 + 2.0}{2} = 1.5$

52c. IR = 1.5 − 0.6 = 0.9

52d. outliers: below 0.6 − 1.5(0.9) = −0.75 or above 1.5 + 1.5(0.9) = 2.85; 3.7

52e.

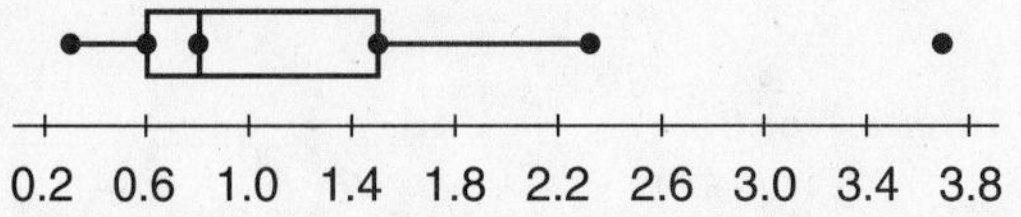

11-3 Geometric Sequences

Pages 666–667 Check for Understanding

1. Each successive term of a geometric sequence is found by multiplying the previous term by a number instead of adding a number to the previous term as in an arithmetic sequence.
2. The common ratio is the factor relating two consecutive terms of a geometric sequence.
3. Find the ratio between each pair of terms. If all pairs have the same ratio, the sequence is a geometric sequence.
4. Sample answer: Let $a_1 = 324$, so 12 would be a_4. Use the general formula for the *n*th term of a geometric sequence to find the value of *r* and then use that value to find the missing terms: 108 and 36. $\left(12 = 324r^{4-1}, \frac{1}{27} = r^3, \frac{1}{3} = r\right)$
5. No, if *r* is negative, the points do not fall into this pattern.
6. $\frac{20}{5} = 4, \frac{80}{20} = 4, \frac{320}{80} = 4$; yes, 4
7. $\frac{-15}{3} = -5, \frac{75}{-15} = -5, \frac{-375}{75} = -5$; yes, −5
8. $\frac{20}{5} = 4, \frac{35}{20} = \frac{7}{4}, \frac{50}{35} = \frac{10}{7}$; no
9. $\frac{4}{9} \div \frac{2}{3} = \frac{4}{9} \cdot \frac{3}{2} = \frac{2}{3}, \frac{8}{27} \div \frac{4}{9} = \frac{8}{27} \cdot \frac{9}{4} = \frac{2}{3}, \frac{16}{81} \div \frac{8}{27} = \frac{16}{81} \cdot \frac{27}{8} = \frac{2}{3}$; yes, $\frac{2}{3}$
10. $r = \frac{30}{20}$ or $\frac{3}{2}$; $45 \cdot \frac{3}{2} = 67.5$, $67.5 \cdot \frac{3}{2} = 101.25$; 67.5, 101.25
11. $r = \frac{-1}{\frac{1}{2}}$ or −2; −1(−2) = 2, 2(−2) = −4; 2, −4
12. −2 · 3 = −6, −6 · 3 = −18, −18 · 3 = −54, −54 · 3 = −162; −2, −6, −18, −54, −162
13. $a_4 = 7(2)^{4-1}$
 $= 56$
14. $32 = a_1(-0.5)^{3-1}$
 $32 = a_1(0.25)$
 $128 = a_1$
 $a_6 = 128(-0.5)^{6-1}$
 $= -4$
15. $r = \frac{30}{60} = \frac{1}{2}$
 $a_9 = 60\left(\frac{1}{2}\right)^{9-1}$
 $= \frac{60}{256}$ or $\frac{15}{64}$

16a. $a_1 = 1, a_4 = 8$
$8 = 1 \cdot r^{4-1}$
$8 = r^3$
$2 = r$
1 · 2 = 2, 2 · 2 = 4; 2, 4

16b.

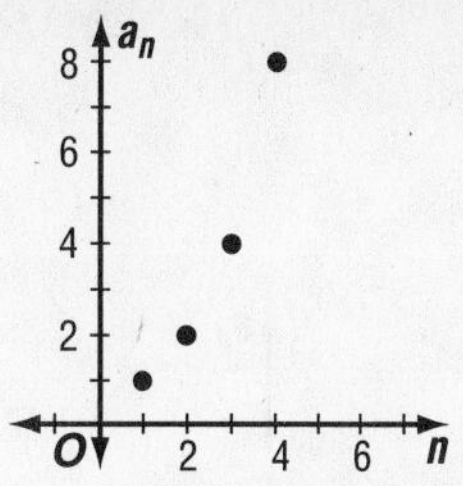

17. 5 · 2 = 10, 10 · 2 = 20,
 20 · 2 = 40, 40 · 2 = 80,
 80 · 2 = 160, 160 · 2 = 320;
 5 + 10 + 20 + 40 + 80 + 160 + 320 = 635

Page 667–669 Exercises

18. $r = \frac{135}{405}$ or $\frac{1}{3}$
 $45 \cdot \frac{1}{3} = 15$,
 $15 \cdot \frac{1}{3} = 5$; 15, 5
19. $r = \frac{108}{81}$ or $\frac{4}{3}$
 $144 \cdot \frac{4}{3} = 192$,
 $192 \cdot \frac{4}{3} = 256$; 192, 256
20. $r = \frac{24}{16}$ or $\frac{3}{2}$
 $36 \cdot \frac{3}{2} = 54$,
 $54 \cdot \frac{3}{2} = 81$; 54, 81
21. $r = \frac{108}{162}$ or $\frac{2}{3}$
 $72 \cdot \frac{2}{3} = 48$,
 $48 \cdot \frac{2}{3} = 32$; 48, 32
22. $r = -\frac{4}{9} \div \frac{4}{27}$
 $= -\frac{4}{9} \cdot \frac{27}{4}$
 $= -3$
 $\frac{4}{3}(-3) = -4$
 $-4(-3) = 12$; −4, 12
23. $r = -\frac{16}{64}$ or $-\frac{1}{4}$
 $4\left(-\frac{1}{4}\right) = -1$
 $-1\left(-\frac{1}{4}\right) = \frac{1}{4}$; −1, $\frac{1}{4}$
24. 2(−3) = −6, −6(−3) = 18, 18(−3) = −54, −54(−3) = 162; 2, −6, 18, −54, 162
25. $243\left(\frac{1}{3}\right) = 81, 81\left(\frac{1}{3}\right) = 27, 27\left(\frac{1}{3}\right) = 9$,
 $9\left(\frac{1}{3}\right) = 3$; 243, 81, 27, 9, 3
26. 576(−0.5) = −288, −288(−0.5) = 144, 144(−0.5) = −72, −72(−0.5) = 36; 576, −288, 144, −72, 36
27. $a_8 = \frac{1}{3}(3)^{8-1}$
 $= 729$
28. $a_9 = \frac{1}{64}(4)^{9-1}$
 $= 1024$
29. $a_6 = 16{,}807\left(\frac{3}{7}\right)^{6-1}$
 $= 243$
30. $a_8 = 4096\left(\frac{1}{4}\right)^{8-1}$
 $= \frac{1}{4}$
31. $16 = a_1(0.5)^{4-1}$
 $16 = a_1(0.125)$
 $128 = a_1$
 $a_8 = 128(0.5)^{8-1}$
 $= 1$
32. $3 = a_1(2)^{6-1}$
 $3 = a_1(32)$
 $\frac{3}{32} = a_1$
 $a_{12} = \left(\frac{3}{32}\right)(2)^{12-1}$
 $= 192$
33. $r = \frac{1}{\frac{1}{5}}$ or 5
 $a_9 = \frac{1}{5}(5)^{9-1}$
 $= 78{,}125$
34. $r = \frac{1}{16} \div \frac{1}{32}$
 $= \frac{1}{16} \cdot \frac{32}{1}$
 $= 2$
 $a_7 = \left(\frac{1}{32}\right)(2)^{7-1}$
 $= 2$
35. $r = -\frac{12}{4}$ or −3
 $a_8 = 4(-3)^{8-1}$
 $= -8748$

36. $r = \frac{90}{540}$ or $\frac{1}{6}$

$a_6 = 540\left(\frac{1}{6}\right)^{6-1}$

$= \frac{540}{7776}$ or $\frac{5}{72}$

37. $144 = 9(r)^{5-1}$

$16 = r^4$

$\pm 2 = r$

$9(\pm 2) = \pm 18$

$(\pm 18)(\pm 2) = 36$

$36(\pm 2) = \pm 72$

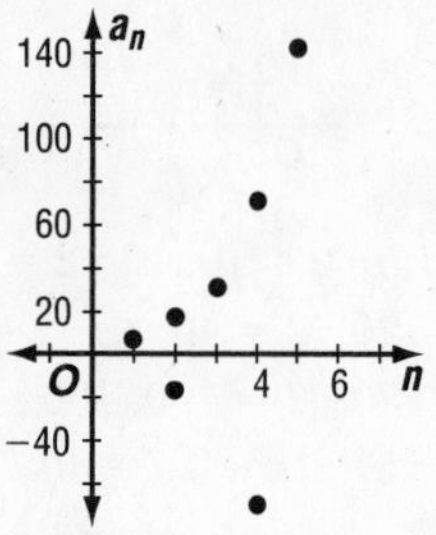

38. $324 = 4(r)^{5-1}$

$81 = r^4$

$\pm 3 = r$

$4(\pm 3) = \pm 12$

$(\pm 12)(\pm 3) = 36$

$36(\pm 3) = \pm 108$

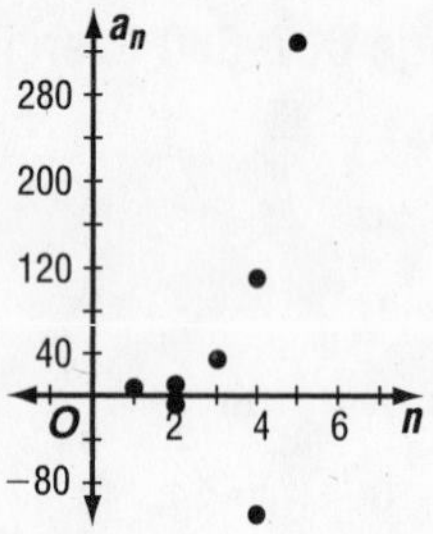

39. $1 = 32(r)^{6-1}$

$\frac{1}{32} = r^5$

$\frac{1}{2} = r$

$32\left(\frac{1}{2}\right) = 16$

$16\left(\frac{1}{2}\right) = 8$

$8\left(\frac{1}{2}\right) = 4$

$4\left(\frac{1}{2}\right) = 2$

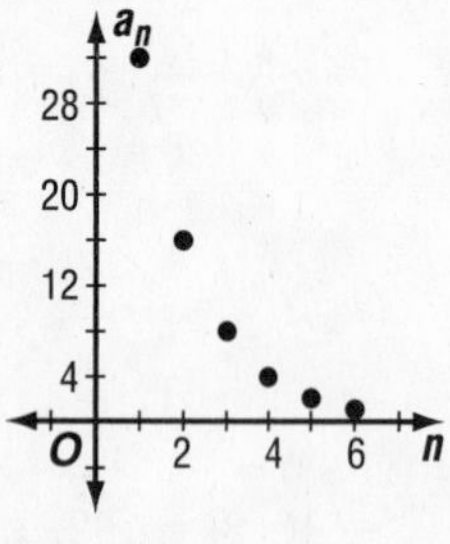

40. $96 = 12(r)^{4-1}$

$8 = r^3$

$2 = r$

$12 \div 2 = 6$

$6 \div 2 = 3$

$12(2) = 24$

$24(2) = 48$

3, 6, 24, 48

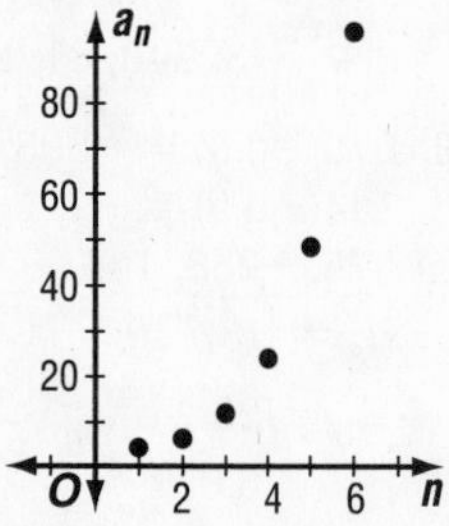

41. $r = \frac{8}{2}$ or 4

$32(4) = 5y + 3$

$128 = 5y + 3$

$125 = 5y$

$25 = y$

42. $r = \frac{6}{3}$ or 2

$6(2) = 2y + 18$

$12 = 2y + 18$

$-6 = 2y$

$-3 = y$

43. $r = \frac{y}{y+1}$

$y\left(\frac{y}{y+1}\right) = y - 4$

$\frac{y^2}{y+1} = y - 4$

$y^2 = y^2 - 3y - 4$

$0 = -3y - 4$

$4 = -3y$

$-\frac{4}{3} = y$

44. $r = \frac{2y-1}{y+1}$

$2y - 1\left(\frac{2y-1}{y+1}\right) = 4y - 3$

$\frac{4y^2 - 4y + 1}{y+1} = 4y - 3$

$4y^2 - 4y + 1 = 4y^2 + y - 3$

$-4y + 1 = y - 3$

$-5y = -4$

$y = \frac{4}{5}$

45. $r = \frac{4}{2}$ or 2

$a_n = 2 \cdot 2^{n-1}$

$= 2^n$

46. $r = \frac{12}{36}$ or $\frac{1}{3}$

$a_n = 36\left(\frac{1}{3}\right)^{n-1}$

47. $r = \frac{100}{-20}$ or -5

$a_n = \frac{4}{25}(-5)^{n-1}$

48a. $a_7 = 0.6(4)^{7-1}$

$= 2457.6$

48b. $a_n = 0.6(4)^{n-1}$

49. Clear L_1, L_2, and Y=. [2nd] [LIST] 5 [ALPHA] [N] [,] [ALPHA] [N] [,] 1 [,] 5 [,] 1 [)] [STO▸] [2nd] [L1] [ENTER] [2nd] [LIST] 5 2 [×] 2 [^] [(] [ALPHA] [N] [−] 1 [)] [,] [ALPHA] [N] [,] 1 [,] 5 [,] 1 [)] [STO▸] [2nd] [L2] [ENTER]

WINDOW: [−1, 7] by [−5, 35] with Xscl = 1, Yscl = 5. [2nd] [STAT PLOT] [ENTER] [ENTER] [GRAPH]

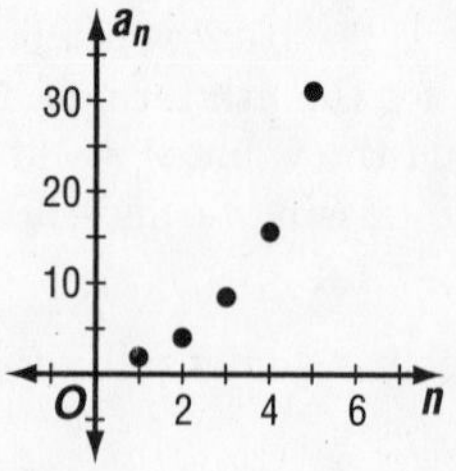

2, 4, 8, 16, 32

50. Clear L_1, L_2, and Y=. [2nd] [LIST] 5 [ALPHA] [N] [,] [ALPHA] [N] [,] 1 [,] 10 [,] 1 [)] [STO▸] [2nd] [L1] [ENTER] [2nd] [LIST] 5 12 [×] .5 [^] [(] [ALPHA] [N] [−] 1 [)] [,] [ALPHA] [N] [,] 1 [,] 10 [,] 1 [)] [STO▸] [2nd] [L2] [ENTER]

WINDOW: [−2, 14] by [−2, 14] with Xscl = 2, Yscl = 2. [2nd] [STAT PLOT] [ENTER] [ENTER] [GRAPH]

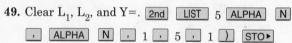

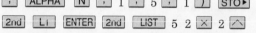

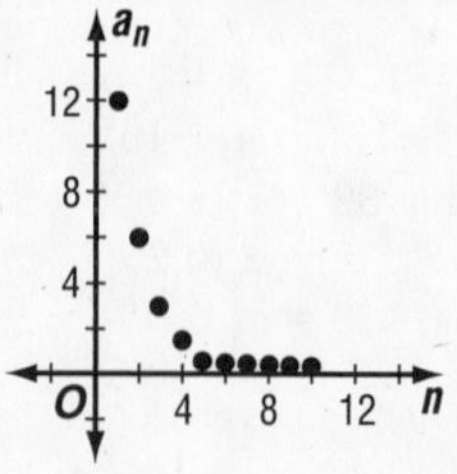

12, 6, 3, 1.5, 0.75, 0.375, 0.1875, 0.09375, 0.046875, 0.0234375

51. Clear L_1, L_2, and Y=. [2nd] [LIST] 5 [ALPHA] [N] [,] [ALPHA] [N] [,] 1 [,] 8 [,] 1 [)] [STO▸] [2nd] [L1] [ENTER] [2nd] [LIST] 5 243 [×] [(] 1 [÷] 3 [)] [^] [(] [ALPHA] [N] [−] 1 [)] [,] [ALPHA] [N] [,] 1 [,] 8 [,] 1 [)] [STO▸] [2nd] [L2] [ENTER] WINDOW: [−1, 8] by [−40, 280] with Xscl = 1, Yscl = 40. [2nd] [STAT PLOT] [ENTER] [ENTER] [GRAPH]

243, 81, 27, 9, 3, 1, $\frac{1}{3}$, $\frac{1}{9}$

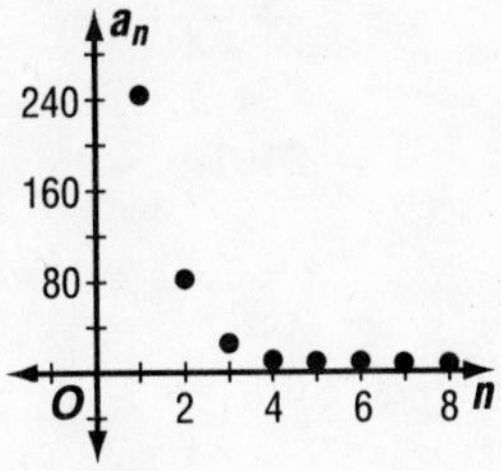

52. $r = \frac{b}{a}$

$c = b \cdot \frac{b}{a}$

$= \frac{b^2}{a}$

53. Sample answer: In a geometric sequence, each subsequent term can be found by multiplying the preceding term by r. So the nth term of a sequence a_n would equal $a_{n-1}r$. Each term of the sequence can be expressed in terms of the first term. The second term is $a_1 \times r$, the third term is $a_1 \times r \times r$ or a_1r^2, the fourth term is $a_1 \times r \times r \times r$ or a_1r^3, and so on. Notice each term is a product of a_1 and $n-1$ factors of r. So the nth term would be a_1r^{n-1}. Since $a_{n-1}r$ and a_1r^{n-1} both describe the nth term, they are equivalent.

54. Yes, both sequences have the same value of r.

55. $1000 \cdot \frac{1}{5} = 200$, $1000 - 200 = 800$;

$800 \cdot \frac{1}{5} = 160$; $800 - 160 = 640$;

$640 \cdot \frac{1}{5} = 128$, $640 - 128 = 512$;

$512 \cdot \frac{1}{5} = 102.4$; $512 - 102.4 = 409.6$;

$409.6 \cdot \frac{1}{5} = 81.92$, $409.6 - 81.92 = 327.68$;

$327.68 \cdot \frac{1}{5} = 65.536$; $327.68 - 65.536 = 262.144$;

262.144 pounds

56. $n = 6$

$a_6 = 64\left(\frac{1}{2}\right)^{6-1}$

$= 2$; 2 milligrams

57a. $a_5 = 320(0.99)^{5-1}$

≈ 307; 307 mg/L

57b. $320 \times 0.75 = 240$

$$240 = 320(0.99)^{n-1}$$
$$\frac{3}{4} = 0.99^{n-1}$$
$$\log \frac{3}{4} = \log 0.99^{n-1}$$
$$\log 3 - \log 4 = (n - 1) \log 0.99$$
$$\frac{\log 3 - \log 4}{\log 0.99} = n - 1$$
$$28.624 \approx n - 1$$
$$29.624 \approx n; \text{ 29 tiers}$$

57c.
$$200 = 320(0.99)^{n-1}$$
$$\frac{5}{8} = 0.99^{n-1}$$
$$\log \frac{5}{8} = \log 0.99^{n-1}$$
$$\log 5 - \log 8 = (n - 1) \log 0.99$$
$$\frac{\log 5 - \log 8}{\log 0.99} = n - 1$$
$$46.765 \approx n - 1$$
$$47.765 \approx n; \text{ at most 47 tiers}$$

58. $S_{23} = \frac{23}{2}(11 + 44)$

$= 632.5$

59.
$$\log_5 4 + \log_5 x = \log_5 36$$
$$\log_5 4x = \log_5 36$$
$$4x = 36$$
$$x = 9$$

60.
$$\frac{4800}{90{,}000} = \frac{x}{219{,}000}$$
$$90{,}000x = 1{,}051{,}200{,}000$$
$$x = 11{,}680; \$11{,}680$$

61.
$$x - 7\sqrt{x} - 8 = 0$$
$$\left(x^{\frac{1}{2}}\right)^2 - 7\left(x^{\frac{1}{2}}\right) - 8 = 0$$
$$\left(x^{\frac{1}{2}} - 8\right)\left(x^{\frac{1}{2}} + 1\right) = 0$$
$$x^{\frac{1}{2}} - 8 = 0 \text{ or } x^{\frac{1}{2}} + 1 = 0$$
$$x^{\frac{1}{2}} = 8 \qquad x^{\frac{1}{2}} = -1$$
$$\left(x^{\frac{1}{2}}\right)^2 = (8)^2 \qquad \left(x^{\frac{1}{2}}\right)^2 = (-1)^2$$
$$x = 64 \qquad x = 1$$

Check:
$$x - 7\sqrt{x} - 8 = 0$$
$$64 - 7\sqrt{64} - 8 \stackrel{?}{=} 0$$
$$64 - 56 - 8 \stackrel{?}{=} 0$$
$$0 = 0 \checkmark$$
$$x - 7\sqrt{x} - 8 = 0$$
$$1 - 7\sqrt{1} - 8 \stackrel{?}{=} 0$$
$$1 - 7 - 8 \stackrel{?}{=} 0$$
$$-14 \neq 0$$

62. $f(x) = x^4 - 8x^2 + 10$

x	$f(x)$
−3	19
−2	−6
−1	3
0	10

x	$f(x)$
1	3
2	−6
3	19

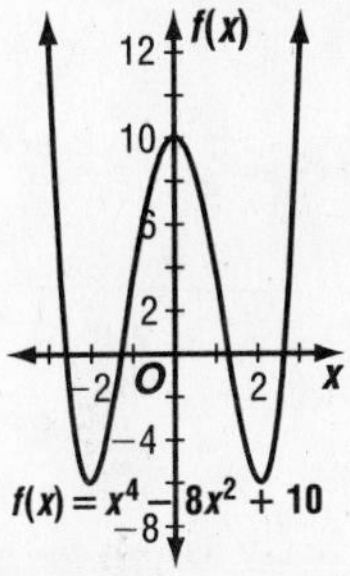

63.
$$\sqrt{(x - 7)^2 + (y + 7)^2} = \sqrt{(x + 2)^2 + (y - y)^2}$$
$$(x - 7)^2 + (y + 7)^2 = (x + 2)^2$$
$$x^2 - 14x + 49 + (y + 7)^2 = x^2 + 4x + 4$$
$$(y + 7)^2 = 18x - 45$$
$$(y + 7)^2 + 45 = 18x$$
$$\frac{1}{18}(y + 7)^2 + \frac{5}{2} = x$$

64. $(x - 7)(x + 2) > 0$

$x - 7 > 0$ and $x + 2 > 0$ or $x - 7 < 0$ and $x + 2 < 0$

$x > 7$ $\quad x > -2$ $\quad x < 7$ $\quad x < -2$

$x > 7$ or $x < -2$

$\{x \mid x < -2 \text{ or } x > 7\}$

65. $(5 + \boldsymbol{i})(2 - 3\boldsymbol{i}) = 10 - 15\boldsymbol{i} + 2\boldsymbol{i} - 3\boldsymbol{i}^2$

$= 13 - 13\boldsymbol{i}$

66. $3y^2 + 5y + 2 = (3y + 2)(y + 1)$

67. Let x = number at Heathrow and $x + 7.2$ = number at O'Hare.

$x + x + 7.2 = 55.2$

$2x = 48$

$x = 24$; 24 million at Heathrow

$x + 7.2 = 31.2$; 31.2 million at O'Hare

11-4 Geometric Series

Page 673 Check for Understanding

1. Both are the sums of the terms of a sequence.

2a. $S_n = \frac{a_1 - a_1 r^n}{1 - r}$ 2b. $S_n = \frac{a_1 - a_n r}{1 - r}$

2c. $S_n = a_1 n$

3. $a_1 = 1$, $r = -\frac{3}{1}$ or -3, and $n = 6$; $\sum_{n=1}^{6} (-3)^{n-1}$

4. no change

5. 6, $r = -\frac{18}{6}$ or -3, -162, 4

6. 7, $r = \frac{3.5}{7}$ or 0.5, 0.875, 4

7. $r = \frac{36}{12}$ or 3, $a_1 = 12 \div 3$ or 4, 3, 324, 5

8. $r = -\frac{36}{18}$ or -2, $a_1 = 18 \div (-2)$ or -9, -2, $a_5 = 72(-2)$ or -144, 5

9. $S_5 = \frac{12 - 972(-3)}{1 - (-3)} = \frac{2928}{4} = 732$

10. $S_n = \frac{3 - (46{,}875)(-5)}{1 - (-5)} = \frac{234{,}378}{6} = 39{,}063$

11. $S_{14} = \frac{5 - 5(2^{14})}{1 - 2} = \frac{-81{,}915}{-1} = 81{,}915$

12. $S_5 = \frac{243 - 243\left(-\frac{2}{3}\right)^5}{1 - \left(-\frac{2}{3}\right)} = \frac{275}{\frac{5}{3}} = 165$

13. $r = \frac{36}{54}$ or $\frac{2}{3}$

$S_6 = \frac{54 - 54\left(\frac{2}{3}\right)^6}{1 - \frac{2}{3}} = \frac{\frac{35{,}910}{729}}{\frac{1}{3}} = \frac{35{,}910}{243} = \frac{1330}{9}$ or $147\frac{7}{9}$

14. $r = -\frac{6}{3}$ or -2

$S_7 = \frac{3 - 3(-2)7}{1 - (-2)} = \frac{387}{3} = 129$

15. $81\left(\frac{1}{3}\right)^{1-1} = 81$, $81\left(\frac{1}{3}\right)^{2-1} = 27$, $81\left(\frac{1}{3}\right)^{3-1} = 9$, $81\left(\frac{1}{3}\right)^{4-1} = 3$, $81\left(\frac{1}{3}\right)^{5-1} = 1$, $81\left(\frac{1}{3}\right)^{6-1} = \frac{1}{3}$, $81\left(\frac{1}{3}\right)^{7-1} = \frac{1}{9}$;

$81 + 27 + 9 + 3 + 1 + \frac{1}{3} + \frac{1}{9} = 121\frac{4}{9}$

16. $S_5 = \frac{1 - 1(3)^5}{1 - 3} = \frac{-242}{-2} = 121$; 121 inches or about 10 feet

Pages 674–675 Exercises

17. $S_5 = \frac{625 - 625\left(\frac{3}{5}\right)^5}{1 - \frac{3}{5}} = \frac{576.4}{\frac{2}{5}} = 1441$

18. $S_8 = \frac{4 - 4(0.5)^8}{1 - 0.5} = \frac{3.984375}{0.5} = 7.96875$

19. $S_{12} = \frac{5 - 5(3)^{12}}{1 - 3} = \frac{-2{,}657{,}200}{-2} = 1{,}328{,}600$

20. $S_5 = \frac{2401 - 2401\left(-\frac{1}{7}\right)^5}{1 - \left(-\frac{1}{7}\right)} = \frac{2401.142857}{\frac{8}{7}} = 2101$

21. $S_5 = \frac{4 - 4(-3)^5}{1 - (-3)} = \frac{976}{4} = 244$

22. $S_8 = \frac{625 - 625(0.4)^8}{1 - 0.4} = \frac{624.5904}{0.6} = 1040.984$

23. $S_5 = \frac{1296 - 1\left(-\frac{1}{6}\right)}{1 - \left(-\frac{1}{6}\right)} = \frac{1296\frac{1}{6}}{\frac{7}{6}} = 1111$

24. $S_8 = \frac{3 - 384(2)}{1 - 2} = \frac{-765}{-1} = 765$

25. $S_4 = \frac{343 - (-1)\left(-\frac{1}{7}\right)}{1 - \left(-\frac{1}{7}\right)} = \frac{342\frac{6}{7}}{\frac{8}{7}} = 300$

26. $S_{10} = \frac{64 - \left(-\frac{1}{8}\right)\left(-\frac{1}{6}\right)}{1 - \left(-\frac{1}{6}\right)} = \frac{63\frac{47}{48}}{\frac{7}{6}} = 54\frac{47}{56}$

27. $S_6 = \frac{4 - 0.125(0.5)}{1 - 0.5} = \frac{3.9375}{0.5} = 7.875$

28. $a_5 = a_2 \cdot r^3$

$972 = (-36)(r^3)$

$-27 = r^3$

$-3 = r$

$a_1 = \frac{-36}{-3}$ or 12

$S_7 = \frac{12 - 12(-3)^7}{1 - (-3)} = \frac{26256}{4} = 6564$

29. $r = \frac{100}{250}$ or $\frac{2}{5}$

$a_1 = 250 \div \frac{2}{5} = 625$

$S_8 = \frac{625 - 625\left(\frac{2}{5}\right)^8}{1 - \frac{2}{5}} = \frac{624.5904}{\frac{3}{5}} = 1040.984$

30. $a_6 = a_3 \cdot r^3$

$-972 = -36 \cdot r^3$

$27 = r^3$

$3 = r$

$a_1 = -36 \div 3 \div 3 = -4$

$S_{10} = \frac{-4 - (-4)(3)^{10}}{1 - 3} = \frac{236{,}192}{-2} = -118{,}096$

31. $r = 1$
$S = 12(12)$
$= 144$

32. $r = \frac{21}{7}$ or 3
$S_{10} = \frac{7 - 7(3)^{10}}{1 - 3}$
$= \frac{-413{,}336}{-2}$
$= 206{,}668$

33. $r = \frac{-343}{2401}$ or $-\frac{1}{7}$
$S_5 = \frac{2401 - 2401\left(-\frac{1}{7}\right)^5}{1 - \left(-\frac{1}{7}\right)}$
$= \frac{2401.142857}{\frac{8}{7}}$
$= 2101$

34. $r = \frac{-\frac{1}{3}}{\frac{1}{9}} = -3$
$S_6 = \frac{\frac{1}{9} - \frac{1}{9}(-3)^6}{1 - (-3)}$
$= \frac{-\frac{728}{9}}{4}$
$= -\frac{182}{9}$

35. $5(2)^{1-1} = 5$, $5(2)^{2-1} = 10$, $5(2)^{3-1} = 20$, $5(2)^{4-1} = 40$, $5(2)^{5-1} = 80$, $5(2)^{6-1} = 160$, $5(2)^{7-1} = 320$, $5(2)^{8-1} = 640$, $5(2)^{9-1} = 1280$; $5 + 10 + 20 + 40 + 80 + 160 + 320 + 640 + 1280 = 2555$

36. $64\left(\frac{3}{4}\right)^{1-1} = 64$, $64\left(\frac{3}{4}\right)^{2-1} = 48$, $64\left(\frac{3}{4}\right)^{3-1} = 36$, $64\left(\frac{3}{4}\right)^{4-1} = 27$, $64\left(\frac{3}{4}\right)^{5-1} = 20\frac{1}{4}$, $64\left(\frac{3}{4}\right)^{6-1} = 15\frac{3}{16}$, $64\left(\frac{3}{4}\right)^{7-1} = 11\frac{25}{64}$, $64\left(\frac{3}{4}\right)^{8-1} = 8\frac{139}{256}$; $64 + 48 + 36 + 27 + 20\frac{1}{4} + 15\frac{3}{16} + 11\frac{25}{64} + 8\frac{139}{256} = 230\frac{95}{256}$

37. $2(-3)^{1-1} = 2$, $2(-3)^{2-1} = -6$, $2(-3)^{3-1} = 18$, $2(-3)^{4-1} = -54$, $2(-3)^{5-1} = 162$, $2(-3)^{6-1} = -486$; $2 - 6 + 18 - 54 + 162 - 486 = -364$

38. $Sn = \frac{a_1(1 - r^n)}{1 - r}$
$-364 = \frac{a_1(1 - (-3)^6)}{1 - (-3)}$
$-364 = \frac{a_1(-728)}{4}$
$-1456 = a_1(-728)$
$2 = a_1$

39. $S_n = \frac{a_1(1 - r^n)}{1 - r}$
$\frac{215}{64} = \frac{a_1\left(1 - \left(-\frac{1}{2}\right)^7\right)}{1 - \left(-\frac{1}{2}\right)}$
$\frac{215}{64} = \frac{a_1(1.0078125)}{\frac{3}{2}}$
$\frac{645}{128} = a_1(1.0078125)$
$5 = a_1$

40. $S_n = \frac{a_1 - a_n r}{1 - r}$
$315 = \frac{a_1 - 5(0.5)}{1 - 0.5}$
$157.5 = a_1 - 2.5$
$160 = a_1$

41. $S_n = \frac{a_1 - a_n r}{1 - r}$
$165 = \frac{a_1 - 48\left(-\frac{2}{3}\right)}{1 - \left(-\frac{2}{3}\right)}$
$275 = a_1 + 32$
$243 = a_1$

42. $r = \frac{15}{75}$ or $\frac{1}{5}$
$a_n = 75\left(\frac{1}{5}\right)^{n-1}$
$\sum_{n=1}^{10} 75\left(\frac{1}{5}\right)^{n-1}$
$S_{10} = \frac{75 - 75\left(\frac{1}{5}\right)^{10}}{1 - \left(\frac{1}{5}\right)}$
$= \frac{74.99999232}{\frac{4}{5}}$
≈ 93.75

43. $r = \frac{162}{243}$ or $\frac{2}{3}$
$a_n = 243\left(\frac{2}{3}\right)^{n-1}$
$\sum_{n=1}^{12} 243\left(\frac{2}{3}\right)^{n-1}$
$S_{12} = \frac{243 - 243\left(\frac{2}{3}\right)^{12}}{1 - \frac{2}{3}}$
$= \frac{241.1271148}{\frac{1}{3}}$
≈ 723.38

44. [2nd] [LIST] [▶] 5 [2nd] [LIST] 5 [(] 1 [÷] 3 [)] [(] 4 [÷] 3 [)] [^] [(] [ALPHA] [N] [−] 1 [)] [,] [ALPHA] [N] [,] 1 [,] 10 [,] 1 [)] [ENTER]
16.75772663

45. [2nd] [LIST] [▶] 5 [2nd] [LIST] 5 [(] 3 [)] [(] [(−)] 2 [)] [^] [(] [ALPHA] [N] [−] 1 [)] [,] [ALPHA] [N] [,] 1 [,] 20 [,] 1 [)] [ENTER]
−1,048,575

46.

	Sequence	Sum of First 5 Terms	Sum of First 10 Terms	Sum of First 15 Terms	Sum of First 20 Terms
A:	75 + 15 + 3 + . . .	93.72	93.7499904	93.75	93.75
B:	1 + 2 + 4 + 8 + . . .	31	1023	32,767	1,048,575
C:	$a_1 = 25$, $r = 2$	775	25,575	819,175	26,214,375
D:	$a_1 = 4$, $r = 0.5$	7.75	7.9921875	7.999755859	7.999992371

46a. A levels out to 93.75; B and C get increasingly larger; D gets closer to 8.

46b. B and C would continue to increase; A would be 93.75; D would be close to 8.

46c. If $r > 1$, sum gets larger and larger. If $0 < r < 1$, the sum approaches a number.

47a. $S_{10} = \frac{1 - 1(2)^{10}}{1 - 2}$
$= 1023$; 1023 pennies or $10.23
$S_{20} = \frac{1 - 1(2)^{20}}{1 - 2}$
$= 1048575$; l048575 pennies or $10,485.75

47b. The amount you have to put away each day exceeds the funds available to anyone.

48. $S_{10} = \frac{4 - 4(0.40)^{10}}{1 - 0.40}$
$= \frac{3.99958057}{0.6}$
≈ 6.67; 6.67 inches

49. $r = \frac{54}{9}$ or 6
$a_2 = \frac{3}{2} \div 6$
$= \frac{1}{4}$
$a_1 = \frac{1}{4} \div 6$
$= \frac{1}{24}$

50. $a_{11} = -3 + (11 - 1)(-9)$
$= -93$

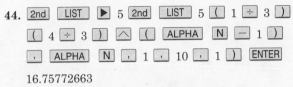

51. $6^x = 216$

$\log 6^x = \log 216$

$x \cdot \log 6 = \log 216$

$x = \dfrac{\log 216}{\log 6}$

$x = 3$

52.

0	12	4	−3	−1	0
		0	0	0	0
$-\frac{1}{3}$	12	4	−3	−1	0
		−4	0	1	
	12	0	−3	0	

$12x^2 - 3 = 0$

$x^2 = \frac{1}{4}$

$x = \pm\frac{1}{2}$

$0, -\frac{1}{3}, \frac{1}{2}, -\frac{1}{2}$

53. $x^2 + y^2 - 3x + 8y = 20$

$\left(x^2 - 3x + \frac{9}{4}\right) + (y^2 + 8y + 16) = 20 + \frac{9}{4} + 16$

$\left(y - \frac{3}{2}\right)^2 + (y + 4)^2 = 38\frac{1}{4}$

$\left(\frac{3}{2}, -4\right)$; $r = \sqrt{38\frac{1}{4}}$ or about 6.2 units

54. $\bar{x} = \dfrac{2(49) + 2(54) + 61 + 51 + 56 + 58}{8}$

$= \frac{432}{8}$ or 54

$\text{SD} = \sqrt{\dfrac{2(49-54)^2 + 2(54-54)^2 + (61-54)^2 + (51-54)^2 + (56-54)^2 + (58-54)^2}{8}}$

$= \sqrt{\dfrac{50 + 0 + 49 + 9 + 4 + 16}{8}}$

$= 4$; 4 centimeters

55. $f(x,y) = 3x + 2y$

$f(5, 2) = 3(5) + 2(-2)$

$= 11$

56. $|x - 15| < 45$

$-45 < x - 15 < 45$

$-30 < \quad x \quad < 60$

$\{x \mid -30 < x < 60\}$

Page 675 Self–Test

1. $a_{14} = 7 + (14 - 1)3$

$= 46$

2. $a_8 = 2 + (8 - 1)\left(\frac{1}{2}\right)$

$= \frac{11}{2}$

3. $d = 12 - 6$ or 6

$a_n = a_1 + (n - 1)d$

$96 = 6 + (n - 1)6$

$90 = 6n - 6$

$96 = 6n$

$16 = n$

$S_{16} = \frac{16}{2}(6 + 96)$

$= 816$

4. $2(1) - 1 = 1$, $2(2) - 1 = 3$,

$d = 3 - 1$ or 2

$S_{30} = \frac{30}{2}[2(1) + (30 - 1)2]$

$= 15[60]$

$= 900$

5. $a_5 = a_1 + (n - 1)d$

$48 = 24 + (5 - 1)d$

$24 = 4d$

$6 = d$

$24 + 6 = 30,$

$30 + 6 = 36,$

$36 + 6 = 42$

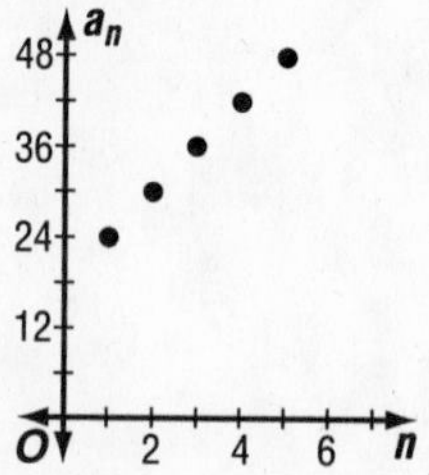

6. $d = 8 - 6$ or 2

$S_{12} = \frac{12}{2}[2(6) + (12 - 1)2]$

$= 6[34]$

$= 204$; 204 cans

7. $a_3 = 4(5)^{3-1}$

$= 100$

8. $a_5 = 243\left(-\frac{1}{3}\right)^{5-1}$

$= 3$

9. $a_5 = 3(r)^{5-1}$

$48 = 3r^4$

$16 = r^4$

$\pm 2 = r$

$3(\pm 2) = \pm 6,$

$\pm 6(\pm 2) = 12,$

$12(\pm 2) = \pm 24$

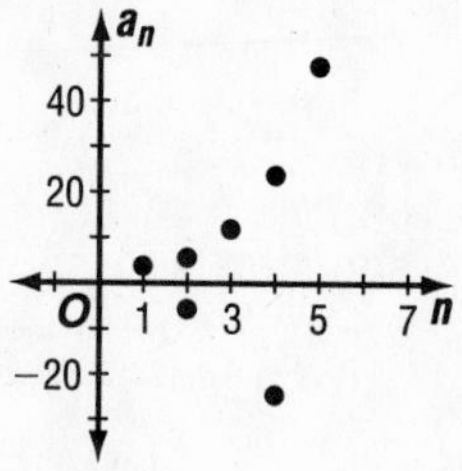

10. $S_{12} = \dfrac{5 - 5(3)^{12}}{1 - 3}$

$= \dfrac{-2{,}657{,}200}{-2}$

$= 1{,}328{,}600$

11. $2(-3)^{1-1} = 2$

$2(-3)^{2-1} = -6$

$r = -\frac{6}{2}$ or -3

$S_6 = \dfrac{2 - 2(-3)^6}{1 - (-3)}$

$= -\dfrac{1456}{4}$

$= -364$

11-5 Infinite Geometric Series

Pages 679–680 Check for Understanding

1. $S = \dfrac{a_1}{1 - r}$; $S_n = \dfrac{a_1 - a_1r^n}{1 - r} = \dfrac{a_1}{1 - r} - \dfrac{a_1r^n}{1 - r}$.
For $|r| < 1$, as n approaches ∞, r^n approaches 0, so the second fraction approaches 0. Thus S_n for $n = \infty$ becomes $\dfrac{a_1}{1 - r}$.

2. No, because $|r| > 1$.

3a. $S_n = \dfrac{3 - 3(0.8)^n}{1 - 0.8}$

3b. It approaches 0.

3c. The numerator approaches the value of 3.

3d. $\dfrac{3}{1 - 0.8} = 15$; It approaches 15.

4. 25

5. Trent; $r = \frac{3}{8} \div \frac{1}{2}$ or $\frac{6}{8}$.

6. See students' work.

7. 36, $r = \frac{24}{36}$ or $\frac{2}{3}$; $S = \frac{36}{1 - \frac{2}{3}}$

$= \frac{36}{\frac{1}{3}}$

$= 36 \cdot 3$

$= 108$

8. 16, $r = -\frac{24}{16}$ or $-\frac{3}{2}$; none

9. 6, $r = -\frac{4}{6}$ or $-\frac{2}{3}$; $S = \frac{6}{1 - \left(-\frac{2}{3}\right)}$

$= \frac{6}{\frac{5}{3}}$

$= 6 \cdot \frac{3}{5}$

$= \frac{18}{5}$

10. $\frac{1}{4}$, $r = \frac{\frac{1}{6}}{\frac{1}{4}}$ or $\frac{2}{3}$; $S = \frac{\frac{1}{4}}{1 - \frac{2}{3}}$

$= \frac{\frac{1}{4}}{\frac{1}{3}}$

$= \frac{1}{4} \cdot \frac{3}{1}$

$= \frac{3}{4}$

11. 16, $r = \frac{24}{16}$ or $\frac{3}{2}$; none

12. 40, $\frac{3}{5}$, $S = \frac{40}{1 - \frac{3}{5}}$

$= \frac{40}{\frac{2}{5}}$

$= 40 \cdot \frac{5}{2}$

$= 100$

13. $S = \frac{\frac{5}{10}}{1 - \frac{1}{10}}$

$= \frac{\frac{5}{10}}{\frac{9}{10}}$

$= \frac{5}{10} \cdot \frac{10}{9}$

$= \frac{5}{9}$

14. $S = \frac{\frac{37}{100}}{1 - \frac{1}{100}}$

$= \frac{\frac{37}{100}}{\frac{99}{100}}$

$= \frac{37}{100} \cdot \frac{100}{99}$

$= \frac{37}{99}$

15. $S = \frac{\frac{175}{1000}}{1 - \frac{1}{1000}}$

$= \frac{\frac{175}{1000}}{\frac{999}{1000}}$

$= \frac{175}{1000} \cdot \frac{1000}{999}$

$= \frac{175}{999}$

16. $S = \frac{80}{1 - 0.90}$

$= \frac{80}{0.1}$

$= 800$; 800 feet

Pages 680–682 Exercises

17. $S = \frac{4}{1 - \frac{5}{7}}$

$= \frac{4}{\frac{2}{7}}$

$= 4 \cdot \frac{7}{2}$

$= 14$

18. $S = \frac{12}{1 - \left(-\frac{3}{5}\right)}$

$= \frac{12}{\frac{8}{5}}$

$= 12 \cdot \frac{5}{8}$

$= 7.5$

19. $S = \frac{18}{1 - 0.6}$

$= \frac{18}{0.4}$

$= 45$

20. does not exist

21. $r = \frac{10}{15}$ or $\frac{2}{3}$

$S = \frac{15}{1 - \frac{2}{3}}$

$= \frac{15}{\frac{1}{3}}$

$= 15 \cdot 3$

$= 45$

22. $r = \frac{\frac{25}{3}}{\frac{5}{3}}$

$= \frac{25}{3} \cdot \frac{3}{5}$

$= 5$

does not exist

23. $r = \frac{\frac{2}{3}}{1}$ or $\frac{2}{3}$

$S = \frac{1}{1 - \frac{2}{3}}$

$= \frac{1}{\frac{1}{3}}$

$= 1 \cdot 3$

$= 3$

24. $r = \frac{1.8}{3}$ or 0.6

$S = \frac{3}{1 - 0.6}$

$= \frac{3}{0.4}$

$= 7.5$

25. $r = -\frac{12}{18}$ or $-\frac{2}{3}$

$S = \frac{18}{1 - \left(-\frac{2}{3}\right)}$

$= \frac{18}{\frac{5}{3}}$

$= 18 \cdot \frac{3}{5}$

$= \frac{54}{5}$

26. $r = -\frac{18}{12}$ or $-\frac{3}{2}$

does not exist

27. $r = \frac{\frac{10}{9}}{\frac{5}{3}}$

$= \frac{10}{9} \cdot \frac{3}{5}$ or $\frac{2}{3}$

$S = \frac{\frac{5}{3}}{1 - \frac{2}{3}}$

$= \frac{\frac{5}{3}}{\frac{1}{3}}$

$= \frac{5}{3} \cdot \frac{3}{1}$

$= 5$

28. $r = \frac{-\frac{3}{4}}{\frac{3}{2}}$

$= -\frac{3}{4} \cdot \frac{2}{3}$ or $-\frac{1}{2}$

$S = \frac{\frac{3}{2}}{1 - \left(-\frac{1}{2}\right)}$

$= \frac{\frac{3}{2}}{\frac{3}{2}}$

$= 1$

29. $S = \dfrac{48}{1 - \frac{2}{3}}$

$= \dfrac{48}{\frac{1}{3}}$

$= 48 \cdot 3$

$= 144$

30. $S = \dfrac{\frac{3}{8}}{1 - \frac{3}{4}}$

$= \dfrac{\frac{3}{8}}{\frac{1}{4}}$

$= \frac{3}{8} \cdot \frac{4}{1}$

$= \frac{3}{2}$

31. $S = \dfrac{-24}{1 - \left(-\frac{3}{5}\right)}$

$= \dfrac{-24}{\frac{8}{5}}$

$= -24 \cdot \frac{5}{8}$

$= -15$

32. $S = \dfrac{\frac{7}{10}}{1 - \frac{1}{10}}$

$= \dfrac{\frac{7}{10}}{\frac{9}{10}}$

$= \frac{7}{10} \cdot \frac{10}{9}$

$= \frac{7}{9}$

33. $S = \dfrac{\frac{1}{10}}{1 - \frac{1}{10}}$

$= \dfrac{\frac{1}{10}}{\frac{9}{10}}$

$= \frac{1}{10} \cdot \frac{10}{9}$

$= \frac{1}{9}$

34. $S = \dfrac{\frac{36}{100}}{1 - \frac{1}{100}}$

$= \dfrac{\frac{36}{100}}{\frac{99}{100}}$

$= \frac{36}{100} \cdot \frac{100}{99}$

$= \frac{4}{11}$

35. $S = \dfrac{\frac{82}{100}}{1 - \frac{1}{100}}$

$= \dfrac{\frac{82}{100}}{\frac{99}{100}}$

$= \frac{82}{100} \cdot \frac{100}{99}$

$= \frac{82}{99}$

36. $S = \dfrac{\frac{6}{10}}{1 - \frac{1}{10}} + 4$

$= \dfrac{\frac{6}{10}}{\frac{9}{10}} + 4$

$= \frac{6}{10} \cdot \frac{10}{9} + 4$

$= \frac{2}{3} + 4$

$= \frac{14}{3}$

37. $S = \dfrac{\frac{5}{100}}{1 - \frac{1}{10}} + 0.4$

$= \dfrac{\frac{5}{100}}{\frac{9}{10}} + 0.4$

$= \frac{5}{100} \cdot \frac{10}{9} + \frac{4}{10}$

$= \frac{5}{90} + \frac{36}{90}$

$= \frac{41}{90}$

38. $S = \dfrac{\frac{31}{1000}}{1 - \frac{1}{100}} + 0.2$

$= \dfrac{\frac{31}{1000}}{\frac{99}{100}} + 0.2$

$= \frac{31}{1000} \cdot \frac{100}{99} + \frac{2}{10}$

$= \frac{31}{990} + \frac{198}{990}$

$= \frac{229}{990}$

39. $S = \dfrac{\frac{99}{100}}{1 - \frac{1}{100}}$

$= \dfrac{\frac{99}{100}}{\frac{99}{100}}$

$= 1$

40. $r = -\frac{1}{10}$ or -0.1

$\sum_{n=1}^{\infty} 10(-0.1)^{n-1}$

$S = \dfrac{10}{1 - (-0.1)}$

$= \frac{10}{1.1}$ or $\frac{100}{11}$

41. $r = \frac{27}{3}$ or 9

$\sum_{n=1}^{\infty} 3(9)^{n-1}$

sum does not exist

42. $r = -\frac{0.5}{1}$ or -0.5

$\sum_{n=1}^{\infty} 1(-0.5)^{n-1}$

$S = \dfrac{1}{1 - (-0.5)}$

$= \frac{1}{1.5}$

$= \frac{10}{15}$ or $\frac{2}{3}$

43. $81 = \dfrac{a_1}{1 - \frac{2}{3}}$

$81 = \dfrac{a_1}{\frac{1}{3}}$

$27 = a_1$

$27\left(\frac{2}{3}\right) = 18$

$18\left(\frac{2}{3}\right) = 12$

27, 18, 12

44. $125 = \dfrac{a_1}{1 - 0.4}$

$125 = \dfrac{a_1}{0.6}$

$75 = a_1$

$75(0.4) = 30$

$30(0.4) = 12$

75, 30, 12

45. $76\frac{4}{5} = \dfrac{a_1}{1 - \frac{11}{16}}$

$\frac{384}{5} = \dfrac{a_1}{\frac{5}{16}}$

$120 = 5a_1$

$24 = a_1$

$24\left(\frac{11}{16}\right) = 16\frac{1}{2}$

$16\frac{1}{2}\left(\frac{11}{16}\right) = 11\frac{11}{32}$

$11\frac{11}{32}\left(\frac{11}{16}\right) = 7\frac{409}{512}$

$24, 16\frac{1}{2}, 11\frac{11}{32}, 7\frac{409}{512}$

46. $-13\frac{1}{3} = \dfrac{-8}{1 - r}$

$-\frac{40}{3} = \dfrac{-8}{1 - r}$

$-40 + 40r = -24$

$40r = 16$

$r = \frac{16}{40}$ or $\frac{2}{5}$

$-8\left(\frac{2}{5}\right) = -\frac{16}{5}$ or $-3\frac{1}{5}$

$-\frac{16}{5}\left(\frac{2}{5}\right) = -\frac{32}{25}$ or $-1\frac{7}{25}$

$-\frac{32}{25}\left(\frac{2}{5}\right) = -\frac{64}{125}$

$-8, -3\frac{1}{5}, -1\frac{7}{25}, -\frac{64}{125}$

47. Yes, it is possible to have infinite arithmetic series, but a sum does not exist since the sum increases with each term, or decreases with each term if d is negative.

48a. $r = \frac{6}{10}$ or $\frac{3}{5}$; $6\left(\frac{3}{5}\right) = 3.6$, $3.6\left(\frac{3}{5}\right) = 2.16$, $2.16\left(\frac{3}{5}\right) = 1.296$

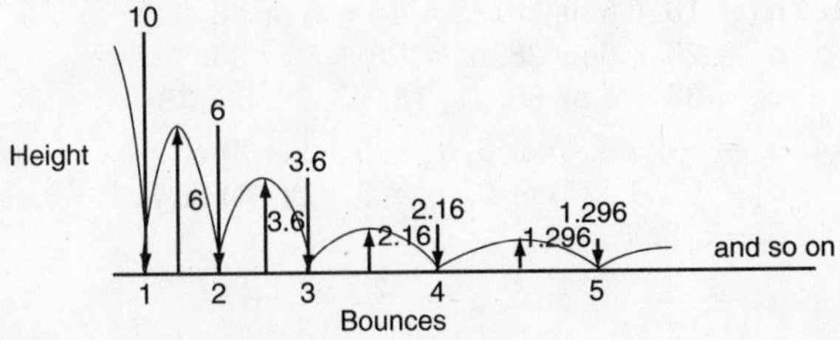

48b. $10 + 6 + 3.6 + 2.6 + \ldots$

$$S = \frac{10}{1 - \frac{3}{5}} = \frac{10}{\frac{2}{5}} = 10 \cdot \frac{5}{2} = 25$$

48c. $6 + 3.6 + 2.16 + \ldots$

$$S = \frac{6}{1 - \frac{3}{5}} = \frac{6}{\frac{2}{5}} = 6 \cdot \frac{5}{2} = 15$$

48d. $S_D = 10 + S_U$

48e. $25 + 15 = 40$; 40 feet

49. $S = \frac{10}{1 - 0.8} = \frac{10}{0.2} = 50$; 50 feet

50a. $P_1 = 40$; $P = 4s$

$40 = 4s$

$10 = s$

$\frac{1}{2}(10) = 5$

side of second square $= \sqrt{5^2 + 5^2}$ or $2\sqrt{5}$

$P_2 = 4(5\sqrt{2}) = 20\sqrt{2}$

$\frac{1}{2}(5\sqrt{2}) = 2.5\sqrt{2}$

side of third square $= \sqrt{(2.5\sqrt{2})^2 + (2.5\sqrt{2})^2}$ or 5

$P_3 = 4(5) = 20$

$40 + 20\sqrt{2} + 20 + \ldots$

50b. $r = \frac{20\sqrt{2}}{40}$ or $\frac{\sqrt{2}}{2}$

$$S = \frac{40}{1 - \frac{\sqrt{2}}{2}} = \frac{40}{\frac{2 - \sqrt{2}}{2}} = 40 \cdot \frac{2}{2 - \sqrt{2}} = \frac{80(2 + \sqrt{2})}{(2 - \sqrt{2})(2 + \sqrt{2})} = \frac{160 + 80\sqrt{2}}{4 - 2} = \frac{160 + 80\sqrt{2}}{2}$$

$= 80 + 40\sqrt{2}$; $(80 + 40\sqrt{2})$ centimeters

51. $r = -\frac{3}{1}$ or -3

$\sum_{n=1}^{6} (-3)^{n-1}$

52. $r = 1 - \frac{1}{5}$ or $\frac{4}{5}$, $a_1 = \frac{4}{5}$

$a_n = a_1 r^{n-1}$

$= \frac{4}{5}\left(\frac{4}{5}\right)^{5-1}$

$= 0.32768$; about 32.8%

53.

$$\frac{3y + 1}{2y - 10} + \frac{1}{y^2 - 2y - 15} = \frac{3y + 1}{2(y - 5)} + \frac{1}{(y - 5)(y + 3)}$$

$$= \frac{(3y + 1)(y + 3)}{2(y - 5)(y + 3)} + \frac{2}{2(y - 5)(y + 3)}$$

$$= \frac{3y^2 + 10y + 3 + 2}{2(y - 5)(y + 3)}$$

$$= \frac{3y^2 + 10y + 5}{2(y - 5)(y + 3)}$$

54. $2a = 28{,}900$

$a = 14{,}450$

$b^2 = a^2 - c^2$

$b^2 = 14{,}450^2 - 8000^2$

$b^2 = 144{,}802{,}500$

$$\frac{x^2}{(14{,}450)^2} + \frac{y^2}{144{,}802{,}500} = 1$$

$$\frac{x^2}{208{,}802{,}500} + \frac{y^2}{144{,}802{,}500} = 1$$

55a. 34% + 34% = 68%; 500(0.68) = 340; 340 items

55b. 13.5% + 34% + 34% + 13.% = 95%; 500(0.95) = 475; 475 items

55c. 2% + 13.5% + 34% + 34% + 13.5% + 2% = 99%; 500(0.99) = 495; 495 items

55d. (0.34)(500) = 170; 170 items

55e. 34% + 13.5% = 47.5%; 500(0.475) = 237.5; 237.5 items

56.

$$A = \ell \cdot w$$

$$6x^2 + 38x + 56 = \ell(2x + 8)$$

$$\frac{6x^2 + 38x + 56}{2x + 8} = \ell$$

$$\frac{2(3x + 7)(x + 4)}{2(x + 4)} = \ell$$

$$3x + 7 = \ell$$

57.

$$\left[\begin{array}{ccc|c} 1 & \frac{1}{2} & -3 & 19 \\ \frac{1}{2} & -1 & 2 & -16 \\ 5 & 2 & -2 & 50 \end{array}\right] = \left[\begin{array}{ccc|c} 1 & \frac{1}{2} & -3 & 19 \\ \frac{11}{2} & 1 & 0 & 34 \\ 5 & 2 & 2 & 50 \end{array}\right]$$

$$= \left[\begin{array}{ccc|c} -2 & -1 & 6 & -38 \\ \frac{11}{2} & 1 & 0 & 34 \\ 5 & 2 & -2 & 50 \end{array}\right] = \left[\begin{array}{ccc|c} 13 & 5 & 0 & 112 \\ \frac{11}{2} & 1 & 0 & 34 \\ 5 & 2 & -2 & 50 \end{array}\right]$$

$$= \left[\begin{array}{ccc|c} -14.5 & 0 & 0 & -58 \\ \frac{11}{2} & 1 & 0 & 34 \\ 5 & 2 & -2 & 50 \end{array}\right] = \left[\begin{array}{ccc|c} 1 & 0 & 0 & 4 \\ \frac{11}{2} & 1 & 0 & 34 \\ 5 & 2 & -2 & 50 \end{array}\right]$$

$$= \left[\begin{array}{ccc|c} 1 & 0 & 0 & 4 \\ 0 & 1 & 0 & 12 \\ 5 & 2 & -2 & 50 \end{array}\right] = \left[\begin{array}{ccc|c} 1 & 0 & 0 & 4 \\ 0 & 1 & 0 & 12 \\ 0 & 2 & -2 & 30 \end{array}\right]$$

$$= \left[\begin{array}{ccc|c} 1 & 0 & 0 & 4 \\ 0 & 1 & 0 & 12 \\ 0 & 0 & -2 & 6 \end{array}\right] = \left[\begin{array}{ccc|c} 1 & 0 & 0 & 4 \\ 0 & 1 & 0 & 12 \\ 0 & 0 & 1 & -3 \end{array}\right]; (4, 12, -3)$$

58. $25 + 1.75x = 46$
$1.75x = 21$
$x = 12;\ 12 + 10 = 22$

59. $y - y_1 = m(x - x_1)$
$y - 2 = \frac{3}{4}(x - 8)$
$y - 2 = \frac{3}{4}x - 6$
$y = \frac{3}{4}x - 4$

11-6 Recursion and Special Sequences

Page 686 Check for Understanding

1. $a_n = a_{n-1} + d$; This formula uses the previous term (a_{n-1}) to find a_n.
2. Iteration is the composition of a function to itself. For $f(x) = 5x - 1$, the iterate is $f(f(x)) = 5(5x - 1) - 1$ or $f(f(x)) = 25x - 6$.
3. $a_n = 2a_{n-1} + 1$
4. $a_2 = 12 - 3$ or 9, $a_3 = 9 - 3$ or 6, $a_4 = 6 - 3$ or 3, $a_5 = 3 - 3$ or 0, $a_6 = 0 - 3$ or -3; 12, 9, 6, 3, 0, -3
5. $a_3 = 4(2) - 3(1)$ or 5, $a_4 = 4(5) - 3(2)$ or 14, $a_5 = 4(14) - 3(5)$ or 41, $a_6 = 4(41) - 3(14)$ or 122; 1, 2, 5, 14, 41, 122
6. $f(x_0) = f(3)$
$= 3(3) - 4$ or 5
$f(x_1) = f(5)$
$= 3(5) - 4$ or 11
$f(x_2) = f(11)$
$= 3(11) - 4$ or 29
5, 11, 29
7. $f(x_0) = f(-1)$
$= (-1)^2 + 2$ or 3
$f(x_1) = f(3)$
$= 3^2 + 2$ or 11
$f(x_2) = f(11)$
$= 11^2 + 2$ or 123
3, 11, 123
8. $f(x_0) = f(-7)$
$= 2(-7) - 8$ or -22
$f(x_1) = f(-22)$
$= 2(-22) - 8$ or -52
$f(x_2) = f(-52)$
$= 2(-52) - 8$ or -112
$f(x_3) = f(-112)$
$= 2(-112) - 8$ or -232
$f(x_4) = f(-232)$
$= 2(-232) - 8$ or -472
$-22, -52, -112, -232, -472$
9. $f(x_0) = f(0.4)$
$= 2(0.4) - 8$ or -7.2
$f(x_1) = f(-7.2)$
$= 2(-7.2) - 8$ or -22.4
$f(x_2) = f(-22.4)$
$= 2(-22.4) - 8$ or -52.8
$f(x_3) = f(-52.8)$
$= 2(-52.8) - 8$ or -113.6
$f(x_4) = f(-113.6)$
$= 2(-113.6) - 8$ or -235.2
$-7.2, -22.4, -52.8, -113.6, -235.2$
10. $c(x) = x(1.03)^n$
$= 1.80(1.03)^{10}$
≈ 2.42; about \$2.42

Pages 686–687 Exercises

11. $a_2 = 2(9) - 4$ or 14, $a_3 = 2(14) - 4$ or 24, $a_4 = 2(24) - 4$ or 44, $a_5 = 2(44) - 4$ or 84, $a_6 = 2(84) - 4$ or 164; 9, 14, 24, 44, 84, 164
12. $a_2 = -6 + 3$ or -3, $a_3 = -3 + 3$ or 0, $a_4 = 0 + 3$ or 3, $a_5 = 3 + 3$ or 6, $a_6 = 6 + 3$ or 9; $-6, -3, 0, 3, 6, 9$
13. $a_2 = 13 + 5$ or 18, $a_3 = 18 + 5$ or 23, $a_4 = 23 + 5$ or 28, $a_5 = 28 + 5$ or 33, $a_6 = 33 + 5$ or 38; 13, 18, 23, 28, 33, 38
14. $a_3 = -3 + 2(4)$ or 5, $a_4 = 5 + 2(-3)$ or -1, $a_5 = -1 + 2(5)$ or 9, $a_6 = 9 + 2(-1)$ or 7; 4, -3, 5, -1, 9, 7
15. $a_2 = \frac{1}{1+1} \cdot 1$ or $\frac{1}{2}$, $a_3 = \frac{2}{2+1} \cdot \frac{1}{2}$ or $\frac{1}{3}$, $a_4\ \frac{3}{3+1} \cdot \frac{1}{3}$ or $\frac{1}{4}$, $a_5 = \frac{4}{4+1} \cdot \frac{1}{4}$ or $\frac{1}{5}$, $a_6 = \frac{5}{5+1} \cdot \frac{1}{5}$ or $\frac{1}{6}$; 1, $\frac{1}{2}$, $\frac{1}{3}$, $\frac{1}{4}$, $\frac{1}{5}$, $\frac{1}{6}$
16. $a_2 = 6 + (1 + 3)$ or 10, $a_3 = 10 + (2 + 3)$ or 15, $a_4 = 15 + (3 + 3)$ or 21, $a_5 = 21 + (4 + 3)$ or 28, $a_6 = 28 + (5 + 3)$ or 36; 6, 10, 15, 21, 28, 36
17. $f(x_0) = f(2)$
$= 9(2) - 2$ or 16
$f(x_1) = f(16)$
$= 9(16) - 2$ or 142
$f(x_2) = f(142)$
$= 9(142) - 2$ or 1276
16, 142, 1276
18. $f(x_0) = f(2)$
$= 4(2) - 3$ or 5
$f(x_1) = f(5)$
$= 4(5) - 3$ or 17
$f(x_2) = f(17)$
$= 4(17) - 3$ or 65
5, 17, 65
19. $f(x_0) = f(-4)$
$= 3(-4) + 5$ or -7
$f(x_1) = f(-7)$
$= 3(-7) + 5$ or -16
$f(x_2) = f(-16)$
$= 3(-16) + 5$ or -43
$-7, -16, -43$
20. $f(x_0) = f(-1)$
$= 2(-1)^2 - 5$ or -3
$f(x_1) = f(-3)$
$= 2(-3)^2 - 5$ or 13
$f(x_2) = f(13)$
$= 2(13)^2 - 5$ or 333
$-3, 13, 333$
21. $f(x_0) = f(1)$
$= 3(1)^2 - 4$ or -1
$f(x_1) = f(-1)$
$= 3(-1)^2 - 4$ or -1
$f(x_2) = f(-1)$
$= 3(-1)^2 - 4$ or -1
$-1, -1, -1$

22. $f(x_0) = f(1)$
$= 1^2 + 3(1) + 1$ or 5
$f(x_1) = f(5)$
$= 5^2 + 3(5) + 1$ or 41
$f(x_2) = f(41)$
$= 41^2 + 3(41) + 1$ or 1805
5, 41, 1805

23. $f(x_0) = f(6)$
$= 4(6) - 5$ or 19
$f(x_1) = f(19)$
$= 4(19) - 5$ or 71
$f(x_2) = f(71)$
$= 4(71) - 5$ or 279
$f(x_3) = f(279)$
$= 4(279) - 5$ or 1111
$f(x_4) = f(1111)$
$= 4(1111) - 5$ or 4439
19, 71, 279, 1111, 4439

24. $f(x_0) = f(-2)$
$= 4(-2) - 5$ or -13
$f(x_1) = f(-13)$
$= 4(-13) - 5$ or -57
$f(x_2) = f(-57)$
$= 4(-57) - 5$ or -233
$f(x_3) = f(-233)$
$= 4(-233) - 5$ or -937
$f(x_4) = f(-937)$
$= 4(-937) - 5$ or -3753
$-13, -57, -233, -937, -3753$

25. $f(x_0) = f\left(\frac{1}{2}\right)$
$= 4\left(\frac{1}{2}\right) - 5$ or -3
$f(x_1) = f(-3)$
$= 4(-3) - 5$ or -17
$f(x_2) = f(-17)$
$= 4(-17) - 5$ or -73
$f(x_3) = f(-73)$
$= 4(-73) - 5$ or -297
$f(x_4) = f(-297)$
$= 4(-297) - 5$ or -1193
$-3, -17, -73, -297, -1193$

26. $f(x_0) = f(0.85)$
$= 4(0.85) - 5$ or -1.6
$f(x_1) = f(-1.6)$
$= 4(-1.6) - 5$ or -11.4
$f(x_2) = f(-11.4)$
$= 4(-11.4) - 5$ or -50.6
$f(x_3) = f(-50.6)$
$= 4(-50.6) - 5$ or -207.4
$f(x_4) = f(-207.4)$
$= 4(-207.4) - 5$ or -834.6
$-1.6, -11.4, -50.6, -207.4, -834.6$

27. $a_1 = 7 + 12$ or 19
$a_2 = 19 + 12$ or 31
$a_3 = 31 + 12$ or 43
$a_4 = 43 + 12$ or 55
$a_5 = 55 + 12$ or 67

28. $a_1 = -2.1$
$a_2 = -2.1$
$a_3 = -2.1$
$a_4 = -2.1$

29. $f(x_0) = f(0.3)$
$= 0.1(0.3) + 0.3$ or 0.33
$f(x_1) = f(0.33)$
$= 0.1(0.33) + 0.3$ or 0.333
$f(x_2) = f(0.333)$
$= 0.1(0.333) + 0.3$ or 0.3333
0.33, 0.333, 0.3333, . . .
The values approach $\frac{1}{3}$.

30. $B_1 = (120{,}000)(1.0075) - 942.55$
$= 119{,}957.45$; \$119,957.45
$B_2 = (119{,}957.45)(1.0075) - 942.55$
$= 119{,}914.5809$; \$119,914.58
$B_3 = (119{,}914.5809)(1.0075) - 942.55$
$= 119{,}871.3903$; \$119,871.39
$B_4 = (119{,}871.3903)(1.0075) - 942.55$
$= 119{,}827.8757$; \$119,827.88
$B_5 = (119{,}827.8757)(1.0075) - 942.55$
$= 119{,}784.0348$; \$119,784.03
$B_6 = (119{,}784.0348)(1.0075) - 942.55$
$= 119{,}739.8651$; \$119,739.87
$B_7 = (119{,}739.8651)(1.0075) - 942.55$
$= 119{,}695.364$; \$119,695.36
$B_8 = (119{,}695.364)(1.0075) - 942.55$
$= 119{,}650.5293$; \$119,650.53

31a. 1, 3, 6, 10, 15

31b. $a_1 = 1,\ a_{n+1} = a_n + (n + 1)$

31c. $a_n = \frac{n(n+1)}{2}$
$a_{80} = \frac{80(80+1)}{2}$
$= \frac{6480}{2}$ or 3240

32.

F_1	F_2	F_3	F_4	F_5	F_6	F_7	F_8	F_9
1	1	2	3	5	8	13	21	34

$L_1 = 1$ $\quad L_5 = F_6 + F_4 = 8 + 3 = 11$
$L_2 = F_3 + F_1 = 2 + 1 = 3$ $\quad L_6 = F_7 + F_5 = 13 + 5 = 18$
$L_3 = F_4 + F_2 = 3 + 1 = 4$ $\quad L_7 = F_8 + F_6 = 21 + 8 = 29$
$L_4 = F_5 + F_3 = 5 + 2 = 7$ $\quad L_8 = F_9 + F_7 = 34 + 13 = 47$
1, 3, 4, 7, 11, 18, 29, 47

33. $r = \frac{6}{9}$ or $\frac{2}{3}$
$S = \frac{9}{1 - \frac{2}{3}}$
$= \frac{9}{\frac{1}{3}}$
$= 9 \cdot 3$
$= 27$

34. $\frac{x_1}{y_2} = \frac{x_2}{y_1}$
$\frac{1}{d^2} = \frac{2}{12^2}$
$144 = 2d^2$
$72 = d^2$
$6\sqrt{2} = d$; $6\sqrt{2}$ meters

35. center: $\left(3, \frac{1.5 - 0.5}{2}\right) = (3, 0.5)$
$2a = 2$ $\quad 2c = 7$ $\quad c^2 = a^2 + b^2$
$a = 1$ $\quad c = 3.5$ $\quad (3.5)^2 = 1^2 + b^2$
$11.25 = b^2$
$$\frac{(y - 0.5)^2}{1} - \frac{(x - 3)^2}{11.25} = 1$$

36. $3\begin{bmatrix}4\\1\\7\end{bmatrix} + 2\begin{bmatrix}3\\-2\\6\end{bmatrix} - 5\begin{bmatrix}-2\\3\\6\end{bmatrix} = \begin{bmatrix}12\\3\\21\end{bmatrix} + \begin{bmatrix}6\\-4\\12\end{bmatrix} + \begin{bmatrix}10\\-15\\-30\end{bmatrix}$
$= \begin{bmatrix}28\\-16\\3\end{bmatrix}$

37. 10, 13, 15, 16, 17, 19 , 21, 23, 24, 25, 39, 39

37a.

37b.

Stem	Leaf
1	0 3 5 6 7 9
2	1 3 4 5
3	9 9

2|1 = 21

37c. $\frac{19+21}{2} = 20$; 39;

$\frac{10+13+15+16+17+19+21+23+24+25+39+39}{12}$

$= \frac{261}{12} = 21.75$

11-7 Fractals

Page 692 Check for Understanding

1. See students' work.
2. A rule is applied to smaller and smaller parts.
3. Small parts of the frond look like the entire frond.
4.

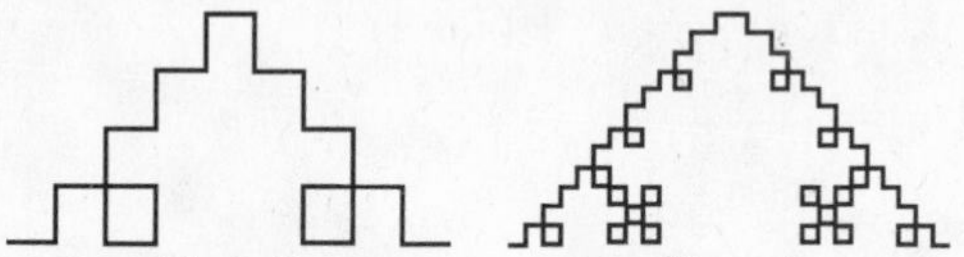

Stage 3 Stage 4

5a. $a_1 = 1, a_{n+1} = 3a_n$

5b. $a_2 = 3(1)$ or 3
$a_3 = 3(3)$ or 9
$a_4 = 3(9)$ or 27
$a_5 = 3(27)$ or 81

6. Small parts look like the entire tree.

Pages 693–694 Exercises

7.

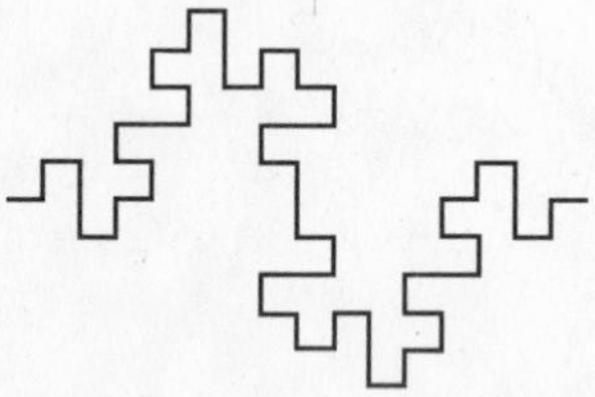

8.

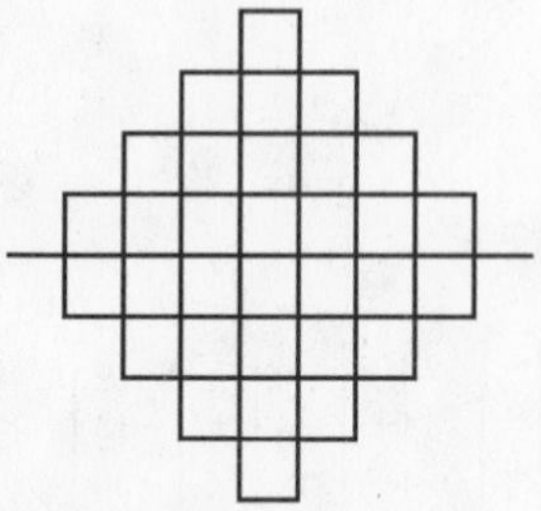

9a.

Stage 3 Stage 4

9b. $a_1 = 1, a_{n+1} = 8a_n$

9c. $a_2 = 8(1)$ or 8
$a_3 = 8(8)$ or 64
$a_4 = 8(64)$ or 512
$a_5 = 8(512)$ or 4096
$a_6 = 8(4096)$ or 32,768

9d. $a_1 = 81, a_{n+1} = \frac{8}{9}a_n$

9e. The area approaches zero.

10. Finite; the series of areas is an infinite series with $r = \frac{3}{4}$; therefore it has a sum.
11. Sample answer: Small changes produced unexpected results.
12. Sample answer: Within each mountain range, you can see features of the whole range.
13. See students' work.
14. $a_2 = 2(3) + 5$ or 11, $a_3 = 2(11) + 5$ or 27, $a_4 = 2(27) + 5$ or 59, $a_5 = 2(59) + 5$ or 123; 3, 11, 27, 59, 123
15. −2.8824
16.

$$E = I \cdot Z$$
$$(430 - j330) = (35 - j40)Z$$
$$\frac{(430 - j330)}{(35 - j40)} = Z$$
$$\frac{(430 - j330)(35 + j40)}{(35 - j40)(35 + j40)} = Z$$
$$\frac{15050 + j5650 - j^2 13200}{1225 - j^2 1600} = Z$$
$$\frac{28250 + j5650}{2825} = Z$$
$$10 + j2 = Z;\ (10 + j2) \text{ ohms}$$

17.

$$\begin{bmatrix} 5 & 1 \\ 2 & -3 \end{bmatrix} \cdot \begin{bmatrix} x \\ y \end{bmatrix} = \begin{bmatrix} 26 \\ 41 \end{bmatrix}$$
$$\begin{bmatrix} 5x + y \\ 2x - 3y \end{bmatrix} = \begin{bmatrix} 26 \\ 41 \end{bmatrix}$$

$5x + y = 26$
$2x - 3y = 41$

18. $|x - 7| = 12$

$x - 7 = 12$ or $x - 7 = -12$
$x = 19$ $\quad$ $x = -5$

Page 694 Mathematics and Society

1. Sample answer: to cause more rotation
2. The roller coaster and merry-go-round produce motions that are cyclical, repetitive, and predictable. The motions of the Tilt-a-Whirl are not repetitive or predictable; they vary with each ride.
3. A mathemaatical model can provide information about speed and direction of motions, forces exerted on riders, cars, platforms, or supports, and design parameters for supports and restraints.

11-8 The Binomial Theorem

Page 699 Check for Understanding

1. For each coefficient, add the pair of coefficients above its location.
2. Neither; consecutive terms have neither a common difference nor a common ratio.

3a. Sample answer: The exponent of b is one less than the number of the term. The sum of the exponents must equal the degree of the expansion.

3b. Sample answer: The degree of expansion is used as factorial in the numerator. Factorials in the denominator are the exponents of the variables.

3c. Sample answer: n is the degree of expansion, k is one less than the number of the term, the sum of the exponents of a and b equals the degree of expansion, and in the denominator, k and $n - k$ are the exponents of the variables.

4. Sample answers: Pascals triangle, binomial theorem, multiplication, factorials

5. 40,320 **6.** 17,160 **7.** 66

8. $p^5 + 5p^4q + 10p^3q^2 + 10p^2q^3 + 5pq^4 + q^5$

9. $t^6 + 6t^5 \cdot 2 + 15t^4 \cdot 2^2 + 20t^3 \cdot 2^3 + 15t^2 \cdot 2^4 + 6t \cdot 2^5 + 2^6 = t^2 + 12t^5 + 60t^4 + 160t^3 + 240t^2 + 192t + 64$

10. $x^4 - 4x^3y + 6x^2y^2 - 4xy^3 + y^4$

11. $(a + b)^8 = \sum_{k=0}^{8} \frac{8!}{k!(8-k)!} a^{8-k}b^k;\ k = 3$

$$\frac{8!}{3!(8-3)!} a^{8-3}b^3 = \frac{8 \cdot 7 \cdot 6}{3 \cdot 2 \cdot 1} a^5b^3 = 56a^5b^3$$

12. $(2a + 3b)^{10} = \sum_{k=0}^{10} \frac{10!}{k!(10-k)!} (2a)^{10-k}(3b)^k;\ k = 4$

$$\frac{10!}{4!(10-4)!} (2a)^{10-4}(3b)^4 = \frac{10 \cdot 9 \cdot 8 \cdot 7}{4 \cdot 3 \cdot 2 \cdot 1} (2a)^6(3b)^4 = 210(64a^6)(81b^4) = 1{,}088{,}640a^6b^4$$

13. $V = s^3$

$= (2x - 3)^3$

$= \sum_{k=0}^{3} \frac{3!}{k!(3-k)!} (2x)^{3-k}(-3)^k$

$= \frac{3!}{0!\,3!}(2x)^3(-3)^0 + \frac{3!}{1!\,2!}(2x)^2(-3)^1 + \frac{3!}{2!\,1!}(2x)^1(-3)^2 + \frac{3!}{3!\,0!}(2x)^0(-3)^3$

$= 1(8x^3)1 + 3(4x^2)(-3) + 3(2x)(9) + 1(1)(-27)$

$= 8x^3 - 36x^2 + 54x - 27;$

$(8x^3 - 36x^2 + 54x - 27)$ cm^3

Pages 699–701 Exercises

14. 362,880 **15.** 120 **16.** 6,227,020,800

17. 72 **18.** 210 **19.** 32,760

20. 495 **21.** 210 **22.** 2002

23. $r^7 + 7r^6s + 21r^5s^2 + 35r^4s^3 + 35r^3s^4 + 21r^2s^5 + 7rs^6 + s^7$

24. $a^3 - 3a^2b + 3ab^2 - b^3$

25. $m^5 - 5m^4a + 10m^3a^2 - 10m^2a^3 + 5ma^4 - a^5$

26. $(2a)^6 + 6(2a)^5b + 15(2a)^4b^2 + 20(2a)^3b^3 + 15(2a)^2b^4 + 6(2a)b^5 + b^6 = 64a^6 + 192a^5b + 240a^4b^2 + 160a^3b^3 + 60a^2b^4 + 12ab^5 + b^6$

27. $(2b)^4 + 4(2b)^3(-x) + 6(2b)^2(-x)^2 + 4(2b)(-x)^3 + (-x)^4 = 16b^4 - 32b^3x + 24b^2x^2 - 8bx^3 + x^4$

28. $(3x)^5 + 5(3x)^4(-2y) + 10(3x)^3(-2y)^2 + 10(3x)^2(-2y)^3 + 5(3x)(-2y)^4 + (-2y)^5 = 243x^5 - 810x^4y + 1080x^3y^2 - 720x^2y^3 + 240xy^4 - 32y^5$

29. $(3x)^4 + 4(3x)^3(2y) + 6(3x)^2(2y)^2 + 4(3x)(2y)^3 + (2y)^4 = 81x^4 + 216x^3y + 216x^2y^2 + 96xy^3 + 16y^4$

30. $\left(\frac{a}{2}\right)^5 + 5\left(\frac{a}{2}\right)^4(2) + 10\left(\frac{a}{2}\right)^3(2)^2 + 10\left(\frac{a}{2}\right)^2(2)^3 + 5\left(\frac{a}{2}\right)(2)^4 + (2)^5 = \frac{a^5}{32} + \frac{5a^4}{8} + 5a^3 + 20a^2 + 40a + 32$

31. $(3)^5 + 5(3)^4\left(\frac{m}{3}\right) + 10(3)^3\left(\frac{m}{3}\right)^2 + 10(3)^2\left(\frac{m}{3}\right)^3 + 5(3)\left(\frac{m}{3}\right)^4 + \left(\frac{m}{3}\right)^5 = 243 + 135m + 30m^2 + \frac{10m^3}{3} + \frac{5m^4}{27} + \frac{m^5}{243}$

32. $(x + 2)^7 = \sum_{k=0}^{7} \frac{7!}{k!(7-k)!} (x)^{7-k}(2)^k;\ k = 3$

$$\frac{7!}{3!(7-3)!} (x)^{7-3}(2)^3 = \frac{7 \cdot 6 \cdot 5}{3 \cdot 2 \cdot 1} x^4(8) = 280x^4$$

33. $(x + y)^{12} = \sum_{k=0}^{12} \frac{12!}{k!(12-k)!} x^{12-k}y^k;\ k = 6$

$$\frac{12!}{6!(12-6)!} x^{12-6}y^6 = \frac{12 \cdot 11 \cdot 10 \cdot 9 \cdot 8 \cdot 7}{6 \cdot 5 \cdot 4 \cdot 3 \cdot 2 \cdot 1} x^6y^6 = 924x^6y^6$$

34. $(x - y)^9 = \sum_{k=0}^{9} \frac{9!}{k!(9-k)!} x^{9-k}(-y)^k;\ k = 5$

$$\frac{9!}{5!(9-5)!} x^{9-5}(-y)^5 = \frac{9 \cdot 8 \cdot 7 \cdot 6 \cdot 5}{5 \cdot 4 \cdot 3 \cdot 2 \cdot 1} x^4(-y^5) = -126x^4y^5$$

35. $(2x + 3y)^9 = \sum_{k=0}^{9} \frac{9!}{k!(9-k)!} (2x)^{9-k}(3y)^k;\ k = 3$

$$\frac{9!}{3!(9-3)!} (2x)^{9-3}(3y)^3 = \frac{9 \cdot 8 \cdot 7}{3 \cdot 2 \cdot 1} (2x)^6(3y)^3 = 84(64x^6)(27y^3) = 145{,}152x^6y^3$$

36. $(2a + 3b)^{10} = \sum_{k=0}^{10} \frac{10!}{k!(10-k)!} (2a)^{10-k}(3b)^k;\ k = 4$

$$\frac{10!}{4!(10-4)!} (2a)^{10-4}(3b)^4 = \frac{10 \cdot 9 \cdot 8 \cdot 7}{4 \cdot 3 \cdot 2 \cdot 1} (2a)^6(3b)^4 = 210(64a^6)(81b^4) = 1{,}088{,}640a^6b^4$$

37. $\left(\frac{2}{5} + \frac{3}{5}\right)^{10} = \sum_{k=0}^{10} \frac{10!}{k!(10-k)!} \left(\frac{2}{5}\right)^{10-k}\left(\frac{3}{5}\right)^k;\ k = 4$

$$\frac{10!}{4!(10-4)!} \left(\frac{2}{5}\right)^{10-4}\left(\frac{3}{5}\right)^4 = \frac{10 \cdot 9 \cdot 8 \cdot 7}{4 \cdot 3 \cdot 2 \cdot 1} \left(\frac{2}{5}\right)^6\left(\frac{3}{5}\right)^4 = 210\left(\frac{64}{15{,}625}\right)\left(\frac{81}{625}\right) \approx 0.111477$$

38. $\frac{(k+1)!}{k!} = \frac{(k+1)k(k-1)(k-2)\ldots 1}{k(k-1)(k-2)\ldots 1} = k + 1$

39. $(k + 2)!\,(k + 3) = (k + 2)(k + 1)k(k - 1)\ldots 1\,(k + 3) = (k + 3)!$

40. $\frac{(n+3)!}{(n+1)!} = \frac{(n+3)(n+2)(n+1)\ldots 1}{(n+1)n(n-1)\ldots 1}$

$= (n+3)(n+2)$ or $n^2 + 5n + 6$

41. $\frac{8!(n-4)!}{8 \cdot 6!\,(n-3)!}$

$= \frac{8 \cdot 7 \cdot 6 \cdot 5 \cdot 4 \cdot 3 \cdot 2 \cdot 1\,(n-4)(n-5)(n-6)\ldots 1}{8 \cdot 6 \cdot 5 \cdot 4 \cdot 3 \cdot 2 \cdot 1\,(n-3)(n-4)(n-5)\ldots 1}$

$= \frac{7}{n-3}$

42. enter program

42a. execute program; 7 ENTER press ENTER 8 more times; 1, 7, 21, 35, 35, 21, 7, 1

42b. execute program; 8 ENTER press ENTER 9 more times; 1, 8, 28, 56, 70, 56, 28, 8, 1

42c. execute program; 10 ENTER press ENTER 11 more times; 1, 10, 45, 120, 210, 252, 210, 120, 45, 10, 1

43a. eighth

43b. 15 + 7 = 22; 22nd power

43c. $\frac{22!}{8!(22-8)!}a^{22-8}b^8$

$= \frac{22 \cdot 21 \cdot 20 \cdot 19 \cdot 18 \cdot 17 \cdot 16 \cdot 15}{8 \cdot 7 \cdot 6 \cdot 5 \cdot 4 \cdot 3 \cdot 2 \cdot 1}a^{14}b^8$

$= 319{,}770a^{14}b^8$

44a. There are 4 levels; using the expression $(a+b)^4$, the coefficients would be 1, 4, 6, 4, 1 whose total is 16.

44b. The probability for each tray section is in the same ratio. Multiply by 64 ÷ 16 or 4 to get 4, 16, 24, 16, 4.

44c. If there are 5 levels, use the coefficients of the expression $(a+b)^5$ which are 1, 5, 10, 10, 5, 1 whose total is 32. Multiply by 64 ÷ 32 or 2 to get 2, 10, 20, 20, 10, 2.

44d. Sample answer: For any row, the number of ball bearings in each section is proportional to the numbers in that row of Pascal's triangle.

45. 1, 1 + 1 = 2, 1 + 2 + 1 = 4, 1 + 3 + 3 + 1 = 8, 1 + 4 + 6 + 4 + 1 = 16; $2^9 = 512$

46. Let p = probability of completed pass, or 0.68.
Let q = probability of incompleted pass, or 0.32.
$(p+q)^4 = p^4 + 4p^3q + 6p^2q^2 + 4pq^3 + q^4$
$P(\text{exactly 3 completions}) = 4p^3q$
$= 4(0.68)^3(0.32)$
≈ 0.402 or 40.2%

47. Let p = probability of owning cats or 0.30.
Let q = probability of not owning cats or 0.70.
$(p+q)^8 = p^8 + 8p^7q + 28p^6q^2 + 56p^5q^3 + 70p^4q^4 + 56p^3q^5 + 28p^2q^6 + 8pq^7 + q^8$
$P(\text{exactly half (4) own cats}) = 70p^4q^4$
$= 70(0.30)^4(0.70)^4$
≈ 0.136 or 13.6%

48a. Let p = probability of hiring a man or 0.60.
Let q = probability of hiring a woman or 0.40.
$(p+q)^7 = p^7 + 7p^6q + 21p^5q^2 + 35p^4q^3 + 35p^3q^4 + 21p^2q^5 + 7pq^6 + q^7$
$P(\text{5 men hired}) = 21p^5q^2$
$= 21(0.60)^5(0.40)^2$
≈ 0.261 or 26.1%

48b. See students' work.

48c. No, since 26.1% is greater than 5%.

49. $r = \frac{\frac{1}{3}}{\frac{1}{2}}$ or $\frac{2}{3}$

$S = \frac{\frac{1}{2}}{1 - \frac{2}{3}}$

$= \frac{\frac{1}{2}}{\frac{1}{3}}$

$= \frac{1}{2} \cdot \frac{3}{1}$

$= \frac{3}{2}$

50. If $a_1 = 14$, then $a_7 = -1$.
$a_n = a_1 + (n-1)d$
$-1 = 14 + (7-1)d$
$-15 = 6d$
$-2.5 = d$
$a_2 = 14 - (-2.5)$ or 16.5
$a_1 = 16.5 - (-2.5)$ or 19
$a_4 = 14 + (-2.5)$ or 11.5
19, 16.5, 14, 11.5

51.
$y = ne^{kt}$
$164 = 80e^{k(3)}$
$\frac{164}{80} = e^{3k}$
$\ln \frac{164}{80} = \ln e^{3k}$
$\ln 164 - \ln 80 = 3k$
$\frac{\ln 164 - \ln 80}{3} = k$
$0.2393 \approx k$

52. $\log_3 243 = x$
$3^x = 243$
$3^x = 3^5$
$x = 5$

53. $\frac{x_1}{y_2} = \frac{x_2}{y_1}$
$\frac{30}{100} = \frac{x_2}{140}$
$4200 = 100x_2$
$42 = x_2$; 42 lb/in²

54. $[f \circ g](x) = f(g(x))$
$= f(3x - 4)$
$= (3x-4)^2 + 6$
$= 9x^2 - 24x + 16 + 6$
$= 9x^2 - 24x + 22$

55.
$x^2 + y^2 - 8x + 6y + 24 = 0$
$x^2 - 8x + y^2 + 6y = -24$
$(x^2 - 8x + 16) + (y^2 + 6y + 9) = -24 + 16 + 9$
$(x-4)^2 + (y+3)^2 = 1$; circle

56. $5 - \sqrt{b+2} = 0$
$5 = \sqrt{b+2}$
$5^2 = (\sqrt{b+2})^2$
$25 = b + 2$
$23 = b$

57. parallel slope $= \frac{2}{3}$
$y - y_1 = m(x - x_1)$
$y - 6 = \frac{2}{3}(x - 4)$
$y - 6 = \frac{2}{3}x - \frac{8}{3}$
$y = \frac{2}{3}x + \frac{10}{3}$

Chapter 11 Highlights

Page 703 Understanding and Using the Vocabulary

1. k	**2.** i	**3.** l	**4.** a
5. d	**6.** f	**7.** b, e	**8.** m
9. c	**10.** g		

Chapter 11 Study Guide and Assessment

Pages 704–706 Skills and Concepts

11. $a_5 = 6 + (5 - 1)8$
$= 38$

12. $a_{22} = -5 + (22 - 1)7$
$= 142$

13. $a_9 = 5 + (9 - 1)(-2)$
$= -11$

14. $a_{15} = -2 + (15 - 1)(-3)$
$= -44$

15. $a_{32} = 4 + (32 - 1)3$
$= 97$

16. $a_{10} = 8 + (10 - 1)(-5)$
$= -37$

17. $d = 2 - (-5)$ or 7
$72 = -5 + (n - 1)7$
$77 = 7n - 7$
$84 = 7n$
$12 = n$

18. $d = -1 - 1$ or -2
$-37 = 1 + (n - 1)(-2)$
$-38 = -2n + 2$
$-40 = -2n$
$20 = n$

19. $d = 9 - 4$ or 5
$49 = 4 + (n - 1)5$
$45 = 5n - 5$
$50 = 5n$
$10 = n$

20. $d = 2 - 2\frac{1}{4}$ or $-\frac{1}{4}$
$-\frac{17}{4} = \frac{21}{4} + (n - 1)\left(-\frac{1}{4}\right)$
$-\frac{26}{4} = -\frac{1}{4}n + \frac{1}{4}$
$-\frac{27}{4} = -\frac{1}{4}n$
$27 = n$

21. $9 = -7 + (5 - 1)d$
$16 = 4d$
$4 = d$
$a_2 = -7 + 4$ or -3
$a_3 = -3 + 4$ or 1
$a_4 = 1 + 4$ or 5

22. $4 = 12 + (4 - 1)d$
$-8 = 3d$
$-\frac{8}{3} = d$
$a_2 = 12 + \left(-\frac{8}{3}\right)$ or $\frac{28}{3}$
$a_3 = \frac{28}{3} + \left(-\frac{8}{3}\right)$ or $\frac{20}{3}$

23. If $a_1 = 6$, then $a_4 = -3$
$-3 = 6 + (4 - 1)d$
$-9 = 3d$
$-3 = d$
$a_1 = 6 - (-3)$ or 9
$a_3 = 6 + (-3)$ or 3
$a_4 = 3 + (-3)$ or 0
$a_6 = -3 + (-3) = -6$

24. If $a_1 = 49$, then $a_4 = 28$
$28 = 49 + (4 - 1)d$
$-21 = 3d$
$-7 = d$
$a_1 = 49 - (-7)$ or 56
$a_3 = 49 + (-7)$ or 42
$a_4 = 42 + (-7)$ or 35

25. $S_{36} = \frac{36}{2}(12 + 117)$
$= 18(129)$
$= 2322$

26. $d = 10 - 4$ or 6
$106 = 4 + (n - 1)6$
$102 = 6n - 6$
$108 = 6n$
$18 = n$
$S_{18} = \frac{18}{2}(4 + 106)$
$= 9(110)$
$= 990$

27. $S_{21} = \frac{21}{2}(85 + 25)$
$= \frac{21}{2}(110)$
$= 1155$

28. $d = 4 - 10$ or -6
$-50 = 10 + (n - 1)(-6)$
$-60 = -6n + 6$
$-66 = -6n$
$11 = n$
$S_{11} = \frac{11}{2}(10 + (-50))$
$= \frac{11}{2}(-40)$
$= -220$

29. $3(2) + 1 = 7$, $3(3) + 1 = 10$, $3(4) + 1 = 13$, $3(5) + 1 = 16$, $3(6) + 1 = 19$, $3(7) + 1 = 22$, $3(8) + 1 = 25$, $3(9) + 1 = 28$, $3(10) + 1 = 31$, $3(11) + 1 = 34$, $3(12) + 1 = 37$, $3(13) + 1 = 40$;
$7 + 10 + 13 + 16 + 19 + 22 + 25 + 28 + 31 + 34 + 37 + 40 = 282$

30. $108 = \frac{n}{2}(3 + 24)$
$108 = \frac{n}{2}(27)$
$4 = \frac{n}{2}$
$8 = n$
$a_8 = a_1 + (n - 1)d$
$24 = 3 + (8 - 1)d$
$21 = 7d$
$3 = d$
$a_2 = 3 + 3$ or 6
$a_3 = 6 + 3$ or 9
3, 6, 9

31. $r = \frac{\frac{4}{3}}{\frac{2}{3}} = \frac{4}{3} \cdot \frac{3}{2}$ or 2
$a_6 = \frac{2}{3}(2)^{6-1}$
$= \frac{64}{3}$

32. $a_5 = 2(2)^{5-1}$
$= 32$

33. $a_4 = 7(2)^{4-1}$
$= 56$

34. $a_5 = 243\left(-\frac{1}{3}\right)^{5-1}$
$= 3$

35. $48 = 3r^{5-1}$
$16 = r^4$
$\pm 2 = r$
$3(\pm 2) = \pm 6$
$(\pm 6)(\pm 2) = 12$
$12(\pm 2) = \pm 24$

36. $120 = 7.5r^{5-1}$
$16 = r^4$
$\pm 2 = r$
$7.5\ (\pm 2) = \pm 15$
$(\pm 15)(\pm 2) = 30$
$30\ (\pm 2) = \pm 60$

37. $\frac{1}{4} = 8r^{6-1}$
$\frac{1}{32} = r^5$
$\frac{1}{2} = r$
$8\left(\frac{1}{2}\right) = 4$
$4\left(\frac{1}{2}\right) = 2$
$2\left(\frac{1}{2}\right) = 1$
$1\left(\frac{1}{2}\right) = \frac{1}{2}$

38. $80 = 5r^{5-1}$
$16 = r^4$
$\pm 2 = r$
$5(\pm 2) = \pm 10$
$(\pm 10)(\pm 2) = 20$
$20(\pm 2) = \pm 40$

39. $-98 = -2r^{3-1}$
$49 = r^2$
$\pm 7 = r$
$-2(\pm 7) = \pm 14$
$-98(\pm 7) = \pm 686$
$\pm 686(\pm 7) = -4802$

40. $S_5 = \frac{12 - 12(3^5)}{1 - 3}$
$= \frac{-2904}{-2}$
$= 1452$

41. $S_6 = \frac{4 - 4\left(-\frac{1}{2}\right)^6}{1 - \left(-\frac{1}{2}\right)}$
$= \frac{\frac{63}{16}}{\frac{3}{2}}$
$= \frac{63}{16} \cdot \frac{2}{3}$
$= \frac{21}{8}$

42. $S_9 = \frac{256 - 256(0.75)^9}{1 - (0.75)}$
$= \frac{236.7783203}{0.25}$
≈ 947.11

43. $S_5 = \frac{1 - \left(\frac{1}{16}\right)\left(-\frac{1}{2}\right)}{1 - \left(-\frac{1}{2}\right)}$
$= \frac{\frac{33}{32}}{\frac{3}{2}}$
$= \frac{33}{32} \cdot \frac{2}{3}$
$= \frac{11}{16}$

44. $S_5 = \frac{625 - (81)\left(\frac{3}{5}\right)}{1 - \frac{3}{5}}$
$= \frac{576.4}{\frac{2}{5}}$
$= 576.4 \cdot \frac{5}{2}$
$= 1441$

45. $1031 = \frac{a_1\left(1 - \left(\frac{2}{5}\right)^5\right)}{1 - \frac{2}{5}}$
$1031 = \frac{a_1\left(1 - \frac{32}{3125}\right)}{\frac{3}{5}}$
$618.6 = a_1\left(\frac{3093}{3125}\right)$
$625 = a_1$

46. $30 = \frac{a_1(1 - (-2)^4)}{1 - (-2)}$
$30 = \frac{a_1(-15)}{3}$
$90 = a_1(-15)$
$-6 = a_1$

47. $-61 = \frac{a_1(1 - (-1)^5)}{1 - (-1)}$
$-61 = \frac{a_1(2)}{2}$
$-61 = a_1$

48. $244 = \frac{a_1(1 - (-3)^5)}{1 - (-3)}$
$244 = \frac{a_1(244)}{4}$
$976 = a_1(244)$
$4 = a_1$

49. $S = \frac{6}{1 - \frac{11}{12}}$
$= \frac{6}{\frac{1}{12}}$
$= 6 \cdot 12$
$= 72$

50. $r = \frac{-\frac{3}{16}}{\frac{1}{8}}$
$= -\frac{3}{16} \cdot \frac{8}{1}$ or $-\frac{3}{2}$
does not exist

51. $S = \frac{-2}{1 - \left(-\frac{5}{8}\right)}$
$= \frac{-2}{\frac{13}{8}}$
$= -2 \cdot \frac{8}{13}$
$= -\frac{16}{13}$

52. $r = \frac{-\frac{5}{2}}{10}$
$= -\frac{5}{2} \cdot \frac{1}{10}$ or $-\frac{1}{4}$
$S = \frac{10}{1 - \left(-\frac{1}{4}\right)}$
$= \frac{10}{\frac{5}{4}}$
$= 10 \cdot \frac{4}{5}$
$= 8$

53. $f(x_0) = f(1)$
$= -2(1) + 3$ or 1
$f(x_1) = f(1)$
$= -2(1) + 3$ or 1
$f(x_2) = f(1)$
$= -2(1) + 3$ or 1
1, 1, 1

54. $f(x_0) = f(2)$
$= 7(2) - 4$ or 10
$f(x_1) = f(10)$
$= 7(10) - 4$ or 66
$f(x_2) = f(66)$
$= 7(66) - 4$ or 458
10, 66, 458

55. $f(x_0) = f(-1)$
$= (-1)^2 - 6$ or -5
$f(x_1) = f(-5)$
$= (-5)^2 - 6$ or 19
$f(x_2) = f(19)$
$= (19)^2 - 6$ or 355
−5, 19, 355

56. $f(x_0) = f(-2)$
$= -2(-2)^2 - (-2) + 5$ or -1
$f(x_1) = f(-1)$
$= -2(-1)^2 - (-1) + 5$ or 4
$f(x_2) = f(4)$
$= -2(4)^2 - (4) + 5$ or -31
−1, 4, −31

57. $x^3 + 3x^2y + 3xy^2 + y^3$

58. $x^4 + 4x^3(-2) + 6x^2(-2)^2 + 4x(-2)^3 + (-2)^4 = x^4 - 8x^3 + 24x^2 - 32x + 16$

59. $(3r)^5 + 5(3r)^4s + 10(3r)^3s^2 + 10(3r)^2s^3 + 5(3r)s^4 + s^5 = 243r^5 + 405r^4s + 270r^3s^2 + 90r^2s^3 + 15rs^4 + s^5$

60. $(x + 2y)^6 = \sum_{k=0}^{6} \frac{6!}{k!\,(6-k)!} x^{6-k}(2y)^k$; $k = 3$
$\frac{6!}{3!\,(6-3)!} x^{6-3}(2y)^3 = \frac{6 \cdot 5 \cdot 4}{3 \cdot 2 \cdot 1} x^3(8y^3)$
$= 160x^3y^3$

61. $(4x - 5)^{10} = \sum_{k=0}^{10} \frac{10!}{k!\,(10-k)!} (4x)^{10-k}(-5)^k$; $k = 1$
$\frac{10!}{1!\,(10-1)!} (4x)^{10-1}(-5)^1 = \frac{10}{1}(4x)^9(-5)$
$= 10(262{,}144x^9)(-5)$
$= -13{,}107{,}200x^9$

62. $(x - y)^{15} = \sum_{k=0}^{15} \frac{15!}{k!\,(15-k)!} x^{15-k}(-y)^k$; $k = 6$
$\frac{15!}{6!\,(15-6)!} x^{15-6}(-y)^6 = \frac{15 \cdot 14 \cdot 13 \cdot 12 \cdot 11 \cdot 10}{6 \cdot 5 \cdot 4 \cdot 3 \cdot 2 \cdot 1} x^9y^6$
$= 5005x^9y^6$

Page 706 Applications and Problem Solving

63. $d = 7 - 5$ or 2

$a_{20} = 5 + (20 - 1)2$
$= 43$

64. triangle 1: $P = 3(20)$ or 60

triangle 2: $s = 10$;
$P = 3(10)$ or 30

triangle3: $s = 5$;
$P = 3(5)$ or 15

$r = \frac{30}{60}$ or $\frac{1}{2}$

$S = \frac{60}{1 - \frac{1}{2}}$

$= \frac{60}{\frac{1}{2}}$

$= 60 \cdot 2$

$= 120$; 120 inches

Page 707 Alternative Assessment; Thinking Critically

- No, the same number is not added to each term.
- Sample answers: 1, 2, 3, 4, 5, 6, . . . , $a_n = n$, where $n \geq 1$; 1, 2, 3, 6, 11, 20, . . . , $a_{n+1} = a_{n-2} + a_{n-1} + a_n$, where $n \geq 3$.

College Entrance Exam Practice, Chapters 1–11

Pages 708–709

1. B

2. $\begin{vmatrix} x & 7 & 5 \\ 0 & 3 & 4 \\ 3 & 2 & -2 \end{vmatrix} = 11$

$x\begin{vmatrix} 3 & 4 \\ 2 & -2 \end{vmatrix} - 7\begin{vmatrix} 0 & 4 \\ 3 & -2 \end{vmatrix} + 5\begin{vmatrix} 0 & 3 \\ 3 & 2 \end{vmatrix} = 11$

$x(-14) - 7(-12) + 5(-9) = 11$

$-14x + 84 - 45 = 11$

$-14x = -28$

$x = 2$

D

3. $1716 = \frac{n}{2}(6 + 306)$

$1716 = 156n$

$11 = n$

$306 = 6 + (11 - 1)d$

$300 = 10d$

$30 = d$

$a_2 = 6 + 30$ or 36

$a_3 = 36 + 30$ or 66

A

4. $(4^{\sqrt{3}})^{\sqrt{2}} = 4^{\sqrt{6}}$

C

5. $3x - 2y + 2z = -2 \rightarrow \quad 3x - 2y + 2z = -2$

$x - 3y + z = -2 \rightarrow (+) -3x + 9y - 3z = 6$

$7y - z = 4$

$x - 3y + z = -2 \rightarrow \quad -2x + 6y - 2z = 4$

$2x - y + 4z = 7 \rightarrow \quad (+) 2x - y + 4z = 7$

$5y + 2z = 11$

$7y - z = 4 \rightarrow \quad 14y - 2z = 8$

$5y + 2z = 11 \rightarrow (+) 5y + 2z = 11$

$19y = 19$

$y = 1$

$7y - z = 4$

$7(1) - z = 4$

$3 = z$

$x - 3y + z = -2$

$x - 3(1) + 3 = -2$

$x = -2$

(−2, 1, 3); A

6. 4×5; B

7. $207 = a_1 + (14 - 1)3$; C

8. $\dfrac{\frac{3x}{4x-1}}{1 + \frac{3x}{x-1}} = \dfrac{\frac{3x}{4x-1}}{\frac{x - 1 + 3x}{x-1}}$

$= \frac{3x}{4x - 1} \cdot \frac{x - 1}{4x - 1}$

$= \frac{3x(x-1)}{(4x-1)^2}$; B

9. D

10. $(5ab^2)(a^3b)(-3c^2) + (7bc)(3ac)(a^3b)^2$

$= (5(-3)a \cdot a^3 \cdot b^2 \cdot b \cdot c^2)$

$+ (7 \cdot 3 \cdot a \cdot a^{3 \cdot 2} \cdot b \cdot b^2 \cdot c \cdot c)$

$= -15a^4b^3c^2 + 21a^7b^3c^2$; C

11. Let w = width and $w + 6$ = length.

$A = \ell \cdot w$

$315 = (w + 6)w$

$315 = w^2 + 6w$

$0 = w^2 + 6w - 315$

$0 = (w + 21)(w - 15)$

$w + 21 = 0$ or $w - 15 = 0$

$w = -21$ $\quad w = 15$

$w + 6 = 15 + 6$ or 21

21 inches by 15 inches

12. $V_n = P(1 + r)^n$

$15{,}000 = 75{,}000(1 - 0.08)^n$

$\frac{1}{5} = 0.92^n$

$\log \frac{1}{5} = \log 0.92^n$

$\log 1 - \log 5 = n \log 0.92$

$\frac{\log 1 - \log 5}{\log 0.92} = n$

$19.3 \approx n$; 19.3 years

13. Let w = width, $2w + 3$ = length, and $w - 2$ = height.

$V = \ell \cdot w \cdot h$

$2475 = (2w + 3)w(w - 2)$

$2475 = 2w^3 - w^2 - 6w$

$0 = 2w^3 - w^2 - 6w - 2475$

11⌋	2	−1	−6	−2475
		22	231	2475
	2	21	225	0

$w = 11$ $\quad \ell = 2(11) + 3$ or 25

$h = 11 - 2$ or 9

$9 \times 11 \times 25$ units

14. $a_1 = 2, r = 2$

$S_n = \frac{a_1(1 - r^n)}{1 - r}$

$S_6 = \frac{2(1 - 2^6)}{1 - 2}$

$= 2 \cdot 63$

$= 126$; 126 teachers

1 principal + 126 teachers = 127 people

15.

$\underline{-1}\rfloor$	1	−5	−13	53	60
		−1	6	7	−60
	1	−6	−7	60	0

$a^3 - 6a^2 - 7a + 60$

16. $S = \frac{120}{1 - \frac{2}{3}}$ $\quad 120 \cdot \frac{2}{3} = 80$

$= \frac{120}{\frac{1}{3}}$ $\quad S = \frac{80}{1 - \frac{2}{3}}$

$= 360$ $\quad = \frac{80}{\frac{1}{3}}$ or 240

360 + 240 = 600; 600 feet

17. 4.45, 5.50, 5.50. 6.30, 7.80, 11.00, 12.20, 17.20;

$\frac{6.30 + 7.80}{2} = 7.05$; \$7.05; \$5.50;

(4.45 + 5.50 + 5.50 + 6.30 + 7.80 + 11.00 + 12.20 + 17.20) ÷ 8 = 69.95 ÷ 8 = 8.74375, \$8.74;

$$\text{SD} = \sqrt{\frac{\left[\begin{array}{c}(4.45 - 8.74)^2 + 2(5.50 - 8.74)^2 \\ + (6.30 - 8.74)^2 + (7.80 - 8.74)^2 \\ + (11.00 - 8.74)^2 + (12.20 - 8.74)^2 + (17.20 - 8.74)^2\end{array}\right]}{8}}$$

$$= \sqrt{\frac{\left[\begin{array}{c}18.4041 + 20.9952 \\ + 5.9536 + 0.8836 + 5.1076 + 11.9716 + 71.5716\end{array}\right]}{8}}$$

$= \sqrt{16.8609125}$

≈ 4.11; \$4.11

18. $r = \frac{1}{2}\sqrt{\frac{S}{\pi}}$

$= \frac{1}{2}\sqrt{\frac{616}{\pi}}$

≈ 7.0014; about 7 inches

19. Let x = Josh's age and y = Yuji's age.

$x + y = 32$

$y = 32 - x$

$2x = 2y + 4$

$2x = 2(32 - x) + 4$

$2x = 64 - 2x + 4$

$4x = 68$

$x = 17$

$y = 32 - x$

$= 32 - 17$

$= 15$; Josh, 17; Yuji, 15

20. $\frac{3.00 \times 10^5}{1} = \frac{36}{x}$

$(3.00 \times 10^5)x = 36$

$x = \frac{36}{3.00 \times 10^5}$

$x = \frac{3.6 \times 10^1}{3.00 \times 10^5}$

$x = 1.2 \times 10^{-4}$ or 0.00012 seconds

21. $\frac{a}{b} = \frac{7}{3}$ $\quad 12a = 12\left(\frac{7b}{3}\right)$ $\quad$ C

$3a = 7b$ $\quad = 28b$

$a = \frac{7b}{3}$

22. $5^{x+2} = 15.3$ $\quad 9^{x-4} = 6.28$

$\log 5^{x+2} = \log 15.3$ $\quad \log 9^{x-4} = \log 6.28$

$(x + 2)\log 5 = \log 15.3$ $\quad (x - 4)\log 9 = \log 6.28$

$x + 2 = \frac{\log 15.3}{\log 5}$ $\quad x - 4 = \frac{\log 6.28}{\log 9}$

$x + 2 \approx 1.6949$ $\quad x - 4 \approx 0.8362$

$x \approx -0.3051$ $\quad x \approx 4.8362$

B

23.

$$\begin{array}{r} 2x^2 + 9x - 5 \\ x + 3\overline{)2x^3 + 15x^2 + 22x - 15} \\ \underline{2x^3 + 6x^2} \qquad\qquad \\ 9x^2 + 22x \qquad \\ \underline{9x^2 + 27x} \qquad \\ -5x - 15 \\ \underline{-5x - 15} \\ 0 \end{array}$$

$$\begin{array}{r} x^2 + 4x - 3 - \frac{4}{x-1} \\ x - 1\overline{)x^3 + 3x^2 - 7x - 1} \\ \underline{x^3 - x^2} \qquad\qquad \\ 4x^2 - 7x \qquad \\ \underline{4x^2 - 4x} \qquad \\ -3x - 1 \\ \underline{-3x + 3} \\ -4 \end{array}$$

For $x > 1$

$2x^2 + 9x - 5 > x^2 + 4x - 3 - \frac{4}{x - 1}$

A

24. D

25. $x = \frac{5y + 2}{2}$ $\quad \frac{x - 1}{2\sqrt{5}} \cdot \frac{4}{\sqrt{5}} = \frac{4x - 4}{2 \cdot 5}$

$2x = 5y + 2$ $\quad = \frac{2(2x - 2)}{2 \cdot 5}$

$2x - 2 = 5y$ $\quad = \frac{2x - 2}{5}$

$\frac{2x - 2}{5} = y$

C

12-1 The Counting Principle

Page 715 Check for Understanding

1. Sample answer: The fundamental counting principle allows you to determine the total number of ways independent events can happen in sequence given the number of choices for each event occurring.
2. With independent events, one choice for an event does not affect any of the possibilities for another event. Examples include rolling dice and picking a marble out of a sack, replacing the marble, and picking again. With dependent events, each choice is affected by the previous choice. Examples include choosing numbers in a lottery and selecting members of a team from a group.
3. 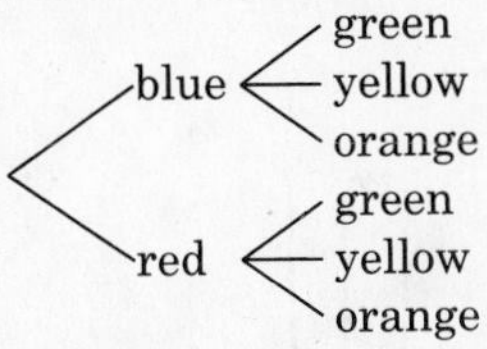

6 possibilities
4. Sample answer: In solving a simpler problem, a pattern or shortcut may emerge that can be applied to the more difficult problem.
5. $8 \cdot 10 \cdot 10 = 800$ possible area codes
6. 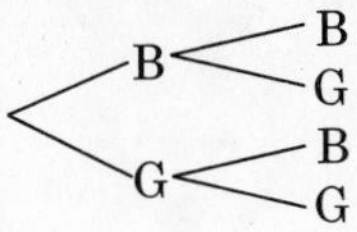

4 possibilities
7. 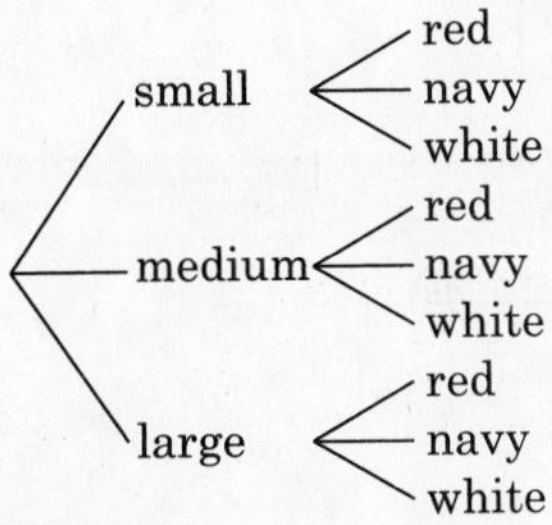

9 possibilities
8. independent
9. dependent
10. $6 \cdot 5 \cdot 4 \cdot 3 \cdot 2 \cdot 1 = 720$; 720 schedules
11. $2 \cdot 2 \cdot 2 \cdot 2 \cdot 2 \cdot 2 \cdot 2 \cdot 2 = 2^8 = 256$; 256 choices

Pages 715–717 Exercises

12. 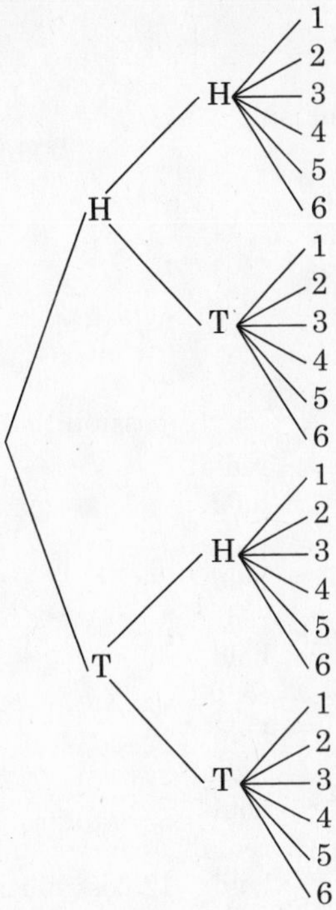

24 possibilities
13. 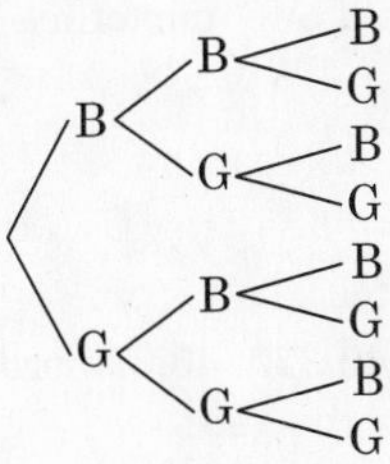

8 possibilites
14. 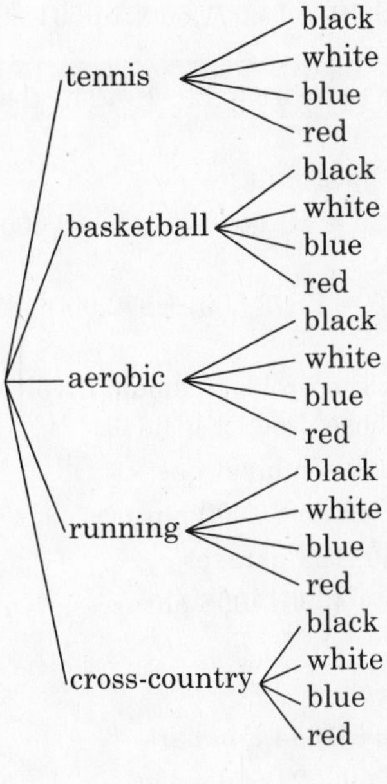

20 possibilities

15.

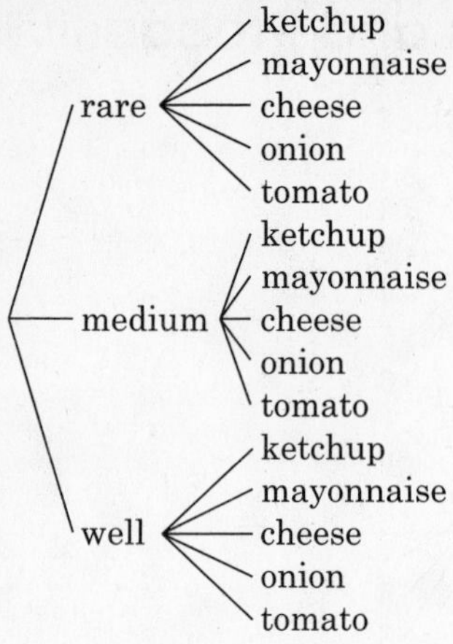

15 possibilities

16.

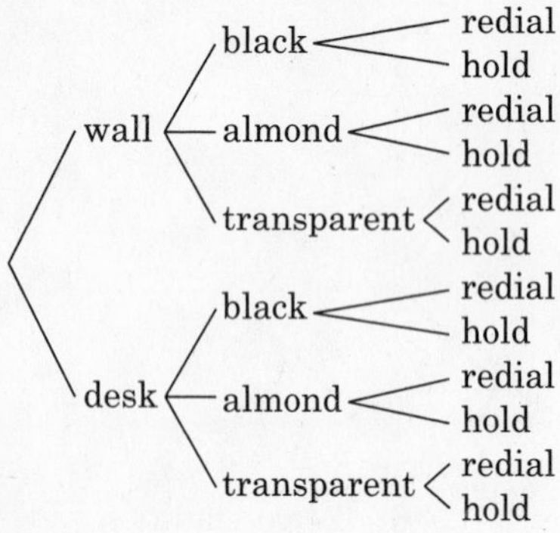

12 possibilities

17. dependent, if a person can hold only one office
18. independent
19. dependent
20. independent
21. $5 \cdot 4 \cdot 3 \cdot 2 \cdot 1 = 120$; 120 routes
22. $8 \cdot 7 \cdot 6 \cdot 5 \cdot 4 \cdot 3 \cdot 2 \cdot 1 \cdot 1 = 40{,}320$; 40,320 orders
23. $5 \cdot 5 \cdot 5 \cdot 5 \cdot 5 = 5^5 = 3125$; 3125 passwords
24. $24 \cdot 26 \cdot 26 \cdot 10 \cdot 10 \cdot 9 = 14{,}601{,}600$; 14,601,600 license plates
25. $5 \cdot 4 \cdot 3 \cdot 2 \cdot 1 \cdot 1 + 1 \cdot 5 \cdot 4 \cdot 3 \cdot 2 \cdot 1 = 240$; 240 ways
26. $5 \cdot 16 \cdot 8 = 640$; 640 possibilities
27a. $26 \cdot 25 \cdot 24 \cdot 26 \cdot 25 = 10{,}140{,}000$; 10,140,000 possibilities
27b. $26 \cdot 25 \cdot 24 \cdot 6 \cdot 20 = 1{,}872{,}000$; 1,872,000 possibilities
28. See students' work; the problem should involve finding numbers whose product is 2340.
29. $7 \cdot 3 \cdot 5 \cdot 2 = 210$; 210 combinations
30a. $10 \cdot 10 \cdot 10 = 10^3 = 1000$; 1000 phrases
30b. $5 \cdot 5 \cdot 5 = 5^3 = 125$; 125 phrases
30c. $16 \cdot 16 \cdot 16 = 16^3 = 4096$; 4096 phrases
30d. Answers will vary.
31. $4 \cdot 3 \cdot 8 = 96$; 96 meals
32. $1 \cdot 4 \cdot 8 \cdot 7 \cdot 6 = 1344$; 1344 numbers
33. $2 \cdot 25 \cdot 24 \cdot 23 = 27{,}600$; 27,600 ways
34. $(2m-3)^6 = (2m)^6 + 6(2m)^5(-3) + 15(2m)^4(-3)^2 + 20(2m)^3(-3)^3 + 15(2m)^2(-3)^4 + 6(2m)(-3)^5 + (-3)^6 = 64m^6 - 576m^5 + 2160m^4 - 4320m^3 + 4860m^2 - 2916m + 729$

35. $\ln 9.5 = \ln (e^{0.2x})$
$2.2513 \approx 0.2x$
$11.26 \approx x$

36. $11{,}160 \div 36{,}000 = 0.31$; 31%
$6480 \div 36{,}000 = 0.18$; 18%
$5400 \div 36{,}000 = 0.15$; 15%
$3240 \div 36{,}000 = 0.09$; 9%
$2160 \div 36{,}000 = 0.06$; 6%
$1800 \div 36{,}000 = 0.05$; 5%
$5760 \div 36{,}000 = 0.16$; 16%

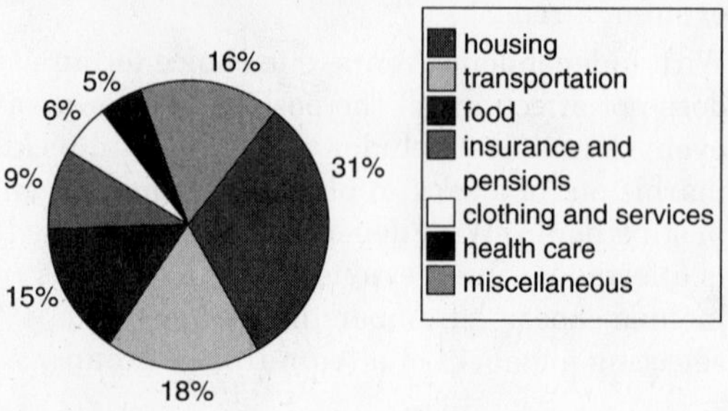

37. $f(x) = x^6$

x	$f(x)$
−2	64
−1	6
0	0
1	6

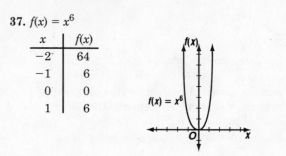

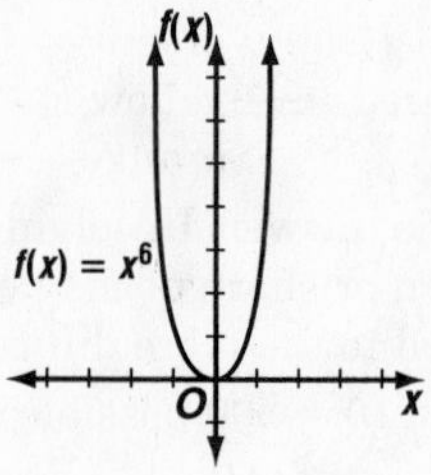

38. $y = \frac{1}{10}x^2$
$h = 0, k = 0, a = \frac{1}{10}$
$\left(0, 0 + \frac{1}{4\left(\frac{1}{10}\right)}\right) = \left(0, 2\frac{1}{2}\right)$

39. $\frac{\sqrt{3} + n\sqrt{6}}{4 - \sqrt{n}} = \frac{(\sqrt{3} + n\sqrt{6})(4 + \sqrt{n})}{(4 - \sqrt{n})(4 + \sqrt{n})}$
$= \frac{4\sqrt{3} + \sqrt{3n} + 4n\sqrt{6} + n\sqrt{6n}}{16 - n}$

12-2 Permutations

Pages 722–723 Check for Understanding

1. $6 \cdot 5 \cdot 4 \cdot 3 \cdot 2 \cdot 1$
2. Order is important.
3. There are five different letters and each letter is used once.
4. In a circular permutation, there is no reference point for the exact beginning of the arrangement.
5. Denise; the number of linear permutations is 8! or 40,320, and the number of circular permutations is 7! or 5040.

6. R = red, B = blue, Y = yellow, G = green

R B Y G	R Y B G	R G Y B	B R Y G
R B G Y	R Y G B	R G B Y	B R G Y
Y R B G	Y B R G	Y G R B	B Y R G
Y R G B	Y B G R	Y G B R	B Y G R
G R B Y	G B R Y	G Y B R	B G Y R
G R Y B	G B Y R	G Y R B	B G R Y

24

7. $4! = 24$

8. $3! = 6$

9. $\frac{3!}{2!} = 3$

10. $6! = 720$

11. linear, not reflection; $9! = 362{,}880$

12. circular, not reflection; $\frac{6!}{6} = 120$

13a. Order is important since each place winner receives a different cash prize and awards.

13b. $\underset{\text{winner}}{\underline{52}}\ \underset{\text{1st}}{\underline{51}}\ \underset{\text{2nd}}{\underline{50}}\ \underset{\text{3rd}}{\underline{49}}$

13c. $52 \cdot 51 \cdot 50 \cdot 49 = 6{,}497{,}400$; 6,497,400 ways

Pages 723–725 Exercises

14. $\frac{5!}{2!2!} = 30$

15. $7! = 5040$

16. $\frac{3!}{2!} = 3$

17. $\frac{8!}{2!3!} = 3360$

18. $\frac{6!}{3!} = 120$

19. $\frac{4!}{2!} = 12$

20. $\frac{5!}{2!} = 60$

21. $5! = 120$

22. $\frac{11!}{4!4!2!} = 34{,}650$

23. $\frac{7!}{2!} = 2520$

24. $\frac{9!}{2!2!} = 90{,}720$

25. $\frac{10!}{2!2!2!} = 453{,}600$

26. linear, reflection; $\frac{10!}{2} = 1{,}814{,}400$

27. circular, not reflection; $\frac{5!}{5} = 24$

28. circular, not reflection; $\frac{6!}{6} = 120$

29. circular, not reflection; $\frac{8!}{8} = 5040$

30. linear, not reflection; $7! = 5040$

31. circular, reflection; $\frac{5!}{2} = 60$

32. $\frac{P(6, 4)}{P(5, 3)} = \frac{\frac{6!}{(6-4)!}}{\frac{5!}{(5-3)!}} = \frac{6 \cdot 5 \cdot 4 \cdot 3}{5 \cdot 4 \cdot 3} = 6$

33. $\frac{P(6, 3)\,P(4, 2)}{P(5, 2)} = \frac{\left(\frac{6!}{(6-3)!}\right)\left(\frac{4!}{(4-2)!}\right)}{\frac{5!}{(5-2)!}} = \frac{(6 \cdot 5 \cdot 4 \cdot 3)(4 \cdot 3)}{5 \cdot 4 \cdot 3}$

$= 72$

34. $\frac{P(12, 6)}{P(12, 3)\,P(8, 2)} = \frac{\frac{12!}{(12-6)!}}{\left(\frac{12!}{(12-3)!}\right)\left(\frac{8!}{(8-2)!}\right)}$

$= \frac{12 \cdot 11 \cdot 10 \cdot 9 \cdot 8 \cdot 7}{(12 \cdot 11 \cdot 10)(8 \cdot 7)} = 9$

35.
$$P(n, 4) = 40[P(n-1, 2)]$$
$$\frac{n!}{(n-4)!} = 40\left[\frac{(n-1)!}{(n-1-2)!}\right]$$
$$n(n-1)(n-2)(n-3) = 40[(n-1)(n-2)]$$
$$n(n-3) = 40$$
$$n^2 - 3n - 40 = 0$$
$$(n-8)(n+5) = 0$$
$$n - 8 = 0 \quad \text{or} \quad n + 5 = 0$$
$$n = 8 \qquad\qquad n = -5$$
-5 is not a reasonable solution.

36.
$$P(n, 4) = 3[P(n, 3)]$$
$$\frac{n!}{(n-4)!} = 3\left[\frac{n!}{(n-3)!}\right]$$
$$n(n-1)(n-2)(n-3) = 3[n(n-1)(n-2)]$$
$$n - 3 = 3$$
$$n = 6$$

37. $n[P(5, 3)] = P(7, 5)$
$$n\left(\frac{5!}{(5-3)!}\right) = \frac{7!}{(7-5)!}$$
$$n(5 \cdot 4 \cdot 3) = 7 \cdot 6 \cdot 5 \cdot 4 \cdot 3$$
$$n = 42$$

38.
$$208\,P(n, 2) = P(16, 4)$$
$$208\left(\frac{n!}{(n-2)!}\right) = \frac{16!}{(16-4)!}$$
$$208\,n(n-1) = 16 \cdot 15 \cdot 14 \cdot 13$$
$$n^2 - n = 210$$
$$n^2 - n - 210 = 0$$
$$(n-15)(n+14) = 0$$
$$n - 15 = 0 \quad \text{or} \quad n + 14 = 0$$
$$n = 15 \qquad\qquad n = -14$$
-14 is not a reasonable solution.

39. $6! = 720$; 720 ways

40. See students' work.

41. $7! = 5040$; 5040 ways

42. $10 \cdot 10 \cdot 10 - 6 = 994$; 994 numbers

43. $6 \cdot 5 \cdot 4 \cdot 2 \cdot 1 \cdot 3 \cdot 2 \cdot 1 = 1440$; 1440 ways

44a. $\frac{6!}{6} = 120$; 120 arrangements

44b. $5! = 120$; 120 arrangements

45. $2^8 - 1 = 255$; 255 combinations

46a. $5! = 120$; 120 ways

46b. $6! = 720$; 720 ways
$\frac{6!}{2!} = 360$; 360 ways

46c. MODEL, COUNT, LINEAR, CIRCLE; $\frac{5!}{2!} = 60$; 60 ways

46d. ORDER

46e. $12! = 479{,}001{,}600$; 479,001,600 arrangements

47. Q = quarter, D = dime, N = nickle, P = penny; 2Q; 1Q, 2D, 1N; 1Q, 1D, 3N; 1Q, 5N; 1Q, 2D, 5P; 1Q, 1D, 2N, 5P; 1Q, 1D, 1N, 10P; 1Q, 1D, 15P; 1Q, 4N, 5P; 1Q, 3N, 10P; 1Q, 2N, 15P; 1Q, 1N, 20P; 1Q, 25P; 13 ways

48. $r = \dfrac{\frac{1}{3}}{\frac{2}{3}}$ $\quad S = \dfrac{\frac{2}{3}}{1 - \frac{1}{2}}$

$= \frac{1}{3} \cdot \frac{3}{2}$ $\quad = \dfrac{\frac{2}{3}}{\frac{1}{2}}$

$= \frac{1}{2}$ $\quad = \frac{2}{3} \cdot \frac{2}{1}$

$\quad = \frac{4}{3}$

49. $y = 2^x$
$4096 = 2^x$
$2^{12} = 2^x$
$12 = x$; 12 hours

50. $\frac{x_1}{y_2} = \frac{x_2}{y_1}$
$\frac{1.5}{-3} = \frac{x_2}{-8}$
$-3x_2 = -12$
$x_2 = 4$

51. $f(x) = 3x^5 - 8x^2 + 1$; 2 or 0 positive real zeros
$f(-x) = 3(-x)^5 - 8(-x)^2 + 1 = -3x^5 - 8x^2 + 1$;
1 negative real zero
2 or 4 imaginary zeros

52. $133{,}000 \times 60 = 7{,}980{,}000$ or 7.98×10^6

53. $\begin{bmatrix} 3 & -1 \\ 2 & 5 \end{bmatrix} \cdot \begin{bmatrix} 4 & -1 & -2 \\ -3 & 5 & 4 \end{bmatrix} = \begin{bmatrix} 12 + 3 & -3 - 5 & -6 - 4 \\ 8 - 15 & -2 + 25 & -4 + 20 \end{bmatrix}$
$= \begin{bmatrix} 15 & -8 & -10 \\ -7 & 23 & 16 \end{bmatrix}$

54. $x \le 5$
$y \ge -3x$
$2y \le x + 7$
$y \le \frac{x}{2} + \frac{7}{2}$
$y \ge x - 4$
$f(x, y) = 4x - 3y$

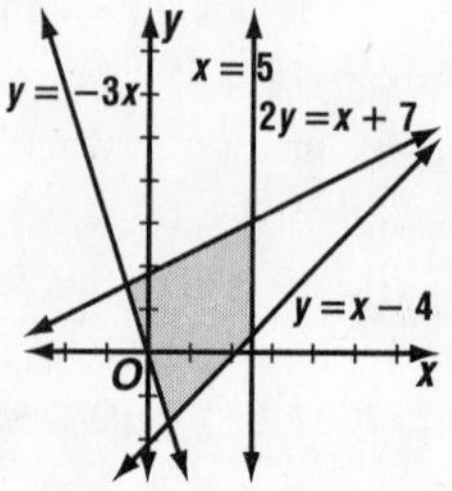

vertices: (1, −3), (−1, 3), (5, 6), (5, 1)

(x, y)	$4x - 3y$	$f(x, y)$
(1, −3)	4(1) − 3(−3)	13
(−1, 3)	4(−1) − 3(3)	−13
(5, 6)	4(5) − 3(6)	2
(5, 1)	4(5) − 3(1)	17

max: $f(5, 1) = 17$
min: $f(-1, 3) = -13$

55. $p \le 400$

12-3 Combinations

Pages 728–729 Check for Understanding

1. A permutation is an arrangement in which the order is important. Order is not important in a combination.
2. $C(11, 5)$
3.

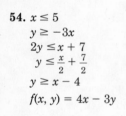

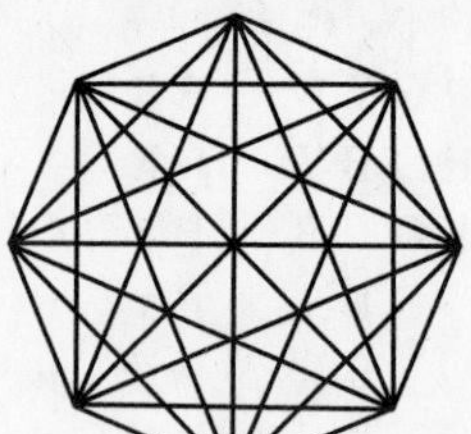

4. Find the product of the two combinations, $C(4, 3)$ and $C(5, 2)$.
5. The principal is mathematically correct because the order is important.
6. permutation
7. combination
8. combination
9. $C(4, 2) = \frac{4!}{(4-2)!2!}$
$= \frac{4 \cdot 3 \cdot 2!}{2 \cdot 2!}$
$= 6$
10. $C(7, 2) = \frac{7!}{(7-2)!2!}$
$= \frac{7 \cdot 6 \cdot 5!}{5! \cdot 2}$
$= 21$
11. $C(3, 2) \cdot C(8, 3) = \frac{3!}{(3-2)!2!} \cdot \frac{8!}{(8-3)!3!}$
$= \frac{3 \cdot 2!}{1 \cdot 2!} \cdot \frac{8 \cdot 7 \cdot 6 \cdot 5!}{5! \cdot 3 \cdot 2 \cdot 1}$
$= 3 \cdot 56$
$= 168$
12. $C(8, 5) \cdot C(7, 3) = \frac{8!}{(8-5)!5!} \cdot \frac{7!}{(7-3)!3!}$
$= \frac{8 \cdot 7 \cdot 6 \cdot 5!}{3 \cdot 2 \cdot 1 \cdot 5!} \cdot \frac{7 \cdot 6 \cdot 5 \cdot 4!}{4! \cdot 3 \cdot 2 \cdot 1}$
$= 56 \cdot 35$
$= 1960$
13. $C(8, 2) \cdot C(5, 1) \cdot C(4, 2) = \frac{8!}{(8-2)!2!} \cdot \frac{5!}{(5-1)!1!} \cdot \frac{4!}{(4-2)!2!}$
$= \frac{8 \cdot 7 \cdot 6!}{6! \cdot 2} \cdot \frac{5 \cdot 4!}{4! \cdot 1} \cdot \frac{4 \cdot 3 \cdot 2!}{2 \cdot 2!}$
$= 28 \cdot 5 \cdot 6$
$= 840$; 840 bouquets
14. $C(12, 6) = \frac{12!}{(12-6)!6!}$
$= \frac{12 \cdot 11 \cdot 10 \cdot 9 \cdot 8 \cdot 7 \cdot 6!}{6 \cdot 5 \cdot 4 \cdot 3 \cdot 2 \cdot 1 \cdot 6!}$
$= 924$; 924 teams

Pages 729–731 Exercises

15. permutation
16. combination
17. permutation
18. combination
19. combination
20. combination
21. permutation
22. combination
23. $C(5, 2) = \frac{5!}{(5-2)!2!}$
$= \frac{5 \cdot 4 \cdot 3!}{3! \cdot 2}$
$= 10$
24. $C(10, 5) = \frac{10!}{(10-5)!5!}$
$= \frac{10 \cdot 9 \cdot 8 \cdot 7 \cdot 6 \cdot 5!}{5 \cdot 4 \cdot 3 \cdot 2 \cdot 1 \cdot 5!}$
$= 252$

25. $C(8, 4) = \frac{8!}{(8-4)!4!}$
$= \frac{8 \cdot 7 \cdot 6 \cdot 5 \cdot 4!}{4 \cdot 3 \cdot 2 \cdot 1 \cdot 4!}$
$= 70$

26. $C(24, 21) = \frac{24!}{(24-21)!21!}$
$= \frac{24 \cdot 23 \cdot 22 \cdot 21!}{3 \cdot 2 \cdot 1 \cdot 21!}$
$= 2024$

27. $C(12, 7) = \frac{12!}{(12-7)!7!}$
$= \frac{12 \cdot 11 \cdot 10 \cdot 9 \cdot 8 \cdot 7!}{5 \cdot 4 \cdot 3 \cdot 2 \cdot 1 \cdot 7!}$
$= 792$

28. $C(10, 4) = \frac{10!}{(10-6)!6!}$
$= \frac{10 \cdot 9 \cdot 8 \cdot 7 \cdot 6!}{4 \cdot 3 \cdot 2 \cdot 1 \cdot 6!}$
$= 210$

29. $C(12, 4) \cdot C(8, 3) = \frac{12!}{(12-4)!4!} \cdot \frac{8!}{(8-3)!3!}$
$= \left(\frac{12 \cdot 11 \cdot 10 \cdot 9 \cdot 8!}{8! \cdot 4 \cdot 3 \cdot 2 \cdot 1}\right)\left(\frac{8 \cdot 7 \cdot 6 \cdot 5!}{5! \cdot 3 \cdot 2 \cdot 1}\right)$
$= 495 \cdot 56$
$= 27{,}720$

30. $C(9, 3) \cdot C(6, 2) = \frac{9!}{(9-3)!3!} \cdot \frac{6!}{(6-2)!2!}$
$= \left(\frac{9 \cdot 8 \cdot 7 \cdot 6!}{6! \cdot 3 \cdot 2 \cdot 1}\right)\left(\frac{6 \cdot 5 \cdot 4!}{4! \cdot 2 \cdot 1}\right)$
$= 84 \cdot 15$
$= 1260$

31. $C(10, 4) \cdot C(5, 3) = \frac{10!}{(10-4)!4!} \cdot \frac{5!}{(5-3)!3!}$
$= \left(\frac{10 \cdot 9 \cdot 8 \cdot 7 \cdot 6!}{6! \cdot 4 \cdot 3 \cdot 2 \cdot 1}\right)\left(\frac{5 \cdot 4 \cdot 3!}{2 \cdot 1 \cdot 3!}\right)$
$= 210 \cdot 10$
$= 2100$

32. $C(8, 2) \cdot C(5, 1) \cdot C(4, 2) = \frac{8!}{(8-2)!2!} \cdot \frac{5!}{(5-1)!1!} \cdot \frac{4!}{(4-2)!2!}$
$= \left(\frac{8 \cdot 7 \cdot 6!}{6! \cdot 2 \cdot 1}\right)\left(\frac{5 \cdot 4!}{4! \cdot 1}\right)\left(\frac{4 \cdot 3 \cdot 2!}{2 \cdot 1 \cdot 2!}\right)$
$= 28 \cdot 5 \cdot 6$
$= 840$

33. $C(8, 3) = \frac{8!}{(8-3)!3!}$
$= \frac{8 \cdot 7 \cdot 6 \cdot 5!}{5! \cdot 3 \cdot 2 \cdot 1}$
$= 56$

34a. $C(9, 3) = \frac{9!}{(9-3)!3!}$
$= \frac{9 \cdot 8 \cdot 7 \cdot 6!}{6! \cdot 3 \cdot 2 \cdot 1}$
$= 84$

34b. $C(9, 8) = \frac{9!}{(9-8)!8!}$
$= \frac{9 \cdot 8!}{1 \cdot 8!}$
$= 9$

34c. $C(9, 5) = \frac{9!}{(9-5)!5!}$
$= \frac{9 \cdot 8 \cdot 7 \cdot 6 \cdot 5!}{4 \cdot 3 \cdot 2 \cdot 1 \cdot 5!}$
$= 126$

34d. $C(9, 4) = \frac{9!}{(9-4)!4!}$
$= \frac{9 \cdot 8 \cdot 7 \cdot 6 \cdot 5!}{5! \cdot 4 \cdot 3 \cdot 2 \cdot 1}$
$= 126$

34e. $C(9, 10)$ not possible; none

34f. $C(9, 6) = \frac{9!}{(9-6)!6!}$
$= \frac{9 \cdot 8 \cdot 7 \cdot 6!}{3 \cdot 2 \cdot 1 \cdot 6!}$
$= 84$

35. $C(n, 5) = C(n, 7)$
$\frac{n!}{(n-5)!5!} = \frac{n!}{(n-7)!7!}$
$n!(n-7)!\,7! = n!(n-5)!\,5!$
$(n-7)!\,7! = (n-5)!\,5!$
$\frac{7!}{5!} = \frac{(n-5)!}{(n-7)!}$
$7 \cdot 6 = (n-5)(n-6)$
$42 = n^2 - 11n - 30$
$0 = n^2 - 11n - 72$
$0 = (n-12)(n+6)$
$n - 12 = 0$ or $n + 6 = 0$
$n = 12$ $\quad n = -6$
-6 is not a reasonable solution.

36. $C(11, 8) = C(11, n)$
$\frac{11!}{(11-8)!8!} = \frac{11!}{(11-n)!n!}$
$(11-8)!\,8! = (11-n)!\,n!$
$3!\,8! = (11-n)!\,n!$
$n = 3$ or 8

37. $C(14, 3) = C(n, 11)$
$\frac{14!}{(14-3)!3!} = \frac{n!}{(n-11)!\,11!}$
$14!(n-11)!\,11! = n!\,(11)!\,3!$
$14!(n-11)! = n!\,3!$
$n = 14$

38. $C(n, 7) = C(n, 2)$
$\frac{n!}{(n-7)!7!} = \frac{n!}{(n-2)!2!}$
$n!(n-2)!\,2! = n!(n-7)!\,7!$
$(n-2)!\,2! = (n-7)!\,7!$
$\frac{(n-2)!}{(n-7)!} = \frac{7!}{2!}$
$(n-2)(n-3)(n-4)(n-5)(n-6) = 7 \cdot 6 \cdot 5 \cdot 4 \cdot 3$
$n = 9$

39. $C(n, r) = \frac{n!}{(n-r)!r!}$ or $\frac{n!}{(n-r)!} \cdot \frac{1}{r!}$; $P(n, r) = \frac{n!}{(n-r)!}$
By substituting, $C(n, r) = P(n, r) \cdot \frac{1}{r!}$ or $\frac{P(n, r)}{r!}$.

40. $C(22, 2) \cdot C(16, 3) = \frac{22!}{(22-2)!2!} \cdot \frac{16!}{(16-3)!3!}$
$= \left(\frac{22 \cdot 21 \cdot 20!}{20! \cdot 2 \cdot 1}\right)\left(\frac{16 \cdot 15 \cdot 14 \cdot 13!}{13! \cdot 3 \cdot 2 \cdot 1}\right)$
$= 231 \cdot 560$
$= 129{,}360$; 129,360 study groups

41a. $C(8, 5) = \frac{8!}{(8-5)!5!}$
$= \frac{8 \cdot 7 \cdot 6 \cdot 5!}{3 \cdot 2 \cdot 1 \cdot 5!}$
$= 56$; 56 committees

41b. $C(10, 5) = \frac{10!}{(10-5)!5!}$
$= \frac{10 \cdot 9 \cdot 8 \cdot 7 \cdot 6 \cdot 5!}{5 \cdot 4 \cdot 3 \cdot 2 \cdot 1 \cdot 5!}$
$= 252$; 252 committees

41c. $C(8, 1) \cdot C(10, 4) = \frac{8!}{(8-1)!1!} \cdot \frac{10!}{(10-4)!4!}$
$= \frac{8 \cdot 7!}{7! \cdot 1} \cdot \frac{10 \cdot 9 \cdot 8 \cdot 7 \cdot 6!}{6! \cdot 4 \cdot 3 \cdot 2 \cdot 1}$
$= 8 \cdot 210$
$= 1680$; 1680 committees

41d. $C(8, 3) \cdot C(10, 2) = \frac{8!}{(8-3)!3!} \cdot \frac{10!}{(10-2)!2!}$
$= \frac{8 \cdot 7 \cdot 6 \cdot 5!}{5! \cdot 3 \cdot 2 \cdot 1} \cdot \frac{10 \cdot 9 \cdot 8!}{8! \cdot 2 \cdot 1}$
$= 56 \cdot 45$
$= 2520$; 2520 committees

42. $C(10, 2) = \frac{10!}{(10-2)!2!}$
$= \frac{10 \cdot 9 \cdot 8!}{8! \cdot 2 \cdot 1}$
$= 45$; 45 line segments

43a. $C(6, 5) = \frac{6!}{(6-5)!5!}$
$= \frac{6 \cdot 5!}{1! \cdot 5!}$
$= 6$; 6 ways

43b. $C(4, 5)$; not possible; 0 ways

43c. $C(9, 5) = \frac{9!}{(9-5)!5!}$
$= \frac{9 \cdot 8 \cdot 7 \cdot 6 \cdot 5!}{4 \cdot 3 \cdot 2 \cdot 1 \cdot 5!}$
$= 126$; 126 ways

43d. 2 dark, 3 milk: $C(9, 2) \cdot C(6, 3) = \frac{9!}{(9-2)!2!} \cdot \frac{6!}{(6-3)!3!}$
$= \frac{9 \cdot 8 \cdot 7!}{7! \cdot 2 \cdot 1} \cdot \frac{6 \cdot 5 \cdot 4 \cdot 3!}{3 \cdot 2 \cdot 1 \cdot 3!}$
$= 36 \cdot 20$ or 720

2 dark, 3 nuts: $C(9, 2) \cdot C(4, 3) = \frac{9!}{(9-2)!2!} \cdot \frac{4!}{(4-3)!3!}$
$= \frac{9 \cdot 8 \cdot 7!}{7! \cdot 2 \cdot 1} \cdot \frac{4 \cdot 3!}{1 \cdot 3!}$
$= 36 \cdot 4$ or 144

2 milk, 3 dark: $C(6, 2) \cdot C(9, 3) = \frac{6!}{(6-2)!2!} \cdot \frac{9!}{(9-3)!3!}$
$= \frac{6 \cdot 5 \cdot 4!}{4! \cdot 2 \cdot 1} \cdot \frac{9 \cdot 8 \cdot 7 \cdot 6!}{6! \cdot 3 \cdot 2 \cdot 1}$
$= 15 \cdot 84$ or 1260

2 milk, 3 nuts: $C(6, 2) \cdot C(4, 3) = \frac{6!}{(6-2)!2!} \cdot \frac{4!}{(4-3)!3!}$
$= \frac{6 \cdot 5 \cdot 4!}{4! \cdot 2 \cdot 1} \cdot \frac{4 \cdot 3!}{1 \cdot 3!}$
$= 15 \cdot 4$ or 60

2 nuts, 3 dark: $C(4, 2) \cdot C(9, 3) = \frac{4!}{(4-2)!2!} \cdot \frac{9!}{(9-3)!3!}$
$= \frac{4 \cdot 3 \cdot 2!}{2 \cdot 1 \cdot 2!} \cdot \frac{9 \cdot 8 \cdot 7 \cdot 6!}{6! \cdot 3 \cdot 2 \cdot 1}$
$= 6 \cdot 84$ or 504

2 nuts, 3 milk: $C(4, 2) \cdot C(6, 3) = \frac{4!}{(4-2)!2!} \cdot \frac{6!}{(6-3)!3!}$
$= \frac{4 \cdot 3 \cdot 2!}{2! \cdot 2 \cdot 1} \cdot \frac{6 \cdot 5 \cdot 4 \cdot 3!}{3! \cdot 3 \cdot 2 \cdot 1}$
$= 6 \cdot 20$ or 120

$720 + 144 + 1260 + 60 + 504 + 120 = 2808$;
2808 ways

43e. $C(4, 2) \cdot C(6, 2) \cdot C(9, 1) = 6 \cdot 15 \cdot \frac{9!}{(9-1)!1!}$
$= 6 \cdot 15 \cdot \frac{9 \cdot 8!}{8! \cdot 1}$
$= 6 \cdot 15 \cdot 9$
$= 108$; 108 ways

44. $C(44, 6) = \frac{44!}{(44-6)!6!}$
$= \frac{44 \cdot 43 \cdot 42 \cdot 41 \cdot 40 \cdot 39 \cdot 38!}{38! \cdot 6 \cdot 5 \cdot 4 \cdot 3 \cdot 2 \cdot 1}$
$= 7{,}059{,}052$; 7,059,052 combinations

45. $C(100, 5) = \frac{100!}{(100-5)!5!}$
$= \frac{100 \cdot 99 \cdot 98 \cdot 97 \cdot 96 \cdot 95!}{95! \cdot 5 \cdot 4 \cdot 3 \cdot 2 \cdot 1}$
$= 75{,}287{,}520$;
75,287,520 senatorial committees

46. $P(12, 2) \cdot C(4, 3) \cdot C(4, 4) = \frac{12!}{(12-2)!} \cdot \frac{4!}{(4-3)!3!} \cdot \frac{4!}{(4-4)!4!}$
$= \frac{12 \cdot 11 \cdot 10!}{10!} \cdot \frac{4 \cdot 3!}{1 \cdot 3!} \cdot \frac{4!}{1 \cdot 4!}$
$= 132 \cdot 4 \cdot 1$
$= 528$; 528 ways

47. $5! = 120$

48. $\sum_{s=1}^{4} 2s\left(-\frac{1}{2}\right)^2$
$= 2(1)\left(-\frac{1}{2}\right)^2 + 2(2)\left(-\frac{1}{2}\right)^2 + 2(3)\left(-\frac{1}{2}\right)^2 + 2(4)\left(-\frac{1}{2}\right)^2$
$= \frac{1}{2} + 1 + \frac{3}{2} + 2$
$= 5$

49a. $y = 100(1.08)^n$

49b. $y = 100(1.08)^{16}$
≈ 342.59; \$342.59

50. $s_1 + s_2 = -2 + (-7)$ $\quad -\frac{b}{a} = -9$; $\frac{c}{a} = 14$
$= -9$ $\quad a = 1, b = 9, c = 14$
$s_1(s_2) = -2(-7)$ $\quad x^2 + 9x + 14 = 0$
$= 14$

51. $19.9(6.02 \times 10^{23}) = (19.9 \cdot 6.02) \times 10^{23}$
$= (119.798) \times 10^{23}$
$= (1.19798 \times 10^2) \times 10^{23}$
$\approx 1.20 \times 10^{25}$;
1.20×10^{25} molecules

52. $x + y = 1$
$y = -x + 1$
$3x - 2y = -7$
$-2y = -3x - 7$
$y = \frac{3}{2}x + \frac{7}{2}$
$(-1, 2)$

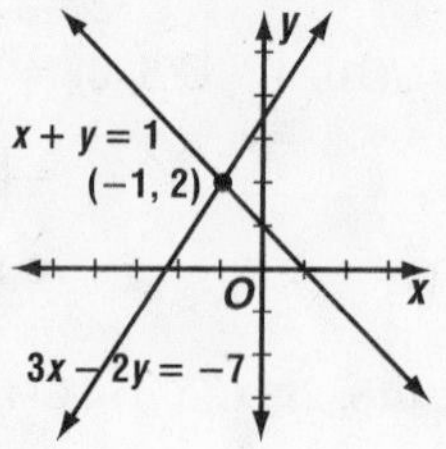

53. $3x - 4y = -10$
$-4y = -3x - 10$
$y = \frac{3}{4}x + \frac{5}{2}$; $m = \frac{3}{4}$, $b = \frac{5}{2}$

54. $|x + 4| = 5$
$x + 4 = 5$ or $x + 4 = -5$
$x = 1$ $\quad x = -9$

Page 731 Mathematics and Society

1. $C(16, 3) + C(16, 2) \cdot C(2, 1) + C(16, 1)$
$= \frac{16!}{(16-3)!3!} + \left(\frac{16!}{(16-2)!2!} \cdot \frac{2!}{(2-1)!1!}\right) + \left(\frac{16!}{(16-1)!1!}\right)$
$= \frac{16 \cdot 15 \cdot 14 \cdot 13!}{13! \cdot 3 \cdot 2 \cdot 1} + \left(\frac{16 \cdot 15 \cdot 14!}{14! \cdot 2 \cdot 1} \cdot \frac{2 \cdot 1}{1 \cdot 1}\right) + \frac{16 \cdot 15!}{15! \cdot 1}$
$= 560 + (120 \cdot 2) + 16$
$= 560 + 240 + 16$
$= 816$
2. See students' work.
3. See students' work.
4. See students' work.

12-4 Probability

Page 735 Check for Understanding

1. The chance that an event will happen.
2. No; the probability of an event can never be greater than 1.
3. 1:5
4. 5:2
5. $P(3 \text{ coins, } 2 \text{ heads}) = \frac{1}{2} \cdot \frac{1}{2} \cdot \frac{1}{2} \cdot C(3, 2)$
$= \frac{1}{8} \cdot \frac{3!}{1!2!} = \frac{1}{8}(3) = \frac{3}{8}$
$P(4 \text{ coins, } 2 \text{ heads}) = \frac{1}{2} \cdot \frac{1}{2} \cdot \frac{1}{2} \cdot \frac{1}{2} \cdot C(4, 2)$
$= \frac{1}{16} \cdot \frac{4!}{2!2!} = \frac{1}{16}(6) = \frac{6}{16} \text{ or } \frac{3}{8}$
Neither is right. The probability for both is $\frac{3}{8}$.
6. Answers will vary.
7. $s = 3$
$f = 4 - 3$ or 1
odds = 3:1
8. $s = 2$
$f = 9 - 2$ or 7
odds = 2:7
9. $s = 6, f = 5$
$s + f = 11$
probability = $\frac{6}{11}$
10. $s = 1, f = 1$
$s + f = 2$
probability = $\frac{1}{2}$
11. $s = 4$
$f = 5 - 4$ or 1
odds of not earning scholarship = 1:4
12. $s = 1, f = 9$
$s + f = 10$
probability = $\frac{1}{10}$
13. $P(2 \text{ vowels}) = \frac{C(3, 2)}{C(7, 2)}$
$= \frac{\frac{3!}{1!2!}}{\frac{7!}{5!2!}}$
$= \frac{3}{21} \text{ or } \frac{1}{7}$
14. $P(2 \text{ consonants}) = \frac{C(4, 2)}{C(7, 2)}$
$= \frac{\frac{4!}{2!2!}}{\frac{7!}{5!2!}}$
$= \frac{6}{21} \text{ or } \frac{2}{7}$
15. $P(1 \text{ vowel, } 1 \text{ consonant}) = \frac{C(3, 1) \cdot C(4, 1)}{C(7, 2)}$
$= \frac{\frac{3!}{2!1!} \cdot \frac{4!}{3!1!}}{\frac{7!}{5!2!}}$
$= \frac{3 \cdot 4}{21}$
$= \frac{12}{21} \text{ or } \frac{4}{7}$

16a. $s = 2, f = 1$
$s + f = 3$
probability = $\frac{2}{3}$

16b. $s = 1, f = 6$
$s + f = 7$
probability = $\frac{1}{7}$

16c. $s = 1, f = 16$
$s + f = 17$
probability = $\frac{1}{17}$

Pages 736–738 Exercises

17. $s = 1$
$f = 2 - 1$ or 1
odds = 1:1
18. $s = 3$
$f = 8 - 3$ or 5
odds = 3:5
19. $s = 11$
$f = 12 - 11$ or 1
odds = 11:1
20. $s = 4$
$f = 7 - 4$ or 3
odds = 4:3
21. $s = 1$
$f = 5 - 1$ or 4
odds = 1:4
22. $s = 4$
$f = 11 - 4$ or 7
odds = 4:7
23. $s = 6, f = 1$
$s + f = 7$
probability = $\frac{6}{7}$
24. $s = 3, f = 7$
$s + f = 10$
probability = $\frac{3}{10}$
25. $s = 5, f = 6$
$s + f = 11$
probability = $\frac{5}{11}$
26. $s = 9, f = 8$
$s + f = 17$
probability = $\frac{9}{17}$
27. $s = 1, f = 8$
$s + f = 9$
probability = $\frac{1}{9}$
28. $s = 7, f = 9$
$s + f = 16$
probability = $\frac{7}{16}$

29a. $\frac{C(40, 1)}{C(160, 1)} = \frac{\frac{40!}{39!1!}}{\frac{160!}{159!1!}}$
$= \frac{40}{160} \text{ or } \frac{1}{4}$

29b. $\frac{C(80, 1)}{C(200, 1)} = \frac{\frac{80!}{79!1!}}{\frac{200!}{199!1!}}$
$= \frac{80}{200} \text{ or } \frac{2}{5}$

29c. $2\left(\frac{1}{4}\right) = \frac{1}{2}$ Double the probability.
$\frac{40 + x}{160 + x} = \frac{1}{2}$ Add x Polynesian Punch jelly beans to original probability and set equal to $\frac{1}{2}$.
$80 + 2x = 160 + x$ Solve.
$x = 80$; 80 jelly beans

30. $P(2 \text{ gray kittens}) = \frac{C(4, 2)}{C(11, 2)}$
$= \frac{\frac{4!}{2!2!}}{\frac{11!}{9!2!}}$
$= \frac{6}{55}$
$s = 6$
$f = 55 - 6$ or 49
odds = 6:49

31. $P(2 \text{ white kittens}) = \frac{C(7, 2)}{C(11, 2)}$
$= \frac{\frac{7!}{5!2!}}{\frac{11!}{9!2!}}$
$= \frac{21}{55}$
$s = 21$
$f = 55 - 21$ or 34
odds = 21:34

32. $P(\text{1 gray, 1 white}) = \dfrac{C(4, 1) \cdot C(7, 1)}{C(11, 2)}$

$= \dfrac{\frac{4!}{3!1!} \cdot \frac{7!}{6!1!}}{\frac{11!}{9!2!}}$

$= \dfrac{4 \cdot 7}{55}$

$= \dfrac{28}{55}$

$s = 28$

$f = 55 - 28$ or 27

odds = 28:27

33. $P(\text{all jazz}) = \dfrac{C(8, 3)}{C(25, 3)}$

$= \dfrac{\frac{8!}{5!3!}}{\frac{25!}{22!3!}}$

$= \dfrac{56}{2300}$ or $\dfrac{14}{575}$

34. $P(\text{all rock}) = \dfrac{C(12, 3)}{C(25, 3)}$

$= \dfrac{\frac{12!}{9!3!}}{\frac{25!}{22!3!}}$

$= \dfrac{220}{2300}$ or $\dfrac{11}{115}$

35. $P(\text{1 classical, 2 jazz}) = \dfrac{C(5, 1) \cdot C(8, 2)}{C(25, 3)}$

$= \dfrac{\frac{5!}{4!1!} \cdot \frac{8!}{6!2!}}{\frac{25!}{22!3!}}$

$= \dfrac{5 \cdot 28}{2300}$

$= \dfrac{140}{2300}$ or $\dfrac{7}{115}$

36. $P(\text{2 classical, 1 rock}) = \dfrac{C(5, 2) \cdot C(12, 1)}{C(25, 3)}$

$= \dfrac{\frac{5!}{3!2!} \cdot \frac{12!}{11!1!}}{\frac{25!}{22!3!}}$

$= \dfrac{10 \cdot 12}{2300}$

$= \dfrac{120}{2300}$ or $\dfrac{6}{115}$

37. $P(\text{1 classical, 1 jazz, 1 rock}) = \dfrac{C(5, 1) \cdot C(8, 1) \cdot C(12, 1)}{C(25, 3)}$

$= \dfrac{\frac{5!}{4!1!} \cdot \frac{8!}{7!1!} \cdot \frac{12!}{11!1!}}{\frac{25!}{22!3!}}$

$= \dfrac{5 \cdot 8 \cdot 12}{2300}$

$= \dfrac{480}{2300}$ or $\dfrac{24}{115}$

38. $P(\text{2 jazz, 1 reggae}) = 0$

39. A of a circle $= \pi r^2$ A of square $= s^2$

$= \pi 1^2$ $= 15^2$

$= \pi$ $= 225$

40 circles $= 40\pi$ Probability $= \dfrac{40\pi}{225}$ or about 56%

40a. $6 \cdot 6 \cdot 6 = 216$; 216 combinations

40b. $\dfrac{6}{216} = \dfrac{1}{36}$

40c. $3 \cdot \dfrac{6}{6} \cdot \dfrac{1}{6} \cdot \dfrac{5}{6} = \dfrac{5}{12}$

41. A of circle $= \pi r^2$ A of triangle $= \frac{1}{2}bh$

$= \pi 4^2$ $= \frac{1}{2}(4 + 4)4$

$= 16\pi$ $= 16$

A of shaded region $= 16\pi - 16$

Probability $= \dfrac{16\pi - 16}{16\pi}$ or $\dfrac{\pi - 1}{\pi}$

42. Values of k making $x^2 + kx + 16$ factorable:

$k = 8, 10$

Probability $= \dfrac{2}{11}$

43. sum = 9; (1, 8), (8, 1), (2, 7), (7, 2), (3, 6), (6, 3), (4, 5), (5, 4); 8 ways

total possible rolls: $8 \cdot 8 = 64$

$P(\text{sum} = 9) = \dfrac{8}{64}$ or $\dfrac{1}{8}$

44. $\dfrac{5000}{250{,}000} = \dfrac{x}{50}$

$250{,}000 = 250{,}000x$

$1 = x$; 1 person

45a. P(next to the Pacific Ocean) $= \dfrac{5}{50}$ or $\dfrac{1}{10}$

45b. P(has at least one representative in the House of Representatives) = 1

45c. P(has at least five neighboring states) $= \dfrac{21}{50}$

45d. P(has three U.S. Senators) = 0

46. $P(\text{winning}) = \dfrac{C(6, 6)}{C(49, 6)}$

$= \dfrac{\frac{6!}{0!6!}}{\frac{49!}{43!6!}}$

$= \dfrac{1}{13{,}983{,}816}$

47. P(white short fur) $= \dfrac{3}{16}$

48a. area of $A = \pi 4^2 - \pi 2^2$ or 12π

area of dart board $= \pi 8^2$ or 64π

$P(A) = \dfrac{12\pi}{64\pi} = \dfrac{3}{16}$

48b. area of $B = \pi 6^2 - \pi 4^2$ or 20π

$P(B) = \dfrac{20\pi}{64\pi} = \dfrac{5}{16}$

48c. area of $C = \pi 8^2 - \pi 6^2$ or 28π

$P(C) = \dfrac{28\pi}{64\pi} = \dfrac{7}{16}$

49. $C(6, 2) \cdot C(8, 2) = \dfrac{6!}{4!2!} \cdot \dfrac{8!}{6!2!}$

$= 15 \cdot 28$

$= 420$; 420 ways

50. $5! = 120$

51. $r = \dfrac{9}{3}$ or 3

$a_3 = 3 \div 3$ or 1

$a_2 = 1 \div 3$ or $\frac{1}{3}$

$a_1 = \frac{1}{3} \div 3$ or $\frac{1}{9}$

52.

x	$f(x)$
1	0
−1	0
1.8	0.5376
1.7	−0.2079

x	$f(x)$
1.6	−0.6864
−1.8	0.5376
−1.7	−0.2079
−1.6	−0.6864

1, −1, 1.7, −1.7

53. $f(m) = (2m - 5)^2$
$= 4m^2 - 20m + 25$

54. $\sqrt[4]{5} + 6\sqrt[4]{5} - 2\sqrt[4]{5} = 5\sqrt[4]{5}$

55. $x + 2y \le 7$ $\quad x + 2y \le 7$ $\quad x + 2y \le 7$
$0 + 2(0) \overset{?}{\le} 7$ $\quad 1 + 2(2) \overset{?}{\le} 7$ $\quad -3 + 2(1) \overset{?}{\le} 7$
$0 \le 7$ ✓ $\quad 5 \le 7$ ✓ $\quad -1 \le 7$ ✓

56. $x = 4y + 7$
$x - 7 = 4y$
$\frac{1}{4}x - \frac{7}{4} = y$; perpendicular slope $= -4$

57. $2 \le \frac{x}{3} + 5 \le 13$
$-3 \le \frac{x}{3} \le 8$
$-9 \le x \le 24$

Page 738 Self Test

1a. tree diagram

1b. $2 \cdot 2 \cdot 2 \cdot 3 = 24$

2. $6 \cdot 18 \cdot 7 = 756$

3. There are $P(5, 5)$ or 5! ways of arranging the books in the algebra group.
There are $P(4, 4)$ or 4! ways of arranging the books in the geometry group.
There are 5 ways that the algebra books can be together.
$5! \cdot 4! \cdot 5 = 14{,}400$

4. $P(100, 100) = \frac{100!}{(100 - 100)!}$
$= \frac{100!}{0!}$
$= 100!$

5. permutation

6. combination

7. $P(12, 3) = \frac{12!}{(12 - 3)!}$
$= \frac{12!}{9!}$
$= 1320$

8. $C(8, 3) = \frac{8!}{(8 - 3)!3!}$
$= \frac{8!}{5!3!}$
$= 56$

9. $C(13, 6) = \frac{13!}{(13 - 6)!6!}$
$= \frac{13!}{7!6!}$
$= 1716$; 1716 terms

10. $C(52, 13) = \frac{52!}{(52 - 13)!13!}$
$= \frac{52!}{39!13!}$

12-5 Multiplying Probabilities

Page 742 Check for Understanding

1. Multiply their individual probabilities.
2. Events that are affected by previous choices.
3. Events A and B are independent since the outcome of each die rolled does not affect the other.
4. See students' work.

5a. no; Since you are replacing the marbles, you may not have picked all of the marbles and there may be a black marble in the bag.

5b. no; You can not be sure you have picked every marble in the bag at least once.

5c. Sample answer: As the number of trials increases, the results become more reliable. However, you cannot be absolutely certain there are no black marbles in the bag without looking at the marbles.

6.

		First Choice: Black 5/8	First Choice: Green 3/8
Second Choice	Black 5/8	$\frac{25}{64}$	$\frac{15}{64}$
	Green 3/8	$\frac{15}{64}$	$\frac{9}{64}$

7. dependent; $P(\text{blue, then black, then blue}) = \frac{7}{12} \cdot \frac{3}{11} \cdot \frac{6}{10} = \frac{21}{220}$

8. independent; $P(\text{2 on green, 6 on red}) = \frac{1}{6} \cdot \frac{1}{6} = \frac{1}{36}$

9a. independent; $P(\$1, \$5, \$10) = \frac{3}{9} \cdot \frac{4}{9} \cdot \frac{2}{9} = \frac{8}{243}$

9b. dependent; $P(\$1, \$5, \$10) = \frac{3}{9} \cdot \frac{4}{8} \cdot \frac{2}{7} = \frac{1}{21}$

10. $P(\text{selecting 2 movie videos}) = \frac{8}{16} \cdot \frac{7}{15} = \frac{7}{30}$

11. $P(\text{selecting 2 movie videos}) = \frac{8}{16} \cdot \frac{8}{16} = \frac{1}{4}$

12. $P(\text{selecting an exercise video, then a cartoon video}) = \frac{3}{16} \cdot \frac{5}{15} = \frac{1}{16}$

Pages 743–745 Exercises

13. dependent; $P(\text{2 diet cola}) = \frac{3}{8} \cdot \frac{2}{7} = \frac{3}{28}$

14. independent; $P(\text{2 apricots}) = \frac{5}{9} \cdot \frac{5}{9} = \frac{25}{81}$

15. independent; $P(\text{reach highest level in 4 games}) = \frac{3}{7} \cdot \frac{3}{7} \cdot \frac{3}{7} \cdot \frac{3}{7} = \frac{81}{2401}$

16. $P(\text{selecting 2 consonants}) = \frac{5}{7} \cdot \frac{5}{7} = \frac{25}{49}$

17. $P(\text{selecting 2 consonants}) = \frac{5}{7} \cdot \frac{4}{6} = \frac{10}{21}$

18. $P(\text{selecting the same letter twice}) = \frac{1}{7} \cdot \frac{0}{7} = 0$

19a. (2, 6), (6, 2), (4, 4), (3, 5), (5, 3)

19b. (4, 4) is one of 5 possible outcomes when rolling a sum of 8.

20. $P(\text{breaking 2 vases}) = \frac{3}{10} \cdot \frac{2}{9} = \frac{1}{15}$

21. $P(\text{breaking 2 statues}) = \frac{4}{10} \cdot \frac{3}{9} = \frac{2}{15}$

22. $P(\text{breaking a picture frame, then a vase}) = \frac{3}{10} \cdot \frac{3}{9} = \frac{1}{10}$

23. $P(\text{breaking a picture frame and a vase}) = \frac{3}{10} \cdot \frac{3}{9} \cdot C(2, 1) = \frac{1}{10} \cdot \frac{2!}{1!1!} = \frac{1}{10} \cdot 2 = \frac{1}{5}$

24a. First Spin Second Spin

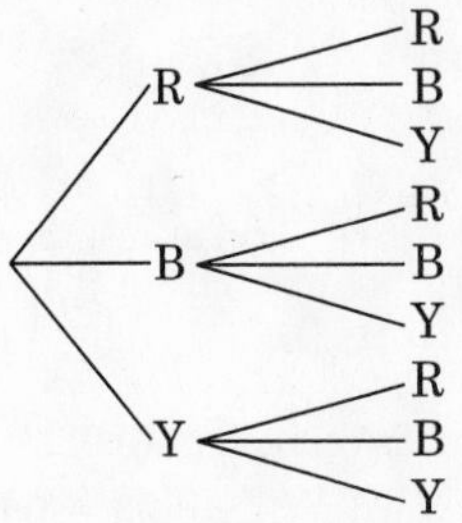

9 possibilities
$P(R, B) = \frac{1}{3} \cdot \frac{1}{3} = \frac{1}{9}$

24b–c.

		Blue 1/3	Yellow 1/3	Red 1/3
		First Spin		
Second Spin	Blue 1/3	BB 1/9	BY 1/9	BR 1/9
	Yellow 1/3	YB 1/9	YY 1/9	YR 1/9
	Red 1/3	RB 1/9	RY 1/9	RR 1/9

24d. $P(\text{same color both spins}) = \frac{3}{9}$ or $\frac{1}{3}$

24e. $P(\text{same color twice was red}) = \frac{1}{3}$

25. $P(2 \text{ and } 3) = \frac{1}{6} \cdot \frac{1}{6} = \frac{1}{36}$

26. $P(\text{no 6s}) = \frac{5}{6} \cdot \frac{5}{6} = \frac{25}{36}$

27. $P(\text{two 4s}) = \frac{1}{6} \cdot \frac{1}{6} = \frac{1}{36}$

28. $P(1 \text{ and any other number}) = \frac{1}{6} \cdot \frac{6}{6} = \frac{6}{36}$ or $\frac{1}{6}$

29. $P(\text{two numbers alike}) = \frac{6}{6} \cdot \frac{1}{6} = \frac{6}{36}$ or $\frac{1}{6}$

30. $P(\text{two different numbers}) = \frac{6}{6} \cdot \frac{5}{6} = \frac{30}{36}$ or $\frac{5}{6}$

31a. $P(3 \text{ different colors}) = \frac{7}{17} \cdot \frac{4}{16} \cdot \frac{6}{15} = \frac{7}{170}$

31b. $P(3 \text{ different colors}) = \frac{7}{17} \cdot \frac{4}{17} \cdot \frac{6}{17} = \frac{168}{4913}$

32a. $P(3 \text{ different chocolates}) = \frac{8}{16} \cdot \frac{3}{15} \cdot \frac{5}{14} = \frac{1}{28}$

32b. $P(3 \text{ different chocolates}) = \frac{8}{16} \cdot \frac{3}{16} \cdot \frac{5}{16} = \frac{15}{512}$

33. $P(\text{all clubs}) = \frac{13}{52} \cdot \frac{12}{51} \cdot \frac{11}{50} \cdot \ldots \cdot \frac{1}{40} = \frac{1}{635{,}013{,}559{,}600}$

34. $P(\text{all black cards}) = \frac{26}{52} \cdot \frac{25}{51} \cdot \frac{24}{50} \cdot \ldots \cdot \frac{14}{40} = \frac{19}{1{,}160{,}054}$

35. $P(\text{all one suit}) = \frac{52}{52} \cdot \frac{12}{51} \cdot \frac{11}{50} \cdot \frac{10}{49} \cdot \ldots \cdot \frac{1}{40}$

$= \frac{4}{635{,}013{,}559{,}600}$ or $\frac{1}{158{,}753{,}389{,}900}$

36. $P(\text{all face cards}) = \frac{12}{52} \cdot \frac{11}{51} \cdot \frac{10}{50} \cdot \ldots \cdot \frac{0}{52} = 0$

37a.

		Green 1/3	Blue 1/3	Red 1/3
		Spinner 1		
Spinner 2	Green 1/4	GG 1/12	BG 1/12	RG 1/12
	Blue 1/4	GB 1/12	BB 1/12	RB 1/12
	Red 1/2	GR 1/6	BR 1/6	RR 1/6

$\frac{1}{12}$

37b. $P(\text{red}) = \frac{1}{3} \cdot \frac{1}{2} = \frac{1}{6}$

37c. 6 outcomes: GR, GB, BR, BG, RG, RB

38. See students' work.

39a. $P(3 \text{ men get own hats}) = \frac{1}{12} \cdot \frac{1}{11} \cdot \frac{1}{10} = \frac{1}{1320}$

39b. $P(5 \text{ get own hats}) = \frac{1}{12} \cdot \frac{1}{12} \cdot \frac{1}{12} \cdot \frac{1}{12} \cdot \frac{1}{12} = \left(\frac{1}{12}\right)^5$
$= \frac{1}{248{,}832}$

40a. 93% = 0.93; $P(\text{first 5 words correct}) = (0.93)^5 \approx 0.7$

40b. chance of misspelling word = 1 − 0.93 = 0.07;
P(first 3 correct, next 2 incorrect)
$= (0.93)^3 \cdot (0.07)^2 \approx 0.004$

40c. $P(30 \text{ words correct}) = (0.93)^{30} \approx 0.11$

41a. $P(3 \text{ red gumballs}) = \frac{C(7, 3)}{C(36, 3)}$

$= \frac{\frac{7!}{4!3!}}{\frac{36!}{33!3!}}$

$= \frac{35}{7140}$ or $\frac{1}{204}$

41b. P(2 white gumballs, 1 purple gumball)

$= \frac{C(7, 2) \cdot C(9, 1)}{C(36, 3)}$

$= \frac{\frac{7!}{5!2!} \cdot \frac{9!}{8!1!}}{\frac{36!}{33!3!}}$

$= \frac{21 \cdot 9}{7140}$

$= \frac{189}{7140}$ or $\frac{9}{340}$

41c. P(1 purple gumball, 1 orange gumball, 1 yellow gumball)

$= \frac{C(9, 1) \cdot C(8, 1) \cdot C(5, 1)}{C(36, 3)}$

$= \frac{\frac{9!}{8!1!} \cdot \frac{8!}{7!1!} \cdot \frac{5!}{4!1!}}{\frac{36!}{33!3!}}$

$= \frac{9 \cdot 8 \cdot 5}{7140}$

$= \frac{360}{7140}$ or $\frac{6}{119}$

42. $d = 33 - 50 = -17$

$a_n = a_1 + (n - 1)d$
$-52 = 50 + (n - 1)(-17)$
$-102 = -17n + 17$
$-119 = -17n$
$7 = n$

$S_n = \frac{n}{2}(a_1 + a_n)$
$S_7 = \frac{7}{2}(50 + (-52))$
$= \frac{7}{2}(-2)$
$= -7$

43.
$\frac{1}{y + 1} - \frac{3}{y - 3} = 2$
$(y + 1)(y - 3)\left(\frac{1}{y + 1} - \frac{3}{y - 3}\right) = (y + 1)(y - 3)(2)$
$y - 3 - 3(y + 1) = (y^2 - 2y - 3)2$
$y - 3 - 3y - 3 = 2y^2 - 4y - 6$
$0 = 2y^2 - 2y$
$0 = 2y(y - 1)$
$2y = 0$ or $y - 1 = 0$
$y = 0$ $\quad y = 1$

44.
$x^2 - 22x = -117$
$x^2 - 22x + 117 = 0$
$(x - 9)(x - 13) = 0$
$x - 9 = 0$ or $x - 13 = 0$
$x = 9$ $\quad x = 13$

45. $A = A_0(2.7)^{-\frac{3}{5}}$
$= 500(2.7)^{-\frac{3}{5}}$
$\approx 500(0.5510)$
≈ 275.52; 276 milligrams

46. $3x - y = 4$
$-y = -3x + 4$
$y = 3x - 4$
$9x - 6 = 3y$
$3x - 2 = y$
No solution, inconsistent

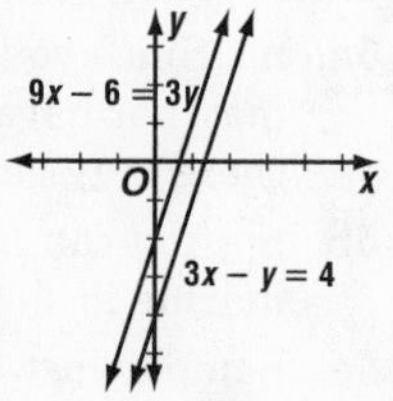

47. $m = \frac{-4-4}{0-7}$
$= \frac{-8}{-7}$
$= \frac{8}{7}$; perpendicular slope $= -\frac{7}{8}$

48. $12a^2 + bc = 12(3)^2 + (7)(-2)$
$= 12(9) + (-14)$
$= 108 - 14$
$= 94$

12-6 Adding Probabilities

Page 748 Check for Understanding

1. Mutually exclusive events cannot occur at the same time, whereas inclusive events can.
2. Sample answer: going to school, eating pizza, or watching TV.
3. $134 - 62 = 72$
   $108 - 62 = 46$

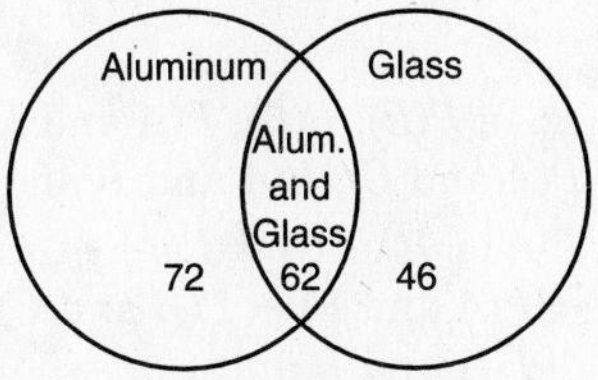

4a. The events are not mutally exclusive.

4b. probability of rain on both days

5a. mutually exclusive; $P(5 \text{ or ace}) = P(5) + P(\text{ace})$
$= \frac{4}{52} + \frac{4}{52}$
$= \frac{8}{52}$ or $\frac{2}{13}$

5b. inclusive;
$P(\text{jack or diamond})$
$= P(\text{jack}) + P(\text{diamond}) - P(\text{jack and diamond})$
$= \frac{4}{52} + \frac{13}{52} - \frac{1}{52}$
$= \frac{16}{52}$ or $\frac{4}{13}$

6a. $P(\text{at least 4 heads})$
$= P(4 \text{ heads}) + P(5 \text{ heads}) + P(6 \text{ heads})$
$= \frac{1}{2} \cdot \frac{1}{2} \cdot \frac{1}{2} \cdot \frac{1}{2} \cdot \frac{1}{2} \cdot \frac{1}{2} \cdot C(6, 4) +$
$\frac{1}{2} \cdot \frac{1}{2} \cdot \frac{1}{2} \cdot \frac{1}{2} \cdot \frac{1}{2} \cdot \frac{1}{2} \cdot C(6, 5) +$
$\frac{1}{2} \cdot \frac{1}{2} \cdot \frac{1}{2} \cdot \frac{1}{2} \cdot \frac{1}{2} \cdot \frac{1}{2} \cdot C(6, 6)$
$= \frac{1}{64}\left(\frac{6!}{2!4!}\right) + \frac{1}{64}\left(\frac{6!}{1!5!}\right) + \frac{1}{64}\left(\frac{6!}{0!6!}\right)$
$= \frac{1}{64}(15) + \frac{1}{64}(6) + \frac{1}{64}(1)$
$= \frac{22}{64}$ or $\frac{11}{32}$

6b. $P(3 \text{ tails or } 2 \text{ heads})$
$= \frac{1}{2} \cdot \frac{1}{2} \cdot \frac{1}{2} \cdot \frac{1}{2} \cdot \frac{1}{2} \cdot \frac{1}{2} \cdot C(6, 3) +$
$\frac{1}{2} \cdot \frac{1}{2} \cdot \frac{1}{2} \cdot \frac{1}{2} \cdot \frac{1}{2} \cdot \frac{1}{2} \cdot C(6, 2)$
$= \frac{1}{64}\left(\frac{6!}{3!3!}\right) + \frac{1}{64}\left(\frac{6!}{4!2!}\right)$
$= \frac{1}{64}(20) + \frac{1}{64}(15)$
$= \frac{35}{64}$

6c. $P(4 \text{ tails or } 1 \text{ head})$
$= \frac{1}{2} \cdot \frac{1}{2} \cdot \frac{1}{2} \cdot \frac{1}{2} \cdot \frac{1}{2} \cdot \frac{1}{2} \cdot C(6, 4) +$
$\frac{1}{2} \cdot \frac{1}{2} \cdot \frac{1}{2} \cdot \frac{1}{2} \cdot \frac{1}{2} \cdot \frac{1}{2} \cdot C(6, 1)$
$= \frac{1}{64}\left(\frac{6!}{2!4!}\right) + \frac{1}{64}\left(\frac{6!}{5!1!}\right)$
$= \frac{1}{64}(15) + \frac{1}{64}(6)$
$= \frac{21}{64}$

6d. $P(\text{all heads or all tails})$
$= \frac{1}{2} \cdot \frac{1}{2} \cdot \frac{1}{2} \cdot \frac{1}{2} \cdot \frac{1}{2} \cdot \frac{1}{2} \cdot C(6, 6) +$
$\frac{1}{2} \cdot \frac{1}{2} \cdot \frac{1}{2} \cdot \frac{1}{2} \cdot \frac{1}{2} \cdot \frac{1}{2} \cdot C(6, 6)$
$= \frac{1}{64}\left(\frac{6!}{0!6!}\right) + \frac{1}{64}\left(\frac{6!}{0!6!}\right)$
$= \frac{1}{64} + \frac{1}{64}$
$= \frac{2}{64}$ or $\frac{1}{32}$

7. $P(\text{vowel or letter from equation}) = \frac{5}{26} + \frac{3}{26}$
$= \frac{8}{26}$

8. $P(\text{French or algebra}) = \frac{550}{1400} + \frac{700}{1400} - \frac{400}{1400}$
$= \frac{850}{1400}$
$= \frac{17}{28}$

Pages 749–751 Exercises

9. mutally exclusive;
$P(\text{physics book or history book}) = \frac{3}{9} + \frac{2}{9}$
$= \frac{5}{9}$

10. inclusive;
$P(\text{black card or face card}) = \frac{26}{52} + \frac{12}{52} - \frac{6}{52}$
$= \frac{32}{52}$ or $\frac{8}{13}$

11. inclusive;
$P(\text{tossing 5 or number greater than 3}) = \frac{1}{6} + \frac{3}{6} - \frac{1}{6}$
$= \frac{3}{6}$ or $\frac{1}{2}$

12. inclusive;
$P(\text{boy or a senior}) = \frac{14}{34} + \frac{11}{34} - \frac{4}{34}$
$= \frac{21}{34}$

13. $P(\text{exactly 2 silver}) = \frac{C(4, 2) \cdot C(5, 1)}{C(9,3)}$
$= \frac{6 \cdot 5}{84}$
$= \frac{30}{84}$ or $\frac{5}{14}$

14. $P(\text{all 3 gold or all 3 silver}) = P(3 \text{ gold}) + P(3 \text{ silver})$
$= \frac{C(5, 3)}{C(9, 3)} + \frac{C(4, 3)}{C(9, 3)}$
$= \frac{10}{84} + \frac{4}{84}$
$= \frac{14}{84}$ or $\frac{1}{6}$

15. $P(\text{at least 2 gold}) = P(2 \text{ gold}) + P(3 \text{ gold})$
$= \frac{C(5, 2) \cdot C(4, 1)}{C(9, 3)} + \frac{C(5, 3) \cdot C(4, 0)}{C(9, 3)}$
$= \frac{10 \cdot 4}{84} + \frac{10 \cdot 1}{84}$
$= \frac{40}{84} + \frac{10}{84}$
$= \frac{50}{84}$ or $\frac{25}{42}$

16. $P(\text{at least 1 silver})$
$= P(\text{1 silver}) + P(\text{2 silver}) + P(\text{3 silver})$
$= \frac{C(4, 1) \cdot C(5, 2)}{C(9, 3)} + \frac{C(4, 2) \cdot C(5, 1)}{C(9, 3)} + \frac{C(4, 3) \cdot C(5, 0)}{C(9, 3)}$
$= \frac{4 \cdot 10}{84} + \frac{6 \cdot 5}{84} + \frac{4 \cdot 1}{84}$
$= \frac{40}{84} + \frac{30}{84} + \frac{4}{84}$
$= \frac{74}{84}$ or $\frac{37}{42}$

17. $P(\text{both kings or both black})$
$= P(\text{both kings}) + P(\text{both black}) - P(\text{both black kings})$
$= \frac{4}{52} \cdot \frac{3}{51} + \frac{26}{52} \cdot \frac{25}{51} - \frac{2}{52} \cdot \frac{1}{51}$
$= \frac{12}{2652} + \frac{650}{2652} - \frac{2}{2652}$
$= \frac{660}{2652}$ or $\frac{55}{221}$

18. $P(\text{both kings or both face cards})$
$= P(\text{both kings}) + P(\text{both face cards}) - P(\text{both kings})$
$= \frac{4}{52} \cdot \frac{3}{51} + \frac{12}{52} \cdot \frac{11}{51} - \frac{4}{52} \cdot \frac{3}{51}$
$= \frac{12}{2652} + \frac{132}{2652} - \frac{12}{2652}$
$= \frac{132}{2652}$ or $\frac{11}{221}$

19. $P(\text{both face cards or both red})$
$= P(\text{both face cards}) + P(\text{both red})$
$- P(\text{both red face cards})$
$= \frac{12}{52} \cdot \frac{11}{52} + \frac{26}{52} \cdot \frac{25}{51} - \frac{6}{52} \cdot \frac{5}{51}$
$= \frac{132}{2652} + \frac{650}{2652} - \frac{30}{2652}$
$= \frac{752}{2652}$ or $\frac{188}{663}$

20. $P(\text{both either red or a king})$
$= P(\text{both red or both kings})$
$+ P(\text{red but not a king, 1 king})$
$= [P(\text{both red}) + P(\text{both kings})$
$- P(\text{both red kings})] + \frac{C(24, 1) \cdot C(4, 1)}{C(52, 2)}$
$= \left[\frac{26}{52} \cdot \frac{25}{51} + \frac{4}{52} \cdot \frac{3}{51} - \frac{2}{52} \cdot \frac{1}{51}\right] + \frac{24 \cdot 4}{1326}$
$= \frac{55}{221} + \frac{96}{1326}$
$= \frac{426}{1326}$ or $\frac{71}{221}$

21. $P(\text{4 women, 1 man or 4 men, 1 woman})$
$= P(\text{4 women, 1 man}) + P(\text{4 men, 1 woman})$
$= \frac{C(7, 4) \cdot C(6, 1)}{C(13, 5)} + \frac{C(6, 4) \cdot C(7, 1)}{C(13, 5)}$
$= \frac{35 \cdot 6}{1287} + \frac{15 \cdot 7}{1287}$
$= \frac{315}{1287}$ or $\frac{35}{143}$

22. $P(\text{3 women, 2 men or 3 men, 2 women})$
$= P(\text{3 women, 2 men}) + P(\text{3 men, 2 women})$
$= \frac{C(7, 3) \cdot C(6, 2)}{C(13, 5)} + \frac{C(6, 3) \cdot C(7, 2)}{C(13, 5)}$
$= \frac{35 \cdot 15}{1287} + \frac{20 \cdot 21}{1287}$
$= \frac{945}{1287}$ or $\frac{105}{143}$

23. $P(\text{all women or all men})$
$= P(\text{all men}) + P(\text{all women})$
$= \frac{C(6, 5) \cdot C(7, 0)}{C(13, 5)} + \frac{C(7, 5) \cdot C(6, 0)}{C(13, 5)}$
$= \frac{6 \cdot 1}{1287} + \frac{21 \cdot 1}{1287}$
$= \frac{27}{1287}$ or $\frac{3}{143}$

24. $P(\text{at least 3 women})$
$= P(\text{3 women}) + P(\text{4 women}) + P(\text{5 women})$
$= \frac{C(7, 3) \cdot C(6, 2)}{C(13, 5)} + \frac{C(7, 4) \cdot C(6, 1)}{C(13, 5)} + \frac{C(7, 5) \cdot C(6, 0)}{C(13, 5)}$
$= \frac{35 \cdot 15}{1287} + \frac{35 \cdot 6}{1287} + \frac{21 \cdot 1}{1287}$
$= \frac{756}{1287}$ or $\frac{84}{143}$

25. $P(\text{each is a 25}) = \frac{1}{30} \cdot \frac{1}{26}$
$= \frac{1}{780}$

26. $P(\text{neither is a 20}) = \frac{29}{30} \cdot \frac{25}{26}$
$= \frac{145}{156}$

27. $P(\text{at least one is a 30}) = \frac{1}{30} \cdot \frac{26}{26} + \frac{30}{30} \cdot \frac{1}{26} - \frac{1}{30} \cdot \frac{1}{26}$
$= \frac{26}{780} + \frac{30}{780} - \frac{1}{780}$
$= \frac{55}{780}$ or $\frac{11}{156}$

28. $P(\text{each is greater than 15}) = \frac{15}{30} \cdot \frac{26}{26}$
$= \frac{1}{2}$

29. $P(A)$, $P(B)$, $P(C)$, $P(A \text{ and } B)$, $P(B \text{ and } C)$, $P(A \text{ and } C)$, $P(A \text{ and } B \text{ and } C)$;
$P(A \text{ or } B \text{ or } C) = P(A) + P(B) + P(C)$
$- P(A \text{ and } B) - P(B \text{ and } C) - P(A \text{ and } C)$
$+ P(A \text{ and } B \text{ and } C)$

30. Sample answer: Let A stand for a white counter in the bag in the beginning, B for a black counter, and C for the added white counter. After a white counter is taken, there are three equally possible situations:

1. C has been taken, leaving A.
2. A has been taken, leaving C.
3. C has been taken, leaving B.

Since a white counter remains in the bag for the first two cases and a black counter remains in the third case, the answer is therefore $\frac{2}{3}$.

31. $P(\text{woman or person in his or her 20s})$
$= P(\text{woman}) + P(\text{person in his or her 20s})$
$- P(\text{woman in 20s})$
$= 52\% + 74\% - \frac{1800}{6000}$
$= 52\% + 74\% - 30\%$
$= 96\%$

32a.

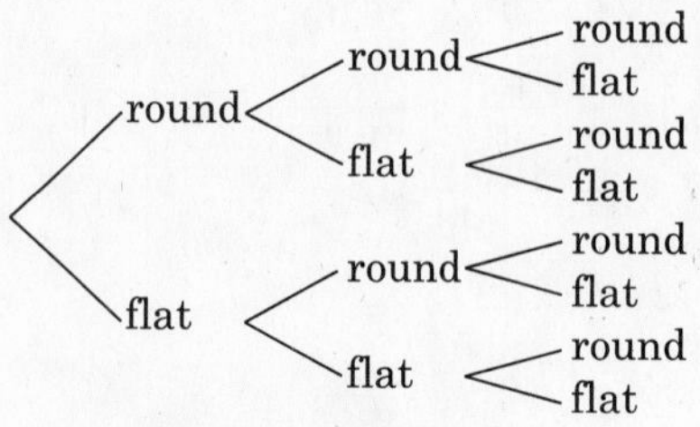

32b. $P(\text{advancing 2 lines}) = \frac{1}{8}$
$P(\text{advancing 1 line}) = \frac{1}{8}$
$P(\text{advancing at least 1 line}) = \frac{1}{8} + \frac{1}{8}$
$= \frac{1}{4}$
$P(\text{losing a turn}) = \frac{6}{8}$ or $\frac{3}{4}$

33a.

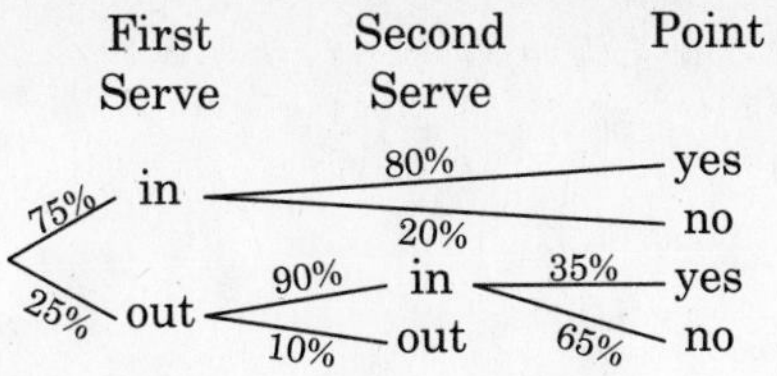

33b. $0.75(0.80) + 0.25(0.90)(0.35)$
$= 0.67875$ or about 67.9%

33c. $\dfrac{0.75(0.80)}{0.75(0.80) + 0.25(0.90)(0.35)}$
$= 0.8839779$ or about 88.4%

34a. P(being intoxicated and having an unimpeded trip) =
$0.02 \cdot 0.99911 = 0.0199822$

34b. P(being unintoxicated and having an unimpeded trip) =
$0.98 \cdot 0.99984 = 0.9798432$

34c. P(being intoxicated, arrested, and convicted) =
$0.02 \cdot 0.00044 \cdot 0.70 = 0.00000616$

34d. P(being intoxicated, arrested, and dismissed) =
$0.02 \cdot 0.00044 \cdot 0.30 = 0.00000264$

35a. P(1 red gumball, then another red gumball, then another red gumball) $= \frac{7}{36} \times \frac{6}{35} \times \frac{5}{34}$
$= \frac{210}{42840}$ or $\frac{1}{204}$

35b. P(1 purple gumball, then 1 orange gumball, then 1 yellow gumball) $= \frac{9}{36} \times \frac{8}{35} \times \frac{5}{34}$
$= \frac{360}{42840}$ or $\frac{1}{119}$

35c. P(1 white gumball, then another white gumball, then 1 purple gumball) $= \frac{7}{36} \times \frac{6}{35} \times \frac{9}{34}$
$= \frac{378}{42840}$ or $\frac{3}{340}$

36. $d = 15 - 6$ or 9
$a_{57} = 6 + (57 - 1)9$
$= 510$

37.
$$\frac{\frac{3x+5}{3x+1} - 2}{3 + \frac{3x}{1-2x}} = \frac{\frac{3x+5}{3x+1} - \frac{2(3x+1)}{3x+1}}{\frac{3(1-2x)}{1-2x} + \frac{3x}{1-2x}}$$
$$= \frac{\frac{3x+5-6x-2}{3x+1}}{\frac{3-6x+3x}{1-2x}}$$
$$= \frac{-3x+3}{3x+1} \cdot \frac{1-2x}{-3x+3}$$
$$= \frac{1-2x}{3x+1}$$

38. $f(x) = -3x^3 + 2$
$f(2) = -3(2)^3 + 2$
$= -22$

39a. $a = 23$, $b = 48$
$\frac{x^2}{2304} + \frac{y^2}{529} = 1$

39b. The desk is at one focus point.
$c^2 = 2304 - 529$
$c^2 = 1775$
$c \approx 42$
He had to stand about 84 feet away.

40. $M^{-1} = \frac{1}{-21+25}\begin{bmatrix} -7 & 5 \\ -5 & 3 \end{bmatrix}$
$= \frac{1}{4}\begin{bmatrix} -7 & 5 \\ -5 & 3 \end{bmatrix}$

$$\begin{bmatrix} 3 & -5 \\ 5 & 7 \end{bmatrix} \cdot \begin{bmatrix} x \\ y \end{bmatrix} = \begin{bmatrix} 4 \\ 8 \end{bmatrix}$$

$$\frac{1}{4}\begin{bmatrix} -7 & 5 \\ -5 & 3 \end{bmatrix} \cdot \begin{bmatrix} 3 & -5 \\ 5 & -7 \end{bmatrix} \cdot \begin{bmatrix} x \\ y \end{bmatrix} = \frac{1}{4}\begin{bmatrix} -7 & 5 \\ -5 & 3 \end{bmatrix} \cdot \begin{bmatrix} 4 \\ 8 \end{bmatrix}$$

$$\begin{bmatrix} x \\ y \end{bmatrix} = \frac{1}{4}\begin{bmatrix} -28+40 \\ -20+24 \end{bmatrix}$$

$$\begin{bmatrix} x \\ y \end{bmatrix} = \frac{1}{4}\begin{bmatrix} 12 \\ 4 \end{bmatrix}$$

$$\begin{bmatrix} x \\ y \end{bmatrix} = \begin{bmatrix} 3 \\ 1 \end{bmatrix}; (3, 1)$$

12-7 Binomial Experiments and Simulations

Pages 755–756 Check for Understanding

1. A binomial experiment exists if and only if these conditions occur.
   a. There are exactly 2 possible outcomes for any trial.
   b. There is a fixed number of trials.
   c. The trials are independent.
   d. The probability of each trial is the same.

2.

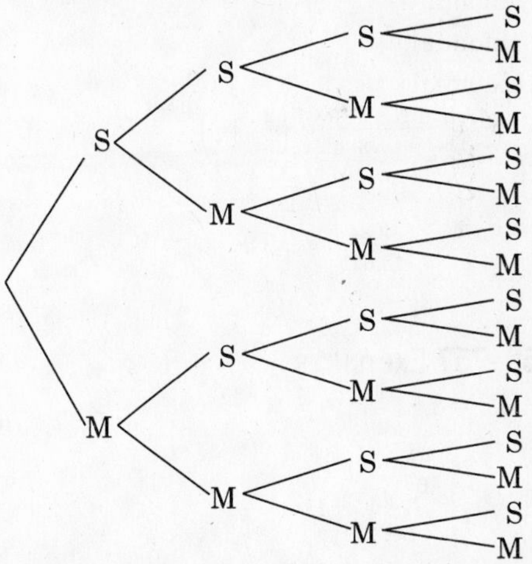

3. Sample answer: coins, dice, spinners, random draws from a bag
4. See students' work.
5. The results will be closer to the theoretical probability.

6a. $(G + W)^4 = G^4 + 4G^3W + 6G^2W^2 + 4GW^3 + W^4$
P(at least one white)
$= 4G^3W + 6G^2W^2 + 4GW^3 + W^4$
$= 4\left(\frac{3}{4}\right)^3\left(\frac{1}{4}\right) + 6\left(\frac{3}{4}\right)^2\left(\frac{1}{4}\right)^2 + 4\left(\frac{3}{4}\right)\left(\frac{1}{4}\right)^3 + \left(\frac{1}{4}\right)^4$
$= \frac{27}{64} + \frac{27}{128} + \frac{3}{64} + \frac{1}{256}$
$= \frac{175}{256}$
≈ 0.6836 or about 68.4%

6b. See students' work.

7. Modeling could be done using coins. Toss 4 coins, let heads be one gender and tails be the other.
$(B + G)^4 = B^4 + 4B^3G + 6B^2G^2 + 4BG^3 + G^4$
$P(\text{at least 2 boys}) = B^4 + 4B^3G + 6B^2G^2$
$= \left(\frac{1}{2}\right)^4 + 4\left(\frac{1}{2}\right)^3\left(\frac{1}{2}\right) + 6\left(\frac{1}{2}\right)^2\left(\frac{1}{2}\right)^2$
$= \frac{1}{16} + \frac{1}{4} + \frac{3}{8}$
$= \frac{11}{16}$

8. binomial; $P(\text{1 head, 2 tails}) = C(3, 1)H^1T^2$
$= \frac{3}{1}\left(\frac{1}{2}\right)\left(\frac{1}{2}\right)^2$
$= \frac{3}{8}$

9a. binomial; $P(\text{4 jacks}) = C(4, 4)J^4$
$= 1 \cdot \left(\frac{4}{52}\right)^4$
$= \frac{1}{28{,}561}$

9b. not binomial

10a. $P(\text{both diet}) = C(2, 2)D^2$
$= 1 \cdot \left(\frac{8}{18}\right)^2$
$= \frac{16}{81} \approx 0.198$

10b. $P(\text{both root beer}) = C(2, 2)R^2$
$= 1 \cdot \left(\frac{4}{18}\right)^2$
$= \frac{4}{81} \approx 0.049$

10c. $P(\text{both orange}) = C(2, 2)\ O^2$
$= 1 \cdot \left(\frac{6}{18}\right)^2$
$= \frac{1}{9} \approx 0.111$

10d. not binomial

10e. not binomial

10f. not binomial

11. $C(7, 4)S^4G^3 = \frac{7 \cdot 6 \cdot 5 \cdot 4!}{3!\ 4!}\left(\frac{2}{5}\right)^4\left(\frac{3}{5}\right)^3$
$= 35\left(\frac{16}{625}\right)\left(\frac{27}{125}\right)$
$= \frac{3024}{15{,}625} \approx 0.194$

Pages 756–757 Exercises

12. $C(4, 4)T^4 = 1 \cdot \left(\frac{1}{2}\right)^4$
$= \frac{1}{16} \approx 0.063$

13. $C(4, 2)H^2T^2 = 6\left(\frac{1}{2}\right)^2\left(\frac{1}{2}\right)^2$
$= \frac{3}{8} = 0.375$

14. $C(4, 3)T^3H + C(4, 4)T^4 = 4\left(\frac{1}{2}\right)^3\left(\frac{1}{2}\right) + 1\left(\frac{1}{2}\right)^4$
$= \frac{1}{4} + \frac{1}{16}$
$= \frac{5}{16} \approx 0.313$

15. $C(5, 1)WL^4 = 5\left(\frac{1}{6}\right)\left(\frac{5}{6}\right)^4$
$= \frac{3125}{7776} \approx 0.402$

16. $C(5, 3)W^3L^2 + C(5, 4)W^4L + C(5, 5)W^5$
$= 10\left(\frac{1}{6}\right)^3\left(\frac{5}{6}\right)^2 + 5\left(\frac{1}{6}\right)^4\left(\frac{5}{6}\right) + 1\left(\frac{1}{6}\right)^5$
$= \frac{250}{7776} + \frac{25}{7776} + \frac{1}{7776}$
$= \frac{276}{7776} = \frac{23}{648} \approx 0.035$

17. $C(5, 0)L^5 + C(5, 1)WL^4 + C(5, 2)W^2L^3$
$= 1\left(\frac{5}{6}\right)^5 + 5\left(\frac{1}{6}\right)\left(\frac{5}{6}\right)^4 + 10\left(\frac{1}{6}\right)^2\left(\frac{5}{6}\right)^3$
$= \frac{3125}{7776} + \frac{3125}{7776} + \frac{1250}{7776}$
$= \frac{625}{648} \approx 0.965$

18. $C(5, 0)W^5 = 1\left(\frac{3}{4}\right)^5$
$= \frac{243}{1024} \approx 0.237$

19. $C(5, 4)W^1R^4 + C(5, 5)R^5 = 5\left(\frac{3}{4}\right)\left(\frac{1}{4}\right)^4 + 1\left(\frac{1}{4}\right)^5$
$= \frac{15}{1024} + \frac{1}{1024}$
$= \frac{1}{64} \approx 0.016$

20. $C(5, 0)W^5 + C(5, 1)W^4R + C(5, 2)W^3R^2 + C(5, 3)W^2R^3 + C(5, 4)WR^4$
$= 1\left(\frac{3}{4}\right)^5 + 5\left(\frac{3}{4}\right)^4\left(\frac{1}{4}\right) + 10\left(\frac{3}{4}\right)^3\left(\frac{1}{4}\right)^2 + 10\left(\frac{3}{4}\right)^2\left(\frac{1}{4}\right)^3 + 5\left(\frac{3}{4}\right)\left(\frac{1}{4}\right)^4$
$= \frac{243}{1024} + \frac{405}{1024} + \frac{270}{1024} + \frac{90}{1024} + \frac{15}{1024}$
$= \frac{1023}{1024} \approx 0.999$

21. $C(5, 3)W^2R^3 = 10\left(\frac{3}{4}\right)^2\left(\frac{1}{4}\right)^3$
$= \frac{90}{1024}$
$= \frac{45}{512} \approx 0.088$

22. $C(10, 6)R^6W^4 = 210\left(\frac{1}{2}\right)^6\left(\frac{1}{2}\right)^4$
$= \frac{105}{512} \approx 0.205$

23. $C(10, 5)R^5W^5 + C(10, 6)R^6W^4 + C(10, 7)R^7W^3 + C(10, 8)R^8W^2 + C(10, 9)R^9W^1 + C(10, 10)R^{10}$
$= 252\left(\frac{1}{2}\right)^5\left(\frac{1}{2}\right)^5 + 210\left(\frac{1}{2}\right)^6\left(\frac{1}{2}\right)^4 + 120\left(\frac{1}{2}\right)^7\left(\frac{1}{2}\right)^3 + 45\left(\frac{1}{2}\right)^8\left(\frac{1}{2}\right)^2 + 10\left(\frac{1}{2}\right)^9\left(\frac{1}{2}\right) + 1\left(\frac{1}{2}\right)^{10}$
$= \frac{252}{1024} + \frac{210}{1024} + \frac{120}{1024} + \frac{45}{1024} + \frac{10}{1024} + \frac{1}{1024}$
$= \frac{319}{512} \approx 0.623$

24. $C(10, 10)W^{10} = 1\left(\frac{1}{2}\right)^{10}$
$= \frac{1}{1024} \approx 0.001$

25. $C(5, 2)H^2M^3 = 10\left(\frac{3}{10}\right)^2\left(\frac{7}{10}\right)^3$
$= \frac{3087}{10{,}000} \approx 0.309$

26. $C(5, 2)H^2M^3 + C(5, 3)H^3M^2 + C(5, 4)H^4M + C(5, 5)H^5$
$= 10\left(\frac{3}{10}\right)^2\left(\frac{7}{10}\right)^3 + 10\left(\frac{3}{10}\right)^3\left(\frac{7}{10}\right)^2 + 5\left(\frac{3}{10}\right)^4\left(\frac{7}{10}\right) + 1\left(\frac{3}{10}\right)^5$
$= \frac{30{,}870}{100{,}000} + \frac{13{,}230}{100{,}000} + \frac{2835}{100{,}000} + \frac{243}{100{,}000}$
$= \frac{47{,}178}{100{,}000} \approx 0.472$

27. $C(5, 4)H^4M + C(5, 5)H^5 = 5\left(\frac{3}{10}\right)^4\left(\frac{7}{10}\right) + 1\left(\frac{3}{10}\right)^5$
$= \frac{2835}{100{,}000} + \frac{243}{100{,}000}$
$= \frac{3078}{100{,}000} \approx 0.031$

28. $C(12, 4)U^4D^8 = 495\left(\frac{2}{5}\right)^4\left(\frac{3}{5}\right)^8$

$= \frac{10,392,624}{48,828,125} \approx 0.213$

29. $C(12, 12)U^{12} = 1\left(\frac{2}{5}\right)^{12}$

$= \frac{4096}{244,140,625} \approx 0.0000168$

30. $C(12, 5)U^5D^7 + C(12, 6)U^6D^6 + C(12, 7)U^7D^5 + C(12, 8)U^8D^4 + C(12, 9)U^9D^3 + C(12, 10)U^{10}D^2 + C(12, 11)U^{11}D + C(12, 12)U^{12}$

$= 792\left(\frac{2}{5}\right)^5\left(\frac{3}{5}\right)^7 + 924\left(\frac{2}{5}\right)^6\left(\frac{3}{5}\right)^6 + 792\left(\frac{2}{5}\right)^7\left(\frac{3}{5}\right)^5 + 495\left(\frac{2}{5}\right)^8\left(\frac{3}{5}\right)^4 + 220\left(\frac{2}{5}\right)^9\left(\frac{3}{5}\right)^3 + 66\left(\frac{2}{5}\right)^{10}\left(\frac{3}{5}\right)^2 + 12\left(\frac{2}{5}\right)^{11}\left(\frac{3}{5}\right) + 1\left(\frac{2}{5}\right)^{12}$

$= \frac{55,427,328}{244,140,625} + \frac{43,110,144}{244,140,625} + \frac{24,634,368}{244,140,625} + \frac{10,264,320}{244,140,625} + \frac{3,041,280}{244,140,625} + \frac{608,256}{244,140,625} + \frac{73,728}{244,140,625} + \frac{4096}{244,140,625}$

$= \frac{137,163,520}{244,140,625} \approx 0.562$

31. 0.95

32a. $(B + N)^6$

$= B^6 + 6B^5N + 15B^4N^2 + 20B^3N^3 + 15B^2N^4 + 6BN^5 + N^6$

$= \left(\frac{1}{2}\right)^6 + 6\left(\frac{1}{2}\right)^5\left(\frac{1}{2}\right) + 15\left(\frac{1}{2}\right)^4\left(\frac{1}{2}\right)^2 + 20\left(\frac{1}{2}\right)^3\left(\frac{1}{2}\right)^3 + 15\left(\frac{1}{2}\right)^2\left(\frac{1}{2}\right)^4 + 6\left(\frac{1}{2}\right)\left(\frac{1}{2}\right)^5 + \left(\frac{1}{2}\right)^6$

$= \frac{1}{64} + \frac{6}{64} + \frac{15}{64} + \frac{20}{64} + \frac{15}{64} + \frac{6}{64} + \frac{1}{64}$

Outcomes	Points	Probability
6 black	5	1/64
5 black, 1 neutral	1	6/64
4 black, 2 neutral	0	15/64
3 black, 3 neutral	0	20/64
2 black, 4 neutral	0	15/64
1 black, 5 neutral	1	6/64
6 neutral	5	1/64

32b. $P(\text{at least 5 black}) + P(\text{at least 5 neutral})$

$= \frac{1}{64} + \frac{6}{64} + \frac{6}{64} + \frac{1}{64}$

$= \frac{14}{64}$ or $\frac{7}{32}$

33. $C(6, 1)PO^5 + C(6, 2)P^2O^4 + C(6, 3)P^3O^3 + C(6, 4)P^4O^2 + C(6, 5)P^5O + C(6, 6)P^6$

$= 6\left(\frac{7}{100}\right)\left(\frac{93}{100}\right)^5 + 15\left(\frac{7}{100}\right)^2\left(\frac{93}{100}\right)^4 + 20\left(\frac{7}{100}\right)^3\left(\frac{93}{100}\right)^3 + 15\left(\frac{7}{100}\right)^4\left(\frac{93}{100}\right)^2 + 6\left(\frac{7}{100}\right)^5\left(\frac{93}{100}\right) + 1\left(\frac{7}{100}\right)^6$

$= \frac{42 \cdot 6,956,883,693}{1,000,000,000,000} + \frac{15 \cdot 3,665,454,849}{1,000,000,000,000} + \frac{5,517,889,020}{1,000,000,000,000} + \frac{311,493,735}{1,000,000,000,000} + \frac{9,378,306}{1,000,000,000,000} + \frac{117,649}{1,000,000,000,000}$

≈ 0.353

34. $P(\text{not a junior}) = \frac{16 - 3}{16}$

$= \frac{13}{16}$

35. 2.5440; 2; 0.5440

36. $y = \frac{-3x}{x - 1}$

x	y
−4	−2.4
−2	−2
0	0
$\frac{1}{2}$	3
1	undefined

x	y
$1\frac{1}{2}$	−9
2	−6
4	−4
6	−3.6

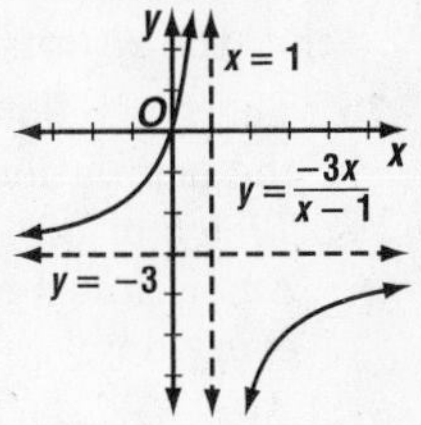

37. $d = \sqrt{(8 - 9)^2 + (0 - 6)^2}$

$= \sqrt{1 + 36}$

$= \sqrt{37}$; $\sqrt{37}$ units

38a. profit = income − cost

$y = (120 - 5x)(21 + 3x) - 75(21 + 3x)$

$= 2520 + 255x - 15x^2 - 1575 - 225x$

$= -15x^2 + 30x + 945$

$= -15(x^2 - 2x + 1) + 945 + 15$

$= -15(x - 1)^2 + 960$

The vertex is (1,960). The profit is maximized when $x = 1$.

So, they should charge 120 − 5(1) or $115 for a camera.

38b. $960

39. $\begin{bmatrix} -3 & 14 & 12 \\ -2 & -1 & 7 \end{bmatrix} + \begin{bmatrix} 1 & -5 & 10 \\ 22 & 13 & -8 \end{bmatrix} = \begin{bmatrix} -2 & 9 & 22 \\ 20 & 12 & -1 \end{bmatrix}$

12-8 Sampling and Testing Hypotheses

Pages 760–761 Check for Understanding

1. See students' work.
2. The margin of sampling error decreases when the size of the sample n increases. As n increases, $\frac{p(1 - p)}{n}$ decreases.
3. Yes, all numbers have an equal chance to be selected.
4. No, advanced chemistry students probably require more study time than other students.
5. $ME = 2\sqrt{\frac{0.68(1 - 0.68)}{520}}$

≈ 0.0409; 4%

There is a 95% probability that the value of p in the population is between 68 − 4 or 64% and 68 + 4 or 72% and that 64% to 72% of high school students are involved in extracurricular activities.

6. $ME = 2\sqrt{\frac{0.45(1 - 0.45)}{1730}}$

≈ 0.0239; 2%

There is a 95% probability that the value of p in the population is between 45 − 2 or 43% and 45 + 2 or 47% and that 43% to 47% of adults believe that the results of call-in polls are believable.

7a. There is a 95% probability that the value of p in the population is between 77 − 5 or 72% and 77 + 5 or 82% and that 72% to 82% of Americans age 12 or older listen to the radio every day.

7b. $ME = 2\sqrt{\frac{p(1 - p)}{n}}$

$0.05 = 2\sqrt{\frac{0.77(1 - 0.77)}{n}}$

$0.025 = \sqrt{\frac{0.77(0.23)}{n}}$

$0.000625 = \frac{0.1771}{n}$

$n = 283.36$; 283 people

8. See students' work.

Pages 671–672 Exercises

9. Yes, all girls in your high school have their names in the yearbook.
10. Yes, a wide variety of people would be called since almost everyone is listed in a phone book.
11. No, not everyone in the city belongs to a health spa and the ones that do generally exercise often.
12. No, polling only freshmen would not give an accurate average for a school, you must poll all grade levels.
13. Yes, all students have a lunch break.
14. $ME = 2\sqrt{\frac{0.46(1 - 0.46)}{800}}$

≈ 0.0352; 4%

There is a 95% probability that the value of p in the population is between 46 − 4 or 42% and 46 + 4 or 50% and that 42% to 50% of the population believe that crime is the most serious problem facing the country.

15. $ME = 2\sqrt{\frac{0.33(1 - 0.33)}{2406}}$

≈ 0.0192; 2%

There is a 95% probability that the value of p in the population is between 33 − 2 or 31% and 33 + 2 or 35% and that 31% to 35% of adults believe that skim milk is a good calcium source.

16. $0.04 = 2\sqrt{\frac{0.34(1 - 0.34)}{n}}$

$0.02 = \sqrt{\frac{0.34(0.66)}{n}}$

$0.0004 = \frac{0.2244}{n}$

$n = 561$; 561 people

17a. See students' work. 17b. See students' work.

17c. See students' work.

18. Sample answer: The reported margin of error is too small, or the polls reach different populations.

19a. There is a 95% probability that the value of p in the population is between 90 − 2 or 88% and 90 + 2 or 92% and that 88% to 92% of people registered to vote actually vote on election day.

19b. $0.02 = 2\sqrt{\frac{0.90(1 - 0.90)}{n}}$

$0.01 = \sqrt{\frac{0.90(0.1)}{n}}$

$0.0001 = \frac{0.09}{n}$

$n = 900$; 900 people

20a. $ME = 2\sqrt{\frac{0.60(1 - 0.60)}{1500}}$

≈ 0.0253; 2.5%

20b. $ME = 2\sqrt{\frac{0.20(1 - 0.20)}{1500}}$

≈ 0.0207; 2.1%

20c. $ME = 2\sqrt{\frac{0.10(1 - 0.10)}{1500}}$

≈ 0.01549; 1.5%

21. See students' work.

22. $C(10, 10)C^{10} = 1\left(\frac{1}{2}\right)^{10}$

$= \frac{1}{1024} \approx 0.001$

23. $2 \log_6 3 + 3 \log_6 2 = \log_6 x$

$\log_6 3^2 + \log_6 2^3 = \log_6 x$

$\log_6 3^2 \cdot 2^3 = \log_6 x$

$9 \cdot 8 = x$

$72 = x$

24.

$$\begin{array}{r|rrr} 3 & 2 & -8 & 6 \\ & & 6 & -6 \\ \hline & 2 & -2 & 0 \end{array} \qquad \begin{array}{r|rrr} -2 & 2 & -8 & 6 \\ & & -4 & 24 \\ \hline & 2 & -12 & 30 \end{array}$$

25. $x^2 \le 6$

$-\sqrt{6} \le x \le \sqrt{6}$; $\{x \mid -\sqrt{6} \le x \le \sqrt{6}\}$

26. $|m - 4| + 2 \ge 0$

$|m - 4| \ge -2$

all reals

Chapter 12 Highlights

Page 763 Understanding and Using the Vocabulary

1. e	2. l
3. b	4. a
5. d	6. k
7. i	8. c
9. f	10. g
11. h	12. j

Chapter 12 Study Guide and Assessment

Pages 764–766 Skills and Concepts

13. $10! = 3,628,800$; 3,628,800 batting orders

14. $6^6 = 46,656$; 46,656 passwords

15. $10 \cdot 9 \cdot 8 \cdot 7 = 5040$; 5040 patterns

16. $6! = 720$

17. $\frac{11!}{2!} = 19,958,400$

18. $\frac{8!}{2!2!} = 10,080$

19. $\frac{10!}{3!} = 604,800$

20. $3 \cdot 3 \cdot 2 \cdot 1 = 18$; 18 arrangements

21. $\frac{8!}{8} = 5040$; 5040 ways

22. $C(13, 5) = \frac{13!}{8!5!}$
$= 1287$; 1287 ways

23. $C(8, 2) = \frac{8!}{6!2!}$
$= 28$; 28 pizzas

24. $C(16, 2) = \frac{16!}{14!2!}$
$= 120$
$120 - 16 = 104$; 104 diagonals

25. $\frac{C(5, 3)}{C(9, 3)} = \frac{\frac{5!}{2!3!}}{\frac{9!}{6!3!}}$
$= \frac{10}{84}$ or $\frac{5}{42}$

26. $\frac{C(17 + x, 1)}{C(45 + x, 1)} = \frac{3}{7}$
$\frac{\frac{(17 + x)!}{(16 + x)!\,1!}}{\frac{(45 + x)!}{(44 + x)!\,1!}} = \frac{3}{7}$
$\frac{17 + x}{45 + x} = \frac{3}{7}$
$135 + 3x = 119 + 7x$
$16 = 4x$
$4 = x$; 4 colas

27. P(1st number greater than 14, 2nd number greater than 25 or less than 6) $= \frac{14}{28} \cdot \frac{8}{28}$
$= \frac{1}{7}$

28. P(6 odd numbers) $= \frac{23}{46} \cdot \frac{22}{45} \cdot \frac{21}{44} \cdot \frac{20}{43} \cdot \frac{19}{42} \cdot \frac{18}{41}$
$= \frac{19}{1763}$

29. mutually exclusive;
P(geometry book or pre-calculus book) $= \frac{15}{60} + \frac{15}{60}$
$= \frac{30}{60}$ or $\frac{1}{2}$

30. mutually exclusive;
P(a king or less than a 6) $= \frac{4}{52} + \frac{16}{52}$
$= \frac{20}{52}$ or $\frac{5}{13}$

31. mutually exclusive;
P(a 6 or less than 3) $= \frac{1}{6} + \frac{2}{6}$
$= \frac{3}{6}$ or $\frac{1}{2}$

32. inclusive;
P(both jacks or both red)
$= P$(both jacks) $+ P$(both red) $- P$(both red jacks)
$= \frac{4}{52} \cdot \frac{3}{51} + \frac{26}{52} \cdot \frac{25}{51} - \frac{2}{52} \cdot \frac{1}{51}$
$= \frac{12}{2652} + \frac{650}{2652} - \frac{2}{2652}$
$= \frac{660}{2652}$ or $\frac{55}{221}$

33. $C(8, 7)H^7T^1 = 8\left(\frac{1}{2}\right)^7\left(\frac{1}{2}\right)^1$
$= \frac{1}{32}$

34. $C(7, 5)B^5G^2 = 21\left(\frac{1}{2}\right)^5\left(\frac{1}{2}\right)^2$
$= \frac{21}{128}$

35a. $C(12, 12)N^{12} = 1\left(\frac{1}{6}\right)^{12}$
$= \frac{1}{2,176,782,336}$

35b. $C(12, 1)N^1W^{11} = 12\left(\frac{1}{6}\right)^1\left(\frac{5}{6}\right)^{11}$
$= \frac{585,937,500}{2,176,782,336}$

35c. $C(12, 6)N^6W^6 = 924\left(\frac{1}{6}\right)^6\left(\frac{5}{6}\right)^6$
$= \frac{14,437,500}{2,176,782,336}$

36. $ME = 2\sqrt{\frac{0.51(1 - 0.51)}{625}}$
≈ 0.03999; 4%

37. $0.045 = 2\sqrt{\frac{0.63(1 - 0.63)}{n}}$
$0.0225 = \sqrt{\frac{0.63(0.37)}{n}}$
$0.00050625 = \frac{0.2331}{n}$
$n = 460.4$; 460 mothers

Page 766 Applications and Problem Solving

38. $36^3 = 46,656$; 46,656 combinations

39. $9 \cdot 7 \cdot 5 \cdot 4 = 1260$; 1260 varieties

Page 767 Alternative Assessment; Thinking Critically

- Sample answer: 1 out of every 7 dogs sold at the local pet store last year was a retriever. Suppose a salesperson sells 9 dogs per week. What is the probability he or she sells exactly 3 retrievers in a week.

  Let R represent the probability that the dog is a retriever.

  Let N represent the probability that the dog is not a retriever.

  $C(9, 3)R^3N^6 = 84\left(\frac{1}{7}\right)^3\left(\frac{6}{7}\right)^6$
  $= \frac{3,919,104}{40,353,607}$
  ≈ 0.0971; 9.7%

13-1 An Introduction to Trigonometry

Page 777 Check for Understanding

1. hypotenuse, c; adjacent, b; opposite, a
2. triangle measure
3. $\sin \theta = \frac{8}{10}$ or 0.8 $\quad \csc \theta = \frac{10}{8}$ or 1.25

   $\cos \theta = \frac{6}{10}$ or 0.6 $\quad \sec \theta = \frac{10}{6}$ or about 1.6667

   $\tan \theta = \frac{8}{6}$ or about 1.3333 $\quad \cot \theta = \frac{6}{8}$ or 0.75
4. 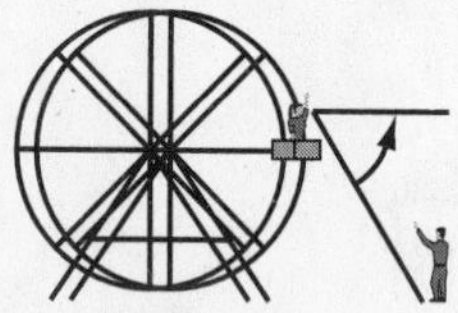
5. See students' work.
6. $\sin \theta = \frac{\sqrt{3}}{2}$

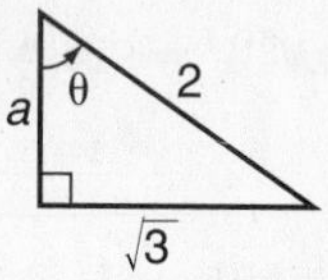

$a^2 + b^2 = c^2$
$a^2 + (\sqrt{3})^2 = 2^2$
$a^2 + 3 = 4$
$a^2 = 1$
$a = 1$

$\cos \theta = \frac{1}{2}$ or 0.5

$\tan \theta = \frac{\sqrt{3}}{1}$ or about 1.7321

$\csc \theta = \frac{2}{\sqrt{3}} \cdot \frac{\sqrt{3}}{\sqrt{3}} = \frac{2\sqrt{3}}{3}$ or about 1.1547

$\sec \theta = 2$

$\cot \theta = \frac{1}{\sqrt{3}} \cdot \frac{\sqrt{3}}{\sqrt{3}} = \frac{\sqrt{3}}{3}$ or about 0.5774

7. $\tan \theta = 2$

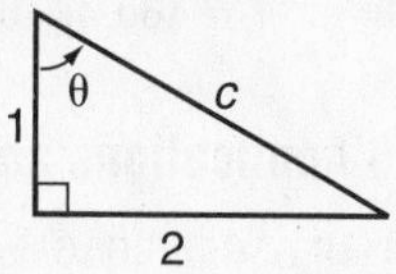

$a^2 + b^2 = c^2$
$1^2 + 2^2 = c^2$
$1 + 4 = c^2$
$5 = c^2$
$\sqrt{5} = c$

$\sin \theta = \frac{2}{\sqrt{5}} \cdot \frac{\sqrt{5}}{\sqrt{5}} = \frac{2\sqrt{5}}{5}$ or about 0.8944

$\cos \theta = \frac{1}{\sqrt{5}} \cdot \frac{\sqrt{5}}{\sqrt{5}} = \frac{\sqrt{5}}{5}$ or about 0.4472

$\csc \theta = \frac{\sqrt{5}}{2}$ or about 1.1180

$\sec \theta = \sqrt{5}$ or about 2.2361

$\cot \theta = \frac{1}{2}$ or 0.5

8. $\sin 42° = \frac{x}{39}$
   $0.6691 \approx \frac{x}{39}$
   $x \approx 26.1$

9. $\tan x° = \frac{33}{15}$
   $\tan x° = 2.2$
   $x \approx 66°$

10. 47°

11. 8°

12. $63° + B = 90°$ $\quad \tan 63° = \frac{9.70}{b}$ $\quad \sin 63° = \frac{9.70}{c}$

    $B = 27°$ $\quad 1.9626 \approx \frac{9.70}{b}$ $\quad 0.8910 \approx \frac{9.70}{c}$

    $b \approx 4.9$ $\quad c \approx 10.9$

13. $a^2 + b^2 = c^2$ $\quad \sin A = \frac{12}{13}$ $\quad \cos B = \frac{12}{13}$

    $12^2 + b^2 = 13^2$ $\quad \sin A \approx 0.9231$ $\quad \cos B \approx 0.9231$

    $144 + b^2 = 169$ $\quad A \approx 67°$ $\quad B \approx 23°$

    $b^2 = 25$

    $b = 5$

14. $54° + B = 90°$ $\quad \cos 54° = \frac{b}{17.8}$ $\quad \sin 54° = \frac{a}{17.8}$

    $B = 36°$ $\quad 0.5878 \approx \frac{b}{17.8}$ $\quad 0.8090 \approx \frac{a}{17.8}$

    $b \approx 10.5$ $\quad a \approx 14.4$

15. $\tan 30° = \frac{173}{b}$

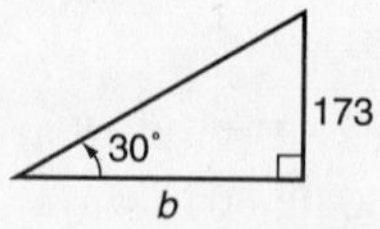

$0.5774 \approx \frac{173}{b}$
$b \approx 300$
about 300 feet

Pages 778–779 Exercises

16. $\tan \theta = \frac{12}{5}$

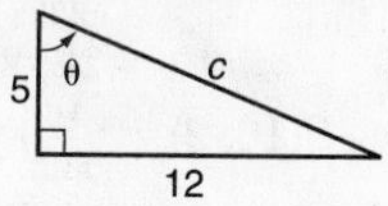

$a^2 + b^2 = c^2$
$5^2 + 12^2 = c^2$
$25 + 144 = c^2$
$169 = c^2$
$13 = c$

$\sin \theta = \frac{12}{13}$ or about 0.9231

$\cos \theta = \frac{5}{13}$ or about 0.3846

$\cot \theta = \frac{5}{12}$ or about 0.4167

$\csc \theta = \frac{13}{12}$ or about 1.0833

$\sec \theta = \frac{13}{5}$ or about 2.6

17. $\cos \theta = \frac{1}{4}$

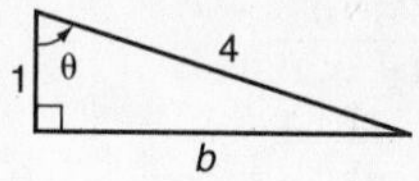

$a^2 + b^2 = c^2$
$1^2 + b^2 = 4^2$
$1 + b^2 = 16$
$b^2 = 15$
$b = \sqrt{15}$

$\sin \theta = \frac{\sqrt{15}}{4}$ or about 0.9682

$\tan \theta = \sqrt{15}$ or about 3.8730

$\csc \theta = \frac{4}{\sqrt{15}} \cdot \frac{\sqrt{15}}{\sqrt{15}} = \frac{4\sqrt{15}}{15}$ or about 1.0328

$\sec \theta = 4$

$\cot \theta = \frac{1}{\sqrt{15}} \cdot \frac{\sqrt{15}}{\sqrt{15}} = \frac{\sqrt{15}}{15}$ or about 0.2582

18. $\cot \theta = 2$

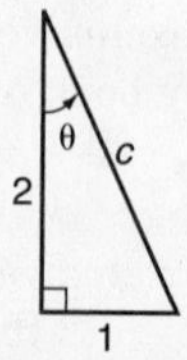

$a^2 + b^2 = c^2$
$1^2 + 2^2 = c^2$
$1 + 4 = c^2$
$5 = c^2$
$\sqrt{5} = c$

$\sin \theta = \frac{1}{\sqrt{5}} \cdot \frac{\sqrt{5}}{\sqrt{5}} = \frac{\sqrt{5}}{5}$ or about 0.4472

$\cos \theta = \frac{2}{\sqrt{5}} \cdot \frac{\sqrt{5}}{\sqrt{5}} = \frac{2\sqrt{5}}{5}$ or about 0.8944

$\tan \theta = \frac{1}{2}$ or 0.5

$\csc \theta = \sqrt{5}$ or about 2.2361

$\sec \theta = \frac{\sqrt{5}}{2}$ or about 1.1180

19. $\csc \theta = \frac{5}{2}$

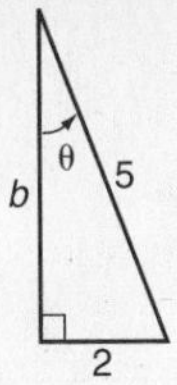

$a^2 + b^2 = c^2$
$2^2 + b^2 = 5^2$
$4 + b^2 = 25$
$b^2 = 21$
$b = \sqrt{21}$

$\sin \theta = \frac{2}{5}$ or 0.4
$\cos \theta = \frac{\sqrt{21}}{5}$ or about 0.9165
$\tan \theta = \frac{2}{\sqrt{21}} \cdot \frac{\sqrt{21}}{\sqrt{21}} = \frac{2\sqrt{21}}{21}$ or about 0.4364
$\sec \theta = \frac{5}{\sqrt{21}} \cdot \frac{\sqrt{21}}{\sqrt{21}} = \frac{5\sqrt{21}}{21}$ or about 1.0911
$\cot \theta = \frac{\sqrt{21}}{2}$ or about 2.2913

20. $\sec \theta = 3$

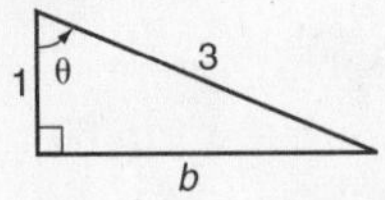

$a^2 + b^2 = c^2$
$1^2 + b^2 = 3^2$
$1 + b^2 = 9$
$b^2 = 8$
$b = \sqrt{8}$ or $2\sqrt{2}$

$\sin \theta = \frac{2\sqrt{2}}{3}$ or about 0.9428
$\cos \theta = \frac{1}{3}$ or about 0.3333
$\tan \theta = 2\sqrt{2}$ or about 2.8284
$\csc \theta = \frac{3}{2\sqrt{2}} \cdot \frac{\sqrt{2}}{\sqrt{2}} = \frac{3\sqrt{2}}{4}$ or about 1.0607
$\cot \theta = \frac{1}{2\sqrt{2}} \cdot \frac{\sqrt{2}}{\sqrt{2}} = \frac{\sqrt{2}}{4}$ or about 0.3536

21. $\sin \theta = 0.5$

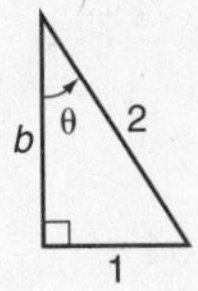

$a^2 + b^2 = c^2$
$1^2 + b^2 = 2^2$
$1 + b^2 = 4$
$b^2 = 3$
$b = \sqrt{3}$

$\cos \theta = \frac{\sqrt{3}}{2}$ or about 0.8660
$\tan \theta = \frac{1}{\sqrt{3}} \cdot \frac{\sqrt{3}}{\sqrt{3}} = \frac{\sqrt{3}}{3}$ or about 0.5774
$\sec \theta = \frac{2}{\sqrt{3}} \cdot \frac{\sqrt{3}}{\sqrt{3}} = \frac{2\sqrt{3}}{3}$ or about 1.1547
$\csc \theta = 2$
$\cot \theta = \sqrt{3}$ or about 1.7321

22. $\cos 23° = \frac{32}{x}$
$0.9205 \approx \frac{32}{x}$
$x \approx 34.8$

23. $\sin 54° = \frac{17.8}{x}$
$0.8090 \approx \frac{17.8}{x}$
$x \approx 22.0$

24. $\tan 17.5° = \frac{x}{23.7}$
$0.3153 \approx \frac{x}{23.7}$
$x \approx 7.5$

25. $\tan x° = \frac{15}{21}$
$\tan x° \approx 0.7143$
$x \approx 36°$

26. $\cos x° = \frac{5}{13}$
$\cos x° \approx 0.3846$
$x \approx 67°$

27. $\sin x° = \frac{18}{33}$
$\sin x° \approx 0.5455$
$x \approx 33°$

28. 31° **29.** 58° **30.** 12°

31. 89° **32.** 1° **33.** 30°

34. $a^2 + b^2 = c^2$
$a^2 + 6^2 = 13^2$
$a^2 + 36 = 169$
$a^2 = 133$
$a \approx 11.5$

$\cos A = \frac{6}{13}$
$\cos A \approx 0.4615$
$A \approx 63°$
$63° + B \approx 90°$
$B \approx 27°$

35. $\sin 16° = \frac{a}{14}$
$0.2756 \approx \frac{a}{14}$
$a \approx 3.9$

$16° + B = 90°$
$B = 74°$

$\cos 16° = \frac{b}{14}$
$0.9613 \approx \frac{b}{14}$
$b \approx 13.5$

36. $a^2 + b^2 = c^2$
$4^2 + b^2 = 9^2$
$16 + b^2 = 81$
$b^2 = 65$
$b \approx 8.1$

$\sin A = \frac{4}{9}$
$\sin A \approx 0.4444$
$A \approx 26°$

$\cos B = \frac{4}{9}$
$\cos B \approx 0.4444$
$B \approx 64°$

37. $A + 18° = 90°$
$A = 72°$

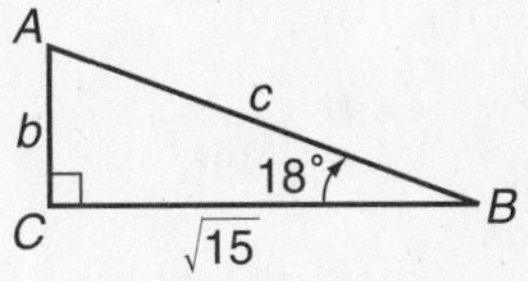

$\tan 18° = \frac{b}{\sqrt{15}}$
$0.3249 \approx \frac{b}{3.8730}$
$b \approx 1.3$
$\cos 18° = \frac{\sqrt{15}}{c}$
$0.9511 \approx \frac{3.8730}{c}$
$c \approx 4.1$

38. $56° + B = 90°$
$B = 34°$

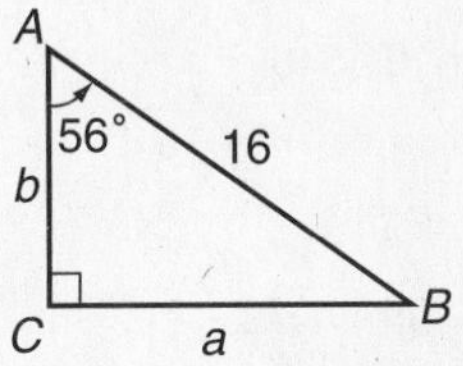

$\sin 56° = \frac{a}{16}$
$0.8290 \approx \frac{a}{16}$
$a \approx 13.3$
$\cos 56° = \frac{b}{16}$
$0.5592 \approx \frac{b}{16}$
$b \approx 8.9$

39. $45° + B = 90°$
$B = 45°$

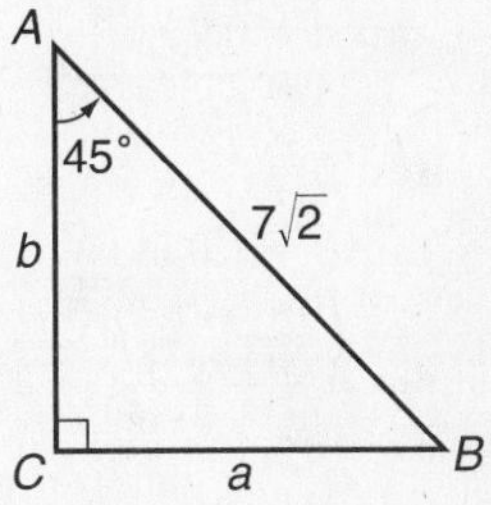

$\sin 45° = \frac{a}{7\sqrt{2}}$
$0.7071 \approx \frac{a}{9.8995}$
$a \approx 7$
$\cos 45° = \frac{b}{7\sqrt{2}}$
$0.7071 \approx \frac{b}{9.8995}$
$b \approx 7$

40. $15° + B = 90°$
$B = 75°$

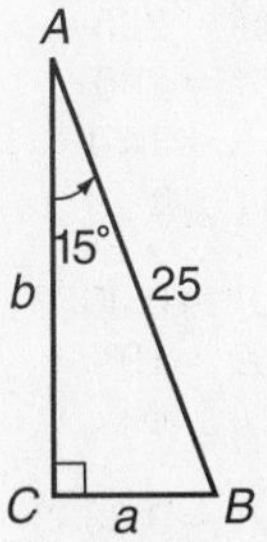

$\sin 15° = \frac{a}{25}$
$0.2588 \approx \frac{a}{25}$
$a \approx 6.5$
$\cos 15° = \frac{b}{25}$
$0.9659 \approx \frac{b}{25}$
$b \approx 24.1$

41. $a + 30° = 90°$
$A = 60°$

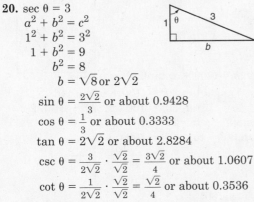

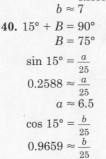

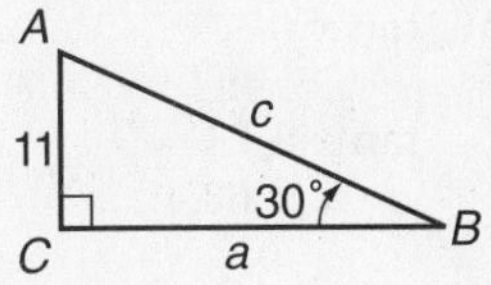

$\tan 30° = \frac{11}{a}$
$0.5774 \approx \frac{11}{a}$
$a \approx 19.1$
$\sin 30° = \frac{11}{c}$
$0.5 = \frac{11}{c}$
$c = 22$

42. $b = 8$

$a^2 + b^2 = c^2$

$7^2 + 8^2 = c^2$

$49 + 64 = c^2$

$113 = c^2$

$c \approx 10.6$

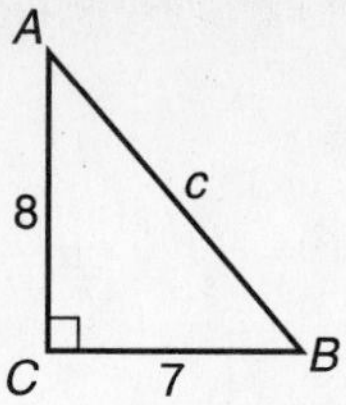

$\tan A = \frac{7}{8}$

$\tan A = 0.875$

$A \approx 41°$

$\tan B = \frac{8}{7}$

$\tan B \approx 1.1429$

$B \approx 49°$

43. $27° + B = 90°$

$B = 63°$

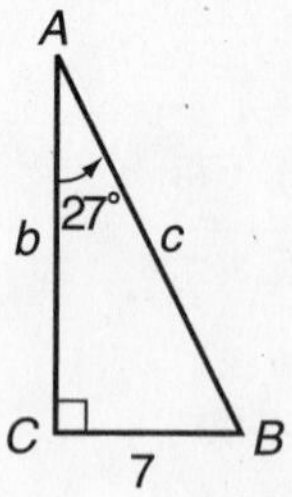

$\tan 27° = \frac{7}{b}$

$0.5095 \approx \frac{7}{b}$

$b \approx 13.7$

$\sin 27° = \frac{7}{c}$

$0.4540 \approx \frac{7}{c}$

$c \approx 15.4$

44. $a = 6$

$a^2 + b^2 = c^2$

$6^2 + 8^2 = c^2$

$36 + 64 = c^2$

$100 = c^2$

$10 = c$

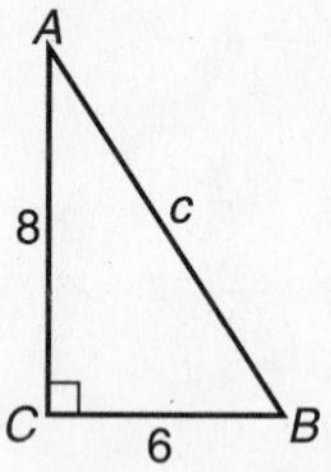

$\tan A = \frac{6}{8}$

$\tan A = 0.75$

$A \approx 37°$

$\tan B = \frac{8}{6}$

$\tan B \approx 1.3333$

$B \approx 53°$

45. $\sin A = \frac{1}{3} = \frac{5}{15}$

$c = 15$

$a^2 + b^2 = c^2$

$5^2 + b^2 = 15^2$

$25 + b^2 = 225$

$b^2 = 200$

$b \approx 14.1$

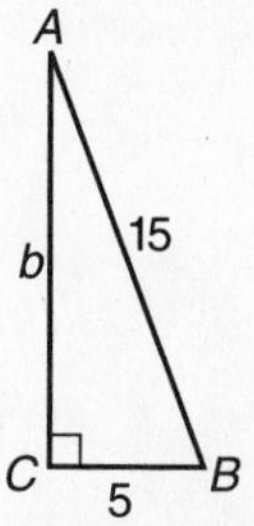

$\sin A = \frac{1}{3}$

$\sin A \approx 0.3333$

$A \approx 19°$

$\cos B = \frac{1}{3}$

$\cos B \approx 0.3333$

$B \approx 71°$

46. $\tan x = \frac{n}{\frac{1}{2}n}$

$\tan x = 2$

$x \approx 63.4°$

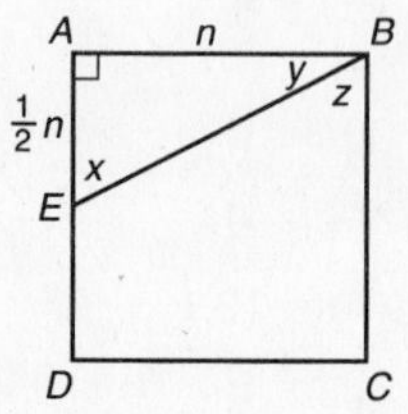

$\tan y = \frac{\frac{1}{2}n}{n}$

$\tan y = 0.5$

$y \approx 26.6°$

$26.6° + z \approx 90°$

$z \approx 63.4°$

47. $\tan 39° = \frac{h}{5}$

$0.8098 \approx \frac{h}{5}$

$h \approx 4.05;$

4.05 centimeters

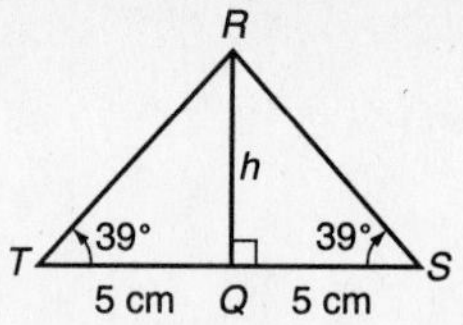

48. Sample answer: if you know two acute angles and no sides

49. Sample answer: The legs of a right triangle are never greater than the hypotenuse, but one leg may be greater than the other leg.

50. $\frac{6}{9} = \frac{64}{x}$

$6x = 576$

$x = 96$; 96 feet

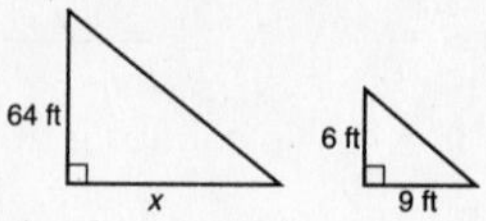

51. $\tan 30° = \frac{h}{x}$

$h = x \tan 30°$

$\tan 20° = \frac{h}{100 + x}$

$h = (100 + x) \tan 20°$

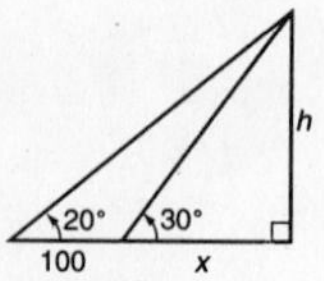

$x \tan 30° = (100 + x) \tan 20°$

$x \tan 30° = 100 \tan 20° + x \tan 20°$

$x \tan 30° - x \tan 20° = 100 \tan 20°$

$x(\tan 30° - \tan 20°) = 100 \tan 20°$

$x = \frac{100 \tan 20°}{\tan 30° - \tan 20°}$

$x \approx 170.57$

$h = x \tan 30°$

$h \approx 170.57(0.5774)$

$h \approx 99$; 99 feet

52. $\sin \theta = \frac{2900}{8395}$

$\sin \theta \approx 0.3454$

$\theta \approx 20.2°$

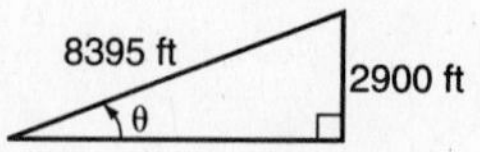

53. $\cos 51.8° = \frac{115}{c}$

$0.6184 = \frac{115}{c}$

$c \approx 186$

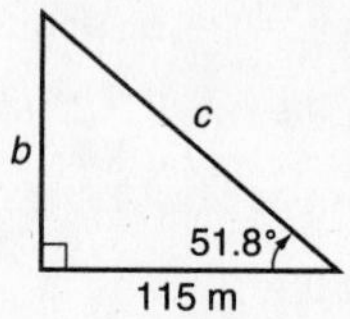

$\tan \theta = \frac{186}{115}$

$\tan \theta \approx 1.6174$

$\theta \approx 58.3°$

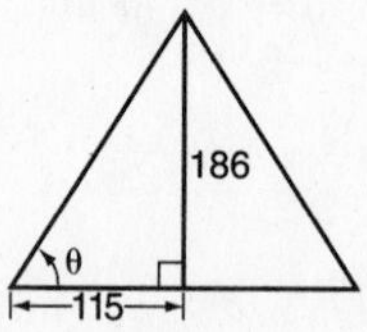

54a. $\tan 20° = \frac{b}{500{,}000}$

$0.3640 \approx \frac{b}{500{,}000}$

$b \approx 181{,}985$

$\cos 20° = \frac{500{,}000}{c}$

$0.9397 \approx \frac{500{,}000}{c}$

$c \approx 532{,}089$

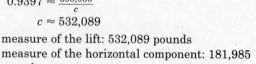

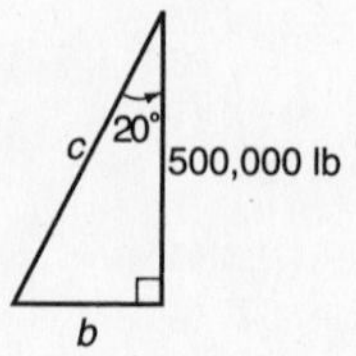

measure of the lift: 532,089 pounds

measure of the horizontal component: 181,985 pounds

54b. $\cos\theta = \frac{500{,}000}{650{,}000}$

$\cos\theta \approx 0.7692$

$\theta \approx 39.7°$

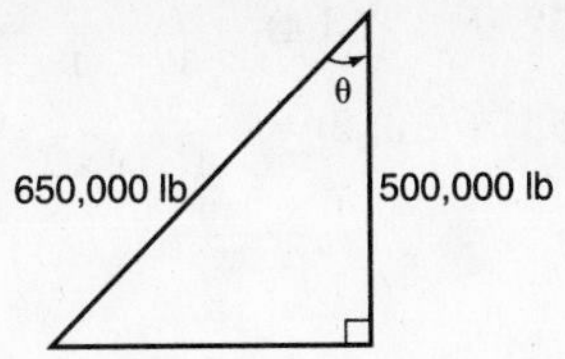

55. no

56. $P(\text{4 strikes, 1 not a strike}) = C(5, 4)\ S^4N^1$

$= 5\left(\frac{4}{7}\right)^4\left(\frac{3}{7}\right) = \frac{3840}{16{,}870} \approx 22.8\%$

57. $s = 5, f = 1, s + f = 6$, probability $= \frac{5}{6}$

58. $(r + s)^6 = r^6 + 6r^5s + 15r^4s^2 + 20r^3s^3 + 15r^2s^4 + 6rs^5 + s^6$

59. $a_n = a_1r^{n-1}$

$a_3 = 4(5)^{3-1}$

$a_3 = 4(5)^2$

$a_3 = 4(25)$

$a_3 = 100$

60. $\log_4(x + 2) + \log_4(x - 4) = 2$

$\log_4(x + 2)(x - 4) = 2$

$(x + 2)(x - 4) = 4^2$

$x^2 - 2x - 8 = 16$

$x^2 - 2x - 24 = 0$

$(x - 6)(x + 4) = 0$

$x - 6 = 0$ or $x + 4 = 0$

$x = 6$ $x = -4$

-4 is not a valid answer

61. $(x^{\sqrt{2}})^{\sqrt{8}} = x^{\sqrt{16}}$

$= x^4$

62. $d = \sqrt{(x_2 - x_1)^2 + (y_2 - y_1)^2}$

$= \sqrt{(3 - \sqrt{3})^2 + (3 - \sqrt{3})^2}$

$= \sqrt{(9 - 6\sqrt{3} + 3) + (9 - 6\sqrt{3} + 3)}$

$= \sqrt{24 - 12\sqrt{3}}$

$= \sqrt{4(6 - 3\sqrt{3})}$

$= 2\sqrt{6 - 3\sqrt{3}}$ or about 1.8 units

63. $\frac{1.8 \times 10^{24}}{6.02 \times 10^{23}} \approx 0.299 \times 10^1$ or 2.99

64. distributive property

13-2 Angles and Angle Measure

Pages 783–784 Check for Understanding

1. when an angle has its vertex at the origin and its initial side along the positive x-axis

2.

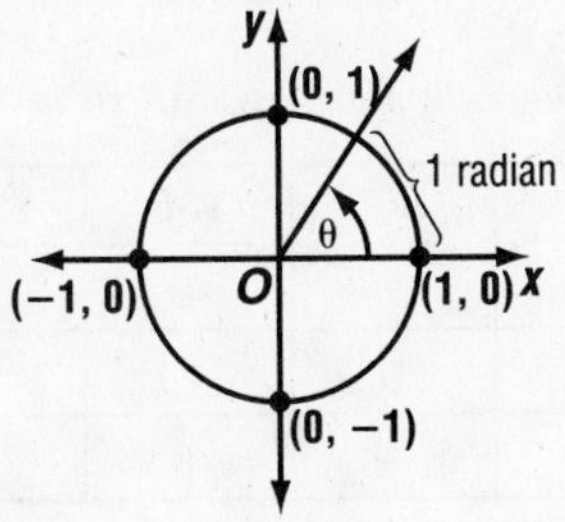

3. c

4. 360° is one complete revolution.

5. Toshi; their difference is not a multiple of 360.

6. b, d **7.** a **8.** f, h **9.** g

10. $45°\left(\frac{\pi \text{ radians}}{180°}\right) = \frac{45\pi}{180}$ radians or $\frac{\pi}{4}$ radians

11. $-120°\left(\frac{\pi \text{ radians}}{180°}\right) = -\frac{120\pi}{180}$ radians or $-\frac{2\pi}{3}$ radians

12. $540°\left(\frac{\pi \text{ radians}}{180°}\right) = \frac{540\pi}{180}$ radians or 3π radians

13. $\frac{2\pi}{3}$ radians $\left(\frac{180°}{\pi \text{ radians}}\right) = \frac{360°\pi}{3\pi} = 120°$

14. $\frac{-7\pi}{4}$ radians $\left(\frac{180°}{\pi \text{ radians}}\right) = \frac{-1260°\pi}{4\pi} = -315°$

15. 5 radians $\left(\frac{180°}{\pi \text{ radians}}\right) = \frac{900°}{\pi} \approx 286.48°$

16. Sample answer:
positive angle, $-60° + 360° = 300°$
negative angle, $-60° - 360° = -420°$

17. Sample answer:
positive angle, $\frac{\pi}{4} + 2\pi = \frac{9\pi}{4}$
negative angle, $\frac{\pi}{4} - 2\pi = \frac{-7\pi}{4}$

18. Sample answer:
positive angle, $750° - 360° = 390°$
negative angle, $750° - 360°(3) = 750° - 1080° = -330°$

19. $\frac{360}{12} = 30°$

$-2(30°) = -60°$

$-60°\left(\frac{\pi \text{ radians}}{180°}\right) = \frac{-60\pi}{180}$ radians or $\frac{-\pi}{3}$ radians

Pages 784–785 Exercises

20. $-90°\left(\frac{\pi \text{ radians}}{180°}\right) = \frac{-90\pi}{180}$ radians or $-\frac{\pi}{2}$ radians

21. $180°\left(\frac{\pi \text{ radians}}{180°}\right) = \frac{180\pi}{180}$ radians or π radians

22. $135°\left(\frac{\pi \text{ radians}}{180°}\right) = \frac{135\pi}{180}$ radians or $\frac{3\pi}{4}$ radians

23. $1200°\left(\frac{\pi \text{ radians}}{180°}\right) = \frac{1200\pi}{180}$ radians or $\frac{20\pi}{3}$ radians

24. $-315°\left(\frac{\pi \text{ radians}}{180°}\right) = \frac{-315\pi}{180}$ radians or $-\frac{7\pi}{4}$ radians

25. $-800°\left(\frac{\pi \text{ radians}}{180°}\right) = \frac{-800\pi}{180}$ radians or $-\frac{40\pi}{9}$ radians

26. $150°\left(\frac{\pi \text{ radians}}{180°}\right) = \frac{150\pi}{180}$ radians or $\frac{5\pi}{6}$ radians

27. $540°\left(\frac{\pi \text{ radians}}{180°}\right) = \frac{540\pi}{180}$ radians or 3π radians

28. $3600°\left(\frac{\pi \text{ radians}}{180°}\right) = \frac{3600\pi}{180}$ radians or 20π radians

29. π radians $\left(\frac{180°}{\pi \text{ radians}}\right) = \frac{180°\pi}{\pi}$ or $180°$

30. $-\frac{\pi}{2}$ radians $\left(\frac{180°}{\pi \text{ radians}}\right) = -\frac{180°\pi}{2\pi}$ or $-90°$

31. $\frac{-8\pi}{2}$ radians $\left(\frac{180°}{\pi \text{ radians}}\right) = -\frac{1440°\pi}{3\pi}$ or $-480°$

32. $\frac{3\pi}{4}$ radians $\left(\frac{180°}{\pi \text{ radians}}\right) = \frac{540°\pi}{4\pi}$ or $135°$

33. 5π radians $\left(\frac{180°}{\pi \text{ radians}}\right) = \frac{900°\pi}{\pi} = 900°$

34. $\frac{5\pi}{2}$ radians $\left(\frac{180°}{\pi \text{ radians}}\right) = \frac{900°\pi}{2\pi} = 450°$

35. 7 radians $\left(\frac{180°}{\pi \text{ radians}}\right) = \frac{1260°}{\pi} \approx 401.07$

36. 3.5 radians $\left(\frac{180°}{\pi \text{ radians}}\right) = \frac{630°}{\pi} \approx 200.54°$

37. -1.5 radians $\left(\frac{180°}{\pi \text{ radians}}\right) = -\frac{270°}{\pi} \approx -85.94°$

38. Sample answer:
positive angle, $-120° + 360° = 240°$
negative angle, $-120° - 360° = -480°$

39. Sample answer:
positive angle, $310° + 360° = 670°$
negative angle, $310° - 360° = -50°$

40. Sample answer:
positive angle, $-5\pi + 3(2\pi) = -5\pi + 6\pi = \pi$
negative angle, $-5\pi + 2\pi = -3\pi$

41. Sample answer:
positive angle, $\frac{9\pi}{4} - 2\pi = \frac{\pi}{4}$
negative angle, $\frac{9\pi}{4} - 2(2\pi) = \frac{9\pi}{4} - 4\pi = -\frac{7\pi}{4}$

42. Sample answer:
positive angle, $-450° + 2(360°) =$
$-450° + 720° = 270°$
negative angle, $-450° + 360° = -90°$

43. Sample answer:
positive angle, $720° - 360° = 360°$
negative angle, $720° - 3(360°) = 720° - 1080°$
$= -360°$

44. Sample answer:
positive angle, $\frac{\pi}{8} + 2\pi = \frac{17\pi}{8}$
negative angle, $\frac{\pi}{8} - 2\pi = -\frac{15\pi}{8}$

45. Sample answer:
positive angle, $-900° + 3(360°) =$
$-900° + 1080° = 180°$
negative angle, $-900° + 2(360°) =$
$-900° + 720° = -180°$

46. Sample answer:
positive angle, $-\frac{8\pi}{3} + 3(2\pi) = -\frac{8\pi}{3} + 6\pi = \frac{4\pi}{3}$
negative angle, $-\frac{8\pi}{3} + 2\pi = -\frac{2\pi}{3}$

47a. $a^2 + (-b)^2 = a^2 + b^2 = 1$

47b. $b^2 + a^2 = a^2 + b^2 = 1$

47c. $b^2 + (-a)^2 = a^2 + b^2 = 1$

48a. $300° \cdot \frac{24 \text{ hour}}{360°} = 20$ hour

48b. $\frac{2\pi}{3} \cdot \frac{24 \text{ hour}}{2\pi} = 8$ hour

49. $w = \frac{2\pi \text{ radians}}{1 \text{ revolution}} \cdot \frac{2 \text{ revolutions}}{3 \text{ seconds}}$
$= \frac{4\pi}{3}$ radians/second

50a. $\angle ACB + 42.4° = 90°$
$\angle ACB = 47.6°$

50b. $\sin 47.6° = \frac{AB}{3960}$
$0.7385 \approx \frac{AB}{3960}$
$AB \approx 2924$; 2924 miles

50c. $C = 2\pi r$
$C \approx 2\pi(2924)$
$C \approx 18{,}374$; 18,374 miles

50d. $\frac{18{,}374 \text{ miles}}{1 \text{ day}} \cdot \frac{1 \text{ day}}{24 \text{ hour}} = 766$ miles/hour

51. $\tan 47° = \frac{x}{120}$
$1.0724 \approx \frac{x}{120}$
$x \approx 128.7$; 128.7 meters

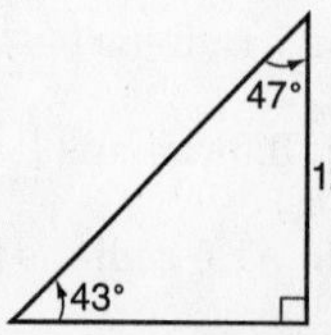

52. $P(3 \text{ and } 4) = \frac{2}{36} = \frac{1}{18} = 0.0\overline{5}$

53. $C(10, 2) = \frac{10!}{(10-2)!\,2!}$
$= \frac{10!}{8!\,2!}$
$= 45$
$45 - 10 = 35$ diagonals

54. $S_n = \frac{a_1(1 - r^n)}{1 - r}$
$S_3 = \frac{48\left(1 - \left(\frac{1}{2}\right)^3\right)}{1 - \frac{1}{2}}$
$= \frac{48\left(\frac{7}{8}\right)}{\frac{1}{2}}$
$= \frac{42}{\frac{1}{2}}$
$= 84$

55. $\frac{7}{m-3} = \frac{m+4}{m-3}$
$7 = m + 4$
$m = 3$
m cannot equal 3, no solution

56. $g[h(x)] = g(x^2)$
$= (x^2) - 1$
$= x^2 - 1$

57. $s_1 + s_2 = 6 + 4$
$= 10$
$s_1(s_2) = 6(4)$
$= 24$
$-\frac{b}{a} = \frac{10}{1};\ \frac{c}{a} = \frac{24}{1}$
$a = 1,\ b = -10,\ c = 24$
$x^2 - 10x + 24 = 0$

58. $\begin{bmatrix} 5 & 3 \\ 7 & 5 \end{bmatrix}\begin{bmatrix} x \\ y \end{bmatrix} = \begin{bmatrix} -5 \\ -11 \end{bmatrix}$

$M^{-1} = \frac{1}{4}\begin{bmatrix} 5 & -3 \\ -7 & 5 \end{bmatrix}$

$\frac{1}{4}\begin{bmatrix} 5 & -3 \\ -7 & 5 \end{bmatrix}\begin{bmatrix} 5 & 3 \\ 7 & 5 \end{bmatrix}\begin{bmatrix} x \\ y \end{bmatrix} = \frac{1}{4}\begin{bmatrix} 5 & -3 \\ -7 & 5 \end{bmatrix}\begin{bmatrix} -5 \\ -11 \end{bmatrix}$

$\frac{1}{4}\begin{bmatrix} 4 & 0 \\ 0 & 4 \end{bmatrix}\begin{bmatrix} x \\ y \end{bmatrix} = \frac{1}{4}\begin{bmatrix} 8 \\ -20 \end{bmatrix}$

$\begin{bmatrix} 1 & 0 \\ 0 & 1 \end{bmatrix}\begin{bmatrix} x \\ y \end{bmatrix} = \begin{bmatrix} 2 \\ -5 \end{bmatrix}$

$\begin{bmatrix} x \\ y \end{bmatrix} = \begin{bmatrix} 2 \\ -5 \end{bmatrix}$ (2, −5)

59. additive identity

13-3 Trigonometric Functions of General Angles

Pages 789–790 Check for Understanding

1. I

2. trigonometric expressions that are equal for all values of θ

3. $\frac{1}{\cos\theta} = \frac{1}{\frac{x}{r}} = \frac{r}{x} = \sec\theta$

4. Luisa; sin θ increases as θ goes from 0° to 90°.

5.

Function	0°	90°	180°	270°
sin θ	0	1	0	−1
cos θ	1	0	−1	0
tan θ	0	–	0	–

6. negative **7.** zero **8.** positive

9. $x = 1, y = -8$

$r = \sqrt{x^2 + y^2}$
$= \sqrt{1^2 + (-8)^2}$
$= \sqrt{65}$

$\sin\theta = \frac{y}{r}$
$= \frac{-8}{\sqrt{65}} \cdot \frac{\sqrt{65}}{\sqrt{65}}$
$= \frac{-8\sqrt{65}}{65}$

$\cos\theta = \frac{x}{r}$
$= \frac{1}{\sqrt{65}} \cdot \frac{\sqrt{65}}{\sqrt{65}}$
$= \frac{\sqrt{65}}{65}$

$\tan\theta = \frac{y}{x}$
$= \frac{-8}{1}$
$= -8$

10. $x = -3, y = -4$

$r = \sqrt{x^2 + y^2}$
$= \sqrt{(-3)^2 + (-4)^2}$
$= \sqrt{25}$
$= 5$

$\sin\theta = \frac{y}{r}$
$= \frac{-4}{5}$

$\cos\theta = \frac{x}{r}$
$= \frac{-3}{5}$

$\tan\theta = \frac{y}{x}$
$= \frac{-4}{-3}$
$= \frac{4}{3}$

11. $\cos 120° = \frac{x}{r}$
$= -\frac{1}{2}$

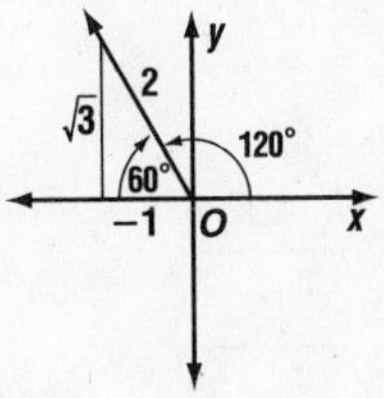

12. $\tan\left(-\frac{\pi}{3}\right) = \frac{y}{x}$
$= \frac{-\sqrt{3}}{1}$
$= -\sqrt{3}$

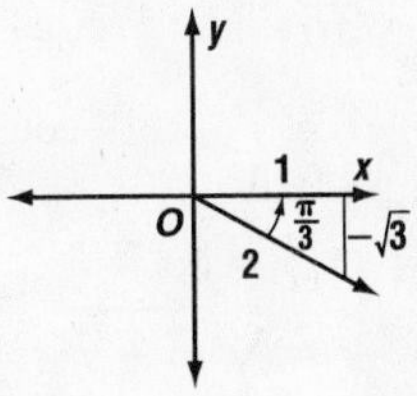

13. $\sin 225° = \frac{y}{r}$
$= \frac{-\sqrt{2}}{2}$

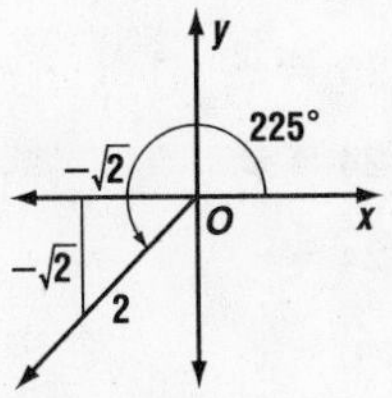

14. $\sin\theta = \frac{-4}{5} = \frac{y}{r}$

$y = -4, r = 5$
$r = \sqrt{x^2 + y^2}$
$5 = \sqrt{x^2 + (-4)^2}$
$25 = x^2 + 16$
$9 = x^2$
$3 = x$

$\cos\theta = \frac{x}{r} = \frac{3}{5}$
$\tan\theta = \frac{y}{x} = \frac{-4}{3}$
$\csc\theta = \frac{r}{y} = \frac{-5}{4}$
$\sec\theta = \frac{r}{x} = \frac{5}{3}$
$\cot\theta = \frac{x}{y} = \frac{-3}{4}$

15. $\tan\theta = 2 = \frac{y}{x}$

$x = 1, y = 2$
$r = \sqrt{x^2 + y^2}$
$= \sqrt{1^2 + 2^2}$
$= \sqrt{5}$

$\sin\theta = \frac{y}{r} = \frac{2}{\sqrt{5}} \cdot \frac{\sqrt{5}}{\sqrt{5}} = \frac{2\sqrt{5}}{5}$
$\cos\theta = \frac{x}{r} = \frac{1}{\sqrt{5}} \cdot \frac{\sqrt{5}}{\sqrt{5}} = \frac{\sqrt{5}}{5}$
$\csc\theta = \frac{r}{y} = \frac{\sqrt{5}}{2}$
$\sec\theta = \frac{r}{x} = \frac{\sqrt{5}}{1}$ or $\sqrt{5}$
$\cot\theta = \frac{x}{y} = \frac{1}{2}$

16. $6077 - 31\cos 2\theta = 6077 - 31\cos 2(30°)$
$= 6077 - 31\cos 60°$
$= 6077 - 31(.5)$
$= 6061.5$; 6061.5 feet

Pages 790–791 Exercises

17. negative **18.** positive **19.** negative
20. zero **21.** positive **22.** positive
23. undefined **24.** zero **25.** negative

26. $x = -15, y = 8$

$r = \sqrt{x^2 + y^2}$
$= \sqrt{(-15)^2 + 8^2}$
$= \sqrt{289}$
$= 17$

$\sin\theta = \frac{y}{r} = \frac{8}{17}$
$\cos\theta = \frac{x}{r} = -\frac{15}{17}$
$\tan\theta = \frac{y}{x} = -\frac{8}{15}$

27. $x = -3, y = 0$

$r = \sqrt{x^2 + y^2}$
$= \sqrt{(-3)^2 + 0^2}$
$= \sqrt{9}$
$= 3$

$\sin\theta = \frac{y}{r} = \frac{0}{3}$ or 0
$\cos\theta = \frac{x}{r} = \frac{-3}{3}$ or -1
$\tan\theta = \frac{y}{x} = \frac{0}{-3}$ or 0

28. $x = -\sqrt{2}, y = \sqrt{2}$

$r = \sqrt{x^2 + y^2}$
$= \sqrt{(-\sqrt{2})^2 + (\sqrt{2})^2}$
$= \sqrt{4}$
$= 2$

$\sin\theta = \frac{y}{r} = \frac{\sqrt{2}}{2}$
$\cos\theta = \frac{x}{r} = -\frac{\sqrt{2}}{2}$
$\tan\theta = \frac{y}{x} = -\frac{\sqrt{2}}{\sqrt{2}}$ or -1

29. $x = 5, y = -3$

$r = \sqrt{x^2 + y^2}$
$= \sqrt{(5)^2 + (-3)^2}$
$= \sqrt{25 + 9}$
$= \sqrt{34}$

$\sin\theta = \frac{y}{r} = -\frac{3}{\sqrt{34}} \cdot \frac{\sqrt{34}}{\sqrt{34}} = -\frac{3\sqrt{34}}{34}$
$\cos\theta = \frac{x}{r} = \frac{5}{\sqrt{34}} \cdot \frac{\sqrt{34}}{\sqrt{34}} = \frac{5\sqrt{34}}{34}$
$\tan\theta = \frac{y}{x} = -\frac{3}{5}$

30. $x = 0, y = 2$

$r = \sqrt{x^2 + y^2}$
$= \sqrt{0^2 + 2^2}$
$= \sqrt{4}$
$= 2$

$\sin\theta = \frac{y}{r} = \frac{2}{2}$ or 1
$\cos\theta = \frac{x}{r} = \frac{0}{2}$ or 0
$\tan\theta = \frac{y}{x} = \frac{2}{0}$ or undefined

31. $x = 4, y = 4$

$r = \sqrt{x^2 + y^2}$
$= \sqrt{4^2 + 4^2}$
$= \sqrt{32}$
$= 4\sqrt{2}$

$\sin\theta = \frac{y}{r} = \frac{4}{4\sqrt{2}} \cdot \frac{\sqrt{2}}{\sqrt{2}} = \frac{\sqrt{2}}{2}$
$\cos\theta = \frac{x}{r} = \frac{4}{4\sqrt{2}} \cdot \frac{\sqrt{2}}{\sqrt{2}} = \frac{\sqrt{2}}{2}$
$\tan\theta = \frac{y}{x} = \frac{4}{4}$ or 1

32.

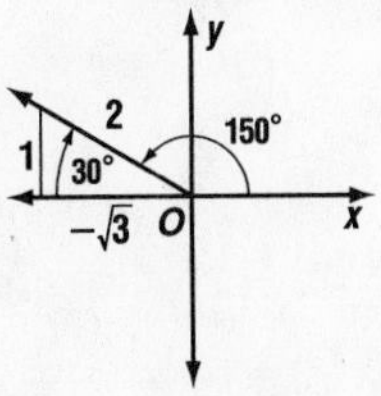

$\cos 150° = \frac{x}{r}$
$= -\frac{\sqrt{3}}{2}$

33.

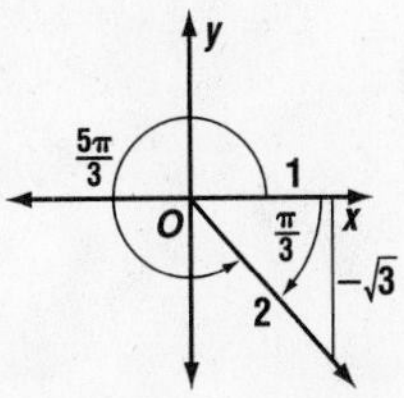

$\cos\frac{11\pi}{3} = \frac{x}{r}$
$= \frac{1}{2}$

34. 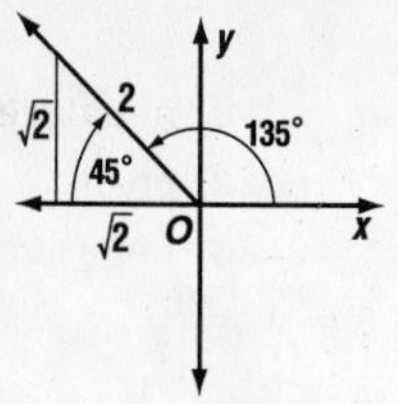

$\tan 135° = \frac{y}{x}$
$= \frac{\sqrt{2}}{-\sqrt{2}}$
$= -1$

35. 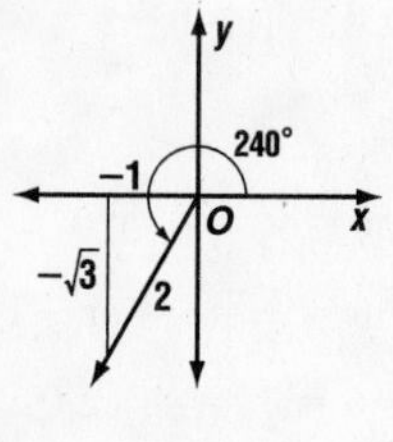

$\sin 240° = \frac{y}{r}$
$= -\frac{\sqrt{3}}{2}$

36. 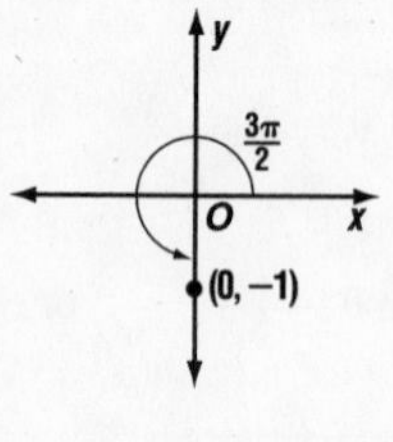

$\sin \frac{3\pi}{2} = \frac{-1}{1}$ or -1

37. 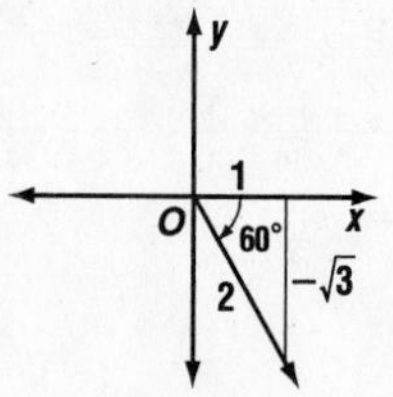

$\cos(-60°) = \frac{x}{r}$
$= \frac{1}{2}$

38. 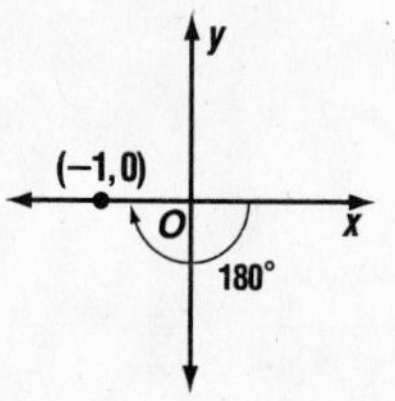

$\sin(-180°) = -\frac{0}{1}$ or 0

39. 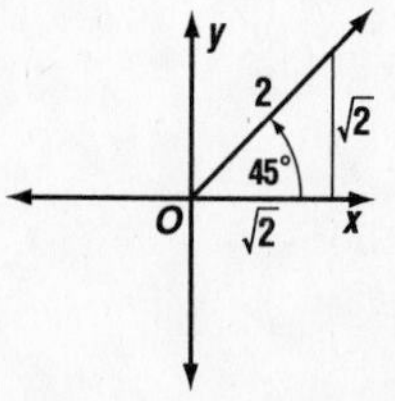

$\tan 405° = \tan 45°$
$\tan 405° = \frac{y}{x}$
$= \frac{\sqrt{2}}{\sqrt{2}}$
$= 1$

40. 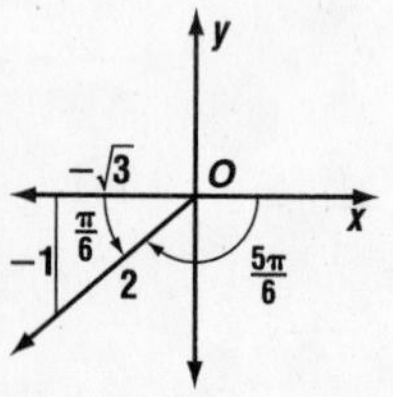

$\tan\left(\frac{-5\pi}{6}\right) = \frac{y}{x}$
$= \frac{-1}{-\sqrt{3}} \cdot \frac{\sqrt{3}}{\sqrt{3}}$
$= \frac{\sqrt{3}}{3}$

41. $\cos\theta = -\frac{1}{2}$
$x = -1, r = 2$
$r = \sqrt{x^2 + y^2}$
$2 = \sqrt{(-1)^2 + y^2}$
$2 = \sqrt{1 + y^2}$
$4 = 1 + y^2$
$3 = y^2$
$y = \sqrt{3}$

$\sin\theta = \frac{y}{r} = \frac{\sqrt{3}}{2}$
$\tan\theta = \frac{y}{x} = \frac{\sqrt{3}}{-1}$ or $-\sqrt{3}$
$\csc\theta = \frac{r}{y} = \frac{2}{\sqrt{3}} \cdot \frac{\sqrt{3}}{\sqrt{3}}$ or $\frac{2\sqrt{3}}{3}$
$\sec\theta = \frac{r}{x} = \frac{2}{-1}$ or -2
$\cot\theta = \frac{x}{y} = \frac{-1}{\sqrt{3}} \cdot \frac{\sqrt{3}}{\sqrt{3}}$ or $-\frac{\sqrt{3}}{3}$

42. $\sec\theta = \sqrt{3}$
$r = \sqrt{3}, x = 1$
$r = \sqrt{x^2 + y^2}$
$\sqrt{3} = \sqrt{1^2 + y^2}$
$3 = 1 + y^2$
$2 = y^2$
$-\sqrt{2} = y$

$\sin\theta = \frac{y}{r} = -\frac{\sqrt{2}}{\sqrt{3}} \cdot \frac{\sqrt{3}}{\sqrt{3}} = -\frac{\sqrt{6}}{3}$
$\tan\theta = \frac{y}{x} = -\frac{\sqrt{2}}{1}$ or $-\sqrt{2}$
$\csc\theta = \frac{r}{y} = -\frac{\sqrt{3}}{\sqrt{2}} \cdot \frac{\sqrt{2}}{\sqrt{2}} = -\frac{\sqrt{6}}{2}$
$\sec\theta = \frac{r}{x} = \frac{\sqrt{3}}{1}$ or $\sqrt{3}$
$\cot\theta = \frac{x}{y} = \frac{1}{-\sqrt{2}} \cdot \frac{\sqrt{2}}{\sqrt{2}} = -\frac{\sqrt{2}}{2}$

43. $\tan\theta = 3$
$-x = 1, -y = 3$
$r = \sqrt{x^2 + y^2}$
$r = \sqrt{1^2 + 3^2}$
$r = \sqrt{10}$

$\sin\theta = \frac{y}{r} = \frac{-3}{\sqrt{10}} \cdot \frac{\sqrt{10}}{\sqrt{10}} = -\frac{3\sqrt{10}}{10}$
$\cos\theta = \frac{x}{r} = \frac{-1}{\sqrt{10}} \cdot \frac{\sqrt{10}}{\sqrt{10}} = -\frac{\sqrt{10}}{10}$
$\csc\theta = \frac{r}{y} = -\frac{\sqrt{10}}{3}$
$\sec\theta = \frac{r}{x} = -\frac{\sqrt{10}}{1}$ or $-\sqrt{10}$
$\cot\theta = \frac{x}{y} = \frac{-1}{-3}$ or $\frac{1}{3}$

44. $\sin\theta = -\frac{1}{5}$
$y = -1, r = 5$
$r = \sqrt{x^2 + y^2}$
$5 = \sqrt{x^2 + (-1)^2}$
$25 = x^2 + 1$
$24 = x^2$
$\sqrt{24} = x$
$-2\sqrt{6} = x$

$\cos\theta = \frac{x}{r} = -\frac{2\sqrt{6}}{5}$
$\tan\theta = \frac{y}{x} = \frac{-1}{-2\sqrt{6}} \cdot \frac{\sqrt{6}}{\sqrt{6}}$
$= \frac{\sqrt{6}}{12}$
$\csc\theta = \frac{r}{y} = \frac{5}{-1}$ or -5
$\sec\theta = \frac{r}{x} = \frac{5}{-2\sqrt{6}} \cdot \frac{\sqrt{6}}{\sqrt{6}}$
$= -\frac{5\sqrt{6}}{12}$
$\cot\theta = \frac{x}{y} = \frac{-2\sqrt{6}}{-1}$ or $2\sqrt{6}$

45. $\cot\theta = -5$
$x = -5, y = 1$
$r = \sqrt{x^2 + y^2}$
$= \sqrt{(-5)^2 + 1^2}$
$= \sqrt{26}$

$\sin\theta = \frac{y}{r} = \frac{1}{\sqrt{26}} \cdot \frac{\sqrt{26}}{\sqrt{26}} = \frac{\sqrt{26}}{26}$
$\cos\theta = \frac{x}{r} = -\frac{5}{\sqrt{26}} \cdot \frac{\sqrt{26}}{\sqrt{26}} = -\frac{5\sqrt{26}}{26}$
$\tan\theta = \frac{y}{x} = -\frac{1}{5}$
$\csc\theta = \frac{r}{y} = \frac{\sqrt{26}}{1}$ or $\sqrt{26}$
$\sec\theta = \frac{r}{x} = -\frac{\sqrt{26}}{5}$

46. $\csc\theta = -3$
$y = -1, r = 3$
$r = \sqrt{x^2 + y^2}$
$3 = \sqrt{x^2 + (-1)^2}$
$9 = x^2 + 1$
$8 = x^2$
$2\sqrt{2} = x$

$\sin\theta = \frac{y}{r} = -\frac{1}{3}$
$\cos\theta = \frac{x}{r} = \frac{2\sqrt{2}}{3}$
$\tan\theta = \frac{x}{y} = -\frac{1}{2\sqrt{2}} \cdot \frac{\sqrt{2}}{\sqrt{2}}$
$= -\frac{\sqrt{2}}{4}$
$\sec\theta = \frac{r}{x} = \frac{3}{2\sqrt{2}} \cdot \frac{\sqrt{2}}{\sqrt{2}} = \frac{3\sqrt{2}}{4}$
$\cot\theta = \frac{x}{y} = \frac{2\sqrt{2}}{-1}$ or $-2\sqrt{2}$

47. $\cos\theta = \frac{2}{3}$

$x = 2,\ r = 3$ $\qquad \sin\theta = \frac{y}{r} = \pm\frac{\sqrt{5}}{3}$

$r = \sqrt{x^2 + y^2}$

$3 = \sqrt{2^2 + y^2}$

$9 = 4 + y^2$

$5 = y^2$

$\pm\sqrt{5} = y$

48. $\sec\theta = -3$

$r = 3,\ x = -1$ $\qquad \sin\theta = \frac{y}{r} = \pm\frac{2\sqrt{2}}{3}$

$r = \sqrt{x^2 + y^2}$

$3 = \sqrt{(-1)^2 + y^2}$ $\qquad \cos\theta = \frac{x}{r} = -\frac{1}{3}$

$9 = 1 + y^2$

$8 = y^2$

$\pm 2\sqrt{2} = y$

49. $\cos\theta = 0$

$r = 1,\ x = 0$ $\qquad \sin\theta = \frac{y}{r} = \pm\frac{1}{1}$ or ± 1

$r = \sqrt{x^2 + y^2}$

$1 = \sqrt{0^2 + y^2}$ $\qquad \tan\theta = \frac{y}{x} = \pm\frac{1}{0}$ or undefined

$1 = y^2$

$\pm 1 = y$

50. Quadrants I and II

51. Quadrant II

52. Quadrant III

53. $\frac{\cos\theta}{\sin\theta} = \frac{\frac{x}{r}}{\frac{y}{r}} = \frac{x}{r}\cdot\frac{r}{y} = \frac{x}{y} = \cot\theta$

54a. $R = \frac{v_0{}^2 \sin 2\theta}{g}$

$= \frac{(100)^2 \sin 2(45°)}{32}$

≈ 312.5; 312.5 feet

54b. 45°; $2 \times 45°$ or 90° yields the greatest value for $\sin 2\theta$.

55. $H = \frac{v_0{}^2 \sin^2\theta}{2g}$

$= \frac{(25)^2 \sin^2 65°}{2(32)}$

≈ 8; 8 feet

56. $\frac{5\pi}{6}$ radians $\left(\frac{180°}{\pi} \text{ radians}\right) = \frac{900°\pi}{6\pi}$ or 150°

57. $a^2 + b^2 = c^2$ $\qquad \cos A = \frac{18}{21}$ $\qquad \sin B = \frac{18}{21}$

$a^2 + 18^2 = 21^2$ $\qquad \cos A \approx 0.8571$ $\qquad \sin B \approx 0.8571$

$a^2 + 324 = 441$ $\qquad A \approx 31°$ $\qquad B \approx 59°$

$a^2 = 117$

$a \approx 10.8$

58. P(boy or red-haired person)

$= P(\text{boy}) + P(\text{red-haired person}) - P(\text{red-haired boy})$

$= \frac{15}{31} + \frac{5}{31} - \frac{2}{31}$

$= \frac{18}{31} \approx 0.581$

59. $r = \frac{-\frac{2}{3}}{\frac{4}{3}} = -\frac{1}{2}$ $\qquad S = \frac{a_1}{1 - r} = \frac{\frac{4}{3}}{1 - \left(-\frac{1}{2}\right)}$

$= \frac{\frac{4}{3}}{\frac{3}{2}}$

$= \frac{4}{3}\cdot\frac{2}{3}$

$= \frac{8}{9}$

60. $d = 15 - 21$

$= -6$

$9 + (-6) = 3$

$3 + (-6) = -3$

$-3 + (-6) = -9$

$-9 + (-6) = -15$ $\qquad 3, -3, -9, -15$

61. $\frac{10^7}{10^5} = 10^2$ or 100

100 times more acidic

62. $\frac{w + 12}{4w - 16} - \frac{w + 4}{2w - 8} = \frac{w + 12}{4(w - 4)} - \frac{(w + 4)}{2(w - 4)}\cdot\frac{2}{2}$

$= \frac{w + 12}{4(w - 4)} - \frac{2w + 8}{4(w - 4)}$

$= \frac{w + 12 - (2w + 8)}{4(w - 4)}$

$= \frac{-w + 4}{4(w - 4)}$

$= \frac{-(w - 4)}{4(w - 4)}$

$= -\frac{1}{4}$

63. $(x - 6)(x - 4 + 2\boldsymbol{i})(x - 4 - 2\boldsymbol{i})$

$= (x - 6)(x^2 - 8x + 20)$

$= x^3 - 8x^2 + 20x - 6x^2 + 48x - 120$

$= x^3 - 14x^2 + 68x - 120$

64. $m = \frac{y_2 - y_1}{x_2 - x_1}$ $\qquad y - y_1 = m(x - x_1)$

$= \frac{1 - 5}{3 - (-2)}$ $\qquad y - 1 = -\frac{4}{5}(x - 3)$

$= -\frac{4}{5}$ $\qquad y - 1 = -\frac{4}{5}x + \frac{12}{5}$

$y = -\frac{4}{5}x + \frac{17}{5}$

65. $-1.6m + 5 = -7.8$

$-1.6m = -12.8$

$m = 8$

13-4 Law of Sines

Page 796 Check for Understanding

1. $\frac{\sin A}{a} = \frac{\sin B}{b} = \frac{\sin C}{c}$
2. Sample answer: two sides and the angle opposite one of them
3. if $A < 90°$ and $a < b \sin A$ or if $A > 90°$ and $a < b$
4. 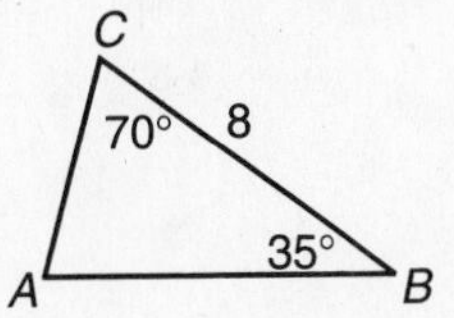

5. $a > 10$

6. $A = \frac{1}{2}ab \sin C$

$= \frac{1}{2}(15)(20)\sin 63°$

≈ 133.6

7. $A = \frac{1}{2}bc \sin A$

$= \frac{1}{2}(12)(23)\sin 100°$

≈ 135.9

8. $A = B$ $\qquad \frac{\sin C}{c} = \frac{\sin B}{b}$

$A + A + 50° = 180°$ $\qquad \frac{\sin 50°}{c} = \frac{\sin 65°}{12}$

$2A = 130°$ $\qquad c = \frac{12 \sin 50°}{\sin 65°}$

$A = 65°$ $\qquad c \approx 10.1$

$B = 65°$

9. $40° + B + 60° = 180°$

$B = 80°$

$$\frac{\sin A}{a} = \frac{\sin B}{b} \qquad \frac{\sin C}{c} = \frac{\sin B}{b}$$

$$\frac{\sin 40°}{a} = \frac{\sin 80°}{20} \qquad \frac{\sin 60°}{c} = \frac{\sin 80°}{20}$$

$$a = \frac{20 \sin 40°}{\sin 80°} \qquad c = \frac{20 \sin 60°}{\sin 80°}$$

$a \approx 13.1 \qquad c \approx 17.6$

10. $49° + 57° + C = 180°$

$C = 74°$

$$\frac{\sin A}{a} = \frac{\sin B}{b} \qquad \frac{\sin A}{a} = \frac{\sin C}{c}$$

$$\frac{\sin 49°}{8} = \frac{\sin 57°}{b} \qquad \frac{\sin 49°}{8} = \frac{\sin 74°}{c}$$

$$b = \frac{8 \sin 57°}{\sin 49°} \qquad c = \frac{8 \sin 74°}{\sin 49°}$$

$b \approx 8.9 \qquad c \approx 10.2$

11. two solutions $8 > 6 > 8 \sin 36°$

$$\frac{\sin B}{b} = \frac{\sin A}{a}$$

$$\frac{\sin B}{8} = \frac{\sin 36°}{6}$$

$$\sin B = \frac{8 \sin 36°}{6}$$

$B \approx 51.6°$

$36° + 51.6° + C \approx 180°$

$C \approx 92.4°$

$$\frac{\sin C}{c} = \frac{\sin A}{a}$$

$$\frac{\sin 92.4°}{c} \approx \frac{\sin 36°}{6}$$

$$c \approx \frac{6 \sin 92.4°}{\sin 36°}$$

$c \approx 10.2$

$B \approx 51.6°, C \approx 92.4°, c \approx 10.2$

$B + 51.6° \approx 180°$

$B \approx 128.4°$

$36° + 128.4° + C \approx 180$

$C \approx 15.6°$

$$\frac{\sin C}{c} = \frac{\sin A}{a}$$

$$\frac{\sin 15.6°}{c} \approx \frac{\sin 36}{6}$$

$$c \approx \frac{6 \sin 15.6°}{\sin 36°}$$

$c \approx 2.7$

$B \approx 128.4°, C \approx 15.6°, c \approx 2.7$

12. $A \geq 90°, 6 \leq 8$

no solution

13. $c \geq 98°, 90 > 64$

one solution

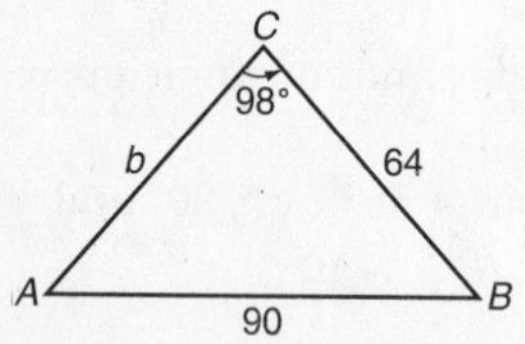

$$\frac{\sin C}{c} = \frac{\sin A}{a}$$

$$\frac{\sin 98°}{90} = \frac{\sin A}{64}$$

$$\sin A = \frac{64 \sin 98°}{90}$$

$A \approx 44.8°$

$44.8° + B + 98° \approx 180$

$B \approx 37.2°$

$$\frac{\sin B}{b} = \frac{\sin C}{c}$$

$$\frac{\sin 37.2°}{b} \approx \frac{\sin 98°}{90}$$

$$b \approx \frac{90 \sin 37.2°}{\sin 98°}$$

$b \approx 55.0$

$A \approx 44.8°, B \approx 37.2°, b \approx 55.0$

14.

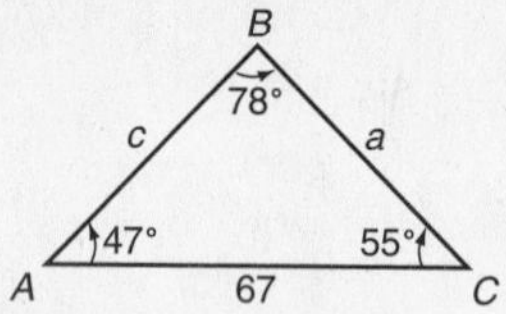

$47° + B + 55° = 180°$

$B = 78°$

$$\frac{\sin A}{a} = \frac{\sin B}{b}$$

$$\frac{\sin 47°}{a} = \frac{\sin 78°}{67}$$

$$a = \frac{67 \sin 47°}{\sin 78°}$$

$a \approx 50.1$

$$\frac{\sin C}{c} = \frac{\sin B}{b}$$

$$\frac{\sin 55°}{c} = \frac{\sin 78°}{67}$$

$$c = \frac{67 \sin 55°}{\sin 78°}$$

$c \approx 56.1$

$B = 78°, a \approx 50.1, c \approx 56.1$

Pages 796–798 Exercises

15. $A = \frac{1}{2}ab \sin C$

$= \frac{1}{2}(18)(13) \sin 34°$

$= 65.4$

16. $A = \frac{1}{2}bc \sin A$

$= \frac{1}{2}(12)(10) \sin 120°$

$= 52.0$

17. $A = \frac{1}{2}ab \sin C$

$= \frac{1}{2}(20)(24) \sin 73°$

$= 229.5$

18. $A = \frac{1}{2}bc \sin A$

$= \frac{1}{2}(35)(47) \sin 67°$

$= 757.1$

19. $A = \frac{1}{2}ac \sin B$

$= \frac{1}{2}(11.5)(19) \sin 20°$

$= 37.4$

20. $A = \frac{1}{2}ac \sin B$

$= \frac{1}{2}(9.4)(13.5) \sin 95°$

$= 63.2$

21. $49° + 57° + C = 180°$

$C = 74°$

$$\frac{\sin A}{a} = \frac{\sin B}{b} \qquad \frac{\sin A}{a} = \frac{\sin C}{c}$$

$$\frac{\sin 49°}{8} = \frac{\sin 57°}{b} \qquad \frac{\sin 49°}{8} = \frac{\sin 74°}{c}$$

$$b = \frac{8 \sin 57°}{\sin 49°} \qquad c = \frac{8 \sin 74°}{\sin 49°}$$

$b \approx 8.9 \qquad c \approx 10.2$

22. $43° + 68° + C = 180°$

$C = 69°$

$$\frac{\sin C}{c} = \frac{\sin B}{b} \qquad \frac{\sin C}{c} = \frac{\sin A}{a}$$

$$\frac{\sin 69°}{22} = \frac{\sin 68°}{b} \qquad \frac{\sin 69°}{22} = \frac{\sin 43°}{a}$$

$$b = \frac{22 \sin 68°}{\sin 69°} \qquad a = \frac{22 \sin 43°}{\sin 69°}$$

$b \approx 21.8 \qquad a \approx 16.1$

23. $110° + B + 35.3° \approx 180°$

$B \approx 34.7°$

$$\frac{\sin A}{a} = \frac{\sin C}{c} \qquad \frac{\sin A}{a} = \frac{\sin B}{b}$$

$$\frac{\sin 110°}{13} = \frac{\sin C}{8} \qquad \frac{\sin 110°}{13} \approx \frac{\sin 34.7°}{b}$$

$$\sin C = \frac{8 \sin 110°}{13} \qquad b \approx \frac{13 \sin 34.7°}{\sin 110°}$$

$C \approx 35.3° \qquad b \approx 7.9$

24. $36° + 49° + C \approx 180°$
$C \approx 95°$

$\frac{\sin B}{b} = \frac{\sin A}{a}$ $\frac{\sin C}{c} = \frac{\sin B}{b}$

$\frac{\sin 49°}{14.9} = \frac{\sin A}{11.6}$ $\frac{\sin 95°}{c} \approx \frac{\sin 49°}{14.9}$

$\sin A = \frac{11.6 \sin 49°}{14.9}$ $c \approx \frac{14.9 \sin 95°}{\sin 49°}$

$A \approx 36.0°$ $c \approx 19.7$

25. $A + 75° + 38° = 180°$
$A = 67°$

$\frac{\sin A}{a} = \frac{\sin B}{b}$ $\frac{\sin A}{a} = \frac{\sin C}{c}$

$\frac{\sin 67°}{45} = \frac{\sin 75°}{b}$ $\frac{\sin 67°}{45} = \frac{\sin 38°}{c}$

$b = \frac{45 \sin 75°}{\sin 67°}$ $c = \frac{45 \sin 38°}{\sin 67°}$

$b \approx 47.2$ $c \approx 30.1$

26. $105° + 48.7° + C \approx 180°$
$C \approx 26.3°$

$\frac{\sin A}{a} = \frac{\sin B}{b}$ $\frac{\sin C}{c} = \frac{\sin A}{a}$

$\frac{\sin 105°}{18} = \frac{\sin B}{14}$ $\frac{\sin 26.3°}{c} \approx \frac{\sin 105°}{18}$

$\sin B = \frac{14 \sin 105°}{18}$ $c \approx \frac{18 \sin 26.3°}{\sin 105°}$

$B \approx 48.7°$ $c \approx 8.3$

27.

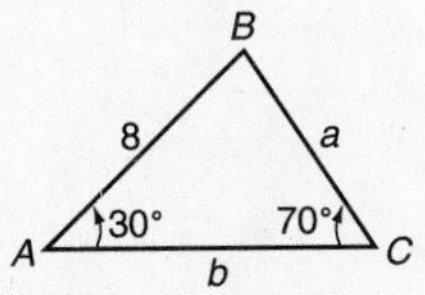

$30° + B + 70° = 180°$
$B = 80°$

$\frac{\sin C}{c} = \frac{\sin A}{a}$ $\frac{\sin C}{c} = \frac{\sin B}{b}$

$\frac{\sin 70°}{8} = \frac{\sin 30°}{a}$ $\frac{\sin 70°}{8} = \frac{\sin 80°}{b}$

$a = \frac{8 \sin 30°}{\sin 70°}$ $b = \frac{8 \sin 80°}{\sin 70°}$

$a \approx 4.3$ $b \approx 8.4$

28.

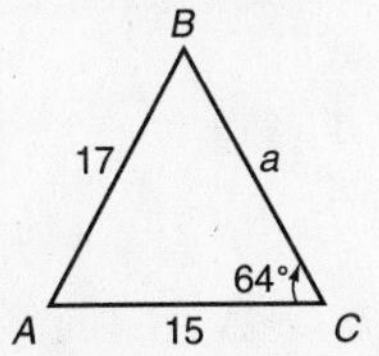

$A + 52.5° + 64° \approx 180°$
$A \approx 63.5°$

$\frac{\sin C}{c} = \frac{\sin B}{b}$ $\frac{\sin A}{a} = \frac{\sin C}{c}$

$\frac{\sin 64°}{17} = \frac{\sin B}{15}$ $\frac{\sin 63.5°}{a} \approx \frac{\sin 64°}{17}$

$\sin B = \frac{15 \sin 64°}{17}$ $a \approx \frac{17 \sin 63.5°}{\sin 64°}$

$B \approx 52.5°$ $a \approx 16.9$

29.

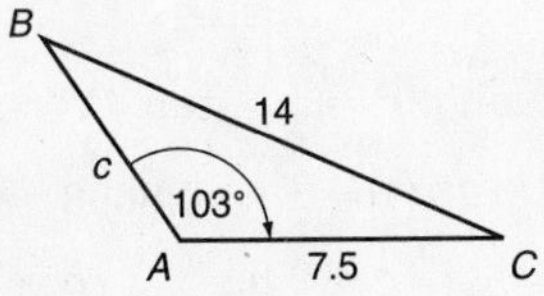

$103° + 31.5° + C \approx 180°$
$C \approx 45.5°$

$\frac{\sin A}{a} = \frac{\sin B}{b}$ $\frac{\sin C}{c} = \frac{\sin A}{a}$

$\frac{\sin 103°}{14} = \frac{\sin B}{7.5}$ $\frac{\sin 45.5°}{c} \approx \frac{\sin 103°}{14}$

$\sin B = \frac{7.5 \sin 103°}{14}$ $c \approx \frac{14 \sin 45.5°}{\sin 103°}$

$B \approx 31.5°$ $c \approx 10.2$

30.

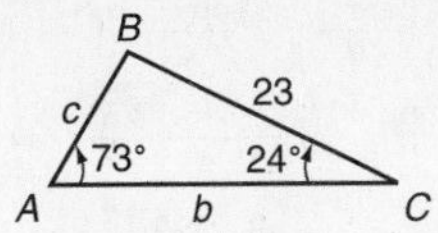

$73° + B + 24° = 180°$
$B = 83°$

$\frac{\sin A}{a} = \frac{\sin C}{c}$ $\frac{\sin A}{a} = \frac{\sin B}{b}$

$\frac{\sin 73°}{23} = \frac{\sin 24°}{c}$ $\frac{\sin 73°}{23} = \frac{\sin 83°}{b}$

$c = \frac{23 \sin 24°}{\sin 73°}$ $b = \frac{23 \sin 83°}{\sin 73°}$

$c \approx 9.8$ $b \approx 23.9$

31. $A \geq 90°$, $7 \leq 9$
no solution

32. $A < 90°$, $14 > 12$
one solution
$45° + 37.3° + C = 180°$
$C \approx 97.7°$

$\frac{\sin A}{a} = \frac{\sin B}{b}$ $\frac{\sin A}{a} = \frac{\sin C}{c}$

$\frac{\sin 45°}{14} = \frac{\sin B}{12}$ $\frac{\sin 45°}{14} = \frac{\sin 97.7°}{c}$

$\sin B = \frac{12 \sin 45°}{14}$ $c \approx \frac{14 \sin 97.7°}{\sin 45°}$

$B \approx 37.3°$ $c \approx 19.6$

33. $A < 90°$, $12 < 19 \sin 57°$ no solution

34. $A < 90°$, $9 < 20 \sin 31°$ no solution

35. $A \geq 90°$, $12 \leq 14$ no solution

36. $A < 90°$, $150 > 125 > 150 \sin 25°$
two solutions

$\frac{\sin A}{a} = \frac{\sin B}{b}$

$\frac{\sin 25°}{125} = \frac{\sin B}{150}$

$\sin B = \frac{150 \sin 25°}{125}$

$B \approx 30.5°$

$25° + 30.5° + C \approx 180°$
$C \approx 124.5°$

$\frac{\sin A}{a} = \frac{\sin C}{c}$

$\frac{\sin 25°}{125} \approx \frac{\sin 124.5°}{c}$

$c \approx \frac{125 \sin 124.5°}{\sin 25°}$

$c \approx 243.8$

$B \approx 30.5°$, $C \approx 124.5°$,
$c = 243.8$

$B + 30.5° \approx 180$
$B \approx 149.5°$
$25° + 149.5° + C \approx 180°$
$C \approx 5.5°$

$\frac{\sin A}{a} = \frac{\sin C}{c}$

$\frac{\sin 25°}{125} \approx \frac{\sin 5.5°}{c}$

$c \approx \frac{125 \sin 5.5°}{\sin 25°}$

$c \approx 28.4$

$B \approx 149.5°$, $C \approx 5.5°$,
$c \approx 28.4$

37. $A < 90°$, $10 < 16 \sin 40°$
no solution

38. $A \geq 90°$, $18 \leq 20$
no solution

39. $A < 90°$, $10 > 8 > 10 \sin 40°$
two solutions

$\frac{\sin A}{a} = \frac{\sin B}{b}$

$\frac{\sin 40°}{8} = \frac{\sin B}{10}$

$\sin B = \frac{10 \sin 40°}{8}$

$B \approx 53.5°$

$40° + 53.5° + C \approx 180°$
$C \approx 86.5°$

$B + 53.5° \approx 180°$
$B \approx 126.5°$
$40° + 126.5° + C \approx 180°$
$C \approx 13.5°$

(Continued next page)

$\frac{\sin A}{a} = \frac{\sin C}{c}$

$\frac{\sin 40°}{8} \approx \frac{\sin 86.5°}{c}$

$c \approx \frac{8 \sin 86.5°}{\sin 40°}$

$c \approx 12.4$

$B \approx 53.5°$, $C \approx 86.5°$, $c = 12.4$

$\frac{\sin A}{a} = \frac{\sin C}{c}$

$\frac{\sin 40°}{8} = \frac{\sin 13.5°}{c}$

$c = \frac{8 \sin 13.5°}{\sin 40°}$

$c \approx 2.9$

$B \approx 126.5°$, $C \approx 13.5°$, $c \approx 2.9$

40.

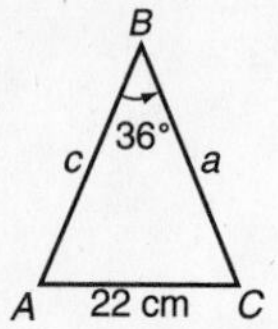

$A = C$

$A + 36° + A = 180°$

$2A = 144°$

$A = 72°$

$\frac{\sin B}{b} = \frac{\sin A}{a}$

$\frac{\sin 36°}{22} = \frac{\sin 72°}{a}$

$a = \frac{22 \sin 72°}{\sin 36°}$

$a \approx 35.6$

$P \approx 35.6 + 35.6 + 22$
≈ 93.2; 93.2 centimeters

41. $8 + 13 < 22$ There is no solution.

42. See students' work.

43.

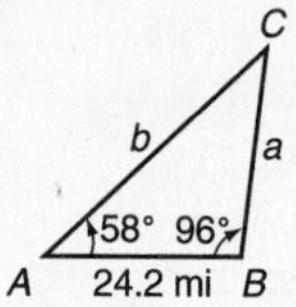

$58° + 96° + C = 180°$

$C = 26°$

$\frac{\sin A}{a} = \frac{\sin C}{c}$

$\frac{\sin 58°}{a} = \frac{\sin 26°}{24.2}$

$a = \frac{24.2 \sin 58°}{\sin 26°}$

$a \approx 46.8$

46.8 miles to Norfolk.

44.

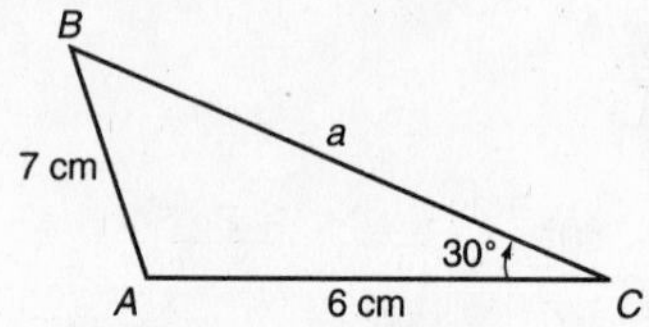

$\frac{\sin B}{b} = \frac{\sin C}{c}$

$\frac{\sin B}{6} = \frac{\sin 30°}{7}$

$\sin B = \frac{6 \sin 30°}{7}$

$B \approx 25.8°$

$A + 25.8° + 30° \approx 180°$

$A \approx 124.2°$

$\frac{\sin A}{a} = \frac{\sin C}{c}$

$\frac{\sin 124.2°}{a} \approx \frac{\sin 30°}{7}$

$a \approx \frac{7 \sin 124.2°}{\sin 30°}$

$a \approx 11.5$

yes, 11.5 centimeters

45.

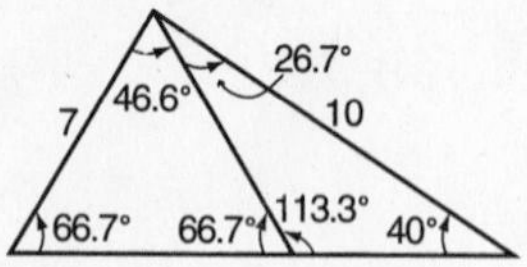

$\frac{\sin 40°}{7} = \frac{\sin x°}{10}$

$\sin x° = \frac{10 \sin 40°}{7}$

$x \approx 66.7°$

$\frac{\sin 26.7}{y} = \frac{\sin 40°}{7}$

$y = \frac{7 \sin 26.7}{\sin 40°}$

$y \approx 4.9$

$\frac{\sin 40°}{7} = \frac{\sin 73.3°}{y}$

$y = \frac{7 \sin 73.3°}{\sin 40}$

$y \approx 10.4$

between 4.9 and 10.4 miles

46a.

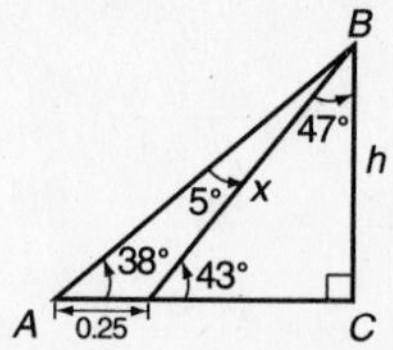

$\frac{\sin 5°}{0.25} = \frac{\sin 38°}{x}$

$x = \frac{0.25 \sin 38°}{\sin 5°}$

$x \approx 1.8$

$\frac{\sin 90°}{1.8} \approx \frac{\sin 43°}{h}$

$h \approx \frac{1.8 \sin 43°}{\sin 90°}$

$h \approx 1.2$ km

46b. See students' work.

47.

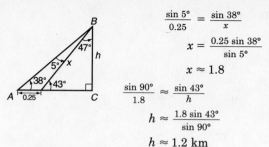

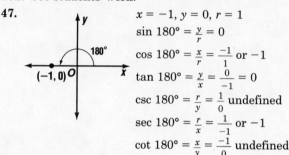

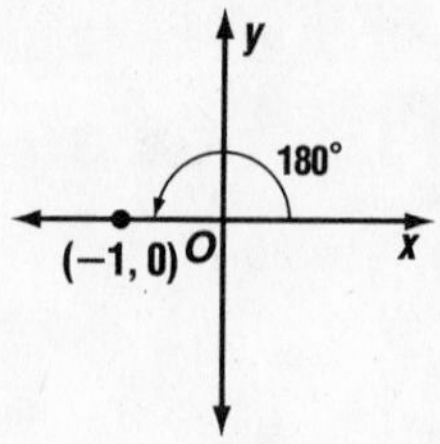

$x = -1, y = 0, r = 1$

$\sin 180° = \frac{y}{r} = 0$

$\cos 180° = \frac{x}{r} = \frac{-1}{1}$ or -1

$\tan 180° = \frac{y}{x} = \frac{0}{-1} = 0$

$\csc 180° = \frac{r}{y} = \frac{1}{0}$ undefined

$\sec 180° = \frac{r}{x} = \frac{1}{-1}$ or -1

$\cot 180° = \frac{x}{y} = \frac{-1}{0}$ undefined

48. $P(6, 6) = 6!$ or 720

49. $S_n = \frac{n}{2}[2a_1 + (n - 1)d]$

$S_{50} = \frac{50}{2}[2(5) + (50 - 1)25]$

$= 25(10 + 1225)$

$= 30{,}875$

50. $A = Pe^{rt}$

$= 1000\, e^{0.07(16)}$

$= \$3064.85$

Yes; Sean has $3064.85 in his account.

51. $\frac{3x - 21}{x^2 - 49} \div \frac{3x}{x^2 + 7x} = \frac{3x - 21}{x^2 - 49} \cdot \frac{x^2 + 7x}{3x}$

$= \frac{\cancel{3}(\cancel{x - 7})}{(\cancel{x + 7})(\cancel{x - 7})} \cdot \frac{\cancel{x}(\cancel{x + 7})}{\cancel{3x}}$

$= 1$

52. $a = 6, c = 2$

$b^2 = a^2 - c^2$

$b^2 = 6^2 - 2^2$

$b^2 = 36 - 4$

$b^2 = 32$

$\frac{x^2}{b^2} + \frac{y^2}{a^2} = 1$

$\frac{x^2}{32} + \frac{y^2}{36} = 1$

53. $2x^2 - 11x - 21 = (2x + 3)(x - 7)$

54. $\begin{vmatrix} 6 & 4 \\ -3 & 2 \end{vmatrix} = 6(2) - 4(-3)$

$= 12 + 12$

$= 24$

Page 798 Self Test

1. $49° + B + 90° = 180°$

$B = 41°$

$\sin 49° = \frac{7}{c}$

$0.7547 \approx \frac{7}{c}$

$c \approx 9.3$

$\tan 41° = \frac{b}{7}$

$0.8693 \approx \frac{b}{7}$

$b \approx 6.1$

2. $90°\left(\frac{\pi \text{ radians}}{180°}\right) = \frac{90\pi}{180}$ radians or $\frac{\pi}{2}$ radians

3. $150°\left(\frac{\pi \text{ radians}}{180°}\right) = \frac{150\pi}{180}$ radians or $\frac{5\pi}{6}$ radians

4. $-135°\left(\frac{\pi \text{ radians}}{180°}\right) = -\frac{135\pi}{180}$ radians or $-\frac{3\pi}{4}$ radians

5. $\frac{3\pi}{2}$ radians $\left(\frac{180°}{\pi \text{ radians}}\right) = \frac{540°\pi}{2\pi}$ or 270°

6. $-\frac{7\pi}{4}$ radians $\left(\frac{180°}{\pi \text{ radians}}\right) = -\frac{1260°\pi}{4\pi}$ or −315°

7. 2 radians $\left(\frac{180°}{\pi \text{ radians}}\right) = \frac{360°}{\pi} \approx 114.6°$

8. $x = -2, y = 0$

$r = \sqrt{x^2 + y^2} = \sqrt{(-2)^2 + 0^2} = \sqrt{4} = 2$

$\sin\theta = \frac{y}{r} = \frac{0}{2}$ or 0

$\cos\theta = \frac{x}{r} = \frac{-2}{2}$ or −1

$\tan\theta = \frac{y}{x} = \frac{0}{-2}$ or 0

9. $P = IV\cos\theta$
$= (2)(120)\cos 70°$
≈ 82.1; 82.1 watts

10. $A < 90°$, $5 < 12 \sin 40°$
no solution

13-5 Law of Cosines

Pages 802 Check for Understanding

1. Sample answer: if you know the measure of three sides
2. $a^2 = 8^2 + 10^2 - 2 \cdot 8 \cdot 10 \cos 40°$
3. a, c
4. You do not know two parts of one ratio.
5. See students' work.
6. See students' work.
7. cosines; $c^2 = a^2 + b^2 - 2ab\cos C$

$c^2 = 11^2 + 17^2 - 2(11)(17)\cos 42°$

$c^2 \approx 132.06$

$c \approx 11.5$

$\frac{\sin C}{c} = \frac{\sin B}{b}$

$\frac{\sin 42°}{11.5} \approx \frac{\sin B}{17}$

$\sin B \approx \frac{17 \sin 42°}{11.5}$

$B \approx 81.6°$

$A + 81.6° + 42° \approx 180°$

$A \approx 56.4°$

8. sines; $\frac{\sin C}{c} = \frac{\sin B}{b}$

$\frac{\sin C}{8} = \frac{\sin 71°}{16}$

$\sin C = \frac{8 \sin 71°}{16}$

$C \approx 28.2°$

$A + 71° + 28.2° \approx 180°$

$A \approx 80.8°$

$\frac{\sin A}{a} = \frac{\sin B}{b}$

$\frac{\sin 80.8°}{a} \approx \frac{\sin 71°}{16}$

$a \approx \frac{16 \sin 80.8°}{\sin 71°}$

$a \approx 16.7$

9. sines; $\frac{\sin A}{a} = \frac{\sin C}{c}$

$\frac{\sin 34°}{12} = \frac{\sin C}{15}$

$\sin C = \frac{15 \sin 34°}{12}$

$C \approx 44.3°$

$34° + B + 44.3° \approx 180°$

$B \approx 101.7°$

$\frac{\sin A}{a} = \frac{\sin B}{b}$

$\frac{\sin 34°}{12} \approx \frac{\sin 101.7°}{b}$

$b \approx \frac{12 \sin 101.7°}{\sin 34°}$

$b \approx 21.0$

10. cosines; $a^2 = b^2 + c^2 - 2bc\cos A$

$15^2 = 18^2 + 19^2 - 2(18)(19)\cos A$

$2(18)(19)\cos A = 18^2 + 19^2 - 15^2$

$\cos A = \frac{18^2 + 19^2 - 15^2}{2(18)(19)}$

$\cos A \approx 0.6725$

$A \approx 47.7°$

$\frac{\sin A}{a} = \frac{\sin B}{b}$

$\frac{\sin 47.7°}{15} \approx \frac{\sin B}{18}$

$\sin B \approx \frac{18 \sin 47.7°}{15}$

$B \approx 62.6°$

$47.7° + 62.6° + C \approx 180°$

$C \approx 69.7°$

11. $c^2 = a^2 + b^2 - 2ab\cos C$

$4.9^2 = 6.8^2 + 8.4^2 - 2(6.8)(8.4)\cos C$

$2(6.8)(8.4)\cos C = 6.8^2 + 8.4^2 - 4.9^2$

$\cos C = \frac{6.8^2 + 8.4^2 - 4.9^2}{2(6.8)(8.4)}$

$\cos C \approx 0.81223$

$C \approx 35.7°$

The smallest angle is about 35.7°.

Pages 802–804 Exercises

12. cosines; $a^2 = b^2 + c^2 - 2bc\cos A$

$a^2 = 6^2 + 7^2 - 2(6)(7)\cos 40°$

$a^2 \approx 20.65$

$a \approx 4.5$

$\frac{\sin C}{c} = \frac{\sin A}{a}$

$\frac{\sin C}{7} \approx \frac{\sin 40°}{4.5}$

$\sin C \approx 7\ \frac{\sin 40°}{4.5}$

$C \approx 89.2°$

$40° + B + 89.2° \approx 180°$

$B \approx 50.8°$

13. cosines; $c^2 = a^2 + b^2 - 2ab\cos C$

$c^2 = 11^2 + 10.5^2 - 2(11)(10.5)\cos 35°$

$c^2 \approx 42.03$

$C \approx 6.5$

$\frac{\sin C}{c} = \frac{\sin A}{a}$

$\frac{\sin 35°}{6.5} \approx \frac{\sin A}{11}$

$\sin A \approx \frac{11 \sin 35°}{6.5}$

$A \approx 76.1$

$76.1° + B + 35° \approx 180°$

$B \approx 68.9°$

14. sines; $\frac{\sin C}{c} = \frac{\sin A}{a}$

$\frac{\sin 70°}{14} = \frac{\sin 40°}{a}$

$a = \frac{14 \sin 40°}{\sin 70°}$

$a \approx 9.6$

$\frac{\sin B}{b} = \frac{\sin C}{c}$

$\frac{\sin 70°}{b} = \frac{\sin 70°}{14}$

$b = \frac{14 \sin 70°}{\sin 70°}$

$b \approx 14$

$40° + B + 70° = 180°$

$B = 70°$

15. cosines; $a^2 = b^2 + c^2 - 2bc\cos A$

$140^2 = 185^2 + 166^2 - 2(185)(166)\cos A$

$2(185)(166)\cos A = 185^2 + 166^2 - 140^2$

$\cos A = \frac{185^2 + 166^2 - 140^2}{2(185)(166)}$

$\cos A \approx 0.6868$

$A \approx 46.6°$

(Continued next page)

$$\frac{\sin A}{a} = \frac{\sin B}{b}$$
$$\frac{\sin 46.6°}{140} \approx \frac{\sin B}{185}$$
$$\sin B \approx \frac{185 \sin 46.6°}{140}$$
$$B \approx 73.8°$$
$$46.6° + 73.8° + C \approx 180°$$
$$C \approx 59.6°$$

16. sines; $\frac{\sin C}{c} = \frac{\sin A}{a}$ $\quad$ $\frac{\sin B}{b} = \frac{\sin A}{a}$

$$\frac{\sin 22°}{c} = \frac{\sin 56°}{12.2} \qquad \frac{\sin 102°}{b} = \frac{\sin 56°}{12.2}$$
$$c = \frac{12.2 \sin 22°}{\sin 56°} \qquad b = \frac{12.2 \sin 102°}{\sin 56°}$$
$$c \approx 5.5 \qquad b \approx 14.4$$
$$56° + B + 22° = 180°$$
$$B = 102°$$

17. cosines; $a^2 = b^2 + c^2 - 2bc \cos A$

$$13^2 = 12^2 + 5^2 - 2(12)(5) \cos A$$
$$2(12)(5) \cos A = 12^2 + 5^2 - 13^2$$
$$\cos A = \frac{12^2 + 5^2 - 13^2}{2(12)(5)}$$
$$\cos A = 0$$
$$A = 90.0°$$
$$\frac{\sin B}{b} = \frac{\sin A}{a} \qquad 90.0° + 67.4° + C \approx 180°$$
$$\frac{\sin B}{12} = \frac{\sin 90°}{13} \qquad C \approx 22.6°$$
$$\sin B = \frac{12 \sin 90°}{13}$$
$$B \approx 67.4°$$

18. cosines; $a^2 = b^2 + c^2 - 2bc \cos A$

$$a^2 = 16^2 + 19^2 - 2(16)(19) \cos 35°$$
$$a^2 \approx 118.96$$
$$a \approx 10.9$$
$$\frac{\sin A}{a} = \frac{\sin B}{b} \qquad 35° + 57.3° + C \approx 180°$$
$$\frac{\sin 35°}{10.9} \approx \frac{\sin B}{16} \qquad C \approx 87.7°$$
$$\sin B \approx \frac{16 \sin 35°}{10.9}$$
$$B \approx 57.3°$$

19. cosines; $b^2 = a^2 + c^2 - 2ac \cos B$

$$b^2 = 20^2 + 24^2 - 2(20)(24) \cos 47°$$
$$b^2 \approx 321.28$$
$$b \approx 17.9$$
$$\frac{\sin B}{b} = \frac{\sin A}{a} \qquad 54.8° + 47° + C \approx 180°$$
$$\frac{\sin 47°}{17.9} \approx \frac{\sin A}{20} \qquad C \approx 78.2°$$
$$\sin A \approx \frac{20 \sin 47°}{17.9}$$
$$A \approx 54.8°$$

20. cosines; $c^2 = a^2 + b^2 - 2ab \cos C$

$$c^2 = 21.5^2 + 13^2 - 2(21.5)(13) \cos 38.3°$$
$$c^2 \approx 192.56$$
$$c \approx 13.9$$
$$\frac{\sin C}{c} = \frac{\sin A}{a} \qquad A + 35.4° + 38.3° \approx 180°$$
$$\frac{\sin 38.3°}{13.9} \approx \frac{\sin B}{13} \qquad A \approx 106.3°$$
$$\sin B \approx \frac{13 \sin 38.3°}{13.9}$$
$$B \approx 35.4°$$

21. sines; $40° + 59° + C = 180°$

$$C = 81°$$
$$\frac{\sin C}{c} = \frac{\sin A}{a} \qquad \frac{\sin B}{b} = \frac{\sin C}{c}$$
$$\frac{\sin 81°}{14} = \frac{\sin 40°}{a} \qquad \frac{\sin 59°}{b} = \frac{\sin 81°}{14}$$
$$a = \frac{14 \sin 40°}{\sin 81°} \qquad b = \frac{14 \sin 59°}{\sin 81°}$$
$$a \approx 9.1 \qquad b \approx 12.1$$

22. cosines; $b^2 = a^2 + c^2 - 2ac \cos B$

$$b^2 = 51^2 + 61^2 - 2(51)(61) \cos 19°$$
$$b^2 \approx 438.98$$
$$b \approx 21.0$$
$$\frac{\sin C}{c} = \frac{\sin B}{b} \qquad A + 19° + 71.0° \approx 180°$$
$$\frac{\sin C}{61} \approx \frac{\sin 19°}{21} \qquad A \approx 90.0°$$
$$\sin C \approx \frac{61 \sin 19°}{21}$$
$$C \approx 71.0°$$

23. sines; $25° + 78° + C = 180°$

$$C = 77°$$
$$\frac{\sin B}{b} = \frac{\sin A}{a} \qquad \frac{\sin A}{a} = \frac{\sin C}{c}$$
$$\frac{\sin 78°}{b} = \frac{\sin 25°}{13.7} \qquad \frac{\sin 25°}{13.7} \approx \frac{\sin 77°}{c}$$
$$b = \frac{13.7 \sin 78°}{\sin 25°} \qquad c \approx \frac{13.7 \sin 77°}{\sin 25°}$$
$$b \approx 31.7 \qquad c \approx 31.6$$

24. $15 + 25 \not> 40$; no solution

25. cosines; $a^2 = b^2 + c^2 - 2bc \cos A$

$$345^2 = 648^2 + 442^2 - 2(648)(442) \cos A$$
$$2(648)(442) \cos A = 648^2 + 442^2 - 345^2$$
$$\cos A = \frac{648^2 + 442^2 - 345^2}{2(648)(442)}$$
$$\cos A \approx 0.8663$$
$$A \approx 30.0°$$
$$\frac{\sin B}{b} = \frac{\sin A}{a} \qquad 30.0° + 69.2° + C \approx 180°$$
$$\frac{\sin B}{648} = \frac{\sin 30°}{345} \qquad C \approx 80.8°$$
$$\sin B = \frac{645 \sin 30°}{345}$$
$$B \approx 69.2°$$

26. cosines; $a^2 = b^2 + c^2 - 2bc \cos A$

$$21.5^2 = 16.7^2 + 10.3^2 - 2(16.7)(10.3) \cos A$$
$$2(16.7)(10.3) \cos A = 16.7^2 + 10.3^2 - 21.5^2$$
$$\cos A = \frac{16.7^2 + 10.3^2 - 21.5^2}{2(16.7)(10.3)}$$
$$\cos A \approx -0.2246$$
$$A \approx 103°$$
$$\frac{\sin A}{a} = \frac{\sin B}{b} \qquad 103° + 49.2° + C \approx 180°$$
$$\frac{\sin 103°}{21.5} \approx \frac{\sin B}{16.7} \qquad C \approx 27.8°$$
$$\sin B \approx \frac{16.7 \sin 103°}{21.5}$$
$$B \approx 49.2°$$

27. cosines;
$$a^2 = b^2 + c^2 - 2bc \cos A$$
$$a^2 = 5^2 + 4.9^2 - 2(5)(4.9) \cos 28°$$
$$a^2 \approx 5.7$$
$$a \approx 2.4$$
$$\frac{\sin B}{b} = \frac{\sin A}{a} \qquad 28° + 78.0° + C \approx 180°$$
$$C \approx 74.0°$$
$$\frac{\sin B}{5} \approx \frac{\sin 28°}{2.4}$$
$$\sin B \approx \frac{5 \sin 28°}{2.4}$$
$$B \approx 78.0°$$

28. cosines;
$$a^2 = b^2 + c^2 - 2bc \cos A$$
$$a^2 = 7.6^2 + 14.1^2 - 2(7.6)(14.1) \cos 29°$$
$$a^2 \approx 69.12$$
$$a \approx 8.3$$
$$\frac{\sin B}{b} = \frac{\sin A}{a} \qquad 29° + 26.4° + C \approx 180°$$
$$C \approx 124.6°$$
$$\frac{\sin B}{7.6} \approx \frac{\sin 29°}{8.3}$$
$$\sin B \approx \frac{7.6 \sin 29°}{8.3}$$
$$B \approx 26.4°$$

29. cosines;
$$a^2 = b^2 + c^2 - 2bc \cos A$$
$$8^2 = 24^2 + 18^2 - 2(24)(18) \cos A$$
$$2(24)(18) \cos A = 24^2 + 18^2 - 8^2$$
$$\cos A = \frac{24^2 + 18^2 - 8^2}{2(24)(18)}$$
$$\cos A \approx 0.9676$$
$$A \approx 14.6°$$
$$\frac{\sin A}{a} = \frac{\sin C}{c} \qquad 14.6° + B + 34.6° \approx 180°$$
$$B \approx 130.8°$$
$$\frac{\sin 14.6°}{8} \approx \frac{\sin C}{18}$$
$$\sin C \approx \frac{18 \sin 14.6°}{8}$$
$$C \approx 34.6°$$

30.

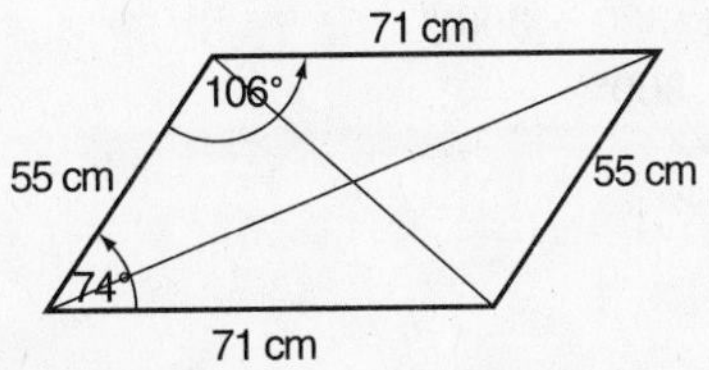

$$a^2 = b^2 + c^2 - 2bc \cos A$$
$$a^2 = 55^2 + 71^2 - 2(55)(71) \cos 74°$$
$$a^2 \approx 5913.27$$
$$a \approx 76.9$$
$$a^2 = b^2 + c^2 - 2bc \cos A$$
$$a^2 = 55^2 + 71^2 - 2(55)(71) \cos 106°$$
$$a^2 \approx 10218.73$$
$$a \approx 101.1$$
The diagonals measure 76.9 cm and 101.1 cm

31. $q^2 = 15^2 + 15^2 - 2(15)(15) \cos 123°$
$q^2 \approx 695.09$
$q \approx 26.4$; 26.4 centimeters

32.

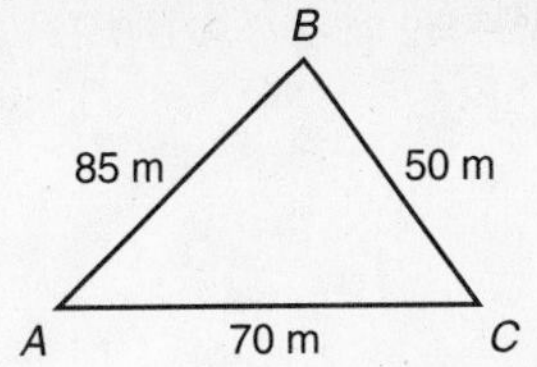

$$a^2 = b^2 + c^2 - 2bc \cos A$$
$$50^2 = 70^2 + 85^2 - 2(70)(85) \cos A$$
$$2(70)(85) \cos A = 70^2 + 85^2 - 50^2$$
$$\cos A = \frac{70^2 + 85^2 - 50^2}{2(70)(85)}$$
$$\cos A \approx 0.8088$$
$$A \approx 36°$$
The smallest angle measures about 36°.

33a. $A = 4.08$ **33b.** $A = 14.15$

33c. $A = 9.12$

34. Since $\cos 90° = 0$, $c^2 = a^2 + b^2 - 2ab \cos C$ becomes $c^2 = a^2 + b^2$.

35.

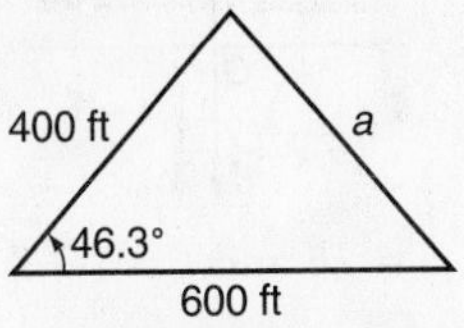

$$A = \frac{1}{2} ab \sin C$$
$$= \frac{1}{2}(400)(600) \sin 46.3°$$
$\approx 86{,}756.06$; 86,756.06 square feet
$$a^2 = b^2 + c^2 - 2bc \cos A$$
$$a^2 = 400^2 + 600^2 - 2(400)(600) \cos 46.3°$$
$$a^2 \approx 188{,}376.44$$
$$a \approx 434$$
$$P \approx 400 + 600 + 434$$
≈ 1434; 1434 feet

36. $a^2 = b^2 + c^2 - 2bc \cos A$
$a^2 = 45^2 + 35^2 - 2(45)(35) \cos 125°$
$a^2 = 5056.77$
$a \approx 71.1$; 71.1 miles

37.

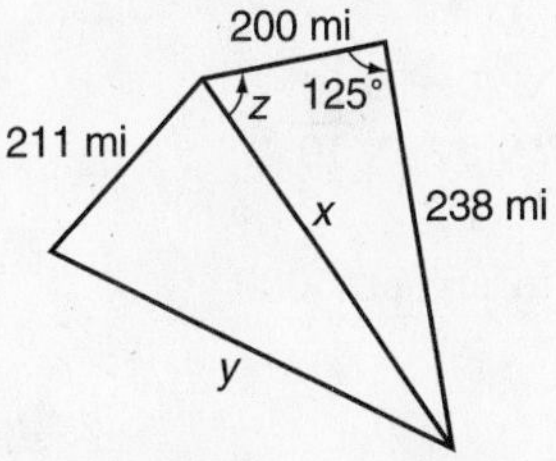

$$x^2 = 200^2 + 238^2 - 2(200)(238) \cos 125°$$
$$x^2 = 151248.48$$
$$x \approx 388.9$$
$$\frac{\sin z}{238} \approx \frac{\sin 125°}{389}$$
$$\sin z \approx \frac{238 \sin 125°}{389}$$
$$z \approx 30°$$
$$166° - 30° = 136°$$
$$y^2 \approx 211^2 + (388.9)^2 - 2(211)(388.9) \cos 136°$$
$$y^2 \approx 313819.2$$
$y \approx 561$; 561 miles

38. $\frac{\sin B}{b} = \frac{\sin A}{a}$

$\frac{\sin B}{79} = \frac{\sin 45°}{83}$

$\sin B = \frac{79 \sin 45°}{83}$

$B \approx 42.3°$

$\frac{\sin A}{a} = \frac{\sin C}{c}$

$\frac{\sin 45°}{83} \approx \frac{\sin 92.7°}{c}$

$c \approx \frac{83 \sin 92.7°}{\sin 45°}$

$c \approx 117.3$

$45° + 42.3° + C \approx 180°$

$C \approx 92.7°$

39. $-45°\left(\frac{\pi \text{ radians}}{180°}\right) = \frac{-45\pi}{180}$ radians $= \frac{-\pi}{4}$ radians

40. $\frac{7!}{1!\,3!\,2!\,1!} = 420$

41.

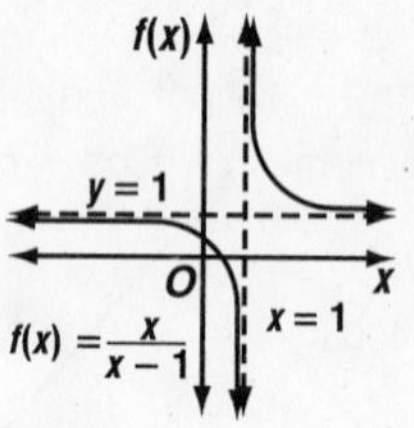

42. Let h = the height, then $w = 2h$ and $\ell = 7 + h$.

$V = \ell wh$

$72 = h(2h)(7 + h)$

$72 = 14h^2 + 2h^3$

$0 = 2h^3 + 14h^2 - 72$

$0 = h^3 + 7h^2 - 36$

$h = 2$

$w = 2h = 2(2)$ or 4

$\ell = 7 + h = 7 + 2$ or 9

4 units by 9 units by 2 units

43. $z^2 + 4z = 96$

$z^2 + 4z + 4 = 96 + 4$

$(z + 2)^2 = 100$

$z + 2 = \pm 10$

$z = -2 \pm 10$

$z = -12$ or 8

44. $(3 + \sqrt{2})(\sqrt{10} + \sqrt{5})$

$= 3\sqrt{10} + 3\sqrt{5} + \sqrt{20} + \sqrt{10}$

$= 3\sqrt{10} + 3\sqrt{5} + 2\sqrt{5} + \sqrt{10}$

$= 4\sqrt{10} + 5\sqrt{5}$

45a. Sample answer: y-intercept: 5000

(1907, 5000)

(1994, 26,689)

$m = \frac{y_2 - y_1}{x_2 - x_1}$

$= \frac{26{,}689 - 5000}{1994 - 1907}$

$= 249$

$y = mx + b$

$y = 249x + 5000$

45b. Sample answer based on the equation in 45a.

$2000 - 1907 = 93$

$y = 249x + 5000$

$= 249(93) + 5000$

$= 28{,}157$; 28,157 movie screens

Page 804 Mathematics and Society

1. Sample answer: measurements of angles, directions, depths, and distances along each segment
2. Sample answer: flooding, water leakage, fire, inadequate ventilation

13-6 Circular Functions

Page 808 Check for Understanding

1. $\cos \theta = x$, $\sin \theta = y$
2. Sample answer: sin θ is positive until 180° and is negative until 360°.
3. Sample answer: Graphs have same shape but cross the x-axis at different points.
4. See students' work.

5. $\sin \theta = y = \frac{4}{5}$

$\cos \theta = x = -\frac{3}{5}$

$\tan \theta = \frac{\sin \theta}{\cos \theta}$

$= \frac{\frac{4}{5}}{-\frac{3}{5}}$

$= -\frac{4}{3}$

6. $\sin \theta = y = -\frac{5}{13}$

$\cos \theta = x = -\frac{12}{13}$

$\tan \theta = \frac{\sin \theta}{\cos \theta}$

$= \frac{-\frac{5}{13}}{-\frac{12}{13}}$

$= \frac{5}{12}$

7. 9

8. $\cos\left(-\frac{3\pi}{4}\right) = \cos\left(-\frac{3\pi}{4} + 2\pi\right)$

$= \cos\left(\frac{5\pi}{4}\right)$

$= -\frac{\sqrt{2}}{2}$

9. $\sin 660° = \sin (300 + 360)°$

$= \sin 300°$

$= -\frac{\sqrt{3}}{2}$

10. yes; 7 white keys

Pages 809–810 Exercises

11. $\sin \theta = y = \frac{\sqrt{2}}{2}$

$\cos \theta = x = \frac{\sqrt{2}}{2}$

$\tan \theta = \frac{\sin \theta}{\cos \theta}$

$= \frac{\frac{\sqrt{2}}{2}}{\frac{\sqrt{2}}{2}}$

$= 1$

12. $\sin \theta = y = -\frac{12}{13}$

$\cos \theta = x = \frac{5}{13}$

$\tan \theta = \frac{\sin \theta}{\cos \theta}$

$= \frac{-\frac{12}{13}}{\frac{5}{13}}$

$= -\frac{12}{5}$

13. $\sin \theta = y = 0$

$\cos \theta = x = 1$

$\tan \theta = \frac{\sin \theta}{\cos \theta}$

$= \frac{0}{1}$

$= 0$

14. 2π **15.** 720° **16.** 6

17. $\sin 1020° = \sin (300 + 720)°$

$= \sin 300°$

$= -\frac{\sqrt{3}}{2}$

18. $\cos(-450°) = \cos(-450 + 720)°$
$= \cos 270°$
$= 0$

19. $\sin(-180°) = \sin(-180 + 360)°$
$= \sin 180°$
$= 0$

20. $\sin\left(-\frac{13\pi}{6}\right) = \sin\left(-\frac{13\pi}{6} + 4\pi\right)$
$= \sin\left(\frac{11\pi}{6}\right)$
$= -\frac{1}{2}$

21. $\sin\frac{3\pi}{2} = -1$

22. $\cos\frac{9\pi}{2} = \cos\left(\frac{9\pi}{2} - 2\pi\right)$
$= \cos\frac{\pi}{2}$
$= 0$

23. $4(\sin 30°)(\cos 60°) = 4\left(\frac{1}{2}\right)\left(\frac{1}{2}\right)$
$= 1$

24. $\frac{\sin 30° + \cos 60°}{2} = \frac{\frac{1}{2} + \frac{1}{2}}{2}$
$= \frac{1}{2}$

25. $\frac{4\sin 300° + 2\cos 30°}{3} = \frac{4\left(-\frac{\sqrt{3}}{2}\right) + 2\left(\frac{\sqrt{3}}{2}\right)}{3}$
$= \frac{-2\sqrt{3} + \sqrt{3}}{3}$
$= -\frac{\sqrt{3}}{3}$

26. $\sin 30° + \cos 60° = \frac{1}{2} + \frac{\sqrt{3}}{2}$
$= \frac{1 + \sqrt{3}}{2}$

27. $(\sin 60°)^2 + (\cos 60°)^2 = \left(\frac{\sqrt{3}}{2}\right)^2 + \left(\frac{1}{2}\right)^2$
$= \frac{3}{4} + \frac{1}{4}$
$= 1$

28. $8(\sin 120°)(\cos 120°) = 8\left(\frac{\sqrt{3}}{2}\right)\left(-\frac{1}{2}\right)$
$= -2\sqrt{3}$

29. See students' work.

30. sine: D = {all reals}, R = $\{-1 \le x \le 1\}$
cosine: D = {all reals}, R = $\{-1 \le x \le 1\}$
tangent: D = {all reals except 90, 270, . . .},
R = {all reals}

31.
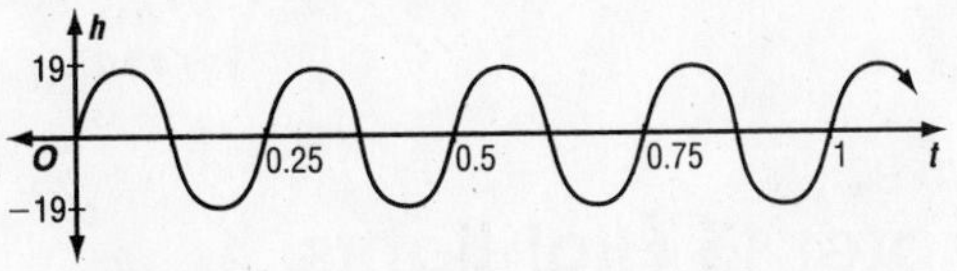

32.
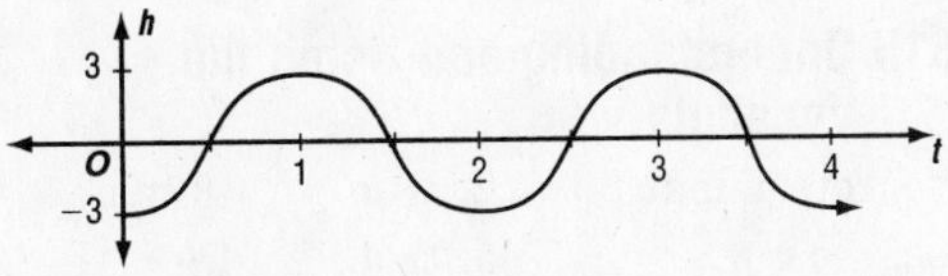

33. $a^2 = 75^2 + 300^2 - 2(75)(300)\cos 15°$
$a^2 \approx 52158.34$
$a \approx 228.4$; 228 miles

34.
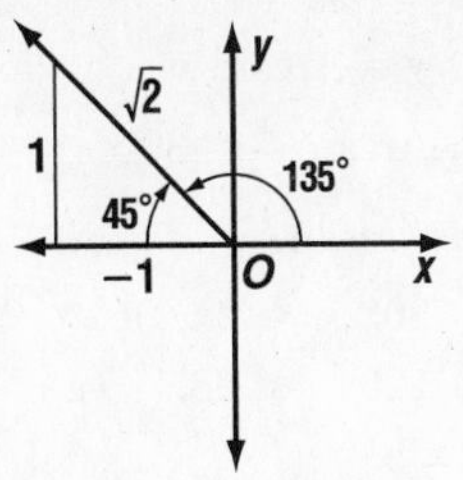

$\tan 135° = \frac{y}{x}$
$= \frac{-1}{1}$ or -1

35. No, the figure is not self-similar.

36. $4^x = 24$
$\log 4^x = \log 24$
$x \log 4 = \log 24$
$x = \frac{\log 24}{\log 4}$
$x \approx 2.2925$

37. $x^4 - 13x^2 + 36 = 0$
$(x^2)^2 - 13(x^2) + 36 = 0$
$(x^2 - 9)(x^2 - 4) = 0$
$(x + 3)(x - 3)(x + 2)(x - 2) = 0$
$x + 3 = 0$ or $x - 3 = 0$ or $x + 2 = 0$ or $x - 2 = 0$
$x = -3$ $x = 3$ $x = -2$ $x = 2$

38. $A^{-1} = \frac{1}{12 - 5}\begin{bmatrix} -4 & -5 \\ -1 & -3 \end{bmatrix}$
$= \frac{1}{7}\begin{bmatrix} -4 & -5 \\ -1 & -3 \end{bmatrix}$

39. $x + 2y = -2$
$(+)3x - 2y = 10$
$4x = 8$
$x = 2$

$x + 2y = -2$
$2 + 2y = -2$
$2y = -4$
$y = -2$ (2, −2)

13-7 Inverse Trigonometric Functions

Page 813 Check for Understanding

1. They are inverses of each other.
2. The trigonometric functions are not one–to–one functions.
3. Restricted domains are denoted with a capital letter.
4. $\theta = \text{Arcsin } x$
5. $y = \text{Arctan} - 3$
6. 0°
7. 45°
8. $r = \sqrt{x^2 + y^2}$
$3 = \sqrt{2^2 + y^2}$
$9 = 4 + y^2$
$5 = y^2$
$\sqrt{5} = y$
$\sin\left(\text{Cos}^{-1}\left(\frac{2}{3}\right)\right) = \frac{\sqrt{5}}{3}$
9. $\frac{4}{5}$
10. $\frac{1}{2}$
11. −45°
12. $\frac{1}{2}$
13. 90°
14. $\sin\theta = \frac{8}{16}$
$\sin\theta = \frac{1}{2}$
$\theta = \sin^{-1}\frac{1}{2}$
$\theta = 30°$

Pages 813–814 Exercises

15. $b = \text{Arccos } a$ **16.** $y = \text{Arcsin } x$

17. $\alpha = \text{Arctan } \beta$ **18.** $\text{Arcsin } \frac{1}{2} = 30°$

19. $\text{Arccos } y = 45°$ **20.** $\text{Arctan } \left(-\frac{4}{3}\right) = x$

21. 90° **22.** 45° **23.** 30° **24.** 0°

25. 30° **26.** 45° **27.** 120° **28.** $\frac{1}{2}$

29. 0°

30.
$$\begin{aligned} r &= \sqrt{x^2 + y^2} \\ 7 &= \sqrt{6^2 + y^2} \\ 49 &= 36 + y^2 \\ 13 &= y^2 \\ \sqrt{13} &= y \end{aligned}$$
$$\tan\left(\text{Cos}^{-1}\frac{6}{7}\right) = \frac{\sqrt{13}}{6}$$

31.
$$\begin{aligned} r &= \sqrt{x^2 + y^2} \\ 6 &= \sqrt{x^2 + 5^2} \\ 36 &= x^2 + 25 \\ 11 &= x^2 \\ \sqrt{11} &= x \end{aligned}$$
$$\cot\left(\text{Sin}^{-1}\frac{5}{6}\right) = \frac{\sqrt{11}}{5}$$

32.
$$\begin{aligned} r &= \sqrt{x^2 + y^2} \\ 9 &= \sqrt{x^2 + 7^2} \\ 81 &= x^2 + 49 \\ 32 &= x^2 \\ 4\sqrt{2} &= x \end{aligned}$$
$$\cot\left(\text{Sin}^{-1}\frac{7}{9}\right) = \frac{4\sqrt{2}}{7}$$

33.
$$\begin{aligned} r &= \sqrt{x^2 + y^2} \\ r &= \sqrt{3^2 + (\sqrt{3})^2} \\ r &= \sqrt{9 + 3} \\ r &= \sqrt{12} \\ &= 2\sqrt{3} \end{aligned}$$
$$\sin\left(\text{Arctan } \frac{\sqrt{3}}{3}\right) = \frac{1}{2}$$

34.
$$\begin{aligned} r &= \sqrt{x^2 + y^2} \\ 5^2 &= \sqrt{x^2 + 3^2} \\ 25 &= x^2 + 9 \\ 16 &= x^2 \\ 4 &= x \end{aligned}$$
$$\cos\left(\text{Arcsin } \frac{3}{5}\right) = \frac{4}{5}$$

35. 3 **36.** $\frac{\pi}{2}$ or 90°

37. 60° **38.** 30°

39.
$$\begin{aligned} r &= \sqrt{x^2 + y^2} \\ r &= \sqrt{1^2 + \sqrt{3}^2} \\ r &= \sqrt{1 + 3} \\ r &= \sqrt{4} \\ &= 2 \end{aligned}$$
$$\cos\left(\text{Tan}^{-1} \sqrt{3}\right) = \frac{1}{2}$$

40.
$$\begin{aligned} r &= \sqrt{x^2 + y^2} \\ 2 &= \sqrt{x^2 + (-1)^2} \\ 4 &= x^2 + 1 \\ 3 &= x^2 \\ \sqrt{3} &= x \end{aligned}$$
$$\cos\left[\text{Arcsin}\left(-\frac{1}{2}\right)\right] = \frac{\sqrt{3}}{2}$$

41.
$$\begin{aligned} r &= \sqrt{x^2 + y^2} \\ r &= \sqrt{1^2 + 1^2} \\ r &= \sqrt{2} \end{aligned}$$
$$\cos\left(\text{Tan}^{-1} 1\right) = \frac{1}{\sqrt{2}} \text{ or } \frac{\sqrt{2}}{2}$$

42.
$$\begin{aligned} \cos\left[\text{Cos}^{-1}\left(\frac{\sqrt{2}}{2}\right) - \frac{\pi}{2}\right] &= \frac{\sqrt{2}}{2} - \cos\frac{\pi}{2} \\ &= \frac{\sqrt{2}}{2} - 0 \\ &= \frac{\sqrt{2}}{2} \end{aligned}$$

43.
$$\begin{aligned} \sin\left(2 \sin^{-1}\frac{1}{2}\right) &= \sin 60° \\ &= \frac{\sqrt{3}}{2} \end{aligned}$$

44.
$$\begin{aligned} \sin\left(2 \cos^{-1}\frac{3}{5}\right) &\approx \sin\,[2(53.13)] \\ &\approx \sin 106.26 \\ &\approx 0.96 \text{ or } \frac{24}{25} \end{aligned}$$

45. See students' work.

46.

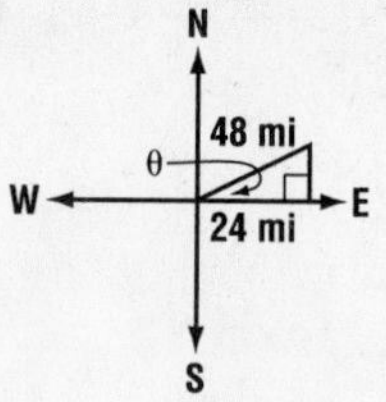

$$\begin{aligned} \cos\theta &= \frac{1}{2} \\ \theta &= \text{Cos}^{-1}\frac{1}{2} \\ \theta &= 30° \\ \theta + x &= 90° \\ 30° + x &= 90° \\ x &= 60° \end{aligned}$$
60° north of east

47.
$$\begin{aligned} \cos\theta &= \sqrt{\frac{I_t}{I_o}} \\ \cos\theta &= \sqrt{\frac{1}{4}} \\ \cos\theta &= 0.5 \\ \theta &= 60° \end{aligned}$$

48. π

49.

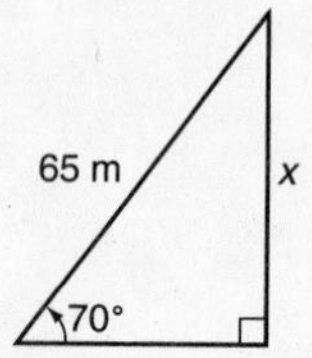

$$\begin{aligned} \sin 70° &= \frac{x}{65} \\ x &= 65 \sin 70° \\ x &\approx 61.1; \text{ 61.1 meters} \end{aligned}$$

50.
$$\begin{aligned} \sum_{k=1}^{10} (2 + k) &= (2 + 1) + (2 + 2) + (2 + 3) + (2 + 4) \\ &\quad + (2 + 5) + (2 + 6) + (2 + 7) \\ &\quad + (2 + 8) + (2 + 9) + (2 + 10) \\ &= 3 + 4 + 5 + 6 + 7 + 8 + 9 + 10 \\ &\quad + 11 + 12 \\ &= 75 \end{aligned}$$

51.
$$\begin{aligned} y &= ne^{kt} \\ 164 &= 80e^{3k} \\ 2.05 &= e^{3k} \\ \ln 2.05 &= \ln e^{3k} \\ \ln 2.05 &= 3k \ln e \\ \ln 2.05 &= 3k \\ \frac{\ln 2.05}{3} &= k \\ 0.2392 &\approx k \end{aligned}$$

52. center: (4, 9)
radius: 2

53.
$$\begin{aligned} x^2 - 7x &= 0 \\ x(x - 7) &= 0 \\ x = 0 \quad \text{or} \quad x - 7 &= 0 \\ x &= 7 \end{aligned}$$
0, 7

54.
$$AA = \begin{bmatrix} 2 & 7 \\ 0 & -1 \end{bmatrix}\begin{bmatrix} 2 & 7 \\ 0 & 1 \end{bmatrix} = \begin{bmatrix} 4 & 7 \\ 0 & 1 \end{bmatrix}$$

55. $x + y > 2$ $y > 3$
$y > -x + 2$

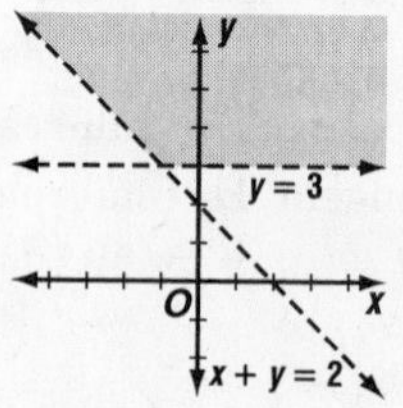

Chapter 13 Highlights

Page 815 Understanding and Using the Vocabulary

1. false, coterminal **2.** true **3.** true

4. false, sec θ **5.** true

6. false, law of cosines **7.** true

8. false, an angle that has its terminal side on an axis where x or y is equal to zero

9. false, tan θ **10.** false, terminal

Chapter 13 Study Guide and Assessment

Pages 816–818 Skills and Concepts

11. $x = 2, r = 15$

$r = \sqrt{x^2 + y^2}$

$15 = \sqrt{2^2 + y^2}$

$225 = 4 + y^2$

$221 = y^2$

$\sqrt{221} = y$

$\cos\theta = \frac{2}{15}$

$\sin\theta = \frac{\sqrt{221}}{15}$ or 0.9911

$\tan\theta = \frac{\sqrt{221}}{2}$ or 7.4330

$\csc\theta = \frac{15}{\sqrt{221}} = \frac{15\sqrt{221}}{221}$ or 1.0090

$\sec\theta = \frac{15}{2}$ or 7.5000

$\cot\theta = \frac{2}{\sqrt{221}} = \frac{2\sqrt{221}}{221}$ or 0.1345

12. $\tan\theta = 0.5 = \frac{1}{2}$

$x = 2, y = 1$

$r = \sqrt{x^2 + y^2}$

$r = \sqrt{2^2 + 1^2}$

$r = \sqrt{5}$

$\sin\theta = \frac{1}{\sqrt{5}} = \frac{\sqrt{5}}{5}$ or 0.4472

$\cos\theta = \frac{2}{\sqrt{5}} = \frac{2\sqrt{5}}{5}$ or 0.8944

$\csc\theta = \sqrt{5}$ or 2.2361

$\sec\theta = \frac{\sqrt{5}}{2}$ or 1.1180

$\cot\theta = 2.000$

13. $\sin\theta = \frac{3}{4}$

$y = 3, r = 4$

$r = \sqrt{x^2 + y^2}$

$4 = \sqrt{x^2 + 3^2}$

$16 = x^2 + 9$

$7 = x^2$

$\sqrt{7} = x$

$\cos\theta = \frac{\sqrt{7}}{4}$ or 0.6614

$\tan\theta = \frac{\sqrt{7}}{3}$ or 1.1339

$\csc\theta = \frac{4}{3}$ or 1.3333

$\sec\theta = \frac{4}{\sqrt{7}} = \frac{4\sqrt{7}}{7}$ or 1.5119

$\cot\theta = \frac{3}{\sqrt{7}} = \frac{3\sqrt{7}}{3}$ or 0.8819

14. $\sec\theta = 2\frac{1}{2}$ or $\frac{5}{2}$

$r = 5, x = 2$

$r = \sqrt{x^2 + y^2}$

$5 = \sqrt{2^2 + y^2}$

$25 = 4 + y^2$

$21 = y^2$

$\sqrt{21} = y$

$\sin\theta = \frac{\sqrt{21}}{5}$ or 0.9165

$\cos\theta = \frac{2}{5}$ or 0.400

$\tan\theta = \frac{\sqrt{21}}{2}$ or 2.2913

$\csc\theta = \frac{5}{\sqrt{21}} = \frac{5\sqrt{21}}{21}$ or 1.0911

$\cot\theta = \frac{2}{\sqrt{21}} = \frac{2\sqrt{21}}{21}$ or 0.4364

15. 15° **16.** 33° **17.** 75° **18.** 47°

19. $a^2 + b^2 = c^2$

$7^2 + b^2 = 16^2$

$49 + b^2 = 256$

$b^2 = 207$

$b = \sqrt{207}$

$b \approx 14.4$

$\sin A = \frac{7}{16}$

$\sin A = 0.4375$

$A \approx 26°$

$A + B = 90°$

$26° + B = 90°$

$B \approx 64°$

20. $25° + B = 90°$, $B = 65°$

$\sin 25° = \frac{a}{6}$, $a = 6\sin 25°$, $a \approx 2.5$

$\sin 65° = \frac{b}{6}$, $b = 6\sin 65°$, $b \approx 5.4$

21. $A + 45° = 90°$, $A = 45°$

$\sin 45° = \frac{b}{12}$, $b = 12\sin 45°$, $b \approx 8.5$

$\sin 45° = \frac{a}{12}$, $a = 12\sin 45°$, $a \approx 8.5$

22. $A + 83° = 90°$, $A = 7°$

$\sin 83° = \frac{\sqrt{31}}{c}$, $c = \frac{\sqrt{31}}{\sin 83°}$, $c \approx 5.6$

$\sin 7° = \frac{a}{5.6}$, $a = 5.6\sin 7°$, $a \approx 0.7$

23. $A + 49° = 90°$, $A = 41°$

$\sin 41° = \frac{9}{c}$, $c = \frac{9}{\sin 41°}$, $c \approx 13.7$

$\tan 49° = \frac{b}{9}$, $b = 9\tan 49°$, $b \approx 10.4$

24. $\cos A = \frac{1}{4}$, $A \approx 76°$

$76° + B \approx 90°$, $B \approx 14°$

$\sin 76° = \frac{4}{c}$, $c = \frac{4}{\sin 76°}$, $c \approx 4.1$

$\sin 14° = \frac{b}{4.1}$, $b = 4.1\sin 14°$, $b \approx 1.0$

25. $255° \cdot \left(\frac{\pi \text{ radians}}{180°}\right) = \frac{255\pi}{180}$ radians or $\frac{17\pi}{12}$ radians

26. $-210° \left(\frac{\pi \text{ radians}}{180°}\right) = -\frac{210\pi}{180}$ radians or $-\frac{7\pi}{6}$ radians

27. $65° \left(\frac{\pi \text{ radians}}{180°}\right) = \frac{65\pi}{180}$ radians or $\frac{13\pi}{36}$ radians

28. $120° \left(\frac{\pi \text{ radians}}{180°}\right) = \frac{120\pi}{180}$ radians or $\frac{2\pi}{3}$ radians

29. $\frac{7\pi}{4}$ radians $\cdot \frac{180°}{\pi \text{ radians}} = \frac{1260°\pi}{4\pi}$ or 315°

30. $-\frac{5\pi}{12}$ radians $\cdot \frac{180°}{\pi \text{ radians}} = -\frac{900°\pi}{12\pi}$ or −75°

31. -4π radians $\cdot \frac{180°}{\pi \text{ radians}} = -\frac{720°\pi}{\pi}$ or −720°

32. $\frac{5\pi}{3}$ radians $\cdot \frac{180°}{\pi \text{ radians}} = \frac{900°\pi}{3\pi}$ or 300°

33.

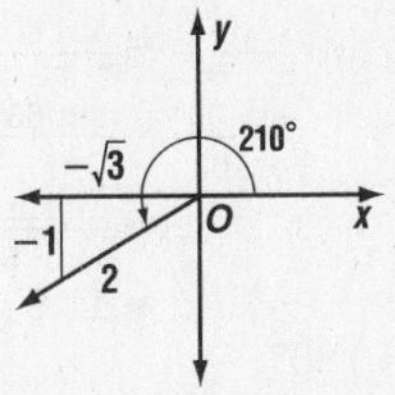

$\cos 210° = \frac{x}{r}$

$= \frac{-\sqrt{3}}{2}$

34.

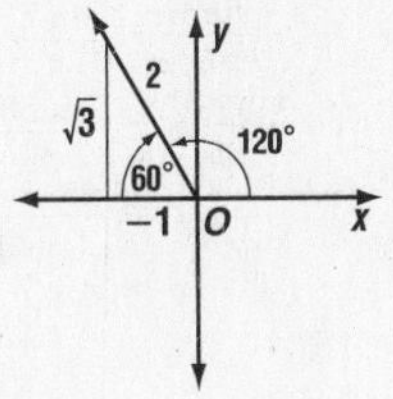

$\tan 120° = \frac{y}{x}$

$= -\sqrt{3}$

35.

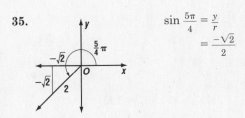

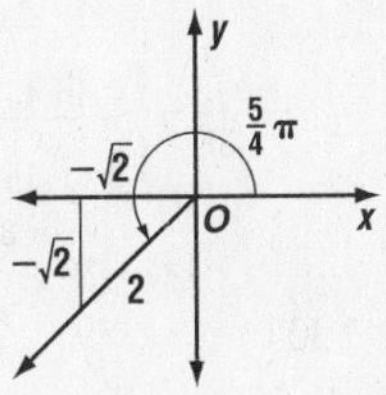

$\sin \frac{5\pi}{4} = \frac{y}{r}$

$= \frac{-\sqrt{2}}{2}$

36.

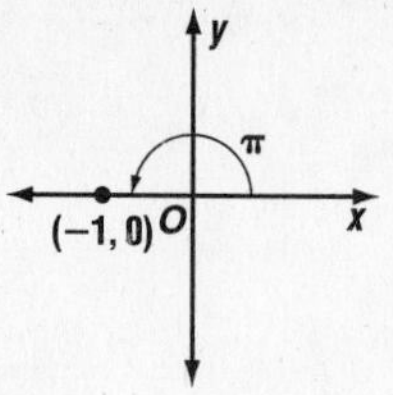

$\cos 3\pi = \frac{x}{r}$

$= -1$

37.

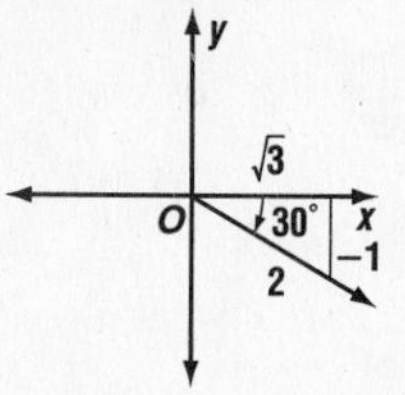

$\sec(-30°) = \frac{r}{x}$

$= \frac{2}{\sqrt{3}} \cdot \frac{\sqrt{3}}{\sqrt{3}}$

$= \frac{2\sqrt{3}}{3}$

38.

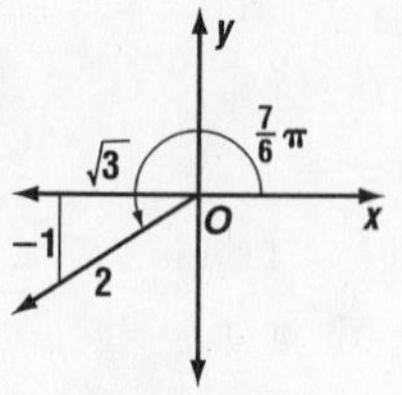

$\cot \frac{7\pi}{6} = \frac{x}{y}$

$= \frac{-\sqrt{3}}{-1}$

$= \sqrt{3}$

39. $x = 2, y = 5$

$r = \sqrt{x^2 + y^2}$

$r = \sqrt{2^2 + 5^2}$

$r = \sqrt{29}$

$\sin \theta = \frac{y}{r} = \frac{5}{\sqrt{29}} \cdot \frac{\sqrt{29}}{\sqrt{29}} = \frac{5\sqrt{29}}{29}$

$\cos \theta = \frac{x}{r} = \frac{2}{\sqrt{29}} \cdot \frac{\sqrt{29}}{\sqrt{29}} = \frac{2\sqrt{29}}{29}$

$\tan \theta = \frac{y}{x} = \frac{5}{2}$

40. $x = 15, y = -8$

$r = \sqrt{x^2 + y^2}$

$r = \sqrt{15^2 + (-8)^2}$

$r = \sqrt{225 + 64}$

$r = \sqrt{289}$ or 17

$\sin \theta = \frac{y}{r} = -\frac{8}{17}$

$\cos \theta = \frac{x}{r} = \frac{15}{17}$

$\tan \theta = \frac{y}{x} = -\frac{8}{15}$

41. $\frac{\sin A}{a} = \frac{\sin B}{b}$

$\frac{\sin 50°}{10} = \frac{\sin B}{12}$

$\sin B = \frac{12 \sin 50°}{10}$

$B \approx 67°$

$\frac{\sin A}{a} = \frac{\sin C}{c}$

$\frac{\sin 50°}{10} \approx \frac{\sin 63°}{c}$

$c \approx \frac{10 \sin 63°}{\sin 50°}$

$c \approx 11.6$

$50° + 67° + C \approx 180°$

$C \approx 63°$

42. $\frac{\sin A}{a} = \frac{\sin B}{b}$

$\frac{\sin 51°}{a} = \frac{\sin 46°}{65}$

$a = \frac{65 \sin 51°}{\sin 46°}$

$a \approx 70.2$

$\frac{\sin B}{b} = \frac{\sin C}{c}$

$\frac{\sin 46°}{65} = \frac{\sin 83°}{c}$

$c = \frac{65 \sin 83°}{\sin 46°}$

$c \approx 89.7$

$A + 46° + 83° = 180°$

$A = 51°$

43. $\frac{\sin B}{b} = \frac{\sin C}{c}$

$\frac{\sin 30°}{20} = \frac{\sin 105°}{c}$

$c = \frac{20 \sin 105°}{\sin 30°}$

$c \approx 38.6$

$\frac{\sin B}{b} = \frac{\sin A}{a}$

$\frac{\sin 30°}{20} = \frac{\sin 45°}{a}$

$a = \frac{20 \sin 45°}{\sin 30°}$

$a \approx 28.3$

$45° + 30° + C = 180°$

$C = 105°$

44. $\frac{\sin A}{a} = \frac{\sin B}{b}$

$\frac{\sin 105°}{18} = \frac{\sin B}{14}$

$\sin B = \frac{14 \sin 105°}{18}$

$B \approx 49°$

$\frac{\sin A}{a} = \frac{\sin C}{c}$

$\frac{\sin 105°}{18} \approx \frac{\sin 26°}{c}$

$c \approx \frac{18 \sin 26°}{\sin 105°}$

$c \approx 8.2$

$105° + 49° + C \approx 180°$

$C \approx 26°$

45. $A < 90°$

$36 < 24 \sin 64°$

no solution

46. $A < 90°$

$17 < 21 \sin 64°$

no solution

47. $C < 90°$

$15 > 10$

one solution

$\frac{\sin C}{c} = \frac{\sin B}{b}$

$\frac{\sin 66°}{15} = \frac{\sin B}{10}$

$\sin B = \frac{10 \sin 66°}{15}$

$B \approx 38°$

$A + 38° + 66° \approx 180°$

$A \approx 76°$

$\frac{\sin A}{a} = \frac{\sin C}{c}$

$\frac{\sin 76°}{a} \approx \frac{\sin 66°}{15}$

$a \approx \frac{15 \sin 76°}{\sin 66°}$

$a \approx 15.9$

48. $A < 90°$

$9 < 12 \sin 82°$

no solution

49. $c^2 = a^2 + b^2 - 2ab \cos C$

$c^2 = 4^2 + 7^2 - 2(4)(7) \cos 65°$

$c^2 \approx 41.33$

$c \approx 6.4$

$\frac{\sin A}{a} = \frac{\sin C}{c}$

$\frac{\sin A}{4} \approx \frac{\sin 65°}{6.4}$

$\sin A \approx \frac{4 \sin 65°}{6.4}$

$A \approx 35°$

$35° + B + 65° \approx 180°$

$B \approx 80°$

50. $a^2 = b^2 + c^2 - 2bc \cos A$

$a^2 = 2^2 + 5^2 - 2(2)(5) \cos 60°$

$a^2 \approx 19$

$a \approx 4.4$

$\frac{\sin B}{b} = \frac{\sin A}{a}$

$\frac{\sin B}{2} \approx \frac{\sin 60°}{4.4}$

$\sin B \approx \frac{2 \sin 60°}{4.4}$

$B \approx 23°$

$60° + 23° + C \approx 180°$

$C \approx 97°$

51. $c^2 = a^2 + b^2 - 2ab \cos C$

$c^2 = 6^2 + 7^2 - 2(6)(7) \cos 40°$

$c^2 \approx 20.65$

$c \approx 4.5$

$\frac{\sin C}{c} = \frac{\sin A}{a}$

$\frac{\sin 40°}{4.5} \approx \frac{\sin A}{6}$

$\sin A \approx \frac{6 \sin 40°}{4.5}$

$A \approx 59°$

$59° + B + 40° \approx 180°$

$B \approx 81°$

52. $b^2 = a^2 + c^2 - 2ac \cos B$

$b^2 = 42^2 + 6.5^2 - 2(42)(6.5)$

$\cos 24°$

$b^2 \approx 1307.45$

$b \approx 36.2$

$\frac{\sin B}{b} = \frac{\sin A}{a}$

$\frac{\sin 24°}{36.2} \approx \frac{\sin A}{42}$

$\sin A \approx \frac{42 \sin 24°}{36.2}$

$A \approx 28°$

$28° + 24° + C \approx 180°$

$C \approx 128°$

53. $c^2 = a^2 + b^2 - 2ab\cos C$

$15^2 = 11^2 + 13^2 - 2(11)(13)\cos C$

$2(11)(13)\cos C = 11^2 + 13^2 - 15^2$

$\cos C = \frac{11^2 + 13^2 - 15^2}{2(11)(13)}$

$\cos C \approx 0.2273$

$C \approx 77°$

$\frac{\sin B}{b} = \frac{\sin C}{c}$ $\quad A + 58° + 77° \approx 180°$

$\frac{\sin B}{13} \approx \frac{\sin 77°}{15}$ $\quad A \approx 45°$

$\sin B \approx \frac{13 \sin 77°}{15}$

$B \approx 58°$

54. $\sin(-150°) = \sin(-150 + 360)°$
$= \sin 210°$
$= -\frac{1}{2}$

55. $\cos 300° = \frac{1}{2}$

56. $(\sin 45°)(\sin 225°) = \left(\frac{\sqrt{2}}{2}\right)\left(-\frac{\sqrt{2}}{2}\right)$
$= -\frac{1}{2}$

57. $\sin \frac{5}{4}\pi = -\frac{\sqrt{2}}{2}$

58. $(\sin 30°)^2 + (\cos 30°)^2 = \left(\frac{1}{2}\right)^2 + \left(\frac{\sqrt{3}}{2}\right)^2$
$= \frac{1}{4} + \frac{3}{4}$
$= 1$

59. $\frac{4\cos 150° + 2\sin 300°}{3} = \frac{4\left(-\frac{\sqrt{3}}{2}\right) + 2\left(-\frac{\sqrt{3}}{2}\right)}{3}$
$= \frac{-2\sqrt{3} + (-\sqrt{3})}{3}$
$= \frac{-3\sqrt{3}}{3}$
$= -\sqrt{3}$

60. $\text{Sin}^{-1}(-1) = -90°$ 61. $\text{Cos}^{-1}\left(\frac{\sqrt{3}}{2}\right) = 30°$

62. $\text{Tan}^{-1}(\sqrt{3}) = 60°$

63. $\cos(\text{Sin}^{-1} 1) = \cos 90°$
$= 0$

64. $y = 3, r = 5$
$r = \sqrt{x^2 + y^2}$
$5 = \sqrt{x^2 + 3^2}$
$25 = x^2 + 9$
$16 = x^2$
$4 = x$
$\tan\left(\text{Arcsin}\frac{3}{5}\right) = \frac{3}{4}$

65. $\cot\left(\text{Tan}^{-1}\frac{8}{15}\right) = \frac{15}{8}$

Page 818 Applications and Problem Solving

66.

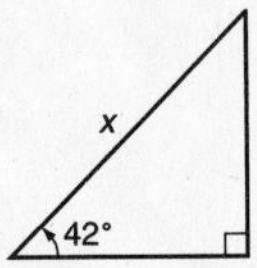

$\sin 42° = \frac{3000}{x}$

$x = \frac{3000}{\sin 42°}$

$x = 4483.43$; 4483.43 feet

67. $430^2 = 400^2 + 500^2 - 2(400)(500)\cos x$

$2(400)(500)\cos x = 400^2 + 500^2 - 430^2$

$\cos x = \frac{400^2 + 500^2 - 430^2}{2(400)(500)}$

$\cos x \approx 0.5628$

$x \approx 55.75°$

Page 819 Alternative Assessment; Thinking Critically

- If you know the measure of any two sides of a right triangle or the measure of one side and one acute angle, you can determine the measure of all sides and angles of the triangle.
- Since tangent and cotangent have the same sign in every quadrant, the quadrant cannot be determined.

College Entrance Exam Practice, Chapters 1–13

Pages 820–821

1. $\frac{6}{9}$ or $\frac{2}{3}$; C

2. $\sqrt{c+4} = \sqrt{c+20} - 2$
$(\sqrt{c+4})^2 = (\sqrt{c+20} - 2)^2$
$c + 4 = c + 20 - 4\sqrt{c+20} + 4$
$-20 = -4\sqrt{c+20}$
$5 = \sqrt{c+20}$
$(5)^2 = (\sqrt{c+20})^2$
$25 = c + 20$
$5 = c$; D

3. $5 \cdot 4 \cdot 2 = 40$ outfits; A

4. $\frac{30 + x}{84} = \frac{60}{100}$
$\frac{30 + x}{84} = \frac{3}{5}$
$5(30 + x) = 252$
$150 + 5x = 252$
$5x = 102$
$x = 20.4$
21 games; A

5.

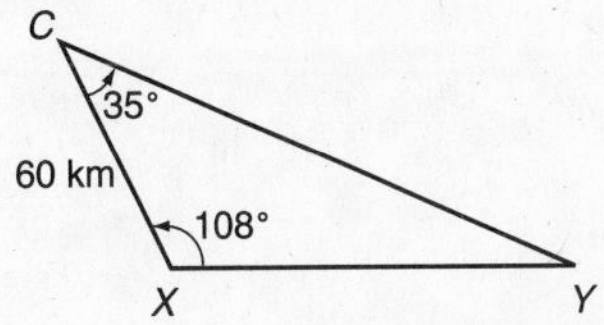

$y + 108° + 35° = 180°$
$y = 37°$
$\frac{\sin 35°}{XY} = \frac{\sin 37°}{60}$
$XY = \frac{60 \sin 35°}{\sin 37°}$
$XY = 57.2$;
57.2 kilometers; B

6. 2 weeks $\cdot \frac{7 \text{ days}}{1 \text{ week}} \cdot \frac{5¢}{\text{day}} = 70¢$
D

7. $\sin x = \frac{40}{41} = \frac{y}{r}$ $\quad \tan\theta = \frac{y}{x} = \frac{40}{9}$
$r = \sqrt{x^2 + y^2}$ $\quad$ A
$41 = \sqrt{x^2 + 40^2}$
$1681 = x^2 + 1600$
$81 = x^2$
$9 = x$

8. B

9. $\frac{n!}{n} = \frac{12!}{12}$ or 39,916,800

10. $m + 3c = 0.75$

$3c = 0.75 - m$

$c = 0.25 - \frac{1}{3}m$

$p + m = 0.95$

$p = 0.95 - m$

$2p + 2m + c = 2.05$

$2(0.95 - m) + 2m + 0.25 - \frac{1}{3}m = 2.05$

$1.90 - 2m + 2m + 0.25 - \frac{1}{3}m = 2.05$

$-\frac{1}{3}m = -0.10$

$m = 0.30$

$c = 0.25 - \frac{1}{3}m$ $\qquad p = 0.95 - m$

$= 0.25 - \frac{1}{3}(0.30)$ $\qquad = 0.95 - 0.30$

$= 0.25 - 0.10$ $\qquad = 0.65$

$= 0.15$

65¢, 30¢, 15¢

11.

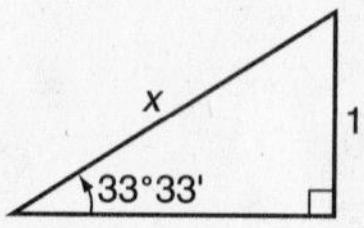

$\sin 33° 33' = \frac{10}{x}$

$x = 18.09$

18.09 feet or 18 feet 1 inch

12.

3	4	−35	78	28	−165
		12	−69	27	165
	4	−23	9	55	0

$-\frac{5}{4}$	4	−23	9	55
		−5	35	−55
	4	−28	44	0

$4x^2 - 28x + 44 = 0$

$x^2 - 7x + 11 = 0$

$x = \frac{-(-7) \pm \sqrt{(-7)^2 - 4(1)(11)}}{2(1)}$

$= \frac{7 \pm \sqrt{5}}{2}$

$3, -\frac{5}{4}, \frac{7 \pm \sqrt{5}}{2}$

13. P (blueberry and bran) $= \frac{10}{24} \cdot \frac{6}{23} = \frac{5}{46}$

14. $25x^2 - 4x^2 = 100$

$\frac{x^2}{4} - \frac{y^2}{25} = 1$

vertices: $(\pm 2, 0)$

foci: $c^2 = a^2 + b^2$

$c^2 = 4 + 25$

$c = \pm\sqrt{29}$

$(\pm\sqrt{29}, 0)$

15. $a^2 + b^2 = c^2$

$48^2 + 20^2 = c^2$

$2704 = c^2$

$52 = c$

$\tan A = \frac{48}{20}$ or 2.4000

$\sin A = \frac{48}{52}$ or 0.9231

$\cos A = \frac{20}{52}$ or 0.3846

$\cot A = \frac{20}{48}$ or 0.4167

$\csc A = \frac{52}{48}$ or 1.0833

$\sec A = \frac{52}{20} = 2.6000$

16. $-2x + 7y = -21$

$7y = 2x - 21$

$y = \frac{2}{7}x - 3$

$y - y_1 = m(x - x_1)$

$y - 4 = \frac{2}{7}[x - (-3)]$

$y - 4 = \frac{2}{7}x + \frac{6}{7}$

$y = \frac{2}{7}x + \frac{34}{7}$

y-intercept: $\frac{34}{7}$

$y - y_1 = m(x - x_1)$

$y - 9 = -\frac{7}{2}[x - (-2)]$

$y - 9 = -\frac{7}{2}x - 7$

$y = -\frac{7}{2}x + 2$

y-intercept: 2

A

17. $a^2 + b^2 = c^2$

$a^2 + 2^2 = 6^2$

$a^2 = 32$

$a \approx 5.7$

$a^2 + b^2 = c^2$

$5^2 + b^2 = 11^2$

$b^2 = 96$

$b \approx 9.8$

B

18. $\log_2 0.75 = \log_2 \frac{3}{4}$

$= \log_2 3 - 2 \log_2 2$

$= 1.585 - 2$

$= -0.415$

$\log_2 \frac{36}{49} = \log_2 \frac{2^2 \cdot 3^2}{7^2}$

$= (2 \log_2 2 + 2 \log_2 3) - 2 \log_2 7$

$= 2 + 2(1.585) - 2(2.807)$

$= 2 + 3.17 - 5.614$

$= -0.444$

A

19. 8:11; 8:11; C

20. $\frac{a + 3b}{7} = 3$ $\qquad r + 11 = 8t$

$11a - b = -7$ $\qquad 8(r - t) = 3$

D

14-1A Graphing Technology: Trigonometric Functions

Page 825 Exercises

1. Enter: Y= TAN X,T,θ,n ZOOM 7

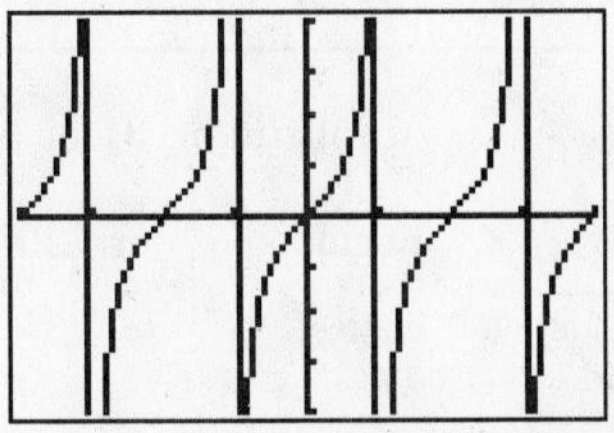

2. Enter: Y= COS X,T,θ,n ZOOM 7

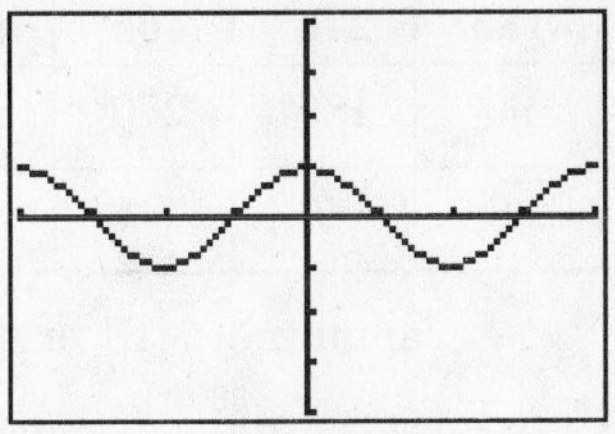

3. Enter: Y= COS ((–) X,T,θ,n) ZOOM 7

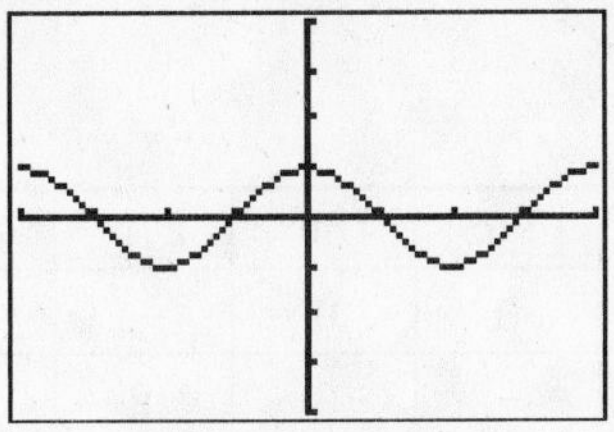

4. Enter: Y= 1 ÷ SIN X,T,θ,n ZOOM 7

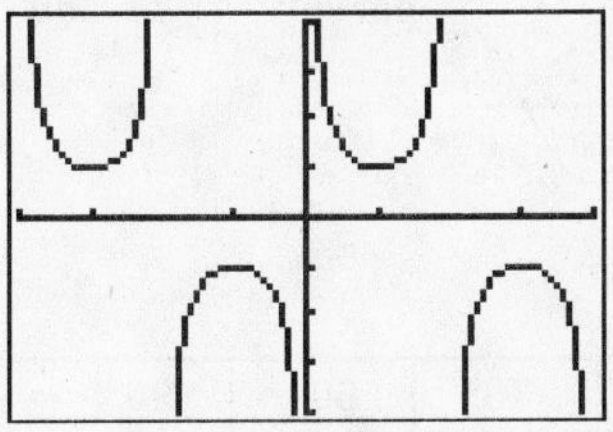

5. Enter: Y= 1 ÷ TAN X,T,θ,n ZOOM 7

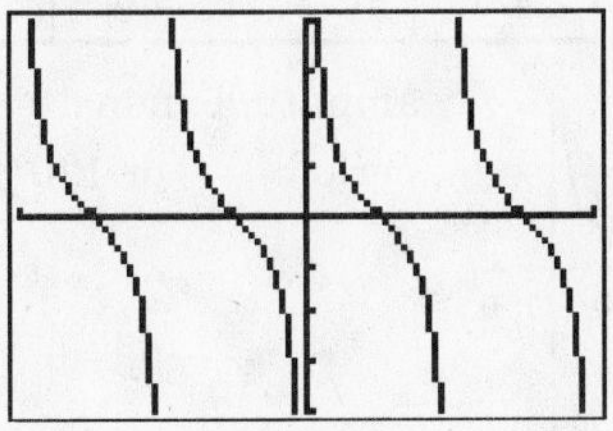

6. Enter: Y= TAN (X,T,θ,n – 180) ZOOM 7

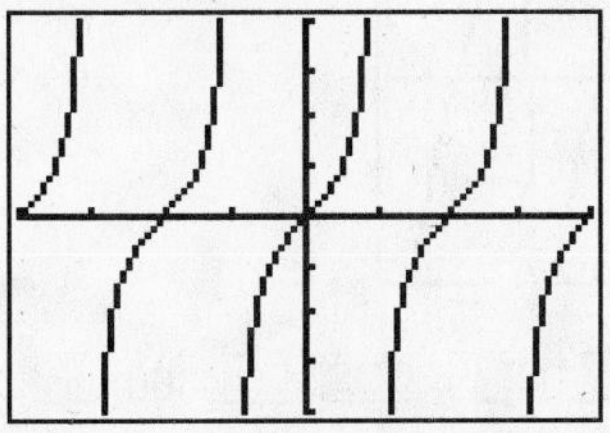

7. Enter: Y= TAN 5 X,T,θ,n ZOOM 7
Window: [−90, 90] by [−4, 4] with Xscl = 18 and Yscl = 1

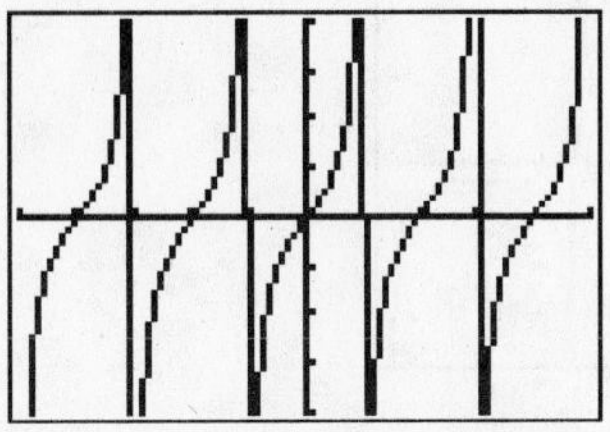

8. Enter: Y= 3 (1 ÷ COS ((–) X,T,θ,n)) ZOOM 7

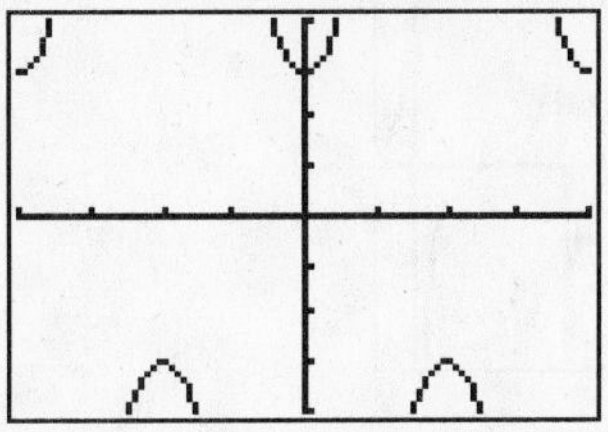

9. Enter: Y= 12 SIN (X,T,θ,n + 45)
Window: [−360, 360] by [−12, 12] with Xscl = 90 and Yscl = 3

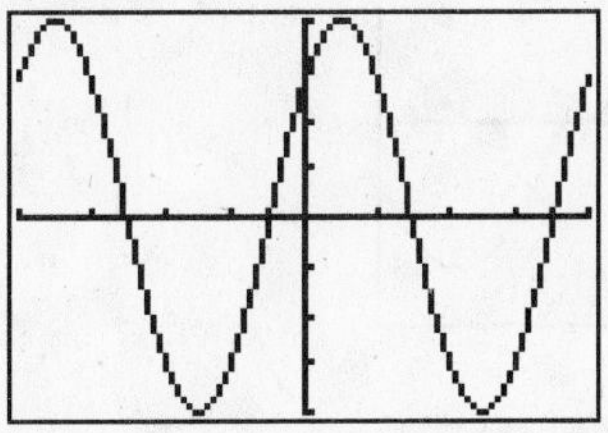

10. Enter: Y= 0.5 (1 ÷ SIN (2 X,T,θ,n + 90))
Window: [−180, 180] by [−4, 4] with Xscl = 45 and Yscl = 1

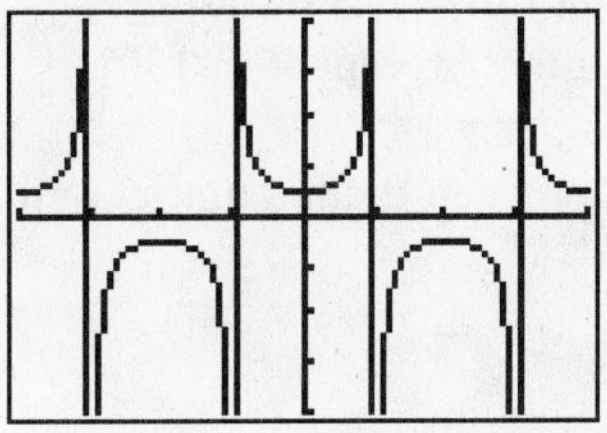

11. Enter: Y= 3 TAN (90 − X,T,θ,n) ZOOM 7

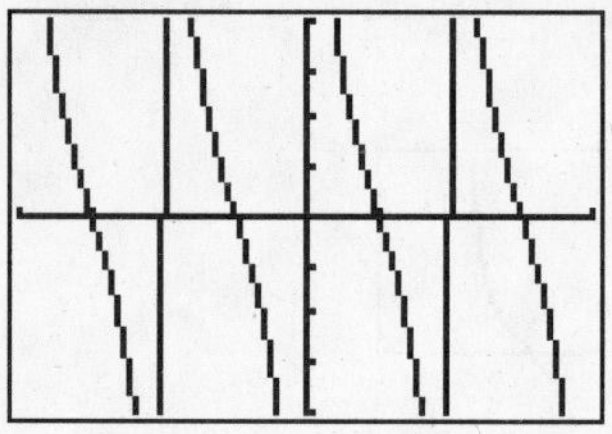

12. Enter: Y= 0.1 (1 ÷ COS (360 + 2 X,T,θ,n))

Window: [−135, 135] by [1, 1] with Xscl = 45 and Yscl = 1

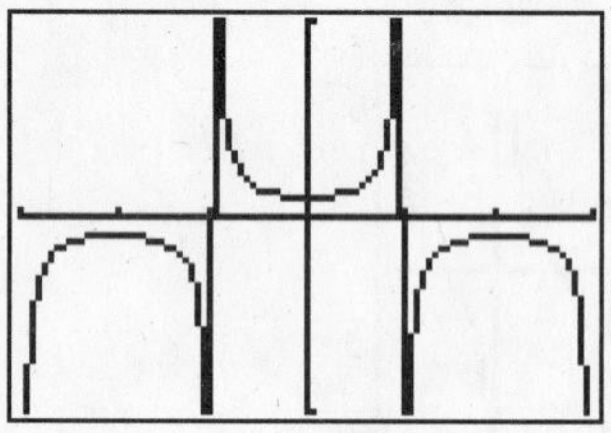

13. Enter: Y= 0.5 (1 ÷ TAN (X,T,θ,n + 45)) ZOOM 7

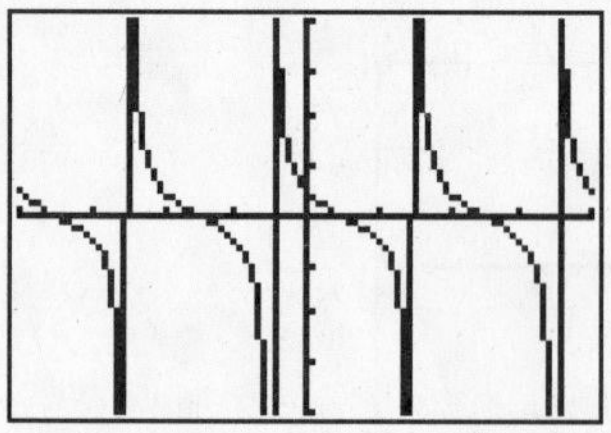

14. Enter: Y= 3 COS (2 ÷ 3) X,T,θ,n ZOOM 7

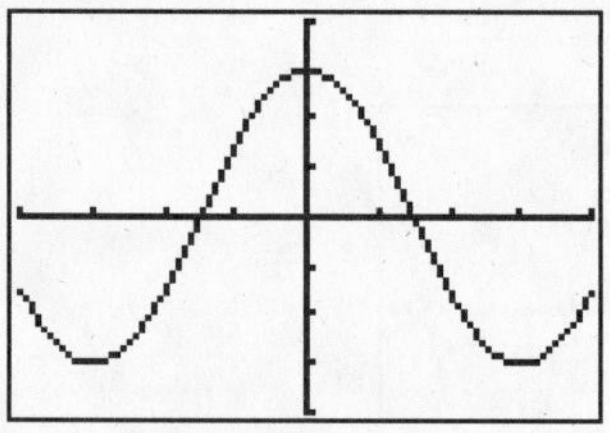

14-1 Graphing Trigonometric Functions

Pages 831–832 Check for Understanding

1. The values of the function repeat in 180° intervals.
2. half the distance between the maximum and minimum values

3a. yes; 2 **3b.** yes; 5

3c. no

4. Tina; a possible equation is $y = 10 \sin 524\pi t$.

5. Both functions have the same shape, period and amplitude; they have different x- and y-intercepts, and the cosine function is translated to the right 90° on the x-axis.

6. c **7.** a **8.** d **9.** b

10.

θ	0°	180°	360°	540°	720°
$\frac{1}{2}\theta$	0°	90°	180°	270°	360°
$3 \cos \frac{1}{2}\theta$	3	0	−3	0	3

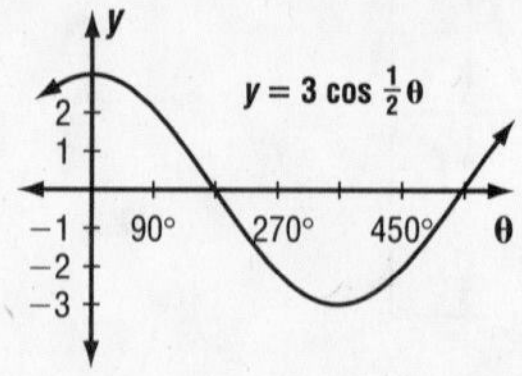

amplitude: $|3|$ or 3

period: $\frac{360°}{\left|\frac{1}{2}\right|}$ or 720°

11.

θ	0°	135°	270°	405°	540°
$\frac{2}{3}\theta$	0°	90°	180°	270°	360°
$6 \sin \frac{2}{3}\theta$	0	6	0	−6	0

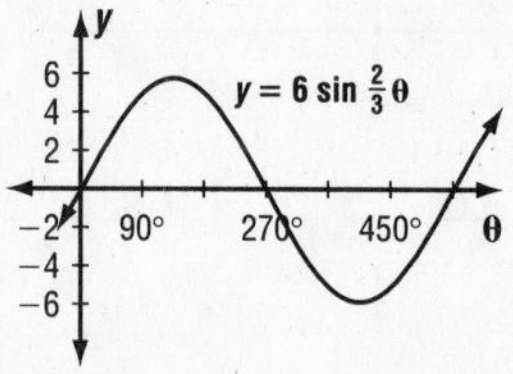

amplitude: $|6|$ or 6

period: $\frac{360°}{\left|\frac{2}{3}\right|}$ or 540°

12.

θ	0°	90°	180°	270°	360°
$\sin \theta$	0	1	0	−1	0
$-2 \sin \theta$	0	−2	0	2	0

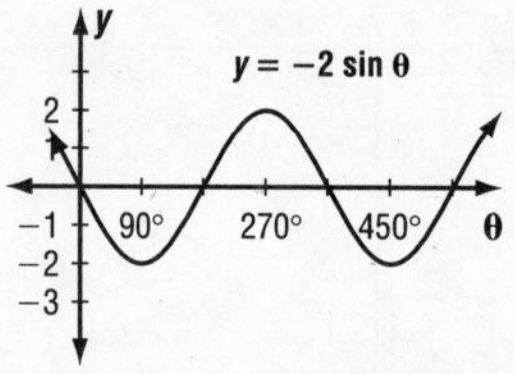

amplitude: $|-2|$ or 2

period: $\frac{360°}{|1|}$ or 360°

13.

θ	0°	30°	60°	90°	120°
3θ	0°	90°	180°	270°	360°
$\sec 3\theta$	1	nd	−1	nd	1

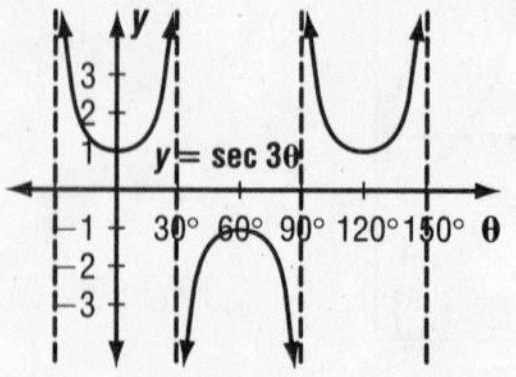

amplitude: none

period: $\frac{360°}{|3|}$ or 120°

14.

θ	0°	90°	180°	270°	360°
$\tan\theta$	0	–	0	–	0
$3\tan\theta$	0	nd	0	nd	0

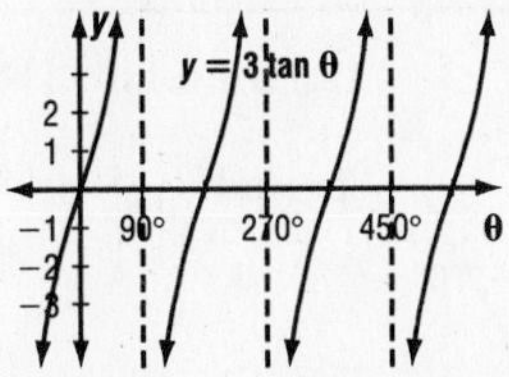

amplitude: none
period: $\frac{180°}{|1|}$ or 180°

15.

θ	0°	18°	36°	54°	72°
5θ	0°	90°	180°	270°	360°
$\cot 5\theta$	nd	0	nd	0	–

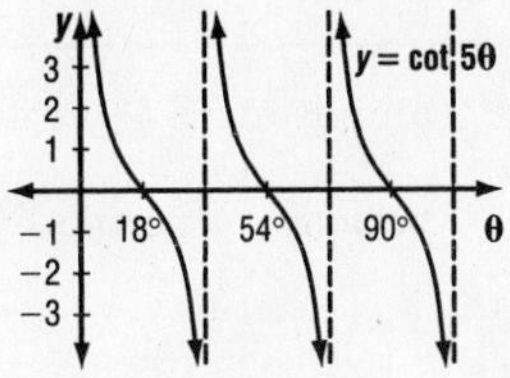

amplitude: none
period: $\frac{180°}{|5|}$ or 36°

16. Exercises 10, 11, and 12

17. c

Pages 832–834 Exercises

18.

θ	0°	90°	180°	270°	360°
$\sin\theta$	0	1	0	−1	0
$\frac{1}{2}\sin\theta$	0	$\frac{1}{2}$	0	$-\frac{1}{2}$	0

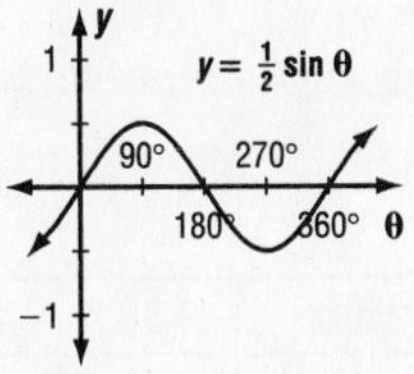

amplitude: $\left|\frac{1}{2}\right|$ or $\frac{1}{2}$
period: $\frac{360°}{|1|}$ or 360°

19.

θ	0°	90°	180°	270°	360°
$\sin\theta$	0	1	0	−1	0
$3\sin\theta$	0	3	0	−3	0

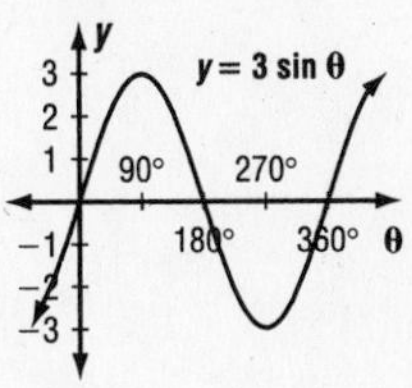

amplitude: $|3|$ or 3
period: $\frac{360°}{|1|}$ or 360°

20.

θ	0°	30°	60°	90°	120°
3θ	0°	90°	180°	270°	360°
$\cos 3\theta$	1	0	−1	0	1

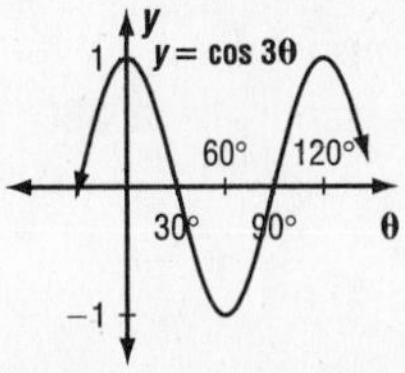

amplitude: $|1|$ or 1
period: $\frac{360°}{|3|}$ or 120°

21.

θ	0°	22.5°	45°	67.5°	90°
4θ	0°	90°	180°	270°	360°
$\sin 4\theta$	0	1	0	−1	0

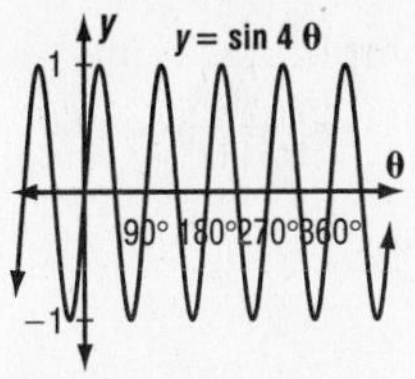

amplitude: $|1|$ or 1
period: $\frac{360°}{|4|}$ or 90°

22.

θ	0°	45°	90°	135°	180°
2θ	0°	90°	180°	270°	360°
$\cos 2\theta$	1	0	−1	0	1

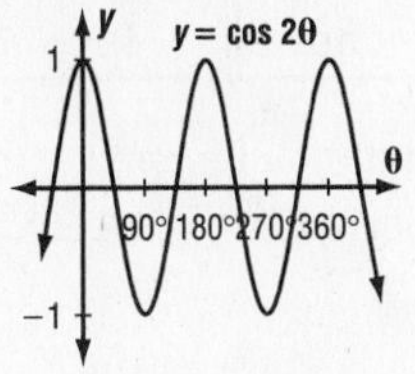

amplitude: $|1|$ or 1
period: $\frac{360°}{|2|}$ or 180°

23.

θ	0°	90°	180°	270°	360°
$\sin\theta$	0	1	0	−1	0
$-3\sin\theta$	0	−3	0	3	0

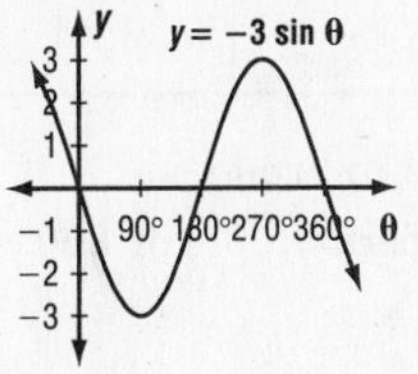

amplitude: $|-3|$ or 3
period: $\frac{360°}{|1|}$ or 360°

24.

θ	0°	90°	180°	270°	360°
$\cot\theta$	nd	0	nd	0	nd

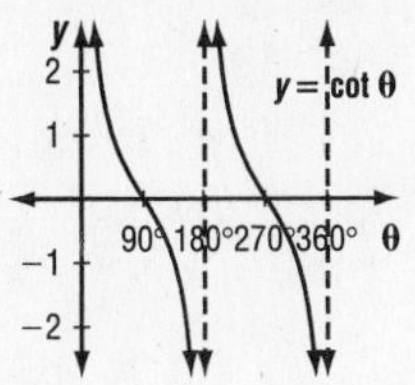

amplitude: none
period: $\frac{180°}{|1|}$ or 180°

25.

θ	0°	90°	180°	270°	360°
cos θ	1	0	−1	0	1
$\frac{2}{3}$ cos θ	$\frac{2}{3}$	0	$-\frac{2}{3}$	0	$\frac{2}{3}$

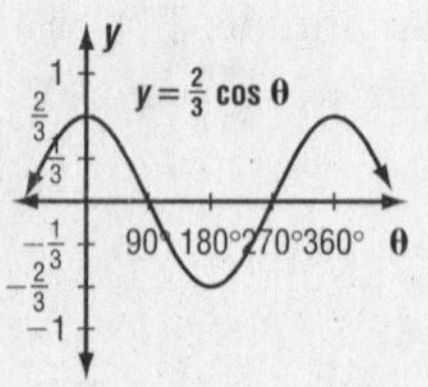

amplitude: $\left|\frac{2}{3}\right|$ or $\frac{2}{3}$
period: $\frac{360°}{|1|}$ or 360°

26.

θ	0°	90°	180°	270°	360°
sec θ	1	nd	−1	nd	1
3 sec θ	3	nd	−3	nd	3

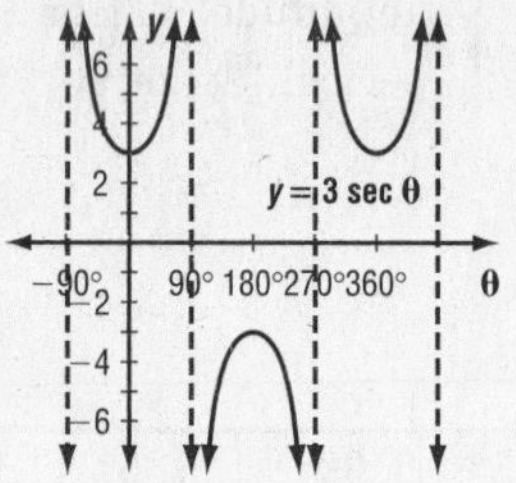

amplitude: none
period: $\frac{360°}{|1|}$ or 360°

27.

θ	0°	45°	90°	135°	180°
2θ	0°	90°	180°	270°	360°
csc 2θ	nd	1	nd	−1	nd

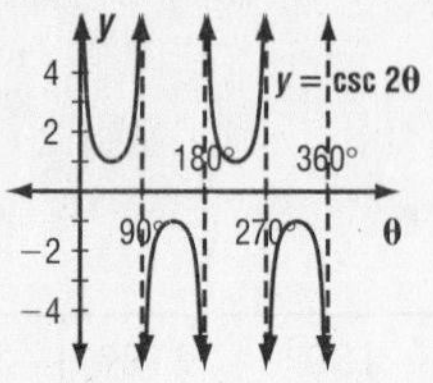

amplitude: none
period: $\frac{360°}{|2|}$ or 180°

28.

θ	0°	90°	180°	270°	360°
sec θ	1	nd	−1	nd	1
$\frac{1}{3}$ sec θ	$\frac{1}{3}$	nd	$-\frac{1}{3}$	nd	$\frac{1}{3}$

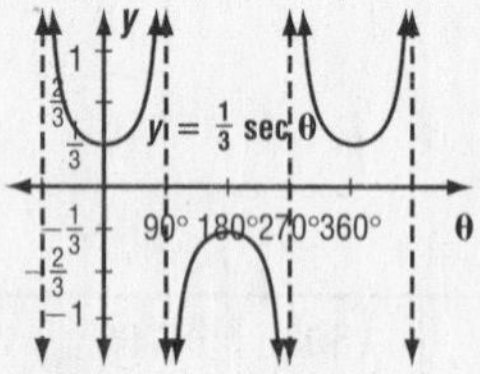

amplitude: none
period: $\frac{360°}{|1|}$ or 360°

29.

θ	0°	180°	360°	540°	720°
$\frac{1}{2}$ θ	0°	90°	180°	270°	360°
4 sin $\frac{1}{2}$ θ	0	4	0	−4	0

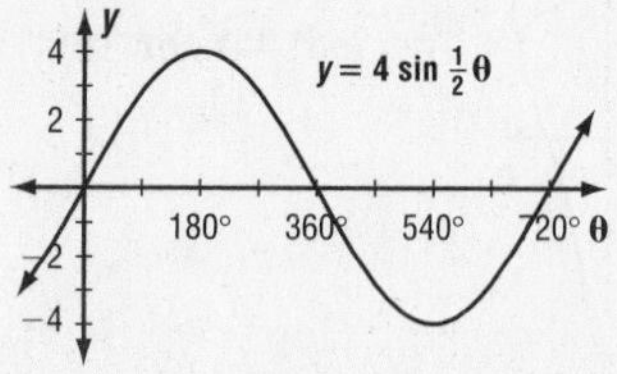

amplitude: |4| or 4
period: $\frac{360°}{\left|\frac{1}{2}\right|}$ or 720°

30.

θ	0°	120°	240°	360°	480°
$\frac{3}{4}$ θ	0°	90°	180°	270°	360°
4 cos $\frac{3}{4}$ θ	4	0	−4	0	4

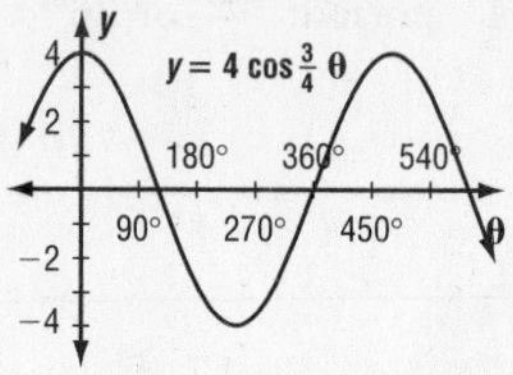

amplitude: |4| or 4
period: $\frac{360°}{\left|\frac{3}{4}\right|}$ or 480°

31.

θ	0°	180°	360°	540°	720°
$\frac{1}{2}$θ	0°	90°	180°	270°	360°
3 csc $\frac{1}{2}$ θ	nd	3	nd	−3	nd

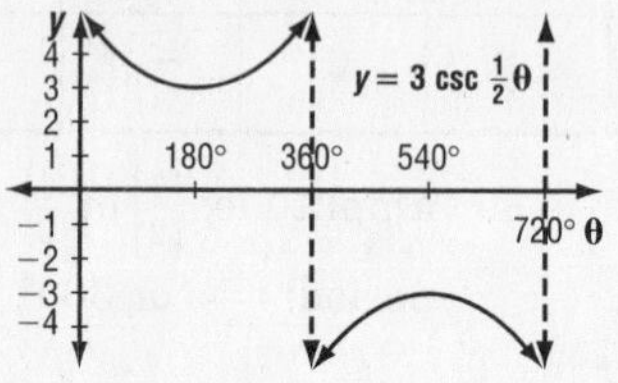

amplitude: none
period: $\frac{360°}{\left|\frac{1}{2}\right|}$ or 720°

32.

θ	0°	45°	90°	135°	180°
2θ	0°	90°	180°	270°	360°
$-\frac{1}{2}$ cot 2θ	nd	0	nd	0	nd

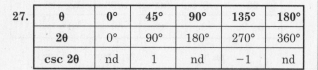

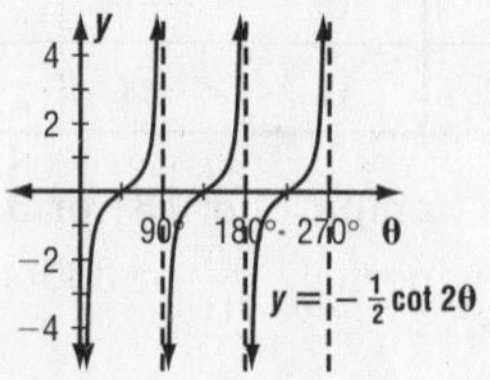

amplitude: none
period: $\frac{180°}{|2|}$ or 90°

33. $2y = \tan \theta$

$y = \frac{1}{2} \tan \theta$

θ	0°	90°	180°	270°	360°
$\tan \theta$	0	nd	0	nd	0
$\frac{1}{2} \tan \theta$	0	nd	0	nd	0

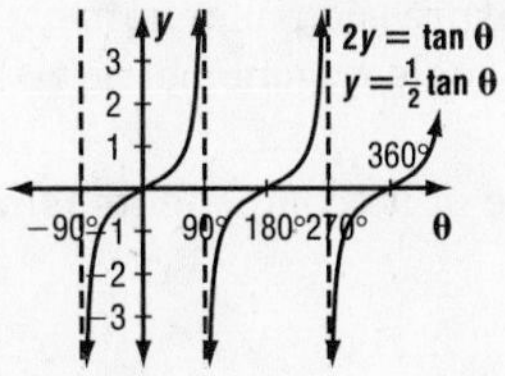

amplitude: none

period: $\frac{180°}{|1|}$ or 180°

34. $3y = 2 \sin \frac{1}{2} \theta$

$y = \frac{2}{3} \sin \frac{1}{2} \theta$

θ	0°	180°	360°	540°	720°
$\frac{1}{2}\theta$	0°	90°	180°	270°	360°
$\frac{2}{3} \sin \frac{1}{2} \theta$	0	$\frac{2}{3}$	0	$\frac{2}{3}$	0

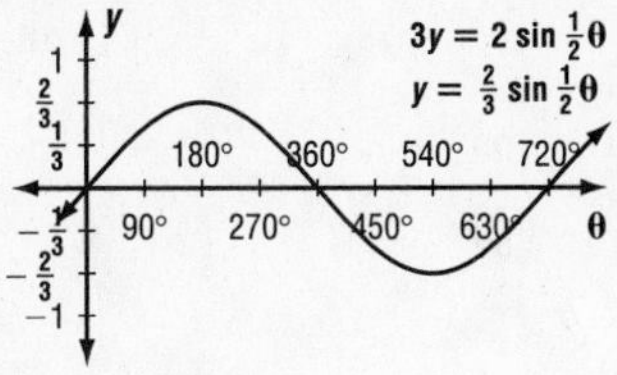

amplitude: $\left|\frac{2}{3}\right|$ or $\frac{2}{3}$

period: $\frac{360°}{\left|\frac{1}{2}\right|}$ or 720°

35. $\frac{3}{4}y = \frac{2}{3} \sin \frac{3}{5} \theta$

$y = \frac{8}{9} \sin \frac{3}{5} \theta$

θ	0°	150°	300°	450°	600°
$\frac{3}{5}\theta$	0°	90°	180°	270°	360°
$\frac{8}{9} \sin \frac{3}{5} \theta$	0	$\frac{8}{9}$	0	$-\frac{8}{9}$	0

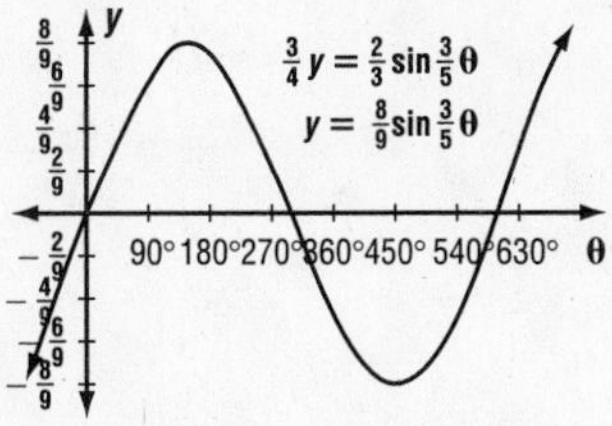

amplitude: $\left|\frac{8}{9}\right|$ or $\frac{8}{9}$

period: $\frac{360°}{\left|\frac{3}{5}\right|}$ or 600°

36. $y = 4 \sin \theta$

37. $y = 0.6 \cos \frac{1}{2} \theta$

38. $y = 5 \sin 2\theta$

39. $y = \frac{1}{3} \cos 4\theta$

40. $y = 4.25 \cos \theta$

41. $y = 6.7 \sin 3\theta$

42. $y = 3 \sin \theta$

43. $y = \cos 2\theta$

44. $y = \sin \frac{1}{2} \theta$

45a.

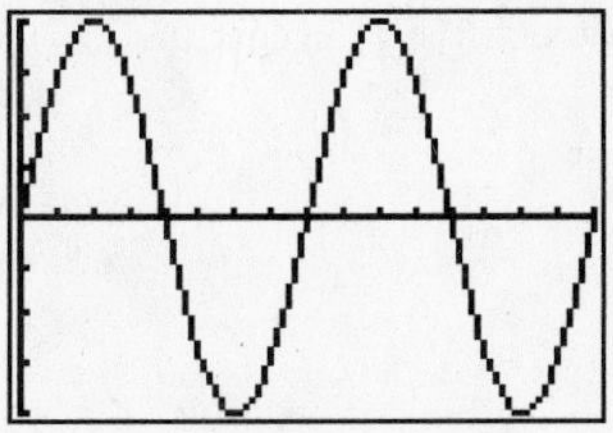

45b.

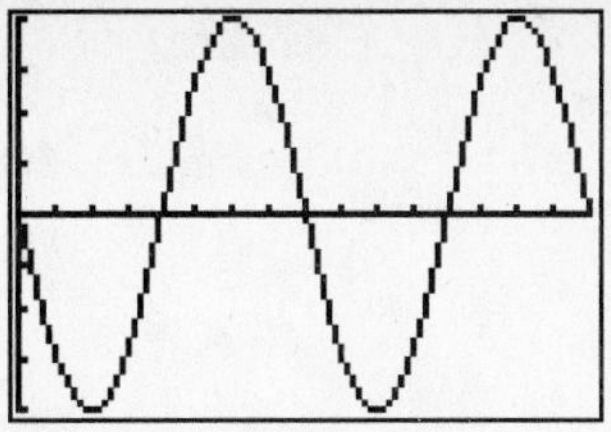

45c.

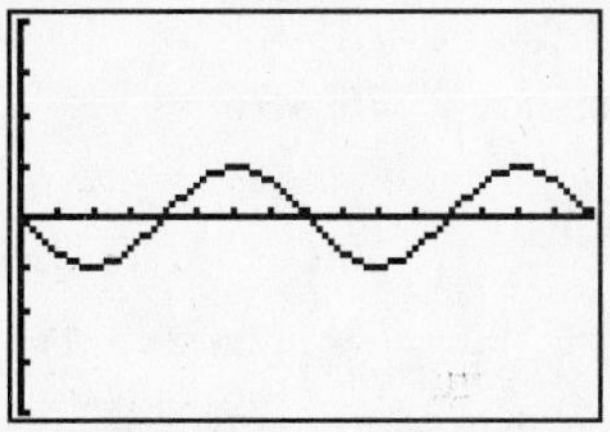

45d. The greater the absolute value of a, the greater the amplitude. If a is negative, then the curve is the same as would be obtained by reflecting the curve $y = -a \sin \theta$ about the x-axis.

46. By trial and error, using simple values for θ. For example, if $\theta = 0$, then $\sin \theta = 0 = \cos d$. Thus, a possible value for d is 90° since $\cos 90° = 0$. Next, use a calculator to check several values of θ in the equation $\sin \theta = \cos (\theta + 90°)$ to show that the conjecture is plausible.

47a.

t	0	1	2	3	4	5	6
$\frac{\pi t}{2}$	0	$\frac{\pi}{2}$	π	$\frac{3\pi}{2}$	2π	$\frac{5\pi}{2}$	3π
$250 \sin \frac{\pi t}{2}$	0	250	0	−250	0	250	0
$1000 + 250 \sin \frac{\pi t}{2}$	1000	1250	1000	750	1000	1250	1000

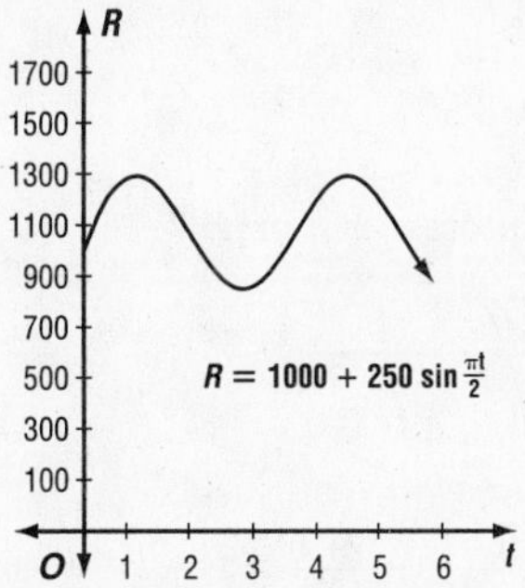

47b. 1000

47c. 1250; January 1, 1991

47d. 750; January 1, 1993

48. $\frac{2\pi}{|10^7 \cdot 2\pi|} = \frac{1}{10^7}$ second

49.

$$r = \sqrt{x^2 + y^2}$$
$$17 = \sqrt{15^2 + y^2}$$
$$289 = \sqrt{225 + y^2}$$
$$64 = y^2$$
$$8 = y$$

$$\sin\left(\text{Cos}^{-1} \frac{15}{17}\right) = \frac{8}{17}$$

50. $P(0 \text{ correct, } 4 \text{ incorrect}) = C(4, 0)\, R^0\, W^4$

$$= 1\left(\frac{1}{3}\right)^0\left(\frac{2}{3}\right)^4 \text{ or } \frac{16}{81}$$

51. $r = \frac{a_n}{a_{n-1}} = \frac{38}{19}$ or 2

$$a_n = a_1 r^{n-1}$$
$$38 = a_1(2)^4$$
$$38 = 16a_1$$
$$2.375 = a_1$$
$$a_2 = a_1 \cdot r = 2.375 \cdot 2 = 4.75$$

The missing terms are 2.375, 4.75.

52. 4.0413

53.
$$\frac{x-3}{2x} = \frac{x-2}{2x+1} - \frac{1}{2}$$
$$2x(2x+1)\left(\frac{x-3}{2x}\right) = \left(\frac{x-2}{2x+1} - \frac{1}{2}\right)(2x)(2x+1)$$
$$(2x+1)(x-3) = 2x(x-2) - x(2x+1)$$
$$2x^2 - 5x - 3 = 2x^2 - 4x - 2x^2 - x$$
$$2x^2 - 5x - 3 = -5x$$
$$2x^2 - 3 = 0$$
$$2x^2 = 3$$
$$x^2 = \frac{3}{2}$$
$$x = \pm\sqrt{\frac{3}{2}}$$
$$x = \pm\sqrt{\frac{3}{2}\cdot\frac{\sqrt{2}}{\sqrt{2}}}$$
$$x = \pm\frac{\sqrt{6}}{2}$$

54. $\frac{(x-1)^2}{9} - \frac{(y+4)^2}{16} = 1$, $a = \pm\sqrt{9}$ or ± 3, $b = \pm\sqrt{16}$ or ± 4

center: $(1, -4)$

vertices: $(1 \pm 3, -4)$ or $(-2, -4)$, $(4, -4)$

foci: $c^2 = a^2 + b^2$

$$c^2 = 9 + 16$$
$$c^2 = 25$$
$$c = \pm 5$$

$(1 \pm 5, -4)$ or $(6, -4)$, $(-4, -4)$

slopes of the asymptotes: $\pm\frac{b}{a}$ or $\pm\frac{4}{3}$

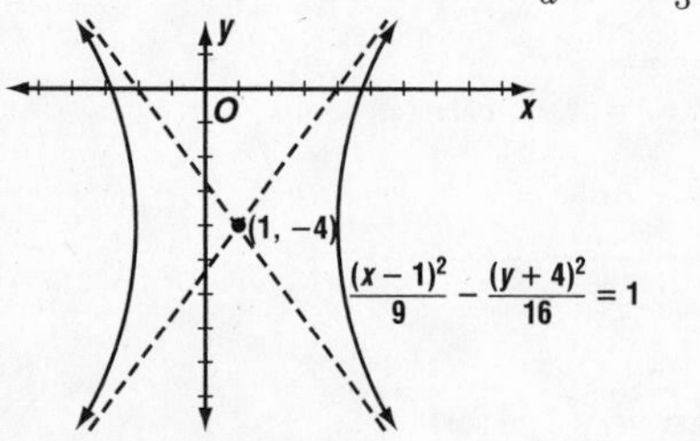

55. $\sqrt[3]{16a^5b^7} = (16a^5b^7)^{\frac{1}{3}}$

$$= 16^{\frac{1}{3}}a^{\frac{5}{3}}b^{\frac{7}{3}}$$

56.

(x, y)	x − y	f(x − y)
(0, 0)	0 − 0	0
(0, 5)	0 − 5	−5
(3, 4)	3 − 4	−1
(6, 0)	6 − 0	6

maximum: 6

minimum: −5

57. Sample answer: $a(b + c) = ab + ac$

14-2 Trigonometric Identities

Page 839 Check for Understanding

1. Given an angle in standard position whose measurement is θ and which intersects the circle at point (x, y), $x = \cos\theta$ and $y = \sin\theta$.
2. It means to write the expression as a numerical value or in terms of a single trigonometric function.
3. II or IV, where only one of its components (sin or cos) is negative
4. $\cot\theta = 2$
$$\tan\theta = \frac{1}{\cot\theta}$$
$$\tan\theta = \frac{1}{2}$$
5. $\cos^2\theta + \sin^2\theta = 1$
$$\cos^2\theta = 1 - \sin^2\theta$$
$$\cos^2\theta = 1 - \left(\frac{4}{5}\right)^2$$
$$\cos^2\theta = 1 - \frac{16}{25}$$
$$\cos^2\theta = \frac{9}{25}$$
$$\cos\theta = \frac{3}{5}$$
6. $\cos^2\theta + \sin^2\theta = 1$
$$\sin^2\theta = 1 - \cos^2\theta$$
$$\sin^2\theta = 1 - \left(\frac{2}{3}\right)^2$$
$$\sin^2\theta = 1 - \frac{4}{9}$$
$$\sin^2\theta = \frac{5}{9}$$
$$\sin\theta = \frac{\sqrt{5}}{3}$$
7. $\cos^2\theta + \sin^2\theta = 1$
$$\sin^2\theta = 1 - \cos^2\theta$$
$$\sin^2\theta = 1 - \left(\frac{2}{3}\right)^2$$
$$\sin^2\theta = 1 - \frac{4}{9}$$
$$\sin^2\theta = \frac{5}{9}$$
$$\left(\frac{1}{\csc^2\theta}\right) = \frac{5}{9}$$
$$\csc^2\theta = \frac{9}{5}$$
$$\csc\theta = \frac{\sqrt{9}}{\sqrt{5}}$$
$$\csc\theta = \frac{3\sqrt{5}}{5}$$
8. $\sin x \sec x \stackrel{?}{=} \tan x$
$$\sin x \frac{1}{\cos x} \stackrel{?}{=} \tan x$$
$$\frac{\sin x}{\cos x} \stackrel{?}{=} \tan x$$
$$\tan x = \tan x$$
9. $\tan\theta\cos^2\theta = \left(\frac{\sin\theta}{\cos\theta}\right)\cdot\cos^2\theta$
$$= \sin\theta\cos\theta$$
10. $\csc^2\theta - \cot^2\theta = (\cot^2\theta + 1) - \cot^2\theta$
$$= 1$$

11. $\dfrac{\cos x \csc x}{\tan x} = \dfrac{\cos x\left(\dfrac{1}{\sin x}\right)}{\tan x}$

$= \dfrac{\cot x}{\tan x}$

$= \cot x \cdot \dfrac{1}{\tan x}$

$= \cot x \cdot \cot x$

$= \cot^2 x$

12. The functions cos θ and sin θ can be thought of as the lengths of the legs of a right triangle and the number 1 can be thought of as the measure of the corresponding hypotenuse.

Pages 839–840 Exercises

13. $\cos^2\theta + \sin^2\theta = 1$

$\sin^2\theta = 1 - \cos^2\theta$

$\sin^2\theta = 1 - \left(-\frac{3}{5}\right)^2$

$\sin^2\theta = 1 - \frac{9}{25}$

$\sin^2\theta = \frac{16}{25}$

$\left(\frac{1}{\csc^2\theta}\right) = \frac{16}{25}$

$\csc^2\theta = \frac{25}{16}$

$\csc\theta = \frac{5}{4}$

14. $\cos^2\theta + \sin^2\theta = 1$

$\cos^2\theta = 1 - \sin^2\theta$

$\cos^2\theta = 1 - \left(\frac{1}{2}\right)^2$

$\cos^2\theta = 1 - \frac{1}{4}$

$\cos^2\theta = \frac{3}{4}$

$\cos\theta = -\frac{\sqrt{3}}{2}$

$\tan\theta = \dfrac{\sin\theta}{\cos\theta}$

$= \dfrac{\frac{1}{2}}{-\frac{\sqrt{3}}{2}}$

$= -\dfrac{1}{\sqrt{3}}$

$= -\dfrac{\sqrt{3}}{3}$

15. $\cos^2\theta + \sin^2\theta = 1$

$\cos^2\theta = 1 - \sin^2\theta$

$\cos^2\theta = 1 - \left(\frac{3}{5}\right)^2$

$\cos^2\theta = 1 - \frac{9}{25}$

$\cos^2\theta = \frac{16}{25}$

$\cos\theta = -\frac{4}{5}$

16. $\tan^2\theta + 1 = \sec^2\theta$

$(-2)^2 + 1 = \sec^2\theta$

$4 + 1 = \sec^2\theta$

$5 = \sec^2\theta$

$-\sqrt{5} = \sec\theta$

17. $\cos^2\theta + \sin^2\theta = 1$

$\sin^2\theta = 1 - \cos^2\theta$

$\sin^2\theta = 1 - \left(-\frac{3}{5}\right)^2$

$\sin^2\theta = 1 - \frac{9}{25}$

$\sin^2\theta = \frac{16}{25}$

$\left(\frac{1}{\csc^2\theta}\right) = \frac{16}{25}$

$\csc^2\theta = \frac{25}{16}$

$\csc\theta = -\frac{5}{4}$

18. $\tan^2\theta + 1 = \sec^2\theta$

$\tan^2\theta = \sec^2\theta - 1$

$\tan^2\theta = (-3)^2 - 1$

$\tan^2\theta = 9 - 1$

$\tan^2\theta = 8$

$\tan\theta = 2\sqrt{2}$

19. $\cot^2\theta + 1 = \csc^2\theta$

$\left(\frac{1}{4}\right)^2 + 1 = \csc^2\theta$

$\frac{1}{16} + 1 = \csc^2\theta$

$\frac{17}{16} = \csc^2\theta$

$-\frac{\sqrt{17}}{4} = \csc\theta$

20. $\cos^2\theta + \sin^2\theta = 1$

$\cos^2\theta = 1 - \sin^2\theta$

$\cos^2\theta = 1 - \left(-\frac{1}{2}\right)^2$

$\cos^2\theta = 1 - \frac{1}{4}$

$\cos^2\theta = \frac{3}{4}$

$\cos\theta = -\frac{\sqrt{3}}{2}$

21. $\cos^2\theta + \sin^2\theta = 1$

$\sin^2\theta = 1 - \cos^2\theta$

$\sin^2\theta = 1 - \left(\frac{5}{13}\right)^2$

$\sin^2\theta = 1 - \frac{25}{169}$

$\sin^2\theta = \frac{144}{169}$

$\sin\theta = -\frac{12}{13}$

22. $\tan^2\theta + 1 = \sec^2\theta$

$(-1)^2 + 1 = \sec^2\theta$

$1 + 1 = \sec^2\theta$

$2 = \sec^2\theta$

$\sqrt{2} = \sec\theta$

23. $\cos\theta = \dfrac{1}{\sec\theta}$

$\cos\theta = \dfrac{1}{\frac{5}{3}}$

$\cos\theta = \frac{3}{5}$

24. $\sin\theta = \dfrac{1}{\csc\theta}$

$= \dfrac{1}{-\frac{5}{3}}$

$= -\frac{3}{5}$

$\cos^2\theta + \sin^2\theta = 1$

$\cos^2\theta = 1 - \sin^2\theta$

$\cos^2\theta = 1 - \left(-\frac{3}{5}\right)^2$

$\cos^2\theta = 1 - \frac{9}{25}$

$\cos^2\theta = \frac{16}{25}$

$\cos\theta = \frac{4}{5}$

25. $\csc\alpha\cos\alpha\tan\alpha = \left(\frac{1}{\sin\alpha}\right)\cos\alpha\left(\frac{\sin\alpha}{\cos\alpha}\right)$

$= \frac{\cos\alpha\sin\alpha}{\sin\alpha\cos\alpha}$

$= 1$

26. $\cos\alpha\ \csc\alpha = \cos\alpha\left(\frac{1}{\sin\alpha}\right)$

$= \frac{\cos\alpha}{\sin\alpha}$

$= \cot\alpha$

27. $\sec^2\theta - 1 = (\tan^2\theta + 1) - 1$

$= \tan^2\theta$

28. $\sin x + \cos x\tan x = \sin x + \cos x\left(\frac{\sin x}{\cos x}\right)$

$= \sin x + \frac{\cos x\sin x}{\cos x}$

$= \sin x + \sin x$

$= 2\sin x$

29. $\frac{\tan\beta}{\sin\beta} = \frac{\frac{\sin\beta}{\cos\beta}}{\sin\beta}$

$= \frac{1}{\cos\beta}$

$= \sec\beta$

30. $\frac{1-\sin^2\alpha}{\sin^2\alpha} = \frac{(\cos^2\alpha + \sin^2\alpha) - \sin^2\alpha}{\sin^2\alpha}$

$= \frac{\cos^2\alpha}{\sin^2\alpha}$

$= \cot^2\alpha$

31. $\tan\beta\cot\beta = \tan\beta\left(\frac{1}{\tan\beta}\right)$

$= \frac{\tan\beta}{\tan\beta}$

$= 1$

32. $\tan x\csc x = \left(\frac{\sin x}{\cos x}\right)\left(\frac{1}{\sin x}\right)$

$= \frac{\sin x}{\cos x\sin x}$

$= \frac{1}{\cos x}$

$= \sec x$

33. $\sin\beta\,(1 + \cot^2\beta) = \sin\beta\,(\csc^2\beta)$

$= \sin\beta\left(\frac{1}{\sin^2\beta}\right)$

$= \frac{\sin\beta}{\sin^2\beta}$

$= \frac{1}{\sin\beta}$

$= \csc\beta$

34. $\frac{1}{\sin^2\theta} - \frac{\cos^2\theta}{\sin^2\theta} = \frac{1-\cos^2\theta}{\sin^2\theta}$

$= \frac{(\sin^2\theta + \cos^2\theta) - \cos^2\theta}{\sin^2\theta}$

$= \frac{\sin^2\theta}{\sin^2\theta}$

$= 1$

35. $\frac{\tan^2\theta - \sin^2\theta}{\tan^2\theta\sin^2\theta} = \frac{\tan^2\theta}{\tan^2\theta\sin^2\theta} - \frac{\sin^2\theta}{\tan^2\theta\sin^2\theta}$

$= \frac{1}{\sin^2\theta} - \frac{1}{\tan^2\theta}$

$= \csc^2\theta - \cot^2\theta$

$= (\cot^2\theta + 1) - \cot^2\theta$

$= 1$

36. $2(\csc^2\theta - \cot^2\theta) = 2[(\cot^2\theta + 1) - \cot^2\theta]$

$= 2(1)$

$= 2$

37. $1 + \tan^2\theta \stackrel{?}{=} \sec^2\theta$

$1 + \frac{\sin^2\theta}{\cos^2\theta} \stackrel{?}{=} \sec^2\theta$

$\frac{\cos^2\theta}{\cos^2\theta} + \frac{\sin^2\theta}{\cos^2\theta} \stackrel{?}{=} \sec^2\theta$

$\frac{\cos^2\theta + \sin^2\theta}{\cos^2\theta} \stackrel{?}{=} \sec^2\theta$

$\frac{1}{\cos^2\theta} \stackrel{?}{=} \sec^2\theta$

$\sec^2\theta = \sec^2\theta$

38. $1 + \cot^2\theta \stackrel{?}{=} \csc^2\theta$

$1 + \frac{\cos^2\theta}{\sin^2\theta} \stackrel{?}{=} \csc^2\theta$

$\frac{\sin^2\theta}{\sin^2\theta} + \frac{\cos^2\theta}{\sin^2\theta} \stackrel{?}{=} \csc^2\theta$

$\frac{\sin^2\theta + \cos^2\theta}{\sin^2\theta} \stackrel{?}{=} \csc^2\theta$

$\frac{1}{\sin^2\theta} \stackrel{?}{=} \csc^2\theta$

$\csc^2\theta = \csc^2\theta$

39. $\sec\alpha - \cos\alpha \stackrel{?}{=} \sin\alpha\tan\alpha$

$\frac{1}{\cos\alpha} - \cos\alpha \stackrel{?}{=} \sin\alpha\tan\alpha$

$\frac{1}{\cos\alpha} - \frac{\cos^2\alpha}{\cos\alpha} \stackrel{?}{=} \sin\alpha\tan\alpha$

$\frac{1-\cos^2\alpha}{\cos\alpha} \stackrel{?}{=} \sin\alpha\tan\alpha$

$\frac{\sin^2\alpha}{\cos\alpha} \stackrel{?}{=} \sin\alpha\tan\alpha$

$\sin\alpha\cdot\frac{\sin\alpha}{\cos\alpha} \stackrel{?}{=} \sin\alpha\tan\alpha$

$\sin\alpha\tan\alpha = \sin\alpha\tan\alpha$

40. $\frac{\sec\theta}{\csc\theta} \stackrel{?}{=} \tan\theta$

$\frac{\frac{1}{\cos\theta}}{\frac{1}{\sin\theta}} \stackrel{?}{=} \tan\theta$

$\frac{1}{\cos\theta}\cdot\frac{\sin\theta}{1} \stackrel{?}{=} \tan\theta$

$\frac{\sin\theta}{\cos\theta} \stackrel{?}{=} \tan\theta$

$\tan\theta = \tan\theta$

41. $\frac{\sin\beta\sec\beta}{\cot\beta} = \frac{\sin\beta\cdot\frac{1}{\cos\beta}}{\cot\beta}$

$= \frac{\frac{\sin\beta}{\cos\beta}}{\cot\beta}$

$= \frac{\tan\beta}{\cot\beta}$

$= \frac{\tan\beta}{\frac{1}{\tan\beta}}$

$= \tan^2\beta$

$= \left(\frac{3}{4}\right)^2$

$= \frac{9}{16}$

42. The length of $\overline{AB}$ (the segment touching circle O) represents $\tan\theta$ and the length of $\overline{OB}$ (the segment "cutting" circle O) represents $\sec\theta$. Then, since $OA = 1$, the identity reflects the Pythagorean relationship between the lengths of the three sides of right triangle OAB.

43. $\sin\theta = \frac{1}{4}$

$\theta \approx 14.5°$

44. $\sin\theta = \frac{1}{5}$

$\theta \approx 11.5°$

$\cos^2\theta + \sin^2\theta = 1$

$\cos^2 = 1 - \sin^2\theta$

$\cos^2\theta = 1 - \left(\frac{1}{5}\right)^2$

$\cos^2\theta = 1 - \frac{1}{25}$

$\cos^2\theta = \frac{24}{25}$

$\cos\theta = \frac{2\sqrt{6}}{5}$

$\tan\theta = \frac{\sin\theta}{\cos\theta}$

$= \frac{\frac{1}{5}}{\frac{2\sqrt{6}}{5}}$

$= \frac{1}{2\sqrt{6}}$

$= \frac{\sqrt{6}}{12}$

≈ 0.2041

$d = 2r$

$16 = 2r$

$8 = r$

$\tan\theta = \frac{v^2}{gR}$

$0.2041 \approx \frac{v^2}{9.8(8)}$

$v^2 \approx 16.001$

$v \approx \pm 4$

The speed of the runner is about 4 m/s.

45.

θ	0°	90°	180°	270°	360°
cos θ	1	0	−1	0	1
3 cos θ	3	0	−3	0	3

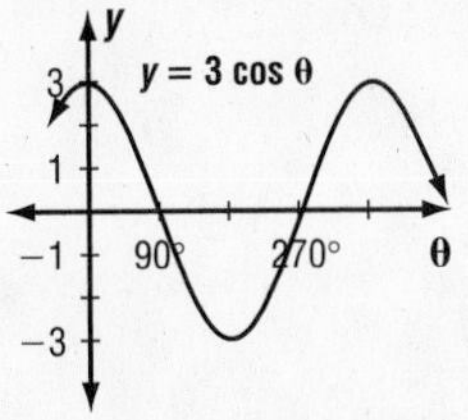

amplitude: $|3|$ or 3

period: $\frac{360°}{|1|}$ or 360°

46. $\tan(-390°) = \tan(-390 + 720)°$
$= \tan 330°$
$= -\frac{\sqrt{3}}{3}$ or about -0.5774

47. $C(125) = \frac{12!}{(12-5)!\,5!}$
$= \frac{12!}{7!\,5!}$
$= 792$

48. 15(12)(10) or 1800 combinations

49. $d = 13 - 8 = 5$
$13 + 5 = 18$
$18 + 5 = 23$
$23 + 5 = 28$
18, 23, 28

50. possible rational roots: ± 1, ± 2, ± 4, ± 8

2⌋	1	3	−6	−8
		2	10	8
	1	5	4	0

$x^2 + 5x + 4 = 0$
$(x + 4)(x + 1) = 0$
$x + 4 = 0$ or $x + 1 = 0$
$x = -4$ $\quad x = -1$
−4, −1, 2

51. $y^2 + 4y - 21 = 0$
$(y + 7)(y - 3) = 0$
$y + 7 = 0$ or $y - 3 = 0$
$y = -7$ $\quad y = 3$

52.
$$\begin{vmatrix} 4 & 3 & 6 \\ 2 & 2n & 7 \\ -4 & -3n & 3 \end{vmatrix} = -582$$

$4(2n)(3) + 3(7)(-4) + 6(2)(-3n) -$
$(-4)(2n)(6) - (-3n)(7)(4) - 3(2)(3) = -582$
$24n - 84 - 36n + 48n + 84n - 18 = -582$
$120n - 102 = -582$
$120n = -480$
$n = -4$

14-3A Graphing Technology Verifying Trigonometric Identities

Page 841 Exercises

1. Enter: [Y=] [(] 1 [+] [SIN] [X,T,θ,n] [)] [(] 1 [−] [SIN] [X,T,θ,n] [)] [ENTER] [(] [COS] [X,T,θ,n] [)] [x²] [ZOOM] 7 yes

2. Enter: [Y=] 1 [÷] [(] [TAN] [X,T,θ,n] [)] [+] [TAN] [X,T,θ,n] [ENTER] [(] 1 [÷] [(] [SIN] [X,T,θ,n] [)] [)] [(] 1 [÷] [(] [TAN] [X,T,θ,n] [)] [)] [ZOOM] 7 no

3. Enter: [Y=] [(] 1 [÷] [(] [COS] [X,T,θ,n] [)] [x²] [÷] [(] [TAN] [X,T,θ,n] [)] [ENTER] [(] 1 [÷] [(] [COS] [X,T,θ,n] [)] [)] [(] 1 [÷] [(] [SIN] [X,T,θ,n] [)] [)] [ZOOM] 7 yes

4. Enter: [Y=] 1 [÷] [(] 1 [÷] [(] [COS] [X,T,θ,n] [)] [)] [+] 1 [÷] [(] 1 [÷] [(] [SIN] [X,T,θ,n] [)] [)] [ENTER] 1 [ZOOM] 7 no

5. Enter: [Y=] [SIN] [(] 90 [−] [X,T,θ,n] [)] [ENTER] cos [X,T,θ,n] [ZOOM] 7 yes

6. Enter: [Y=] 1 [÷] [(] 1 [÷] [COS] [(] [X,T,θ,n] [)] [)] [(] [TAN] [X,T,θ,n] [)] [ENTER] 1 [÷] [SIN] [X,T,θ,n] [−] [SIN] [X,T,θ,n] [ZOOM] 7 yes

7. Enter: [Y=] [TAN] [X,T,θ,n] [÷] [(] 1 [+] [TAN] [X,T,θ,n] [)] [ENTER] [SIN] [X,T,θ,n] [÷] [(] [SIN] [X,T,θ,n] [+] [COS] [X,T,θ,n] [)] [ZOOM] 7 yes

8. Enter: [Y=] 1 [÷] [(] [TAN] [X,T,θ,n] [)] [x²] [(] [(] 1 [÷] [(] [COS] [X,T,θ,n] [)] [)] [x²] [−] 1 [)] [ENTER] 1 [ZOOM] 7 yes

9. Enter: [Y=] [COS] 2 [X,T,θ,n] [ENTER] 1 [−] 2 [(] [SIN] [X,T,θ,n] [)] [x²] [ZOOM] 7 yes

10. Enter: [Y=] 1 [÷] [SIN] [(−)] [X,T,θ,n] [÷] [(] 1 [÷] [COS] [(−)] [X,T,θ,n] [)] [ENTER] [(−)] 1 [÷] [TAN] [X,T,θ,n] [ZOOM] 7 yes

11. Enter: [Y=] [COS] 3 [X,T,θ,n] [+] 1 [ENTER] 2 [COS] [X,T,θ,n] [x²] [ZOOM] 7 yes

12. Enter: [Y=] 1 [÷] [SIN] [X,T,θ,n] [x²] [÷] [(] 1 [÷] [SIN] [X,T,θ,n] [−] 1 [)] [ENTER] [(] 1 [+] [SIN] [X,T,θ,n] [)] [÷] [SIN] [X,T,θ,n] no

14-3 Verifying Trigonometric Identities

Page 845 Check for Understanding

1. See students' work.

2. $\dfrac{g \sec \theta}{w^2} = \dfrac{g\left(\dfrac{1}{\cos \theta}\right)}{w^2}$ $\qquad$ $\dfrac{g \tan \theta}{w^2 \sin \theta} = \dfrac{g\left(\dfrac{\sin \theta}{\cos \theta}\right)}{w^2 \sin \theta}$

$= \dfrac{g}{w^2} \cdot \dfrac{1}{\cos \theta}$ $\qquad$ $= \dfrac{g}{w^2} \cdot \dfrac{\sin \theta}{\cos \theta} \cdot \dfrac{1}{\sin \theta}$

$= \dfrac{g}{w^2 \cos \theta}$ $\qquad$ $= \dfrac{g}{w^2 \cos \theta}$

3. $\sin \theta \sec \theta \cot \theta \stackrel{?}{=} 1$

$\sin \theta \cdot \dfrac{1}{\cos \theta} \cdot \dfrac{\cos \theta}{\sin \theta} \stackrel{?}{=} 1$

$1 = 1$

4. $\tan^2 x \cos^2 x \stackrel{?}{=} 1 - \cos^2 x$

$\dfrac{\sin^2 x}{\cos^2 x} \cdot \cos^2 x \stackrel{?}{=} \sin^2 x$

$\sin^2 x = \sin^2 x$

5. $\csc y \sec y \stackrel{?}{=} \cot y + \tan y$

$\csc y \sec y \stackrel{?}{=} \dfrac{\cos y}{\sin y} + \dfrac{\sin y}{\cos y}$

$\csc y \sec y \stackrel{?}{=} \dfrac{\sin^2 y + \cos^2 y}{\sin y \cos y}$

$\csc y \sec y \stackrel{?}{=} \dfrac{1}{\sin y \cos y}$

$\csc y \sec y = \csc y \sec y$

6. $\tan \alpha \ \sin \alpha \ \cos \alpha \ \csc^2 \alpha \stackrel{?}{=} 1$

$\dfrac{\sin \alpha}{\cos \alpha} \cdot \sin \alpha \cdot \cos \alpha \cdot \dfrac{1}{\sin^2 \alpha} \stackrel{?}{=} 1$

$1 = 1$

7. $\dfrac{\sec \beta + \csc \beta}{1 + \tan \beta} \stackrel{?}{=} \csc \beta$

$\dfrac{\dfrac{1}{\cos \beta} + \dfrac{1}{\sin \beta}}{1 + \dfrac{\sin \beta}{\cos \beta}} \stackrel{?}{=} \csc \beta$

$\dfrac{\dfrac{\sin \beta + \cos \beta}{\sin \beta \cos \beta}}{\dfrac{\sin \beta + \cos \beta}{\cos \beta}} \stackrel{?}{=} \csc \beta$

$\dfrac{\sin \beta + \cos \beta}{\sin \beta \cos \beta} \cdot \dfrac{\cos \beta}{\sin \beta + \cos \beta} \stackrel{?}{=} \csc \beta$

$\dfrac{\cos \beta}{\sin \beta \cos \beta} \stackrel{?}{=} \csc \beta$

$\dfrac{1}{\sin \beta} \stackrel{?}{=} \csc \beta$

$\csc \beta = \csc \beta$

8. $\dfrac{1 - 2\cos^2 \beta}{\sin \beta \cos \beta} \stackrel{?}{=} \tan \beta - \cot \beta$

$\dfrac{(1 - \cos^2 \beta) - \cos^2 \beta}{\sin \beta \cos \beta} \stackrel{?}{=} \tan \beta - \cot \beta$

$\dfrac{\sin^2 \beta - \cos^2 \beta}{\sin \beta \cos \beta} \stackrel{?}{=} \tan \beta - \cot \beta$

$\dfrac{\sin^2 \beta}{\sin \beta \cos \beta} - \dfrac{\cos^2 \beta}{\sin \beta \cos \beta} \stackrel{?}{=} \tan \beta - \cot \beta$

$\dfrac{\sin \beta}{\cos \beta} - \dfrac{\cos \beta}{\sin \beta} \stackrel{?}{=} \tan \beta - \cot \beta$

$\tan \beta - \cot \beta = \tan \beta - \cot \beta$

9. $L = \dfrac{g \tan \theta}{w^2 \sin \theta}$

$= \dfrac{980 \tan 40°}{8^2 \sin 40°}$

≈ 20; 20 centimeters

Pages 845–846 Exercises

10. $\sec^2 x - \tan^2 x \stackrel{?}{=} \tan x \cot x$

$\dfrac{1}{\cos^2 x} - \dfrac{\sin^2 x}{\cos^2 x} \stackrel{?}{=} \dfrac{\sin x}{\cos x} \cdot \dfrac{\cos x}{\sin x}$

$\dfrac{1 - \sin^2 x}{\cos^2 x} \stackrel{?}{=} 1$

$\dfrac{\cos^2 x}{\cos^2 x} \stackrel{?}{=} 1$

$1 = 1$

11. $\dfrac{1}{\sec^2 \theta} + \dfrac{1}{\csc^2 \theta} \stackrel{?}{=} 1$

$\cos^2 \theta + \sin^2 \theta \stackrel{?}{=} 1$

$1 = 1$

12. $\tan^2 \theta - \sin^2 \theta \stackrel{?}{=} \tan^2 \theta \sin^2 \theta$

$\dfrac{\sin^2 \theta}{\cos^2 \theta} - \sin^2 \theta \stackrel{?}{=} \tan^2 \theta \sin^2 \theta$

$\dfrac{\sin^2 \theta}{\cos^2 \theta} - \dfrac{\sin^2 \theta \cos^2 \theta}{\cos^2 \theta} \stackrel{?}{=} \tan^2 \theta \sin^2 \theta$

$\dfrac{\sin^2 - \sin^2 \theta \cos^2 \theta}{\cos^2 \theta} \stackrel{?}{=} \tan^2 \theta \sin^2 \theta$

$\dfrac{\sin^2 \theta\,(1 - \cos^2 \theta)}{\cos^2 \theta} \stackrel{?}{=} \tan^2 \theta \sin^2 \theta$

$\dfrac{\sin^2 \theta}{\cos^2 \theta} \cdot \sin^2 \theta \stackrel{?}{=} \tan^2 \theta \sin^2 \theta$

$\tan^2 \theta \sin^2 \theta = \tan^2 \theta \sin^2 \theta$

13. $\dfrac{\sec \alpha}{\sin \alpha} - \dfrac{\sin \alpha}{\cos \alpha} \stackrel{?}{=} \cot \alpha$

$\dfrac{\dfrac{1}{\cos \alpha}}{\sin \alpha} - \dfrac{\sin \alpha}{\cos \alpha} \stackrel{?}{=} \cot \alpha$

$\dfrac{1}{\sin \alpha \cos \alpha} - \dfrac{\sin^2 \alpha}{\sin \alpha \cos \alpha} \stackrel{?}{=} \cot \alpha$

$\dfrac{1 - \sin^2 \alpha}{\sin\alpha \cos \alpha} \stackrel{?}{=} \cot \alpha$

$\dfrac{\cos^2 \alpha}{\sin \alpha \cos \alpha} \stackrel{?}{=} \cot \alpha$

$\dfrac{\cos \alpha}{\sin \alpha} \stackrel{?}{=} \cot \alpha$

$\cot \alpha = \cot \alpha$

14. $\dfrac{\sin \alpha}{1 - \cos \alpha} + \dfrac{1 - \cos \alpha}{\sin \alpha} \stackrel{?}{=} 2 \csc \alpha$

$\dfrac{\sin \alpha}{\sin \alpha} \cdot \dfrac{\sin \alpha}{1 - \cos \alpha} + \dfrac{1 - \cos \alpha}{1 - \cos \alpha} \cdot \dfrac{1 - \cos \alpha}{\sin \alpha} \stackrel{?}{=} 2 \csc \alpha$

$\dfrac{\sin^2 \alpha}{\sin \alpha\,(1 - \cos \alpha)} + \dfrac{1 - 2\cos \alpha + \cos^2 \alpha}{\sin \alpha\,(1 - \cos \alpha)} \stackrel{?}{=} 2 \csc \alpha$

$\dfrac{\sin^2 \alpha + \cos^2 \alpha + 1 - 2\cos \alpha}{\sin \alpha\,(1 - \cos)} \stackrel{?}{=} 2 \csc \alpha$

$\dfrac{2 - 2\cos \alpha}{\sin \alpha\,(1 - \cos \alpha)} \stackrel{?}{=} 2 \csc \alpha$

$\dfrac{2(1 - \cos \alpha)}{\sin \alpha\,(1 - \cos \alpha)} \stackrel{?}{=} 2\csc \alpha$

$\dfrac{2}{\sin \alpha} \stackrel{?}{=} 2 \csc \alpha$

$2 \csc \alpha = 2 \csc \alpha$

15. $\dfrac{\sin \theta}{\sec \theta} \stackrel{?}{=} \dfrac{1}{\tan \theta + \cot \theta}$

$\dfrac{\sin \theta}{\sec \theta} \stackrel{?}{=} \dfrac{1}{\dfrac{\sin \theta}{\cos \theta} + \dfrac{\cos \theta}{\sin \theta}}$

$\dfrac{\sin \theta}{\sec \theta} \stackrel{?}{=} \dfrac{1}{\dfrac{\sin^2 \theta + \cos^2 \theta}{\sin \theta \cos \theta}}$

$\dfrac{\sin \theta}{\sec \theta} \stackrel{?}{=} \dfrac{\sin \theta \cos \theta}{\sin^2 \theta + \cos^2 \theta}$

$\dfrac{\sin \theta}{\sec \theta} \stackrel{?}{=} \dfrac{\sin \theta \cos \theta}{1}$

$\dfrac{\sin \theta}{\sec \theta} = \dfrac{\sin \theta}{\sec \theta}$

16. $$\frac{1-\cos x}{\sin x} \stackrel{?}{=} \frac{\sin x}{1+\cos x}$$
$$\frac{1-\cos x}{\sin x} \cdot \frac{1+\cos x}{1+\cos x} \stackrel{?}{=} \frac{\sin x}{1+\cos x}$$
$$\frac{1-\cos^2 x}{\sin x(1+\cos x)} \stackrel{?}{=} \frac{\sin x}{1+\cos x}$$
$$\frac{\sin^2 x}{\sin x(1+\cos x)} \stackrel{?}{=} \frac{\sin x}{1+\cos x}$$
$$\frac{\sin x}{1+\cos x} = \frac{\sin x}{1+\cos x}$$

17. $$\frac{\sec\theta+1}{\tan\theta} \stackrel{?}{=} \frac{\tan\theta}{\sec\theta-1}$$
$$\frac{\sec\theta+1}{\tan\theta} \stackrel{?}{=} \frac{\tan\theta}{\sec\theta-1} \cdot \frac{\sec\theta+1}{\sec\theta+1}$$
$$\frac{\sec\theta+1}{\tan\theta} \stackrel{?}{=} \frac{\tan\theta \cdot (\sec\theta+1)}{\sec^2\theta-1}$$
$$\frac{\sec\theta+1}{\tan\theta} \stackrel{?}{=} \frac{\tan\theta \cdot (\sec\theta+1)}{\tan^2\theta}$$
$$\frac{\sec\theta+1}{\tan\theta} = \frac{\sec\theta+1}{\tan\theta}$$

18. $$\frac{1-\cos x}{1+\cos x} \stackrel{?}{=} (\csc x - \cot x)^2$$
$$\frac{1-\cos x}{1+\cos x} \stackrel{?}{=} \csc^2 x - 2\cot x \csc x + \cot^2 x$$
$$\frac{1-\cos x}{1+\cos x} \stackrel{?}{=} \frac{1}{\sin^2 x} - 2 \cdot \frac{\cos x}{\sin x} \cdot \frac{1}{\sin x} + \frac{\cos^2 x}{\sin^2 x}$$
$$\frac{1-\cos x}{1+\cos x} \stackrel{?}{=} \frac{1}{\sin^2 x} - \frac{2\cos x}{\sin^2 x} + \frac{\cos^2 x}{\sin^2 x}$$
$$\frac{1-\cos x}{1+\cos x} \stackrel{?}{=} \frac{1-2\cos x+\cos^2 x}{\sin^2 x}$$
$$\frac{1-\cos x}{1+\cos x} \stackrel{?}{=} \frac{1-\cos x+\cos^2 x-\cos x}{\sin^2 x}$$
$$\frac{1-\cos x}{1+\cos x} \stackrel{?}{=} \frac{1-\cos x+\cos x(\cos x-1)}{1-\cos^2 x}$$
$$\frac{1-\cos x}{1+\cos x} \stackrel{?}{=} \frac{(1-\cos x)-\cos x(1-\cos x)}{(1-\cos x)(1+\cos x)}$$
$$\frac{1-\cos x}{1+\cos x} \stackrel{?}{=} \frac{(1-\cos x)(1-\cos x)}{(1-\cos x)(1+\cos x)}$$
$$\frac{1-\cos x}{1+\cos x} = \frac{1-\cos x}{1+\cos x}$$

19. $$\cos^2 x + \tan^2 x \cos^2 x \stackrel{?}{=} 1$$
$$\cos^2 x + \frac{\sin^2 x}{\cos^2 x} \cdot \cos^2 x \stackrel{?}{=} 1$$
$$\cos^2 x + \sin^2 x \stackrel{?}{=} 1$$
$$1 = 1$$

20. $$\frac{\cot\theta+\csc\theta}{\sin\theta+\tan\theta} \stackrel{?}{=} \cot\theta\csc\theta$$
$$\frac{\frac{\cos\theta}{\sin\theta}+\frac{1}{\sin\theta}}{\sin\theta+\frac{\sin\theta}{\cos\theta}} \stackrel{?}{=} \cot\theta\csc\theta$$
$$\frac{\frac{\cos\theta+1}{\sin\theta}}{\frac{\sin\theta\cos\theta+\sin\theta}{\cos\theta}} \stackrel{?}{=} \cot\theta\csc\theta$$
$$\frac{\frac{\cos\theta+1}{\sin\theta}}{\frac{\sin\theta(\cos\theta+1)}{\cos\theta}} \stackrel{?}{=} \cot\theta\csc\theta$$
$$\frac{\cos\theta+1}{\sin\theta} \cdot \frac{\cos\theta}{\sin\theta(\cos\theta+1)} \stackrel{?}{=} \cot\theta\csc\theta$$
$$\frac{\cos\theta}{\sin\theta} \cdot \frac{1}{\sin\theta} \stackrel{?}{=} \cot\theta\csc\theta$$
$$\cot\theta\csc\theta = \cot\theta\csc\theta$$

21. $$\frac{1+\tan^2\theta}{\csc^2\theta} \stackrel{?}{=} \tan^2\theta$$
$$\frac{\sec^2\theta}{\csc^2\theta} \stackrel{?}{=} \tan^2\theta$$
$$\frac{\frac{1}{\cos^2\theta}}{\frac{1}{\sin^2\theta}} \stackrel{?}{=} \tan^2\theta$$
$$\frac{1}{\cos^2\theta} \cdot \sin^2\theta \stackrel{?}{=} \tan^2\theta$$
$$\tan^2\theta = \tan^2\theta$$

22. $$\frac{1+\sin x}{\sin x} \stackrel{?}{=} \frac{\cot^2 x}{\csc x-1}$$
$$\frac{1+\sin x}{\sin x} \stackrel{?}{=} \frac{\cot^2 x}{\csc x-1} \cdot \frac{\csc x+1}{\csc x+1}$$
$$\frac{1+\sin x}{\sin x} \stackrel{?}{=} \frac{\cot^2 x(\csc x+1)}{\csc^2 x-1}$$
$$\frac{1+\sin x}{\sin x} \stackrel{?}{=} \frac{\cot^2 x(\csc x+1)}{\cot^2 x}$$
$$\frac{1+\sin x}{\sin x} \stackrel{?}{=} \csc x+1$$
$$\frac{1+\sin x}{\sin x} \stackrel{?}{=} \frac{1}{\sin x}+\frac{\sin x}{\sin x}$$
$$\frac{1+\sin x}{\sin x} = \frac{1+\sin x}{\sin x}$$

23. $$\frac{\cos y}{1+\sin y}+\frac{\cos y}{1-\sin y} \stackrel{?}{=} 2\sec y$$
$$\frac{\cos y}{1+\sin y} \cdot \frac{1-\sin y}{1-\sin y}+\frac{\cos y}{1-\sin y} \cdot \frac{1+\sin y}{1+\sin y} \stackrel{?}{=} 2\sec y$$
$$\frac{\cos y(1-\sin y)+\cos y(1+\sin y)}{(1+\sin y)(1-\sin y)} \stackrel{?}{=} 2\sec y$$
$$\frac{\cos y-\sin y\cos y+\cos y+\sin y\cos y}{1-\sin^2 y} \stackrel{?}{=} 2\sec y$$
$$\frac{2\cos y}{\cos^2 y} \stackrel{?}{=} 2\sec y$$
$$\frac{2}{\cos y} \stackrel{?}{=} 2\sec y$$
$$2\sec y = 2\sec y$$

24. $$\cos^4\theta-\sin^4\theta \stackrel{?}{=} \cos^2\theta-\sin^2\theta$$
$$(\cos^2\theta-\sin^2\theta)(\cos^2\theta+\sin^2\theta) \stackrel{?}{=} \cos^2\theta-\sin^2\theta$$
$$(\cos^2\theta-\sin^2\theta)\cdot 1 \stackrel{?}{=} \cos^2\theta-\sin^2\theta$$
$$\cos^2\theta-\sin^2\theta = \cos^2\theta-\sin^2\theta$$

25. $$\cot x(\cot x+\tan x) \stackrel{?}{=} \csc^2 x$$
$$\cot^2 x+\cot x\tan x \stackrel{?}{=} \csc^2 x$$
$$\csc^2 x-1+\frac{\sin x}{\cos x}\cdot\frac{\cos x}{\sin x} \stackrel{?}{=} \csc^2 x$$
$$\csc^2 x-1+1 \stackrel{?}{=} \csc^2 x$$
$$\csc^2 x = \csc^2 x$$

26. $$\frac{\tan^2 x}{\sec x-1} \stackrel{?}{=} 1+\frac{1}{\cos x}$$
$$\frac{\tan^2 x}{\sec x-1}\cdot\frac{\sec x+1}{\sec x+1} \stackrel{?}{=} 1+\frac{1}{\cos x}$$
$$\frac{\tan^2 x(\sec x+1)}{\sec^2 x-1} \stackrel{?}{=} 1+\frac{1}{\cos x}$$
$$\frac{\tan^2 x(\sec x+1)}{\tan^2 x} \stackrel{?}{=} 1+\frac{1}{\cos x}$$
$$\sec x+1 \stackrel{?}{=} 1+\frac{1}{\cos x}$$
$$1+\frac{1}{\cos x} = 1+\frac{1}{\cos x}$$

27. $$\frac{1+\tan\alpha}{1+\cot\alpha} \stackrel{?}{=} \frac{\sin\alpha}{\cos\alpha}$$
$$\frac{1+\frac{\sin\alpha}{\cos\alpha}}{1+\frac{\cos\alpha}{\sin\alpha}} \stackrel{?}{=} \frac{\sin\alpha}{\cos\alpha}$$
$$\frac{\frac{\sin\alpha+\cos\alpha}{\cos\alpha}}{\frac{\sin\alpha+\cos\alpha}{\sin\alpha}} \stackrel{?}{=} \frac{\sin\alpha}{\cos\alpha}$$
$$\frac{\sin\alpha+\cos\alpha}{\cos\alpha}\cdot\frac{\sin\alpha}{\sin\alpha+\cos\alpha} \stackrel{?}{=} \frac{\sin\alpha}{\cos\alpha}$$
$$\frac{\sin\alpha}{\cos\alpha} = \frac{\sin\alpha}{\cos\alpha}$$

28. $$\sin\theta+\cos\theta \stackrel{?}{=} \frac{1+\tan\theta}{\sec\theta}$$
$$\sin\theta+\cos\theta \stackrel{?}{=} \frac{1+\frac{\sin\theta}{\cos\theta}}{\frac{1}{\cos\theta}}$$
$$\sin\theta+\cos\theta \stackrel{?}{=} \frac{\frac{\sin\theta+\cos\theta}{\cos\theta}}{\frac{1}{\cos\theta}}$$
$$\sin\theta+\cos\theta \stackrel{?}{=} \frac{\sin\theta+\cos\theta}{\cos\theta}\cdot\cos\theta$$
$$\sin\theta+\cos\theta = \sin\theta+\cos\theta$$

29. $$1+\sec^2 x\sin^2 x \stackrel{?}{=} \sec^2 x$$
$$1+\frac{1}{\cos^2 x}\cdot\sin^2 x \stackrel{?}{=} \sec^2 x$$
$$1+\tan^2 x \stackrel{?}{=} \sec^2 x$$
$$\sec^2 x = \sec^2 x$$

30. See students' work.

31. \$10.25 + \$7.45 = \$17.70
\$17.70 × 2 = \$35.40
\$35.40 × 2 = \$70.80
\$70.80 + \$15.00 = \$85.80
The amount of Estrella's paycheck was \$85.80.

32a. $$\frac{v_0^2\tan^2\theta}{2g\sec^2\theta} \stackrel{?}{=} \frac{v_0^2\sin^2\theta}{2g}$$
$$\frac{v_0^2\left(\frac{\sin^2\theta}{\cos^2\theta}\right)}{2g\left(\frac{1}{\cos^2\theta}\right)} \stackrel{?}{=} \frac{v_0^2\sin^2\theta}{2g}$$
$$\frac{v_0^2\sin^2\theta}{2g} = \frac{v_0^2\sin^2\theta}{2g}$$

32b. $$h = \frac{v_0^2\sin^2\theta}{2g}$$
$$= \frac{47^2\sin^2 50°}{2(9.8)}$$
$$\approx 66$$
No, its maximum height will be about 66 meters.

32c. $$h = \frac{v_0^2\sin^2\theta}{2g}$$
$$50 = \frac{v_0^2\sin^2 45°}{2(9.8)}$$
$$v_0^2 = \frac{2(9.8)(50)}{\sin^2 45}$$
$$v_0^2 \approx 1960$$
$$v_0 \approx 44$$
about 44 meters per second

33. $$\frac{\sec\alpha}{\sin\alpha} - \frac{\sin\alpha}{\cos\alpha} = \frac{\frac{1}{\cos\alpha}}{\sin\alpha}$$
$$= \frac{1}{\cos\alpha}\cdot\frac{1}{\sin\alpha} - \frac{\sin\alpha}{\cos\alpha}$$
$$= \frac{1}{\cos\alpha\sin\alpha} - \frac{\sin\alpha}{\cos\alpha}$$
$$= \frac{1}{\cos\alpha\sin\alpha} - \frac{\sin\alpha}{\cos\alpha}\cdot\frac{\sin\alpha}{\sin\alpha}$$
$$= \frac{1-\sin^2\alpha}{\cos\alpha\sin\alpha}$$
$$= \frac{\cos^2\alpha}{\cos\alpha\sin\alpha}$$
$$= \frac{\cos\alpha}{\sin\alpha}$$
$$= \cot\alpha$$

34. $$\cos\frac{17\pi}{3} = \cos\left(\frac{17\pi}{3} - \frac{12\pi}{3}\right)$$
$$= \cos\frac{5\pi}{3}$$
$$= \frac{1}{2}$$

35. $P(3 \text{ and } 4) = \frac{2}{36}$ or $\frac{1}{18}$

36. $$r = \frac{6}{12} = \frac{1}{2}$$
$$S = \frac{a_1}{1-r}$$
$$= \frac{12}{1-\frac{1}{2}}$$
$$= \frac{12}{\frac{1}{2}}$$
$$= 12(2)$$
$$= 24$$

37. $$(x^2y^2)^2x^3y^3 = (x^2)^2(y^2)^2x^3y^3$$
$$= x^4\cdot y^4\cdot x^3\cdot y^3$$
$$= x^7y^7$$

38. $$h(-2.1) = [3(-2.1) - 1]$$
$$= [-6.3 - 1]$$
$$= [-7.3]$$
$$= -8$$

Page 846 Self Test

1. amplitude: $|1|$ or 1
period: $\frac{2\pi}{|4|}$ or $\frac{\pi}{2}$
$\frac{360°}{|4|}$ or 90°

2. amplitude: $|3|$ or 3
period: $\frac{2\pi}{|1|}$ or 2π
$\frac{360°}{|1|}$ or 360°

3. amplitude: none
period: $\frac{\pi}{\left|\frac{1}{5}\right|}$ or 5π
$\frac{180°}{\left|\frac{1}{5}\right|}$ or 900°

4.

θ	0°	90°	180°	270°	360°
cos θ	1	0	−1	0	1
$\frac{1}{2}\cos\theta$	$\frac{1}{2}$	0	$-\frac{1}{2}$	0	$\frac{1}{2}$

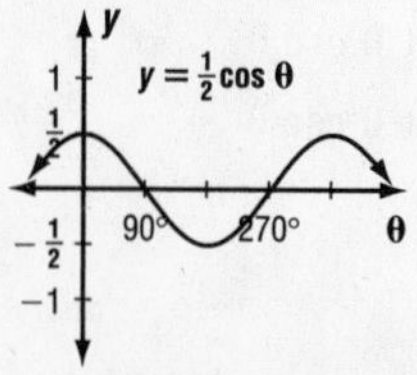

amplitude: $\left|\frac{1}{2}\right|$ or $\frac{1}{2}$
period: $\frac{360°}{|1|}$ or 360°

5.

θ	0°	90°	180°	270°	360°
sin θ	0	1	0	−1	0
5 sin θ	0	5	0	−5	0

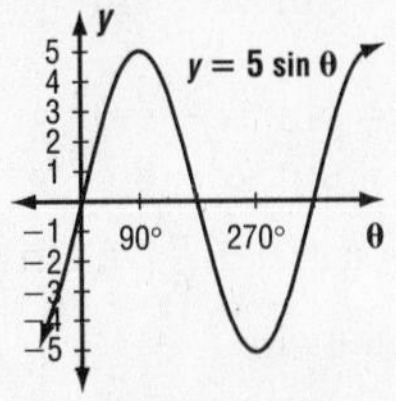

amplitude: $|5|$ or 5
period: $\frac{360°}{|1|}$ or 360°

6. $1 + \cot^2 \theta = \csc^2 \theta$
$1 + \left(-\frac{2}{5}\right)^2 = \csc^2 \theta$
$1 + \frac{4}{25} = \csc^2 \theta$
$\frac{29}{25} = \csc^2 \theta$
$\frac{\sqrt{29}}{5} = \csc \theta$

7. $\cos^2 \alpha + \sin^2 \alpha = 1$
$\sin^2 \alpha = 1 - \cos^2 \alpha$
$\sin^2 \alpha = 1 - \left(-\frac{1}{2}\right)^2$
$\sin^2 \alpha = 1 - \frac{1}{4}$
$\sin^2 \alpha = \frac{3}{4}$
$\sin \alpha = \pm\frac{\sqrt{3}}{2}$

$\tan \alpha = \frac{\sin \alpha}{\cos \alpha}$
$\tan \alpha = \frac{\frac{\pm\sqrt{3}}{2}}{-\frac{1}{2}}$
$\tan \alpha = \frac{\pm\sqrt{3}}{2} \cdot 2$
$\tan \alpha = \pm\sqrt{3}$

8. $\sec \theta - \tan \theta \sin \theta \stackrel{?}{=} \cos \theta$
$\frac{1}{\cos \theta} - \frac{\sin \theta}{\cos \theta} \cdot \sin \theta \stackrel{?}{=} \cos \theta$
$\frac{1 - \sin^2 \theta}{\cos \theta} \stackrel{?}{=} \cos \theta$
$\frac{\cos^2 \theta}{\cos \theta} \stackrel{?}{=} \cos \theta$
$\cos \theta = \cos \theta$

9. $(1 - \sin^2 \theta)(1 + \tan^2 \theta) \stackrel{?}{=} 1$
$\cos^2 \theta \left(1 + \frac{\sin^2 \theta}{\cos^2 \theta}\right) \stackrel{?}{=} 1$
$\cos^2 \theta + \sin^2 \theta \stackrel{?}{=} 1$
$1 = 1$

10. Let x = one number and y = the other number.
$x + y = 4$
$xy = 7$

$\frac{1}{x} + \frac{1}{y} = \frac{y}{y} \cdot \frac{1}{x} + \frac{x}{x} \cdot \frac{1}{y}$
$= \frac{y}{xy} + \frac{x}{xy}$
$= \frac{x + y}{xy}$
$= \frac{4}{7}$

The sum of the reciprocals is $\frac{4}{7}$.

14-4 Sum and Difference of Angles Formulas

Page 850 Check for Understanding

1. No; a counter example is:
$\cos (30° + 45°) \stackrel{?}{=} \cos 30° + \cos 45°$
$= \frac{\sqrt{3}}{2} + \frac{\sqrt{2}}{2}$
$= 1.5731$
Since a cosine value cannot be greater than 1, this statement must be false.

2. See students' work.
$\sin 15° = \sin (45° - 30°)$
$= \sin 45° \cos 30° - \cos 45° \sin 30°$
$= \frac{\sqrt{2}}{2} \cdot \frac{\sqrt{3}}{2} - \frac{\sqrt{2}}{2} \cdot \frac{1}{2}$
$= \frac{\sqrt{6}}{4} - \frac{\sqrt{2}}{4}$
$= \frac{\sqrt{6} - \sqrt{2}}{4}$

3. $\cos 75° = \cos (30° + 45°)$
$= \cos 30° \cos 45° - \sin 30° \sin 45°$
$= \frac{\sqrt{3}}{2} \cdot \frac{\sqrt{2}}{2} - \frac{1}{2} \cdot \frac{\sqrt{2}}{2}$
$= \frac{\sqrt{6} - \sqrt{2}}{4}$

4. $\sin 165° = \sin (120° + 45°)$
$= \sin 120° \cos 45° + \cos 120° \sin 45°$
$= \frac{\sqrt{3}}{2} \cdot \frac{\sqrt{2}}{2} + \left(-\frac{1}{2}\right)\left(\frac{\sqrt{2}}{2}\right)$
$= \frac{\sqrt{6} - \sqrt{2}}{4}$

5. $\cos 255° = \cos (210° + 45°)$
$= \cos 210° \cos 45° - \sin 210° \sin 45°$
$= \left(-\frac{\sqrt{3}}{2}\right)\left(\frac{\sqrt{2}}{2}\right) - \left(-\frac{1}{2}\right)\left(\frac{\sqrt{2}}{2}\right)$
$= -\frac{\sqrt{6}}{4} + \frac{\sqrt{2}}{4}$
$= \frac{\sqrt{2} - \sqrt{6}}{4}$

6. $\cos 80° \cos 20° + \sin 80° \sin 20° = \cos (80° - 20°)$
$= \cos 60°$
$= \frac{1}{2}$

7. $\sin (270° - \theta) \stackrel{?}{=} -\cos \theta$
$\sin 270° \cos \theta - \cos 270° \sin \theta \stackrel{?}{=} -\cos \theta$
$-1 \cos \theta - 0 \stackrel{?}{=} -\cos \theta$
$-\cos \theta = -\cos \theta$

8. $\cos (90° + \theta) \stackrel{?}{=} -\sin \theta$
$\cos 90° \cos \theta - \sin 90° \sin \theta \stackrel{?}{=} -\sin \theta$
$0 - 1 \sin \theta \stackrel{?}{=} -\sin \theta$
$-\sin \theta = -\sin \theta$

9. $\sin (x + 30°) + \cos(x + 60°) \stackrel{?}{=} \cos x$
$\sin x \sin 30° + \cos x \cos 30° +$
$\cos x \cos 60° - \sin x \sin 60° \stackrel{?}{=} \cos x$
$\frac{\sqrt{3}}{2} \sin x + \frac{1}{2} \cos x + \frac{1}{2} \cos x -$
$\frac{\sqrt{3}}{2} x \sin \stackrel{?}{=} \cos x$
$\frac{1}{2} \cos x + \frac{1}{2} \cos x \stackrel{?}{=} \cos x$
$\cos x = \cos x$

10. When the difference formula is used, roundings occur in the intermediate steps. These produce small errors, which accumulate.

Pages 850–852 Exercises

11. $\sin 285° = \sin (240° + 45°)$
$= \sin 240° \cos 45° + \cos 240° \sin 45°$
$= -\frac{\sqrt{3}}{2} \frac{\sqrt{2}}{2} + \left(-\frac{1}{2}\right)\left(\frac{\sqrt{2}}{2}\right)$
$= \frac{-\sqrt{6} - \sqrt{2}}{4}$

12. $\sin 75° = \sin (30° + 45°)$
$= \sin 30° \cos 45° + \cos 30° \sin 45°$
$= \frac{1}{2} \cdot \frac{\sqrt{2}}{2} + \frac{\sqrt{3}}{2} \cdot \frac{\sqrt{2}}{2}$
$= \frac{\sqrt{2} + \sqrt{6}}{4}$

13. $\cos 195° = \cos(60° + 135°)$
$= \cos 60° \cos 135° - \sin 60° \sin 135°$
$= \frac{1}{2}\left(-\frac{\sqrt{2}}{2}\right) - \left(\frac{\sqrt{3}}{2}\right)\left(\frac{\sqrt{2}}{2}\right)$
$= -\frac{\sqrt{2}}{4} - \frac{\sqrt{6}}{4}$
$= \frac{-\sqrt{6} - \sqrt{2}}{4}$

14. $\cos 105° = \cos(60° + 45°)$
$= \cos 60° \cos 45° - \sin 60° \sin 45°$
$= \frac{1}{2} \cdot \frac{\sqrt{2}}{2} - \frac{\sqrt{3}}{2} \cdot \frac{\sqrt{2}}{2}$
$= \frac{\sqrt{2} - \sqrt{6}}{4}$

15. $\cos 345° = \cos(300° + 45°)$
$= \cos 300° \cos 45° - \sin 300° \sin 45°$
$= \frac{1}{2} \cdot \frac{\sqrt{2}}{2} - \left(-\frac{\sqrt{3}}{2}\right) \cdot \frac{\sqrt{2}}{2}$
$= \frac{\sqrt{2} + \sqrt{6}}{4}$

16. $\cos 165° = \cos(120° + 45°)$
$= \cos 120° \cos 45° - \sin 120° \sin 45°$
$= -\frac{1}{2} \cdot \frac{\sqrt{2}}{2} - \frac{\sqrt{3}}{2} \cdot \frac{\sqrt{2}}{2}$
$= \frac{-\sqrt{2} - \sqrt{6}}{4}$

17. $\sin 65° \cos 35° - \cos 65° \sin 35° = \sin(65° - 35°)$
$= \sin 30°$
$= \frac{1}{2}$

18. $\sin 40° \cos 20° + \cos 40° \sin 20° = \sin(40° + 20°)$
$= \sin 60°$
$= \frac{\sqrt{3}}{2}$

19. $\cos 25° \cos 5° - \sin 25° \sin 5° = \cos(25° + 5°)$
$= \cos 30°$
$= \frac{\sqrt{3}}{2}$

20. $\cos(270° - \theta) \stackrel{?}{=} -\sin\theta$
$\cos 270° \cos\theta + \sin 270° \sin\theta \stackrel{?}{=} -\sin\theta$
$0 + (-1 \cdot \sin\theta) \stackrel{?}{=} -\sin\theta$
$-\sin\theta = -\sin\theta$

21. $\sin(90° + \theta) \stackrel{?}{=} \cos\theta$
$\sin 90° \cos\theta + \cos 90° \sin\theta \stackrel{?}{=} \cos\theta$
$1 \cdot \cos\theta + 0 \stackrel{?}{=} \cos\theta$
$\cos\theta = \cos\theta$

22. $\sin(180° + \theta) \stackrel{?}{=} -\sin\theta$
$\sin 180° \cos\theta + \cos 180° \sin\theta \stackrel{?}{=} -\sin\theta$
$0 + (-1 \cdot \sin\theta) \stackrel{?}{=} -\sin\theta$
$-\sin\theta = -\sin\theta$

23. $\sin(90° - \theta) \stackrel{?}{=} \cos\theta$
$\sin 90° \cos\theta - \cos 90° \sin\theta \stackrel{?}{=} \cos\theta$
$1 \cdot \cos\theta - 0 \stackrel{?}{=} \cos\theta$
$\cos\theta = \cos\theta$

24. $\sin(60° + \theta) + \sin(60° - \theta) \stackrel{?}{=} \sqrt{3}\cos\theta$
$\sin 60° \cos\theta + \cos 60° \sin\theta +$
$\sin 60° \cos\theta - \cos 60° \sin\theta \stackrel{?}{=} \sqrt{3}\cos\theta$
$\frac{\sqrt{3}}{2}\cos\theta + \frac{1}{2}\sin\theta + \frac{\sqrt{3}}{2}\cos\theta - \frac{1}{2}\sin\theta \stackrel{?}{=} \sqrt{3}\cos\theta$
$\sqrt{3}\cos\theta = \sqrt{3}\cos\theta$

25. $\sin(x + y)\sin(x - y) \stackrel{?}{=} \sin^2 x - \sin^2 y$
$(\sin x \cos y + \cos x \sin y)$
$(\sin x \cos y - \cos x \sin y) \stackrel{?}{=} \sin^2 x - \sin^2 y$
$\sin^2 x \cos^2 y - \cos^2 x \sin^2 y \stackrel{?}{=} \sin^2 x - \sin^2 y$
$\sin^2 x(1 - \sin^2 y) -$
$(1 - \sin^2 x)\sin^2 y \stackrel{?}{=} \sin^2 x - \sin^2 y$
$\sin^2 x - \sin^2 x \sin^2 y -$
$\sin^2 y + \sin^2 x \sin^2 y \stackrel{?}{=} \sin^2 x - \sin^2 y$
$\sin^2 x - \sin^2 y = \sin^2 x - \sin^2 y$

26. $\sin\left(\theta + \frac{\pi}{3}\right) - \cos\left(\theta + \frac{\pi}{6}\right) \stackrel{?}{=} \sin\theta$
$\sin\theta \cos\frac{\pi}{3} + \cos\theta \sin\frac{\pi}{3} -$
$\cos\theta \cos\frac{\pi}{6} + \sin\theta \sin\frac{\pi}{6} \stackrel{?}{=} \sin\theta$
$\frac{1}{2}\sin\theta + \frac{\sqrt{3}}{2}\cos\theta - \frac{\sqrt{3}}{2}\cos\theta + \frac{1}{2}\sin\theta \stackrel{?}{=} \sin\theta$
$\frac{1}{2}\sin\theta + \frac{1}{2}\sin\theta \stackrel{?}{=} \sin\theta$
$\sin\theta = \sin\theta$

27. $\tan(225° - 120°) = \frac{\tan 225° - \tan 120°}{1 + \tan 225° \tan 120°}$
$= \frac{1 - (-\sqrt{3})}{1 + (1)(-\sqrt{3})}$
$= \frac{(1 + \sqrt{3})}{(1 - \sqrt{3})} \frac{(1 + \sqrt{3})}{(1 + \sqrt{3})}$
$= \frac{1 + 2\sqrt{3} + 3}{1 - 3}$
$= \frac{4 + 2\sqrt{3}}{-2}$
$= -2 - \sqrt{3}$

28. $\tan(315° - 120°) = \frac{\tan 315° - \tan 120°}{1 + \tan 315° \tan 120°}$
$= \frac{-1 - (-\sqrt{3})}{1 + (-1)(-\sqrt{3})}$
$= \frac{-1 + \sqrt{3}}{1 + \sqrt{3}}$
$= \frac{(-1 + \sqrt{3})}{(1 + \sqrt{3})} \frac{(1 - \sqrt{3})}{(1 - \sqrt{3})}$
$= \frac{-1 + 2\sqrt{3} - 3}{1 - 3}$
$= \frac{-4 + 2\sqrt{3}}{-2}$
$= 2 - \sqrt{3}$

29. $\tan(30° + 30°) = \frac{\tan 30° + \tan 30°}{1 - \tan 30° \tan 30°}$
$= \frac{\frac{\sqrt{3}}{3} + \frac{\sqrt{3}}{3}}{1 - \frac{\sqrt{3}}{3}\left(\frac{\sqrt{3}}{3}\right)}$
$= \frac{\frac{2\sqrt{3}}{3}}{1 - \frac{1}{3}}$
$= \frac{\frac{2\sqrt{3}}{3}}{\frac{2}{3}} = \sqrt{3}$

30. $\tan 195° = \tan(315° - 120°)$
$= \frac{\tan 315° - \tan 120°}{1 + \tan 315° \tan 120°}$
$= \frac{-1 - (-\sqrt{3})}{1 + (-1)(-\sqrt{3})}$
$= \frac{-1 + \sqrt{3}}{1 + \sqrt{3}}$
$= \frac{(-1 + \sqrt{3})}{(1 + \sqrt{3})} \frac{(1 - \sqrt{3})}{(1 - \sqrt{3})}$
$= \frac{-1 + 2\sqrt{3} - 3}{1 - 3}$
$= \frac{-4 + 2\sqrt{3}}{-2} = 2 - \sqrt{3}$

31. 90° **32.** −90° or 270°

33. 90° **34.** 180°

35. $\tan(\alpha + \beta) = \frac{\sin(\alpha + \beta)}{\cos(\alpha + \beta)}$

$= \frac{\sin\alpha\cos\beta + \cos\alpha\sin\beta}{\cos\alpha\cos\beta - \sin\alpha\sin\beta}$

$= \frac{\frac{\sin\alpha\cos\beta}{\cos\alpha\cos\beta} + \frac{\cos\alpha\sin\beta}{\cos\alpha\cos\beta}}{\frac{\cos\alpha\cos\beta}{\cos\alpha\cos\beta} - \frac{\sin\alpha\sin\beta}{\cos\alpha\cos\beta}}$

$= \frac{\tan\alpha + \tan\beta}{1 - \tan\alpha\tan\beta}$

36a. $\sin(113.5° - 61.2°) \approx 0.9171 \cos 61.2° + 0.3987 \sin 61.2°$
$\approx 0.9171 \cdot 0.4818 + 0.3987 \cdot 0.8763$
$\approx 0.4418 + 0.3494$
≈ 0.7912; 0.7912 E

36b. $\sin(113.5° - 44.8°) \approx 0.9171 \cos 44.8° + 0.3987 \sin 44.8°$
$\approx 0.9171 \cdot 0.7096 + 0.3987 \cdot 0.7046$
$\approx 0.6508 + 0.2809$
≈ 0.9317; 0.9317 E

36c. $\sin(113.5° - 24.6°) \approx 0.9171 \cos 24.6° + 0.3987 \sin 24.6°$
$\approx 0.9171 \cdot 0.9092 + 0.3987 \cdot 0.4163$
$\approx 0.8338 + 0.1660$
≈ 0.9998; 0.9998 E

36d. See students' work.

37a. $\sin(113.5° + 32.8°) \approx 0.9171 \cos 32.8° - 0.3987 \sin 32.8°$
$\approx 0.9171 \cdot 0.8406 - 0.3987 \cdot 0.5417$
$\approx 0.7709 - 0.2160$
≈ 0.5549; 0.5549 E

37b. $\sin(113.5° + 45.5°) \approx 0.9171 \cos 45.5° - 0.3987 \sin 45.5°$
$\approx 0.9171 \cdot 0.7009 - 0.3987 \cdot 0.7133$
$\approx 0.6428 - 0.2844$
≈ 0.3584; 0.3584 E

37c. $\sin(113.5° + 0.0°) \approx 0.9171 \cos 0.0° - 0.3987 \sin 0.0°$
$\approx 0.9171 \cdot 1 - 0.3987 \cdot 0$
≈ 0.9171; 0.9171 E

38. $\sin 30° = \frac{x}{100}$

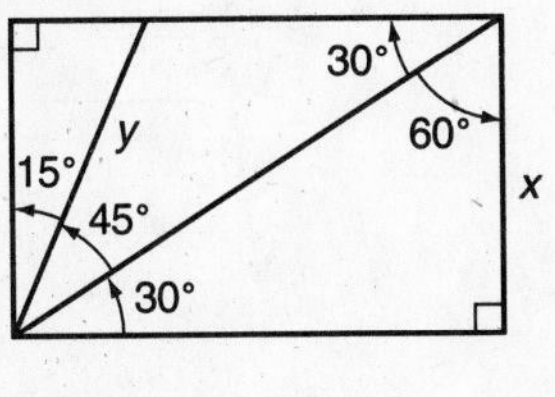

$x = 100 \sin 30°$
$= 50$

$\cos 15° = \frac{50}{y}$

$\cos(45° - 30°) = \frac{50}{y}$

$\cos 45° \cos 30° + \sin 45° \sin 30° = \frac{50}{y}$

$\frac{\sqrt{2}}{2} \cdot \frac{\sqrt{3}}{2} + \frac{\sqrt{2}}{2} \cdot \frac{1}{2} = \frac{50}{y}$

(Continued next column)

$\frac{\sqrt{6} + \sqrt{2}}{4} = \frac{50}{y}$

$(\sqrt{6} + \sqrt{2})y = 200$

$y = \frac{200}{(\sqrt{6} + \sqrt{2})} \cdot \frac{(\sqrt{6} - \sqrt{2})}{(\sqrt{6} - \sqrt{2})}$

$y = 50(\sqrt{6} - \sqrt{2})$

$y = 50\sqrt{6} - 50\sqrt{2}$

or about 51.8 yards

39. $\sin\theta \sec\theta \cot\theta \stackrel{?}{=} 1$

$\sin\theta \left(\frac{1}{\cos\theta}\right)\left(\frac{\cos\theta}{\sin\theta}\right) \stackrel{?}{=} 1$

$1 = 1$

40. $a^2 = b^2 + c^2 - 2bc \cos A$

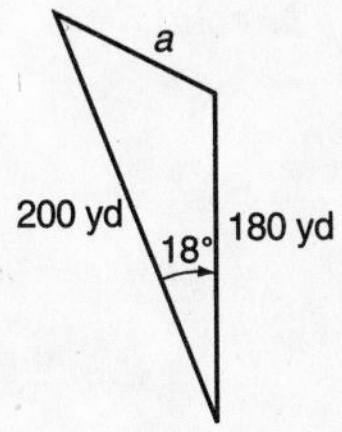

$a^2 = 180^2 + 200^2 - 2(180)(200) \cos 18°$

$a^2 \approx 3923.93$

$a \approx 63$; 63 yards

41. $P(\text{black card or ace}) = 1 - P(\text{not a black card or ace})$

$= 1 - \frac{24}{52}\left(\frac{23}{51}\right)$

$= \frac{2100}{2652}$ or $\frac{175}{221}$

42a. $\frac{0.50(0.08p)}{6} + \frac{0.50(0.08p)}{4}$

42b. $\frac{0.50(0.08p)}{6} + \frac{0.50(0.08p)}{4} = \frac{0.04p}{6} + \frac{0.04p}{4}$

$= \frac{0.08p}{12} + \frac{0.12p}{12}$

$= \frac{0.20p}{12}$ or $\frac{p}{60}$

42c. $\frac{0.04p}{6}$ or $\frac{p}{150}$

43.

x	$f(x)$
−2	$\frac{1}{2}$
−1	$\frac{1}{3}$
0	0
1	−1
2	undefined
3	3
4	2
5	$\frac{5}{3}$

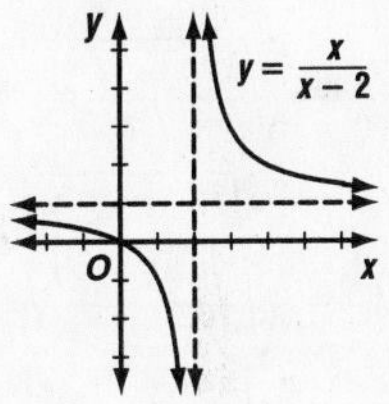

44.

2⌋	1	1	1	1	1
		2	6	14	30
	1	3	7	15	31

$f(2) = 31$

−1⌋	1	1	1	1	1
		−1	0	−1	0
	1	0	1	0	1

$f(-1) = 1$

45. $r + c \leq 60$
$r \geq 3c$

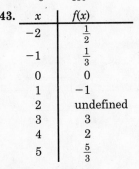

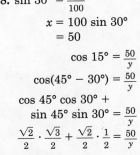

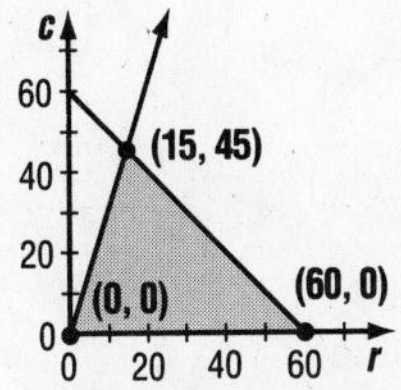

(r, c)	$4500r + 5000c$	$f(r, c)$
(0, 0)	4500(0) + 5000(0)	0
(60, 0)	4500(60) + 5000(0)	270,000
(15, 45)	4500(15) + 5000(45)	292,500

She should build 15 colonial and 45 ranch.

46. See students' work.

14-5 Double Angle and Half-Angle Formulas

Page 857 Check for Understanding

1. x will be in Quadrant II. Use the double-angle formula for sine knowing that $\sin x$ will be positive.

2. $\cos^2 x = 1 - \sin^2 x$
$\cos^2 x = 1 - \left(-\frac{9}{41}\right)^2$
$\cos^2 x = 1 - \frac{81}{1681}$
$\cos^2 x = \frac{1600}{1681}$
$\cos x = \frac{40}{41}$

$\sin \frac{x}{2} = \sqrt{\frac{1 - \frac{40}{41}}{2}}$
$= \sqrt{\frac{1}{82}}$
$= \frac{\sqrt{82}}{82}$

3. Jack is right only for small angles such as those he tested. The pattern fails for angles with much greater measure. For example, $\sin 90° = 1$ and $\sin 180° = 0$.

4. $\cos^2 x = 1 - \sin^2 x$
$\cos^2 x = 1 - \left(\frac{5}{13}\right)^2$
$\cos^2 x = \frac{144}{169}$
$\cos x = -\frac{12}{13}$

$\sin 2x = 2 \sin x \cos x$
$= 2\left(\frac{5}{13}\right)\left(-\frac{12}{13}\right)$
$= -\frac{120}{169}$

$\cos 2x = 1 - 2 \sin^2 x$
$= 1 - 2\left(\frac{5}{13}\right)^2$
$= 1 - 2\left(\frac{25}{169}\right)$
$= \frac{119}{169}$

$\sin \frac{x}{2} = \sqrt{\frac{1 - \cos x}{2}}$
$= \sqrt{\frac{1 - \left(-\frac{12}{13}\right)}{2}}$
$= \sqrt{\frac{25}{26}}$
$= \frac{5}{\sqrt{26}} \cdot \frac{\sqrt{26}}{\sqrt{26}}$
$= \frac{5\sqrt{26}}{26}$

$\cos \frac{x}{2} = \sqrt{\frac{1 + \cos x}{2}}$
$= \sqrt{\frac{1 + \left(-\frac{12}{13}\right)}{2}}$
$= \sqrt{\frac{1}{26}}$
$= \frac{\sqrt{26}}{26}$

5. $\sin^2 x = 1 - \cos^2 x$
$\sin^2 x = 1 - \left(\frac{1}{5}\right)^2$
$\sin^2 x = \frac{24}{25}$
$\sin x = -\frac{2\sqrt{6}}{5}$

$\sin 2x = 2 \sin x \cos x$
$= 2\left(-\frac{2\sqrt{6}}{5}\right)\left(\frac{1}{5}\right)$
$= -\frac{4\sqrt{6}}{25}$

$\cos 2x = 2 \cos^2 x - 1$
$= 2\left(\frac{1}{5}\right)^2 - 1$
$= -\frac{23}{25}$

$\sin \frac{x}{2} = \sqrt{\frac{1 - \cos x}{2}}$
$= \sqrt{\frac{1 - \frac{1}{5}}{2}}$
$= \sqrt{\frac{2}{5}}$
$= \frac{\sqrt{10}}{5}$

$\cos \frac{x}{2} = -\sqrt{\frac{1 + \cos x}{2}}$
$= -\sqrt{\frac{1 + \frac{1}{5}}{2}}$
$= -\sqrt{\frac{3}{5}}$
$= -\frac{\sqrt{15}}{5}$

6. $\cos \frac{\pi}{8} = \cos \frac{\frac{\pi}{4}}{2}$
$= \sqrt{\frac{1 + \cos \frac{\pi}{4}}{2}}$
$= \sqrt{\frac{1 + \frac{\sqrt{2}}{2}}{2}}$
$= \sqrt{\frac{2 + \sqrt{2}}{4}}$
$= \frac{\sqrt{2 + \sqrt{2}}}{2}$

7. $\sin 22\frac{1}{2}° = \sin \frac{45°}{2}$
$= \sqrt{\frac{1 - \cos 45°}{2}}$
$= \sqrt{\frac{1 - \frac{\sqrt{2}}{2}}{2}}$
$= \sqrt{\frac{2 - \sqrt{2}}{4}}$
$= \frac{\sqrt{2 - \sqrt{2}}}{2}$

8. $(\sin x + \cos x)^2 \stackrel{?}{=} 1 + \sin 2x$
$\sin^2 x + 2 \sin x \cos x + \cos^2 x \stackrel{?}{=} 1 + \sin 2x$
$\sin^2 x + \cos^2 x + 2 \sin x \cos x \stackrel{?}{=} 1 + \sin 2x$
$1 + 2 \sin x \cos x \stackrel{?}{=} 1 + \sin 2x$
$1 + \sin 2x = 1 + \sin 2x$

9. $\frac{1}{\sin x \cos x} - \frac{\cos x}{\sin x} \stackrel{?}{=} \tan x$
$\frac{1 - \cos^2 x}{\sin x \cos x} \stackrel{?}{=} \tan x$
$\frac{\sin^2 x}{\sin x \cos x} \stackrel{?}{=} \tan x$
$\tan x = \tan x$

10. $\sin \frac{\theta}{2} = \frac{1}{m}$
$\sin \frac{\theta}{2} = \frac{1}{1.4}$
$\sin \frac{\theta}{2} = 0.714286$
$\frac{\theta}{2} \approx 45.58$
$\theta \approx 91°$

Pages 857–859 Exercises

11. $\cos^2 x = 1 - \sin^2 x$
$\cos^2 x = 1 - \left(\frac{4}{5}\right)^2$
$\cos^2 x = \frac{9}{25}$
$\cos x = -\frac{3}{5}$

$\sin 2x = 2 \sin x \cos x$
$= 2\left(\frac{4}{5}\right)\left(-\frac{3}{5}\right)$
$= -\frac{24}{25}$

$\cos 2x = 1 - 2 \sin^2 x$
$= 1 - 2\left(\frac{4}{5}\right)^2$
$= -\frac{7}{25}$

$\sin \frac{x}{2} = \sqrt{\frac{1 - \cos x}{2}}$
$= \sqrt{\frac{1 - \left(-\frac{3}{5}\right)}{2}}$
$= \sqrt{\frac{4}{5}} \cdot \frac{\sqrt{5}}{\sqrt{5}}$
$= \frac{2\sqrt{5}}{5}$

$\cos \frac{x}{2} = \sqrt{\frac{1 + \cos x}{2}}$
$= \sqrt{\frac{1 + \left(-\frac{3}{5}\right)}{2}}$
$= \sqrt{\frac{1}{5}} \cdot \frac{\sqrt{5}}{\sqrt{5}}$
$= \frac{\sqrt{5}}{5}$

12. $\sin^2 x = 1 - \cos^2 x$

$\sin^2 x = 1 - \left(\frac{3}{5}\right)^2$

$\sin^2 x = \frac{16}{25}$

$\sin x = \frac{4}{5}$

$\sin 2x = 2 \sin x \cos x = 2\left(\frac{4}{5}\right)\left(\frac{3}{5}\right) = \frac{24}{25}$

$\cos 2x = 2\cos^2 x - 1 = 2\left(\frac{3}{5}\right)^2 - 1 = -\frac{7}{25}$

$\sin \frac{x}{2} = \sqrt{\frac{1 - \cos x}{2}} = \sqrt{\frac{1 - \left(\frac{3}{5}\right)}{2}} = \sqrt{\frac{1}{5}} \cdot \frac{\sqrt{5}}{\sqrt{5}} = \frac{\sqrt{5}}{5}$

$\cos \frac{x}{2} = \sqrt{\frac{1 + \cos x}{2}} = \sqrt{\frac{1 + \left(\frac{3}{5}\right)}{2}} = \sqrt{\frac{4}{5}} \cdot \frac{\sqrt{5}}{\sqrt{5}} = \frac{2\sqrt{5}}{5}$

13. $\sin^2 x = 1 - \cos^2 x$

$\sin^2 x = 1 - \left(-\frac{1}{3}\right)^2$

$\sin^2 x = \frac{8}{9}$

$\sin x = -\frac{2\sqrt{2}}{3}$

$\sin 2x = 2 \sin x \cos x = 2\left(-\frac{2\sqrt{2}}{3}\right)\left(-\frac{1}{3}\right) = \frac{4\sqrt{2}}{9}$

$\cos 2x = 2\cos^2 x - 1 = 2\left(-\frac{1}{3}\right)^2 - 1 = -\frac{7}{9}$

$\sin \frac{x}{2} = \sqrt{\frac{1 - \cos x}{2}} = \sqrt{\frac{1 - \left(-\frac{1}{3}\right)}{2}} = \sqrt{\frac{2}{3}} = \frac{\sqrt{6}}{3}$

$\cos \frac{x}{2} = \sqrt{\frac{1 + \cos x}{2}} = \sqrt{\frac{1 + \left(-\frac{1}{3}\right)}{2}} = \sqrt{\frac{1}{3}} \cdot \frac{\sqrt{3}}{\sqrt{3}} = -\frac{\sqrt{3}}{3}$

14. $\sin^2 x = 1 - \cos^2 x$

$\sin^2 x = 1 - \left(-\frac{2}{3}\right)^2$

$\sin^2 x = \frac{5}{9}$

$\sin x = -\frac{\sqrt{5}}{3}$

$\sin 2x = 2 \sin x \cos x = 2\left(-\frac{\sqrt{5}}{3}\right)\left(-\frac{2}{3}\right) = \frac{4\sqrt{5}}{9}$

$\cos 2x = 2\cos^2 x - 1 = 2\left(-\frac{2}{3}\right)^2 - 1 = -\frac{1}{9}$

$\sin \frac{x}{2} = \sqrt{\frac{1 - \cos x}{2}} = \sqrt{\frac{1 - \left(-\frac{2}{3}\right)}{2}} = \sqrt{\frac{5}{6}} \cdot \frac{\sqrt{6}}{\sqrt{6}} = \frac{\sqrt{30}}{6}$

$\cos \frac{x}{2} = \sqrt{\frac{1 + \cos x}{2}} = \sqrt{\frac{1 + \left(-\frac{2}{3}\right)}{2}} = \sqrt{\frac{1}{6}} \cdot \frac{\sqrt{6}}{\sqrt{6}} = -\frac{\sqrt{6}}{6}$

15. $\cos^2 x = 1 - \sin^2 x$

$\cos^2 x = 1 - \left(-\frac{3}{5}\right)^2$

$\cos^2 x = \frac{16}{25}$

$\cos x = -\frac{4}{5}$

$\sin 2x = 2 \sin x \cos x = 2\left(-\frac{3}{5}\right)\left(-\frac{4}{5}\right) = \frac{24}{25}$

$\cos 2x = 1 - 2\sin^2 x = 1 - 2\left(-\frac{3}{5}\right)^2 = \frac{7}{25}$

$\sin \frac{x}{2} = \sqrt{\frac{1 - \cos x}{2}} = \sqrt{\frac{1 - \left(-\frac{4}{5}\right)}{2}} = \frac{3}{\sqrt{10}} \cdot \frac{\sqrt{10}}{\sqrt{10}} = \frac{3\sqrt{10}}{10}$

$\cos \frac{x}{2} = \sqrt{\frac{1 + \cos x}{2}} = \sqrt{\frac{1 + \left(-\frac{4}{5}\right)}{2}} = \sqrt{\frac{1}{10}} \cdot \frac{\sqrt{10}}{\sqrt{10}} = -\frac{\sqrt{10}}{10}$

16. $\cos^2 x = 1 - \sin^2 x$

$\cos^2 x = 1 - \left(-\frac{3}{4}\right)^2$

$\cos^2 x = \frac{7}{16}$

$\cos x = \frac{\sqrt{7}}{4}$

$\sin 2x = 2 \sin x \cos x = 2\left(-\frac{3}{4}\right)\left(\frac{\sqrt{7}}{4}\right) = -\frac{3\sqrt{7}}{8}$

$\cos 2x = 1 - 2\sin^2 x = 1 - 2\left(-\frac{3}{4}\right)^2 = -\frac{2}{16} = -\frac{1}{8}$

$\sin \frac{x}{2} = \sqrt{\frac{1 - \cos x}{2}} = \sqrt{\frac{1 - \frac{\sqrt{7}}{4}}{2}} = \sqrt{\frac{4 - \sqrt{7}}{8}} = \frac{\sqrt{8 - 2\sqrt{7}}}{4}$

$\cos \frac{x}{2} = \sqrt{\frac{1 + \cos x}{2}} = \sqrt{\frac{1 + \left(\frac{\sqrt{7}}{4}\right)}{2}} = \sqrt{\frac{4 + \sqrt{7}}{8}} = \frac{\sqrt{8 + 2\sqrt{7}}}{4}$

17. $\sin^2 x = 1 - \cos^2 x$

$\sin^2 x = 1 - \left(-\frac{1}{3}\right)^2$

$\sin^2 x = \frac{8}{9}$

$\sin x = \frac{2\sqrt{2}}{3}$

$\sin 2x = 2 \sin x \cos x = 2\left(\frac{2\sqrt{2}}{3}\right)\left(-\frac{1}{3}\right) = -\frac{4\sqrt{2}}{9}$

$\cos 2x = 2\cos^2 x - 1 = 2\left(-\frac{1}{3}\right)^2 - 1 = -\frac{7}{9}$

$\sin \frac{x}{2} = \sqrt{\frac{1 - \cos x}{2}} = \sqrt{\frac{1 - \left(-\frac{1}{3}\right)}{2}} = \frac{2}{\sqrt{6}} \cdot \frac{\sqrt{6}}{\sqrt{6}} = \frac{\sqrt{6}}{3}$

$\cos \frac{x}{2} = \sqrt{\frac{1 + \cos x}{2}} = \sqrt{\frac{1 + \left(-\frac{1}{3}\right)}{2}} = \sqrt{\frac{1}{3}} \cdot \frac{\sqrt{3}}{\sqrt{3}} = \frac{\sqrt{3}}{3}$

18. $\cos^2 x = 1 - \sin^2 x$

$\cos^2 x = 1 - \left(-\frac{1}{4}\right)^2$

$\cos^2 x = \frac{15}{16}$

$\cos x = -\frac{\sqrt{15}}{4}$

$\sin 2x = 2 \sin x \cos x = 2\left(-\frac{1}{4}\right)\left(-\frac{\sqrt{15}}{4}\right) = \frac{\sqrt{15}}{8}$

$\cos 2x = 1 - 2\sin^2 x = 1 - 2\left(-\frac{1}{4}\right)^2 = \frac{7}{8}$

$\sin \frac{x}{2} = \sqrt{\frac{1 - \cos x}{2}} = \sqrt{\frac{1 - \left(-\frac{\sqrt{15}}{4}\right)}{2}} = \sqrt{\frac{4 + \sqrt{15}}{2}} = \frac{\sqrt{8 + 2\sqrt{15}}}{2}$

$\cos \frac{x}{2} = \sqrt{\frac{1 + \cos x}{2}} = \sqrt{\frac{1 + \left(-\frac{\sqrt{15}}{4}\right)}{2}} = \sqrt{\frac{4 - \sqrt{15}}{8}} = \frac{\sqrt{8 - 2\sqrt{15}}}{4}$

19. $\sin 105° = \sin \frac{210°}{2} = \sqrt{\frac{1 - \cos 210°}{2}} = \sqrt{\frac{1 - \left(-\frac{\sqrt{3}}{2}\right)}{2}} = \sqrt{\frac{2 + \sqrt{3}}{4}} = \frac{\sqrt{2 + \sqrt{3}}}{2}$

20. $\sin 195° = \sin \frac{390°}{2} = -\sqrt{\frac{1 - \cos 390°}{2}} = -\sqrt{\frac{1 - \frac{\sqrt{3}}{2}}{2}} = -\sqrt{\frac{2 - \sqrt{3}}{4}} = -\frac{\sqrt{2 - \sqrt{3}}}{2}$

21. $\sin \frac{7\pi}{8} = \sin \frac{\frac{7\pi}{4}}{2} = \sqrt{\frac{1 - \cos \frac{7\pi}{4}}{2}} = \sqrt{\frac{1 - \frac{\sqrt{2}}{2}}{2}} = \sqrt{\frac{2 - \sqrt{2}}{4}} = \frac{\sqrt{2 - \sqrt{2}}}{2}$

22. $\cos \frac{19\pi}{12} = \cos \frac{\frac{19\pi}{6}}{2} = \sqrt{\frac{1 + \cos \frac{19\pi}{6}}{2}} = \sqrt{\frac{1 + \left(-\frac{\sqrt{3}}{2}\right)}{2}} = \sqrt{\frac{2 - \sqrt{3}}{4}} = \frac{\sqrt{2 - \sqrt{3}}}{2}$

23. $\cos^2 2x + 4\sin^2 x \cos^2 x \stackrel{?}{=} 1$

$\cos^2 2x + \sin^2 2x \stackrel{?}{=} 1$

$1 = 1$

24. $\sin^2 \theta \stackrel{?}{=} \frac{1}{2}(1 - \cos 2\theta)$

$\sin^2 \theta \stackrel{?}{=} \frac{1}{2}[1 - (1 - 2\sin^2 \theta)]$

$\sin^2 \theta \stackrel{?}{=} \frac{1}{2}(2\sin^2 \theta)$

$\sin^2 \theta = \sin^2 \theta$

25. $\sin 2x \stackrel{?}{=} 2 \cot x \sin^2 x$

$2 \sin x \cos x \stackrel{?}{=} 2 \frac{\cos x}{\sin x} \cdot \sin^2 x$

$2 \sin x \cos x = 2 \sin x \cos x$

26. $\sin^4 x - \cos^4 x \stackrel{?}{=} 2\sin^2 x - 1$

$(\sin^2 x - \cos^2 x)(\sin^2 x + \cos^2 x) \stackrel{?}{=} 2\sin^2 x - 1$

$(\sin^2 x - \cos^2 x) \cdot 1 \stackrel{?}{=} 2\sin^2 x - 1$

$[\sin^2 x - (1 - \sin^2 x)] \cdot 1 \stackrel{?}{=} 2\sin^2 x - 1$

$\sin^2 x - 1 + \sin^2 x \stackrel{?}{=} 2\sin^2 x - 1$

$2\sin^2 x - 1 = 2\sin^2 x - 1$

27. $2\cos^2 \frac{x}{2} \stackrel{?}{=} 1 + \cos x$

$2\left(\pm\sqrt{\frac{1 + \cos x}{2}}\right)^2 \stackrel{?}{=} 1 + \cos x$

$2\left(\frac{1 + \cos x}{2}\right) \stackrel{?}{=} 1 + \cos x$

$1 + \cos x = 1 + \cos x$

28. $\tan^2 \frac{x}{2} \stackrel{?}{=} \frac{1 - \cos x}{1 + \cos x}$

$\frac{\sin^2 \frac{x}{2}}{\cos^2 \frac{x}{2}} \stackrel{?}{=} \frac{1 - \cos x}{1 + \cos x}$

$\frac{\left(\pm\sqrt{\frac{1 - \cos x}{2}}\right)^2}{\left(\pm\sqrt{\frac{1 + \cos x}{2}}\right)^2} \stackrel{?}{=} \frac{1 - \cos x}{1 + \cos x}$

$\frac{1 - \cos x}{1 + \cos x} = \frac{1 - \cos x}{1 + \cos x}$

29. $\cos^2 4x = 1 - \sin^2 4x$

$\cos^2 4x = 1 - \left(\frac{2}{3}\right)^2$

$\cos^2 4x = 1 - \frac{4}{9}$

$\cos^2 4x = \frac{5}{9}$

$\cos 4x = -\frac{\sqrt{5}}{3}$

$\sin 2x = \sin\left(\frac{4x}{2}\right) = \pm\sqrt{\frac{1 - \left(-\frac{\sqrt{5}}{3}\right)}{2}} = \pm\sqrt{\frac{3 + \sqrt{5}}{6}} = \pm\frac{\sqrt{18 + 6\sqrt{5}}}{6}$

$\cos^2 2x = 1 - \sin^2 x$

$\cos^2 2x = 1 - \frac{18 + 6\sqrt{5}}{36}$

$\cos^2 2x = \frac{18 - 6\sqrt{5}}{36}$

$\cos 2x = \frac{\sqrt{18 - 6\sqrt{5}}}{6}$

$\sin x = \sin\left(\frac{2x}{2}\right) = \pm\sqrt{\frac{1 - (\sqrt{18 - 6\sqrt{5}})}{6}} = \pm\sqrt{\frac{6 - \sqrt{18 - 6\sqrt{5}}}{12}} = \pm\frac{\sqrt{18 - 3\sqrt{18 - 6\sqrt{5}}}}{6}$

30. $\sin\frac{\theta}{2} = \sqrt{\frac{1-\cos\theta}{2}}$

$= \sqrt{\frac{1-\cos 60°}{2}}$

$= \sqrt{\frac{1-\frac{1}{2}}{2}}$

$= \sqrt{\frac{1}{4}}$

$= \frac{1}{2}$

$\sin\frac{\theta}{2} = \frac{1}{m}$

$\frac{1}{2} = \frac{1}{m}$

$m = 2$

$s \approx 2.740$

≈ 1480; 1480 mph

31. $n = \frac{\sin\left(\frac{\theta}{2}+\frac{\alpha}{2}\right)}{\sin\frac{\alpha}{2}}$

$1.9 = \frac{\sin\left(\frac{90°}{2}+\frac{\alpha}{2}\right)}{\sin\frac{\alpha}{2}}$

$1.9 = \frac{\sin 45° \cos\frac{\alpha}{2} + \cos 45° \sin\frac{\alpha}{2}}{\sin\frac{\alpha}{2}}$

$1.9 = \frac{\frac{\sqrt{2}}{2}\cos\frac{\alpha}{2}}{\sin\frac{\alpha}{2}} + \frac{\frac{\sqrt{2}}{2}\sin\frac{\alpha}{2}}{\sin\frac{\alpha}{2}}$

$1.9 = \frac{\sqrt{2}}{2}\cot\frac{\alpha}{2} + \frac{\sqrt{2}}{2}$

$1.129 \approx \frac{\sqrt{2}}{2}\cot\frac{\alpha}{2}$

$1.687 \approx \frac{1}{\tan\frac{\alpha}{2}}$

$\tan\frac{\alpha}{2} \approx \frac{1}{1.687}$

$\frac{\alpha}{2} \approx 30.66°$

$\alpha \approx 61.3°$

32a. $\sin 1° = \sin 13° \cos 12° - \cos 13° \sin 12°$

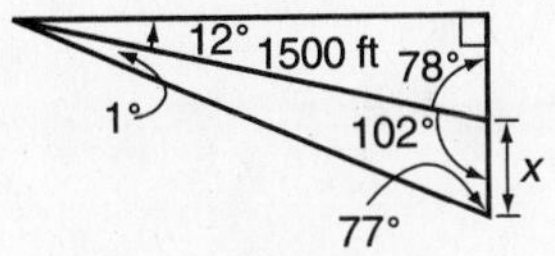

32b. $\frac{\sin 77°}{1500} = \frac{\sin 1°}{x}$

$x = \frac{1500 \sin 1°}{\sin 77°}$

$x \approx 26.9$; 26.9 feet

33. $\frac{a}{\sin A} = \frac{b}{\sin B}$

$\frac{8}{\sin 40°} = \frac{b}{\sin 62°}$

$b = \frac{8 \sin 62°}{\sin 40°}$

$b \approx 11.0$

$40° + 62° + C = 180°$

$C = 78°$

$\frac{a}{\sin A} = \frac{c}{\sin C}$

$\frac{8}{\sin 40°} = \frac{c}{\sin 78°}$

$c = \frac{8 \sin 78°}{\sin 40°}$

$c \approx 12.2$

34. $\frac{n!}{n} = \frac{12!}{12}$ or $11! = 39{,}916{,}800$

35. 1.814

36. not defined

37. $V = \frac{1}{3}\pi r^2 h$

$3V = \pi r^2 h$

$\frac{3V}{\pi r^2} = \frac{\pi r^2 h}{\pi r^2}$

$\frac{3V}{\pi r^2} = h$

14-6A Graphing Technology Solving Trigonometric Equations

Page 860 Exercises

1. $\sin x = 0.2$

$\sin x - 0.2 = 0$

Enter: [Y=] [SIN] [X,T,θ,n] [–] .2 [GRAPH]

approximate solutions: 11.5°, 168.5°

2. $0.5 \cos x = 1.4$

$0.5 \cos x - 1.4 = 0$

Enter: [Y=] 0.5 [COS] [X,T,θ,n] [–] 1.4 [GRAPH]

approximate solutions: none

3. $\sin 2x = \sin x$

$\sin 2x - \sin x = 0$

Enter: [Y=] [SIN] 2 [X,T,θ,n] [–] [SIN] [X,T,θ,n] [GRAPH]

approximate solutions: 0°, 60°, 180° 300°

4. $\tan x = \sin x$

$\tan x - \sin x = 0$

Enter: [Y=] [TAN] [X,T,θ,n] [–] [SIN] [X,T,θ,n] [GRAPH]

approximate solutions: 0°, 180°

5. $3 \sin 2x - 5 \sin x = 1$

$3 \sin 2x - 5 \sin x - 1 = 0$

Enter: [Y=] 3 [SIN] 2 [X,T,θ,n] [–] 5 [SIN] [X,T,θ,n] [–] 1 [GRAPH]

approximate solutions: −174.8°, −51.6°, 185.2°, 308.4°

6. $\tan^2 x \cos x + 5 \cos x = 0$

Enter: [Y=] [(] [TAN] [X,T,θ,n] [)] [x^2] [COS] [X,T,θ,n] [+] 5 [COS] [X,T,θ] [GRAPH]

approximate solutions: none

14-6 Solving Trigonometric Equations

Pages 864–865 Check for Understanding

1. Sample answer: The function is periodic with two solutions in each of its infinite number of periods.
2. All values of cos x are between −1 and 1, inclusive.
3. False; an identity is an equation that is true for all values of the variable.
4. $\cos^2\theta = 1$

$\cos^2\theta - 1 = 0$

$(\cos\theta + 1)(\cos\theta - 1) = 0$

$\cos\theta + 1 = 0$ or $\cos\theta - 1 = 0$

$\cos\theta = -1$ $\qquad$ $\cos\theta = 1$

$\theta = 180°$ $\qquad$ $\theta = 0$

0°, 180°

5. Let $x = 2\theta$; $0° \le x < 720°$

$\sin x = \frac{1}{2}$

$x = 30°, 150°, 390°, 510°$

$\theta = \frac{x}{2}$

$= 15°, 75°, 195°, 255°$

$15°, 75°, 195°, 255°$

6.
$$2\cos^2\theta + 2 = 5\cos\theta$$
$$2\cos^2\theta - 5\cos\theta + 2 = 0$$
$$(2\cos\theta - 1)(\cos\theta - 2) = 0$$

$2\cos\theta - 1 = 0$ or $\cos\theta - 2 = 0$

$2\cos\theta = 1$ $\quad$ $\cos\theta = 2$

$\cos\theta = \frac{1}{2}$ $\quad$ not possible

$\theta = 60°$ or $300°$

$60°, 300°$

7. $\sin\theta + \sin\theta\cos\theta = 0$

$\sin\theta(1 + \cos\theta) = 0$

$\sin\theta = 0$ or $\cos\theta + 1 = 0$

$\theta = 0°$ $\quad$ $\cos\theta = -1$

$\theta = 180°$

$0°, 180°$

8.
$$\cos 2\theta = \cos\theta$$
$$(2\cos^2\theta - 1) = \cos\theta$$
$$2\cos^2\theta - \cos\theta - 1 = 0$$
$$(2\cos\theta + 1)(\cos\theta - 1) = 0$$

$2\cos\theta + 1 = 0$ or $\cos\theta - 1 = 0$

$2\cos\theta = -1$ $\quad$ $\cos\theta = 1$

$\cos\theta = -\frac{1}{2}$ $\quad$ $\theta = 0$ or 2π

$\theta = \frac{2\pi}{3}$ or $\frac{4\pi}{3}$

$0 + \frac{2\pi k}{3}$

9.
$$\cos 2\theta + \cos\theta + 1 = 0$$
$$(2\cos^2\theta - 1) + \cos\theta + 1 = 0$$
$$2\cos^2\theta + \cos\theta = 0$$
$$\cos\theta(2\cos\theta + 1) = 0$$

$\cos\theta = 0$ or $2\cos\theta + 1 = 0$

$\theta = \frac{\pi}{2}$ or $\frac{3\pi}{2}$ $\quad$ $2\cos\theta = -1$

$\cos\theta = -\frac{1}{2}$

$\theta = \frac{2\pi}{3}$ or $\frac{4\pi}{3}$

$\frac{\pi}{2} + k\pi, \frac{2\pi}{3} + 2\pi k, \frac{4\pi}{3} + 2\pi k$

10.
$$3\sin^2\theta - \cos^2\theta = 0$$
$$3\sin^2\theta - (1 - \sin^2\theta) = 0$$
$$4\sin^2\theta - 1 = 0$$
$$(2\sin\theta + 1)(2\sin\theta - 1) = 0$$

$2\sin\theta + 1 = 0$ or $2\sin\theta - 1 = 0$

$\sin\theta = -\frac{1}{2}$ $\quad$ $\sin\theta = \frac{1}{2}$

$\theta = \frac{\pi}{6}$ or $\frac{5\pi}{6}$ $\quad$ $\theta = \frac{\pi}{3}$ or $\frac{5\pi}{3}$

$\frac{\pi}{6} + 2k\pi, \frac{5\pi}{6} + 2k\pi$

11. $4\cos^2\theta - 4\cos\theta + 1 = 0$

$(2\cos\theta - 1)^2 = 0$

$2\cos\theta - 1 = 0$

$2\cos\theta = 1$

$\cos\theta = \frac{1}{2}$

$\theta = \frac{\pi}{3}$ or $\frac{5\pi}{3}$

$\frac{\pi}{3} + 2k\pi, \frac{5\pi}{3} + 2k\pi$

12. Every day from February 19 to October 20; explanations will vary. Sample explanation: Since the longest day of the year occurs around June 22, the days between February 19 and October 20 must increase in length until June 22 and then decrease in length until October 20.

Pages 865–867 Exercises

13.
$$4\cos^2 x = 1$$
$$4\cos^2 x - 1 = 0$$
$$(2\cos x + 1)(2\cos x - 1) = 0$$

$2\cos x + 1 = 0$ or $2\cos x - 1 = 0$

$2\cos x = -1$ $\quad$ $2\cos x = 1$

$\cos x = -\frac{1}{2}$ $\quad$ $\cos x = \frac{1}{2}$

$x = 120°$ or $240°$ $\quad$ $x = 60°$ or $300°$

$60°, 120°, 240°, 300°$

14. $2\sin^2 x - 1 = 0$

$2\sin^2 x = 1$

$\sin^2 x = \frac{1}{2}$

$\sin x = \pm\sqrt{\frac{1}{2}}$ or $\pm\frac{\sqrt{2}}{2}$

$x = 45°, 135°, 225°, 315°$

$45°, 135°, 225°, 315°$

15.
$$\sin 2x = 2\cos x$$
$$2\sin x\cos x = 2\cos x$$
$$2\sin x\cos x - 2\cos x = 0$$
$$2\cos x(\sin x - 1) = 0$$

$\cos x = 0$ or $\sin x - 1 = 0$

$x = 90°$ or $270°$ $\quad$ $\sin x = 1$

$x = 90°$ or $270°$

$90°, 270°$

16.
$$2\cos^2 x = \sin x + 1$$
$$2(1 - \sin^2 x) = \sin x + 1$$
$$2 - 2\sin^2 x = \sin x + 1$$
$$0 = 2\sin^2 x + \sin x - 1$$
$$0 = (2\sin x - 1)(\sin x + 1)$$

$2\sin x - 1 = 0$ or $\sin x + 1 = 0$

$\sin x = \frac{1}{2}$ $\quad$ $\sin x = -1$

$x = 30°$ or $150°$ $\quad$ $x = 270°$

$30°, 150°, 270°$

17. $4\sin^2 x - 4\sin x + 1 = 0$

$(2\sin x - 1)^2 = 0$

$2\sin x - 1 = 0$

$\sin x = \frac{1}{2}$

$x = 30°$ or $150°$

$30°, 150°$

18.
$$\sin 2x = \cos x$$
$$2\sin x\cos x = \cos x$$
$$2\sin x\cos x - \cos x = 0$$
$$\cos x(2\sin x - 1) = 0$$

$\cos x = 0$ or $2\sin x - 1 = 0$

$x = 90°$ or $270°$ $\quad$ $\sin x = \frac{1}{2}$

$x = 30°$ or $150°$

$30°, 90°, 150°, 270°$

19. $2 \sin \theta = -1$

$\sin \theta = -\frac{1}{2}$

$\theta = \frac{7\pi}{6}$ or $\frac{11\pi}{6}$

$\frac{7\pi}{6}, \frac{11\pi}{6}$

20. $2 \cos \theta - 1 = 0$

$\cos \theta = \frac{1}{2}$

$\theta = \frac{\pi}{3}$ or $\frac{5\pi}{3}$

$\frac{\pi}{3}, \frac{5\pi}{3}$

21. $2 \sin \theta = -\sqrt{3}$

$\sin \theta = -\frac{\sqrt{3}}{2}$

$\theta = \frac{4\pi}{3}$ or $\frac{5\pi}{3}$

$\frac{4\pi}{3}, \frac{5\pi}{3}$

22. $4 \sin^2 \theta = 1$

$\sin^2 \theta = \frac{1}{4}$

$\sin \theta = \pm\sqrt{\frac{1}{4}}$ or $\pm\frac{1}{2}$

$\theta = \frac{\pi}{6}, \frac{5\pi}{6}, \frac{7\pi}{6}, \frac{11\pi}{6}$

$\frac{\pi}{6}, \frac{5\pi}{6}, \frac{7\pi}{6}, \frac{11\pi}{6}$

23. $2 \sin^2 \theta - \sin \theta = 1$

$2 \sin^2 \theta - \sin \theta - 1 = 0$

$(2 \sin \theta + 1)(\sin \theta - 1) = 0$

$2 \sin \theta + 1 = 0$ or $\sin \theta - 1 = 0$

$\sin \theta = -\frac{1}{2}$ | $\sin \theta = 1$

$\theta = \frac{7\pi}{6}$ or $\frac{11\pi}{6}$ | $\theta = \frac{\pi}{2}$

$\frac{\pi}{2}, \frac{7\pi}{6}, \frac{11\pi}{6}$

24. $2\sin^2 \theta = -\sin \theta$

$2 \sin^2 \theta + \sin \theta = 0$

$\sin \theta\ (2 \sin \theta + 1) = 0$

$\sin \theta = 0$ or $2 \sin \theta + 1 = 0$

$\theta = 0$ or π | $\sin \theta = -\frac{1}{2}$

$\theta = \frac{7\pi}{6}$ or $\frac{11\pi}{6}$

$0, \pi, \frac{7\pi}{6}, \frac{11\pi}{6}$

25. $\sin x = \cos x$

$x = 45°$

$45° + k \cdot 180°$

26. $\sin^2 x - 2 \sin x - 3 = 0$

$(\sin x + 1)(\sin x - 3) = 0$

$\sin x + 1 = 0$ or $\sin x - 3 = 0$

$\sin x = -1$ | $\sin x = 3$

$x = 270°$ | not possible

$270° + k \cdot 360°$

27. $\tan x = \sin x$

$\frac{\sin x}{\cos x} = \sin x$

$\sin x = \cos x \sin x$

$0 = \cos x \sin x - \sin x$

$0 = \sin x(\cos x - 1)$

$\sin x = 0$ or $\cos x - 1 = 0$

$x = 0°$ or $180°$ | $\cos x = 1$

$x = 0°$

$0° + k \cdot 180°$

28. $\sin x = 1 + \cos x$

$\sin^2 x = (1 + \cos x)^2$

$\sin^2 x = 1 + 2 \cos x + \cos^2 x$

$1 - \cos^2 x = 1 + 2 \cos x + \cos^2 x$

$0 = 2 \cos^2 x + 2 \cos x$

$0 = 2 \cos x(\cos x + 1)$

$\cos x = 0$ or $\cos x + 1 = 0$

$x = 90°$ | $\cos x = -1$

$x = 180°$

$90° + k \cdot 360°, 180° + k \cdot 360°$

29. $3 \cos 2x - 5 \cos x = 1$

$3(2 \cos^2 x - 1) - 5 \cos x = 1$

$6 \cos^2 x - 3 - 5 \cos x = 1$

$6 \cos^2 x - 5 \cos x - 4 = 0$

$(3 \cos x - 4)(2 \cos x + 1) = 0$

$3 \cos x - 4 = 0$ or $2 \cos x + 1 = 0$

$\cos x = \frac{4}{3}$ | $\cos x = -\frac{1}{2}$

not possible | $x = 120°$ or $240°$

$120° + k \cdot 360°, 240° + k \cdot 360°$

30. $\tan^2 x - \sqrt{3} \tan x = 0$

$\tan x(\tan x - \sqrt{3}) = 0$

$\tan x = 0$ or $\tan x - \sqrt{3} = 0$

$x = 0°$ or $180°$ | $\tan x = \sqrt{3}$

$x = 60°$ or $240°$

$0° + k \cdot 180°, 60° + k \cdot 180°$

31. $\sin^2 x - \sin x = 0$

$\sin x(\sin x - 1) = 0$

$\sin x = 0$ or $\sin x - 1 = 0$

$x = 0°$ or $180°$ | $\sin x = 1$

$x = 90°$

$0° + k \cdot 180°, 90° + k \cdot 360°$

32. $\cos x \tan x - \sin^2 x = 0$

$\cos x\left(\frac{\sin x}{\cos x}\right) - \sin^2 x = 0$

$\sin x - \sin^2 x = 0$

$\sin x(1 - \sin x) = 0$

$\sin x = 0$ or $1 - \sin x = 0$

$x = 0°$ or $180°$ | $1 = \sin x$

$90° = x$

$0° + k \cdot 180°$

33. $2 \sin^2 \theta - 3 \sin \theta - 2 = 0$

$(2 \sin \theta + 1)(\sin \theta - 2) = 0$

$2 \sin \theta + 1 = 0$ or $\sin \theta - 2 = 0$

$\sin \theta = -\frac{1}{2}$ | $\sin \theta = 2$

not possible

$\theta = \frac{7\pi}{6}$ or $\frac{11\pi}{6}$

$\frac{7\pi}{6} + 2k \cdot \pi, \frac{11\pi}{6} + 2k \cdot \pi$

34. $\cos 2\theta + 3 \cos \theta - 1 = 0$

$(2 \cos^2 \theta - 1) + 3 \cos \theta - 1 = 0$

$2 \cos^2 \theta + 3 \cos \theta - 2 = 0$

$(2 \cos \theta - 1)(\cos \theta + 2) = 0$

$2 \cos \theta - 1 = 0$ or $\cos \theta + 2 = 0$

$\cos \theta = \frac{1}{2}$ | $\cos \theta = -2$

not possible

$\theta = \frac{\pi}{3}$ or $\frac{5\pi}{3}$

$\frac{\pi}{3} + 2k\pi, \frac{5\pi}{3} + 2k\pi$

35. $2 \sin^2 \theta - \cos \theta - 1 = 0$

$2(1 - \cos^2 \theta) - \cos \theta - 1 = 0$

$2 - 2 \cos^2 \theta - \cos \theta - 1 = 0$

$2 \cos^2 + \cos \theta - 1 = 0$

$(2 \cos \theta - 1)(\cos \theta + 1) = 0$

$2 \cos \theta - 1 = 0$ or $\cos \theta + 1 = 0$

$\cos \theta = \frac{1}{2}$ | $\cos \theta = -1$

$\theta = \frac{\pi}{3}$ or $\frac{5\pi}{3}$ | $\theta = \pi$

$\frac{\pi}{3} + 2k\pi, \pi + 2k\pi, \frac{5\pi}{3} + 2k\pi$

36. $\cos^2\theta - \frac{5}{2}\cos\theta - \frac{3}{2} = 0$

$2\cos^2\theta - 5\cos\theta - 3 = 0$

$(2\cos\theta + 1)(\cos\theta - 3) = 0$

$2\cos\theta + 1 = 0$ or $\cos\theta - 3 = 0$

$\cos\theta = -\frac{1}{2}$ $\qquad$ $\cos\theta = 3$

$\theta = \frac{2\pi}{3}$ or $\frac{4\pi}{3}$ $\qquad$ not possible

$\frac{2\pi}{3} + 2k\pi, \frac{4\pi}{3} + 2k\pi$

37. $\cos^2\theta - \frac{7}{2}\cos\theta - 2 = 0$

$2\cos^2\theta - 7\cos\theta - 4 = 0$

$(2\cos\theta + 1)(\cos\theta - 4) = 0$

$2\cos\theta + 1 = 0$ or $\cos\theta - 4 = 0$

$\cos\theta = -\frac{1}{2}$ $\qquad$ $\cos\theta = 4$

$\theta = \frac{2\pi}{3}$ or $\frac{4\pi}{3}$ $\qquad$ not possible

$\frac{2\pi}{3} + 2k\pi, \frac{4\pi}{3} + 2k\pi$

38. $2\cos^2\theta + 3\sin\theta - 3 = 0$

$2(1 - \sin^2\theta) + 3\sin\theta - 3 = 0$

$2 - 2\sin^2\theta + 3\sin\theta - 3 = 0$

$2\sin^2\theta - 3\sin\theta + 1 = 0$

$(2\sin\theta - 1)(\sin\theta - 1) = 0$

$2\sin\theta - 1 = 0$ or $\sin\theta - 1 = 0$

$\sin\theta = \frac{1}{2}$ $\qquad$ $\sin\theta = 1$

$\theta = \frac{\pi}{6}$ or $\frac{5\pi}{6}$ $\qquad$ $\theta = \frac{\pi}{2}$

$\frac{\pi}{6} + 2k\pi, \frac{5\pi}{6} + 2k\pi, \frac{\pi}{2} + 2k\pi$

39. $\cos 2\theta = 1 - \sin\theta$

$1 - 2\sin^2\theta = 1 - \sin\theta$

$2\sin^2\theta - \sin\theta = 0$

$\sin\theta(2\sin\theta - 1) = 0$

$\sin\theta = 0$ or $2\sin\theta - 1 = 0$

$\theta = 0°$ or π $\qquad$ $\sin\theta = \frac{1}{2}$

$\theta = \frac{\pi}{6}$ or $\frac{5\pi}{6}$

$0 + k\pi, \frac{\pi}{6} + 2k\pi, \frac{5\pi}{6} + 2k\pi$

40. $\cos\theta = 3\cos\theta - 2$

$2 = 2\cos\theta$

$1 = \cos\theta$

$\theta = 0°$

$0 + 2k\pi$

41a. two times; 90° and 270°

41b. Exercise 15; yes $\qquad$ **41c.** They are the same.

41d. If the equation is an identity then the two curves are identical. Otherwise, the curves only intersect at certain points.

42a. Disp: "2 (cos x)^2 + 3 cos (x) − 2 = 0" $\qquad$ Line 2
A = 0°, B = 180°
(2 (cos Y)^2 + 3 cos (Y) − 2) → F $\qquad$ Line 11
ONE SOLUTION IS 60°

42b. Disp: "2 cos (x) − sin (2x) = 0" $\qquad$ Line 2
A = 0°, B = 180°
(2 cos (Y) − sin (2 * Y)) → F $\qquad$ Line 11
ONE SOLUTION IS 90°
ONE SOLUTION IS 270°

42c. Disp: "2 (sin x)^2 + sin (x) − 1 = 0" $\qquad$ Line 2
A = 180°, B = 240°
(2 (sin Y)^2 + sin (Y) − 1) → F $\qquad$ Line 11
NO SOLUTIONS BETWEEN 180 AND 240 DEGREES

42d. Disp: "sin (x) + cos (x) * (tan x)^2 = 0" $\qquad$ Line 2
A = −360°, B = 0°
(sin (Y) + cos (Y) * (tan Y)^2) → F $\qquad$ Line 11
ONE SOLUTION IS −360°
ONE SOLUTION IS −225°
ONE SOLUTION IS −180°
ONE SOLUTION IS −45°
ONE SOLUTION IS 0°

42e. Disp: "cos (2 * x) + sin (x) − 1 = 0" $\qquad$ Line 2
A = 0°, B = 720°
(cos (2 * Y) + sin (Y) − 1) → F $\qquad$ Line 11
ONE SOLUTION IS 0°
ONE SOLUTION IS 30°
ONE SOLUTION IS 150°
ONE SOLUTION IS 180°
ONE SOLUTION IS 360°
ONE SOLUTION IS 390°
ONE SOLUTION IS 510°
ONE SOLUTION IS 540°
ONE SOLUTION IS 720°

43. $\frac{\tan x - \sin x}{\tan x + \sin x} = \frac{\sec x - 1}{\sec x + 1}$

$\frac{\frac{\sin x}{\cos x} - \sin x}{\frac{\sin x}{\cos x} + \sin x} = \frac{\frac{1}{\cos x} - 1}{\frac{1}{\cos x} + 1}$

$\frac{\sin x - \sin x\cos x}{\sin x + \sin x\cos x} = \frac{1 - \cos x}{1 + \cos x}$

$\frac{1 - \cos x}{1 + \cos x} = \frac{1 - \cos x}{1 + \cos x}$ identity

excluded values

$\sec x + 1 = 0$ $\qquad$ $\tan x + \sin x = 0$

$\sec x = -1$ $\qquad$ $\frac{\sin x + \sin x\cos x}{\cos x} = 0$

$x = \pi$ $\qquad$ $\sin x(1 + \cos x) = 0$

$\sin x = 0$ $\qquad$ $\cos x = -1$

$x = 0$ or π $\qquad$ $x = \pi$

all reals except $0 + \frac{k\pi}{2}$, where k is any integer

44. Let $u = \frac{2\pi}{365}t_1$

$12.85 = 2.3\sin u + 11.7$

$1.15 = 2.3\sin u$

$0.5 = \sin u$

$0.5 = \sin u$

$u = \frac{\pi}{6}$ or $\frac{5\pi}{6}$

$\frac{\pi}{6} = \frac{2\pi}{365}t$ $\qquad$ $\frac{5\pi}{6} = \frac{2\pi}{365}t$

$30.4 \approx t$ $\qquad$ $152.1 \approx t$

April 20 and August 20

45. $\sin\alpha = 1.33\sin\beta$

$\sin\alpha = 1.33\sin\alpha$

$0 = 0.33\sin\alpha$

$\alpha = 0°$

46. Quadrant I

47. $\tan A = \frac{\sqrt{5}}{2} = \frac{a}{b}$

$a^2 + b^2 = c^2$

$(\sqrt{5})^2 + 2^2 = c^2$

$5 + 4 = c^2$

$9 = c^2$

$3 = c$

$\cos A = \frac{b}{c}$

$= \frac{2}{3}$

48a. $P(\text{2 pineapple}) = \frac{C(5, 2)}{C(20, 2)}$

$= \frac{1}{19} \approx 0.053$

48b. $P(\text{1 pineapple and 1 lemon}) = \frac{2 \cdot C(5, 1) \cdot (6, 1)C}{C(20, 2)}$

$= \frac{3}{19} \approx 0.158$

49. $C(6, 4)(0.8)^4 (0.2)^2 = 15(0.8)^4(0.2)^2$
$= 0.24576$ or 24.576%

50.
$$2^{2x} = \frac{1}{8}$$
$$2^{2x} = \frac{1}{2^3}$$
$$2^{2x} = 2^{-3}$$
$$2x = -3$$
$$x = -\frac{3}{2}$$

51.
$$b^2 - \frac{3}{4}b + \frac{1}{8} = 0$$
$$b^2 - \frac{3}{4}b = -\frac{1}{8}$$
$$b^2 - \frac{3}{4}b + \frac{9}{64} = -\frac{1}{8} + \frac{9}{64}$$
$$(b - \frac{3}{8})^2 = \frac{1}{64}$$
$$6 - \frac{3}{8} = \pm \frac{1}{8}$$
$$b = \frac{3}{8} \pm \frac{1}{8}$$
$b = \frac{3}{8} + \frac{1}{8}$ or $b = \frac{3}{8} - \frac{1}{8}$

$b = \frac{1}{2}$ $\quad$ $b = \frac{1}{4}$

52a. 134, 144, 153, 154, 154, 158, 163, 166, 166, 167, 167, 167, 170, 172, 176, 187, 188, 201
$Q_2 = \frac{166 + 167}{2}$ or 166.5; $Q_1 = 154$; $Q_3 = 172$;
IQR = 172 − 154 = 18; 154 − 1.5(18) or 127, 172 + 1.5(18) or 199, 201 is an outlier

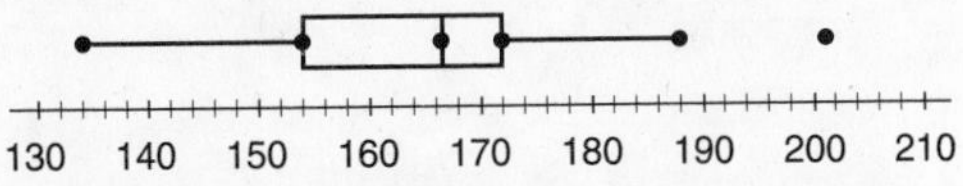

52b. She usually bowled between 154 and 172.

53. $29x \leq 609$
$x \leq 21$

Page 867 Mathematics and Society

1. Change the size, shape, tension, or material composition of the drumhead
2. See students' work.
3. Sample answer: Tell the geophysicist to be very cautious in his or her assumptions and conclusions. Just because two or more underground structures produced identical frequency spectra does not mean that structures are identical. The drum experiments indicate that identical spectra can, in fact, be produced by structures that are not identical.

Chapter 14 Highlights

Page 869 Understanding and Using the Vocabulary

1. h	**2.** e	**3.** b	**4.** d
5. f	**6.** c	**7.** i	**8.** g
9. a			

Chapter 14 Study Guide and Assessment

Pages 870–872 Skills and Concepts

10.

θ	0°	90°	180°	270°	360°
$\cos\theta$	1	0	−1	0	1
$-\frac{1}{2}\cos\theta$	$-\frac{1}{2}$	0	$\frac{1}{2}$	0	$-\frac{1}{2}$

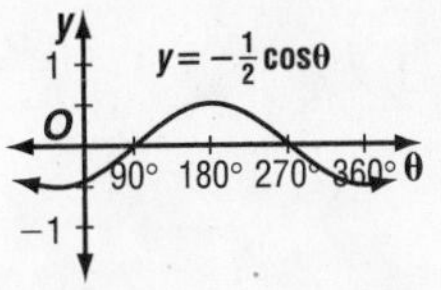

amplitude: $\left|-\frac{1}{2}\right|$ or $\frac{1}{2}$
period: $\frac{360°}{|1|}$ or 360°

11.

θ	0°	45°	90°	135°	180°
2θ	0	90°	180°	270°	360°
$4\sin 2\theta$	0	4	0	−4	0

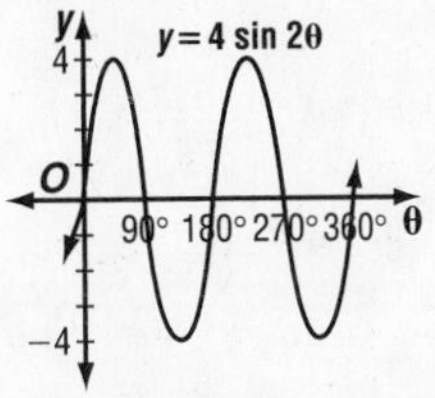

amplitude: |4| or 4
period: $\frac{360°}{|2|}$ or 180°

12.

θ	0°	180°	360°	540°	720°
$\frac{1}{2}\theta$	0°	90°	180°	270°	360°
$\sin\frac{1}{2}\theta$	0	1	0	−1	0

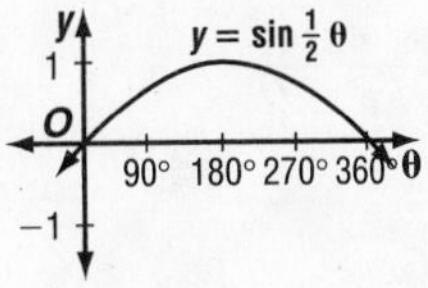

amplitude: |1| or 1
period: $\frac{360°}{\left|\frac{1}{2}\right|}$ or 720°

13.

θ	0°	90°	180°	270°	360°
$5\sec\theta$	5	nd	−5	nd	5

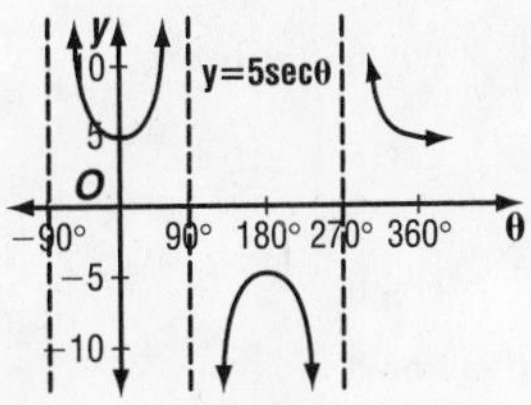

amplitude: none
period: $\frac{360°}{|1|}$ or 360°

14.

θ	0°	135°	270°	405°	540°
$\frac{2}{3}\theta$	0°	90°	180°	270°	360°
$\frac{1}{2}\csc\frac{2}{3}\theta$	nd	$\frac{1}{2}$	nd	$-\frac{1}{2}$	nd

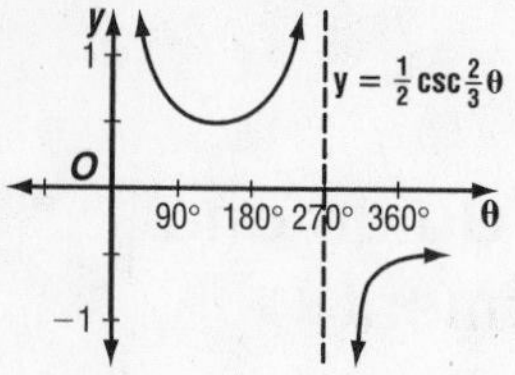

amplitude: none

period: $\frac{360°}{\left|\frac{2}{3}\right|}$ or 540°

15.

θ	0°	15°	22.5°	30°	45°
4θ	0°	60°	90°	120°	180°
$\tan 4\theta$	0	$\sqrt{3}$	nd	$-\sqrt{3}$	0

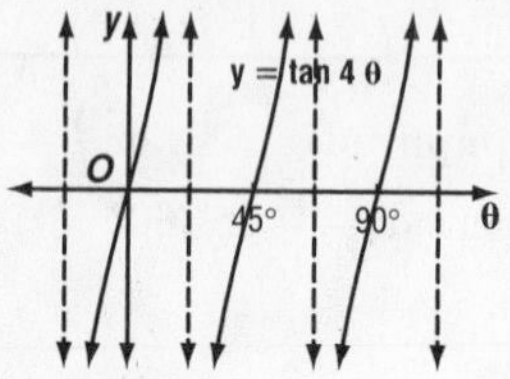

amplitude: none

period: $\frac{180°}{|4|}$ or 45°

16. $1 + \cot^2\theta = \csc^2\theta$

$\cot^2\theta = \csc^2\theta - 1$

$\cot^2\theta = \left(-\frac{5}{3}\right)^2 - 1$

$\cot^2\theta = \frac{16}{9}$

$\cot\theta = -\frac{4}{3}$

17. $\cos^2\theta = 1 - \sin^2\theta$

$\cos^2\theta = 1 - \left(-\frac{1}{2}\right)^2$

$\cos^2\theta = \frac{3}{4}$

$\cos\theta = \frac{\sqrt{3}}{2}$

$\sec\theta = \frac{1}{\cos\theta}$

$\sec\theta = \frac{1}{\frac{\sqrt{3}}{2}}$

$\sec\theta = \frac{2}{\sqrt{3}} \cdot \frac{\sqrt{3}}{\sqrt{3}}$

$= \frac{2\sqrt{3}}{3}$

18. $\sin\alpha\csc\alpha - \cos^2\alpha$

$= \sin\alpha\left(\frac{1}{\sin\alpha}\right) - \cos^2\alpha$

$= 1 - \cos^2\alpha$

$= \sin^2\alpha$

19. $\cos^2\theta\sec\theta\csc\theta$

$= \cos^2\theta\left(\frac{1}{\cos\theta}\right)\left(\frac{1}{\sin\theta}\right)$

$= \frac{\cos\theta}{\sin\theta}$

$= \cot\theta$

20. $\cos\beta + \sin\beta\tan\beta = \cos\beta + \sin\beta\left(\frac{\sin\beta}{\cos\beta}\right)$

$= \cos\beta + \frac{\sin^2\beta}{\cos\beta}$

$= \frac{\cos^2\beta + \sin^2\beta}{\cos\beta}$

$= \frac{1}{\cos\beta}$

$= \sec\beta$

21. $\sin\alpha(1 + \cot^2\alpha) = \sin\alpha(\csc^2\alpha)$

$= \sin\alpha\left(\frac{1}{\sin^2\alpha}\right)$

$= \frac{1}{\sin\alpha}$

$= \csc\alpha$

22. $\frac{\sin\theta}{\tan\theta} + \frac{\cos\theta}{\cot\theta} \stackrel{?}{=} \cos\theta + \sin\theta$

$\frac{\sin\theta}{\frac{\sin\theta}{\cos\theta}} + \frac{\cos\theta}{\frac{\cos\theta}{\sin\theta}} \stackrel{?}{=} \cos\theta + \sin\theta$

$\sin \cdot \frac{\cos\theta}{\sin\theta} + \cos\theta \cdot \frac{\sin\theta}{\cos\theta} \stackrel{?}{=} \cos\theta + \sin\theta$

$\cos\theta + \sin\theta = \cos\theta + \sin\theta$

23. $\frac{\sin\theta}{1 - \cos\theta} \stackrel{?}{=} \csc\theta + \cot\theta$

$\frac{\sin\theta}{1 - \cos\theta} \stackrel{?}{=} \frac{1}{\sin\theta} + \frac{\cos\theta}{\sin\theta}$

$\frac{\sin\theta}{1 - \cos\theta} \stackrel{?}{=} \frac{1 + \cos\theta}{\sin\theta}$

$\frac{\sin\theta}{1 - \cos\theta} \stackrel{?}{=} \frac{(1 + \cos\theta)}{\sin\theta} \cdot \frac{(1 - \cos\theta)}{(1 - \cos\theta)}$

$\frac{\sin\theta}{1 - \cos\theta} \stackrel{?}{=} \frac{1 - \cos^2\theta}{\sin\theta(1 - \cos\theta)}$

$\frac{\sin\theta}{1 - \cos\theta} \stackrel{?}{=} \frac{\sin^2\theta}{\sin\theta(1 - \cos\theta)}$

$\frac{\sin\theta}{1 - \cos\theta} = \frac{\sin\theta}{1 - \cos\theta}$

24. $\cot^2\theta\sec^2\theta \stackrel{?}{=} 1 + \cot^2\theta$

$\frac{\cos^2}{\sin^2\theta} \cdot \frac{1}{\cos^2\theta} \stackrel{?}{=} 1 + \cot^2\theta$

$\frac{1}{\sin^2\theta} \stackrel{?}{=} 1 + \cot^2\theta$

$\csc^2\theta \stackrel{?}{=} 1 + \cot^2\theta$

$1 + \cot^2\theta = 1 + \cot^2\theta$

25. $\sec x(\sec x - \cos x) \stackrel{?}{=} \tan^2 x$

$\frac{1}{\cos x}\left(\frac{1}{\cos x} - \cos x\right) \stackrel{?}{=} \tan^2 x$

$\frac{1}{\cos^2 x} - 1 \stackrel{?}{=} \tan^2 x$

$\sec^2 x - 1 \stackrel{?}{=} \tan^2 x$

$\tan^2 x = \tan^2 x$

26. $\frac{\cos x}{\csc x} - \frac{\sin x}{\cos x} \stackrel{?}{=} -\sin^2 x\tan x$

$\frac{\cos x}{\frac{1}{\sin x}} - \frac{\sin x}{\cos x} \stackrel{?}{=} -\sin^2 x\tan x$

$\cos x \cdot \sin x - \frac{\sin x}{\cos x} \stackrel{?}{=} \sin^2 x\tan x$

$\frac{\cos^2 x\sin x - \sin x}{\cos x} \stackrel{?}{=} -\sin^2\tan x$

$\frac{\sin x(\cos^2 x - 1)}{\cos x} \stackrel{?}{=} -\sin^2 x\tan x$

$\frac{\sin x(-\sin^2 x)}{\cos x} \stackrel{?}{=} -\sin^2 x\tan x$

$-\sin^2 x \cdot \frac{\sin x}{\cos x} \stackrel{?}{=} -\sin^2 x\tan x$

$-\sin^2 x\tan x = -\sin^2 x\tan x$

27. $\frac{\csc\theta + 1}{\cot\theta} \stackrel{?}{=} \frac{\cot\theta}{\csc\theta - 1}$

$\frac{\csc\theta + 1}{\cot\theta} \stackrel{?}{=} \frac{\cot\theta}{\csc\theta - 1} \cdot \frac{\csc\theta + 1}{\csc\theta + 1}$

$\frac{\csc\theta + 1}{\cot\theta} \stackrel{?}{=} \frac{\cot\theta(\csc\theta + 1)}{\csc^2 - 1}$

$\frac{\csc\theta + 1}{\cot\theta} \stackrel{?}{=} \frac{\cot\theta(\csc\theta + 1)}{\cot^2\theta}$

$\frac{\csc\theta + 1}{\cot\theta} = \frac{\csc\theta + 1}{\cot\theta}$

28. $\cos 15° = \cos(45° - 30°)$

$= \cos 45°\cos 30° + \sin 45°\sin 30°$

$= \frac{\sqrt{2}}{2} \cdot \frac{\sqrt{3}}{2} + \frac{\sqrt{2}}{2} \cdot \frac{1}{2}$

$= \frac{\sqrt{6}}{4} + \frac{\sqrt{2}}{4}$

$= \frac{\sqrt{6} + \sqrt{2}}{4}$

29. $\cos 285° = \cos(240° + 45°)$

$= \cos 240°\cos 45° - \sin 240°\sin 45°$

$= -\frac{1}{2} \cdot \frac{\sqrt{2}}{2} - \left(-\frac{\sqrt{3}}{2}\right)\left(\frac{\sqrt{2}}{2}\right)$

$= -\frac{\sqrt{2}}{4} + \frac{\sqrt{6}}{4}$

$= \frac{\sqrt{6} - \sqrt{2}}{4}$

30. $\sin 195° = \sin(150° + 45°)$
$= \sin 150° \cos 45° + \cos 150° \sin 45°$
$= \frac{1}{2} \cdot \frac{\sqrt{2}}{2} + \left(-\frac{\sqrt{3}}{2}\right) \cdot \frac{\sqrt{2}}{2}$
$= \frac{\sqrt{2}}{4} - \frac{\sqrt{6}}{4}$
$= \frac{\sqrt{2} - \sqrt{6}}{4}$

31. $\sin 255° = \sin(210° + 45°)$
$= \sin 210° \cos 45° + \cos 210° \sin 45°$
$= -\frac{1}{2} \cdot \frac{\sqrt{2}}{2} + \left(-\frac{\sqrt{3}}{2}\right) \cdot \frac{\sqrt{2}}{2}$
$= -\frac{\sqrt{2}}{4} - \frac{\sqrt{6}}{4}$
$= \frac{-\sqrt{2} - \sqrt{6}}{4}$ or $\frac{\sqrt{2} + \sqrt{6}}{-4}$

32. $\sin 165° = \sin(120° + 45°)$
$= \sin 120° \cos 45° + \cos 120° \sin 45°$
$= \frac{\sqrt{3}}{2} \cdot \frac{\sqrt{2}}{2} + \left(-\frac{1}{2}\right) \cdot \frac{\sqrt{2}}{2}$
$= \frac{\sqrt{6}}{4} - \frac{\sqrt{2}}{4}$
$= \frac{\sqrt{6} - \sqrt{2}}{4}$

33. $\cos(-210°) = \cos(90° - 300°)$
$= \cos 90° \cos 300° + \sin 90° \sin 300°$
$= 0 \cdot \frac{1}{2} + 1 \cdot \left(-\frac{\sqrt{3}}{2}\right)$
$= -\frac{\sqrt{3}}{2}$

34. $\cos(\theta + 270°) \stackrel{?}{=} \sin\theta$
$\cos\theta \cos 270° - \sin\theta \sin 270° \stackrel{?}{=} \sin\theta$
$\cos\theta \cdot 0 - \sin\theta \cdot -1 \stackrel{?}{=} \sin\theta$
$\sin\theta = \sin\theta$

35. $\cos(180° - \alpha) \stackrel{?}{=} -\cos\alpha$
$\cos 180° \cos\alpha + \sin 180° \sin\alpha \stackrel{?}{=} -\cos\alpha$
$-1 \cdot \cos\alpha + 0 \cdot \sin\alpha \stackrel{?}{=} -\cos\alpha$
$-\cos\alpha = -\cos\alpha$

36. $\cos^2 x = 1 - \sin^2 x$
$\cos^2 x = 1 - \left(\frac{1}{4}\right)^2$
$\cos^2 x = \frac{15}{16}$
$\cos x = \frac{\sqrt{15}}{4}$

$\sin 2x = 2 \sin x \cos x$
$= 2\left(\frac{1}{4}\right)\left(\frac{\sqrt{15}}{4}\right)$
$= \frac{\sqrt{15}}{8}$

$\cos 2x = 1 - 2\sin^2 x$
$= 1 - 2\left(\frac{1}{4}\right)^2$
$= \frac{7}{8}$

$\sin \frac{x}{2} = \sqrt{\frac{1 - \cos x}{2}}$
$= \sqrt{\frac{1 - \frac{\sqrt{15}}{4}}{2}}$
$= \sqrt{\frac{8 - 2\sqrt{15}}{16}}$
$= \frac{\sqrt{8 - 2\sqrt{15}}}{4}$

$\cos \frac{x}{2} = \sqrt{\frac{1 + \cos x}{2}}$
$= \sqrt{\frac{1 + \frac{\sqrt{15}}{4}}{2}}$
$= \sqrt{\frac{8 + 2\sqrt{15}}{16}}$
$= \frac{\sqrt{8 + 2\sqrt{15}}}{4}$

37. $\cos^2 x = 1 - \sin^2 x$
$\cos^2 x = 1 - \left(-\frac{5}{13}\right)^2$
$\cos^2 x = \frac{144}{169}$
$\cos x = -\frac{12}{13}$

$\sin 2x = 2 \sin x \cos x$
$= 2\left(-\frac{5}{13}\right)\left(-\frac{12}{13}\right)$
$= \frac{120}{169}$

$\cos 2x = 1 - 2\sin^2 x$
$= 1 - 2\left(-\frac{5}{13}\right)^2$
$= \frac{119}{169}$

$\sin \frac{x}{2} = \sqrt{\frac{1 - \cos x}{2}}$
$= \sqrt{\frac{1 - (-\frac{12}{13})}{2}}$
$= \sqrt{\frac{25}{26}}$
$= \frac{5}{\sqrt{26}} \cdot \frac{\sqrt{26}}{\sqrt{26}}$
$= \frac{5\sqrt{26}}{26}$

$\cos \frac{x}{2} = \sqrt{\frac{1 + \cos x}{2}}$
$= \sqrt{\frac{1 + (-\frac{12}{13})}{2}}$
$= \sqrt{\frac{1}{26}}$
$= -\frac{1}{\sqrt{26}} \cdot \frac{\sqrt{26}}{\sqrt{26}}$
$= -\frac{\sqrt{26}}{26}$

38. $\sin^2 x = 1 - \cos^2 x$
$\sin^2 x = 1 - \left(-\frac{15}{17}\right)^2$
$\sin^2 x = \frac{64}{289}$
$\sin x = \frac{8}{17}$

$\sin 2x = 2 \sin x \cos x$
$= 2\left(\frac{8}{17}\right)\left(-\frac{15}{17}\right)$
$= -\frac{240}{289}$

$\cos 2x = 2\cos^2 x - 1$
$= 2\left(-\frac{15}{17}\right)^2 - 1$
$= \frac{161}{289}$

$\sin \frac{x}{2} = \sqrt{\frac{1 - \cos x}{2}}$
$= \sqrt{\frac{1 - (-\frac{15}{17})}{2}}$
$= \sqrt{\frac{32}{34}}$
$= \sqrt{\frac{16}{17}}$
$= \frac{4\sqrt{17}}{17}$

$\cos \frac{x}{2} = \sqrt{\frac{1 + (-\frac{15}{17})}{2}}$
$= \sqrt{\frac{1 + \cos x}{2}}$
$= \sqrt{\frac{1}{17}}$
$= \frac{\sqrt{17}}{17}$

39. $\sin^2 x = 1 - \cos^2 x$

$\sin^2 x = 1 - \left(\frac{12}{13}\right)^2$

$\sin^2 x = \frac{25}{169}$

$\sin x = -\frac{5}{13}$

$\sin 2x = 2 \sin x \cos x$
$= 2\left(-\frac{5}{13}\right)\left(\frac{12}{13}\right)$
$= -\frac{120}{169}$

$\cos 2x = 2\cos^2 x - 1$
$= 2\left(\frac{12}{13}\right)^2 - 1$
$= \frac{119}{169}$

$\sin \frac{x}{2} = \sqrt{\frac{1 - \cos x}{2}}$
$= \sqrt{\frac{1 - \frac{12}{13}}{2}}$
$= \sqrt{\frac{1}{26}}$
$= \frac{\sqrt{26}}{26}$

$\cos \frac{x}{2} = \sqrt{\frac{1 + \cos x}{2}}$
$= \sqrt{\frac{1 + \frac{12}{13}}{2}}$
$= \sqrt{\frac{25}{26}}$
$= -\frac{5\sqrt{26}}{26}$

40. $\sin^4 \theta - \cos^4 \theta \stackrel{?}{=} -\cos 2\theta$

$(\sin^2 \theta + \cos^2 \theta)(\sin^2 \theta - \cos^2 \theta) \stackrel{?}{=} -\cos 2\theta$

$1(\sin^2 \theta - \cos^2 \theta) \stackrel{?}{=} -\cos 2\theta$

$-(\cos^2 \theta - \sin^2 \theta) \stackrel{?}{=} -\cos 2\theta$

$-\cos 2\theta = -\cos 2\theta$

41. $\frac{1}{2} \sin 2x \stackrel{?}{=} \frac{\tan x}{1 + \tan^2 x}$

$\frac{1}{2} \sin 2x \stackrel{?}{=} \frac{\frac{\sin x}{\cos x}}{\sec^2 x}$

$\frac{1}{2} \sin 2x \stackrel{?}{=} \frac{\sin x}{\cos x} \cdot \cos^2 x$

$\frac{1}{2} \sin 2x \stackrel{?}{=} \frac{2 \sin x \cos x}{2}$

$\frac{1}{2} \sin 2x = \frac{1}{2} \sin 2x$

42. $\frac{\sin 2\theta}{1 - \cos 2\theta} \stackrel{?}{=} \cot \theta$

$\frac{2 \sin \theta \cos \theta}{1 - (1 - 2\sin^2 \theta)} \stackrel{?}{=} \cot \theta$

$\frac{2 \sin \theta \cos \theta}{2 \sin^2 \theta} \stackrel{?}{=} \cot \theta$

$\frac{\cos \theta}{\sin \theta} \stackrel{?}{=} \cot \theta$

$\cot \theta = \cot \theta$

43. $2\cos^2 \theta + \sin^2 \theta = 2 \cos \theta$

$2\cos^2 \theta + (1 - \cos^2 \theta) = 2 \cos \theta$

$\cos^2 \theta - 2\cos \theta + 1 = 0$

$(\cos \theta - 1)^2 = 0$

$\cos \theta - 1 = 0$

$\cos \theta = 1$

$\theta = 0°$

44. $\cos \theta = 1 - \sin \theta$

$\cos^2 \theta = (1 - \sin \theta)^2$

$\cos^2 \theta = 1 - 2\sin \theta + \sin^2 \theta$

$1 - \sin^2 \theta = 1 - 2 \sin \theta + \sin^2 \theta$

$0 = 2\sin^2 \theta - 2 \sin \theta$

$0 = 2 \sin \theta (\sin \theta - 1)$

$2 \sin \theta = 0$ or $\sin \theta - 1 = 0$

$\sin \theta = 0$ $\quad$ $\sin \theta = 1$

$\theta = 0°$ or $180°$ $\quad$ $\theta = 90°$

$0°, 90°$

45. Let $u = 2\theta$.

$2 \sin u = 1$

$\sin u = \frac{1}{2}$

$u = 30°, 150°, 390°, 510°$

$2\theta = u$

$\theta = \frac{1}{2} u$

$\theta = 15°, 75°, 195°, 255°$

46. $6 \sin^2 x - 5 \sin x - 4 = 0$

$(3 \sin x - 4)(2 \sin x + 1) = 0$

$3 \sin x - 4 = 0$ or $2 \sin x + 1 = 0$

$\sin x = \frac{4}{3}$ $\quad$ $\sin x = -\frac{1}{2}$

not possible $\quad$ $x = 210°$ or $330°$

$210° + k \cdot 360°, 330° + k \cdot 360°$

47. $2\cos^2 x = 3 \sin x$

$2(1 - \sin^2 x) = 3 \sin x$

$0 = 2 \sin^2 x + 3 \sin x - 2$

$0 = (2 \sin x - 1)(\sin x + 2)$

$2 \sin x - 1 = 0$ or $\sin x + 2 = 0$

$\sin x = \frac{1}{2}$ $\quad$ $\sin x = -2$

$x = 30°$ or $150°$ $\quad$ not possible

$30° + k \cdot 360°, 150° + k \cdot 360°$

48. $2 \sin x \cos x = 1$

$\sin 2x = 1$

Let $u = 2x$

$\sin u = 1$

$u = 90°$

$2x = u$

$x = \frac{1}{2} u$

$x = 45°$

$45° + k \cdot 180°$

Page 872 Applications and Problem Solving

49.

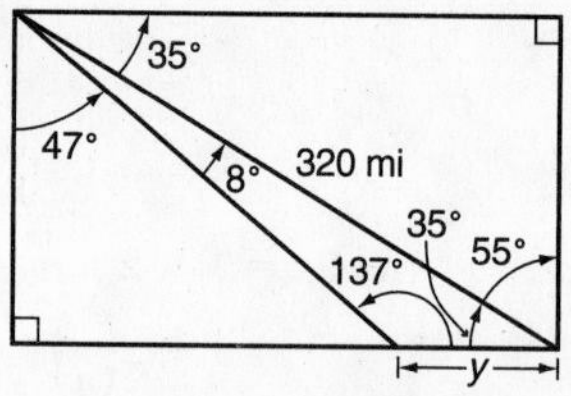

$\sin \frac{8°}{y} = \sin \frac{137°}{320}$

$y = \frac{320 \sin 8°}{\sin 137°}$

$y \approx 65.3$;
65.3 miles

50. $\sin x + \cos x = \sqrt{2}$

$(\sin x + \cos x)^2 = (\sqrt{2})^2$

$\sin^2 x + 2 \sin x \cos x + \cos^2 x = 2$

$1 + 2 \sin x \cos x = 2$

$2 \sin x \cos x = 1$

$\sin 2x = 1$

$x = \frac{\pi}{4}$

Page 873 Alternative Assessment; Thinking Critically

- Use $\cot (A - B) = \frac{\cos(A - B)}{\sin (A - B)}$ or $\cot (A - B) = \frac{1}{\tan (A - B)}$
- $\tan 2\theta = \tan (\theta + \theta)$
  $= \frac{\tan \theta + \tan \theta}{1 - \tan \theta(\tan \theta)}$
  $= \frac{2 \tan \theta}{1 - \tan^2 \theta}$

Extra Practice

Page 876 Lesson 1-1

1. $3(2^2 + 3) = 3(4 + 3) = 3(7) = 21$

2. $2(3 + 8) - 3 = 2(11) - 3 = 22 - 3 = 19$

3. $5 + 3^2 - 16 + 4 = 5 + 9 - 16 + 4 = 2$

4. $(5 + 3) - 16 \div 4 = 8 - 16 \div 4 = 8 - 4 = 4$

5. $4 + 8(4) \div 2 - 10 = 4 + 32 \div 2 - 10 = 4 + 16 - 10 = 10$

6. $15 \div 3 \times 5 + 1 = 5 \times 5 + 1 = 25 + 1 = 26$

7. $[(4 + 8)^2 \div 9] \cdot 5 = [(12)^2 \div 9] \cdot 5 = [144 \div 9] \cdot 5 = 16 \cdot 5 = 80$

8. $5 + 8^2 \div 4 \cdot 3 = 5 + 64 \div 4 \cdot 3 = 5 + 16 \cdot 3 = 5 + 48 = 53$

9. $5 \cdot 7 - 2(5 + 1) \div 3 = 35 - 2(6) \div 3 = 35 - 12 \div 3 = 35 - 4 = 31$

10. $3 + 7^2 - 16 \div 2 = 3 + 49 - 16 \div 2 = 3 + 49 - 8 = 44$

11. $12 + 20 \div 4 - 5 = 12 + 5 - 5 = 12$

12. $[7 - (8 - 6)^2] - 1 = [7 - (2)^2] - 1 = [7 - 4] - 1 = 3 - 1 = 2$

13. $\frac{1}{2}(3^2 + 5 \cdot 7) - 8 = \frac{1}{2}(9 + 35) - 8 = \frac{1}{2}(44) - 8 = 22 - 8 = 14$

14. $\frac{3 \cdot 5 + 3^2}{2^3} = \frac{15 + 9}{8} = \frac{24}{8} = 3$

15. $\frac{6^2 + 4(2^4)}{28 + 9 \cdot 8} = \frac{36 + 4(16)}{28 + 72} = \frac{36 + 64}{28 + 72} = \frac{100}{100} = 1$

16. $3b + 4d = 3(4) + 4(-3) = 12 + (-12) = 0$

17. $ab^2 + c = (-0.5)(4)^2 + 5 = (-0.5)(16) + 5 = -8 + 5 = -3$

18. $bc + d \div a = 4(5) + (-3) \div (-0.5) = 20 + 6 = 26$

19. $7ab - 3d = 7(-0.5)(4) - 3(-3) = -14 + 9 = -5$

20. $ad + b^2 - c = -0.5(-3) + 4^2 - 5 = 1.5 + 16 - 5 = 12.5$

21. $d(b + d)^3 = -3(4 + (-3))^3 = -3(1)^3 = -3(1) = -3$

22. $\frac{4a + 3c}{3b} = \frac{4(-0.5) + 3(5)}{3(4)} = \frac{-2 + 15}{12} = \frac{13}{12}$

23. $\frac{3ab^2 - d^3}{a} = \frac{3(-0.5)4^2 - (-3)^3}{-0.5} = \frac{3(-0.5)16 - (-27)}{-0.5} = \frac{-24 + 27}{-0.5} = \frac{3}{-0.5} = -6$

24. $\frac{5a + ad}{bc} = \frac{5(-0.5) + (-0.5)(-3)}{4(5)} = \frac{-2.5 + 1.5}{20} = \frac{-1}{20} = -\frac{1}{20}$

Page 876 Lesson 1-2

1. $4.1 + 8.2 = 12.3$; Q, R

2. $-54 \div 6 = -9$; Z, Q, R

3. $\sqrt{36} - 3 = 6 - 3 = 3$; N, W, Z, Q, R

4. $\sqrt{81 - 4} = \sqrt{77} \approx 8.775$; I, R

5. commutative (×)

6. multiplicative inverse

7. distributive

8. additive inverse

9. additive identity

10. associative (×)

11. $-3; \frac{1}{3}$

12. $\frac{1}{8}; -8$

13. $-\frac{2}{7}; \frac{7}{2}$

14. $-0.2; \frac{10}{2} = 5$

15. $6(2a + 3b) + 5(3a - 4b) = 12a + 18b + 15a - 20b = 12a + 15a + 18b - 20b = 27a - 2b$

16. $7s + 9t + 2s - 7t = 7s + 2s + 9t - 7t = 9s + 2t$

17. $4(3x - 5y) - 8(2x + y) = 12x - 20y - 16x - 8y = 12x - 16x - 20y - 8y = -4x - 28y$

18. $0.2(5m - 8) + 0.3(6 - 2m) = 1m - 1.6 + 1.8 - 0.6m = 1m - 0.6m - 1.6 + 1.8 = 0.4m + 0.2$

19. $\frac{1}{2}(7p + 3q) + \frac{3}{4}(6p - 4q) = \frac{7}{2}p + \frac{3}{2}q + \frac{9}{2}p - 3q = \frac{7}{2}p + \frac{9}{2}p + \frac{3}{2}q - 3q = \frac{16}{2}p - \frac{3}{2}q = 8p - \frac{3}{2}q$

20. $\frac{4}{5}(3v - 2w) - \frac{1}{5}(7v - 2w) = \frac{12}{5}v - \frac{8}{5}w - \frac{7}{5}v + \frac{2}{5}w$
$= \frac{12}{5}v - \frac{7}{5}v - \frac{8}{5}w + \frac{2}{5}w$
$= v - \frac{6}{5}w$

Page 876 Lesson 1-3

1. 1, 1, 1, 2, 4; 1; 1
$\frac{1+1+1+2+4}{5} = \frac{9}{5} = 1.8$

2. 179, 180, 216, 219, 399, 399
$\frac{216+219}{2} = \frac{435}{2} = 217.5;$
$399; \frac{179+180+216+219+399+399}{6} =$
$\frac{1592}{6} = 265.\overline{3}$ or 265.3

3. 49, 50, 52, 56, 58, 60, 61, 61
$\frac{56+58}{2} = \frac{114}{2} = 57; 61;$
$\frac{49+50+52+56+58+60+61+61}{8} =$
$\frac{447}{8} = 55.875$ or 55.9

4. 20.9, 23.4, 24.0, 25.5, 25.7, 26.7, 26.8
25.5; no mode;
$\frac{20.9+23.4+24.0+25.5+25.7+26.7+26.8}{7} =$
$\frac{173}{7} \approx 24.7$

5.
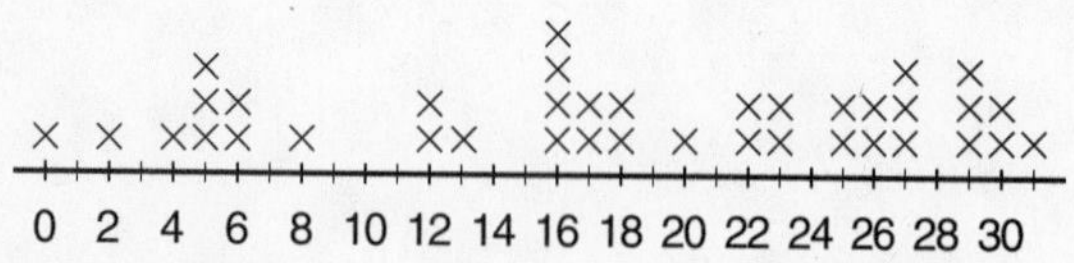

6.

Stem	Leaf
0	0 2 4 5 5 5 6 6 8
1	2 2 3 6 6 6 6 7 7 8 8
2	0 2 2 3 3 5 5 6 6 7 7 7 9 9 9
3	0 0 1

$3|0 = 30°$

7. $\frac{18+18}{2} = 18$

8. 16

9. $(0 + 2 + 4 + 5 + 5 + 5 + 6 + 6 + 8 + 12 + 12 + 13 + 16 + 16 + 16 + 16 + 17 + 17 + 18 + 18 + 20 + 22 + 22 + 23 + 23 + 25 + 25 + 26 + 26 + 27 + 27 + 27 + 29 + 29 + 29 + 30 + 30 + 31) \div 38 = 683 \div 38 \approx 17.97$

Page 877 Lesson 1-4

1. $2(x + 7)$ 2. $12 - x^2$ 3. $6x^2$ 4. $3(x - 1)$
5. $8 + 4x$ 6. $(x + 11)^2$
7. symmetric (=) 8. substitution (=)
9. reflexive (=) 10. multiplication (=)
11. subtraction (=) 12. transitive (=)

13. $5t + 8 = 88$
$5t + 8 - 8 = 88 - 8$
$5t = 80$
$t = 16$

14. $27 - x = -4$
$27 - 27 - x = -4 - 27$
$-x = -31$
$x = 31$

15. $17a = -8 + 9a$
$17a - 9a = -8 + 9a - 9a$
$8a = -8$
$a = -1$

16. $6 = \frac{3x-6}{3}$
$18 = 3x - 6$
$24 = 3x$
$8 = x$

17. $\frac{3a+3}{4} = \frac{5}{2}$
$2(3a + 3) = 5 \cdot 4$
$6a + 6 = 20$
$6a = 14$
$a = \frac{7}{3}$

18. $\frac{3}{4}y = \frac{2}{3}y + 5$
$\frac{3}{4}y - \frac{2}{3}y = 5$
$\frac{9}{12}y - \frac{8}{12}y = 5$
$\frac{1}{12}y = 5$
$y = 60$

19. $-6 = 3.1s + 6.4$
$-12.4 = 3.1s$
$-4 = s$

20. $8s - 3 = 5(2s + 1)$
$8s - 3 = 10s + 5$
$-3 = 2s + 5$
$-8 = 2s$
$-4 = s$

21. $0.4(p - 9) = 0.3(p + 4)$
$0.4p - 3.6 = 0.3p + 1.2$
$0.1p - 3.6 = 1.2$
$0.1p = 4.8$
$p = 48$

22. $2(m - 4) + 5 = 9$
$2m - 8 + 5 = 9$
$2m - 3 = 9$
$2m = 12$
$m = 6$

23. $5(a - 1) = 2(a + 5)$
$5a - 5 = 2a + 10$
$3a - 5 = 10$
$3a = 15$
$a = 5$

24. $4c - 3 = 7c + 18$
$-3 = 3c + 18$
$-21 = 3c$
$-7 = c$

25. $0.5z + 10 = z + 4$
$10 = 0.5z + 4$
$6 = 0.5z$
$12 = z$

26. $3(k - 2) = k + 4$
$3k - 6 = k + 4$
$2k - 6 = 4$
$2k = 10$
$k = 5$

27. $4(y + 1) + 7 = y + 17$
$4y + 4 + 7 = y + 17$
$4y + 11 = y + 17$
$3y + 11 = 17$
$3y = 6$
$y = 2$

28. $\frac{2r-3}{-7} = 5$
$2r - 3 = -35$
$2r = -32$
$r = -16$

29. $8q - \frac{q}{3} = 46$
$\frac{24}{3}q - \frac{1}{3}q = 46$
$\frac{23}{3}q = 46$
$q = 6$

30. $\frac{1}{3}(3d - 1) = \frac{1}{2}(d + 2)$
$d - \frac{1}{3} = \frac{1}{2}d + 1$
$\frac{1}{2}d - \frac{1}{3} = 1$
$\frac{1}{2}d = \frac{4}{3}$
$d = \frac{8}{3}$

Page 877 Lesson 1-5

1. $|2x| = |2(-5)|$
$= |-10|$
$= 10$

2. $|-3y| = |-3(3)|$
$= |-9|$
$= 9$

3. $|2x + y| = |2(-5) + 3|$
$= |-10 + 3|$
$= |-7|$
$= 7$

4. $|y + 5z| = |3 + 5(-2.5)|$
$= |3 - 12.5|$
$= |-9.5|$
$= 9.5$

5. $-|x + z| = -|-5 + (-2.5)|$
$= -|-7.5|$
$= -7.5$

6. $8 - |5y - 3| = 8 - |5(3) - 3|$
$= 8 - |15 - 3|$
$= 8 - |12|$
$= 8 - 12$
$= -4$

7. $2|x| - 4|2 + y| = 2|-5| - 4|2 + 3|$
$= 2|-5| - 4|5|$
$= 2(5) - 4(5)$
$= 10 - 20$
$= -10$

8. $|x + y| - 6|z| = |-5 + 3| - 6|-2.5|$
$= |-2| - 6|-2.5|$
$= 2 - 6(2.5)$
$= 2 - 15$
$= -13$

9. $|d + 1| = 7$
$d + 1 = 7$ or $d + 1 = -7$
$d = 6$ $\quad d = -8$

10. $|a - 6| = 10$
$a - 6 = 10$ or $a - 6 = -10$
$a = 16$ $\quad a = -4$

11. $2|x - 5| = 22$
$|x - 5| = 11$
$x - 5 = 11$ or $x - 5 = -11$
$x = 16$ $\quad x = -6$

12. $|t + 9| - 8 = 5$
$|t + 9| = 13$
$t + 9 = 13$ or $t + 9 = -13$
$t = 4$ $\quad t = -22$

13. $|p + 1| + 10 = 5$
$|p + 1| = -5$
no solution

14. $6|g - 3| = 42$
$|g - 3| = 7$
$g - 3 = 7$ or $g - 3 = -7$
$g = 10$ $\quad g = -4$

15. $2|y + 4| = 14$
$|y + 4| = 7$
$y + 4 = 7$ or $y + 4 = -7$
$y = 3$ $\quad y = -11$

16. $|3b - 10| = 2b$
$3b - 10 = 2b$ or $3b - 10 = -2b$
$-10 = -b$ $\quad -10 = -5b$
$10 = b$ $\quad 2 = b$

17. $|3x + 7| + 4 = 0$
$|3x + 7| = -4$
no solution

18. $|2c + 3| - 15 = 0$
$|2c + 3| = 15$
$2c + 3 = 15$ or $2c + 3 = -15$
$2c = 12$ $\quad 2c = -18$
$c = 6$ $\quad c = -9$

19. $7 - |m - 1| = 3$
$-|m - 1| = -4$
$|m - 1| = 4$
$m - 1 = 4$ or $m - 1 = -4$
$m = 5$ $\quad m = -3$

20. $3 + |z + 5| = 10$
$|z + 5| = 7$
$z + 5 = 7$ or $z + 5 = -7$
$z = 2$ $\quad z = -12$

21. $4|h + 1| = 32$
$|h + 1| = 8$
$h + 1 = 8$ or $h + 1 = -8$
$h = 7$ $\quad h = -9$

22. $2|2x + 3| = 34$
$|2x + 3| = 17$
$2x + 3 = 17$ or $2x + 3 = -17$
$2x = 14$ $\quad 2x = -20$
$x = 7$ $\quad x = -10$

23. $3|a - 5| - 4 = 14$
$3|a - 5| = 18$
$|a - 5| = 6$
$a - 5 = 6$ or $a - 5 = -6$
$a = 11$ $\quad a = -1$

24. $2|2d - 7| + 1 = 35$
$2|2d - 7| = 34$
$|2d - 7| = 17$
$2d - 7 = 17$ or $2d - 7 = -17$
$2d = 24$ $\quad 2d = -10$
$d = 12$ $\quad d = -5$

25. $|3t + 6| + 9 = 30$
$|3t + 6| = 21$
$3t + 6 = 21$ or $3t + 6 = -21$
$3t = 15$ $\quad 3t = -27$
$t = 5$ $\quad t = -9$

26. $|d - 3| = 2d + 9$
$d - 3 = 2d + 9$ or $d - 3 = -(2d + 9)$
$-3 = d + 9$ $\quad d - 3 = -2d - 9$
$-12 = d$ $\quad 3d - 3 = -9$
$3d = -6$
$d = -2$

Check:
$|d - 3| = 2d + 9$
$|-12 - 3| \stackrel{?}{=} 2(-12) + 9$ $\quad |-2 - 3| \stackrel{?}{=} 2(-2) + 9$
$|-15| \stackrel{?}{=} -24 + 9$ $\quad |-5| \stackrel{?}{=} -4 + 9$
$15 \neq -15$ $\quad 5 = 5$ ✓

27. $|4y - 5| + 4 = 7y + 8$
$|4y - 5| = 7y + 4$
$4y - 5 = 7y + 4$ or $4y - 5 = -(7y + 4)$
$-5 = 3y + 4$ $\quad 4y - 5 = -7y - 4$
$-9 = 3y$ $\quad 11y - 5 = -4$
$-3 = y$ $\quad 11y = 1$
$y = \frac{1}{11}$

(Continued next page)

Check:

$|4y - 5| + 4 = 7y + 8$

$|4(-3) - 5| + 4 \stackrel{?}{=} 7(-3) + 8$

$|-17| + 4 \stackrel{?}{=} -21 + 8$

$17 + 4 \stackrel{?}{=} -13$

$21 \neq -13$

$\left|4\left(\frac{1}{11}\right) - 5\right| + 4 \stackrel{?}{=} 7\left(\frac{1}{11}\right) + 8$

$\left|-\frac{51}{11}\right| + 4 \stackrel{?}{=} \frac{7}{11} + 8$

$\frac{51}{11} + \frac{44}{11} \stackrel{?}{=} \frac{7}{11} + \frac{88}{11}$

$\frac{95}{11} = \frac{95}{11}$ ✓

28. $|2b + 4| - 3 = 6b + 1$

$|2b + 4| = 6b + 4$

$2b + 4 = 6b + 4$	or	$2b + 4 = -(6b + 4)$
$4 = 4b + 4$		$2b + 4 = -6b - 4$
$0 = 4b$		$8b + 4 = -4$
$0 = b$		$8b = -8$
		$b = -1$

Check:

$|2b + 4| - 3 = 6b + 1$

$|2(0) + 4| - 3 \stackrel{?}{=} 6(0) + 1$

$|4| - 3 \stackrel{?}{=} 0 + 1$

$4 - 3 \stackrel{?}{=} 0 + 1$

$1 = 1$ ✓

$|2(-1) + 4| - 3 \stackrel{?}{=} 6(-1) + 1$

$|2| - 3 \stackrel{?}{=} -6 + 1$

$2 - 3 \stackrel{?}{=} -6 + 1$

$-1 \neq -5$

29. $|5t| + 2 = 3t + 18$

$|5t| = 3t + 16$

$5t = 3t + 16$	or	$5t = -(3t + 16)$
$2t = 16$		$5t = -3t - 16$
$t = 8$		$8t = -16$
		$t = -2$

Page 877 Lesson 1-6

1. $2z + 5 \leq 7$

$2z \leq 2$

$z \leq 1$; $\{z \mid z \leq 1\}$

2. $3r - 8 > 7$

$3r > 15$

$r > 5$; $\{r \mid r > 5\}$

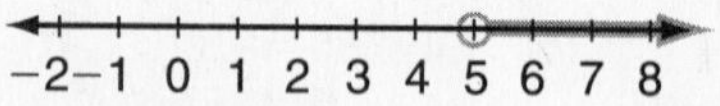

3. $-3x > 6$

$x < -2$; $\{x \mid x < -2\}$

4. $0.75b < 3$

$b < 4$; $\{b \mid b < 4\}$

5. $2(3f + 5) \geq 28$

$6f + 10 \geq 28$

$6f \geq 18$

$f \geq 3$; $\{f \mid f \geq 3\}$

6. $-33 > 5g + 7$

$-40 > 5g$

$-8 > g$; $\{g \mid g < -8\}$

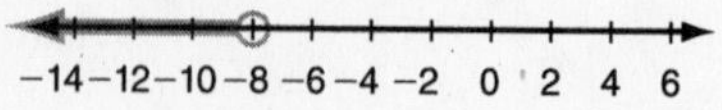

7. $-3(y - 2) \geq -9$

$-3y + 6 \geq -9$

$-3y \geq -15$

$y \leq 5$; $\{y \mid y \leq 5\}$

8. $7a + 5 > 4a - 7$

$3a + 5 > -7$

$3a > -12$

$a > -4$; $\{a \mid a > -4\}$

9. $5(b - 3) \leq b - 7$

$5b - 15 \leq b - 7$

$4b - 15 \leq -7$

$4b \leq 8$

$b \leq 2$; $\{b \mid b \leq 2\}$

10. $3(2x - 5) < 5(x - 4)$

$6x - 15 < 5x - 20$

$x - 15 < -20$

$x < -5$; $\{x \mid x < -5\}$

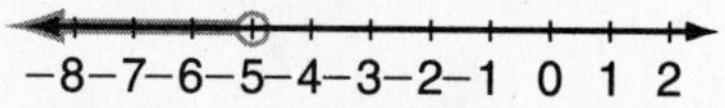

11. $2(4m - 1) + 3(m + 4) \geq 6m$

$8m - 2 + 3m + 12 \geq 6m$

$11m + 10 \geq 6m$

$5m + 10 \geq 0$

$5m \geq -10$

$m \geq -2$; $\{m \mid m \geq -2\}$

12. $8(2c - 1) > 11c + 22$

$16c - 8 > 11c + 22$

$5c - 8 > 22$

$5c > 30$

$c > 6$; $\{c \mid c > 6\}$

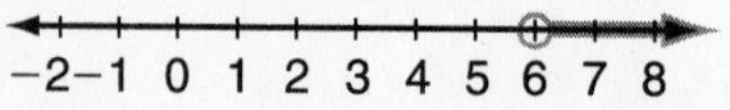

13. $5y - 4(2y + 1) \leq 2(0.5 - 2y)$
$5y - 8y - 4 \leq 1 - 4y$
$-3y - 4 \leq 1 - 4y$
$y - 4 \leq 1$
$y \leq 5; \{y \mid y \leq 5\}$

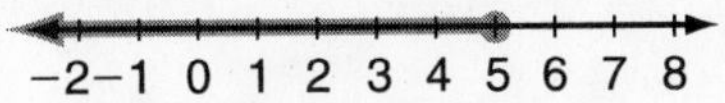

14. $2(d + 4) - 5 \geq 5(d + 3)$
$2d + 8 - 5 \geq 5d + 15$
$2d + 3 \geq 5d + 15$
$-3d + 3 \geq 15$
$-3d \geq 12$
$d \leq -4; \{d \mid d \leq -4\}$

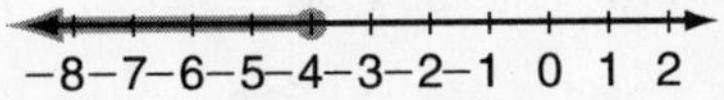

15. $8 - 3t < 4(3 - t)$
$8 - 3t < 12 - 4t$
$8 + t < 12$
$t < 4; \{t \mid t < 4\}$

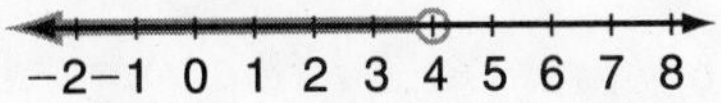

16. $-x \geq \frac{x + 4}{7}$
$-7x \geq x + 4$
$-8x \geq 4$
$x \leq -\frac{1}{2}; \left\{x \mid x \leq -\frac{1}{2}\right\}$

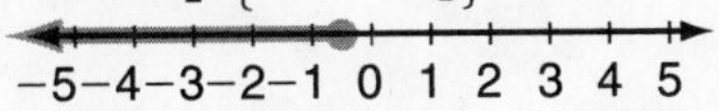

17. $\frac{a + 8}{4} \leq \frac{7 + a}{3}$
$3(a + 8) \leq 4(7 + a)$
$3a + 24 \leq 28 + 4a$
$-1a + 24 \leq 28$
$-1a \leq 4$
$a \geq -4; \{a \mid a \geq -4\}$

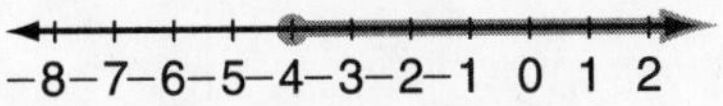

18. $-y < \frac{y + 8}{3}$
$-3y < y + 8$
$-4y < 8$
$y > -2; \{y \mid y > -2\}$

19. $2 + 4(d - 2) \leq 3 - (d - 1)$
$2 + 4d - 8 \leq 3 - d + 1$
$4d - 6 \leq 4 - d$
$5d - 6 \leq 4$
$5d \leq 10$
$d \leq 2; \{d \mid d \leq 2\}$

20. $5(x - 1) - 4x \geq 3(3 - x)$
$5x - 5 - 4x \geq 9 - 3x$
$-5 + x \geq 9 - 3x$
$-5 + 4x \geq 9$
$4x \geq 14$
$x \geq 3.5; \{x \mid x \geq 3.5\}$

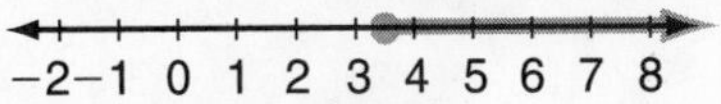

21. $6s - (4s + 7) > 5 - s$
$6s - 4s - 7 > 5 - s$
$2s - 7 > 5 - s$
$3s - 7 > 5$
$3s > 12$
$s > 4; \{s \mid s > 4\}$

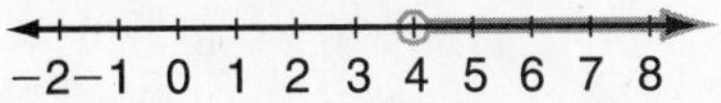

22. $7x > 42$
$x > 6; \{x \mid x > 6\}$

23. $2x - 3 \leq 11$
$2x \leq 14$
$x \leq 7; \{x \mid x \leq 7\}$

24. $-4x \geq 16$
$x \leq -4; \{x \mid x \leq -4\}$

25. $54 < 18x$
$3 < x; \{x \mid x > 3\}$

26. $30 - x < 2x + 3$
$30 - 3x < 3$
$-3x < -27$
$x > 9; \{x \mid x > 9\}$

Page 878 Lesson 1-7

1. $|x| < 5.5$

2. $|x| > 9$

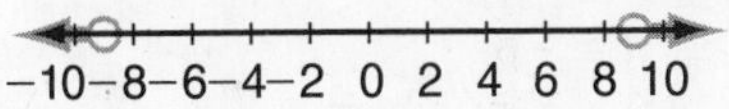

3. $|x| \leq 6$

4. $|a + 3| < 1$
$a + 3 < 1$ and $a + 3 > -1$
$a < -2$ $a > -4$
$\{a \mid -4 < a < -2\}$

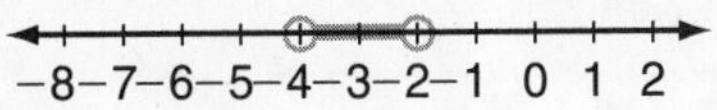

5. $|t - 4| > 1$
$t - 4 > 1$ or $t - 4 < -1$
$t > 5$ $t < 3$
$\{t \mid t < 3 \text{ or } t > 5\}$

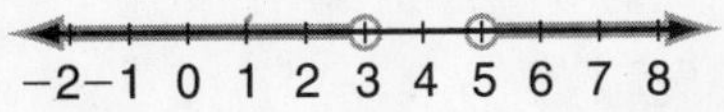

6. $|7x| \geq 21$
$7x \geq 21$ or $7x \leq -21$
$x \geq 3$ $x \leq -3$
$\{x \mid x \leq -3 \text{ or } x \geq 3\}$

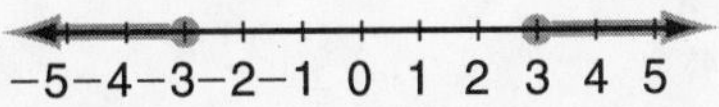

7. $|8p| \leq 16$

$8p \leq 16$ and $8p \geq -16$

$p \leq 2$ $\quad$ $p \geq -2$

$\{p \mid -2 \leq p \leq 2\}$

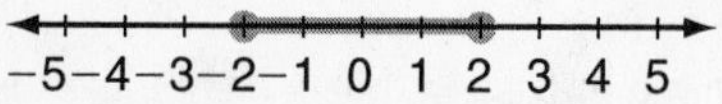

8. $|2y - 5| < 3$

$2y - 5 < 3$ and $2y - 5 > -3$

$2y < 8$ $\quad$ $2y > 2$

$y < 4$ $\quad$ $y > 1$

$\{y \mid 1 < y < 4\}$

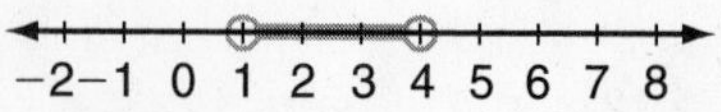

9. $|3d + 6| \geq 3$

$3d + 6 \geq 3$ or $3d + 6 \leq -3$

$3d \geq -3$ $\quad$ $3d \leq -9$

$d \geq -1$ $\quad$ $d \leq -3$

$\{d \mid d \leq -3 \text{ or } d \geq -1\}$

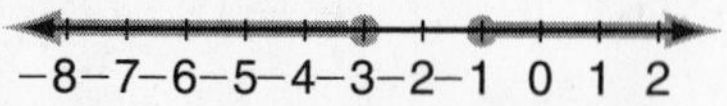

10. $2 < n + 4 < 7$

$-2 < n < 3$

$\{n \mid -2 < n < 3\}$

11. $-3 \leq s - 2 \leq 5$

$-1 \leq s \leq 7$

$\{s \mid -1 \leq s \leq 7\}$

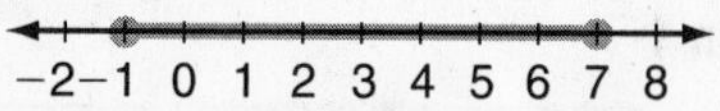

12. $|7d| \geq -42$

$7d \geq -42$ or $7d \leq 42$

$d \geq -6$ $\quad$ $d \leq 6$

all real numbers

13. $|4x - 1| < 5$

$4x - 1 < 5$ and $4x - 1 > -5$

$4x < 6$ $\quad$ $4x > -4$

$x < 1.5$ $\quad$ $x > -1$

$\{x \mid -1 < x < 1.5\}$

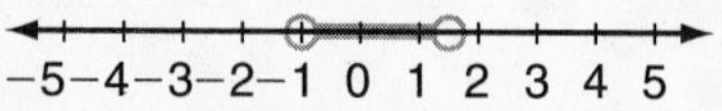

14. $|6v + 12| > 18$

$6v + 12 > 18$ or $6v + 12 < -18$

$6v > 6$ $\quad$ $6v < -30$

$v > 1$ $\quad$ $v < -5$

$\{v \mid v < -5 \text{ or } v > 1\}$

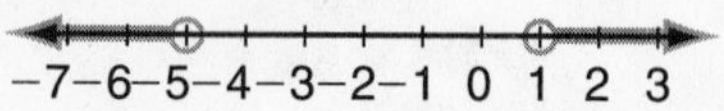

15. $7 < 4x + 3 < 19$

$4 < 4x < 16$

$1 < x < 4$

$\{x \mid 1 < x < 4\}$

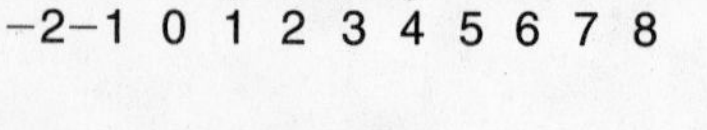

16. $3m - 2 < 7$ or $2m + 1 > 13$

$3m < 9$ $\quad$ $2m > 12$

$m < 3$ $\quad$ $m > 6$

$\{m \mid m < 3 \text{ or } m > 6\}$

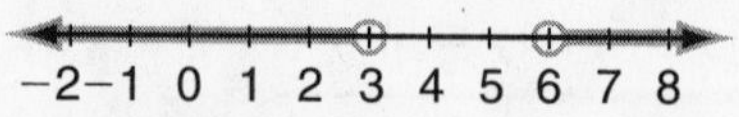

17. $|z + 2| \geq z$

$z + 2 \geq z$ or $z + 2 \leq -z$

$2 \geq 0$ $\quad$ $2z + 2 \leq 0$

true $\quad$ $2z \leq -3$

$z \leq -1$

all reals

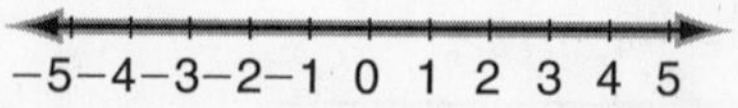

18. $5t + 3 \leq -7$ or $4t - 2 \geq 8$

$5t \leq -10$ $\quad$ $4t \geq 10$

$t \leq -2$ $\quad$ $t \geq 2.5$

$\{t \mid t \leq -2 \text{ or } t \geq 2.5\}$

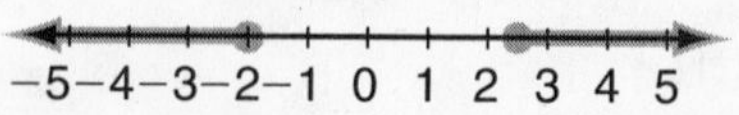

19. $12 + |2q| < 0$

$|2q| < -12$

$2q < -12$ and $2q > 12$

$q < -6$ $\quad$ $q > 6$

$\varnothing$

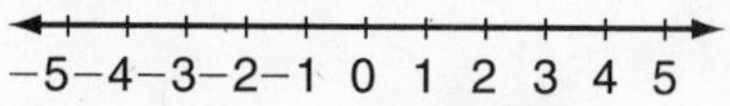

20. $|2r + 4| < 6$

$2r + 4 < 6$ and $2r + 4 > -6$

$2r < 2$ $\quad$ $2r > -10$

$r < 1$ $\quad$ $r > -5$

$\{r \mid -5 < r < 1\}$

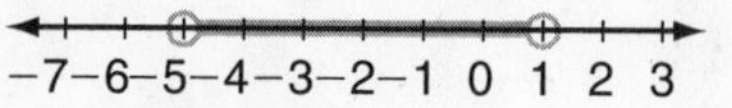

21. $|5w - 3| \geq 9$

$5w - 3 \geq 9$ or $5w - 3 \leq -9$

$5w \geq 12$ $\quad$ $5w \leq -6$

$w \geq 2.4$ $\quad$ $w \leq -1.2$

$\{w \mid w \leq -1.2 \text{ or } w \geq 2.4\}$

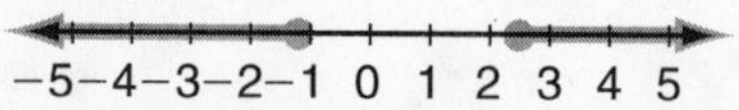

22. $|3h| + 15 < 0$

$|3h| < -15$

$3h < -15$ and $3h > 15$

$h < -5$ $\quad$ $h > 5$

$\varnothing$

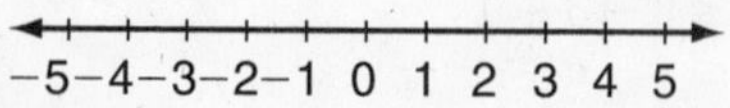

23. $|5n| - 16 \geq 4$

$|5n| \geq 20$

$5n \geq 20$ or $5n \leq -20$

$n \geq 4$ $\quad$ $n \leq -4$

$\{n \mid n \leq -4 \text{ or } n \geq 4\}$

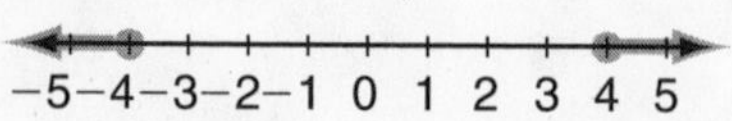

24. $4x + 7 < 5$ or $2x - 4 > 12$
$4x < -2$ $\quad 2x > 16$
$x < -0.5$ $\quad x > 8$
$\{x \mid x < -0.5 \text{ or } x > 8\}$

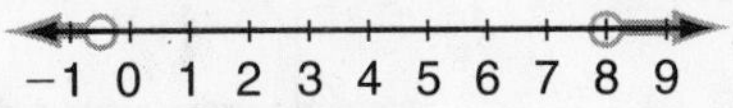

Page 878 Lesson 2-1

1. D = {1, 2, 3, 4}
R = {2, 3, 4, 5}
function, discrete

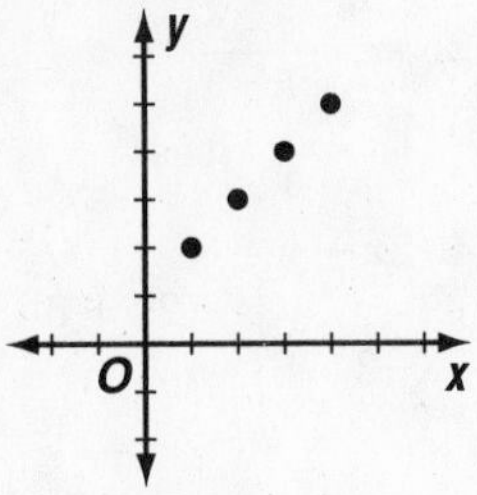

2. D = {0}
R = {0, 1, 2, 3}
not a function

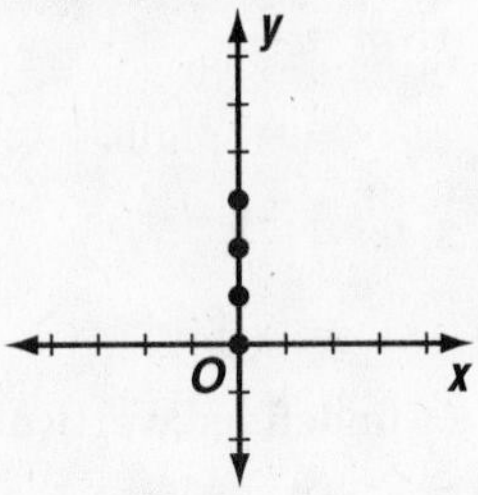

3. D = all reals
R = $\{y \mid y \geq 0\}$
function, continuous

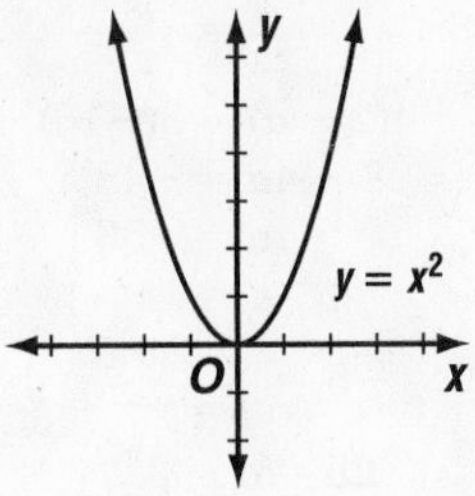

4. D = all reals
R = all reals
function, continuous

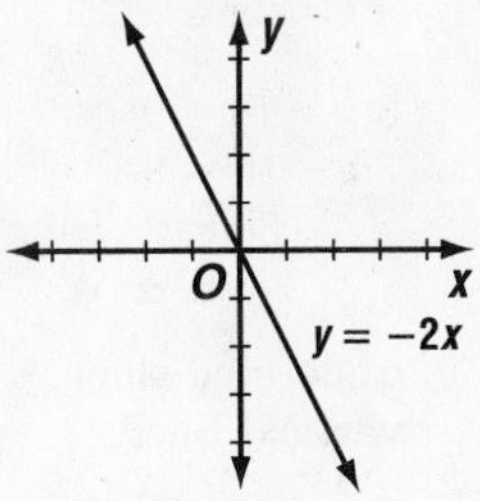

5. D = all reals
R = all reals
function, continuous

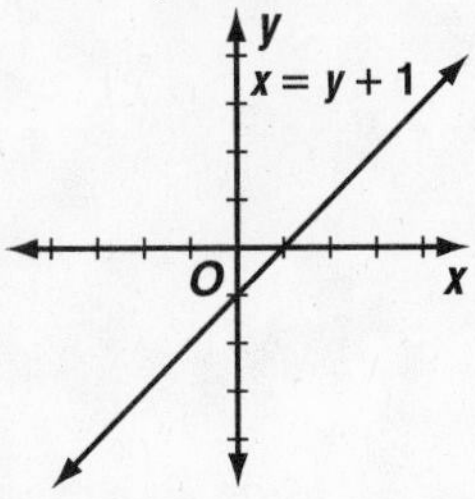

6. D = $\{x \mid x \geq 0\}$
R = all reals
not a function

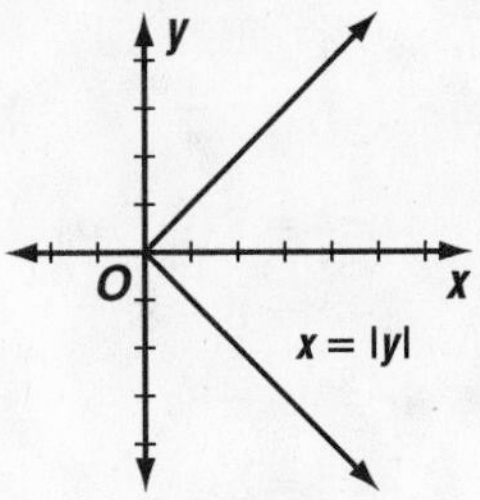

7. no **8.** yes **9.** yes **10.** no

11. $f(x) = \frac{1}{2}(x + 7)$
$f(2) = \frac{1}{2}(2 + 7)$
$= \frac{1}{2}(9)$
$= \frac{9}{2}$

12. $f(x) = \frac{1}{2}(x + 7)$
$f(-4) = \frac{1}{2}(-4 + 7)$
$= \frac{1}{2}(3)$
$= \frac{3}{2}$

13. $f(x) = \frac{1}{2}(x + 7)$
$f\left(\frac{1}{2}\right) = \frac{1}{2}\left(\frac{1}{2} + 7\right)$
$= \frac{1}{2}\left(\frac{15}{2}\right)$
$= \frac{15}{4}$

14. $f(x) = \frac{1}{2}(x + 7)$
$f(a + 2) = \frac{1}{2}(a + 2 + 7)$
$= \frac{1}{2}(a + 9)$
$= \frac{a + 9}{2}$

15. $g(x) = (x + 1)^2 - \frac{2}{x}$
$g(4) = (4 + 1)^2 - \frac{2}{4}$
$= 5^2 - \frac{1}{2}$
$= 25 - \frac{1}{2}$
$= \frac{49}{2}$

16. $g(x) = (x + 1)^2 - \frac{2}{x}$
$g(-2) = (-2 + 1)^2 - \frac{2}{(-2)}$
$= (-1)^2 + 1$
$= 1 + 1$
$= 2$

17. $g(x) = (x + 1)^2 - \frac{2}{x}$
$g\left(\frac{1}{2}\right) = \left(\frac{1}{2} + 1\right)^2 - \frac{2}{\frac{1}{2}}$
$= \left(\frac{3}{2}\right)^2 - 4$
$= \frac{9}{4} - 4$
$= -\frac{7}{4}$

18. $g(x) = (x + 1)^2 - \frac{2}{x}$
$g(b - 1) = (b - 1 + 1)^2 - \frac{2}{b - 1}$
$= b^2 - \frac{2}{b - 1}$

Page 878 Lesson 2-2

1. yes **2.** no **3.** no
4. yes **5.** yes **6.** no

7. $x + 7 = y$
$x - y + 7 = 0$
$x - y = -7$
1; −1; −7

8. $5x - 7y = \frac{1}{2}$
$10x - 14y = 1$
10; −14; 1

9. $y = \frac{2}{3}x + 8$
$-\frac{2}{3}x + y = 8$
$2x - 3y = -24$
2; −3; −24

10. $0.05x + 0.02y = 4$
$0.05x + 0.02(0) = 4$
$0.05x = 4$
$x = 80$
$0.05x + 0.02y = 4$
$0.05(0) + 0.02y = 4$
$0.02y = 4$
$y = 200$

11. $x = 3y$ $\quad x = 3y$
$x = 3(0)$ $\quad 0 = 3y$
$x = 0$ $\quad 0 = y$

12. $x = 7$; none

13. $2y = 3x$
$2(0) = 3x$
$0 = 3x$
$0 = x$

x	y
2	3
−2	−3

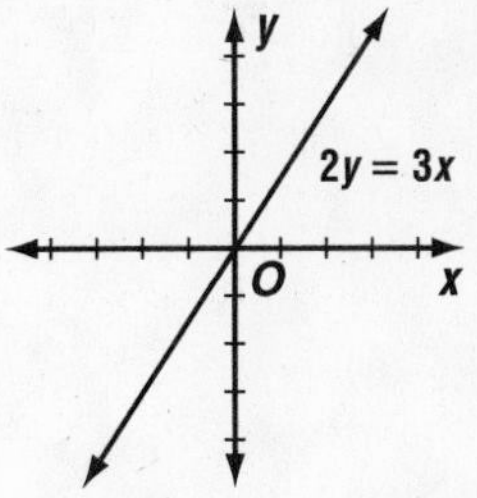

14. $y = x - 4$
$0 = x - 4$
$4 = x$
$y = x - 4$
$y = 0 - 4$
$y = -4$

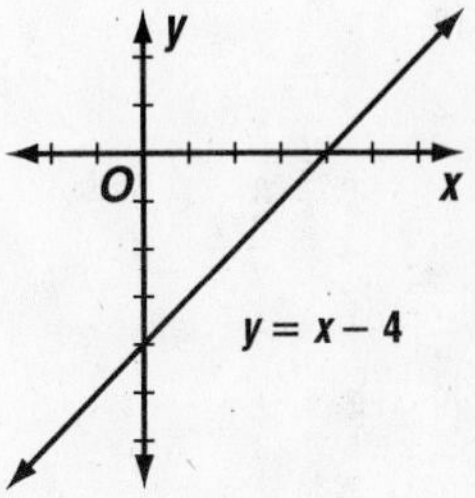

15. $2x + y = 6$
$2x + 0 = 6$
$2x = 6$
$x = 3$
$2x + y = 6$
$2(0) + y = 6$
$y = 6$

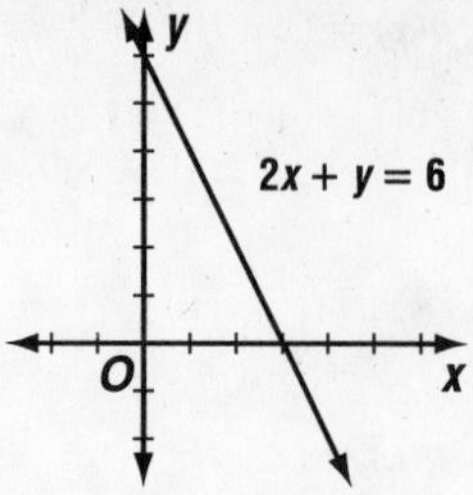

16. $3x - 2y = -12$
$3x - 2(0) = -12$
$3x = -12$
$x = -4$
$3x - 2y = -12$
$3(0) - 2y = -12$
$-2y = -12$
$y = 6$

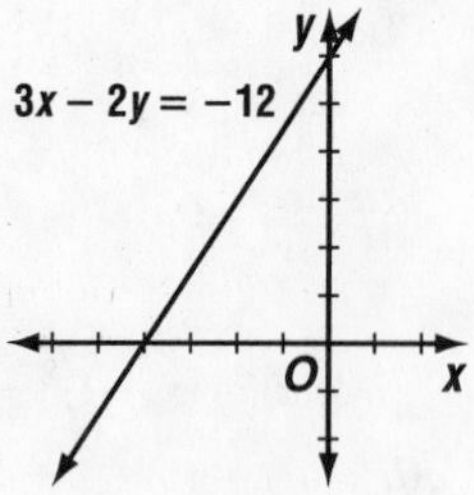

17. $0.2x - 0.5y = 1$
$0.2x - 0.5(0) = 1$
$0.2x = 1$
$x = 5$
$0.2x - 0.5y = 1$
$0.2(0) - 0.5y = 1$
$-0.5y = 1$
$y = -2$

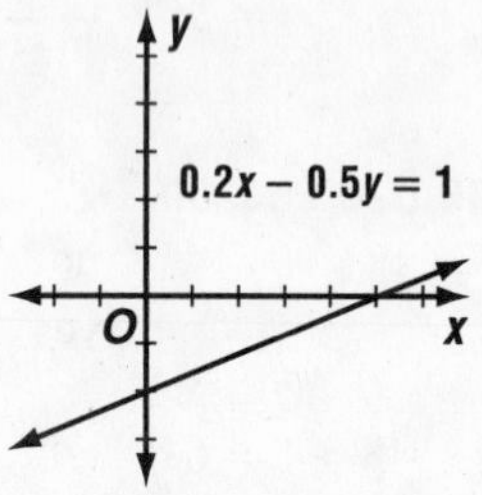

18. $5x = 20$
$x = 4$

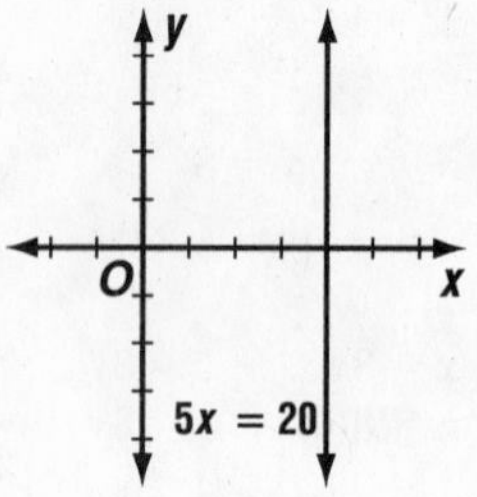

19. $3y + 7 = 12$
$3y = 5$
$y = \frac{5}{3}$

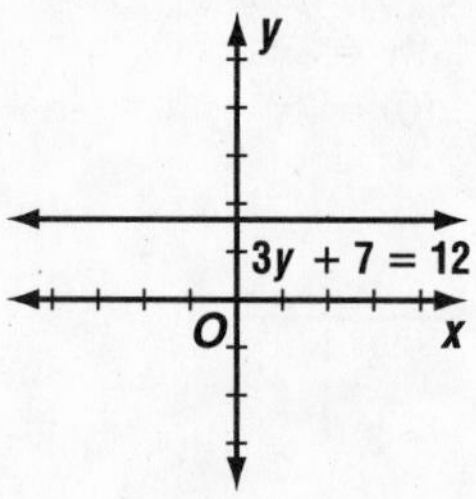

20. $\frac{x}{2} - \frac{y}{5} = \frac{1}{3}$
$\frac{x}{2} - \frac{0}{5} = \frac{1}{3}$
$\frac{x}{2} = \frac{1}{3}$
$x = \frac{2}{3}$
$\frac{x}{2} - \frac{y}{5} = \frac{1}{3}$
$\frac{0}{2} - \frac{y}{5} = \frac{1}{3}$
$-\frac{y}{5} = \frac{1}{3}$
$y = -\frac{5}{3}$

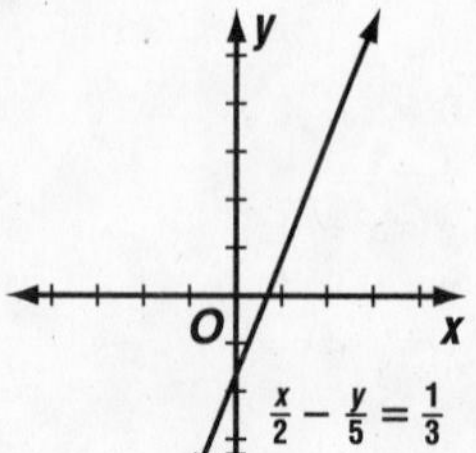

21. $\frac{3}{4}y - x = 1$
$\frac{3}{4}(0) - x = 1$
$-x = 1$
$x = -1$
$\frac{3}{4}y - x = 1$
$\frac{3}{4}y - 0 = 1$
$\frac{3}{4}y = 1$
$y = \frac{4}{3}$

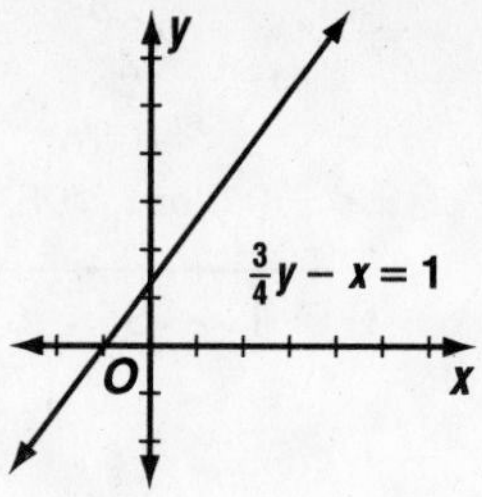

Page 879 Lesson 2-3

1. $m = \frac{0 - 3}{5 - 0}$
$= -\frac{3}{5}$; falls

2. $m = \frac{7 - 3}{5 - 2}$
$= \frac{4}{3}$; rises

3. $m = \frac{-8 - 8}{2 - 2}$
$= -\frac{16}{0}$
undefined; vertical

4. $2x + y = 8$
$y = -2x + 8$
-2

5. $x - 5y = -15$
$-5y = -x - 15$
$y = \frac{1}{5}x + 3$
$\frac{1}{5}$

6. $y = 7$
0

7. $3 = \frac{9 - 0}{a - 5}$
$3(a - 5) = 9$
$3a - 15 = 9$
$3a = 24$
$a = 8$

8. $\frac{4}{3} = \frac{-8 - 8}{2 - a}$
$4(2 - a) = 3(-16)$
$8 - 4a = -48$
$-4a = -56$
$a = 14$

9. undefined slope; vertical line; $a = 7$

10. $-5 = \frac{a - 3}{5 - 0}$
$-25 = a - 3$
$-22 = a$

11. $-\frac{1}{8} = \frac{\frac{3}{4} - a}{\frac{1}{2} - \frac{1}{4}}$
$-\frac{1}{8} = \frac{\frac{3}{4} - a}{\frac{1}{4}}$
$-\frac{1}{4} = 8\left(\frac{3}{4} - a\right)$
$-\frac{1}{4} = 6 - 8a$
$-\frac{25}{4} = -8a$
$\frac{25}{32} = a$

12. $-1 = \frac{a - 1.2}{4.8 - 3.6}$
$-1.2 = a - 1.2$
$0 = a$

Page 879 Lesson 2-4

1. 3; 2

2. 0.12; -3.75

3. $-y = 6x + 4$
$y = -6x - 4$
$-6; -4$

4. $6y = 3x - 9$
$y = \frac{1}{2}x - \frac{3}{2}$
$\frac{1}{2}; -\frac{3}{2}$

5. $2 - 5x = 5y$
$\frac{2}{5} - x = y$
$-1; \frac{2}{5}$

6. $6y + 42 = 5x$
$6y = 5x - 42$
$y = \frac{5}{6}x - 7$
$\frac{5}{6}; -7$

7. $y - y_1 = m(x - x_1)$
$y - 0 = \frac{5}{8}(x - 0)$
$y = \frac{5}{8}x$

8. $y - y_1 = m(x - x_1)$
$y - 7 = -0.3(x - (-2))$
$y - 7 = -0.3x - 0.6$
$y = -0.3x + 6.4$

9. $m = \frac{-3 - 3}{-5 - 5}$
$= \frac{-6}{-10}$
$= \frac{3}{5}$
$y - y_1 = m(x - x_1)$
$y - 3 = \frac{3}{5}(x - 5)$
$y - 3 = \frac{3}{5}x - 3$
$y = \frac{3}{5}x$

10. $(2, 0), (0, 7); m = \frac{7 - 0}{0 - 2}$
$= -\frac{7}{2}$
$y - y_1 = m(x - x_1)$
$y - 0 = -\frac{7}{2}(x - 2)$
$y = -\frac{7}{2}x + 7$

11. $m = \frac{5}{3}; y - y_1 = m(x - x_1)$
$y - 1 = \frac{5}{3}(x - 7)$
$y - 1 = \frac{5}{3}x - \frac{35}{3}$
$y = \frac{5}{3}x - \frac{32}{3}$

12. perpendicular slope $= -\frac{3}{5}; y - y_1 = m(x - x_1)$
$y - 1 = -\frac{3}{5}(x - 7)$
$y - 1 = -\frac{3}{5}x + \frac{21}{5}$
$y = -\frac{3}{5}x + \frac{26}{5}$

13. $m = \frac{4 - 8}{2 - 7}$
$= \frac{-4}{-5}$
$= \frac{4}{5}$
perpendicular slope $= -\frac{5}{4}; y - y_1 = m(x - x_1)$
$y - 5 = -\frac{5}{4}(x - 0)$
$y - 5 = -\frac{5}{4}x$
$y = -\frac{5}{4}x + 5$

Page 879 Lesson 2-5

1a.

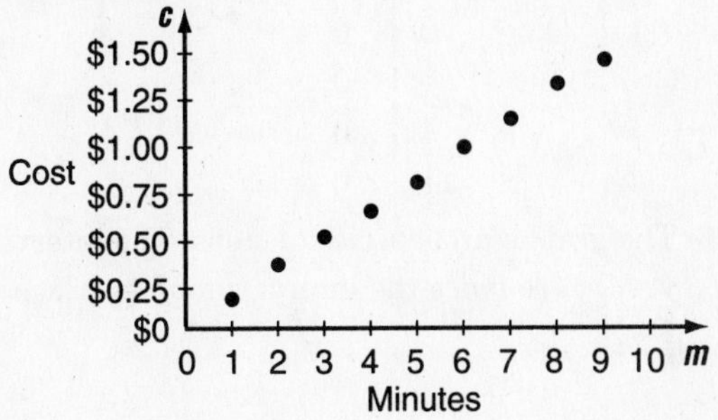

1b. $m = \frac{0.36 - 0.20}{2 - 1}$
$= \frac{0.16}{1}$
$= 0.16$

$y - y_1 = m(x - x_1)$
$y - 0.20 = 0.16(x - 1)$
$y - 0.20 = 0.16x - 0.16$
$y = 0.16x + 0.04$

1c. $y = 0.16x + 0.04$
$= 0.16(15) + 0.04$
$= 2.4 + 0.04$
$= 2.44$; \$2.44

2a.

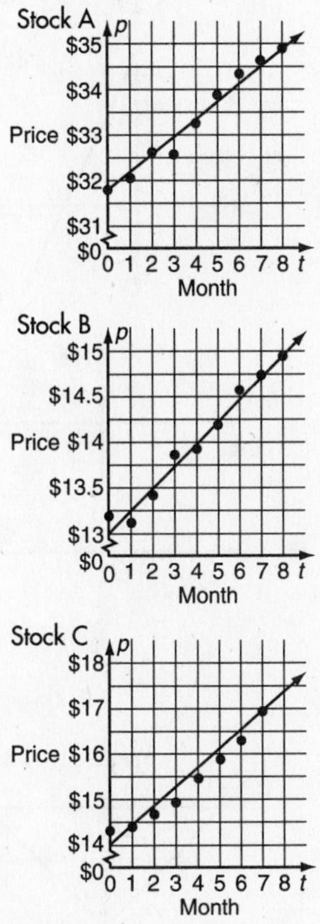

2b. Sample answers:
Stock A:
$p = 0.42m + 31.60$
Stock B:
$p = 0.23m + 13.04$
Stock C:
$p = 0.35m + 14.25$

2c. Sample answer:
$p \approx 0.35m + 14.25$
$\approx 0.35(8) + 14.25$
$\approx 2.80 + 14.25$
≈ 17.05;
about \$17.05

Page 880 Lesson 2-6

1. $g(x) = \left[-\frac{x}{3}\right] - 2$
$g(6) = \left[-\frac{6}{3}\right] - 2$
$= [-2] - 2$
$= -2 - 2$
$= -4$

2. $g(x) = \left[-\frac{x}{3}\right] - 2$
$g(-6) = \left[-\frac{-6}{3}\right] - 2$
$= [2] - 2$
$= 2 - 2$
$= 0$

3. $g(x) = \left[-\frac{x}{3}\right] - 2$
$g(-3) = \left[-\frac{-3}{3}\right] - 2$
$= [1] - 2$
$= 1 - 2$
$= -1$

4. $g(x) = \left[-\frac{x}{3}\right] - 2$
$g(10) = \left[-\frac{10}{3}\right] - 2$
$= \left[-3\frac{1}{3}\right] - 2$
$= -4 - 2$
$= -6$

5. $g(x) = \left[-\frac{x}{3}\right] - 2$
$g\left(\frac{2}{3}\right) = \left[-\frac{\frac{2}{3}}{3}\right] - 2$
$= \left[-\frac{2}{9}\right] - 2$
$= -1 - 2$
$= -3$

6. $g(x) = \left[-\frac{x}{3}\right] - 2$
$g(-25.5) = \left[-\frac{-25.5}{3}\right] - 2$
$= [8.5] - 2$
$= 8 - 2$
$= 6$

7. $g(x) = \left[-\frac{x}{3}\right] - 2$

$g\left(\frac{9}{2}\right) = \left[-\frac{\frac{9}{2}}{3}\right] - 2$

$= \left[-\frac{9}{6}\right] - 2$

$= -2 - 2$

$= -4$

8. $g(x) = \left[-\frac{x}{3}\right] - 2$

$g(23.7) = \left[-\frac{23.7}{3}\right] - 2$

$= [-7.9] - 2$

$= -8 - 2$

$= -10$

9. D; $f(x) = -2x + 5$

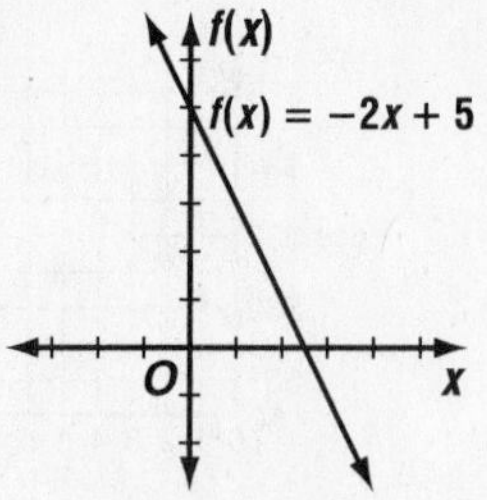

10. C; $f(x) = \frac{17}{4}$

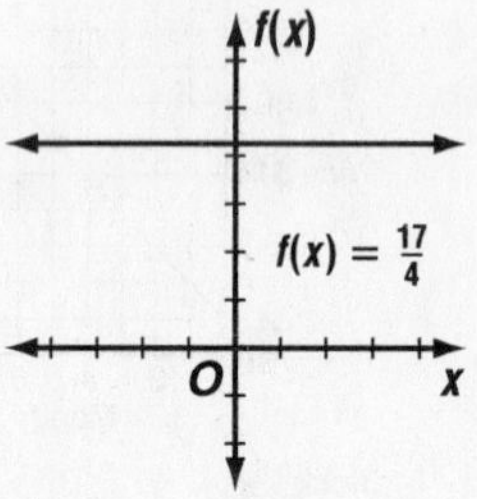

11. A; $h(x) = |x| - 4$

x	$h(x)$
−2	−2
−1	−3
0	−4
1	−3
2	−2

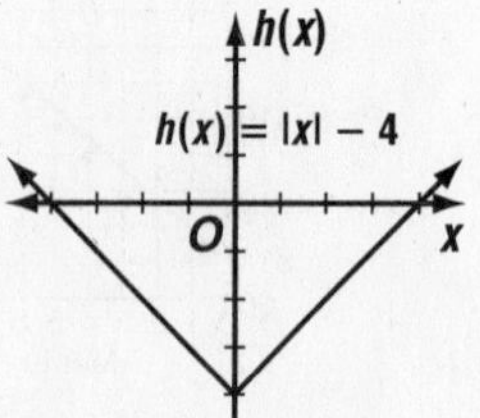

12. G; $g(x) = -2[x + 5]$

x	$g(x)$
−5	0
$-4\frac{1}{2}$	0
−4	−2
$-3\frac{1}{2}$	−2
−3	−4

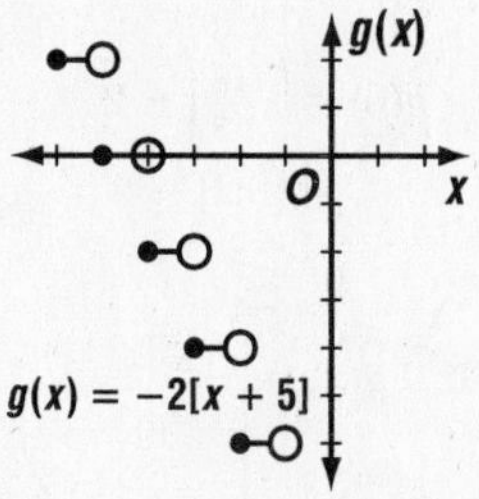

13. D; $g(x) = \frac{x}{2}$

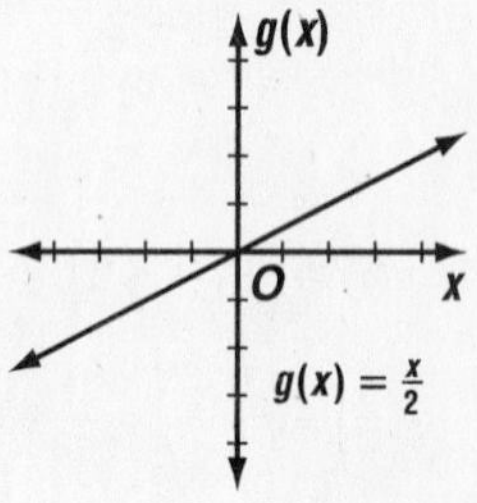

14. A; $h(x) = |-2x| - 8$

x	$h(x)$
−4	0
−2	−4
0	−8
2	−4
4	0

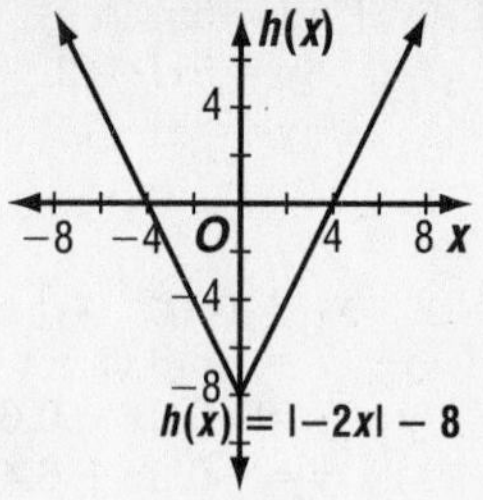

15. $y = |x| - 4$ $y = |x - 4|$

x	y
−1	−2
0	−4
1	−3
2	−2

x	y
3	1
4	0
5	1
6	2

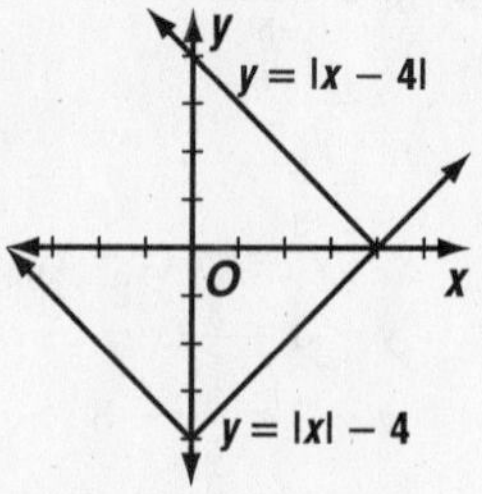

The shapes of the graphs are similar. The vertex of the graph of $|x| - 4$ is (0, −4) and the vertex of the graph of $|x - 4|$ is (4, 0)

16. $y = [-2x]$ $y = -[2x]$

x	y
−1	3
$-\frac{1}{2}$	1
0	0
$\frac{1}{2}$	−1
1	−2

x	y
−1	2
$-\frac{1}{2}$	1
0	0
$\frac{1}{2}$	−1
1	−2

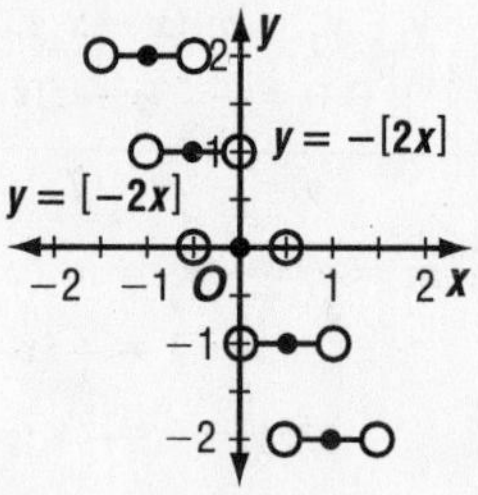

The graphs are series of steps. In the graph of $[-2x]$, the left end is open. In the graph of $-[2x]$, the right is open.

17. $y = |x - 5|$ $y = |5 - x|$

x	y
3	2
4	1
5	0
6	1

x	y
3	2
4	1
5	0
6	1

The graphs are the same.

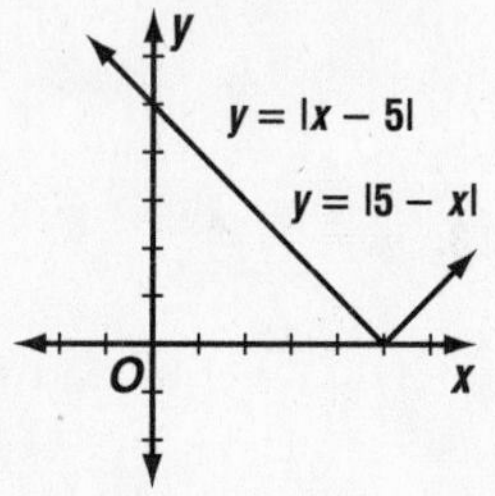

18. $y = [x]$ $y = \left[\frac{x}{2}\right]$

x	y
−1	−1
$-\frac{1}{2}$	−1
0	0
$\frac{1}{2}$	0
1	1

x	y
−2	−1
$-1\frac{1}{2}$	−1
−1	−1
$-\frac{1}{2}$	−1
0	0
$\frac{1}{2}$	0
1	0
$1\frac{1}{2}$	0

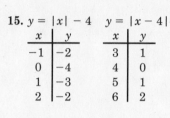

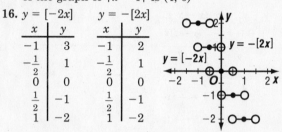

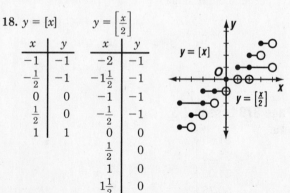

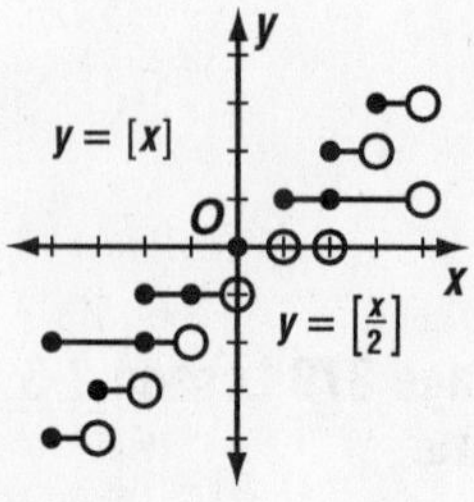

The graphs are a series of steps. The intervals for $y = \left[\frac{x}{2}\right]$ are twice the intervals for $y = [x]$.

Page 880 Lesson 2-7

1. $y \geq x - 15$

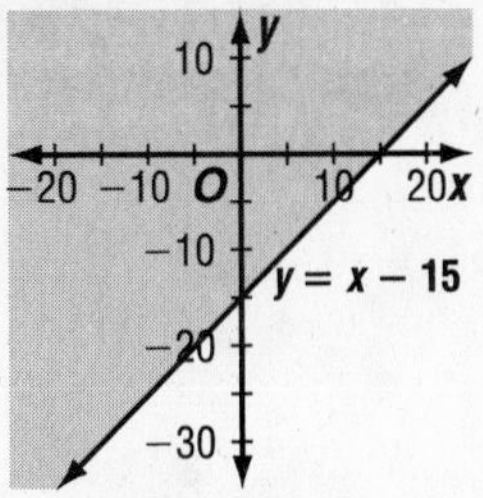

2. $y \leq -3x - 1$

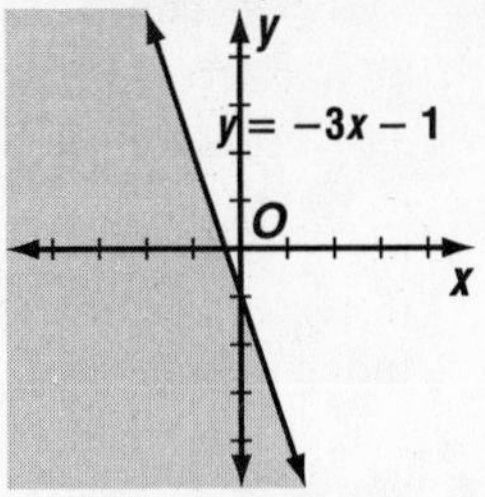

3. $4y \leq 2x - 3y + 8$
$7y \leq 2x + 8$
$y \leq \frac{2}{7}x + \frac{8}{7}$

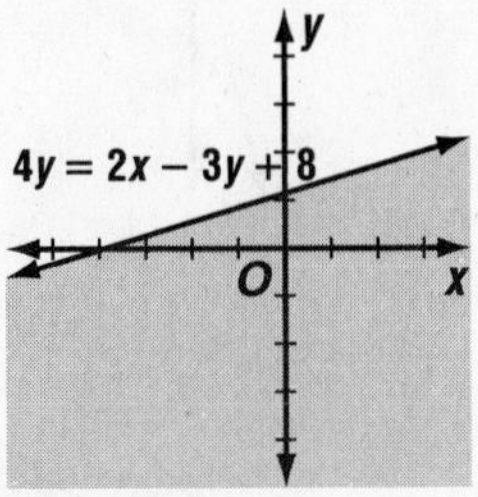

4. $3x > y$
$y < 3x$

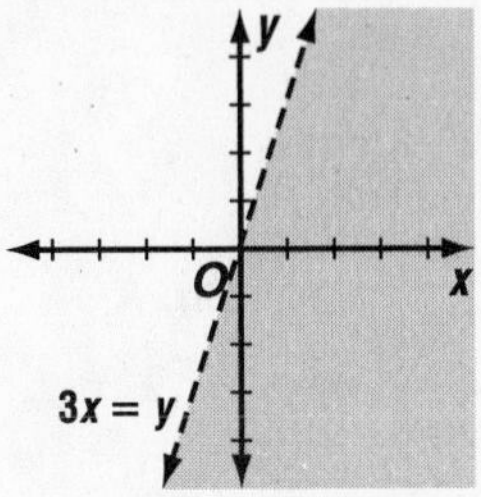

5. $5x + 3 < 18$
$5x < 15$
$x < 3$

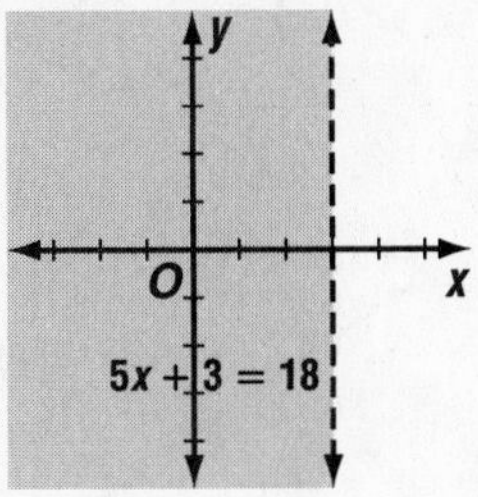

6. $x + 2 \geq y - 7$
$x + 9 \geq y$
$y \leq x + 9$

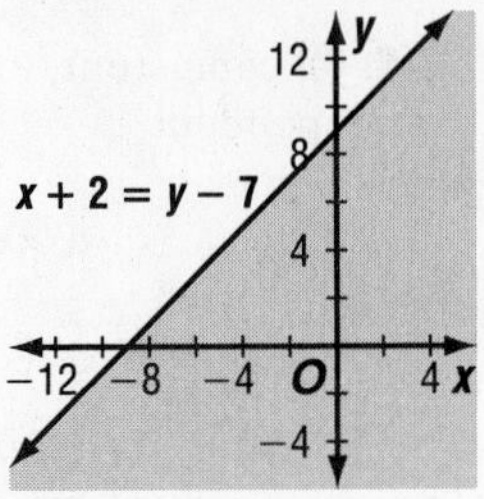

7. $7 > y - 7$
$14 > y$
$y < 14$

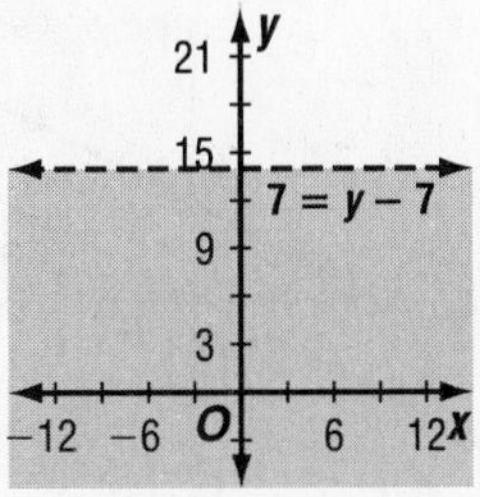

8. $2x < 5 - y$
$2x + y < 5$
$y < -2x + 5$

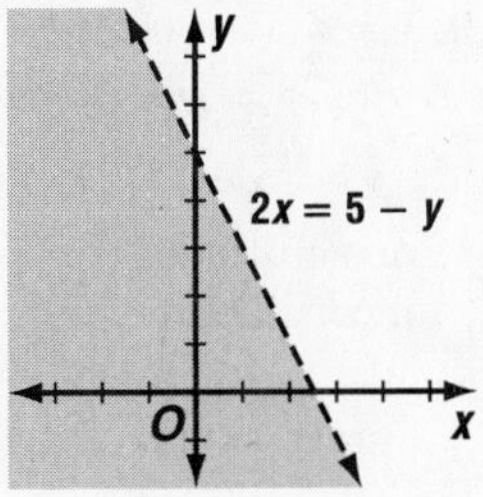

9. $y > \frac{1}{5}x - 8$

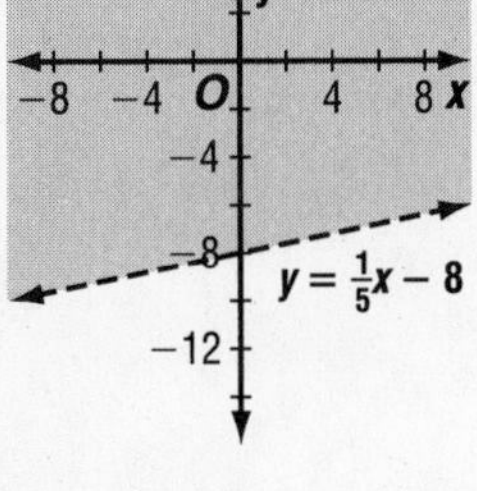

10. $2y - 5x \leq 8$
$2y \leq 5x + 8$
$y \leq \frac{5}{2}x + 4$

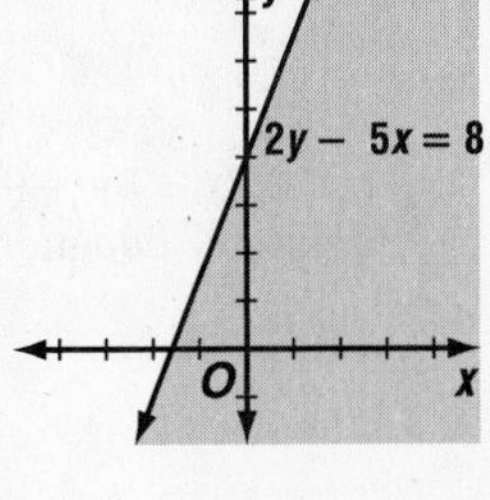

11. $-2x + 5 \leq 3y$
$-\frac{2}{3}x + \frac{5}{3} \leq y$
$y \geq -\frac{2}{3}x + \frac{5}{3}$

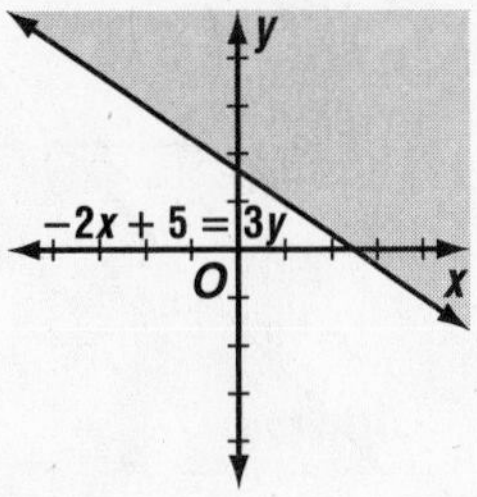

12. $3x + 2y \geq 0$
$2y \geq -3x$
$y \geq -\frac{3}{2}x$

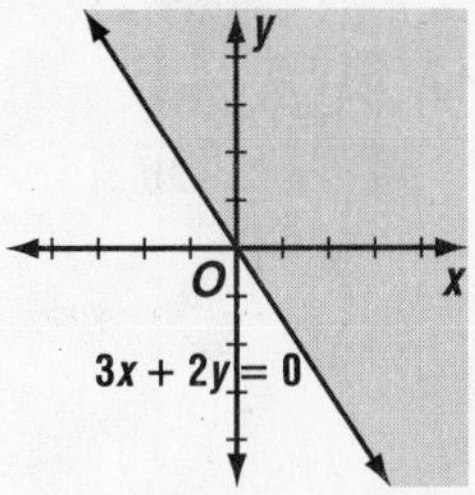

13. $x - 3 < 5$
$x < 8$

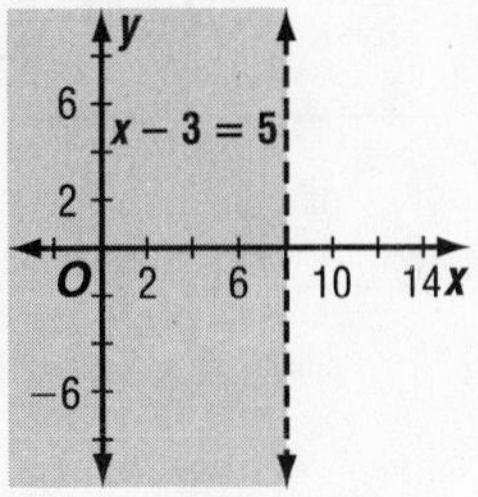

14. $y > 5x - 3$

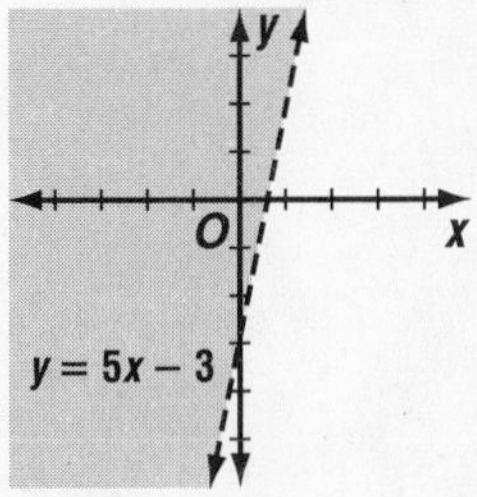

15. $3x + 4y < 9$
$4y < -3x + 9$
$y < -\frac{3}{4}x + \frac{9}{4}$

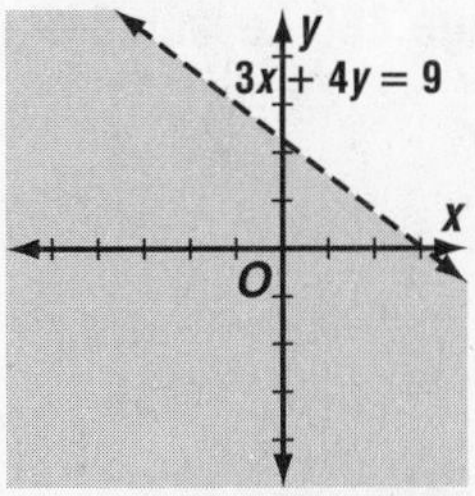

16. $|x| \leq y + 3$
$|x| - 3 \leq y$
$y \geq |x| - 3$

x	y
−2	−1
−1	−2
0	−3
1	−2
2	−1

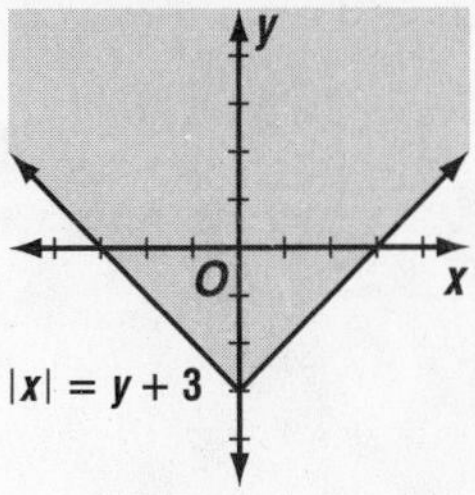

17. $\frac{y}{2} \leq x - 1$
$y \leq 2x - 2$

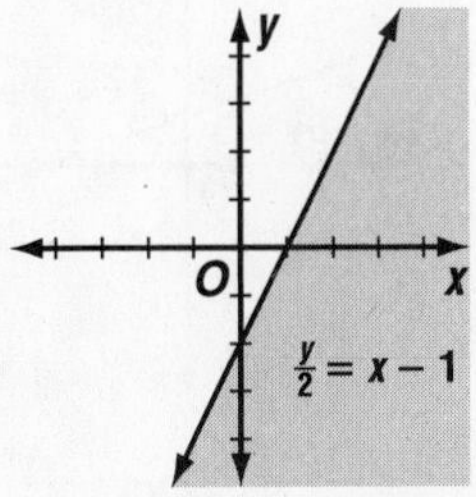

18. $2x - 3y \leq 18$
$-3y \leq -2x + 18$
$y \geq \frac{2}{3}x - 6$

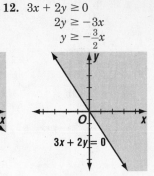

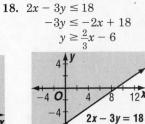

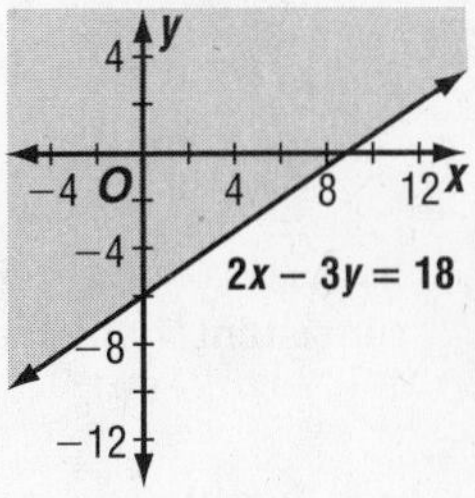

19. $-y < \frac{2x}{3} + 5$

$y > -\frac{2}{3}x - 5$

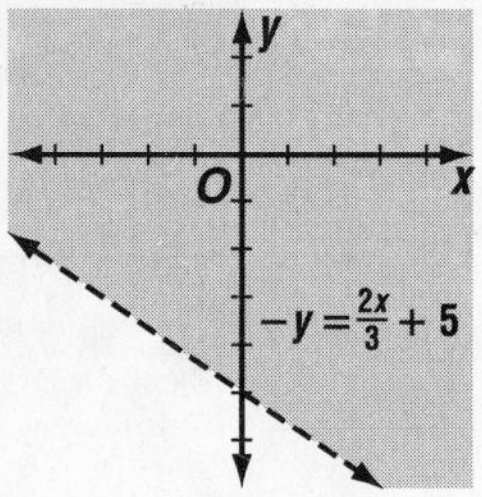

20. $-y \geq 8 - x$

$y \leq -8 + x$

$y \leq x - 8$

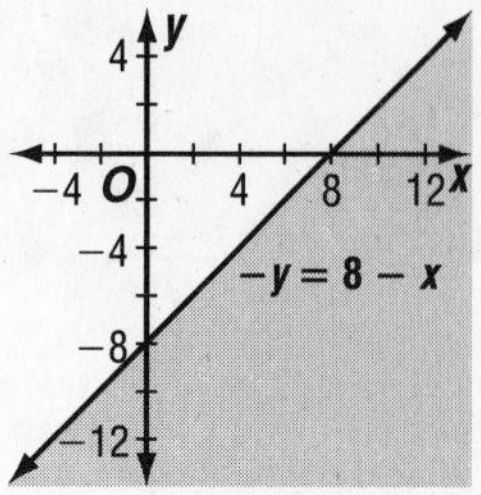

21. $|y| < 7$

$y < 7$ and $y > -7$

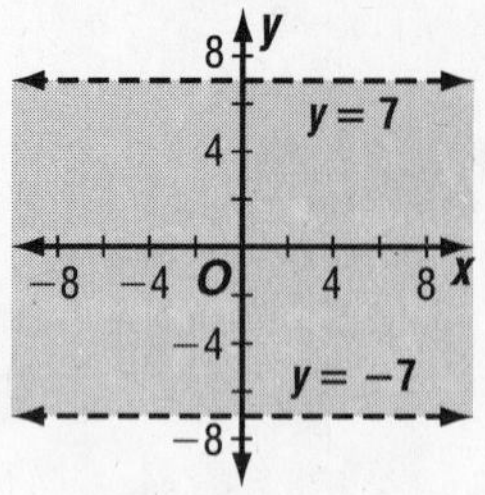

Page 880 Lesson 3-1

1. $x - y = 2$

$-y = -x + 2$

$y = x - 2$

$2x - 2y = 10$

$-2y = -2x + 10$

$y = x - 5$

no solutions; inconsistent

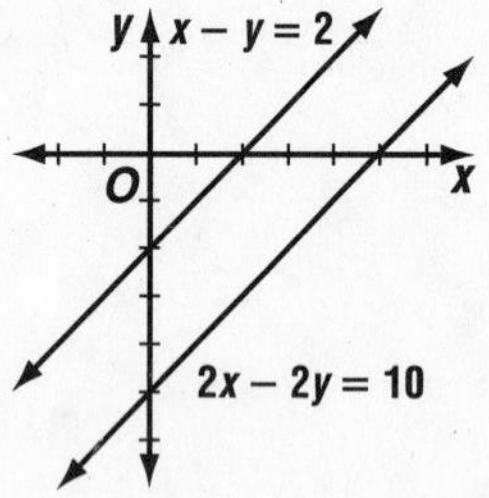

2. $x + 3y = 18$

$3y = -x + 18$

$y = -\frac{1}{3}x + 6$

$-x + 2y = 7$

$2y = x + 7$

$y = \frac{1}{2}x + \frac{7}{2}$

(3, 5); consistent, independent

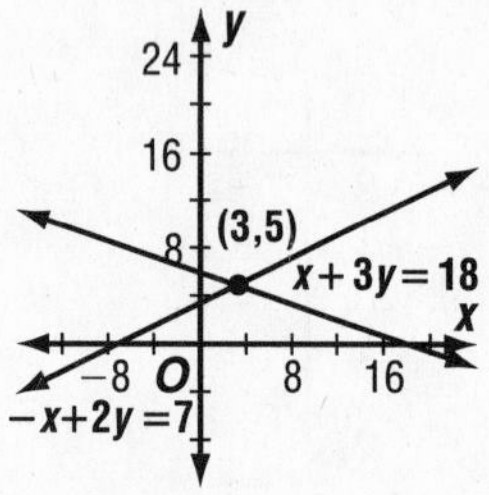

3. $2x + 6y = 6$

$6y = -2x + 6$

$y = -\frac{1}{3}x + 1$

$\frac{1}{3}x + y = 1$

$y = -\frac{1}{3}x + 1$

$\{(x, y) \mid 2x + 6y = 6\}$; consistent, dependent

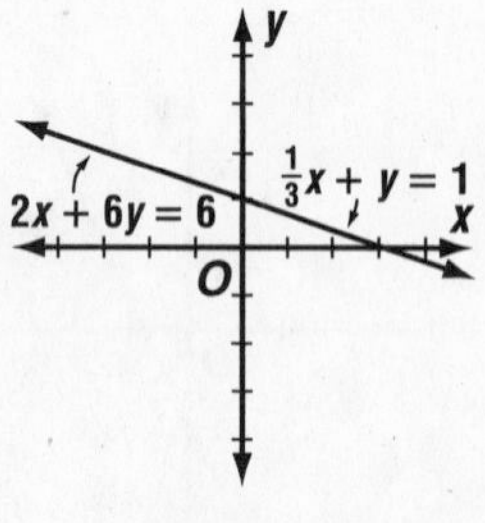

4. $x + 3y = 0$

$3y = -x$

$y = -\frac{1}{3}x$

$2x + 6y = 5$

$6y = -2x + 5$

$y = -\frac{1}{3}x + \frac{5}{6}$

no solutions; inconsistent

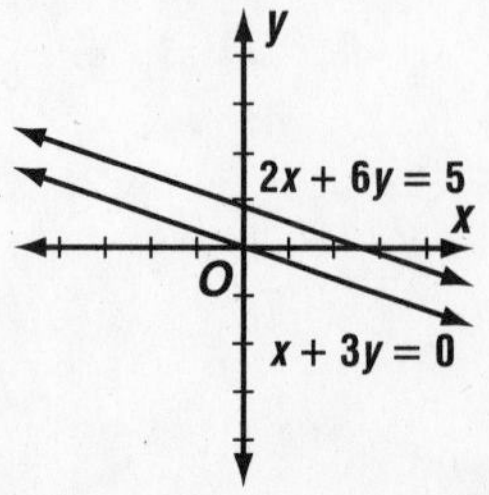

5. $2x - y = 7$

$-y = -2x + 7$

$y = 2x - 7$

$\frac{2}{5}x - \frac{4}{3}y = -2$

$-\frac{4}{3}y = -\frac{2}{5}x - 2$

$y = \frac{3}{10}x + \frac{3}{2}$

(5, 3); consistent, independent

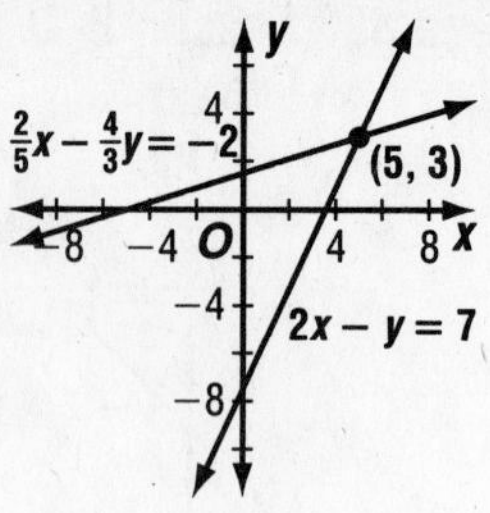

6. $y = \frac{1}{3}x + 1 \quad y = 4x + 1$

(0, 1); consistent, independent

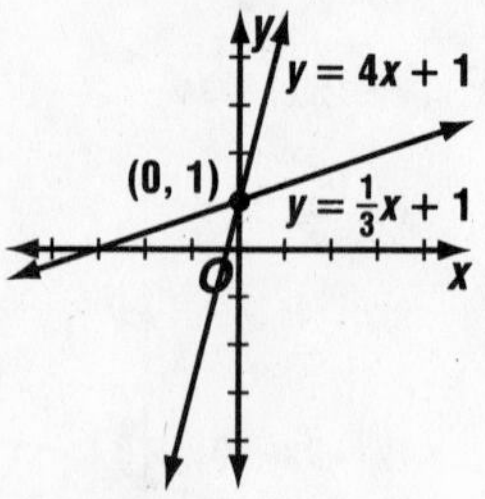

7. $\frac{3}{4}x - y = 0$

$-y = -\frac{3}{4}x$

$y = \frac{3}{4}x$

$\frac{y}{3} + \frac{x}{2} = 6$

$\frac{y}{3} = -\frac{x}{2} + 6$

$y = -\frac{3}{2}x + 18$

(8, 6); consistent, independent

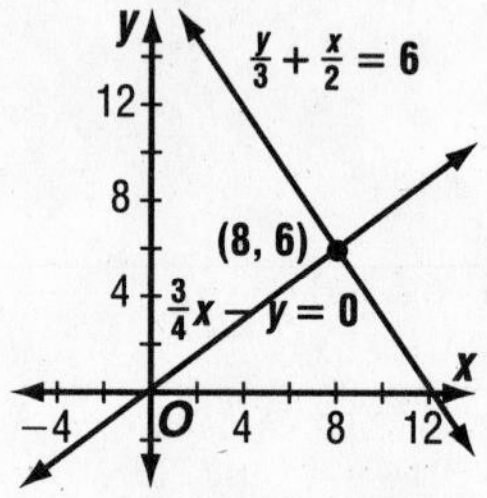

8. $2x + 3y = 5$

$3y = -2x + 5$

$y = -\frac{2}{3}x + \frac{5}{3}$

$-6x - 9y = -15$

$-9y = 6x - 15$

$y = -\frac{2}{3}x + \frac{5}{3}$

$\{(x, y) \mid 2x + 3y = 5\}$; consistent, dependent

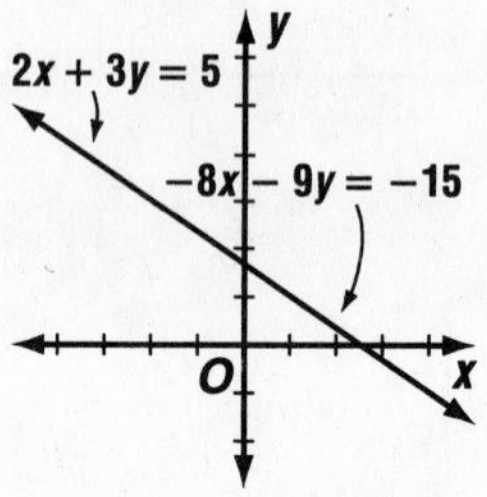

9. $y = \frac{x}{2}$

$2y = x + 4$

$y = \frac{1}{2}x + 2$

no solutions; inconsistent

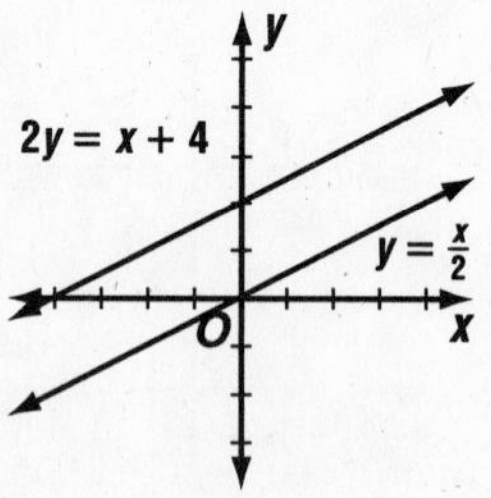

10. $\frac{2}{3}x = \frac{5}{3}y$

$\frac{2}{5}x = y$

$2x - 5y = 0$

$-5y = -2x$

$y = \frac{2}{5}x$

$\{(x, y) \mid 2x - 5y = 0\}$; consistent, dependent

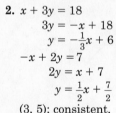

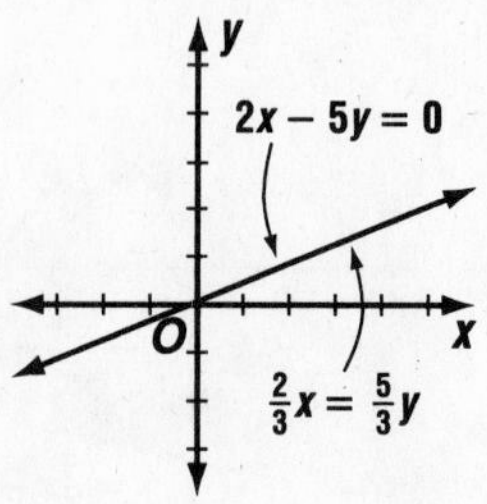

11. $9x - 5 = 7y$

$\frac{9}{7}x - \frac{5}{7} = y$

$4\frac{1}{2}x - 3\frac{1}{2}y = 2\frac{1}{2}$

$\frac{9}{2}x - \frac{7}{2}y = \frac{5}{2}$

$-\frac{7}{2}y = -\frac{9}{2}x + \frac{5}{2}$

$y = \frac{9}{7}x - \frac{5}{7}$

$\{(x, y) \mid 9x - 5 = 7y\}$; consistent, dependent

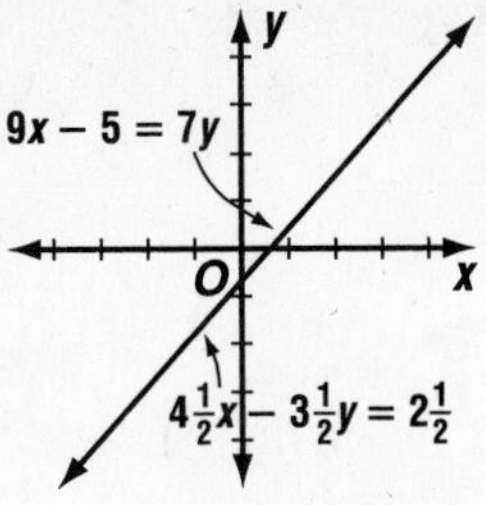

12. $x - 2y = 4$

$-2y = -x + 4$

$y = \frac{1}{2}x - 2$

$y = x - 2$

$(0, -2)$; consistent, independent

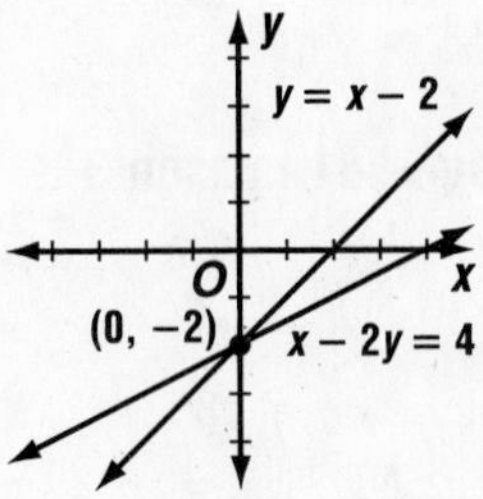

Page 881 Lesson 3-2

1.
$$\begin{aligned} 7x + y &= 9 \\ (+)\ 5x - y &= 15 \\ \hline 12x \quad &= 24 \\ x &= 2 \end{aligned}$$

$$\begin{aligned} 7x + y &= 9 \\ 7(2) + y &= 9 \\ 14 + y &= 9 \\ y &= -5 \end{aligned}$$

$(2, -5)$

2. $x + 6y = 32$

$x = 32 - 6y$

$$\begin{aligned} 2x + 3y &= 10 \\ 2(32 - 6y) + 3y &= 10 \\ 64 - 12y + 3y &= 10 \\ 64 - 9y &= 10 \\ -9y &= -54 \\ y &= 6 \end{aligned}$$

$$\begin{aligned} x &= 32 - 6y \\ &= 32 - 6(6) \\ &= 32 - 36 \\ &= -4 \end{aligned}$$

$(-4, 6)$

3. $x = 4y - 10$

$$\begin{aligned} 5x + 3y &= -4 \\ 5(4y - 10) + 3y &= -4 \\ 20y - 50 + 3y &= -4 \\ 23y - 50 &= -4 \\ 23y &= 46 \\ y &= 2 \end{aligned}$$

$$\begin{aligned} x &= 4y - 10 \\ &= 4(2) - 10 \\ &= 8 - 10 \\ &= -2 \end{aligned}$$

$(-2, 2)$

4. $r + 5s = -17$

$r = -5s - 17$

$$\begin{aligned} 2r - 6s &= -2 \\ 2(-5s - 17) - 6s &= -2 \\ -10s - 34 - 6s &= -2 \\ -16s - 34 &= -2 \\ -16s &= 32 \\ s &= -2 \end{aligned}$$

$$\begin{aligned} r &= -5s - 17 \\ &= -5(-2) - 17 \\ &= 10 - 17 \\ &= -7 \end{aligned}$$

$(-7, -2)$

5. $2x - 3y = 7 \rightarrow 4x - 6y = 14$

$3x + 6y = 42 \rightarrow (+)\ 3x + 6y = 42$

$$\begin{aligned} 7x &= 56 \\ x &= 8 \end{aligned}$$

$$\begin{aligned} 2x - 3y &= 7 \\ 2(8) - 3y &= 7 \\ 16 - 3y &= 7 \\ -3y &= -9 \\ y &= 3 \end{aligned}$$

$(8, 3)$

6. $2a + 5b = -13 \rightarrow 8a + 20b = -52$

$3a - 4b = 38 \rightarrow (+)15a - 20b = 190$

$$\begin{aligned} 23a &= 138 \\ a &= 6 \end{aligned}$$

$$\begin{aligned} 2a + 5b &= -13 \\ 2(6) + 5b &= -13 \\ 12 + 5b &= -13 \\ 5b &= -25 \\ b &= -5 \end{aligned}$$

$(6, -5)$

7. $6p + 8q = 20 \rightarrow 6p + 8q = 20$

$5p - 4q = -26 \rightarrow (+)\ 10p - 8q = -52$

$$\begin{aligned} 16p &= -32 \\ p &= -2 \end{aligned}$$

$$\begin{aligned} 5p - 4q &= -26 \\ 5(-2) - 4q &= -26 \\ -10 - 4q &= -26 \\ -4q &= -16 \\ q &= 4 \end{aligned}$$

$(-2, 4)$

8. $\frac{5}{2}x + \frac{1}{3}y = 13 \rightarrow 15x + 2y = 78$

$\frac{1}{2}x - y = -7 \rightarrow (+)\ x - 2y = -14$

$$\begin{aligned} 16x &= 64 \\ x &= 4 \end{aligned}$$

$$\begin{aligned} \tfrac{1}{2}x - y &= -7 \\ \tfrac{1}{2}(4) - y &= -7 \\ 2 - y &= -7 \\ -y &= -9 \\ y &= 9 \end{aligned}$$

$(4, 9)$

9. $\frac{2}{7}c - \frac{4}{3}d = 16 \rightarrow \frac{4}{7}c - \frac{8}{3}d = 32$

$\frac{4}{7}c + \frac{8}{3}d = -16 \rightarrow (+)\ \frac{4}{7}c + \frac{8}{3}d = -16$

$$\begin{aligned} \tfrac{8}{7}c &= 16 \\ c &= 14 \end{aligned}$$

$$\begin{aligned} \tfrac{2}{7}c - \tfrac{4}{3}d &= 16 \\ \tfrac{2}{7}(14) - \tfrac{4}{3}d &= 16 \\ 4 - \tfrac{4}{3}d &= 16 \\ -\tfrac{4}{3}d &= 12 \\ d &= -9 \end{aligned}$$

$(14, -9)$

10. $2x + y = -7$

$y = -2x - 7$

$3x - 4y = -27$
$3x - 4(-2x - 7) = -27$
$3x + 8x + 28 = -27$
$11x + 28 = -27$
$11x = -55$
$x = -5$

$y = -2x - 7$
$= -2(-5) - 7$
$= 10 - 7$
$= 3$
$(-5, 3)$

11. $3c + 4d = -1 \rightarrow 3c + 4d = -1$
$6c - 2d = 3 \rightarrow (+)12c - 4d = 6$
$15c = 5$
$c = \frac{1}{3}$

$6c - 2d = 3$
$6\left(\frac{1}{3}\right) - 2d = 3$
$2 - 2d = 3$
$-2d = 1$
$d = -\frac{1}{2}$
$\left(\frac{1}{3}, -\frac{1}{2}\right)$

12. $5x + 3y = -4 \rightarrow 5x + 3y = -4$
$7x - y = 36 \rightarrow (+)21x - 3y = 108$
$26x = 104$
$x = 4$

$7x - y = 36$
$7(4) - y = 36$
$28 - y = 36$
$-y = 8$
$y = -8$
$(4, -8)$

13. $x = 2y - 1$

$4x - 3y = 21$
$4(2y - 1) - 3y = 21$
$8y - 4 - 3y = 21$
$5y - 4 = 21$
$5y = 25$
$y = 5$

$x = 2y - 1$
$= 2(5) - 1$
$= 10 - 1$
$= 9$
$(9, 5)$

14. $3m + 4n = 28 \rightarrow 9m + 12n = 84$
$5m - 3n = -21 \rightarrow (+)20m - 12n = -84$
$29m = 0$
$m = 0$

$5m - 3n = -21$
$5(0) - 3n = -21$
$0 - 3n = -21$
$-3n = -21$
$n = 7$
$(0, 7)$

15. $y = 5x - 19$

$7x - y = 35$
$7x - (5x - 19) = 35$
$7x - 5x + 19 = 35$
$2x + 19 = 35$
$2x = 16$
$x = 8$

$y = 5x - 19$
$= 5(8) - 19$
$= 40 - 19$
$= 21$
$(8, 21)$

Page 881 Lesson 3-3

1. $\begin{vmatrix} 7 & 6 \\ 2 & 5 \end{vmatrix} = 7(5) - 2(6)$
$= 35 - 12$
$= 23$

2. $\begin{vmatrix} -4 & 5 \\ 6 & 2 \end{vmatrix} = -4(2) - 6(5)$
$= -8 - 30$
$= -38$

3. $\begin{vmatrix} 5 & 1 \\ 7 & -2 \end{vmatrix} = 5(-2) - 7(1)$
$= -10 - 7$
$= -17$

4.
$x = \dfrac{\begin{vmatrix} 19 & -3 \\ 8 & 2 \end{vmatrix}}{\begin{vmatrix} 5 & -3 \\ 7 & 2 \end{vmatrix}} = \dfrac{19(2) - 8(-3)}{5(2) - 7(-3)} = \dfrac{62}{31} = 2$

$y = \dfrac{\begin{vmatrix} 5 & 19 \\ 7 & 8 \end{vmatrix}}{\begin{vmatrix} 5 & -3 \\ 7 & 2 \end{vmatrix}} = \dfrac{5(8) - 7(19)}{5(2) - 7(-3)} = \dfrac{-93}{31} = -3$

$(2, -3)$

5.
$p = \dfrac{\begin{vmatrix} 22 & -3 \\ 30 & 8 \end{vmatrix}}{\begin{vmatrix} 4 & -3 \\ 2 & 8 \end{vmatrix}} = \dfrac{22(8) - 30(-3)}{4(8) - 2(-3)} = \dfrac{266}{38} = 7$

$q = \dfrac{\begin{vmatrix} 4 & 22 \\ 2 & 30 \end{vmatrix}}{\begin{vmatrix} 4 & -3 \\ 2 & 8 \end{vmatrix}} = \dfrac{4(30) - 2(22)}{4(8) - 2(-3)} = \dfrac{76}{38} = 2$

$(7, 2)$

6.
$x = \dfrac{\begin{vmatrix} 5 & 1 \\ 38 & 4 \end{vmatrix}}{\begin{vmatrix} -1 & 1 \\ 2 & 4 \end{vmatrix}} = \dfrac{5(4) - 38(1)}{-1(4) - 2(1)} = \dfrac{-18}{-6} = 3$

$y = \dfrac{\begin{vmatrix} -1 & 5 \\ 2 & 38 \end{vmatrix}}{\begin{vmatrix} -1 & 1 \\ 2 & 4 \end{vmatrix}} = \dfrac{-1(38) - 2(5)}{-1(4) - 2(1)} = \dfrac{-48}{-6} = 8$

$(3, 8)$

7.
$a = \dfrac{\begin{vmatrix} 7 & -3 \\ -55 & 7 \end{vmatrix}}{\begin{vmatrix} 2 & -3 \\ 5 & 7 \end{vmatrix}} = \dfrac{7(7) - (-55)(-3)}{2(7) - 5(-3)} = \dfrac{-116}{29} = -4$

$b = \dfrac{\begin{vmatrix} 2 & 7 \\ 5 & -55 \end{vmatrix}}{\begin{vmatrix} 2 & -3 \\ 5 & 7 \end{vmatrix}} = \dfrac{2(-55) - 5(7)}{2(7) - 5(-3)} = \dfrac{-145}{29} = -5$

$(-4, -5)$

8. $m = \dfrac{\begin{vmatrix} -6 & 6 \\ -18 & 3 \end{vmatrix}}{\begin{vmatrix} 2 & 6 \\ 4 & 3 \end{vmatrix}}$ $\quad n = \dfrac{\begin{vmatrix} 2 & -6 \\ 4 & -18 \end{vmatrix}}{\begin{vmatrix} 2 & 6 \\ 4 & 3 \end{vmatrix}}$

$= \dfrac{-6(3) - (-18)6}{2(3) - 4(6)}$ $\quad = \dfrac{2(-18) - 4(-6)}{2(3) - 4(6)}$

$= \dfrac{90}{-18}$ $\quad = \dfrac{-12}{-18}$

$= -5$ $\quad = \dfrac{2}{3}$ $\quad \left(-5, \dfrac{2}{3}\right)$

9. $r = \dfrac{\begin{vmatrix} 5 & 3 \\ -9 & -2 \end{vmatrix}}{\begin{vmatrix} 8 & 3 \\ 6 & -2 \end{vmatrix}}$ $\quad s = \dfrac{\begin{vmatrix} 8 & 5 \\ 6 & -9 \end{vmatrix}}{\begin{vmatrix} 8 & 3 \\ 6 & -2 \end{vmatrix}}$

$= \dfrac{5(-2) - (-9)3}{8(-2) - 6(3)}$ $\quad = \dfrac{8(-9) - 6(5)}{8(-2) - 6(3)}$

$= \dfrac{17}{-34}$ $\quad = \dfrac{-102}{-34}$

$= -\dfrac{1}{2}$ $\quad = 3$ $\quad \left(-\dfrac{1}{2}, 3\right)$

10. $x = \dfrac{\begin{vmatrix} -8 & -\frac{1}{2} \\ -4 & \frac{5}{6} \end{vmatrix}}{\begin{vmatrix} \frac{1}{3} & -\frac{1}{2} \\ \frac{3}{5} & \frac{5}{6} \end{vmatrix}}$ $\quad y = \dfrac{\begin{vmatrix} \frac{1}{3} & -8 \\ \frac{3}{5} & -4 \end{vmatrix}}{\begin{vmatrix} \frac{1}{3} & -\frac{1}{2} \\ \frac{3}{5} & \frac{5}{6} \end{vmatrix}}$

$= \dfrac{-8\left(\frac{5}{6}\right) - (-4)\left(-\frac{1}{2}\right)}{\frac{1}{3}\left(\frac{5}{6}\right) - \frac{3}{5}\left(-\frac{1}{2}\right)}$ $\quad = \dfrac{\frac{1}{3}(-4) - \frac{3}{5}(-8)}{\frac{1}{3}\left(\frac{5}{6}\right) - \frac{3}{5}\left(-\frac{1}{2}\right)}$

$= \dfrac{-\frac{20}{3} - 2}{\frac{5}{18} + \frac{3}{10}}$ $\quad = \dfrac{-\frac{4}{3} + \frac{24}{5}}{\frac{5}{18} + \frac{3}{10}}$

$= \dfrac{-\frac{26}{3}}{\frac{52}{90}}$ $\quad = \dfrac{\frac{52}{15}}{\frac{52}{90}}$

$= -15$ $\quad = 6$ $\quad (-15, 6)$

11. $c = \dfrac{\begin{vmatrix} 6 & \frac{2}{3} \\ -4 & -\frac{5}{3} \end{vmatrix}}{\begin{vmatrix} \frac{1}{4} & \frac{2}{3} \\ \frac{3}{4} & -\frac{5}{3} \end{vmatrix}}$ $\quad d = \dfrac{\begin{vmatrix} \frac{1}{4} & 6 \\ \frac{3}{4} & -4 \end{vmatrix}}{\begin{vmatrix} \frac{1}{4} & \frac{2}{3} \\ \frac{3}{4} & -\frac{5}{3} \end{vmatrix}}$

$= \dfrac{6\left(-\frac{5}{3}\right) - (-4)\frac{2}{3}}{\frac{1}{4}\left(-\frac{5}{3}\right) - \frac{3}{4}\left(\frac{2}{3}\right)}$ $\quad = \dfrac{\frac{1}{4}(-4) - \frac{3}{4}(6)}{\frac{1}{4}\left(-\frac{5}{3}\right) - \frac{3}{4}\left(\frac{2}{3}\right)}$

$= \dfrac{-10 + \frac{8}{3}}{-\frac{5}{12} - \frac{1}{2}}$ $\quad = \dfrac{-1 - \frac{9}{2}}{-\frac{5}{12} - \frac{1}{2}}$

$= \dfrac{-\frac{22}{3}}{-\frac{11}{12}}$ $\quad = \dfrac{-\frac{11}{2}}{-\frac{11}{12}}$

$= 8$ $\quad = 6$ $\quad (8, 6)$

12. $a = \dfrac{\begin{vmatrix} 0.44 & 1.6 \\ 0.66 & 2.5 \end{vmatrix}}{\begin{vmatrix} 0.3 & 1.6 \\ 0.4 & 2.5 \end{vmatrix}}$ $\quad b = \dfrac{\begin{vmatrix} 0.3 & 0.44 \\ 0.4 & 0.66 \end{vmatrix}}{\begin{vmatrix} 0.3 & 1.6 \\ 0.4 & 2.5 \end{vmatrix}}$

$= \dfrac{0.44(2.5) - 0.66(1.6)}{0.3(2.5) - 0.4(1.6)}$ $\quad = \dfrac{0.3(0.66) - 0.4(0.44)}{0.3(2.5) - 0.4(1.6)}$

$= \dfrac{0.044}{0.11}$ $\quad = \dfrac{0.022}{0.11}$

$= 0.4$ $\quad = 0.2$ $\quad (0.4, 0.2)$

13. $m = \dfrac{\begin{vmatrix} -\frac{1}{3} & -\frac{5}{3} \\ 1 & \frac{7}{6} \end{vmatrix}}{\begin{vmatrix} \frac{2}{3} & -\frac{5}{3} \\ \frac{5}{9} & \frac{7}{6} \end{vmatrix}}$ $\quad n = \dfrac{\begin{vmatrix} \frac{2}{3} & -\frac{1}{3} \\ \frac{5}{9} & 1 \end{vmatrix}}{\begin{vmatrix} \frac{2}{3} & -\frac{5}{3} \\ \frac{5}{9} & \frac{7}{6} \end{vmatrix}}$

$= \dfrac{-\frac{1}{3}\left(\frac{7}{6}\right) - 1\left(-\frac{5}{3}\right)}{\frac{2}{3}\left(\frac{7}{6}\right) - \frac{5}{9}\left(-\frac{5}{3}\right)}$ $\quad = \dfrac{\frac{2}{3}(1) - \frac{5}{9}\left(-\frac{1}{3}\right)}{\frac{2}{3}\left(\frac{7}{6}\right) - \frac{5}{9}\left(-\frac{5}{3}\right)}$

$= \dfrac{-\frac{7}{18} + \frac{5}{3}}{\frac{7}{9} + \frac{25}{27}}$ $\quad = \dfrac{\frac{2}{3} + \frac{5}{27}}{\frac{7}{9} + \frac{25}{27}}$

$= \dfrac{\frac{23}{18}}{\frac{46}{27}}$ $\quad = \dfrac{\frac{23}{27}}{\frac{46}{27}}$

$= \dfrac{3}{4}$ $\quad = \dfrac{1}{2}$ $\quad \left(\dfrac{3}{4}, \dfrac{1}{2}\right)$

14. $3y = 4x + 28$

$-4x + 3y = 28$

$5x + 7y = 8$

$x = \dfrac{\begin{vmatrix} 28 & 3 \\ 8 & 7 \end{vmatrix}}{\begin{vmatrix} -4 & 3 \\ 5 & 7 \end{vmatrix}}$ $\quad y = \dfrac{\begin{vmatrix} -4 & 28 \\ 5 & 8 \end{vmatrix}}{\begin{vmatrix} -4 & 3 \\ 5 & 7 \end{vmatrix}}$

$= \dfrac{28(7) - 8(3)}{-4(7) - 5(3)}$ $\quad = \dfrac{-4(8) - 5(28)}{-4(7) - 5(3)}$

$= \dfrac{172}{-43}$ $\quad = \dfrac{-172}{-43}$

$= -4$ $\quad = 4$ $\quad (-4, 4)$

15. $4.5x = 3y$

$4.5x - 3y = 0$

$2(x - 4y) = -20$

$2x - 8y = -20$

$x = \dfrac{\begin{vmatrix} 0 & -3 \\ -20 & -8 \end{vmatrix}}{\begin{vmatrix} 4.5 & -3 \\ 2 & -8 \end{vmatrix}}$ $\quad y = \dfrac{\begin{vmatrix} 4.5 & 0 \\ 2 & -20 \end{vmatrix}}{\begin{vmatrix} 4.5 & -3 \\ 2 & -8 \end{vmatrix}}$

$= \dfrac{0(-8) - (-20)(-3)}{4.5(-8) - 2(-3)}$ $\quad = \dfrac{4.5(-20) - 2(0)}{4.5(-8) - 2(-3)}$

$= \dfrac{-60}{-30}$ $\quad = \dfrac{-90}{-30}$

$= 2$ $\quad = 3$ $\quad (2, 3)$

Page 881 Lesson 3-4

1. $x \le 5$
   $y \ge -3$

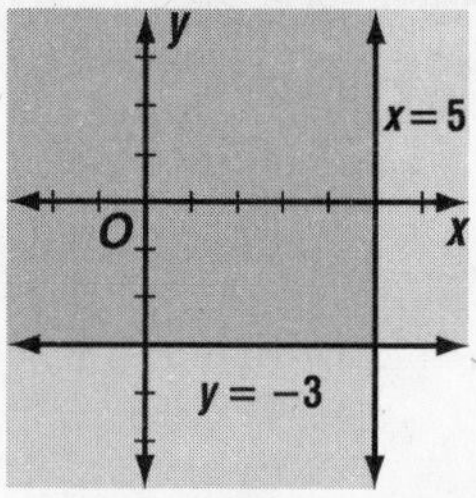

2. $x + y \le 2$
   $y \le -x + 2$
   $y - x \le 4$
   $y \le x + 4$

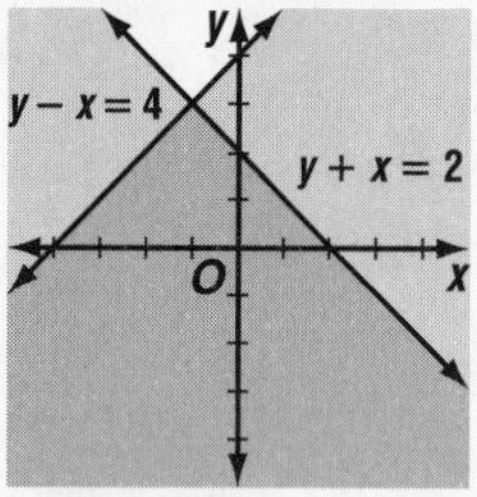

3. $x + y < 5$
   $y < -x + 5$
   $x < 2$

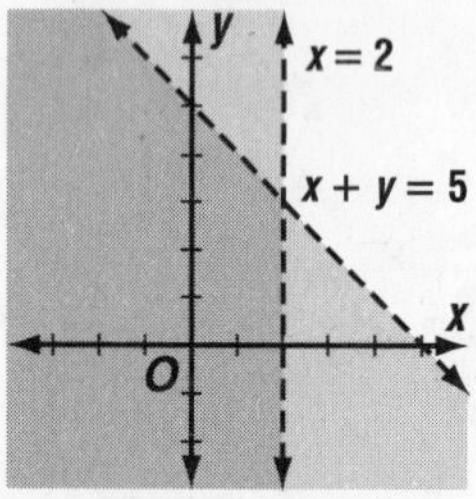

4. $y + x < 2$
   $y < -x + 2$
   $y \ge x$

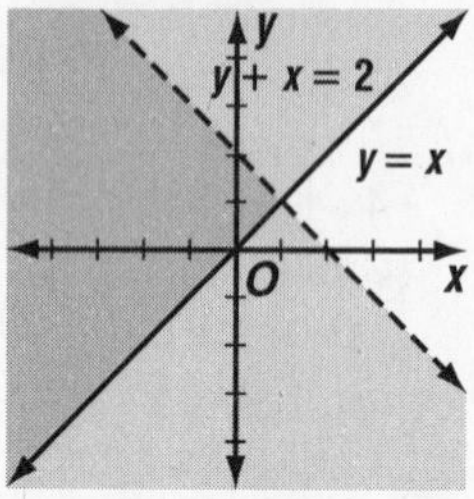

5. $y < 3$
   $y - x \ge -1$
   $y \ge x - 1$

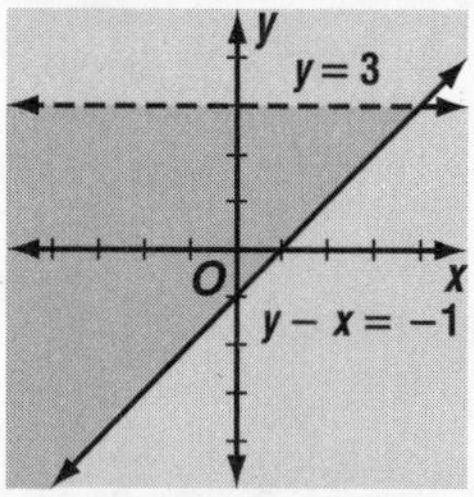

6. $y \le x + 4$
   $x + y \ge 1$
   $y \ge -x + 1$

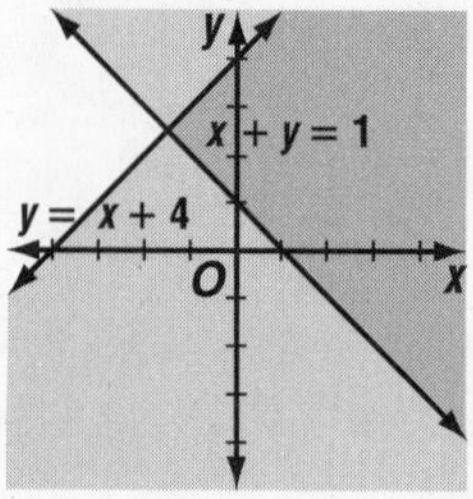

7. $y < \frac{1}{3}x + 5$
   $y < 2x + 1$

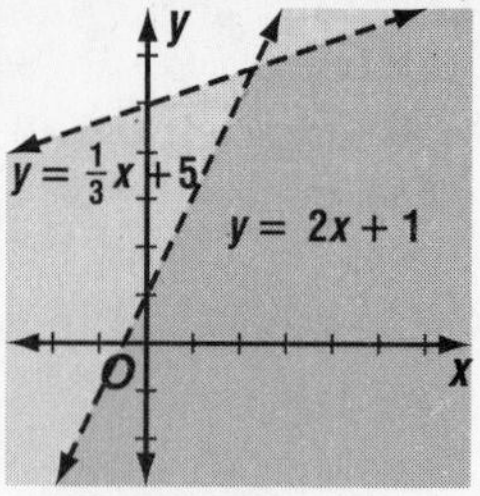

8. $y + x \ge 1$
   $y \ge -x + 1$
   $y - x \ge -1$
   $y \ge x - 1$

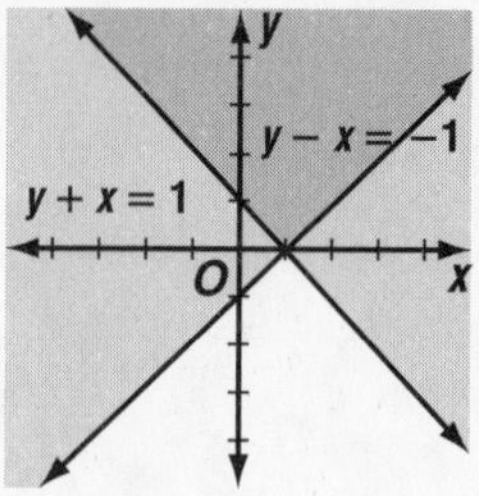

9. $|x| > 2$
   $x > 2$ or $x < -2$
   $|y| \le 5$
   $y \le 5$ and $y \ge -5$

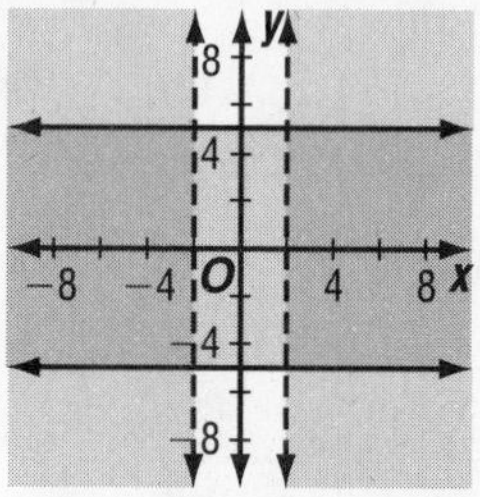

10. $|x - 2| \le 3$
    $x - 2 \le 3$ and $x - 2 \ge -3$
    $x \le 5$ $\quad$ $x \ge -1$
    $4y - 2x \ge 6$
    $4y \ge 2x + 6$
    $y \ge \frac{1}{2}x + \frac{3}{2}$

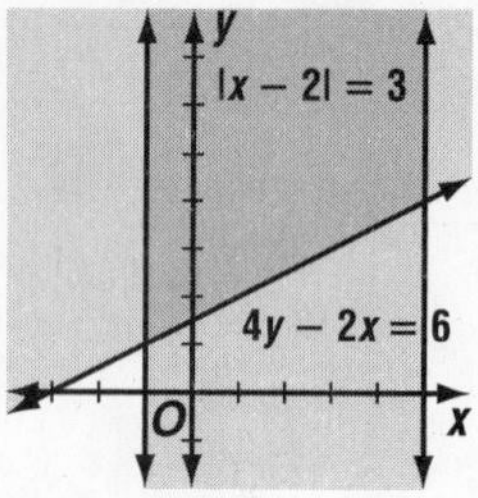

11. $4x + 3y \ge 12$
    $3y \ge -4x + 12$
    $y \ge -\frac{4}{3}x + 4$

    $2y - x \ge 1$
    $2y \ge x + 1$
    $y \ge \frac{1}{2}x + \frac{1}{2}$

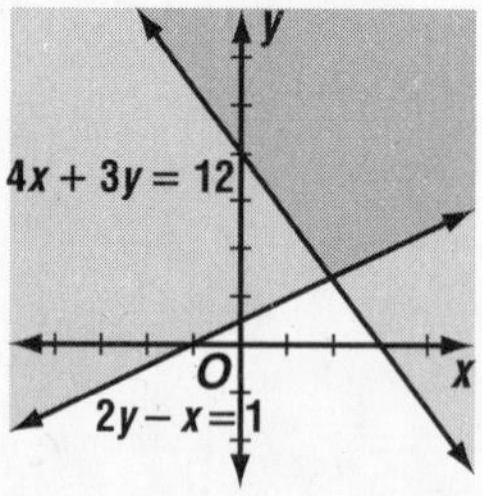

12. $y \le -1$

    $3x - 2y \ge 6$
    $-2y \ge -3x + 6$
    $y \le \frac{3}{2}x - 3$

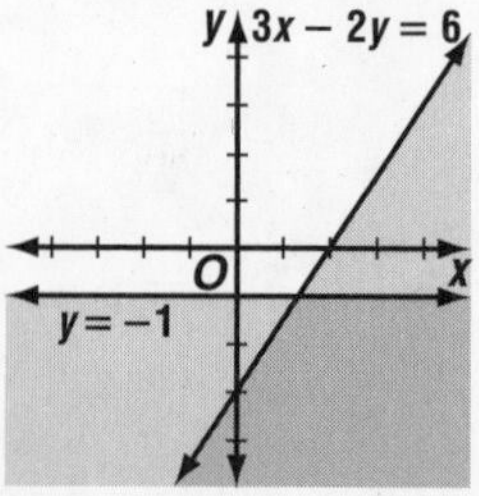

13. $y > 1$
$y < -3x + 3$
$y > -3x + 1$

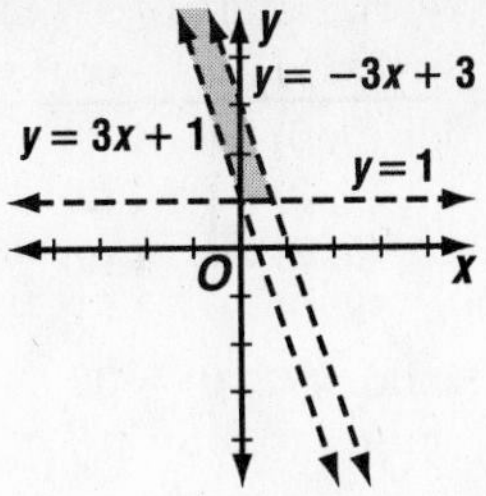

14. $y \geq -\frac{1}{2}x + 1$
$y \leq -3x + 5$
$y \leq 2x + 2$

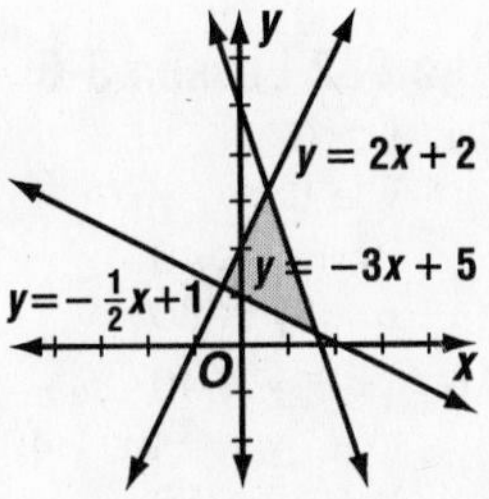

15. $2x + 5y < 25$
$5y < -2x + 25$
$y < -\frac{2}{5}x + 5$
$y < 3x - 2$

$5x - 7y < 14$
$-7y < -5x + 14$
$y > \frac{5}{7}x - 2$

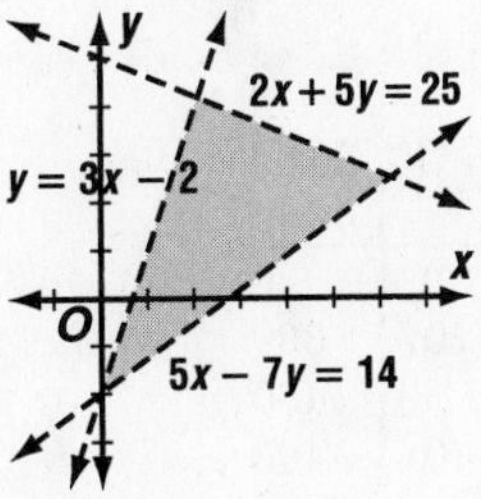

Page 882 Lesson 3-5

1.

(x, y)	$2x - y$	$f(x, y)$
(−3, 2)	2(−3) − 2	−8
(1, 3)	2(1) − 3	−1
(6, 1)	2(6) − 1	11
(2, −2)	2(2) − (−2)	6

max: $f(6, 1) = 11$
min: $f(-3, 2) = -8$

2.

(x, y)	$x + 5y$	$f(x, y)$
(−3, 2)	−3 + 5(2)	7
(1, 3)	1 + 5(3)	16
(6, 1)	6 + 5(1)	11
(2, −2)	2 + 5(−2)	−8

max: $f(1, 3) = 16$
min: $f(2, -2) = -8$

3.

(x, y)	$y - 4x$	$f(x, y)$
(−3, 2)	2 − 4(−3)	14
(1, 3)	3 − 4(1)	−1
(6, 1)	1 − 4(6)	−23
(2, −2)	−2 − 4(2)	−10

max: $f(-3, 2) = 14$
min: $f(6, 1) = -23$

4.

(x, y)	$-x + 3y$	$f(x, y)$
(−3, 2)	−(−3) + 3(2)	9
(1, 3)	−1 + 3(3)	8
(6, 1)	−6 + 3(1)	−3
(2, −2)	−2 + 3(−2)	−8

max: $f(-3, 2) = 9$
min: $f(2, -2) = -8$

5.

(x, y)	$3x - y$	$f(x, y)$
(−3, 2)	3(−3) − 2	−11
(1, 3)	3(1) − 3	0
(6, 1)	3(6) − 1	17
(2, −2)	3(2) − (−2)	8

max: $f(6, 1) = 17$
min: $f(-3, 2) = -11$

6.

(x, y)	$2y - 2x$	$f(x, y)$
(−3, 2)	2(2) − 2(−3)	10
(1, 3)	2(3) − 2(1)	4
(6, 1)	2(1) − 2(6)	−10
(2, −2)	2(−2) − 2(2)	−8

max: $f(-3, 2) = 10$
min: $f(6, 1) = -10$

7. $4x - 5y \geq -10$
$-5y \geq -4x - 10$
$y \leq \frac{4}{5}x + 2$
$y \leq 6$
$2x - 5y \leq -10$
$-5y \leq -2x - 10$
$y \geq \frac{2}{5}x + 2$

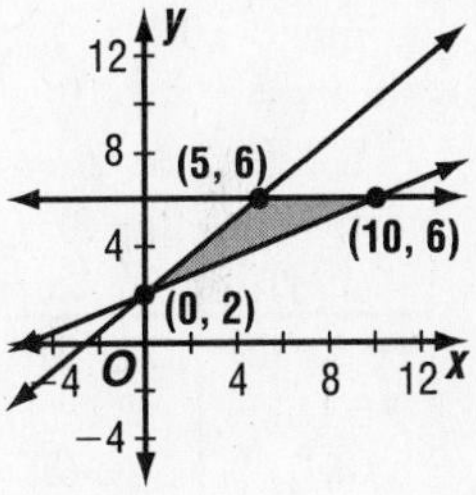

vertices: (0, 2), (5, 6), (10, 6)

(x, y)	$x + y$	$f(x, y)$
(0, 2)	0 + 2	2
(5, 6)	5 + 6	11
(10, 6)	10 + 6	16

max: $f(10, 6) = 16$
min: $f(0, 2) = 2$

8. $x \leq 5$
$y \geq 2$
$2x - 5y \geq -10$
$-5y \geq -2x - 10$
$y \leq \frac{2}{5}x + 2$

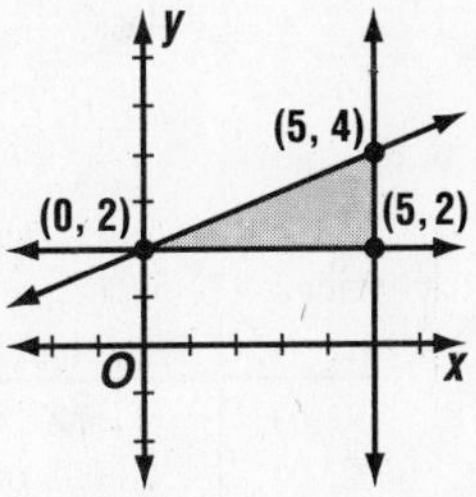

vertices: (0, 2), (5, 4), (5, 2)

(x, y)	$3x + y$	$f(x, y)$
(0, 2)	3 (0) + 2	2
(5, 4)	3 (5) + 4	19
(5, 2)	3 (5) + 2	17

max: $f(5, 4) = 19$
min: $f(0, 2) = 2$

9. $x - 2y \geq -7$

$-2y \geq -x - 7$

$y \leq \frac{1}{2}x + \frac{7}{2}$

$x + y \geq 8$

$y \geq -x + 8$

$2x - y \leq 7$

$-y \leq -2x + 7$

$y \geq 2x - 7$

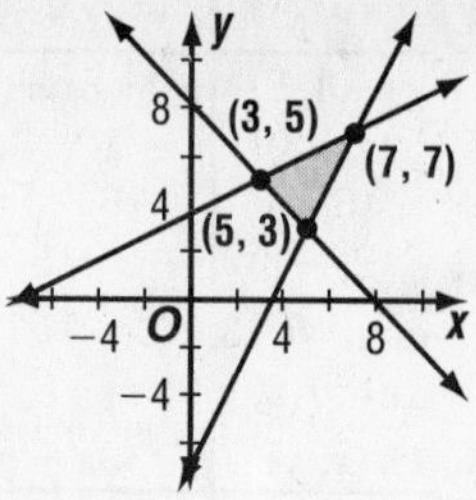

vertices: (5, 3), (3, 5), (7, 7)

(x, y)	$3x - 4y$	$f(x, y)$
(5, 3)	3 (5) − 4(3)	3
(3, 5)	3 (3) − 4 (5)	−11
(7, 7)	3 (7) − 4 (7)	−7

max: $f(5, 3) = 3$

min: $f(3, 5) = -11$

10. $y \leq 4x + 6$

$x + 4y \leq 7$

$4y \leq -x + 7$

$y \leq -\frac{1}{4}x + \frac{7}{4}$

$2x + y \leq 7$

$y \leq -2x + 7$

$x - 6y \leq 10$

$-6y \leq -x + 10$

$y \geq \frac{1}{6}x - \frac{5}{3}$

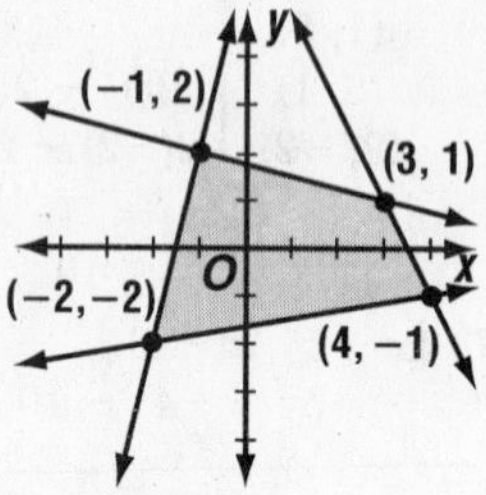

vertices: (−2, −2), (−1, 2), (3, 1), (4, −1)

(x, y)	$2x - y$	$f(x, y)$
(−2, −2)	2 (−2) − (−2)	−2
(−1, 2)	2 (−1) − 2	−4
(3, 1)	2 (3) − 1	5
(4, −1)	2 (4) − (−1)	9

max: $f(4, -1) = 9$

min: $f(-1, 2) = -4$

11. $y \geq 0$

$y \leq 5$

$y \leq -x + 7$

$5x + 3y \geq 20$

$3y \geq -5x + 20$

$y \geq -\frac{5}{3}x + \frac{20}{3}$

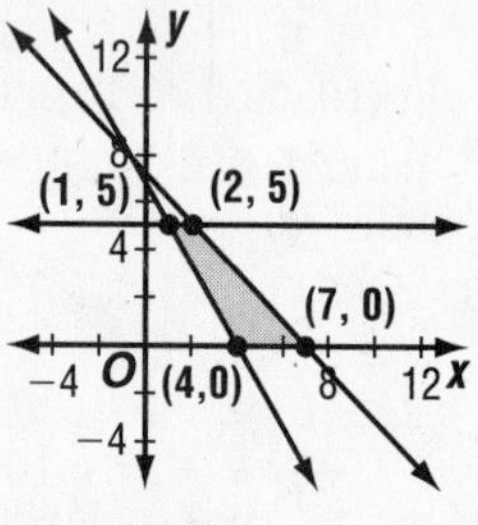

vertices: (1, 5), (2, 5), (7, 0), (4, 0)

(x, y)	$x + 2y$	$f(x, y)$
(1, 5)	1 + 2 (5)	11
(2, 5)	2 + 2 (5)	12
(7, 0)	7 + 2 (0)	7
(4, 0)	4 + 2 (0)	4

max: $f(2, 5) = 12$

min: $f(4, 0) = 4$

12. $y \geq 0$

$3x - 2y \geq 0$

$-2y \geq -3x$

$y \leq \frac{3}{2}x$

$x + 3y \leq 11$

$3y \leq -x + 11$

$y \leq -\frac{1}{3}x + \frac{11}{3}$

$2x + 3y \leq 16$

$3y \leq -2x + 16$

$y \leq -\frac{2}{3}x + \frac{16}{3}$

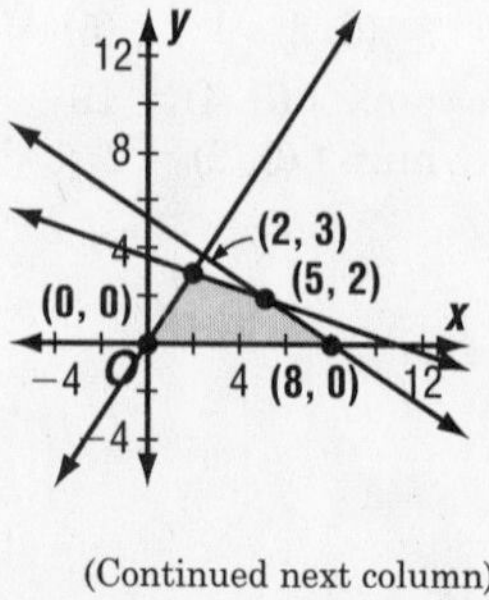

(Continued next column)

vertices: (0, 0), (2, 3), (5, 2), (8, 0)

(x, y)	$4x + y$	$f(x, y)$
(0, 0)	4 (0) + 0	0
(2, 3)	4 (2) + 3	11
(5, 2)	4 (5) + 2	22
(8, 0)	4 (8) + 0	32

max: $f(8, 0) = 32$

min: $f(0, 0) = 0$

Page 882 Lesson 3-6

1a. $x \geq 0$

$y \geq 0$

$2x + y \leq 40$

$x + 3y \leq 60$

1b. $2x + y \leq 40$

$y \leq -2x + 40$

$x + 3y \leq 60$

$3y \leq -x + 60$

$y \leq -\frac{1}{3}x + 20$

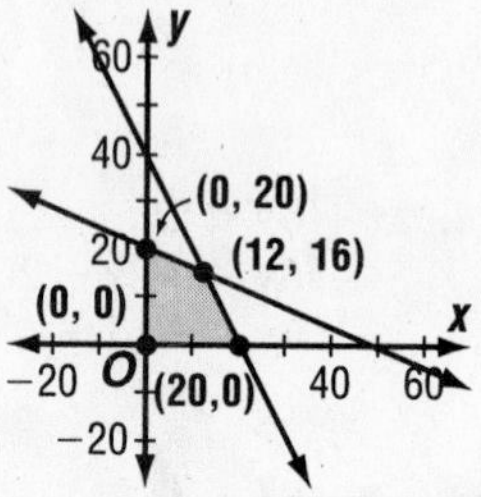

1c. $20x + 15y$

1d. vertices: (0, 0), (0, 20), (12, 16), (20, 0)

(x, y)	$20x + 15y$	$f(x, y)$
(0, 0)	20 (0) + 15 (0)	0
(0, 20)	20 (0) + 15 (20)	300
(12, 16)	20 (12) + 15 (16)	480
(20, 0)	20 (20) + 15 (0)	400

12 outdoor pair, 16 indoor pair; $480

2a. Let x = 100 yo-yos and y = 100 tops.

$3x + 4y \leq 450$

$4y \leq -3x + 450$

$y \leq -\frac{3}{4}x + 112.5$

$5x + 2y \leq 400$

$2y \leq -5x + 400$

$y \leq -\frac{5}{2}x + 200$

$x \geq 0$

$y \geq 0$

$f(x) = 3x + 3y$

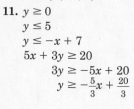

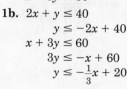

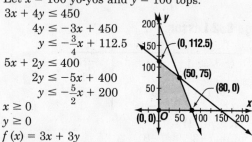

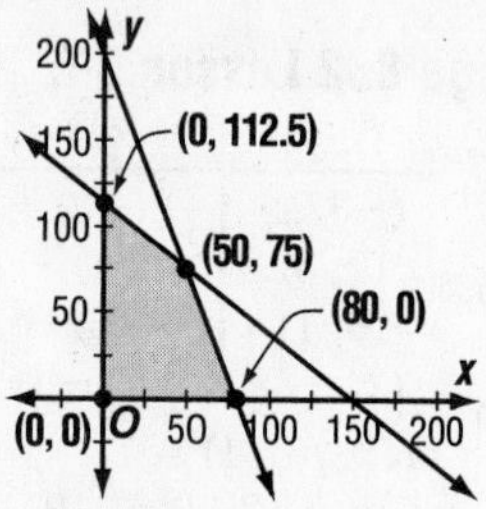

vertices: (0, 0), (0, 112.5), (50, 75), (80, 0)

(x, y)	$3x + 3y$	$f(x, y)$
(0, 0)	3 (0) + 3 (0)	0
(0, 112.5)	3 (0) + 3 (112.5)	337.5
(50, 75)	3 (50) + 3 (75)	375
(80, 0)	3 (80) + 3 (0)	320

max: $f(50, 75) = 375$

$100 \cdot 50 = 5000$; 5000 yo-yos

$100 \cdot 75 = 7500$; 7500 tops

2b. $37,500

Page 882 Lesson 3-7

1. $4x + 2y - 6z \stackrel{?}{=} -38$
$4(-3) + 2(2) - 6(5) \stackrel{?}{=} -38$
$-38 = -38$

$5x - 4y + z \stackrel{?}{=} -18$
$5(-3) - 4(2) + 5 \stackrel{?}{=} -18$
$-18 = -18$

$x + 3y + 7z \stackrel{?}{=} 38$
$-3 + 3(2) + 7(5) \stackrel{?}{=} 38$
$38 = 38$

yes

2. $u + 3v + w \stackrel{?}{=} 14$
$1 + 3(5) + (-2) \stackrel{?}{=} 14$
$14 = 14$

$2u - v + 3w \stackrel{?}{=} -9$
$2(1) - 5 + 3(-2) \stackrel{?}{=} -9$
$-9 = -9$

$4u - 5v - 2w \stackrel{?}{=} -2$
$4(1) - 5(5) - 2(-2) \stackrel{?}{=} -2$
$-17 \neq -2$

no

3. $x + y \stackrel{?}{=} -6$
$-4 + 2 \stackrel{?}{=} -6$
$-2 \neq -6$; no

4. $5a = 5$
$a = 1$

$2a + 7c = -5$
$2(1) + 7c = -5$
$2 + 7c = -5$
$7c = -7$
$c = -1$

$6b - 3c = 15$
$6b - 3(-1) = 15$
$6b + 3 = 15$
$6b = 12$
$b = 2$

$(1, 2, -1)$

5. $2t = 8$
$t = 4$

$s + 2t = 5$
$s + 2(4) = 5$
$s + 8 = 5$
$s = -3$

$7r - 3s + t = 20$
$7r - 3(-3) + 4 = 20$
$7r + 9 + 4 = 20$
$7r + 13 = 20$
$7r = 7$
$r = 1$

$(1, -3, 4)$

6.
$$\begin{array}{rl} 3v + w &= -3 \\ (+)\ 4u \qquad - w &= 2 \\ \hline 4u + 3v \qquad &= -1 \end{array} \qquad \begin{array}{rl} 2u - 3v &= 13 \\ (+)\ 4u + 3v &= -1 \\ \hline 6u \qquad &= 12 \\ u &= 2 \end{array}$$

$2u - 3v = 13$
$2(2) - 3v = 13$
$4 - 3v = 13$
$-3v = 9$
$v = -3$

$3v + w = -3$
$3(-3) + w = 3$
$-9 + w = -3$
$w = 6$

$(2, -3, 6)$

7. $4a + 2b - c = 5 \rightarrow 4a + 2b - c = 5$
$2a + b - 5c = -11 \rightarrow (+)\ -4a - 2b + 10c = 22$
$9c = 27$
$c = 3$

$2a + b - 5c = -11 \rightarrow 4a + 2b - 10c = -22$
$a - 2b + 3c = 6 \rightarrow (+)\ a - 2b + 3c = 6$
$5a - 7c = -16$

$5a - 7c = -16$
$5a - 7(3) = -16$
$5a - 21 = -16$
$5a = 5$
$a = 1$

$2a + b - 5c = -11$
$2(1) + b - 5(3) = -11$
$2 + b - 15 = -11$
$b - 13 = -11$
$b = 2$

$(1, 2, 3)$

8.
$$\begin{array}{rl} x + 2y - z &= 1 \\ (-)x + 3y + 2z &= 7 \\ \hline -y - 3z &= -6 \end{array}$$

$x + 2y - z = 1 \rightarrow -2x - 4y + 2z = -2$
$2x + 6y + z = 8 \rightarrow (+)\ 2x + 6y + z = 8$
$2y + 3z = 6$

(Continued next column)

$$\begin{array}{rl} -y - 3z &= -6 \\ (+)\ 2y + 3z &= 6 \\ \hline y &= 0 \end{array}$$

$2y + 3z = 6$
$2(0) + 3z = 6$
$3z = 6$
$z = 2$

$x + 2y - z = 1$
$x + 2(0) - 2 = 1$
$x - 2 = 1$
$x = 3$

$(3, 0, 2)$

9. $2x + y - z = 7 \rightarrow 4x + 2y - 2z = 14$
$3x - y + 2z = 15 \rightarrow (+)\ 3x - y + 2z = 15$
$7x + y = 29$

$$\begin{array}{rl} 2x + y - z &= 7 \\ (+)\ x - 4y + z &= 2 \\ \hline 3x - 3y &= 9 \end{array}$$

$7x + y = 29 \rightarrow 21x + 3y = 87$
$3x - 3y = 9 \rightarrow (+)\ 3x - 3y = 9$
$24x = 96$
$x = 4$

$7x + y = 29$
$7(4) + y = 29$
$28 + y = 29$
$y = 1$

$x - 4y + z = 2$
$4 - 4(1) + z = 2$
$4 - 4 + z = 2$
$z = 2$

$(4, 1, 2)$

Page 883 Lesson 4-1

1. $\frac{3}{2}\begin{bmatrix} 8 & 4 & 3 \end{bmatrix} = \begin{bmatrix} 12 & 6 & \frac{9}{2} \end{bmatrix}$

2. $-10\begin{bmatrix} 1.26 & 8.95 \\ 2.47 & -3.62 \end{bmatrix} = \begin{bmatrix} -12.6 & -89.5 \\ -24.7 & 36.2 \end{bmatrix}$

3. $-5\begin{bmatrix} 7.5 \\ -3.8 \end{bmatrix} = \begin{bmatrix} -37.5 \\ 19 \end{bmatrix}$

4. $-z = 15$
$z = -15$

$3y = -z$
$3y = -(-15)$
$3y = 15$
$y = 5$

$2x = 2y$
$2x = 2(5)$
$2x = 10$
$x = 5$

5. $x + y = 1 \rightarrow 3x + 3y = 3$
$4x - 3y = 11 \rightarrow (+)\ 4x - 3y = 11$
$7x = 14$
$x = 2$

$x + y = 1$
$2 + y = 1$
$y = -1$

6. $-2\begin{bmatrix} w + 5 & x - z \\ 3y & 8 \end{bmatrix} = \begin{bmatrix} -16 & -4 \\ 6 & 2x + 8z \end{bmatrix}$

$\begin{bmatrix} -2w - 10 & -2x + 2z \\ -6y & -16 \end{bmatrix} = \begin{bmatrix} -16 & -4 \\ 6 & 2x + 8z \end{bmatrix}$

$-2w - 10 = -16$
$-2w = -6$
$w = 3$

$$\begin{array}{rl} -2x + 2z &= -4 \\ (+)\ 2x + 8z &= -16 \\ \hline 10z &= -20 \\ z &= -2 \end{array}$$

$-6y = 6$
$y = -1$

$2x + 8z = -16$
$2x + 8(-2) = -16$
$2x - 16 = -16$
$2x = 0$
$x = 0$

7. $y\begin{bmatrix} 2 & x \\ 5 & 1 \end{bmatrix} = \begin{bmatrix} 4 & -10 \\ 10 & 2z \end{bmatrix}$

$\begin{bmatrix} 2y & xy \\ 5y & y \end{bmatrix} = \begin{bmatrix} 4 & -10 \\ 10 & 2z \end{bmatrix}$

$2y = 4$
$y = 2$

$5y = 10$
$y = 2$

$xy = -10$
$x(2) = -10$
$x = -5$

$y = 2z$
$2 = 2z$
$1 = z$

8. $2x = 16$ $\quad -y = 18 \quad$ $3z = -21$

$x = 8 \quad y = -18 \quad z = -7$

9. $$\begin{bmatrix} x - 3y \\ 4y - 3x \end{bmatrix} = -5\begin{bmatrix} 2 \\ x \end{bmatrix} \qquad \begin{aligned} x - 3y &= -10 \\ 4y - 3x &= -5x \\ 4y + 2x &= 0 \end{aligned}$$

$$\begin{bmatrix} x - 3y \\ 4y - 3x \end{bmatrix} = \begin{bmatrix} -10 \\ -5x \end{bmatrix}$$

$$\begin{aligned} x - 3y &= -10 && \rightarrow & -2x + 6y &= 20 \\ 2x + 4y &= 0 && \rightarrow & (+)\ 2x + 4y &= 0 \\ &&&& \hline 10y &= 20 \\ &&&& y &= 2 \end{aligned}$$

$$\begin{aligned} x - 3y &= -10 \\ x - 3(2) &= -10 \\ x - 6 &= -10 \\ x &= -4 \end{aligned}$$

10. $$\begin{aligned} y - 4 &= 2 \\ y &= 6 \end{aligned} \qquad \begin{aligned} x + y &= 5 \\ x + 6 &= 5 \\ x &= -1 \end{aligned} \qquad \begin{aligned} 5 - y &= x \\ 5 - y &= -1 \\ -y &= -6 \\ y &= 6 \end{aligned} \qquad \begin{aligned} x^2 + 1 &= 2 \\ x^2 &= 1 \\ x &= \pm 1 \end{aligned}$$

11. $$\begin{aligned} 6 &= 4 - 2x \\ 2 &= -2x \\ -1 &= x \end{aligned} \qquad \begin{aligned} x + y &= 0 \\ -1 + y &= 0 \\ y &= 1 \end{aligned} \qquad \begin{aligned} 3 &= 2y - x \\ 3 &= 2y - (-1) \\ 2 &= 2y \\ 1 &= y \end{aligned} \qquad \begin{aligned} y &= z^2 \\ 1 &= z^2 \\ \pm 1 &= z \end{aligned}$$

Page 883 Lesson 4-2

1. $$\begin{bmatrix} 3 & 5 \\ -7 & 2 \end{bmatrix} + \begin{bmatrix} -2 & 6 \\ 8 & -1 \end{bmatrix} = \begin{bmatrix} 1 & 11 \\ 1 & 1 \end{bmatrix}$$

2. $$\begin{bmatrix} 45 & 36 \\ 18 & 63 \end{bmatrix} - 9\begin{bmatrix} 5 & 4 \\ 2 & 7 \end{bmatrix} = \begin{bmatrix} 45 & 36 \\ 18 & 63 \end{bmatrix} - \begin{bmatrix} 45 & 36 \\ 18 & 63 \end{bmatrix} = \begin{bmatrix} 0 & 0 \\ 0 & 0 \end{bmatrix}$$

3. $$\begin{aligned} &4\,[-8 \quad 2 \quad 9] - 3\,[2 \quad -7 \quad 6] \\ &= [-32 \quad 8 \quad 36] - [6 \quad -21 \quad 18] \\ &= [-38 \quad 29 \quad 18] \end{aligned}$$

4. $$\frac{4}{5}\begin{bmatrix} -5 \\ 6 \\ 8 \end{bmatrix} + \frac{1}{4}\begin{bmatrix} 9 \\ -6 \\ 12 \end{bmatrix} - \frac{1}{2}\begin{bmatrix} 5 \\ 4 \\ 7 \end{bmatrix}$$

$$= \begin{bmatrix} -4 \\ 4.8 \\ 6.4 \end{bmatrix} + \begin{bmatrix} 2.25 \\ -1.5 \\ 3 \end{bmatrix} - \begin{bmatrix} 2.5 \\ 2 \\ 3.5 \end{bmatrix}$$

$$= \begin{bmatrix} -4.25 \\ 1.3 \\ 5.9 \end{bmatrix}$$

5. $$\begin{bmatrix} -3 & 6 & -9 \\ 4 & -3 & 0 \\ 8 & -2 & 3 \end{bmatrix} - \begin{bmatrix} 1 & 5 & 7 \\ 5 & 2 & -6 \\ 3 & 0 & -2 \end{bmatrix} = \begin{bmatrix} -4 & 1 & -16 \\ -1 & -5 & 6 \\ 5 & -2 & 5 \end{bmatrix}$$

6. $$5\begin{bmatrix} 3 & 1 & 0 \\ 0 & 0 & 2 \\ 1 & -1 & -1 \end{bmatrix} - 3\begin{bmatrix} 2 & 0 & 3 \\ 1 & 1 & 2 \\ 2 & 1 & -1 \end{bmatrix}$$

$$= \begin{bmatrix} 15 & 5 & 0 \\ 0 & 0 & 10 \\ 5 & -5 & -5 \end{bmatrix} - \begin{bmatrix} 6 & 0 & 9 \\ 3 & 3 & 6 \\ 6 & 3 & -3 \end{bmatrix}$$

$$= \begin{bmatrix} 9 & 5 & -9 \\ -3 & -3 & 4 \\ -1 & -8 & -2 \end{bmatrix}$$

7. $$5\begin{bmatrix} 6 & -2 \\ 5 & 4 \end{bmatrix} - 2\begin{bmatrix} 6 & -2 \\ 5 & 4 \end{bmatrix} + 4\begin{bmatrix} 7 & -6 \\ -4 & 2 \end{bmatrix}$$

$$= \begin{bmatrix} 30 & -10 \\ 25 & 20 \end{bmatrix} - \begin{bmatrix} 12 & -4 \\ 10 & 8 \end{bmatrix} + \begin{bmatrix} 28 & -24 \\ -16 & 8 \end{bmatrix}$$

$$= \begin{bmatrix} 46 & -30 \\ -1 & 20 \end{bmatrix}$$

8. $$1.3\begin{bmatrix} 3.7 & 4.8 \\ -5.4 & 9.5 \end{bmatrix} + 4.1\begin{bmatrix} 6.4 & -1.9 \\ -3.7 & -2.8 \end{bmatrix} - 6.2\begin{bmatrix} -0.8 & 5.1 \\ 3.2 & 7.4 \end{bmatrix}$$

$$= \begin{bmatrix} 4.81 & 6.24 \\ -7.02 & 12.35 \end{bmatrix} + \begin{bmatrix} 26.24 & -7.79 \\ -15.17 & -11.48 \end{bmatrix} - \begin{bmatrix} -4.96 & 31.62 \\ 19.84 & 45.88 \end{bmatrix}$$

$$= \begin{bmatrix} 36.01 & -33.17 \\ -42.03 & -45.01 \end{bmatrix}$$

Page 883 Lesson 4-3

1. 4×4
2. not defined
3. not defined
4. 3×2
5. not defined
6. 5×6
7. $m \times p$
8. 2×7

9. $$[7 \quad 2] \cdot \begin{bmatrix} -3 \\ 5 \end{bmatrix} = [7\,(-3) + 2\,(5)] = [-11]$$

10. $$\begin{bmatrix} 2 & -4 \\ 0 & 5 \end{bmatrix} \cdot \begin{bmatrix} 1 & 3 \\ -2 & -1 \end{bmatrix}$$

$$= \begin{bmatrix} 2(1) + (-4)(-2) & 2(3) + (-4)(-1) \\ 0(1) + 5(-2) & 0(3) + 5(-1) \end{bmatrix}$$

$$= \begin{bmatrix} 10 & 10 \\ -10 & -5 \end{bmatrix}$$

11. $$\begin{bmatrix} 1 & 3 \\ -2 & -1 \end{bmatrix} \cdot \begin{bmatrix} 2 & -4 \\ 0 & 5 \end{bmatrix}$$

$$= \begin{bmatrix} 1\,(2) + 3\,(0) & 1\,(-4) + 3\,(5) \\ -2\,(2) + -1\,(0) & -2\,(-4) + (-1)\,(5) \end{bmatrix}$$

$$= \begin{bmatrix} 2 & 11 \\ -4 & 3 \end{bmatrix}$$

12. $$\begin{bmatrix} 3 & 2 \\ 5 & 2 \end{bmatrix} \cdot \begin{bmatrix} -8 \\ 15 \end{bmatrix} = \begin{bmatrix} 3\,(-8) + 2\,(15) \\ 5\,(-8) + 2\,(15) \end{bmatrix} = \begin{bmatrix} 6 \\ -10 \end{bmatrix}$$

13. not defined

14. $$\begin{bmatrix} 0 & 1 & -2 \\ 5 & 3 & -4 \\ -1 & 0 & 0 \end{bmatrix} \cdot \begin{bmatrix} 1 & -3 & 0 \\ 2 & 0 & -1 \\ 0 & 1 & -2 \end{bmatrix}$$

$$= \begin{bmatrix} 0(1) + 1(2) + (-2)0 & 0(-3) + 1(0) + (-2)1 & 0(0) + 1(-1) + (-2)(-2) \\ 5\,(1) + 3(2) + (-4)0 & 5(-3) + 3(0) + (-4)1 & 5(0) + 3(-1) + -4(-2) \\ -1(1) + 0(2) + 0(0) & -1(-3) + 0(0) + 0(1) & -1(0) + 0(-1) + 0(-2) \end{bmatrix}$$

$$= \begin{bmatrix} 2 & -2 & 3 \\ 11 & -19 & 5 \\ -1 & 3 & 0 \end{bmatrix}$$

15. $$\begin{bmatrix} 3 & -2 \\ 4 & 5 \end{bmatrix} \cdot \begin{bmatrix} 1 & 0 \\ 0 & 1 \end{bmatrix} = \begin{bmatrix} 3(1) + (-2)0 & 3(0) + (-2)1 \\ 4(1) + 5(0) & 4(0) + 5(1) \end{bmatrix} = \begin{bmatrix} 3 & -2 \\ 4 & 5 \end{bmatrix}$$

16. $\begin{bmatrix} 3 & -2 \\ 4 & 5 \end{bmatrix} \cdot \begin{bmatrix} \frac{5}{7} & -\frac{2}{7} \\ \frac{4}{7} & -\frac{3}{7} \end{bmatrix} = \begin{bmatrix} 3\left(\frac{5}{7}\right) + (-2)\left(\frac{4}{7}\right) & 3\left(-\frac{2}{7}\right) + (-2)\left(-\frac{3}{7}\right) \\ 4\left(\frac{5}{7}\right) + (-5)\left(\frac{4}{7}\right) & 4\left(-\frac{2}{7}\right) + (-5)\left(-\frac{3}{7}\right) \end{bmatrix}$

$= \begin{bmatrix} 1 & 0 \\ 0 & 1 \end{bmatrix}$

Page 884 Lesson 4-4

1. no

2. yes; $\begin{vmatrix} 1 & -5 \\ 3 & 4 \end{vmatrix} = 1(4) - 3(-5)$
$= 19$

3. yes; $\begin{vmatrix} -1 & 6 & 1 \\ 0 & 5 & 1 \\ -5 & 2 & 3 \end{vmatrix} = -1\begin{vmatrix} 5 & 1 \\ 2 & 3 \end{vmatrix} - 6\begin{vmatrix} 0 & 1 \\ -5 & 3 \end{vmatrix} + 1\begin{vmatrix} 0 & 5 \\ -5 & 2 \end{vmatrix}$
$= -1(15 - 2) - 6(0 + 5) + 1(0 + 25)$
$= -13 - 30 + 25$
$= -18$

4. no

5. $\begin{vmatrix} 2 & -3 & 5 \\ 1 & -2 & -7 \\ -1 & 4 & -3 \end{vmatrix} = 2\begin{vmatrix} -2 & -7 \\ 4 & -3 \end{vmatrix} - (-3)\begin{vmatrix} 1 & -7 \\ -1 & -3 \end{vmatrix} + 5\begin{vmatrix} 1 & -2 \\ -1 & 4 \end{vmatrix}$
$= 2(6 + 28) + 3(-3 - 7) + 5(4 - 2)$
$= 68 - 30 + 10$
$= 48$

6. $\begin{vmatrix} 0 & -1 & 2 \\ -2 & 1 & 0 \\ 2 & 0 & -1 \end{vmatrix} = 0\begin{vmatrix} 1 & 0 \\ 0 & -1 \end{vmatrix} - (-1)\begin{vmatrix} -2 & 0 \\ 2 & -1 \end{vmatrix} + 2\begin{vmatrix} -2 & 1 \\ 2 & 0 \end{vmatrix}$
$= 0(-1 - 0) + 1(2 - 0) + 2(0 - 2)$
$= 0 + 2 - 4$
$= -2$

7. $\begin{vmatrix} 4 & 3 & -2 \\ 2 & 5 & -8 \\ 6 & 4 & -1 \end{vmatrix} = 4\begin{vmatrix} 5 & -8 \\ 4 & -1 \end{vmatrix} - 3\begin{vmatrix} 2 & -8 \\ 6 & -1 \end{vmatrix} + (-2)\begin{vmatrix} 2 & 5 \\ 6 & 4 \end{vmatrix}$
$= 4(-5 + 32) - 3(-2 + 48) - 2(8 - 30)$
$= 108 - 138 + 44$
$= 14$

8. $\begin{vmatrix} -3 & 0 & 2 \\ 1 & -2 & -1 \\ 0 & 5 & 0 \end{vmatrix} = -3\begin{vmatrix} -2 & -1 \\ 5 & 0 \end{vmatrix} - 0\begin{vmatrix} 1 & -1 \\ 0 & 0 \end{vmatrix} + 2\begin{vmatrix} 1 & -2 \\ 0 & 5 \end{vmatrix}$
$= -3(0 + 5) - 0(0 - 0) + 2(5 - 0)$
$= -15 - 0 + 10$
$= -5$

9. $\left|\begin{matrix} 3 & 2 & -1 \\ 2 & 3 & 0 \\ -1 & 0 & 3 \end{matrix}\right| \begin{matrix} 3 & 2 \\ 2 & 3 \\ -1 & 0 \end{matrix}$
$= 3 \cdot 3 \cdot 3 + 2 \cdot 0(-1) + (-1)2 \cdot 0 - (-1)3(-1) -$
$0 \cdot 0 \cdot 3 - 3 \cdot 2 \cdot 2$
$= 27 + 0 + 0 - 3 - 0 - 12$
$= 12$

10. $\left|\begin{matrix} 1 & 0 & 0 \\ 0 & 1 & 0 \\ 0 & 0 & 1 \end{matrix}\right| \begin{matrix} 1 & 0 \\ 0 & 1 \\ 0 & 0 \end{matrix}$
$= 1 \cdot 1 \cdot 1 + 0 \cdot 0 \cdot 0 + 0 \cdot 0 \cdot 0 - 0 \cdot 1 \cdot 0 -$
$0 \cdot 0 \cdot 1 - 1 \cdot 0 \cdot 0$
$= 1 + 0 + 0 - 0 - 0 - 0$
$= 1$

11. $\left|\begin{matrix} 4 & 3 & -2 \\ 2 & 5 & -8 \\ 6 & 4 & -1 \end{matrix}\right| \begin{matrix} 4 & 3 \\ 2 & 5 \\ 6 & 4 \end{matrix}$
$= 4 \cdot 5(-1) + 3(-8)6 + (-2)2 \cdot 4 - 6 \cdot 5(-2) -$
$4(-8)4 - (-1) \cdot 2 \cdot 3$
$= -20 - 144 - 16 + 60 + 128 + 6$
$= 14$

12. $\left|\begin{matrix} 6 & 12 & 15 \\ 9 & 3 & 14 \\ 5 & 6 & 3 \end{matrix}\right| \begin{matrix} 6 & 12 \\ 9 & 3 \\ 5 & 6 \end{matrix}$
$= 6 \cdot 3 \cdot 3 + 12 \cdot 14 \cdot 5 + 15 \cdot 9 \cdot 6 - 5 \cdot 3 \cdot 15 -$
$6 \cdot 14 \cdot 6 - 3 \cdot 9 \cdot 12$
$= 54 + 840 + 810 - 225 - 504 - 324$
$= 651$

13. $A = \frac{1}{2}\begin{vmatrix} 2 & 3 & 1 \\ 5 & 6 & 1 \\ 0 & 0 & 1 \end{vmatrix}$
$= \frac{1}{2}\left|\begin{matrix} 2 & 3 & 1 \\ 5 & 6 & 1 \\ 0 & 0 & 1 \end{matrix}\right| \begin{matrix} 2 & 3 \\ 5 & 6 \\ 0 & 0 \end{matrix}$
$= \frac{1}{2}(2 \cdot 6 \cdot 1 + 3 \cdot 1 \cdot 0 + 1 \cdot 5 \cdot 0 - 0 \cdot 6 \cdot 1 -$
$0 \cdot 1 \cdot 2 - 1 \cdot 5 \cdot 3)$
$= \frac{1}{2}(12 + 0 + 0 - 0 - 0 - 15)$
$= \frac{1}{2}(-3)$
$= -1.5$; $|-1.5| = 1.5$; 1.5 square units

14. $A = \frac{1}{2}\begin{vmatrix} -5 & -8 & 1 \\ 2 & 7 & 1 \\ 6 & -3 & 1 \end{vmatrix}$
$= \frac{1}{2}\left|\begin{matrix} -5 & -8 & 1 \\ 2 & 7 & 1 \\ 6 & -3 & 1 \end{matrix}\right| \begin{matrix} -5 & -8 \\ 2 & 7 \\ 6 & -3 \end{matrix}$
$= \frac{1}{2}(-5 \cdot 7 \cdot 1 + (-8) \cdot 1 \cdot 6 + 1 \cdot 2(-3) -$
$6 \cdot 7 \cdot 1 - (-3)1(-5) - 1 \cdot 2(-8))$
$= \frac{1}{2}(-35 - 48 - 6 - 42 - 15 + 16)$
$= \frac{1}{2}(-130)$
$= -65$; $|-65| = 65$; 65 square units

15. $A = \frac{1}{2}\begin{vmatrix} -2 & 2 & 1 \\ 2 & 2 & 1 \\ 2 & -2 & 1 \end{vmatrix}$
$= \frac{1}{2}\left|\begin{matrix} -2 & 2 & 1 \\ 2 & 2 & 1 \\ 2 & -2 & 1 \end{matrix}\right| \begin{matrix} -2 & 2 \\ 2 & 2 \\ 2 & -2 \end{matrix}$
$= \frac{1}{2}(-2 \cdot 2 \cdot 1 + 2 \cdot 1 \cdot 2 + 1 \cdot 2\,(-2) - 2 \cdot 2 \cdot 1 -$
$(-2)1(-2) - 1 \cdot 2 \cdot 2)$
$= \frac{1}{2}(-4 + 4 - 4 - 4 - 4 - 4)$
$= \frac{1}{2}(-16)$
$= -8$; $|-8| = 8$; 8 square units

Page 884 Lesson 4-5

1. $M^{-1} = \frac{1}{2 \cdot 1 - 1 \cdot 3}\begin{bmatrix} 1 & -3 \\ -1 & 2 \end{bmatrix}$

$= \frac{1}{-1}\begin{bmatrix} 1 & -3 \\ -1 & 2 \end{bmatrix}$

$= \begin{bmatrix} -1 & 3 \\ 1 & -2 \end{bmatrix}$

2. $M^{-1} = \frac{1}{3(-4) - 0 \cdot 2}\begin{bmatrix} -4 & -2 \\ 0 & 3 \end{bmatrix}$

$= \frac{1}{-12}\begin{bmatrix} -4 & -2 \\ 0 & 3 \end{bmatrix}$

$= \begin{bmatrix} \frac{1}{3} & \frac{1}{6} \\ 0 & -\frac{1}{4} \end{bmatrix}$

3. not square

4. det = 0

5. $M^{-1} = \frac{1}{2 \cdot 3 - 2 \cdot 4}\begin{bmatrix} 3 & -4 \\ -2 & 2 \end{bmatrix}$

$= \frac{1}{-2}\begin{bmatrix} 3 & -4 \\ -2 & 2 \end{bmatrix}$

$= \begin{bmatrix} -1.5 & 2 \\ 1 & -1 \end{bmatrix}$

6. $M^{-1} = \frac{1}{8 \cdot 4 - 6 \cdot 5}\begin{bmatrix} 4 & -5 \\ -6 & 8 \end{bmatrix}$

$= \frac{1}{2}\begin{bmatrix} 4 & -5 \\ -6 & 8 \end{bmatrix}$

$= \begin{bmatrix} 2 & -2.5 \\ -3 & 4 \end{bmatrix}$

7. $M^{-1} = \frac{1}{10 \cdot 2 - 5 \cdot 3}\begin{bmatrix} 2 & -3 \\ -5 & 10 \end{bmatrix}$

$= \frac{1}{5}\begin{bmatrix} 2 & -3 \\ -5 & 10 \end{bmatrix}$

$= \begin{bmatrix} 0.4 & -0.6 \\ -1 & 2 \end{bmatrix}$

8. $M^{-1} = \frac{1}{-3 \cdot 8 - (-4)4}\begin{bmatrix} 8 & -4 \\ 4 & -3 \end{bmatrix}$

$= \frac{1}{-8}\begin{bmatrix} 8 & -4 \\ 4 & -3 \end{bmatrix}$

$= \begin{bmatrix} -1 & \frac{1}{2} \\ -\frac{1}{2} & \frac{3}{8} \end{bmatrix}$

9. $\begin{bmatrix} -7 & -6 \\ 8 & 7 \end{bmatrix} \cdot \begin{bmatrix} -7 & -6 \\ 8 & 7 \end{bmatrix} \stackrel{?}{=} I$

$\begin{bmatrix} -7(-7) + (-6)8 & -7(-6) + (-6)7 \\ 8(-7) + 7(8) & 8(-6) + 7(7) \end{bmatrix} \stackrel{?}{=} I$

$\begin{bmatrix} 1 & 0 \\ 0 & 1 \end{bmatrix} = I$ ✓ true

10. $\begin{bmatrix} -3 & 4 \\ 2 & -2 \end{bmatrix} \cdot \begin{bmatrix} -2 & -2 \\ -4 & -3 \end{bmatrix} \stackrel{?}{=} I$

$\begin{bmatrix} -3(-2) + 4(-4) & -3(-2) + 4(-3) \\ 2(-2) - 2(-4) & 2(-2) + (-2)(-3) \end{bmatrix} \stackrel{?}{=} I$

$\begin{bmatrix} -10 & -6 \\ 4 & 2 \end{bmatrix} \neq I$ false

11. $\begin{bmatrix} 1 & 0 \\ 0 & 1 \end{bmatrix} \cdot \begin{bmatrix} -3 & 7 \\ 1 & 8 \end{bmatrix} \stackrel{?}{=} \begin{bmatrix} -3 & 7 \\ 1 & 8 \end{bmatrix}$

$\begin{bmatrix} 1(-3) + 0 \cdot 1 & 1 \cdot 7 + 0 \cdot 8 \\ 0(-3) + 1 \cdot 1 & 0 \cdot 7 + 1 \cdot 8 \end{bmatrix} \stackrel{?}{=} \begin{bmatrix} -3 & 7 \\ 1 & 8 \end{bmatrix}$

$\begin{bmatrix} -3 & 7 \\ 1 & 8 \end{bmatrix} = \begin{bmatrix} -3 & 7 \\ 1 & 8 \end{bmatrix}$ ✓ true

Page 884 Lesson 4-6

1. $\begin{bmatrix} 5 & 3 \\ 2 & -1 \end{bmatrix} \cdot \begin{bmatrix} x \\ y \end{bmatrix} = \begin{bmatrix} 6 \\ 9 \end{bmatrix}$

2. $\begin{bmatrix} 3 & 4 \\ 2 & -3 \end{bmatrix} \cdot \begin{bmatrix} x \\ y \end{bmatrix} = \begin{bmatrix} -8 \\ 6 \end{bmatrix}$

3. $\begin{bmatrix} 1 & 3 \\ 4 & -1 \end{bmatrix} \cdot \begin{bmatrix} x \\ y \end{bmatrix} = \begin{bmatrix} 1 \\ -22 \end{bmatrix}$

4. $\begin{bmatrix} 4 & -3 \\ 5 & -2 \end{bmatrix} \cdot \begin{bmatrix} x \\ y \end{bmatrix} = \begin{bmatrix} -1 \\ 39 \end{bmatrix}$

5. $\begin{bmatrix} 3 & 4 \\ 2 & -5 \end{bmatrix} \cdot \begin{bmatrix} x \\ y \end{bmatrix} = \begin{bmatrix} 33 \\ -1 \end{bmatrix}$

$\frac{1}{23}\begin{bmatrix} 5 & 4 \\ 2 & -3 \end{bmatrix} \cdot \begin{bmatrix} 3 & 4 \\ 2 & -5 \end{bmatrix} \cdot \begin{bmatrix} x \\ y \end{bmatrix} = \frac{1}{23}\begin{bmatrix} 5 & 4 \\ 2 & -3 \end{bmatrix} \cdot \begin{bmatrix} 33 \\ -1 \end{bmatrix}$

$\begin{bmatrix} x \\ y \end{bmatrix} = \frac{1}{23}\begin{bmatrix} 165 - 4 \\ 66 + 3 \end{bmatrix}$

$\begin{bmatrix} x \\ y \end{bmatrix} = \frac{1}{23}\begin{bmatrix} 161 \\ 69 \end{bmatrix}$

$\begin{bmatrix} x \\ y \end{bmatrix} = \begin{bmatrix} 7 \\ 3 \end{bmatrix}$; (7, 3)

6. $\begin{bmatrix} 1 & 2 & -1 \\ -2 & 3 & 1 \\ 1 & 1 & 3 \end{bmatrix} \cdot \begin{bmatrix} x \\ y \\ z \end{bmatrix} = \begin{bmatrix} 6 \\ 1 \\ 8 \end{bmatrix}$

$\frac{1}{27}\begin{bmatrix} 8 & -7 & 5 \\ 7 & 4 & 1 \\ -5 & 1 & 7 \end{bmatrix} \cdot \begin{bmatrix} 1 & 2 & -1 \\ -2 & 3 & 1 \\ 1 & 1 & 3 \end{bmatrix} \cdot \begin{bmatrix} x \\ y \\ z \end{bmatrix} = \frac{1}{27}\begin{bmatrix} 8 & -7 & 5 \\ 7 & 4 & 1 \\ -5 & 1 & 7 \end{bmatrix} \cdot \begin{bmatrix} 6 \\ 1 \\ 8 \end{bmatrix}$

$\begin{bmatrix} x \\ y \\ z \end{bmatrix} = \frac{1}{27}\begin{bmatrix} 48 - 7 + 40 \\ 42 + 4 + 8 \\ -30 + 1 + 56 \end{bmatrix}$

$\begin{bmatrix} x \\ y \\ z \end{bmatrix} = \frac{1}{27}\begin{bmatrix} 81 \\ 54 \\ 27 \end{bmatrix}$

$\begin{bmatrix} x \\ y \\ z \end{bmatrix} = \begin{bmatrix} 3 \\ 2 \\ 1 \end{bmatrix}$; (3, 2, 1)

7. $M^{-1} = \frac{1}{1(-0.08) - 0.1(1)}\begin{bmatrix} -0.08 & -1 \\ -0.1 & 1 \end{bmatrix}$

$= \frac{1}{-0.18}\begin{bmatrix} -0.08 & -1 \\ -0.1 & 1 \end{bmatrix}$

$\begin{bmatrix} 1 & 1 \\ 0.1 & -0.08 \end{bmatrix} \cdot \begin{bmatrix} x \\ y \end{bmatrix} = \begin{bmatrix} 18{,}000 \\ 0 \end{bmatrix}$

$-\frac{1}{0.18}\begin{bmatrix} -0.08 & -1 \\ -0.1 & 1 \end{bmatrix} \cdot \begin{bmatrix} 1 & 1 \\ 0.1 & -0.08 \end{bmatrix} \cdot \begin{bmatrix} x \\ y \end{bmatrix}$

$= -\frac{1}{0.18}\begin{bmatrix} -0.08 & -1 \\ -0.1 & 1 \end{bmatrix} \cdot \begin{bmatrix} 18{,}000 \\ 0 \end{bmatrix}$

$\begin{bmatrix} x \\ y \end{bmatrix} = -\frac{1}{0.18}\begin{bmatrix} -1440 - 0 \\ -1800 + 0 \end{bmatrix}$

$\begin{bmatrix} x \\ y \end{bmatrix} = -\frac{1}{0.18}\begin{bmatrix} -1440 \\ -1800 \end{bmatrix}$

$\begin{bmatrix} x \\ y \end{bmatrix} = \begin{bmatrix} 8000 \\ 10{,}000 \end{bmatrix}$; (8000, 10,000)

8. $M^{-1} = \frac{1}{-1(-6) - 7 \cdot 1}\begin{bmatrix} -6 & -1 \\ -7 & -1 \end{bmatrix}$

$= \frac{1}{-1}\begin{bmatrix} -6 & -1 \\ -7 & -1 \end{bmatrix}$

$\begin{bmatrix} -1 & 1 \\ 7 & -6 \end{bmatrix} \cdot \begin{bmatrix} x \\ y \end{bmatrix} = \begin{bmatrix} 0 \\ 3 \end{bmatrix}$

$-1\begin{bmatrix} -6 & -1 \\ -7 & -1 \end{bmatrix} \cdot \begin{bmatrix} -1 & 1 \\ 7 & -6 \end{bmatrix} \cdot \begin{bmatrix} x \\ y \end{bmatrix} = -1\begin{bmatrix} -6 & -1 \\ -7 & -1 \end{bmatrix} \cdot \begin{bmatrix} 0 \\ 3 \end{bmatrix}$

$\begin{bmatrix} x \\ y \end{bmatrix} = -1\begin{bmatrix} 0 - 3 \\ 0 - 3 \end{bmatrix}$

$\begin{bmatrix} x \\ y \end{bmatrix} = -1\begin{bmatrix} -3 \\ -3 \end{bmatrix}$

$\begin{bmatrix} x \\ y \end{bmatrix} = \begin{bmatrix} 3 \\ 3 \end{bmatrix}$; (3, 3)

9. $\begin{bmatrix} 5 & -1 \\ 8 & 2 \end{bmatrix} \cdot \begin{bmatrix} x \\ y \end{bmatrix} = \begin{bmatrix} 7 \\ 4 \end{bmatrix}$ $\quad M^{-1} = \frac{1}{5 \cdot 2 - 8(-1)}\begin{bmatrix} 2 & 1 \\ -8 & 5 \end{bmatrix}$

$= \frac{1}{18}\begin{bmatrix} 2 & 1 \\ -8 & 5 \end{bmatrix}$

$\begin{bmatrix} 5 & -1 \\ 8 & 2 \end{bmatrix} \cdot \begin{bmatrix} x \\ y \end{bmatrix} = \begin{bmatrix} 7 \\ 4 \end{bmatrix}$

$\frac{1}{18}\begin{bmatrix} 2 & 1 \\ -8 & 5 \end{bmatrix} \cdot \begin{bmatrix} 5 & -1 \\ 8 & 2 \end{bmatrix} \cdot \begin{bmatrix} x \\ y \end{bmatrix} = \frac{1}{18}\begin{bmatrix} 2 & 1 \\ -8 & 5 \end{bmatrix} \cdot \begin{bmatrix} 7 \\ 4 \end{bmatrix}$

$\begin{bmatrix} x \\ y \end{bmatrix} = \frac{1}{18}\begin{bmatrix} 14 + 4 \\ -56 + 20 \end{bmatrix}$

$\begin{bmatrix} x \\ y \end{bmatrix} = \frac{1}{18}\begin{bmatrix} 18 \\ -36 \end{bmatrix}$

$\begin{bmatrix} x \\ y \end{bmatrix} = \begin{bmatrix} 1 \\ -2 \end{bmatrix}$; (1, −2)

10. $\begin{bmatrix} 3 & 1 \\ 2 & 2 \end{bmatrix} \cdot \begin{bmatrix} x \\ y \end{bmatrix} = \begin{bmatrix} 4 \\ 3 \end{bmatrix}$ $\quad M^{-1} = \frac{1}{3 \cdot 2 - 2 \cdot 1}\begin{bmatrix} 2 & -1 \\ -2 & 3 \end{bmatrix}$

$= \frac{1}{4}\begin{bmatrix} 2 & -1 \\ -2 & 3 \end{bmatrix}$

$\begin{bmatrix} 3 & 1 \\ 2 & 2 \end{bmatrix} \cdot \begin{bmatrix} x \\ y \end{bmatrix} = \begin{bmatrix} 4 \\ 3 \end{bmatrix}$

$\frac{1}{4}\begin{bmatrix} 2 & -1 \\ -2 & 3 \end{bmatrix} \cdot \begin{bmatrix} 3 & 1 \\ 2 & 2 \end{bmatrix} \cdot \begin{bmatrix} x \\ y \end{bmatrix} = \frac{1}{4}\begin{bmatrix} 2 & -1 \\ -2 & 3 \end{bmatrix} \cdot \begin{bmatrix} 4 \\ 3 \end{bmatrix}$

$\begin{bmatrix} x \\ y \end{bmatrix} = \frac{1}{4}\begin{bmatrix} 8 - 3 \\ -8 + 9 \end{bmatrix}$

$\begin{bmatrix} x \\ y \end{bmatrix} = \frac{1}{4}\begin{bmatrix} 5 \\ 1 \end{bmatrix}$

$\begin{bmatrix} x \\ y \end{bmatrix} = \begin{bmatrix} \frac{5}{4} \\ \frac{1}{4} \end{bmatrix}$; $\left(\frac{5}{4}, \frac{1}{4}\right)$

11. $\begin{bmatrix} 6 & 5 \\ 3 & -10 \end{bmatrix} \cdot \begin{bmatrix} x \\ y \end{bmatrix} = \begin{bmatrix} 7 \\ -4 \end{bmatrix}$ $\quad M^{-1} = \frac{1}{6(-10) - 3 \cdot 5}\begin{bmatrix} -10 & -5 \\ -3 & 6 \end{bmatrix}$

$= \frac{1}{-75}\begin{bmatrix} -10 & -5 \\ -3 & 6 \end{bmatrix}$

(Continued next column)

$\begin{bmatrix} 6 & 5 \\ 3 & 10 \end{bmatrix} \cdot \begin{bmatrix} x \\ y \end{bmatrix} = \begin{bmatrix} 7 \\ -4 \end{bmatrix}$

$-\frac{1}{75}\begin{bmatrix} -10 & -5 \\ -3 & 6 \end{bmatrix} \cdot \begin{bmatrix} 6 & 5 \\ 3 & -10 \end{bmatrix} \cdot \begin{bmatrix} x \\ y \end{bmatrix} = -\frac{1}{75}\begin{bmatrix} -10 & -5 \\ -3 & 6 \end{bmatrix} \cdot \begin{bmatrix} 7 \\ -4 \end{bmatrix}$

$\begin{bmatrix} x \\ y \end{bmatrix} = -\frac{1}{75}\begin{bmatrix} -70 + 20 \\ -21 - 24 \end{bmatrix}$

$\begin{bmatrix} x \\ y \end{bmatrix} = -\frac{1}{75}\begin{bmatrix} -50 \\ -45 \end{bmatrix}$

$\begin{bmatrix} x \\ y \end{bmatrix} = \begin{bmatrix} \frac{2}{3} \\ \frac{3}{5} \end{bmatrix}$; $\left(\frac{2}{3}, \frac{3}{5}\right)$

12. $\begin{bmatrix} 3 & -5 \\ 1 & 3 \end{bmatrix} \cdot \begin{bmatrix} x \\ y \end{bmatrix} = \begin{bmatrix} 1 \\ 5 \end{bmatrix}$ $\quad M^{-1} = \frac{1}{3 \cdot 3 - 1(-5)}\begin{bmatrix} 3 & 5 \\ -1 & 3 \end{bmatrix}$

$= \frac{1}{14}\begin{bmatrix} 3 & 5 \\ -1 & 3 \end{bmatrix}$

$\begin{bmatrix} 3 & -5 \\ 1 & 3 \end{bmatrix} \cdot \begin{bmatrix} x \\ y \end{bmatrix} = \begin{bmatrix} 1 \\ 5 \end{bmatrix}$

$\frac{1}{14}\begin{bmatrix} 3 & 5 \\ -1 & 3 \end{bmatrix} \cdot \begin{bmatrix} 3 & -5 \\ 1 & 3 \end{bmatrix} \cdot \begin{bmatrix} x \\ y \end{bmatrix} = \frac{1}{14}\begin{bmatrix} 3 & 5 \\ -1 & 3 \end{bmatrix} \cdot \begin{bmatrix} 1 \\ 5 \end{bmatrix}$

$\begin{bmatrix} x \\ y \end{bmatrix} = \frac{1}{14}\begin{bmatrix} 3 + 25 \\ -1 + 15 \end{bmatrix}$

$\begin{bmatrix} x \\ y \end{bmatrix} = \frac{1}{14}\begin{bmatrix} 28 \\ 14 \end{bmatrix}$

$\begin{bmatrix} x \\ y \end{bmatrix} = \begin{bmatrix} 2 \\ 1 \end{bmatrix}$; (2, 1)

Page 885 Lesson 4-7

1. $y = 2x + 3 \qquad y = 4x - 1$

$-2x + y = 3 \qquad -4x + y = -1$

$\left[\begin{array}{cc|c} -2 & 1 & 3 \\ -4 & 1 & -1 \end{array}\right]; \left[\begin{array}{cc|c} -2 & 1 & 3 \\ -4 & 1 & -1 \end{array}\right] = \left[\begin{array}{cc|c} -2 & 0 & -4 \\ -4 & 1 & -1 \end{array}\right]$

$= \left[\begin{array}{cc|c} 1 & 0 & 2 \\ -4 & 1 & -1 \end{array}\right] = \left[\begin{array}{cc|c} 1 & 0 & 2 \\ 0 & 1 & 7 \end{array}\right]$ $\quad$ (2, 7)

2. $\left[\begin{array}{cc|c} 3 & 4 & -6 \\ 5 & -3 & 19 \end{array}\right] = \left[\begin{array}{cc|c} 9 & 12 & -18 \\ 5 & -3 & 19 \end{array}\right] = \left[\begin{array}{cc|c} 29 & 0 & 58 \\ 5 & -3 & 19 \end{array}\right]$

$= \left[\begin{array}{cc|c} 1 & 0 & 2 \\ 5 & -3 & 19 \end{array}\right] = \left[\begin{array}{cc|c} 1 & 0 & 2 \\ 0 & -3 & 9 \end{array}\right] = \left[\begin{array}{cc|c} 1 & 0 & 2 \\ 0 & 1 & -3 \end{array}\right]$ $\quad$ (2, −3)

3. $\left[\begin{array}{ccc|c} 3 & 2 & 4 & 9 \\ 2 & 5 & -2 & -7 \\ 4 & 1 & -3 & -3 \end{array}\right] = \left[\begin{array}{ccc|c} 7 & 12 & 0 & -5 \\ 2 & 5 & -2 & -7 \\ 4 & 1 & -3 & -3 \end{array}\right]$

$= \left[\begin{array}{ccc|c} 7 & 12 & 0 & -5 \\ -6 & -15 & 6 & 21 \\ 4 & 1 & -3 & -3 \end{array}\right] = \left[\begin{array}{ccc|c} 7 & 12 & 0 & -5 \\ 2 & -13 & 0 & 15 \\ 4 & 1 & 3 & -3 \end{array}\right]$

$= \left[\begin{array}{ccc|c} 7 & 12 & 0 & -5 \\ 14 & -91 & 0 & 105 \\ 4 & 1 & -3 & -3 \end{array}\right] = \left[\begin{array}{ccc|c} 7 & 12 & 0 & -5 \\ 0 & -115 & 0 & 115 \\ 4 & 1 & -3 & -3 \end{array}\right]$

$= \left[\begin{array}{ccc|c} 7 & 12 & 0 & -5 \\ 0 & 1 & 0 & -1 \\ 4 & 1 & -3 & -3 \end{array}\right] = \left[\begin{array}{ccc|c} 7 & 12 & 0 & -5 \\ 0 & 1 & 0 & -1 \\ 4 & 0 & -3 & -2 \end{array}\right] = \left[\begin{array}{ccc|c} 7 & 0 & 0 & 7 \\ 0 & 1 & 0 & -1 \\ 4 & 0 & -3 & -2 \end{array}\right]$

$= \left[\begin{array}{ccc|c} 1 & 0 & 0 & 1 \\ 0 & 1 & 0 & -1 \\ 4 & 0 & -3 & -2 \end{array}\right] = \left[\begin{array}{ccc|c} 1 & 0 & 0 & 1 \\ 0 & 1 & 0 & -1 \\ 0 & 0 & -3 & -6 \end{array}\right] = \left[\begin{array}{ccc|c} 1 & 0 & 0 & 1 \\ 0 & 1 & 0 & -1 \\ 0 & 0 & 1 & 2 \end{array}\right]$

(1, −1, 2)

4. $\left[\begin{array}{ccc|c} 1 & 2 & -3 & 12 \\ 5 & -3 & 1 & -11 \\ 2 & 1 & 4 & -5 \end{array}\right] = \left[\begin{array}{ccc|c} 1 & 2 & -3 & 12 \\ 0 & -13 & 16 & -71 \\ 2 & 1 & 4 & -5 \end{array}\right]$

$= \left[\begin{array}{ccc|c} 1 & 2 & -3 & 12 \\ 0 & -13 & 16 & -71 \\ 0 & -3 & 10 & -29 \end{array}\right] = \left[\begin{array}{ccc|c} 1 & 2 & -3 & 12 \\ 0 & 65 & -80 & 355 \\ 0 & -3 & 10 & -29 \end{array}\right]$

$= \left[\begin{array}{ccc|c} 1 & 2 & -3 & 12 \\ 0 & 41 & 0 & 123 \\ 0 & -3 & 10 & -29 \end{array}\right] = \left[\begin{array}{ccc|c} 1 & 2 & -3 & 12 \\ 0 & 1 & 0 & 3 \\ 0 & -3 & 10 & -29 \end{array}\right]$

$= \left[\begin{array}{ccc|c} 1 & 2 & -3 & 12 \\ 0 & 1 & 0 & 3 \\ 0 & 0 & 10 & -20 \end{array}\right] = \left[\begin{array}{ccc|c} 1 & 2 & -3 & 12 \\ 0 & 1 & 0 & 3 \\ 0 & 0 & 1 & -2 \end{array}\right] = \left[\begin{array}{ccc|c} 1 & 0 & -3 & 6 \\ 0 & 1 & 0 & 3 \\ 0 & 0 & 1 & -2 \end{array}\right]$

$= \left[\begin{array}{ccc|c} 1 & 0 & 0 & 0 \\ 0 & 1 & 0 & 3 \\ 0 & 0 & 1 & -2 \end{array}\right]$ $(0, 3, -2)$

5. $\left[\begin{array}{cc|c} -2 & 0 & -12 \\ 0 & 4 & 48 \end{array}\right] = \left[\begin{array}{cc|c} 1 & 0 & 6 \\ 0 & 1 & 12 \end{array}\right]$ $(6, 12)$

6. $x + 2y = 9$ $\quad 3y + z = 6$

$x = 9 - 2y$ $\quad z = 6 - 3y$; $(9 - 2y, y, 6 - 3y)$

7. $0 = -2$; no solution

8. $2x = 3y - 31$ $\quad 3x + 5y = 1$

$2x - 3y = -31$

$\left[\begin{array}{cc|c} 2 & -3 & -31 \\ 3 & 5 & 1 \end{array}\right] = \left[\begin{array}{cc|c} 2 & -3 & -31 \\ -6 & -10 & -2 \end{array}\right] = \left[\begin{array}{cc|c} 2 & -3 & -31 \\ 0 & -19 & -95 \end{array}\right]$

$= \left[\begin{array}{cc|c} 2 & -3 & -31 \\ 0 & 1 & 5 \end{array}\right] = \left[\begin{array}{cc|c} 2 & 0 & -16 \\ 0 & 1 & 5 \end{array}\right] = \left[\begin{array}{cc|c} 1 & 0 & -8 \\ 0 & 1 & 5 \end{array}\right]$; $(-8, 5)$

9. $6y = 4x - 9$ $\quad 3x = 7y - 2$

$-4x + 6y = -9$ $\quad 3x - 7y = -2$

$\left[\begin{array}{cc|c} -4 & 6 & -9 \\ 3 & -7 & -2 \end{array}\right] = \left[\begin{array}{cc|c} -4 & 6 & -9 \\ 12 & -28 & -8 \end{array}\right] = \left[\begin{array}{cc|c} -4 & 6 & -9 \\ 0 & -10 & -35 \end{array}\right]$

$= \left[\begin{array}{cc|c} -4 & 6 & -9 \\ 0 & 1 & 3.5 \end{array}\right] = \left[\begin{array}{cc|c} -4 & 0 & -30 \\ 0 & 1 & 3.5 \end{array}\right] = \left[\begin{array}{cc|c} 1 & 0 & 7.5 \\ 0 & 1 & 3.5 \end{array}\right]$; $(7.5, 3.5)$

10. $\left[\begin{array}{cc|c} 7 & 5 & 27 \\ 5 & -5 & 5 \end{array}\right] = \left[\begin{array}{cc|c} 12 & 0 & 32 \\ 5 & -5 & 5 \end{array}\right] = \left[\begin{array}{cc|c} 1 & 0 & \frac{8}{3} \\ 5 & -5 & 5 \end{array}\right]$

$= \left[\begin{array}{cc|c} 1 & 0 & \frac{8}{3} \\ 0 & -5 & -\frac{25}{3} \end{array}\right] = \left[\begin{array}{cc|c} 1 & 0 & \frac{8}{3} \\ 0 & 1 & \frac{5}{3} \end{array}\right]$; $\left(\frac{8}{3}, \frac{5}{3}\right)$

11. $\left[\begin{array}{cc|c} 4 & 2 & 0 \\ 3 & 5 & 7 \end{array}\right] = \left[\begin{array}{cc|c} -20 & -10 & 0 \\ 3 & 5 & 7 \end{array}\right] = \left[\begin{array}{cc|c} -14 & 0 & 14 \\ 3 & 5 & 7 \end{array}\right]$

$= \left[\begin{array}{cc|c} 1 & 0 & -1 \\ 3 & 5 & 7 \end{array}\right] = \left[\begin{array}{cc|c} 1 & 0 & -1 \\ 0 & 5 & 10 \end{array}\right] = \left[\begin{array}{cc|c} 1 & 0 & -1 \\ 0 & 1 & 2 \end{array}\right]$; $(-1, 2)$

12. $\left[\begin{array}{ccc|c} 2 & -3 & 4 & -15 \\ 5 & -1 & -3 & 8 \\ 3 & -2 & 5 & -5 \end{array}\right] = \left[\begin{array}{ccc|c} -13 & 0 & 13 & -39 \\ 5 & -1 & -3 & 8 \\ 3 & -2 & 5 & -5 \end{array}\right]$

$= \left[\begin{array}{ccc|c} -13 & 0 & 13 & -39 \\ 5 & -1 & -3 & 8 \\ -7 & 0 & 11 & -21 \end{array}\right] = \left[\begin{array}{ccc|c} -1 & 0 & 1 & -3 \\ 5 & -1 & -3 & 8 \\ -7 & 0 & 11 & -21 \end{array}\right]$

$= \left[\begin{array}{ccc|c} -1 & 0 & 1 & -3 \\ 2 & -1 & 0 & -1 \\ -7 & 0 & 11 & -21 \end{array}\right] = \left[\begin{array}{ccc|c} -1 & 0 & 1 & -3 \\ 2 & -1 & 0 & -1 \\ 0 & 0 & 4 & 0 \end{array}\right]$

$= \left[\begin{array}{ccc|c} -1 & 0 & 1 & -3 \\ 2 & -1 & 0 & 1 \\ 0 & 0 & 1 & 0 \end{array}\right] = \left[\begin{array}{ccc|c} -1 & 0 & 0 & -3 \\ 2 & -1 & 0 & -1 \\ 0 & 0 & 1 & 0 \end{array}\right]$

$= \left[\begin{array}{ccc|c} 1 & 0 & 0 & 3 \\ 2 & -1 & 0 & -1 \\ 0 & 0 & 1 & 0 \end{array}\right] = \left[\begin{array}{ccc|c} 1 & 0 & 0 & 3 \\ 0 & -1 & 0 & -7 \\ 0 & 0 & 1 & 0 \end{array}\right] = \left[\begin{array}{ccc|c} 1 & 0 & 0 & 3 \\ 0 & 1 & 0 & 7 \\ 0 & 0 & 1 & 0 \end{array}\right]$;

$(3, 7, 0)$

13. $\left[\begin{array}{ccc|c} 2 & -1 & -4 & -8 \\ 4 & 1 & 3 & 6 \\ 6 & 0 & -1 & -2 \end{array}\right] = \left[\begin{array}{ccc|c} 2 & -1 & -4 & -8 \\ 6 & 0 & -1 & -2 \\ 6 & 0 & -1 & -2 \end{array}\right]$

$= \left[\begin{array}{ccc|c} 2 & -1 & -4 & -8 \\ 0 & 0 & 0 & 0 \\ 6 & 0 & -1 & -2 \end{array}\right] = \left[\begin{array}{ccc|c} 2 & -1 & -4 & -8 \\ 0 & 0 & 0 & 0 \\ -24 & 0 & 4 & 8 \end{array}\right]$

$= \left[\begin{array}{ccc|c} -22 & -1 & 0 & 0 \\ 0 & 0 & 0 & 0 \\ -24 & 0 & 4 & 8 \end{array}\right]$

$-22x - y = 0$ $\quad -24x + 4z = 8$

$-22x = y$ $\quad -6x + z = 2$

$z = 6x + 2$

$(x, -22x, 6x + 2)$

14. $\left[\begin{array}{ccc|c} 1 & -4 & 2 & 4 \\ 2 & 3 & 2 & -5 \\ 2 & -5 & 1 & 2 \end{array}\right] = \left[\begin{array}{ccc|c} 1 & -4 & 2 & 4 \\ -2 & 13 & 0 & -9 \\ 2 & -5 & 1 & 2 \end{array}\right]$

$= \left[\begin{array}{ccc|c} -3 & 6 & 0 & 0 \\ -2 & 13 & 0 & -9 \\ 2 & -5 & 1 & 2 \end{array}\right] = \left[\begin{array}{ccc|c} -3 & 6 & 0 & 0 \\ -2 & 13 & 0 & -9 \\ 0 & 8 & 1 & -7 \end{array}\right]$

$= \left[\begin{array}{ccc|c} 1 & -2 & 0 & 0 \\ -2 & 13 & 0 & -9 \\ 0 & 8 & 1 & -7 \end{array}\right] = \left[\begin{array}{ccc|c} 1 & -2 & 0 & 0 \\ 0 & 9 & 0 & -9 \\ 0 & 8 & 1 & -7 \end{array}\right]$

$= \left[\begin{array}{ccc|c} 1 & -2 & 0 & 0 \\ 0 & 1 & 0 & -1 \\ 0 & 8 & 1 & -7 \end{array}\right] = \left[\begin{array}{ccc|c} 1 & 0 & 0 & -2 \\ 0 & 1 & 0 & -1 \\ 0 & 8 & 1 & -7 \end{array}\right] = \left[\begin{array}{ccc|c} 1 & 0 & 0 & -2 \\ 0 & 1 & 0 & -1 \\ 0 & 0 & 1 & 1 \end{array}\right]$;

$(-2, -1, 1)$

15. $\left[\begin{array}{ccc|c} 3 & -2 & -4 & 13 \\ 2 & 3 & 3 & 4 \\ 2 & -2 & -5 & 5 \end{array}\right] = \left[\begin{array}{ccc|c} 1 & 0 & 1 & 8 \\ 2 & 3 & 3 & 4 \\ 2 & -2 & -5 & 5 \end{array}\right]$

$= \left[\begin{array}{ccc|c} 1 & 0 & 1 & 8 \\ 0 & 3 & 1 & -12 \\ 2 & -2 & -5 & 5 \end{array}\right] = \left[\begin{array}{ccc|c} 1 & 0 & 1 & 8 \\ 0 & 3 & 1 & -12 \\ 0 & -2 & -7 & -11 \end{array}\right]$

$= \left[\begin{array}{ccc|c} 1 & 0 & 1 & 8 \\ 0 & 21 & 7 & -84 \\ 0 & -2 & -7 & -11 \end{array}\right] = \left[\begin{array}{ccc|c} 1 & 0 & 1 & 8 \\ 0 & 19 & 0 & -95 \\ 0 & -2 & -7 & -11 \end{array}\right]$

$= \left[\begin{array}{ccc|c} 1 & 0 & 1 & 8 \\ 0 & 1 & 0 & -5 \\ 0 & -2 & -7 & -11 \end{array}\right] = \left[\begin{array}{ccc|c} 1 & 0 & 1 & 8 \\ 0 & 1 & 0 & -5 \\ 0 & 0 & -7 & -21 \end{array}\right]$

$= \left[\begin{array}{ccc|c} 1 & 0 & 1 & 8 \\ 0 & 1 & 0 & -5 \\ 0 & 0 & 1 & 3 \end{array}\right] = \left[\begin{array}{ccc|c} 1 & 0 & 0 & 5 \\ 0 & 1 & 0 & -5 \\ 0 & 0 & 1 & 3 \end{array}\right]$; (5, −5, 3)

Page 885 Lesson 4-8

1. 135 − 30 = 105
2. 50%
3. 25%
4. 100%
5. 10, 13, 13, 16, 17, 17, 17, 18, 19, 20, 20, 20, 20, 20, 20, 20, 21, 22, 22, 23, 23, 23, 24, 24, 24, 24
24 − 10 = 14; Q_2 lies between 13th and 14th terms, $\frac{20 + 20}{2} = 20$; Q_1 is 7th term = 17; Q_3 is 20th term = 23; IR = 23 − 17 = 6; outliers: below 17 − 1.5 (6) = 8 or above 23 + 1.5 (6) = 32, no outliers

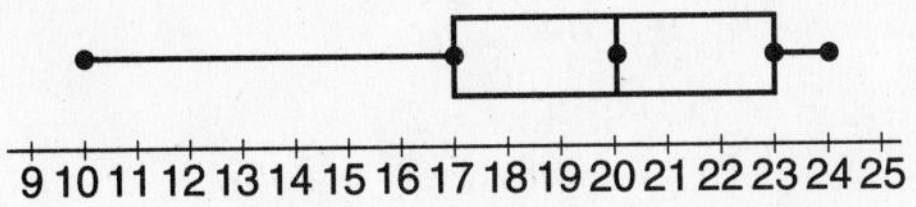

6. 3, 5, 6, 6, 7, 8, 8, 9, 9, 10, 10, 11, 11, 11, 12, 12, 12, 12, 12, 12, 13, 13, 13, 14, 14, 14, 15, 15, 15
15 − 3 = 12; Q_2 is 15th term = 12; Q_1 is between 7th and 8th terms, $\frac{8 + 9}{2} = 8.5$; Q_3 is between 22nd and 23rd terms, $\frac{13 + 13}{2} = 13$; IR = 13 − 8.5 = 4.5; outliers: below 8.5 − 1.5(4.5) = 1.75 or above 13 + 1.5(4.5) = 19.75, no outliers

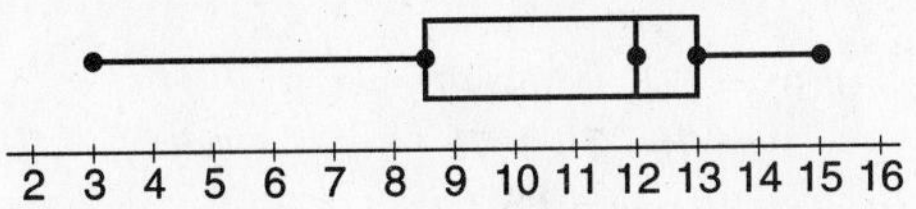

7. 28, 33, 36, 38, 47, 55, 67, 70, 72, 73, 73, 73, 76, 80, 81, 83, 83, 84, 87, 88, 89, 89, 89, 89, 91, 97
97 − 28 = 69; Q_2 is between 13th and 14th terms, $\frac{76 + 80}{2} = 78$; Q_1 is 7th term = 67; Q_3 is 20th term = 88; IR = 88 − 67 = 21; outliers: below 67 − 1.5(21) = 35.5 or above 88 + 1.5(21) = 119.5, 28 and 33

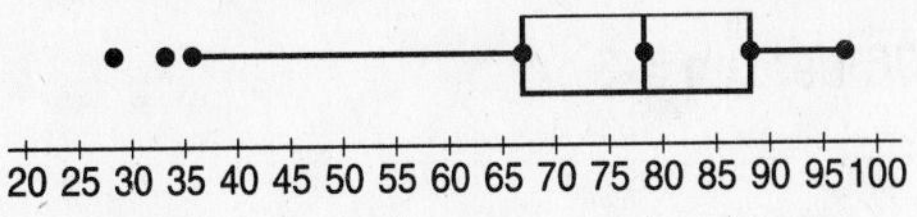

8. 5.2, 5.4, 5.5, 6.2, 8.2, 8.7, 8.8, 11.1, 13.2, 13.6, 18.9, 30.4
30.4 − 5.2 = 25.2; Q_2 is between 6th and 7th terms = $\frac{8.7 + 8.8}{2} = 8.75$; Q_1 is between 3rd and 4th terms = $\frac{5.5 + 6.2}{2} = 5.85$; Q_3 is between 9th and 10th terms = $\frac{13.2 + 13.6}{2} = 13.4$; IR = 13.4 − 5.85 = 7.55; outliers: below 5.85 − 1.5(7.55) = −5.475 or above 13.4 + 1.5 (7.55) = 24.725, 30.4

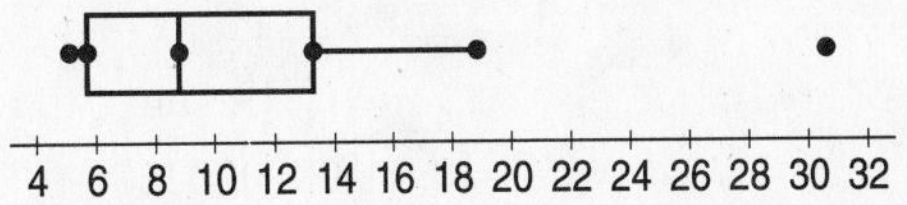

9. 496, 553, 556, 565, 625, 679, 718, 805, 1033, 2064
2064 − 496 = 1568; Q_2 is between 5th and 6th terms = $\frac{625 + 679}{2} = 652$; Q_1 is 3rd term = 556, Q_3 is 8th term = 805; IR = 805 − 556 = 249; outliers: below 556 − 1.5(249) = 182.5 or above 805 + 1.5(249) = 1178.5; 2064

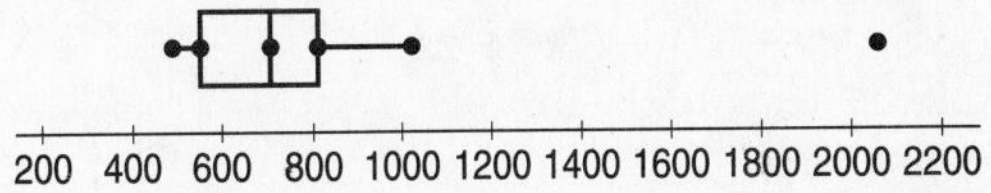

Page 885 Lesson 5-1

1. $x^7x^3x = x^{7+3+1} = x^{11}$
2. $(-3)^4(-3) = (-3)^{4+1} = (-3)^5 = -243$
3. $\frac{t^{12}}{t} = t^{12-1} = t^{11}$
4. $\frac{6^5}{6^3} = 6^{5-3} = 6^2 = 36$
5. $(m^3)^8 = m^{3 \cdot 8} = m^{24}$
6. $-3^4 = -(3^4) = -81$
7. $\left(\frac{x}{5}\right)^2 = \frac{x^2}{5^2} = \frac{x^2}{25}$
8. $(-2y^5)^2 = (-2)^2y^{5 \cdot 2} = 4y^{10}$
9. $3x^0 = 3 \cdot 1 = 3$
10. $\frac{5^6a^{x+y}}{5^4a^{x-y}} = 5^{6-4}a^{x+y-(x-y)} = 5^2a^{x+y-x+y} = 25a^{2y}$
11. $ab^{-1} = a \cdot \frac{1}{b} = \frac{a}{b}$
12. $\frac{b^{-4}}{b^{-5}} = b^{-4-(-5)} = b^{-4+5} = b$
13. $(y^{-5})^{-7} = y^{-5(-7)} = y^{35}$
14. $(5x^2y^{-3})^4 = 5^4x^{2 \cdot 4}y^{-3 \cdot 4} = 625x^8y^{-12} = \frac{625x^8}{y^{12}}$
15. $\frac{1}{x^{-3}} = x^3$
16. $\frac{2^{-1}xy^2}{2^3y^8} = \frac{x}{2^1 \cdot 2^3y^{8-2}} = \frac{x}{2^4y^6} = \frac{x}{16y^6}$

17. $(8.95 \times 10^9)(1.82 \times 10^7) = (8.95 \times 1.82)(10^9 \times 10^7)$
$= (16.289 \times 10^{16})$
$\approx 1.63 \times 10^{17}$
$\approx 163{,}000{,}000{,}000{,}000{,}000$

18. $(-3.1 \times 10^5)(7.9 \times 10^{-8}) = (-3.1 \times 7.9)(10^5 \times 10^{-8})$
$= (-24.49 \times 10^{-3})$
$= -2.449 \times 10^{-2}$
$= -0.02449$

19. $\frac{(2.38 \times 10^{13})(7.56 \times 10^{-5})}{(4.2 \times 10^{18})} = \frac{(2.38 \times 7.56)(10^{13} \times 10^{-5})}{(4.2 \times 10^{18})}$
$= \frac{17.9928 \times 10^8}{4.2 \times 10^{18}}$
$= 4.284 \times 10^{-10}$
$= 0.0000000004284$

Page 886 Lesson 5-2

1. yes; 3 2. yes; 2 3. no 4. no
5. yes; 0

6. $4x^3 + 5x - 7x^2 - 2x^3 + 5x^2 - 7y^2$
$= 4x^3 - 2x^3 - 7x^2 + 5x^2 + 5x - 7y^2$
$= 2x^3 - 2x^2 + 5x - 7y^2$

7. $(2x^2 - 3x + 11) + (7x^2 + 2x - 8)$
$= 2x^2 + 7x^2 - 3x + 2x + 11 - 8$
$= 9x^2 - x + 3$

8. $(-3x^2 + 7x + 23) + (-8x^2 - 5x + 13)$
$= -3x^2 - 8x^2 + 7x - 5x + 23 + 13$
$= -11x^2 + 2x + 36$

9. $(-3x^2 + 7x + 23) - (-8x^2 - 5x + 13)$
$= -3x^2 + 7x + 23 + 8x^2 + 5x - 13$
$= -3x^2 + 8x^2 + 7x + 5x + 23 - 13$
$= 5x^2 + 12x + 10$

10. $5a^2b(4a - 3b) = 5a^2b(4a) - 5a^2b(3b)$
$= 20a^3b - 15a^2b^2$

11. $\frac{7u}{w}\left(4u^2w^3 - 5uw + \frac{w}{7u}\right)$
$= \frac{7u}{w}(4u^2w^3) - \frac{7u}{w}(5uw) + \frac{7u}{w}\left(\frac{w}{7u}\right)$
$= 28u^3w^2 - 35u^2 + 1$

12. $-4x^5(-3x^4 - x^3 + x + 7)$
$= -4x^5(-3x^4) - (-4x^5)(x^3) + (-4x^5)x + (-4x^5)7$
$= 12x^9 + 4x^8 - 4x^6 - 28x^5$

13. $-5x^4(9 - 2x^2 + 4x^3 - 7x^4)$
$= -5x^4(9) - (-5x^4)(2x^2) + (-5x^4)(4x^3) -$
$(-5x^4)(7x^4)$
$= -45x^4 + 10x^6 - 20x^7 + 35x^8$
$= 35x^8 - 20x^7 + 10x^6 - 45x^4$

14. $(2x - 3)(4x + 7) = 2x \cdot 4x + 2x \cdot 7 + (-3)4x + (-3)7$
$= 8x^2 + 14x - 12x - 21$
$= 8x^2 + 2x - 21$

15. $(3x - 5)(-2x - 1)$
$= 3x(-2x) + 3x(-1) + (-5)(-2x) + (-5)(-1)$
$= -6x^2 - 3x + 10x + 5$
$= -6x^2 + 7x + 5$

16. $(2x - 3)(x^2 + 4x + 7)$
$= 2x(x^2 + 4x + 7) - 3(x^2 + 4x + 7)$
$= 2x \cdot x^2 + 2x \cdot 4x + 2x \cdot 7 - 3 \cdot x^2 - 3 \cdot 4x - 3 \cdot 7$
$= 2x^3 + 8x^2 + 14x - 3x^2 - 12x - 21$
$= 2x^3 + 5x^2 + 2x - 21$

17. $(3x - 5)(4x^2 - 2x - 1)$
$= 3x(4x^2 - 2x - 1) - 5(4x^2 - 2x - 1)$
$= 3x \cdot 4x^2 + 3x(-2x) + 3x(-1) - 5 \cdot 4x^2 -$
$5(-2x) - 5(-1)$
$= 12x^3 - 6x^2 - 3x - 20x^2 + 10x + 5$
$= 12x^3 - 26x^2 + 7x + 5$

18. $(2x + 5)(2x - 5)$
$= 2x \cdot 2x + 2x(-5) + 5 \cdot 2x + 5(-5)$
$= 4x^2 - 10x + 10x - 25$
$= 4x^2 - 25$

19. $(3x - 7)(3x + 7) = 3x \cdot 3x + 3x \cdot 7 - 7 \cdot 3x - 7 \cdot 7$
$= 9x^2 + 21x - 21x - 49$
$= 9x^2 - 49$

20. $(x + 4)(x - 4) = x \cdot x + x(-4) + 4 \cdot x + 4(-4)$
$= x^2 - 4x + 4x - 16$
$= x^2 - 16$

21. $(5 + 2w)(5 - 2w)$
$= 5 \cdot 5 + 5(-2w) + 2w \cdot 5 + 2w(-2w)$
$= 25 - 10w + 10w - 4w^2$
$= 25 - 4w^2$

22. $(3a^4 - 5)(3a^4 + 5)$
$= 3a^4 \cdot 3a^4 + 3a^4 \cdot 5 - 5 \cdot 3a^4 - 5 \cdot 5$
$= 9a^8 + 15a^4 - 15a^4 - 25$
$= 9a^8 - 25$

23. $(-4x - 10)(-4x + 10)$
$= -4x(-4x) - 4x \cdot 10 - 10(-4x) - 10 \cdot 10$
$= 16x^2 - 40x + 40x - 100$
$= 16x^2 - 100$

24. $(3x + 7)^2 = (3x + 7)(3x + 7)$
$= 3x \cdot 3x + 3x \cdot 7 + 7 \cdot 3x + 7 \cdot 7$
$= 9x^2 + 21x + 21x + 49$
$= 9x^2 + 42x + 49$

25. $(5x - 2)^2 = (5x - 2)(5x - 2)$
$= 5x \cdot 5x + 5x(-2) - 2 \cdot 5x - 2(-2)$
$= 25x^2 - 10x - 10x + 4$
$= 25x^2 - 20x + 4$

26. $(x + 7)^2 = (x + 7)(x + 7)$
$= x \cdot x + x \cdot 7 + 7 \cdot x + 7 \cdot 7$
$= x^2 + 7x + 7x + 49$
$= x^2 + 14x + 49$

27. $(t - 5)^2 = (t - 5)(t - 5)$
$= t \cdot t + t(-5) - 5 \cdot t - 5(-5)$
$= t^2 - 5t - 5t + 25$
$= t^2 - 10t + 25$

28. $(7b - 0.8)^2 = (7b - 0.8)(7b - 0.8)$
$= 7b \cdot 7b + 7b(-0.8) - 0.8 \cdot 7 -$
$0.8(-0.8)$
$= 49b^2 - 5.6b - 5.6b + 0.64$
$= 49b^2 - 11.2b + 0.64$

29. $(5x - 3x^4)^2 = (5x - 3x^4)(5x - 3x^4)$
$= 5x \cdot 5x + 5x(-3x^4) - 3x^4 \cdot 5x -$
$3x^4(-3x^4)$
$= 25x^2 - 15x^5 - 15x^5 + 9x^8$
$= 25x^2 - 30x^5 + 9x^8$

Page 886 Lesson 5-3

1. $\frac{18r^3s^2 + 36r^2s^3}{9r^2s^2} = \frac{18r^3s^2}{9r^2s^2} + \frac{36r^2s^3}{9r^2s^2}$
$= 2r + 4s$

2. $\frac{15v^3w^2 - 5v^4w^3}{-5v^4w^3} = \frac{15v^3w^2}{-5v^4w^3} - \frac{5v^4w^3}{-5v^4w^3}$
$= \frac{-3}{vw} - (-1)$
$= -\frac{3}{vw} + 1$

3. $\frac{x^2 - x + 1}{x} = \frac{x^2}{x} - \frac{x}{x} + \frac{1}{x}$
$= x - 1 + \frac{1}{x}$

4.
$$\begin{array}{r} 5h \\ b + c\,\overline{)5hb + 5hc} \\ \underline{5hb + 5hc} \\ 0 \end{array}$$

5. $(25c^4d + 10c^3d^2 - cd) \div 5cd$
$= \frac{25c^4d}{5cd} + \frac{10c^3d^2}{5cd} - \frac{cd}{5cd}$
$= 5c^3 + 2c^2d - \frac{1}{5}$

6. $(16f^{18} + 20f^9 - 8f^6) \div 4f^3 = \frac{16f^{18}}{4f^3} + \frac{20f^9}{4f^3} - \frac{8f^6}{4f^3}$
$= 4f^{15} + 5f^6 - 2f^3$

7. $(33m^5 + 55mn^5 - 11m^3)(11m)^{-1}$
$= \frac{33m^5 + 55mn^5 - 11m^3}{11m}$
$= \frac{33m^5}{11m} + \frac{55mn^5}{11m} - \frac{11m^3}{11m}$
$= 3m^4 + 5n^5 - m^2$

8.
$$\begin{array}{r} 8g^2 - 5g + 3 \\ g + 3\,\overline{)8g^3 + 19g^2 - 12g + 9} \\ \underline{8g^3 + 24g^2} \qquad\qquad \\ -5g^2 - 12g \qquad \\ \underline{-5g^2 - 15g} \qquad \\ 3g + 9 \\ \underline{3g + 9} \\ 0 \end{array}$$

9. $(p^{21} + 3p^{14} + p^7 - 2)(p^7 + 2)^{-1} = \frac{p^{21} + 3p^{14} + p^7 - 2}{p^7 + 2}$
$$\begin{array}{r} p^{14} + p^7 - 1 \\ p^7 + 2\,\overline{)p^{21} + 3p^{14} + p^7 - 2} \\ \underline{p^{21} + 2p^{14}} \qquad\qquad \\ p^{14} + p^7 \qquad \\ \underline{p^{14} + 2p^7} \qquad \\ -p^7 - 2 \\ \underline{-p^7 - 2} \\ 0 \end{array}$$

10.
$$\begin{array}{r} 5x^2 - 2xy + y^2 \\ 3x + 5y\,\overline{)15x^3 + 19x^2y - 7xy^2 + 5y^3} \\ \underline{15x^3 + 25x^2y} \qquad\qquad \\ -6x^2y - 7xy^2 \qquad \\ \underline{-6x^2y - 10xy^2} \qquad \\ 3xy^2 + 5y^3 \\ \underline{3xy^2 + 5y^3} \\ 0 \end{array}$$

11.
$$\begin{array}{r} n^2 - 5n + 25 \\ n + 5\,\overline{)n^3 + 0n^2 + 0n + 125} \\ \underline{n^3 + 5n^2} \qquad\qquad \\ -5n^2 + 0n \qquad \\ \underline{-5n^2 - 25n} \qquad \\ 25n + 125 \\ \underline{25n + 125} \\ 0 \end{array}$$

12.
$$\begin{array}{r} 5z^2 + 15z \\ 2z - 6\,\overline{)10z^3 + 0z^2 - 90z} \\ \underline{10z^3 - 30z^2} \qquad \\ 30z^2 - 90z \\ \underline{30z^2 - 90z} \\ 0 \end{array}$$

13.
$$\begin{array}{r} 4k - 14 \\ 2k - 7\,\overline{)8k^2 - 56k + 98} \\ \underline{8k^2 - 28k} \qquad \\ -28k + 98 \\ \underline{-28k + 98} \\ 0 \end{array}$$

14.
$$\begin{array}{r} 2r - 1 \\ r + 3\,\overline{)2r^2 + 5r - 3} \\ \underline{2r^2 + 6r} \qquad \\ -1r - 3 \\ \underline{-1r - 3} \\ 0 \end{array}$$

15. $(6y^2 + 7y - 3)(2y + 3)^{-1} = \frac{6y^2 + 7y - 3}{2y + 3}$
$$\begin{array}{r} 3y - 1 \\ 2y + 3\,\overline{)6y^2 + 7y - 3} \\ \underline{6y^2 + 9y} \qquad \\ -2y - 3 \\ \underline{-2y - 3} \\ 0 \end{array}$$

16.
$$\begin{array}{r|rrrrr} 4 & 6 & -22 & -9 & 9 & -17 \\ & & 24 & 8 & -4 & 20 \\ \hline & 6 & 2 & -1 & 5 & 3 \end{array}$$
$6a^3 + 2a^2 - a + 5 + \frac{3}{a + 4}$

17.
$$\begin{array}{r|rrrrr} -8 & 1 & 8 & 0 & 3 & 17 \\ & & -8 & 0 & 0 & -24 \\ \hline & 1 & 0 & 0 & 3 & -7 \end{array}$$
$q^3 + 3 - \frac{7}{q + 8}$

18. $(15v^3 + 8v^2 - 21v + 6) \div (5v - 4)$
$= \frac{15v^3 + 8v^2 - 21v + 6}{5v - 4}$
$= \frac{(15v^3 + 8v^2 - 21v + 6) \div 5}{(5v - 4) \div 5}$
$= \frac{3v^3 + \frac{8}{5}v^2 - \frac{21}{5}v + \frac{6}{5}}{v - \frac{4}{5}}$
$$\begin{array}{r|rrrr} \frac{4}{5} & 3 & \frac{8}{5} & -\frac{21}{5} & \frac{6}{5} \\ & & \frac{12}{5} & \frac{16}{5} & -\frac{4}{5} \\ \hline & 3 & 4 & -1 & \frac{2}{5} \end{array}$$
$3v^2 + 4v - 1 + \frac{\frac{2}{5}}{v - \frac{4}{5}}$ or $3v^2 + 4v - 1 + \frac{2}{5v - 4}$

19. $(10y^4 + 3y^2 - 7)\,(2y^2 - 1)^{-1} = \dfrac{10y^4 + 3y^2 - 7}{2y^2 - 1}$

$= \dfrac{(10y^4 + 3y^2 - 7) \div 2}{(2y^2 - 1) \div 2}$

$= \dfrac{5y^4 + \frac{3}{2}y^2 - \frac{7}{2}}{y^2 - \frac{1}{2}}$

$\frac{1}{2}\rfloor$	5	$\frac{3}{2}$	$-\frac{7}{2}$
		$\frac{5}{2}$	2
	5	4	$-\frac{3}{2}$

$5y^2 + 4 - \dfrac{\frac{3}{2}}{y^2 - \frac{1}{2}}$ or $5y^2 + 4 - \dfrac{3}{2y^2 - 1}$

20.

$-1\rfloor$	5	1	0	−7
		−5	4	−4
	5	−4	4	−11

$5s^2 - 4s + 4 - \frac{11}{s + 1}$

21.

$-2\rfloor$	1	13	−12	−8
		−2	−22	68
	1	11	−34	60

$x^2 + 11x - 34 + \frac{60}{x + 2}$

22.

$2\rfloor$	1	−2	1	−3	2
		2	0	2	−2
	1	0	1	−1	0

$t^3 + t - 1$

23.

$4\rfloor$	1	−3	−1	−11	−4
		4	4	12	4
	1	1	3	1	0

$z^3 + z^2 + 3z + 1$

24.

$-1\rfloor$	3	−6	−2	1	−6
		−3	9	−7	6
	3	−9	7	−6	0

$3r^3 - 9r^2 + 7r - 6$

25.

$3\rfloor$	2	−11	12	9
		6	−15	−9
	2	−5	−3	0

$2b^2 - 5b - 3$

Page 886 Lesson 5-4

1. $14a^3b^3c - 21a^2b^4c + 7a^2b^3c = 7a^2b^3c\,(2a - 3b + 1)$
2. $10ax - 2xy - 15ab + 3by$
   $= 2x\,(5a - y) - 3b\,(5a - y)$
   $= (5a - y)\,(2x - 3b)$
3. $x^2 + x - 42 = (x + 7)\,(x - 6)$
4. $2x^2 + 5x + 3 = (2x + 3)\,(x + 1)$
5. $6x^2 + 71x - 12 = (6x - 1)\,(x + 12)$
6. $6x^4 - 12x^3 + 3x^2 = 3x^2\,(2x^2 - 4x + 1)$
7. $x^2\,(x + 3) + 2\,(x + 3) = (x + 3)\,(x^2 + 2)$
8. prime
9. $2x^3 + 6x^2 + x + 3 = 2x^2\,(x + 3) + (x + 3)$
   $= (x + 3)\,(2x^2 + 1)$
10. $x^2 - 2x - 15 = (x - 5)\,(x + 3)$
11. $6x^2 + 23x + 20 = (2x + 5)\,(3x + 4)$
12. $24x^2 - 76x + 40 = 4\,(6x^2 - 19x + 10)$
    $= 4\,(2x - 5)\,(3x - 2)$
13. $6p^2 - 13pq - 28q^2 = (2p - 7q)\,(3p + 4q)$
14. prime
15. $x^2 + 49 - 14x = x^2 - 14x + 49$
    $= (x - 7)\,(x - 7)$ or $(x - 7)^2$
16. $9x^2 - 64 = (3x + 8)\,(3x - 8)$
17. $9 - t^{10} = (3 + t^5)\,(3 - t^5)$
18. prime
19. $a^4 - 81b^4 = (a^2 + 9b^2)\,(a^2 - 9b^2)$
    $= (a^2 + 9b^2)\,(a + 3b)\,(a - 3b)$
20. $3a^3 + 12a^2 - 63a = 3a\,(a^2 + 4a - 21)$
    $= 3a\,(a + 7)\,(a - 3)$
21. $x^3 - 8x^2 + 15x = x\,(x^2 - 8x + 15)$
    $= x\,(x - 5)\,(x - 3)$
22. $x^2 + 6x + 9 = (x + 3)\,(x + 3)$ or $(x + 3)^2$
23. $18x^3 - 8x = 2x\,(9x^2 - 4)$
    $= 2x\,(3x + 2)\,(3x - 2)$
24. prime
25. prime
26. $35ac - 3bd - 7ad + 15bc$
    $= 35ac - 7ad + 15bc - 3bd$
    $= 7a\,(5c - d) + 3b\,(5c - d)$
    $= (7a + 3b)\,(5c - d)$
27. $5h^2 - 10hj + h - 2j = 5h\,(h - 2j) + (h - 2j)$
    $= (h - 2j)\,(5h + 1)$
28. $16r^2 - 24r + 9 = (4r - 3)\,(4r - 3)$ or $(4r - 3)^2$
29. $3a^2 + 6a + 9y = 3\,(a^2 + 2a + 3y)$

Page 887 Lesson 5-5

1. $\sqrt{289} = 17$
2. $\sqrt[4]{0.0625} = 0.5$
3. $\sqrt[3]{-343} = -7$
4. $\sqrt{7832} \approx 88.499$
5. $\sqrt[10]{32^4} = 4$
6. $\sqrt[3]{49} \approx 3.659$
7. $\sqrt[5]{5} \approx 1.380$
8. $-\sqrt[4]{25} \approx -2.236$
9. $\sqrt{\left(-\frac{2}{3}\right)^4} = \sqrt{\left[\left(-\frac{2}{3}\right)^2\right]^2}$
   $= \left(-\frac{2}{3}\right)^2$
   $= \frac{4}{9}$
10. $\sqrt[5]{-32} = \sqrt[5]{(-2)^5}$
    $= -2$
11. $-\sqrt{-144}$; no real roots
12. $\sqrt[4]{a^{16}b^8} = \sqrt[4]{(a^4b^2)^4}$
    $= a^4b^2$
13. $\sqrt{9h^{22}} = \sqrt{(3h^{11})^2}$
    $= 3\,|h^{11}|$
14. $\pm\sqrt[4]{81x^4} = \pm\sqrt[4]{(3x)^4}$
    $= \pm\, 3x$
15. $\sqrt[5]{\frac{1}{100000}} = \sqrt[5]{\left(\frac{1}{10}\right)^5}$
    $= \frac{1}{10}$
16. $\sqrt[5]{p^{25}q^{15}r^5s^{20}} = \sqrt[5]{(p^5q^3rs^4)^5}$
    $= p^5q^3rs^4$
17. $\sqrt[3]{-d^6} = \sqrt[3]{(-d^2)^3}$
    $= -d^2$

18. $-\sqrt[4]{(2x^2-y)^8} = -\sqrt[4]{[(2x^2-y)^2]^4}$
$= -(2x^2-y)^2$

19. $\sqrt[5]{0} = 0$

20. $\pm\sqrt{16m^6n^2} = \pm\sqrt{(4m^3n^2)^2}$
$= \pm 4m^3n^2$

21. $\sqrt[3]{(2x-y)^3} = 2x - y$

22. $\sqrt[4]{(r+s)^4} = |r+s|$

23. $\sqrt{9a^2+6a+1} = \sqrt{(3a+1)^2}$
$= |3a+1|$

24. $\sqrt{4y^2+12y+9} = \sqrt{(2y+3)^2}$
$= |2y+3|$

Page 887 Lesson 5-6

1. $\sqrt{75} = \sqrt{5^2 \cdot 3}$
$= 5\sqrt{3}$

2. $7\sqrt{12} = 7\sqrt{2^2 \cdot 3}$
$= 7 \cdot 2\sqrt{3}$
$= 14\sqrt{3}$

3. $\sqrt[3]{81} = \sqrt[3]{3^3 \cdot 3}$
$= 3\sqrt[3]{3}$

4. $\sqrt{5r^5} = \sqrt{(r^2)^2 \cdot 5r}$
$= r^2\sqrt{5r}$

5. $\sqrt[4]{7^8x^5y^6} = \sqrt[4]{(7^2xy)^4xy^2}$
$= 7^2\ |xy|\ \sqrt[4]{xy^2}$
$= 49\ |xy|\ \sqrt[4]{xy^2}$

6. $3\sqrt{5} + 6\sqrt{5} = 9\sqrt{5}$

7. $\sqrt{18} - \sqrt{50} = 3\sqrt{2} - 5\sqrt{2}$
$= -2\sqrt{2}$

8. $4\sqrt[3]{32} + \sqrt[3]{500} = 4\sqrt[3]{2^3 \cdot 4} + \sqrt[3]{5^3 \cdot 4}$
$= 4 \cdot 2\sqrt[3]{4} + 5\sqrt[3]{4}$
$= 8\sqrt[3]{4} + 5\sqrt[3]{4}$
$= 13\sqrt[3]{4}$

9. $\sqrt{12} \cdot \sqrt{27} = \sqrt{324}$
$= \sqrt{18^2}$
$= 18$

10. $\sqrt[3]{6} - \sqrt{6} = \sqrt[3]{6} - \sqrt{6}$

11. $\sqrt{10}\,(2 - \sqrt{5}) = 2\sqrt{10} - \sqrt{50}$
$= 2\sqrt{10} - 5\sqrt{2}$

12. $\sqrt{3}\,(5\sqrt{2} + 4\sqrt{7}) = 5\sqrt{6} + 4\sqrt{21}$

13. $(1 - \sqrt{7})\,(4 + \sqrt{7})$
$= 1 \cdot 4 + 1 \cdot \sqrt{7} - \sqrt{7} \cdot 4 - \sqrt{7} \cdot \sqrt{7}$
$= 4 + \sqrt{7} - 4\sqrt{7} - 7$
$= -3 - 3\sqrt{7}$

14. $(5 + \sqrt{2})\,(3 + \sqrt{3})$
$= 5 \cdot 3 + 5 \cdot \sqrt{3} + \sqrt{2} \cdot 3 + \sqrt{2} \cdot \sqrt{3}$
$= 15 + 5\sqrt{3} + 3\sqrt{2} + \sqrt{6}$

15. $(2 + \sqrt{5})\,(2 - \sqrt{5})$
$= 2 \cdot 2 + 2\,(-\sqrt{5}) + \sqrt{5} \cdot 2 + \sqrt{5}\,(-\sqrt{5})$
$= 4 - 2\sqrt{5} + 2\sqrt{5} - 5$
$= -1$

16. $(x - \sqrt{3y})\,(x + \sqrt{3y})$
$= x \cdot x + x \cdot \sqrt{3y} - \sqrt{3y} \cdot x - \sqrt{3y} \cdot \sqrt{3y}$
$= x^2 + x\sqrt{3y} - x\sqrt{3y} - 3y$
$= x^2 - 3y$

17. $(8 + \sqrt{11})^2 = (8 + \sqrt{11})\,(8 + \sqrt{11})$
$= 8 \cdot 8 + 8 \cdot \sqrt{11} + \sqrt{11} \cdot 8 + \sqrt{11} \cdot \sqrt{11}$
$= 64 + 8\sqrt{11} + 8\sqrt{11} + 11$
$= 75 + 16\sqrt{11}$

18. $(5z - 2\sqrt{7})^2 = (5z - 2\sqrt{7})\,(5z - 2\sqrt{7})$
$= 5z \cdot 5z + 5z\,(-2\sqrt{7}) - 2\sqrt{7} \cdot 5z - 2\sqrt{7}\,(-2\sqrt{7})$
$= 25z^2 - 10z\sqrt{7} - 10z\sqrt{7} + 4 \cdot 7$
$= 25z^2 - 20z\sqrt{7} + 28$

19. $\sqrt{\frac{3m^3}{24n^5}} = \sqrt{\frac{m^3}{8n^5}}$
$= \frac{\sqrt{m^3}}{\sqrt{8n^5}}$
$= \frac{m\sqrt{m}}{2n^2\sqrt{2n}}$
$= \frac{m\sqrt{m} \cdot \sqrt{2n}}{2n^2\sqrt{2n} \cdot \sqrt{2n}}$
$= \frac{m\sqrt{2mn}}{2n^2 \cdot 2n}$
$= \frac{m\sqrt{2mn}}{4n^3}$

20. $\frac{\sqrt{18}}{\sqrt{32}} = \frac{3\sqrt{2}}{4\sqrt{2}}$
$= \frac{3}{4}$

21. $2\sqrt[3]{\frac{r^5}{2s^2t}} = 2\frac{\sqrt[3]{r^5}}{\sqrt[3]{2s^2t}}$
$= 2\ \frac{r\sqrt[3]{r^2}}{\sqrt[3]{2s^2t}}$
$= 2\ \frac{r\sqrt[3]{r^2} \cdot \sqrt[3]{4st^2}}{\sqrt[3]{2s^2t} \cdot \sqrt[3]{4st^2}}$
$= \frac{2r\sqrt[3]{4r^2st^2}}{\sqrt[3]{8s^3t^3}}$
$= \frac{2r\sqrt[3]{4r^2st^2}}{2st}$
$= \frac{r\sqrt[3]{4r^2st^2}}{st}$

22. $\sqrt{\frac{2}{3}} - \sqrt{\frac{3}{8}} = \frac{\sqrt{2}}{\sqrt{3}} - \frac{\sqrt{3}}{\sqrt{8}}$
$= \frac{\sqrt{2} \cdot \sqrt{8}}{\sqrt{3} \cdot \sqrt{8}} - \frac{\sqrt{3} \cdot \sqrt{3}}{\sqrt{8} \cdot \sqrt{3}}$
$= \frac{\sqrt{16}}{\sqrt{24}} - \frac{\sqrt{9}}{\sqrt{24}}$
$= \frac{4-3}{\sqrt{24}}$
$= \frac{1}{2\sqrt{6}}$
$= \frac{1\sqrt{6}}{2\sqrt{6} \cdot \sqrt{6}}$
$= \frac{\sqrt{6}}{12}$

23. $\frac{5}{3 - \sqrt{10}} = \frac{5\,(3 + \sqrt{10})}{(3 - \sqrt{10})\,(3 + \sqrt{10})}$
$= \frac{15 + 5\sqrt{10}}{9 + 3\sqrt{10} - 3\sqrt{10} - 10}$
$= \frac{15 + 5\sqrt{10}}{-1}$
$= -15 - 5\sqrt{10}$

24. $\frac{x + \sqrt{5}}{x - \sqrt{5}} = \frac{(x + \sqrt{5})\,(x + \sqrt{5})}{(x - \sqrt{5})\,(x + \sqrt{5})}$
$= \frac{x^2 + \sqrt{5}x + \sqrt{5}x + 5}{x^2 + \sqrt{5}x - \sqrt{5}x - 5}$
$= \frac{x^2 + 2x\sqrt{5} + 5}{x^2 - 5}$

Page 887 Lesson 5-7

1. $2401^{\frac{1}{4}} = \sqrt[4]{2401}$
$= 7$

2. $27^{\frac{4}{3}} = (\sqrt[3]{27})^4$
$= 3^4$
$= 81$

3. $(-32)^{\frac{2}{5}} = (\sqrt[5]{(-32)}\,)^2$
$= (-2)^2$
$= 4$

4. $-81^{\frac{3}{4}} = (\sqrt[4]{(-81)})^3$
$= (-3)^3$
$= -27$

5. $(-125)^{-\frac{2}{3}} = \dfrac{1}{(-125)^{\frac{2}{3}}}$
$= \dfrac{1}{(\sqrt[3]{-125})^2}$
$= \dfrac{1}{(-5)^2}$
$= \dfrac{1}{25}$

6. $7^{\frac{5}{2}} \cdot 7^{\frac{1}{2}} = 7^3$
$= 343$

7. $8^{-\frac{2}{3}} \cdot 64^{\frac{1}{6}} = 8^{-\frac{2}{3}} \cdot 8^{\frac{2}{6}}$
$= 8^{-\frac{2}{3}} \cdot 8^{\frac{1}{3}}$
$= 8^{-\frac{1}{3}}$
$= \dfrac{1}{8^{\frac{1}{3}}}$
$= \dfrac{1}{\sqrt[3]{8}}$
$= \dfrac{1}{2}$

8. $\left(\dfrac{48}{1875}\right)^{-\frac{5}{4}} = \dfrac{1}{\left(\frac{48}{1875}\right)^{\frac{5}{4}}}$
$= \dfrac{1}{\left(\sqrt[4]{\frac{48}{1875}}\right)^5}$
$= \dfrac{1}{\left(\sqrt[4]{\frac{16}{625}}\right)^5}$
$= \dfrac{1}{\left(\frac{2}{5}\right)^5}$
$= \dfrac{1}{\frac{32}{3125}}$
$= \dfrac{3125}{32}$

9. $7^{\frac{5}{9}} = \sqrt[9]{7^5}$

10. $32^{\frac{2}{3}} = \sqrt[3]{32^2}$
$= \sqrt[3]{1024}$
$= 8\sqrt[3]{2}$

11. $k^{\frac{8}{5}} = \sqrt[5]{k^8}$
$= k\sqrt[5]{k^3}$

12. $x^{\frac{2}{5}} \cdot x^{\frac{5}{8}} = x^{\frac{16}{40}} \cdot x^{\frac{25}{40}}$
$= x^{\frac{41}{40}}$
$= \sqrt[40]{x^{41}}$
$= x\,\sqrt[40]{x}$

13. $m^{\frac{2}{5}} \cdot n^{\frac{4}{5}} = \sqrt[5]{m^2} \cdot \sqrt[5]{n^4}$
$= \sqrt[5]{m^2n^4}$

14. $\left(p^{\frac{5}{4}}q^{\frac{7}{2}}\right)^{\frac{8}{3}} = p^{\frac{10}{3}}q^{\frac{28}{3}}$
$= \sqrt[3]{p^{10}} \cdot \sqrt[3]{q^{28}}$
$= p^3\,\sqrt[3]{p} \cdot q^9\,\sqrt[3]{q}$
$= p^3q^9\,\sqrt[3]{pq}$

15. $3^{\frac{9}{2}}c^{\frac{3}{2}} = \sqrt{3^9} \cdot \sqrt{c^3}$
$= 3^4\,\sqrt{3} \cdot c\sqrt{c}$
$= 81c\,\sqrt{3c}$

16. $\dfrac{7^{\frac{3}{4}}}{7^{\frac{5}{3}}} = \dfrac{7^{\frac{9}{12}}}{7^{\frac{20}{12}}}$
$= \dfrac{1}{7^{\frac{11}{12}}}$
$= \dfrac{1}{\sqrt[12]{7^{11}}}$
$= \dfrac{1}{\sqrt[12]{7^{11}}} \cdot \dfrac{\sqrt[12]{7}}{\sqrt[12]{7}}$
$= \dfrac{\sqrt[12]{7}}{7}$

17. $\dfrac{1}{t^{\frac{9}{5}}} = \dfrac{1}{\sqrt[5]{t^9}}$
$= \dfrac{1}{t\,\sqrt[5]{t^4}}$
$= \dfrac{1 \cdot \sqrt[5]{t}}{t\,\sqrt[5]{t^4} \cdot \sqrt[5]{t}}$
$= \dfrac{\sqrt[5]{t}}{t \cdot t}$
$= \dfrac{\sqrt[5]{t}}{t^2}$ or $\dfrac{t^{\frac{1}{5}}}{t^2}$

18. $a^{-\frac{8}{7}} = \dfrac{1}{a^{\frac{8}{7}}}$
$= \dfrac{1}{\sqrt[7]{a^8}}$
$= \dfrac{1}{a\sqrt[7]{a}}$
$= \dfrac{1 \cdot \sqrt[7]{a^6}}{a\,\sqrt[7]{a} \cdot \sqrt[7]{a^6}}$
$= \dfrac{\sqrt[7]{a^6}}{a \cdot a}$
$= \dfrac{a^{\frac{6}{7}}}{a^2}$

19. $\dfrac{y^{\frac{1}{2}}}{x^{\frac{1}{2}} + y^{\frac{1}{2}}} = \dfrac{\sqrt{y}}{\sqrt{x} + \sqrt{y}}$
$= \dfrac{\sqrt{y}\,(\sqrt{x} - \sqrt{y})}{(\sqrt{x} + \sqrt{y})\,(\sqrt{x} - \sqrt{y})}$
$= \dfrac{\sqrt{xy} - y}{x - \sqrt{xy} + \sqrt{xy} - y}$
$= \dfrac{\sqrt{xy} - y}{x - y}$
$= \dfrac{x^{\frac{1}{2}}y^{\frac{1}{2}} - y}{x - y}$

20. $(a + b)^{-\frac{3}{4}} = \dfrac{1}{(a + b)^{\frac{3}{4}}}$
$= \dfrac{1}{\sqrt[4]{(a + b)^3}}$
$= \dfrac{1}{\sqrt[4]{(a + b)^3}} \cdot \dfrac{\sqrt[4]{(a + b)}}{\sqrt[4]{(a + b)}}$
$= \dfrac{\sqrt[4]{(a + b)}}{a + b}$ or $\dfrac{(a + b)^{\frac{1}{4}}}{a + b}$

21. $\dfrac{r}{r^{\frac{7}{5}}} = \dfrac{r}{\sqrt[5]{r^7}}$
$= \dfrac{r}{r\,\sqrt[5]{r^2}}$
$= \dfrac{1}{\sqrt[5]{r^2}}$
$= \dfrac{\sqrt[5]{r^3}}{\sqrt[5]{r^2} \cdot \sqrt[5]{r^3}}$
$= \dfrac{\sqrt[5]{r^3}}{r}$
$= \dfrac{r^{\frac{3}{5}}}{r}$

22. $\dfrac{8}{5^{\frac{1}{2}} + 3^{\frac{1}{2}}} = \dfrac{8}{\sqrt{5} + \sqrt{3}}$

$= \dfrac{8(\sqrt{5} - \sqrt{3})}{(\sqrt{5} + \sqrt{3})(\sqrt{5} - \sqrt{3})}$

$= \dfrac{8(\sqrt{5} - \sqrt{3})}{5 - \sqrt{15} + \sqrt{15} - 3}$

$= \dfrac{8(\sqrt{5} - \sqrt{3})}{2}$

$= 4\left(5^{\frac{1}{2}} - 3^{\frac{1}{2}}\right)$

23. $\dfrac{v^{\frac{11}{7}} - v^{\frac{4}{7}}}{v^{\frac{4}{7}}} = \dfrac{v^{\frac{11}{7}}}{v^{\frac{4}{7}}} - \dfrac{v^{\frac{4}{7}}}{v^{\frac{4}{7}}}$

$= v^{\frac{7}{7}} - 1$

$= v - 1$

24. $\left(z^{\frac{5}{3}} \cdot z^{-\frac{9}{2}}\right)^{-\frac{12}{17}} = \left(z^{\frac{10}{6}} \cdot z^{\frac{-27}{6}}\right)^{-\frac{12}{17}}$

$= \left(z^{\frac{-17}{6}}\right)^{-\frac{12}{17}}$

$= z^2$

Page 888 Lesson 5-8

1. $\sqrt{x} = 16$
   $x = 256$

2. $\sqrt{z + 3} = 7$
   $z + 3 = 49$
   $z = 46$

3. $\sqrt[4]{a + 5} = 1$
   $a + 5 = 1$
   $a = -4$

4. $5\sqrt{s} - 8 = 3$
   $5\sqrt{s} = 11$
   $\sqrt{s} = \frac{11}{5}$
   $s = \frac{121}{25}$

5. $\sqrt[4]{m + 7} + 11 = 9$
   $\sqrt[4]{m + 7} = -2$
   no real solutions

6. $d + \sqrt{d^2 - 8} = 4$
   $\sqrt{d^2 - 8} = 4 - d$
   $d^2 - 8 = (4 - d)^2$
   $d^2 - 8 = 16 - 8d + d^2$
   $-8 = 16 - 8d$
   $-24 = -8d$
   $3 = d$

7. $g\sqrt{7} + 8 = g$
   $g\sqrt{7} + 8 - g = 0$
   $g\sqrt{7} - g = -8$
   $g(\sqrt{7} - 1) = -8$
   $g = \dfrac{-8}{\sqrt{7} - 1}$
   $g = \dfrac{-8(\sqrt{7} + 1)}{(\sqrt{7} - 1)(\sqrt{7} + 1)}$
   $g = \dfrac{-8\sqrt{7} - 8}{7 + \sqrt{7} - \sqrt{7} - 1}$
   $g = \dfrac{-8\sqrt{7} - 8}{6}$
   $g = \dfrac{-4\sqrt{7} - 4}{3}$

8. $\sqrt{x - 8} = \sqrt{13 + x}$
   $x - 8 = 13 + x$
   $-8 \neq 13$
   no real solutions

9. $\sqrt{3x + 10} = 1 + \sqrt{2x + 5}$
   $(\sqrt{3x + 10})^2 = (1 + \sqrt{2x + 5})^2$
   $3x + 10 = 1 + 2\sqrt{2x + 5} + 2x + 5$
   $x + 10 = 6 + 2\sqrt{2x + 5}$
   $x + 4 = 2\sqrt{2x + 5}$
   $\frac{x + 4}{2} = \sqrt{2x + 5}$
   $\left(\frac{x + 4}{2}\right)^2 = (\sqrt{2x + 5})^2$
   $\frac{x^2 + 8x + 16}{4} = 2x + 5$
   $x^2 + 8x + 16 = 8x + 20$
   $x^2 + 16 = 20$
   $x^2 = 4$
   $x = \pm 2$

10. $\sqrt{3 - x} = \sqrt{11} - \sqrt{x}$
    $(\sqrt{3 - x})^2 = (\sqrt{11} - \sqrt{x})^2$
    $3 - x = 11 - 2\sqrt{11x} + x$
    $3 - 2x = 11 - 2\sqrt{11x}$
    $-8 - 2x = -2\sqrt{11x}$
    $4 + x = \sqrt{11x}$
    $(4 + x)^2 = (\sqrt{11x})^2$
    $16 + 8x + x^2 = 11x$
    $x^2 - 3x + 16 = 0$
    no real solutions

11. $(3x + 8)^{\frac{1}{2}} = 2$
    $[(3x + 8)^{\frac{1}{2}}]^2 = 2^2$
    $3x + 8 = 4$
    $3x = -4$
    $x = -\frac{4}{3}$

12. $\sqrt{3n - 1} = \sqrt{4 - 2n}$
    $3n - 1 = 4 - 2n$
    $5n - 1 = 4$
    $5n = 5$
    $n = 1$

13. $8w + 3 = 4 - w\sqrt{5}$
    $8w + w\sqrt{5} + 3 = 4$
    $8w + w\sqrt{5} = 1$
    $w(8 + \sqrt{5}) = 1$
    $w = \dfrac{1}{8 + \sqrt{5}}$
    $w = \dfrac{1(8 - \sqrt{5})}{(8 + \sqrt{5})(8 - \sqrt{5})}$
    $w = \dfrac{8 - \sqrt{5}}{64 + 8\sqrt{5} - 8\sqrt{5} - 5}$
    $w = \dfrac{8 - \sqrt{5}}{59}$

14. $\sqrt{5y + 4} = 8$
    $5y + 4 = 64$
    $5y = 60$
    $y = 12$

15. $2 - 4\sqrt{21 - 6c} = 6$
    $-4\sqrt{21 - 6c} = 4$
    $\sqrt{21 - 6c} = -1$
    no real solutions

16. $\sqrt{3x + 25} + \sqrt{10 - 2x} = 0$
    $\sqrt{3x + 25} = -\sqrt{10 - 2x}$
    no real solutions

17. $\sqrt{2c + 3} - 7 = 0$
    $\sqrt{2c + 3} = 7$
    $2c + 3 = 49$
    $2c = 46$
    $c = 23$

18. $\sqrt{3z - 5} - 3 = 1$
    $\sqrt{3z - 5} = 4$
    $3z - 5 = 16$
    $3z = 21$
    $z = 7$

19. $\sqrt{5y + 1} + 6 = 10$
    $\sqrt{5y + 1} = 4$
    $5y + 1 = 16$
    $5y = 15$
    $y = 3$

20. $\sqrt{3f + 1} - 2 = 6$
    $\sqrt{3f + 1} = 8$
    $3f + 1 = 64$
    $3f = 63$
    $f = 21$

21. $\sqrt{y-5} - \sqrt{y} = 1$
$\sqrt{y-5} = 1 + \sqrt{y}$
$(\sqrt{y-5})^2 = (1 + \sqrt{y})^2$
$y - 5 = 1 + 2\sqrt{y} + y$
$-5 = 1 + 2\sqrt{y}$
$-6 = 2\sqrt{y}$
$-3 = \sqrt{y}$
no real solutions

Page 888 Lesson 5-9

1. $\sqrt{-289} = 17i$

2. $\sqrt{-\frac{25}{121}} = \frac{5}{11}i$

3. $\sqrt{-625b^8} = 25b^4 i$

4. $\sqrt{-\frac{28f^6}{27g^5}} = \frac{2\,|f^3|}{3g^2} i \sqrt{\frac{7}{3g}}$

5. $(7i)^2 = 49i^2$
$= -49$

6. $(6i)(-2i)(11i) = -132i^3$
$= -132(-i)$
$= 132i$

7. $(\sqrt{-8})(\sqrt{-12}) = 2i\sqrt{2} \cdot 2i\sqrt{3}$
$= 4i^2\sqrt{6}$
$= -4\sqrt{6}$

8. $-i^{22} = -(i^2)^{11}$
$= -(-1)^{11}$
$= 1$

9. $i^{17} \cdot i^{11} \cdot i^{26} = i^{54}$
$= (i^2)^{27}$
$= (-1)^{27}$
$= -1$

10. $3\sqrt{-24} - 7\sqrt{-96} = 3 \cdot 2i\sqrt{6} - 7 \cdot 4i\sqrt{6}$
$= 6i\sqrt{6} - 28i\sqrt{6}$
$= -22i\sqrt{6}$

11. $(14 - 5i) + (-8 + 19i) = (14 - 8) + (-5i + 19i)$
$= 6 + 14i$

12. $(7i) - (2 + 3i) = (-2) + (7i - 3i)$
$= -2 + 4i$

13. $(2 + 2i) - (5 + i) = (2 - 5) + (2i - i)$
$= -3 + i$

14. $(7 + 3i)(7 - 3i) = 7 \cdot 7 + 7(-3i) + 3i \cdot 7 + 3i(-3i)$
$= 49 - 21i + 21i - 9i^2$
$= 49 + 9$
$= 58$

15. $(8 - 2i)(5 + i) = 8 \cdot 5 + 8 \cdot i - 2i \cdot 5 - 2i \cdot i$
$= 40 + 8i - 10i - 2i^2$
$= 40 - 2i + 2$
$= 42 - 2i$

16. $(6 + 8i)^2 = (6 + 8i)(6 + 8i)$
$= 6 \cdot 6 + 6 \cdot 8i + 8i \cdot 6 + 8i \cdot 8i$
$= 36 + 48i + 48i + 64i^2$
$= 36 + 96i - 64$
$= -28 + 96i$

17. $(15 - 3i)(15 + 3i)$
$= 15 \cdot 15 + 15 \cdot 3i - 3i \cdot 15 - 3i \cdot 3i$
$= 225 + 45i - 45i - 9i^2$
$= 225 + 9$
$= 234$

18. $(9 + 5i)^2 + (15 - 3i)^2$
$= (9 + 5i)(9 + 5i) + (15 - 3i)(15 - 3i)$
$= 9 \cdot 9 + 9 \cdot 5i + 5i \cdot 9 + 5i \cdot 5i + 15 \cdot 15 +$
$15(-3i) - 3i \cdot 15 - 3i(-3i)$
$= 81 + 45i + 45i + 25i^2 + 225 - 45i - 45i + 9i^2$
$= 81 - 25 + 225 - 9$
$= 272$

19. $x^2 + 8 = 3$
$x^2 = -5$
$x = \pm\sqrt{-5}$
$x = \pm i\sqrt{5}$

20. $\frac{4x^2}{49} + 6 = 3$
$\frac{4x^2}{49} = -3$
$4x^2 = -147$
$x^2 = -\frac{147}{4}$
$x = \pm\sqrt{-\frac{147}{4}}$
$x = \pm\frac{7i}{2}\sqrt{3}$

21. $8x^2 + 5 = 1$
$8x^2 = -4$
$x^2 = -\frac{1}{2}$
$x = \sqrt{-\frac{1}{2}}$
$x = \pm\frac{i}{\sqrt{2}}$
$x = \pm\frac{i\sqrt{2}}{\sqrt{2} \cdot \sqrt{2}}$
$x = \pm\frac{i\sqrt{2}}{2}$

22. $12 - 9x^2 = 38$
$-9x^2 = 26$
$x^2 = -\frac{26}{9}$
$x = \pm\sqrt{-\frac{26}{9}}$
$x = \pm\frac{i\sqrt{26}}{3}$

Page 888 Lesson 5-10

1. $3 - i$

2. $\sqrt{2} + 3i$

3. $-8 - 7i$

4. $i\sqrt{5}$

5. $7i(-7i) = -49i^2$
$= 49$

6. $(3 - i)(3 + i) = 9 + 3i - 3i - i^2$
$= 9 + 1$
$= 10$

7. $(5 + 3i)(5 - 3i) = 25 - 15i + 15i - 9i^2$
$= 25 + 9$
$= 34$

8. $(3 - 4i)(3 + 4i) = 9 + 12i - 12i - 16i^2$
$= 9 + 16$
$= 25$

9. $\frac{2+i}{i} = \frac{(2+i)(-i)}{i(-i)}$
$= \frac{-2i - i^2}{-i^2}$
$= \frac{-2i + 1}{1}$
$= 1 - 2i$

10. $\frac{8+5i}{4i} = \frac{(8+5i)(-4i)}{(4i)(-4i)}$
$= \frac{-32i - 20i^2}{-16i^2}$
$= \frac{-32i + 20}{16}$
$= -2i + \frac{5}{4}$
$= \frac{5}{4} - 2i$

11. $\frac{3-7i}{5+4i} = \frac{(3-7i)(5-4i)}{(5+4i)(5-4i)}$
$= \frac{15 - 12i - 35i + 28i^2}{25 - 20i + 20i - 16i^2}$
$= \frac{15 - 47i - 28}{25 + 16}$
$= \frac{-13 - 47i}{41}$

12. $\frac{2+10i}{6-i} = \frac{(2+10i)(6+i)}{(6-i)(6+i)}$

$= \frac{12+2i+60i+10i^2}{36+6i-6i-i^2}$

$= \frac{12+62i-10}{36+1}$

$= \frac{2+62i}{37}$

13. $\frac{9+12i}{8+3i} = \frac{(9+12i)(8-3i)}{(8+3i)(8-3i)}$

$= \frac{72-27i+96i-36i^2}{64-24i+24i-9i^2}$

$= \frac{72+69i+36}{64+9}$

$= \frac{108+69i}{73}$

14. $\frac{3}{6-2i} = \frac{3(6+2i)}{(6-2i)(6+2i)}$

$= \frac{18+6i}{36+12i-12i-4i^2}$

$= \frac{18+6i}{36+4}$

$= \frac{18+6i}{40}$

$= \frac{9+3i}{20}$

15. $\frac{5i}{3+4i} = \frac{5i(3-4i)}{(3+4i)(3-4i)}$

$= \frac{15i-20i^2}{9-12i+12i-16i^2}$

$= \frac{15i+20}{9+16}$

$= \frac{15i+20}{25}$

$= \frac{3i+4}{5}$

$= \frac{4+3i}{5}$

16. $\frac{5+3i}{1+i} = \frac{(5+3i)(1-i)}{(1+i)(1-i)}$

$= \frac{5-5i+3i-3i^2}{1-i+i-i^2}$

$= \frac{5-2i+3}{1-(-1)}$

$= \frac{8-2i}{2}$

$= 4 - i$

17. $\frac{5}{\sqrt{3}+2i} = \frac{5(\sqrt{3}-2i)}{(\sqrt{3}+2i)(\sqrt{3}-2i)}$

$= \frac{5\sqrt{3}-10i}{3-2\sqrt{3}i+2\sqrt{3}i-4i^2}$

$= \frac{5\sqrt{3}-10i}{3+4}$

$= \frac{5\sqrt{3}-10i}{7}$

18. $\frac{3i}{1+i\sqrt{2}} = \frac{3i(1-i\sqrt{2})}{(1+i\sqrt{2})(1-i\sqrt{2})}$

$= \frac{3i-3i^2\sqrt{2}}{1-i\sqrt{2}+i\sqrt{2}-2i^2}$

$= \frac{3i+3\sqrt{2}}{1+2}$

$= \frac{3i+3\sqrt{2}}{3}$

$= i+\sqrt{2}$ or $\sqrt{2}+i$

19. $\frac{2-i\sqrt{3}}{2+i\sqrt{3}} = \frac{(2-i\sqrt{3})(2-i\sqrt{3})}{(2+i\sqrt{3})(2-i\sqrt{3})}$

$= \frac{4-2i\sqrt{3}-2i\sqrt{3}+i^2\cdot 3}{4-2i\sqrt{3}+2i\sqrt{3}-3i^2}$

$= \frac{4-4i\sqrt{3}-3}{4+3}$

$= \frac{1-4i\sqrt{3}}{7}$

20. $\frac{1}{\sqrt{5}+i} = \frac{1(\sqrt{5}-i)}{(\sqrt{5}+i)(\sqrt{5}-i)}$

$= \frac{\sqrt{5}-i}{5-i\sqrt{5}+i\sqrt{5}-i^2}$

$= \frac{\sqrt{5}-i}{5+1}$

$= \frac{\sqrt{5}-i}{6}$

21. $\frac{1}{5+2i} = \frac{1(5-2i)}{(5+2i)(5-2i)}$

$= \frac{5-2i}{25-10i+10i-4i^2}$

$= \frac{5-2i}{25+4}$

$= \frac{5-2i}{29}$

22. $\frac{1}{\frac{7i}{3-4i}} = \frac{3-4i}{7i}$

$= \frac{(3-4i)(-7i)}{7i(-7i)}$

$= \frac{-21i+28i^2}{-49i^2}$

$= \frac{-21i-28}{49}$

$= \frac{3i+4}{-7}$

23. $\frac{1}{\frac{3-i}{4+i}} = \frac{4+i}{3-i}$

$= \frac{(4+i)(3+i)}{(3-i)(3+i)}$

$= \frac{12+4i+3i+i^2}{9+3i-3i-i^2}$

$= \frac{12+7i-1}{9+1}$

$= \frac{11+7i}{10}$

24. $\frac{1}{\frac{1+i}{1-i}} = \frac{1-i}{1+i}$

$= \frac{(1-i)(1-i)}{(1+i)(1-i)}$

$= \frac{1-i-i+i^2}{1-i+i-i^2}$

$= \frac{1-2i-1}{1+1}$

$= \frac{-2i}{2}$

$= -i$

Page 889 Lesson 6-1

1. $4x^2$; $-3x$; 8
2. $2r^2$; 0; 1
3. $f(z) = (z+3)^2 - 5$
   $= z^2 + 6z + 9 - 5$
   $= z^2 + 6z + 4$
   z^2; $6z$; 4
4. m^2; 0; -9
5. $g(a) = (2a-4)^2 - 16$
   $= 4a^2 - 16a + 16 - 16$
   $= 4a^2 - 16a$
   $4a^2$; $-16a$; 0
6. $5y^2$; $3y$; 0
7. $h(w) = (3w+5)^2 - 10w$
   $= 9w^2 + 30w + 25 - 10w$
   $= 9w^2 + 20w + 25$
   $9w^2$; $20w$; 25
8. $-6x^2$; $7x$; 2
9. $9x^2$; 0; 0

10. $y = x^2 - 5x + 6$

x	y
0	6
1	2
2	0
3	0
4	2

2, 3

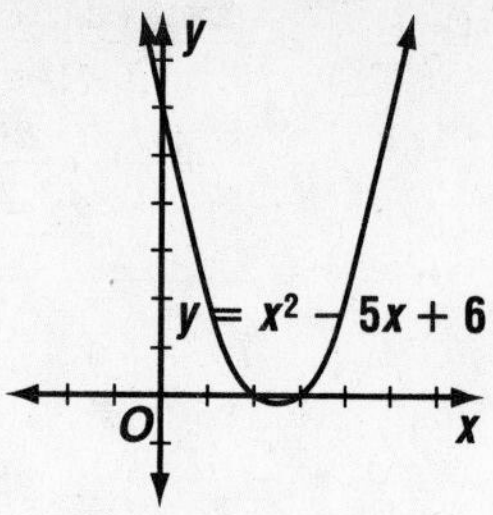

11. $y = x^2 + 2x + 1$

x	y
−2	1
−1	0
0	1
1	4

−1

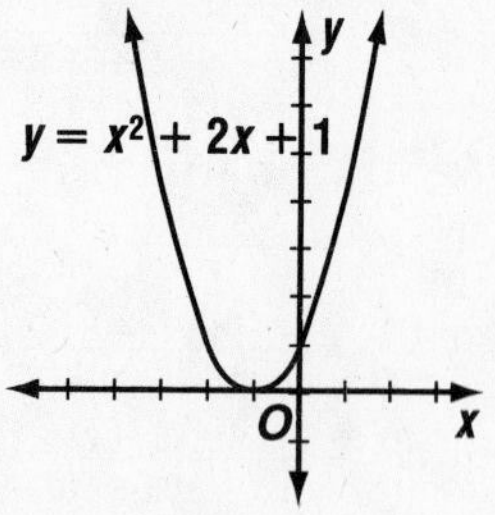

12. $y = x^2 - 2x - 8$

x	y
−2	0
0	−8
2	−8
4	0

−2, 4

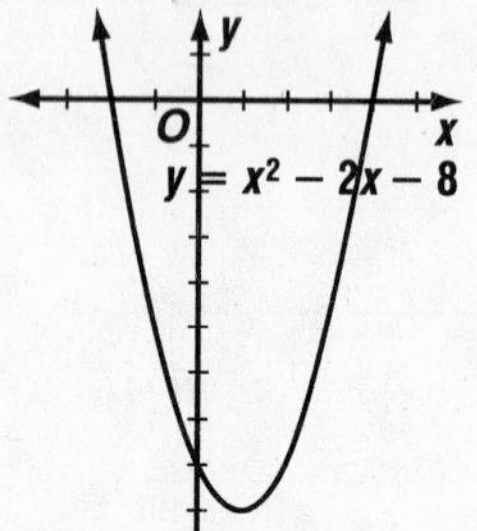

13. $y = x^2 + x - 6$

x	y
−3	0
−1	−6
0	−6
2	0

−3, 2

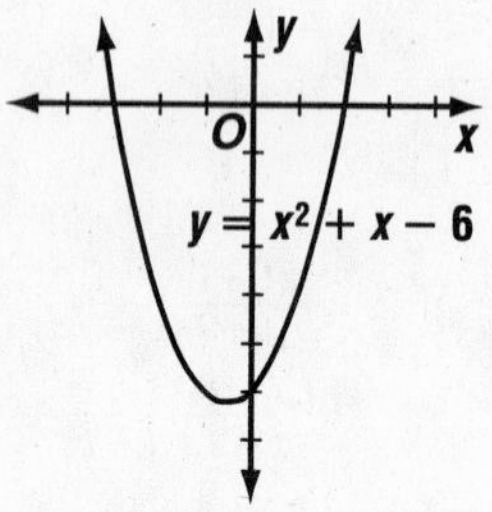

14. $y = 4x^2 - 9$

x	y
−2	7
−1	−5
0	−9
1	−5
2	7

$-\frac{3}{2}, \frac{3}{2}$

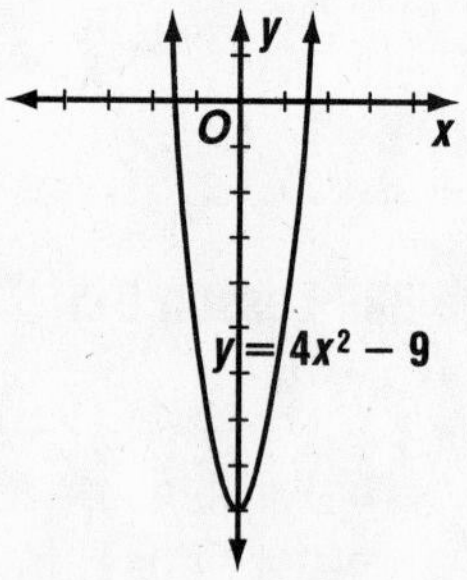

15. $y = 2x^2 + 7x - 4$

x	y
−4	0
−2	−10
0	−4
2	18

$-4, \frac{1}{2}$

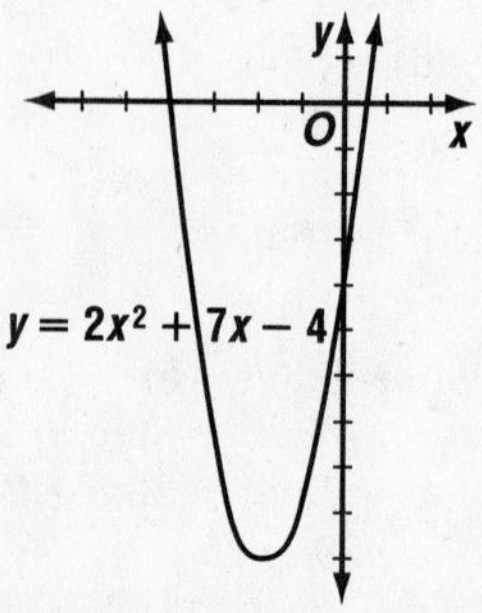

16. $f(x) = -x^2$

x	$f(x)$
−2	−4
−1	−1
0	0
1	−1

(0, 0); $x = 0$

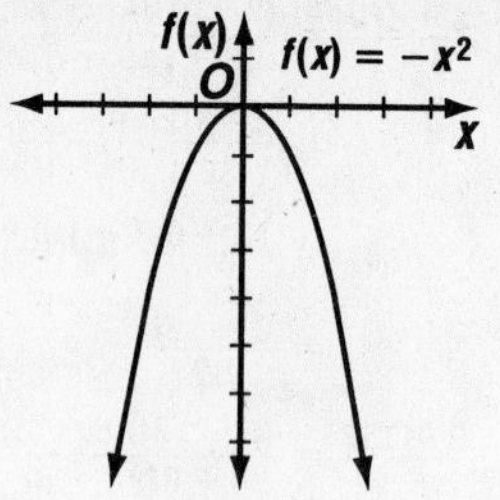

17. $f(x) = x^2 + 6x - 27$

x	$f(x)$
−10	13
−5	−32
0	−27
5	28

(−3, −36); $x = -3$

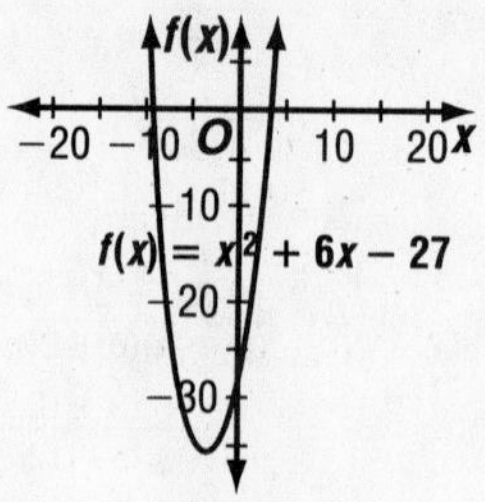

18. $f(x) = 9 - x^2$

x	$f(x)$
−4	−7
−2	5
0	9
2	5

(0, 9); $x = 0$

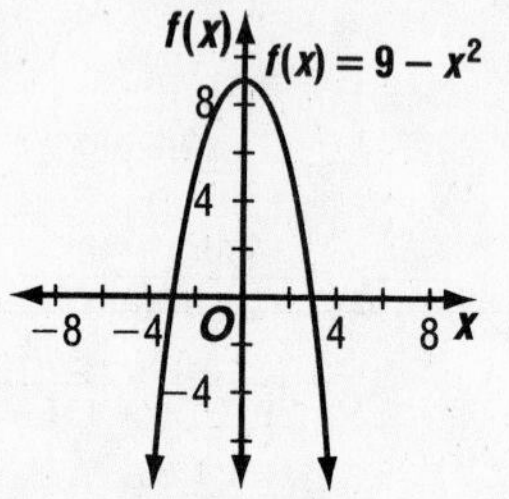

19. $g(x) = x^2 + 5x - 6$

x	$g(x)$
−6	0
−3	−12
0	−6
1	0

(−2.5, −12.25);
$x = -2.5$

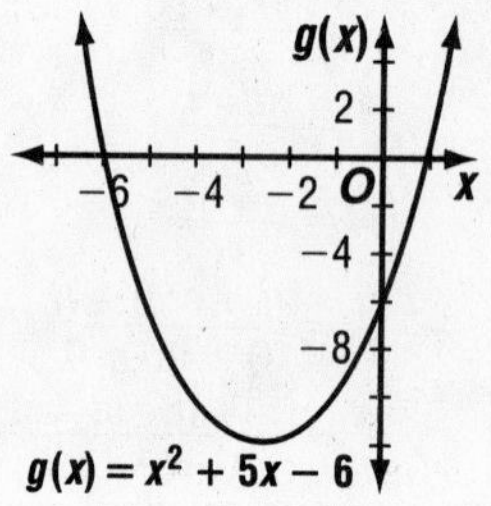

20. $g(x) = x^2 - x + \frac{5}{4}$

x	$g(x)$
−1	$3\frac{1}{4}$
0	$\frac{5}{4}$
1	$\frac{5}{4}$
2	$3\frac{1}{4}$

(0.5, 1); $x = 0.5$

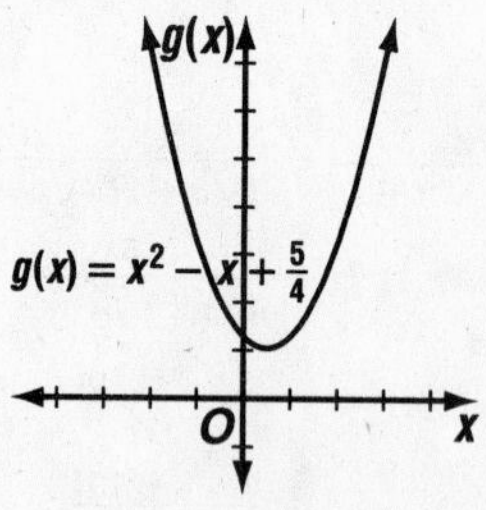

21. $f(x) = x^2 + \frac{14}{3}x + \frac{5}{3}$

x	$f(x)$
−5	$3\frac{1}{3}$
−3	$-3\frac{1}{3}$
−1	−2
1	$7\frac{1}{3}$

$\left(-\frac{7}{3}, -\frac{34}{9}\right)$; $x = -\frac{7}{3}$

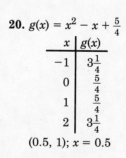

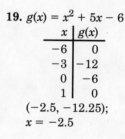

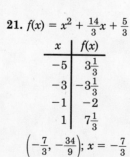

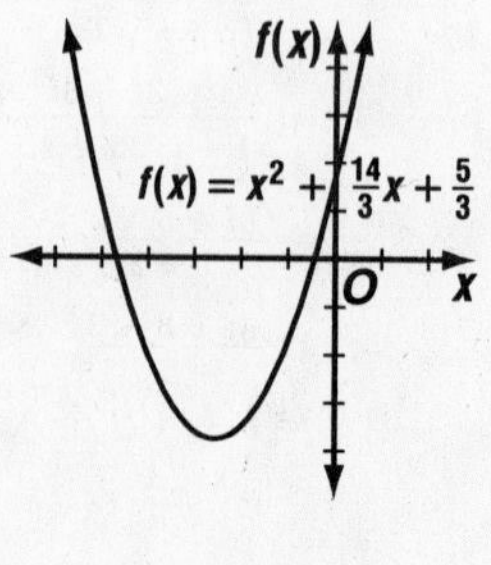

Page 889 Lesson 6-2

1. $(x + 5)(x - 3) = 0$
$x + 5 = 0$ or $x - 3 = 0$
$x = -5$; $x = 3$

2. $(y - 2)(3y + 2) = 0$
$y - 2 = 0$ or $3y + 2 = 0$
$y = 2$; $3y = -2$
$y = -\frac{2}{3}$

3. $s(2s - 1) = 0$
$s = 0$ or $2s - 1 = 0$
$2s = 1$
$s = \frac{1}{2}$

4. $x^2 + 7x + 10 = 0$
$(x + 2)(x + 5) = 0$
$x + 2 = 0$ or $x + 5 = 0$
$x = -2$; $x = -5$

5. $x^2 - 4x - 21 = 0$
$(x - 7)(x + 3) = 0$
$x - 7 = 0$ or $x + 3 = 0$
$x = 7$; $x = -3$

6. $b^2 = 49$
$b^2 - 49 = 0$
$(b - 7)(b + 7) = 0$
$b - 7 = 0$ or $b + 7 = 0$
$b = 7$; $b = -7$

7. $3z^3 = 75z$
$3z^3 - 75z = 0$
$3z(z^2 - 25) = 0$
$3z(z - 5)(z + 5) = 0$
$3z = 0$ or $z - 5 = 0$ or $z + 5 = 0$
$z = 0$; $z = 5$; $z = -5$

8. $2m^2 + 7m = 9$
$2m^2 + 7m - 9 = 0$
$(2m + 9)(m - 1) = 0$
$2m + 9 = 0$ or $m - 1 = 0$
$2m = -9$; $m = 1$
$m = -\frac{9}{2}$

9. $7x(x - 1) = 30(x + 1)$
$7x^2 - 7x = 30x + 30$
$7x^2 - 37x = 30$
$7x^2 - 37x - 30 = 0$
$(7x + 5)(x - 6) = 0$
$7x + 5 = 0$ or $x - 6 = 0$
$7x = -5$; $x = 6$
$x = -\frac{5}{7}$

10. $8x^2 = 48 - 40x$
$8x^2 + 40x - 48 = 0$
$8(x^2 + 5x - 6) = 0$
$8(x + 6)(x - 1) = 0$
$x + 6 = 0$ or $x - 1 = 0$
$x = -6$; $x = 1$

11. $5x^2 = 20x$
$5x^2 - 20x = 0$
$5x(x - 4) = 0$
$5x = 0$ or $x - 4 = 0$
$x = 0$; $x = 4$

12. $12d^2 - 71d - 6 = 0$
$(12d + 1)(d - 6) = 0$
$12d + 1 = 0$ or $d - 6 = 0$
$12d = -1$; $d = 6$
$d = -\frac{1}{12}$

13. $16x^2 - 64 = 0$
$(4x - 8)(4x + 8) = 0$
$4x - 8 = 0$ or $4x + 8 = 0$
$4x = 8$; $4x = -8$
$x = 2$; $x = -2$

14. $5x^2 - 45x + 90 = 0$
$5(x^2 - 9x + 18) = 0$
$5(x - 6)(x - 3) = 0$
$x - 6 = 0$ or $x - 3 = 0$
$x = 6$; $x = 3$

15. $24x^2 - 15 = 2x$
$24x^2 - 2x - 15 = 0$
$(4x + 3)(6x - 5) = 0$
$4x + 3 = 0$ or $6x - 5 = 0$
$4x = -3$; $6x = 5$
$x = -\frac{3}{4}$; $x = \frac{5}{6}$

16. $x^2 = 72 - x$
$x^2 + x - 72 = 0$
$(x + 9)(x - 8) = 0$
$x + 9 = 0$ or $x - 8 = 0$
$x = -9$; $x = 8$

17. $2x^2 + 5x + 3 = 0$
$(2x + 3)(x + 1) = 0$
$2x + 3 = 0$ or $x + 1 = 0$
$2x = -3$; $x = -1$
$x = -\frac{3}{2}$

18. $4p^2 + 9 = 12p$
$4p^2 - 12p + 9 = 0$
$(2p - 3)(2p - 3) = 0$
$2p - 3 = 0$ or $2p - 3 = 0$
$2p = 3$; $2p = 3$
$p = \frac{3}{2}$; $p = \frac{3}{2}$

19. $2x^2 - 8x = 0$
$2x(x - 4) = 0$
$2x = 0$ or $x - 4 = 0$
$x = 0$; $x = 4$

20. $8b^2 + 10b = 3$
$8b^2 + 10b - 3 = 0$
$(4b - 1)(2b + 3) = 0$
$4b - 1 = 0$ or $2b + 3 = 0$
$4b = 1$; $2b = -3$
$b = \frac{1}{4}$; $b = -\frac{3}{2}$

21. $12p^2 - 5p = 3$
$12p^2 - 5p - 3 = 0$
$(4p - 3)(3p + 1) = 0$
$4p - 3 = 0$ or $3p + 1 = 0$
$4p = 3$; $3p = -1$
$p = \frac{3}{4}$; $p = -\frac{1}{3}$

22. $a^2 + 8a + 12 = 0$
$(a + 6)(a + 2) = 0$
$a + 6 = 0$ or $a + 2 = 0$
$a = -6$; $a = -2$

23. $x^2 + 9x + 14 = 0$
$(x + 7)(x + 2) = 0$
$x + 7 = 0$ or $x + 2 = 0$
$x = -7$ $\quad x = -2$

24. $9g^2 + 1 = 6g$
$9g^2 - 6g + 1 = 0$
$(3g - 1)(3g - 1) = 0$
$3g - 1 = 0$ or $3g - 1 = 0$
$3g = 1$ $\quad 3g = 1$
$g = \frac{1}{3}$ $\quad g = \frac{1}{3}$

25. $2x^2 = 6x$
$2x^2 - 6x = 0$
$2x(x - 3) = 0$
$2x = 0$ or $x - 3 = 0$
$x = 0$ $\quad x = 3$

26. $6t^2 + 7t = 3$
$6t^2 + 7t - 3 = 0$
$(3t - 1)(2t + 3) = 0$
$3t - 1 = 0$ or $2t + 3 = 0$
$3t = 1$ $\quad 2t = -3$
$t = \frac{1}{3}$ $\quad t = -\frac{3}{2}$

27. $g^2 - 4g = 21$
$g^2 - 4g - 21 = 0$
$(g - 7)(g + 3) = 0$
$g - 7 = 0$ or $g + 3 = 0$
$g = 7$ $\quad g = -3$

Page 889 Lesson 6-3

1. $c = \left(-\frac{12}{2}\right)^2$
$= (-6)^2$
$= 36$

2. $c = \left(\frac{20}{2}\right)^2$
$= 10^2$
$= 100$

3. $c = \left(-\frac{11}{2}\right)^2$
$= \frac{121}{4}$

4. $c = \left(\frac{-\frac{2}{3}}{2}\right)^2$
$= \left(-\frac{1}{3}\right)^2$
$= \frac{1}{9}$

5. $c = \left(\frac{30}{2}\right)^2$
$= 15^2$
$= 225$

6. $c = \left(\frac{-0.5}{2}\right)^2$
$= (-0.25)^2$
$= 0.0625$

7. $c = \left(\frac{\frac{3}{8}}{2}\right)^2$
$= \left(\frac{3}{16}\right)^2$
$= \frac{9}{256}$

8. $c = \left(\frac{16}{2}\right)^2$
$= 8^2$
$= 64$

9. $c = \left(-\frac{3}{2}\right)^2$
$= \frac{9}{4}$

10. $x^2 + 3x - 4 = 0$
$x^2 + 3x = 4$
$x^2 + 3x + \frac{9}{4} = 4 + \frac{9}{4}$
$\left(x + \frac{3}{2}\right)^2 = \frac{25}{4}$
$x + \frac{3}{2} = \pm\frac{5}{2}$
$x = -\frac{3}{2} \pm \frac{5}{2}$
$x = -\frac{3}{2} + \frac{5}{2}$ or $x = -\frac{3}{2} - \frac{5}{2}$
$= 1$ $\quad = -4$

11. $x^2 + 5x = 0$
$x^2 + 5x + \frac{25}{4} = \frac{25}{4}$
$\left(x + \frac{5}{2}\right)^2 = \frac{25}{4}$
$x + \frac{5}{2} = \pm\frac{5}{2}$
$x = -\frac{5}{2} \pm \frac{5}{2}$
$x = -\frac{5}{2} + \frac{5}{2}$ or $x = -\frac{5}{2} - \frac{5}{2}$
$= 0$ $\quad = -5$

12. $x^2 + 2x - 63 = 0$
$x^2 + 2x = 63$
$x^2 + 2x + 1 = 63 + 1$
$(x + 1)^2 = 64$
$x + 1 = \pm 8$
$x = -1 \pm 8$
$x = -1 + 8$ or $x = -1 - 8$
$= 7$ $\quad = -9$

13. $3x^2 - 16x - 35 = 0$
$x^2 - \frac{16}{3}x - \frac{35}{3} = 0$
$x^2 - \frac{16}{3}x = \frac{35}{3}$
$x^2 - \frac{16}{3}x + \frac{256}{36} = \frac{35}{3} + \frac{256}{36}$
$\left(x - \frac{16}{6}\right)^2 = \frac{676}{36}$
$x - \frac{16}{6} = \pm\frac{26}{6}$
$x = \frac{16}{6} \pm \frac{26}{6}$
$x = \frac{16}{6} + \frac{26}{6}$ or $x = \frac{16}{6} - \frac{26}{6}$
$= 7$ $\quad = -\frac{5}{3}$

14. $x^2 + 7x + 13 = 0$
$x^2 + 7x = -13$
$x^2 + 7x + \frac{49}{4} = -13 + \frac{49}{4}$
$\left(x + \frac{7}{2}\right)^2 = -\frac{3}{4}$
$x + \frac{7}{2} = \pm\sqrt{-\frac{3}{4}}$
$x = -\frac{7}{2} \pm \frac{i\sqrt{3}}{2}$
$x = \frac{-7 \pm i\sqrt{3}}{2}$

15. $5x^2 - 8x + 2 = 0$
$x^2 - \frac{8}{5}x + \frac{2}{5} = 0$
$x^2 - \frac{8}{5}x = -\frac{2}{5}$
$x^2 - \frac{8}{5}x + \frac{64}{100} = -\frac{2}{5} + \frac{64}{100}$
$\left(x - \frac{8}{10}\right)^2 = \frac{24}{100}$
$x - \frac{8}{10} = \pm\frac{2\sqrt{6}}{10}$
$x = \frac{8}{10} \pm \frac{2\sqrt{6}}{10}$
$x = \frac{8 \pm 2\sqrt{6}}{10}$
$x = \frac{4 \pm \sqrt{6}}{5}$

16. $x^2 - 6x + 11 = 0$
$x^2 - 6x = -11$
$x^2 - 6x + 9 = -11 + 9$
$(x - 3)^2 = -2$
$x - 3 = \pm\sqrt{-2}$
$x = 3 \pm i\sqrt{2}$

17. $x^2 - 12x + 36 = 0$
$x^2 - 12x = -36$
$x^2 - 12x + 36 = -36 + 36$
$(x - 6)^2 = 0$
$x - 6 = 0$
$x = 6$

18. $8x^2 + 13x - 4 = 0$
$x^2 + \frac{13}{8}x - \frac{1}{2} = 0$
$x^2 + \frac{13}{8}x = \frac{1}{2}$
$x^2 + \frac{13}{8}x + \frac{169}{256} = \frac{1}{2} + \frac{169}{256}$
$\left(x + \frac{13}{16}\right)^2 = \frac{297}{256}$
$x + \frac{13}{16} = \pm \frac{3\sqrt{33}}{16}$
$x = -\frac{13}{16} \pm \frac{3\sqrt{33}}{16}$
$x = \frac{-13 \pm 3\sqrt{33}}{16}$

19. $3x^2 + 5x + 6 = 0$
$x^2 + \frac{5}{3}x + 2 = 0$
$x^2 + \frac{5}{3}x = -2$
$x^2 + \frac{5}{3}x + \frac{25}{36} = -2 + \frac{25}{36}$
$\left(x + \frac{5}{6}\right)^2 = -\frac{47}{36}$
$x + \frac{5}{6} = \pm \frac{\sqrt{-47}}{6}$
$x = -\frac{5}{6} \pm \frac{i\sqrt{47}}{6}$
$x = \frac{-5 \pm i\sqrt{47}}{6}$

20. $x^2 + 14x - 1 = 0$
$x^2 + 14x = 1$
$x^2 + 14x + 49 = 1 + 49$
$(x + 7)^2 = 50$
$x + 7 = \pm 5\sqrt{2}$
$x = -7 \pm 5\sqrt{2}$

21. $4x^2 - 32x + 15 = 0$
$x^2 - 8x + \frac{15}{4} = 0$
$x^2 - 8x = -\frac{15}{4}$
$x^2 - 8x + 16 = -\frac{15}{4} + 16$
$(x - 4)^2 = \frac{49}{4}$
$x - 4 = \pm\frac{7}{2}$

22. $3x^2 - 11x - 4 = 0$
$x^2 - \frac{11}{3}x - \frac{4}{3} = 0$
$x^2 - \frac{11}{3}x = \frac{4}{3}$
$x^2 - \frac{11}{3}x + \frac{121}{36} = \frac{4}{3} + \frac{121}{36}$
$\left(x - \frac{11}{6}\right)^2 = \frac{169}{36}$
$x - \frac{11}{6} = \pm\frac{13}{6}$
$x = \frac{11}{6} \pm \frac{13}{6}$
$x = \frac{11}{6} - \frac{13}{6}$ or $x = \frac{11}{6} + \frac{13}{6}$
$= -\frac{1}{3}$ $= 4$

23. $x^2 + 8x - 84 = 0$
$x^2 + 8x = 84$
$x^2 + 8x + 16 = 84 + 16$
$(x + 4)^2 = 100$
$x + 4 = \pm 10$
$x = -4 \pm 10$
$x = -4 - 10$ or $x = -4 + 10$
$= -14$ $= 10$

24. $x^2 - 7x + 5 = 0$
$x^2 - 7x = -5$
$x^2 - 7x + \frac{49}{4} = -5 + \frac{49}{4}$
$\left(x - \frac{7}{2}\right)^2 = \frac{29}{4}$
$x - \frac{7}{2} = \pm\frac{\sqrt{29}}{2}$
$x = \frac{7}{2} \pm \frac{\sqrt{29}}{2}$
$x = \frac{7 \pm \sqrt{29}}{2}$

25. $t^2 + 3t - 8 = 0$
$t^2 + 3t = 8$
$t^2 + 3t + \frac{9}{4} = 8 + \frac{9}{4}$
$\left(t + \frac{3}{2}\right)^2 = \frac{41}{4}$
$t + \frac{3}{2} = \pm\frac{\sqrt{41}}{2}$
$t = -\frac{3}{2} \pm \frac{\sqrt{41}}{2}$
$t = \frac{-3 \pm \sqrt{41}}{2}$

26. $a^2 - 5a - 10 = 0$
$a^2 - 5a = 10$
$a^2 - 5a + \frac{25}{4} = 10 + \frac{25}{4}$
$\left(a - \frac{5}{2}\right)^2 = \frac{65}{4}$
$a - \frac{5}{2} = \pm\frac{\sqrt{65}}{2}$
$a = \frac{5}{2} \pm \frac{\sqrt{65}}{2}$
$a = \frac{5 \pm \sqrt{65}}{2}$

27. $3z^2 - 12z + 4 = 0$
$z^2 - 4z + \frac{4}{3} = 0$
$z^2 - 4z = -\frac{4}{3}$
$z^2 - 4z + 4 = -\frac{4}{3} + 4$
$(z - 2)^2 = \frac{8}{3}$
$z - 2 = \pm\frac{2\sqrt{2}}{\sqrt{3}}$
$z = 2 \pm \frac{2\sqrt{6}}{3}$

28. $x^2 + 20x + 75 = 0$
$x^2 + 20x = -75$
$x^2 + 20x + 100 = -75 + 100$
$(x + 10)^2 = 25$
$x + 10 = \pm 5$
$x = -10 \pm 5$
$x = -10 - 5$ or $x = -10 + 5$
$= -15$ $= -5$

29. $x^2 - 5x - 24 = 0$

$x^2 - 5x = 24$

$x^2 - 5x + \frac{25}{4} = 24 + \frac{25}{4}$

$\left(x - \frac{5}{2}\right)^2 = \frac{121}{4}$

$x - \frac{5}{2} = \pm \frac{11}{2}$

$x = \frac{5}{2} \pm \frac{11}{2}$

$x = \frac{5}{2} - \frac{11}{2}$ or $x = \frac{5}{2} + \frac{11}{2}$

$= -3$ $\qquad$ $= 8$

30. $2t^2 + t - 21 = 0$

$t^2 + \frac{1}{2}t - \frac{21}{2} = 0$

$t^2 + \frac{1}{2} = \frac{21}{2}$

$t^2 + \frac{1}{2}t + \frac{1}{16} = \frac{21}{2} + \frac{1}{16}$

$\left(t + \frac{1}{4}\right)^2 = \frac{169}{16}$

$t + \frac{1}{4} = \pm \frac{13}{4}$

$t = -\frac{1}{4} \pm \frac{13}{4}$

$t = -\frac{1}{4} - \frac{13}{4}$ or $t = -\frac{1}{4} + \frac{13}{4}$

$= -\frac{7}{2}$ $\qquad$ $= 3$

Page 890 Lesson 6-4

1. $b^2 - 4ac = 7^2 - 4 \cdot 1 \cdot 13$

$= 49 - 52$

$= -3$

2 imaginary

$x = \frac{-7 \pm \sqrt{-3}}{2 \cdot 1}$

$= \frac{-7 \pm i\sqrt{3}}{2}$

2. $b^2 - 4ac = 6^2 - 4 \cdot 6\,(-21)$

$= 36 + 504$

$= 540$

2 real, irrational

$x = \frac{-6 \pm \sqrt{540}}{2 \cdot 6}$

$= \frac{-6 \pm 6\sqrt{15}}{12}$

$= \frac{-1 \pm \sqrt{15}}{2}$; 1.44, −2.44

3. $b^2 - 4ac = (-5)^2 - 4 \cdot 5 \cdot 4$

$= 25 - 80$

$= -55$

2 imaginary

$x = \frac{5 \pm \sqrt{-55}}{2 \cdot 5}$

$= \frac{5 \pm i\sqrt{55}}{10}$

4. $b^2 - 4ac = (-64)^2 - 4 \cdot 16 \cdot 19$

$= 4096 - 1216$

$= 2880$

2 real, irrational

$x = \frac{64 \pm \sqrt{2880}}{2 \cdot 16}$

$= \frac{64 \pm 24\sqrt{5}}{32}$

$= \frac{8 \pm 3\sqrt{5}}{4}$; 3.68, 0.32

5. $b^2 - 4ac = 42^2 - 4 \cdot 9 \cdot 49$

$= 1764 - 1764$

$= 0$

1 real, rational

$x = \frac{-42 \pm \sqrt{0}}{2 \cdot 9}$

$= -\frac{42}{18}$

$= -\frac{7}{3}$

6. $b^2 - 4ac = (-16)^2 - 4 \cdot 4 \cdot 3$

$= 256 - 48$

$= 208$

2 real, irrational

$x = \frac{16 \pm \sqrt{208}}{2 \cdot 4}$

$= \frac{16 \pm 4\sqrt{13}}{8}$

$= \frac{4 \pm \sqrt{13}}{2}$; 3.80, 0.20

7. $2x^2 = 5x + 3$

$2x^2 - 5x - 3 = 0$

$b^2 - 4ac = (-5)^2 - 4 \cdot 2\,(-3)$

$= 25 + 24$

$= 49$

2 real, rational

$x = \frac{5 \pm \sqrt{49}}{2 \cdot 2}$

$= \frac{5 \pm 7}{4}$

$x = \frac{5 + 7}{4}$ or $x = \frac{5 - 7}{4}$

$= 3$ $\qquad$ $= -\frac{1}{2}$

8. $x^2 + 81 = 18x$

$x^2 - 18x + 81 = 0$

$b^2 - 4ac = (-18)^2 - 4 \cdot 1 \cdot 81$

$= 324 - 324$

$= 0$

1 real, rational

$x = \frac{18 \pm \sqrt{0}}{2 \cdot 1}$

$= \frac{18}{2}$

$= 9$

9. $18x^2 = 6x^2 + 5$

$12x^2 - 5 = 0$

$b^2 - 4ac = 0^2 - 4 \cdot 12\,(-5)$

$= 0 + 240$

$= 240$

2 real, irrational

$x = \frac{0 \pm \sqrt{240}}{2 \cdot 12}$

$= \frac{0 \pm 4\sqrt{15}}{24}$

$= \pm\frac{\sqrt{15}}{6}$; 0.65, −0.65

10. $4x^2 = 49$

$4x^2 - 49 = 0$

$b^2 - 4ac = 0^2 - 4 \cdot 4\,(-49)$

$= 0 + 784$

$= 784$

2 real, rational

$x = \frac{0 \pm \sqrt{784}}{2 \cdot 4}$

$= \frac{\pm 28}{8}$

$= \pm \frac{7}{2}$

11. $b^2 - 4ac = (-30)^2 - 4 \cdot 3 \cdot 75$
$= 900 - 900$
$= 0$

1 real, rational

$x = \frac{30 \pm \sqrt{0}}{2 \cdot 3}$
$= \frac{30}{6}$
$= 5$

12. $24x^2 + 10x = 43$
$24x^2 + 10x - 43 = 0$
$b^2 - 4ac = 10^2 - 4 \cdot 24\,(-43)$
$= 100 + 4128$
$= 4228$

2 real, irrational

$x = \frac{-10 \pm \sqrt{4228}}{2 \cdot 24}$
$= \frac{-10 \pm 2\sqrt{1057}}{48}$
$= \frac{-5 \pm \sqrt{1057}}{24}$; 1.15, −1.56

13. $9x^2 + 4 = 2x$
$9x^2 - 2x + 4 = 0$
$b^2 - 4ac = (-2)^2 - 4 \cdot 9 \cdot 4$
$= 4 - 144$
$= -140$

2 imaginary

$x = \frac{2 \pm \sqrt{-140}}{2 \cdot 9}$
$= \frac{2 \pm 2i\sqrt{35}}{18}$
$= \frac{1 \pm i\sqrt{35}}{9}$

14. $7x = 8x^2$
$-8x^2 + 7x = 0$
$b^2 - 4ac = 7^2 - 4\,(-8)0$
$= 49 + 0$
$= 49$

2 real, rational

$x = \frac{-7 \pm \sqrt{49}}{2\,(-8)}$
$= -\frac{7 \pm 7}{16}$

$x = -\frac{7 + 7}{16}$ or $x = -\frac{7 - 7}{16}$
$= 0$ $= \frac{7}{8}$

15. $18x^2 = 9x + 45$
$18x^2 - 9x - 45 = 0$
$b^2 - 4ac = (-9)^2 - 4 \cdot 18\,(-45)$
$= 81 + 3240$
$= 3321$

2 real, irrational

$x = \frac{9 \pm \sqrt{3321}}{2 \cdot 18}$
$= \frac{9 \pm 9\sqrt{41}}{36}$
$= \frac{1 \pm \sqrt{41}}{4}$; 1.85, −1.35

16. $b^2 - 4ac = (-4)^2 - 4 \cdot 1 \cdot 4$
$= 16 - 16$
$= 0$

1 real, rational

$y = \frac{4 \pm \sqrt{0}}{2 \cdot 1}$
$= \frac{4}{2}$
$= 2$

17. $b^2 - 4ac = 8^2 - 4 \cdot 4 \cdot 3$
$= 64 - 48$
$= 16$

2 real, rational

$x = \frac{-8 \pm \sqrt{16}}{2 \cdot 4}$
$= \frac{-8 \pm 4}{8}$

$x = \frac{-8 + 4}{8}$ or $x = \frac{-8 - 4}{8}$
$= -\frac{1}{2}$ $= -\frac{3}{2}$

18. $b^2 - 4ac = 16^2 - 4 \cdot 4 \cdot 15$
$= 256 - 240$
$= 16$

2 real, rational

$y = \frac{-16 \pm \sqrt{16}}{2 \cdot 4}$
$= \frac{-16 \pm 4}{8}$

$y = \frac{-16 + 4}{8}$ or $y = \frac{-16 - 4}{8}$
$= -\frac{3}{2}$ $= -\frac{5}{2}$

19. $b^2 - 4ac = (-6)^2 - 4 \cdot 1 \cdot 13$
$= 36 - 52$
$= -16$

2 imaginary

$y = \frac{6 \pm \sqrt{-16}}{2 \cdot 1}$
$= \frac{6 \pm 4i}{2}$
$= 3 \pm 2i$

20. $3m^2 = 108m$
$3m^2 - 108m = 0$
$b^2 - 4ac = (-108)^2 - 4 \cdot 3 \cdot 0$
$= 11{,}664 - 0$
$= 11{,}664$

2 real, rational

$m = \frac{108 \pm \sqrt{11{,}664}}{2 \cdot 3}$
$= \frac{108 \pm 108}{6}$

$m = \frac{108 + 108}{6}$ or $m = \frac{108 - 108}{6}$
$= \frac{216}{6}$ $= 0$
$= 36$

21. $b^2 - 4ac = (-1)^2 - 4 \cdot 1 \cdot 1$
$= 1 - 4$
$= -3$

2 imaginary

$x = \frac{1 \pm \sqrt{-3}}{2 \cdot 1}$
$= \frac{1 \pm i\sqrt{3}}{2}$

22. $b^2 - 4ac = 4^2 - 4 \cdot 1 \cdot 29$
$= 16 - 116$
$= -100$

2 imaginary

$n = \frac{-4 \pm \sqrt{-100}}{2 \cdot 1}$
$= \frac{-4 \pm 10i}{2}$
$= -2 \pm 5i$

23. $b^2 - 4ac = 3^2 - 4 \cdot 4\,(-2)$
$= 9 + 32$
$= 41$

2 real, irrational

$a = \frac{-3 \pm \sqrt{41}}{2 \cdot 4}$
$= \frac{-3 \pm \sqrt{41}}{8}$; 0.43, −1.18

24. $2x^2 + 5x = 9$
$2x^2 + 5x - 9 = 0$
$b^2 - 4ac = 5^2 - 4 \cdot 2\,(-9)$
$= 25 + 72$
$= 97$

2 real, irrational

$x = \frac{-5 \pm \sqrt{97}}{2 \cdot 2}$
$= \frac{-5 \pm \sqrt{97}}{4}$; 1.21, −3.71

25. $n^2 = 8n - 16$
$n^2 - 8n + 16 = 0$
$b^2 - 4ac = (-8)^2 - 4 \cdot 1 \cdot 16$
$= 64 - 64$
$= 0$

1 real, rational

$n = \frac{8 \pm \sqrt{0}}{2 \cdot 1}$
$= \frac{8}{2}$
$= 4$

26. $7b^2 = 4b$
$7b^2 - 4b = 0$
$b^2 - 4ac = (-4)^2 - 4 \cdot 7 \cdot 0$
$= 16 - 0$
$= 16$

2 real, rational

$b = \frac{4 \pm \sqrt{16}}{2 \cdot 7}$
$= \frac{4 \pm 4}{14}$

$b = \frac{4 + 4}{14}$ or $b = \frac{4 - 4}{14}$
$= \frac{4}{7}$ $= 0$

27. $b^2 - 4ac = 6^2 - 4 \cdot 2 \cdot 5$
$= 36 - 40$
$= -4$

2 imaginary

$y = \frac{-6 \pm \sqrt{-4}}{2 \cdot 2}$
$= \frac{-6 \pm 2i}{4}$
$= \frac{-3 \pm i}{2}$

28. $b^2 - 4ac = (-30)^2 - 4 \cdot 9 \cdot 25$
$= 900 - 900$
$= 0$

1 real, rational

$a = \frac{30 \pm \sqrt{0}}{2 \cdot 9}$
$= \frac{30}{18}$
$= \frac{5}{3}$

29. $b^2 - 4ac = (-4)^2 - 4 \cdot 3 \cdot 2$
$= 16 - 24$
$= -8$

2 imaginary

$x = \frac{4 \pm \sqrt{-8}}{2 \cdot 3}$
$= \frac{4 \pm 2i\sqrt{2}}{6}$
$= \frac{2 \pm i\sqrt{2}}{3}$

30. $b^2 - 4ac = 3^2 - 4 \cdot 2 \cdot 3$
$= 9 - 24$
$= -15$

2 imaginary

$x = \frac{-3 \pm \sqrt{-15}}{2 \cdot 2}$
$= \frac{-3 \pm i\sqrt{15}}{4}$

Page 890 Lesson 6-5

1. $s_1 + s_2 = 9 + (-7)$
$= 2$
$s_1(s_2) = 9\,(-7)$
$= -63$

$-\frac{b}{a} = 2, \frac{c}{a} = -63$
$a = 1, b = -2, c = -63$
$x^2 - 2x - 63 = 0$

2. $s_1 + s_2 = \frac{2}{3} + 3$
$= \frac{11}{3}$
$s_1(s_2) = \frac{2}{3} \cdot 3$
$= \frac{6}{3}$

$-\frac{b}{a} = \frac{11}{3}, \frac{c}{a} = \frac{6}{3}$
$a = 3, b = -11, c = 6$
$3x^2 - 11x + 6 = 0$

3. $s_1 + s_2 = 2 + \sqrt{5} + 2 - \sqrt{5}$
$= 4$
$s_1(s_2) = (2 + \sqrt{5})(2 - \sqrt{5})$
$= 4 - 2\sqrt{5} + 2\sqrt{5} - 5$
$= -1$

$-\frac{b}{a} = 4, \frac{c}{a} = -1$
$a = 1, b = -4, c = -1$
$x^2 - 4x - 1 = 0$

4. $s_1 + s_2 = \frac{-5 + 3\sqrt{2}}{3} + \frac{-5 - 3\sqrt{2}}{3}$
$= -\frac{10}{3}$ or $-\frac{30}{9}$
$s_1(s_2) = \left(\frac{-5 + 3\sqrt{2}}{3}\right)\left(\frac{-5 - 3\sqrt{2}}{3}\right)$
$= \frac{25 + 15\sqrt{2} - 15\sqrt{2} - 18}{9}$
$= \frac{7}{9}$

$-\frac{b}{a} = -\frac{30}{9}, \frac{c}{a} = \frac{7}{9}$
$a = 9, b = 30, c = 7$
$9x^2 + 30x + 7 = 0$

5. $s_1 + s_2 = 17 + 17$
$= 34$
$s_1(s_2) = 17 \cdot 17$
$= 289$

$-\frac{b}{a} = 34, \frac{c}{a} = 289$
$a = 1, b = -34, c = 289$
$x^2 - 34x + 289 = 0$

6. $s_1 + s_2 = \frac{-6 + 2i\sqrt{3}}{5} + \frac{-6 - 2i\sqrt{3}}{5}$
$= -\frac{12}{5}$ or $-\frac{60}{25}$
$s_1(s_2) = \left(\frac{-6 + 2i\sqrt{3}}{5}\right)\left(\frac{-6 - 2i\sqrt{3}}{5}\right)$
$= \frac{36 + 12i\sqrt{3} - 12i\sqrt{3} - 12i^2}{25}$
$= \frac{36 + 12}{25}$ or $\frac{48}{25}$

$-\frac{b}{a} = -\frac{60}{25}, \frac{c}{a} = \frac{48}{25}$
$a = 25, b = 60, c = 48$
$25x^2 + 60x + 48 = 0$

7. $s_1 + s_2 = 0 + 8$
$= 8$
$s_1(s_2) = 0 \cdot 8$
$= 0$

$-\frac{b}{a} = 8, \frac{c}{a} = 0$
$a = 1, b = -8, c = 0$
$x^2 - 8x = 0$

8. $s_1 + s_2 = \frac{\sqrt{6}}{4} + \left(\frac{-\sqrt{6}}{4}\right)$ $\quad -\frac{b}{a} = 0, \frac{c}{a} = -\frac{3}{8}$

$= 0$ $\quad a = 8, b = 0, c = -3$

$s_1(s_2) = \left(\frac{\sqrt{6}}{4}\right)\left(\frac{-\sqrt{6}}{4}\right)$ $\quad 8x^2 - 3 = 0$

$= -\frac{6}{16}$

$= -\frac{3}{8}$

9. $x = \frac{3 \pm \sqrt{(-3)^2 - 4(4)(-6)}}{2 \cdot 4}$

$= \frac{3 \pm \sqrt{9 + 96}}{8}$

$= \frac{3 \pm \sqrt{105}}{8}$

$s_1 + s_2 = \frac{3 + \sqrt{105}}{8} + \frac{3 - \sqrt{105}}{8}$

$= \frac{6}{8}$ or $\frac{3}{4}$ ✓

$s_1(s_2) = \left(\frac{3 + \sqrt{105}}{8}\right)\left(\frac{3 - \sqrt{105}}{8}\right)$

$= \frac{9 - 3\sqrt{105} + 3\sqrt{105} - 105}{64}$

$= -\frac{96}{64}$ or $-\frac{6}{4}$ ✓

10. $4x^2 = 625$

$x^2 = \frac{625}{4}$

$x = \pm\frac{25}{2}$

$s_1 + s_2 = \frac{25}{2} + \left(-\frac{25}{2}\right)$

$= 0$ ✓

$s_1(s_2) = \left(\frac{25}{2}\right)\left(-\frac{25}{2}\right)$

$= -\frac{625}{4}$ ✓

11. $81x^2 + 4 = 36x$

$81x^2 - 36x + 4 = 0$

$x = \frac{36 \pm \sqrt{(-36)^2 - 4 \cdot 81 \cdot 4}}{2 \cdot 81}$

$= \frac{36 \pm \sqrt{1296 - 1296}}{162}$

$= \frac{36}{162}$ or $\frac{2}{9}$

$s_1 + s_2 = \frac{2}{9} + \frac{2}{9}$

$= \frac{4}{9}$ or $\frac{36}{81}$

$s_1(s_2) = \frac{2}{9}\left(\frac{2}{9}\right)$

$= \frac{4}{81}$ ✓

12. $x = \frac{7 \pm \sqrt{7^2 - 4 \cdot 1 \cdot 3}}{2 \cdot 1}$

$= \frac{7 \pm \sqrt{49 - 12}}{2}$

$= \frac{7 \pm \sqrt{37}}{2}$

$s_1 + s_2 = \frac{7 + \sqrt{37}}{2} + \frac{7 - \sqrt{37}}{2}$

$= \frac{14}{2}$ or 7 ✓

$s_1(s_2) = \left(\frac{7 + \sqrt{37}}{2}\right)\left(\frac{7 - \sqrt{37}}{2}\right)$

$= \frac{49 - 7\sqrt{37} + 7\sqrt{37} - 37}{4}$

$= \frac{12}{4}$ or 3 ✓

13. $7x^2 + 3x + 1 = 3$

$7x^2 + 3x - 2 = 0$

$x = \frac{-3 \pm \sqrt{3^2 - 4 \cdot 7(-2)}}{2 \cdot 7}$

$= \frac{-3 \pm \sqrt{9 + 56}}{14}$

$= \frac{-3 \pm \sqrt{65}}{14}$

$s_1 + s_2 = \frac{-3 + \sqrt{65}}{14} + \frac{-3 - \sqrt{65}}{14}$

$= -\frac{6}{14}$ or $-\frac{3}{7}$ ✓

$s_1(s_2) = \left(\frac{-3 + \sqrt{65}}{14}\right)\left(\frac{-3 - \sqrt{65}}{14}\right)$

$= \frac{9 + 3\sqrt{65} - 3\sqrt{65} - 65}{196}$

$= \frac{-56}{196}$ or $-\frac{2}{7}$ ✓

14. $6x^2 = 13x$

$6x^2 - 13x = 0$

$x = \frac{13 \pm \sqrt{(-13)^2 - 4 \cdot 6 \cdot 0}}{2 \cdot 6}$

$= \frac{13 \pm \sqrt{169}}{12}$

$= \frac{13 \pm 13}{12}$

$x = \frac{26}{12}$ or $\frac{13}{6}$; $x = \frac{0}{12}$ or 0

$s_1 + s_2 = \frac{13}{6} + 0$

$= \frac{13}{6}$ ✓

$s_1(s_2) = \frac{13}{6} \cdot 0$

$= 0$ ✓

15. $x = \frac{-18 \pm \sqrt{18^2 - 4 \cdot 5 \cdot 0}}{2 \cdot 5}$

$= \frac{-18 \pm \sqrt{324}}{10}$

$= \frac{-18 \pm 18}{10}$

$x = \frac{0}{10}$ or 0; $x = -\frac{36}{10}$ or $-\frac{18}{5}$

$s_1 + s_2 = 0 + \left(-\frac{18}{5}\right)$

$= -\frac{18}{5}$ ✓

$s_1(s_2) = 0\left(-\frac{18}{5}\right)$

$= 0$ ✓

16. $x = \frac{8 \pm \sqrt{(-8)^2 - 4 \cdot 1 \cdot 5}}{2 \cdot 1}$

$= \frac{8 \pm \sqrt{64 - 20}}{2}$

$= \frac{8 \pm \sqrt{44}}{2}$

$= \frac{8 \pm 2\sqrt{11}}{2}$

$= 4 \pm \sqrt{11}$

$s_1 + s_2 = (4 + \sqrt{11}) + (4 - \sqrt{11})$

$= 8$ ✓

$s_1(s_2) = (4 + \sqrt{11})(4 - \sqrt{11})$

$= 16 - 4\sqrt{11} + 4\sqrt{11} - 11$

$= 5$ ✓

17. $x = \frac{16 \pm \sqrt{(-16)^2 - 4 \cdot 3\,(-12)}}{2 \cdot 3}$

$= \frac{16 \pm \sqrt{256 + 144}}{6}$

$= \frac{16 \pm \sqrt{400}}{6}$

$= \frac{16 \pm 20}{6}$

$x = \frac{36}{6}$ or 6; $x = -\frac{4}{6}$ or $-\frac{2}{3}$

$s_1 + s_2 = 6 + \left(-\frac{2}{3}\right)$

$= \frac{16}{3}$ ✓

$s_1\,(s_2) = 6\left(-\frac{2}{3}\right)$

$= -\frac{12}{3}$ ✓

18. $n = \frac{0 \pm \sqrt{0^2 - 4\,(9)\,(-1)}}{2 \cdot 9}$

$= \pm\frac{\sqrt{36}}{18}$

$= \pm\frac{6}{18}$

$= \pm\frac{1}{3}$

$s_1 + s_2 = \frac{1}{3} + \left(-\frac{1}{3}\right)$

$= 0$ ✓

$s_1\,(s_2) = \frac{1}{3}\left(-\frac{1}{3}\right)$

$= -\frac{1}{9}$ ✓

19. $2x^2 - 7x = 15$

$2x^2 - 7x - 15 = 0$

$x = \frac{7 \pm \sqrt{(-7)^2 - 4 \cdot 2\,(-15)}}{2 \cdot 2}$

$= \frac{7 \pm \sqrt{49 + 120}}{4}$

$= \frac{7 \pm 13}{4}$

$x = \frac{7 + 13}{4}$ or $x = \frac{7 - 13}{4}$

$= 5$ $\quad$ $= -\frac{3}{2}$

$s_1 + s_2 = 5 + \left(-\frac{3}{2}\right)$

$= \frac{7}{2}$ ✓

$s_1\,(s_2) = 5\left(-\frac{3}{2}\right)$

$= -\frac{15}{2}$ ✓

20. $c = \frac{2 \pm \sqrt{(-2)^2 - 4 \cdot 15\,(-8)}}{2 \cdot 15}$

$= \frac{2 \pm \sqrt{4 + 480}}{30}$

$= \frac{2 \pm 22}{30}$

$c = \frac{2 + 22}{30}$ or $c = \frac{2 - 22}{30}$

$= \frac{4}{5}$ $\quad$ $= -\frac{2}{3}$

$s_1 + s_2 = \frac{4}{5} + \left(-\frac{2}{3}\right)$

$= \frac{2}{15}$ ✓

$s_1\,(s_2) = \frac{4}{5}\left(-\frac{2}{3}\right)$

$= -\frac{8}{15}$ ✓

21. $s = \frac{-5 \pm \sqrt{5^2 - 4 \cdot 7\,(-1)}}{2 \cdot 7}$

$= \frac{-5 \pm \sqrt{25 + 28}}{14}$

$= \frac{-5 \pm \sqrt{53}}{14}$

$s_1 + s_2 = \frac{-5 \pm \sqrt{53}}{14} + \frac{-5 - \sqrt{53}}{14}$

$= -\frac{10}{14}$ or $-\frac{5}{7}$ ✓

$s_1\,(s_2) = \left(\frac{-5 + \sqrt{53}}{14}\right)\left(\frac{-5 - \sqrt{53}}{14}\right)$

$= \frac{25 + 5\sqrt{53} - 5\sqrt{53} - 53}{196}$

$= -\frac{28}{196}$ or $-\frac{1}{7}$ ✓

22. $x = \frac{-19 \pm \sqrt{19^2 - 4\,(12)\,(4)}}{2 \cdot 12}$

$= \frac{-19 \pm \sqrt{361 - 192}}{24}$

$= \frac{-19 \pm 13}{24}$

$x = \frac{-19 + 13}{24}$ or $x = \frac{-19 - 13}{24}$

$= -\frac{6}{24}$ or $-\frac{1}{4}$ $\quad$ $= -\frac{32}{24}$ or $-\frac{4}{3}$

$s_1 + s_2 = -\frac{1}{4} + \left(-\frac{4}{3}\right)$

$= -\frac{19}{12}$ ✓

$s_1\,(s_2) = -\frac{1}{4}\left(-\frac{4}{3}\right)$

$= \frac{4}{12}$ ✓

23. $x = \frac{-1 \pm \sqrt{1^2 - 4 \cdot 1\,(-6)}}{2 \cdot 1}$

$= \frac{-1 \pm \sqrt{1 + 24}}{2}$

$= \frac{-1 \pm 5}{2}$

$x = \frac{-1 + 5}{2}$ or $x = \frac{-1 - 5}{2}$

$= 2$ $\quad$ $= -3$

$s_1 + s_2 = 2 + (-3)$

$= -1$ ✓

$s_1\,(s_2) = 2(-3)$

$= -6$ ✓

24. $m = \frac{-5 \pm \sqrt{5^2 - 4 \cdot 1 \cdot 6}}{2 \cdot 1}$

$= \frac{-5 \pm \sqrt{25 - 24}}{2}$

$= \frac{-5 \pm 1}{2}$

$m = \frac{-5 + 1}{2}$ or $m = \frac{-5 - 1}{2}$

$= -2$ $\quad$ $= -3$

$s_1 + s_2 = -2 + (-3)$

$= -5$ ✓

$s_1\,(s_2) = -2(-3)$

$= 6$ ✓

25. $s = \frac{-5 \pm \sqrt{5^2 - 4 \cdot 1\,(-24)}}{2 \cdot 1}$

$= \frac{-5 \pm \sqrt{25 + 96}}{2}$

$= \frac{-5 \pm 11}{2}$

$s = \frac{-5 + 11}{2}$ or $s = \frac{-5 - 11}{2}$

$= 3$ $\quad$ $= -8$

$s_1 + s_2 = 3 + (-8)$

$= -5$ ✓

$s_1\,(s_2) = 3\,(-8)$

$= -24$ ✓

26. $a = \frac{9 \pm \sqrt{(-9)^2 - 4 \cdot 1 \cdot 20}}{2 \cdot 1}$

$= \frac{9 \pm \sqrt{81 - 80}}{2}$

$= \frac{9 \pm 1}{2}$

$a = \frac{9 + 1}{2}$ or $a = \frac{9 - 1}{2}$

$= 5$ $\quad = 4$

$s_1 + s_2 = 5 + 4$

$= 9$ ✓

$s_1(s_2) = 5 \cdot 4$

$= 20$ ✓

27. $x = \frac{12 \pm \sqrt{(-12)^2 - 4 \cdot 1(-45)}}{2 \cdot 1}$

$= \frac{12 \pm \sqrt{144 + 180}}{2}$

$= \frac{12 \pm 18}{2}$

$x = \frac{12 + 18}{2}$ or $x = \frac{12 - 18}{2}$

$= 15$ $\quad = -3$

$s_1 + s_2 = 15 + (-3)$

$= 12$ ✓

$s_1(s_2) = 15(-3)$

$= -45$ ✓

28. $m = \frac{10 \pm \sqrt{(-10)^2 - 4 \cdot 2 \cdot 9}}{2 \cdot 2}$

$= \frac{10 \pm \sqrt{100 - 72}}{4}$

$= \frac{10 \pm \sqrt{28}}{4}$

$= \frac{10 \pm 2\sqrt{7}}{4}$

$= \frac{5 \pm \sqrt{7}}{2}$

$s_1 + s_2 = \frac{5 + \sqrt{7}}{2} + \frac{5 - \sqrt{7}}{2}$

$= \frac{10}{2}$ ✓

$s_1(s_2) = \left(\frac{5 + \sqrt{7}}{2}\right)\left(\frac{5 - \sqrt{7}}{2}\right)$

$= \frac{25 - 5\sqrt{7} + 5\sqrt{7} - 7}{4}$

$= \frac{18}{4}$ or $\frac{9}{2}$ ✓

29. $x = \frac{0 \pm \sqrt{0^2 - 4 \cdot 3(-11)}}{2 \cdot 3}$

$= \frac{0 \pm \sqrt{132}}{6}$

$= \pm\frac{2\sqrt{33}}{6}$

$= \pm\frac{\sqrt{33}}{3}$

$s_1 + s_2 = \frac{\sqrt{33}}{3} + \left(-\frac{\sqrt{33}}{3}\right)$

$= 0$ ✓

$s_1(s_2) = \frac{\sqrt{33}}{3}\left(-\frac{\sqrt{33}}{3}\right)$

$= -\frac{33}{9}$ or $-\frac{11}{3}$ ✓

Page 890 Lesson 6-6

1. $f(x) = -9(x - 7)^2 + 3$
   $(7, 3)$; $x = 7$; down
2. $f(x) = (x + 6)^2 - 1$
   $(-6, -1)$; $x = -6$; up
3. $f(x) = 2(x - 8)^2 - 5$
   $(8, -5)$; $x = 8$; up
4. $f(x) = -(x + 1)^2 + 7$
   $(-1, 7)$; $x = -1$; down

5. $f(x) = -x^2 + 10x - 3$

$= -1(x^2 - 10x) - 3$

$= -(x^2 - 10x + 25) - 3 - (-1)25$

$= -(x - 5)^2 + 22$

$(5, 22)$; $x = 5$; down

6. $f(x) = -2x^2 + 16x + 7$

$= -2(x^2 - 8x) + 7$

$= -2(x^2 - 8x + 16) + 7 - (-2)16$

$= -2(x - 4)^2 + 39$

$(4, 39)$; $x = 4$; down

7. $f(x) = 3x^2 + 9x + 8$

$= 3(x^2 + 9x) + 8$

$= 3\left(x^2 + 3x + \frac{9}{4}\right) + 8 - 3\left(\frac{9}{4}\right)$

$= 3\left(x + \frac{3}{2}\right)^2 + \frac{5}{4}$

$\left(-\frac{3}{2}, \frac{5}{4}\right)$; $x = -\frac{3}{2}$; up

8. $f(x) = 8x^2 - 3x + 1$

$= 8\left(x^2 - \frac{3}{8}x\right) + 1$

$= 8\left(x^2 - \frac{3}{8}x + \frac{9}{256}\right) + 1 - 8\left(\frac{9}{256}\right)$

$= 8\left(x - \frac{3}{16}\right)^2 + \frac{23}{32}$

$\left(\frac{3}{16}, \frac{23}{32}\right)$; $x = \frac{3}{16}$; up

9. $f(x) = \frac{3}{4}x^2 - 6x - 5$

$= \frac{3}{4}(x^2 - 8x) - 5$

$= \frac{3}{4}(x^2 - 8x + 16) - 5 - \frac{3}{4}(16)$

$= \frac{3}{4}(x - 4)^2 - 17$

$(4, -17)$; $x = 4$; up

10. $f(x) = x^2 - 2x + 4$

$= (x^2 - 2x) + 4$

$= (x^2 - 2x + 1) + 4 - 1$

$= (x - 1)^2 + 3$

$(1, 3)$; $x = 1$; up

11. $f(x) = -3x^2 + 18x$

$= -3(x^2 - 6x)$

$= -3(x^2 - 6x + 9) - (-3)9$

$= -3(x - 3)^2 + 27$

$(3, 27)$; $x = 3$; down

12. $f(x) = -2x^2 - 40x + 10$

$= -2(x^2 + 20x) + 10$

$= -2(x^2 + 20x + 100) + 10 - (-2)(100)$

$= -2(x + 10)^2 + 210$

$(-10, 210)$; $x = -10$; down

13. $f(x) = 2x^2 - 8x + 9$

$= 2(x^2 - 4x) + 9$

$= 2(x^2 - 4x + 4) + 9 - 2(4)$

$= 2(x - 2)^2 + 1$

$(2, 1)$; $x = 2$; up

14. $f(x) = \frac{1}{3}x^2 + 2x + 7$

$= \frac{1}{3}(x^2 + 6x) + 7$

$= \frac{1}{3}(x^2 + 6x + 9) + 7 - \frac{1}{3}(9)$

$= \frac{1}{3}(x + 3)^2 + 4$

$(-3, 4)$; $x = -3$; up

15. $f(x) = x^2 + 6x + 9$
$= (x^2 + 6x) + 9$
$= (x^2 + 6x + 9) + 9 - 9$
$= (x + 3)^2$
$(-3, 0)$; $x = -3$; up

16. $f(x) = x^2 + 3x + 6$
$= (x^2 + 3x) + 6$
$= \left(x^2 + 3x + \frac{9}{4}\right) + 6 - \frac{9}{4}$
$= \left(x + \frac{3}{2}\right)^2 + \frac{15}{4}$
$\left(-\frac{3}{2}, \frac{15}{4}\right)$; $x = -\frac{3}{2}$; up

17. $f(x) = 2x^2 + 8x + 9$
$= 2(x^2 + 4x) + 9$
$= 2(x^2 + 4x + 4) + 9 - 2(4)$
$= 2(x + 2)^2 + 1$
$(-2, 1)$; $x = -2$; up

18. $f(x) = x^2 - 8x + 9$
$= (x^2 - 8x) + 9$
$= (x^2 - 8x + 16) + 9 - 16$
$= (x - 4)^2 - 7$
$(4, -7)$; $x = 4$; up

19. $f(x) = -x^2 - 10x + 10$
$= -1(x^2 + 10x) + 10$
$= -1(x^2 + 10x + 25) + 10 - (-1)25$
$= -1(x + 5)^2 + 35$
$(-5, 35)$; $x = -5$; down

20. $f(x) = -\frac{2}{3}x^2 + 4x - 3$
$= -\frac{2}{3}(x^2 - 6x) - 3$
$= -\frac{2}{3}(x^2 - 6x + 9) - 3 - \left(-\frac{2}{3}\right)(9)$
$= -\frac{2}{3}(x - 3)^2 + 3$
$(3, 3)$; $x = 3$; down

21. $f(x) = -2x^2 - 8x - 1$
$= -2(x^2 + 4x) - 1$
$= -2(x^2 + 4x + 4) - 1 - (-2)(4)$
$= -2(x + 2)^2 + 7$
$(-2, 7)$; $x = -2$; down

22. $(-1, 5)$: $5 = a(-1)^2 + b(-1) + c \rightarrow 5 = a - b + c$
$(2, -4)$: $-4 = a(2)^2 + b(2) + c \rightarrow -4 = 4a + 2b + c$
$(5, 5)$: $5 = a(5)^2 + b(5) + c \rightarrow 5 = 25a + 5b + c$

$$\begin{array}{r} 5 = a - b + c \\ (-)\ -4 = 4a + 2b + c \\ \hline 9 = -3a - 3b \end{array} \qquad \begin{array}{r} 5 = a - b + c \\ (-)\ 5 = 25a + 5b + c \\ \hline 0 = -24a - 6b \end{array}$$

$$\begin{array}{l} 9 = -3a - 3b \rightarrow \\ 0 = -24a - 6b \rightarrow \end{array} \quad \begin{array}{r} -18 = 6a + 6b \\ (+)\ 0 = -24a - 6b \\ \hline -18 = -18a \\ 1 = a \end{array}$$

$$\begin{array}{r} 0 = -24a - 6b \\ 0 = -24(1) - 6b \\ 24 = -6b \\ -4 = b \end{array} \qquad \begin{array}{l} 5 = a - b + c \\ 5 = 1 - (-4) + c \\ 0 = c \end{array}$$

$f(x) = x^2 - 4x$ or
$f(x) = (x^2 - 4x + 4) - 4$
$= (x - 2)^2 - 4$

23. $(-3, 1)$: $1 = a(-3)^2 + b(-3) + c \rightarrow 1 = 9a - 3b + c$
$(-2, -1)$: $-1 = a(-2)^2 + b(-2) + c \rightarrow -1 = 4a - 2b + c$
$(-1, -7)$: $-7 = a(-1)^2 + b(-1) + c \rightarrow -7 = a - b + c$

$$\begin{array}{r} 1 = 9a - 3b + c \\ (-)\ -1 = 4a - 2b + c \\ \hline 2 = 5a - b \end{array} \qquad \begin{array}{r} -1 = 4a - 2b + c \\ (-)\ -7 = a - b + c \\ \hline 6 = 3a - b \end{array}$$

$$\begin{array}{r} 2 = 5a - b \\ (-)\ 6 = 3a - b \\ \hline -4 = 2a \\ -2 = a \end{array}$$

$$\begin{array}{r} 6 = 3a - b \\ 6 = 3(-2) - b \\ 6 = -6 - b \\ 12 = -b \\ -12 = b \end{array} \qquad \begin{array}{r} -7 = a - b + c \\ -7 = -2 - (-12) + c \\ -7 = 10 + c \\ -17 = c \end{array}$$

$f(x) = -2x^2 - 12x - 17$ or
$f(x) = -2(x^2 - 6x) - 17$
$= -2(x^2 - 6x + 9) - 17 - (-2)(9)$
$= -2(x - 3)^2 + 1$

24. $(-5, -3)$: $-3 = a(-5)^2 + b(-5) + c \rightarrow -3 = 25a - 5b + c$
$(-1, 5)$: $5 = a(-1)^2 + b(-1) + c \rightarrow 5 = a - b + c$
$(0, 9.5)$: $9.5 = a(0)^2 + b(0) + c \rightarrow 9.5 = c$

$$\begin{array}{r} -3 = 25a - 5b + c \\ -3 = 25a - 5b + 9.5 \\ -12.5 = 25a - 5b \end{array} \qquad \begin{array}{r} 5 = a - b + c \\ 5 = a - b + 9.5 \\ -4.5 = a - b \end{array}$$

$$\begin{array}{l} -12.5 = 25a - 5b \rightarrow \\ -4.5 = a - b \rightarrow \end{array} \quad \begin{array}{r} -12.5 = 25a - 5b \\ (+)\ 22.5 = -5a + 5b \\ \hline 10 = 20a \\ \frac{1}{2} = a \end{array}$$

$$\begin{array}{r} -4.5 = a - b \\ -4.5 = \frac{1}{2} - b \\ -5 = -b \\ 5 = b \end{array}$$

$f(x) = \frac{1}{2}x^2 + 5x + 9.5$ or
$f(x) = \frac{1}{2}(x^2 + 10x) + 9.5$
$= \frac{1}{2}(x^2 + 10x + 25) + 9.5 - \frac{1}{2}(25)$
$= \frac{1}{2}(x + 5)^2 - 3$

25. $(0, -8)$: $-8 = a \cdot 0^2 + b \cdot 0 + c \rightarrow -8 = c$
$(2, -2)$: $-2 = a \cdot 2^2 + b \cdot 2 + c \rightarrow -2 = 4a + 2b + c$
$(4, -8)$: $-8 = a \cdot 4^2 + b \cdot 4 + c \rightarrow -8 = 16a + 4b + c$

$$\begin{array}{r} -2 = 4a + 2b + c \\ -2 = 4a + 2b - 8 \\ 6 = 4a + 2b \end{array} \qquad \begin{array}{r} -8 = 16a + 4b + c \\ -8 = 16a + 4b - 8 \\ 0 = 16a + 4b \end{array}$$

$$\begin{array}{l} 6 = 4a + 2b \rightarrow \\ 0 = 16a + 4b \rightarrow \end{array} \quad \begin{array}{r} -12 = -8a - 4b \\ (+)\ 0 = 16a + 4b \\ \hline -12 = 8a \\ -\frac{3}{2} = a \end{array}$$

$$\begin{array}{r} 0 = 16a + 4b \\ 0 = 16\left(-\frac{3}{2}\right) + 4b \\ 0 = -24 + 4b \\ 24 = 4b \\ 6 = b \end{array}$$

$f(x) = -\frac{3}{2}x^2 + 6x - 8$ or
$f(x) = -\frac{3}{2}(x^2 - 4x) - 8$
$= -\frac{3}{2}(x^2 - 4x + 4) - 8 - \left(-\frac{3}{2}\right)(4)$
$= -\frac{3}{2}(x - 2)^2 - 2$

26. $(3, 0)$: $0 = a \cdot 3^2 + b \cdot 3 + c \quad \rightarrow 0 = 9a + 3b + c$
$(0, -9)$: $-9 = a \cdot 0^2 + b \cdot 0 + c \rightarrow -9 = c$
$(5, -4)$: $-4 = a \cdot 5^2 + b \cdot 5 + c \quad \rightarrow -4 = 25a + 5b + c$

$$\begin{array}{ll} 0 = 9a + 3b + c & -4 = 25a + 5b + c \\ 0 = 9a + 3b - 9 & -4 = 25a + 5b - 9 \\ 9 = 9a + 3b & 5 = 25a + 5b \end{array}$$

$$\begin{array}{lcr} 9 = 9a + 3b & \rightarrow & 45 = 45a + 15b \\ 5 = 25a + 5b & \rightarrow & (+)\ -15 = -75a - 15b \\ \hline & & 30 = -30a \\ & & -1 = a \end{array}$$

$$\begin{aligned} 9 &= 9a + 3b \\ 9 &= 9(-1) + 3b \\ 18 &= 3b \\ 6 &= b \end{aligned}$$

$f(x) = -1x^2 + 6x - 9$ or
$f(x) = -1(x^2 - 6x) - 9$
$= -1(x^2 - 6x + 9) - 9 - (-1)9$
$= -(x - 3)^2$

27. $(-5, 5)$: $5 = a(-5)^2 + b(-5) + c \rightarrow 5 = 25a - 5b + c$
$(0, 0)$: $0 = a(0)^2 + b(0) + c \quad \rightarrow 0 = c$
$(5, 5)$: $5 = a(5)^2 + b(5) + c \quad \rightarrow 5 = 25a + 5b + c$
Substitute $c = 0$:

$$\begin{array}{lr} 5 = 25a - 5b + c \rightarrow & 5 = 25a - 5b \\ 5 = 25a + 5b + c \rightarrow & (+)\ 5 = 25a + 5b \\ \hline & 10 = 50a \\ & \frac{1}{5} = a \end{array}$$

$$\begin{aligned} 5 &= 25a - 5b \\ 5 &= 25\left(\tfrac{1}{5}\right) - 5b \\ 5 &= 5 - 5b \\ 0 &= -5b \\ 0 &= b \end{aligned}$$

$f(x) = \frac{1}{5}x^2 + 0x + 0$
$= \frac{1}{5}x^2$

28. $(0, -5)$: $-5 = a(0)^2 + b(0) + c \quad \rightarrow -5 = c$
$(-1, -7)$: $-7 = a(-1)^2 + b(-1) + c \rightarrow -7 = a - b + c$
$(-4, -1)$: $-1 = a(-4)^2 + b(-4) + c \rightarrow -1 = 16a - 4b + c$

$$\begin{array}{ll} -7 = a - b + c & -1 = 16a - 4b + c \\ -7 = a - b + -5 & -1 = 16a - 4b + -5 \\ -2 = a - b & 4 = 16a - 4b \end{array}$$

$$\begin{array}{lcr} -2 = a - b & \rightarrow & 8 = -4a + 4b \\ 4 = 16a - 4b & \rightarrow & (+)4 = 16a - 4b \\ \hline & & 12 = 12a \\ & & 1 = a \end{array}$$

$$\begin{aligned} -2 &= a - b \\ -2 &= 1 - b \\ -3 &= -b \\ 3 &= b \end{aligned}$$

$f(x) = x^2 + 3x - 5$ or
$f(x) = (x^2 + 3x) - 5$
$= \left(x^2 + 3x + \frac{9}{4}\right) - 5 - \frac{9}{4}$
$= \left(x + \frac{3}{2}\right)^2 - \frac{29}{4}$

29. $(1, 5)$: $5 = a(1)^2 + b(1) + c \quad \rightarrow 5 = a + b + c$
$(4, -4)$: $-4 = a(4)^2 + b(4) + c \rightarrow -4 = 16a + 4b + c$
$(0, 0)$: $0 = a(0)^2 + b(0) + c \quad \rightarrow 0 = c$
Substitute $c = 0$:

$$\begin{array}{lr} 5 = a + b + c \quad \rightarrow & -20 = -4a - 4b \\ -4 = 16a + 4b + c \rightarrow & (+)\ -4 = 16a + 4b \\ \hline & -24 = 12a \\ & -2 = a \end{array}$$

$$\begin{aligned} 5 &= a + b \\ 5 &= -2 + b \\ 7 &= b \end{aligned}$$

$f(x) = -2x^2 + 7x$ or
$f(x) = -2\left(x^2 - \frac{7}{2}x\right)$
$= -2\left(x^2 - \frac{7}{2}x + \frac{49}{16}\right) - (-2)\frac{49}{16}$
$= -2\left(x - \frac{7}{4}\right)^2 + \frac{49}{8}$

30. $(1, 1.2)$: $1.2 = a(1)^2 + b(1) + c \quad \rightarrow 1.2 = a + b + c$
$(0, 0.8)$: $0.8 = a(0)^2 + b(0) + c \quad \rightarrow 0.8 = c$
$(-2, 3.6)$: $3.6 = a(-2)^2 + b(-2) + c \rightarrow 3.6 = 4a - 2b + c$

$$\begin{array}{ll} 1.2 = a + b + c & 3.6 = 4a - 2b + c \\ 1.2 = a + b + 0.8 & 3.6 = 4a - 2b + 0.8 \\ 0.4 = a + b & 2.8 = 4a - 2b \end{array}$$

$$\begin{array}{lcr} 0.4 = a + b & \rightarrow & 0.8 = 2a + 2b \\ 2.8 = 4a - 2b & \rightarrow & (+)2.8 = 4a - 2b \\ \hline & & 3.6 = 6a \\ & & 0.6 = a \end{array}$$

$$\begin{aligned} 0.4 &= a + b \\ 0.4 &= 0.6 + b \\ -0.2 &= b \end{aligned}$$

$f(x) = 0.6x^2 - 0.2x + 0.8$ or
$f(x) = \frac{3}{5}x^2 - \frac{1}{5}x + \frac{4}{5}$ or
$f(x) = \frac{3}{5}\left(x^2 - \frac{1}{3}x\right) + \frac{4}{5}$
$= \frac{3}{5}\left(x^2 - \frac{1}{3}x + \frac{1}{36}\right) + \frac{4}{5} - \left(\frac{3}{5}\right)\left(\frac{1}{36}\right)$
$= \frac{3}{5}\left(x - \frac{1}{6}\right)^2 + \frac{47}{60}$

Page 891 Lesson 6-7

1. $y \le 5x^2 + 3x - 2$

x	y
-2	12
-1	0
0	-2
1	6

Test $(0, -3)$:
$y \le 5x^2 + 3x - 2$
$-3 \overset{?}{\le} 5(0)^2 + 3(0) - 2$
$-3 \le -2$, true

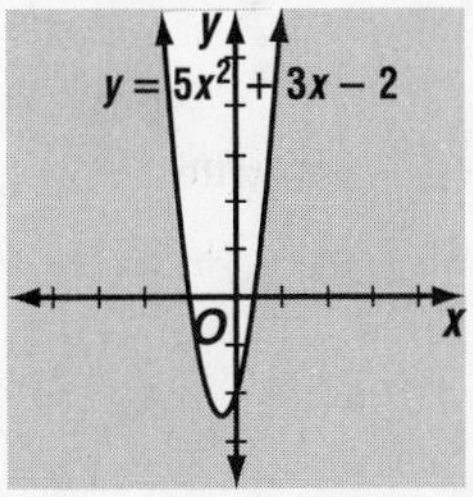

2. $y \geq \frac{1}{2}x^2 - 4x$

x	y
0	0
4	−8
8	0

Test: (0, 4)

$y \geq \frac{1}{2}x^2 - 4x$

$4 \overset{?}{\geq} \frac{1}{2}(0)^2 - 4(0)$

$4 \geq 0$, true

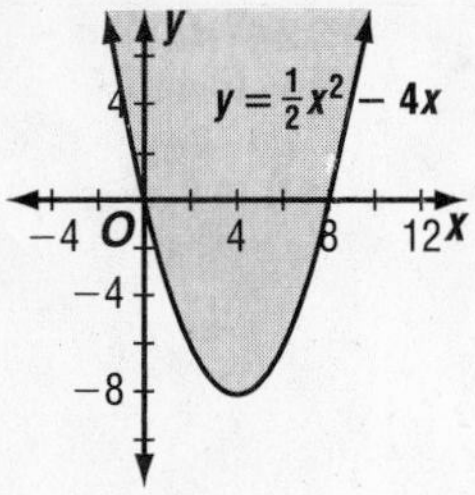

3. $y > -3x^2 + 2$

x	y
−2	−10
−1	−1
0	2
1	−1

Test: (0, 3)

$y > -3x^2 + 2$

$3 \overset{?}{>} -3(0)^2 + 2$

$3 > 2$, true

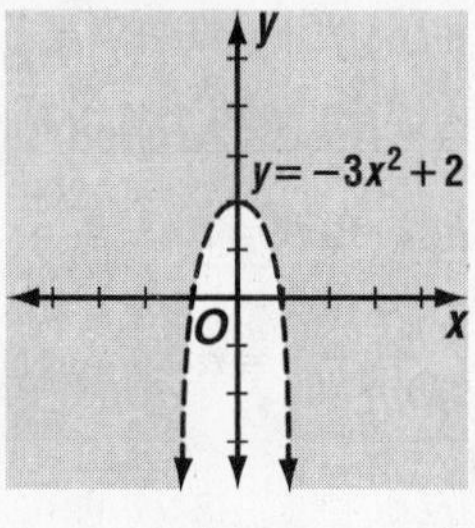

4. $y \geq -x^2 - x + 3$

x	y
−3	−3
−1	3
1	1

Test: (0, 4)

$y \geq -x^2 - x + 3$

$4 \overset{?}{\geq} -0^2 - 0 + 3$

$4 \geq 3$, true

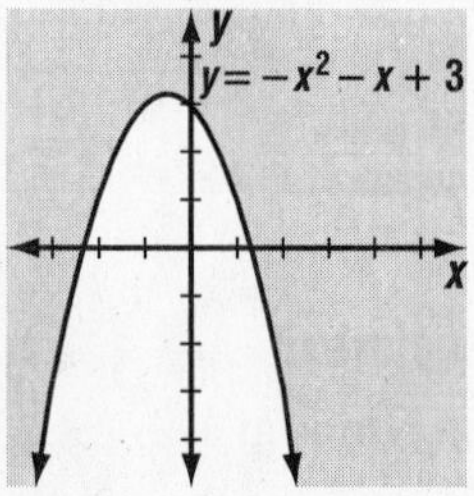

5. $y \leq \frac{3}{8}x^2 + 2x - 1$

x	y
−6	0.5
−4	−3
−2	−3.5
0	−1

Test: (0, −4)

$y \leq \frac{3}{8}x^2 + 2x - 1$

$-4 \overset{?}{\leq} \frac{3}{8}(0)^2 + 2(0) - 1$

$-4 \leq -1$, true

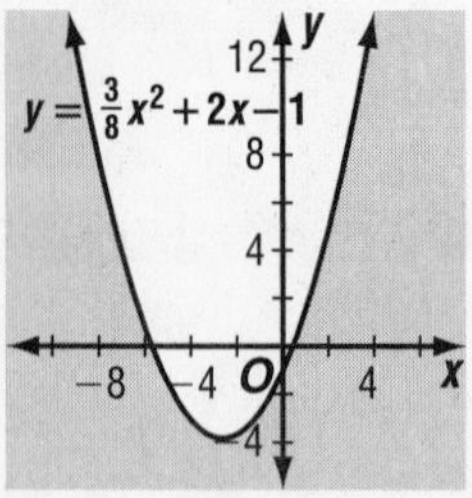

6. $y \leq -5x^2 + 2x - 3$

x	y
−1	−10
0	−3
1	−6

Test: (0, −5)

$y \leq -5x^2 + 2x - 3$

$-5 \overset{?}{\leq} -5(0)^2 + 2(0) - 3$

$-5 \leq -3$, true

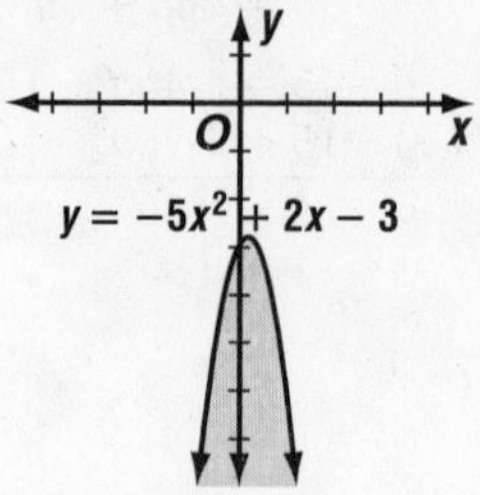

7. $y > 4x^2 + x$

x	y
−1	3
0	0
1	5

Test: (0, 2)

$y > 4x^2 + x$

$2 \overset{?}{>} 4(0)^2 + 0$

$2 > 0$, true

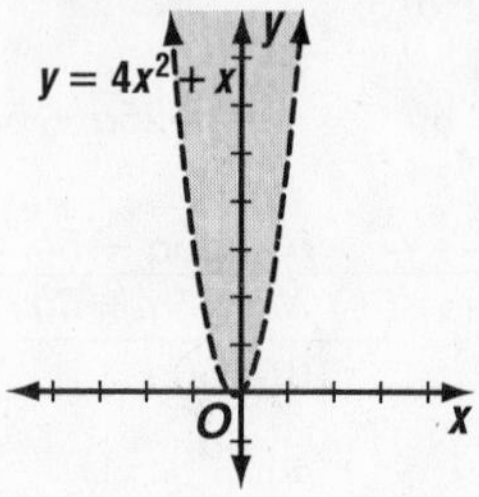

8. $y \geq -x^2 - 7$

x	y
−1	−8
0	−7
1	−8
2	−11

Test: (0, 0)

$y \geq -x^2 - 7$

$0 \overset{?}{\geq} -0^2 - 7$

$0 \geq -7$, true

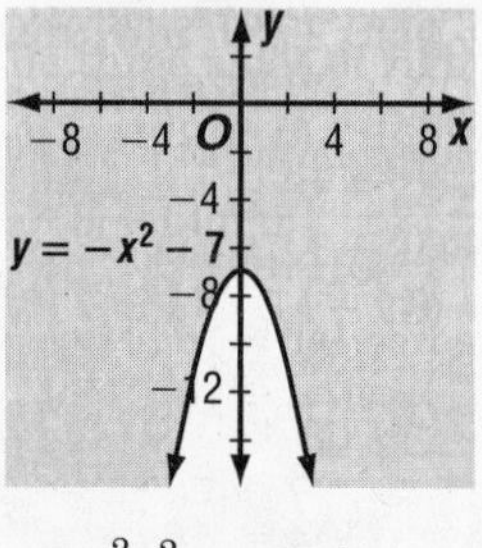

9. $y < -\frac{2}{3}x^2 + x + 6$

x	y
−2	$1\frac{1}{3}$
0	6
1	$6\frac{1}{3}$
2	$5\frac{1}{3}$

Test: (0, 0)

$y < -\frac{2}{3}x^2 + x + 6$

$0 \overset{?}{<} -\frac{2}{3}(0)^2 + 0 + 6$

$0 < 6$, true

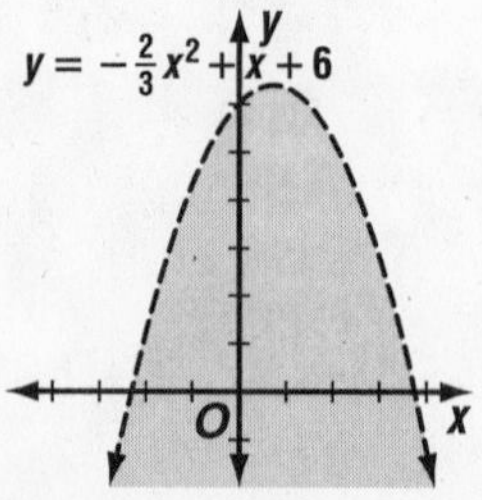

10. $(x + 1)(x - 1) < 0$

$x + 1 < 0$ and $x - 1 > 0$ or $x + 1 > 0$ and $x - 1 < 0$

$x < -1 \qquad x > 1 \qquad x > -1 \qquad x < 1$

$\varnothing$ or $\{x \mid -1 < x < 1\}$

11. $(2x + 3)(5x - 1) \geq 0$

$2x + 3 \geq 0$ and $5x - 1 \geq 0$

$2x \geq -3 \qquad 5x \geq 1$

$x \geq -\frac{3}{2} \qquad x \geq \frac{1}{5}$

or

$2x + 3 \leq 0$ and $5x - 1 \leq 0$

$2x \leq -3 \qquad 5x \leq 1$

$x \leq -\frac{3}{2} \qquad x \leq \frac{1}{5}$

$x \geq \frac{1}{5}$ or $x \leq -\frac{3}{2}$

$\{x \mid x \leq -\frac{3}{2} \text{ or } x \geq \frac{1}{5}\}$

12. $x^2 - 2x - 8 \leq 0$

$(x - 4)(x + 2) \leq 0$

$x - 4 \leq 0$ and $x + 2 \geq 0$

$x \leq 4 \qquad x \geq -2$

or

$x - 4 \geq 0$ and $x + 2 \leq 0$

$x \geq 4 \qquad x \leq -2$

$\{x \mid -2 \leq x \leq 4\}$ or $\varnothing$

13. $-x^2 - 5x - 6 > 0$

$x^2 + 5x + 6 < 0$

$(x + 3)(x + 2) < 0$

$x + 3 < 0$ and $x + 2 > 0$

$x < -3 \qquad x > -2$

or

$x + 3 > 0$ and $x + 2 < 0$

$x > -3 \qquad x < -2$

$\varnothing$ or $\{x \mid -3 < x < -2\}$

14. $-3x^2 \geq 5$

$x^2 \leq -\frac{5}{3}$

$\varnothing$

15. $20x^2 + 9x + 1 < 0$

$(4x + 1)(5x + 1) < 0$

$4x + 1 < 0$ and $5x + 1 > 0$

$4x < -1 \qquad 5x > -1$

$x < -\frac{1}{4} \qquad x > -\frac{1}{5}$

or

$4x + 1 > 0$ and $5x + 1 < 0$

$4x > -1 \qquad 5x < -1$

$x > -\frac{1}{4} \qquad x < -\frac{1}{5}$

$\varnothing$ or $\left\{x \mid -\frac{1}{4} < x < -\frac{1}{5}\right\}$

16. $2x^2 \geq 5x + 12$

$2x^2 - 5x - 12 \geq 0$

$(2x + 3)(x - 4) \geq 0$

$2x + 3 \geq 0$ and $x - 4 \geq 0$

$2x \geq -3 \qquad x \geq 4$

$x \geq -\frac{3}{2} \qquad x \geq 4$

or

$2x + 3 \leq 0$ and $x - 4 \leq 0$

$2x \leq -3 \qquad x \leq 4$

$x \leq -\frac{3}{2} \qquad x \leq 4$

$x \geq 4$ or $x \leq -\frac{3}{2}$

$\left\{x \mid x \leq -\frac{3}{2} \text{ or } x \geq 4\right\}$

17. $x^2 + 3x + 4 > 0$

x	y
−3	4
−2	2
−1	2
0	4

{all real numbers}

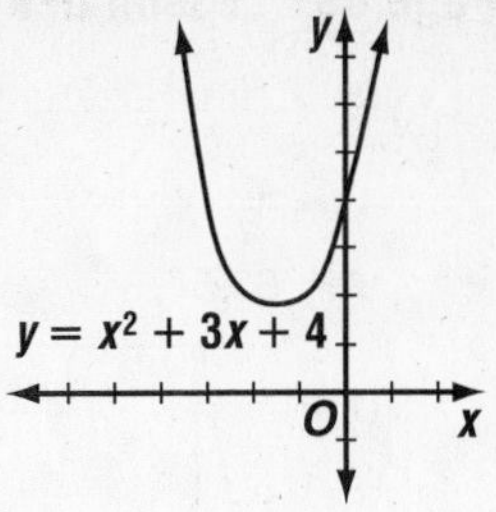

18. $2x - x^2 \leq -15$

$-x^2 + 2x + 15 \leq 0$

$x^2 - 2x - 15 \geq 0$

$(x - 5)(x + 3) \geq 0$

$x - 5 \geq 0$ and $x + 3 \geq 0$

$x \geq 5 \qquad x \geq -3$

or

$x - 5 \leq 0$ and $x + 3 \leq 0$

$x \leq 5 \qquad x \leq -3$

$x \geq 5$ or $x \leq -3$

$\{x \mid x \leq -3 \text{ or } x \geq 5\}$

19. $13x - 28x^2 + 6 < 0$

$-28x^2 + 13x + 6 < 0$

$28x^2 - 13x - 6 > 0$

$(7x + 2)(4x - 3) > 0$

$7x + 2 > 0$ and $4x - 3 > 0$

$7x > -2 \qquad 4x > 3$

$x > -\frac{2}{7} \qquad x > \frac{3}{4}$

or

$7x + 2 < 0$ and $4x - 3 < 0$

$7x < -2 \qquad 4x < 3$

$x < -\frac{2}{7} \qquad x < \frac{3}{4}$

$x > \frac{3}{4}$ or $x < -\frac{2}{7}$

$\left\{x \mid x < -\frac{2}{7} \text{ or } x > \frac{3}{4}\right\}$

20. $3x^2 \leq 36$

$x^2 \leq 12$

$x^2 - 12 \leq 0$

$(x - 2\sqrt{3})(x + 2\sqrt{3}) \leq 0$

$x - 2\sqrt{3} \leq 0$ and $x + 2\sqrt{3} \geq 0$

$x \leq 2\sqrt{3} \qquad x \geq -2\sqrt{3}$

or

$x - 2\sqrt{3} \geq 0$ and $x + 2\sqrt{3} \leq 0$

$x \geq 2\sqrt{3} \qquad x \leq -2\sqrt{3}$

$\{x \mid -2\sqrt{3} \leq x \leq 2\sqrt{3}\}$ or $\varnothing$

21. $x - x^2 \geq 1$

$-x^2 + x - 1 \geq 0$

$x^2 - x + 1 \leq 0$

x	y
−1	3
0	1
1	1
2	3

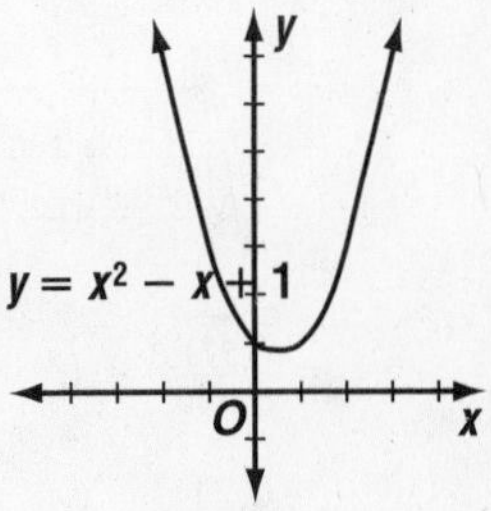

$\varnothing$

Page 891 Lesson 6-8

1. $\bar{x} = \dfrac{86 + 71 + 74 + 65 + 45 + 42 + 76}{7}$

$= \dfrac{459}{7}$

≈ 65.57

$$SD = \sqrt{\frac{\left[\begin{array}{c}(86 - 65.57)^2 + (71 - 65.57)^2 + \\ (74 - 65.57)^2 + (65 - 65.57)^2 + \\ (45 - 65.57)^2 + (42 - 65.57)^2 + (76 - 65.57)^2\end{array}\right]}{7}}$$

$$= \sqrt{\frac{\left[\begin{array}{c}417.3849 + 29.4849 + 71.0649 + \\ 0.3249 + 423.1249 + 555.5449 + 108.7849\end{array}\right]}{7}}$$

$$= \sqrt{\frac{1605.7143}{7}}$$

≈ 15.15

2. $\bar{x} = \dfrac{16 + 20 + 15 + 14 + 24 + 23 + 25 + 10 + 19}{9}$

$= \dfrac{166}{9}$

≈ 18.44

$$SD = \sqrt{\frac{\left[\begin{array}{c}(16 - 18.44)^2 + (20 - 18.44)^2 + (15 - 18.44)^2 + \\ (14 - 18.44)^2 + (24 - 18.44)^2 + (23 - 18.44)^2 + \\ (25 - 18.44)^2 + (10 - 18.44)^2 + (9 - 18.44)^2\end{array}\right]}{9}}$$

$$= \sqrt{\frac{\left[\begin{array}{c}5.9536 + 2.4336 + 11.8336 + 19.7136 + \\ 30.9136 + 20.7936 + 43.0336 + 71.2336 + 89.1136\end{array}\right]}{9}}$$

$$= \sqrt{\frac{295.0224}{9}}$$

≈ 5.73

3. $\bar{x} = \dfrac{2(18) + 5(24) + 3(16) + 4(22) + 13 + 17 + 20 + 7 + 5 + 4}{20}$

$= \dfrac{358}{20}$

≈ 17.9

$$SD = \sqrt{\frac{\left[\begin{array}{c}2(18 - 17.9)^2 + 5(24 - 17.9)^2 + 3(16 - 17.9)^2 + \\ 4(22 - 17.9)^2 + (13 - 17.9)^2 + (17 - 17.9)^2 + \\ (20 - 17.9)^2 + (7 - 17.9)^2 + (5 - 17.9)^2 + (4 - 17.9)^2\end{array}\right]}{20}}$$

$$= \sqrt{\frac{\left[\begin{array}{c}0.02 + 186.05 + 10.83 + 67.24 + 24.01 \\ + 0.81 + 4.41 + 118.81 + 166.41 + 193.21\end{array}\right]}{20}}$$

$$= \sqrt{\frac{771.8}{20}}$$

≈ 6.21

4. $\bar{x} = [364 + 2(305) + 217 + 331 + 2(311) + 352 + 319 + 272 + 2(238) + 2(226) + 220 + 215 + 160 + 123 + 4 + 24 + 99] \div 21$

$= 4860 \div 21$

≈ 231.43

(Continued next column)

$$SD = \sqrt{\frac{\left[\begin{array}{c}(364 - 231.43)^2 + 2(305 - 231.43)^2 + \\ (217 - 231.43)^2 + (331 - 231.43)^2 + 2(311 - 231.43)^2 + \\ (352 - 231.43)^2 + (319 - 231.43)^2 + (272 - 231.43)^2 + \\ 2(238 - 231.43)^2 + 2(226 - 231.43)^2 + (220 - 231.43)^2 + \\ (215 - 231.43)^2 + (160 - 231.43)^2 + (123 - 231.43)^2 + \\ (4 - 231.43)^2 + (24 - 231.43)^2 + (99 - 231.43)^2\end{array}\right]}{21}}$$

$$= \sqrt{\frac{\left[\begin{array}{c}17574.8049 + 10825.0898 + 208.2249 + 9914.1849 + \\ 12662.7698 + 14537.1249 + 7668.5049 + 1645.9249 + \\ 86.3298 + 58.9698 + 130.6449 + 269.9449 + 5102.2449 + \\ 11757.0649 + 51724.4049 + 43027.2049 + 17537.7049\end{array}\right]}{21}}$$

$$= \sqrt{\frac{204{,}731.1429}{21}}$$

≈ 98.74

5. $\bar{x} = [4(55) + 6(50) + 2(65) + 2(45) + 3(35) + 4(40) + 2(70) + 90 + 30 + 75 + 60] \div 27$

$= 1400 \div 27$

≈ 51.85

$$SD = \sqrt{\frac{\left[\begin{array}{c}4(55 - 51.85)^2 + \\ 6(50 - 51.85)^2 + 2(65 - 51.85)^2 + 2(45 - 51.85)^2 + \\ 3(35 - 51.85)^2 + 4(40 - 51.85)^2 + 2(70 - 51.85)^2 + \\ (90 - 51.85)^2 + (30 - 51.85)^2 + (75 - 51.85)^2 + (60 - 51.85)^2\end{array}\right]}{27}}$$

$$= \sqrt{\frac{\left[\begin{array}{c}39.69 + 20.535 + 345.845 + \\ 93.845 + 851.7675 + 561.69 + 658.845 + \\ 1455.4255 + 477.4225 + 535.9225 + 66.4225\end{array}\right]}{27}}$$

$$= \sqrt{\frac{5107.4105}{27}}$$

≈ 13.75

6. $\bar{x} = [2(13.01) + 13.03 + 13.09 + 2(13.17) + 13.21 + 13.22 + 13.23 + 13.25 + 13.26 + 2(13.27) + 2(13.30) + 13.31 + 13.33 + 13.41 + 13.43 + 2(13.44) + 13.45 + 13.46 + 13.48 + 13.49 + 13.50 + 3(13.51) + 13.54 + 13.55 + 13.58 + 13.59 + 13.61 + 13.63 + 13.65] \div 36$

$= 481.21 \div 36$

≈ 13.37

$$SD = \sqrt{\frac{\left[\begin{array}{c}2(13.01 - 13.37)^2 + (13.03 - 13.37)^2 + \\ (13.09 - 13.37)^2 + 2(13.17 - 13.37)^2 + (13.21 - 13.37)^2 + \\ (13.22 - 13.37)^2 + (13.23 - 13.37)^2 + (13.25 - 13.37)^2 + \\ (13.26 - 13.37)^2 + 2(13.27 - 13.37)^2 + 2(13.30 - 13.37)^2 + \\ (13.31 - 13.37)^2 + (13.33 - 13.37)^2 + (13.41 - 13.37)^2 + \\ (13.43 - 13.37)^2 + 2(13.44 - 13.37)^2 + (13.45 - 13.37)^2 + \\ (13.46 - 13.37)^2 + (13.48 - 13.37)^2 + (13.49 - 13.37)^2 + \\ (13.50 - 13.37)^2 + 3(13.51 - 13.37)^2 + (13.54 - 13.37)^2 + \\ (13.55 - 13.37)^2 + (13.58 - 13.37)^2 + (13.59 - 13.37)^2 + \\ (13.61 - 13.37)^2 + (13.63 - 13.37)^2 + (13.65 - 13.37)^2\end{array}\right]}{36}}$$

$$= \sqrt{\frac{\left[\begin{array}{c}0.2592 + 0.1156 + 0.0784 + 0.08 + 0.0256 + \\ 0.0225 + 0.0196 + 0.0144 + 0.0121 + 0.02 + 0.0098 + \\ 0.0036 + 0.0016 + 0.0016 + 0.0036 + 0.0098 + 0.0064 + \\ 0.0081 + 0.0121 + 0.0144 + 0.0169 + 0.0588 + 0.0289 + \\ 0.0324 + 0.0441 + 0.0484 + 0.0576 + 0.0676 + 0.0784\end{array}\right]}{36}}$$

$$= \sqrt{\frac{1.1515}{36}}$$

≈ 0.18

7. $\bar{x} = [7 + 8 + 10 + 2(11) + 12 + 2(13) + 2(14) + 2(15) + 2(16) + 2(17) + 2(19) + 2(20) + 3(21) + 2(22) + 3(23) + 24 + 25] \div 30$
$= 512 \div 30$
≈ 17.07

$$SD = \sqrt{\frac{\begin{bmatrix}(7-17.07)^2+(8-17.07)^2+\\(10-17.07)^2+2(11-17.07)^2+(12-17.07)^2+\\2(13-17.07)^2+2(14-17.07)^2+2(15-17.07)^2+\\2(16-17.07)^2+2(17-17.07)^2+2(19-17.07)^2+\\2(20-17.07)^2+2(21-17.07)^2+2(22-17.07)^2+\\3(23-17.07)^2+(24-17.07)^2+(25-17.07)^2\end{bmatrix}}{30}}$$

$$= \sqrt{\frac{\begin{bmatrix}101.4049+82.2649+49.9849+\\73.6898+25.7049+33.1298+18.8498+\\8.5698+2.2898+0.0098+7.4498+17.1698+\\30.8898+48.6098+105.4947+48.0249+62.8849\end{bmatrix}}{30}}$$

$$= \sqrt{\frac{716.4221}{30}}$$

≈ 4.89

Page 891 Lesson 6-9

1. $7.5 - 0.5 = 7$ $\quad 7.5 + 0.5 = 8$
$7.5 - 2(0.5) = 6.5$ $\quad 7.5 + 2(0.5) = 8.5$
$7.5 - 3(0.5) = 6$ $\quad 7.5 + 3(0.5) = 9$

1a. $34 + 34 = 68$; 68%

1b. 34%

1c. $13.5 + 34 + 34 + 13.5 + 2 + 0.5 = 97.5$; 97.5%

1d. $2 + 13.5 + 34 + 34 + 13.5 = 97$; 97%
$100 \cdot 0.97 = 97$

2. $22 - 7.5 = 14.5$ $\quad 22 + 7.5 = 29.5$
$22 - 2(7.5) = 7$ $\quad 22 + 2(7.5) = 37$
$22 - 3(7.5) = -0.5$ $\quad 22 + 3(7.5) = 44.5$

2a. $34 + 13.5 + 2 + 0.5 = 50$;
50%; $3000 \cdot 0.50 = 1500$

2b. $13.5 + 34 + 34 = 81.5$; 81.5%;
$3000 \cdot 0.815 = 2445$

2c. $2 + 0.5 = 2.5$; 2.5%

3. $510 - 80 = 430$ $\quad 510 + 80 = 590$
$510 - 2(80) = 350$ $\quad 510 + 2(80) = 670$
$510 - 3(80) = 270$ $\quad 510 + 3(80) = 750$

3a. $34 + 13.5 + 2 + 0.5 = 50$; 50%;
$50{,}000 \cdot 0.50 = 25{,}000$

3b. $34 + 34 = 68$; 68%; $50{,}000 \cdot 0.68 = 34{,}000$

3c. $13.5 + 34 + 34 + 13.5 + 2 + 0.5 = 97.5$; 97.5%

3d. 0.5%

Page 892 Lesson 7-1

1. $d = \sqrt{(x_2 - x_1)^2 + (y_2 - y_1)^2}$
$= \sqrt{(5 - 3)^2 + (7 - 19)^2}$
$= \sqrt{4 + 144}$
$= \sqrt{148}$
$= 2\sqrt{37}$

2. $d = \sqrt{(x_2 - x_1)^2 + (y_2 - y_1)^2}$
$= \sqrt{(-2 - 5)^2 + (-1 - 3)^2}$
$= \sqrt{49 + 16}$
$= \sqrt{65}$

3. $d = \sqrt{(x_2 - x_1)^2 + (y_2 - y_1)^2}$
$= \sqrt{(-3 - 7)^2 + [15 - (-8)]^2}$
$= \sqrt{100 + 529}$
$= \sqrt{629}$

4. $d = \sqrt{(x_2 - x_1)^2 + (y_2 - y_1)^2}$
$= \sqrt{[6 - (-4)]^2 + [-3 - (-9)]^2}$
$= \sqrt{100 + 36}$
$= \sqrt{136}$
$= 2\sqrt{34}$

5. $d = \sqrt{(x_2 - x_1)^2 + (y_2 - y_1)^2}$
$= \sqrt{(3.89 - 4.04)^2 + [-0.38 - (-0.18)]^2}$
$= \sqrt{0.0225 + 0.04}$
$= \sqrt{0.0625}$
$= 0.25$

6. $d = \sqrt{(x_2 - x_1)^2 + (y_2 - y_1)^2}$
$= \sqrt{[5\sqrt{3} - (-11\sqrt{3})]^2 + [2\sqrt{2} - (-4\sqrt{2})]^2}$
$= \sqrt{768 + 72}$
$= \sqrt{840}$
$= 2\sqrt{210}$

7. $\left(\frac{x_1 + x_2}{2}, \frac{y_1 + y_2}{2}\right) = \left(\frac{7 + (-11)}{2}, \frac{-3 + 13}{2}\right)$
$= \left(\frac{-4}{2}, \frac{10}{2}\right)$
$= (-2, 5)$

8. $\left(\frac{x_1 + x_2}{2}, \frac{y_1 + y_2}{2}\right) = \left(\frac{16 + (-7)}{2}, \frac{29 + 2}{2}\right)$
$= \left(\frac{9}{2}, \frac{31}{2}\right)$
$= (4.5, 15.5)$

9. $\left(\frac{x_1 + x_2}{2}, \frac{y_1 + y_2}{2}\right) = \left(\frac{43 + (-78)}{2}, \frac{-18 + (-32)}{2}\right)$
$= \left(\frac{-35}{2}, \frac{-50}{2}\right)$
$= (-17.5, -25)$

10. $\left(\frac{x_1 + x_2}{2}, \frac{y_1 + y_2}{2}\right) = \left(\frac{-7.54 + 4.89}{2}, \frac{3.42 + (-9.28)}{2}\right)$
$= \left(\frac{-2.65}{2}, \frac{-5.86}{2}\right)$
$= (-1.325, -2.93)$

11. $\left(\frac{x_1 + x_2}{2}, \frac{y_1 + y_2}{2}\right) = \left(\frac{-8 + 0.34}{2}, \frac{4.19 + 20}{2}\right)$
$= \left(\frac{-7.66}{2}, \frac{24.19}{2}\right)$
$= (-3.83, 12.095)$

12. $\left(\frac{x_1 + x_2}{2}, \frac{y_1 + y_2}{2}\right) = \left(\frac{684 + 528}{2}, \frac{-239 + (-735)}{2}\right)$
$= \left(\frac{1212}{2}, \frac{-974}{2}\right)$
$= (606, -487)$

13. $d = \sqrt{(x_2 - x_1)^2 + (y_2 - y_1)^2}$

$25 = \sqrt{(p - 8)^2 + (3 - 27)^2}$

$625 = (p - 8)^2 + 576$

$49 = (p - 8)^2$

$\pm 7 = p - 8$

$\pm 7 + 8 = p$

$p = 8 + 7 = 15$ or $p = 8 - 7 = 1$

14. $d = \sqrt{(x_2 - x_1)^2 + (y_2 - y_1)^2}$

$25 = \sqrt{[5 - (-2)]^2 + (p - 6)^2}$

$625 = 49 + (p - 6)^2$

$576 = (p - 6)^2$

$\pm 24 = p - 6$

$6 \pm 24 = p$

$p = 6 + 24 = 30$ or $p = 6 - 24 = -18$

15. $d = \sqrt{(x_2 - x_1)^2 + (y_2 - y_1)^2}$

$25 = \sqrt{(15 - p)^2 + [-8 - (-8)]^2}$

$625 = (15 - p)^2$

$\pm 25 = 15 - p$

$-15 \pm 25 = -p$

$15 \pm 25 = p$

$p = 15 + 25 = 40$ or $p = 15 - 25 = -10$

16. $d = \sqrt{(x_2 - x_1)^2 + (y_2 - y_1)^2}$

$25 = \sqrt{(-17 - 7)^2 + (-7 - p)^2}$

$625 = 576 + (-7 - p)^2$

$49 = (-7 - p)^2$

$\pm 7 = -7 - p$

$7 \pm 7 = -p$

$-7 \pm 7 = p$

$p = -7 + 7 = 0$ or $p = -7 - 7 = -14$

17. $d = \sqrt{(x_2 - x_1)^2 + (y_2 - y_1)^2}$

$25 = \sqrt{[8 - (-3)]^2 + [p - (-5)]^2}$

$625 = 121 + (p + 5)^2$

$504 = (p + 5)^2$

$\pm 22.45 \approx p + 5$

$-5 \pm 22.45 \approx p$

$p \approx -5 + 22.45 \approx 17.45$ or $p \approx -5 - 22.45 \approx -27.45$

18. $d = \sqrt{(x_2 - x_1)^2 + (y_2 - y_1)^2}$

$25 = \sqrt{(p - 25)^2 + (-16 - 13)^2}$

$625 = (p - 25)^2 + 841$

$-216 = (p - 25)^2$

$\pm\sqrt{-216} = p - 25$

no real solution

19. $d = \sqrt{(x_2 - x_1)^2 + (y_2 - y_1)^2}$

$25 = \sqrt{(-6.8 - 3.7)^2 + [p - (-8.9)]^2}$

$625 = 110.25 + (p + 8.9)^2$

$514.75 = (p + 8.9)^2$

$\pm 22.69 \approx p + 8.9$

$-8.9 \pm 22.69 \approx p$

$p \approx -8.9 + 22.69 \approx 13.79$ or $p \approx -8.9 - 22.69 \approx -31.59$

20. $d = \sqrt{(x_2 - x_1)^2 + (y_2 - y_1)^2}$

$25 = \sqrt{[p - (-29)]^2 + [-28 - (-35)]^2}$

$625 = (p + 29)^2 + 49$

$576 = (p + 29)^2$

$\pm 24 = p + 29$

$-29 \pm 24 = p$

$p = -29 + 24 = -5$ or $p = -29 - 24 = -53$

21. $(x, y) = \left(\frac{x_1 + x_2}{2}, \frac{y_1 + y_2}{2}\right)$

$(-13, 2) = \left(\frac{5 + x}{2}, \frac{-16 + y}{2}\right)$

$-13 = \frac{5 + x}{2}$ and $2 = \frac{-16 + y}{2}$

$-26 = 5 + x$ $\quad$ $4 = -16 + y$

$-31 = x$ $\quad$ $20 = y$

$B(-31, 20)$

22. $(x, y) = \left(\frac{x_1 + x_2}{2}, \frac{y_1 + y_2}{2}\right)$

$(7.3, 2.8) = \left(\frac{-8.9 + x}{2}, \frac{-3.4 + y}{2}\right)$

$7.3 = \frac{-8.9 + x}{2}$ and $2.8 = \frac{-3.4 + y}{2}$

$14.6 = -8.9 + x$ $\quad$ $5.6 = -3.4 + y$

$23.5 = x$ $\quad$ $9 = y$

$A(23.5, 9)$

23. $(x, y) = \left(\frac{x_1 + x_2}{2}, \frac{y_1 + y_2}{2}\right)$

$\left(\frac{5}{8}, \frac{7}{12}\right) = \left(\frac{\frac{2}{3} + x}{2}, \frac{\frac{5}{4} + y}{2}\right)$

$\frac{5}{8} = \frac{\frac{2}{3} + x}{2}$ and $\frac{7}{12} = \frac{\frac{5}{4} + y}{2}$

$10 = \frac{16}{3} + 8x$ $\quad$ $14 = 15 + 12y$

$\frac{14}{3} = 8x$ $\quad$ $-1 = 12y$

$\frac{7}{12} = x$ $\quad$ $-\frac{1}{12} = y$

$B\left(\frac{7}{12}, -\frac{1}{12}\right)$

Page 892 Lesson 7-2

1. $y + \frac{3}{4} = x^2$

$y = x^2 - \frac{3}{4}$

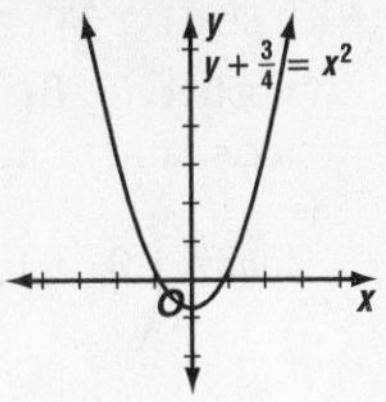

vertex: $\left(0, -\frac{3}{4}\right)$

axis of symmetry: $x = 0$

focus: $\left(0, -\frac{3}{4} + \frac{1}{4(1)}\right)$ or $\left(0, -\frac{1}{2}\right)$

directrix: $y = -\frac{3}{4} - \frac{1}{4(1)}$ or -1

direction of opening: upward, since $a > 0$

length of the latus rectum: $\left|\frac{1}{1}\right|$ or 1 units

2. $\frac{y}{5} = (x + 2)^2$

$y = 5(x + 2)^2$

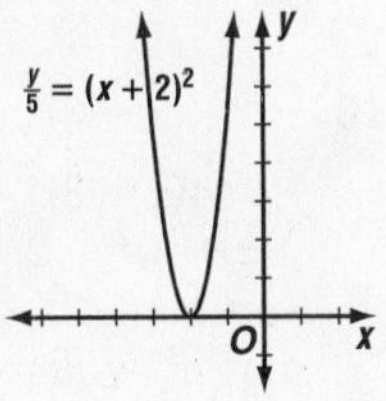

vertex: $(-2, 0)$

axis of symmetry: $x = -2$

focus: $\left(-2, 0 + \frac{1}{4(5)}\right)$ or $\left(-2, \frac{1}{20}\right)$

directrix: $y = 0 - \frac{1}{4(20)}$ or $-\frac{1}{20}$

direction of opening: upward, since $a > 0$

length of the latus rectum: $\left|\frac{1}{5}\right|$ or $\frac{1}{5}$ units

3. $4(y + 2) = 3(x - 1)^2$

$y + 2 = \frac{3}{4}(x - 1)^2$

$y = \frac{3}{4}(x - 1)^2 - 2$

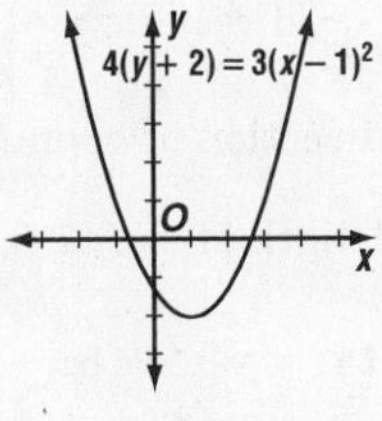

vertex: $(1, -2)$

axis of symmetry: $x = 1$

focus: $\left(1, -2 + \frac{1}{4\left(\frac{3}{4}\right)}\right)$ or

$\left(1, -1\frac{2}{3}\right)$

directrix: $y = -2 - \frac{1}{4\left(\frac{3}{4}\right)}$ or $-2\frac{1}{3}$

direction of opening: upward, since $a > 0$

length of the latus rectum: $\left|\frac{1}{\frac{3}{4}}\right|$ or $\frac{4}{3}$ units

4. $5x + 3y^2 = 15$

$5x = -3y^2 + 15$

$x = -\frac{3}{5}y^2 + 3$

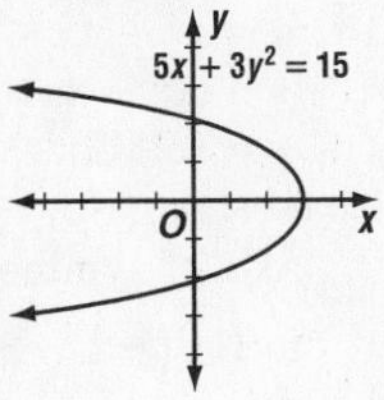

vertex: $(3, 0)$

axis of symmetry: $y = 0$

focus: $\left(3 + \frac{1}{4\left(-\frac{3}{5}\right)}, 0\right)$ or $\left(2\frac{7}{12}, 0\right)$

directrix: $x = 3 - \frac{1}{4\left(-\frac{3}{5}\right)}$ or $3\frac{5}{12}$

direction of opening: left, since $a < 0$

length of the latus rectum: $\left|\frac{1}{\frac{-3}{5}}\right|$ or $\frac{5}{3}$ units

5. $y = 2x^2 - 8x + 7$

$y = 2(x^2 - 4x) + 7$

$y = 2(x^2 - 4x + 4) + 7 - 2(4)$

$y = 2(x - 2)^2 - 1$

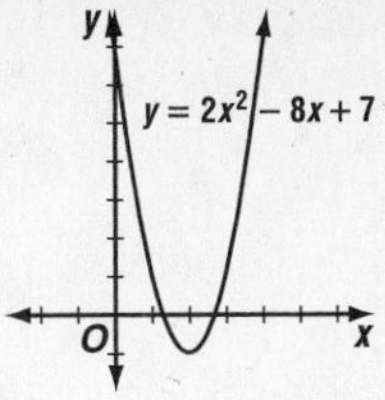

vertex: $(2, -1)$

axis of symmetry: $x = 2$

focus: $\left(2, -1 + \frac{1}{4(2)}\right)$ or $\left(2, -\frac{7}{8}\right)$

directrix: $y = -1 - \frac{1}{4(2)}$ or $-1\frac{1}{8}$

direction of opening: upward, since $a > 0$

length of the latus rectum: $\left|\frac{1}{2}\right|$ or $\frac{1}{2}$ unit

6. $x = 2y^2 - 8y + 7$

$x = 2(y^2 - 4y) + 7$

$x = 2(y^2 - 4y + 4) + 7 - 2(4)$

$x = 2(y - 2)^2 - 1$

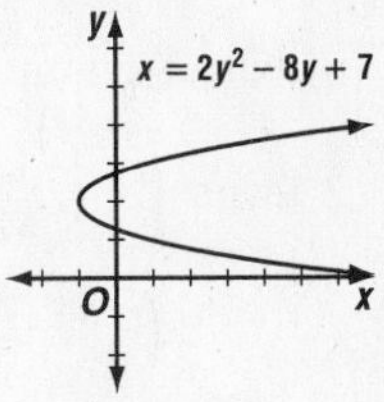

vertex: $(-1, 2)$

axis of symmetry: $y = 2$

focus: $\left(-1 + \frac{1}{4(2)}, 2\right)$ or $\left(-\frac{7}{8}, 2\right)$

directrix: $x = -1 - \frac{1}{4(2)}$ or $-1\frac{1}{8}$

direction of opening: right, since $a > 0$

length of the latus rectum: $\left|\frac{1}{2}\right|$ or $\frac{1}{2}$ unit

7. $3(x - 8)^2 = 5(y + 3)$

$\frac{3}{5}(x - 8)^2 = y + 3$

$\frac{3}{5}(x - 8)^2 - 3 = y$

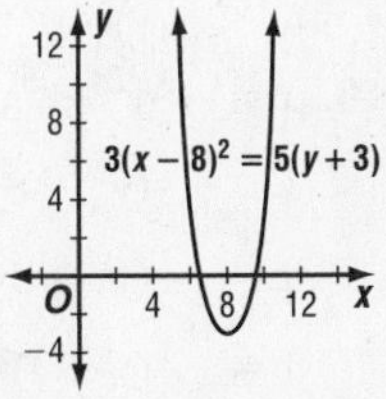

vertex: $(8, -3)$

axis of symmetry: $x = 8$

focus: $\left(8, -3 + \frac{1}{4\left(\frac{3}{5}\right)}\right)$ or

$\left(8, -2\frac{7}{12}\right)$

directrix: $y = -3 - \frac{1}{4\left(\frac{3}{5}\right)}$ or $-3\frac{5}{12}$

direction of opening: upward, since $a > 0$

length of the latus rectum: $\left|\frac{1}{\frac{3}{5}}\right|$ or $\frac{5}{3}$ units

8. $x = 3(y + 4)^2 + 1$

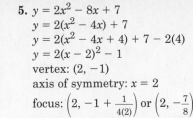

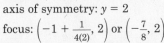

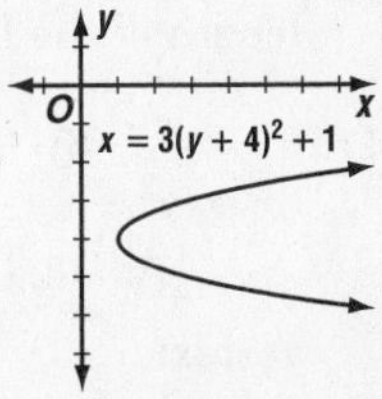

vertex: $(1, -4)$

axis of symmetry: $y = -4$

focus: $\left(1 + \frac{1}{4(3)}, -4\right)$ or $\left(1\frac{1}{2}, -4\right)$

directrix: $x = 1 - \frac{1}{4(3)}$ or $\frac{11}{12}$

direction of opening: right, since $a > 0$

length of the latus rectum: $\left|\frac{1}{3}\right|$ or $\frac{1}{3}$ unit

9. $8y + 5x^2 + 15x + 9 = 0$

$$8y + 9 = -5x^2 - 15x$$
$$8y + 9 = -5(x^2 + 3x)$$
$$8y + 9 = -5\left(x^2 + 3x + \frac{9}{4}\right) + 5\left(\frac{9}{4}\right)$$
$$8y + 9 = -5\left(x + \frac{3}{2}\right)^2 + \frac{45}{4}$$
$$8y = -5\left(x + \frac{3}{2}\right)^2 + \frac{45}{4} - 9$$
$$8y = -5\left(x + \frac{3}{2}\right)^2 + \frac{9}{4}$$
$$y = -\frac{5}{8}\left(x + \frac{3}{2}\right)^2 + \frac{9}{32}$$

vertex: $\left(-\frac{3}{2}, \frac{9}{32}\right)$

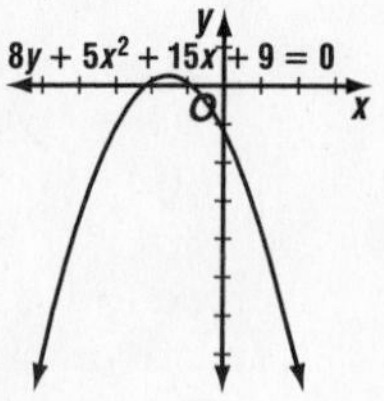

axis of symmetry: $x = -\frac{3}{2}$

focus: $\left(-\frac{3}{2}, \frac{9}{32} + \frac{1}{4\left(-\frac{5}{8}\right)}\right)$ or $\left(-\frac{3}{2}, -\frac{19}{160}\right)$

directrix: $y = \frac{9}{32} - \frac{1}{4\left(-\frac{5}{8}\right)}$ or $\frac{109}{160}$

direction of opening: downward, since $a < 0$

length of the latus rectum: $\left|\frac{1}{-\frac{5}{8}}\right|$ or $\frac{8}{5}$ units

10. $x = -\frac{1}{5}y^2 + \frac{8}{5}y - 7$

$$x = -\frac{1}{5}(y^2 - 8y) - 7$$
$$x = -\frac{1}{5}(y^2 - 8y + 16) - 7 + \frac{1}{5}(16)$$
$$x = -\frac{1}{5}(y - 4)^2 - \frac{19}{5}$$

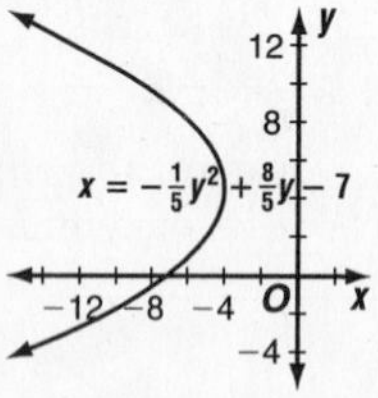

vertex: $\left(-\frac{19}{5}, 4\right)$

axis of symmetry: $y = 4$

focus: $\left(-\frac{19}{5} + \frac{1}{4\left(-\frac{1}{5}\right)}, 4\right)$ or $\left(-\frac{101}{20}, 4\right)$

directrix: $x = -\frac{19}{5} - \frac{1}{4\left(-\frac{1}{5}\right)}$ or $-\frac{51}{20}$

direction of opening: left, since $a < 0$

length of the latus rectum: $\left|\frac{1}{-\frac{1}{5}}\right|$ or 5 units

11. $6x = y^2 - 6y + 39$

$$6x = (y^2 - 6y + 9) + 39 - 9$$
$$x = \frac{1}{6}(y - 3)^2 + 5$$

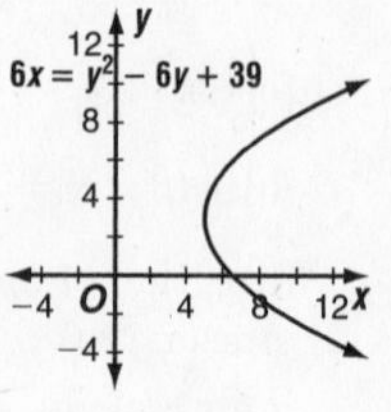

vertex: $(5, 3)$

axis of symmetry: $y = 3$

focus: $\left(5 + \frac{1}{4\left(\frac{1}{6}\right)}, 3\right)$ or $\left(6\frac{1}{2}, 3\right)$

directrix: $x = 5 - \frac{1}{4\left(\frac{1}{6}\right)}$ or $3\frac{1}{2}$

direction of opening: right, since $a > 0$

length of the latus rectum: $\left|\frac{1}{\frac{1}{6}}\right|$ or 6 units

12. $-8y = x^2$

$$y = -\frac{1}{8}x^2$$

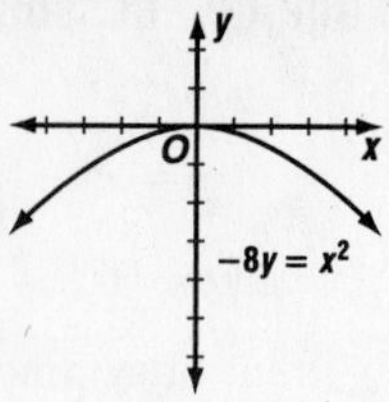

vertex: $(0, 0)$

axis of symmetry: $x = 0$

focus: $\left(0, 0 + \frac{1}{4\left(-\frac{1}{8}\right)}\right)$ or $(0, -2)$

directrix: $y = 0 - \frac{1}{4\left(-\frac{1}{8}\right)}$ or 2

direction of opening: downward, since $a < 0$

length of the latus rectum: $\left|\frac{1}{-\frac{1}{8}}\right|$ or 8 units

13. $(x + 3)^2 = \frac{1}{4}(y + 2)$

$$4(x + 3)^2 = y + 2$$
$$4(x + 3)^2 - 2 = y$$

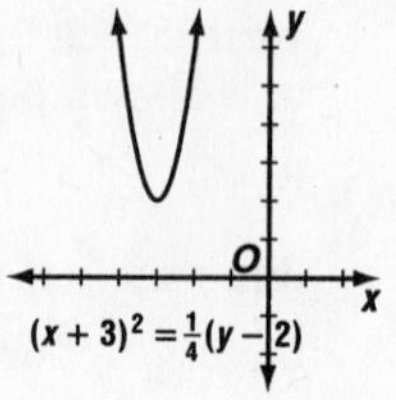

vertex: $(-3, -2)$

axis of symmetry: $x = -3$

focus: $\left(-3, -2 + \frac{1}{4(4)}\right)$ or $\left(-3, -1\frac{15}{16}\right)$

directrix: $y = -2 - \frac{1}{4(4)}$ or $-2\frac{1}{16}$

direction of opening: upward, since $a > 0$

length of the latus rectum: $\left|\frac{1}{4}\right|$ or $\frac{1}{4}$ unit

14. $y = x^2 - 6x + 33$

$$y = (x^2 - 6x + 9) + 33 - 9$$
$$y = (x - 3)^2 + 24$$

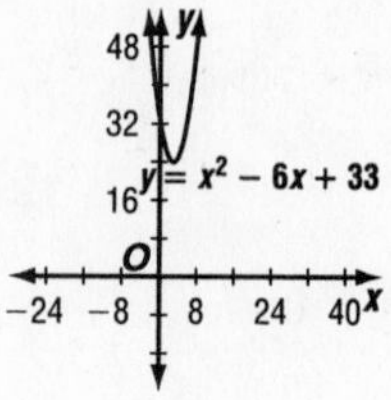

vertex: $(3, 24)$

axis of symmetry: $x = 3$

focus: $\left(3, 24 + \frac{1}{4(1)}\right)$ or $\left(3, 24\frac{1}{4}\right)$

directrix: $y = 24 - \frac{1}{4(1)}$ or $23\frac{3}{4}$

direction of opening: upward, since $a > 0$

length of the latus rectum: $\left|\frac{1}{1}\right|$ or 1 unit

15. $y = x^2 + 4x + 1$

$$y = (x^2 + 4x + 4) + 1 - 4$$
$$y = (x + 2)^2 - 3$$

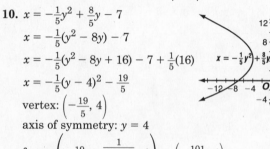

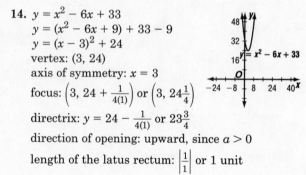

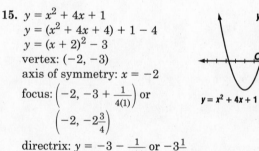

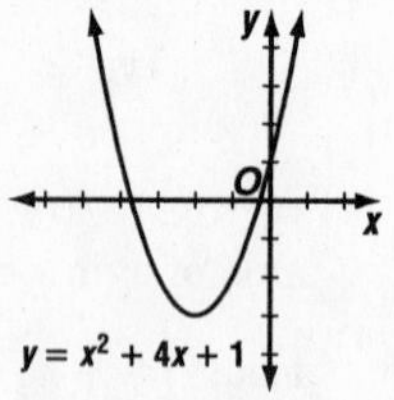

vertex: $(-2, -3)$

axis of symmetry: $x = -2$

focus: $\left(-2, -3 + \frac{1}{4(1)}\right)$ or $\left(-2, -2\frac{3}{4}\right)$

directrix: $y = -3 - \frac{1}{4(1)}$ or $-3\frac{1}{4}$

direction of opening: upward, since $a > 0$

length of the latus rectum: $\left|\frac{1}{1}\right|$ or 1 unit

16. $4(x-2)=(y+3)^2$

$x-2=\frac{1}{4}(y+3)^2$

$x=\frac{1}{4}(y+3)^2+2$

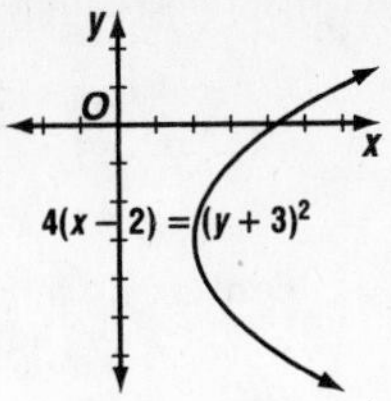

vertex: $(2, -3)$

axis of symmetry: $y=-3$

focus: $\left(2+\frac{1}{4\left(\frac{1}{4}\right)}, -3\right)$ or $(3, -3)$

directrix: $x=2-\frac{1}{4\left(\frac{1}{4}\right)}$ or 1

direction of opening: right, since $a>0$

length of the latus rectum: $\left|\frac{1}{\frac{1}{4}}\right|$ or 4 units

17. $(y-8)^2=-4(x-4)$

$-\frac{1}{4}(y-8)^2=x-4$

$-\frac{1}{4}(y-8)^2+4=x$

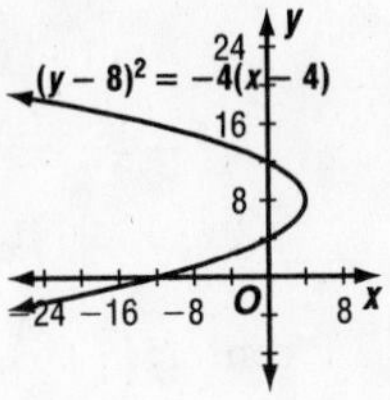

vertex: $(4, 8)$

axis of symmetry: $y=8$

focus: $\left(4+\frac{1}{4\left(-\frac{1}{4}\right)}, 8\right)$ or $(3, 8)$

directrix: $x=4-\frac{1}{4\left(-\frac{1}{4}\right)}$ or 5

direction of opening: left, since $a<0$

length of the latus rectum: $\left|\frac{1}{-\frac{1}{4}}\right|$ or 4 units

18. $6x=y^2+4y+4$

$x=\frac{1}{6}(y+2)^2$

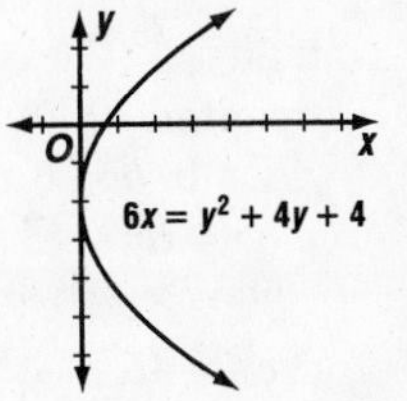

vertex: $(0, -2)$

axis of symmetry: $y=-2$

focus: $\left(0+\frac{1}{4\left(\frac{1}{6}\right)}, -2\right)$ or $\left(\frac{3}{2}, -2\right)$

directrix: $x=0-\frac{1}{4\left(\frac{1}{6}\right)}$ or $-\frac{3}{2}$

direction of opening: right, since $a>0$

length of the latus rectum: $\left|\frac{1}{\frac{1}{6}}\right|$ or 6 units

Page 892 Lesson 7–3

1. $(x-h)^2+(y-k)^2=r^2$

   $(x-3)^2+(y-2)^2=5^2$

   $(x-3)^2+(y-2)^2=25$

2. $(x-h)^2+(y-k)^2=r^2$

   $[x-(-5)]^2+(y-8)^2=3^2$

   $(x+5)^2+(y-8)^2=9$

3. $(x-h)^2+(y-k)^2=r^2$

   $(x-1)^2+[y-(-6)]^2=\left(\frac{2}{3}\right)^2$

   $(x-1)^2+(y+6)^2=\frac{4}{9}$

4. $(x-h)^2+(y-k)^2=r^2$

   $(x-0)^2+(y-7)^2=(\sqrt{6})^2$

   $x^2+(y-7)^2=6$

5. $(x-h)^2+(y-k)^2=r^2$

   $(x-\sqrt{2})^2+(y-4)^2=9^2$

   $(x-\sqrt{2})^2+(y-4)^2=81$

6. $(x-h)^2+(y-k)^2=r^2$

   $[x-(-8)]^2+[y-(-\sqrt{10})]^2=11^2$

   $(x+8)^2+(y+\sqrt{10})^2=121$

7. $(x-h)^2+(y-k)^2=r^2$

   $(x-0.8)^2+(y-0.5)^2=(0.2)^2$

   $(x-0.8)^2+(y-0.5)^2=0.04$

8. $(x-h)^2+(y-k)^2=r^2$

   $[x-(-9)]^2+(y-0)^2=\left(\frac{5}{7}\right)^2$

   $(x+9)^2+y^2=\frac{25}{49}$

9. $(x-h)^2+(y-k)^2=r^2$

   $(x-4)^2+(y-1)^2=4^2$

   $(x-4)^2+(y-1)^2=16$

10. $x^2+y^2=36$

    center: $(0, 0)$

    radius: $\sqrt{36}$ or 6 units

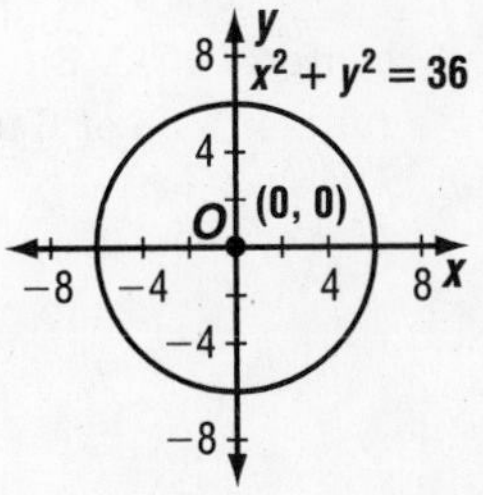

11. $(x-5)^2+(y+4)^2=1$

    center: $(5, -4)$

    radius: $\sqrt{1}$ or 1 unit

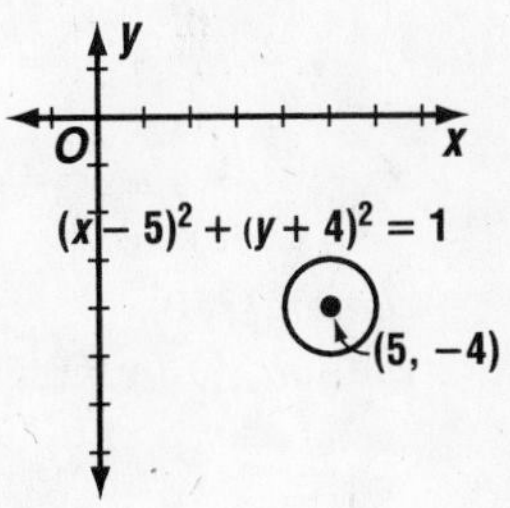

12. $x^2+3x+y^2-5y=\frac{1}{2}$

    $x^2+3x+\frac{9}{4}+y^2-5y+\frac{25}{4}=\frac{1}{2}+\frac{9}{4}-\frac{25}{4}$

    $\left(x+\frac{3}{2}\right)^2+\left(y-\frac{5}{2}\right)^2=\frac{35}{4}$

    center: $\left(-\frac{3}{2}, \frac{5}{2}\right)$

    radius: $\sqrt{\frac{35}{4}}$ or $\frac{\sqrt{35}}{2}$ units

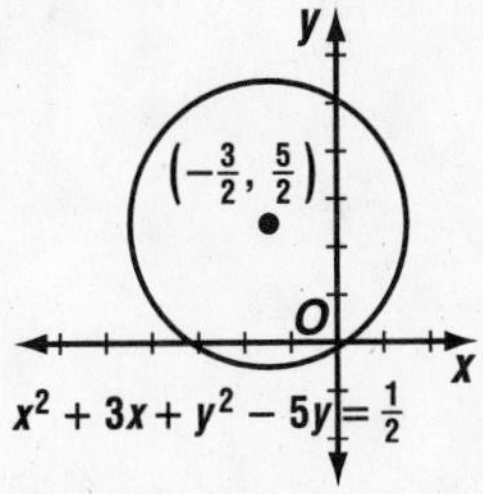

13. $x^2+y^2=14x-24$

    $x^2-14x+y^2=-24$

    $x^2-14x+49+y^2=-24+49$

    $(x-7)^2+y^2=25$

    center: $(7, 0)$

    radius: $\sqrt{25}$ or 5 units

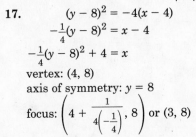

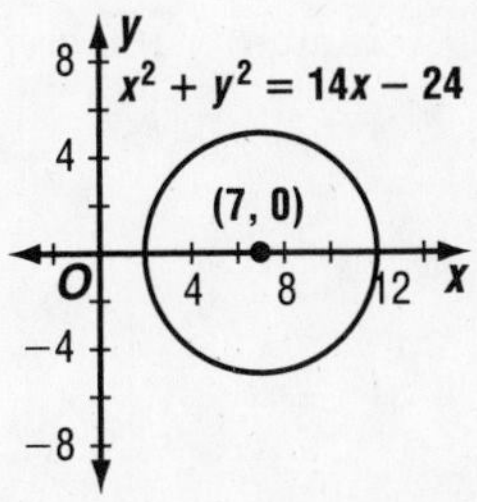

14.

$$x^2 + y^2 = 2(y - x)$$
$$x^2 + y^2 = 2y - 2x$$
$$x^2 + 2x + y^2 - 2y = 0$$
$$x^2 + 2x + 1 + y^2 - 2y + 1 = 1 + 1$$
$$(x + 1)^2 + (y - 1)^2 = 2$$

center: $(-1, 1)$
radius: $\sqrt{2}$ units

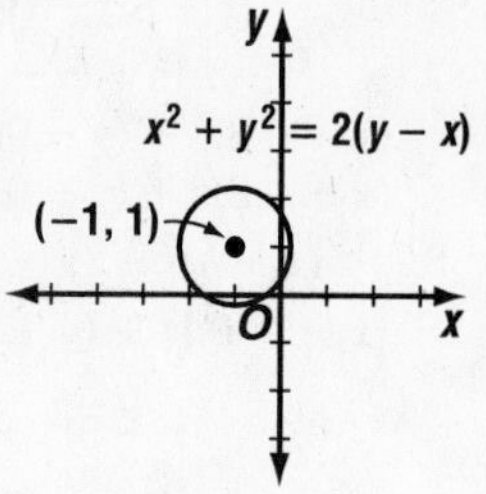

15.

$$x^2 + 10x + (y - \sqrt{3})^2 = 11$$
$$x^2 + 10x + 25 + (y - \sqrt{3})^2 = 11 + 25$$
$$(x + 5)^2 + (y - \sqrt{3})^2 = 36$$

center: $(-5, \sqrt{3})$
radius: $\sqrt{36}$ or 6 units

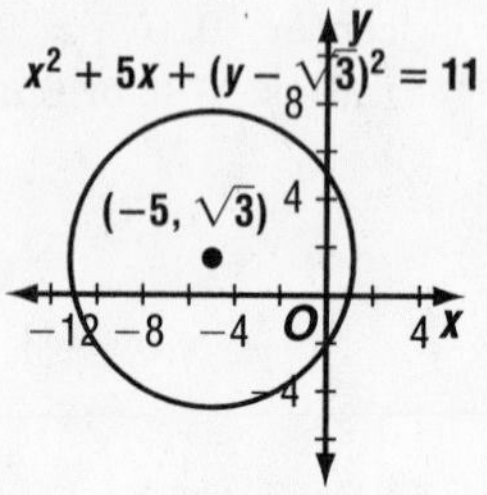

16.

$$x^2 + y^2 = 4x + 9$$
$$x^2 - 4x + y^2 = 9$$
$$x^2 - 4x + 4 + y^2 = 9 + 4$$
$$(x - 2)^2 + y^2 = 13$$

center: $(2, 0)$
radius: $\sqrt{13}$ units

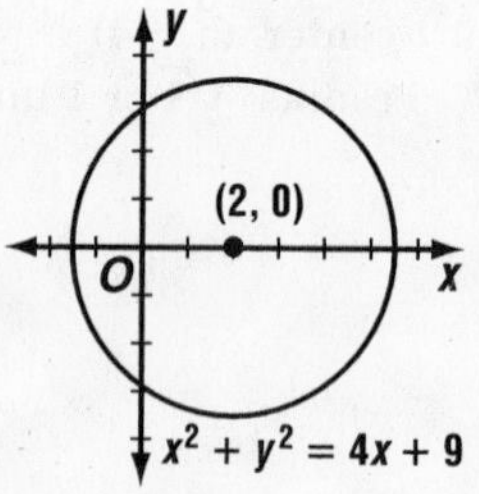

17.

$$x^2 + y^2 + 12x - 10y + 45 = 0$$
$$x^2 + 12x + 36 + y^2 - 10y + 25 = -45 + 36 + 25$$
$$(x + 6)^2 + (y - 5)^2 = 16$$

center: $(-6, 5)$
radius: $\sqrt{16}$ or 4 units

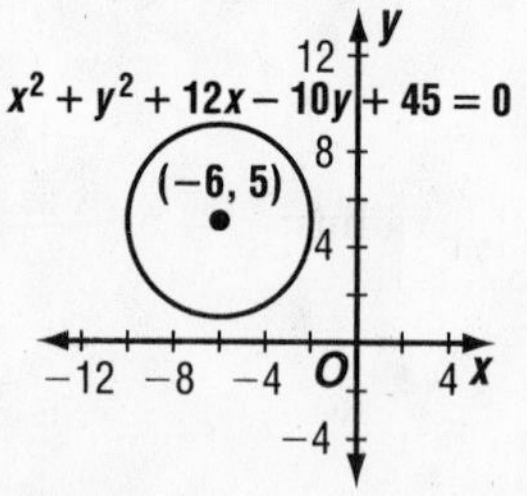

18.

$$x^2 + y^2 - 6x + 4y = 156$$
$$x^2 - 6x + y^2 + 4y = 156$$
$$x^2 - 6x + 9 + y^2 + 4y + 4 = 156 + 9 + 4$$
$$(x - 3)^2 + (y + 2)^2 = 169$$

center: $(3, -2)$
radius: $\sqrt{169}$ or 13 units

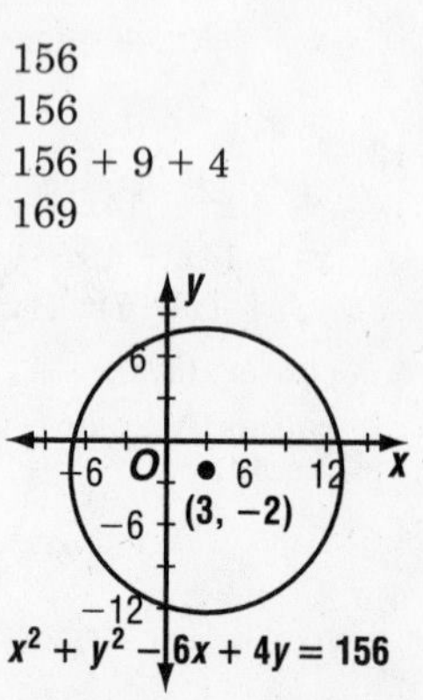

19.

$$x^2 + y^2 - 2(\sqrt{5}x - \sqrt{7}y) = 1$$
$$x^2 - 2\sqrt{5}x + y^2 + 2\sqrt{7}y = 1$$
$$x^2 - 2\sqrt{5}x + 5 + y^2 + 2\sqrt{7}y + 7 = 1 + 5 + 7$$
$$(x - \sqrt{5})^2 + (y + \sqrt{7})^2 = 13$$

center: $(\sqrt{5}, -\sqrt{7})$
radius: $\sqrt{13}$ units

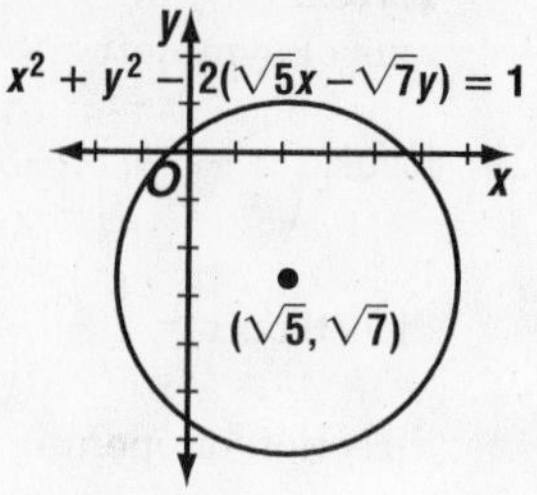

20. $16(x^2 + y^2) - 8(3x + 5y) + 33 = 0$

$$x^2 + y^2 - \frac{1}{2}(3x + 5y) + \frac{33}{16} = 0$$
$$x^2 - \frac{3}{2}x + y^2 - \frac{5}{2}y = -\frac{33}{16}$$
$$x^2 - \frac{3}{2}x + \frac{9}{16} + y^2 - \frac{5}{2}y + \frac{25}{16} = -\frac{33}{16} + \frac{9}{16} + \frac{25}{16}$$
$$\left(x - \frac{3}{4}\right)^2 + \left(y - \frac{5}{4}\right)^2 = \frac{1}{16}$$

center: $\left(\frac{3}{4}, \frac{5}{4}\right)$

radius: $\sqrt{\frac{1}{16}}$ or $\frac{1}{4}$ units

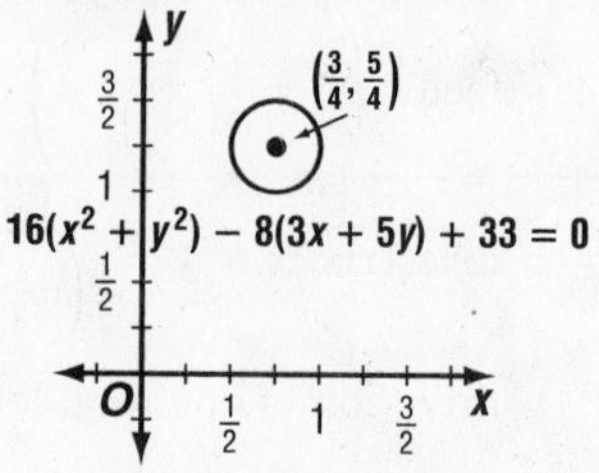

Page 893 Lesson 7-4

1. $\frac{x^2}{36} + \frac{y^2}{81} = 1$

center: $(0, 0)$
$a = 9$, $b = 6$
$b^2 = a^2 - c^2$
$36 = 81 - c^2$
$c^2 = 45$
$c = 3\sqrt{5}$
foci $(0, \pm 3\sqrt{5}$
length of major axis: 2(9) or 18
length of minor axis: 2(6) or 12

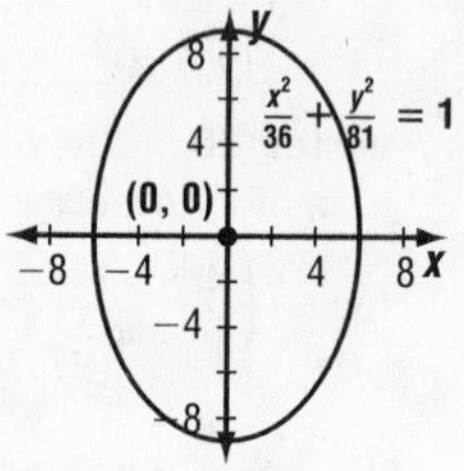

2. $\frac{x^2}{121} + \frac{(y - 5)^2}{16} = 1$

center: $(0, 5)$
$a = 11$, $b = 4$
$b^2 = a^2 - c^2$
$16 = 121 - c^2$
$c^2 = 105$
$c = \sqrt{105}$
foci: $(0 \pm \sqrt{105}, 5)$
length of major axis: 2(11) or 22
length of minor axis: 2(4) or 8

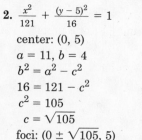

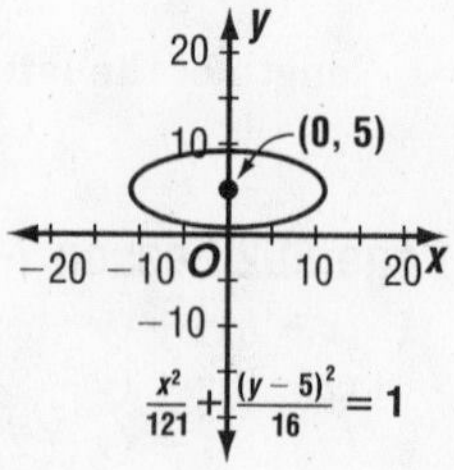

3. $\frac{(x+2)^2}{12} + \frac{(y+1)^2}{16} = 1$

center: $(-2, -1)$
$a = 4$, $b = \sqrt{12}$ or $2\sqrt{3}$
$b^2 = a^2 - c^2$
$12 = 16 - c^2$
$c^2 = 4$
$c = 2$
foci: $(-2, -1 \pm 2)$ or
$(-2, -3), (2, 1)$
length of major axis: 2(4) or 8
length of minor axis: $2(2\sqrt{3})$ or $4\sqrt{3}$

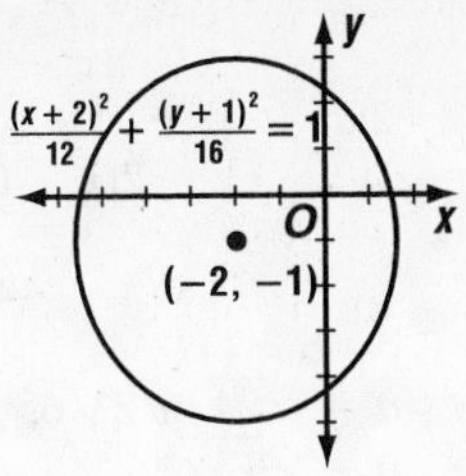

4. $\frac{(x-5)^2}{25} + \frac{(y+3)^2}{75} = 1$

center: $(5, -3)$
$a = \sqrt{75}$ or $5\sqrt{3}$, $b = 5$
$b^2 = a^2 - c^2$
$c^2 = 50$
$25 = 75 - c^2$
$c = 5\sqrt{2}$
foci: $(5, -3 \pm 5\sqrt{2})$
length of major axis: $2(5\sqrt{3})$ or $10\sqrt{3}$
length of minor axis: 2(5) or 10

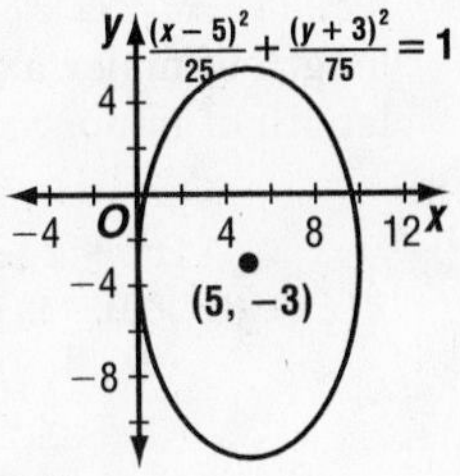

5. $\frac{x^2}{9} + \frac{y^2}{36} = 1$

center: $(0, 0)$
$a = 6$, $b = 3$
$b^2 = a^2 - c^2$
$9 = 36 - c^2$
$c^2 = 27$
$c = 3\sqrt{3}$
foci: $(0, \pm 3\sqrt{3})$
length of major axis: 2(6) or 12
length of minor axis: 2(3) or 6

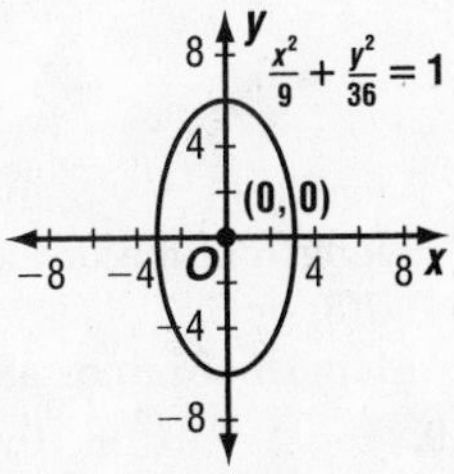

6. $\frac{(x-8)^2}{4} + \frac{(y+8)^2}{1} = 1$

center: $(8, -8)$
$a = 2$, $b = 1$
$b^2 = a^2 - c^2$
$1 = 4 - c^2$
$c^2 = 3$
$c = \pm\sqrt{3}$
foci: $(8 \pm \sqrt{3}, -8)$
length of major axis: 2(2) or 4
length of minor axis: 2(1) or 2

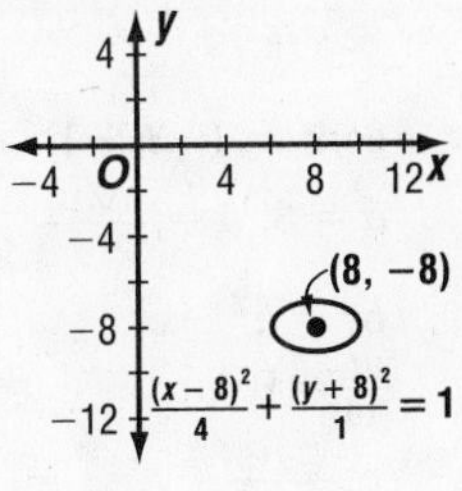

7. $\frac{(x+2)^2}{36} + \frac{(y-4)^2}{40} = 1$

center: $(-2, 4)$
$a = \sqrt{40}$ or $2\sqrt{10}$, $b = 6$
$b^2 = a^2 - c^2$
$36 = 40 - c^2$
$c^2 = 4$
$c = 2$
foci: $(-2, 4 \pm 2)$ or
$(-2, 2), (-2, 6)$
length of major axis: $2(2\sqrt{10})$ or $4\sqrt{10}$
length of minor axis: 2(6) or 12

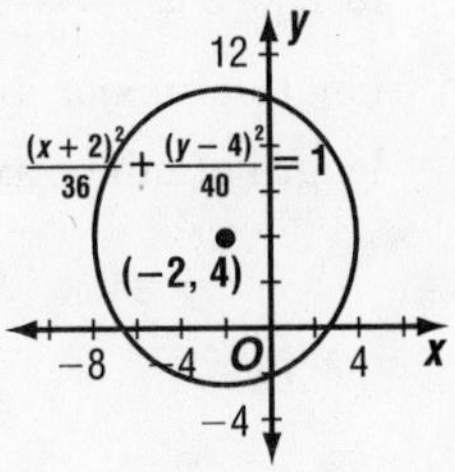

8. $\frac{(x+8)^2}{121} + \frac{(y-7)^2}{64} = 1$

center: $(-8, 7)$
$a = 11$, $b = 8$
$b^2 = a^2 - c^2$
$64 = 121 - c^2$
$c^2 = 57$
$c = \sqrt{57}$
foci: $(-8 \pm \sqrt{57}, 7)$
length of major axis: 2(11) or 22
length of minor axis: 2(8) or 16

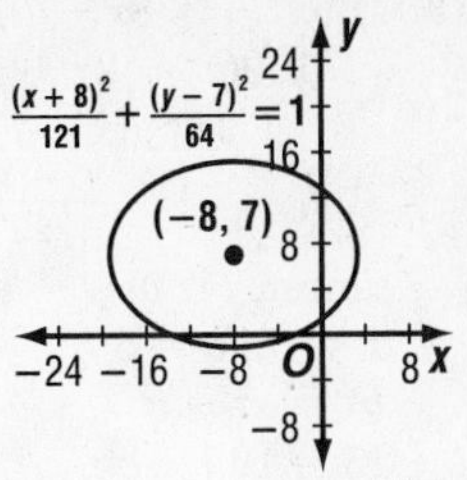

9. $\frac{(x-4)^2}{16} + \frac{(y+1)^2}{9} = 1$

center: $(4, -1)$
$a = 4$, $b = 3$
$b^2 = a^2 - c^2$
$9 = 16 - c^2$
$c^2 = 7$
$c = \sqrt{7}$
foci: $(4 \pm \sqrt{7}, -1)$
length of major axis: 2(4) or 8
length of minor axis: 2(3) or 6

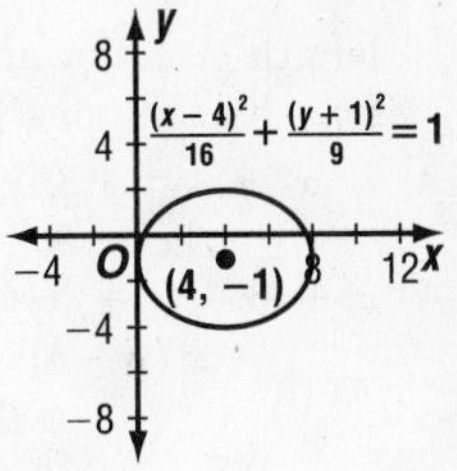

10. $8x^2 + 2y^2 = 32$
$\frac{x^2}{4} + \frac{y^2}{16} = 1$
center: $(0, 0)$
$a = 4$, $b = 2$
$b^2 = a^2 - c^2$
$4 = 16 - c^2$
$c^2 = 12$
$c = 2\sqrt{3}$
foci: $(0, \pm 2\sqrt{3})$
length of major axis: 2(4) or 8
length of minor axis: 2(2) or 4

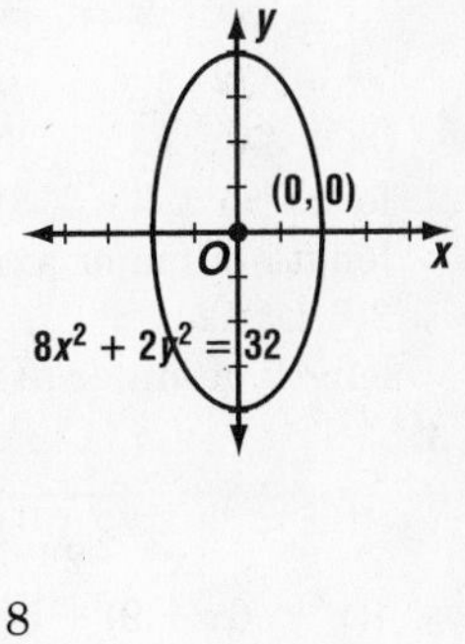

11. $7x^2 + 3y^2 = 84$
$\frac{x^2}{12} + \frac{y^2}{28} = 1$
center: $(0, 0)$
$a = \sqrt{28}$ or $2\sqrt{7}$,
$b = \sqrt{12}$ or $2\sqrt{3}$
$b^2 = a^2 - c^2$
$12 = 28 - c^2$
$c^2 = 16$
$c = 4$
foci: $(0, 4)$ and $(0, -4)$
length of major axis: $2(2\sqrt{7})$ or $4\sqrt{7}$
length of minor axis: $2(2\sqrt{3})$ or $4\sqrt{3}$

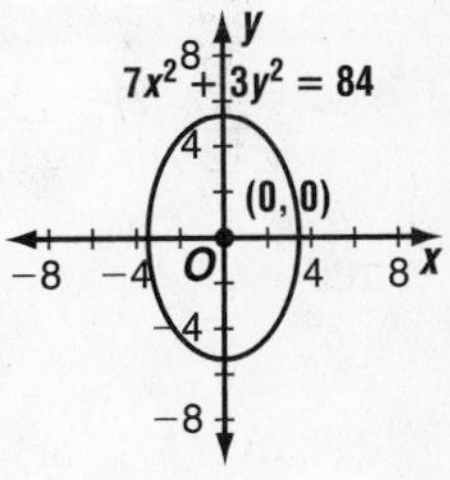

12. $9x^2 + 16y^2 = 144$
$\frac{x^2}{16} + \frac{y^2}{9} = 1$
center: $(0, 0)$
$a = 4$, $b = 3$
$b^2 = a^2 - c^2$
$9 = 16 - c^2$
$c^2 = 7$
$c = \sqrt{7}$
foci: $(\sqrt{7}, 0)$ and $(-\sqrt{7}, 0)$
length of major axis: 2(4) or 8
length of minor axis: 2(3) or 6

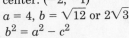

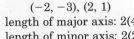

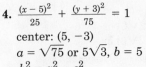

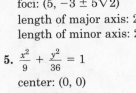

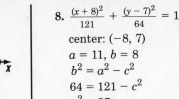

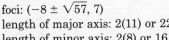

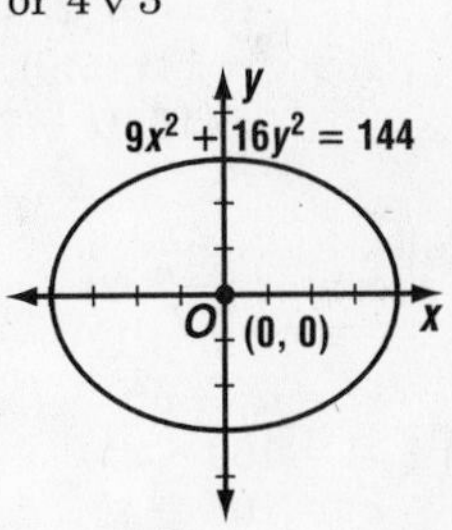

13. $169x^2 - 338x + 169 + 25y^2 = 4225$
$169(x^2 - 2x + 1) + 25y^2 = 4225$
$169(x - 1)^2 + 25y^2 = 4225$
$\frac{(x-1)^2}{25} + \frac{y^2}{169} = 1$

center: (1, 0)
$a = 13, b = 5$
$b^2 = a^2 - c^2$
$25 = 169 - c^2$
$c^2 = 144$
$c = 12$
foci: (1, 12) and (1, −12)
length of major axis: 2(13) or 26
length of minor axis: 2(5) or 10

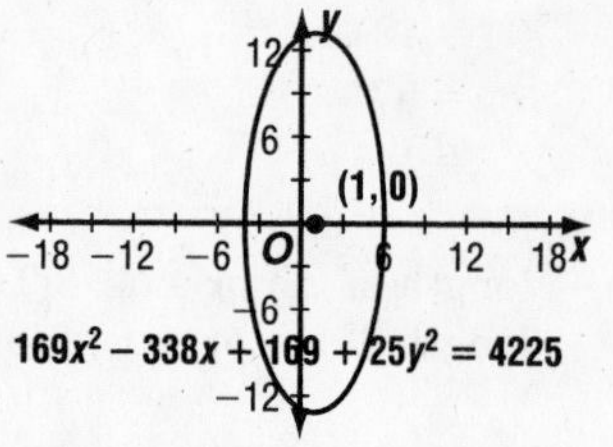

14. $x^2 + 4y^2 + 8x - 64y + 236 = 0$
$x^2 + 8x + 4y^2 - 64y = -236$
$x^2 + 8x + 16 + 4(y^2 - 16y + 64) = -236 + 16 + 256$
$(x + 4)^2 + 4(y - 8)^2 = 36$
$\frac{(x+4)^2}{36} + \frac{(y-8)^2}{9} = 1$

center: (−4, 8)
$a = 6, b = 3$
$b^2 = a^2 - c^2$
$9 = 36 - c^2$
$c^2 = 27$
$c = 3\sqrt{3}$
foci: $(-4 \pm 3\sqrt{3}, 8)$
length of major axis: 2(6) or 12
length of minor axis: 2(3) or 6

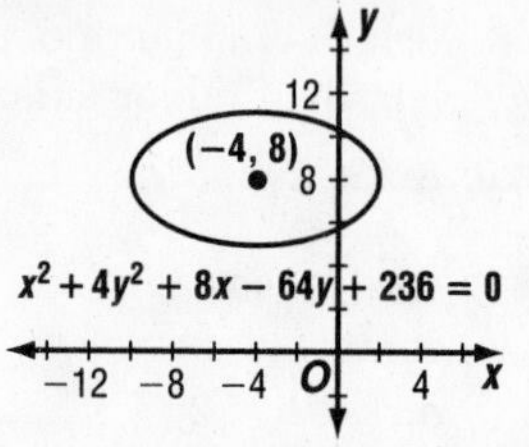

15. $4x^2 + 5y^2 = 4(6x + 5y + 111)$
$4x^2 + 5y^2 = 24x + 20y + 444$
$4x^2 - 24x + 5y^2 - 20y = 444$
$4(x^2 - 6x + 9) + 5(y^2 - 4y + 4) = 444 + 36 + 20$
$4(x - 3)^2 + 5(y - 2)^2 = 500$
$\frac{(x-3)^2}{125} + \frac{(y-2)^2}{100} = 1$

center: (3, 2)
$a = \sqrt{125}$ or $5\sqrt{5}$, $b = 10$
$b^2 = a^2 - c^2$
$100 = 25 - c^2$
$c^2 = 25$
$c = 5$
foci: $(3 \pm 5, 2)$ or (8, 2), (−2, 2)
length of major axis: $2(5\sqrt{5})$ or $10\sqrt{5}$
length of minor axis: 2(10) or 20

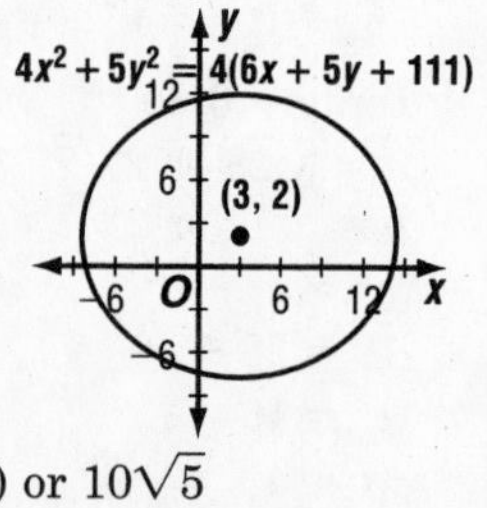

16. $169x^2 + y^2 + 2366x = 4y - 8116$
$169x^2 + 2366x + y^2 - 4y = -8116$
$169(x^2 + 14x + 49) + (y^2 - 4y + 4) = -8116 + 8281 + 4$
$169(x + 7)^2 + (y - 2)^2 = 169$
$\frac{(x+7)^2}{1} + \frac{(y-2)^2}{169} = 1$

center: (−7, 2)
$a = 13, b = 1$
$b^2 = a^2 - c^2$
$1 = 169 - c^2$
$c^2 = 168$
$c = 2\sqrt{42}$
foci: $(-7, 2 \pm 2\sqrt{42})$
length of major axis: 2(13) or 26
length of minor axis: 2(1) or 2

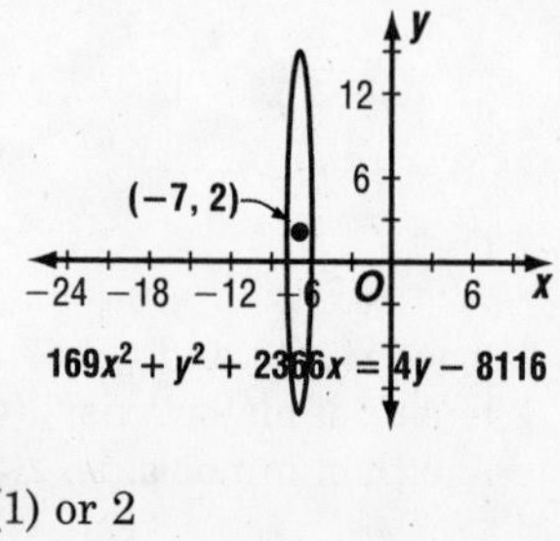

17. $2x^2 + y^2 - 4x + 8y - 6 = 0$
$2x^2 - 4x + y^2 + 8y = 6$
$2(x^2 - 2x + 1) + (y^2 + 8y + 16) = 6 + 2 + 16$
$2(x - 1)^2 + (y + 4)^2 = 24$
$\frac{(x-1)^2}{12} + \frac{(y+4)^2}{24} = 1$

center: (1, −4)
$a = \sqrt{24}$ or $2\sqrt{6}$,
$b = \sqrt{12}$ or $2\sqrt{3}$
$b^2 = a^2 - c^2$
$12 = 24 - c^2$
$c^2 = 12$
$c = 2\sqrt{3}$
foci: $(1, -4 \pm 2\sqrt{3}$
length of major axis: $2(2\sqrt{6})$ or $4\sqrt{6}$
length of minor axis: $2(2\sqrt{3})$ or $4\sqrt{3}$

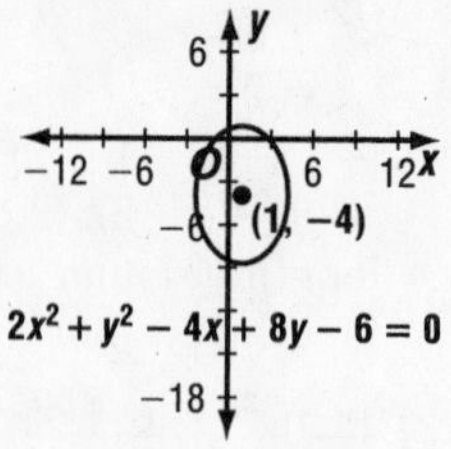

18. $4x^2 + 9y^2 + 24x - 90y = -225$
$4x^2 + 24x + 9y^2 - 90y = -225$
$4(x^2 + 6x + 9) + 9(y^2 - 10y + 25) = -225 + 36 + 225$
$4(x + 3)^2 + 9(y - 5)^2 = 36$
$\frac{(x+3)^2}{9} + \frac{(y-5)^2}{4} = 1$

center: (−3, 5)
$a = 3, b = 2$
$b^2 = a^2 - c^2$
$4 = 9 - c^2$
$c^2 = 5$
$c = \sqrt{5}$
foci: $(-3 \pm \sqrt{5}, 5)$
length of major axis: 2(3) or 6
length of minor axis: 2(2) or 4

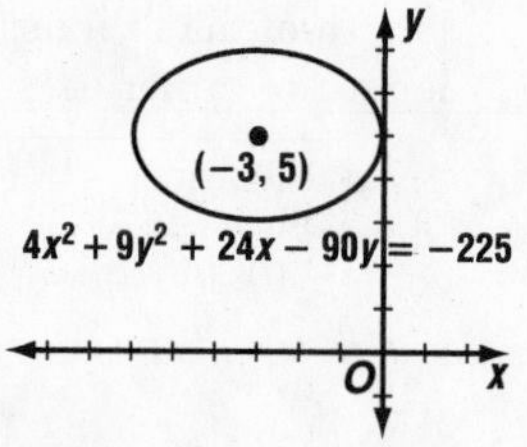

19. $9x^2 + 10y^2 + 54x + 20y = -1$
$9x^2 + 54x + 10y^2 + 20y = -1$
$9(x^2 + 6x + 9) + 10(y^2 + 2y + 1) = -1 + 81 + 1$
$9(x + 3)^2 + 10(y + 1)^2 = 81$
$\frac{(x+3)^2}{9} + \frac{(y+1)^2}{\frac{81}{10}} = 1$

center: (−3, −1)
$a = 3, b = \frac{9\sqrt{10}}{10}$
$b^2 = a^2 - c^2$
$\frac{81}{10} = 9 - c^2$
$c^2 = \frac{19}{10}$
$c = \frac{19\sqrt{10}}{10}$

foci: $\left(-3 \pm \frac{19\sqrt{10}}{10}, \frac{9\sqrt{10}}{10}\right)$
length of major axis: 2(3) or 6
length of minor axis: $2\left(\frac{9\sqrt{10}}{10}\right)$ or $\frac{9\sqrt{10}}{5}$

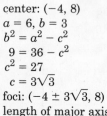

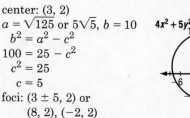

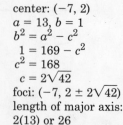

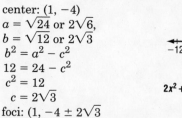

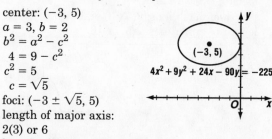

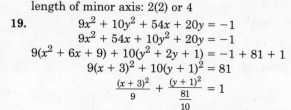

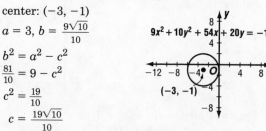

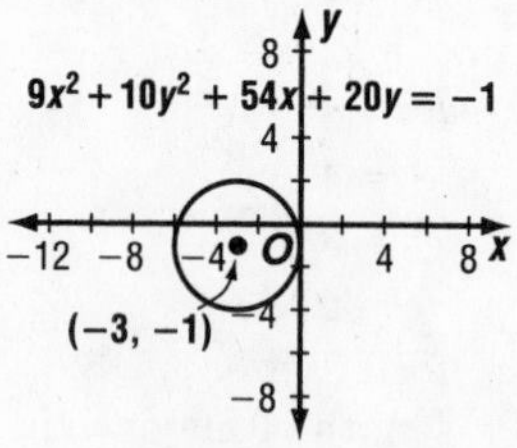

20. $9x^2 + 16y^2 - 54x + 64y + 1 = 0$

$$9x^2 - 54x + 16y^2 + 64y = -1$$
$$9(x^2 - 6x + 9) + 16(y^2 + 4y + 4) = -1 + 81 + 64$$
$$9(x-3)^2 + 16(y+2)^2 = 144$$
$$\frac{(x-3)^2}{16} + \frac{(y+2)^2}{9} = 1$$

center: $(3, -2)$
$a = 4,\ b = 3$
$b^2 = a^2 - c^2$
$9 = 16 - c^2$
$c^2 = 7$
$c = \sqrt{7}$
foci: $(3 \pm \sqrt{7}, -2)$
length of major axis: 2(4) or 8
length of minor axis: 2(3) or 6

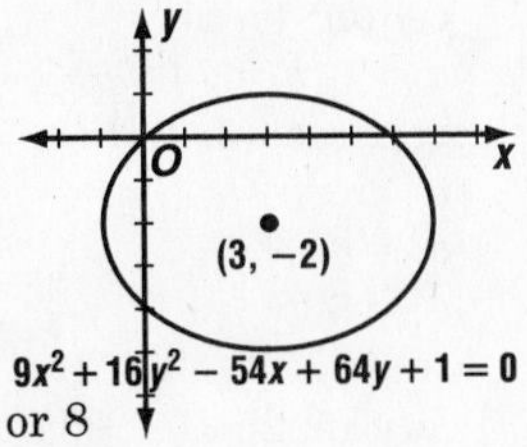

Page 893 Lesson 7-5

1. $\frac{y^2}{25} - \frac{x^2}{9} = 1$
center: $(0, 0)$
$a = 5,\ b = 3$
vertices: $(0, 5), (0, -5)$
$c^2 = a^2 + b^2$
$c^2 = 25 + 9$
$c^2 = 34$
$c = \sqrt{34}$
foci: $(0, \sqrt{34}), (0, -\sqrt{34})$
slopes of asymptotes: $\pm\frac{5}{3}$

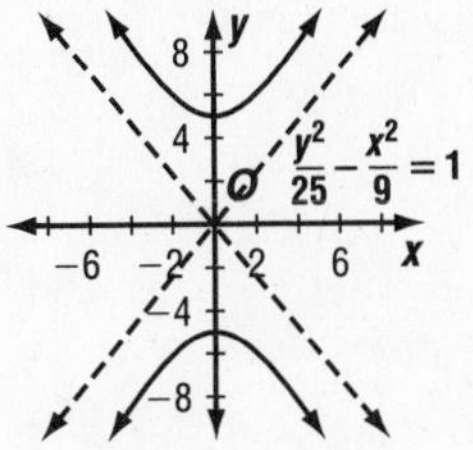

2. $\frac{x^2}{4} - \frac{y^2}{9} = 1$
center: $(0, 0)$
$a = 2,\ b = 3$
vertices: $(2, 0), (-2, 0)$
$c^2 = a^2 + b^2$
$c^2 = 4 + 9$
$c^2 = 13$
$c = \sqrt{13}$
foci: $(\sqrt{13}, 0), (-\sqrt{13}, 0)$
slopes of asymptotes: $\pm\frac{3}{2}$

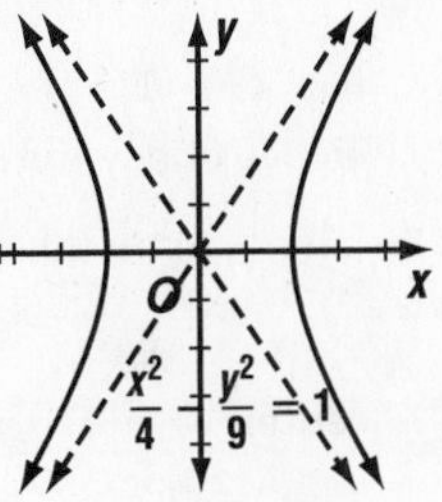

3. $\frac{x^2}{81} - \frac{y^2}{36} = 1$
center: $(0, 0)$
$a = 9,\ b = 6$
vertices: $(9, 0), (-9, 0)$
$c^2 = a^2 + b^2$
$c^2 = 81 + 36$
$c^2 = 117$
$c = \sqrt{117}$ or $3\sqrt{13}$
foci: $(3\sqrt{13}, 0), (-3\sqrt{13}, 0)$
slopes of asymptotes: $\pm\frac{9}{6}$ or $\pm\frac{3}{2}$

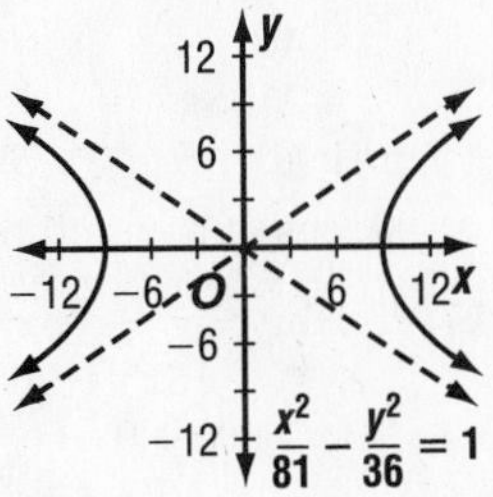

4. $\frac{x^2}{9} - \frac{y^2}{16} = 1$
center: $(0, 0)$
$a = 3,\ b = 4$
vertices: $(3, 0), (-3, 0)$
$c^2 = a^2 + b^2$
$c^2 = 9 + 16$
$c^2 = 25$
$c = 5$
foci: $(5, 0), (-5, 0)$
slopes of asymptotes: $\pm\frac{3}{4}$

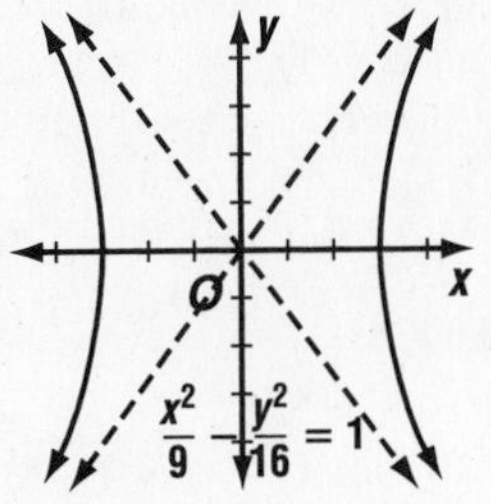

5. $\frac{y^2}{100} - \frac{x^2}{144} = 1$
center: $(0, 0)$
$a = 10,\ b = 12$
vertices: $(0, 10), (0, -10)$
$c^2 = a^2 + b^2$
$c^2 = 100 + 144$
$c^2 = 244$
$c = \sqrt{244}$ or $2\sqrt{61}$
foci: $(0, 2\sqrt{61})$,
$(0, -2\sqrt{61})$
slopes of asymptotes: $\pm\frac{10}{12}$ or $\pm\frac{5}{6}$

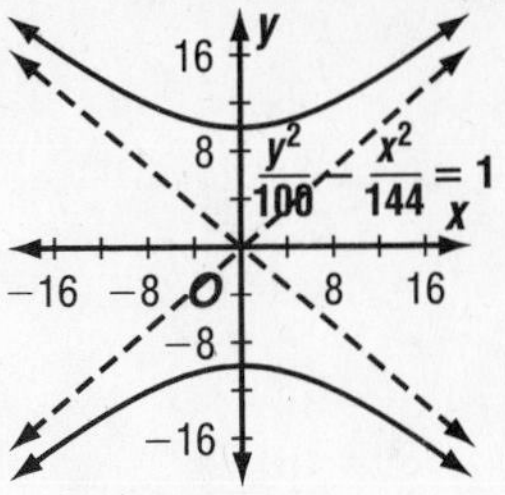

6. $\frac{x^2}{16} - \frac{y^2}{4} = 1$
center: $(0, 0)$
$a = 4,\ b = 2$
vertices: $(4, 0), (-4, 0)$
$c^2 = a^2 + b^2$
$c^2 = 16 + 4$
$c^2 = 20$
$c = 2\sqrt{5}$
foci: $(2\sqrt{5}, 0), (-2\sqrt{5}, 0)$
slopes of asymptotes: $\pm\frac{2}{4}$ or $\pm\frac{1}{2}$

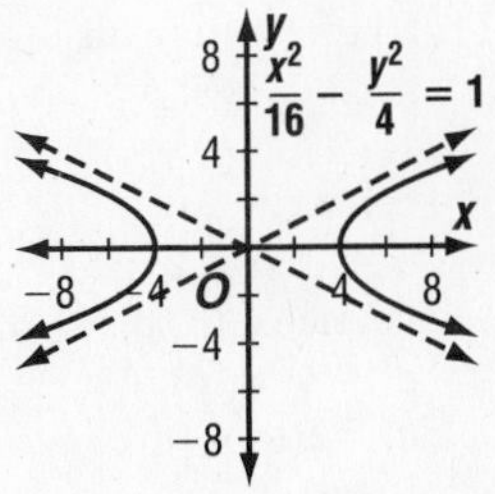

7. $\frac{(x-4)^2}{64} - \frac{(y+1)^2}{16} = 1$
center: $(4, -1)$
$a = 8,\ b = 4$
vertices: $(4 \pm 8, -1)$ or
$(-4, -1), (12, -1)$
$c^2 = a^2 + b^2$
$c^2 = 64 + 16$
$c^2 = 80$
$c = 4\sqrt{5}$
foci: $(4 \pm 4\sqrt{5}, -1)$
slopes of asymptotes: $\pm\frac{4}{8}$ or $\pm\frac{1}{2}$

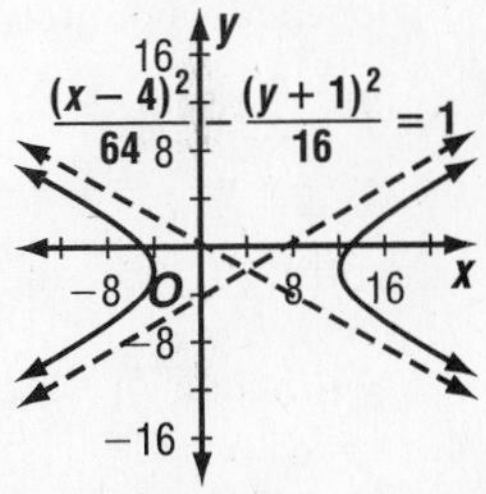

8. $\frac{(y-7)^2}{2.25} - \frac{(x-3)^2}{4} = 1$
center: $(3, 7)$
$a = 1.5,\ b = 2$
vertices: $(3, 7 \pm 1.5)$ or
$(3, 8.5), (3, 5.5)$
$c^2 = a^2 + b^2$
$c^2 = 2.25 + 4$
$c^2 = 6.25$
$c = 2.5$
foci: $(3, 7 \pm 2.5)$ or
$(3, 9.5), (3, 4.5)$
slopes of asymptotes: $\pm\frac{1.5}{2}$

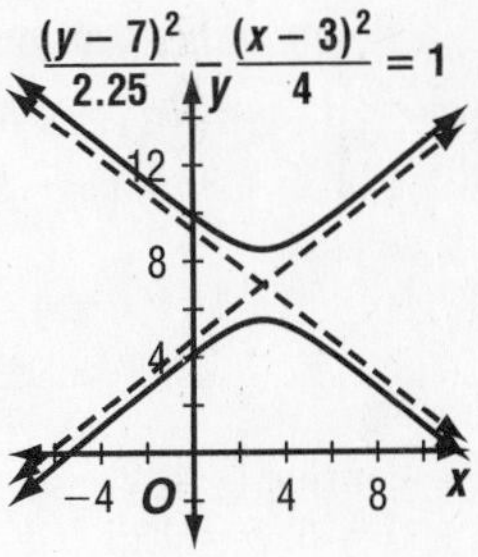

9. $(x+5)^2 - (y+3)^2 = 1$
center: $(-5, -3)$
$a = 1,\ b = 2$
vertices: $(-5 \pm 1, -3)$ or
$(-6, -3), (-4, -3)$
$c^2 = a^2 + b^2$
$c^2 = 1 + 4$
$c^2 = 5$
$c = \sqrt{5}$
foci: $(-5 \pm \sqrt{5}, -3)$
slopes of asymptotes: $\pm\frac{2}{1}$

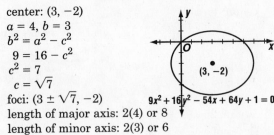

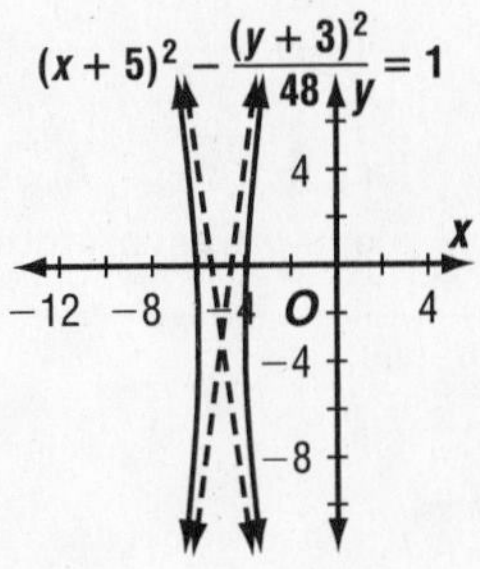

10. $x^2 - 9y^2 = 36$

$\frac{x^2}{36} - \frac{y^2}{4} = 1$

center: (0, 0)
$a = 6, b = 2$
vertices: (6, 0), (−6, 0)
$c^2 = a^2 + b^2$
$c^2 = 36 + 4$
$c^2 = 40$
$c = 2\sqrt{10}$
foci: $(\pm 2\sqrt{10}, 0)$
slopes of asymptotes: $\pm\frac{2}{6}$ or $\pm\frac{1}{3}$

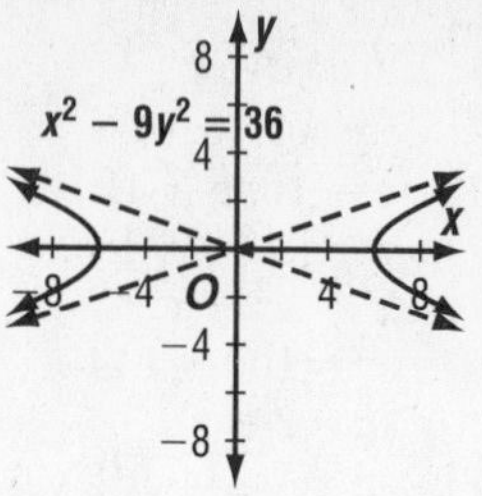

11. $4x^2 - 9y^2 = 36$

$\frac{x^2}{9} - \frac{y^2}{4} = 1$

center: (0, 0)
$a = 3, b = 2$
vertices: (3, 0), (−3, 0)
$c^2 = a^2 + b^2$
$c^2 = 9 + 4$
$c^2 = 13$
$c = \sqrt{13}$
foci: $(\sqrt{13}, 0), (-\sqrt{13}, 0)$
slopes of asymptotes: $\pm\frac{2}{3}$

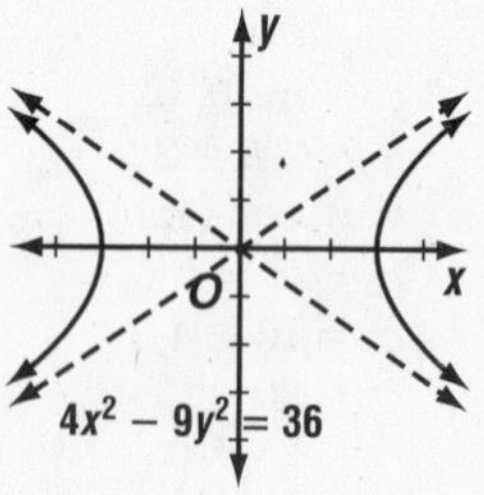

12. $49x^2 - 16y^2 = 784$

$\frac{x^2}{16} - \frac{y^2}{49} = 1$

center: (0, 0)
$a = 4, b = 7$
vertices: (4, 0), (−4, 0)
$c^2 = a^2 + b^2$
$c^2 = 16 + 49$
$c^2 = 65$
$c = \sqrt{65}$
foci: $(\sqrt{65}, 0), (-\sqrt{65}, 0)$
slopes of asymptotes: $\pm\frac{7}{4}$

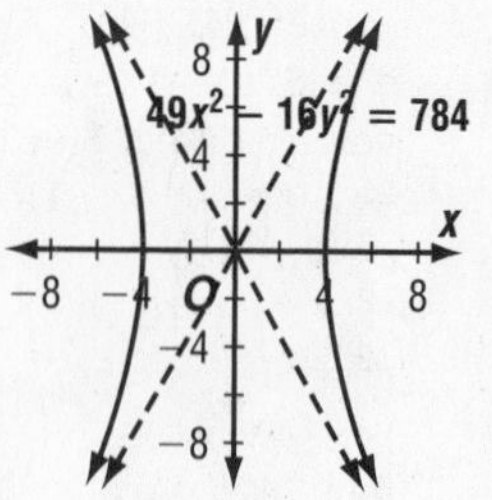

13. $144x^2 + 1152x - 25y^2 - 100y = 1396$

$144(x^2 + 8x + 16) - 25(y^2 - 4y + 4) = 1396 + 2304 - 100$

$144(x + 4)^2 - 25(y - 2)^2 = 3600$

$\frac{(x+4)^2}{25} - \frac{(y-2)^2}{144} = 1$

center: (−4, 2)
$a = 5, b = 12$
vertices: $(-4 \pm 5, 2)$ or (1, 2), (−9, 2)
$c^2 = a^2 + b^2$
$c^2 = 25 + 144$
$c^2 = 169$
$c = 13$
foci: $(-4 \pm 13, 2)$ or (−17, 2), (9, 2)
slopes of asymptotes: $\pm\frac{12}{5}$

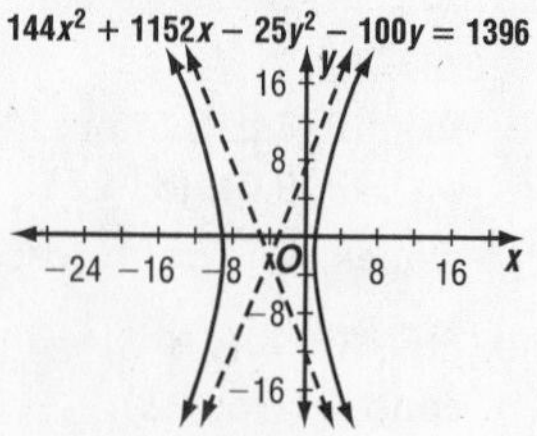

14. $576y^2 = 49x^2 + 490x + 29{,}449$

$576y^2 - 49x^2 - 490x = 29{,}449$

$576y^2 - 49(x^2 - 10x + 25) = 29{,}449 - 1225$

$576y^2 - 49(x - 5)^2 = 28{,}224$

$\frac{y^2}{49} - \frac{(x-5)^2}{576} = 1$

center: (5, 0)
$a = 7, b = 24$
vertices: (5, 7), (5, −7)
$c^2 = a^2 + b^2$
$c^2 = 49 + 576$
$c^2 = 625$
$c = 25$
foci: (5, 25), (5, −25)
slopes of asymptotes: $\pm\frac{7}{24}$

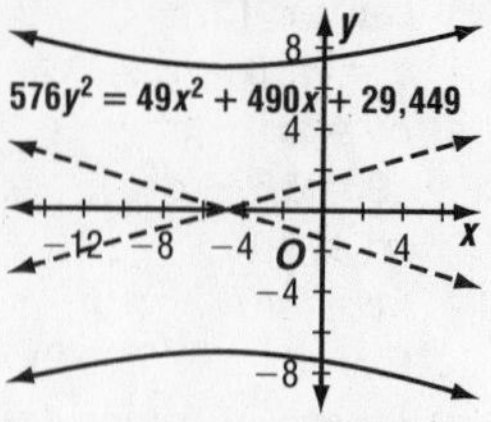

15. $23.04y^2 - 46.08y - 1.96x^2 - 3.92x = 24.0784$

$23.04(y^2 - 2y + 1) - 1.96(x^2 + 2x + 1) = 24.0784 + 23.04 - 1.96$

$23.04(y - 1)^2 - 1.96(x + 1)^2 = 45.1584$

$\frac{(y-1)^2}{1.96} - \frac{(x+1)^2}{23.04} = 1$

center: (−1, 1)
$a = 1.4, b = 4.8$
vertices:
$(-1, 1 \pm 1.4)$ or
(1, 2.4), (1, −0.4)
$c^2 = a^2 + b^2$
$c^2 = 1.96 + 23.04$
$c^2 = 25$
$c = 5$
foci: $(-1, 1 \pm 5)$ or (−1, 6), (−1, −4)
slopes of asymptotes: $\pm\frac{1.4}{4.8}$ or $\pm\frac{7}{24}$

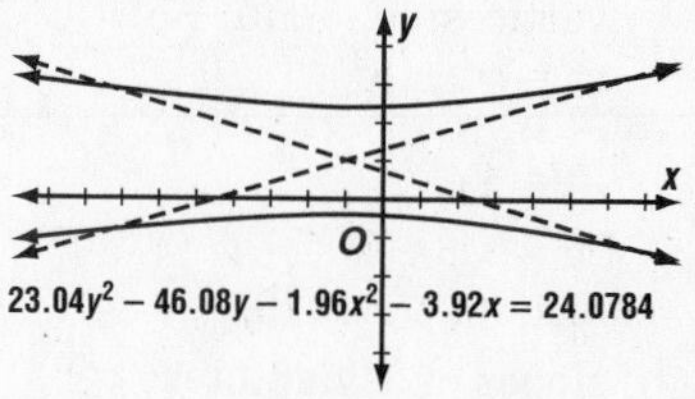

16. $25(y + 5)^2 - 20(x - 1)^2 = 500$

$\frac{(y+5)^2}{20} - \frac{(x-1)^2}{25} = 1$

center: (1, −5)
$a = \sqrt{20}$ or $2\sqrt{5}$, $b = 5$
vertices: $(1, -5 \pm 2\sqrt{5})$
$c^2 = a^2 + b^2$
$c^2 = 20 + 25$
$c^2 = 45$
$c = 3\sqrt{5}$
foci: $(1, -5 \pm 3\sqrt{5})$
slopes of asymptotes: $\pm\frac{2\sqrt{5}}{5}$

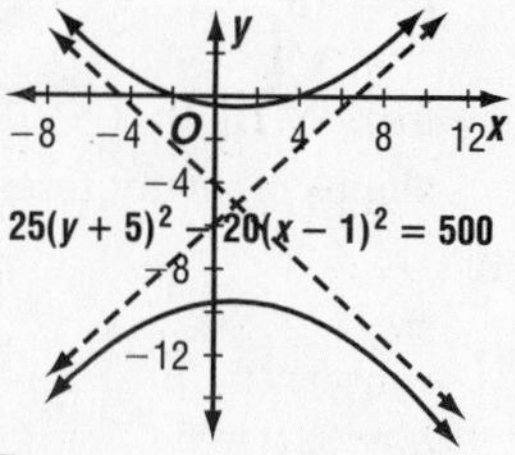

17. $16x^2 - y^2 + 96x + 8y + 112 = 0$

$16x^2 + 96x - y^2 + 8y = -112$

$16(x^2 + 6x + 9) - (y^2 - 8y + 16) = -112 + 144 - 16$

$16(x + 3)^2 - (y - 4)^2 = 16$

$\frac{(x+3)^2}{1} - \frac{(y-4)^2}{16} = 1$

center: (−3, 4)
$a = 1, b = 4$
vertices: $(-3 \pm 1, 4)$ or (−4, 4), (−2, 4)
$c^2 = a^2 + b^2$
$c^2 = 1 + 16$
$c^2 = 17$
$c = \sqrt{17}$
foci: $(-3 \pm \sqrt{17}, 4)$
slopes of asymptotes: $\pm\frac{4}{1}$

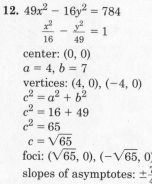

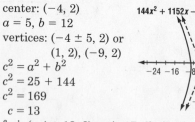

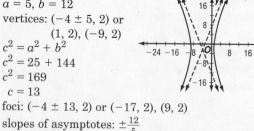

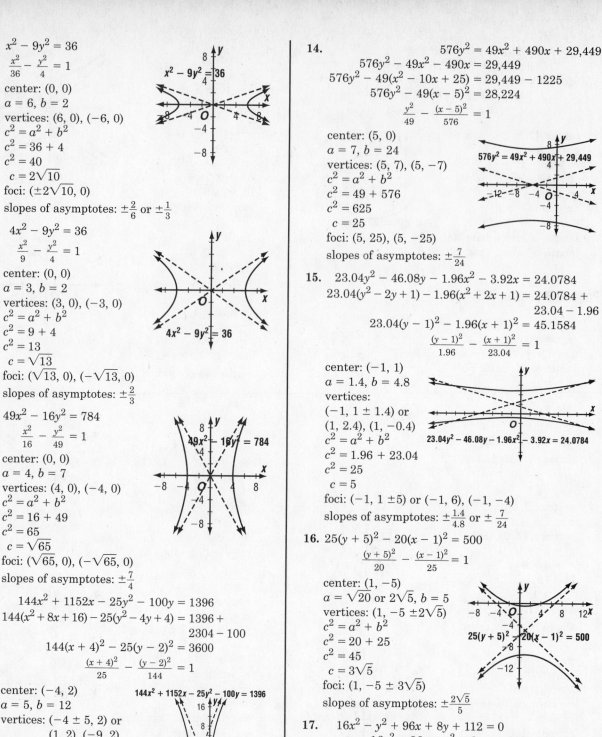

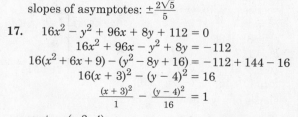

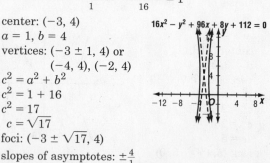

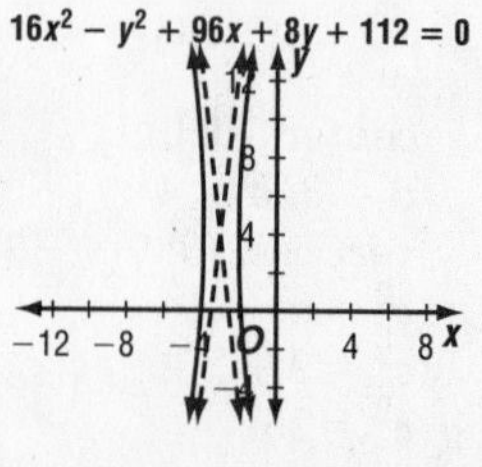

18. $y^2 - 4x^2 - 2y - 16x + 1 = 0$

$y^2 - 2y + 1 - 4x^2 - 16x = 0$

$(y - 1)^2 - 4(x^2 - 4x + 4) = -16$

$4(x - 2)^2 - (y - 1)^2 = 16$

$\frac{(x-2)^2}{4} - \frac{(y-1)^2}{16} = 1$

center: $(2, 1)$

$a = 2, b = 4$

vertices: $(2 \pm 2, 1)$ or $(0, 1), (4, 1)$

$c^2 = a^2 + b^2$

$c^2 = 4 + 16$

$c^2 = 20$

$c = 2\sqrt{5}$

foci: $(2 \pm 2\sqrt{5}, 1)$

slopes of asymptotes: $\pm\frac{4}{2}$ or $\pm\frac{2}{1}$

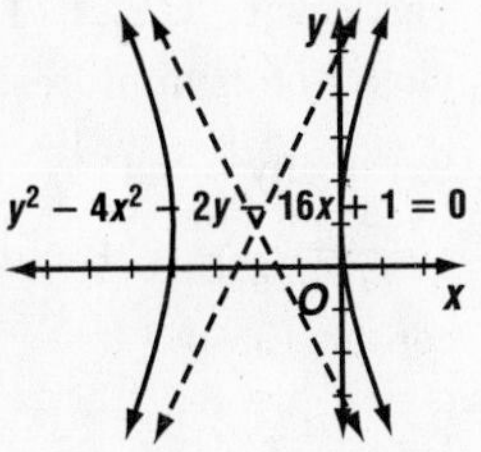

19. $(y - 1)^2 - 4(x - 2)^2 = 168$

$\frac{(y-1)^2}{168} - \frac{(x-2)^2}{42} = 1$

center: $(2, 1)$

$a = \sqrt{168}$ or $2\sqrt{42}$,

$b = \sqrt{42}$

vertices: $(2, 1 \pm \sqrt{168})$

$c^2 = a^2 + b^2$

$c^2 = 168 + 42$

$c^2 = 210$

$c = \sqrt{210}$

foci: $(2, 1 \pm \sqrt{210})$

slopes of asymptotes: $\pm\frac{2\sqrt{42}}{\sqrt{42}}$ or $\pm\frac{2}{1}$

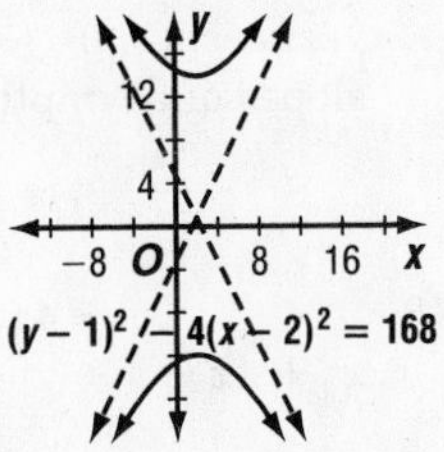

20. $3x^2 - 12y^2 + 45x + 60y = -60$

$3x^2 + 45x - 12y^2 + 60y = -60$

$3\left(x^2 + 15x + \frac{225}{4}\right) - 12\left(y^2 - 5y + \frac{25}{4}\right) = -60 + \frac{675}{4} - 75$

$3\left(x + \frac{15}{2}\right)^2 - 12\left(y - \frac{5}{2}\right)^2 = \frac{135}{4}$

$\frac{\left(x + \frac{15}{2}\right)^2}{11.25} - \frac{\left(y - \frac{5}{2}\right)^2}{2.8125} = 1$

center: $\left(-\frac{15}{2}, \frac{5}{2}\right)$

$a = \sqrt{11.25}, b = \sqrt{2.8125}$

vertices: $\left(-\frac{15}{2} \pm \sqrt{11.25}, \frac{5}{2}\right)$

$c^2 = a^2 + b^2$

$c^2 = 11.25 + 2.8125$

$c^2 = 14.0625$

$c = 3.75$

foci: $\left(-\frac{15}{2} \pm 3.75, \frac{5}{2}\right)$

slopes of asymptotes: $\pm\frac{\sqrt{11.25}}{\sqrt{2.8125}}$ or $\pm\frac{2}{1}$

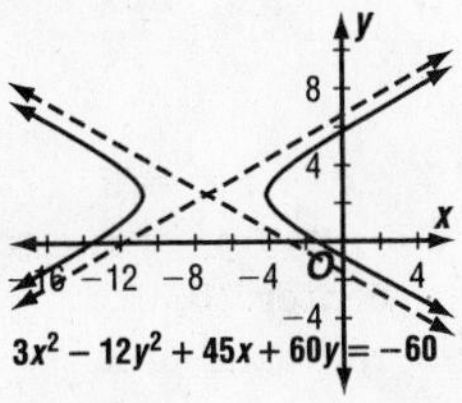

Page 893 Lesson 7-6

1. $9x^2 - 36x + 36 = 4y^2 + 24y + 72$

$9(x^2 - 4x + 4) - 4y^2 - 24y = 72$

$9(x - 2)^2 - 4(y^2 + 6y + 9) = 72 - 36$

$9(x - 2)^2 - 4(y + 3)^2 = 36$

$\frac{(x-2)^2}{4} - \frac{(y+3)^2}{9} = 1$; hyperbola

center: $(2, -3)$

$a = 2, b = 3$

vertices: $(2 \pm 2, -3)$ or $(4, -3), (0, -3)$

slopes of asymptotes: $\pm\frac{3}{2}$

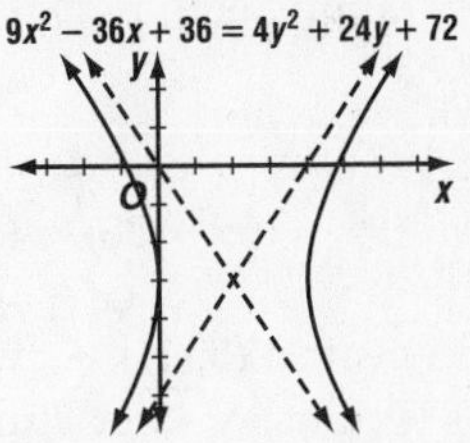

2. $x^2 + 4x + 2y^2 + 16y + 32 = 0$

$x^2 + 4x + 4 + 2(y^2 + 8y + 16) = -32 + 4 + 32$

$(x + 2)^2 + 2(y + 4)^2 = 4$

$\frac{(x+2)^2}{4} + \frac{(y+4)^2}{2} = 1$; ellipse

center: $(-2, -4)$

$a = 2, b = \sqrt{2}$

length of major axis: $2(2)$ or 4

length of minor axis: $2\sqrt{2}$ or $2\sqrt{2}$

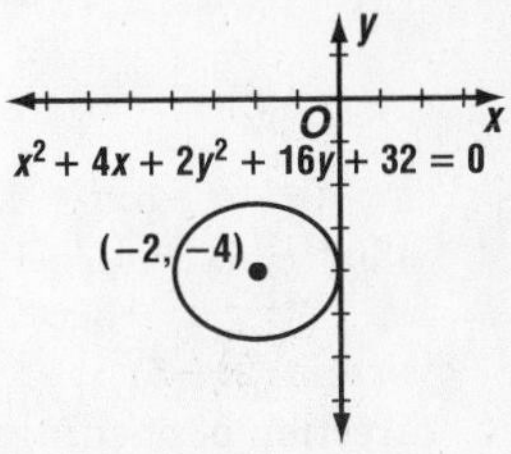

3. $x^2 + 6x + y^2 - 6y + 9 = 0$

$(x^2 + 6x + 9) + (y^2 - 6y + 9) = 9$

$(x + 3)^2 + (y - 3)^2 = 9$; circle

center: $(-3, 3)$

radius: $\sqrt{9}$ or 3 units

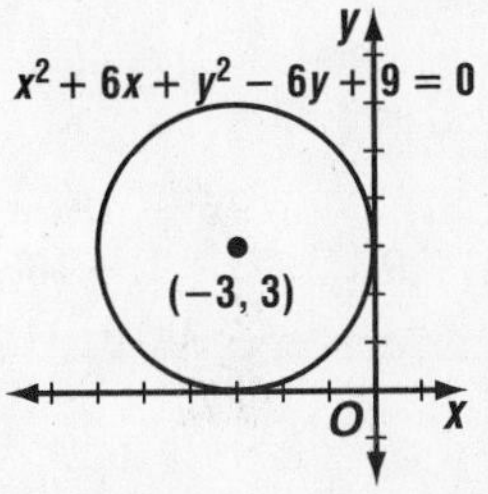

4. $9y^2 = 25x^2 + 400x + 1825$

$9y^2 - 25x^2 - 400x = 1825$

$9y^2 - 25(x^2 + 16x + 64) = 1825 - 1600$

$\frac{y^2}{25} - \frac{(x+8)^2}{9} = 1$; hyperbola

center: $(-8, 0)$

$a = 5, b = 3$

vertices: $(-8, 5), (-8, -5)$

slopes of asymptotes: $\pm\frac{5}{3}$

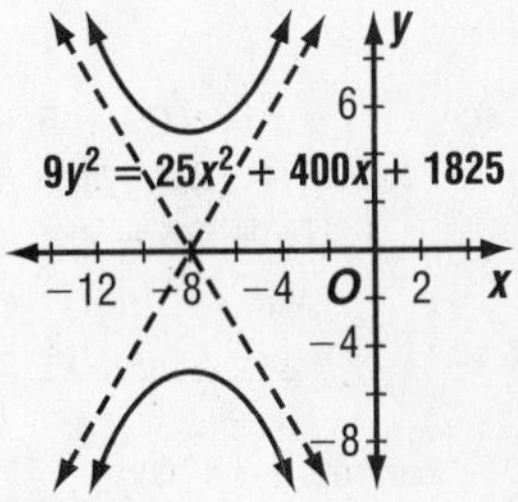

5. $$2y^2 + 12y - x + 6 = 0$$
$$2(y^2 + 6y) + 6 = x$$
$$2(y^2 + 6y + 9) + 6 - 2(9) = x$$
$$2(y + 3)^2 - 12 = x;$$
parabola
vertex: $(-12, -3)$
direction of opening:
right, since $a > 0$

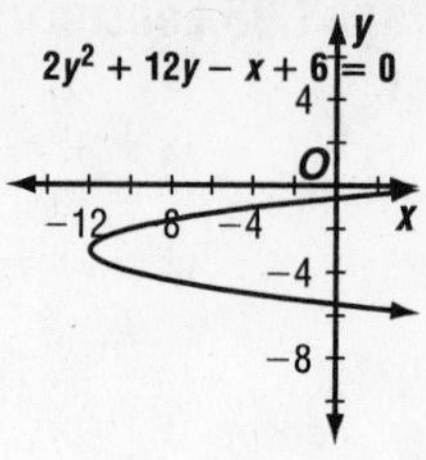

6. $$x^2 + y^2 = 10x + 2y + 23$$
$$x^2 - 10x + y^2 - 2y = 23$$
$$(x^2 - 10x + 25) + (y^2 - 2y + 1) = 23 + 25 + 1$$
$$(x - 5)^2 + (y - 1)^2 = 49;\text{ circle}$$
center: $(5, 1)$
radius: $\sqrt{49}$ or 7 units

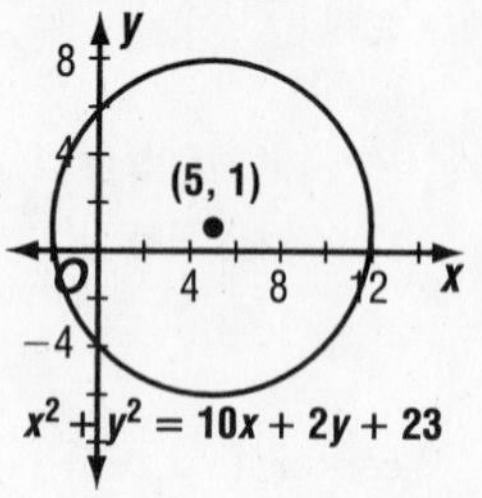

7. $$3x^2 + y = 12x - 17$$
$$-3x^2 + 12x - 17 = y$$
$$-3(x^2 - 4x + 4) - 17 + 3(4) = y$$
$$-3(x - 2)^2 - 5 = y;\text{ parabola}$$
vertex: $(2, -5)$
direction of opening:
downward, since $a < 0$

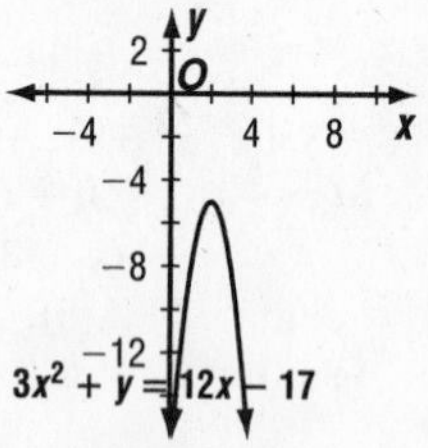

8. $$9x^2 - 18x + 16y^2 + 160y = -265$$
$$9(x^2 - 2x + 1) + 16(y^2 + 10y + 25) = -265 + 9 + 400$$
$$9(x - 1)^2 + 16(y + 5)^2 = 144$$
$$\frac{(x - 1)^2}{16} + \frac{(y + 5)^2}{9} = 1;\text{ ellipse}$$
center: $(1, -5)$
$a = 4$, $b = 3$
length of major axis:
2(4) or 8
length of minor axis:
2(3) or 6

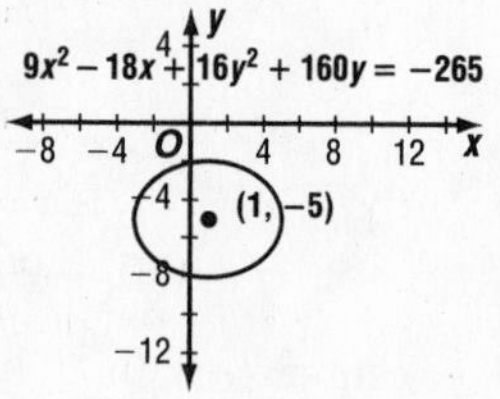

9. $$x^2 + 10x + 5 = 4y^2 + 16$$
$$x^2 + 10x - 4y^2 = 11$$
$$x^2 + 10x + 25 - 4y^2 = 11 + 25$$
$$(x + 5)^2 - 4y^2 = 36$$
$$\frac{(x + 5)^2}{36} - \frac{y^2}{9} = 1;\text{ hyperbola}$$
center: $(-5, 0)$
$a = 6$, $b = 3$
vertices: $(-11, 0)$, $(1, 0)$
slopes of asymptotes: $\pm\frac{3}{6}$ or $\pm\frac{1}{2}$

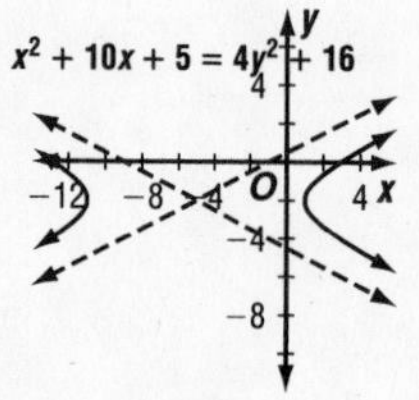

10. $$\frac{(y - 5)^2}{4} - (x + 1)^2 = 4$$
$$\frac{(y - 5)^2}{16} - \frac{(x + 1)^2}{4} = 1;\text{ hyperbola}$$
center: $(-1, 5)$
$a = 4$, $b = 2$
vertices: $(-1, 9)$, $(-1, 1)$
slopes of asymptotes: $\pm\frac{4}{2}$ or $\pm\frac{2}{1}$

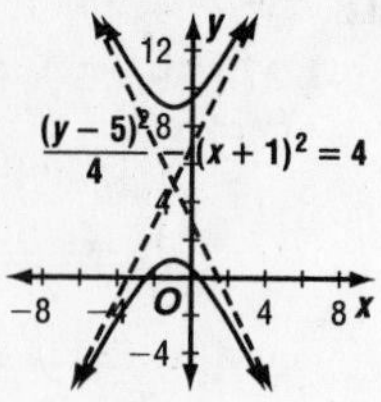

11. $$9x^2 + 49y^2 = 441$$
$$\frac{x^2}{49} + \frac{y^2}{9} = 441;\text{ ellipse}$$
center: $(0, 0)$
$a = 7$, $b = 3$
length of major axis: 2(7) or 14
length of minor axis: 2(3) or 6

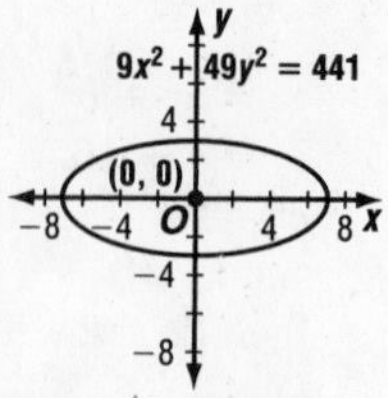

12. $$4x^2 - y^2 = 4$$
$$\frac{x^2}{1} - \frac{y^2}{4} = 1;\text{ hyperbola}$$
center: $(0, 0)$ $a = 1$, $b = 2$
vertices: $(1, 0)$, $(-1, 0)$
slopes of asymptotes: $\pm\frac{2}{1}$

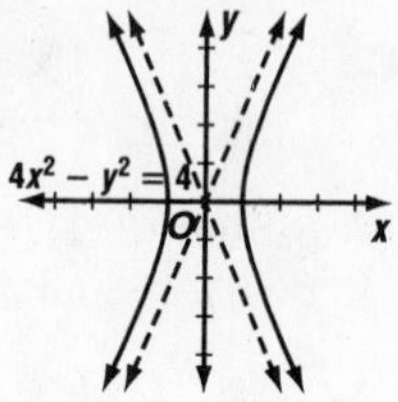

13. $$x^2 + 4x + y^2 - 8y = 2$$
$$x^2 + 4x + 4 + y^2 - 8y + 16 = 2 + 4 + 16$$
$$(x + 2)^2 + (y - 4)^2 = 22;\text{ circle}$$
center: $(-2, 4)$
radius: $\sqrt{22}$ units

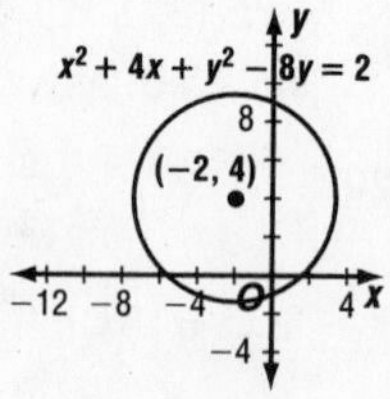

14. $$(x + 3)^2 = 8(y + 2)$$
$$\frac{1}{8}(x + 3)^2 - 2 = y;\text{ parabola}$$
vertex : $(-3, -2)$
direction of opening:
upward, since $a > 0$

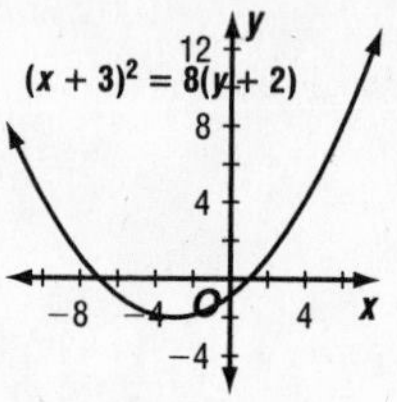

15. $$9x^2 + 9y^2 = 9$$
$$x^2 + y^2 = 1;\text{ circle}$$
center: $(0, 0)$
radius: 1 unit

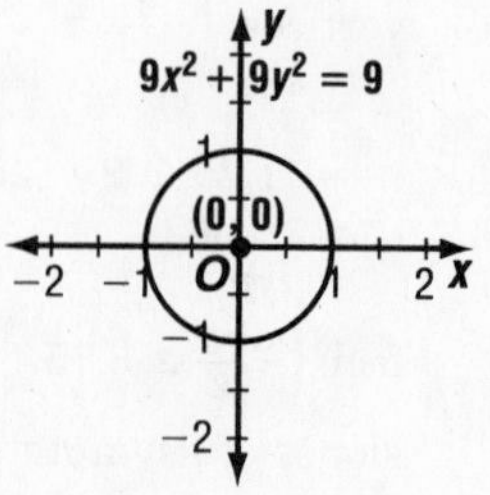

16. $$y - x^2 = x + 3$$
$$y = x^2 + x + 3$$
$$y = \left(x^2 + x + \frac{1}{4}\right) + 3 - \frac{1}{4}$$
$$y = \left(x + \frac{1}{2}\right)^2 + 2\frac{3}{4};\text{ parabola}$$
vertex: $\left(-\frac{1}{2}, 2\frac{3}{4}\right)$
direction of opening: upward, since $a > 0$

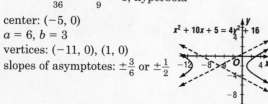

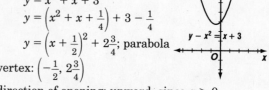

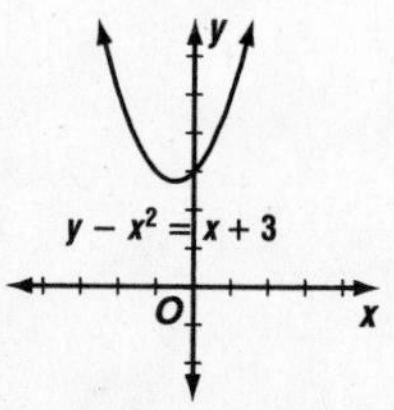

17. $2x^2 - 13y^2 + 5 = 0$

$\frac{13y^2}{5} - \frac{2x^2}{5} = 1$; hyperbola

center: (0, 0)

$a = \sqrt{\frac{5}{13}}$, $b = \sqrt{\frac{5}{2}}$

vertices: $\left(0, \pm\sqrt{\frac{5}{13}}\right)$

slopes of asymptotes: $\pm\sqrt{\frac{2}{13}}$

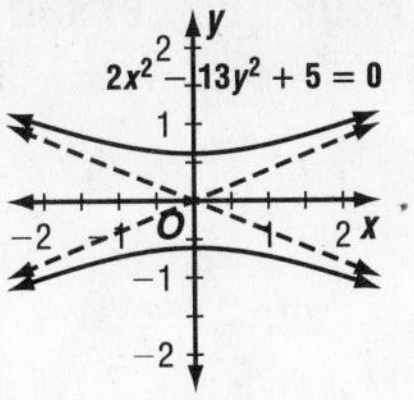

18. $16(x - 3)^2 + 81(y + 4)^2 = 1296$

$\frac{(x-3)^2}{81} + \frac{(y+4)^2}{16} = 1$; ellipse

center: (3, 4)

$a = 9$, $b = 4$

length of major axis: 2(9) or 18

length of minor axis: 2(4) or 8

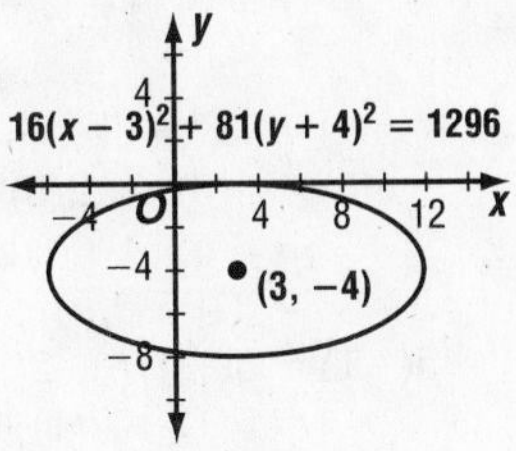

19. $4x^2 - y^2 = 16$

$\frac{x^2}{4} - \frac{y^2}{16} = 1$; hyperbola

center: (0, 0)

$a = 2$, $b = 4$

vertices: (2, 0), (−2, 0)

slopes of asymptotes: $\pm\frac{4}{2}$ or $\pm\frac{2}{1}$

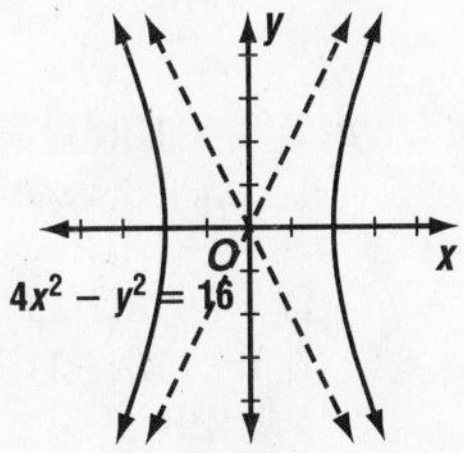

20. $x^2 + 5y^2 = 16$

$\frac{x^2}{16} + \frac{5y^2}{16} = 1$; ellipse

center: (0, 0)

$a = 4$, $b = \sqrt{\frac{16}{5}}$ or $\frac{4\sqrt{5}}{5}$

length of major axis: 2(4) or 8

length of minor axis: $2\left(\frac{4\sqrt{5}}{5}\right)$ or $\frac{8\sqrt{5}}{5}$

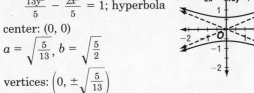

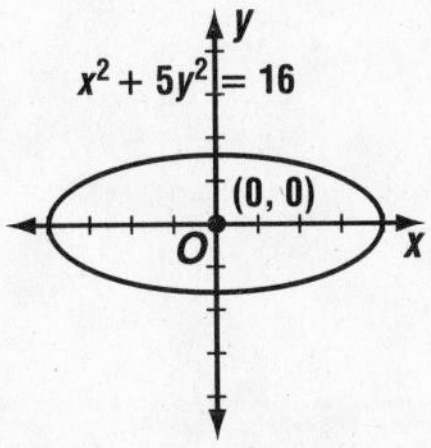

Page 894 Lesson 7-7

1. $4y = x^2 - 4$

$4y + 4 = x^2$

$x^2 + y^2 = 9$

$(4y + 4) + y^2 = 9$

$y^2 + 4y - 5 = 0$

$(y + 5)(y - 1) = 0$

$y + 5 = 0$ or $y - 1 = 0$

~~$y = -5$~~ $\quad y = 1$

$4y + 4 = x^2$

$4(1) + 4 = x^2$

$8 = x^2$

$\pm\sqrt{8} = x$

$\pm 2\sqrt{2} = x$

$(\pm 2\sqrt{2}, 1)$

2. $(x + 3)^2 + y^2 = 53$

$(x + 3)^2 + x = 53$

$x^2 + 6x + 9 + x = 53$

$x^2 + 7x - 44 = 0$

$(x + 11)(x - 4) = 0$

$x + 11 = 0$ or $x - 4 = 0$

~~$x = -11$~~ $\quad x = 4$

$x = y^2$

$4 = y^2$

$\pm 2 = y$

$(4, \pm 2)$

3. $\frac{x^2}{3} - \frac{(y+2)^2}{4} = 1$

$\frac{y^2 + 11}{3} - \frac{(y+2)^2}{4} = 1$

$4(y^2 + 11) - 3(y + 2)^2 = 12$

$4y^2 + 44 - 3(y^2 + 4y + 4) = 12$

$4y^2 + 44 - 3y^2 - 12y - 12 - 12 = 0$

$y^2 - 12y + 20 = 0$

$(y - 10)(y - 2) = 0$

$y - 10 = 0$ or $y - 2 = 0$

$y = 10 \qquad y = 2$

$x^2 = y^2 + 11 \qquad x^2 = y^2 + 11$

$x^2 = 10^2 + 11 \qquad x^2 = 2^2 + 11$

$x^2 = 111 \qquad x^2 = 15$

$x = \pm\sqrt{111} \qquad x = \pm\sqrt{15}$

$(\pm\sqrt{111}, 10)$, $(\pm\sqrt{15}, 2)$

4. $\frac{(x-1)^2}{5} + \frac{y^2}{2} = 1$

$\frac{(x-1)^2}{5} + \frac{(x+1)^2}{2} = 1$

$2(x - 1)^2 + 5(x + 1)^2 = 10$

$2(x^2 - 2x + 1) + 5(x^2 + 2x + 1) = 10$

$2x^2 - 4x + 2 + 5x^2 + 10x + 5 - 10 = 0$

$7x^2 + 6x - 3 = 0$

$x = \frac{-6 \pm \sqrt{36 - 4(7)(-3)}}{2(7)}$

$= \frac{-6 \pm \sqrt{120}}{14}$

$= \frac{-3 \pm \sqrt{30}}{7}$

$y = x + 1$

$= \frac{-3 + \sqrt{30}}{7} + 1$

$= \frac{4 + \sqrt{30}}{7}$

$y = x + 1$

$= \frac{-3 - \sqrt{30}}{7} + 1$

$= \frac{4 - \sqrt{30}}{7}$

$\left(\frac{-3 + \sqrt{30}}{7}, \frac{4 + \sqrt{30}}{7}\right)$, $\left(\frac{-3 - \sqrt{30}}{7}, \frac{4 - \sqrt{30}}{7}\right)$

5. $x^2 + y^2 = 13$

$(+)\ x^2 - y^2 = -5$

$2x^2 = 8$

$x^2 = 4$

$x = \pm 2$

$x^2 + y^2 = 13$

$(\pm 2)^2 + y^2 = 13$

$y^2 = 9$

$y = \pm 3$

$(\pm 2, \pm 3)$

6. $y = x^2 - 4$

$y + 4 = x^2$

$\frac{x^2}{25} - \frac{y^2}{5} = 1$

$\frac{y+4}{25} - \frac{y^2}{5} = 1$

$y + 4 - 5y^2 = 25$

$5y^2 - y + 21 = 0$

$y = \frac{-(-1) \pm \sqrt{(-1)^2 - 4(5)(21)}}{2(5)}$

$= \frac{1 \pm \sqrt{-419}}{10}$ no real solutions

7. $x^2 + y = 0$

$y = -x^2$

$x + y = -2$

$y = -2 - x$

$-x^2 = -2 - x$

$x^2 - x - 2 = 0$

$(x - 2)(x + 1) = 0$

$x - 2 = 0$ or $x + 1 = 0$

$x = 2 \qquad x = -1$

$y = -2 - x$

$= -2 - x$

$= -4$

$(2, -4)$

$y = -2 - x$

$= -2 - (-1)$

$= -1$

$(-1, -1)$

8. $x^2 - 9y^2 = 36$
$x^2 - 9(x)^2 = 36$
$-8x^2 = 36$
$x^2 = -\frac{36}{8}$ no real solutions

9. $y^2 - 16 = 9x^2$
$y^2 = 9x^2 + 16$

$5x^2 + y^2 = 30$	$y^2 = 9x^2 + 16$
$5x^2 + (9x^2 + 16) = 30$	$y^2 = 9(\pm 1)^2 + 16$
$14x^2 = 14$	$y^2 = 9 + 16$
$x^2 = 1$	$y^2 = 25$
$x = \pm 1$	$y = \pm 5$

$(\pm 1, \pm 5)$

10. $\frac{x^2}{16} - \frac{y^2}{1} \geq 1$
center: (0, 0)
vertices: $(\pm 4, 0)$
slopes of asymptotes: $\pm\frac{1}{4}$

$x^2 + y^2 \geq 49$
center: (0, 0)
radius: 7 units

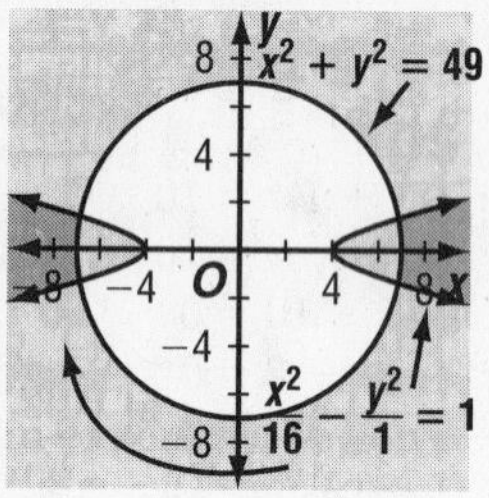

11. $\frac{x^2}{25} - \frac{y^2}{16} \geq 1$
center: (0, 0)
vertices: $(\pm 5, 0)$
slopes of asymptotes: $\pm\frac{4}{5}$

$y \leq x - 2$

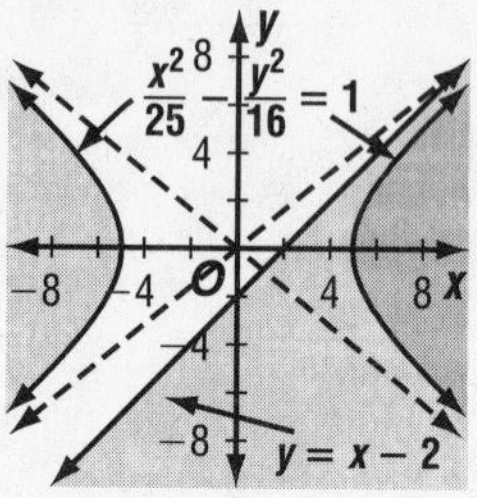

12. $y = x + 3$

$x^2 + y^2 < 25$
center: (0, 0)
radius: 5 units

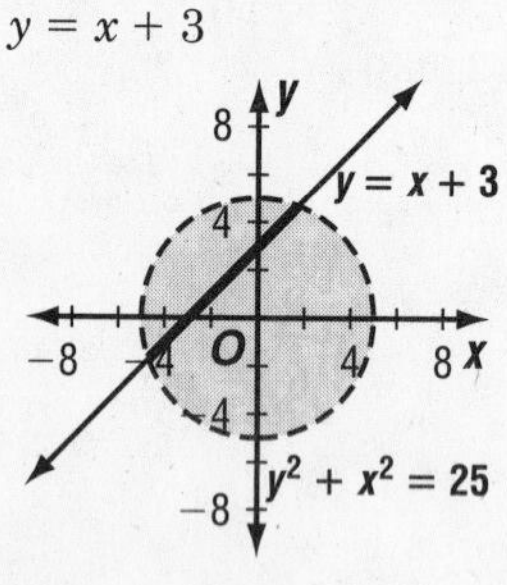

13. $4x^2 + (y - 3)^2 \leq 16$
$\frac{x^2}{4} + \frac{(y-3)^2}{16} \leq 1$
center: (0, 3)
length of major axis:
2(4) or 8
length of minor axis:
2(2) or 4

$x - 2y = -1$
$-2y = -x - 1$
$y = \frac{1}{2}x + \frac{1}{2}$

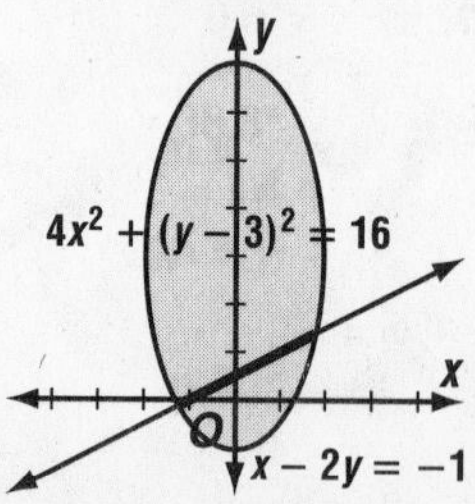

Page 894 Lesson 8-1

1. $p(x) = 7x - 3$
$p(5) = 7(5) - 3$
$= 35 - 3$
$= 32$
$p(-1) = 7(-1) - 3$
$= -7 - 3$
$= -10$

2. $p(x) = x^2 + 5x - 4$
$p(5) = -3\ (5)^2 + 5\ (5) - 4$
$= -3(25) + 25 - 4$
$= -54$
$p(-1) = -3(-1)^2 + 5(-1) - 4$
$= -3(1) - 5 - 4$
$= -12$

3. $p(x) = 5x^4 + 2x^2 - 2x$
$p(5) = 5(5)^4 + 2(5)^2 - 2(5)$
$= 5(625) + 2(25) - 10$
$= 3165$
$p(-1) = 5(-1)^4 + 2(-1)^2 - 2(-1)$
$= 5(1) + 2(1) + 2$
$= 9$

4. $p(x) = -13x^3 + 5x^2 - 3x + 2$
$p(5) = -13(5)^3 + 5(5)^2 - 3(5) + 2$
$= -13(125) + 5(25) - 15 + 2$
$= -1513$
$p(-1) = -13(-1)^3 + 5(-1)^2 - 3(-1) + 2$
$= -13(-1) + 5(1) + 3 + 2$
$= 23$

5. $p(x) = x^6 - 2$
$p(5) = (5)^6 - 2$
$= 15{,}625 - 2$
$= 15{,}623$
$p(-1) = (-1)^6 - 2$
$= 1 - 2$
$= -1$

6. $p(x) = \frac{2}{3}x^2 + 5$
$p(5) = \frac{2}{3}\ (5)^2 + 5\ (5)$
$= \frac{2}{3}(25) + 25$
$= \frac{125}{3}$
$p(-1) = \frac{2}{3}(-1)^2 + 5(-1)$
$= \frac{2}{3}(1) - 5$
$= -\frac{13}{3}$

7. $g(x) = 7x - 3$
$g(a - 2) = 7(a - 2) - 3$
$= 7a - 14 - 3$
$= 7a - 17$

8. $g(x) = 3x + 5$
$g(a - 2) = 3(a - 2) + 5$
$= 3a - 6 + 5$
$= 3a - 1$

9. $g(x) = -(x + 2)^2 + 8$
$g(a - 2) = -[(a - 2) + 2]^2 + 8$
$= -(a)^2 + 8$
$= -a^2 + 8$

10. $g(x) = -2x^3 + 5x$
$g(a - 2) = -2(a - 2)^3 + 5(a - 2)$
$= -2(a - 2)(a^2 - 4a + 4) + 5a - 10$
$= -2(a^3 - 6a^2 + 12a - 8) + 5a - 10$
$= -2a^3 + 12a^2 - 24a + 16 + 5a - 10$
$= -2a^3 + 12a^2 - 19a + 6$

11. $-3[f(x)] = -3(4x^2 + 3x - 7)$
$= -12x^2 - 9x + 21$

12. $-3[f(x)] = -3\left(\frac{x}{6} - \frac{2x^3}{9} + 1\right)$
$= -\frac{x}{2} + \frac{2x^3}{3} - 3$
$= \frac{2x^3}{3} - \frac{x}{2} - 3$

13. $-3[f(x)] = -3\,[5(x^2 + 2x)]$
$= -3(5x^2 + 10x)$
$= -15x^2 - 30x$

14. $-3[f(x)] = -3(8 - x)$
$= -24 + 3x$
$= 3x - 24$

Page 894 Lesson 8-2

1.

-2	1	−1	1	6
		−2	6	−14
	1	−3	7	−8

$(x^3 - x^2 - x + 6) = (x^2 - 3x + 7)(x + 2) - 8$; no

2.

3	5	−17	6	2
		15	−6	0
	5	−2	0	2

$(5x^3 - 17x^2 + 6x + 2) = (5x^2 - 2x)(x - 3) + 2$; no

3.

4	2	−4	3	−6
		8	16	76
	2	4	19	70

$(2x^3 - 4x^2 + 3x - 6) = (2x^2 + 4x + 19)(x - 4) + 70$; no

4.

2	1	0	0	−8
		2	4	8
	1	2	4	0

$(x^3 - 8) = (x^2 + 2x + 4)(x - 2)$; yes

5.

-1	1	6	−3
		−1	−5
	1	5	−8

$(x^2 + 6x - 3) = (x + 5)(x + 1) - 8$; no

6.

-1	1	1	1	1	1
		−1	0	−1	0
	1	0	1	0	1

$(x^4 + x^3 + x^2 + x + 1) = (x^3 + x)(x + 1) + 1$; no

7.

3	3	0	−5	0	2	−8
		9	27	66	198	600
	3	9	22	66	200	592
-2	3	0	−5	0	2	−8
		−6	12	−14	28	−60
	3	−6	7	−14	30	−68

$g(3) = 592$; $g(-2) = -68$

8.

3	−2	7	8	−3	5
		−6	3	33	90
	−2	1	11	30	95
-2	−2	7	8	−3	5
		4	−22	28	−50
	−2	11	−14	25	−45

$g(3) = 95$; $g(-2) = -45$

9.

3	10	0	0	2
		30	90	270
	10	30	90	272
-2	10	0	0	2
		−20	40	−80
	10	−20	40	−78

$g(3) = 272$; $g(-2) = -78$

10.

3	1	1	1	1	1	1
		3	12	39	120	363
	1	4	13	40	121	364
-2	1	1	1	1	1	1
		−2	2	−6	10	−22
	1	−1	3	−5	11	−21

$g(3) = 364$, $g(-2) = -21$

11.

7	1	−8	1	42
		7	−7	−42
	1	−1	−6	0

$x^2 - x - 6 = (x - 3)(x + 2)$

12.

2	6	13	−36	−43	30
		12	50	28	−30
	6	25	14	−15	0

$6x^3 + 25x^2 + 14x - 15 = (3x^2 + 8x - 5)(2x + 3)$

13.

3	1	5	0	−27	−135
		3	24	72	135
	1	8	24	45	0

$x^3 + 8x^2 + 24x + 45 = (x^2 + 3x + 9)(x + 5)$

14.

$-\frac{5}{2}$	2	−15	−2	120
		−5	50	−120
	2	−20	48	0

$x^2 - 10x + 24 = (x - 6)(x - 4)$

Page 895 Lesson 8-3

1.

x	$f(x)$	
0	−7	
1	−1	← zero between $x = 1$ and $x = 2$
2	5	

1.2

2.

x	$f(x)$	
−1	−4	← zero between $x = -1$ and $x = 0$
0	4	

−0.7

3.

x	$f(x)$	
−1	11	← zero between $x = -1$ and $x = 0$
0	−2	
1	−1	
2	−4	
3	−5	← zero between $x = 3$ and $x = 4$
4	26	

−0.4, 3.4

4.

x	$f(x)$	
−2	191	← zero between $x = -2$ and $x = -1$
−1	−1	
0	−5	
1	−1	← zero between $x = 1$ and $x = 2$
2	191	

−1.0, 1.0

5.

x	$f(x)$	
−9	47	← zero between $x = -9$ and $x = -8$
−8	−31	

8.5

6.

x	$f(x)$	
0	0	← zero
1	1	← zero between $x = 1$ and $x = 2$
2	-30	

0, 1.1

7.

x	$f(x)$	
-2	-95	← zero between $x = -2$ and $x = -1$
-1	10	
0	9	← zero between $x = 0$ and $x = 1$
1	-2	
7	-959	← zero between $x = 7$ and $x = 8$
8	2656	

-1.3, 0.9, 7.4

8.

x	$f(x)$	
-1	5	← zero between $x = -1$ and $x = 0$
0	-3	
3	-51	
4	-55	← zero between $x = 4$ and $x = 5$
5	17	

-0.7, 4.9

9.

x	$f(x)$	
-9	-6.925	← zero between $x = -9$ and $x = -8$
-8	0.5	
-4	9.2	
-2	6.2	
0	0.5	← zero between $x = 0$ and $x = 1$
1	-2.425	
4	-7.9	
7	-2.13	← zero between $x = 7$ and $x = 8$
8	3.7	

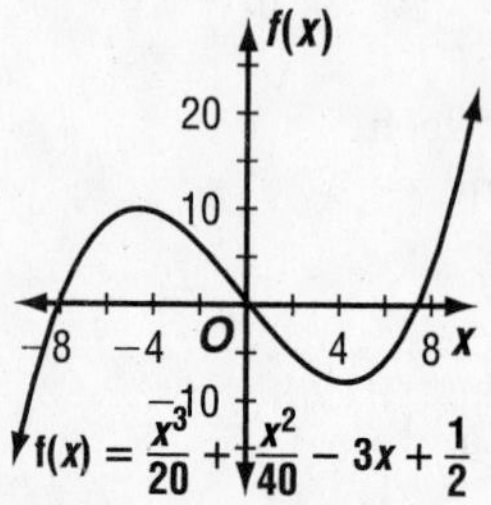

10.

x	$f(x)$	
-9	-0.55	← zero between $x = -9$ and $x = -8$
-8	12.45	
-6	5.45	← zero between $x = -6$ and $x = -5$
-5	-3.75	
-4	-11.55	
-1	-8	← zero between $x = -1$ and $x = 0$
0	1.25	
2	21.45	
4	12.45	← zero between $x = 4$ and $x = 5$
5	-18.75	

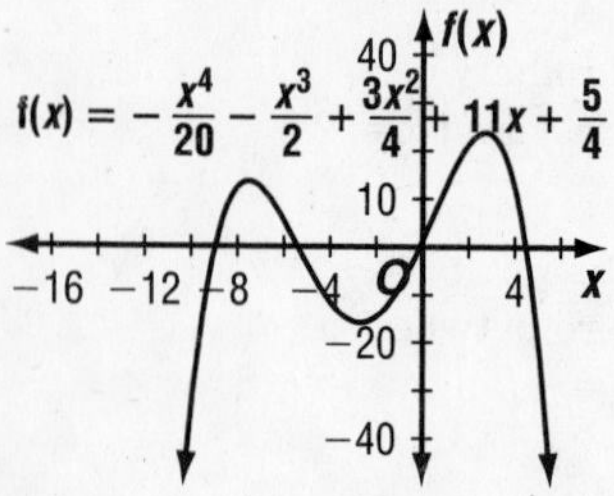

11.

x	$f(x)$	
-11	113	← zero between $x = -11$ and $x = -10$
-10	-1840	
-4	-832	
-3	-111	← zero between $x = -3$ and $x = -2$
-2	464	
0	960	
2	464	← zero between $x = 2$ and $x = 3$
3	-111	
4	-832	
10	-1840	← zero between $x = 10$ and $x = 11$
11	113	

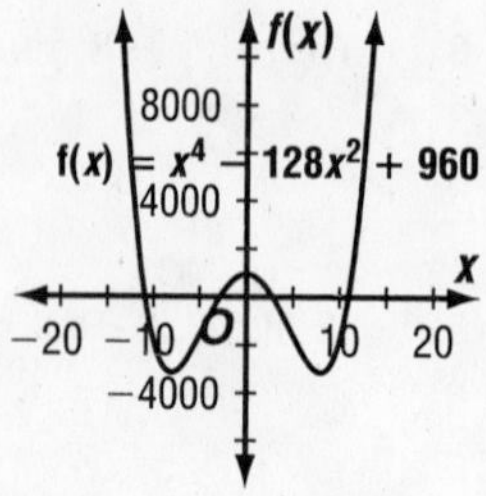

12.

x	$f(x)$	
-6	723	← zero between $x = -6$ and $x = -5$
-5	-2166	
-1	-342	
0	9	← zero between $x = 0$ and $x = 1$
1	-54	
2	-549	

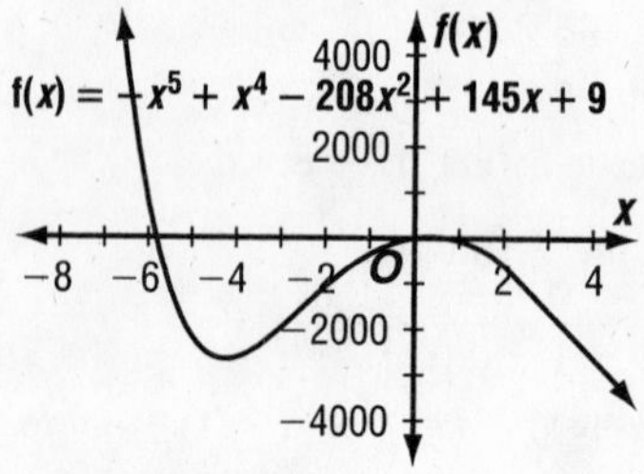

13.

x	$f(x)$	
-6	90929	
-4	28611	
-2	3925	
0	25	← zero between $x = 0$ and $x = 1$
1	-609	
2	-3925	
4	-28611	
6	-90929	

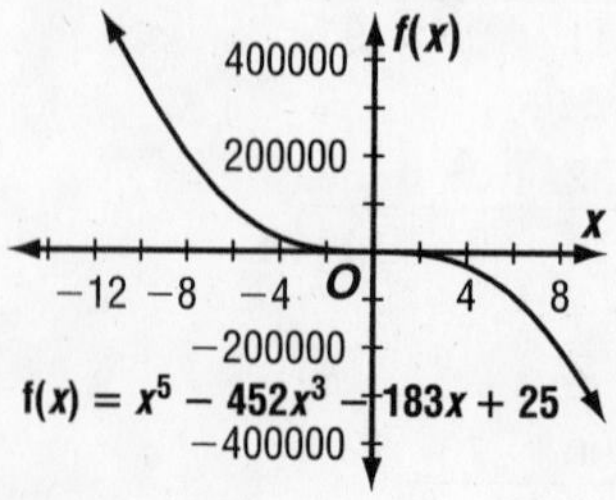

14.

x	$f(x)$	
−2	−20	← zero between $x = -2$ and $x = -1$
−1	59	
0	54	← zero between $x = 0$ and $x = 1$
1	−5	
6	−60	← zero between $x = 6$ and $x = 7$
7	187	

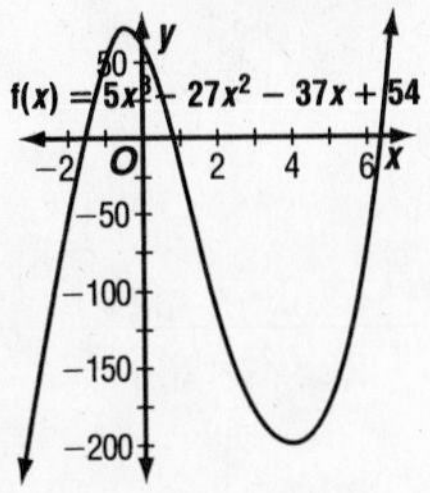

15.

x	$f(x)$	
−1	56	
0	78	
1	76	
2	22	← zero between $x = 2$ and $x = 3$
3	−54	
4	−74	← zero between $x = 4$ and $x = 5$
5	38	

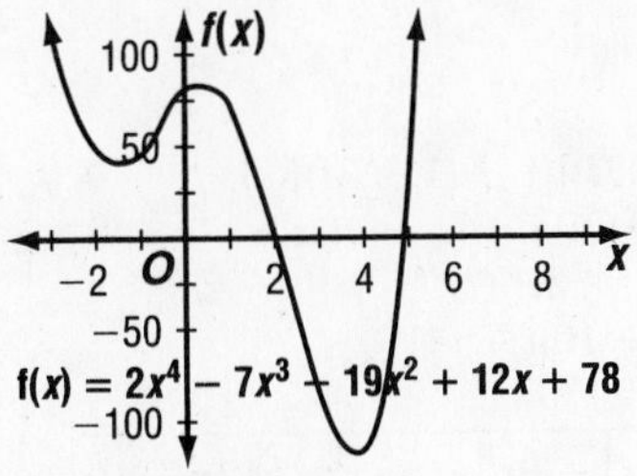

16.

x	$f(x)$	
−3	47	
−2	0	← zero
0	−16	← zero between $x = 0$ and $x = 1$
1	3	
2	32	
8	80	
9	11	← zero between $x = 9$ and $x = 10$
10	−246	

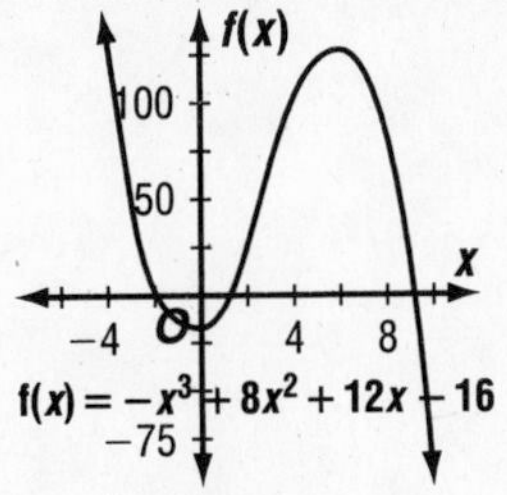

Page 895 Lesson 8-4

1. $f(x) = 5x^8 - x^6 + 7x^4 - 8x^2 - 3$
   yes yes yes no — 3 sign changes
   $f(-x) = 5(-x)^8 - (-x)^6 + 7(-x)^4 - 8(-x)^2 - 3$
   $= 5x^8 - x^6 + 7x^4 - 8x - 3$
   yes yes yes no — 3 sign changes
   positive: 3 or 1; negative: 3 or 1; imaginary: 2, 4, or 6

2. $f(x) = 6x^5 - 7x^2 + 5$
   yes yes — 2 sign changes
   $f(-x) = 6(-x)^5 - 7(-x)^2 + 5$
   $= -6x^5 - 7x^2 + 5$
   no yes — 1 sign change
   positive: 2 or 0; negative: 1; imaginary: 2 or 4

3. $f(x) = -2x^6 - 5x^5 + 8x^2 - 3x + 1$
   no yes yes yes — 3 sign changes
   $f(-x) = -2(-x)^6 - 5(-x)^5 + 8(-x)^2 - 3(-x) + 1$
   $= -2x^6 + 5x^5 + 8x^2 + 3x + 1$
   yes no no no — 1 sign change
   positive: 3 or 1; negative: 1; imaginary: 2 or 4

4. $f(x) = 4x^3 + x^2 - 38x + 56$
   no yes yes — 2 sign changes
   $f(-x) = 4(-x)^3 + (-x)^2 - 38(-x) + 56$
   $= -4x^3 + x^2 + 38x + 56$
   yes no no — 1 sign change
   positive: 2 or 0; negative: 1; imaginary: 0 or 2

5. $f(x) = 3x^8 - 15x^5 - 7x^4 - 8x^3 - 3$
   yes no no no — 1 sign change
   $f(-x) = 3(-x)^8 - 15(-x)^5 - 7(-x)^4 - 8(-x)^3 - 3$
   $= 3x^8 + 15x^5 - 7x^4 + 3x^3 - 3$
   no yes yes yes — 3 sign changes
   positive: 1; negative: 3 or 1; imaginary: 4 or 6

6. $f(x) = -x^6 - 8x^5 - 5x^4 - 11x^3 - 2x^2 - 5x - 1$
   no no no no no no
   no sign changes
   $f(-x) = -(-x)^6 - 8(-x)^5 - 5(-x)^4 - 11(-x)^3 -$
   $2(-x)^2 - 5(-x) - 1$
   $= -x^6 + 8x^5 - 5x^4 + 11x^3 - 2x^2 + 5x - 1$
   yes yes yes yes yes yes
   6 sign changes
   positive: 0; negative: 6, 4, 2, or 0;
   imaginary: 0, 2, 4, or 6

7. $f(x) = 3x^4 - 5x^3 + 2x^2 - 7x + 5$
   yes yes yes yes — 4 sign changes
   $f(-x) = 3(-x)^4 - 5(-x)^3 + 2(-x)^2 - 7(-x) + 5$
   $= 3x^4 + 5x^3 + 2x^2 + 7x + 5$
   no no no no — no sign changes
   positive: 4, 2, or 0; negative: 0; imaginary: 0, 2, or 4

8. $f(x) = x^5 - x^4 + 7x^3 - 25x^2 + 8x - 13$
   yes yes yes yes yes — 5 sign changes
   $f(-x) = (-x)^5 - (-x)^4 + 7(-x)^3 - 25(-x)^2 +$
   $8(-x) - 13$
   $= -x^5 - x^4 - 7x^3 - 25x^2 - 8x - 13$
   no no no no no
   no sign changes
   positive: 5, 3, or 1; negative: 0; imaginary: 0, 2, or 4

9. $f(x) = [x - (3 - i)][x - (3 + i)](?)$
$= [x^2 - (3 - i)x - (3 + i)x + (3 - i)(3 + i)](?)$
$= (x^2 - 6x + 10)(?)$

$$
\begin{array}{r}
x - 1 \\
x^2 - 6x + 10\,\overline{)\,x^3 - 7x^2 + 16x - 10} \\
\underline{(-)x^3 - 6x^2 + 10x} \\
-x^2 + 6x - 10 \\
\underline{-x^2 + 6x - 10} \\
0
\end{array}
$$

$3 - i, 3 + i, 1$

10.

2⌋	1	−4	6	−4
		2	−4	4
	1	−2	2	0

$x^2 - 2x + 2 = 0$

$x = \frac{-(-2) \pm \sqrt{(-2)^2 - 4(1)(2)}}{2(1)}$

$= \frac{2 \pm \sqrt{-4}}{2}$

$= \frac{2 \pm 2i}{2}$ or $1 \pm i$

$1 \pm i, 2$

11. $f(x) = [x - (5 - \sqrt{6})][x - (5 + \sqrt{6})](?)$
$= [x^2 - (5 - \sqrt{6})x - (5 + \sqrt{6})x +$
$(5 - \sqrt{6})(5 + \sqrt{6})](?)$
$= (x^2 - 10x + 19)(?)$

$$
\begin{array}{r}
x - 6 \\
x^2 - 10x + 19\,\overline{)\,x^3 - 16x^2 + 79x - 114} \\
\underline{x^3 - 10x^2 + 19x} \\
-6x^2 + 60x - 114 \\
\underline{-6x^2 + 60x - 114} \\
0
\end{array}
$$

$5 + \sqrt{6}, 5 - \sqrt{6}, 6$

12.

1⌋	−3	6	5	−8
		−3	3	8
	−3	3	8	0

$-3x^2 + 3x + 8 = 0$

$x = \frac{-3 \pm \sqrt{(3)^2 - 4(-3)(8)}}{2(-3)}$

$= \frac{-3 \pm \sqrt{105}}{-6}$

$\frac{3 \pm \sqrt{105}}{6}, 1$

13. $f(x) = \left[x - \left(\frac{2}{3} + i\right)\right]\left[x - \left(\frac{2}{3} - i\right)\right](?)$
$= \left[x^2 - \left(\frac{2}{3} + i\right)x - \left(\frac{2}{3} - i\right)x + \left(\frac{2}{3} + i\right)\left(\frac{2}{3} - i\right)\right](?)$
$= \left(x^2 - \frac{4}{3}x + \frac{13}{9}\right)(?)$

$$
\begin{array}{r}
45x^2 - 162x - 72 \\
x^2 - \frac{4}{3}x + \frac{13}{9}\,\overline{)\,45x^4 - 222x^3 + 209x^2 - 138x - 104} \\
\underline{45x^4 - 60x^3 + 65x^2} \\
-162x^3 + 144x^2 - 138x \\
\underline{-162x^3 + 216x^2 - 234x} \\
-72x^2 + 96x - 104 \\
\underline{-72x^2 + 96x - 104} \\
0
\end{array}
$$

(Continued next column)

$45x^2 - 162x - 72 = 0$
$9(5x^2 - 18x - 8) = 0$
$9(5x + 2)(x - 4) = 0$
$5x - 2 = 0$ or $x - 4 = 0$
$5x = 2$ $x = 4$
$x = \frac{2}{5}$

$\frac{2}{3} + i, \frac{2}{3} - i, 4, -\frac{2}{5}$

14. $f(x) = \left(x + \frac{5}{2}i\right)\left(x - \frac{5}{2}i\right)(?)$
$= \left(x^2 + \frac{25}{4}\right)(?)$

$$
\begin{array}{r}
4x^2 + 36x + 32 \\
x^2 + \frac{25}{4}\,\overline{)\,4x^4 + 36x^3 + 57x^2 + 225x + 200} \\
\underline{4x^4 + 25x^2} \\
36x^3 + 32x^2 + 225x \\
\underline{36x^3 + 225x} \\
32x + 200 \\
\underline{32x + 200} \\
0
\end{array}
$$

$4x^2 + 36x + 32 = 0$
$4(x^2 + 9x + 8) = 0$
$4(x + 8)(x + 1) = 0$
$x + 8 = 0$ or $x + 1 = 0$
$x = -8$ $x = -1$

$\frac{5}{2}i, -\frac{5}{2}i, -8, -1$

15. $f(x) = [x - (1 + 3i)][x - (1 - 3i)](?)$
$= [x^2 - (1 - 3i)x - (1 + 3i)x +$
$(1 + 3i)(1 - 3i)](?)$
$= (x^2 - 2x + 10)(?)$

$$
\begin{array}{r}
-x^2 + 4x - 1 \\
x^2 - 2x + 10\,\overline{)\,-x^4 + 6x^3 - 19x^2 + 42x - 10} \\
\underline{-x^4 + 2x^3 - 10x^2} \\
4x^3 - 9x^2 + 42x \\
\underline{4x^3 - 8x^2 + 40x} \\
-x^2 + 2x - 10 \\
\underline{-x^2 + 2x - 10} \\
0
\end{array}
$$

$-x^2 + 4x - 1 = 0$

$x = \frac{-4 \pm \sqrt{4^2 - 4(-1)(-1)}}{-2}$

$= \frac{-4 \pm \sqrt{12}}{-2}$

$= \frac{-4 \pm 2\sqrt{3}}{-2}$

$= 2 \pm \sqrt{3}$

$2 \pm \sqrt{3}, 1 + 3i, 1 - 3i$

Page 895 Lesson 8-5

1. factors of p: $\pm 1, \pm 2, \pm 3, \pm 6$; factors of q: $\pm 1, \pm 3$
possible rational zeros: $\pm 1, \pm\frac{1}{3}, \pm\frac{2}{3}, \pm 2, \pm 6$
2. factors of p: $\pm 1, \pm 2, \pm 4, \pm 8$;
factors of q: $\pm 1, \pm 2, \pm 4$
possible rational zeros: $\pm 1, \pm 2, \pm 4, \pm 8, \pm\frac{1}{2}, \pm\frac{1}{4}$
3. factors of p: $\pm 1, \pm 7$; factors of q: $\pm 1, \pm 2, \pm 3, \pm 6$
possible rational zeros: $\pm 1, \pm 7, \pm\frac{1}{6}, \pm\frac{7}{6}, \pm\frac{1}{2}, \pm\frac{7}{2}, \pm\frac{1}{3}, \pm\frac{7}{3}$

4. factors of p: $\pm1, \pm2, \pm4, \pm5, \pm10, \pm20, \pm25, \pm50, \pm100$; factors of q: $\pm1, \pm2, \pm3, \pm4, \pm6, \pm12$
possible rational zeros: $\pm1, \pm2, \pm4, \pm5, \pm10, \pm20, \pm25, \pm50, \pm100, \pm\frac{1}{2}, \pm\frac{5}{2}, \pm\frac{25}{2}, \pm\frac{1}{3}, \pm\frac{2}{3}, \pm\frac{4}{3}, \pm\frac{5}{3}, \pm\frac{10}{3}, \pm\frac{20}{3}, \pm\frac{25}{3}, \pm\frac{50}{3}, \pm\frac{100}{3}, \pm\frac{1}{4}, \pm\frac{5}{4}, \pm\frac{25}{4}, \pm\frac{1}{6}, \pm\frac{5}{6}, \pm\frac{25}{6}, \pm\frac{1}{12}, \pm\frac{5}{12}, \pm\frac{25}{12}$

5. factors of p: $\pm1, \pm2, \pm3, \pm6, \pm9, \pm18$;
factors of q: ±1
possible rational zeros: $\pm1, \pm2, \pm3, \pm6, \pm9, \pm18$

$$\begin{array}{r|rrrrr} 3 & 1 & 3 & -7 & -27 & -18 \\ & & 3 & 18 & 33 & 18 \\ \hline & 1 & 6 & 11 & 6 & 0 \end{array}$$

$$\begin{array}{r|rrrr} -3 & 1 & 6 & 11 & 6 \\ & & -3 & -9 & -6 \\ \hline & 1 & 3 & 2 & 0 \end{array}$$

$x^2 + 3x + 2 = 0$
$(x + 2)(x + 1) = 0$
$x + 2 = 0$ or $x + 1 = 0$
$x = -2$ $\quad$ $x = -1$
$\pm3, -1, -2$

6.
$$\begin{array}{r|rrrrr} 7 & 6 & -31 & -119 & 214 & 560 \\ & & 42 & 77 & -294 & -560 \\ \hline & 6 & 11 & -42 & -80 & 0 \end{array}$$

$$\begin{array}{r|rrrr} -2 & 6 & 11 & -42 & -80 \\ & & -12 & 2 & 80 \\ \hline & 6 & -1 & -40 & 0 \end{array}$$

$6x^2 - x - 40 = 0$
$(3x - 8)(2x + 5) = 0$
$3x - 8 = 0$ or $2x + 5 = 0$
$x = \frac{8}{3}$ $\quad$ $x = -\frac{5}{3}$
$-\frac{5}{2}, -2, \frac{8}{3}, 7$

7. factors of p: $\pm1, \pm3$
factors of q: $\pm1, \pm2, \pm4, \pm5, \pm10, \pm20$
possible rational zeros: $\pm1, \pm\frac{1}{2}, \pm\frac{1}{4}, \pm\frac{1}{5}, \pm\frac{1}{10}, \pm\frac{1}{20}, \pm3, \pm\frac{3}{2}, \pm\frac{3}{4}, \pm\frac{3}{5}, \pm\frac{3}{10}, \pm\frac{3}{20}$

$$\begin{array}{r|rrrrr} 1 & 20 & -16 & 11 & -12 & -3 \\ & & 20 & 4 & 15 & 3 \\ \hline & 20 & 4 & 15 & 3 & 0 \end{array}$$

$$\begin{array}{r|rrrr} -\frac{1}{5} & 20 & 4 & 15 & 3 \\ & & -4 & 0 & -3 \\ \hline & 20 & 0 & 15 & 0 \end{array}$$

$20x^2 + 15 = 0$
$20x^2 = -15$
$x^2 = -\frac{15}{20}$ not a real solution
$1, -\frac{1}{5}$

8.
$$\begin{array}{r|rrrrr} 7 & 2 & -30 & 117 & -75 & 280 \\ & & 14 & -112 & 35 & -280 \\ \hline & 2 & -16 & 5 & -40 & \end{array}$$

(Continued next column)

$$\begin{array}{r|rrrr} 8 & 2 & -16 & 5 & -40 \\ & & 16 & 0 & 40 \\ \hline & 2 & 0 & 5 & 0 \end{array}$$

$2x^2 + 5 = 0$
$2x^2 = -5$
$x^2 = -\frac{5}{2}$ not a real solution
7, 8

9. factors of p: $\pm1, \pm3, \pm7, \pm21$; factors of q: $\pm1, \pm3$
possible rational zeros: $\pm1, \pm3, \pm7, \pm21\ \pm\frac{1}{3}, \pm\frac{7}{3}$

$$\begin{array}{r|rrrrrr} 3 & 3 & -17 & 33 & -19 & -31 & 21 \\ & & 9 & -24 & 27 & 24 & -21 \\ \hline & 3 & -8 & 9 & 8 & -7 & 0 \end{array}$$

3

10. factors of p: $\pm1, \pm3, \pm9$; factors of q: $\pm1, \pm2$
possible rational zeros: $\pm1, \pm3, \pm9, \pm\frac{1}{2}, \pm\frac{3}{2}, \pm\frac{9}{2}$

$$\begin{array}{r|rrrrrrr} 1 & 2 & -12 & 17 & 6 & -10 & 6 & -9 \\ & & 2 & -10 & 7 & 13 & 3 & 9 \\ \hline & 2 & -10 & 7 & 13 & 3 & 9 & 0 \end{array}$$

$$\begin{array}{r|rrrrrr} -1 & 2 & -10 & 7 & 13 & 3 & 9 \\ & & -2 & 12 & -19 & 6 & -9 \\ \hline & 2 & -12 & 19 & -6 & 9 & 0 \end{array}$$

$$\begin{array}{r|rrrrr} 3 & 2 & -12 & 19 & -6 & 9 \\ & & 6 & -18 & 3 & -9 \\ \hline & 2 & -6 & 1 & -3 & 0 \end{array}$$

$3, \pm1$

11. factors of p: ±1
factors of q: $\pm1, \pm2, \pm3, \pm4, \pm6, \pm8, \pm12, \pm24, \pm48$
possible rational
zeros: $\pm1, \pm\frac{1}{2}, \pm\frac{1}{3}, \pm\frac{1}{4}, \pm\frac{1}{6}, \pm\frac{1}{8}, \pm\frac{1}{12}, \pm\frac{1}{24}, \pm\frac{1}{48}$

$$\begin{array}{r|rrrrrr} \frac{1}{2} & 48 & 16 & -24 & -8 & 3 & 1 \\ & & 24 & 20 & -2 & -5 & -1 \\ \hline & 48 & 40 & -4 & -10 & -2 & 0 \end{array}$$

$$\begin{array}{r|rrrrr} -\frac{1}{2} & 48 & 40 & -4 & -10 & -2 \\ & & -24 & -8 & 6 & 2 \\ \hline & 48 & 16 & -12 & -4 & 0 \end{array}$$

$$\begin{array}{r|rrrr} -\frac{1}{3} & 48 & 16 & -12 & -4 \\ & & -16 & 0 & 4 \\ \hline & 48 & 0 & -12 & 0 \end{array}$$

$48x^2 - 12 = 0$
$48x^2 = 12$
$x^2 = \frac{1}{4}$
$x = \pm\frac{1}{2}$
$\pm\frac{1}{2}, -\frac{1}{3}$

12. $f(x) = x^5 - x^4 + x^3 + 3x^2 - x$
$= x(x^4 - x^3 + x^2 + 3x - 1)$
possible rational zeros: ±1
0

13.

$-\frac{1}{2}$	90	−99	−64	36	16
		−45	72	−4	−16
	90	−144	8	32	0

$-\frac{2}{5}$	90	−144	8	32
		−36	72	−32
	90	−180	80	0

$90x^2 - 180x + 80 = 0$

$10(9x^2 - 18x + 8) = 0$

$(3x - 2)(3x - 4) = 0$

$3x - 2 = 0$ or $3x - 4 = 0$

$x = \frac{2}{3}$ $\quad x = \frac{4}{3}$

$-\frac{1}{2}, -\frac{2}{5}, \frac{2}{3}, \frac{4}{3}$

14.

8	2	−13	−34	65	120
		16	24	−80	−120
	2	3	−10	−15	0

$-\frac{3}{2}$	2	3	−10	−15
		−3	0	15
	2	0	−10	0

$2x^2 - 10 = 0$

$2x^2 = 10$

$x^2 = 5$

$x = \pm\sqrt{5}$

$8, -\frac{3}{2}, \sqrt{5}, -\sqrt{5}$

15.

2	6	5	−8	−45	−14
		12	34	52	14
	6	17	26	7	0

$-\frac{1}{3}$	6	17	26	7
		−2	−5	−7
	6	15	21	0

$6x^2 + 15x + 21 = 0$

$3(2x^2 + 5x + 7) = 0$

$x = \frac{-5 \pm \sqrt{5^2 - 4(2)(7)}}{2(2)}$

$= \frac{-5 \pm \sqrt{-31}}{4}$

$= \frac{-5 \pm i\sqrt{31}}{4}$

$2, -\frac{1}{3}, \frac{-5 + i\sqrt{31}}{4}, \frac{-5 - i\sqrt{31}}{4}$

16.

$\frac{3}{2}$	4	0	19	0	−63
		6	9	42	63
	4	6	28	42	0

$-\frac{3}{2}$	4	6	28	42
		−6	0	−42
	4	0	28	0

$4x^2 + 28 = 0$

$4x^2 = -28$

$x^2 = -7$

$x = \pm i\sqrt{7}$

$\frac{3}{2}, -\frac{3}{2}, i\sqrt{7}, -i\sqrt{7}$

Page 896 Lesson 8-6

1. $5x^{10} - 6x^5 = 3$

$5x^{10} - 6x^5 - 3 = 0$

$5(x^5)^2 - 6(x^5) - 3 = 0$

2. $3r + 2\sqrt{r} - 7 = 0$

$3(\sqrt{r})^2 + 2(\sqrt{r}) - 7 = 0$

3. $z^9 = 8z^3$

$z^9 - 8z^3 = 0$

impossible; $(z^3)^2 \neq z^9$

4. $2y^6 + 3y^4 = 10$

$2y^6 + 3y^4 - 10 = 0$

impossible; $(y^4)^2 \neq y^6$

5. $x - 10x^{\frac{1}{2}} + 25 = 0$

$(x^{\frac{1}{2}})^2 - 10(x^{\frac{1}{2}}) + 25 = 0$

6. $x^{\frac{4}{3}} - 7x^{\frac{2}{3}} + 12 = 0$

$(x^{\frac{2}{3}})^2 - 7(x^{\frac{2}{3}}) + 12 = 0$

7. $y^{\frac{1}{2}} - 10y^{\frac{1}{4}} + 16 = 0$

$(y^{\frac{1}{4}})^2 - 10(y^{\frac{1}{4}}) + 16 = 0$

8. $r^{\frac{2}{3}} - 5r^{\frac{1}{3}} + 6 = 0$

$(r^{\frac{1}{3}})^2 - 5(r^{\frac{1}{3}}) + 6 = 0$

9. $x^{\frac{1}{2}} + 7x^{\frac{1}{4}} + 12 = 0$

$(x^{\frac{1}{4}})^2 + 7(x^{\frac{1}{4}}) + 12 = 0$

10. $8x^3 + 27 = 0$

$(2x + 3)(4x^2 - 6x + 9) = 0$

$2x + 3 = 0$ or $4x^2 - 6x + 9 = 0$

$x = -\frac{3}{2}$ $\quad x = \frac{-(-6) \pm \sqrt{(-6)^2 - 4(4)(9)}}{2(4)}$

$= \frac{6 \pm \sqrt{-108}}{8}$

$= \frac{6 \pm 6i\sqrt{3}}{8}$

$= \frac{3 \pm 3i\sqrt{3}}{4}$

11. $5\sqrt[3]{z^2} - \sqrt[3]{z} = 4$

$5\sqrt[3]{z^2} - \sqrt[3]{z} - 4 = 0$

$5(\sqrt[3]{z})^2 - (\sqrt[3]{z}) - 4 = 0$

$(5\sqrt[3]{z} + 4)(\sqrt[3]{z} - 1) = 0$

$5\sqrt[3]{z} + 4 = 0$ or $\sqrt[3]{z} - 1 = 0$

$5\sqrt[3]{z} = -4$ $\quad \sqrt[3]{z} = 1$

$\sqrt[3]{z} = -\frac{4}{5}$ $\quad z = 1$

$z = -\frac{64}{125}$

12. $2m^4 = 3m^2 + 5$

$2m^4 - 3m^2 - 5 = 0$

$2(m^2)^2 - 3(m^2) - 5 = 0$

$(2m^2 - 5)(m^2 + 1) = 0$

$2m^2 - 5 = 0$ or $m^2 + 1 = 0$

$2m^2 = 5$ $\quad m^2 = -1$

$m^2 = \frac{5}{2}$ $\quad m = \pm i$

$m = \pm\sqrt{\frac{5}{2}}$ or $\pm\frac{\sqrt{10}}{2}$

13. $3b^5 = 7b^3$
$3b^5 - 7b^3 = 0$
$b^3(3b^2 - 7) = 0$
$b^3 = 0$ or $3b^2 - 7 = 0$
$b = 0$ $\quad 3b^2 = 7$
$b^2 = \frac{7}{3}$
$b = \pm\sqrt{\frac{7}{3}}$ or $\pm\frac{\sqrt{21}}{3}$

14. $x^3 + 10x^2 + 16x = 0$
$x(x^2 + 10x + 16) = 0$
$x(x + 8)(x + 2) = 0$
$x = 0$ or $x + 8 = 0$ or $x + 2 = 0$
$x = -8$ $\quad x = -2$

15. $y^4 - 3y^2 + 2 = 0$
$(y^2)^2 - 3(y^2) + 2 = 0$
$(y^2 - 2)(y^2 - 1) = 0$
$y^2 - 2 = 0$ or $y^2 - 1 = 0$
$y^2 = 2$ $\quad y^2 = 1$
$y = \pm\sqrt{2}$ $\quad y = \pm 1$

16. $a^3 = 125$
$a^3 - 125 = 0$
$(a - 5)(a^2 + 5a + 25) = 0$
$a - 5 = 0$ or $a^2 + 5a + 25 = 0$
$a = 5$ $\quad a = \frac{-(5) \pm \sqrt{(5)^2 - 4(1)(25)}}{2(1)}$
$= \frac{-5 \pm \sqrt{-75}}{2}$
$= \frac{-5 \pm 5i\sqrt{3}}{2}$

17. $m - 9\sqrt{m} + 8 = 0$
$(\sqrt{m})^2 - 9(\sqrt{m}) + 8 = 0$
$(\sqrt{m} - 8)(\sqrt{m} - 1) = 0$
$\sqrt{m} - 8 = 0$ or $\sqrt{m} - 1 = 0$
$\sqrt{m} = 8$ $\quad \sqrt{m} = 1$
$m = 64$ $\quad m = 1$

18. $r^{\frac{2}{3}} - 12r^{\frac{1}{3}} + 20 = 0$
$(r^{\frac{1}{3}})^2 - 12(r^{\frac{1}{3}}) + 20 = 0$
$(r^{\frac{1}{3}} - 10)(r^{\frac{1}{3}} - 2) = 0$
$r^{\frac{1}{3}} - 10 = 0$ or $r^{\frac{1}{3}} - 2 = 0$
$r^{\frac{1}{3}} = 10$ $\quad r^{\frac{1}{3}} = 2$
$r = 1000$ $\quad r = 8$

19. $x^{\frac{2}{3}} - 8x^{\frac{1}{3}} + 15 = 0$
$(x^{\frac{1}{3}})^2 - 8(x^{\frac{1}{3}}) + 15 = 0$
$(x^{\frac{1}{3}} - 3)(x^{\frac{1}{3}} - 5) = 0$
$x^{\frac{1}{3}} - 3 = 0$ or $x^{\frac{1}{3}} - 5 = 0$
$x^{\frac{1}{3}} = 3$ $\quad x^{\frac{1}{3}} = 5$
$x = 27$ $\quad x = 125$

20. $m - 11m^{\frac{1}{2}} + 30 = 0$
$(m^{\frac{1}{2}})^2 - 11(m^{\frac{1}{2}}) + 30 = 0$
$(m^{\frac{1}{2}} - 5)(m^{\frac{1}{2}} - 6) = 0$
$m^{\frac{1}{2}} - 5 = 0$ or $m^{\frac{1}{2}} - 6 = 0$
$m^{\frac{1}{2}} = 5$ $\quad m^{\frac{1}{2}} = 6$
$m = 25$ $\quad m = 36$

21. $y^3 - 8y^{\frac{3}{2}} + 16 = 0$
$(y^{\frac{3}{2}})^2 - 8(y^{\frac{3}{2}}) + 16 = 0$
$(y^{\frac{3}{2}} - 4)^2 = 0$
$y^{\frac{3}{2}} - 4 = 0$
$y^{\frac{3}{2}} = 4$
$y = 4^{\frac{2}{3}}$ or $\sqrt[3]{16}$

22. $3g^{\frac{2}{3}} - 10g^{\frac{1}{3}} + 8 = 0$
$3(g^{\frac{1}{3}})^2 - 10(g^{\frac{1}{3}}) + 8 = 0$
$(3g^{\frac{1}{3}} - 4)(g^{\frac{1}{3}} - 2) = 0$
$3g^{\frac{1}{3}} - 4 = 0$ or $g^{\frac{1}{3}} - 2 = 0$
$3g^{\frac{1}{3}} = 4$ $\quad g^{\frac{1}{3}} = 2$
$g^{\frac{1}{3}} = \frac{4}{3}$ $\quad g = 8$
$g = \frac{64}{27}$

23. $3m + m^{\frac{1}{2}} - 2 = 0$
$3(m^{\frac{1}{2}})^2 + (m^{\frac{1}{2}}) - 2 = 0$
$(3m^{\frac{1}{2}} - 2)(m^{\frac{1}{2}} + 1) = 0$
$3m^{\frac{1}{2}} - 2 = 0$ or $m^{\frac{1}{2}} + 1 = 0$
$3m^{\frac{1}{2}} = 2$ $\quad m^{\frac{1}{2}} = -1$
$m^{\frac{1}{2}} = \frac{2}{3}$ $\quad m = \boldsymbol{i}$
$m = \frac{4}{9}$

24. $x^{\frac{1}{2}} - 6x^{\frac{1}{4}} + 8 = 0$
$(x^{\frac{1}{4}})^2 - 6(x^{\frac{1}{4}}) + 8 = 0$
$(x^{\frac{1}{4}} - 4)(x^{\frac{1}{4}} - 2) = 0$
$x^{\frac{1}{4}} - 4 = 0$ or $x^{\frac{1}{4}} - 2 = 0$
$x^{\frac{1}{4}} = 4$ $\quad x^{\frac{1}{4}} = 2$
$x = 256$ $\quad x = 16$

Page 896 Lesson 8-7

1. $[f \circ g](-4) = f[g(-4)]$
$= f[(-4) - 3]$
$= f(-7)$
$= 3(-7) + 5$
$= -16$

$[g \circ f](-4) = g[f(-4)]$
$= g[3(-4) + 5]$
$= g(-7)$
$= (-7) - 3$
$= -10$

2. $[f \circ g](-4) = f[g(-4)]$
$= f[(-4)^2]$
$= f(16)$
$= \sqrt{16}$
$= 4$

$[g \circ f](-4) = g[f(-4)]$
$= g[\sqrt{-4}]$
$= g(2\boldsymbol{i})$
$= (2\boldsymbol{i})^2$
$= -4$

3. $[f \circ g](-4) = f[g(-4)]$
$= f\left[\frac{(-4) - 8}{3}\right]$
$= f(-4)$
$= 2(-4)^2 - 5(-4) + 8$
$= 60$

$[g \circ f](-4) = g[f(-4)]$
$= g[2(-4)^2 - 5(-4) + 8]$
$= g(60)$
$= \frac{(60) - 8}{3}$
$= \frac{52}{3}$

4. $[f \circ g](-4) = f[g(-4)] = f(0) = 5$ $[g \circ f](-4) = g[f(-4)] = g(2) = 3$

5. $[f \circ g](-4) = f[g(-4)] = f(1) = -7$ $[g \circ f](-4) = g[f(-4)] = g(0) = 11$

6. $[f \circ g](-4) = f[g(-4)] = f[(-4) + 1] = f(-3) = (-3)^2 + 1 = 10$ $[g \circ f](-4) = g[f(-4)] = g[(-4)^2 + 1] = g(17) = (17) + 1 = 18$

7. $g[h(x)] = g(3x) = 8 - 2(3x) = 8 - 6x$ $h[g(x)] = h(8 - 2x) = 3(8 - 2x) = 24 - 6x$

8. $g[h(x)] = g(3x + 2) = (3x + 2)^2 - 7 = (9x^2 + 12x + 4) - 7 = 9x^2 + 12x - 3$ $h[g(x)] = h(x^2 - 7) = 3(x^2 - 7) + 2 = 3x^2 - 19$

9. $g[h(x)] = g\left(\frac{x-7}{2}\right) = 2\left(\frac{x-7}{2}\right) + 7 = x$
$h[g(x)] = h(2x + 7) = \frac{(2x + 7) - 7}{2} = x$

10. $g[h(x)] = g(5 - 3x) = |2(5 - 3x) + 3| = |13 - 6x|$
$h[g(x)] = h(|2x + 3|) = 5 - 3|2x + 3|$

11. $g[f(1)] = g[(1)^2] = g(1) = 3(1) = 3$

12. $[f \circ h](3) = f[h(3)] = f[(3) - 1] = f(2) = (2)^2 = 4$

13. $[h \circ f](3) = h[f(3)] = h[(3)^2] = h(9) = (9) - 1 = 8$

14. $[g \circ f](-2) = g[f(-2)] = g[(-2)^2] = g(4) = 3(4) = 12$

15. $g[h(-20)] = g[(-20) - 1] = g(-21) = 3(-21) = -63$

16. $f[h(-3)] = f[(-3) - 1] = f(-4) = (-4)^2 = 16$

17. $g[f(x)] = g[x^2] = 3(x^2) = 3x^2$

18. $[f \circ (g \circ h)](x) = f[g[h(x)]] = f[g(x - 1)] = f[3(x - 1)] = f(3x - 3) = (3x - 3)^2 = 9x^2 - 18x + 9$

Page 896 Lesson 8-8

1. {(7, −2), (0, 3), (−8, 5)}; yes
2. {(9, −3), (4, −2), (9, 3), (1, −1)}; no
3. {(5, 1), (3, 2), (3, 4), (5, −1)}; no

4. $f(x) = x - 5$
$y = x - 5$
$x = y - 5$
$x + 5 = y$
$f^{-1}(x) = x + 5$

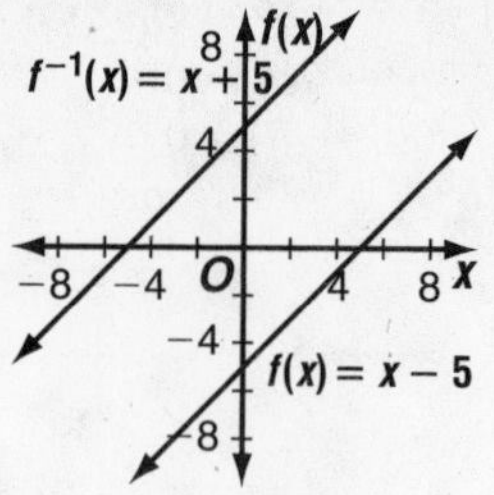

5. $y = 2x + 8$
$x = 2y + 8$
$\frac{x-8}{2} = y$
$y^{-1} = \frac{x-8}{2}$

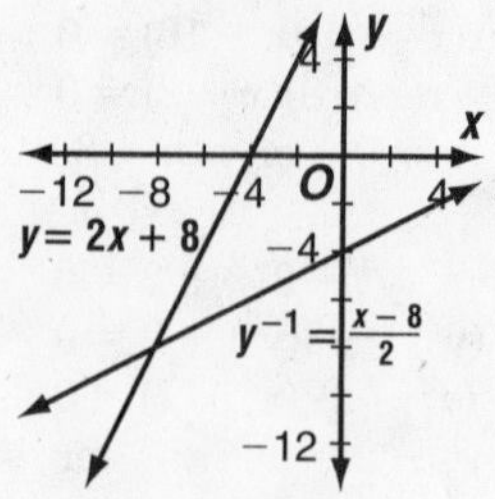

6. $g(x) = 2x^2 - 3$
$y = 2x^2 - 3$
$x = 2y^2 - 3$
$\frac{x+3}{2} = y^2$
$y = \pm\sqrt{\frac{x+3}{2}}$
$g^{-1}(x) = \pm\frac{\sqrt{2x+6}}{2}$

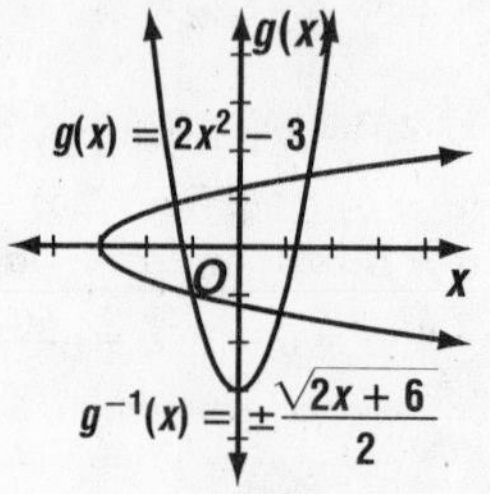

7. $h(x) = \frac{x}{5} + 1$
$y = \frac{x}{5} + 1$
$x = \frac{y}{5} + 1$
$5(x - 1) = y$
$h^{-1}(x) = 5(x - 1)$

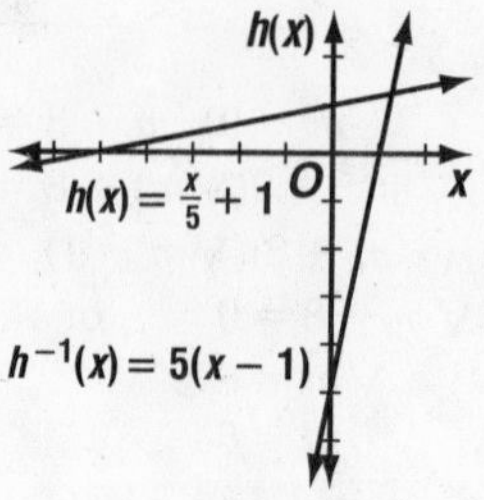

8. $y = -2$
$x = -2$

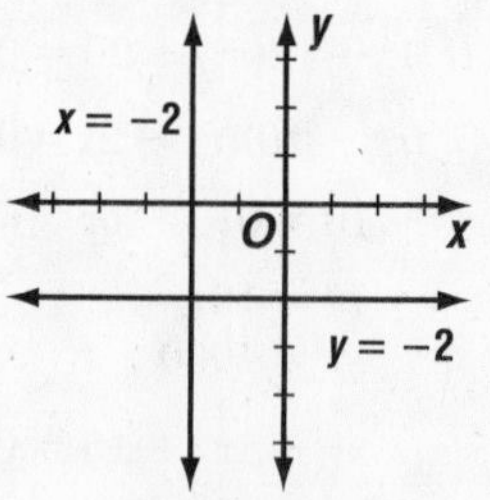

9. $g(x) = 5 - 2x$
$y = 5 - 2x$
$x = 5 - 2y$
$\frac{x-5}{-2} = y$
$g^{-1}(x) = \frac{5-x}{2}$

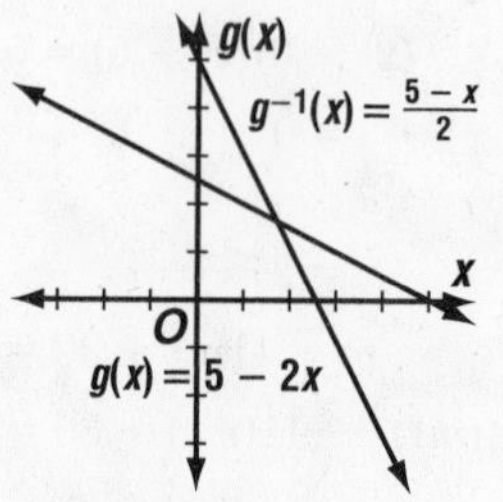

10.
$$y = -x^2 + 2$$
$$x = -y^2 + 2$$
$$x - 2 = -y^2$$
$$\pm\sqrt{2 - x} = y$$
$$y^{-1} = \pm\sqrt{2 - x}$$

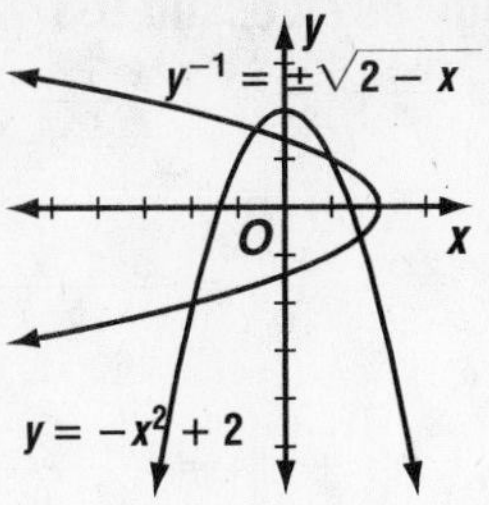

11. $h(x) = -\frac{2}{3}x$
$$y = -\frac{2}{3}x$$
$$x = -\frac{2}{3}y$$
$$-\frac{3}{2}x = y$$
$$h^{-1}(x) = -\frac{3}{2}x$$

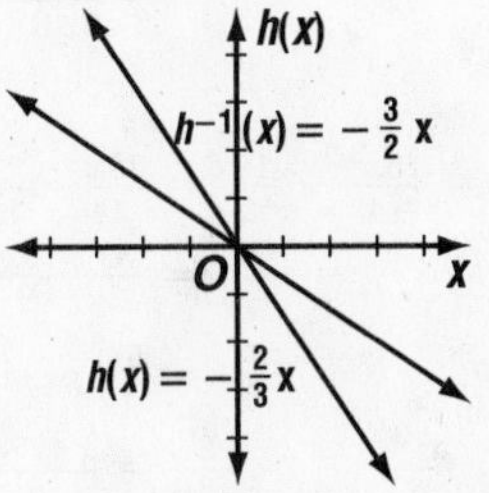

12. $f[g(x)] = f\left(\frac{3x - 5}{3}\right) = \frac{2\left(\frac{3x-5}{3}\right) - 3}{5} = \frac{6x - 10 - 9}{15} = \frac{6x - 19}{15}$

$g[f(x)] = g\left(\frac{2x - 3}{5}\right) = \frac{3\left(\frac{2x-3}{5}\right) - 5}{3} = \frac{6x - 9 - 25}{15} = \frac{6x - 34}{15}$

no

13. $f[g(x)] = f\left(\frac{x + 6}{5}\right) = 5\left(\frac{x+6}{5}\right) - 6 = x + 6 - 6 = x$

$g[f(x)] = g(5x - 6) = \frac{(5x - 6) + 6}{5} = \frac{5x}{5} = x$

yes

14. $f[g(x)] = f\left(2 - \frac{1}{3}x\right) = 6 - 3\left(2 - \frac{1}{3}x\right) = 6 - 6 + x = x$

$g[f(x)] = g(6 - 3x) = 2 - \frac{1}{3}(6 - 3x) = 2 - 2 + x = x$

yes

15. $f[g(x)] = f\left(\frac{1}{3}x + 7\right) = 3\left(\frac{1}{3}x + 7\right) - 7 = x + 21 - 7 = x + 14$

$g[f(x)] = g(3x - 7) = \frac{1}{3}(3x - 7) + 7 = x - \frac{7}{3} + 7 = x + \frac{14}{3}$

no

Page 897 Lesson 9-1

1. $x + 4 = 0$
$x = -4$
$y = 0$

2. $x + 3 = 0$
$x = -3$
$y = 1$

3. $x + 1 = 0$ or $x - 8 = 0$
$x = -1$ $\quad x = 8$
$y = 0$

4. $x + 2 = 0$
$x = -2$
$y = 1$

5. $x + 2 = 0$
$x = -2$
none

6. $x = 0 \qquad y = 0$

7.

x	$f(x)$
0	−0.2
3	−0.5
4.5	−2
5	undefined
5.5	2
6	1
7	0.5

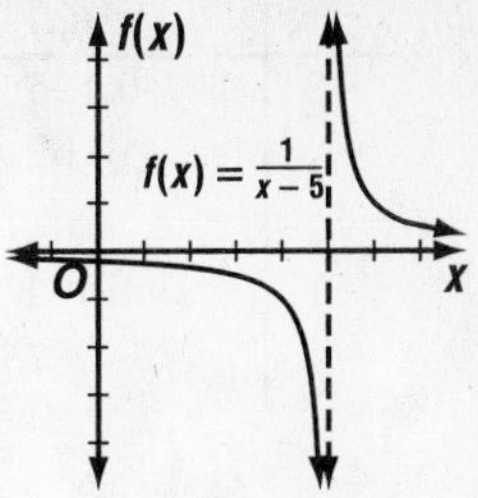

8.

x	$f(x)$
−3	4.5
−2	6
$-1\frac{1}{2}$	9
−1	undefined
$-\frac{1}{2}$	−3
0	0
2	2

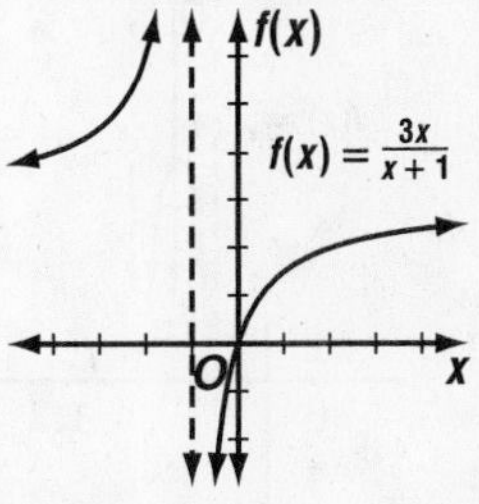

9.

x	$f(x)$
−6	−3
−5	−2
−4	−1
−3	undefined
−2	1
−1	2
0	3

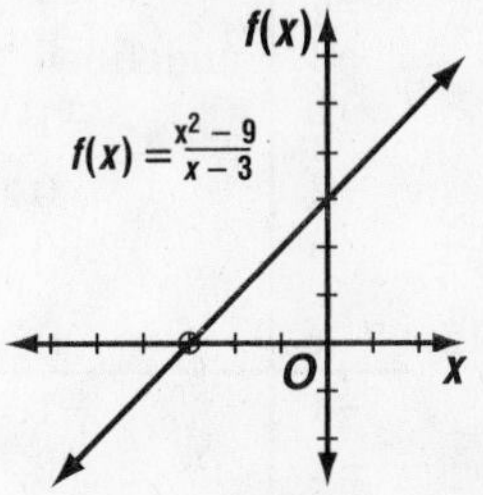

10.

x	$f(x)$
0	0
4	−2
5.5	−11
6	undefined
6.5	13
8	4
12	2

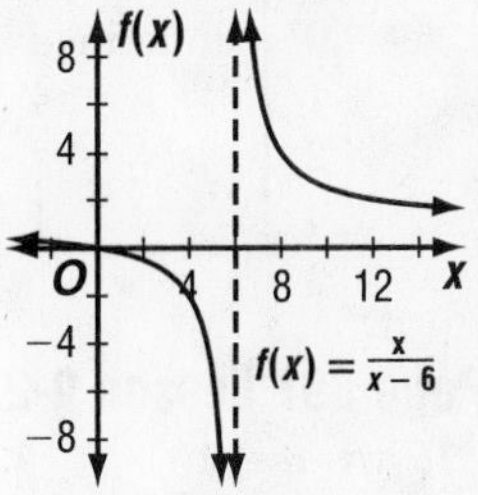

11.

x	$f(x)$
0	0.11
2	1
2.5	4
3	undefined
3.5	4
4	1
6	0.11

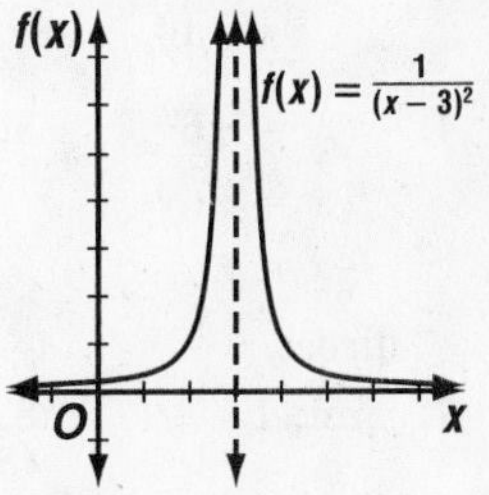

12.

x	$f(x)$
−8	0.03
−4	0.25
−3.5	0.53
−3	undefined
−2.5	−0.62

x	$f(x)$
0	−0.17
3.5	−0.62
4	undefined
4.5	0.53
6	0.11

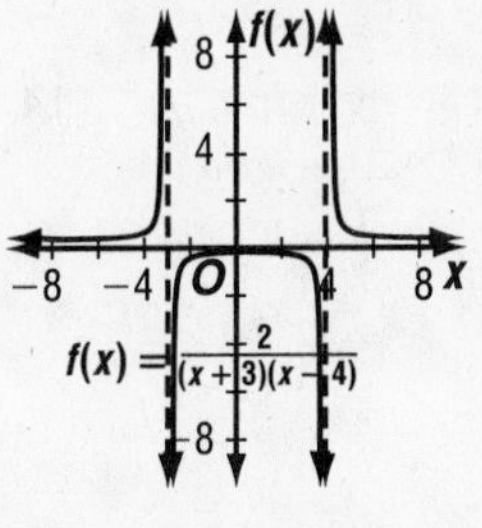

13.

x	$f(x)$
-3	0.125
-2	0.67
$-1\frac{1}{2}$	2
-1	undefined
$-\frac{1}{2}$	-4.67

x	$f(x)$
0	-4
$\frac{1}{2}$	-6
1	undefined
$1\frac{1}{2}$	4.4
3	0.875

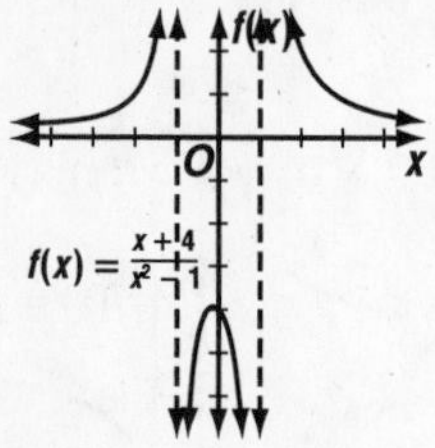

14.

x	$f(x)$
-6	1.3
-4	2
$-3\frac{1}{2}$	15
-3	undefined
$-2\frac{1}{2}$	-1
-2	0
0	0.66

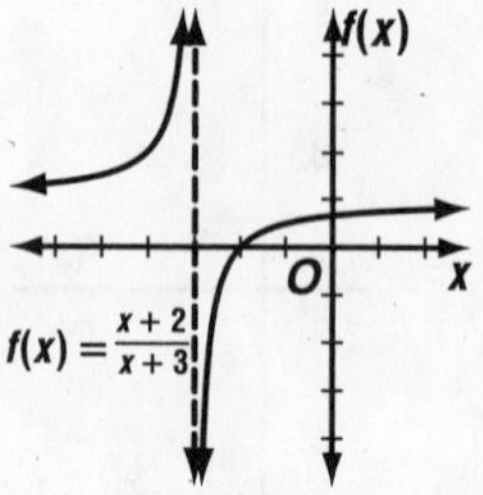

15.

x	$f(x)$
-4	-1
-2	-2
-1	-4
0	undefined
1	4
2	2
4	1

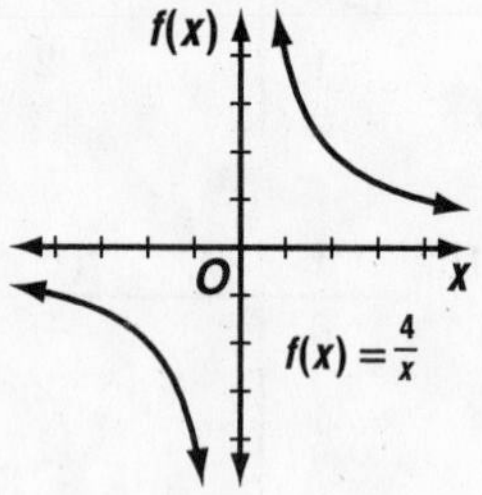

Page 897 Lesson 9-2

1. inverse, 10

2. $x = 6y$
$\frac{1}{6}x = y$
direct, $\frac{1}{6}$

3. direct, $\frac{1}{7}$

4. $\frac{x}{y} = -6$
$x = -6y$
$-\frac{1}{6}x = y$
direct, $-\frac{1}{6}$

5. direct, 10

6. $x = \frac{2}{y}$
$xy = 2$
inverse, 2

7. joint, 1

8. $\frac{1}{4}b = -\frac{3}{5}c$
$-\frac{5}{12}b = c$
direct, $-\frac{5}{12}$

9. joint, 1

10. $y = kx$
$16 = k \cdot 4$
$4 = k$
$y = 4x$
$= 4(12)$
$= 48$

11. $xy = k$
$12(-3) = k$
$-36 = k$
$xy = -36$
$x(-18) = -36$
$x = 2$

12. $m = kw$
$-15 = k \cdot 2.5$
$-6 = k$
$m = -6w$
$= -6(12.5)$
$= -75$

13. $y = kxz$
$10 = k \cdot 5 \cdot 4$
$\frac{1}{2} = k$
$y = \frac{1}{2}xz$
$= \frac{1}{2} \cdot 4 \cdot 2$
$= 4$

14. $xy = k$
$24\left(\frac{1}{4}\right) = k$
$6 = k$
$xy = 6$
$\frac{3}{4}y = 6$
$y = 8$

15. $y = kxz$
$45 = k \cdot 9 \cdot 15$
$\frac{1}{3} = k$
$y = \frac{1}{3}xz$
$= \frac{1}{3} \cdot 25 \cdot 12$
$= 100$

Page 897 Lesson 9-3

1. $\frac{3x^3}{-2} \cdot \frac{-4}{9x} = \frac{3 \cdot x \cdot x \cdot x \cdot (-1) \cdot 2 \cdot 2}{-1 \cdot 2 \cdot 3 \cdot 3 \cdot x}$
$= \frac{2x^2}{3}$

2. $\frac{21x^2}{-5} \cdot \frac{10}{7x^3} = \frac{3 \cdot 7 \cdot x \cdot x \cdot 2 \cdot 5}{-1 \cdot 5 \cdot 7 \cdot x \cdot x \cdot x}$
$= -\frac{6}{x}$

3. $\frac{2u^2}{3} \div \frac{6u^3}{5} = \frac{2u^2}{3} \cdot \frac{5}{6u^3}$
$= \frac{2 \cdot u \cdot u \cdot 5}{3 \cdot 2 \cdot 3 \cdot u \cdot u \cdot u}$
$= \frac{5}{9u}$

4. $\frac{15x^3}{14} \div \frac{18x}{7} = \frac{15x^3}{14} \cdot \frac{7}{18x}$
$= \frac{3 \cdot 5 \cdot x \cdot x \cdot x \cdot 7}{2 \cdot 7 \cdot 2 \cdot 3 \cdot 3 \cdot x}$
$= \frac{5x^2}{12}$

5. $\frac{xy^2}{2} \cdot \frac{x^2}{2y} \cdot \frac{2}{x^2y} = \frac{x \cdot y \cdot y \cdot x \cdot x \cdot 2}{2 \cdot 2 \cdot y \cdot x \cdot x \cdot y}$
$= \frac{x}{2}$

6. $axy \div \frac{ax}{y} \div \frac{ay}{x} = axy \cdot \frac{y}{ax} \cdot \frac{x}{ay}$
$= \frac{a \cdot x \cdot y \cdot y \cdot x}{a \cdot x \cdot a \cdot y}$
$= \frac{xy}{a}$

7. $\frac{9u^2}{28v} \div \frac{27u^2}{8v^2} \div \frac{4u^2}{21} = \frac{9u^2}{28v} \cdot \frac{8v^2}{27u^2} \cdot \frac{21}{4u^2}$
$= \frac{3 \cdot 3 \cdot u \cdot u \cdot 2 \cdot 2 \cdot 2 \cdot v \cdot v \cdot 3 \cdot 7}{2 \cdot 2 \cdot 7 \cdot v \cdot 3 \cdot 3 \cdot 3 \cdot u \cdot u \cdot 2 \cdot 2 \cdot u \cdot u}$
$= \frac{v}{2u^2}$

8. $\frac{x^2 - 4}{4x^2 - 1} \cdot \frac{2x - 1}{x + 2} = \frac{(x - 2)(x + 2)}{(2x - 1)(2x + 1)} \cdot \frac{2x - 1}{x + 2}$
$= \frac{x - 2}{2x + 1}$

9. $\frac{x^2 - 1}{2x^2 - x - 1} \div \frac{x^2 - 4}{2x^2 - 3x - 2}$
$= \frac{x^2 - 1}{2x^2 - x - 1} \cdot \frac{2x^2 - 3x - 2}{x^2 - 4}$
$= \frac{(x - 1)(x + 1)}{(2x + 1)(x - 1)} \cdot \frac{(2x + 1)(x - 2)}{(x - 2)(x + 2)}$
$= \frac{x + 1}{x + 2}$

10. $\frac{2x^2 + x - 1}{2x^2 + 3x - 2} \div \frac{x^2 - 2x + 1}{x^2 + x - 2}$
$= \frac{2x^2 + x - 1}{2x^2 + 3x - 2} \cdot \frac{x^2 + x - 2}{x^2 - 2x + 1}$
$= \frac{(2x - 1)(x + 1)}{(2x - 1)(x + 2)} \cdot \frac{(x + 2)(x - 1)}{(x - 1)(x - 1)}$
$= \frac{x + 1}{x - 1}$

11. $\frac{\frac{x^4 - y^4}{x^3 + y^3}}{\frac{x^3 - y^3}{x + y}} = \frac{x^4 - y^4}{x^3 + y^3} \div \frac{x^3 - y^3}{x + y}$
$= \frac{x^4 - y^4}{x^3 + y^3} \cdot \frac{x + y}{x^3 - y^3}$
$= \frac{(x^2 + y^2)(x - y)(x + y)}{(x + y)(x^2 - xy + y^2)} \cdot \frac{x + y}{(x - y)(x^2 + xy + y^2)}$
$= \frac{(x^2 + y^2)(x + y)}{(x^2 - xy + y^2)(x^2 + xy + y^2)}$

Page 898 Lesson 9-4

1. $\frac{12}{7d} - \frac{3}{14d} = \frac{12(2)}{7d(2)} - \frac{3}{14d}$
$= \frac{24}{14d} - \frac{3}{14d}$
$= \frac{21}{14d}$
$= \frac{3}{2d}$

2. $\frac{x+1}{x} - \frac{x-1}{x^2} = \frac{(x+1)x}{x \cdot x} - \frac{x-1}{x^2}$
$= \frac{x^2+x}{x^2} - \frac{x-1}{x^2}$
$= \frac{x^2+x-x+1}{x^2}$
$= \frac{x^2+1}{x^2}$

3. $\frac{2x+1}{4x^2} - \frac{x+3}{6x} = \frac{(2x+1)3}{(4x^2)3} - \frac{(x+3)(2x)}{6x(2x)}$
$= \frac{6x+3}{12x^2} - \frac{2x^2+6x}{12x^2}$
$= \frac{6x+3-2x^2-6x}{12x^2}$
$= \frac{-2x^2+3}{12x^2}$

4. $\frac{5}{x} - \frac{3}{x+5} = \frac{5(x+5)}{x(x+5)} - \frac{3 \cdot x}{(x+5)x}$
$= \frac{5x+25}{x(x+5)} - \frac{3x}{x(x+5)}$
$= \frac{2x+25}{x(x+5)}$

5. $\frac{x}{x-1} + \frac{1}{1-x} = \frac{x(1-x)}{(x-1)(1-x)} + \frac{1(x-1)}{(1-x)(x-1)}$
$= \frac{x-x^2}{(x-1)(1-x)} + \frac{x-1}{(x-1)(1-x)}$
$= \frac{-x^2+2x-1}{(x-1)(1-x)}$
$= \frac{-1(x-1)(x-1)}{(x-1)(-1)(x-1)}$
$= 1$

6. $\frac{1}{3v^2} + \frac{1}{uv} + \frac{3}{4u^2} = \frac{1 \cdot 4u^2}{3v^2 \cdot 4u^2} + \frac{1 \cdot 12uv}{uv \cdot 12uv} + \frac{3 \cdot 3v^2}{4u^2 \cdot 3v^2}$
$= \frac{4u^2}{12u^2v^2} + \frac{12uv}{12u^2v^2} + \frac{9v^2}{12u^2v^2}$
$= \frac{4u^2+12uv+9v^2}{12u^2v^2}$
$= \frac{(2u+3v)^2}{12u^2v^2}$

7. $\frac{1}{x^2-x} + \frac{1}{x^2+x} = \frac{1}{x(x-1)} + \frac{1}{x(x+1)}$
$= \frac{x+1}{x(x-1)(x+1)} + \frac{x-1}{x(x+1)(x-1)}$
$= \frac{2x}{x(x-1)(x+1)}$
$= \frac{2}{(x-1)(x+1)}$

8. $\frac{1}{x^2-1} - \frac{1}{(x-1)^2}$
$= \frac{1}{(x-1)(x+1)} - \frac{1}{(x-1)(x-1)}$
$= \frac{x-1}{(x-1)(x+1)(x-1)} - \frac{x+1}{(x-1)(x-1)(x+1)}$
$= \frac{x-1-x-1}{(x-1)^2(x+1)}$
$= \frac{-2}{(x-1)^2(x+1)}$

9. $\frac{7x}{13y^2} + \frac{4y}{6x^2} = \frac{7x \cdot 6x^2}{13y^2 \cdot 6x^2} + \frac{4y \cdot 13y^2}{6x^2 \cdot 13y^2}$
$= \frac{42x^3}{78x^2y^2} + \frac{52y^3}{78x^2y^2}$
$= \frac{42x^3+52y^3}{78x^2y^3}$
$= \frac{21x^3+26y^3}{39x^2y^2}$

10. $y - 1 + \frac{1}{y-1} = \frac{y(y-1)}{y-1} - \frac{1(y-1)}{y-1} + \frac{1}{y-1}$
$= \frac{y^2-y-y+1+1}{y-1}$
$= \frac{y^2-2y+2}{y-1}$

11. $3m + 1 - \frac{2m}{3m+1} = \frac{3m(3m+1)}{3m+1} + \frac{1(3m+1)}{3m+1} - \frac{2m}{3m+1}$
$= \frac{9m^2+3m+3m+1-2m}{3m+1}$
$= \frac{9m^2+4m+1}{3m+1}$

12. $\frac{3x}{x-y} + \frac{4x}{y-x} = \frac{3x}{x-y} - \frac{4x}{x-y}$
$= \frac{-x}{x-y}$

13. $\frac{6}{4m^2-12mn+9n^2} + \frac{2}{2mn-3n^2}$
$= \frac{6}{(2m-3n)(2m-3n)} + \frac{2}{n(2m-3n)}$
$= \frac{6n}{n(2m-3n)^2} + \frac{2(2m-3n)}{n(2m-3n)^2}$
$= \frac{6n+4m-6n}{n(2m-3n)^2}$
$= \frac{4m}{n(2m-3n)^2}$

14. $\frac{3}{x^2+5ax+6a^2} + \frac{2}{x^2-4a^2}$
$= \frac{3}{(x+2a)(x+3a)} + \frac{2}{(x-2a)(x+2a)}$
$= \frac{3(x-2a)}{(x+2a)(x+3a)(x-2a)} + \frac{2(x+3a)}{(x-2a)(x+2a)(x+3a)}$
$= \frac{3x-6a+2x+6a}{(x+3a)(x+2a)(x-2a)}$
$= \frac{5x}{(x+3a)(x+2a)(x-2a)}$

15. $\frac{4}{a^2-4} - \frac{3}{a^2+4a+4} = \frac{4}{(a-2)(a+2)} - \frac{3}{(a+2)(a+2)}$
$= \frac{4(a+2)}{(a-2)(a+2)^2} - \frac{3(a-2)}{(a+2)^2(a-2)}$
$= \frac{4a+8-3a+6}{(a+2)^2(a-2)}$
$= \frac{a+14}{(a+2)^2(a-2)}$

16. $\frac{4}{3-3z^2} - \frac{2}{z^2+5z+4}$
$= \frac{4}{3(1-z)(1+z)} - \frac{2}{(z+1)(z+4)}$
$= \frac{4(z+4)}{3(1-z)(1+z)(z+4)} - \frac{2 \cdot 3(1-z)}{(z+1)(z+4)3(1-z)}$
$= \frac{4z+16-6+6z}{3(1-z)(z+1)(z+4)}$
$= \frac{10z+10}{3(1-z)(z+1)(z+4)}$
$= \frac{10(z+1)}{3(1-z)(z+1)(z+4)}$
$= \frac{10}{3(1-z)(z+4)}$ or $-\frac{10}{3(z-1)(z+4)}$

17. $\dfrac{\frac{1}{x+y}}{\frac{1}{x}+\frac{1}{y}} = \dfrac{\frac{1}{x+y}}{\frac{y}{xy}+\frac{x}{xy}}$

$= \dfrac{\frac{1}{x+y}}{\frac{y+x}{xy}}$

$= \dfrac{1}{x+y} \div \dfrac{y+x}{xy}$

$= \dfrac{1}{x+y} \cdot \dfrac{xy}{y+x}$

$= \dfrac{xy}{(x+y)^2}$

18. $\dfrac{1-\frac{1}{x+1}}{1+\frac{1}{x-1}} = \dfrac{\frac{x+1}{x+1}-\frac{1}{x+1}}{\frac{x-1}{x-1}+\frac{1}{x-1}}$

$= \dfrac{\frac{x}{x+1}}{\frac{x}{x-1}}$

$= \dfrac{x}{x+1} \div \dfrac{x}{x-1}$

$= \dfrac{x}{x+1} \cdot \dfrac{x-1}{x}$

$= \dfrac{x-1}{x+1}$

Page 898 Lesson 9-5

1. $\frac{5}{x} + \frac{3}{5} = \frac{2}{x}$

$5x\left(\frac{5}{x} + \frac{3}{5}\right) = 5x\left(\frac{2}{x}\right)$

$25 + 3x = 10$

$3x = -15$

$x = -5$

2. $\frac{1}{2+3x} + \frac{2}{2-3x} = 0$

$(2+3x)(2-3x)\left(\frac{1}{2+3x} + \frac{2}{2-3x}\right)$

$= (2+3x)(2-3x)0$

$2 - 3x + 2(2 + 3x) = 0$

$2 - 3x + 4 + 6x = 0$

$6 + 3x = 0$

$3x = -6$

$x = -2$

3. $\frac{x-2}{x} = \frac{x-4}{x-6}$

$x(x-6)\left(\frac{x-2}{x}\right) = x(x-6)\left(\frac{x-4}{x-6}\right)$

$(x-6)(x-2) = x(x-4)$

$x^2 - 8x + 12 = x^2 - 4x$

$-8x + 12 = -4x$

$12 = 4x$

$3 = x$

4. $x(x+2)\left(\frac{1}{x} + \frac{x}{x+2}\right) = x(x+2)1$

$x + 2 + x^2 = x^2 + 2x$

$x + 2 = 2x$

$2 = x$

5. $\frac{1}{x+1} + \frac{1}{x-1} = \frac{2}{x^2-1}$

$(x-1)(x+1)\left(\frac{1}{x+1} + \frac{1}{x-1}\right)$

$= (x-1)(x+1)\left(\frac{2}{x^2-1}\right)$

$x - 1 + x + 1 = 2$

$2x = 2$

$x = 1$

But, $x \neq 1$ because the denominators $x - 1$ and $x^2 - 1$ would equal 0. ∅

6. $\frac{2}{x} + \frac{1}{x-2} = 1$

$x(x-2)\left(\frac{2}{x} + \frac{1}{x-2}\right) = x(x-2)1$

$2(x-2) + x = x^2 - 2x$

$2x - 4 + x = x^2 - 2x$

$-4 = x^2 - 5x$

$0 = x^2 - 5x + 4$

$0 = (x-4)(x-1)$

$x - 4 = 0$ or $x - 1 = 0$

$x = 4$ $\quad x = 1$

7. $\frac{1}{x-3} + \frac{1}{x+5} = \frac{x+1}{x-3}$

$(x-3)(x+5)\left(\frac{1}{x-3} + \frac{1}{x+5}\right) = (x-3)(x+5)\left(\frac{x+1}{x-3}\right)$

$x + 5 + x - 3 = (x+5)(x+1)$

$2x + 2 = x^2 + 6x + 5$

$2 = x^2 + 4x + 5$

$0 = x^2 + 4x + 3$

$0 = (x+3)(x+1)$

$x + 3 = 0$ or $x + 1 = 0$

$x = -3$ $\quad x = -1$

8. $\frac{4}{x^2-2x-3} = \frac{-x}{3-x} - \frac{1}{x+1}$

$\frac{4}{(x-3)(x+1)} = \frac{x}{x-3} - \frac{1}{x+1}$

$(x+1)(x-3)\left(\frac{4}{(x-3)(x+1)}\right)$

$= (x+1)(x-3)\left(\frac{x}{x-3} - \frac{1}{x+1}\right)$

$4 = x(x+1) - 1(x-3)$

$4 = x^2 + x - x + 3$

$4 = x^2 + 3$

$1 = x^2$

$\pm 1 = x$

But, $x \neq -1$ because the denominator $x + 1$ would equal 0.

9. $\frac{x}{x+1} + \frac{3}{x-3} + 1 = 0$

$(x+1)(x-3)\left(\frac{x}{x+1} + \frac{3}{x-3} + 1\right) = (x+1)(x-3)0$

$x(x-3) + 3(x+1) + (x+1)(x-3) = 0$

$x^2 - 3x + 3x + 3 + x^2 - 2x - 3 = 0$

$2x^2 - 2x = 0$

$2x(x-1) = 0$

$2x = 0$ or $x - 1 = 0$

$x = 0$ $\quad x = 1$

10. $\frac{3x}{x^2+2x-8} = \frac{1}{x-2} + \frac{x}{x+4}$

$\frac{3x}{(x-2)(x+4)} = \frac{1}{x-2} + \frac{x}{x+4}$

$(x-2)(x+4)\left(\frac{3x}{(x-2)(x+4)}\right)$

$= (x-2)(x+4)\left(\frac{1}{x-2} + \frac{x}{x+4}\right)$

$3x = x + 4 + x(x-2)$

$3x = x + 4 + x^2 - 2x$

$3x = x^2 + x + 4$

$0 = x^2 - 2x + 4$

$x = \frac{2 \pm \sqrt{(-2)^2 - 4 \cdot 1 \cdot 4}}{2 \cdot 1}$

$= \frac{2 \pm \sqrt{-12}}{2}$

∅

11. $\frac{5x+2}{x^2-4} = \frac{-5x}{2-x} + \frac{2}{x+2}$

$\frac{5x+2}{(x-2)(x+2)} = \frac{5x}{x-2} + \frac{2}{x+2}$

$(x-2)(x+2)\left(\frac{5x+2}{(x-2)(x+2)}\right)$

$= (x-2)(x+2)\left(\frac{5x}{x-2} + \frac{2}{x+2}\right)$

$5x + 2 = 5x(x+2) + 2(x-2)$

$5x + 2 = 5x^2 + 10x + 2x - 4$

$5x + 2 = 5x^2 + 12x - 4$

$2 = 5x^2 + 7x - 4$

$0 = 5x^2 + 7x - 6$

$0 = (5x-3)(x+2)$

$5x - 3 = 0$ or $x + 2 = 0$

$5x = 3$ $\quad x = -2$

$x = \frac{3}{5}$

But $x \neq -2$ because the denominator $x + 2$ would equal 0.

12. $\frac{1}{x-3} + \frac{2}{x^2-9} = \frac{5}{x+3}$

$\frac{1}{x-3} + \frac{2}{(x-3)(x+3)} = \frac{5}{x+3}$

$(x-3)(x+3)\left(\frac{1}{x-3} + \frac{2}{(x-3)(x+3)}\right)$

$= (x-3)(x+3)\left(\frac{5}{x+3}\right)$

$x + 3 + 2 = 5(x-3)$

$x + 5 = 5x - 15$

$5 = 4x - 15$

$20 = 4x$

$5 = x$

13. $\frac{1}{x^2-1} = \frac{2}{x^2+x-2}$

$\frac{1}{(x-1)(x+1)} = \frac{2}{(x+2)(x-1)}$

$(x-1)(x+1)(x+2)\left(\frac{1}{(x-1)(x+1)}\right)$

$= (x-1)(x+1)(x+2)\left(\frac{2}{(x+2)(x-1)}\right)$

$x + 2 = 2(x+1)$

$x + 2 = 2x + 2$

$2 = x + 2$

$0 = x$

14. $\frac{12}{x^2-16} - \frac{24}{x-4} = 3$

$\frac{12}{(x-4)(x+4)} - \frac{24}{x-4} = 3$

$(x-4)(x+4)\left(\frac{12}{(x-4)(x+4)} - \frac{24}{x-4}\right)$

$= (x-4)(x+4)(3)$

$12 - 24(x+4) = (x^2 - 16)3$

$12 - 24x - 96 = 3x^2 - 48$

$-84 = 3x^2 + 24x - 48$

$0 = 3x^2 + 24x + 36$

$0 = 3(x+2)(x+6)$

$x + 2 = 0$ or $x + 6 = 0$

$x = -2$ $\quad x = -6$

15. $(x-2)(x+1)\left(\frac{4}{x-2} - \frac{x+6}{x+1}\right) = (x-2)(x+1)1$

$4(x+1) - (x+6)(x-2) = (x-2)(x+1)$

$4x + 4 - (x^2 + 4x - 12) = x^2 - x - 2$

$4x + 4 - x^2 - 4x + 12 = x^2 - x - 2$

$16 = 2x^2 - x - 2$

$0 = 2x^2 - x - 18$

$x = \frac{1 \pm \sqrt{(-1)^2 - 4(2)(-18)}}{2 \cdot 2}$

$= \frac{1 \pm \sqrt{145}}{4}$

Page 898 Lesson 10-1

1. $\left(4^{\sqrt{2}}\right)\left(4^{\sqrt{8}}\right) = \left(4^{\sqrt{2}}\right)\left(4^{2\sqrt{2}}\right)$

$= 4^{\sqrt{2} + 2\sqrt{2}}$

$= 4^{3\sqrt{2}}$

$= 64^{\sqrt{2}}$

2. $\left(5^{\sqrt{5}}\right)^{\sqrt{45}} = 5^{\sqrt{5} \cdot \sqrt{45}}$

$= 5^{\sqrt{225}}$

$= 5^{15}$

3. $\left(x^{\sqrt{3}} + x^{\sqrt{5}}\right)^2 = \left(x^{\sqrt{3}} + x^{\sqrt{5}}\right)\left(x^{\sqrt{3}} + x^{\sqrt{5}}\right)$

$= x^{2\sqrt{3}} + x^{\sqrt{3} + \sqrt{5}} + x^{\sqrt{5} + \sqrt{3}} + x^{2\sqrt{5}}$

$= x^{2\sqrt{3}} + 2x^{\sqrt{3} + \sqrt{5}} + x^{2\sqrt{5}}$

4. $\left(w^{\sqrt{6}}\right)^{\sqrt{3}} = w^{\sqrt{6} \cdot \sqrt{3}}$

$= w^{\sqrt{18}}$

$= w^{3\sqrt{2}}$

5. $27^{\sqrt{5}} \div 3^{\sqrt{5}} = 3^{3\sqrt{5}} \div 3^{\sqrt{5}}$

$= 3^{3\sqrt{5}} \cdot \frac{1}{3^{\sqrt{5}}}$

$= \frac{3^{3\sqrt{5}}}{3^{\sqrt{5}}}$

$= 3^{2\sqrt{5}}$

$= 9^{\sqrt{5}}$

6. $8^{2\sqrt{3}} \times 4^{\sqrt{3}} = \left(2^3\right)^{2\sqrt{3}} \times \left(2^2\right)^{\sqrt{3}}$

$= 2^{6\sqrt{3}} \times 2^{2\sqrt{3}}$

$= 2^{8\sqrt{3}}$

$= 256^{\sqrt{3}}$

7. $5\left(2^{\sqrt{7}}\right)\left(4^{-\sqrt{7}}\right) = 5\left(2^{\sqrt{7}}\right)\left(\frac{1}{4^{\sqrt{7}}}\right)$

$= 5\left(2^{\sqrt{7}}\right)\left(\frac{1}{2^{2\sqrt{7}}}\right)$

$= 5\left(\frac{1}{2^{\sqrt{7}}}\right)$

$= \frac{5}{2^{\sqrt{7}}}$

8. $\left(y^{\sqrt{x}}\right)^{\sqrt{x}} = y^{\sqrt{x} \cdot \sqrt{x}}$

$= y^{\sqrt{x^2}}$

$= y^x$

9. $5^{\sqrt{2}} \times 5^{\sqrt{3}} = 5^{\sqrt{2} + \sqrt{3}}$

10. $\left(6^{\sqrt{5}}\right)^{\sqrt{2}} = 6^{\sqrt{5} \cdot \sqrt{2}}$

$= 6^{\sqrt{10}}$

11. $7^{\sqrt{3}} \times 7^{2\sqrt{3}} = 7^{\sqrt{3} + 2\sqrt{3}}$

$= 7^{3\sqrt{3}}$

12. $\left(y^{\sqrt{3}}\right)^{\sqrt{27}} = y^{\sqrt{3} \cdot \sqrt{27}}$

$= y^{\sqrt{81}}$

$= y^9$

13. $3^x = \frac{1}{27}$

$3^x = 3^{-3}$

$x = -3$

14. $5^x = \sqrt{125}$

$5^x = 5^{\frac{3}{2}}$

$x = \frac{3}{2}$

15. $8^{2+x} = 2$
$(2^3)^{2+x} = 2$
$2^{6+3x} = 2$
$6 + 3x = 1$
$3x = -5$
$x = -\frac{5}{3}$

16. $27^{2x-1} = 3$
$(3^3)^{2x-1} = 3$
$3^{6x-3} = 3$
$6x - 3 = 1$
$6x = 4$
$x = \frac{2}{3}$

17. $4^{2x+5} = 16^{x+1}$
$4^{2x+5} = (4^2)^{x+1}$
$4^{2x+5} = 4^{2x+2}$
$2x + 5 = 2x + 2$
$5 \neq 2$
$\varnothing$

18. $49^{x-2} = 7\sqrt{7}$
$(7^2)^{x-2} = 7(7^{\frac{1}{2}})$
$7^{2x-4} = 7^{1+\frac{1}{2}}$
$2x - 4 = 1 + \frac{1}{2}$
$2x = \frac{11}{2}$
$x = \frac{11}{4}$

19. $6^{x+1} = 36^{x-1}$
$6^{x+1} = (6^2)^{x-1}$
$6^{x+1} = 6^{2x-2}$
$x + 1 = 2x - 2$
$1 = x - 2$
$3 = x$

20. $10^{x-1} = 100^{4-x}$
$10^{x-1} = (10^2)^{4-x}$
$10^{x-1} = 10^{8-2x}$
$x - 1 = 8 - 2x$
$3x - 1 = 8$
$3x = 9$
$x = 3$

21. $\left(\frac{1}{5}\right)^{x-3} = 125$
$(5^{-1})^{x-3} = 5^3$
$5^{-x+3} = 5^3$
$-x + 3 = 3$
$-x = 0$
$x = 0$

22. $2^{x^2+1} = 32$
$2^{x^2+1} = 2^5$
$x^2 + 1 = 5$
$x^2 = 4$
$x = \pm 2$

23. $36^x = 6^{x^2-3}$
$(6^2)^x = 6^{x^2-3}$
$6^{2x} = 6^{x^2-3}$
$2x = x^2 - 3$
$0 = x^2 - 2x - 3$
$0 = (x - 3)(x + 1)$
$x - 3 = 0$ or $x + 1 = 0$
$x = 3$ $\quad x = -1$

24. $9^{x^2-2x} = 27^{x^2+1}$
$(3^2)^{x^2-2x} = (3^3)^{x^2+1}$
$3^{2x^2-4x} = 3^{3x^2+3}$
$2x^2 - 4x = 3x^2 + 3$
$-4x = x^2 + 3$
$0 = x^2 + 4x + 3$
$0 = (x + 3)(x + 1)$
$x + 3 = 0$ or $x + 1 = 0$
$x = -3$ $\quad x = -1$

25.

x	y
−4	0.0095
−2	0.0977
0	1
1	3.2
2	10.24

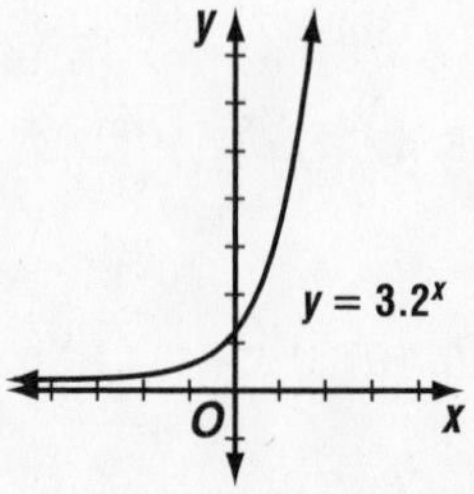

26.

x	y
−4	−0.0048
−2	−0.1953
0	−0.5
1	−1.6
2	−5.12

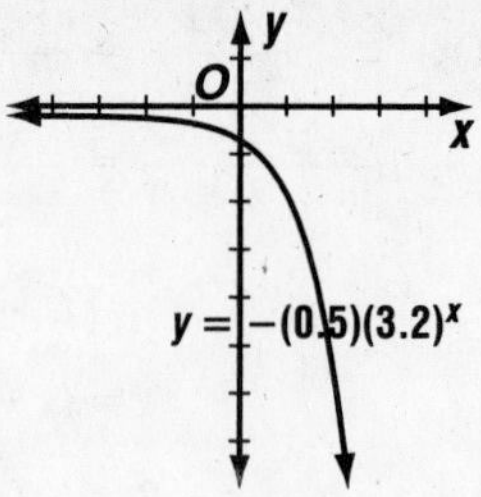

27.

x	y
−4	0.0029
−2	0.0293
0	0.3
1	0.96
2	3.072

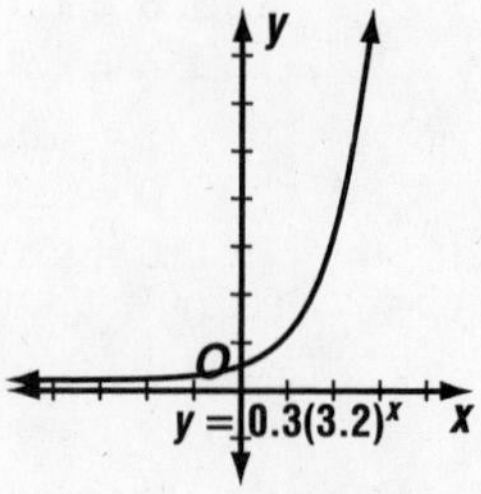

28.

x	y
−6	−0.0093
−4	−0.0954
−2	−0.9766
−1	−3.125
0	−10

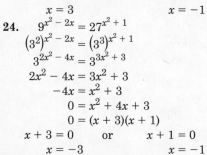

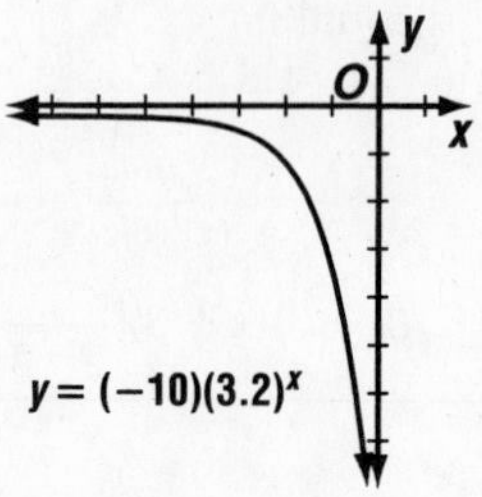

Page 899 Lesson 10-2

1. $\log_4 16 = x$
$4^x = 16$
$4x = 4^2$
$x = 2$

2. $\log_5 125 = x$
$5^x = 125$
$5^x = 5^3$
$x = 3$

3. $\log_3 \frac{1}{9} = x$
$3^x = \frac{1}{9}$
$3^x = 3^{-2}$
$x = -2$

4. $\log_2 \frac{1}{8} = x$
$2^x = \frac{1}{8}$
$2^x = 2^{-3}$
$x = -3$

5. $\log_6 6\sqrt{6} = x$
$6^x = 6\sqrt{6}$
$6^x = 6 \cdot 6^{\frac{1}{2}}$
$6^x = 6^{\frac{3}{2}}$
$x = \frac{3}{2}$

6. $\log_8 4 = x$
$8^x = 4$
$2^{3x} = 2^2$
$3x = 2$
$x = \frac{2}{3}$

7. $\log_7 \sqrt{49} = x$
$7^x = \sqrt{49}$
$7^x = 7$
$x = 1$

8. $\log_{\frac{1}{2}} 8 = x$
$\left(\frac{1}{2}\right)^x = 8$
$\left(\frac{1}{2}\right)^x = \left(\frac{1}{2}\right)^{-3}$
$x = -3$

9. $\log_8 x = 2$
$8^2 = x$
$64 = x$

10. $\log_5 x = 3$
$5^3 = x$
$125 = x$

11. $\log_{10} x = -\frac{1}{2}$
$10^{-\frac{1}{2}} = x$
$\frac{1}{10^{\frac{1}{2}}} = x$
$\frac{1}{\sqrt{10}} = x$
$\frac{\sqrt{10}}{10} = x$

12. $\log_{\frac{1}{9}} x = -\frac{1}{2}$

$\left(\frac{1}{9}\right)^{-\frac{1}{2}} = x$

$\frac{1}{\left(\frac{1}{9}\right)^{\frac{1}{2}}} = x$

$\frac{1}{\frac{1}{3}} = x$

$3 = x$

13. $\log_x 5 = -\frac{1}{2}$

$x^{-\frac{1}{2}} = 5$

$\frac{1}{x^{\frac{1}{2}}} = 5$

$x^{\frac{1}{2}} = \frac{1}{5}$

$x = \frac{1}{25}$

14. $\log_x 7 = 1$

$x^1 = 7$

$x = 7$

15. $\log_x 2 = 0$

$x^0 \neq 2$

$\varnothing$

16. $\log_5(\log_3 x) = 0$

$5^0 = \log_3 x$

$1 = \log_3 x$

$3^1 = x$

$3 = x$

17. $\log_4(\log_3(\log_2 x)) = 0$

$4^0 = \log_3(\log_2 x)$

$1 = \log_3(\log_2 x)$

$3^1 = \log_2 x$

$3 = \log_2 x$

$2^3 = x$

$8 = x$

18. $\log_2(x^2 - 9) = 4$

$2^4 = x^2 - 9$

$16 = x^2 - 9$

$25 = x^2$

$\pm 5 = x$

19. $\log_b(x^2 + 7) = \frac{2}{3}\log_b 64$

$\log_b(x^2 + 7) = \log_b 64^{\frac{2}{3}}$

$x^2 + 7 = 64^{\frac{2}{3}}$

$x^2 + 7 = 16$

$x^2 = 9$

$x = \pm 3$

20. $\log_{10}(x - 1)^2 = \log_{10} 0.01$

$(x - 1)^2 = 0.01$

$x^2 - 2x + 1 = 0.01$

$x^2 - 2x + 0.99 = 0$

$x = \frac{2 \pm \sqrt{(-2)^2 - 4 \cdot 1 \cdot 0.99}}{2 \cdot 1}$

$= \frac{2 \pm \sqrt{0.04}}{2}$

$= \frac{2 \pm 0.2}{2}$

$x = \frac{2 + 0.2}{2}$ or $x = \frac{2 - 0.2}{2}$

$= 1.1$ $\quad$ $= 0.9$

21. $\log_{12}(7x - 3) = \log_{12}(5 - x^2)$

$7x - 3 = 5 - x^2$

$x^2 + 7x - 3 = 5$

$x^2 + 7x - 8 = 0$

$(x + 8)(x - 1) = 0$

$x + 8 = 0$ or $x - 1 = 0$

$x = -8$ $\quad$ $x = 1$

$x \neq -8$ because logarithms are not defined for negative numbers.

22. $\log_9(x^2 + 9x) = \log_9 10$

$x^2 + 9x = 10$

$x^2 + 9x - 10 = 0$

$(x + 10)(x - 1) = 0$

$x + 10 = 0$ or $x - 1 = 0$

$x = -10$ $\quad$ $x = 1$

Page 899 Lesson 10-3

1. $\log_3 \frac{7}{5} = \log_3 7 - \log_3 5$

$= 1.771 - 1.465$

$= 0.306$

2. $\log_3 245 = \log_3(7^2 \cdot 5)$

$= \log_3 7^2 + \log_3 5$

$= 2\log_3 7 + \log_3 5$

$= 2(1.771) + 1.465$

$= 5.007$

3. $\log_3 35 = \log_3(5 \cdot 7)$

$= \log_3 5 + \log_3 7$

$= 1.465 + 1.771$

$= 3.236$

4. $\log_2 x + \log_2(x - 2) = \log_2 3$

$\log_2 x(x - 2) = \log_2 3$

$x(x - 2) = 3$

$x^2 - 2x = 3$

$x^2 - 2x - 3 = 0$

$(x - 3)(x + 1) = 0$

$x - 3 = 0$ or $x + 1 = 0$

$x = 3$ $\quad$ $x = -1$

$x \neq -1$ because logarithms are not defined for negative numbers.

5. $\log_3 x = 2\log_3 3 + \log_3 5$

$\log_3 x = \log_3 3^2 + \log_3 5$

$\log_3 x = \log_3 3^2 \cdot 5$

$x = 3^2 \cdot 5$

$x = 45$

6. $\log_5(x^2 + 7) = \frac{2}{3}\log_5 64$

$\log_5(x^2 + 7) = \log_5 64^{\frac{2}{3}}$

$x^2 + 7 = 64^{\frac{2}{3}}$

$x^2 + 7 = 16$

$x^2 = 9$

$x = \pm 3$

7. $\log_7(3x + 5) - \log_7(x - 5) = \log_7 8$

$\log_7 \frac{3x + 5}{x - 5} = \log_7 8$

$\frac{3x + 5}{x - 5} = 8$

$3x + 5 = 8(x - 5)$

$3x + 5 = 8x - 40$

$5 = 5x - 40$

$45 = 5x$

$9 = x$

8. $\log_2(x^2 - 9) = 4$

$2^4 = x^2 - 9$

$16 = x^2 - 9$

$25 = x^2$

$\pm 5 = x$

9. $\log_3(x + 2) + \log_3 6 = 3$
$$\log_3 6(x + 2) = 3$$
$$3^3 = 6(x + 2)$$
$$27 = 6x + 12$$
$$15 = 6x$$
$$\frac{5}{2} = x$$

10. $\log_6 x + \log_6(x - 5) = 2$
$$\log_6 x(x - 5) = 2$$
$$6^2 = x(x - 5)$$
$$36 = x^2 - 5x$$
$$0 = x^2 - 5x - 36$$
$$0 = (x - 9)(x + 4)$$
$$x - 9 = 0 \quad \text{or} \quad x + 4 = 0$$
$$x = 9 \qquad x = -4$$
$x \neq -4$ because logarithms are not defined for negative numbers.

11. $\log_5(x + 3) = \log_5 8 - \log_5 2$
$$\log_5(x + 3) = \log_5 \frac{8}{2}$$
$$x + 3 = \frac{8}{2}$$
$$x = 1$$

12. $2\log_3 x - \log_3(x - 2) = 2$
$$\log_3 x^2 - \log_3(x - 2) = 2$$
$$\log_3 \frac{x^2}{x - 2} = 2$$
$$3^2 = \frac{x^2}{x - 2}$$
$$9 = \frac{x^2}{x - 2}$$
$$9(x - 2) = x^2$$
$$9x - 18 = x^2$$
$$0 = x^2 - 9x + 18$$
$$0 = (x - 6)(x - 3)$$
$$x - 6 = 0 \quad \text{or} \quad x - 3 = 0$$
$$x = 6 \qquad x = 3$$

13. $\log_6 x = \frac{3}{2}\log_6 9 + \log_6 2$
$$\log_6 x = \log_6 9^{\frac{3}{2}} + \log_6 2$$
$$\log_6 x = \log_6 27 \cdot 2$$
$$x = 54$$

14. $\log_{10}(x + 6) + \log_{10}(x - 6) = 2$
$$\log_{10}(x + 6)(x - 6) = 2$$
$$10^2 = (x + 6)(x - 6)$$
$$100 = x^2 - 36$$
$$136 = x^2$$
$$\pm 2\sqrt{34} = x$$
$x \neq -2\sqrt{34}$ because logarithms are not defined for negative numbers.

15. $\frac{1}{2}\log_4(x + 2) + \frac{1}{2}\log_4(x - 2) = \frac{2}{3}\log_4 27$
$$\log_4(x + 2)^{\frac{1}{2}} + \log_4(x - 2)^{\frac{1}{2}} = \log_4 27^{\frac{2}{3}}$$
$$(x + 2)^{\frac{1}{2}}(x - 2)^{\frac{1}{2}} = 9$$
$$\sqrt{(x + 2)(x - 2)} = 9$$
$$(x + 2)(x - 2) = 81$$
$$x^2 - 4 = 81$$
$$x^2 = 85$$
$$x = \pm\sqrt{85}$$
$x \neq -\sqrt{85}$ because logarithms are not defined for negative numbers.

16. $\log_3 14 + \log_3 x = \log_3 42$
$$\log_3 14x = \log_3 42$$
$$14x = 42$$
$$x = 3$$

17. $\log_{10} x = \frac{1}{2}\log_{10} 81$
$$\log_{10} x = \log_{10} 81^{\frac{1}{2}}$$
$$\log_{10} x = \log_{10} 9$$
$$x = 9$$

Page 899 Lesson 10-4

1. 1.7427; 0.7427; 1
2. -1.1739; $(-1.1739 + 10) - 10 = 8.8261 - 10$; 0.8261; $8 - 10 = -2$
3. 2.5248; 0.5248; 2
4. -3.0969; $(-3.0969 + 10) - 10 = 6.9031 - 10$; 0.9031; $6 - 10 = -4$
5. 3.5258; 0.5258; 3
6. -0.4377; $(-0.4377 + 10) - 10 = 9.5623 - 10$; 0.5623; $9 - 10 = -1$
7. 1.9984; 0.9984; 1
8. 0.7700; 0.7700; 0

9. 0.0022	**10.** 1.2204	**11.** 0.0238	**12.** 1.8005
13. 4.9969	**14.** 1.0104	**15.** 0.0010	**16.** 1.0014
17. 1.8138	**18.** 167.8418	**19.** 10.0554	**20.** 0.5513

Page 900 Lesson 10-5

1. 2.1102	**2.** 3.7728	**3.** 0.9648	**4.** −3.2189
5. 0.8936	**6.** 2.7346	**7.** 0.0867	**8.** 0.3679
9. 3.7839	**10.** 0.9886	**11.** −7.6009	**12.** 3.4903

Page 900 Lesson 10-6

1. $\log_3 21 = \frac{\log 21}{\log 3} \approx \frac{1.3222}{0.4771} \approx 2.771$

2. $\log_4 62 = \frac{\log 62}{\log 4} \approx \frac{1.7924}{0.6021} \approx 2.977$

3. $\log_5 28 = \frac{\log 28}{\log 5} \approx \frac{1.4472}{0.6990} \approx 2.070$

4. $\log_2 25 = \frac{\log 25}{\log 2} \approx \frac{1.3979}{0.3010} \approx 4.644$

5. $\log_{12} 30 = \frac{\log 30}{\log 12} \approx \frac{1.4771}{1.0792} \approx 1.369$

6. $\log_4 63 = \frac{\log 63}{\log 4} \approx \frac{1.7993}{0.6021} \approx 2.989$

7. $\log_7 35 = \frac{\log 35}{\log 7} \approx \frac{1.5441}{0.8451} \approx 1.827$

8. $\log_6 100 = \frac{\log 100}{\log 6} \approx \frac{2}{0.7782} \approx 2.570$

9. $5^x \cdot 5^{-7x} = 5^{-18}$
$5^{-6x} = 5^{-18}$
$-6x = -18$
$x = 3$

10. $3^b = 19$
$\log 3^b = \log 19$
$b \log 3 = \log 19$
$b = \frac{\log 19}{\log 3}$
$b \approx \frac{1.2788}{0.4771}$
$b \approx 2.680$

11. $6^x = 12$
$\log 6^x = \log 12$
$x \log 6 = \log 12$
$x = \frac{\log 12}{\log 6}$
$x \approx \frac{1.0792}{0.7782}$
$x \approx 1.387$

12. $9^{2x+1} = 62.4$
$\log 9^{2x+1} = \log 62.4$
$(2x + 1)\log 9 = \log 62.4$
$2x + 1 = \frac{\log 62.4}{\log 9}$
$2x + 1 \approx \frac{1.7952}{0.9542}$
$2x + 1 \approx 1.881$
$2x \approx 0.881$
$x \approx 0.441$

13. $7^{3x-2} = 0.834$
$\log 7^{3x-2} = \log 0.834$
$(3x - 2)\log 7 = \log 0.834$
$3x - 2 = \frac{\log 0.834}{\log 7}$
$3x - 2 \approx \frac{-0.0788}{0.8451}$
$3x - 2 \approx -0.093$
$3x \approx 1.907$
$x \approx 0.636$

14. $4 = 9^{2x-3}$
$\log 4 = \log 9^{2x-3}$
$\log 4 = (2x - 3)\log 9$
$\frac{\log 4}{\log 9} = 2x - 3$
$\frac{0.6021}{0.9542} \approx 2x - 3$
$0.631 \approx 2x - 3$
$3.631 \approx 2x$
$1.815 \approx x$

15. $6 = 15^{1-x}$
$\log 6 = \log 15^{1-x}$
$\log 6 = (1 - x) \log 15$
$\frac{\log 6}{\log 15} = 1 - x$
$\frac{0.7782}{1.1761} \approx 1 - x$
$0.662 \approx 1 - x$
$-0.338 \approx -x$
$0.338 \approx x$

16. $1.76^x = 23.4$
$\log 1.76^x = \log 23.4$
$x \log 1.76 = \log 23.4$
$x = \frac{\log 23.4}{\log 1.76}$
$x \approx \frac{1.3692}{0.2455}$
$x \approx 5.577$

17. $8 = 3 \times 5^x$
$\frac{8}{3} = 5^x$
$\log \frac{8}{3} = \log 5^x$
$\log 8 - \log 3 = x \log 5$
$\frac{\log 8 - \log 3}{\log 5} = x$
$\frac{0.9031 - 0.4771}{0.6990} = x$
$0.609 = x$

18. $3^x = 4 \times 2^x$
$\frac{3^x}{2^x} = 4$
$\log \left(\frac{3}{2}\right)^x = \log 4$
$x \log \frac{3}{2} = \log 4$
$x = \frac{\log 4}{\log \frac{3}{2}}$
$x = \frac{\log 4}{\log 3 - \log 2}$
$x \approx \frac{0.6021}{0.4771 - 0.3010}$
$x \approx 3.419$

19. $2 \times 5^{x+1} = 5 \times 2^{x+2}$
$\frac{5^{x+1}}{2^{x+2}} = \frac{5}{2}$
$\log\left(\frac{5^{x+1}}{2^{x+2}}\right) = \log \frac{5}{2}$
$\log 5^{x+1} - \log 2^{x+2} = \log 5 - \log 2$
$(x + 1)\log 5 - (x + 2)\log 2 = \log 5 - \log 2$
$(x + 1)(0.6990) - (x + 2)(0.3010)$
$\approx 0.6990 - 0.3010$
$0.6990x + 0.6990 - 0.3010x - 0.6020$
≈ 0.3979
$0.3980x + 0.097 \approx 0.3979$
$0.3980x \approx 0.3009$
$x \approx 0.756$

20. $2^{6x-3} = 4 \times 2^{4x}$
$\frac{2^{6x-3}}{2^{4x}} = 4$
$2^{2x-3} = 4$
$\log 2^{2x-3} = \log 4$
$(2x - 3)\log 2 = \log 4$
$2x - 3 = \frac{\log 4}{\log 2}$
$2x - 3 \approx \frac{0.6021}{0.3010}$
$2x - 3 \approx 2$
$2x \approx 5$
$x \approx 2.5$

Page 900 Lesson 10-7

1. $B = B_0e^{kt}$
$700 = 400e^{k3}$
$1.75 = e^{3k}$
$\ln 1.75 = \ln e^{3k}$
$0.5596 = 3k$
$0.1865 = k$

$B = B_0e^{kt}$
$= 400e^{(0.1865)(12)}$
$= 400e^{2.238}$
≈ 3750; 3750 bacteria

2. $A = Pe^{rt}$
$1000 = 785e^{0.0875t}$
$\frac{1000}{785} = e^{0.0875t}$
$\ln \frac{1000}{785} = \ln e^{0.0875t}$
$0.2421 \approx 0.0875t$
$2.77 \approx t$; 2.77 years

3a. $P = 50e^{\frac{t}{250}}$
$= 50e^{\frac{365}{250}}$
$= 50e^{1.46}$
≈ 215.3; 215.3 watts

3b. $25 = 50e^{\frac{t}{250}}$
$\frac{1}{2} = e^{\frac{t}{250}}$
$\ln \frac{1}{2} = \ln e^{\frac{t}{250}}$
$-0.6931 = \frac{t}{250}$
$-173.3 \approx t$; 173.3 days

3c. $10 = 50e^{\frac{t}{250}}$
$\frac{1}{5} = e^{\frac{t}{250}}$
$\ln \frac{1}{5} = \ln e^{\frac{t}{250}}$
$-1.6094 = \frac{t}{250}$
$-402.4 \approx t$; 402.4 days

4. $T(x) = 18 + 80e^{-0.28x}$
$30 = 18 + 80e^{-0.28x}$
$12 = 80e^{-0.28x}$
$0.15 = e^{-0.28x}$
$\ln 0.15 = \ln e^{-0.28x}$
$-1.8971 \approx -0.28x$
$6.78 \approx x$; 6.78 min
$0.78 \times 60 = 46.8$
6 min 47 s

5. $P = P_0e^{kt}$
$705{,}300 = 350{,}000e^{k \cdot 10}$
$\ln \frac{705{,}300}{350{,}000} = e^{10k}$
$\frac{705{,}300}{350{,}000} = \ln e^{10k}$
$0.7007 \approx 10k$
$0.0701 \approx k$
$P = 350{,}000e^{(0.0701)30}$
$= 350{,}000e^{2.103}$
$\approx 2{,}866{,}747$; 2,866,747 people

Page 901 Lesson 11-1

1. $d = 7 - 9 = -2$
$5 - 2 = 3$
$3 - 2 = 1$
$1 - 2 = -1$
$-1 - 2 = -3$
3, 1, −1, −3

2. $d = 4.5 - 3 = 1.5$
$6 + 1.5 = 7.5$
$7.5 + 1.5 = 9$
$9 + 1.5 = 10.5$
$10.5 + 1.5 = 12$
7.5, 9, 10.5, 12

3. $d = 35 - 40 = -5$
$30 - 5 = 25$
$25 - 5 = 20$
$20 - 5 = 15$
$15 - 5 = 10$
25, 20, 15, 10

4. $d = 5 - 2 = 3$
$8 + 3 = 11$
$11 + 3 = 14$
$14 + 3 = 17$
$17 + 3 = 20$
11, 14, 17, 20

5. $a_{10} = 4 + (10 - 1)5$
$= 4 + 45$
$= 49$

6. $a_5 = -30 + (5 - 1)(-6)$
$= -30 - 24$
$= -54$

7. $a_{72} = \frac{3}{4} + (72 - 1)\left(-\frac{1}{4}\right)$
$= \frac{3}{4} - \frac{71}{4}$
$= -\frac{68}{4}$
$= -17$

8. $a_8 = -3 + (8 - 1)32$
$= -3 + 224$
$= 221$

9. $a_{17} = -\frac{1}{5} + (17 - 1)\left(\frac{3}{5}\right)$
$= -\frac{1}{5} + \frac{48}{5}$
$= \frac{47}{5}$

10. $a_{16} = 20 + (16 - 1)(-3)$
$= 20 - 45$
$= -25$

11. $d = 5 - 3 = 2$
$a_n = 3 + (n - 1)2$
$= 3 + 2n - 2$
$= 2n + 1$

12. $d = -1 - 2 = -3$
$a_n = 2 + (n - 1)(-3)$
$= 2 - 3n + 3$
$= -3n + 5$

13. $d = 28 - 20 = 8$
$a_n = 20 + (n - 1)8$
$= 20 + 8n - 8$
$= 8n + 12$

Page 901 Lesson 11-2

1. $S_6 = \frac{6}{2}(3 + 20)$
$= 3(23)$
$= 69$

2. $S_{30} = \frac{30}{2}(15 - 12)$
$= 15(3)$
$= 45$

3. $S_{10} = \frac{10}{2}(90 - 4)$
$= 5(86)$
$= 430$

4. $S_{12} = \frac{12}{2}(16 + 14)$
$= 6(30)$
$= 180$

5. $S_{18} = \frac{18}{2}(-80 + 120)$
$= 9(40)$
$= 360$

6. $S_{14} = \frac{14}{2}(-3 - 72)$
$= 7(-75)$
$= -525$

7. $d = 12 - 3 = 9$
$a_n = a_1 + (n - 1)d$
$57 = 3 + (n - 1)9$
$57 = 3 + 9n - 9$
$63 = 9n$
$7 = n$
$S_7 = \frac{7}{2}(3 + 57)$
$= \frac{7}{2}(60)$
$= 210$

8. $d = 4 - 1 = 3$
$a_n = a_1 + (n - 1)d$
$31 = 1 + (n - 1)3$
$31 = 1 + 3n - 3$
$33 = 3n$
$11 = n$
$S_{11} = \frac{11}{2}(1 + 31)$
$= \frac{11}{2}(32)$
$= 176$

9. $d = 16 - 8 = 8$
$a_n = a_1 + (n - 1)d$
$80 = 8 + (n - 1)8$
$80 = 8 + 8n - 8$
$80 = 8n$
$10 = n$
$S_{10} = \frac{10}{2}(8 + 80)$
$= 5(88)$
$= 440$

10. $\sum_{n=1}^{6} n + 2 = (1 + 2) + (2 + 2) + (3 + 2) + (4 + 2) + (5 + 2) + (6 + 2)$
$= 3 + 4 + 5 + 6 + 7 + 8$
$= 33$

11. $\sum_{n=5}^{10} 2n - 5 = (2 \cdot 5 - 5) + (2 \cdot 6 - 5) + (2 \cdot 7 - 5) + (2 \cdot 8 - 5) + (2 \cdot 9 - 5) + (2 \cdot 10 - 5)$
$= 5 + 7 + 9 + 11 + 13 + 15$
$= 60$

12. $\sum_{k=1}^{5} 40 - 2k = (40 - 2 \cdot 1) + (40 - 2 \cdot 2) + (40 - 2 \cdot 3) + (40 - 2 \cdot 4) + (40 - 2 \cdot 5)$
$= 38 + 36 + 34 + 32 + 30$
$= 170$

13. $\sum_{k=8}^{12} 6 - 3k = (6 - 3 \cdot 8) + (6 - 3 \cdot 9) + (6 - 3 \cdot 10) + (6 - 3 \cdot 11) + (6 - 3 \cdot 12)$
$= (-18) + (-21) + (-24) + (-27) + (-30)$
$= -120$

14. $\sum_{n=6}^{10} 2 + 3n = (2 + 3 \cdot 6) + (2 + 3 \cdot 7) + (2 + 3 \cdot 8) + (2 + 3 \cdot 9) + (2 + 3 \cdot 10)$
$= 20 + 23 + 26 + 29 + 32$
$= 130$

15. $\sum_{n=1}^{4} 10n + 2 = (10 \cdot 1 + 2) + (10 \cdot 2 + 2) + (10 \cdot 3 + 2) + (10 \cdot 4 + 2)$
$= 12 + 22 + 32 + 42$
$= 108$

Page 901 Lesson 11-3

1. $r = \frac{15}{5}$ or 3
$45 \cdot 3 = 135$
$135 \cdot 3 = 405$
$405 \cdot 3 = 1215$
$1215 \cdot 3 = 3645$
135, 405, 1215, 3645

2. $r = \frac{10}{2}$ or 5
$50 \cdot 5 = 250$
$250 \cdot 5 = 1250$
$1250 \cdot 5 = 6250$
$6250 \cdot 5 = 31{,}250$
250, 1250, 6250, 31,250

3. $r = \frac{16}{64}$ or $\frac{1}{4}$
$4 \cdot \frac{1}{4} = 1$
$1 \cdot \frac{1}{4} = \frac{1}{4}$
$\frac{1}{4} \cdot \frac{1}{4} = \frac{1}{16}$
$\frac{1}{16} \cdot \frac{1}{4} = \frac{1}{64}$
$1, \frac{1}{4}, \frac{1}{16}, \frac{1}{64}$

4. $r = \frac{27}{-9}$ or -3
$-81(-3) = 243$
$243(-3) = -729$
$-729(-3) = 2187$
$2187(-3) = -6561$
243, −729, 2187, −6561

5. $a_6 = 5 \cdot 7^{6-1}$
$= 5 \cdot 16{,}807$
$= 84{,}035$

6. $a_{10} = 200\left(-\frac{1}{2}\right)^{10-1}$
$= 200\left(-\frac{1}{512}\right)$
$= -\frac{25}{64}$

7. $a_4 = 60(-2)^{4-1}$
$= 60(-8)$
$= -480$

8. $a_6 = 300\left(\frac{1}{4}\right)^{6-1}$
$= 300\left(\frac{1}{1024}\right)$
$= \frac{75}{256}$

9. $a_8 = 8(-2)^{8-1}$
$= 8(-128)$
$= -1024$

10. $a_{30} = 1(-1)^{30-1}$
$= 1(-1)$
$= -1$

11. $r = -\frac{6}{3}$ or -2
$12(-2) = 2y - 12$
$-24 = 2y - 12$
$-12 = 2y$
$-6 = y$

12. $r = -\frac{2}{2}$ or -1
$2(-1) = 4y + 2$
$-2 = 4y + 2$
$-4 = 4y$
$-1 = y$

13. $r = \frac{50}{-10}$ or -5
$(-250)(-5) = 20y - 100$
$1250 = 20y - 100$
$1350 = 20y$
$67.5 = y$

Page 902 Lesson 11-4

1. $S_6 = \frac{\frac{1}{81} - \frac{1}{81}(3)^6}{1-3}$
$= \frac{\frac{1}{81} - \frac{729}{81}}{-2}$
$= \frac{-\frac{728}{81}}{-2}$
$= -\frac{728}{81} \div -2$
$= -\frac{728}{81} \cdot \frac{1}{-2} = \frac{364}{81}$

2. $S_7 = \frac{1 - 1(-2)^7}{1-(-2)}$
$= \frac{1 - 1(-128)}{3}$
$= \frac{129}{3}$
$= 43$

3. $S_5 = \frac{5 - 5(4)^5}{1-4}$
$= \frac{5 - 5(1024)}{-3}$
$= \frac{-5115}{-3}$
$= 1705$

4. $S_6 = \frac{-27 - (-27)\left(-\frac{1}{3}\right)^6}{1 - \left(-\frac{1}{3}\right)}$
$= \frac{-27 - (-27)\left(\frac{1}{729}\right)}{\frac{4}{3}}$
$= \frac{-27 + \frac{1}{27}}{\frac{4}{3}}$
$= \frac{-728}{27} \div \frac{4}{3}$
$= \frac{-728}{27} \cdot \frac{3}{4}$
$= -\frac{182}{9}$

5. $S_7 = \frac{1000 - 1000\left(\frac{1}{2}\right)^7}{1 - \frac{1}{2}}$
$= \frac{1000 - 1000\left(\frac{1}{128}\right)}{\frac{1}{2}}$
$= \frac{127{,}000}{128} \div \frac{1}{2}$
$= \frac{127{,}000}{128} \times \frac{2}{1}$
$= \frac{15{,}875}{8}$

6. $S_5 = \frac{125 - 125\left(-\frac{2}{5}\right)^5}{1 - \left(-\frac{2}{5}\right)}$
$= \frac{125 - 125\left(-\frac{32}{3125}\right)}{\frac{7}{5}}$
$= \frac{3157}{25} \div \frac{5}{7}$
$= \frac{3175}{25} \cdot \frac{5}{7}$
$= \frac{451}{5}$

7. $S_6 = \frac{10 - 10(3)^6}{1-3}$
$= \frac{10 - 10(729)}{-2}$
$= \frac{-7280}{-2}$
$= 3640$

8. $S_5 = \frac{1250 - 1250\left(-\frac{1}{5}\right)^5}{1 - \left(-\frac{1}{5}\right)}$
$= \frac{1250 - 1250\left(-\frac{1}{3125}\right)}{\frac{6}{5}}$
$= \frac{6252}{5} \div \frac{6}{5}$
$= \frac{6252}{5} \cdot \frac{5}{6}$
$= 1042$

9. $S_n = \frac{1215 - 5\left(\frac{1}{3}\right)}{1 - \frac{1}{3}}$
$= \frac{3640}{3} \div \frac{2}{3}$
$= \frac{3640}{3} \cdot \frac{3}{2}$
$= 1820$

10. $S_5 = \frac{16 - 16\left(\frac{3}{2}\right)^5}{1 - \frac{3}{2}}$
$= \frac{16 - 16\left(\frac{243}{32}\right)}{-\frac{1}{2}}$
$= -\frac{211}{2} \div -\frac{1}{2}$
$= -\frac{211}{2} \cdot -\frac{2}{1}$
$= 211$

11. $S_7 = \frac{7 - 7(2)^7}{1-2}$
$= \frac{7 - 7(128)}{-1}$
$= 889$

12. $-\frac{3}{2} = a_1\left(-\frac{1}{2}\right)^{6-1}$

$-\frac{3}{2} = a_1\left(-\frac{1}{32}\right)$

$48 = a_1$

$S_6 = \dfrac{48 - 48\left(-\frac{1}{2}\right)^6}{1 - \left(-\frac{1}{2}\right)}$

$= \dfrac{48 - 48\left(\frac{1}{64}\right)}{\frac{3}{2}}$

$= \frac{189}{4} \div \frac{3}{2}$

$= \frac{189}{4} \cdot \frac{2}{3}$

$= \frac{63}{2}$ or 31.5

13. $S_{10} = \dfrac{16 - 16\left(-\frac{1}{2}\right)^{10}}{1 - \left(-\frac{1}{2}\right)}$

$= \dfrac{16 - 16\left(\frac{1}{1024}\right)}{\frac{3}{2}}$

$= \frac{1023}{64} \div \frac{3}{2}$

$= \frac{1023}{64} \cdot \frac{2}{3}$

$= \frac{341}{32}$

14. $S_5 = \dfrac{243 - 243\left(-\frac{2}{3}\right)^5}{1 - \left(-\frac{2}{3}\right)}$

$= \dfrac{243 - 243\left(-\frac{32}{243}\right)}{\frac{5}{3}}$

$= 275 \div \frac{5}{3}$

$= 275 \cdot \frac{3}{5}$

$= 165$

15. $S_{12} = \dfrac{5 - 5(3)^{12}}{1 - 3}$

$= \dfrac{5 - 5(531{,}441)}{-2}$

$= \dfrac{-2{,}657{,}200}{-2}$

$= 1{,}328{,}600$

16. $\sum_{k=1}^{5} 2^k = 2^1 + 2^2 + 2^3 + 2^4 + 2^5$

$= 2 + 4 + 8 + 16 + 32$

$= 62$

17. $\sum_{n=0}^{3} 3^{-n} = 3^{-0} + 3^{-1} + 3^{-2} + 3^{-3}$

$= 1 + \frac{1}{3} + \frac{1}{9} + \frac{1}{27}$

$= \frac{40}{27}$

18. $\sum_{n=0}^{3} 2(5^n) = 2(5^0) + 2(5^1) + 2(5^2) + 2(5^3)$

$= 2 + 10 + 50 + 250$

$= 312$

19. $\sum_{k=2}^{5} -(-3)^{k-1} = -(-3)^{2-1} - (-3)^{3-1} - (-3)^{4-1} - (-3)^{5-1}$

$= 3 + (-9) + 27 + (-81)$

$= -60$

20. $\sum_{n=1}^{6} \left(\frac{1}{2}\right)^{n-1} = \left(\frac{1}{2}\right)^{1-1} + \left(\frac{1}{2}\right)^{2-1} + \left(\frac{1}{2}\right)^{3-1} + \left(\frac{1}{2}\right)^{4-1} + \left(\frac{1}{2}\right)^{5-1} + \left(\frac{1}{2}\right)^{6-1}$

$= 1 + \frac{1}{2} + \frac{1}{4} + \frac{1}{8} + \frac{1}{16} + \frac{1}{32}$

$= \frac{63}{32}$

21. $\sum_{n=0}^{4} 8\left(-\frac{1}{2}\right)^{n-1} = 8\left(-\frac{1}{2}\right)^{0-1} + 8\left(-\frac{1}{2}\right)^{1-1} + 8\left(-\frac{1}{2}\right)^{2-1} + 8\left(-\frac{1}{2}\right)^{3-1} + 8\left(-\frac{1}{2}\right)^{4-1}$

$= -16 + 8 + (-4) + 2 + (-1)$

$= -11$

Page 902 Lesson 11-5

1. $r = \frac{18}{54}$ or $\frac{1}{3}$

$S = \dfrac{54}{1 - \frac{1}{3}}$

$= \dfrac{54}{\frac{2}{3}}$

$= 54 \cdot \frac{3}{2}$

$= 81$

2. $r = -\frac{2}{2}$ or -1

does not exist

3. $r = -\frac{200}{1000}$ or $-\frac{1}{5}$

$S = \dfrac{1000}{1 - \left(-\frac{1}{5}\right)}$

$= \dfrac{1000}{\frac{6}{5}}$

$= 1000 \cdot \frac{5}{6}$

$= 833\frac{1}{3}$

4. $r = \frac{3}{7}$

$S = \dfrac{7}{1 - \frac{3}{7}}$

$= \dfrac{7}{\frac{4}{7}}$

$= 7 \cdot \frac{7}{4}$

$= \frac{49}{4}$

5. $r = \dfrac{\frac{2}{25}}{\frac{4}{5}} = \frac{2}{25} \cdot \frac{5}{4} = \frac{1}{10}$

$S = \dfrac{\frac{4}{5}}{1 - \frac{1}{10}}$

$= \dfrac{\frac{4}{5}}{\frac{9}{10}}$

$= \frac{4}{5} \cdot \frac{10}{9}$

$= \frac{8}{9}$

6. $r = \frac{14}{49}$ or $\frac{2}{7}$

$S = \dfrac{49}{1 - \frac{2}{7}}$

$= \dfrac{49}{\frac{5}{7}}$

$= 49 \cdot \frac{7}{5}$

$= \frac{343}{5}$

7. $r = \dfrac{\frac{1}{2}}{\frac{3}{4}} = \frac{1}{2} \cdot \frac{4}{3} = \frac{2}{3}$

$S = \dfrac{\frac{3}{4}}{1 - \frac{2}{3}}$

$= \dfrac{\frac{3}{4}}{\frac{1}{3}}$

$= \frac{3}{4} \cdot \frac{3}{1}$

$= \frac{9}{4}$

8. $r = \dfrac{-\frac{1}{4}}{1}$ or $-\frac{1}{4}$

$S = \dfrac{1}{1 - \left(-\frac{1}{4}\right)}$

$= \dfrac{1}{\frac{5}{4}}$

$= \frac{4}{5}$

9. $r = -\frac{4}{12}$ or $-\frac{1}{3}$

$S = \dfrac{12}{1 - \left(-\frac{1}{3}\right)}$

$= \dfrac{12}{\frac{4}{3}}$

$= 12 \cdot \frac{3}{4}$

$= 9$

10. $r = -\frac{9}{3}$ or -3

does not exist

11. $r = -\frac{2}{3}$

$S = \dfrac{3}{1 - \left(-\frac{2}{3}\right)}$

$= \dfrac{3}{\frac{5}{3}}$

$= 3 \cdot \frac{3}{5}$

$= \frac{9}{5}$

12. $r = -\frac{1}{10}$

$S = \dfrac{10}{1 - \left(-\frac{1}{10}\right)}$

$= \dfrac{10}{\frac{11}{10}}$

$= 10 \cdot \frac{10}{11}$

$= \frac{100}{11}$

13. $r = \frac{1}{4}, a_1 = 3$

$S = \frac{3}{1 - \frac{1}{4}}$

$= \frac{3}{\frac{3}{4}}$

$= 3 \cdot \frac{4}{3}$

$= 4$

14. $r = -\frac{1}{10}, a_1 = 5$

$S = \frac{5}{1 - \left(-\frac{1}{10}\right)}$

$= \frac{5}{\frac{11}{10}}$

$= 5 \cdot \frac{10}{11}$

$= \frac{50}{11}$

15. $r = -\frac{3}{4}, a_1 = -\frac{2}{3}$

$S = \frac{-\frac{2}{3}}{1 - \left(-\frac{3}{4}\right)}$

$= \frac{-\frac{2}{3}}{\frac{7}{4}}$

$= -\frac{2}{3} \cdot \frac{4}{7}$

$= -\frac{8}{21}$

Page 902 Lesson 11-6

1. $a_1 = 4, a_{n+1} = 2a_n + 1$

$a_{1+1} = 2a_1 + 1$
$a_2 = 2(4) + 1$
$= 9$

$a_{2+1} = 2a_2 + 1$
$a_3 = 2(9) + 1$
$= 19$

$a_{3+1} = 2a_3 + 1$
$a_4 = 2(19) + 1$
$= 39$

$a_{4+1} = 2a_4 + 1$
$a_5 = 2(39) + 1$
$= 79$

$a_{5+1} = 2a_5 + 1$
$a_6 = 2(79) + 1$
$= 159$

4, 9, 19, 39, 79, 159

2. $a_1 = 6, a_{n+1} = a_n + 7$

$a_{1+1} = a_1 + 7$
$a_2 = 6 + 7$
$= 13$

$a_{2+1} = a_2 + 7$
$a_3 = 13 + 7$
$= 20$

$a_{3+1} = a_3 + 7$
$a_4 = 20 + 7$
$= 27$

$a_{4+1} = a_4 + 7$
$a_5 = 27 + 7$
$= 34$

$a_{5+1} = a_5 + 7$
$a_6 = 34 + 7$
$= 41$

6, 13, 20, 27, 34, 41

3. $a_1 = 16, a_{n+1} = a_n + (n + 4)$

$a_{1+1} = a_1 + (1 + 4)$
$a_2 = 16 + 5$
$= 21$

$a_{2+1} = a_2 + (2 + 4)$
$a_3 = 21 + 6$
$= 27$

$a_{3+1} = a_3 + (3 + 4)$
$a_4 = 27 + 7$
$= 34$

$a_{4+1} = a_4 + (4 + 4)$
$a_5 = 34 + 8$
$= 42$

$a_{5+1} = a_5 + (5 + 4)$
$a_6 = 42 + 9$
$= 51$

16, 21, 27, 34, 42, 51

4. $a_1 = 1, a_{n+1} = \frac{n}{n+2} \cdot a_n$

$a_{1+1} = \frac{1}{1+2} \cdot a_1$
$a_2 = \frac{1}{3} \cdot 1$
$= \frac{1}{3}$

$a_{2+1} = \frac{2}{2+2} \cdot a_2$
$a_3 = \frac{2}{4} \cdot \frac{1}{3}$
$= \frac{1}{6}$

$a_{3+1} = \frac{3}{3+2} \cdot a_3$
$a_4 = \frac{3}{5} \cdot \frac{1}{6}$
$= \frac{1}{10}$

$a_{4+1} = \frac{4}{4+2} \cdot a_4$
$a_5 = \frac{4}{6} \cdot \frac{1}{10}$
$= \frac{1}{15}$

$a_{5+1} = \frac{5}{5+2} \cdot a_5$
$a_6 = \frac{5}{7} \cdot \frac{1}{15}$
$= \frac{1}{21}$

$1, \frac{1}{3}, \frac{1}{6}, \frac{1}{10}, \frac{1}{15}, \frac{1}{21}$

5. $f(x_0) = f(3)$
$= 3(3) - 1$
$= 8$

$f(x_1) = f(8)$
$= 3(8) - 1$
$= 23$

$f(x_2) = f(23)$
$= 3(23) - 1$
$= 68$

8, 23, 68

6. $f(x_0) = f(-1)$
$= 2(-1)^2 - 8$
$= -6$

$f(x_1) = f(-6)$
$= 2(-6)^2 - 8$
$= 64$

$f(x_2) = f(64)$
$= 2(64)^2 - 8$
$= 8184$

−6, 64, 8184

7. $f(x_0) = f(3)$
$= 4(3) + 5$
$= 17$

$f(x_1) = f(17)$
$= 4(17) + 5$
$= 73$

$f(x_2) = f(73)$
$= 4(73) + 5$
$= 297$

17, 73, 297

8. $f(x_0) = f(1)$
$= 3(1)^2 + 1$
$= 4$

$f(x_1) = f(4)$
$= 3(4)^2 + 1$
$= 49$

$f(x_2) = f(49)$
$= 3(49)^2 + 1$
$= 7204$

4, 49, 7204

9. $f(x_0) = f(1)$
$= 1^2 + 4 \cdot 1 + 4$
$= 9$

$f(x_1) = f(9)$
$= 9^2 + 4 \cdot 9 + 4$
$= 121$

$f(x_2) = f(121)$
$= 121^2 + 4 \cdot 121 + 4$
$= 15{,}129$

9, 121, 15,129

10. $f(x_0) = f(2)$
$= 2^2 + 9$
$= 13$

$f(x_1) = f(13)$
$= 13^2 + 9$
$= 178$

$f(x_2) = f(178)$
$= 178^2 + 9$
$= 31{,}693$

13, 178, 31, 693

Page 903 Lesson 11-7

1.

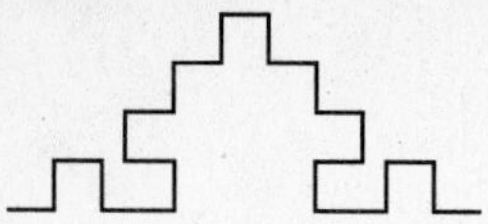

2.

3. Lightning bolts break off into smaller and smaller parts that are of the same pattern and shape as the bigger lightning bolts.

Page 903 Lesson 11-8

1. 720 2. 24 3. 8,648,640 4. 3,991,680

5. 120 6. 1001 7. 21 8. 9

9. $(x + y)^3 = x^3 + 3x^2y + 3xy^2 + y^3$

10. $(2x - y)^4 = (2x)^4 + 4(2x)^3(-y) + 6(2x)^2(-y)^2 + 4(2x)(-y)^3 + (-y)^4$
$= 16x^4 - 32x^3y + 24x^2y^2 - 8xy^3 + y^4$

11. $(3r + 4s)^5 = (3r)^5 + 5(3r)^4(4s) + 10(3r)^3(4s)^2 + 10(3r)^2(4s)^3 + 5(3r)(4s)^4 + (4s)^5$
$= 243r^5 + 1620r^4s + 4320r^3s^2 + 5760r^2s^3 + 3840rs^4 + 1024s^5$

12. $\frac{8!}{5!(8-5)!}x^{8-5}(3)^5 = \frac{8 \cdot 7 \cdot 6 \cdot 5!}{5! \cdot 3 \cdot 2 \cdot 1}x^3(243)$
$= 13{,}608x^3$

13. $\frac{9!}{3!(9-3)!}x^{9-3}(-y)^3 = \frac{9 \cdot 8 \cdot 7 \cdot 6!}{3 \cdot 2 \cdot 1 \cdot 6!}x^6(-y^3) = -84x^6y^3$

14. $\frac{10!}{4!(10-4)!}(3x)^{10-4}(5y)^4 = \frac{10 \cdot 9 \cdot 8 \cdot 7 \cdot 6!}{4 \cdot 3 \cdot 2 \cdot 1 \cdot 6!}(729x^6)(625y^4)$
$= 95{,}681{,}250x^6y^4$

15. $\frac{7!}{5!(7-5)!}x^{7-5}(4y)^5 = \frac{7 \cdot 6 \cdot 5!}{5! \cdot 2 \cdot 1}x^2(1024y^5)$
$= 21{,}504x^2y^5$

Page 903 Lesson 12-1

1.

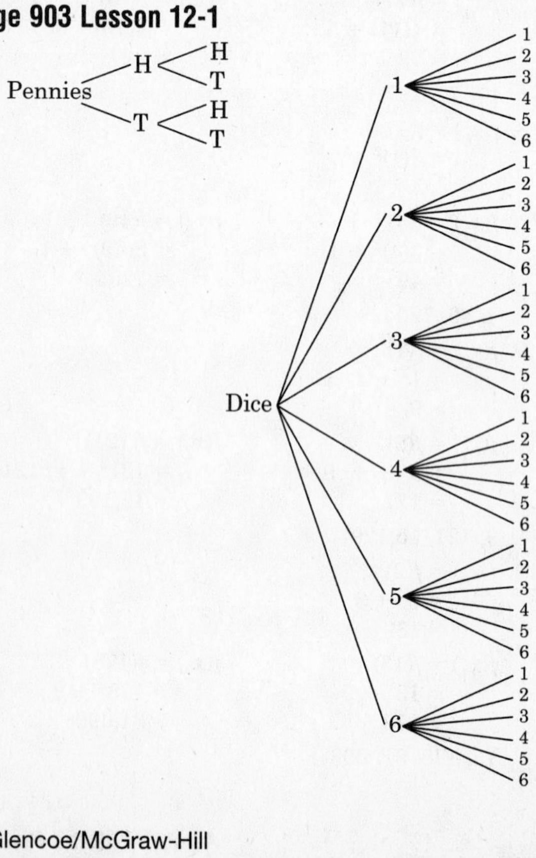

2.

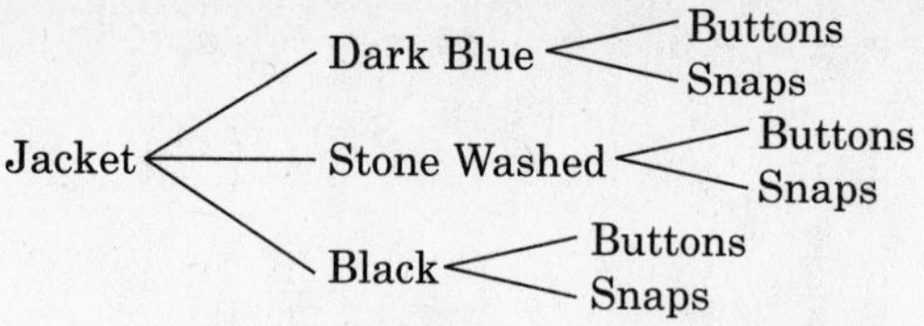

3.

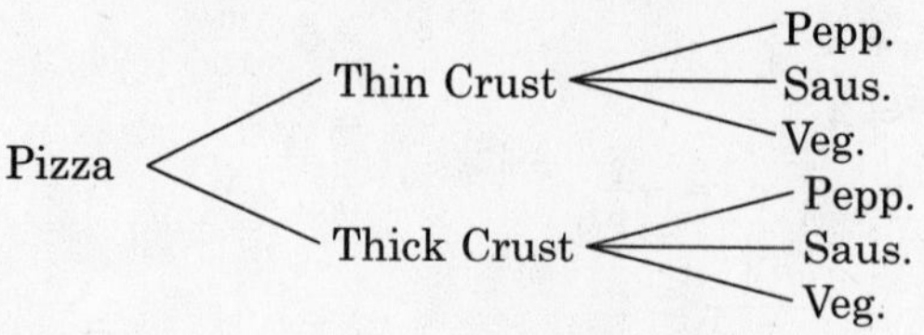

4. independent 5. dependent

6. $10 \cdot 6 \cdot 4 = 240$ 7. $2^{10} = 1024$

8. $26 \cdot 25 \cdot 24 = 15{,}600$ 9. $6 \cdot 5 \cdot 1 = 30$

10. $26 \cdot 10 \cdot 10 \cdot 10 \cdot 10 = 260{,}000$

Page 904 Lesson 12-2

1. $6! = 720$ 2. $5! = 120$

3. $\frac{10!}{2!\,3!\,3!} = 50{,}400$ 4. $\frac{7!}{2!\,2!\,2!} = 630$

5. $\frac{P(5, 3)}{P(3, 2)} = \frac{\frac{5!}{(5-3)!}}{\frac{3!}{(3-2)!}}$
$= \frac{\frac{5 \cdot 4 \cdot 3 \cdot 2!}{2!}}{\frac{3 \cdot 2 \cdot 1}{1!}}$
$= \frac{60}{6}$
$= 10$

6. $\frac{P(5, 2)\,P(4, 3)}{P(6, 3)} = \frac{\frac{5!}{(5-2)!} \cdot \frac{4!}{(4-3)!}}{\frac{6!}{(6-3)!}}$
$= \frac{\frac{5 \cdot 4 \cdot 3!}{3!} \cdot \frac{4 \cdot 3 \cdot 2 \cdot 1}{1!}}{\frac{6 \cdot 5 \cdot 4 \cdot 3!}{3!}}$
$= \frac{20 \cdot 24}{120}$
$= 4$

7. $\frac{P(10, 6)}{P(12, 2)\,P(7, 2)} = \frac{\frac{10!}{(10-6)!}}{\frac{12!}{(12-2)!} \cdot \frac{7!}{(7-2)!}}$
$= \frac{\frac{10 \cdot 9 \cdot 8 \cdot 7 \cdot 6 \cdot 5 \cdot 4!}{4!}}{\frac{12 \cdot 11 \cdot 10!}{10!} \cdot \frac{7 \cdot 6 \cdot 5!}{5!}}$
$= \frac{151{,}200}{132 \cdot 42}$
$= 27.\overline{27}$

Page 904 Lesson 12-3

1. combination 2. permutation

3. combination 4. permutation

5. $C(8, 6) = \frac{8!}{(8-6)!\,6!}$
$= \frac{8 \cdot 7 \cdot 6!}{2 \cdot 1 \cdot 6!}$
$= 28$

6. $C(20, 17) = \frac{20!}{(20-17)!\,17!}$
$= \frac{20 \cdot 19 \cdot 18 \cdot 17!}{3 \cdot 2 \cdot 1 \cdot 17!}$
$= 1140$

7. $C(9, 4) \cdot C(5, 3) = \frac{9!}{(9-4)!\,4!} \cdot \frac{5!}{(5-3)!\,3!}$
$= \frac{9 \cdot 8 \cdot 7 \cdot 6 \cdot 5!}{5!\,4 \cdot 3 \cdot 2 \cdot 1} \cdot \frac{5 \cdot 4 \cdot 3!}{2 \cdot 1 \cdot 3!}$
$= 126 \cdot 10$
$= 1260$

8. $C(6, 1) \cdot C(4, 1) \cdot C(9, 8)$
$= \frac{6!}{(6-1)!\,1!} \cdot \frac{4!}{(4-1)!\,1!} \cdot \frac{9!}{(9-8)!\,8!}$
$= \frac{6 \cdot 5!}{5! \cdot 1} \cdot \frac{4 \cdot 3!}{3! \cdot 1} \cdot \frac{9 \cdot 8!}{1 \cdot 8!}$
$= 6 \cdot 4 \cdot 9$
$= 216$

9. $C(10, 5) \cdot C(8, 4) = \frac{10!}{(10-5)!\,5!} \cdot \frac{8!}{(8-4)!\,4!}$
$= \frac{10 \cdot 9 \cdot 8 \cdot 7 \cdot 6 \cdot 5!}{5 \cdot 4 \cdot 3 \cdot 2 \cdot 1 \cdot 5!} \cdot \frac{8 \cdot 7 \cdot 6 \cdot 5 \cdot 4!}{4 \cdot 3 \cdot 2 \cdot 1 \cdot 4!}$
$= 252 \cdot 70$
$= 17{,}640$

10. $C(7, 6) \cdot C(3, 1) = \frac{7!}{(7-6)!\,6!} \cdot \frac{3!}{(3-1)!\,1!}$
$= \frac{7 \cdot 6!}{1 \cdot 6!} \cdot \frac{3 \cdot 2!}{2! \cdot 1}$
$= 7 \cdot 3$
$= 21$

11. $P(4, 2) \cdot C(13, 4) \cdot C(13, 1)$
$= \frac{4!}{2!} \cdot \frac{13!}{(13-4)!\,4!} \cdot \frac{13!}{(13-1)!\,1!}$
$= \frac{4 \cdot 3 \cdot 2!}{2!} \cdot \frac{13 \cdot 12 \cdot 11 \cdot 10 \cdot 9!}{9! \cdot 4 \cdot 3 \cdot 2 \cdot 1} \cdot \frac{13 \cdot 12!}{12! \cdot 1}$
$= 12 \cdot 715 \cdot 13$
$= 111{,}540$

12. $C(7, 3) = \frac{7!}{(7-3)!\,3!}$
$= \frac{7 \cdot 6 \cdot 5 \cdot 4!}{4! \cdot 3 \cdot 2 \cdot 1}$
$= 35$

13. $C(10, 8) = \frac{10!}{(10-8)!\,8!}$
$= \frac{10 \cdot 9 \cdot 8!}{2 \cdot 1 \cdot 8!}$
$= 45$

Page 904 Lesson 12-4

1. $s = 5, f = 9$
$s + f = 14$
probability $= \frac{5}{14}$

2. $s = 4, f = 8$
$s + f = 12$
probability $= \frac{4}{12}$ or $\frac{1}{3}$

3. $s = 3, f = 10$
$s + f = 13$
probability $= \frac{3}{13}$

4. $s = 2, f = 7$
$s + f = 9$
probability $= \frac{2}{9}$

5. $s = 6, f = 13$
$s + f = 19$
probability $= \frac{6}{19}$

6. $s = 1, f = 19$
$s + f = 20$
probability $= \frac{1}{20}$

7. $\frac{C(4, 3)}{C(12, 3)} = \frac{\frac{4!}{1!\,3!}}{\frac{12!}{9!\,3!}}$
$= \frac{4}{220}$
$= \frac{1}{55}$

8. $\frac{C(3, 1) \cdot C(9 \cdot 2)}{C(12, 3)} = \frac{\frac{3!}{2!\,1!} \cdot \frac{9!}{7!\,2!}}{\frac{12!}{9!\,3!}}$
$= \frac{3 \cdot 36}{220}$
$= \frac{108}{220}$ or $\frac{27}{55}$

9. $\frac{C(5, 2) \cdot C(7, 1)}{C(12, 3)} = \frac{\frac{5!}{3!\,2!} \cdot \frac{7!}{6!\,1!}}{\frac{12!}{9!\,3!}}$
$= \frac{10 \cdot 7}{220}$
$= \frac{7}{22}$

10. $\frac{C(13, 4)}{C(52, 4)} = \frac{\frac{13!}{9!\,4!}}{\frac{52!}{48!\,4!}}$
$= \frac{715}{270{,}725}$
$= \frac{11}{4165}$

11. $\frac{C(48, 13)}{C(52, 13)} = \frac{\frac{48!}{35!\,13!}}{\frac{52!}{39!\,13!}}$
$= \frac{192{,}928{,}249{,}300}{635{,}013{,}559{,}600}$
$= \frac{6327}{20{,}825}$

12. $\frac{C(26, 13)}{C(52, 13)} = \frac{\frac{26!}{13!\,13!}}{\frac{52!}{39!\,13!}}$
$= \frac{10{,}400{,}600}{635{,}013{,}559{,}600}$
$= \frac{19}{1{,}160{,}054}$

Page 905 Lesson 12-5

1a. $P(\text{2 girls and 2 boys}) = \frac{C(7, 2) \cdot C(5, 2)}{C(12, 4)}$
$= \frac{\frac{7!}{5!\,2!} \cdot \frac{5!}{3!\,2!}}{\frac{12!}{8!\,4!}}$
$= \frac{21 \cdot 10}{495}$
$= \frac{14}{33}$

1b. $P(\text{3 girls and 1 boy}) = \frac{C(7, 3) \cdot C(5, 1)}{C(12, 4)}$
$= \frac{\frac{7!}{4!\,3!} \cdot \frac{5!}{4!\,1!}}{\frac{12!}{8!\,4!}}$
$= \frac{35 \cdot 5}{495}$
$= \frac{35}{99}$

1c. $P(\text{2 senior boys and 2 senior girls})$
$= \frac{C(3, 2) \cdot C(3, 2)}{C(12, 4)}$
$= \frac{\frac{3!}{2!\,1!} \cdot \frac{3!}{2!\,1!}}{\frac{12!}{8!\,4!}}$
$= \frac{3 \cdot 3}{495}$
$= \frac{1}{55}$

1d. $P(\text{all seniors of whom at least 2 are girls})$
$= \frac{C(3, 2) \cdot C(3, 2)}{C(12, 4)} + \frac{C(3, 3) \cdot C(3, 1)}{C(12, 4)}$
$= \frac{\frac{3!}{2!\,1!} \cdot \frac{3!}{2!\,1!}}{\frac{12!}{8!\,4!}} + \frac{\frac{3!}{0!\,3!} \cdot \frac{3!}{2!\,1!}}{\frac{12!}{8!\,4!}}$
$= \frac{3 \cdot 3}{495} + \frac{1 \cdot 3}{495}$
$= \frac{12}{495}$ or $\frac{4}{165}$

2a. P(Paula will ask and Leon will ask.)

$= \frac{1}{3} \cdot \frac{1}{4}$

$= \frac{1}{12}$

2b. P(Ray and Paula will ask, but Leon will not.)

$= \frac{3}{4} \cdot \frac{1}{3} \cdot \frac{3}{4}$

$= \frac{3}{16}$

2c. P(At least two out of three will ask.)

$= P$(only 2 will ask) + P(all three will ask)

$= \frac{1}{4} \cdot \frac{1}{3} \cdot \frac{1}{4} + \frac{1}{3} \cdot \frac{3}{4} \cdot \frac{3}{4} + \frac{1}{4} \cdot \frac{3}{4} \cdot \frac{2}{3} + \frac{1}{4} \cdot \frac{1}{3} \cdot \frac{3}{4}$

$= \frac{1}{48} + \frac{9}{48} + \frac{6}{48} + \frac{3}{48}$

$= \frac{19}{48}$

2d. P(at least one out of three will ask)

$= 1 - P$(none will ask)

$= 1 - \frac{3}{4} \cdot \frac{2}{3} \cdot \frac{1}{4}$

$= 1 - \frac{1}{8}$

$= \frac{7}{8}$

3a. P(It will rain in Yellow Falls, but not in Copper Creek.)

$= 0.70 \cdot 0.50$

$= 0.35$; 35%

3b. P(It will rain in both cities.) $= 0.70 \cdot 0.50$

$= 0.35$; 35%

3c. P(It will rain in neither city.) $= 0.30 \cdot 0.50$

$= 0.15$; 15%

3d. P(It will rain in at least one of the cities.)

$= P$(rain in Yellow Falls) + P(rain in Copper Creek) + P(rain in both)

$= 0.70 \cdot 0.50 + 0.30 \cdot 0.50 + 0.70 \cdot 0.50$

$= 0.35 + 0.15 + 0.35$

$= 0.85$; 85%

Page 905 Lesson 12-6

1. $\frac{C(3, 2)}{C(5, 2)} \cdot \frac{C(2, 2)}{C(6, 2)} + \frac{C(2, 2)}{C(5, 2)} \cdot \frac{C(4, 2)}{C(6, 2)}$

$= \frac{\frac{3!}{1!\,2!}}{\frac{5!}{3!\,2!}} \cdot \frac{\frac{2!}{0!\,2!}}{\frac{6!}{4!\,2!}} + \frac{\frac{2!}{0!\,2!}}{\frac{5!}{3!\,2!}} \cdot \frac{\frac{4!}{2!\,2!}}{\frac{6!}{4!\,2!}}$

$= \frac{3}{10} \cdot \frac{1}{15} + \frac{1}{10} \cdot \frac{6}{15}$

$= \frac{1}{50} + \frac{1}{25}$

$= \frac{3}{50}$

2. P(8 correct) + P(9 correct) + P(10 correct)

$= \frac{C(10, 8)}{2^{10}} + \frac{C(10, 9)}{2^{10}} + \frac{C(10, 10)}{2^{10}}$

$= \frac{45}{1024} + \frac{10}{1024} + \frac{1}{1024}$

$= \frac{56}{1024}$ or $\frac{7}{128}$

3a. P(All three dice show the same number.)

$= \frac{1}{6} \cdot \frac{1}{6} \cdot \frac{1}{6} \cdot C(6, 1)$

$= \frac{1}{216} \cdot 6$

$= \frac{1}{36}$

3b. P(Exactly 2 of the dice show the same number.)

$= \frac{1}{6} \cdot \frac{1}{6} \cdot \frac{5}{6} \cdot C(6, 1) + \frac{1}{6} \cdot \frac{5}{6} \cdot \frac{1}{6} \cdot C(6, 1) + \frac{5}{6} \cdot \frac{1}{6} \cdot \frac{1}{6} \cdot C(6, 1)$

$= \frac{5}{216} \cdot 6 + \frac{5}{216} \cdot 6 + \frac{5}{216} \cdot 6$

$= \frac{5}{36} + \frac{5}{36} + \frac{5}{36}$

$= \frac{15}{36}$

$= \frac{5}{12}$

4a. P(at least 1 red marble)

$= P$(1 red) + P(2 red)

$= \frac{3}{14} \cdot \frac{11}{13} \cdot C(2, 1) + \frac{3}{14} \cdot \frac{2}{13}$

$= \frac{33}{182} \cdot 2 + \frac{3}{91}$

$= \frac{33}{91} + \frac{3}{91}$

$= \frac{36}{91}$

4b. P(at least 1 green marble)

$= P$(1 green) + P(2 green)

$= \frac{6}{14} \cdot \frac{8}{13} \cdot C(2, 1) + \frac{6}{14} \cdot \frac{5}{13}$

$= \frac{24}{91} \cdot 2 + \frac{15}{91}$

$= \frac{48}{91} + \frac{15}{91}$

$= \frac{63}{91}$ or $\frac{9}{13}$

4c. P(2 marbles of the same color)

$= P$(2 red) + P(2 blue) + P(2 green)

$= \frac{3}{14} \cdot \frac{2}{13} + \frac{5}{14} \cdot \frac{4}{13} + \frac{6}{14} \cdot \frac{5}{13}$

$= \frac{3}{91} + \frac{10}{91} + \frac{15}{91}$

$= \frac{28}{91}$ or $\frac{4}{13}$

4d. P(two marbles of different colors)

$= P$(1 red, 1 blue) + P(1 red, 1 green) + P(1 blue, 1 green)

$= \frac{3}{14} \cdot \frac{5}{13} \cdot C(2, 1) + \frac{3}{14} \cdot \frac{6}{13} \cdot C(2, 1) + \frac{5}{14} \cdot \frac{6}{13} \cdot C(2, 1)$

$= \frac{15}{91} + \frac{18}{91} + \frac{30}{91}$

$= \frac{63}{91}$ or $\frac{9}{13}$

Page 905 Lesson 12-7

1. P(Die is even.) $= \frac{3}{6}$ or $\frac{1}{2}$

P(heads) $= \frac{1}{2}$

$\frac{1}{2} \cdot \frac{1}{2} = \frac{1}{4}$

2.

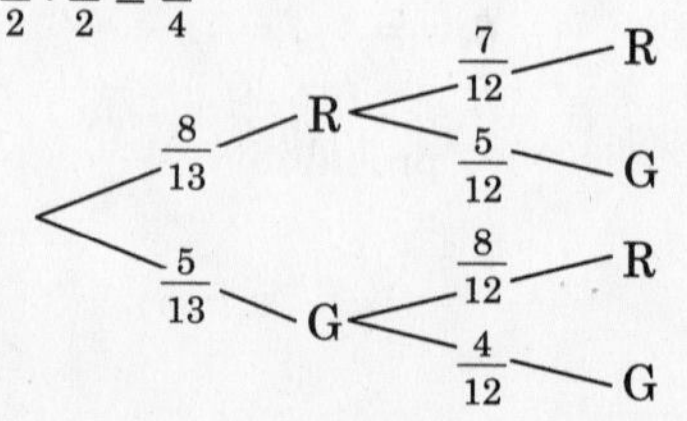

$\frac{8}{13} \cdot \frac{5}{12} = \frac{10}{39}$

$\frac{5}{13} \cdot \frac{8}{12} = \frac{10}{39}$

$\frac{10}{39} + \frac{10}{39} = \frac{20}{39}$

3. $P(D) = \frac{1}{10}$, $P(G) = \frac{9}{10}$

$(D + G)^5 = D^5 + 5D^4G + 10D^3G^2 + 10D^2G^3 + 5DG^4 + G^5$

3a. $P(\text{None are defective.}) = \left(\frac{9}{10}\right)^5$

$= \frac{59049}{100,000}$

$= 0.59049$ or about 0.59

3b. $P(\text{Exactly one is defective.}) = 5\left(\frac{1}{10}\right)\left(\frac{9}{10}\right)^4$

$= \frac{6561}{20,000}$

$= 0.32805$ or about 0.328

3c. $P(\text{At least three are defective.})$

$= \left(\frac{1}{10}\right)^5 + 5\left(\frac{1}{10}\right)^4\left(\frac{9}{10}\right) + 10\left(\frac{1}{10}\right)^3\left(\frac{9}{10}\right)^2$

$= \frac{1}{100,000} + \frac{45}{100,000} + \frac{810}{100,000}$

$= \frac{856}{100,000}$

$= 0.00856$ or about 0.009

3d. $P(\text{Less than three are defective.})$

$= 10\left(\frac{1}{10}\right)^2\left(\frac{9}{10}\right)^3 + 5\left(\frac{1}{10}\right)\left(\frac{9}{10}\right)^4 + \left(\frac{9}{10}\right)^5$

$= \frac{7290}{100,000} + \frac{32,805}{100,000} + \frac{59,049}{100,000}$

$= \frac{99,144}{100,000}$

$= 0.99144$ or about 0.991

4a. $P(\text{Each question is right.}) = C(80, 80)\left(\frac{1}{2}\right)^{80}$

$= 1\left(\frac{1}{2}\right)^{80}$

$= 8.27 \times 10^{-25}$

4b. $P(\text{Exactly 35 are right.}) = C(80, 35)\left(\frac{1}{2}\right)^{35}\left(\frac{1}{2}\right)^{45}$

$= 0.04789$

Page 906 Lesson 12-8

1. No; the doctors in one hospital in one town do not represent a good sample of all doctors in the country. The hospital might have a contract with the makers of a certain pain reliever.
2. Yes; this would be a random sampling because it is an unbiased and thorough representation.
3. No; by frequenting the pizza parlor, it is probably their favorite restaurant. This would not be a good random sample.
4. $ME = 2\sqrt{\frac{p(1-p)}{n}}$

   $= 2\sqrt{\frac{0.72(1-0.72)}{2500}}$

   $= 2\sqrt{0.00008064}$

   ≈ 0.01796; 1.8%

   There is a 95% pobability that between 70.2 – 73.8% of students choose oatmeal as their favorite breakfast meal.
5. $ME = 2\sqrt{\frac{p(1-p)}{n}}$

   $= 2\sqrt{\frac{0.56(1-0.56)}{420}}$

   $= 2\sqrt{0.000587}$

   ≈ 0.04844; 4.8%

   There is a 95% probability that between 51.2 – 60.8% of people feel that they are impulse buyers at the supermarket.
6. $ME = 2\sqrt{\frac{p(1-p)}{n}}$

   $= 2\sqrt{\frac{0.45(1-0.45)}{3000}}$

   $= 2\sqrt{0.0000825}$

   ≈ 0.01817; 1.8%

   There is a 95% probability that between 43.2 – 46.8% of women take the recommended daily allowance of calcium, as recommended by the NIH.

Page 906 Lesson 13-1

1. $\cos\theta = \frac{3}{5} = \frac{b}{c}$

   $a^2 + b^2 = c^2$

   $a^2 + 3^2 = 5^2$

   $a^2 = 16$

   $a = 4$

   $\sin\theta = \frac{4}{5}$ or 0.8000 $\quad \sec\theta = \frac{5}{3}$ or 1.6667

   $\tan\theta = \frac{4}{3}$ or 1.3333 $\quad \cot\theta = \frac{3}{4}$ or 0.7500

   $\csc\theta = \frac{5}{4}$ or 1.2500
2. $\tan\theta = \frac{8}{15} = \frac{a}{b}$

   $a^2 + b^2 = c^2$

   $8^2 + 15^2 = c^2$

   $289 = c^2$

   $17 = c$

   $\sin\theta = \frac{8}{17}$ or 0.4706 $\quad \sec\theta = \frac{17}{15}$ or 1.1333

   $\cos\theta = \frac{15}{17}$ or 0.8824 $\quad \cot\theta = \frac{15}{8}$ or 1.8750

   $\csc\theta = \frac{17}{8}$ or 2.1250
3. $\sec\theta = \frac{13}{5} = \frac{c}{b}$

   $a^2 + b^2 = c^2$

   $a^2 + 5^2 = 13^2$

   $a^2 = 144$

   $a = 12$

   $\sin\theta = \frac{12}{13}$ or 0.9231 $\quad \csc\theta = \frac{13}{12}$ or 1.0833

   $\cos\theta = \frac{5}{13}$ or 0.3846 $\quad \cot\theta = \frac{5}{12}$ or 0.4167

   $\tan\theta = \frac{12}{5}$ or 2.4000
4. $\csc\theta = \frac{25}{7} = \frac{c}{a}$

   $a^2 + b^2 = c^2$

   $7^2 + b^2 = 25^2$

   $b^2 = 576$

   $b = 24$

   $\sin\theta = \frac{7}{25}$ or 0.2800 $\quad \sec\theta = \frac{25}{24}$ or 1.0417

   $\cos\theta = \frac{24}{25}$ or 0.9600 $\quad \cot\theta = \frac{24}{7}$ or 3.4286

   $\tan\theta = \frac{7}{24}$ or 0.2917

5. $\cot \theta = 1 = \frac{b}{a}$
$a^2 + b^2 = c^2$
$1^2 + 1^2 = c^2$
$2 = c^2$
$\sqrt{2} = c$
$\sin \theta = \frac{\sqrt{2}}{2}$ or 0.7071 $\csc \theta = \sqrt{2}$ or 1.4142
$\cos \theta = \frac{\sqrt{2}}{2}$ or 0.7071 $\sec \theta = \sqrt{2}$ or 1.4142
$\tan \theta = 1$ or 1.0000

6. 76° **7.** 67° **8.** 54° **9.** 84°
10. 37° **11.** 9° **12.** 52° **13.** 12°
14. 38° **15.** 63° **16.** 21° **17.** 71°

18. $a^2 + b^2 = c^2$
$8^2 + b^2 = 10^2$
$b^2 = 36$
$b = 6$
$\sin A = \frac{8}{10}$ $53.1° + B \approx 90°$
$\sin A = 0.8000$ $B \approx 36.9°$
$A \approx 53.1°$

19. $a^2 + b^2 = c^2$
$2^2 + 7^2 = c^2$
$53 = c^2$
$c \approx 7.3$
$\tan A = \frac{2}{7}$ $15.9° + B \approx 90°$
$\tan A \approx 0.2857$ $B \approx 74.1°$
$A \approx 15.9°$

20. $a^2 + b^2 = c^2$
$11^2 + 21^2 = c^2$
$562 = c^2$
$23.7 \approx c$
$\tan A = \frac{11}{21}$ $27.6° + B \approx 90°$
$\tan A \approx 0.5238$ $B \approx 62.4°$
$A \approx 27.6°$

21. $A + 64° = 90°$
$A = 26°$
$\sin 64° = \frac{b}{18.2}$ $a^2 + b^2 = c^2$
$b = 18.2 \sin 64°$ $a^2 + (16.4)^2 \approx (18.2)^2$
$b \approx 16.4$ $a^2 \approx 62.28$
$a \approx 7.9$

22. $A + 33° = 90°$
$A = 57°$
$\tan 33° = \frac{b}{33}$ $a^2 + b^2 = c^2$
$b = 33 \tan 33°$ $(33)^2 + (21.4)^2 \approx c^2$
$b \approx 21.4$ $1546.96 \approx c^2$
$39.3 \approx c$

23. $A + 13° = 90°$
$A = 77°$
$\sin 77° = \frac{a}{6}$ $\sin 13° = \frac{b}{6}$
$a = 6 \sin 77°$ $b = 6 \sin 13°$
$a \approx 5.8$ $b \approx 1.3$

24. $77° + B = 90°$
$B = 13°$
$\tan 13° = \frac{42}{a}$ $a^2 + b^2 = c^2$
$a = \frac{42}{\tan 13°}$ $(181.9)^2 + (42)^2 \approx c^2$
$34851.61 \approx c^2$
$a \approx 181.9°$ $186.7 \approx c$

25. $57° + B = 90°$ $a^2 + b^2 = c^2$
$B = 33°$ $a^2 + (9.8)^2 \approx 18°$
$\sin 33° = \frac{b}{18}$ $a^2 \approx 227.96$
$a \approx 15.1$
$b = 18 \sin 33°$
$b \approx 9.8$

26. $35° + B = 90°$
$B = 55°$
$\tan 55° = \frac{b}{7}$ $a^2 + b^2 = c^2$
$b = 7 \tan 55°$ $7^2 + 10^2 \approx c^2$
$b \approx 10.0$ $149 \approx c^2$
$12.2 \approx c$

27. $A + 36° = 90°$
$A = 54°$
$\sin 54° = \frac{a}{18}$ $\sin 36° = \frac{b}{18}$
$a = 18 \sin 54°$ $b = 18 \sin 36°$
$a \approx 14.6$ $b \approx 10.6$

28. $\cos A = \frac{3}{5}$ $53.1° + B \approx 90°$
$\cos A = 0.6000$ $B \approx 36.9°$
$A \approx 53.1°$
$\cos A = \frac{3}{5}$ or $\frac{6}{10}$ $b = 6.0$
$a^2 + b^2 = c^2$
$a^2 + 6^2 = 10^2$
$a^2 = 64$
$a = 8$

29. $\tan B = \frac{1}{2} = \frac{7}{14}$ $a = 14$
$\tan B = 0.5000$ $A + 26.6° \approx 90°$
$B \approx 26.6°$ $A \approx 63.4°$
$a^2 + b^2 = c^2$
$14^2 + 7^2 \approx c^2$
$245 \approx c^2$
$15.7 \approx c$

Page 906 Lesson 13-2

1. $(60°)\left(\frac{\pi \text{ radians}}{180°}\right) = \frac{60\pi}{180}$ radians or $\frac{\pi}{3}$ radians
2. $(270°)\left(\frac{\pi \text{ radians}}{180°}\right) = \frac{270\pi}{180}$ radians or $\frac{3\pi}{2}$ radians
3. $(315°)\left(\frac{\pi \text{ radians}}{180°}\right) = \frac{315\pi}{180}$ radians or $\frac{7\pi}{4}$ radians
4. $(150°)\left(\frac{\pi \text{ radians}}{180°}\right) = \frac{150\pi}{180}$ radians or $\frac{5\pi}{6}$ radians
5. $(-135°)\left(\frac{\pi \text{ radians}}{180°}\right) = -\frac{135\pi}{180}$ radians or $-\frac{3\pi}{4}$ radians
6. $(-315°)\left(\frac{\pi \text{ radians}}{180°}\right) = -\frac{315\pi}{180}$ radians or $-\frac{7\pi}{4}$ radians
7. $(45°)\left(\frac{\pi \text{ radians}}{180°}\right) = \frac{45\pi}{180}$ radians or $\frac{\pi}{4}$ radians
8. $(80°)\left(\frac{\pi \text{ radians}}{180°}\right) = \frac{80\pi}{180}$ radians or $\frac{4\pi}{9}$ radians
9. $(24°)\left(\frac{\pi \text{ radians}}{180°}\right) = \frac{24\pi}{180}$ radians or $\frac{2\pi}{15}$ radians
10. $(-54°)\left(\frac{\pi \text{ radians}}{180°}\right) = -\frac{54\pi}{180}$ radians or $-\frac{3\pi}{10}$ radians
11. $-\pi$ radians $\left(\frac{180°}{\pi \text{ radians}}\right) = -\frac{180°\pi}{\pi}$ or $-180°$
12. $\frac{9\pi}{4}$ radians $\left(\frac{180°}{\pi \text{ radians}}\right) = \frac{1620°\pi}{4\pi}$ or 405°
13. $\frac{3\pi}{2}$ radians $\left(\frac{180°}{\pi \text{ radians}}\right) = \frac{540°\pi}{2\pi}$ or 270°

14. $-\frac{7\pi}{4}$ radians $\left(\frac{180°}{\pi \text{ radians}}\right) = -\frac{1260°\pi}{4\pi} = -315°$

15. $\frac{7\pi}{12}$ radians $\left(\frac{180°}{\pi \text{ radians}}\right) = \frac{1260°\pi}{12\pi} = 105°$

16. $\frac{9\pi}{10}$ radians $\left(\frac{180°}{\pi \text{ radians}}\right) = \frac{1620°\pi}{10\pi} = 162°$

17. $-\frac{17\pi}{30}$ radians $\left(\frac{180°}{\pi \text{ radians}}\right) = -\frac{3060°\pi}{30\pi} = -102°$

18. 1 radians $\left(\frac{180°}{\pi \text{ radians}}\right) = \frac{180°}{\pi} \approx 57.30°$

19. $-2\frac{1}{3}$ or $-\frac{7}{3}$ radians $\left(\frac{180°}{\pi \text{ radians}}\right) = -\frac{1260°}{3\pi} \approx 133.69°$

20. $6\frac{1}{2}$ or $\frac{13}{2}$ radians $\left(\frac{180°}{\pi \text{ radians}}\right) = \frac{2340°}{2\pi} \approx 372.42°$

21. Sample answer: positive angle, 50° + 360° or 410° negative angle, 50° − 360° or −310°

22. Sample answer: positive angle, −75° + 360° or 285°; negative angle, −75° − 360° or −435°

23. Sample answer: positive angle, 125° + 360° or 485°; negative angle, 125° − 360° or −235°

24. Sample answer: positive angle, −400° + 2(360°) or 320°; negative angle, −400° + 360° or −40

25. Sample answer: positive angle, 550° − 360° or 190°; negative angle, 550° − 2(360°) or −170°

26. Sample answer: positive angle, $3\pi - 2\pi$ or π negative angle, $3\pi - 2(2\pi)$ or $-\pi$

27. Sample answer: positive angle, $-2\pi + 2(2\pi)$ or 2π negative angle, $-2\pi - 2\pi$ or -4π

28. Sample answer: positive angle, $\frac{2\pi}{3} + 2\pi$ or $\frac{8\pi}{3}$ negative angle, $\frac{2\pi}{3} - 2\pi$ or $-\frac{4\pi}{3}$

29. Sample answer: positive angle, $\frac{12\pi}{5} - 2\pi$ or $\frac{2\pi}{5}$ negative angle, $\frac{12\pi}{5} - 2(2\pi)$ or $-\frac{8\pi}{5}$

30. Sample answer: positive angle, $-\frac{9\pi}{5} + 2\pi$ or $\frac{\pi}{5}$ negative angle, $-\frac{9\pi}{5} - 2\pi$ or $-\frac{19\pi}{5}$

Page 907 Lesson 13-3

1. Quadrant II, positive
2. Quadrant III, negative
3. zero
4. Quadrant IV, negative
5. zero
6. undefined
7. Quadrant IV, negative
8. Quadrant III, negative
9. Quadrant III, positive
10. negative

11. $P(3, -4)$

$r = \sqrt{x^2 + y^2}$
$= \sqrt{3^2 + (-4)^2}$
$= \sqrt{25}$ or 5

$\sin\theta = \frac{y}{r} = -\frac{4}{5}$ $\quad \cos\theta = \frac{x}{r} = \frac{3}{5}$ $\quad \tan\theta = \frac{y}{x} = -\frac{4}{3}$

12. $P(1, \sqrt{3})$

$r = \sqrt{x^2 + y^2}$
$= \sqrt{1^2 + (\sqrt{3})^2}$
$= \sqrt{4}$ or 2

$\sin\theta = \frac{y}{r} = \frac{\sqrt{3}}{2}$ $\quad \cos\theta = \frac{x}{r} = \frac{1}{2}$ $\quad \tan\theta = \frac{y}{x} = \frac{\sqrt{3}}{1}$ or $\sqrt{3}$

13. $P(0, -4)$

$r = \sqrt{x^2 + y^2}$
$= \sqrt{0^2 + (-4)^2}$
$= \sqrt{16}$ or 4

$\sin\theta = \frac{y}{r} = -\frac{4}{4} = -1$ $\quad \cos\theta = \frac{x}{r} = \frac{0}{4} = 0$ $\quad \tan\theta = \frac{y}{x} = -\frac{4}{0}$ undefined

14. $P(-5, -5)$

$r = \sqrt{x^2 + y^2}$
$= \sqrt{(-5)^2 + (-5)^2}$
$= \sqrt{50}$ or $5\sqrt{2}$

$\sin\theta = \frac{y}{r} = -\frac{5}{5\sqrt{2}} = -\frac{\sqrt{2}}{2}$ $\quad \cos\theta = \frac{x}{r} = -\frac{5}{5\sqrt{2}} = -\frac{\sqrt{2}}{2}$ $\quad \tan\theta = \frac{y}{x} = \frac{-5}{-5} = 1$

15. $P(2.5, 0)$

$r = \sqrt{x^2 + y^2}$
$= \sqrt{2.5^2 + 0^2}$
$= \sqrt{6.25}$ or 2.5

$\sin\theta = \frac{y}{r} = \frac{0}{2.5} = 0$ $\quad \cos\theta = \frac{x}{r} = \frac{2.5}{2.5} = 1$ $\quad \tan\theta = \frac{y}{x} = \frac{0}{2.5} = 0$

16. $\cos 150° = \frac{x}{r} = -\frac{\sqrt{3}}{2}$

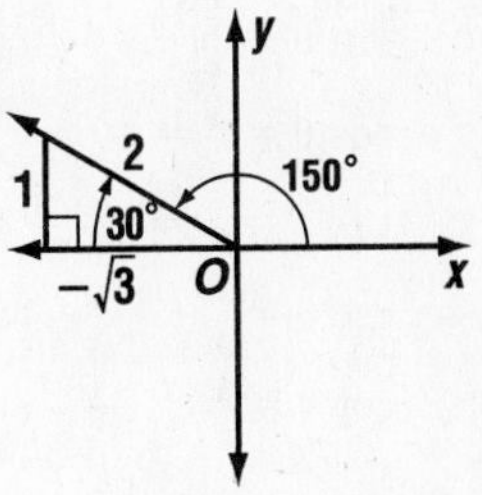

17. $\sin\left(-\frac{5\pi}{3}\right) = \frac{y}{r} = \frac{\sqrt{3}}{2}$

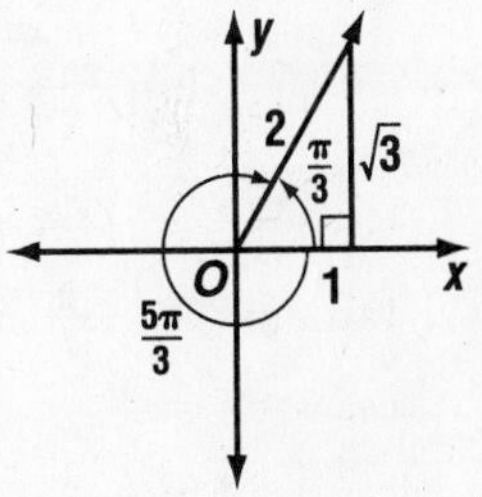

18. $\tan\frac{7\pi}{6} = \frac{y}{x} = \frac{-1}{-\sqrt{3}} = \frac{\sqrt{3}}{3}$

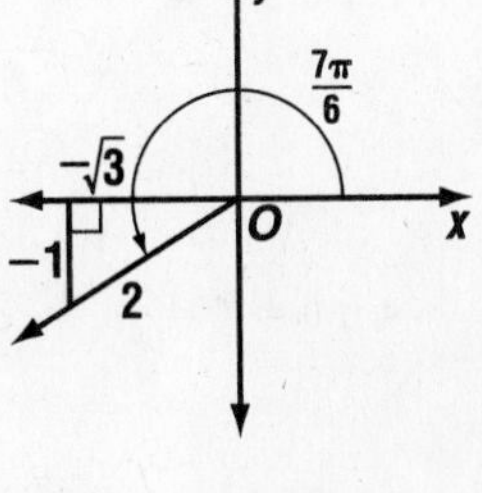

19. $\tan(-300°) = \frac{y}{x} = \frac{\sqrt{3}}{1} = \sqrt{3}$

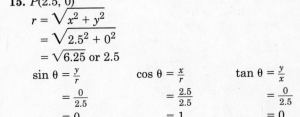

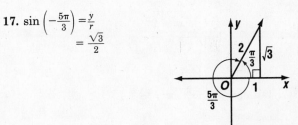

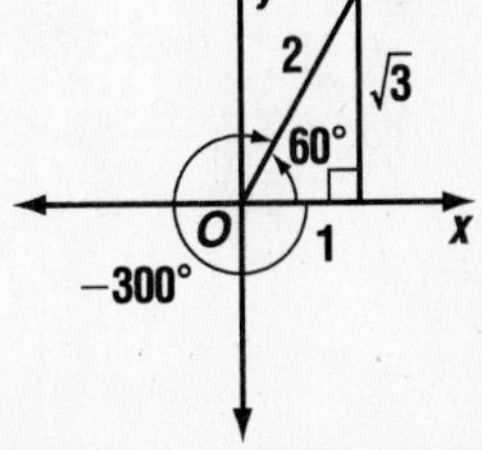

20. $\cos \frac{7\pi}{4} = \frac{x}{r}$
$= \frac{\sqrt{2}}{2}$

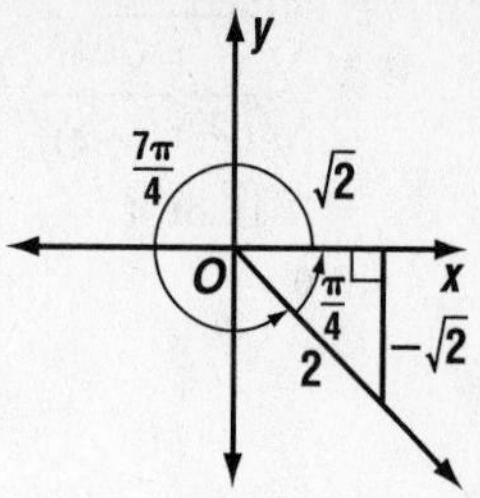

21.
$r = \sqrt{x^2 + y^2}$
$3 = \sqrt{(-1)^2 + y^2}$
$9 = 1 + y^2$
$y = \sqrt{8}$ or $-2\sqrt{2}$
$\sin \theta = \frac{y}{r} = -\frac{2\sqrt{2}}{3}$
$\tan \theta = \frac{y}{x} = \frac{-2\sqrt{2}}{-1}$ or $2\sqrt{2}$
$\csc \theta = \frac{r}{y} = \frac{3}{-2\sqrt{2}}$ or $-\frac{3\sqrt{2}}{4}$
$\sec \theta = \frac{r}{x} = -\frac{3}{1}$ or -3
$\cot \theta = \frac{x}{y} = \frac{-1}{-2\sqrt{2}}$ or $\frac{\sqrt{2}}{4}$

22.
$r = \sqrt{x^2 + y^2}$
$2 = \sqrt{1^2 + y^2}$
$4 = 1 + y^2$
$y = -\sqrt{3}$
$\sin \theta = \frac{y}{r} = -\frac{\sqrt{3}}{2}$
$\cos \theta = \frac{x}{r} = \frac{1}{2}$
$\tan \theta = \frac{y}{x} = -\frac{\sqrt{3}}{1}$ or $-\sqrt{3}$
$\csc \theta = \frac{r}{y} = \frac{2}{-\sqrt{3}}$ or $-\frac{2\sqrt{3}}{3}$
$\cot \theta = \frac{x}{y} = \frac{1}{-\sqrt{3}}$ or $-\frac{\sqrt{3}}{3}$

23.
$r = \sqrt{x^2 + y^2}$
$3 = \sqrt{x^2 + 2^2}$
$9 = x^2 + 4$
$x = -\sqrt{5}$
$\cos \theta = \frac{x}{r} = -\frac{\sqrt{5}}{3}$
$\tan \theta = \frac{y}{x} = -\frac{2}{\sqrt{5}}$ or $-\frac{2\sqrt{5}}{5}$
$\csc \theta = \frac{r}{y} = \frac{3}{2}$
$\sec \theta = \frac{r}{x} = -\frac{3}{\sqrt{5}}$ or $-\frac{3\sqrt{5}}{5}$
$\cot \theta = \frac{x}{y} = -\frac{\sqrt{5}}{2}$

24.
$r = \sqrt{x^2 + y^2}$
$r = \sqrt{1^2 + (-4)^2}$
$r = \sqrt{17}$
$\sin \theta = \frac{y}{r} = -\frac{4}{\sqrt{17}}$ or $-\frac{4\sqrt{17}}{17}$
$\cos \theta = \frac{x}{r} = \frac{1}{\sqrt{17}}$ or $\frac{\sqrt{17}}{17}$
$\csc \theta = \frac{r}{y} = -\frac{\sqrt{17}}{4}$
$\sec \theta = \frac{r}{x} = \sqrt{17}$
$\cot \theta = \frac{x}{y} = -\frac{1}{4}$

25.
$r = \sqrt{x^2 + y^2}$
$5 = \sqrt{x^2 + (-1)^2}$
$25 = x^2 + 1$
$x = \sqrt{24}$ or $-2\sqrt{6}$
$\sin \theta = \frac{y}{r} = -\frac{1}{5}$
$\cos \theta = \frac{x}{r} = -\frac{2\sqrt{6}}{5}$
$\tan \theta = \frac{y}{x} = \frac{-1}{-2\sqrt{6}}$ or $\frac{\sqrt{6}}{12}$
$\sec \theta = \frac{r}{x} = -\frac{5}{2\sqrt{6}}$ or $-\frac{5\sqrt{6}}{12}$
$\cot \theta = \frac{x}{y} = \frac{-2\sqrt{6}}{-1}$ or $2\sqrt{6}$

26.
$r = \sqrt{x^2 + y^2}$
$r = \sqrt{(-2)^2 + (1)^2}$
$r = \sqrt{5}$
$\sin \theta = \frac{y}{r} = \frac{1}{\sqrt{5}}$ or $\frac{\sqrt{5}}{5}$
$\cos \theta = \frac{x}{r} = -\frac{2}{\sqrt{5}}$ or $-\frac{2\sqrt{5}}{5}$
$\tan \theta = \frac{y}{x} = -\frac{1}{2}$
$\csc \theta = \frac{r}{y} = \frac{\sqrt{5}}{1}$ or $\sqrt{5}$
$\sec \theta = \frac{r}{x} = -\frac{\sqrt{5}}{2}$

27.
$r = \sqrt{x^2 + y^2}$
$r = \sqrt{(-3)^2 + (-1)^2}$
$r = \sqrt{10}$
$\sin \theta = \frac{y}{r} = -\frac{1}{\sqrt{10}}$ or $-\frac{\sqrt{10}}{10}$
$\cos \theta = \frac{x}{r} = -\frac{3}{\sqrt{10}}$ or $-\frac{3\sqrt{10}}{10}$
$\csc \theta = \frac{r}{y} = \frac{\sqrt{10}}{-1}$ or $-\sqrt{10}$
$\sec \theta = \frac{r}{x} = -\frac{\sqrt{10}}{3}$
$\cot \theta = \frac{x}{y} = \frac{3}{1}$ or 3

28.
$r = \sqrt{x^2 + y^2}$
$4 = \sqrt{1^2 + y^2}$
$16 = 1 + y^2$
$y = \sqrt{15}$
$\sin \theta = \frac{y}{r} = \frac{\sqrt{15}}{4}$
$\tan \theta = \frac{y}{x} = \frac{\sqrt{15}}{1}$ or $\sqrt{15}$
$\csc \theta = \frac{r}{y} = \frac{4}{\sqrt{15}}$ or $\frac{4\sqrt{15}}{15}$
$\sec \theta = \frac{r}{x} = \frac{4}{1}$ or 4
$\cot \theta = \frac{x}{y} = \frac{1}{\sqrt{15}}$ or $\frac{\sqrt{15}}{15}$

29.
$r = \sqrt{x^2 + y^2}$
$5 = \sqrt{x^2 + (-2)^2}$
$25 = x^2 + 4$
$x = \sqrt{21}$
$\sin \theta = \frac{y}{r} = -\frac{2}{5}$
$\cos \theta = \frac{x}{r} = \frac{\sqrt{21}}{5}$
$\tan \theta = \frac{y}{x} = -\frac{2}{\sqrt{21}}$ or $-\frac{2\sqrt{21}}{21}$
$\sec \theta = \frac{r}{x} = \frac{5}{\sqrt{21}}$ or $\frac{5\sqrt{21}}{21}$
$\cot \theta = \frac{x}{y} = -\frac{\sqrt{21}}{2}$

Page 907 Lesson 13-4

1. $A = \frac{1}{2}ab\sin C$
$= \frac{1}{2}(11)(13)\sin 31°$
≈ 36.8

2. $A = \frac{1}{2}ab\sin C$
$= \frac{1}{2}(15)(22)\sin 90°$
$= 165$

3. $A = \frac{1}{2}ab\sin C$
$= \frac{1}{2}(12)(12)\sin 50°$
≈ 55.2

4. $A = \frac{1}{2}ac\sin B$
$= \frac{1}{2}(6)(4)\sin 52°$
≈ 9.5

5. $A = \frac{1}{2}bc\sin A$
$= \frac{1}{2}(10)(17)\sin 46°$
≈ 61.1

6. $A = \frac{1}{2}bc\sin A$
$= \frac{1}{2}(4)(19)\sin 73°$
≈ 36.3

7. $A = \frac{1}{2}ac\sin B$
$= \frac{1}{2}(11)(5)\sin 55°$
≈ 22.5

8. $A = \frac{1}{2}bc\sin A$
$= \frac{1}{2}(8)(12)\sin 75°$
≈ 46.4

9. $A = \frac{1}{2}ab\sin C$
$= \frac{1}{2}(12)(9)\sin 35°$
≈ 31.0

10. one solution

$40° + 60° + C = 180°$
$C = 80°$

$\frac{a}{\sin A} = \frac{c}{\sin C}$
$\frac{a}{\sin 40°} = \frac{20}{\sin 80°}$
$a = \frac{20 \sin 40°}{\sin 80°}$
$a \approx 13.1$

$\frac{b}{\sin B} = \frac{c}{\sin C}$
$\frac{b}{\sin 60°} = \frac{20}{\sin 80°}$
$b = \frac{20 \sin 60°}{\sin 80°}$
$b \approx 17.6$

11. one solution

$A + 70° + 58° = 180°$
$A = 52°$

$\frac{a}{\sin A} = \frac{b}{\sin B}$
$\frac{84}{\sin 52°} = \frac{b}{\sin 70°}$
$b = \frac{84 \sin 70°}{\sin 52°}$
$b \approx 100.2$

$\frac{a}{\sin A} = \frac{c}{\sin C}$
$\frac{84}{\sin 52°} = \frac{c}{\sin 58°}$
$c = \frac{84 \sin 58°}{\sin 52°}$
$c \approx 90.4$

12. $5 < 12 \sin 40°$
$5 < 7.71$
no solution

13. $29 > 26 > 29 \sin 58°$
two solutions

$\frac{a}{\sin A} = \frac{b}{\sin B}$
$\frac{26}{\sin 58°} = \frac{29}{\sin B}$
$\sin B = \frac{29 \sin 58°}{26}$
$\sin B \approx 0.9459$
$B \approx 71.0°$

$58° + 71° + C \approx 180°$
$C \approx 51°$

$\frac{a}{\sin A} = \frac{c}{\sin C}$
$\frac{26}{\sin 58°} \approx \frac{c}{\sin 51°}$
$c \approx \frac{24 \sin 51°}{\sin 58°}$
$c \approx 23.8$

$B \approx 180° - 71.0°$
$\approx 109.0°$
$58° + 109° + C \approx 180°$
$C \approx 13°$

$\frac{a}{\sin A} = \frac{c}{\sin C}$
$\frac{26}{\sin 58°} \approx \frac{c}{\sin 13°}$
$c \approx \frac{26 \sin 13°}{\sin 58°}$
$c \approx 7.0$

14. one solution

$38° + 63° + C = 180°$
$C = 79°$

$\frac{a}{\sin A} = \frac{c}{\sin C}$
$\frac{a}{\sin 38°} = \frac{15}{\sin 79°}$
$a = \frac{15 \sin 38°}{\sin 79°}$
$a \approx 9.4$

$\frac{c}{\sin C} = \frac{b}{\sin B}$
$\frac{15}{\sin 79°} = \frac{b}{\sin 63°}$
$b = \frac{15 \sin 63°}{\sin 79°}$
$b \approx 13.6$

15. $A \geq 90°$
$6 \leq 8$ no solution

16. $12 < 19 \sin 57°$
no solution

17. $150 > 125 > 150 \sin 25°$
two solutions

$\frac{a}{\sin A} = \frac{b}{\sin B}$
$\frac{125}{\sin 25°} = \frac{150}{\sin B}$
$\sin B = \frac{150 \sin 25°}{125}$
$\sin B \approx 0.5071$
$B \approx 30.5°$

$25° + 30.5° + c \approx 180°$
$c \approx 124.5°$

$\frac{a}{\sin A} = \frac{c}{\sin C}$
$\frac{125}{\sin 25°} \approx \frac{c}{\sin 124.5°}$
$c \approx \frac{125 \sin 124.5°}{\sin 25°}$
$c \approx 243.8$

$B \approx 180 - 30.5°$
$\approx 149.5°$
$25° + 149.5° + C \approx 180°$
$C \approx 5.5°$

$\frac{c}{\sin C} = \frac{a}{\sin A}$
$\frac{c}{\sin 5.5°} \approx \frac{125}{\sin 25°}$
$c \approx \frac{125 \sin 5.5°}{\sin 25°}$
$c \approx 28.3°$

18. one solution

$\frac{a}{\sin A} = \frac{c}{\sin C}$
$\frac{64}{\sin A} = \frac{90}{\sin 98°}$
$\sin A = \frac{64 \sin 98°}{90}$
$\sin A \approx 0.7041$
$A \approx 44.8°$

$44.8° + B + 98° \approx 180°$
$B \approx 37.2°$

$\frac{c}{\sin C} = \frac{b}{\sin B}$
$\frac{90}{\sin 98°} \approx \frac{b}{\sin 37.2°}$
$b \approx \frac{90 \sin 37.2°}{\sin 98°}$
$b \approx 55.0$

19. one solution

$40° + 60° + C = 180°$
$C = 80°$

$\frac{a}{\sin A} = \frac{c}{\sin C}$
$\frac{a}{\sin 40°} = \frac{20}{\sin 80°}$
$a = \frac{20 \sin 40°}{\sin 80°}$
$a \approx 13.1$

$\frac{b}{\sin B} = \frac{c}{\sin C}$
$\frac{b}{\sin 60°} = \frac{20}{\sin 80°}$
$b = \frac{20 \sin 60°}{\sin 80°}$
$b \approx 17.6$

20. $A \geq 90°$
$33 \leq 50$ no solution

21. one solution

$\frac{a}{\sin A} = \frac{b}{\sin B}$
$\frac{83}{\sin 45°} = \frac{79}{\sin B}$
$\sin B = \frac{79 \sin 45°}{83}$
$\sin B \approx 0.6730$
$B \approx 42.3°$

$45° + 42.3° + C \approx 180°$
$C \approx 92.7°$

$\frac{a}{\sin A} = \frac{c}{\sin C}$
$\frac{83}{\sin 45°} \approx \frac{c}{\sin 92.7°}$
$c \approx \frac{83 \sin 92.7°}{\sin 45°}$
$c \approx 117.2$

Page 907 Lesson 13-5

1. law of cosines

$a^2 = b^2 + c^2 - 2bc \cos A$

$a^2 = 40^2 + 45^2 - 2(40)(45) \cos 51°$

$a^2 \approx 1359.4$

$a \approx 36.9$

$\frac{a}{\sin A} = \frac{b}{\sin B}$

$\frac{36.9}{\sin 51°} \approx \frac{40}{\sin B}$

$\sin B \approx \frac{40 \sin 51°}{36.9}$

$\sin B \approx 0.8424$

$B \approx 57.4°$

$51° + 57.4° + C \approx 180°$

$C \approx 71.6°$

2. law of sines

$\frac{a}{\sin A} = \frac{c}{\sin C}$

$\frac{10}{\sin 40°} = \frac{8}{\sin C}$

$\sin C = \frac{8 \sin 40°}{10}$

$\sin C \approx 0.5142$

$C \approx 30.9°$

$40° + B + 30.9° \approx 180°$

$B \approx 109.1°$

$\frac{a}{\sin A} = \frac{b}{\sin B}$

$\frac{10}{\sin 40°} \approx \frac{b}{\sin 109.1°}$

$b \approx \frac{10 \sin 109.1°}{\sin 40°}$

$b \approx 14.7$

3. law of cosines

$b^2 = a^2 + c^2 - 2ac \cos B$

$b^2 = 14^2 + 21^2 - 2(14)(21) \cos 60°$

$b^2 \approx 343$

$b \approx 18.5$

$\frac{a}{\sin A} = \frac{b}{\sin B}$

$\frac{14}{\sin A} \approx \frac{18.5}{\sin 60°}$

$\sin A \approx \frac{14 \sin 60°}{18.5}$

$\sin A \approx 0.6554$

$A \approx 40.9°$

$40.9° + 60° + C \approx 80°$

$C \approx 79.1°$

4. law of cosines

$a^2 = b^2 + c^2 - 2bc \cos A$

$14^2 = 15^2 + 16^2 - 2(15)(16) \cos A$

$2(15)(16) \cos A = 15^2 + 16^2 - 14^2$

$\cos A = \frac{15^2 + 16^2 - 14^2}{2(15)(16)}$

$\cos A \approx 0.5938$

$A \approx 53.6°$

$\frac{a}{\sin A} = \frac{b}{\sin B}$

$\frac{14}{\sin 53.6°} \approx \frac{15}{\sin B}$

$\sin B \approx \frac{15 \sin 53.6°}{14}$

$\sin B \approx 0.8624$

$B \approx 59.6°$

$53.6° + 59.6° + C \approx 180°$

$C \approx 66.8°$

5. law of sines

$\frac{b}{\sin B} = \frac{c}{\sin C}$

$\frac{b}{\sin 41°} = \frac{27}{\sin 52°}$

$b = \frac{27 \sin 41°}{\sin 52°}$

$b \approx 22.5$

$A + 41° + 52° = 180°$

$A = 87°$

$\frac{a}{\sin A} = \frac{c}{\sin C}$

$\frac{a}{\sin 87°} = \frac{27}{\sin 52°}$

$a = \frac{27 \sin 87°}{\sin 52°}$

$a \approx 34.2$

6. law of cosines

$a^2 = b^2 + c^2 - 2bc \cos A$

$19^2 = 24.3^2 + 21.8^2 - 2(24.3)(21.8) \cos A$

$2(24.3)(21.8) \cos A = 24.3^2 + 21.8^2 - 19^2$

$\cos A = \frac{24.3^2 + 21.8^2 - 19^2}{2(24.3)(21.8)}$

$\cos A \approx 0.6652$

$A \approx 49.3°$

$\frac{a}{\sin A} = \frac{b}{\sin B}$

$\frac{19}{\sin 49.3°} \approx \frac{24.3}{\sin B}$

$\sin B \approx \frac{24.3 \sin 49.3°}{19}$

$\sin B \approx 0.9696$

$B \approx 75.8°$

$49.3 + 75.8° + C \approx 180°$

$C \approx 54.9°$

7. law of sines

$\frac{a}{\sin A} = \frac{c}{\sin C}$

$\frac{32}{\sin 112°} = \frac{20}{\sin C}$

$\sin C = \frac{20 \sin 112°}{32}$

$\sin C \approx 0.5795$

$C \approx 35.4°$

$112° + B + 35.4° \approx 180°$

$B \approx 32.6°$

$\frac{b}{\sin B} = \frac{a}{\sin A}$

$\frac{b}{\sin 32.6°} \approx \frac{32}{\sin 112°}$

$b \approx \frac{32 \sin 32.6°}{\sin 112°}$

$b \approx 18.6$

8. law of cosines

$a^2 = b^2 + c^2 - 2bc \cos A$

$a^2 = 8^2 + 7^2 - 2(8)(7) \cos 28°$

$a^2 \approx 14.1$

$a \approx 3.8$

$\frac{a}{\sin A} = \frac{b}{\sin B}$

$\frac{3.8}{\sin 28°} \approx \frac{8}{\sin B}$

$\sin B \approx \frac{8 \sin 28°}{3.8}$

$\sin B \approx 0.9884$

$B \approx 81.2°$

$28° + 81.2° + C \approx 180°$

$C \approx 70.8°$

9. law of cosines

$a^2 = b^2 + c^2 - 2bc \cos A$

$5^2 = 6^2 + 7^2 - 2(6)(7) \cos A$

$2(6)(7) \cos A = 6^2 + 7^2 - 5^2$

$\cos A = \frac{6^2 + 7^2 - 5^2}{2(6)(7)}$

$\cos A \approx 0.7143$

$A \approx 44.4°$

$\frac{a}{\sin A} = \frac{b}{\sin B}$

$\frac{5}{\sin 44.4°} \approx \frac{6}{\sin B}$

$\sin B \approx \frac{6 \sin 44.4°}{5}$

$\sin B \approx 0.8396$

$B \approx 57.1°$

$44.4° + 57.1° + C \approx 180°$

$C \approx 78.5°$

10. law of cosines

$c^2 = a^2 + b^2 - 2ab \cos C$

$c^2 = 11^2 + 10.5^2 - 2(11)(10.5) \cos 35°$

$c^2 \approx 42.03$

$c \approx 6.5$

$\frac{c}{\sin C} = \frac{a}{\sin A}$

$\frac{6.5}{\sin 35°} \approx \frac{11}{\sin A}$

$\sin A \approx \frac{11 \sin 35°}{6.5}$

$\sin A \approx 0.9701$

$A \approx 76.1°$

$76.1° + B + 35° \approx 180°$

$B \approx 68.9°$

11. law of sines

$\frac{a}{\sin A} = \frac{b}{\sin B}$

$\frac{8}{\sin 49°} = \frac{b}{\sin 58°}$

$b = \frac{8 \sin 58°}{\sin 49°}$

$b \approx 8.99$

$49° + 58° + C = 180°$

$C = 73°$

$\frac{a}{\sin A} = \frac{c}{\sin C}$

$\frac{8}{\sin 49°} = \frac{c}{\sin 73°}$

$c = \frac{8 \sin 73°}{\sin 49°}$

$c \approx 10.1$

12. law of cosines

$a^2 = b^2 + c^2 - 2bc \cos A$

$a^2 = 120^2 + 160^2 - 2(120)(160) \cos 42°$

$a^2 \approx 11463.24$

$a \approx 107.1$

$\frac{a}{\sin A} = \frac{b}{\sin B}$

$\frac{107.1}{\sin 42°} \approx \frac{120}{\sin B}$

$\sin B \approx \frac{120 \sin 42°}{107.1}$

$\sin B \approx 0.7497$

$B \approx 48.6°$

$42° + 48.6° + C \approx 180°$

$C \approx 89.4°$

13. law of sines

$\frac{a}{\sin A} = \frac{c}{\sin C}$

$\frac{a}{\sin 40°} = \frac{14}{\sin 70°}$

$a = \frac{14 \sin 40°}{\sin 70°}$

$a \approx 9.6 \qquad b = 14$

$40° + B + 70° = 180°$

$B = 70°$

14. law of cosines

$a^2 = b^2 + c^2 - 2bc \cos A$

$10^2 = 16^2 + 19^2 - 2(16)(19) \cos A$

$2(16)(19) \cos A = 16^2 + 19^2 - 10^2$

$\cos A = \frac{16^2 + 19^2 - 10^2}{2(16)(19)}$

$\cos A \approx 0.8503$

$A \approx 31.8°$

$\frac{a}{\sin A} = \frac{b}{\sin B}$

$\frac{10}{\sin 31.8°} \approx \frac{16}{\sin B}$

$\sin B \approx \frac{16 \sin 31.8°}{10}$

$\sin B \approx 0.8431$

$B \approx 57.5$

$31.8° + 57.5° + C \approx 180°$

$C \approx 90.7°$

15. law of cosines

$b^2 = a^2 + c^2 - 2ac \cos B$

$b^2 = 20^2 + 24^2 - 2(20)(24) \cos 47°$

$b^2 \approx 321.28$

$b \approx 17.9$

$\frac{b}{\sin B} = \frac{a}{\sin A}$

$\frac{17.9}{\sin 47°} \approx \frac{20}{\sin A}$

$\sin A \approx \frac{20 \sin 47°}{17.9}$

$\sin A \approx 0.8172$

$A \approx 54.8°$

$54.8° + 47° + C \approx 180°$

$C \approx 78.2°$

16. law of cosines

$b^2 = a^2 + c^2 - 2ab \cos B$

$b^2 = 10^2 + 8^2 - 2(10)(8) \cos 100°$

$b^2 \approx 191.78$

$b \approx 13.8$

$\frac{b}{\sin B} = \frac{a}{\sin A}$

$\frac{13.8}{\sin 100°} \approx \frac{10}{\sin A}$

$\sin A \approx \frac{10 \sin 100°}{13.8}$

$\sin A \approx 0.7136$

$A \approx 45.5°$

$45.5° + 100° + C \approx 180°$

$C \approx 34.5°$

17. law of sines

$40° + 45° + C = 180°$

$C = 95°$

$\frac{c}{\sin C} = \frac{b}{\sin B}$

$\frac{4}{\sin 95°} = \frac{b}{\sin 45°}$

$b = \frac{4 \sin 45°}{\sin 95°}$

$b \approx 2.8$

$\frac{c}{\sin C} = \frac{a}{\sin A}$

$\frac{4}{\sin 95°} = \frac{a}{\sin 40°}$

$a = \frac{4 \sin 40°}{\sin 95°}$

$a \approx 2.6$

18. law of sines

$\frac{a}{\sin A} = \frac{c}{\sin C}$

$\frac{64}{\sin A} = \frac{90}{\sin 98°}$

$\sin A = \frac{64 \sin 98°}{90}$

$\sin A \approx 0.7042$

$A \approx 44.8°$

$44.8° + B + 98° \approx 180°$

$B \approx 57.2°$

$\frac{b}{\sin B} = \frac{c}{\sin C}$

$\frac{b}{\sin 37.2°} \approx \frac{90}{\sin 98°}$

$b \approx \frac{90 \sin 37.2°}{\sin 98°}$

$b \approx 54.9$

19. law of sines

$\frac{c}{\sin C} = \frac{b}{\sin B}$

$\frac{8}{\sin C} = \frac{16}{\sin 71°}$

$\sin C = \frac{8 \sin 71°}{16}$

$\sin C \approx 0.4727$

$C \approx 29.2°$

$A + 71° + 29.2° \approx 180°$

$A \approx 79.8°$

$\frac{a}{\sin A} = \frac{b}{\sin B}$

$\frac{a}{\sin 79.8°} \approx \frac{16}{\sin 71°}$

$a \approx \frac{16 \sin 79.8°}{\sin 71°}$

$a \approx 16.7$

20. law of cosines

$a^2 = b^2 + c^2 - 2bc \cos A$

$a^2 = 100^2 + 84^2 - 2(100)(84) \cos 20°$

$a^2 \approx 1269.2$

$a \approx 35.6$

$\frac{a}{\sin A} = \frac{b}{\sin B}$

$\frac{35.6}{\sin 20°} = \frac{100}{\sin B}$

$\sin B = \frac{100 \sin 20°}{35.6}$

$\sin B \approx 0.9607$

$B \approx 73.9°$

$20° + 73.9° + C \approx 180°$

$C \approx 86.1°$

21. law of sines

$\frac{c}{\sin C} = \frac{b}{\sin B}$

$\frac{49}{\sin C} = \frac{40}{\sin 53°}$

$\sin C = \frac{49 \sin 53°}{40}$

$\sin C \approx 0.9783$

$C \approx 78.0°$

$A + 53° + 78.0° \approx 180°$

$A \approx 49°$

$\frac{a}{\sin A} = \frac{b}{\sin B}$

$\frac{a}{\sin 49°} \approx \frac{40}{\sin 53°}$

$a \approx \frac{40 \sin 49°}{\sin 53°}$

$a \approx 37.8$

Page 908 Lesson 13-6

1. 270°

2. 3π

3. $\sin 210° = -\frac{1}{2}$

4. $\cos 150° = -\frac{\sqrt{3}}{2}$

5. $\cos(-135)° = \cos(-135° + 360°)$

$= \cos 225°$

$= -\frac{\sqrt{2}}{2}$

6. $\cos \frac{3\pi}{4} = -\frac{\sqrt{2}}{2}$

7. $\sin 570° = \sin(570° - 360°)$

$= \sin 210°$

$= -\frac{1}{2}$

8. $\sin 390° = \sin(390° - 360°)$

$= \sin 30°$

$= \frac{1}{2}$

9. $\sin \frac{4\pi}{3} = -\frac{\sqrt{3}}{2}$

10. $\cos\left(-\frac{7\pi}{3}\right) = \cos\left(-\frac{7\pi}{3} + 4\pi\right)$
$= \cos\left(\frac{5\pi}{3}\right)$
$= \frac{1}{2}$

11. $\cos 30° + \cos 60° = \frac{1}{2} + \frac{\sqrt{3}}{2}$
$= \frac{1 + \sqrt{3}}{2}$

12. $5(\sin 45°)(\cos 45°) = 5\left(\frac{\sqrt{2}}{2}\right)\left(\frac{\sqrt{2}}{2}\right)$
$= \frac{5}{2}$

13. $\frac{\sin 210° + \cos 240°}{2} = \frac{-\frac{1}{2} + \left(-\frac{1}{2}\right)}{2}$
$= -\frac{1}{2}$

14. $\frac{6 \cos 120° + 4 \sin 150°}{5} = \frac{6\left(-\frac{1}{2}\right) + 4\left(\frac{1}{2}\right)}{5}$
$= \frac{-3 + 2}{5}$
$= -\frac{1}{5}$

Page 908 Lesson 13-7

1. $\text{Arcsin } n = m$
2. $\text{Arctan } 1 = 45°$
3. $\text{Arccos } \frac{3}{2} = x$
4. $\text{Arcsin } a = 65°$
5. $\text{Arctan } \sqrt{3} = 60°$
6. 45°
7. 45°
8. 30°
9. 0°
10. 60°
11. 135°
12. −90°
13. $\frac{\sqrt{2}}{2}$

14. $r = \sqrt{x^2 + y^2}$
$13 = \sqrt{x^2 + 5^2}$
$169 = x^2 + 25$
$144 = x^2$
$12 = x$
$\tan\left(\text{Sin}^{-1}\left(\frac{5}{13}\right)\right) = \frac{5}{12}$

15. $\sin 2\left(\text{Arccos } \frac{1}{2}\right) = \sin 2(60°)$
$= \sin 120°$
$= \frac{\sqrt{3}}{2}$

16. $r = \sqrt{x^2 + y^2}$
$17 = \sqrt{15^2 + y^2}$
$289 = 225 + y^2$
$64 = y^2$
$8 = y$
$\sin\left(\text{Arccos } \frac{15}{17}\right) = \frac{8}{17}$

17. $r = \sqrt{x^2 + y^2}$
$r = \sqrt{12^2 + 5^2}$
$r^2 = 144 + 25$
$r^2 = 169$
$r = 13$
$\sin\left(\text{Tan}^{-1} \frac{5}{12}\right) = \frac{5}{13}$

18. $r = \sqrt{x^2 + y^2}$
$2 = \sqrt{-(\sqrt{3})^2 + y^2}$
$4 = 3 + y^2$
$1 = y^2$
$1 = y$
$\tan\left(\text{Arccos}\left(-\frac{\sqrt{3}}{2}\right)\right) = -\frac{1}{\sqrt{3}}$ or $-\frac{\sqrt{3}}{3}$

Page 908 Lesson 14-1

1.

θ	0°	270°	540°	810°	1080°
$\frac{1}{3}\theta$	0°	90°	180°	270°	360°
$\csc \frac{1}{3}\theta$	nd	1	nd	−1	nd

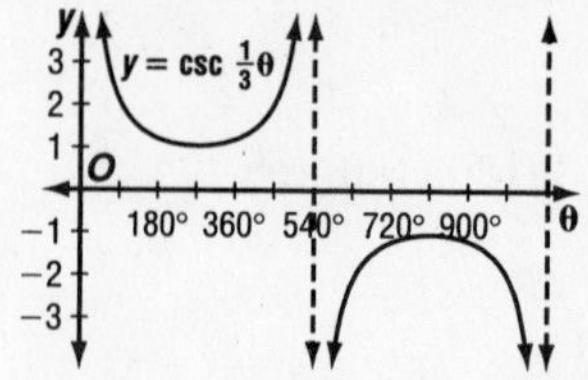

amplitude: none
period: $\frac{360°}{\left|\frac{1}{3}\right|}$ or 1080°

2.

θ	0°	90°	180°	270°	360°
$2 \sec \theta$	2	nd	−2	nd	2

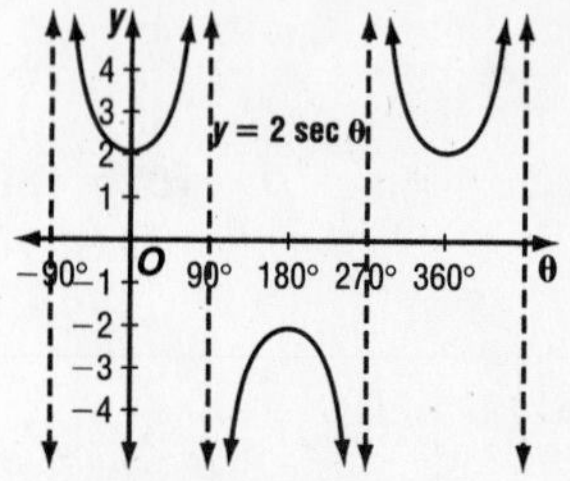

amplitude: none
period: $\frac{360°}{|1|}$ or 360°

3.

θ	0°	45°	90°	135°	180°
$2 \tan \theta$	0	2	nd	−2	0

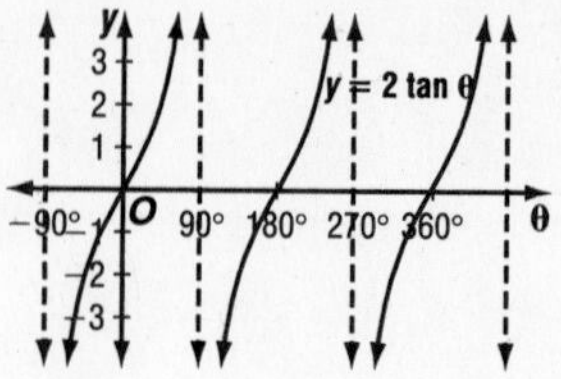

amplitude: none
period: $\frac{180°}{|1|}$ or 180°

4.

θ	0°	135°	270°	405°	540°
$\frac{2}{3}\theta$	0°	90°	180°	270°	360°
$-3 \sin \frac{2}{3}\theta$	0	−3	0	3	0

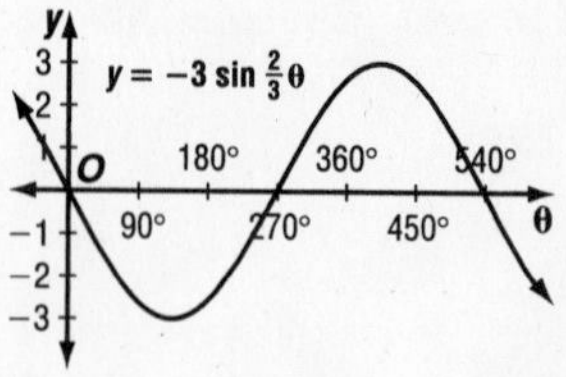

amplitude:
$|-3|$ or 3 units
period: $\frac{360°}{\left|\frac{2}{3}\right|}$ or 540°

5.

θ	0°	450°	900°	1350°	1800°
$\frac{1}{5}\theta$	0°	90°	180°	270°	360°
$2 \sin \frac{1}{5}\theta$	0	2	0	−2	0

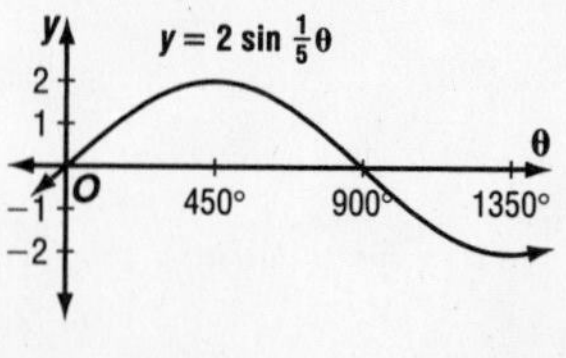

amplitude:
$|2|$ or 2 units
period: $\frac{360°}{\left|\frac{1}{5}\right|}$ or 1800°

6. $\frac{1}{2}y = 3 \sin 2\theta$

$y = 6 \sin 2\theta$

θ	0°	45°	90°	135°	180°
2θ	0°	90°	180°	270°	360°
$6 \sin 2\theta$	0	6	0	6	0

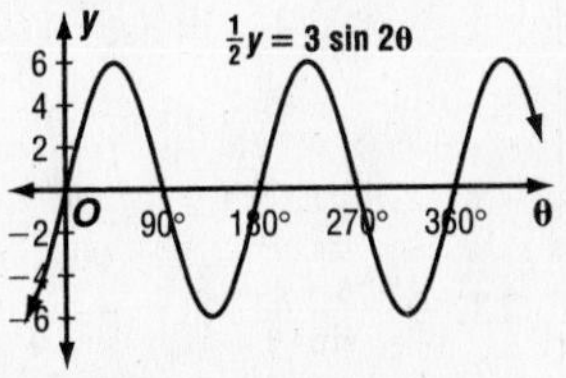

amplitude: $|6|$ or 6 units

period: $\frac{360°}{|2|}$ or 180°

7.

θ	0°	120°	240°	360°	480°
$\frac{3}{4}\theta$	0°	90°	180°	270°	360°
$-\frac{1}{2} \cos \frac{3}{4}\theta$	$\frac{1}{2}$	0	$\frac{1}{2}$	0	$-\frac{1}{2}$

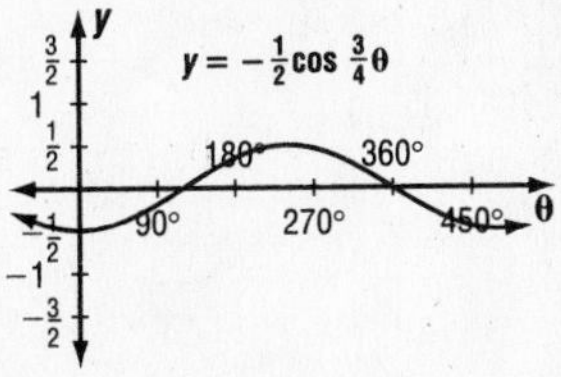

amplitude: $\left|\frac{1}{2}\right|$ or $\frac{1}{2}$unit

period: $\frac{360°}{\left|\frac{3}{4}\right|}$ or 480°

8. $\frac{1}{2}y = 5 \csc 3\theta$

$y = 10 \csc 3\theta$

θ	0°	30°	60°	90°	120°
3θ	0°	90°	180°	270°	360°
$10 \csc 3\theta$	nd	10	nd	−10	nd

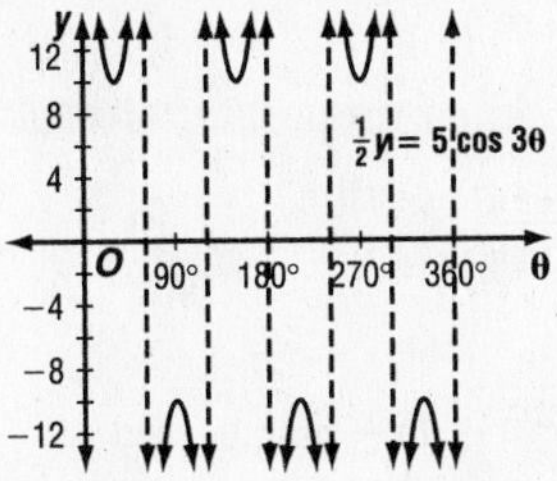

amplitude: none

period: $\frac{360°}{|3|}$ or 120°

9.

θ	0°	15°	30°	45°	60°
6θ	0°	90°	180°	270°	360°
$2 \cot 6\theta$	nd	0	nd	0	nd

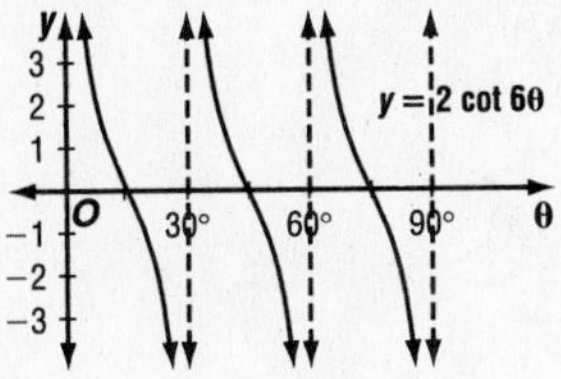

amplitude: none

period: $\frac{360°}{|6|}$ or 60°

10.

θ	0°	15°	30°	45°	60°
6θ	0°	90°	180°	270°	360°
$\csc 6\theta$	nd	1	nd	−1	nd

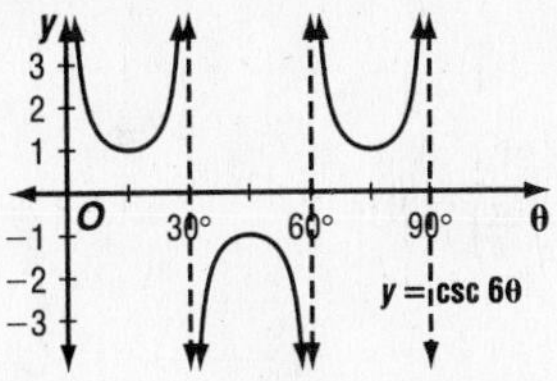

amplitude: none

period: $\frac{360°}{|6|}$ or 60°

11.

θ	0°	90°	270°	450°	540°
$\frac{1}{3}\theta$	0°	30°	90°	150°	180°
$3 \tan \frac{1}{3}\theta$	0°	$\sqrt{3}$	nd	$-\sqrt{3}$	0

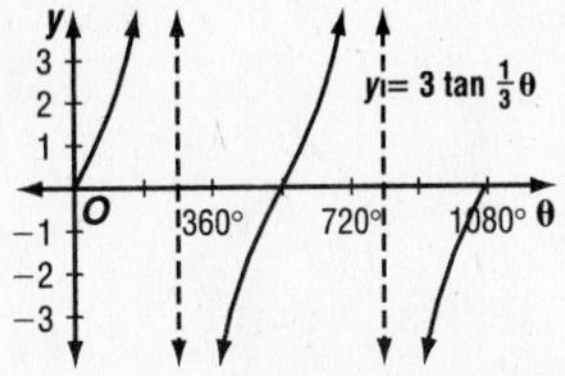

amplitude: none

period: $\frac{180°}{\left|\frac{1}{3}\right|}$ or 540°

12.

θ	0°	60°	120°	180°	240°	300°	360°
$\frac{1}{2}\theta$	0°	30°	60°	90°	120°	150°	180°
$\frac{4}{3} \cot \frac{1}{2}\theta$	0	$\frac{4\sqrt{3}}{9}$	$-\frac{4\sqrt{3}}{9}$	nd	$\frac{4\sqrt{3}}{9}$	$-\frac{4\sqrt{3}}{9}$	nd

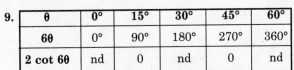

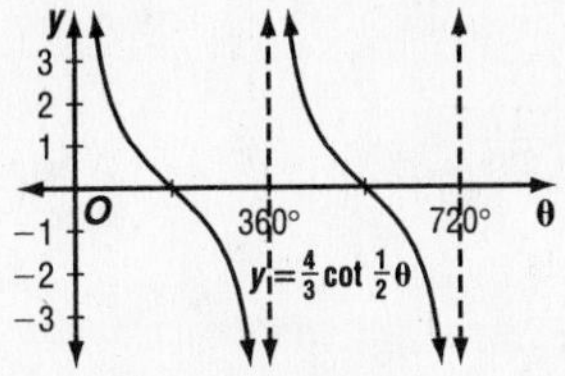

amplitude: none

period: $\frac{180°}{\left|\frac{1}{2}\right|}$ or 360°

13. $y = 3 \sin \theta$

14. $y = 4.8 \sin 3\theta$

15. $y = 0.45 \sin 6\theta$

16. $y = 5 \sin \frac{1}{3}\theta$

17. $y = \frac{1}{3} \sin 12\theta$

18. $y = 0.8 \cos \theta$

19. $y = 5 \cos 6\theta$

20. $y = \frac{1}{4} \cos 4\theta$

21. $y = 3 \cos \frac{1}{2}\theta$

22. $y = 6.5 \cos 3\theta$

Page 909 Lesson 14-2

1. $\sin^2 \theta + \cos^2 \theta = 1$

$$\sin^2 \theta = 1 - \cos^2 \theta$$

$$\sin^2 \theta = 1 - \left(\frac{4}{5}\right)^2$$

$$\sin^2 \theta = \frac{9}{25}$$

$$\sin\theta = \frac{3}{5}$$

$$\tan\theta = \frac{\sin \theta}{\cos \theta}$$

$$= \frac{\frac{3}{5}}{\frac{4}{5}}$$

$$= \frac{3}{4}$$

2. $\sin^2\theta + \cos^2\theta = 1$
$\cos^2\theta = 1 - \sin^2\theta$
$\cos^2\theta = 1 - \left(\frac{1}{2}\right)^2$
$\cos^2\theta = \frac{3}{4}$
$\cos\theta = \frac{\sqrt{3}}{2}$

3. $\sin^2\theta + \cos^2\theta = 1$
$\cos^2\theta = 1 - \sin^2\theta$
$\cos^2\theta = 1 - \left(\frac{3}{4}\right)^2$
$\cos^2\theta = \frac{7}{16}$
$\cos\theta = \frac{\sqrt{7}}{4}$
$\sec\theta = \frac{1}{\cos\theta}$
$= \frac{1}{\frac{\sqrt{7}}{4}}$
$= \frac{4}{\sqrt{7}}$
$= \frac{4\sqrt{7}}{7}$

4. $\tan^2\theta + 1 = \sec^2\theta$
$(4)^2 + 1 = \sec^2\theta$
$17 = \sec^2\theta$
$\sqrt{17} = \sec\theta$
$\sec\theta = \frac{1}{\cos\theta}$
$\sqrt{17} = \frac{1}{\cos\theta}$
$\cos\theta = \frac{1}{\sqrt{17}}$ or $\frac{\sqrt{17}}{17}$
$\cos^2\theta + \sin^2\theta = 1$
$\left(\frac{\sqrt{17}}{17}\right) + \sin^2\theta = 1$
$\frac{17}{289} + \sin^2\theta = 1$
$\sin^2\theta = 1 - \frac{17}{289}$
$\sin^2\theta = \frac{272}{289}$
$\sin\theta = \frac{4\sqrt{17}}{17}$

5. $\tan^2\theta + 1 = \sec^2\theta$
$4^2 + 1 = \sec^2\theta$
$17 = \sec^2\theta$
$17 = \frac{1}{\cos^2\theta}$
$\cos^2\theta = \frac{1}{17}$
$\cos\theta = \sqrt{\frac{1}{17}}$ or $\frac{\sqrt{17}}{17}$

6. $\cot^2\theta + 1 = \csc^2\theta$
$\left(\frac{1}{4}\right)^2 + 1 = \csc^2\theta$
$\frac{17}{16} = \csc^2\theta$
$\frac{\sqrt{17}}{4} = \csc\theta$

7. $\tan^2\theta + 1 = \sec^2\theta$
$\tan^2\theta = \sec^2\theta - 1$
$\tan^2\theta = (-3)^2 - 1$
$\tan^2\theta = 8$
$\tan\theta = 2\sqrt{2}$

8. $\cos^2\theta + \sin^2\theta = 1$
$\sin^2\theta = 1 - \cos^2\theta$
$\sin^2\theta = 1 - \left(-\frac{3}{5}\right)^2$
$\sin^2\theta = \frac{16}{25}$
$\frac{1}{\csc^2\theta} = \frac{16}{25}$
$\csc^2\theta = \frac{25}{16}$
$\csc\theta = -\frac{5}{4}$

9. $\sin^2\theta + \cos^2\theta = 1$
$\cos^2\theta = 1 - \sin^2\theta$
$\cos^2\theta = 1 - \left(-\frac{1}{2}\right)^2$
$\cos^2\theta = \frac{3}{4}$
$\cos\theta = -\frac{\sqrt{3}}{2}$

10. $\cot^2\theta + 1 = \csc^2\theta$
$\left(\frac{1}{4}\right)^2 + 1 = \csc^2\theta$
$\frac{17}{16} = \csc^2\theta$
$-\frac{\sqrt{17}}{4} = \csc\theta$

11. $\cot^2\theta + 1 = \csc^2\theta$
$\left(\frac{3}{5}\right)^2 + 1 = \csc^2\theta$
$\frac{34}{25} = \csc^2\theta$
$-\frac{\sqrt{34}}{5} = \csc\theta$

12. $\tan^2\theta + 1 = \sec^2\theta$
$4^2 + 1 = \sec^2\theta$
$17 = \sec^2\theta$
$17 = \frac{1}{\cos^2\theta}$
$\cos^2\theta = \frac{1}{17}$
$\cos\theta = -\sqrt{\frac{1}{17}}$ or $-\frac{\sqrt{17}}{17}$

13. $\frac{\sin^2\theta + \cos^2\theta}{\sin^2\theta} = \frac{1}{\sin^2\theta}$
$= \csc^2\theta$

14. $\frac{1 + \tan^2\theta}{1 + \cot^2\theta} = \frac{\sec^2\theta}{\csc^2\theta}$
$= \frac{\frac{1}{\cos^2\theta}}{\frac{1}{\sin^2\theta}}$
$= \frac{\sin^2\theta}{\cos^2\theta}$
$= \tan^2\theta$

15. $\frac{1}{1 + \sin\theta} + \frac{1}{1 - \sin\theta}$
$= \frac{1 - \sin\theta}{(1 + \sin\theta)(1 - \sin\theta)} + \frac{1 + \sin\theta}{(1 + \sin\theta)(1 - \sin\theta)}$
$= \frac{2}{(1 + \sin\theta)(1 - \sin\theta)}$
$= \frac{2}{1 - \sin^2\theta}$
$= \frac{2}{\cos^2\theta}$
$= 2\sec^2\theta$

16. $\frac{1 - \sin^2\theta}{\sin^2\theta} = \frac{1}{\sin^2\theta} - \frac{\sin^2\theta}{\sin^2\theta}$
$= \csc^2\theta - 1$
$= \cot^2\theta$

17. $\csc^2\theta - \cot^2\theta = (\cot^2\theta + 1) - \cot^2\theta$
$= 1$

18. $\cos\theta(\csc\theta) = \cos\theta\left(\frac{1}{\sin\theta}\right)$
$= \frac{\cos\theta}{\sin\theta}$
$= \cot\theta$

19. $\tan\theta\csc\theta = \frac{\sin\theta}{\csc\theta}\left(\frac{1}{\sin\theta}\right)$
$= \frac{1}{\cos\theta}$
$= \sec\theta$

20. $\sin\theta\cot\theta = \sin\theta\left(\frac{\cos\theta}{\sin\theta}\right)$
$= \cos\theta$

Page 909 Lesson 14-3

1. $1 + \tan^2\theta \stackrel{?}{=} \sec^2\theta$
$\sec^2\theta = \sec^2\theta$

2.

$$\frac{\tan\theta}{\sin\theta} \overset{?}{=} \sec\theta$$
$$\tan\theta \cdot \frac{1}{\sin\theta} \overset{?}{=} \sec\theta$$
$$\frac{\sin\theta}{\cos\theta} \cdot \frac{1}{\sin\theta} \overset{?}{=} \sec\theta$$
$$\frac{1}{\cos\theta} \overset{?}{=} \sec\theta$$
$$\sec\theta = \sec\theta$$

3.

$$\frac{\tan\theta}{\cot\theta} \overset{?}{=} \tan^2\theta$$
$$\tan\theta \cdot \frac{1}{\cot\theta} \overset{?}{=} \tan^2\theta$$
$$\tan\theta \cdot \tan\theta \overset{?}{=} \tan^2\theta$$
$$\tan^2\theta = \tan^2\theta$$

4.

$$\frac{\cos^2\theta}{1-\sin\theta} \overset{?}{=} 1+\sin\theta$$
$$\frac{1-\sin^2\theta}{1-\sin\theta} \overset{?}{=} 1+\sin\theta$$
$$\frac{(1+\sin\theta)(1-\sin\theta)}{1-\sin\theta} \overset{?}{=} 1+\sin\theta$$
$$1+\sin\theta = 1+\sin\theta$$

5.

$$1-\cot^4\theta \overset{?}{=} 2\csc^2\theta - \csc^4\theta$$
$$1-(\csc^2\theta-1)^2 \overset{?}{=} 2\csc^2\theta - \csc^4\theta$$
$$1-(\csc^4\theta - 2\csc^2\theta + 1) \overset{?}{=} 2\csc^2\theta - \csc^4\theta$$
$$2\csc^2\theta - \csc^4\theta = 2\csc^2\theta - \csc^4\theta$$

6.

$$\sin^4\theta - \cos^4\theta \overset{?}{=} \sin^2\theta - \cos^2\theta$$
$$(\sin^2\theta + \cos^2\theta)(\sin^2\theta - \cos^2\theta) \overset{?}{=} \sin^2\theta - \cos^2\theta$$
$$\sin^2\theta - \cos^2\theta = \sin^2\theta - \cos^2\theta$$

7.

$$\cos^2\theta + \tan^2\theta\cos^2\theta \overset{?}{=} 1$$
$$\cos^2\theta\,(1+\tan^2\theta) \overset{?}{=} 1$$
$$\cos^2\theta\,(\sec^2\theta) \overset{?}{=} 1$$
$$\cos^2\theta\left(\frac{1}{\cos^2\theta}\right) \overset{?}{=} 1$$
$$1 = 1$$

8.

$$\frac{\sec\theta}{\sin\theta} - \frac{\sin\theta}{\cos\theta} \overset{?}{=} \cot\theta$$
$$\frac{1}{\cos\theta}\cdot\frac{1}{\sin\theta} - \frac{\sin\theta}{\cos\theta} \overset{?}{=} \cot\theta$$
$$\frac{1}{\cos\theta\sin\theta} - \frac{\sin^2\theta}{\cos\theta\sin\theta} \overset{?}{=} \cot\theta$$
$$\frac{1-\sin^2\theta}{\cos\theta\sin\theta} \overset{?}{=} \cot\theta$$
$$\frac{\cos^2\theta}{\cos\theta\sin\theta} \overset{?}{=} \cot\theta$$
$$\frac{\cos\theta}{\sin\theta} \overset{?}{=} \cot\theta$$
$$\cot\theta = \cot\theta$$

9.

$$\frac{\cos\theta}{\sec\theta-1} + \frac{\cos\theta}{\sec\theta+1} \overset{?}{=} 2\cot^2\theta$$
$$\frac{\cos\theta\,(\sec\theta+1) + \cos\theta\,(\sec\theta-1)}{(\sec\theta-1)(\sec\theta+1)} \overset{?}{=} 2\cot^2\theta$$
$$\frac{2\cos\theta\sec\theta}{\sec^2\theta-1} \overset{?}{=} 2\cot^2\theta$$
$$\frac{2\cos\theta\sec\theta}{\tan^2\theta} \overset{?}{=} 2\cot^2\theta$$
$$\frac{2\cos\theta\left(\frac{1}{\cos\theta}\right)}{\tan^2\theta} \overset{?}{=} 2\cot^2\theta$$
$$\frac{2}{\tan^2\theta} \overset{?}{=} 2\cot^2\theta$$
$$2\cot^2\theta = 2\cot^2\theta$$

10.

$$\tan\theta + \cot\theta \overset{?}{=} \csc\theta\sec\theta$$
$$\frac{\sin\theta}{\cos\theta} + \frac{\cos\theta}{\sin\theta} \overset{?}{=} \csc\theta\sec\theta$$
$$\frac{\sin^2\theta + \cos^2\theta}{\cos\theta\sin\theta} \overset{?}{=} \csc\theta\sec\theta$$
$$\frac{1}{\cos\theta\sin\theta} \overset{?}{=} \csc\theta\sec\theta$$
$$\csc\theta\sec\theta = \csc\theta\sec\theta$$

11.

$$\frac{1-\cos\theta}{\sin\theta} \overset{?}{=} \frac{\sin\theta}{1+\cos\theta}$$
$$\frac{1-\cos\theta}{\sin\theta}\cdot\frac{1+\cos\theta}{1+\cos\theta} \overset{?}{=} \frac{\sin\theta}{1+\cos\theta}$$
$$\frac{1-\cos^2\theta}{\sin\theta\,(1+\cos\theta)} \overset{?}{=} \frac{\sin\theta}{1+\cos\theta}$$
$$\frac{\sin^2\theta}{\sin\theta\,(1+\cos\theta)} \overset{?}{=} \frac{\sin\theta}{1+\cos\theta}$$
$$\frac{\sin\theta}{1+\cos\theta} = \frac{\sin\theta}{1+\cos\theta}$$

12.

$$\cot^2\theta + \sin^2\theta \overset{?}{=} \csc^2\theta - \cos^2\theta$$
$$(\csc^2\theta - 1) + (1-\cos^2\theta) \overset{?}{=} \csc^2\theta - \cos^2\theta$$
$$\csc^2\theta - \cos^2\theta = \csc^2\theta + \cos^2\theta$$

13.

$$\sec\theta + \tan\theta \overset{?}{=} \frac{\cos\theta}{1-\sin\theta}$$
$$\frac{1}{\cos\theta} + \frac{\sin\theta}{\cos\theta} \overset{?}{=} \frac{\cos\theta}{1-\sin\theta}$$
$$\frac{1+\sin\theta}{\cos\theta} \overset{?}{=} \frac{\cos\theta}{1-\sin\theta}$$
$$\frac{1+\sin\theta}{\cos\theta}\cdot\frac{\cos\theta}{\cos\theta} \overset{?}{=} \frac{\cos\theta}{1-\sin\theta}$$
$$\frac{\cos\theta\,(1+\sin\theta)}{\cos^2\theta} \overset{?}{=} \frac{\cos\theta}{1-\sin\theta}$$
$$\frac{\cos\theta\,(1+\sin\theta)}{1-\sin^2\theta} \overset{?}{=} \frac{\cos\theta}{1-\sin\theta}$$
$$\frac{\cos\theta\,(1+\sin\theta)}{(1+\sin\theta)(1-\sin\theta)} \overset{?}{=} \frac{\cos\theta}{1-\sin\theta}$$
$$\frac{\cos\theta}{1-\sin\theta} = \frac{\cos\theta}{1-\sin\theta}$$

14.

$$\frac{\cot^2\theta}{1+\cot^2\theta} \overset{?}{=} 1-\sin^2\theta$$
$$\frac{\cot^2\theta}{\csc^2\theta} \overset{?}{=} 1-\sin^2\theta$$
$$\frac{\cos^2\theta}{\sin^2\theta}\cdot\frac{\sin^2\theta}{1} \overset{?}{=} 1-\sin^2\theta$$
$$\cos^2\theta \overset{?}{=} 1-\sin^2\theta$$
$$1-\sin^2\theta = 1-\sin^2\theta$$

15.

$$\frac{\tan\theta - \sin\theta}{\sec\theta} = \frac{\sin^3\theta}{1+\cos\theta}$$
$$\frac{\tan\theta}{\sec\theta} - \frac{\sin\theta}{\sec\theta} \overset{?}{=} \frac{\sin^3\theta}{1+\cos\theta}$$
$$\frac{\sin\theta}{\cos\theta}\cdot\cos\theta - \sin\theta\cdot\cos\theta \overset{?}{=} \frac{\sin^3\theta}{1+\cos\theta}$$
$$\sin\theta - \sin\theta\cos\theta \overset{?}{=} \frac{\sin^3\theta}{1+\cos\theta}$$
$$\sin\theta(1-\cos\theta) \overset{?}{=} \frac{\sin^3\theta}{1+\cos\theta}$$
$$\frac{\sin\theta(1-\cos\theta)(1+\cos\theta)}{(1+\cos\theta)} \overset{?}{=} \frac{\sin^3\theta}{1+\cos\theta}$$
$$\frac{\sin\theta(1-\cos^2\theta)}{1+\cos\theta} \overset{?}{=} \frac{\sin^3\theta}{1+\cos\theta}$$
$$\frac{\sin\theta(\sin^2\theta)}{1+\cos\theta} \overset{?}{=} \frac{\sin^3\theta}{1+\cos\theta}$$
$$\frac{\sin^3\theta}{1+\cos\theta} = \frac{\sin^3\theta}{1+\cos\theta}$$

16.

$$\sin^2\theta + \sin^2\theta\tan^2\theta \overset{?}{=} \tan^2\theta$$
$$\sin^2\theta(1+\tan^2\theta) \overset{?}{=} \tan^2\theta$$
$$\sin^2\theta(\sec^2\theta) \overset{?}{=} \tan^2\theta$$
$$\sin^2\theta\left(\frac{1}{\cos^2\theta}\right) \overset{?}{=} \tan^2\theta$$
$$\tan^2\theta = \tan^2\theta$$

17.
$$\frac{\sec\theta - 1}{\sec\theta + 1} + \frac{\cos\theta - 1}{\cos\theta + 1} \stackrel{?}{=} 0$$
$$\frac{(\sec\theta - 1)(\cos\theta + 1) + (\cos\theta - 1)(\sec\theta + 1)}{(\sec\theta + 1)(\cos\theta + 1)} \stackrel{?}{=} 0$$
$$\frac{\sec\theta\cos\theta - \cos\theta + \sec\theta - 1 + \sec\theta\cos\theta + \cos\theta - \sec\theta - 1}{(\sec\theta + 1)(\cos\theta + 1)} \stackrel{?}{=} 0$$
$$\frac{\left(\frac{1}{\cos\theta}\right)\cos\theta - 1 + \left(\frac{1}{\cos\theta}\right)\cos\theta - 1}{(\sec\theta + 1)(\cos\theta + 1)} \stackrel{?}{=} 0$$
$$\frac{0}{(\sec\theta + 1)(\cos\theta + 1)} \stackrel{?}{=} 0$$
$$0 = 0$$

18.
$$1 + \sec^2\theta\sin^2\theta \stackrel{?}{=} \sec^2\theta$$
$$1 + \frac{1}{\cos^2\theta}\cdot\sin^2\theta \stackrel{?}{=} \sec^2\theta$$
$$1 + \tan^2\theta \stackrel{?}{=} \sec^2\theta$$
$$\sec^2\theta = \sec^2\theta$$

19.
$$\tan\theta + \frac{\cos\theta}{1 + \sin\theta} \stackrel{?}{=} \sec\theta$$
$$\frac{\sin\theta}{\cos\theta} + \frac{\cos\theta}{1 + \sin\theta} \stackrel{?}{=} \sec\theta$$
$$\frac{\sin\theta(1 + \sin\theta) + \cos\theta(\cos\theta)}{\cos\theta(1 + \sin\theta)} \stackrel{?}{=} \sec\theta$$
$$\frac{\sin\theta + \sin^2\theta + \cos^2\theta}{\cos\theta(1 + \sin\theta)} \stackrel{?}{=} \sec\theta$$
$$\frac{1 + \sin\theta}{\cos\theta\,(1 + \sin\theta)} \stackrel{?}{=} \sec\theta$$
$$\frac{1}{\cos\theta} \stackrel{?}{=} \sec\theta$$
$$\sec\theta = \sec\theta$$

20.
$$\frac{\tan\theta}{\sec\theta + 1} \stackrel{?}{=} \frac{1 - \cos\theta}{\sin\theta}$$
$$\frac{\frac{\sin\theta}{\cos\theta}}{\frac{1}{\cos\theta} + 1} \stackrel{?}{=} \frac{1 - \cos\theta}{\sin\theta}$$
$$\frac{\sin\theta}{1 + \cos\theta} \stackrel{?}{=} \frac{1 - \cos\theta}{\sin\theta}$$
$$\frac{\sin\theta}{1 + \cos\theta}\cdot\frac{1 - \cos\theta}{1 - \cos\theta} \stackrel{?}{=} \frac{1 - \cos\theta}{\sin\theta}$$
$$\frac{\sin\theta(1 - \cos\theta)}{1 - \cos^2\theta} \stackrel{?}{=} \frac{1 - \cos\theta}{\sin\theta}$$
$$\frac{\sin\theta(1 - \cos\theta)}{\sin^2\theta} \stackrel{?}{=} \frac{1 - \cos\theta}{\sin\theta}$$
$$\frac{1 - \cos\theta}{\sin\theta} = \frac{1 - \cos\theta}{\sin\theta}$$

21.
$$\csc\theta - \frac{\sin\theta}{1 + \cos\theta} \stackrel{?}{=} \cot\theta$$
$$\frac{1}{\sin\theta} - \frac{\sin\theta}{1 + \cos\theta} \stackrel{?}{=} \cot\theta$$
$$\frac{1 + \cos\theta - \sin^2\theta}{\sin\theta(1 + \cos\theta)} \stackrel{?}{=} \cot\theta$$
$$\frac{\cos^2\theta + \cos\theta}{\sin\theta(1 + \cos\theta)} \stackrel{?}{=} \cot\theta$$
$$\frac{\cos\theta((1 + \cos\theta)}{\sin\theta(1 + \cos\theta)} \stackrel{?}{=} \cot\theta$$
$$\frac{\cos\theta}{\sin\theta} \stackrel{?}{=} \cot\theta$$
$$\cot\theta = \cot\theta$$

Page 909 Lesson 14-4

1.
$$\begin{aligned}\sin 195° &= \sin(150° + 45°)\\ &= \sin 150°\cos 45° + \cos 150°\sin 45°\\ &= \frac{1}{2}\cdot\frac{\sqrt{2}}{2} + \left(-\frac{\sqrt{3}}{2}\right)\frac{\sqrt{2}}{2}\\ &= \frac{\sqrt{2}}{4} - \frac{\sqrt{6}}{4}\\ &= \frac{\sqrt{2} - \sqrt{6}}{4}\end{aligned}$$

2.
$$\begin{aligned}\cos 285° &= \cos(240° + 45°)\\ &= \cos 240°\cos 45° - \sin 240°\sin 45°\\ &= -\frac{1}{2}\left(\frac{\sqrt{2}}{2}\right) - \left(-\frac{\sqrt{3}}{2}\right)\left(\frac{\sqrt{2}}{2}\right)\\ &= -\frac{\sqrt{2}}{4} + \frac{\sqrt{6}}{4}\\ &= \frac{\sqrt{6} - \sqrt{2}}{4}\end{aligned}$$

3.
$$\begin{aligned}\sin 255° &= \sin(210° + 45°)\\ &= \sin 210°\cos 45° + \cos 210°\sin 45°\\ &= -\frac{1}{2}\cdot\frac{\sqrt{2}}{2} + -\frac{\sqrt{3}}{2}\cdot\frac{\sqrt{2}}{2}\\ &= -\frac{\sqrt{2}}{4} - \frac{\sqrt{6}}{4}\\ &= \frac{-\sqrt{6} - \sqrt{2}}{4}\end{aligned}$$

4.
$$\begin{aligned}\sin 105° &= \sin(60° + 45°)\\ &= \sin 60°\cos 45° + \cos 60°\sin 45°\\ &= \frac{\sqrt{3}}{2}\cdot\frac{\sqrt{2}}{2} + \frac{1}{2}\cdot\frac{\sqrt{2}}{2}\\ &= \frac{\sqrt{6}}{4} + \frac{\sqrt{2}}{4}\\ &= \frac{\sqrt{6} + \sqrt{2}}{4}\end{aligned}$$

5.
$$\begin{aligned}\cos 15° &= \cos(45° - 30°)\\ &= \cos 45°\cos 30° + \sin 45°\sin 30°\\ &= \frac{\sqrt{2}}{2}\cdot\frac{\sqrt{3}}{2} + \frac{\sqrt{2}}{2}\cdot\frac{1}{2}\\ &= \frac{\sqrt{6}}{4} + \frac{\sqrt{2}}{4}\\ &= \frac{\sqrt{6} + \sqrt{2}}{4}\end{aligned}$$

6.
$$\begin{aligned}\sin 15° &= \sin(45° - 30°)\\ &= \sin 45°\cos 30° - \cos 45°\sin 30°\\ &= \frac{\sqrt{2}}{2}\cdot\frac{\sqrt{3}}{2} - \frac{\sqrt{2}}{2}\cdot\frac{1}{2}\\ &= \frac{\sqrt{6}}{4} - \frac{\sqrt{2}}{4}\\ &= \frac{\sqrt{6} - \sqrt{2}}{4}\end{aligned}$$

7.
$$\begin{aligned}\cos 375° &= \cos(330° + 45°)\\ &= \cos 330°\cos 45° - \sin 330°\sin 45°\\ &= \frac{\sqrt{3}}{2}\cdot\frac{\sqrt{2}}{2} - \left(-\frac{1}{2}\right)\left(\frac{\sqrt{2}}{2}\right)\\ &= \frac{\sqrt{6}}{4} + \frac{\sqrt{2}}{4}\\ &= \frac{\sqrt{6} + \sqrt{2}}{4}\end{aligned}$$

8.
$$\begin{aligned}\sin 165° &= \sin(120° + 45°)\\ &= \sin 120°\cos 45° + \cos 120°\sin 45°\\ &= \frac{\sqrt{3}}{2}\cdot\frac{\sqrt{2}}{2} + \left(-\frac{1}{2}\right)\cdot\frac{\sqrt{2}}{2}\\ &= \frac{\sqrt{6}}{4} - \frac{\sqrt{2}}{4}\\ &= \frac{\sqrt{6} - \sqrt{2}}{4}\end{aligned}$$

9.
$$\sin(270° - \theta) \stackrel{?}{=} -\cos\theta$$
$$\sin 270°\cos\theta - \cos 270°\sin\theta \stackrel{?}{=} -\cos\theta$$
$$-1\cdot\cos\theta - 0\cdot\sin\theta \stackrel{?}{=} -\cos\theta$$
$$-\cos\theta = -\cos\theta$$

10.
$$\cos(90° + \theta) \stackrel{?}{=} -\sin\theta$$
$$\cos 90°\cos\theta - \sin 90°\sin\theta \stackrel{?}{=} -\sin\theta$$
$$0\cdot\cos\theta - 1\cdot\sin\theta \stackrel{?}{=} -\sin\theta$$
$$-\sin\theta = -\sin\theta$$

11.
$$\sin\left(\frac{\pi}{2} + x\right) \stackrel{?}{=} \cos x$$
$$\sin\frac{\pi}{2}\cos x + \cos\frac{\pi}{2}\sin x \stackrel{?}{=} \cos x$$
$$1\cdot\cos x + 0\cdot\sin x \stackrel{?}{=} \cos x$$
$$\cos x = \cos x$$

12. $\sin(x + 30°) + \cos(x + 60°) \stackrel{?}{=} \cos x$

$\sin x \cos 30° + \cos x \sin 30° +$

$\cos x \cos 60° - \sin x \sin 60° \stackrel{?}{=} \cos x$

$\sin x \cdot \frac{\sqrt{3}}{2} + \cos x \cdot \frac{1}{2} + \cos x \cdot \frac{1}{2} - \sin x \cdot \frac{\sqrt{3}}{2} \stackrel{?}{=} \cos x$

$\frac{1}{2} \cos x + \frac{1}{2} \cos x \stackrel{?}{=} \cos x$

$\cos x = \cos x$

13. $\cos(30° - x) + \cos(30° + x) \stackrel{?}{=} \sqrt{3} \cos x$

$\cos 30° \cos x + \sin 30° \sin x +$

$\cos 30° \cos x - \sin 30° \sin x \stackrel{?}{=} \sqrt{3} \cos x$

$\frac{\sqrt{3}}{2} \cdot \cos x + \frac{1}{2} \sin x + \frac{\sqrt{3}}{2} \cos x - \frac{1}{2} \sin x \stackrel{?}{=} \sqrt{3} \cos x$

$\sqrt{3} \cos x = \sqrt{3} \cos x$

14. $\tan(60° + 45°) = \frac{\tan 60° + \tan 45°}{1 - \tan 60° \tan 45°}$

$= \frac{(\sqrt{3} + 1)(1 + \sqrt{3})}{(1 - \sqrt{3})(1 + \sqrt{3})}$

$= \frac{4 + 2\sqrt{3}}{-2}$

$= -2 - \sqrt{3}$

15. $\tan(135° + 120°) = \frac{\tan 135° + \tan 120°}{1 - \tan 135° \tan 120°}$

$= \frac{-1 - \sqrt{3}}{1 - (-1)(-\sqrt{3})}$

$= \frac{(-1 - \sqrt{3})(1 + \sqrt{3})}{(1 - \sqrt{3})(1 + \sqrt{3})}$

$= \frac{-2\sqrt{3} - 4}{-2}$

$= 2 + \sqrt{3}$

16. $\tan 165° = \tan(120° + 45°)$

$= \frac{\tan 120° + \tan 45°}{1 - \tan 120° \tan 45°}$

$= \frac{-\sqrt{3} + 1}{1 - (-\sqrt{3})(1)}$

$= \frac{(-\sqrt{3} + 1)(1 - \sqrt{3})}{(1 + \sqrt{3})(1 - \sqrt{3})}$

$= \frac{4 - 2\sqrt{3}}{-2}$

$= -2 + \sqrt{3}$

17. $\tan 255° = \tan(135° + 120°)$

$= \frac{\tan 135° + \tan 120°}{1 - \tan 135° \tan 120°}$

$= \frac{-1 - \sqrt{3}}{1 - (-1)(-\sqrt{3})}$

$= \frac{(-1 - \sqrt{3})(1 + \sqrt{3})}{(1 - \sqrt{3})(1 + \sqrt{3})}$

$= \frac{-2\sqrt{3} - 4}{-2}$

$= 2 + \sqrt{3}$

Page 910 Lesson 14-5

1. $\cos^2 x + \sin^2 x = 1$

$\sin^2 x = 1 - \cos^2 x$

$\sin^2 x = 1 - \left(\frac{7}{25}\right)^2$

$\sin^2 x = \frac{576}{625}$

$\sin x = \frac{24}{25}$

$\cos 2x = 2 \cos^2 x - 1$

$= 2\left(\frac{7}{25}\right)^2 - 1$

$= 2\left(\frac{49}{625}\right) - 1$

$= -\frac{527}{625}$

(Continued next column)

$\cos \frac{x}{2} = \sqrt{\frac{1 + \cos x}{2}}$

$= \sqrt{\frac{1 + \frac{7}{25}}{2}}$

$= \sqrt{\frac{32}{50}}$

$= \frac{4}{5}$

$\sin 2x = 2 \sin x \cos x$

$= 2\left(\frac{24}{25}\right)\left(\frac{7}{25}\right)$

$= \frac{336}{625}$

$\sin \frac{x}{2} = \sqrt{\frac{1 - \cos x}{2}}$

$= \sqrt{\frac{1 - \frac{7}{25}}{2}}$

$= \sqrt{\frac{18}{50}}$

$= \frac{3}{5}$

2. $\cos^2 x + \sin^2 x = 1$

$\cos^2 x = 1 - \left(\frac{2}{5}\right)^2$

$\cos^2 x = \frac{21}{25}$

$\cos x = \frac{\sqrt{21}}{5}$

$\sin 2x = 2 \sin x \cos x$

$= 2\left(\frac{2}{5}\right)\left(\frac{\sqrt{21}}{5}\right)$

$= \frac{4\sqrt{21}}{25}$

$\cos 2x = 1 - 2 \sin^2 x$

$= 1 - 2\left(\frac{2}{5}\right)^2$

$= \frac{17}{25}$

$\sin \frac{x}{2} = \sqrt{\frac{1 - \cos x}{2}}$

$= \sqrt{\frac{1 - \frac{\sqrt{21}}{5}}{2}}$

$= \sqrt{\frac{5 - \sqrt{21}}{10}}$

$= \frac{\sqrt{50 - 10\sqrt{21}}}{10}$

$\cos \frac{x}{2} = \sqrt{\frac{1 + \cos x}{2}}$

$= \sqrt{\frac{1 + \frac{\sqrt{21}}{5}}{2}}$

$= \sqrt{\frac{5 + \sqrt{21}}{10}}$

$= \frac{\sqrt{50 + 10\sqrt{21}}}{10}$

3. $\cos^2 x + \sin^2 x = 1$

$\sin^2 x = 1 - \cos^2 x$

$\sin^2 x = 1 - \left(-\frac{1}{8}\right)^2$

$\sin^2 x = \frac{63}{64}$

$\sin x = -\frac{3\sqrt{7}}{8}$

$\sin 2x = 2 \sin x \cos x$

$= 2\left(-\frac{3\sqrt{7}}{8}\right)\left(-\frac{1}{8}\right)$

$= \frac{3\sqrt{7}}{32}$

$\cos 2x = 2 \cos^2 x - 1$

$= 2\left(-\frac{1}{8}\right)^2 - 1$

$= -\frac{31}{32}$

$\sin \frac{x}{2} = \sqrt{\frac{1 - \cos x}{2}}$

$= \sqrt{\frac{1 - \left(-\frac{1}{8}\right)}{2}}$

$= \sqrt{\frac{9}{16}}$

$= \frac{3}{4}$

$\cos \frac{x}{2} = -\sqrt{\frac{1 + \cos x}{2}}$

$= -\sqrt{\frac{1 - \frac{1}{8}}{2}}$

$= -\sqrt{\frac{7}{16}}$

$= -\sqrt{\frac{7}{4}}$

4. $\cos^2 x + \sin^2 x = 1$

$$\cos^2 x = 1 - \sin^2 x$$
$$\cos^2 x = 1 - \left(-\tfrac{5}{13}\right)^2$$
$$\cos^2 x = \tfrac{144}{169}$$
$$\cos x = \tfrac{12}{13}$$

$$\sin 2x = 2 \sin x \cos x = 2\left(-\tfrac{5}{13}\right)\left(\tfrac{12}{13}\right) = -\tfrac{120}{169}$$

$$\cos 2x = 1 - 2 \sin^2 x = 1 - 2\left(-\tfrac{5}{13}\right)^2 = \tfrac{119}{169}$$

$$\sin \tfrac{x}{2} = \sqrt{\frac{1 - \cos x}{2}} = \sqrt{\frac{1 - \frac{12}{13}}{2}} = \sqrt{\frac{1}{26}} = \frac{\sqrt{26}}{26}$$

$$\cos \tfrac{x}{2} = -\sqrt{\frac{1 + \cos x}{2}} = -\sqrt{\frac{1 + \frac{12}{13}}{2}} = -\sqrt{\frac{25}{26}} = -\frac{5\sqrt{26}}{26}$$

5. $\cos^2 x + \sin^2 x = 1$

$$\cos^2 x = 1 - \sin^2 x$$
$$\cos^2 x = 1 - \left(\tfrac{\sqrt{35}}{6}\right)^2$$
$$\cos^2 x = \tfrac{1}{36}$$
$$\cos x = -\tfrac{1}{6}$$

$$\sin 2x = 2 \sin x \cos x = 2\left(\tfrac{\sqrt{35}}{6}\right)\left(-\tfrac{1}{6}\right) = -\tfrac{\sqrt{35}}{18}$$

$$\cos 2x = 1 - 2 \sin^2 x = 1 - 2\left(\tfrac{\sqrt{35}}{6}\right)^2 = -\tfrac{34}{36} = -\tfrac{17}{18}$$

$$\sin \tfrac{x}{2} = \sqrt{\frac{1 - \cos x}{2}} = \sqrt{\frac{1 - \left(-\frac{1}{6}\right)}{2}} = \sqrt{\frac{7}{12}} = \frac{\sqrt{21}}{6}$$

$$\cos \tfrac{x}{2} = \sqrt{\frac{1 + \cos x}{2}} = \sqrt{\frac{1 + \left(-\frac{1}{6}\right)}{2}} = \sqrt{\frac{5}{12}} = \frac{\sqrt{15}}{6}$$

6. $\cos^2 x + \sin^2 x = 1$

$$\sin^2 x = 1 - \cos^2 x$$
$$\sin^2 x = 1 - \left(-\tfrac{17}{18}\right)^2$$
$$\sin^2 x = \tfrac{35}{324}$$
$$\sin x = \tfrac{\sqrt{35}}{18}$$

$$\sin 2x = 2\sin x \cos x = 2\left(\tfrac{\sqrt{35}}{18}\right)\left(-\tfrac{17}{18}\right) = -\tfrac{17\sqrt{35}}{162}$$

$$\cos 2x = 2 \cos^2 x - 1 = 2\left(-\tfrac{17}{18}\right)^2 - 1 = \tfrac{127}{162}$$

$$\sin \tfrac{x}{2} = \sqrt{\frac{1 - \cos x}{2}} = \sqrt{\frac{1 - \left(-\frac{17}{18}\right)}{2}} = \frac{\sqrt{35}}{6}$$

$$\cos \tfrac{x}{2} = \sqrt{\frac{1 + \cos x}{2}} = \sqrt{\frac{1 + \left(-\frac{17}{18}\right)}{2}} = \sqrt{\frac{1}{36}} = \frac{1}{6}$$

7. $\sin 15° = \sin \frac{30°}{2}$

$$= \sqrt{\frac{1 - \cos 30°}{2}} = \sqrt{\frac{1 - \frac{\sqrt{3}}{2}}{2}} = \frac{\sqrt{2 - \sqrt{3}}}{2}$$

8. $\cos 75° = \cos \frac{150°}{2}$

$$= \sqrt{\frac{1 + \cos 150°}{2}} = \sqrt{\frac{1 + \left(-\frac{\sqrt{3}}{2}\right)}{2}} = \frac{\sqrt{2 - \sqrt{3}}}{2}$$

9. $\sin \frac{\pi}{8} = \sin \frac{\frac{\pi}{4}}{2}$

$$= \sqrt{\frac{1 - \cos \frac{\pi}{4}}{2}} = \sqrt{\frac{1 - \frac{\sqrt{2}}{2}}{2}} = \frac{\sqrt{2 - \sqrt{2}}}{2}$$

10. $\cos \frac{13\pi}{12} = \cos \frac{\frac{13\pi}{6}}{2}$

$$= -\sqrt{\frac{1 + \cos \frac{13\pi}{6}}{2}} = -\sqrt{\frac{1 + \frac{\sqrt{3}}{2}}{2}} = -\frac{\sqrt{2 + \sqrt{3}}}{2}$$

11.

$$\frac{\sin 2x}{2 \sin^2 x} \stackrel{?}{=} \cot x$$
$$\frac{2 \sin x \cos x}{2 \sin^2 x} \stackrel{?}{=} \cot x$$
$$\frac{\cos x}{\sin x} \stackrel{?}{=} \cot x$$
$$\cot x = \cot x$$

12.

$$1 + \cos 2x \stackrel{?}{=} \frac{2}{1 + \tan^2 x}$$
$$1 + \cos 2x \stackrel{?}{=} \frac{2}{\sec^2 x}$$
$$1 + \cos 2x \stackrel{?}{=} 2 \cos^2 x$$
$$1 + \cos 2x \stackrel{?}{=} 1 + 2 \cos^2 x - 1$$
$$1 + \cos 2x = 1 + \cos 2x$$

13.

$$\csc x \sec x \stackrel{?}{=} 2 \csc 2x$$
$$\csc x \sec x \stackrel{?}{=} \frac{2}{\sin 2x}$$
$$\csc x \sec x \stackrel{?}{=} \frac{2}{2 \sin x \cos x}$$
$$\csc x \sec x \stackrel{?}{=} \frac{1}{\sin x \cos x}$$
$$\csc x \sec x = \csc x \sec x$$

14.

$$\frac{1 - \tan^2 x}{1 + \tan^2 x} \stackrel{?}{=} \cos 2x$$
$$\frac{1 - (\sec^2 x - 1)}{\sec^2 x} \stackrel{?}{=} \cos 2x$$
$$\frac{2 - \sec^2 x}{\sec^2 x} \stackrel{?}{=} \cos 2x$$
$$\frac{2}{\sec^2 x} - \frac{\sec^2 x}{\sec^2 x} \stackrel{?}{=} \cos 2x$$
$$2 \cos^2 x - 1 \stackrel{?}{=} \cos 2x$$
$$\cos 2x = \cos 2x$$

15.

$$\sin 2x(\cot x + \tan x) \stackrel{?}{=} 2$$
$$2 \sin x \cos x\left(\frac{\cos x}{\sin x} + \frac{\sin x}{\cos x}\right) \stackrel{?}{=} 2$$
$$2 \cos^2 x + 2 \sin^2 x \stackrel{?}{=} 2$$
$$2(\cos^2 x + \sin^2 x) \stackrel{?}{=} 2$$
$$2(1) \stackrel{?}{=} 2$$
$$2 = 2$$

16. $\sin^2 x \stackrel{?}{=} \frac{1}{2}(1 - \cos 2x)$

$\sin^2 x \stackrel{?}{=} \frac{1}{2}[1 - (1 - 2\sin^2 x)]$

$\sin^2 x \stackrel{?}{=} \frac{1}{2}(2\sin^2 x)$

$\sin^2 x = \sin^2 x$

17. $$\frac{\cos x + \sin x}{\cos x - \sin x} \stackrel{?}{=} \frac{1 + \sin 2x}{\cos 2x}$$

$$\frac{\cos x + \sin x}{\cos x - \sin x} \cdot \frac{\cos x + \sin x}{\cos x + \sin x} \stackrel{?}{=} \frac{1 + \sin 2x}{\cos 2x}$$

$$\frac{\cos^2 x + 2\cos x \sin x + \sin^2 x}{\cos^2 x - \sin^2 x} \stackrel{?}{=} \frac{1 + \sin 2x}{\cos 2x}$$

$$\frac{1 + 2\cos x \sin x}{\cos 2x} \stackrel{?}{=} \frac{1 + \sin 2x}{\cos 2x}$$

$$\frac{1 + \sin 2x}{\cos 2x} = \frac{1 + \sin 2x}{\cos 2x}$$

18. $$\frac{\sin \frac{x}{2}}{\cos \frac{x}{2}} \stackrel{?}{=} \frac{\sin x}{1 + \cos x}$$

$$\frac{\sqrt{\frac{1 - \cos x}{2}}}{\sqrt{\frac{1 + \cos x}{2}}} \stackrel{?}{=} \frac{\sin x}{1 + \cos x}$$

$$\sqrt{\frac{1 - \cos x}{1 + \cos x}} \stackrel{?}{=} \frac{\sin x}{1 + \cos x}$$

$$\sqrt{\frac{1 - \cos x}{1 + \cos x}}\sqrt{\frac{1 + \cos x}{1 + \cos x}} \stackrel{?}{=} \frac{\sin x}{1 + \cos x}$$

$$\frac{\sqrt{1 - \cos^2 x}}{1 + \cos x} \stackrel{?}{=} \frac{\sin x}{1 + \cos x}$$

$$\frac{\sqrt{\sin^2 x}}{1 + \cos x} \stackrel{?}{=} \frac{\sin x}{1 + \cos x}$$

$$\frac{\sin x}{1 + \cos x} = \frac{\sin x}{1 + \cos x}$$

19. $\cot x \stackrel{?}{=} \frac{\sin 2x}{1 - \cos 2x}$

$\cot x \stackrel{?}{=} \frac{2\sin x \cos x}{1 - (1 - 2\sin^2 x)}$

$\cot x \stackrel{?}{=} \frac{2\sin x \cos x}{2\sin^2 x}$

$\cot x \stackrel{?}{=} \frac{\cos x}{\sin x}$

$\cot x = \cot x$

Page 910 Lesson 14-6

1. $\cos x = -\frac{\sqrt{3}}{2}$

$x = 150°$ or $210°$

$150°, 210°$

2. Let $u = 2x$.

$\sin 2x = -\frac{\sqrt{3}}{2}$

$\sin u = -\frac{\sqrt{3}}{2}$

$u = 240°, 300°, 600°, 660°$

$x = 120°, 150°, 300°, 330°$

3. $\cos 2x = 8 - 15\sin x$

$1 - 2\sin^2 x = 8 - 15\sin x$

$2\sin^2 x - 15\sin x + 7 = 0$

$(2\sin x - 1)(\sin x - 7) = 0$

$2\sin x - 1 = 0$ or $\sin x - 7 = 0$

$\sin x = \frac{1}{2}$ $\sin x = 7$

$x = 30°, 150°$ not possible

$30°, 150°$

4. $\sin x + \cos x = 1$

$(\sin x + \cos x)^2 = (1)^2$

$\sin^2 x + 2\sin x \cos x + \cos^2 x = 1$

$1 + 2\sin x \cos x = 1$

$\sin 2x = 0$

$x = 0°$ or $90°$

$0°, 90°$

5. $2\sin^2 x + \sin x = 0$

$\sin x(2\sin x + 1) = 0$

$\sin x = 0$ or $2\sin x + 1 = 0$

$x = 0°$ or $180°$ $\sin x = -\frac{1}{2}$

$x = 210°$ or $330°$

$0°, 180°, 210°, 330°$

6. $\sin 2x = \cos x$

$2\sin x \cos x = \cos x$

$2\sin x \cos x - \cos x = 0$

$\cos x(2\sin x - 1) = 0$

$\cos x = 0$ $2\sin x - 1 = 0$

$x = 90°$ or $270°$ $\sin x = \frac{1}{2}$

$x = 30°$ or $150°$

$30°, 90°, 150°, 270°$

7. $\tan \theta = 1$

$\theta = \frac{\pi}{4}$ or $\frac{5\pi}{4}$

8. $\cos 8\theta = 1$

$8\theta = 0, 2\pi, 4\pi, 6\pi, 8\pi, 10\pi, 12\pi, 14\pi$

$\theta = 0, \frac{\pi}{4}, \frac{\pi}{2}, \frac{3\pi}{4}, \pi, \frac{5\pi}{4}, \frac{3\pi}{2}, \frac{7\pi}{4}$

9. $\sin \theta + 1 = \cos 2\theta$

$\sin \theta + 1 = 1 - 2\sin^2 \theta$

$2\sin^2 \theta + \sin \theta = 0$

$\sin \theta(2\sin \theta + 1) = 0$

$\sin \theta = 0$ or $2\sin \theta + 1 = 0$

$\theta = 0$ or π $\sin \theta = -\frac{1}{2}$

$\theta = \frac{7\pi}{6}$ or $\frac{11\pi}{6}$

$0, \pi, \frac{7\pi}{6}, \frac{11\pi}{6}$

10. $8\sin \theta \cos \theta = 2\sqrt{3}$

$2\sin \theta \cos \theta = \frac{\sqrt{3}}{2}$

$\sin 2\theta = \frac{\sqrt{3}}{2}$

$2\theta = \frac{\pi}{3}, \frac{2\pi}{3}, \frac{7\pi}{3}, \frac{8\pi}{3}$

$\theta = \frac{\pi}{6}, \frac{\pi}{3}, \frac{7\pi}{6}, \frac{4\pi}{3}$

11. $\cos \theta = 1 + \sin \theta$

$\cos^2 \theta = (1 + \sin \theta)^2$

$\cos^2 \theta = 1 + 2\sin \theta + \sin^2 \theta$

$1 - \sin^2 \theta = 1 + 2\sin \theta + \sin^2 \theta$

$2\sin^2 \theta + 2\sin \theta = 0$

$2\sin \theta(\sin \theta + 1) = 0$

$2\sin \theta = 0$ or $\sin \theta + 1 = 0$

$\sin \theta = 0$ $\sin \theta = -1$

$\theta = 0$ or ~~π~~ $\theta = \frac{3\pi}{2}$

$0, \frac{3\pi}{2}$

12. $2\cos^2\theta = \cos\theta$

$2\cos^2\theta - \cos\theta = 0$

$\cos\theta(2\cos\theta - 1) = 0$

$\cos\theta = 0$ or $2\cos\theta - 1 = 0$

$\theta = \frac{\pi}{2}$ or $\frac{3\pi}{2}$ $\quad$ $\cos\theta = \frac{1}{2}$

$\theta = \frac{\pi}{3}$ or $\frac{5\pi}{3}$

$\frac{\pi}{3}, \frac{\pi}{2}, \frac{3\pi}{2}, \frac{5\pi}{3}$

13. $2\sin^2 x - 1 = 0$

$2\sin^2 x = 1$

$\sin^2 x = \frac{1}{2}$

$\sin x = \pm\frac{\sqrt{2}}{2}$

$x = 45°, 135°$

$45° + 90k°$

14. $\cos x - 2\cos x \sin x = 0$

$\cos x\,(1 - 2\sin x) = 0$

$\cos x = 0$ or $1 - 2\sin x = 0$

$x = 90°$ or $270°$ $\quad$ $\sin x = \frac{1}{2}$

$x = 30°$ or $150°$

$90° + 180k°, 30° + 360k°, 150° + 360k°$

15. $\cos 2x \sin x = 1$

$\sin x = \frac{1}{2\cos^2 x - 1}$

$\sin^2 x = \left(\frac{1}{2\cos^2 x - 1}\right)^2$

$1 - \cos^2 x = \frac{1}{4\cos^4 x - 4\cos^2 x + 1}$

$-4\cos^6 x + 8\cos^4 x - 5\cos^2 x = 0$

$-\cos^2 x(2\cos^2 x - 5)(2\cos^2 x + 1) = 0$

$\cos x = 0$ or $2\cos^2 x - 5 = 0$ or $2\cos^2 x + 1 = 0$

$x = 270°$ $\quad$ $2\cos^2 x = 5$ $\quad$ $2\cos^2 x = -1$

$\cos^2 x = \frac{5}{2}$ $\quad$ $\cos^2 x = -\frac{1}{2}$

not possible $\quad$ not possible

$270° + 360k°$

16. $(\tan x - 1)(2\cos x + 1) = 0$

$\tan x - 1 = 0$ or $2\cos x + 1 = 0$

$\tan x = 1$ $\quad$ $\cos x = -\frac{1}{2}$

$x = 45°, 225°$ $\quad$ $x = 120°, 240°$

$45° + 180k°, 120° + 360k°, 240° + 360k°$

17. $2\cos^2 x = 0.5$

$\cos^2 x = 0.25$

$\cos x = \pm 0.5$

$x = 60°, 120°, 240°, 300°$

$60° + 360k°, 120° + 360k°, 240° + 360k°, 300° + 360k°$

18. $\sin x \tan x - \tan x = 0$

$\tan x\,(\sin x - 1) = 0$

$\tan x = 0$ or $\sin x - 1 = 0$

$x = 0°$ or $180°$ $\quad$ $\sin x = 1$

$x = 90°$

$180k°, 90° + 360k°$

19. $\cos 2\theta \sin\theta = 1$

$(2\cos^2\theta - 1)\sin\theta = 1$

$\sin\theta = \frac{1}{2\cos^2\theta - 1}$

$\sin^2\theta = \left(\frac{1}{2\cos^2\theta - 1}\right)^2$

$1 - \cos^2\theta = \frac{1}{4\cos^4\theta - 4\cos^2\theta - 1}$

(Continued next column)

$-4\cos^6\theta + 8\cos^4\theta - 5\cos^2\theta = 0$

$-\cos^2\theta(2\cos^2\theta - 5)(2\cos^2\theta + 1) = 0$

$\cos^2\theta = 0$ or $2\cos^2\theta - 5 = 0$ or $2\cos^2\theta + 1 = 0$

$\cos\theta = 0$ $\quad$ $2\cos^2\theta = 5$ $\quad$ $2\cos^2\theta = -1$

$\theta = \frac{\pi}{2}$ or $\frac{3\pi}{2}$ $\quad$ $\cos^2\theta = \frac{5}{2}$ $\quad$ $\cos^2\theta = -\frac{1}{2}$

not possible $\quad$ not possible

$\frac{3\pi}{2} + 2k\pi$

20. $\sin\frac{\theta}{2} + \cos\frac{\theta}{2} = \sqrt{2}$

$\left(\sin\frac{\theta}{2} + \cos\frac{\theta}{2}\right)^2 = 2$

$\sin^2\frac{\theta}{2} + 2\sin\frac{\theta}{2}\cos\frac{\theta}{2} + \cos^2\frac{\theta}{2} = 2$

$1 + 2\sin\frac{\theta}{2}\cos\frac{\theta}{2} = 2$

$\sin\theta = 1$

$\theta = \frac{\pi}{2}$

$\frac{\pi}{2} + 2k\pi$

21. $\cos 2\theta + 4\cos\theta = -3$

$2\cos^2\theta - 1 + 4\cos\theta = -3$

$2\cos^2\theta + 4\cos\theta + 2 = 0$

$\cos^2\theta + 2\cos\theta + 1 = 0$

$(\cos\theta + 1)^2 = 0$

$\cos\theta + 1 = 0$

$\cos\theta = -1$

$\theta = \pi$

$\pi + 2k\pi$

22. $\sin\frac{\theta}{2} + \cos\theta = 1$

$\sin\frac{\theta}{2} = 1 - \cos\theta$

$\sqrt{\frac{1 - \cos\theta}{2}} = 1 - \cos\theta$

$\frac{1 - \cos\theta}{2} = (1 - \cos\theta)^2$

$\frac{1 - \cos\theta}{2} = 1 - 2\cos\theta + \cos^2\theta$

$1 - \cos\theta = 2 - 4\cos\theta + 2\cos^2\theta$

$2\cos^2\theta - 3\cos\theta + 1 = 0$

$(2\cos\theta - 1)(\cos\theta - 1) = 0$

$2\cos\theta - 1 = 0$ or $\cos\theta - 1 = 0$

$2\cos\theta = 1$ $\quad$ $\cos\theta = 1$

$\cos\theta = \frac{1}{2}$ $\quad$ $\theta = 0$

$\theta = \frac{\pi}{3}$ or $\frac{5\pi}{3}$

$2k\pi, \frac{\pi}{3} + 2k\pi, \frac{5\pi}{3} + 2k\pi$

23. $3\tan^2\theta - \sqrt{3}\tan\theta = 0$

$\tan\theta\,(3\tan\theta - \sqrt{3}) = 0$

$\tan\theta = 0$ or $3\tan\theta - \sqrt{3} = 0$

$\theta = 0$ or π $\quad$ $3\tan\theta = \sqrt{3}$

$\tan\theta = \frac{\sqrt{3}}{3}$

$\theta = \frac{\pi}{6}$ or $\frac{7\pi}{6}$

$k\pi, \frac{\pi}{6} + k\pi$

24. $4\sin\theta\cos\theta = -\sqrt{3}$

$2\sin\theta\cos\theta = -\frac{\sqrt{3}}{2}$

$\sin 2\theta = -\frac{\sqrt{3}}{2}$

$\theta = \frac{2\pi}{3}$ or $\frac{5\pi}{6}$

$\frac{2\pi}{3} + k\pi, \frac{5\pi}{6} + k\pi$

Page 912 Chapter 1 Test

1. associative (×) 2. symmetric (=)
3. reflexive (=) 4. substitution (=)
5. commutative (×) 6. transitive (=)

7. $[2 + 3^3 - 4] \div 2 = [2 + 27 - 4] \div 2$
$= 25 \div 2$
$= 12.5$

8. $(2 + 3)^3 - 4 \div 2 = 5^3 - 4 \div 2$
$= 125 - 4 \div 2$
$= 125 - 2$
$= 123$

9. $(4^5 - 4^2) + 4^3 = (1024 - 16) + 64$
$= 1008 + 64$
$= 1072$

10. $[5(17 - 2) \div 3] - 2^4 = [5(17 - 2) \div 3] - 16$
$= [5(15) \div 3] - 16$
$= [75 \div 3] - 16$
$= 25 - 16$
$= 9$

11. $\frac{db + 4c}{a} = \frac{(-6)\left(\frac{2}{3}\right) + 4(8)}{-9}$
$= \frac{-4 + 32}{-9}$
$= -\frac{28}{9}$

12. $\frac{a}{b^2} + c = \frac{-9}{\left(\frac{2}{3}\right)^2} + 8$
$= \frac{-9}{\frac{4}{9}} + 8$
$= -9 \cdot \frac{9}{4} + 8$
$= -20.25 + 8$
$= -12.25$

13. $2b(4a + a^2) = 2\left(\frac{2}{3}\right)[4(-9) + (-9)^2]$
$= 2\left(\frac{2}{3}\right)[4(-9) + 81]$
$= 2\left(\frac{2}{3}\right)[-36 + 81]$
$= 2\left(\frac{2}{3}\right)(45)$
$= 60$

14. $\frac{4a + 3c}{3b} = \frac{4(-9) + 3(8)}{3\left(\frac{2}{3}\right)}$
$= \frac{-36 + 24}{2}$
$= \frac{-12}{2}$
$= -6$

15. I, R 16. Q, R
17. N, W, Z, Q, R 18. Z, Q, R

19. $5t - 3 = -2t + 10$
$7t - 3 = 10$
$7t = 13$
$t = \frac{13}{7}$

20. $2x - 7 - (x - 5) = 0$
$2x - 7 - x + 5 = 0$
$x - 7 + 5 = 0$
$x - 2 = 0$
$x = 2$

21. $5m - (5 + 4m) = (3 + m) - 8$
$5m - 5 - 4m = 3 + m - 8$
$m - 5 = -5 + m$
$-5 = -5$
all reals

22. $|8w + 2| + 2 = 0$
$|8w + 2| = -2$
no solution

23. $12\left|\frac{1}{2}y + 3\right| = 6$
$\left|\frac{1}{2}y + 3\right| = \frac{1}{2}$
$\frac{1}{2}y + 3 = \frac{1}{2}$ or $\frac{1}{2}y + 3 = -\frac{1}{2}$
$\frac{1}{2}y = -\frac{5}{2}$ $\frac{1}{2}y = -\frac{7}{2}$
$y = -5$ $y = -7$

24. $2|2y - 6| + 4 = 8$
$2|2y - 6| = 4$
$|2y - 6| = 2$
$2y - 6 = 2$ or $2y - 6 = -2$
$2y = 8$ $2y = 4$
$y = 4$ $y = 2$

25. $4 > b + 1$
$3 > b$
$\{b \mid b < 3\}$

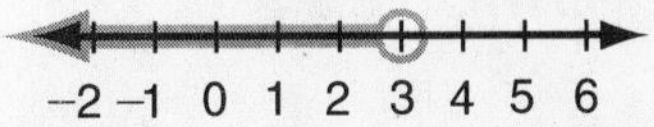

26. $3q + 7 \geq 13$
$3q \geq 6$
$q \geq 2$
$\{q \mid q \geq 2\}$

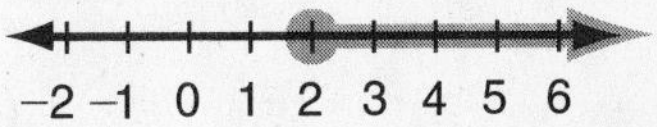

27. $5(3x - 5) + x < 2(4x - 1) + 1$
$15x - 25 + x < 8x - 2 + 1$
$16x - 25 < 8x - 1$
$8x - 25 < -1$
$8x < 24$
$x < 3$
$\{x \mid x < 3\}$

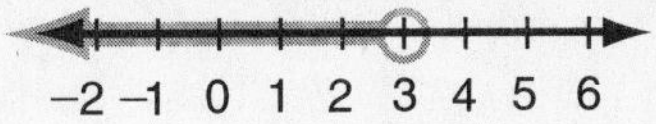

28. $|9y - 4| + 8 > 4$
$|9y - 4| > -4$
$9y - 4 > -4$ or $9y - 4 < 4$
$9y > 0$ $9y < 8$
$y > 0$ $y < \frac{8}{9}$
all reals

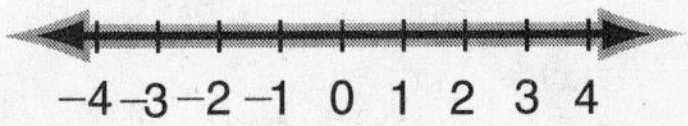

29. $-12 < 7s - 5 \leq 9$
$-7 < 7s \leq 14$
$-1 < s \leq 2$
$\{s \mid -1 < s \leq 2\}$

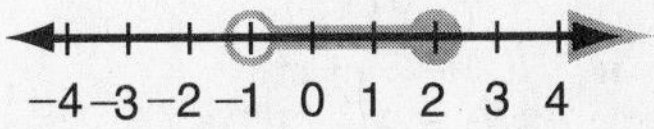

30. $|5 + k| \leq 8$
$5 + k \leq 8$ and $5 + k \geq -8$
$k \leq 3$ $k \geq -13$
$\{k \mid -13 \leq k \leq 3\}$

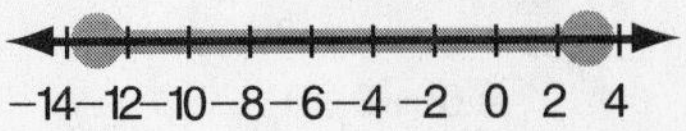

31. males: 250, 260, 300, 370, 400, 420, 420, 430, 450, 480, 510, 660, 670
420; 420; (250 + 260 + 300 + 370 + 400 + 420 + 420 + 430 + 450 + 480 + 510 + 660 + 670) ÷ 13 = 5620 ÷ 13 ≈ 432.3

(Continued next page)

females: 200, 210, 240, 240, 260, 270, 290, 310, 350, 360, 410, 440, 490
290; 240; (200 + 210 + 240 + 240 + 260 + 270 + 290 + 310 + 350 + 360 + 410 + 440 + 490) ÷ 13 = 4070 ÷ 13 ≈ 313.1

32. Let s = score on last test.
$s + 87 + 89 + 76 + 77 = 400$
$s + 329 = 400$
$s = 71$

33. Let m = miles traveled.
$19.50 + 0.18m = 33$
$0.18m = 13.5$
$m = 75$; 75 miles

Page 913 Chapter 2 Test

1. D = {−4, −2, 0, 2, 4}
R = {−81, 21, 51, 33, −9}
yes

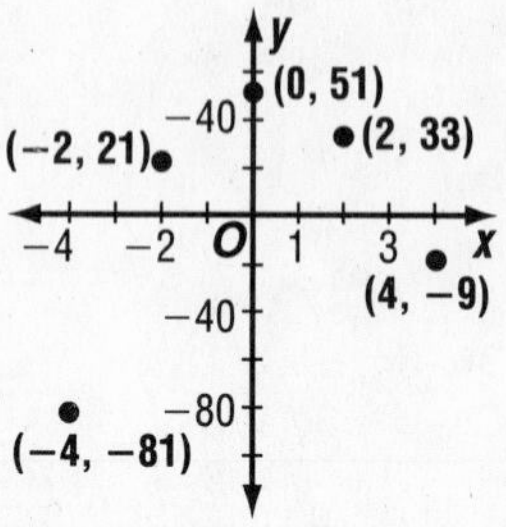

2. D = {−5, −3, −1}
R = {0, 1, 2, 3, 4}
no

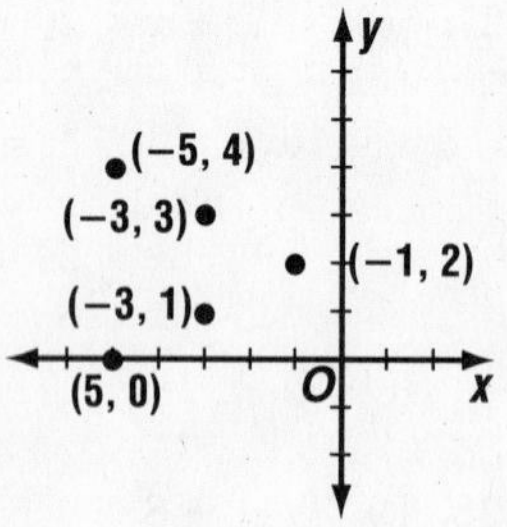

3. $f(x) = 2x^2 - 3x + 5$
$f(-3) = 2(-3)^2 - 3(-3) + 5$
$= 2(9) - 3(-3) + 5$
$= 18 + 9 + 5$
$= 32$

4. $f(x) = 11x^3 - x + 1$
$f(5) = 11(5)^3 - 5 + 1$
$= 11(125) - 5 + 1$
$= 1375 - 5 + 1$
$= 1371$

5. $f(x) = 7 - x^2$
$f(3.7) = 7 - (3.7)^2$
$= 7 - 13.69$
$= -6.69$

6. $f(x) = x - 3x^2$
$f(0) = 0 - 3(0)^2$
$= 0 - 0$
$= 0$

7. $-2x + 5 \le 3y$
$-2x + 5 = 3(0)$ $\quad -2(0) + 5 = 3y$
$-2x + 5 = 0$ $\quad 5 = 3y$
$-2x = -5$ $\quad \frac{5}{3} = y$
$x = \frac{5}{2}$

(Continued next column)

Test: (0, 3)
$-2x + 5 \le 3y$
$-2(0) + 5 \overset{?}{\le} 3(3)$
$5 \le 9$; true

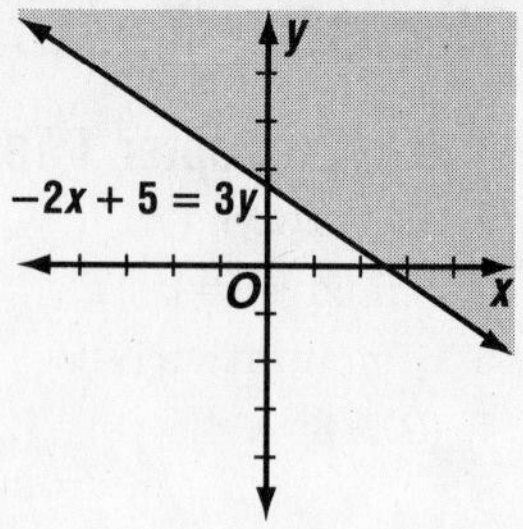

8. $4x - y + 2 = 0$
$4x - 0 + 2 = 0$ $\quad 4(0) - y + 2 = 0$
$4x = -2$ $\quad -y + 2 = 0$
$x = -\frac{1}{2}$ $\quad 2 = y$

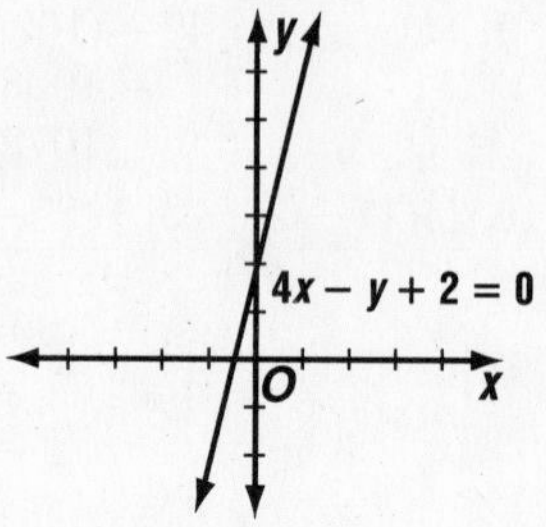

9. $x = -4$

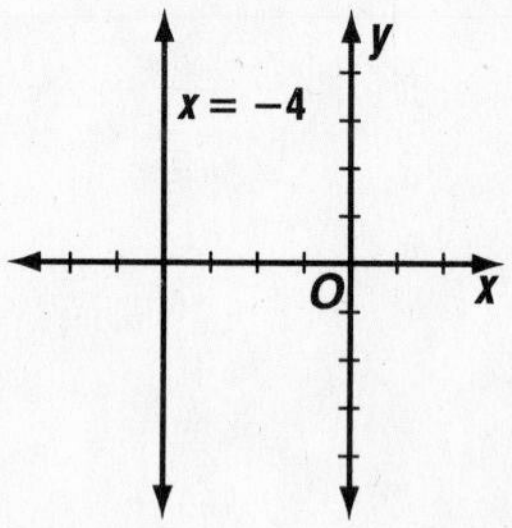

10. $y = 2x - 5$
$0 = 2x - 5$ $\quad y = 2(0) - 5$
$5 = 2x$ $\quad y = -5$
$\frac{5}{2} = x$

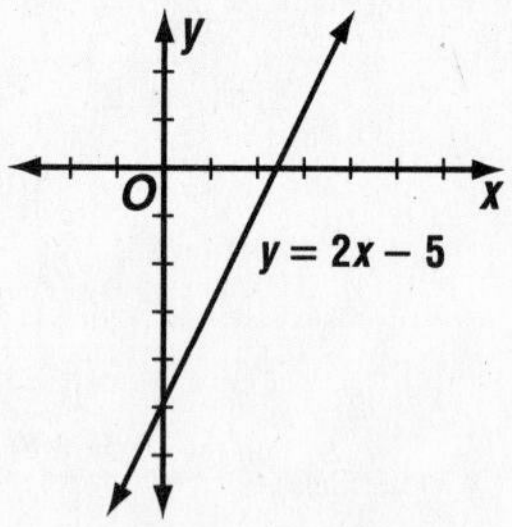

11. $y \le 10$
Test: (0, 0)
$y \le 10$
$0 \overset{?}{\le} 10$; true

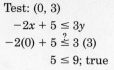

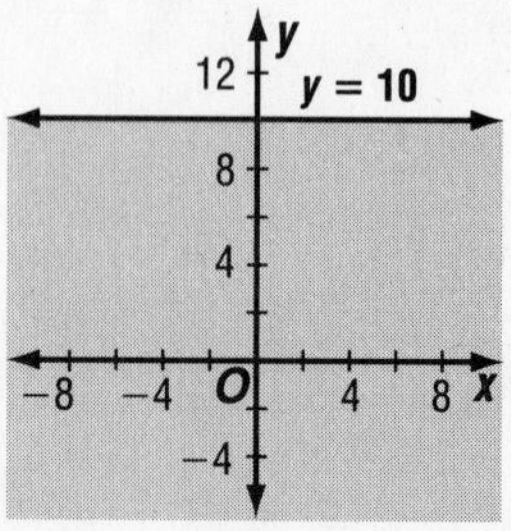

12. $x > 6$

Test: (7, 0)

$x > 6$

$7 \overset{?}{>} 6$; true

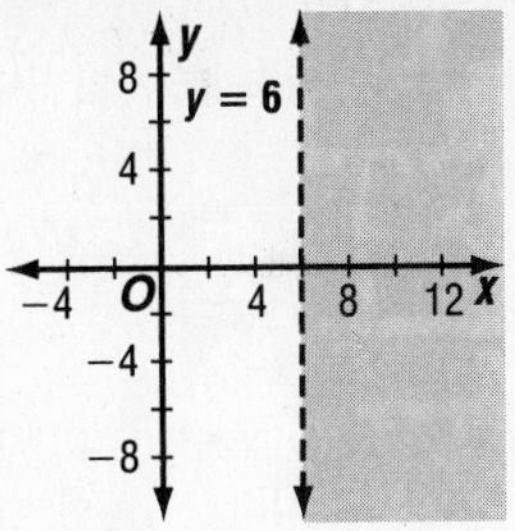

13. $-8x + 4y \geq 32$

$-8x + 4(0) = 32$ $\quad$ $-8(0) + 4y = 32$

$-8x = 32$ $\quad$ $4y = 32$

$x = -4$ $\quad$ $y = 8$

Test: (0, 9)

$-8x + 4y \overset{?}{\geq} 32$

$-8(0) + 4(9) \overset{?}{\geq} 32$

$36 \geq 32$; true

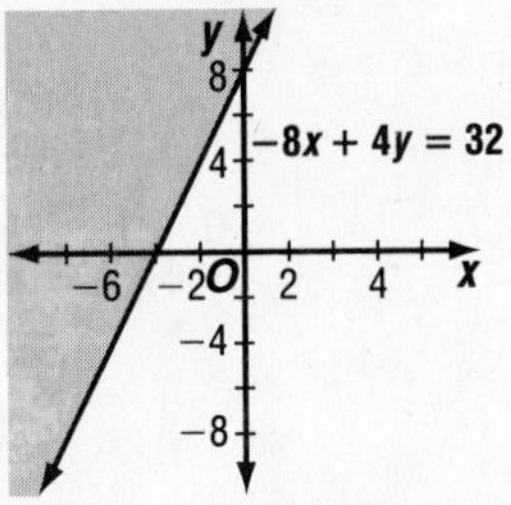

14. $f(x) = [3x] + 3$

x	$[3x] + 3$	$f(x)$
0	$[3 \cdot 0] + 3$	3
$\frac{1}{4}$	$\left[3 \cdot \frac{1}{4}\right] + 3$	3
$\frac{1}{3}$	$\left[3 \cdot \frac{1}{3}\right] + 3$	4
$\frac{1}{2}$	$\left[3 \cdot \frac{1}{2}\right] + 3$	4
$\frac{2}{3}$	$\left[3 \cdot \frac{2}{3}\right] + 3$	5
$\frac{3}{4}$	$\left[3 \cdot \frac{3}{4}\right] + 3$	5

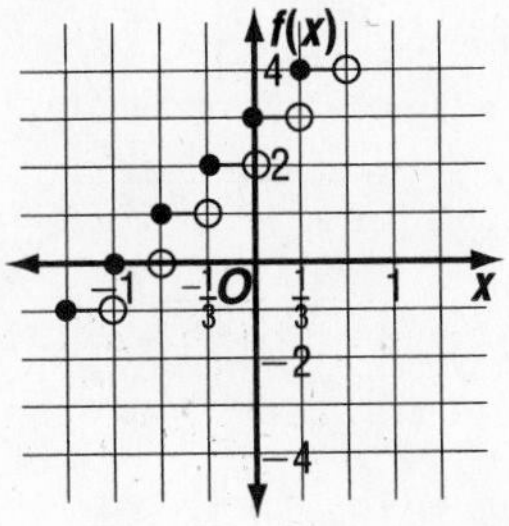

15. $y < 4|x - 1|$

x	$4\|x - 1\|$	y
0	$4\|0 - 1\|$	4
1	$4\|1 - 1\|$	0
2	$4\|2 - 1\|$	4
3	$4\|3 - 1\|$	8

Test: (0, 0) $y < 4|x - 1|$

$0 \overset{?}{<} 4|0 - 1|$

$0 < 4$; true

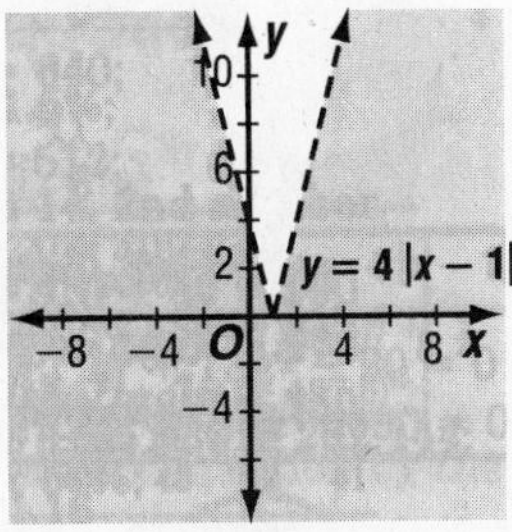

16. $f(x) = 3x - 1$

$0 = 3x - 1$ $\quad$ $y = 3(0) - 1$

$1 = 3x$ $\quad$ $y = -1$

$\frac{1}{3} = x$

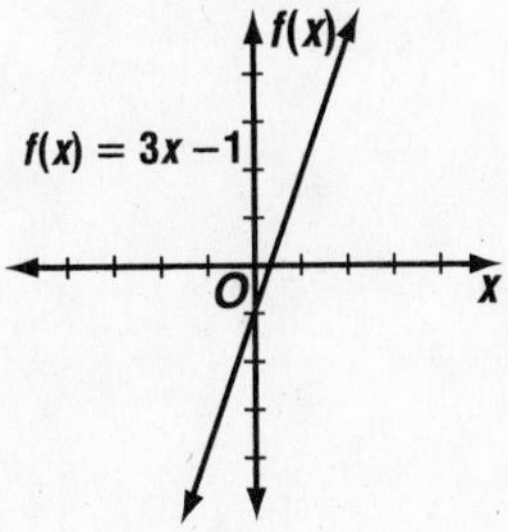

17. $g(x) = -\frac{1}{2}x$

x	$g(x)$
−2	1
0	0
2	−1

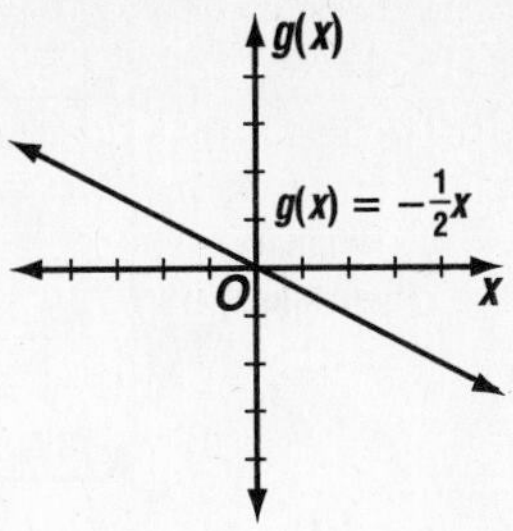

18. $y = \frac{3}{5}x - 4$

$0 = \frac{3}{5}x - 4$ $\quad$ $y = \frac{3}{5}(0) - 4$

$4 = \frac{3}{5}x$ $\quad$ $y = -4$

$\frac{20}{3} = x$

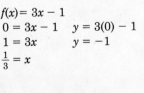

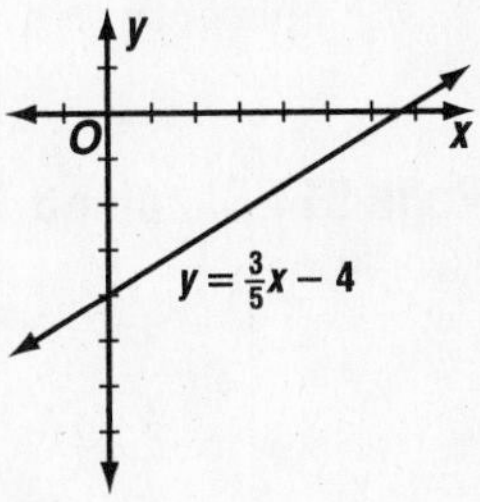

19. $m = \frac{1 - (-4)}{6 - 8}$

$= \frac{5}{-2}$ or $-\frac{5}{2}$

20. $m = \frac{5 - 5}{4 - (-2)}$

$= \frac{0}{6}$ or 0

21. $m = \frac{-6 - 7}{4 - 5}$

$= \frac{-13}{-1}$ or 13

22. $m = \frac{-3 - 5}{4 - 4}$

$= -\frac{8}{0}$; undefined

23. $m = \frac{2 - (-4)}{5 - (-5)}$

$= \frac{6}{10}$ or $\frac{3}{5}$

24. $m = \frac{-1 - (-5)}{9 - (-3)}$

$= \frac{4}{12}$ or $\frac{1}{3}$

25. $y = mx + b$

$y = -5x + 11$

26. $y - y_1 = m(x - x_1)$

$y - 15 = \frac{2}{3}(x + 6)$

$y - 15 = \frac{2}{3}x + 4$

$y = \frac{2}{3}x + 19$

27. $m = \frac{-8 - 7}{7 - (-3)}$

$= \frac{-15}{10}$ or $-\frac{3}{2}$

$y - y_1 = m(x - x_1)$

$y - 7 = -\frac{3}{2}(x + 3)$

$y - 7 = -\frac{3}{2}x - \frac{9}{2}$

$y = -\frac{3}{2}x + \frac{5}{2}$

28. (9, 0), (0, −4)

$m = \frac{-4 - 0}{0 - 9}$

$= \frac{-4}{-9}$ or $\frac{4}{9}$

$y - 0 = \frac{4}{9}(x - 9)$

$y = \frac{4}{9}x - 4$

29. (4, −2), (0, 0)

$m = \frac{0 - (-2)}{0 - 4}$

$= \frac{2}{-4}$ or $-\frac{1}{2}$

$y - 0 = -\frac{1}{2}(x - 0)$

$y = -\frac{1}{2}x$

30. $6x - y = 7$

$-y = -6x + 7$

$y = 6x - 7$

parallel slope = 6

$y - 8 = 6(x + 2)$

$y - 8 = 6x + 12$

$y = 6x + 20$

31. $x + 3y = 7$

$3y = -x + 7$

$y = -\frac{1}{3}x + \frac{7}{3}$

perpendicular slope = 3

$y - 2 = 3(x - 5)$

$y - 2 = 3x - 15$

$y = 3x - 13$

32.

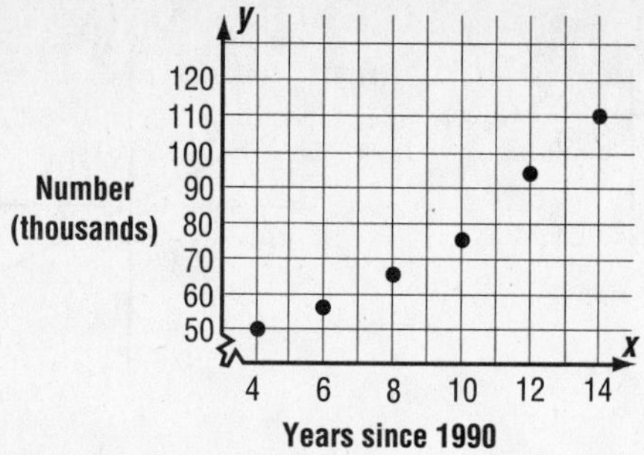

33. Sample answer: $y = 6000x + 20{,}000$

Page 914 Chapter 3 Test

1. $-4x + y = -5$
$y = 4x - 5$
$2x + y = 7$
$y = -2x + 7$

(2, 3)

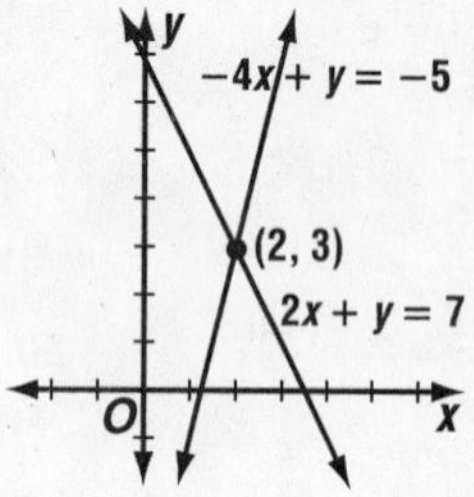

2. $x + y = -8$
$y = -x - 8$
$-3x + 2y = 9$
$2y = 3x + 9$
$y = \frac{3}{2}x + \frac{9}{2}$

(−5, −3)

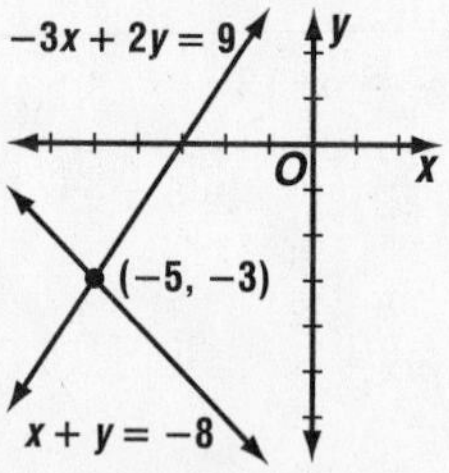

3. $-6x + 3y = 33$
$3y = 6x + 33$
$y = 2x + 11$
$-4x + y = 16$
$y = 4x + 16$

(−2.5, 6)

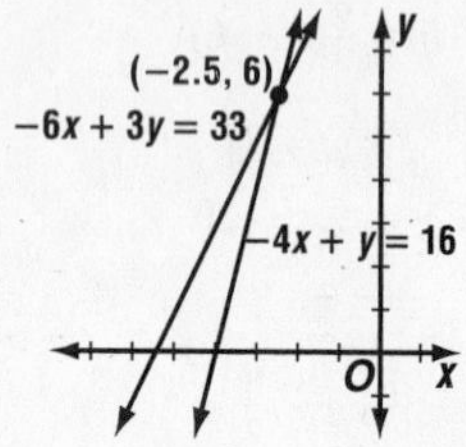

4. $3x - 2y = 8$
$3x - 2(6x + 11) = 8$
$3x - 12x - 22 = 8$
$-9x - 22 = 8$
$-9x = 30$
$x = -\frac{30}{9}$ or $-\frac{10}{3}$

$y = 6x + 11$
$= 6\left(-\frac{10}{3}\right) + 11$
$= -20 + 11$
$= -9$

$\left(-\frac{10}{3}, -9\right)$

5. $x + y = -1$
$y = -x - 1$
$2y = 5x - 1$
$2(-x - 1) = 5x - 1$
$-2x - 2 = 5x - 1$
$-7x - 2 = -1$
$-7x = 1$
$x = -\frac{1}{7}$

$y = -x - 1$
$= -\left(-\frac{1}{7}\right) - 1$
$= \frac{1}{7} - 1$
$= -\frac{6}{7}$

$\left(-\frac{1}{7}, -\frac{6}{7}\right)$

6. $-7x + 6y = 42 \rightarrow 14x - 12y = -84$
$3x + 4y = 28 \rightarrow 9x + 12y = 84$
$23x = 0$
$x = 0$

$3x + 4y = 28$
$3(0) + 4y = 28$
$4y = 28$
$y = 7$ (0, 7)

7. $\begin{vmatrix} -4 & 3 \\ 5 & -2 \end{vmatrix} = -4(-2) - 5 \cdot 3$
$= 8 - 15$
$= -7$

8. $\begin{vmatrix} 1 & -6 \\ 8 & 7 \end{vmatrix} = 1 \cdot 7 - 8(-6)$
$= 7 - (-48)$
$= 55$

9. $\begin{vmatrix} 0 & -4 \\ 2 & 11 \end{vmatrix} = 0 \cdot 11 - 2(-4)$
$= 0 - (-8)$
$= 8$

10. $x = \dfrac{\begin{vmatrix} 60 & 5 \\ -20 & 4 \end{vmatrix}}{\begin{vmatrix} 4 & 5 \\ 5 & 4 \end{vmatrix}}$
$= \frac{60 \cdot 4 - (-20)5}{4 \cdot 4 - 5 \cdot 5}$
$= \frac{240 + 100}{16 - 25}$
$= \frac{340}{-9}$ or $-\frac{340}{9}$

$y = \dfrac{\begin{vmatrix} 4 & 60 \\ 5 & -20 \end{vmatrix}}{\begin{vmatrix} 4 & 5 \\ 5 & 4 \end{vmatrix}}$
$= \frac{4(-20) - 5 \cdot 60}{4 \cdot 4 - 5 \cdot 5}$
$= \frac{-80 - 300}{16 - 25}$
$= \frac{-380}{-9}$ or $\frac{380}{9}$

$\left(-\frac{340}{9}, \frac{380}{9}\right)$

11. $x = \dfrac{\begin{vmatrix} 15 & 1 \\ -16 & -4 \end{vmatrix}}{\begin{vmatrix} 6 & 1 \\ 1 & -4 \end{vmatrix}}$
$= \frac{15(-4) - (-16)1}{6(-4) - 1 \cdot 1}$
$= \frac{-60 + 16}{-24 - 1}$
$= \frac{-44}{-25}$ or 1.76

$y = \dfrac{\begin{vmatrix} 6 & 15 \\ 1 & -16 \end{vmatrix}}{\begin{vmatrix} 6 & 1 \\ 1 & -4 \end{vmatrix}}$
$= \frac{6(-16) - 1 \cdot 15}{6(-4) - 1 \cdot 1}$
$= \frac{-96 - 15}{-24 - 1}$
$= \frac{-111}{-25}$ or 4.44

(1.76, 4.44)

12. $x = \dfrac{\begin{vmatrix} 23 & -8 \\ 24 & 1 \end{vmatrix}}{\begin{vmatrix} 3 & -8 \\ 5 & 1 \end{vmatrix}}$
$= \frac{23 \cdot 1 - 24(-8)}{3 \cdot 1 - 5(-8)}$
$= \frac{23 + 192}{3 + 40}$
$= \frac{215}{43}$ or 5

$y = \dfrac{\begin{vmatrix} 3 & 23 \\ 5 & 24 \end{vmatrix}}{\begin{vmatrix} 3 & -8 \\ 5 & 1 \end{vmatrix}}$
$= \frac{3 \cdot 24 - 5 \cdot 23}{3 \cdot 1 - 5(-8)}$
$= \frac{72 - 115}{3 + 40}$
$= \frac{-43}{43}$ or −1 (5, −1)

13. $y \geq x - 3$
$y \geq -x + 1$

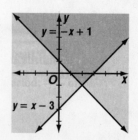

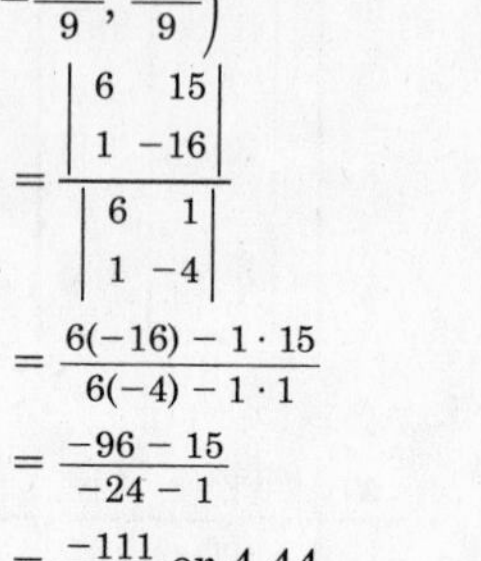

14. $x + 2y \geq 7$
$2y \geq -x + 7$
$y \geq -\frac{1}{2}x + \frac{7}{2}$
$3x - 4y < 12$
$-4y < -3x + 12$
$y > \frac{3}{4}x - 3$

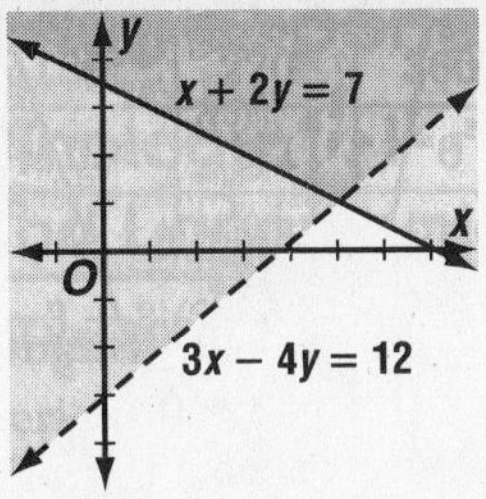

15. $|x| > 5$ $\quad x + y < 6$
$y < -x + 6$

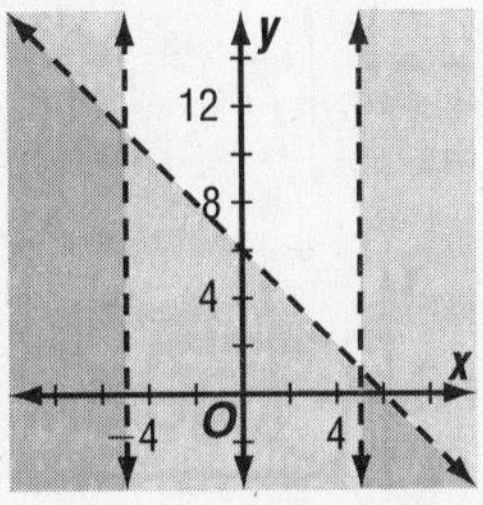

16. $y \leq 5$
$y \geq -3$
$4x + y \leq 5$
$y \leq -4x + 5$
$-2x + y \leq 5$
$y \leq 2x + 5$

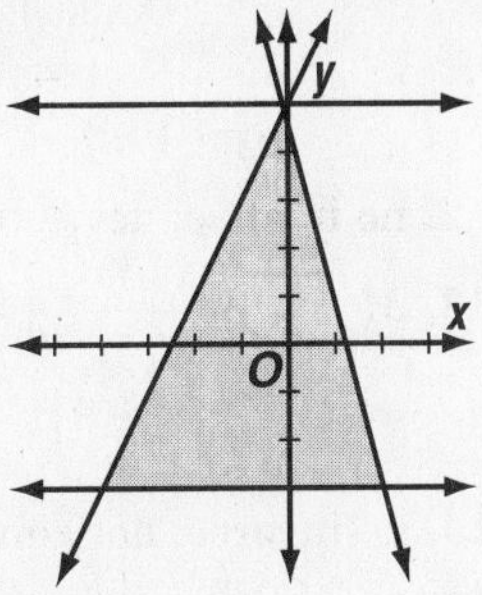

vertices: $(-4, -3)$, $(0, 5)$, $(2, -3)$

(x, y)	$4x - 3y$	$f(x, y)$
$(-4, -3)$	$4(-4) - 3(-3)$	-7
$(0, 5)$	$4(0) - 3(5)$	-15
$(2, -3)$	$4(2) - 3(-3)$	17

max: $f(2, -3) = 17$
min: $f(0, 5) = -15$

17. $x \geq -10$
$y \geq -6$
$y \leq 1$
$\frac{3}{4}x + y \leq -2$
$y \leq -\frac{3}{4}x - 2$
$y \geq \frac{1}{2}x - 5$

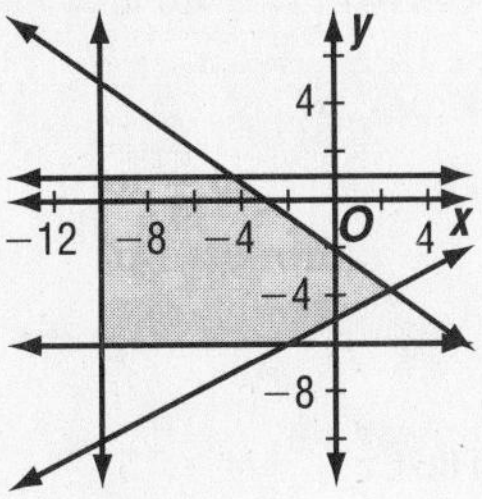

vertices: $(-10, -6)$, $(-10, 1)$, $(-4, 1)$, $(2.4, -3.8)$, $(-2, -6)$

(x, y)	$2x + y$	$f(x, y)$
$(-10, -6)$	$2(-10) + (-6)$	-26
$(-10, 1)$	$2(-10) + 1$	-19
$(-4, 1)$	$2(-4) + 1$	-7
$(2.4, -3.8)$	$2(2.4) + (-3.8)$	1
$(-2, -6)$	$2(-2) + (-6)$	-10

max: $f(2.4, -3.8) = 1$
min: $f(-10, -6) = -26$

18. Let x = soccer balls and y = volleyballs.
$2x + 3y \leq 500$
$3y \leq -2x + 500$
$y \leq -\frac{2}{3}x + 166\frac{2}{3}$
$3x + 2y \leq 450$
$2y \leq -3x + 450$
$y \leq -\frac{3}{2}x + 225$
$x \geq 0$
$y \geq 0$

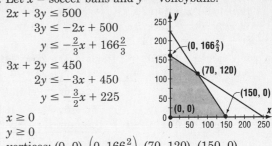

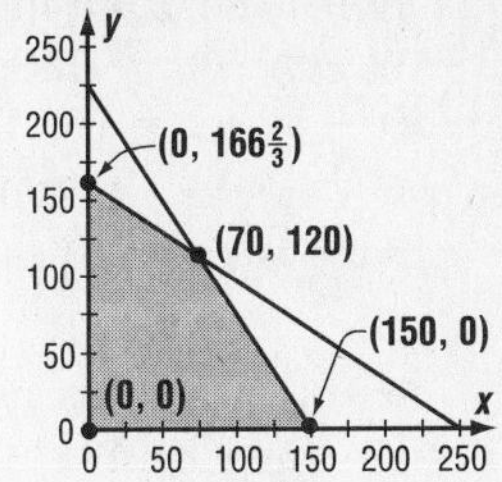

vertices: $(0, 0)$, $\left(0, 166\frac{2}{3}\right)$, $(70, 120)$, $(150, 0)$
$f(x, y) = 5x + 4y$

(x, y)	$(75x, 60y)$	$5x + 4y$	$f(x, y)$
$(0, 0)$	$(0, 0)$	$5(0) + 4(0)$	0
$\left(0, 166\frac{2}{3}\right)$	$(0, 10{,}000)$	$5(0) + 4(10{,}000)$	$40{,}000$
$(70, 120)$	$(5250, 7200)$	$5(5250) + 4(7200)$	$55{,}050$
$(150, 0)$	$(11{,}250, 0)$	$5(11{,}250) + 4(0)$	$56{,}250$

11,250 soccer balls and 0 volleyballs

19. \$56,250

20.
$$\begin{array}{rl} & x + y + z = -1 \\ (-) & 2x + 4y + z = 1 \\ \hline & -x - 3y = -2 \end{array}$$

$x + y + z = -1 \rightarrow 3x + 3y - 3z = -3$
$x + 2y - 3z = -3 \rightarrow (+)\ x + 2y - 3z = -3$
$4x + 5y = -6$

$-x - 3y = -2 \rightarrow -4x - 12y = -8$
$4x + 5y = -6 \rightarrow (+)\ 4x + 5y = -6$
$-7y = -14$
$y = 2$

$-x - 3y = -2$
$-x - 3(2) = -2$
$-x - 6 = -2$
$-x = 4$
$x = -4$

$x + y + z = -1$
$-4 + 2 + z = -1$
$-2 + z = -1$
$z = 1$
$(-4, 2, 1)$

21.
$$\begin{array}{rl} & x + z = 7 \\ (+) & 2y - z = -3 \\ \hline & x + 2y = 4 \end{array}$$

$2y - z = -3 \rightarrow 4y - 2z = -6$
$-x - 3y + 2z = 11 \rightarrow (+)\ -x - 3y + 2z = 11$
$-x + y = 5$

$x + 2y = 4$
$(+)\ -x + y = 5$
$3y = 9$
$y = 3$

$x + 2y = 4$
$x + 2(3) = 4$
$x + 6 = 4$
$x = -2$

$x + z = 7$
$-2 + z = 7$
$z = 9$ $\quad (-2, 3, 9)$

22.
$$\begin{array}{rl} & x - y + z = 0.5 \\ (-) & -x - y + z = 0 \\ \hline & 2x = 0.5 \end{array}$$
$x = 0.25$

$x - y + z = 0.5$
$(-)\ 7x - y + 4z = 4.25$
$-6x - 3z = -3.75$
$-6(0.25) - 3z = -3.75$
$-1.5 - 3z = -3.75$
$-3z = -2.25$
$z = 0.75$

$x - y + z = 0.5$
$0.25 - y + 0.75 = 0.5$
$-y + 1 = 0.5$
$-y = -0.5$
$y = 0.5$ $\quad (0.25, 0.5, 0.75)$

23. Let x = shirt, y = pants, and z = shoes.

$3x + 4y + 2z = 149.79$
$5x + 3y + 3z = 183.19$
$6x + 5y + z = 181.14$

$3x + 4y + 2z = 149.79 \rightarrow \quad 3x + 4y + 2z = 149.79$
$6x + 5y + z = 181.14 \rightarrow (+) -12x - 10y - 2z = -362.28$
$9x - 6y = -212.49$

$5x + 3y + 3z = 183.19 \rightarrow \quad 5x + 3y + 3z = 183.19$
$6x + 5y + z = 181.14 \rightarrow (+) -18x - 15y - 3z = -543.42$
$-13x - 12y = -360.23$

$-9x - 6y = -212.49 \rightarrow \quad 18x + 12y = 424.98$
$-13x - 12y = -360.23 \rightarrow (+) -13x - 12y = -360.23$
$5x = 64.75$
$x = 12.95$

$12.95

24.
$-9x - 6y = -212.49$
$-9(12.95) - 6y = -212.49$
$-116.55 - 6y = -212.49$
$-6y = -95.94$
$y = 15.99$

$15.99

25.
$6x + 5y + z = 181.14$
$6(12.95) + 5(15.99) + z = 181.14$
$77.70 + 79.95 + z = 181.14$
$z = 23.49$

$23.49

Page 915 Chapter 4 Test

1. $\begin{bmatrix} 1 & 2 \\ -4 & 3 \\ 5 & 2 \end{bmatrix} \cdot \begin{bmatrix} 5 \\ 4 \end{bmatrix} = \begin{bmatrix} 1(5) + 2(4) \\ -4(5) + 3(4) \\ 5(5) + 2(4) \end{bmatrix}$

$= \begin{bmatrix} 13 \\ -8 \\ 33 \end{bmatrix}$

2. $\begin{bmatrix} 2 & -4 & 1 \\ 3 & 8 & -2 \end{bmatrix} - 2\begin{bmatrix} 1 & 2 & -4 \\ -2 & 3 & 7 \end{bmatrix} = \begin{bmatrix} 2 & -4 & 1 \\ 3 & 8 & -2 \end{bmatrix} - \begin{bmatrix} 2 & 4 & -8 \\ -4 & 6 & 14 \end{bmatrix}$

$= \begin{bmatrix} 0 & -8 & 9 \\ 7 & 2 & -16 \end{bmatrix}$

3. not possible

4. $-4\begin{bmatrix} -5 & 7 \\ 2 & -6 \end{bmatrix} + 0.5\begin{bmatrix} -2 & 8 \\ 2 & -4 \end{bmatrix} = \begin{bmatrix} 20 & -28 \\ -8 & 24 \end{bmatrix} + \begin{bmatrix} -1 & 4 \\ 1 & -2 \end{bmatrix}$

$= \begin{bmatrix} 19 & -24 \\ -7 & 22 \end{bmatrix}$

5. $\begin{bmatrix} -5 & 7 \\ 2 & -6 \end{bmatrix} \cdot \begin{bmatrix} 2 & -4 & 1 \\ 3 & 8 & -2 \end{bmatrix}$

$= \begin{bmatrix} -5(2) + 7(3) & -5(-4) + 7(8) & -5(1) + 7(-2) \\ 2(2) + (-6)(3) & 2(-4) + (-6)(8) & 2(1) + (-6)(-2) \end{bmatrix}$

$= \begin{bmatrix} 11 & 76 & -19 \\ -14 & -56 & 14 \end{bmatrix}$

6. not possible

7. yes; $\begin{vmatrix} -1 & 4 \\ -6 & 3 \end{vmatrix} = -1(3) - (-6)4$

$= -3 + 24$
$= 21$

8. yes; $\begin{vmatrix} -2 & 0 & 5 \\ -3 & 4 & 0 \\ 1 & 3 & -1 \end{vmatrix}$

$= -2\begin{vmatrix} 4 & 0 \\ 3 & -1 \end{vmatrix} - 0\begin{vmatrix} -3 & 0 \\ 1 & -1 \end{vmatrix} + 5\begin{vmatrix} -3 & 4 \\ 1 & 3 \end{vmatrix}$

$= -2(-4 - 0) - 0(3 - 0) + 5(-9 - 4)$
$= 8 - 0 - 65$
$= -57$

9. no; not square

10. yes; $\begin{vmatrix} 5 & -3 & 2 \\ -6 & 1 & 3 \\ -1 & 4 & -7 \end{vmatrix}$

$= 5\begin{vmatrix} 1 & 3 \\ 4 & -7 \end{vmatrix} + 3\begin{vmatrix} -6 & 3 \\ -1 & -7 \end{vmatrix} + 2\begin{vmatrix} -6 & 1 \\ -1 & 4 \end{vmatrix}$

$= 5(-7 - 12) + 3(42 + 3) + 2(-24 + 1)$
$= -95 + 135 - 46$
$= -6$

11. $M^{-1} = \frac{1}{-2(1) - 3(5)}\begin{bmatrix} 1 & -5 \\ -3 & -2 \end{bmatrix}$

$= \frac{1}{-17}\begin{bmatrix} 1 & -5 \\ -3 & -2 \end{bmatrix}$

12. no inverse; det = 0

13. $M^{-1} = \frac{1}{5(3) - 6(-2)}\begin{bmatrix} 3 & 2 \\ -6 & 5 \end{bmatrix}$

$= \frac{1}{27}\begin{bmatrix} 3 & 2 \\ -6 & 5 \end{bmatrix}$

14. no inverse; not square

15. $5a + 2b = -49$
$2a + 9b = 5$ $\rightarrow \begin{bmatrix} 5 & 2 \\ 2 & 9 \end{bmatrix} \cdot \begin{bmatrix} a \\ b \end{bmatrix} = \begin{bmatrix} -49 \\ 5 \end{bmatrix}$

$M^{-1} = \frac{1}{5(9) - 2(2)}\begin{bmatrix} 9 & -2 \\ -2 & 5 \end{bmatrix}$

$= \frac{1}{41}\begin{bmatrix} 9 & -2 \\ -2 & 5 \end{bmatrix}$

$\frac{1}{41}\begin{bmatrix} 9 & -2 \\ -2 & 5 \end{bmatrix} \cdot \begin{bmatrix} 5 & 2 \\ 2 & 9 \end{bmatrix} \cdot \begin{bmatrix} a \\ b \end{bmatrix} = \frac{1}{41}\begin{bmatrix} 9 & -2 \\ -2 & 5 \end{bmatrix} \cdot \begin{bmatrix} -49 \\ 5 \end{bmatrix}$

$\begin{bmatrix} a \\ b \end{bmatrix} = \frac{1}{41}\begin{bmatrix} 9(-49) + (-2)5 \\ -2(-49) + 5(5) \end{bmatrix}$

$\begin{bmatrix} a \\ b \end{bmatrix} = \frac{1}{41}\begin{bmatrix} -451 \\ 123 \end{bmatrix}$

$\begin{bmatrix} a \\ b \end{bmatrix} = \begin{bmatrix} -11 \\ 3 \end{bmatrix}$; $(-11, 3)$

16. $6x - y = -15$
$5x + 4 = -2y$
$5x = -2y - 4$
$5x + 2y = -4$

$\begin{bmatrix} 6 & -1 \\ 5 & 2 \end{bmatrix} \cdot \begin{bmatrix} x \\ y \end{bmatrix} = \begin{bmatrix} -15 \\ -4 \end{bmatrix}$

$M^{-1} = \frac{1}{6(2) - 5(-1)}\begin{bmatrix} 2 & 1 \\ -5 & 6 \end{bmatrix}$

$= \frac{1}{17}\begin{bmatrix} 2 & 1 \\ -5 & 6 \end{bmatrix}$

$\frac{1}{17} \cdot \begin{bmatrix} 2 & 1 \\ -5 & 6 \end{bmatrix} \cdot \begin{bmatrix} 6 & -1 \\ 5 & 2 \end{bmatrix} \cdot \begin{bmatrix} x \\ y \end{bmatrix} = \frac{1}{17}\begin{bmatrix} 2 & 1 \\ -5 & 6 \end{bmatrix} \cdot \begin{bmatrix} -15 \\ -4 \end{bmatrix}$

$\begin{bmatrix} x \\ y \end{bmatrix} = \frac{1}{17}\begin{bmatrix} 2(-15) + 1(-4) \\ -5(-15) + 6(-4) \end{bmatrix}$

$\begin{bmatrix} x \\ y \end{bmatrix} = \frac{1}{17}\begin{bmatrix} -34 \\ 51 \end{bmatrix}$

$\begin{bmatrix} x \\ y \end{bmatrix} = \begin{bmatrix} -2 \\ 3 \end{bmatrix}$; $(-2, 3)$

17. $\left[\begin{array}{ccc|c} 2 & -1 & 3 & 1 \\ 1 & -1 & 4 & 0 \\ 3 & -2 & 1 & -5 \end{array}\right] = \left[\begin{array}{ccc|c} 1 & 0 & -1 & 1 \\ 1 & -1 & 4 & 0 \\ 3 & -2 & 1 & -5 \end{array}\right] =$

$\left[\begin{array}{ccc|c} 1 & 0 & -1 & 1 \\ 1 & -1 & 4 & 0 \\ 1 & 0 & -7 & -5 \end{array}\right] = \left[\begin{array}{ccc|c} 1 & 0 & -1 & 1 \\ 1 & -1 & 4 & 0 \\ 0 & 0 & -6 & -6 \end{array}\right] =$

$\left[\begin{array}{ccc|c} 1 & 0 & -1 & 1 \\ 1 & -1 & 4 & 0 \\ 0 & 0 & 1 & 1 \end{array}\right] = \left[\begin{array}{ccc|c} 1 & 0 & 0 & 2 \\ 1 & -1 & 4 & 0 \\ 0 & 0 & 1 & 1 \end{array}\right] = \left[\begin{array}{ccc|c} 1 & 0 & 0 & 2 \\ 0 & -1 & 4 & -2 \\ 0 & 0 & 1 & 1 \end{array}\right] =$

$\left[\begin{array}{ccc|c} 1 & 0 & 0 & 2 \\ 0 & -1 & 0 & -6 \\ 0 & 0 & -1 & 1 \end{array}\right] = \left[\begin{array}{ccc|c} 1 & 0 & 0 & 2 \\ 0 & 1 & 0 & 6 \\ 0 & 0 & 1 & 1 \end{array}\right]$; (2, 6, 1)

18. $M^{-1} = \frac{1}{1(-6) - 2(8)}\begin{bmatrix} -6 & -8 \\ -2 & 1 \end{bmatrix}$

$= \frac{1}{-22}\begin{bmatrix} -6 & -8 \\ -2 & 1 \end{bmatrix}$

$\begin{bmatrix} 1 & 8 \\ 2 & -6 \end{bmatrix} \cdot \begin{bmatrix} x \\ y \end{bmatrix} = \begin{bmatrix} -3 \\ -17 \end{bmatrix}$

$-\frac{1}{22} \cdot \begin{bmatrix} -6 & -8 \\ -2 & 1 \end{bmatrix} \cdot \begin{bmatrix} 1 & 8 \\ 2 & -6 \end{bmatrix} \cdot \begin{bmatrix} x \\ y \end{bmatrix} = -\frac{1}{22}\begin{bmatrix} -6 & -8 \\ -2 & 1 \end{bmatrix} \cdot \begin{bmatrix} -3 \\ -17 \end{bmatrix}$

$\begin{bmatrix} x \\ y \end{bmatrix} = -\frac{1}{22}\begin{bmatrix} -6(-3) + (-8)(-17) \\ -2(-3) + 1(-17) \end{bmatrix}$

$\begin{bmatrix} x \\ y \end{bmatrix} = -\frac{1}{22}\begin{bmatrix} 154 \\ -11 \end{bmatrix}$

$\begin{bmatrix} x \\ y \end{bmatrix} = \begin{bmatrix} -7 \\ \frac{1}{2} \end{bmatrix}$; $\left(-7, \frac{1}{2}\right)$

19. $\begin{bmatrix} 2 & 0 & 1 \\ 4 & 1 & 2 \\ 2 & 0 & 4 \end{bmatrix} \cdot \begin{bmatrix} a \\ b \\ c \end{bmatrix} = \begin{bmatrix} 10 \\ 19 \\ 22 \end{bmatrix}$

$\frac{1}{6}\begin{bmatrix} 4 & 0 & -1 \\ -12 & 6 & 0 \\ -2 & 0 & 2 \end{bmatrix} \cdot \begin{bmatrix} 2 & 0 & 1 \\ 4 & 1 & 2 \\ 2 & 0 & 4 \end{bmatrix} \cdot \begin{bmatrix} a \\ b \\ c \end{bmatrix} = \frac{1}{6}\begin{bmatrix} 4 & 0 & -1 \\ -12 & 6 & 0 \\ -2 & 0 & 2 \end{bmatrix} \cdot \begin{bmatrix} 10 \\ 19 \\ 22 \end{bmatrix}$

$\begin{bmatrix} a \\ b \\ c \end{bmatrix} = \frac{1}{6}\begin{bmatrix} 4(10) + 0(19) + (-1)(22) \\ -12(10) + 6(19) + 0(22) \\ -2(10) + 0(19) + 2(22) \end{bmatrix}$

$\begin{bmatrix} a \\ b \\ c \end{bmatrix} = \frac{1}{6}\begin{bmatrix} 18 \\ -6 \\ 24 \end{bmatrix}$

$\begin{bmatrix} a \\ b \\ c \end{bmatrix} = \begin{bmatrix} 3 \\ -1 \\ 4 \end{bmatrix}$ (3, −1, 4)

20. $490 - 10 = 480$; Q_2 is between 16th and 17th terms, $\frac{250 + 280}{2} = 265$; Q_1 is between 8th and 9th terms, $\frac{150 + 170}{2} = 160$; Q_3 is between 24th and 25th terms, $\frac{330 + 360}{2} = 345$; IR $= 345 - 160 = 185$; outliers: below $160 - 1.5(185) = -117.5$ or above $345 + 1.5(185) = 622.5$, no outliers

21. 19, 93, 94, 94, 95, 96, 98, 99, 100, 100, 101, 104, 104, 106, 108, 109, 125
$125 - 19 = 106$; Q_2 is 9th term $= 100$; Q_1 is between 4th and 5th terms, $\frac{94 + 95}{2} = 94.5$; Q_3 is between 13th and 14th terms, $\frac{104 + 106}{2} = 105$; IR $= 105 - 94.5 = 10.5$; outliers: below $94.5 - 1.5(10.5) = 78.75$ or above $105 + 1.5(10.5) = 120.75$, 19 and 125

22. 40, 50, 60, 70, 75, 79, 80, 80, 85, 90, 90, 100, 120, 120, 125, 148, 149, 150, 160, 190, 400
Q_2 is 11th term $= 90$; Q_1 is between 5th and 6th terms, $\frac{75 + 79}{2} = 77$; Q_3 is between 16th and 17th terms, $\frac{148 + 149}{2} = 148.5$; IR $= 148.5 - 77 = 71.5$; outliers: below $77 - 1.5(71.5) = -30.25$ or above $148.5 + 1.5(71.5) = 255.75$, 400

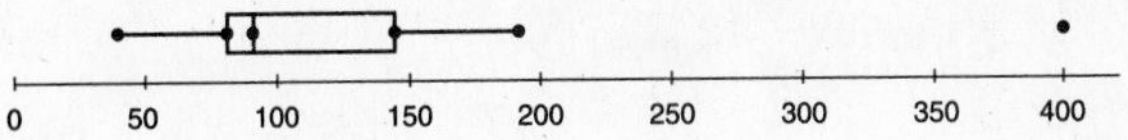

23. $A = \frac{1}{2}\begin{vmatrix} 6 & 3 & 1 \\ 1 & 5 & 1 \\ -1 & 4 & 1 \end{vmatrix}$

$= \frac{1}{2}[6 \cdot 5 \cdot 1 + 3 \cdot 1(-1) + 1 \cdot 1 \cdot 4 - (-1)5 \cdot 1 - 4 \cdot 1 \cdot 6 - 1 \cdot 1 \cdot 3]$

$= \frac{1}{2}[30 - 3 + 4 + 5 - 24 - 3]$

$= \frac{1}{2}[9]$

$= 4\frac{1}{2}$; $4\frac{1}{2}$ square units

24. translation of x−coordinate: $1 + x = 3$
$x = 2$
translation of y−coordinate: $5 + y = 1$
$y = -4$

$\begin{bmatrix} 6 & 1 & -1 \\ 3 & 5 & 4 \end{bmatrix} + \begin{bmatrix} 2 & 2 & 2 \\ -4 & -4 & -4 \end{bmatrix} = \begin{bmatrix} 8 & 3 & 1 \\ -1 & 1 & 0 \end{bmatrix}$

$A^1 = (8, -1)$, $C^1 = (1, 0)$

25. Sample answer:
$5\begin{bmatrix} 6 & 1 & -1 \\ 3 & 5 & 4 \end{bmatrix} = \begin{bmatrix} 30 & 5 & -5 \\ 15 & 25 & 20 \end{bmatrix}$

$A^1 = (30, 15)$, $B^1 = (5, 25)$, $C^1 = (-5, 20)$

Page 916 Chapter 5 Test

1. $(5b)^4(6c)^2 = 5^4 \cdot b^4 \cdot 6^2 \cdot c^2$
$= 625 \cdot b^4 \cdot 36 \cdot c^2$
$= 22{,}500b^4c^2$

2. $(13x - 1)(x + 3) = 13x(x) + 13x(3) - 1(x) - 1(3)$
$= 13x^2 + 39x - x - 3$
$= 13x^2 + 38x - 3$

3. $(2h - 6)^3 = (2h - 6)(2h - 6)(2h - 6)$
$= (2h - 6)[2h \cdot 2h + 2h(-6) - 6 \cdot 2h - 6(-6)]$
$= (2h - 6)(4h^2 - 12h - 12h + 36)$
$= (2h - 6)(4h^2 - 24h + 36)$
$= 2h(4h^2 - 24h + 36) - 6(4h^2 - 24h + 36)$
$= 2h \cdot 4h^2 + 2h(-24h) + 2h \cdot 36 - 6 \cdot 4h^2 - 6(-24h) - 6 \cdot 36$
$= 8h^3 - 48h^2 + 72h - 24h^2 + 144h - 216$
$= 8h^3 - 72h^2 + 216h - 216$

4. $(3.16 \times 10^3)(24 \times 10^2) = (3.16 \times 24)(10^3 \times 10^2)$
$= 75.84 \times 10^5$
$= 7.584 \times 10^1 \times 10^5$
$= 7.584 \times 10^6$
$= 7{,}584{,}000$

5. $\frac{7{,}200{,}000 \cdot 0.0011}{0.018} = \frac{(7.2 \times 10^6)(1.1 \times 10^{-3})}{(1.8 \times 10^{-2})}$
$= \frac{(7.2 \times 1.1)(10^6 \times 10^{-3})}{(1.8 \times 10^{-2})}$
$= \frac{7.92 \times 10^3}{1.8 \times 10^{-2}}$
$= 4.4 \times 10^5$
$= 440{,}000$

6. 2⌋	1	−1	−10	4	24
		2	2	−16	−24
	1	1	−8	−12	0

$x^3 + x^2 - 8x - 12$

7. | −2⌋ | 2 | 9 | −2 | 7 |
|---|---|---|---|---|
| | | −4 | −10 | 24 |
| | 2 | 5 | −12 | 31 |

$2x^2 + 5x - 12 + \frac{31}{x+2}$

8. $x^2 - 14x + 45 = (x - 5)(x - 9)$

9. $2r^2 + 3pr - 2p^2 = (2r - p)(r + 2p)$

10. $x^2 + 2\sqrt{3}x + 3 = (x + \sqrt{3})(x + \sqrt{3})$ or $(x + \sqrt{3})^2$

11. $\sqrt{175} = \sqrt{5^2 \cdot 7}$
$= 5\sqrt{7}$

12. $(5 + \sqrt{3})(7 - 2\sqrt{3}) = 35 - 10\sqrt{3} + 7\sqrt{3} - 6$
$= 29 - 3\sqrt{3}$

13. $3\sqrt{6} + 5\sqrt{54} = 3\sqrt{6} + 5\sqrt{3^2 \cdot 6}$
$= 3\sqrt{6} + 15\sqrt{6}$
$= 18\sqrt{6}$

14. $\frac{9}{5 - \sqrt{3}} = \frac{9(5 + \sqrt{3})}{(5 - \sqrt{3})(5 + \sqrt{3})}$
$= \frac{45 + 9\sqrt{3}}{25 + 5\sqrt{3} - 5\sqrt{3} - 3}$
$= \frac{45 + 9\sqrt{3}}{22}$

15. $\left(9^{\frac{1}{2}} \cdot 9^{\frac{2}{3}}\right)^{\frac{1}{6}} = \left(9^{\frac{1}{2} + \frac{2}{3}}\right)^{\frac{1}{6}}$
$= \left(9^{\frac{7}{6}}\right)^{\frac{1}{6}}$
$= 9^{\frac{7}{36}}$

16. $11^{\frac{1}{2}} \cdot 11^{\frac{7}{3}} \cdot 11^{\frac{1}{6}} = 11^{\frac{1}{2} + \frac{7}{3} + \frac{1}{6}}$
$= 11^3$
$= 1331$

17. $\sqrt[6]{256s^{11}t^{18}} = \sqrt[6]{2^6 \cdot 4 \cdot s^6 \cdot s^5(t^3)^6}$
$= 2st^3\sqrt[6]{4s^5}$

18. $v^{-\frac{7}{11}} = \frac{1}{v^{\frac{7}{11}}}$

$=$

$= \frac{v^{\frac{4}{11}}}{v}$

19. $\frac{b^{\frac{1}{2}}}{b^{\frac{3}{2}} - b^{\frac{1}{2}}} = \frac{b^{\frac{1}{2}}}{(b^{\frac{3}{2}} - b^{\frac{1}{2}})} \cdot \frac{(b^{\frac{3}{2}} + b^{\frac{1}{2}})}{(b^{\frac{3}{2}} + b^{\frac{1}{2}})}$
$= \frac{b^2 + b}{b^3 + b^2 - b^2 - b}$
$= \frac{b^2 + b}{b^3 - b}$
$= \frac{b(b + 1)}{b(b^2 - 1)}$
$= \frac{b + 1}{(b - 1)(b + 1)}$
$= \frac{1}{b - 1}$

20. $\sqrt{b + 15} = \sqrt{3b + 1}$
$b + 15 = 3b + 1$
$15 = 2b + 1$
$14 = 2b$
$7 = b$
Check: $\sqrt{b + 15} = \sqrt{3b + 1}$
$\sqrt{7 + 15} \stackrel{?}{=} \sqrt{3(7) + 1}$
$\sqrt{22} = \sqrt{22}$ ✓

21. $\sqrt{2x} = x - 4$
$2x = (x - 4)^2$
$2x = x^2 - 8x + 16$
$0 = x^2 - 10x + 16$
$0 = (x - 2)(x - 8)$
$x - 2 = 0$ or $x - 8 = 0$
$x = 2$ $x = 8$
Check: $\sqrt{2x} = x - 4$
$\sqrt{2 \cdot 2} \stackrel{?}{=} 2 - 4$
$2 \neq -2$; false
$\sqrt{2x} = x - 4$
$\sqrt{2 \cdot 8} \stackrel{?}{=} 8 - 4$
$4 = 4$ ✓

22. $\sqrt[4]{y + 2} + 9 = 14$
$\sqrt[4]{y + 2} = 5$
$y + 2 = 5^4$
$y + 2 = 625$
$y = 623$
Check: $\sqrt[4]{y + 2} + 9 = 14$
$\sqrt[4]{623 + 2} + 9 \stackrel{?}{=} 14$
$\sqrt[4]{625} + 9 \stackrel{?}{=} 14$
$5 + 9 \stackrel{?}{=} 14$
$14 = 14$ ✓

23. $\sqrt[3]{2w - 1} + 11 = 18$
$\sqrt[3]{2w - 1} = 7$
$2w - 1 = 7^3$
$2w - 1 = 343$
$2w = 344$
$w = 172$
Check: $\sqrt[3]{2w - 1} + 11 = 18$
$\sqrt[3]{2(172) - 1} + 11 \stackrel{?}{=} 18$
$\sqrt[3]{343} + 11 \stackrel{?}{=} 18$
$7 + 11 \stackrel{?}{=} 18$
$18 = 18$ ✓

24. $\sqrt{4x+28} = \sqrt{6x+38}$
$4x + 28 = 6x + 38$
$28 = 2x + 38$
$-10 = 2x$
$-5 = x$
Check: $\sqrt{4x+28} = \sqrt{6x+38}$
$\sqrt{4(-5)+28} \stackrel{?}{=} \sqrt{6(-5)+38}$
$\sqrt{8} = \sqrt{8}$ ✓

25. $1 + \sqrt{x+5} = \sqrt{2x+5}$
$(1 + \sqrt{x+5})^2 = 2x + 5$
$1 + \sqrt{x+5} + \sqrt{x+5} + x + 5 = 2x + 5$
$2\sqrt{x+5} + x + 6 = 2x + 5$
$2\sqrt{x+5} + 6 = x + 5$
$2\sqrt{x+5} = x - 1$
$\sqrt{x+5} = \frac{x}{2} - \frac{1}{2}$
$x + 5 = \left(\frac{x}{2} - \frac{1}{2}\right)^2$
$x + 5 = \frac{x^2}{4} - \frac{x}{4} - \frac{x}{4} + \frac{1}{4}$
$x + 5 = \frac{x^2}{4} - \frac{x}{2} + \frac{1}{4}$
$4x + 20 = x^2 - 2x + 1$
$20 = x^2 - 6x + 1$
$0 = x^2 - 6x - 19$

$x = \frac{6 \pm \sqrt{(-6)^2 - 4(1)(-19)}}{2(1)}$
$= \frac{6 \pm \sqrt{36 + 76}}{2}$
$= \frac{6 \pm \sqrt{112}}{2}$
$= \frac{6 \pm 4\sqrt{7}}{2}$
$= 3 \pm 2\sqrt{7}$

Check: $1 + \sqrt{x+5} = \sqrt{2x+5}$
$1 + \sqrt{3 + 2\sqrt{7} + 5} \stackrel{?}{=} \sqrt{2(3 + 2\sqrt{7}) + 5}$
$1 + \sqrt{8 + 2\sqrt{7}} \stackrel{?}{=} \sqrt{6 + 4\sqrt{7} + 5}$
$1 + \sqrt{8 + 2\sqrt{7}} \stackrel{?}{=} \sqrt{11 + 4\sqrt{7}}$
$4.645751311 = 4.645751311$ ✓
$1 + \sqrt{x+5} = \sqrt{2x+5}$
$1 + \sqrt{3 - 2\sqrt{7} + 5} \stackrel{?}{=} \sqrt{2(3 - 2\sqrt{7}) + 5}$
$1 + \sqrt{8 - 2\sqrt{7}} \stackrel{?}{=} \sqrt{6 - 4\sqrt{7} + 5}$
$1 + \sqrt{8 - 2\sqrt{7}} \stackrel{?}{=} \sqrt{11 - 4\sqrt{7}}$
$2.645751311 \neq 0.6457513111$

26. $(5 - 2\boldsymbol{i}) - (8 - 11\boldsymbol{i}) = (5 - 2\boldsymbol{i}) + (-8 + 11\boldsymbol{i})$
$= (5 - 8) + (-2\boldsymbol{i} + 11\boldsymbol{i})$
$= -3 + 9\boldsymbol{i}$

27. $(4 + 3\boldsymbol{i})(9 - 2\boldsymbol{i}) = 36 - 8\boldsymbol{i} + 27\boldsymbol{i} - 6\boldsymbol{i}^2$
$= 36 + 19\boldsymbol{i} + 6$
$= 42 + 19\boldsymbol{i}$

28. $(14 - 5\boldsymbol{i})^2 = (14 - 5\boldsymbol{i})(14 - 5\boldsymbol{i})$
$= 196 - 70\boldsymbol{i} - 70\boldsymbol{i} + 25\boldsymbol{i}^2$
$= 196 - 140\boldsymbol{i} - 25$
$= 171 - 140\boldsymbol{i}$

29. $t = \sqrt{\frac{d}{16}}$
$11 = \sqrt{\frac{d}{16}}$
$121 = \frac{d}{16}$
$1936 = d$; 1936 feet

30. $c^2 = a^2 + b^2$
$c^2 = 120^2 + 60^2$
$c^2 = 14{,}400 + 3600$
$c^2 = 18{,}000$
$c = \sqrt{18{,}000}$
$c = 60\sqrt{5}$; $60\sqrt{5}$ yards

31. $E = I \cdot Z$
$= (6 + 4\boldsymbol{j})(3 - \boldsymbol{j})$
$= 18 - 6\boldsymbol{j} + 12\boldsymbol{j} - 4\boldsymbol{j}^2$
$= 18 + 6\boldsymbol{j} + 4$
$= 22 + 6\boldsymbol{j}$

32. $s = \frac{1}{2}(a + b + c)$
$= \frac{1}{2}(6 + 9 + 12)$
$= \frac{1}{2}(27)$
$= 13.5$
$A = \sqrt{s(s - a)(s - b)(s - c)}$
$= \sqrt{13.5(13.5 - 6)(13.5 - 9)(13.5 - 12)}$
$= \sqrt{13.5(7.5)(4.5)(1.5)}$
$= \sqrt{683.4375}$
≈ 26.14; 26.14 square feet

33. $4^{\frac{1}{4}} f^{\frac{3}{5}} g^{\frac{5}{8}} = 4^{\frac{10}{40}} f^{\frac{24}{40}} g^{\frac{25}{40}}$
$= \sqrt[40]{4^{10} f^{24} g^{25}}$

Page 917 Chapter 6 Test

1. $y = x^2 + 3x - 40$

x	y
−8	0
−5	−30
−2	−42
1	−36
4	−12

−8, 5

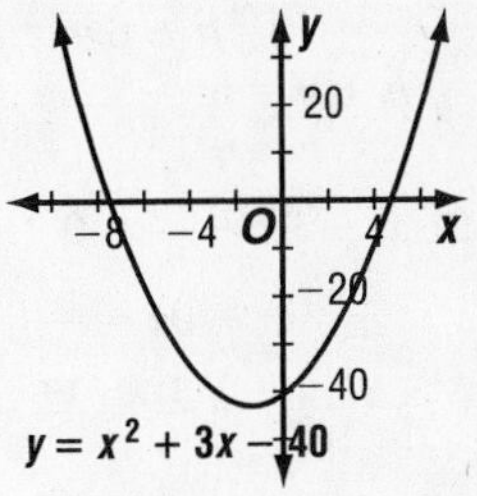

2. $y = 4x^2 - 11x - 3$

x	y
−1	12
0	−3
1	−10
2	−9
3	0

$-\frac{1}{4}$, 3

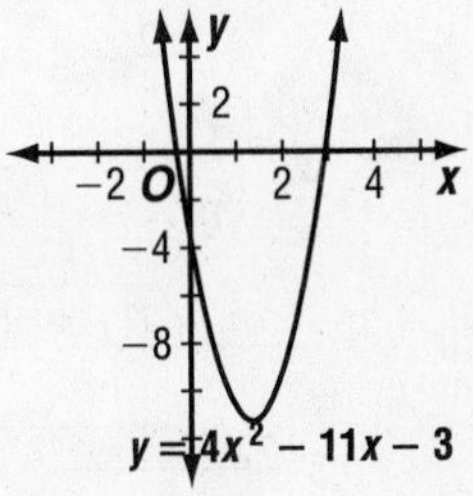

3. $y = 6x^2 - 216$

x	y
-6	0
-3	-162
0	-216
3	-162
6	0

6, -6

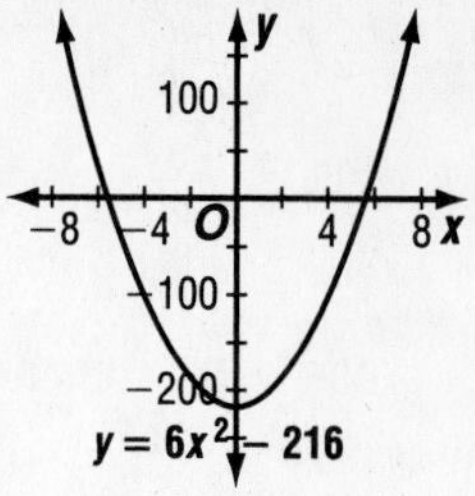

4. $-1.6x^2 - 3.2x + 18 = 0$
$8x^2 + 16x - 90 = 0$
$4x^2 + 8x - 45 = 0$
$(2x + 9)(2x - 5) = 0$
$2x + 9 = 0$ or $2x - 5 = 0$
$2x = -9$ $\quad$ $2x = 5$
$x = -\frac{9}{2}$ $\quad$ $x = \frac{5}{2}$

5. $c^2 + c - 42 = 0$
$(c + 7)(c - 6) = 0$
$c + 7 = 0$ or $c - 6 = 0$
$c = -7$ $\quad$ $c = 6$

6. $15x^2 + 16x - 7 = 0$
$(5x + 7)(3x - 1) = 0$
$5x + 7 = 0$ or $3x - 1 = 0$
$5x = -7$ $\quad$ $3x = 1$
$x = -\frac{7}{5}$ $\quad$ $x = \frac{1}{3}$

7. $b^2 + 8b - 48 = 0$
$b^2 + 8b = 48$
$b^2 + 8b + 16 = 48 + 16$
$(b + 4)^2 = 64$
$b + 4 = \pm 8$
$b + 4 = 8$ or $b + 4 = -8$
$b = 4$ $\quad$ $b = -12$

8. $h^2 + 12h + 11 = 0$
$h^2 + 12h = -11$
$h^2 + 12h + 36 = -11 + 36$
$(h + 6)^2 = 25$
$h + 6 = \pm 5$
$h + 6 = 5$ or $h + 6 = -5$
$h = -1$ $\quad$ $h = -11$

9. $x^2 - 9x - \frac{19}{4} = 0$
$x^2 - 9x = \frac{19}{4}$
$x^2 - 9x + \frac{81}{4} = \frac{19}{4} + \frac{81}{4}$
$\left(x - \frac{9}{2}\right)^2 = 25$
$x - \frac{9}{2} = \pm 5$
$x - \frac{9}{2} = 5$ or $x - \frac{9}{2} = -5$
$x = \frac{19}{2}$ $\quad$ $x = -\frac{1}{2}$

10. $x = \frac{-7 \pm \sqrt{7^2 - 4(3)(-31)}}{2 \cdot 3}$
$= \frac{-7 \pm \sqrt{49 + 372}}{6}$
$= \frac{-7 \pm \sqrt{421}}{6}$

11. $10v^2 + 3v = 1$
$10v^2 + 3v - 1 = 0$
$v = \frac{-3 \pm \sqrt{3^2 - 4(10)(-1)}}{2 \cdot 10}$
$= \frac{-3 \pm \sqrt{9 + 40}}{20}$
$= \frac{-3 \pm 7}{20}$
$v = \frac{-3 + 7}{20}$ or $v = \frac{-3 - 7}{20}$
$= \frac{1}{5}$ $\quad$ $= -\frac{1}{2}$

12. $x = \frac{174 \pm \sqrt{(-174)^2 - 4(-11)(221)}}{2(-11)}$
$= \frac{174 \pm \sqrt{30{,}276 + 9724}}{-22}$
$= \frac{174 \pm 200}{-22}$
$x = \frac{174 + 200}{-22}$ or $x = \frac{174 - 200}{-22}$
$= -17$ $\quad$ $= \frac{13}{11}$

13. $-\frac{b}{a} = -\frac{8}{2}$ $\quad$ $\frac{c}{a} = -\frac{3}{2}$
$= -4$

14. $5x^2 = 6$
$5x^2 - 6 = 0$
$-\frac{b}{a} = -\frac{0}{5}$
$= 0$
$\frac{c}{a} = -\frac{6}{5}$

15. $-\frac{b}{a} = -\frac{3}{4}$ $\quad$ $\frac{c}{a} = -\frac{12}{4}$
$= -3$

16. $s_1 + s_2 = -2 + 5$ $\quad$ $-\frac{b}{a} = 3, \frac{c}{a} = -10$
$= 3$ $\quad$ $a = 1, b = -3, c = -10$
$s_1(s_2) = -2 \cdot 5$ $\quad$ $x^2 - 3x - 10 = 0$
$= -10$

17. $s_1 + s_2 = -\frac{8}{3} + \frac{7}{3}$ $\quad$ $-\frac{b}{a} = -\frac{3}{9}, \frac{c}{a} = -\frac{56}{9}$
$= -\frac{1}{3}$ or $-\frac{3}{9}$ $\quad$ $a = 9, b = 3, c = -56$
$s_1(s_2) = -\frac{8}{3} \cdot \frac{7}{3}$ $\quad$ $9x^2 + 3x - 56 = 0$
$= -\frac{56}{9}$

18. $s_1 + s_2 = 3 + 4i + 3 - 4i$ $\quad$ $-\frac{b}{a} = 6, \frac{c}{a} = 25$
$= 6$ $\quad$ $a = 1, b = -6, c = 25$
$s_1(s_2) = (3 + 4i)(3 - 4i)$ $\quad$ $x^2 - 6x + 25 = 0$
$= 9 - 12i + 12i - 16i^2$
$= 25$

19. $y = (x + 2)^2 - 3$

x	y
-4	1
-2	-3
0	1

$(-2, -3)$; $x = -2$; up

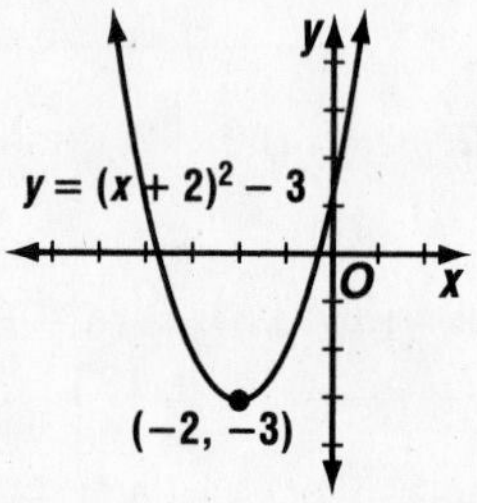

20. $f(x) = x^2 + 10x + 27$
$= (x^2 + 10x + 25) + 27 - 25$
$= (x + 5)^2 + 2$

x	$f(x)$
−7	6
−5	2
−3	6

(−5, 2); $x = -5$; up

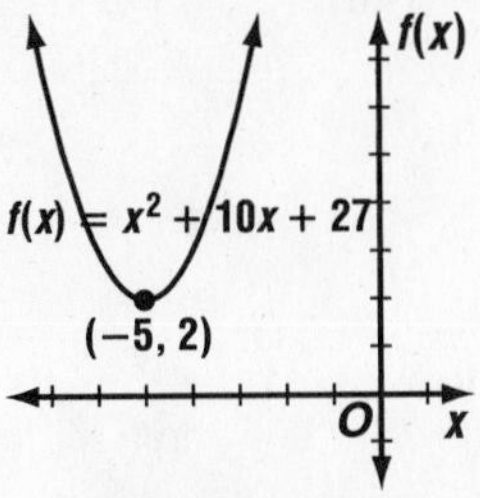

21. $y = (x - 5)^2 - 6$

x	y
2	3
5	−6
8	3

(5, −6); $x = 5$; up

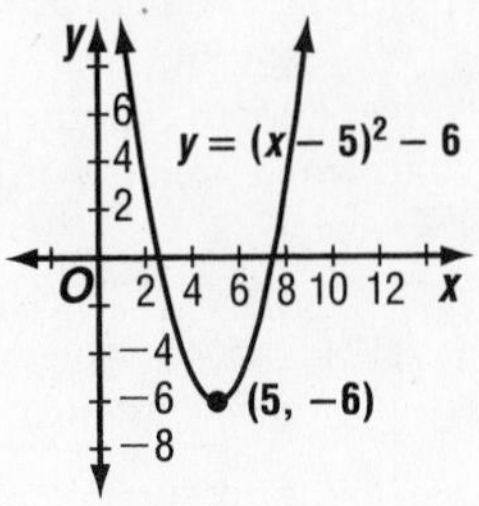

22. $y \le x^2 + 6x - 7$
$y \le (x^2 + 6x + 9) - 7 - 9$
$y \le (x + 3)^2 - 16$

x	y
−7	0
−3	−16
1	0

Test: (0, −12)
$y \le x^2 + 6x - 7$
$-12 \overset{?}{\le} 0^2 + 6 \cdot 0 - 7$
$-12 \le -7$; true

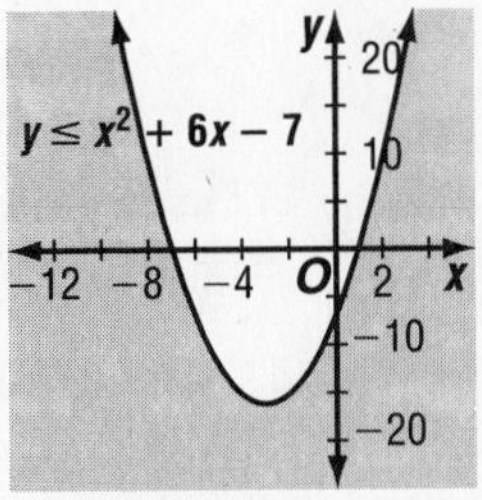

23. $y > -2x^2 + 9$
$y > -2(x + 0)^2 + 9$

x	y
−2	1
0	9
2	1

Test: (0, 10)
$y > -2x^2 + 9$
$10 \overset{?}{>} -2(0)^2 + 9$
$10 > 9$; true

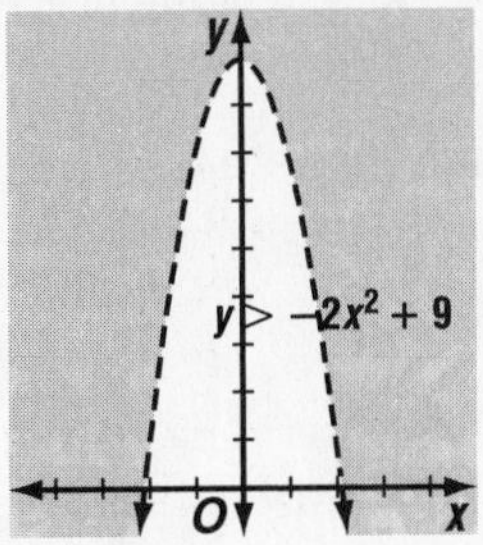

24. $y \ge 3x^2 - 15x + 22$
$y \ge 3(x^2 - 5x) + 22$
$y \ge 3\left(x^2 - 5x + \frac{25}{4}\right) + 22 - 3\left(\frac{25}{4}\right)$
$y \ge 3\left(x - \frac{5}{2}\right)^2 + \frac{13}{4}$

x	y
1	10
$\frac{5}{2}$	$\frac{13}{4}$
4	10

Test: (2, 7)
$y \ge 3x^2 - 15x + 22$
$7 \overset{?}{\ge} 3(2)^2 - 15(2) + 22$
$7 \ge 4$; true

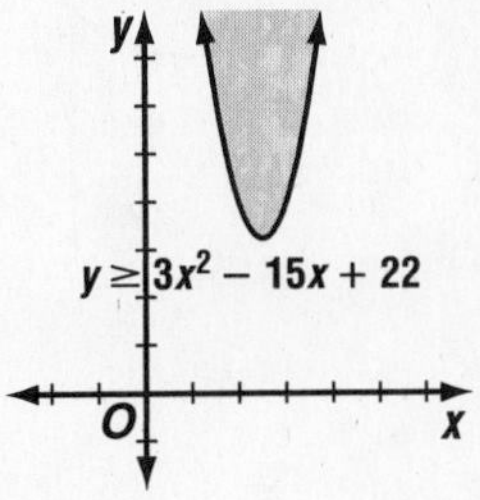

25. $(x - 5)(x + 7) > 0$
$x - 5 > 0$ and $x + 7 > 0$ or $x - 5 < 0$ and $x + 7 < 0$
$x > 5$ $\quad x > -7$ $\quad x < 5$ $\quad x < -7$
$x > 5$ or $x < -7$
$\{x \mid x < -7 \text{ or } x > 5\}$

26. $x^2 - 11x \le 0$
$x(x - 11) \le 0$
$x \le 0$ and $x - 11 \ge 0$ or $x \ge 0$ and $x - 11 \le 0$
$x \ge 11$ $\quad x \le 11$
$\varnothing$ $\quad \{x \mid 0 \le x \le 11\}$

27. $3d^2 \ge 16$
$3d^2 - 16 \ge 0$
$(\sqrt{3}d - 4)(\sqrt{3}d + 4) \ge 0$
$\sqrt{3}d - 4 \ge 0$ and $\sqrt{3}d + 4 \ge 0$
$\sqrt{3}d \ge 4$ $\quad \sqrt{3}d \ge -4$
$d \ge \frac{4}{\sqrt{3}}$ $\quad d \ge -\frac{4}{\sqrt{3}}$
or $\sqrt{3}d - 4 \le 0$ and $\sqrt{3}d + 4 \le 0$
$\sqrt{3}d \le 4$ $\quad \sqrt{3}d \le -4$
$d \le \frac{4}{\sqrt{3}}$ $\quad d \le -\frac{4}{\sqrt{3}}$
$d \ge \frac{4}{\sqrt{3}}$ or $d \le -\frac{4}{\sqrt{3}}$
$d \ge \frac{4\sqrt{3}}{3}$ $\quad d \le -\frac{4\sqrt{3}}{3}$
$\left\{d \mid d \le -\frac{4\sqrt{3}}{3} \text{ or } d \ge \frac{4\sqrt{3}}{3}\right\}$

28a. $\bar{x} = (0 + 0 + 0 + 1 + 1 + 1 + 1 + 1 + 1 + 2 + 2 + 2 + 2 + 2 + 2 + 2 + 2 + 2 + 2 + 3 + 3 + 3 + 4 + 5 + 6) \div 25 = 50 \div 25 = 2$

28b. $SD = \sqrt{\dfrac{\left[\begin{array}{l}3(0-2)^2 + 6(1-2)^2 + 10(2-2)^2 + \\ 3(3-2)^2 + (4-2)^2 + (5-2)^2 + (6-2)^2\end{array}\right]}{25}}$
$= \sqrt{\dfrac{12 + 6 + 0 + 3 + 4 + 9 + 16}{25}}$
$= \sqrt{2}$
$= 1.41$

28c.

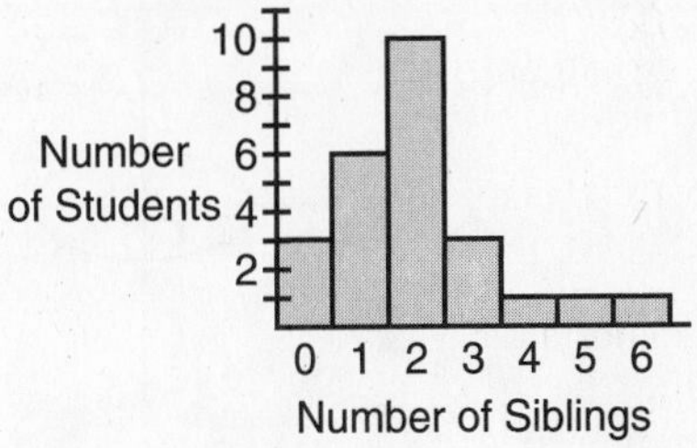

29. $525 - 75 = 450$ $\quad 525 + 75 = 600$
$525 - 2(75) = 375$ $\quad 525 + 2(75) = 675$
$525 - 3(75) = 300$ $\quad 525 + 3(75) = 750$

29a. $13.5 + 2 + 0.5 = 16$, 16%; $65{,}000 \times 0.16 = 10{,}400$

29b. $65{,}000 \times 0.5\% = 325$

29c. $13.5 + 34 + 34 + 13.5 + 2 + 0.5 = 97.5$; 97.5%

Page 918 Chapter 7 Test

1. $d = \sqrt{(x_2 - x_1)^2 + (y_2 - y_1)^2}$
$= \sqrt{(-6 - 3)^2 + (7 - 2)^2}$
$= \sqrt{(-9)^2 + (5)^2}$
$= \sqrt{81 + 25}$
$= \sqrt{106}$

2. $d = \sqrt{(x_2 - x_1)^2 + (y_2 - y_1)^2}$

$= \sqrt{\left(-\frac{3}{4} - \frac{1}{2}\right)^2 + \left(-\frac{11}{4} - \frac{5}{2}\right)^2}$

$= \sqrt{\left(-\frac{5}{4}\right)^2 + \left(-\frac{21}{4}\right)^2}$

$= \sqrt{\frac{466}{16}}$

$= \frac{\sqrt{466}}{4}$

3. $d = \sqrt{(x_2 - x_1)^2 + (y_2 - y_1)^2}$

$= \sqrt{(8 - 8)^2 + [-9 - (-1)]^2}$

$= \sqrt{0^2 + (-8)^2}$

$= \sqrt{64}$

$= 8$

4. $\left(\frac{x_1 + x_2}{2}, \frac{y_1 + y_2}{2}\right) = \left(\frac{7 + (-5)}{2}, \frac{1 + 9}{2}\right)$

$= \left(\frac{2}{2}, \frac{10}{2}\right)$

$= (1, 5)$

5. $\left(\frac{x_1 + x_2}{2}, \frac{y_1 + y_2}{2}\right) = \left(\frac{\frac{3}{8} + \left(-\frac{8}{5}\right)}{2}, \frac{-1 + 2}{2}\right)$

$= \left(\frac{-\frac{49}{40}}{2}, \frac{1}{2}\right)$

$= \left(-\frac{49}{80}, \frac{1}{2}\right)$

6. $\left(\frac{x_1 + x_2}{2}, \frac{y_1 + y_2}{2}\right) = \left(\frac{-13 + (-1)}{2}, \frac{0 + (-8)}{2}\right)$

$= \left(-\frac{14}{2}, -\frac{8}{2}\right)$

$= (-7, -4)$

7. $x^2 + 4y^2 = 25$

$\frac{x^2}{25} + \frac{y^2}{\frac{25}{4}} = 1$; ellipse

center: $(0, 0)$

$a = 5$, $b = \frac{5}{2}$

length of major axis: $2(5)$ or 10

length of minor axis: $2\left(\frac{5}{2}\right)$ or 5

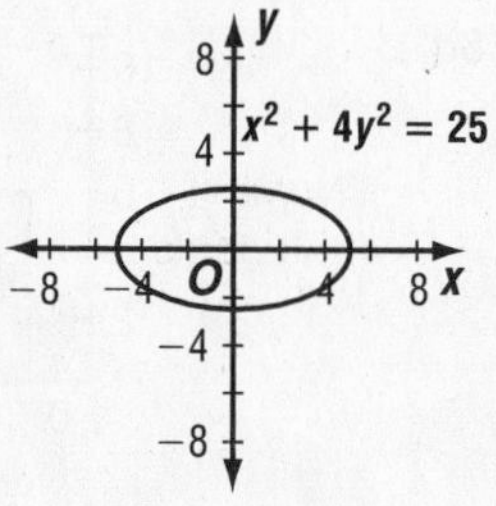

8. $y = 4x^2 + 1$; parabola

vertex: $(0, 1)$

direction of opening: upward, since $a > 0$

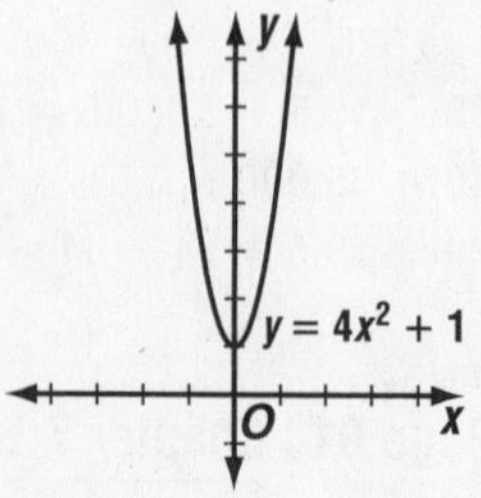

9. $x^2 = 36 - y^2$

$x^2 + y^2 = 36$; circle

center: $(0, 0)$

radius: $\sqrt{36}$ or 6 units

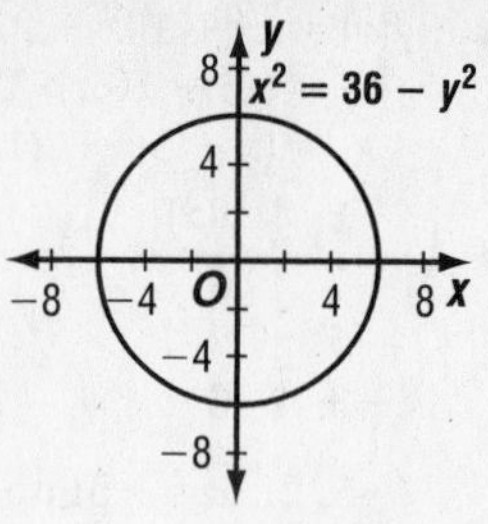

10. $(x + 4)^2 = 7(y + 5)$

$\frac{1}{7}(x + 4)^2 = y + 5$

$\frac{1}{7}(x + 4)^2 - 5 = y$; parabola

vertex: $(-4, -5)$

direction of opening: upward, since $a > 0$

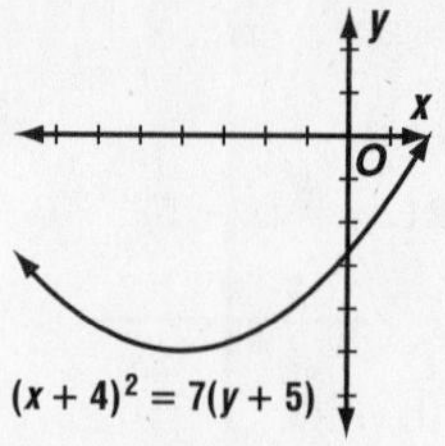

11. $4x^2 - 26y^2 + 10 = 0$

$4x^2 - 26y^2 = -10$

$\frac{4x^2}{-10} - \frac{26y^2}{-10} = 1$

$\frac{y^2}{\frac{5}{13}} - \frac{x^2}{\frac{5}{2}} = 1$; hyperbola

center: $(0, 0)$

$a = \sqrt{\frac{5}{13}}$, $b = \sqrt{\frac{5}{2}}$

slopes of asymptotes: $\pm\sqrt{\frac{2}{13}}$

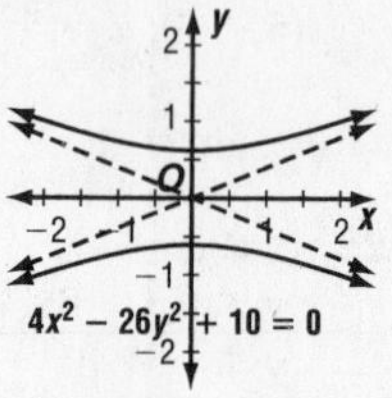

12. $25x^2 + 49y^2 = 1225$

$\frac{x^2}{49} + \frac{y^2}{25} = 1$; ellipse

center: $(0, 0)$

$a = 7$, $b = 5$

length of major axis: $2(7)$ or 14

length of minor axis: $2(5)$ or 10

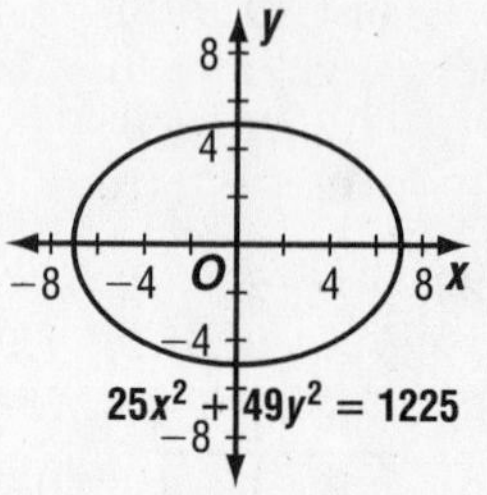

13. $-(y^2 - 24) = x^2 + 10x$

$-y^2 + 24 = x^2 + 10x$

$24 + 25 = x^2 + 10x + 25 + y^2$

$49 = (x + 5)^2 + y^2$; circle

center: $(-5, 0)$

radius: $\sqrt{49}$ or 7 units

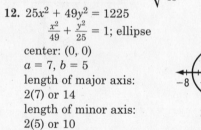

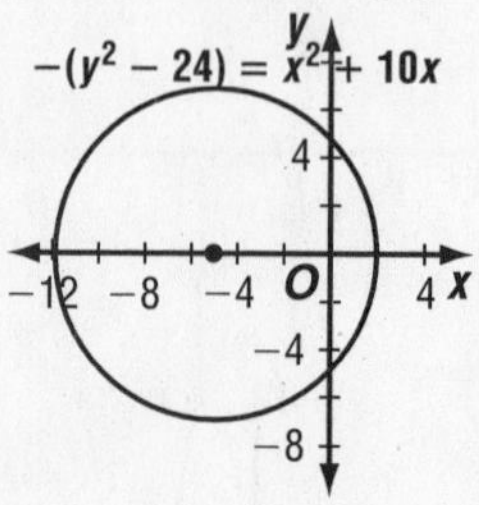

14. $5x^2 - y^2 = 49$

$\frac{5x^2}{49} - \frac{y^2}{49} = 1$

$\frac{x^2}{\frac{49}{5}} - \frac{y^2}{49} = 1$; hyperbola

center: (0, 0)

$a = \sqrt{\frac{49}{5}}$, $b = \sqrt{49}$ or 7

slopes of asymptotes: $\pm\frac{7}{\frac{7\sqrt{5}}{5}}$ or $\pm\sqrt{5}$

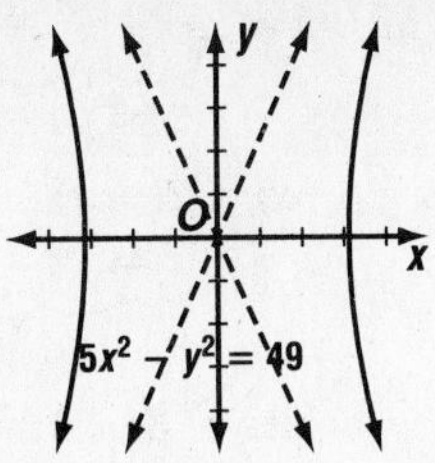

15. $25(x-1)^2 + 121(y+6)^2 = 3025$

$\frac{(x-1)^2}{121} + \frac{(y+6)^2}{25} = 1$; ellipse

center: (1, −6)

$a = 11$, $b = 5$

length of major axis: 2(11) or 22

length of minor axis: 2(5) or 10

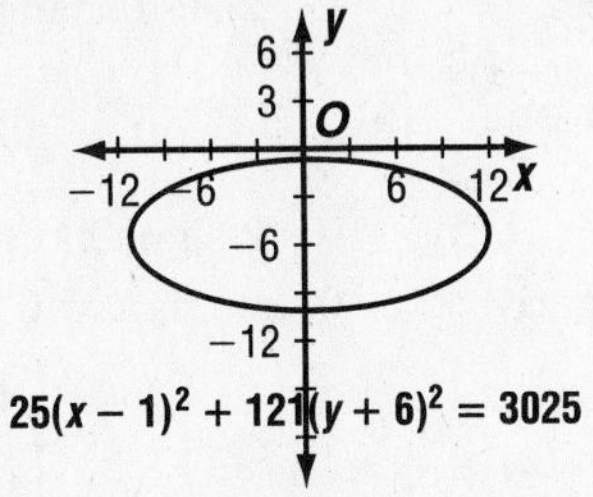

16. $x^2 + 5x + y^2 - 9y = 7$

$x^2 + 5x + \frac{25}{4} + y^2 - 9y + \frac{81}{4} = 7 + \frac{25}{4} + \frac{81}{4}$

$\left(x + \frac{5}{2}\right)^2 + \left(y - \frac{9}{2}\right)^2 = \frac{134}{4}$; circle

center: $\left(-\frac{5}{2}, \frac{9}{2}\right)$

radius: $\sqrt{\frac{134}{4}}$ or $\frac{\sqrt{134}}{2}$ units

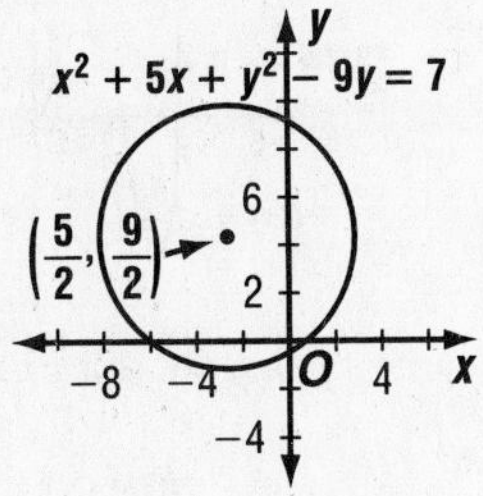

17. $\frac{1}{3}x^2 - 4 = y$; parabola

vertex: (0, −4)

direction of opening:

upward, since $a > 0$

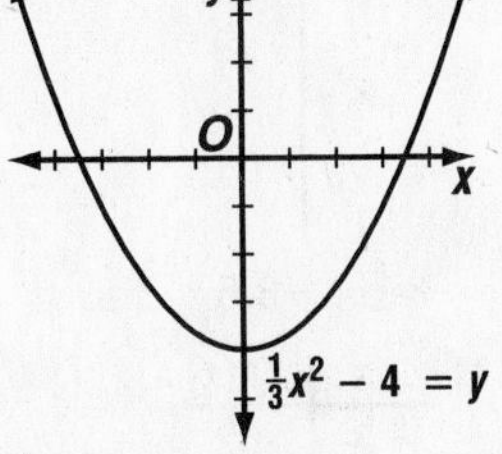

18. $\frac{y^2}{9} - \frac{x^2}{25} = 1$; hyperbola

center: (0, 0)

$a = 3$, $b = 5$

slopes of asymptotes: $\pm\frac{3}{5}$

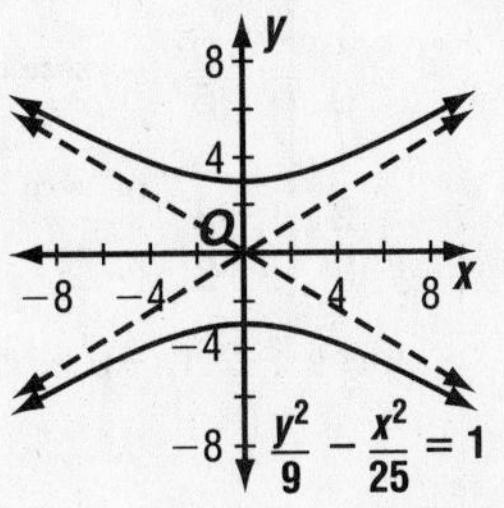

19.

$x^2 + y^2 = 100$	$y = 2 - x$
$x^2 + (2 - x)^2 = 100$	$y = 2 - 8$
$x^2 + 4 - 4x + x^2 = 100$	$y = -6$
$2x^2 - 4x - 96 = 0$	$y = 2 - x$
$x^2 - 2x - 48 = 0$	$y = 2 - (-6)$
$(x - 8)(x + 6) = 0$	$y = 8$

$x - 8 = 0$ or $x + 6 = 0$

$x = 8$ $\quad x = -6$

(8, −6), (−6, 8)

20.

$x^2 - y^2 - 12x + 12y = 36$

$(+)\ x^2 + y^2 - 12x - 12y = -36$

$2x^2 - 24x = 0$

$2x(x - 12) = 0$

$2x = 0$ or $x - 12 = 0$

$x = 0$ $\quad x = 12$

$x^2 - y^2 - 12x + 12y = 36$	$x^2 - y^2 - 12x + 12y = 36$
$0^2 - y^2 - 12(0) + 12y = 36$	$12^2 - y^2 - 12(12) + 12y = 36$
$y^2 - 12y + 36 = 0$	$y^2 - 12y + 36 = 0$
$(y - 6)^2 = 0$	$(y - 6)^2 = 0$
$y = 6$	$y = 6$

(0, 6), (12, 6), (0, 6), (12, 6)

21. $x^2 + y^2 \le 169$

center: (0, 0)

radius: 13 units

$x^2 + y^2 \ge 121$

center: (0, 0)

radius: 11 units

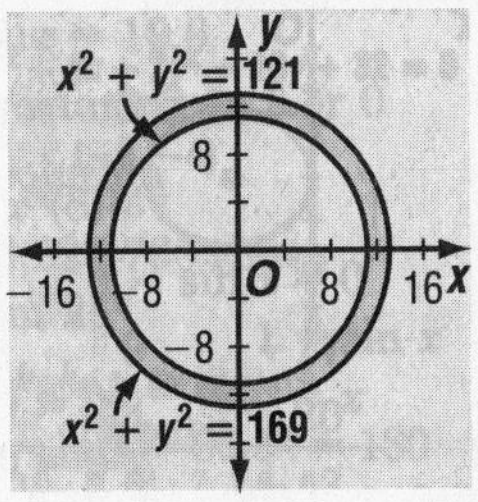

22. $x^2 + y^2 \le 81$ $\qquad y \ge x - 1$

center: (0, 0)

radius: 9 units

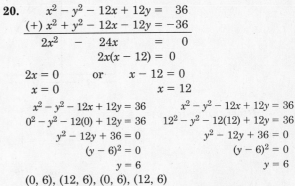

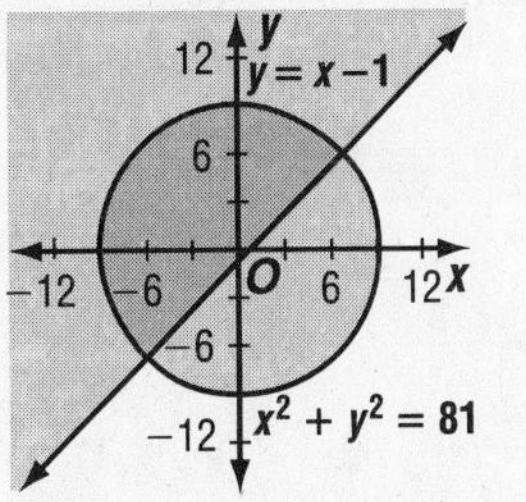

23. $x^2 + y^2 = 25$

$(x - 8)^2 + (y + 8)^2 = 169$

$x^2 - 16x + 64 + y^2 + 16y + 64 = 169$

$x^2 - 16x + y^2 + 16y = 41$

$(x - 11)^2 + (y - 10)^2 = 100$

$x^2 - 22x + 121 + y^2 - 20y + 100 = 100$

$x^2 - 22x + y^2 - 20y = -121$

$x^2 - 16x + y^2 + 16y = 41$

$(-)\ x^2 + y^2 = 25$

$-16x + 16y = 16$

$-x + y = 1$

$x^2 - 22x + y^2 - 20y = -121$

$(-)\ x^2 + y^2 = 25$

$-22x - 20y = -146$

(Continued next page)

$$-x + y = 1 \rightarrow -20x + 20y = 20$$
$$-22x - 20y = -146 \rightarrow (+)\ -22x - 20y = -146$$
$$-42x = -126$$
$$x = 3$$

$$-x + y = 1$$
$$-3 + y = 1$$
$$y = 4$$

The epicenter is at (3, 4).

24. $\frac{x^2}{900} + \frac{y^2}{1600} = 1$

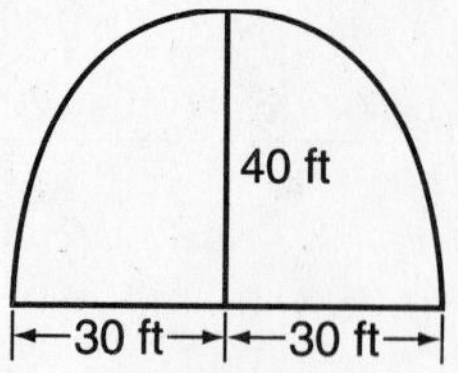

At 6 feet from edge, $x = 24$.

$$\frac{x^2}{900} + \frac{y^2}{1600} = 1$$
$$\frac{24^2}{900} + \frac{y^2}{1600} = 1$$
$$\frac{y^2}{1600} = \frac{36}{100}$$
$$y = 24$$

At 6 feet from the edge, the height is 24 feet.

At 12 feet from edge, $x = 18$.

$$\frac{18^2}{900} + \frac{y^2}{1600} = 1$$
$$\frac{y^2}{1600} = \frac{64}{100}$$
$$y = 32$$

At 12 feet from the edge, the height is 32 feet.

25. $25x^2 - 81y^2 = 30{,}625$

$$\frac{x^2}{1225} - \frac{y^2}{\frac{30{,}625}{81}} = 1$$

$a = \sqrt{1225}$ or 35

length of major axis: 2 (35) or 70 meters

Page 919 Chapter 8 Test

1.
$$\begin{array}{r|rrrr} -1 & 1 & -1 & -5 & -3 \\ & & -1 & 2 & 3 \\ \hline & 1 & -2 & -3 & 0 \end{array}$$

yes; $x^3 - x^2 - 5x - 3 = (x^2 - 2x - 3)(x + 1) + 0$

2.
$$\begin{array}{r|rrrr} -2 & 1 & 0 & 8 & 1 \\ & & -2 & 4 & -24 \\ \hline & 1 & -2 & 12 & -23 \end{array}$$

no; $x^3 + 8x + 1 = (x^2 - 2x + 12)(x + 2) - 23$

3.
$$\begin{array}{r|rrrrr} 2 & 1 & 2 & -7 & -8 & 12 \\ & & 2 & 8 & 2 & -12 \\ \hline & 1 & 4 & 1 & -6 & 0 \end{array}$$

yes; $x^4 + 2x^3 - 7x^2 - 8x + 12 = (x^3 + 4x^2 + x - 6)(x - 2) + 0$

4. $f(x) = x^3 - x^2 - 14x + 24$
yes no yes — 2 sign changes

$f(-x) = (-x)^3 - (-x)^2 - 14(-x) + 24$
$= -x^3 - x^2 + 14x + 24$
no yes no — 1 sign change

positive: 2 or 0; negative: 1; imaginary: 0 or 2

5. $f(x) = 2x^3 - x^2 + 16x - 5$
yes yes yes — 3 sign changes

$f(-x) = 2(-x)^3 - (-x)^2 + 16(-x) - 5$
$= -2x^3 - x^2 - 16x - 5$
no no no — 0 sign changes

positive: 3 or 1; negative: 0; imaginary: 0 or 2

6. $f(x) = x^4 + x^3 - 9x^2 - 17x - 8$
no yes no no — 1 sign change

$f(-x) = (-x)^4 + (-x)^3 - 9(-x)^2 - 17(-x) - 8$
$= x^4 - x^3 - 9x^2 + 17x - 8$
yes no yes yes — 3 sign changes

positive: 1; negative: 3 or 1; imaginary: 0 or 2

7. $f(x) = -7x^4 + 2x^3 + x^2 - 16$
yes no yes — 2 sign changes

$f(-x) = -7(-x)^4 + 2(-x)^3 + (-x)^2 - 16$
$= -7x^4 - 2x^3 + x^2 - 16$
no yes yes — 2 sign changes

positive: 2 or 0; negative: 2 or 0; imaginary: 0 or 4

8.

x	$g(x)$	
−5	−9	← zero between $x = -5$ and $x = -4$
−4	4	
−3	5	
−2	0	← zero
−1	−5	
0	−4	← zero between $x = 0$ and $x = 1$
1	9	

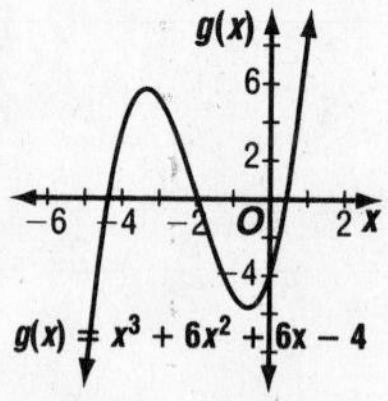

$g(x) = x^3 + 6x^2 + 6x - 4$

zeros: −4.4, −2, 0.4

9.

x	$h(x)$	
−4	4	← zero between $x = -4$ and $x = -3$
−3	−6	← zero between $x = -3$ and $x = -2$
−2	2	
−1	4	
0	0	← zero

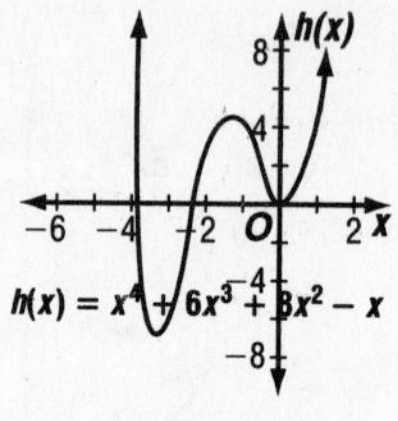

zeros: −3.9, −2.3, 0

$h(x) = x^4 + 6x^3 + 8x^2 - x$

10.

x	$f(x)$	
−4	−7	← zero between $x = -4$ and $x = -3$
−3	7	
−2	9	
−1	5	
0	1	
1	3	

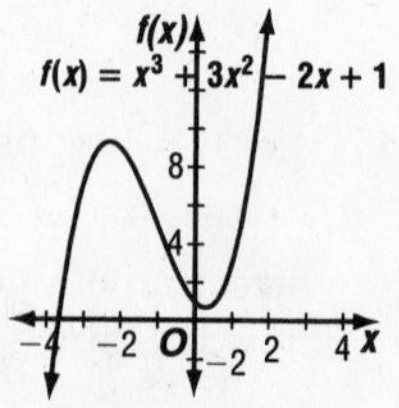

zero: −3.6

$f(x) = x^3 + 3x^2 - 2x + 1$

11.

x	$g(x)$	
−3	62	← zero between $x = -3$ and $x = -2$
−2	−3	
−1	−6	← zero between $x = -1$ and $x = 0$
0	5	
1	6	← zero between $x = 1$ and $x = 2$
2	−3	← zero between $x = 2$ and $x = 3$
3	2	

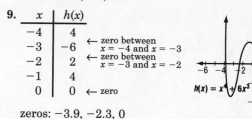

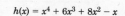

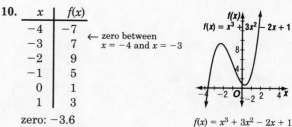

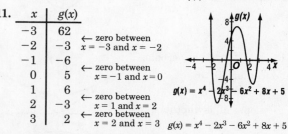

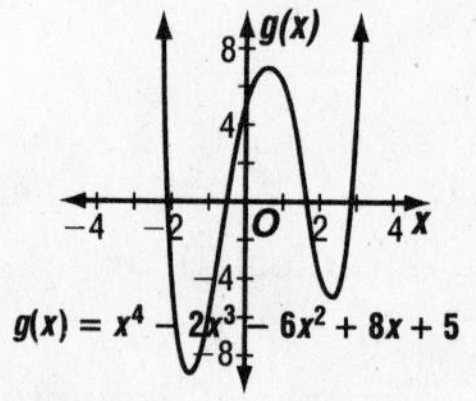

$g(x) = x^4 - 2x^3 - 6x^2 + 8x + 5$

zeros: −2.1, −0.5, 1.7, 2.9

12. possible rational zeros: $\pm1, \pm3, \pm9$

$$\begin{array}{r|rrrr} 9 & 1 & -3 & -53 & -9 \\ & & 9 & 54 & 9 \\ \hline & 1 & 6 & 1 & |\ 0 \end{array}$$

$x^2 + 6x + 1 = 0$ not factorable
rational zero: 9

13. possible rational zeros: $\pm1, \pm2, \pm3, \pm4, \pm6, \pm8, \pm12, \pm24$

$$\begin{array}{r|rrrrr} 4 & 1 & 2 & -23 & 2 & -24 \\ & & 4 & 24 & 4 & 24 \\ \hline & 1 & 6 & 1 & 6 & |\ 0 \end{array}$$

$$\begin{array}{r|rrrr} -6 & 1 & 6 & 1 & 6 \\ & & -6 & 0 & -6 \\ \hline & 1 & 0 & 1 & |\ 0 \end{array}$$

$x^2 + 1 = 0$ not factorable
rational zeros: 4, -6

14. possible rational zeros: $\pm1, \pm2, \pm4, \pm\frac{1}{2}, \pm\frac{1}{3}, \pm\frac{1}{6}, \pm\frac{2}{3}, \pm\frac{4}{3}$

$$\begin{array}{r|rrrr} -2 & 6 & 4 & -14 & 4 \\ & & -12 & 16 & -4 \\ \hline & 6 & -8 & 2 & |\ 0 \end{array}$$

$6x^2 - 8x + 2 = 0$
$3x^2 - 4x + 1 = 0$
$(3x - 1)(x - 1) = 0$
$3x - 1 = 0$ or $x - 1 = 0$
$x = \frac{1}{3}$ $\quad x = 1$

rational zeros: $-2, \frac{1}{3}, 1$

15. possible rational zeros: $\pm1, \pm\frac{1}{2}, \pm\frac{1}{5}, \pm\frac{1}{10}, \pm3, \pm\frac{3}{2}, \pm\frac{3}{5}, \pm\frac{3}{10}, \pm9, \pm\frac{9}{2}, \pm\frac{9}{5}, \pm\frac{9}{10}$

$$\begin{array}{r|rrrr} -3 & 10 & 43 & 36 & -9 \\ & & -30 & -39 & 9 \\ \hline & 10 & 13 & -3 & |\ 0 \end{array}$$

$10x^2 + 13x - 3 = 0$
$(5x - 1)(2x + 3) = 0$
$5x - 1 = 0$ or $2x + 3 = 0$
$x = \frac{1}{5}$ $\quad x = -\frac{3}{2}$

rational zeros: $-3, \frac{1}{5}, -\frac{3}{2}$

16. possible rational zeros: $\pm1, \pm2, \pm4, \pm13, \pm26, \pm52$

$$\begin{array}{r|rrrr} 4 & 1 & 0 & -3 & -52 \\ & & 4 & 16 & 52 \\ \hline & 1 & 4 & 13 & |\ 0 \end{array}$$

$x^2 + 4x + 13 = 0$

$$x = \frac{-4 \pm \sqrt{4^2 - 4(1)(13)}}{2} = \frac{-4 \pm \sqrt{-36}}{2} = \frac{-4 \pm 6i}{2} \text{ or } -2 \pm 3i$$

zeros: 4, $-2 \pm 3i$

17. possible rational zeros: $\pm1, \pm2, \pm3, \pm6$

$$\begin{array}{r|rrrr} 3 & 1 & 4 & -19 & -6 \\ & & 3 & 21 & 6 \\ \hline & 1 & 7 & 2 & |\ 0 \end{array}$$

$x^2 + 7x + 2 = 0$

$$x = \frac{-7 \pm \sqrt{7^2 - 4(1)(2)}}{2} = \frac{-7 \pm \sqrt{41}}{2}$$

zeros: 3, $\frac{-7 \pm \sqrt{41}}{2}$

18. possible rational zeros: $\pm1, \pm2, \pm3, \pm6, \pm9, \pm18, \pm27, \pm54, \pm\frac{1}{2}, \pm\frac{3}{2}, \pm\frac{9}{2}, \pm\frac{27}{2}, \pm\frac{1}{4}, \pm\frac{3}{4}, \pm\frac{9}{4}, \pm\frac{27}{4}$

$$\begin{array}{r|rrrrr} 2 & 4 & 11 & 10 & -69 & -54 \\ & & 8 & 38 & 96 & 54 \\ \hline & 4 & 19 & 48 & 27 & |\ 0 \end{array}$$

$$\begin{array}{r|rrrr} -\frac{3}{4} & 4 & 19 & 48 & 27 \\ & & -3 & -12 & -27 \\ \hline & 4 & 16 & 36 & |\ 0 \end{array}$$

$4x^2 + 16x + 36 = 0$
$x^2 + 4x + 9 = 0$

$$x = \frac{-4 \pm \sqrt{4^2 - 4(1)(9)}}{2} = \frac{-4 \pm \sqrt{-20}}{2} = \frac{-4 \pm 2i\sqrt{5}}{2} \text{ or } -2 \pm i\sqrt{5}$$

zeros: $2, -\frac{3}{4}, -2 \pm i\sqrt{5}$

19. possible rational zeros: $\pm1, \pm2, \pm4, \pm5, \pm8, \pm10, \pm20, \pm40$

$$\begin{array}{r|rrrrr} -1 & 1 & -9 & 11 & -19 & -40 \\ & & -1 & 10 & -21 & 40 \\ \hline & 1 & -10 & 21 & -40 & |\ 0 \end{array}$$

$$\begin{array}{r|rrrr} 8 & 1 & -10 & 21 & -40 \\ & & 8 & -16 & 40 \\ \hline & 1 & -2 & 5 & |\ 0 \end{array}$$

$x^2 - 2x + 5 = 0$

$$x = \frac{-(-2) \pm \sqrt{(-2)^2 - 4(1)(5)}}{2} = \frac{2 \pm \sqrt{-16}}{2} = \frac{2 \pm 4i}{2} \text{ or } 1 \pm 2i$$

zeros: $-1, 8, 1 \pm 2i$

20. $p^3 + 8p^2 - 18p = 0$
$p(p^2 + 8p - 18) = 0$
$p = 0$ or $p^2 + 8p + 18 = 0$

$$p = \frac{-8 \pm \sqrt{8^2 - 4(1)(-18)}}{2} = \frac{-8 \pm \sqrt{136}}{2} = \frac{-8 \pm 2\sqrt{34}}{2} \text{ or } -4 \pm \sqrt{34}$$

$0, -4 \pm \sqrt{34}$

21.
$$16x^4 - x^2 = 0$$
$$x^2(16x^2 - 1) = 0$$
$$x^2(4x + 1)(4x - 1) = 0$$
$$x^2 = 0 \quad \text{or} \quad 4x + 1 = 0 \quad \text{or} \quad 4x - 1 = 0$$
$$x = 0 \qquad 4x = -1 \qquad 4x = 1$$
$$x = -\tfrac{1}{4} \qquad x = \tfrac{1}{4}$$

22.
$$r^4 - 9r^2 + 18 = 0$$
$$(r^2)^2 - 9(r^2) + 18 = 0$$
$$(r^2 - 6)(r^2 - 3) = 0$$
$$r^2 - 6 = 0 \quad \text{or} \quad r^2 - 3 = 0$$
$$r^2 = 6 \qquad r^2 = 3$$
$$r = \pm\sqrt{6} \qquad r = \pm\sqrt{3}$$

23.
$$p^{\frac{3}{2}} - 8 = 0$$
$$p^{\frac{3}{2}} = 8$$
$$(p^{\frac{3}{2}})^{\frac{2}{3}} = 8^{\frac{2}{3}}$$
$$p = 4$$

24.
$$2d + 3\sqrt{d} = 9$$
$$2(\sqrt{d})^2 + 3(\sqrt{d}) - 9 = 0$$
$$(2\sqrt{d} - 3)(2\sqrt{d} + 6) = 0$$
$$2\sqrt{d} - 3 = 0 \quad \text{or} \quad 2\sqrt{d} + 6 = 0$$
$$2\sqrt{d} = 3 \qquad 2\sqrt{d} = -6$$
$$\sqrt{d} = \tfrac{3}{2} \qquad \text{not real}$$
$$d = \tfrac{9}{4}$$

25.
$$z^4 + 6z^3 + 8z^2 = 0$$
$$z^2(z^2 + 6z + 8) = 0$$
$$z^2(z + 2)(z + 4) = 0$$
$$z^2 = 0 \quad \text{or} \quad z + 2 = 0 \quad \text{or} \quad z + 4 = 0$$
$$z = 0 \qquad z = -2 \qquad z = -4$$

26.
$$g(x + h) = (x + h)^2 + 3$$
$$= x^2 + 2xh + h^2 + 3$$

27.
$$f[g(x)] = f(x^2 + 3)$$
$$= 2(x^2 + 3) - 4$$
$$= 2x^2 + 2$$

28.
$$g[f(x)] = g(2x - 4)$$
$$= (2x - 4)^2 + 3$$
$$= 4x^2 - 16x + 19$$

29.
$$g[f(-3)] = g[2(-3) - 4]$$
$$= g(-10)$$
$$= (-10)^2 + 3$$
$$= 103$$

30.
$$f(x) = (x + 1)(x - 3)(x - \boldsymbol{i})(x + \boldsymbol{i})$$
$$= (x^2 - 2x - 3)(x^2 + 1)$$
$$= x^4 - 2x^3 - 2x^2 - 2x - 3$$

31.
$$f(x) = (x - 2)(x - \boldsymbol{i})(x + \boldsymbol{i})$$
$$= (x - 2)(x^2 + 1)$$
$$= x^2 - 2x^2 + x - 2$$

32.
$$f(x) = (x + 2)[x - (1 + \boldsymbol{i})][x - (1 - \boldsymbol{i})]$$
$$= (x + 2)(x^2 - 2x + 2)$$
$$= x^3 - 2x + 4$$

33.
$$f(x) = (x - 1)(x - 4)[x - (1 - \boldsymbol{i})][x - (1 + \boldsymbol{i})]$$
$$= (x^2 - 5x + 4)(x^2 - 2x + 2)$$
$$= x^4 - 7x^3 + 16x^2 - 18x + 8$$

Page 920 Chapter 9 Test

1.
$$\frac{7ab}{9c} \cdot \frac{81c^2}{91a^2b} = \frac{7 \cdot a \cdot b \cdot 3 \cdot 3 \cdot 3 \cdot 3 \cdot c \cdot c}{3 \cdot 3 \cdot c \cdot 7 \cdot 13 \cdot a \cdot a \cdot b}$$
$$= \frac{9c}{13a}$$

2.
$$\frac{4a}{5b} \cdot \frac{15b}{16a} = \frac{2 \cdot 2 \cdot a \cdot 3 \cdot 5 \cdot b}{5 \cdot b \cdot 2 \cdot 2 \cdot 2 \cdot 2 \cdot a}$$
$$= \frac{3}{4}$$

3.
$$\frac{6}{x - 5} + 7 = \frac{6}{x - 5} + \frac{7(x - 5)}{x - 5}$$
$$= \frac{6 + 7x - 35}{x - 5}$$
$$= \frac{7x - 29}{x - 5}$$

4.
$$\frac{m + 5}{2m + 10} = \frac{m + 5}{2(m + 5)}$$
$$= \frac{1}{2}$$

5.
$$\frac{7}{5a} - \frac{10}{3ab} = \frac{7 \cdot 3b}{5a \cdot 3b} - \frac{10 \cdot 5}{3ab \cdot 5}$$
$$= \frac{21b - 50}{15ab}$$

6.
$$\frac{4x}{x^2 - x} = \frac{4x}{x(x - 1)}$$
$$= \frac{4}{x - 1}$$

7.
$$\frac{a^2 - ab}{3a} \div \frac{a - b}{15b^2} = \frac{a^2 - ab}{3a} \cdot \frac{15b^2}{a - b}$$
$$= \frac{a(a - b)}{3a} \cdot \frac{3 \cdot 5 \cdot b \cdot b}{a - b}$$
$$= 5b^2$$

8.
$$\frac{z^2w - z^2}{z^3 - z^3w} = \frac{z^2(w - 1)}{z^3(1 - w)}$$
$$= \frac{z \cdot z \cdot (w - 1)}{z \cdot z \cdot z(-1)(w - 1)}$$
$$= -\frac{1}{z}$$

9.
$$\frac{x^2 - y^2}{y^2} \cdot \frac{y^3}{y - x} = \frac{(x - y)(x + y)}{y^2} \cdot \frac{y^3}{-1\,(x - y)}$$
$$= -y(x + y)$$

10.
$$\frac{4x^2y}{15a^3b^3} \div \frac{2xy^2}{5ab^3} = \frac{4x^2y}{15a^3b^3} \cdot \frac{5ab^3}{2xy^2}$$
$$= \frac{2 \cdot 2 \cdot x \cdot x \cdot y \cdot 5 \cdot a \cdot b \cdot b \cdot b}{3 \cdot 5 \cdot a \cdot a \cdot a \cdot b \cdot b \cdot b \cdot 2 \cdot x \cdot y \cdot y}$$
$$= \frac{2x}{3a^2y}$$

11.
$$\frac{x^2 - 2x + 1}{y - 5} \div \frac{x - 1}{y^2 - 25} = \frac{x^2 - 2x + 1}{y - 5} \cdot \frac{y^2 - 25}{x - 1}$$
$$= \frac{(x - 1)(x - 1)}{y - 5} \cdot \frac{(y - 5)(y + 5)}{x - 1}$$
$$= (x - 1)(y + 5)$$

12.
$$\frac{a^2 - b^2}{2a} \div \frac{a - b}{6a} = \frac{a^2 - b^2}{2a} \cdot \frac{6a}{a - b}$$
$$= \frac{(a - b)(a + b)}{2a} \cdot \frac{2 \cdot 3 \cdot a}{a - b}$$
$$= 3(a + b)$$

13.
$$\frac{\frac{x^2 - 1}{x^2 - 3x - 10}}{\frac{x^2 + 3x + 2}{x^2 - 12x + 35}} = \frac{x^2 - 1}{x^2 - 3x - 10} \div \frac{x^2 + 3x + 2}{x^2 - 12x + 35}$$
$$= \frac{x^2 - 1}{x^2 - 3x - 10} \cdot \frac{x^2 - 12x + 35}{x^2 + 3x + 2}$$
$$= \frac{(x - 1)(x + 1)}{(x - 5)(x + 2)} \cdot \frac{(x - 5)(x - 7)}{(x + 1)(x + 2)}$$
$$= \frac{(x - 1)(x - 7)}{(x + 2)^2}$$

14. $\frac{2x+2}{x^2+5x+6} \div \frac{3x+3}{x^2+2x-3} = \frac{2x+2}{x^2+5x+6} \cdot \frac{x^2+2x-3}{3x+3}$

$= \frac{2(x+1)}{(x+2)(x+3)} \cdot \frac{(x+3)(x-1)}{3(x+1)}$

$= \frac{2(x-1)}{3(x+2)}$

15. $\frac{x-2}{x-1} + \frac{6}{7x-7} = \frac{(x-2)7}{(x-1)7} + \frac{6}{7(x-1)}$

$= \frac{7x-14}{7(x-1)} + \frac{6}{7(x-1)}$

$= \frac{7x-8}{7(x-1)}$

16. $\frac{a^3-b^3}{a+b} \cdot \frac{a^2-b^2}{a^2+ab+b^2} = \frac{(a-b)(a^2+ab+b^2)}{(a+b)} \cdot \frac{(a-b)(a+b)}{a^2+ab+b^2}$

$= (a-b)^2$

17. $\frac{x}{x^2-9} + \frac{1}{2x+6} = \frac{x}{(x-3)(x+3)} + \frac{1}{2(x+3)}$

$= \frac{x \cdot 2}{(x-3)(x+3)2} + \frac{1(x-3)}{2(x+3)(x-3)}$

$= \frac{2x+x-3}{2(x-3)(x+3)}$

$= \frac{3x-3}{2(x-3)(x+3)}$ or $\frac{3(x-1)}{2(x-3)(x+3)}$

18. $\frac{\frac{x^2-5x-14}{x^2+7x+12}}{\frac{3x-21}{x^2-16}} = \frac{x^2-5x-14}{x^2+7x+12} \div \frac{3x-21}{x^2-16}$

$= \frac{x^2-5x-14}{x^2+7x+12} \cdot \frac{x^2-16}{3x-21}$

$= \frac{(x-7)(x+2)}{(x+4)(x+3)} \cdot \frac{(x-4)(x+4)}{3(x-7)}$

$= \frac{(x+2)(x-4)}{3(x+3)}$

19. $x - 3 = 0$

$x = 3$

$y = 0$

x	$f(x)$
-3	0.67
2	4
2.5	8
3	undefined
3.5	-8
4	-4
7	-1

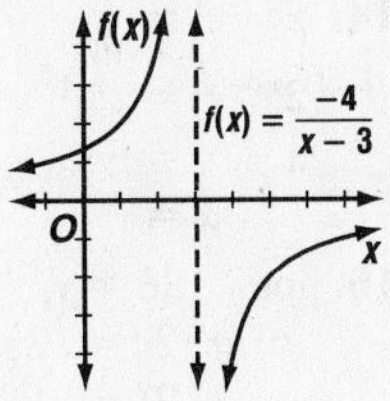

20. $x + 2 = 0$

$x = -2$

$y = 1$

x	$f(x)$
-6	1.5
-3	3
$-2\frac{1}{2}$	5
-2	undefined
$-1\frac{1}{2}$	-3
0	0
4	0.67

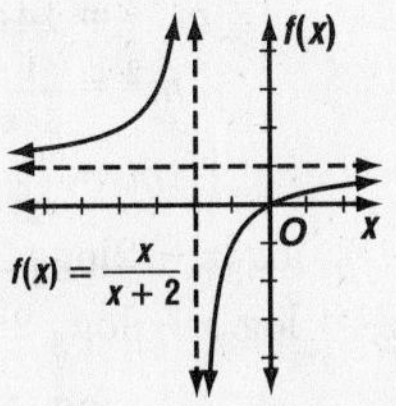

21. $x - 2 = 0$

$x = 2$

$x + 1 = 0$

$x = -1$

$y = 0$

x	$f(x)$
-2	0.5
$-1\frac{1}{2}$	1.14
-1	undefined
$-\frac{1}{2}$	-1.6
1	-1
$1\frac{1}{2}$	-1.6
2	undefined
$2\frac{1}{2}$	1.14
3	0.5

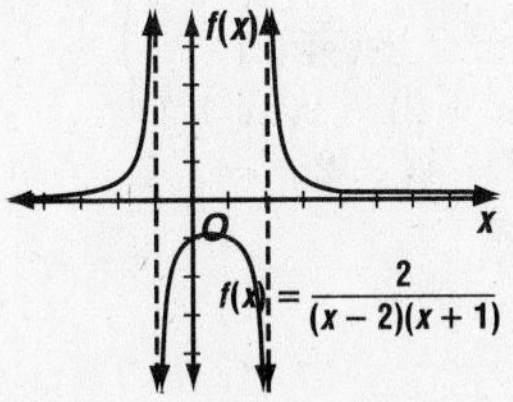

22. $8 - \frac{2-5x}{4} = \frac{4x+9}{3}$

$12\left(8 - \frac{2-5x}{4}\right) = 12\left(\frac{4x+9}{3}\right)$

$96 - 3(2 - 5x) = 4\ (4x + 9)$

$96 - 6 + 15x = 16x + 36$

$90 = x + 36$

$54 = x$

23. $\frac{9}{28} + \frac{3}{z+2} = \frac{3}{4}$

$28(z+2)\left(\frac{9}{28} + \frac{3}{z+2}\right) = 28(z+2)\left(\frac{3}{4}\right)$

$9(z + 2) + 28.3 = 7(z + 2)3$

$9z + 18 + 84 = 21z + 42$

$102 = 12z + 42$

$60 = 12z$

$5 = z$

24. $\frac{3}{x} + \frac{x}{x+2} = \frac{-2}{x+2}$

$x(x+2)\left(\frac{3}{x} + \frac{x}{x+2}\right) = x(x+2)\left(\frac{-2}{x+2}\right)$

$3(x + 2) + x \cdot x = -2x$

$3x + 6 + x^2 = -2x$

$x^2 + 5x + 6 = 0$

$(x + 2)(x + 3) = 0$

$x + 2 = 0$ or $x + 3 = 0$

$x = -2$ $\quad x = -3$

But $x \neq -2$ because the denominator $x + 2$ would equal zero.

25. $x + \frac{12}{x} - 8 = 0$

$x\left(x + \frac{12}{x} - 8\right) = x \cdot 0$

$x^2 + 12 - 8x = 0$

$x^2 - 8x + 12 = 0$

$(x - 6)(x - 2) = 0$

$x - 6 = 0$ or $x - 2 = 0$

$x = 6$ $\quad x = 2$

26. $$\frac{5}{6} - \frac{2m}{2m+3} = \frac{19}{6}$$
$$6(2m+3)\left(\frac{5}{6} - \frac{2m}{2m+3}\right) = 6(2m+3)\left(\frac{19}{6}\right)$$
$$5(2m+3) - 6 \cdot 2m = (2m+3)19$$
$$10m + 15 - 12m = 38m + 57$$
$$15 = 40m + 57$$
$$-42 = 40m$$
$$-\frac{42}{40} = m$$
$$-\frac{21}{20} = m$$

27. $$\frac{x-3}{2x} = \frac{x-2}{2x+1} - \frac{1}{2}$$
$$2x(2x+1)\left(\frac{x-3}{2x}\right) = 2x(2x+1)\left(\frac{x-2}{2x+1} - \frac{1}{2}\right)$$
$$(2x+1)(x-3) = 2x(x-2) - x(2x+1)$$
$$2x^2 - 5x - 3 = 2x^2 - 4x - 2x^2 - x$$
$$2x^2 - 5x - 3 = -5x$$
$$2x^2 - 3 = 0$$
$$2x^2 = 3$$
$$x^2 = \frac{3}{2}$$
$$x = \pm\sqrt{\frac{3}{2}}$$
$$x = \pm\frac{\sqrt{6}}{2}$$

28. $$\frac{2}{x-2} = 3 - \frac{x}{2-x}$$
$$\frac{2}{x-2} = 3 + \frac{x}{x-2}$$
$$(x-2)\left(\frac{2}{x-2}\right) = (x-2)\left(3 + \frac{x}{x-2}\right)$$
$$2 = 3(x-2) + x$$
$$2 = 3x - 6 + x$$
$$2 = 4x - 6$$
$$8 = 4x$$
$$2 = x$$

But, $x \neq 2$ because the demonimator $x - 2$ would equal 0. $\varnothing$

29. $$r + \frac{r^2-5}{r^2-1} = \frac{r^2+r+2}{r+1}$$
$$(r^2-1)\left(r + \frac{r^2-5}{r^2-1}\right) = (r^2-1)\left(\frac{r^2+r+2}{r+1}\right)$$
$$(r^2-1)r + (r^2-1)\left(\frac{r^2-5}{r^2-1}\right) = (r-1)(r+1)\left(\frac{r^2+r+2}{r+1}\right)$$
$$r^3 - r + r^2 - 5 = (r-1)(r^2+r+2)$$
$$r^3 + r^2 - r - 5 = r^3 + r - 2$$
$$r^2 - 2r - 3 = 0$$
$$(r-3)(r+1) = 0$$
$r - 3 = 0$ or $r + 1 = 0$

$r = 3$ $\quad$ $r = -1$

30. $$y = kx$$
$$10 = k(-3)$$
$$-\frac{10}{3} = k$$
$$y = -\frac{10}{3}x$$
$$= -\frac{10}{3}(20)$$
$$= -\frac{200}{3}$$

31. $$xy = k$$
$$\left(-\frac{2}{3}\right)9 = k$$
$$-6 = k$$
$$xy = -6$$
$$x(-7) = -6$$
$$x = \frac{6}{7}$$

32. $$g = kw$$
$$10 = k(-3)$$
$$-\frac{10}{3} = k$$
$$g = -\frac{10}{3}w$$
$$4 = -\frac{10}{3}w$$
$$-\frac{12}{10} = w$$
$$-\frac{6}{5} = w$$

33. $$y = kxz$$
$$250 = k \cdot 10 \cdot 5$$
$$5 = k$$
$$y = 5xz$$
$$2.5 = 5x \cdot 4.5$$
$$\frac{1}{9} = x$$

Page 921 Chapter 10 Test

1. $\log_6 1296 = 4$

2. $\log_3 2187 = 7$

3. $5^4 = 625$

4. $8^{\frac{4}{3}} = 16$

5. $$\log_4 21 = \log_4 7 \cdot 3$$
$$= \log_4 7 + \log_4 3$$
$$\approx 1.4037 + 0.7925$$
$$\approx 2.1962$$

6. $$\log_4 \frac{7}{12} = \log_4 7 - \log_4 (3 \cdot 4)$$
$$= \log_4 7 - (\log_4 3 + \log_4 4)$$
$$\approx 1.4037 - (0.7925 + 1)$$
$$\approx -0.3888$$

7. $$\log_{14} 24 = \frac{\log 24}{\log 14}$$
$$\approx \frac{1.3802}{1.1461}$$
$$\approx 1.204$$

8. $$\log_3 50 = \frac{\log 50}{\log 3}$$
$$\approx \frac{1.6990}{0.4771}$$
$$\approx 3.561$$

9. $4^{\log_4 3} = 3$

10. $$\log_{64} 8 = x$$
$$64^x = 8$$
$$8^{2x} = 8$$
$$2x = 1$$
$$x = \frac{1}{2}$$

11. $$\log_2 \frac{1}{256} = x$$
$$2^x = \frac{1}{256}$$
$$2^x = 2^{-8}$$
$$x = -8$$

12. $$\left(3^{\sqrt{8}}\right)^{\sqrt{2}} = 3^{\sqrt{8}\,.\,\sqrt{2}}$$
$$= 3^{\sqrt{16}}$$
$$= 3^4$$
$$= 81$$

13. $$81^{\sqrt{5}} \div 3^{\sqrt{5}} = 3^{4\sqrt{5}} \div 3^{\sqrt{5}}$$
$$= 3^{4\sqrt{5} - \sqrt{5}}$$
$$= 3^{3\sqrt{5}}$$

14. $$2^{x-3} = \frac{1}{16}$$
$$2^{x-3} = 2^{-4}$$
$$x - 3 = -4$$
$$x = -1$$

15. $$27^{2p+1} = 3^{4p-1}$$
$$(3^3)^{2p+1} = 3^{4p-1}$$
$$3^{6p+3} = 3^{4p-1}$$
$$6p + 3 = 4p - 1$$
$$2p + 3 = -1$$
$$2p = -4$$
$$p = -2$$

16. $$\log_2 128 = y$$
$$2^y = 128$$
$$2^y = 2^7$$
$$y = 7$$

17. $$\log m\ 144 = -2$$
$$m^{-2} = 144$$
$$m^2 = \frac{1}{144}$$
$$m = \frac{1}{12}$$

18. $$\log_3 x - 2\log_3 2 = 3\log_3 3$$
$$\log_3 x - \log_3 2^2 = \log_3 3^3$$
$$\log_3 \frac{x}{4} = \log_3 27$$
$$\frac{x}{4} = 27$$
$$x = 108$$

19. $$\log_9 (x+4) + \log_9 (x-4) = 1$$
$$\log_9 \frac{x+4}{x-4} = 1$$
$$9^1 = \frac{x+4}{x-4}$$
$$9(x-4) = x + 4$$
$$9x - 36 = x + 4$$
$$8x - 36 = 4$$
$$8x = 40$$
$$x = 5$$

20. $\log_5 (8r - 7) = \log_5 (r^2 + 5)$
$8r - 7 = r^2 + 5$
$-7 = r^2 - 8r + 5$
$0 = r^2 - 8r + 12$
$0 = (r - 6)(r - 2)$
$r - 6 = 0$ or $r - 2 = 0$
$r = 6$ $r = 2$

21. $\log_3 3^{(4x-1)} = 15$
$3^{15} = 3^{4x-1}$
$15 = 4x - 1$
$16 = 4x$
$4 = x$

22. $\log_2 3 + \log_2 7 = \log_2 x$
$\log_2 3 \cdot 7 = \log_2 x$
$21 = x$

23. $\log_5 x = -2$
$5^{-2} = x$
$\frac{1}{25} = x$

24. 2.2618

25. 2.7284

26. 2,156,254.407

27. 1.5001

28. $7.6^{x-1} = 431$
$\log 7.6^{x-1} = \log 431$
$(x - 1)\log 7.6 = \log 431$
$x - 1 = \frac{\log 431}{\log 7.6}$
$x - 1 \approx \frac{2.6345}{0.8808}$
$x - 1 \approx 2.9910$
$x \approx 3.9910$

29. $\log_4 37 = x$
$4^x = 37$
$\log 4^x = \log 37$
$x \log 4 = \log 37$
$x = \frac{\log 37}{\log 4}$
$x \approx \frac{1.5682}{0.6021}$
$x \approx 2.6047$

30. $3^x = 5^{x-1}$
$\log 3^x = \log 5^{x-1}$
$x \log 3 = (x - 1) \log 5$
$\frac{x}{x-1} \log 3 = \log 5$
$\frac{x}{x-1} = \frac{\log 5}{\log 3}$
$\frac{x}{x-1} \approx \frac{0.6990}{0.4771}$
$0.6990(x - 1) \approx 0.4771x$
$0.6990x - 0.6990 \approx 0.4771x$
$-0.6990 \approx -0.2218x$
$3.1507 \approx x$

31. $4^{2x-3} = 9^{x+3}$
$\log 4^{2x-3} = \log 9^{x+3}$
$(2x - 3) \log 4 = (x + 3) \log 9$
$\left(\frac{2x-3}{x+3}\right) \log 4 = \log 9$
$\frac{2x-3}{x+3} = \frac{\log 9}{\log 4}$
$\frac{2x-3}{x+3} \approx \frac{0.9542}{0.6021}$
$(2x - 3)0.6021 \approx (x + 3)0.9542$
$1.2042x - 1.8063 \approx 0.9542x + 2.8626$
$0.2499x - 1.8063 \approx 2.8626$
$0.2499x \approx 4.6689$
$x \approx 18.6848$

32. $y = ne^{kt}$
$4000 = 500e^{k(1.5)}$
$8 = e^{1.5k}$
$\ln 8 = \ln e^{1.5k}$
$2.0794 \approx 1.5k$
$1.3863 \approx k$

33. $A = Pe^{rt}$
$75{,}000 = 10e^{0.04t}$
$7500 = e^{0.04t}$
$\ln 7500 = \ln e^{0.04t}$
$8.9227 \approx 0.04t$
$223 \approx t$; 223 years

Page 922 Chapter 11 Test

1. 3, 3, 6, 18, 72, 360, 2160, 15,120
×1 ×2 ×3 ×4 ×5 ×6 ×7

2. $5(-2) = -10, -10(-2) = 20, 20(-2) = -40,$
$-40(-2) = 80, 80(-2) = -160; -160$

3. $a_1 = 27, an = 414, d = 9$
$414 = 27 + (n - 1)9$
$414 = 27 + 9n - 9$
$414 = 18 + 9n$
$396 = 9n$
$44 = n$; 44 integers

4. $S_{31} = \frac{31}{2}(7 + 127)$
$= \frac{31}{2}(134)$
$= 2077$

5. $d = 37 - 42 = -5$
$32 - 5 = 27$
$27 - 5 = 22$
$22 - 5 = 17$
$17 - 5 = 12$
27, 22, 17, 12

6. $a_{27} = 2 + (27 - 1)6$
$= 2 + 156$
$= 158$

7. $r = \frac{\frac{1}{27}}{\frac{1}{81}}$
$= \frac{1}{27} \cdot \frac{81}{1}$
$= 3$
$\frac{1}{9} \cdot 3 = \frac{1}{3}$
$\frac{1}{3} \cdot 3 = 1; \frac{1}{3}, 1$

8. $S_4 = \frac{125 - 125\left(\frac{2}{5}\right)^4}{1 - \frac{2}{5}}$
$= \frac{125 - 125\left(\frac{16}{625}\right)}{\frac{3}{5}}$
$= \frac{609}{5} \div \frac{3}{5}$
$= \frac{609}{5} \cdot \frac{5}{3}$
$= 203$

9. $a_1 = -4, a_5 = 16, n = 5$
$16 = -4 + (5 - 1)d$
$16 = -4 + 4d$
$20 = 4d$
$5 = d$
$-4 + 5 = 1, 1 + 5 = 6, 6 + 5 = 11; 1, 6, 11$

10. $a_1 = 7, a_4 = 189, n = 4$
$189 = 7r^{4-1}$
$27 = r^3$
$3 = r$
$7 \cdot 3 = 21, 21 \cdot 3 = 63; 21, 63$

11. $a_1 = 14 - 2(3) = 8$
$a_2 = 14 - 2(4) = 6$
$d = 6 - 8 = -2$
$Sn = \frac{13}{2}[2 \cdot 8 + (13 - 1)(-2)]$
$= \frac{13}{2}(16 - 24)$
$= \frac{13}{2}(-8)$
$= -52$

12. $a_1 = \frac{1}{3}, r = -2$
no sum

13. $d = 85 - 91 = -6$
$-29 = 91 + (n - 1)(-6)$
$-29 = 91 - 6n + 6$
$-126 = -6n$
$21 = n$
$S_{21} = \frac{21}{2}[2 \cdot 91 + (21 - 1)(-6)]$
$= \frac{21}{2}(182 - 120)$
$= \frac{21}{2}(62)$
$= 651$

14. $r = -\frac{6}{12}$ or $-\frac{1}{2}$
$S = \frac{12}{1 - \left(-\frac{1}{2}\right)}$
$= \frac{12}{\frac{3}{2}}$
$= 12 \cdot \frac{2}{3}$
$= 8$

15. $(2s - 3t)^5 = (2s)^5 + 5(2s)^4(-3t) + 10(2s)^3(-3t)^2 + 10(2s)^2(-3t)^3 + 5(2s)(-3t)^4 + (-3t)^5$
$= 32s^5 - 240s^4t + 720s^3t^2 - 1080s^2t + 810st^4 - 243t^5$

16. $\frac{8!}{2!(8-2)!}x^{8-2}y^2 = \frac{8 \cdot 7 \cdot 6!}{2 \cdot 1 \cdot 6!}x^6y^2$
$= 28x^6y^2$

17. $a_1 = 20, d = -3, a_n = 0$
$0 = 20 + (n - 1)(-3)$
$0 = 20 - 3n + 3$
$-23 = -3n$
$8 \approx n$; 8 rows
$20 + 17 + 14 + 11 + 8 + 5 + 2 = 77$
77 bricks

18. $900{,}000 - 0.25(900{,}000) = 675{,}000$
$675{,}000 - 0.25(675{,}000) = 506{,}250$
$506{,}250 - 0.25(506{,}250) = 379{,}687.50$
$379{,}687.50 - 0.25(379{,}687.50) = 284{,}765.625$
about $284,766

19. $d = 60 - 40 = 20$
$a_{10} = 40 + (10 - 1)20$
$= 40 + 180$
$= 220$; 220 feet

20. $a_1 = 100, r = \frac{1}{2}, n = 5$
$S_5 = \frac{100 - 100\left(\frac{1}{2}\right)^5}{1 - \frac{1}{2}}$
$= \frac{100 - 100\left(\frac{1}{32}\right)}{\frac{1}{2}}$
$= \frac{775}{8} \div \frac{1}{2}$
$= \frac{775}{8} \cdot \frac{2}{1}$
$= \frac{775}{4}$
$= 193.75$; 193.75 feet

Page 923 Chapter 12 Test

1. $P(7, 3) = \frac{7!}{(7-3)!}$
$= \frac{7 \cdot 6 \cdot 5 \cdot 4!}{4!}$
$= 210$

2. $C(7, 3) = \frac{7!}{(7-3)!3!}$
$= \frac{7 \cdot 6 \cdot 5 \cdot 4!}{4! \cdot 3 \cdot 2 \cdot 1}$
$= 35$

3. $P(13, 5) = \frac{13!}{(13-5)!}$
$= \frac{13 \cdot 12 \cdot 11 \cdot 10 \cdot 9 \cdot 8!}{8!}$
$= 154{,}440$

4. $C(13, 5) = \frac{13!}{(13-5)!5!}$
$= \frac{13 \cdot 12 \cdot 11 \cdot 10 \cdot 9 \cdot 8!}{8! \cdot 5 \cdot 4 \cdot 3 \cdot 2 \cdot 1}$
$= 1287$

5. $9! = 362{,}880$
362,880 ways

6. $11 \cdot 9 \cdot 3 \cdot 7 = 2079$
2079 outfits

7. $\frac{11!}{2!2!} = 9{,}979{,}200$
9,979,200 ways

8. $C(18, 11) = \frac{18!}{(18-11)!11!}$
$= 31{,}824$
31,824 teams

9. $P(10, 4) = \frac{10!}{(10-4)!}$
$= 5040$
5040 ways

10. $\frac{1}{6} \cdot 6! = 120$
120 ways

11. $\frac{15}{100} = \frac{3}{20}$

12. $C(11, 5) = \frac{11!}{(11-5)!5!}$
$= \frac{55{,}440}{120}$
$= 462$
462 pentagons

13. $C(3, 2) \cdot C(7, 2) + C(3, 3) \cdot C(7, 1)$
$= \frac{3!}{1!2!} \cdot \frac{7!}{5!2!} + \frac{3!}{0!3!} \cdot \frac{7!}{6!1!}$
$= 3 \cdot 21 + 1 \cdot 7$
$= 63 + 7$
$= 70$; 70 ways

14. $\frac{C(24, 1) \cdot C(23, 1)}{C(52, 1) \cdot C(51, 1)} = \frac{\frac{24!}{23! \cdot 1!} \cdot \frac{23!}{22!1!}}{\frac{52!}{51!1!} \cdot \frac{51!}{50! \cdot 1!}}$
$= \frac{24 \cdot 23}{52 \cdot 51}$
$= \frac{46}{221}$

15. $52 - 22 - 25 = 5, 5 + 10 = 15$
$\frac{C(15, 1)}{C(100, 1)} = \frac{\frac{15!}{14!1!}}{\frac{100!}{99!1!}}$
$= \frac{15}{100}$
$= \frac{3}{20}$

16. $P(H) = \frac{9}{10}, P(M) = \frac{1}{10}$
$(H + M)^7 = H^7 + 7H^6M + 21H^5M^2 + 35H^4M^3 + 35H^3M^4 + 21H^2M^5 + 7HM^6 + M^7$
$35H^4M^3 = 35\left(\frac{9}{10}\right)^4\left(\frac{1}{10}\right)^3$
$= 35\left(\frac{6561}{10{,}000}\right)\left(\frac{1}{1000}\right)$
$= \frac{45{,}927}{2{,}000{,}000}$

17. $C(11, 5) \cdot C(6, 2) \cdot C(4, 4)$

$= \frac{11 \cdot 10 \cdot 9 \cdot 8 \cdot 7 \cdot 6!}{6!5 \cdot 4 \cdot 3 \cdot 2 \cdot 1} \cdot \frac{6 \cdot 5 \cdot 4!}{4!2 \cdot 1} \cdot \frac{4!}{4!}$

$= 462 \cdot 15 \cdot 1$

$= 6930$; 6930 ways

18. $\frac{5}{8} \cdot \frac{5}{8} \cdot \frac{5}{8} + \frac{3}{8} \cdot \frac{3}{8} \cdot \frac{3}{8} = \frac{125}{512} + \frac{27}{512}$

$= \frac{152}{512}$

$= \frac{19}{64}$

19. $P(C) = \frac{1}{4}$, $P(W) = \frac{3}{4}$

19a. $C(10, 6)C^6W^4 = \frac{10 \cdot 9 \cdot 8 \cdot 7 \cdot 6!}{6! \cdot 4 \cdot 3 \cdot 2 \cdot 1}\left(\frac{1}{4}\right)^6\left(\frac{3}{4}\right)^4$

$= 210\left(\frac{1}{4096}\right)\left(\frac{81}{256}\right)$

$= \frac{8505}{524{,}288}$

19b. $C(10, 8)C^8W^2 + C(10, 9)C^9W + C(10, 10)C^{10}$

$= \frac{10 \cdot 9 \cdot 8!}{8! \cdot 2 \cdot 1}\left(\frac{1}{4}\right)^8\left(\frac{3}{4}\right)^2 + \frac{10 \cdot 9!}{9! \cdot 1}\left(\frac{1}{4}\right)^9\left(\frac{3}{4}\right) + \frac{10!}{0!10!}\left(\frac{1}{4}\right)^{10}$

$= 45\left(\frac{1}{65{,}536}\right)\left(\frac{9}{16}\right) + 10\left(\frac{1}{262{,}144}\right)\left(\frac{3}{4}\right) + 1\left(\frac{1}{1{,}048{,}576}\right)$

$= \frac{405}{1{,}048{,}576} + \frac{30}{1{,}048{,}576} + \frac{1}{1{,}048{,}576}$

$= \frac{436}{1{,}048{,}576}$ or $\frac{109}{262{,}144}$

19c. $1 - \frac{109}{262{,}144} = \frac{262{,}035}{262{,}144}$

20. $\text{ME} = 2\sqrt{\frac{p(1-p)}{n}}$

$= 2\sqrt{\frac{0.47(1-0.47)}{1208}}$

$\approx 2\sqrt{0.0002062}$

≈ 0.02872; 2.9%

Page 924 Chapter 13 Test

1. $275°\left(\frac{\pi}{180°}\right) = \frac{275°\pi}{180°} = \frac{55\pi}{36}$

2. $-\frac{\pi}{6}\left(\frac{180°}{\pi}\right) = -\frac{180°\pi}{6\pi} = -30°$

3. $\frac{11\pi}{2}\left(\frac{180°}{\pi}\right) = \frac{1980°\pi}{2\pi} = 990°$

4. $330°\left(\frac{\pi}{180°}\right) = \frac{330°\pi}{180°} = \frac{11\pi}{6}$

5. $-600°\left(\frac{\pi}{180°}\right) = -\frac{600°\pi}{180°} = -\frac{10\pi}{3}$

6. $-\frac{7\pi}{4}\left(\frac{180°}{\pi}\right) = -\frac{1260°\pi}{4\pi} = -315°$

7. $49° + B = 90°$ $\quad \sin 49° = \frac{7}{c}$ $\quad \tan 41° = \frac{b}{7}$

$B = 41°$ $\quad c = \frac{7}{\sin 49°}$ $\quad b = 7 \tan 41°$

$c \approx 9.3$ $\quad b \approx 6.1$

8. $A + 75° = 90°$ $\quad \sin 75° = \frac{6}{c}$ $\quad \tan 15° = \frac{a}{6}$

$A = 15°$ $\quad c = \frac{6}{\sin 75°}$ $\quad a = 6 \tan 15°$

$c \approx 6.2$ $\quad a \approx 1.6$

9. $22° + B = 90°$ $\quad \sin 22° = \frac{a}{8}$ $\quad \sin 68° = \frac{b}{8}$

$B = 68°$ $\quad a = 8 \sin 22°$ $\quad b = 8 \sin 68°$

$a \approx 3.0$ $\quad b \approx 7.4$

10. $a^2 + b^2 = c^2$ $\quad \sin A = \frac{7}{16}$ $\quad 26° + B \approx 90°$

$7^2 + b^2 = 16^2$ $\quad \sin A \approx 0.4375$ $\quad B \approx 64°$

$b^2 = 207$ $\quad A \approx 26°$

$b \approx 14.4$

11.

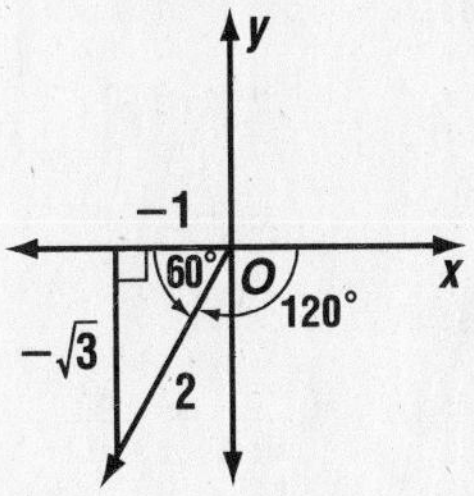

$\cos(-120°) = \frac{x}{r}$

$= -\frac{1}{2}$

12.

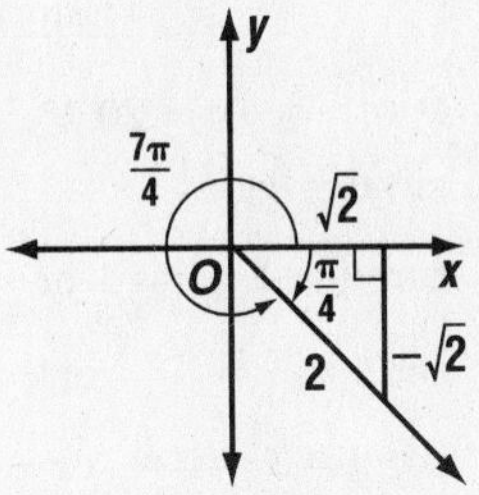

$\sin \frac{7\pi}{4} = \frac{y}{r}$

$= -\frac{\sqrt{2}}{2}$

13.

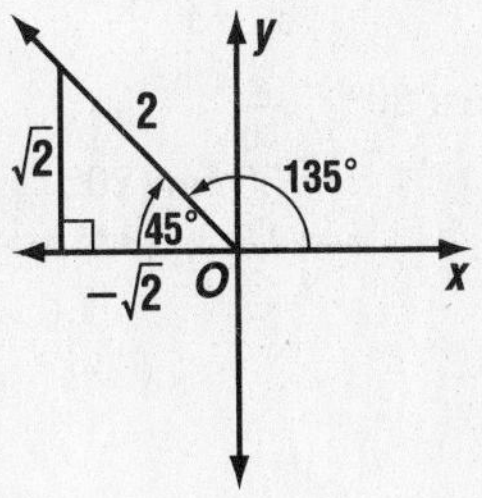

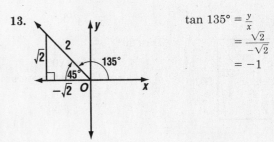

$\tan 135° = \frac{y}{x}$

$= \frac{\sqrt{2}}{-\sqrt{2}}$

$= -1$

14.

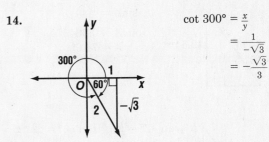

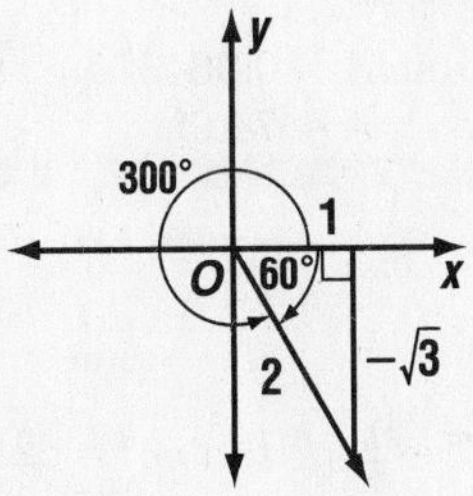

$\cot 300° = \frac{x}{y}$

$= \frac{1}{-\sqrt{3}}$

$= -\frac{\sqrt{3}}{3}$

15.

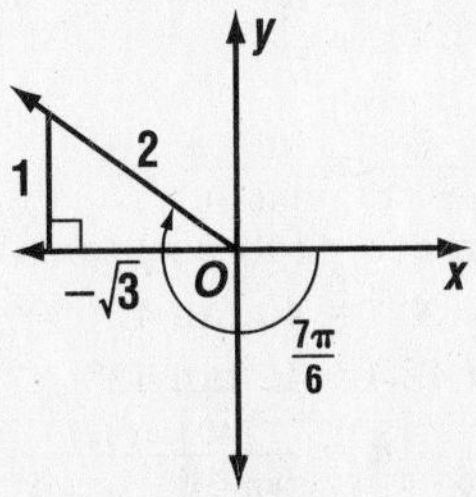

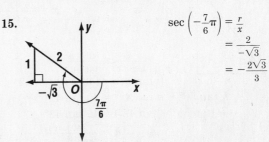

$\sec\left(-\frac{7}{6}\pi\right) = \frac{r}{x}$

$= \frac{2}{-\sqrt{3}}$

$= -\frac{2\sqrt{3}}{3}$

16.

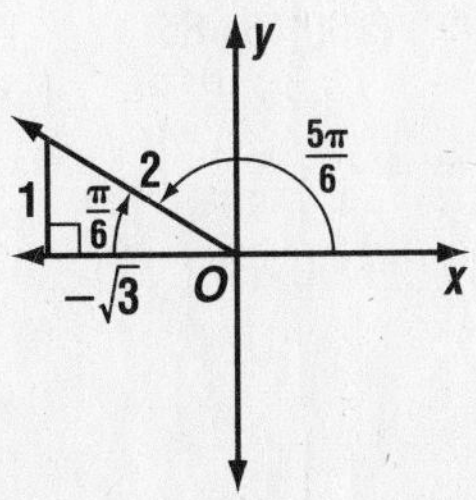

$\csc \frac{5\pi}{6} = \frac{r}{y}$

$= \frac{2}{1}$ or 2

17. $\text{Sin}^{-1}\left(-\frac{\sqrt{3}}{2}\right) = -60°$ 18. Arctan 1 = 45°

19. $\text{Cos}^{-1}(\sin -60°) = \text{Cos}^{-1}\left(-\frac{\sqrt{3}}{2}\right) = 150°$

20. one solution

$$\frac{a}{\sin A} = \frac{b}{\sin B}$$
$$\frac{14}{\sin 40°} = \frac{10}{\sin B}$$
$$\sin B = \frac{10 \sin 40°}{14}$$
$$\sin B \approx 0.4591$$
$$B \approx 27.3°$$
$$40° + 27.3° + C \approx 180°$$
$$C \approx 112.7°$$
$$\frac{a}{\sin A} = \frac{c}{\sin C}$$
$$\frac{14}{\sin 40°} \approx \frac{c}{\sin 112.7°}$$
$$c \approx \frac{14 \sin 112.7°}{\sin 40°}$$
$$c \approx 20.1°$$

21. $r = \sqrt{x^2 + y^2}$

$$2 = \sqrt{(-\sqrt{3})^2 + y^2}$$
$$4 = 3 + y^2$$
$$1 = y^2$$
$$1 = y$$

$$\sin\theta = \frac{y}{r} = \frac{1}{2}$$
$$\tan\theta = \frac{y}{x} = \frac{1}{-\sqrt{3}} \text{ or } -\frac{\sqrt{3}}{3}$$
$$\cot\theta = \frac{x}{y} = \frac{-\sqrt{3}}{1} \text{ or } -\sqrt{3}$$
$$\sec\theta = \frac{r}{x} = \frac{2}{-\sqrt{3}} \text{ or } -\frac{2\sqrt{3}}{3}$$
$$\csc\theta = \frac{r}{y} = \frac{2}{1} \text{ or } 2$$

22.

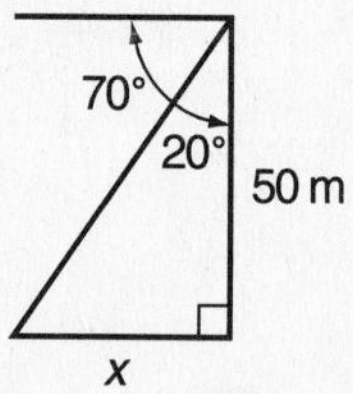

$$\tan 20° = \frac{x}{50}$$
$$x = 50 \tan 20°$$
$x = 18.2$; 18.2 meters

23.

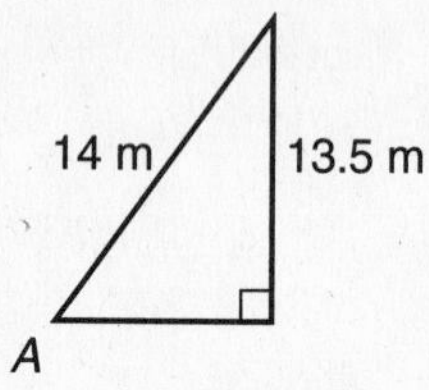

$$\sin A = \frac{13.5}{14}$$
$$\sin A \approx 0.9643$$
$$A \approx 74.6°$$

24.

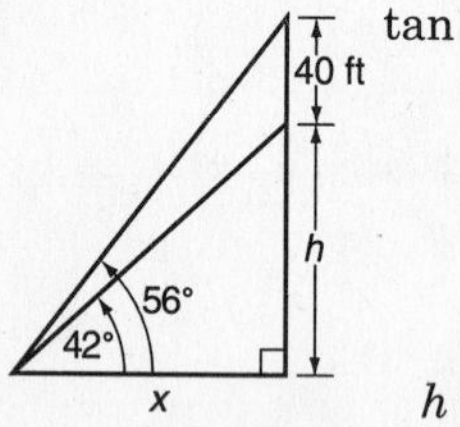

$$\tan 42° = \frac{h}{x} \qquad \tan 56° = \frac{40 + h}{x}$$
$$x = \frac{h}{\tan 42°} \qquad x = \frac{40 + h}{\tan 56°}$$
$$\frac{h}{\tan 42°} = \frac{40 + h}{\tan 56°}$$
$$h \tan 56° = (40 + h) \tan 42°$$
$$h \tan 56° - h \tan 42° = 40 \tan 42°$$
$$h(\tan 56° - \tan 42°) = 40 \tan 42°$$
$$h = \frac{40 \tan 42°}{\tan 56° - \tan 42°}$$
$h \approx 61.87$; 61.87 feet

25. $x^2 = 160^2 + 160^2 - 2(160)(160)\cos 85°$

$$x^2 \approx 46737.42$$
$$x \approx 216.19$$
$$P \approx 160 + 160 + 216.19$$
≈ 536.19; 536.19 feet

Page 925 Chapter 14 Test

1.

x	0°	45°	90°	135°	180°
$2x$	0°	90°	180°	270°	360°
$2 \sin 2x$	0	2	0	−2	0

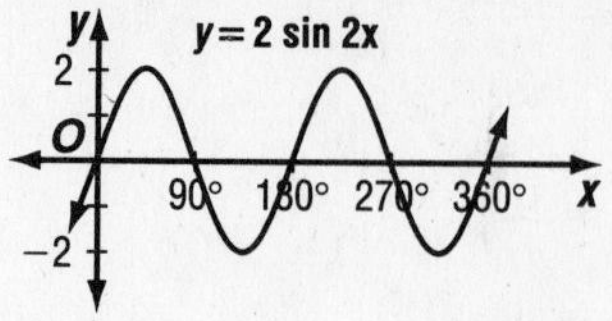

amplitude: |2| or 2 units

period: $\frac{360°}{|2|}$ or 180°

2.

θ	0°	450°	900°	1350°	1800°
$\frac{1}{5}\theta$	0°	90°	180°	270°	360°
$2\cos\frac{1}{5}\theta$	2	0	−2	0	2

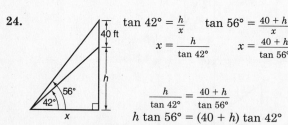

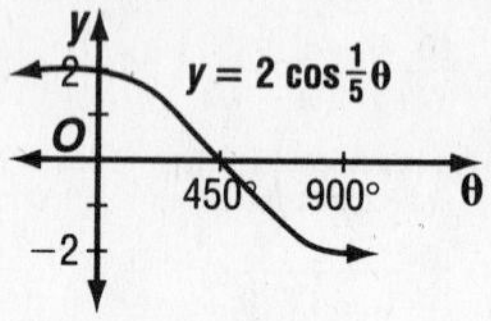

amplitude: |2| or 2 units

units period: $\frac{360°}{\left|\frac{1}{5}\right|}$ or 1800°

3. $\cos^2\theta = 1 - \sin^2\theta$

$$\cos^2\theta = 1 - \left(-\frac{1}{2}\right)^2$$
$$\cos^2\theta = \frac{3}{4}$$
$$\cos\theta = -\frac{\sqrt{3}}{2}$$

$$\tan\theta = \frac{\sin\theta}{\cos\theta} = \frac{-\frac{1}{2}}{-\frac{\sqrt{3}}{2}} = \frac{\sqrt{3}}{3}$$

4. $\csc^2\theta = 1 + \cot^2\theta$

$$\csc^2\theta = 1 + \left(\frac{3}{4}\right)^2$$
$$\csc^2\theta = \frac{25}{16}$$
$$\csc\theta = \frac{5}{4}$$
$$\frac{1}{\sin\theta} = \frac{5}{4}$$
$$\sin\theta = -\frac{4}{5}$$

$$\cot\theta = \frac{\cos\theta}{\sin\theta}$$
$$\frac{3}{4} = \frac{\cos\theta}{-\frac{4}{5}}$$
$$\cos\theta = -\frac{3}{5}$$
$$\frac{1}{\sec\theta} = -\frac{3}{5}$$
$$\sec\theta = -\frac{5}{3}$$

5.

$$(\sin x - \cos x)^2 \stackrel{?}{=} 1 - \sin 2x$$
$$\sin^2 x - 2\sin x\cos x + \cos^2 x \stackrel{?}{=} 1 - \sin 2x$$
$$(\sin^2 x + \cos^2 x) - 2\sin x\cos x \stackrel{?}{=} 1 - \sin 2x$$
$$1 - \sin 2x = 1 - \sin 2x$$

6.

$$\frac{\cos x}{1 - \sin^2 x} \stackrel{?}{=} \sec x$$
$$\frac{\cos x}{\cos^2 x} \stackrel{?}{=} \sec x$$
$$\frac{1}{\cos x} \stackrel{?}{=} \sec x$$
$$\sec x = \sec x$$

7.

$$\frac{\sec x}{\sin x} - \frac{\sin x}{\cos x} \stackrel{?}{=} \cot x$$
$$\frac{1}{\sin x\cos x} - \frac{\sin x}{\cos x} \stackrel{?}{=} \cot x$$
$$\frac{1}{\sin x\cos x} - \frac{\sin^2 x}{\sin x\cos x} \stackrel{?}{=} \cot x$$
$$\frac{\cos^2 x}{\sin x\cos x} \stackrel{?}{=} \cot x$$
$$\frac{\cos x}{\sin x} \stackrel{?}{=} \cot x$$
$$\cot x = \cot x$$

8. $\dfrac{1 + \tan^2\theta}{\cos^2\theta} \stackrel{?}{=} \sec^4\theta$

$\dfrac{\sec^2\theta}{\cos^2\theta} \stackrel{?}{=} \sec^4\theta$

$\sec^2\theta \cdot \sec^2\theta \stackrel{?}{=} \sec^4\theta$

$\sec^4\theta = \sec^4\theta$

9. $\cos 165° = \cos(120° + 45°)$
$= \cos 120° \cos 45° - \sin 120° \sin 45°$
$= -\frac{1}{2} \cdot \frac{\sqrt{2}}{2} - \frac{\sqrt{3}}{2} \cdot \frac{\sqrt{2}}{2}$
$= -\frac{\sqrt{2}}{4} - \frac{\sqrt{6}}{4}$
$= \frac{-\sqrt{2} - \sqrt{6}}{4}$

10. $\sin 255° = \sin(210° + 45°)$
$= \sin 210° \cos 45° + \cos 210° \sin 45°$
$= -\frac{1}{2} \cdot \frac{\sqrt{2}}{2} + \left(-\frac{\sqrt{3}}{2}\right) \cdot \frac{\sqrt{2}}{2}$
$= -\frac{\sqrt{2}}{4} - \frac{\sqrt{6}}{4}$
$= \frac{-\sqrt{2} - \sqrt{6}}{4}$

11. $2 \sin 75° \cos 75° = \sin 2(75°)$
$= \sin 150°$
$= \frac{1}{2}$

12. $(1 - \cos^2\theta)\cot^2\theta = \sin^2\theta \cdot \frac{\cos^2\theta}{\sin^2\theta}$
$= \cos^2\theta$

13. $\sin\beta(\cos\beta + \sin\beta\tan\beta) = \sin\beta\left(\cos\beta + \sin\beta \cdot \frac{\sin\beta}{\cos\beta}\right)$
$= \sin\beta\left(\frac{\cos^2\beta}{\cos\beta} + \frac{\sin^2\beta}{\cos\beta}\right)$
$= \sin\beta\left(\frac{1}{\cos\beta}\right)$
$= \frac{\sin\beta}{\cos\beta}$
$= \tan\beta$

14. $\sin\alpha \cot\alpha = \sin\alpha \cdot \frac{\cos\alpha}{\sin\alpha}$
$= \cos\alpha$

15. $\sin^2 x = 1 - \cos^2 x$
$\sin^2 x = 1 - \left(-\frac{1}{6}\right)^2$
$\sin x = \frac{\sqrt{35}}{6}$
$\sin 2x = 2 \sin x \cos x$
$= 2\left(\frac{\sqrt{35}}{6}\right)\left(-\frac{1}{6}\right)$
$= -\frac{\sqrt{35}}{18}$

$\cos \frac{x}{2} = \sqrt{\frac{1 + \cos x}{2}}$
$= \sqrt{\frac{1 - \left(\frac{1}{6}\right)}{2}}$
$= \sqrt{\frac{5}{12}} \cdot \frac{\sqrt{3}}{\sqrt{3}}$
$= \frac{\sqrt{15}}{6}$

16. $\sin \frac{x}{2} = \sqrt{\frac{1 - \cos x}{2}}$
$= \sqrt{\frac{1 - \frac{3}{4}}{2}}$
$= \sqrt{\frac{1}{8}}$
$= \frac{\sqrt{2}}{4}$

$\cos 2x = 2\cos^2 x - 1$
$= 2\left(\frac{3}{4}\right)^2 - 1$
$= \frac{2}{16}$
$= \frac{1}{8}$

17. $r = \sqrt{x^2 + y^2}$
$= \sqrt{(12)^2 + 5^2}$
$= \sqrt{144 + 25}$
$= \sqrt{169}$
$= 13$

$\cos x = -\frac{12}{13}$

$\tan 2x = \frac{2\tan x}{1 - \tan^2 x}$
$= \frac{2\left(\frac{5}{12}\right)}{1 - \left(\frac{5}{12}\right)^2}$
$= \frac{\frac{5}{6}}{\frac{119}{144}}$
$= \frac{5}{6} \cdot \frac{144}{119}$
$= \frac{120}{119}$

$\tan \frac{x}{2} = -\sqrt{\frac{1 - \cos x}{1 + \cos x}}$
$= -\sqrt{\frac{1 - \left(-\frac{12}{13}\right)}{1 + \left(-\frac{12}{13}\right)}}$
$= -\sqrt{\frac{25}{1}}$
$= -5$

18. $\sec x = 1 + \tan x$
$\sec^2 x = (1 + \tan x)^2$
$1 + \tan^2 x = 1 + 2\tan x + \tan^2 x$
$0 = 2\tan x$
$\tan x = 0$
$x = 0°$ or ~~180°~~

0°

19. $\cos 2x = \cos x$
$2\cos^2 x - 1 = \cos x$
$2\cos^2 x - \cos x - 1 = 0$
$(2\cos x + 1)(\cos x - 1) = 0$
$2\cos x + 1 = 0$ or $\cos x - 1 = 0$
$2\cos x = -1$ $\quad$ $\cos x = 1$
$\cos x = -\frac{1}{2}$ $\quad$ $x = 0°$
$x = 120°$ or $240°$

0°, 120°, 240°

20. $\cos 2x + \sin x = 1$
$1 - 2\sin^2 x + \sin x = 1$
$2\sin^2 x - \sin x = 0$
$\sin x(2\sin x - 1) = 0$
$\sin x = 0$ or $2\sin x - 1 = 0$
$x = 0°$ or $180°$ $\quad$ $2\sin x = 1$
$\sin x = \frac{1}{2}$
$x = 30°$ or $150°$

0°, 30°, 150°, 180°

21. $\sin x = \tan x$
$\sin x = \frac{\sin x}{\cos x}$
$\sin x - \frac{\sin x}{\cos x} = 0$
$\sin x\left(1 - \frac{1}{\cos x}\right) = 0$
$\sin x = 0$ or $1 - \frac{1}{\cos x} = 0$
$x = 0°$ or $180°$ $\quad$ $-\frac{1}{\cos x} = -1$
$\cos x = 1$
$x = 0°$

0°, 180°

22. $2 \sin x \cos x - \sin x = 0$

$\sin x (2 \cos x - 1) = 0$

$\sin x = 0$ or $2 \cos x - 1 = 0$

$x = 0°$ or $180°$ $\quad 2 \cos x = 1$

$\cos x = \frac{1}{2}$

$x = 60°$ or $300°$

0°, 60°, 180°, 300°

23. $\sin x + \sin x \cos x = 0$

$\sin x (1 + \cos x) = 0$

$\sin x = 0$ or $1 + \cos x = 0$

$x = 0°$ or $180°$ $\quad \cos x = -1$

$x = 180°$

0°, 180°

24a. $d = \frac{v_0^2}{g} \sin 2\theta$

$= \frac{100^2}{32} \sin 2\,(60°)$

≈ 270.6; 270.6 feet

24b. $d = \frac{v_0^2}{g} \sin 2\theta$

$= \frac{100^2}{32} \sin 2\,(45°)$

$= 312.5$; 312.5 feet

25. $s = \frac{v_0^2 \sin \theta \cos \theta}{5}$

$20 = \frac{20^2 \sin \theta \cos \theta}{5}$

$\frac{1}{4} = \sin \theta \cos \theta$

$\frac{1}{2} = 2 \sin \theta \cos \theta$

$\frac{1}{2} = \sin 2\theta$

$2\theta = 30°$ or $150°$

$\theta = 15°$ or $75°$

8-8B Square Root Functions and Relations

Page 537 Check for Understanding

1. The graph of $y = \sqrt{x} - 6$ has no x-intercept and its y-intercept is -6. The graph of $y = \sqrt{x - 6}$ has no y-intercept and its x-intercept is 6.

2. $2x + 3 = 0$

$2x = -3$

$x = -\frac{3}{2}$

3a. $y \le \sqrt{\frac{3h}{2}}$

3b.

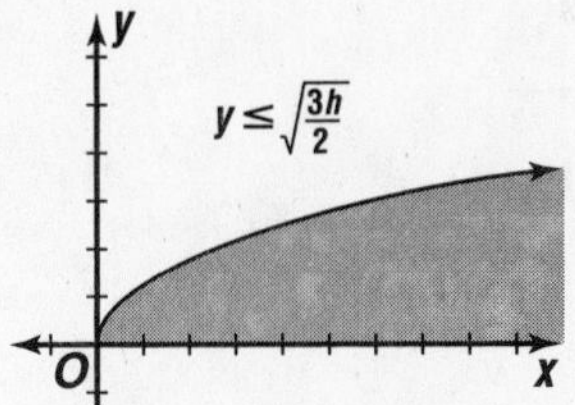

4.

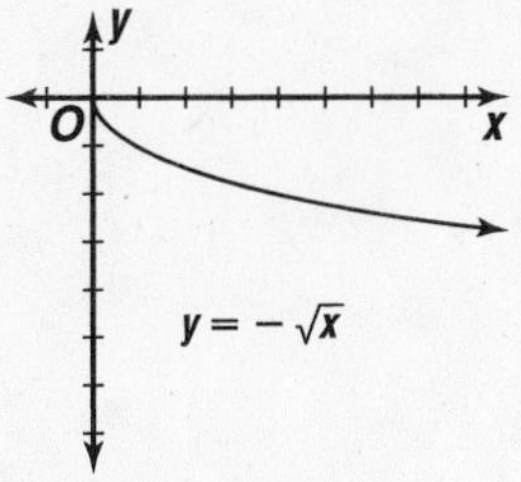

D: $x \ge 0$; R: $y \le 0$

5.

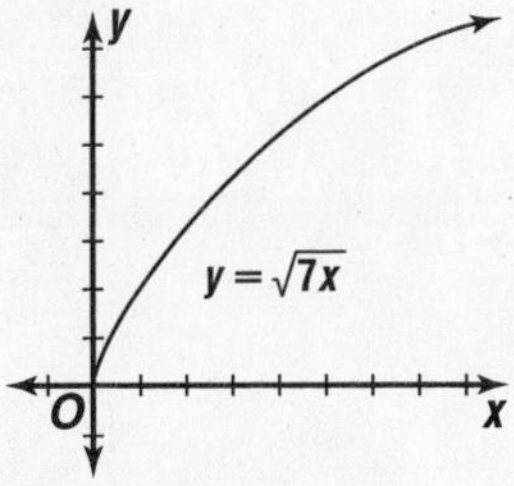

D: $x \ge 0$; R: $y \ge 0$

6.

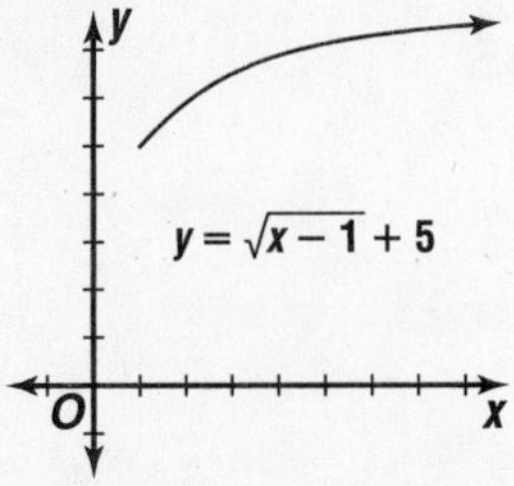

D: $x \ge 1$; R: $y \ge 5$

7.

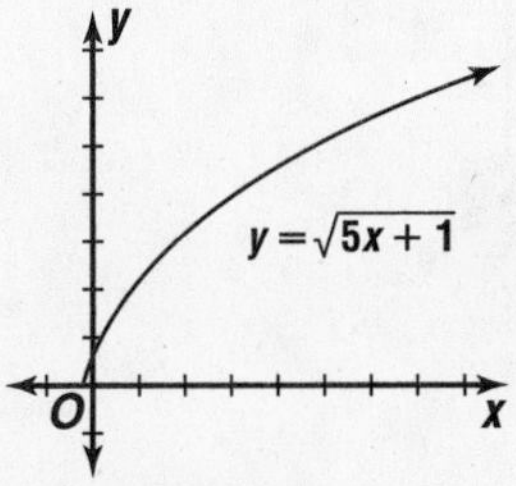

D: $x \ge -\frac{1}{5}$; R: $y \ge 0$

8.

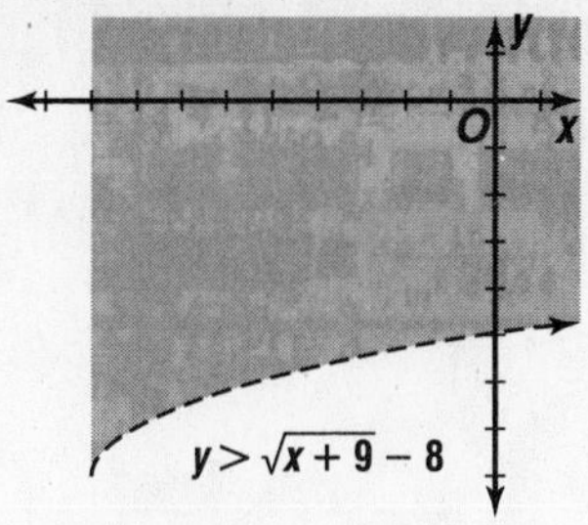

9.

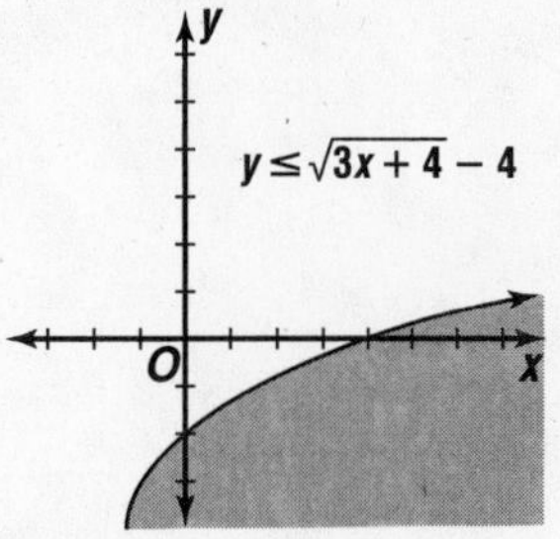

10a. D: $d \ge 0$; R: $s \ge 0$

10b. $s = 3.1\sqrt{10{,}000}$

$= 3.1(100)$

$= 310$ m/s

10c.

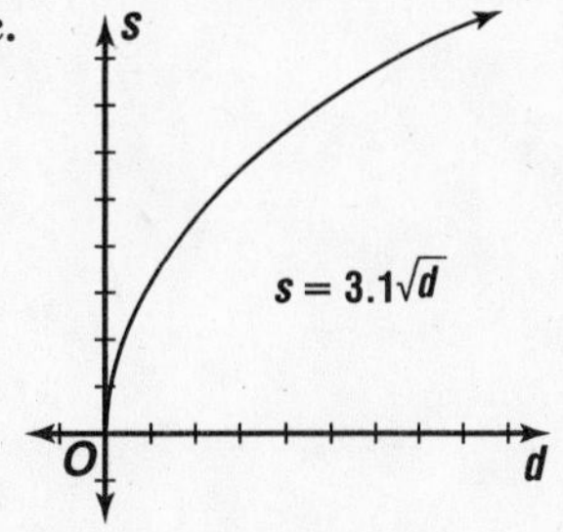

Page 538 Exercises

11.

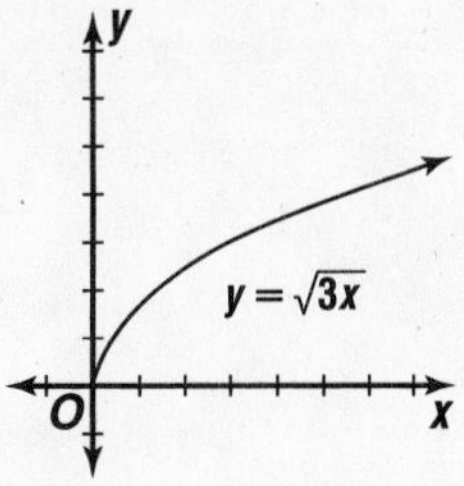

D: $x \ge 0$; R: $y \ge 0$

12.

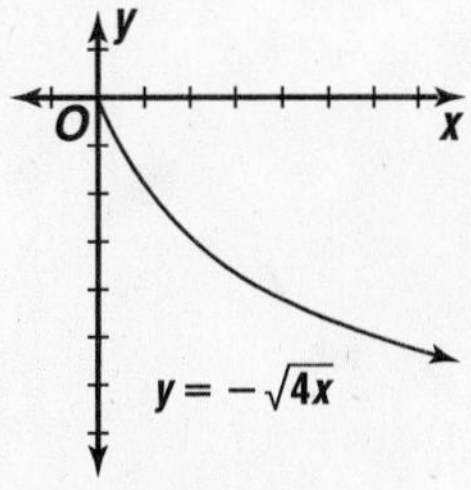

D: $x \ge 0$; R: $y \le 0$

13.

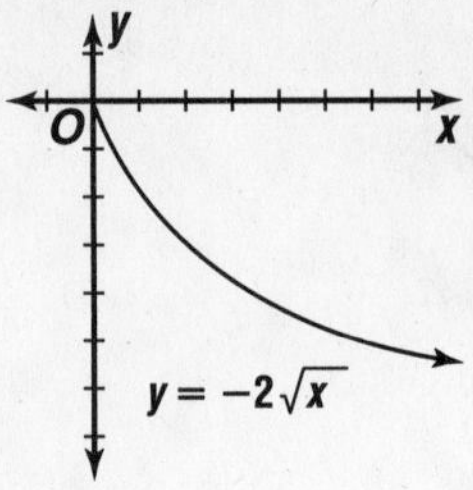

D: $x \geq 0$; R: $y \leq 0$

14.

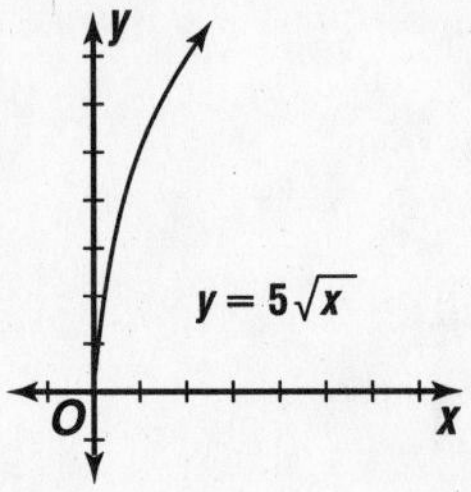

D: $x \geq 0$; R: $y \geq 0$

15.

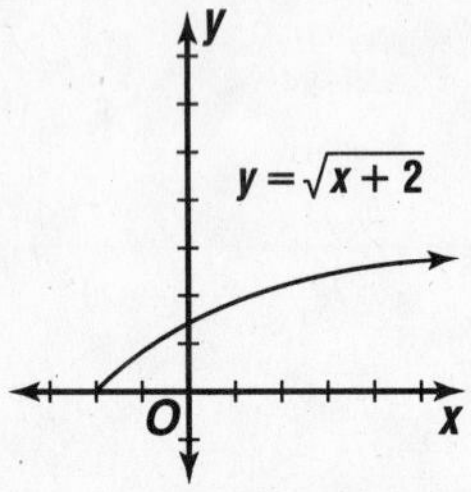

D: $x \geq -2$; R: $y \geq 0$

16.

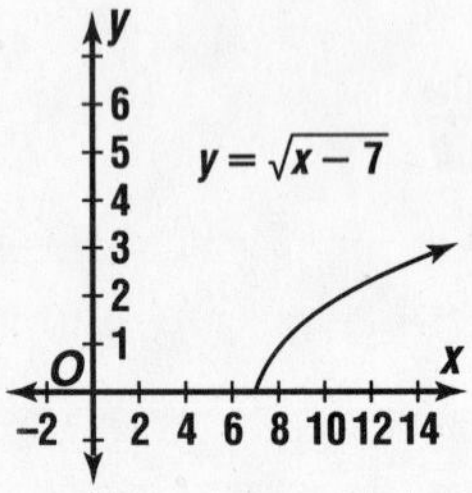

D: $x \geq 7$; R: $y \geq 0$

17.

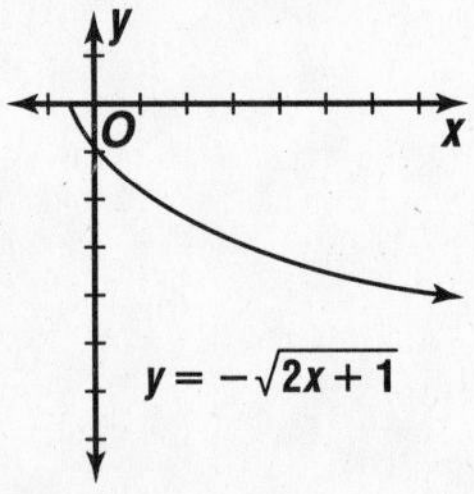

D: $x \geq -\frac{1}{2}$; R: $y \leq 0$

18.

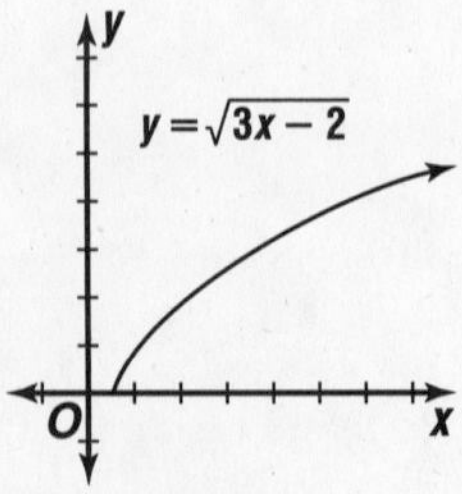

D: $x \geq \frac{2}{3}$; R: $y \geq 0$

19.

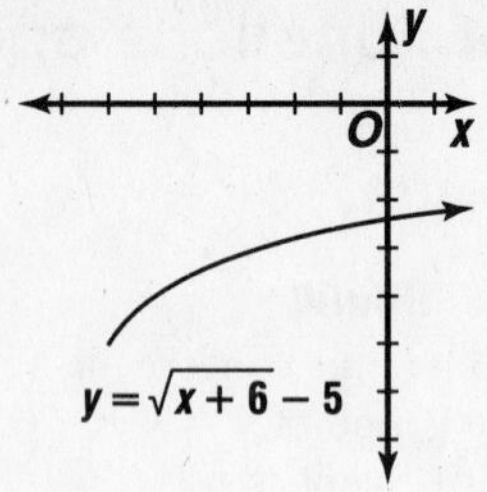

D: $x \geq -6$; R: $y \geq -5$

20.

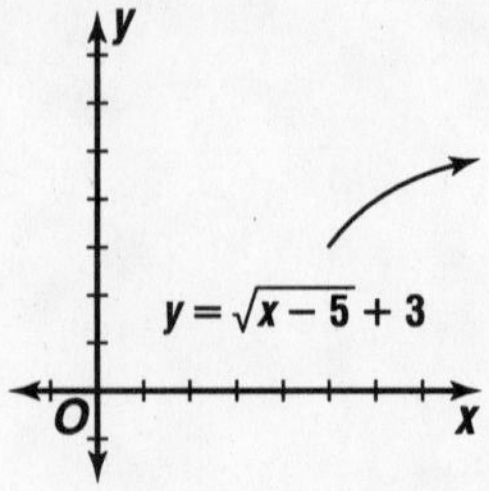

D: $x \geq 5$; R: $y \geq 3$

21.

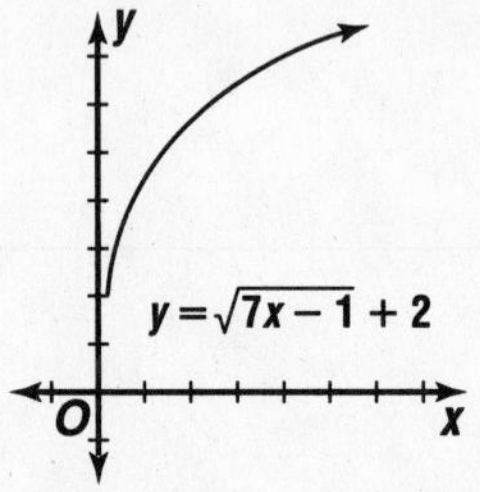

D: $x \geq \frac{1}{7}$; R: $y \geq 2$

22.

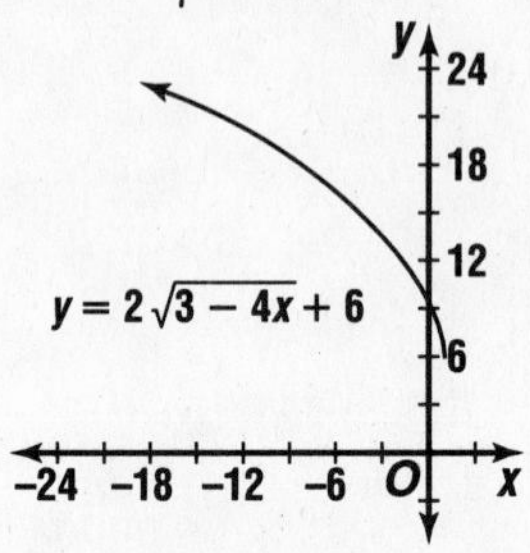

D: $x \leq \frac{3}{4}$; R: $y \geq 6$

23.

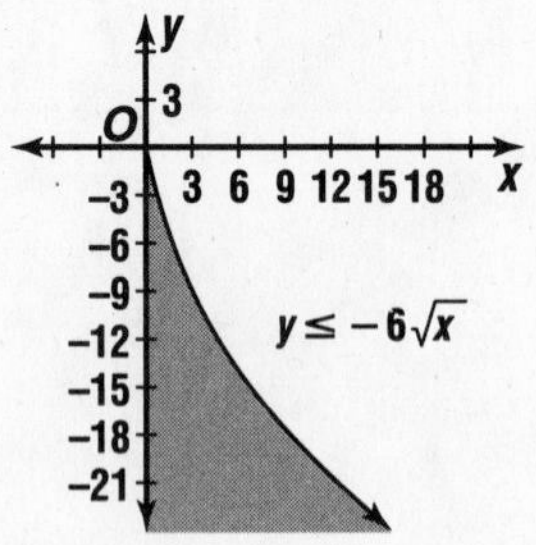

24.

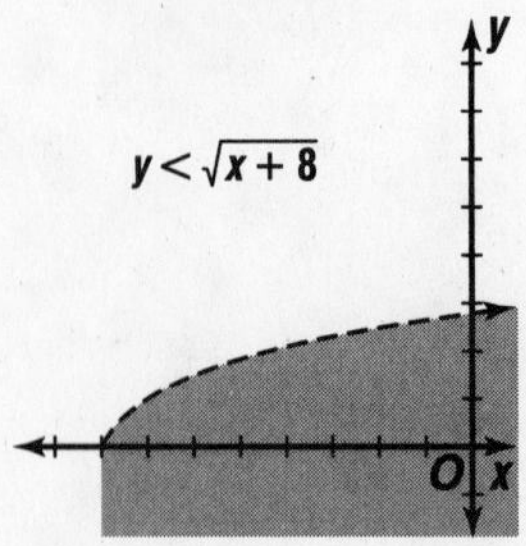

25.

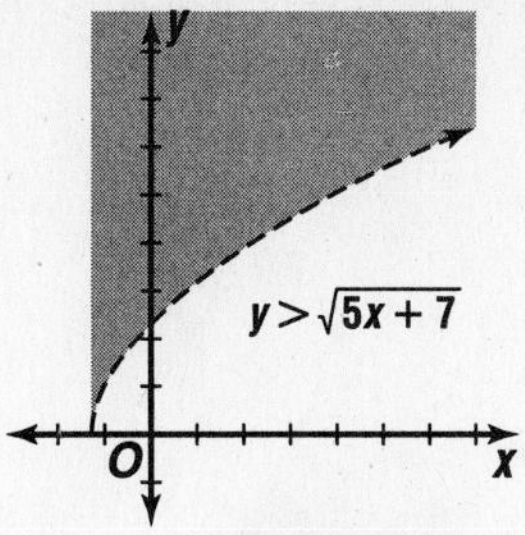

26.

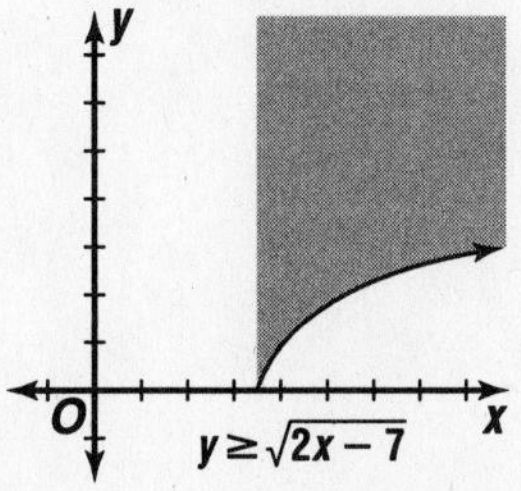

27.

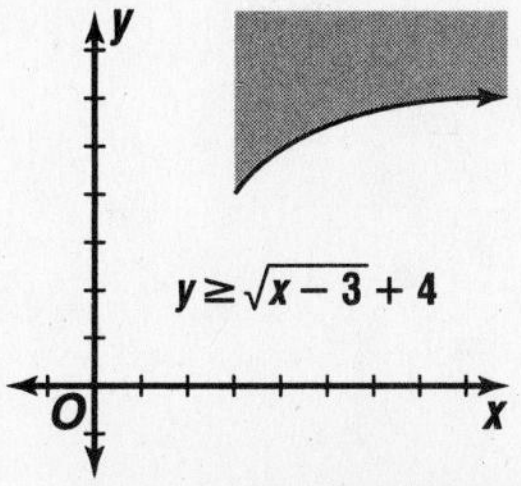

28.

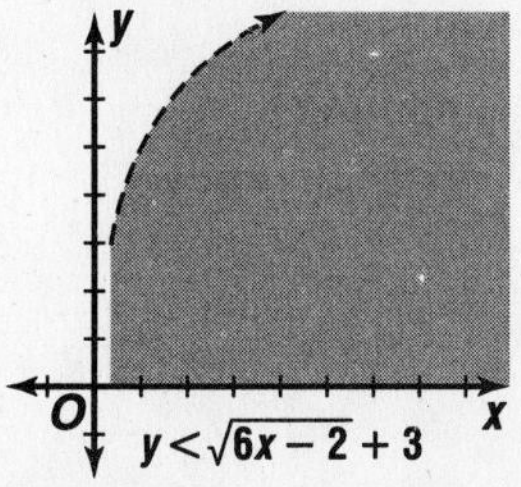

29a.

<table>
<tr><td>If:</td><td>$h > 0$</td><td>$h < 0$</td><td>$k > 0$</td><td>$k < 0$</td></tr>
<tr><td>$a > 0$</td><td rowspan="2">h is minimum value in domain.</td><td rowspan="2">$-h$ is minimum value in domain.</td><td colspan="2">k is minimum value in range.</td></tr>
<tr><td>$a < 0$</td><td colspan="2">k is maximum value in range.</td></tr>
</table>

29b. $y = -2\sqrt{x}$ is a little wider than $y = \sqrt{x}$, and falls downward to the right. $y = \sqrt{x - 4}$ begins at (4, 0). $y = \sqrt{x} + 3$ begins at (0, 3). $y = 3\sqrt{x - 1} + 5$ is wider than $y = \sqrt{x}$, and begins at (1, 5).

30a.

$$V = \frac{1}{3}\pi r^2 h$$
$$V = \frac{1}{3}\pi r^2(5)$$
$$V = \frac{5}{3}\pi r^2$$
$$\left(\frac{3}{5}\right)V = \frac{5}{3}\pi r^2\left(\frac{3}{5}\right)$$
$$\frac{\frac{3}{5}V}{\pi} = \frac{\pi r^2}{\pi}$$
$$\frac{3V}{5\pi} = r^2$$
$$\sqrt{\frac{3V}{5\pi}} = \sqrt{r^2}$$
$$\sqrt{\frac{3V}{5\pi}} = r$$

30b. D: $V \geq 0$; R: $r \geq 0$

30c. $V = \frac{1}{3}\pi r^2 h$

$= \frac{1}{3}\pi(2^2)(5)$

$= \frac{20}{3}\pi$

$\approx 20.9 \text{ in}^3$

30d.

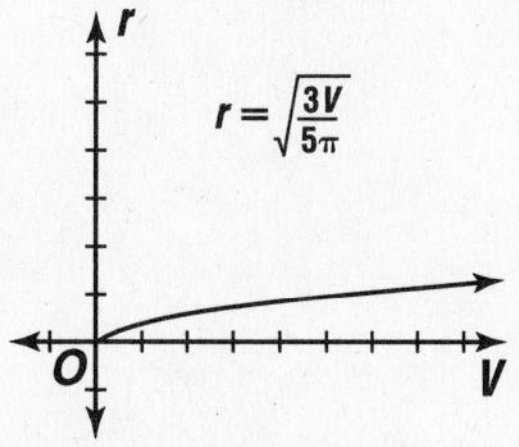

31a. D: $x \geq 0$; R: $y \geq 0$

31b. $V = 0.094\sqrt{A^3}$

$= 0.094\sqrt{12^3}$

$\approx 0.094(41.569)$

$\approx 3.9 \text{ cm}^3$

31c.

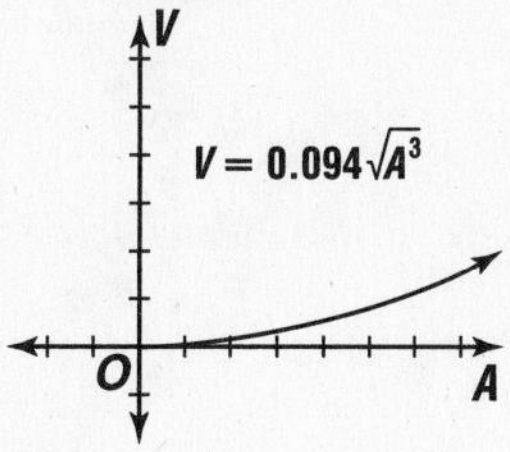

31d. No, it curved upward to the right. The radicand is cubed.